**GALLOP** WITH CONFIDENCE

Consumer line 7/7
+44 (0)1352 746100

**BRONCHIX PULMO**

**BRONCHIX PULMO**

## > FOR PULMONARY SUPPORT AND ELASTICITY

*Richard Hughes; "I have used Bronchix Pulmo syrup and Bronchix Pulmo syringes on two individual horses who have unfortunately been categorised as "bleeders". The product is simple and easy to use and we have had great success with it. We now would not do without it."*

# RACING POST
## MEMBERS' CLUB

**What our current members are saying about**

▶ **Video Replays**

> *I use the race video replay facility to review a horse's form to help to analyse races. I also use the Bloodstock section to follow the sales and stallion results, and the extended racecards which show all details including a horse's breeding.*

## Find out more at
## racingpost.com/members-club

CARPET GALLO...

# *EQUESTRIAN SURFACE SOLUTIONS*

Equestrian surfaces manufactured on professional horse enthusiasts feedback

WE ARE STILL OPEN
E: HELLO@CARPETGALLOP.CO.UK
T; 01785 719 991

The most talked about equestrian surface products on the market; Gallops, Greyhound tracks and equestrian arenas.

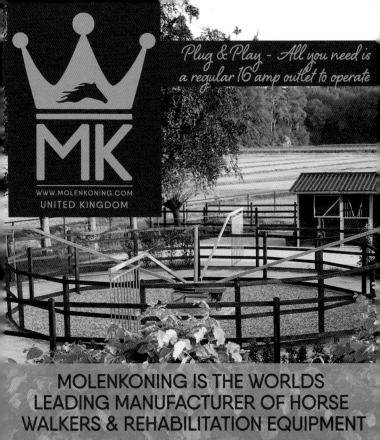

# Tailor Made Insurance Solutions for the Equine Industry

## Equine Liability Insurance

- Property (Buildings, Tack & Machinery)
- Motor (Private, Commercial & Special types)
- Personal Accident Cover
- Bloodstock Insurance
- Care, Custody & Control Cover

**LHK**
Insurance and
Financial Advisors

**Drogheda Office**
12 Trinity Street, Drogheda,
Co. Louth, A92 RH63
Phone: +353 (0) 41 983 7660

**Dublin Office**
Rosemount House,
Dundrum Road, D14 P924
Phone: +353 (0) 1 205 5600

**Email: info@lhkgroup.ie | www.lhkgroup.ie**

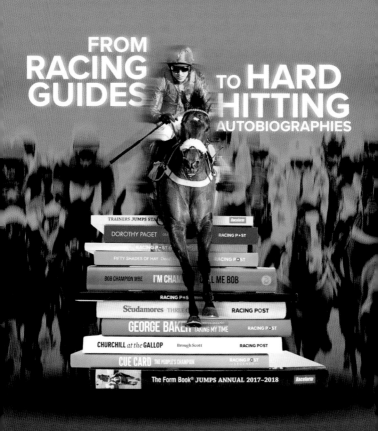

# Download the free must-have Racing Post app.

**RACING POST**

The Must-Have App
For The Must-Have Info

Use your camera phone
and scan the QR code
on the right to download
the free app now.

# HORSES
## IN TRAINING 2021

131st YEAR OF PUBLICATION

*RACING POST*

# INDEX TO GENERAL CONTENTS

**Editor**

**Graham Dench**
E-mail: hitraceform@weatherbys.co.uk

**Production Editor**

**Adrian Gowling**; Bloodstock Services, Weatherbys

**Typesetting**

**Printing Services Department,** Weatherbys,
Sanders Road, Wellingborough, NN8 4BX.

**Orders**

Racing Post Books, Sanders Road, Wellingborough, Northants NN8 4BX.
Tel: 01933 304858
www.racingpost.com/shop
E-mail: Shop@racingpost.com

**Advertisements**

kay.brown@archantdialogue.co.uk and gary.millone@archantdialogue.co.uk

**ISBN**

978-1-83950-068-8

# INDEX TO ADVERTISERS

# 2021

# RACING FIXTURES

# AND SALE DATES

(SUBJECT TO ALTERATION)

Flat fixtures are in **Black Type**; Jump in Light Type; Irish in *Italic*;
asterisk (★) indicates an evening or Twilight meeting;
† indicates an All Weather meeting. Sale dates are at foot of fixtures

# MARCH

| | Mon | Tue | Wed | Thu | Fri | Sat |
|---|---|---|---|---|---|---|
| | **1**<br>Ayr<br>Plumpton<br>**Wolverhampton†★** | **2**<br>Catterick Bridge<br>Leicester<br>**Newcastle†★** | **3**<br>**Kempton Park†★**<br>**Lingfield Park†**<br>Musselburgh<br>Wincanton | **4**<br>**Chelmsford City†★**<br>Ludlow<br>**Southwell†**<br>Taunton<br>*Clonmel* | **5**<br>Doncaster<br>**Lingfield Park†**<br>Newbury<br>**Newcastle†★**<br>*Dundalk (AW-E)* | **6**<br>Doncaster<br>Kelso<br>**Lingfield Park†**<br>Newbury<br>**Southwell†★**<br>*Navan* |
| | **7**<br>Huntingdon<br>Sedgefield<br>*Leopardstown* | **8**<br>Southwell<br>Wetherby<br>**Wolverhampton†★**<br>*Leopardstown* | **9**<br>Exeter<br>Newcastle<br>**Southwell†★**<br><br><br>Tattersalls<br>Ireland Sale | **10**<br>Catterick Bridge<br>Fontwell Park<br>**Kempton Park†★**<br>**Lingfield Park†** | **11**<br>Carlisle<br>**Newcastle†★**<br>**Southwell†**<br>Wincanton<br>*Thules*<br><br>Goffs Sale | **12**<br>Leicester<br>**Lingfield Park†**<br>Sandown Park<br>**Wolverhampton†★**<br>*Dundalk †★* | **13**<br>Ayr<br>**Chelmsford City†★**<br>Hereford<br>Sandown Park<br>**Wolverhampton†★**<br>*Gowran Park*<br>*Navan* |
| | **14**<br>Bangor-On-Dee<br>Warwick<br>*Limerick*<br>*Naas* | **15**<br>Plumpton<br>Stratford-On-Avon<br>Taunton<br>**Wolverhampton†★** | **16**<br>Cheltenham<br>**Newcastle†★**<br>Sedgefield<br>**Southwell†** | **17**<br>Cheltenham<br>Huntingdon<br>**Kempton Park†★**<br>**Lingfield Park†**<br>*Wexford*<br>*Down Royal* | **18**<br>**Chelmsford City†★**<br>Cheltenham<br>Doncaster<br>Hexham | **19**<br>Cheltenham<br>Fakenham<br>**Lingfield Park†**<br>**Southwell†**<br>*Dundalk †★* | **20**<br>Fontwell Park<br>Kempton Park<br>Newcastle<br>Uttoxeter<br>**Wolverhampton†★**<br>*Thules* |
| | **21**<br>Carlisle<br>Chepstow<br>*Downpatrick*<br>*Curragh* | **22**<br>Kelso<br>Plumpton<br>Southwell | **23**<br>Huntingdon<br>Taunton<br>Wetherby<br>*Clonmel* | **24**<br>Haydock Park<br>Hereford<br>Market Rasen | **25**<br>Chepstow<br>Ludlow<br>Sedgefield<br>*Cork* | **26**<br>**Lingfield Park†**<br>Musselburgh<br>Newbury<br>**Newcastle†★**<br>*Dundalk †★* | **27**<br>**Doncaster**<br>Kelso<br>**Kempton Park†**<br>Newbury<br>**Wolverhampton†★**<br>*Navan* |
| | **28**<br>Ascot<br>Carlisle<br>**Doncaster**<br>*Limerick*<br>*Naas* | **29**<br>Fontwell Park<br>Wincanton<br>**Wolverhampton†★** | **30**<br>Newcastle<br>Warwick<br>**Wolverhampton†★** | **31**<br>Hexham<br>**Kempton Park†★**<br>Ludlow<br>Southwell<br>*Dundalk †★*<br><br><br>Tattersalls Sale | | | |

# APRIL

| Sun | Mon | Tue | Wed | Thu | Fri | Sat |
|---|---|---|---|---|---|---|
| | | | | **1** Chelmsford City†★ Ffos Las Uttoxeter Wetherby *Clonmel ★* Tattersalls Sale | **2** Chelmsford City† Lingfield Park† Newcastle† | **3** Carlisle Haydock Park **Kempton Park**† **Musselburgh** Newton Abbot Stratford-On-Avon **Wolverhampton**†★ *Cork* *Fairyhouse* |
| **4** Hereford Market Rasen Plumpton **Southwell**† *Fairyhouse* *Cork* | **5** Chepstow Fakenham Huntingdon Plumpton **Redcar** **Wolverhampton**† *Cork* *Fairyhouse* | **6** **Bath** **Chelmsford City**†★ Exeter Pontefract | **7** Catterick Bridge Lingfield Park† Newcastle†★ **Nottingham** *Gowran Park ★* | **8** Aintree **Chelmsford City**†★ **Southwell**† Taunton *Gowran Park ★* Goffs Sale | **9** Aintree **Kempton Park**†★ **Leicester** Sedgefield *Wexford ★* | **10** Aintree Chepstow **Lingfield Park**† Newcastle **Wolverhampton**† *Dundalk (AW)* |
| **11** Plumpton Warwick *Leopardstown* | **12** Kelso **Redcar** **Windsor** **Wolverhampton**†★ Tattersalls Sale | **13** Newcastle†★ **Newmarket** **Windsor** **Wolverhampton**†★ Tattersalls Sale | **14** **Beverley** Cheltenham **Kempton Park**†★ **Newmarket** *Leopardstown* Tattersalls Sale | **15** Cheltenham Newcastle†★ Newmarket Ripon *Limerick* | **16** Ayr **Bath**★ Exeter★ Fontwell Park **Newbury** *Ballinrobe ★* | **17** Ayr Bangor-On-Dee **Brighton**★ Newbury Nottingham★ **Thirsk** *Curragh* |
| **18** Stratford-On-Avon Wincanton *Dundalk (AW)* *Tramore* | **19** Hexham Kempton Park★ Market Rasen★ **Pontefract** **Windsor** *Tramore ★* | **20** **Epsom Downs** Sedgefield **Southwell**†★ **Wolverhampton**†★ **Yarmouth** Goffs UK Sale | **21** Catterick Bridge **Lingfield Park**†★ Ludlow Perth Taunton★ *Dundalk †★* Goffs UK Sale | **22** **Beverley** **Chelmsford City**†★ Exeter★ Perth Warwick *Tipperary ★* *Kilbeggan ★* Goffs UK Sale | **23** Chepstow★ **Doncaster** Perth **Sandown Park** Worcester★ *Kilbeggan ★* *Cork* | **24** Doncaster★ Haydock Park Leicester Ripon Sandown Park **Wolverhampton**†★ *Navan* *Limerick* |
| **25** Salisbury Wetherby | **26** Ayr **Lingfield Park**† **Southwell**† **Thirsk**★ **Windsor**† *Naas★* | **27** Ayr★ **Brighton** **Lingfield Park**†★ **Nottingham** **Yarmouth** *Punchestown ★* | **28** Ascot **Brighton**★ **Chelmsford City**†★ Pontefract **Wolverhampton**† *Punchestown★* | **29** **Chelmsford City**†★ **Lingfield Park**† Musselburgh Redcar **Southwell**†★ *Punchestown ★* Goffs Sale Tattersalls Sale | **30** Cheltenham★ Chepstow **Goodwood** Musselburgh Newcastle†★ *Punchestown ★* Tattersalls Sale | |

# MAY

| Sun | Mon | Tue | Wed | Thu | Fri | Sat |
|---|---|---|---|---|---|---|
| **30**<br>Fontwell Park<br>Kelso<br>Uttoxeter<br>*Punchestown* | **31**<br>Cartmel<br>Huntingdon<br>**Leicester**<br>Redcar<br>**Windsor**<br>*Roscommon ★* | | | | | **1**<br>Doncaster★<br>**Goodwood**<br>Hexham★<br>**Newmarket**<br>Thirsk<br>Uttoxeter<br>*Punchestown* |
| **2**<br>**Hamilton Park**<br>**Newmarket**<br>**Salisbury**<br>*Sligo* | **3**<br>**Bath**<br>Kempton Park★<br>Warwick<br>**Windsor**<br>*Curragh*<br>*Down Royal* | **4**<br>Ayr<br>Fakenham<br>**Lingfield Park†**<br>**Wolverhampton†**★<br>*Ballinrobe ★*<br>*Gowran Park ★* | **5**<br>**Chester**<br>Fontwell Park★<br>Kelso<br>**Kempton Park†**★<br>Newton Abbot<br>*Gowran Park ★* | **6**<br>**Chelmsford City†**★<br>**Chester**<br>Huntingdon<br>Wincanton★<br>Worcester<br>*Tipperary ★* | **7**<br>**Ascot**<br>**Chester**<br>Market Rasen<br>**Nottingham**<br>**Ripon**★<br>**Wolverhampton†**★<br>*Downpatrick★*<br>*Cork ★* | **8**<br>**Ascot**<br>Haydock Park (Mixed)<br>Hexham<br>**Lingfield Park**<br>**Nottingham**<br>Thirsk★<br>Warwick★<br>*Cork ★*<br>*Naas* |
| **9**<br>Ludlow<br>Plumpton<br>*Killarney*<br>*Leopardstown* | **10**<br>**Catterick Bridge**<br>Ffos Las<br>Southwell★<br>**Windsor**★<br>**Wolverhampton†**<br>*Roscommon ★*<br>*Killarney ★* | **11**<br>**Beverley**<br>**Chepstow**<br>Sedgefield<br>*Killarney ★*<br><br><br>Tattersalls<br>Ireland Sale | **12**<br>**Bath**★<br>Newton Abbot<br>Perth★<br>Worcester<br>**York**<br>*Dundalk †★* | **13**<br>Fontwell Park★<br>**Newmarket**★<br>Perth<br>**Salisbury**<br>**York**<br>*Clonmel ★*<br><br>Arqana Sale | **14**<br>Aintree★<br>**Hamilton Park**★<br>**Newbury**<br>**Newmarket**<br>**York**<br>*Kilbeggan ★*<br>*Leopardstown ★*<br><br>Arqana Sale | **15**<br>Bangor-On-Dee<br>Doncaster★<br>**Newbury**<br>**Newmarket**<br>Thirsk<br>Uttoxeter★<br>*Navan*<br>*Wexford* |
| **16**<br>**Ripon**<br>Stratford-On-Avon<br>*Naas* | **17**<br>Carlisle<br>Ffos Las<br>**Leicester**★<br>Redcar<br>**Windsor**★<br><br><br>Goffs UK Sale | **18**<br>**Brighton**<br>Hexham★<br>Huntingdon★<br>**Nottingham**<br>**Wolverhampton†**<br>*Sligo ★*<br><br>Goffs UK Sale | **19**<br>Ayr<br>**Kempton Park†**★<br>Southwell★<br>Warwick<br>**Yarmouth**<br>*Cork ★*<br><br>Goffs UK Sale | **20**<br>**Chelmsford City†**★<br>**Lingfield Park**<br>Market Rasen<br>**Sandown Park**★<br>**Wolverhampton†**<br>*Tipperary ★*<br><br>Goffs UK Sale | **21**<br>**Bath**<br>**Catterick Bridge**★<br>**Goodwood**<br>**Haydock Park**<br>Worcester★<br>*Downpatrick ★*<br>*Wexford ★*<br><br>Tattersalls<br>Ireland Sale | **22**<br>**Goodwood**<br>**Haydock Park**<br>**Lingfield Park**★<br>**Newmarket**<br>Stratford-On-Avon★<br>**York**<br>*Curragh*<br><br>Arqana Sale |
| **23**<br>Fakenham<br>**Nottingham**<br>*Curragh* | **24**<br>**Brighton**<br>**Windsor**★<br>**Wolverhampton†**<br>*Ballinrobe ★* | **25**<br>Bangor-On-Dee<br>**Lingfield Park†**★<br>**Musselburgh**<br>**Newcastle†**★<br>Southwell<br>*Ballinrobe ★* | **26**<br>**Beverley**<br>**Hamilton Park**<br>Newton Abbot<br>Warwick★<br>*Gowran Park ★* | **27**<br>Carlisle★<br>**Haydock Park**<br>**Ripon**<br>**Sandown Park**★<br>**Yarmouth**<br>*Limerick ★* | **28**<br>**Brighton**<br>Carlisle<br>**Haydock Park**★<br>**Pontefract**★<br>Stratford-On-Avon★<br>**Wolverhampton†**<br>*Fairyhouse ★* | **29**<br>**Beverley**<br>Cartmel<br>**Catterick Bridge**<br>**Chester**<br>Ffos Las★<br>**Haydock Park**<br>**Salisbury**★<br>*Navan*<br>*Punchestown* |

# JUNE

| Sun | Mon | Tue | Wed | Thu | Fri | Sat |
|-----|-----|-----|-----|-----|-----|-----|
| | | **1**<br>Brighton<br>Leicester<br>Lingfield Park★<br>Redcar<br>*Tipperary ★* | **2**<br>Ayr<br>Cartmel<br>Kempton Park†★<br>Nottingham<br>Ripon★<br>*Wexford*<br>*Curragh ★* | **3**<br>Chelmsford City†★<br>Ffos Las<br>Hamilton Park<br>Uttoxeter<br>*Leopardstown★* | **4**<br>Bath★<br>Catterick Bridge<br>Doncaster★<br>Epsom Downs<br>Goodwood★<br>Market Rasen<br>*Down Royal ★*<br>*Tramore ★*<br><br>BBAG Sale | **5**<br>Chepstow★<br>Doncaster<br>Epsom Downs<br>Hexham<br>Lingfield Park★<br>Musselburgh<br>Worcester<br>*Tramore*<br>*Listowel* |
| **6**<br>Goodwood<br>Perth<br>*Listowel*<br>*Kilbeggan* | **7**<br>Leicester<br>Lingfield Park★<br>Pontefract★<br>Windsor★<br>*Gowran Park*<br>*Listowel* | **8**<br>Salisbury<br>Southwell<br>*Roscommon ★*<br><br><br>Goffs Sale | **9**<br>Fontwell Park<br>Hamilton Park★<br>Haydock Park<br>Kempton Park†★<br>Yarmouth<br>*Cork ★*<br><br>Goffs Sale | **10**<br>Haydock Park★<br>Newbury<br>Nottingham<br>Uttoxeter★<br>Yarmouth<br>*Leopardstown★*<br><br>Goffs Sale | **11**<br>Aintree★<br>Chepstow<br>Goodwood★<br>Newton Abbot★<br>Sandown Park<br>York<br>*Fairyhouse ★*<br>*Clonmel ★* | **12**<br>Bath<br>Hexham<br>Leicester★<br>Sandown Park<br>Worcester★<br>York<br>*Limerick*<br>*Downpatrick* |
| **13**<br>Doncaster<br>Salisbury<br>*Downpatrick*<br>*Gowran Park* | **14**<br>Carlisle<br>Lingfield Park★<br>Nottingham★<br>Windsor★<br>*Kilbeggan ★*<br><br>Goffs London Sale | **15**<br>Ascot<br>Beverley★<br>Brighton★<br>Stratford-On-Avon★<br>Thirsk<br>*Sligo ★* | **16**<br>Ascot<br>Chelmsford City†★<br>Hamilton Park<br>Ripon★<br>Uttoxeter<br>*Wexford ★* | **17**<br>Ascot<br>Chelmsford City†<br>Ffos Las★<br>Lingfield Park†★<br>Ripon<br>*Leopardstown ★* | **18**<br>Ascot<br>Goodwood★<br>Market Rasen<br>Newmarket★<br>Redcar<br>*Limerick ★*<br>*Down Royal ★* | **19**<br>Ascot<br>Ayr<br>Haydock Park★<br>Lingfield Park★<br>Newmarket<br>Perth<br>Redcar<br>*Down Royal* |
| **20**<br>Hexham<br>**Pontefract**<br>Worcester | **21**<br>Chepstow<br>Southwell<br>Windsor★<br>Wolverhampton†★<br>*Ballinrobe ★* | **22**<br>Beverley<br>Brighton<br>Newbury★<br>Newton Abbot★ | **23**<br>Bath★<br>Carlisle<br>Kempton Park†★<br>Salisbury<br>Worcester<br>*Naas ★*<br><br>Tattersalls<br>Ireland Sale | **24**<br>Hamilton Park★<br>Leicester★<br>Newcastle†★<br>Newmarket<br>Nottingham<br>*Tipperary ★*<br><br>Tattersalls<br>Ireland Sale | **25**<br>Cartmel<br>Chester★<br>Doncaster<br>Newcastle†★<br>Newmarket†<br>Yarmouth<br>*Curragh ★* | **26**<br>Chester<br>Doncaster★<br>Lingfield Park★<br>Newcastle†<br>Newmarket<br>Windsor<br>*Curragh* |
| **27**<br>Cartmel<br>Uttoxeter<br>**Windsor**<br>*Curragh* | **28**<br>Musselburgh★<br>Pontefract<br>Southwell<br>Windsor★<br><br><br>Arqana Sale | **29**<br>Brighton<br>Chepstow★<br>Hamilton Park<br>Stratford-On-Avon★<br>*Roscommon ★*<br><br>Arqana Sale | **30**<br>Bath★<br>Kempton Park†★<br>Musselburgh<br>Thirsk<br>Worcester<br><br>Arqana Sale | | | |

# JULY

| Sun | Mon | Tue | Wed | Thu | Fri | Sat |
|---|---|---|---|---|---|---|
| | | | | **1**<br>Epsom Downs★<br>Haydock Park★<br>Newbury★<br>Perth<br>Yarmouth<br>*Tipperary ★*<br>*Bellewstown ★*<br><br>Arqana Sale | **2**<br>Beverley★<br>Doncaster<br>Haydock Park★<br>Newton Abbot<br>Sandown Park★<br>*Bellewstown ★*<br>*Wexford ★* | **3**<br>Beverley<br>Carlisle★<br>Haydock Park<br>Leicester<br>Nottingham★<br>Sandown Park<br>*Bellewstown (E)*<br>*Naas* |
| **4**<br>Ayr<br>Market Rasen<br>*Limerick*<br>*Tramore* | **5**<br>Ayr<br>Ripon★<br>Windsor★<br>*Worcester* | **6**<br>Brighton★<br>Pontefract<br>*Uttoxeter*<br>**Wolverhampton†**<br>*Roscommon ★*<br><br>Tattersalls Sale | **7**<br>Bath★<br>Catterick Bridge<br>Kempton Park†<br>Lingfield Park<br>Yarmouth<br>*Fairyhouse ★*<br><br>Tattersalls Sale | **8**<br>Carlisle<br>Doncaster<br>Epsom Downs★<br>Newbury★<br>Newmarket<br>*Leopardstown ★* | **9**<br>Ascot<br>Chepstow★<br>Chester★<br>Newmarket<br>York<br>*Kilbeggan ★*<br>*Cork ★* | **10**<br>Ascot<br>Chester<br>Hamilton Park★<br>Newmarket<br>Salisbury★<br>York<br>*Limerick*<br>*Navan* |
| **11**<br>Perth<br>Stratford-On-Avon<br>*Fairyhouse*<br>*Sligo* | **12**<br>Ayr<br>Newton Abbot<br>**Wolverhampton†**<br>*Dundalk †*<br>*Killarney ★* | **13**<br>Bath<br>Beverley<br>Brighton★<br>*Southwell★*<br>*Killarney ★*<br>*Downpatrick* | **14**<br>Catterick Bridge<br>Lingfield Park<br>Uttoxeter<br>**Wolverhampton†★**<br>*Yarmouth★*<br>*Killarney ★*<br><br>Tattersalls<br>Ireland Sale | **15**<br>Chepstow<br>Epsom Downs★<br>Hamilton Park<br>Leicester<br>*Worcester ★*<br>*Killarney*<br>*Leopardstown ★*<br><br>Tattersalls<br>Ireland Sale | **16**<br>Hamilton Park★<br>Haydock Park<br>Newbury<br>Newmarket★<br>Nottingham<br>Pontefract★<br>*Kilbeggan ★*<br>*Killarney* | **17**<br>Cartmel<br>Doncaster★<br>Haydock Park★<br>Market Rasen<br>Newbury<br>Newmarket<br>Ripon<br>*Curragh* |
| **18**<br>Newton Abbot<br>Redcar<br>Stratford-On-Avon<br>*Curragh*<br>*Tipperary* | **19**<br>Ayr<br>Beverley<br>Cartmel<br>Windsor★<br>*Ballinrobe ★* | **20**<br>Chelmsford City†★<br>Musselburgh<br>**Wolverhampton†**<br>*Ballinrobe ★* | **21**<br>Bath<br>Catterick Bridge<br>Leicester★<br>Lingfield Park<br>Sandown Park★<br>*Naas ★* | **22**<br>Doncaster★<br>Newbury★<br>Sandown Park<br>*Worcester*<br>*Yarmouth*<br>*Leopardstown ★*<br>*Limerick ★* | **23**<br>Ascot<br>Chepstow★<br>Newmarket★<br>Thirsk<br>*Uttoxeter*<br>*York★*<br>*Down Royal ★*<br>*Cork ★* | **24**<br>Ascot<br>Lingfield Park★<br>Newcastle†<br>Newmarket<br>Salisbury★<br>York<br>*Gowran Park* |
| **25**<br>Pontefract<br>*Uttoxeter* | **26**<br>Ayr<br>Newton Abbot<br>Windsor★<br>**Wolverhampton†★**<br>*Galway ★* | **27**<br>Beverley<br>Goodwood<br>*Perth★*<br>*Worcester★*<br>*Yarmouth*<br>*Galway ★* | **28**<br>Goodwood<br>Leicester★<br>*Perth*<br>Redcar<br>Sandown Park★<br>*Galway ★* | **29**<br>Epsom Downs★<br>Ffos Las★<br>Goodwood<br>Newcastle†★<br>Nottingham<br>*Stratford-On-Avon*<br>*Galway* | **30**<br>Bangor-On-Dee<br>Bath★<br>Goodwood<br>Musselburgh★<br>Newmarket★<br>**Wolverhampton†**<br>*Galway ★* | **31**<br>Doncaster<br>Goodwood<br>Hamilton Park★<br>Lingfield Park★<br>Newmarket<br>Thirsk<br>*Galway* |

# AUGUST

| Sun | Mon | Tue | Wed | Thu | Fri | Sat |
|---|---|---|---|---|---|---|
| **1**<br>Chester<br>Market Rasen<br>*Galway* | **2**<br>Carlisle★<br>Kempton Park†<br>Ripon<br>Windsor★<br>*Cork*<br>*Naas* | **3**<br>Catterick Bridge<br>Ffos Las<br>*Roscommon ★* | **4**<br>Bath<br>Brighton<br>Kempton Park★<br>Pontefract<br>Yarmouth★<br>*Sligo*<br><br>Goffs UK Sale | **5**<br>Brighton<br>Doncaster★<br>Haydock Park<br>Newcastle†★<br>Sandown Park★<br>Yarmouth<br>*Sligo ★*<br>*Leopardstown ★*<br>Goffs UK Sale | **6**<br>Brighton<br>Haydock Park★<br>Musselburgh<br>Newmarket★<br>Thirsk<br>*Wexford ★*<br>*Tipperary ★* | **7**<br>Ascot<br>Ayr★<br>Haydock Park★<br>Lingfield Park★<br>Newmarket<br>Redcar<br>*Kilbeggan ★*<br>*Cork* |
| **8**<br>Leicester<br>Windsor<br>*Downpatrick*<br>*Curragh* | **9**<br>Ayr<br>Windsor★<br>Wolverhampton†<br>*Ballinrobe ★* | **10**<br>Chelmsford City†★<br>Lingfield Park<br>Nottingham<br><br><br>Tattersalls<br>Ireland Sale | **11**<br>Beverley<br>Ffos Las★<br>Kempton Park†<br>Salisbury<br>Yarmouth<br>*Gowran Park ★*<br>Tattersalls<br>Ireland Sale | **12**<br>Beverley<br>Ffos Las<br>Lingfield Park★<br>Salisbury<br>*Leopardstown ★*<br>*Tramore ★* | **13**<br>Newbury<br>Newmarket★<br>Nottingham<br>Thirsk★<br>Wolverhampton<br>*Curragh ★*<br>*Tramore ★* | **14**<br>Bath★<br>Doncaster<br>Market Rasen★<br>Newbury<br>Newmarket<br>Perth<br>**Ripon**<br>*Tramore ★*<br>Arqana Sale |
| **15**<br>Pontefract<br>Southwell†<br>*Tramore*<br>*Dundalk †*<br><br>Arqana Sale | **16**<br>Bangor-On-Dee★<br>Catterick Bridge<br>Lingfield Park†<br>Windsor★<br>*Roscommon ★*<br>Arqana Sale | **17**<br>Hamilton Park<br>Kempton Park†<br>*Sligo ★*<br><br>Arqana Sale | **18**<br>Bath<br>Carlisle<br>Kempton Park†★<br>Worcester★<br>**York**<br>Arqana Sale | **19**<br>Chepstow<br>Fontwell Park★<br>Stratford-On-Avon<br>Windsor★<br>York<br>*Killarney ★* | **20**<br>Musselburgh<br>Newcastle†★<br>Salisbury★<br>Sandown Park<br>Wolverhampton†★<br>York<br>*Kilbeggan ★*<br>*Killarney ★* | **21**<br>Chelmsford City†★<br>Chester<br>Lingfield Park★<br>Newton Abbot<br>Sandown Park<br>York<br>*Killarney ★*<br>*Curragh ★* |
| **22**<br>Brighton<br>Worcester<br>*Naas* | **23**<br>Brighton<br>Chepstow<br>*Ballinrobe ★* | **24**<br>Bangor-On-Dee<br>Yarmouth<br>*Bellewstown ★*<br><br><br>Goffs UK Sale | **25**<br>Catterick Bridge<br>Fontwell Park★<br>Kempton Park†★<br>Lingfield Park<br>Musselburgh<br>*Bellewstown ★*<br>Goffs UK Sale | **26**<br>Carlisle<br>Chelmsford City†<br>Ffos Las<br>Lingfield Park†★<br>*Sedgefield★*<br>*Tipperary ★*<br>Goffs UK Sale | **27**<br>Ffos Las<br>Goodwood★<br>Hamilton Park★<br>Newmarket<br>Thirsk<br>*Curragh ★*<br>*Down Royal ★* | **28**<br>Beverley<br>Cartmel<br>Goodwood<br>Newmarket<br>Redcar★<br>Windsor★<br>*Navan* |
| **29**<br>Beverley<br>Goodwood<br>Yarmouth | **30**<br>Cartmel<br>Chepstow<br>Epsom Downs<br>Ripon<br>Southwell†<br>*Roscommon ★*<br>*Downpatrick*<br>Tattersalls Sale | **31**<br>Epsom Downs<br>Newton Abbot★<br>Ripon<br><br><br>Tattersalls Sale | | | | |

# SEPTEMBER

| Sun | Mon | Tue | Wed | Thu | Fri | Sat |
|---|---|---|---|---|---|---|
| | | | **1**<br>**Bath**<br>**Hamilton Park**★<br>**Lingfield Park**<br>Uttoxeter<br>Worcester★<br>Gowran Park<br><br>Tattersalls Sale | **2**<br>Chelmsford City†★<br>**Haydock Park**<br>**Newcastle**†★<br>**Salisbury**<br>Sedgefield<br>Clonmel ★<br>Laytown ★<br><br>Tattersalls Sale | **3**<br>**Ascot**<br>**Haydock Park**<br>**Kempton Park**†★<br>**Newcastle**†<br>Down Royal ★<br>Kilbeggan ★<br><br><br>BBAG Sale | **4**<br>**Ascot**<br>**Haydock Park**<br>**Kempton Park**†<br>Stratford-On-Avon<br>**Thirsk**<br>**Wolverhampton**†★<br>Navan<br>Wexford |
| **5**<br>Fontwell Park<br>**York** | **6**<br>**Brighton**<br>Newton Abbot<br>Perth<br>Galway ★ | **7**<br>**Catterick Bridge**<br>**Goodwood**<br>**Leicester**<br>Galway ★ | **8**<br>**Carlisle**<br>**Doncaster**<br>Uttoxeter<br>Cork (E) | **9**<br>**Chepstow**<br>**Doncaster**<br>**Epsom Downs**<br><br><br>Goffs Yorton Sale | **10**<br>**Chester**<br>**Doncaster**<br>**Salisbury**★<br>**Sandown Park**<br>Ballinrobe ★ | **11**<br>**Bath**<br>**Chester**<br>**Doncaster**<br>**Lingfield Park**<br>**Musselburgh**★<br>Leopardstown<br><br>Goffs Sale |
| **12**<br>**Bath**<br>**Musselburgh**<br>Curragh | **13**<br>**Brighton**<br>**Thirsk**<br>Worcester | **14**<br>**Redcar**<br>Southwell<br>**Yarmouth**<br>Punchestown<br><br>Goffs UK Sale | **15**<br>**Beverley**<br>Kelso★<br>**Sandown Park**<br>**Yarmouth**<br>Sligo<br><br>Goffs UK Sale | **16**<br>**Ayr**<br>**Pontefract**<br>**Yarmouth**<br>Naas | **17**<br>**Ayr**<br>**Newbury**<br>Newton Abbot<br>Downpatrick<br>Dundalk †★ | **18**<br>**Ayr**<br>**Catterick Bridge**<br>**Newbury**<br>**Newmarket**<br>**Wolverhampton**†★<br>Gowran Park<br>Navan |
| **19**<br>**Hamilton Park**<br>Plumpton<br>Listowel | **20**<br>**Hamilton Park**<br>**Leicester**<br>Warwick<br>Fairyhouse ★<br>Listowel | **21**<br>**Beverley**<br>**Lingfield Park**†<br>Warwick<br>Listowel<br><br>Tattersalls<br>Ireland Sale | **22**<br>**Goodwood**<br>Perth<br>**Redcar**<br>Listowel<br><br>Tattersalls<br>Ireland Sale | **23**<br>**Newmarket**<br>Perth<br>**Pontefract**<br>Listowel<br><br>Tattersalls<br>Ireland Sale | **24**<br>**Haydock Park**<br>**Newmarket**<br>Worcester<br>Dundalk †★<br>Listowel | **25**<br>**Haydock Park**<br>Market Rasen<br>**Newmarket**<br>**Ripon**<br>Listowel<br>Curragh |
| **26**<br>**Epsom Downs**<br>Ffos Las<br>Curragh | **27**<br>**Bath**<br>**Hamilton Park**<br>Newton Abbot<br>Roscommon | **28**<br>**Ayr**<br>Sedgefield<br>Southwell<br>Cork<br><br>Goffs Sale | **29**<br>Bangor-On-Dee<br>**Catterick Bridge**<br>**Nottingham**<br>Bellewstown<br><br>Goffs Sale | **30**<br>**Lingfield Park**†<br>**Salisbury**<br>Warwick<br>Bellewstown<br>Clonmel<br><br>Goffs Sale | | |

# OCTOBER

| Sun | Mon | Tue | Wed | Thu | Fri | Sat |
|---|---|---|---|---|---|---|
| **31**<br>Carlisle<br>Huntingdon<br>*Cork*<br>*Naas* | | | | | **1**<br>**Ascot**<br>Fontwell Park<br>Hexham<br>*Dundalk †★*<br>*Gowran Park*<br><br>Goffs Sale | **2**<br>**Ascot**<br>Fontwell Park<br>**Newmarket**<br>Redcar<br>**Wolverhampton†★**<br>*Gowran Park*<br>*Killarney*<br>Arqana Sale |
| **3**<br>Kelso<br>Uttoxeter<br>*Killarney*<br>*Tipperary* | **4**<br>**Pontefract**<br>Stratford-On-Avon<br>**Windsor**<br>*Tipperary* | **5**<br>**Brighton**<br>Huntingdon<br>**Leicester**<br>*Galway*<br><br>Tattersalls Sale | **6**<br>Ludlow<br>**Nottingham**<br>Sedgefield<br>*Navan*<br><br>Tattersalls Sale | **7**<br>**Ayr**<br>Exeter<br>Worcester<br>*Thules*<br><br>Tattersalls Sale | **8**<br>Chepstow<br>**Newmarket**<br>**York**<br>*Downpatrick*<br>*Dundalk †★* | **9**<br>Chepstow<br>Hexham<br>**Newmarket**<br>**York**<br>*Fairyhouse*<br>*Limerick* |
| **10**<br>**Goodwood**<br>Newton Abbot<br>*Limerick*<br>*Curragh* | **11**<br>**Musselburgh**<br>**Windsor**<br>**Yarmouth**<br><br>Tattersalls 2 Sale | **12**<br>Hereford<br>Huntingdon<br>**Leicester**<br>*Punchestown*<br><br>Tattersalls Sale | **13**<br>**Bath**<br>**Nottingham**<br>Wetherby<br>*Punchestown*<br><br>Tattersalls Sale | **14**<br>**Brighton**<br>Carlisle<br>Wincanton<br>*Tramore*<br>*Curragh*<br><br>Tattersalls Sale | **15**<br>Fakenham<br>**Haydock Park**<br>Redcar<br>Uttoxeter<br>*Dundalk †★*<br><br>Tattersalls Sale | **16**<br>**Ascot**<br>**Catterick Bridge**<br>Ffos Las<br>Market Rasen<br>Stratford-On-Avon<br>**Wolverhampton†★**<br>*Leopardstown*<br>Tattersalls Sale |
| **17**<br>Kempton Park<br>Sedgefield<br>*Cork*<br>*Naas* | **18**<br>Plumpton<br>**Pontefract**<br>**Windsor**<br><br>Arqana Sale | **19**<br>Exeter<br>**Newcastle†**<br>**Yarmouth**<br>*Gowran Park*<br><br>Arqana Sale | **20**<br>Fontwell Park<br>**Newmarket**<br>Worcester<br>*Navan*<br><br>Arqana Sale<br>Goffs UK Sale | **21**<br>Carlisle<br>Ludlow<br>Newton Abbot<br>*Thules*<br><br>Arqana Sale<br>Goffs UK Sale | **22**<br>Cheltenham<br>**Doncaster**<br>**Newbury**<br>*Dundalk †★*<br>*Sligo*<br><br>Arqana Sale<br>BBAG Sale | **23**<br>Cheltenham<br>**Doncaster**<br>Kelso<br>**Newbury**<br>*Leopardstown*<br>*Galway*<br>Arqana Sale<br>BBAG Sale |
| **24**<br>Aintree<br>Wincanton<br>*Galway*<br>*Wexford* | **25**<br>Ayr<br>**Leicester**<br>**Redcar**<br>*Wexford*<br>*Galway*<br><br>Tattersalls Sale | **26**<br>Bangor-On-Dee<br>**Catterick Bridge**<br>Chepstow<br>*Curragh*<br><br>Tattersalls Sale | **27**<br>Fakenham<br>**Nottingham**<br>Taunton<br>*Dundalk †*<br><br>Tattersalls Sale | **28**<br>**Lingfield Park†**<br>Southwell<br>Stratford-On-Avon<br>*Clonmel*<br><br>Tattersalls Sale | **29**<br>**Newmarket**<br>Uttoxeter<br>Wetherby<br>*Dundalk †★*<br>*Down Royal*<br><br>Tattersalls Sale | **30**<br>Ascot<br>Ayr<br>**Newmarket**<br>Wetherby<br>*Down Royal* |

# NOVEMBER

| Sun | Mon | Tue | Wed | Thu | Fri | Sat |
|---|---|---|---|---|---|---|
| | **1** | **2** | **3** | **4** | **5** | **6** |
| | Hereford<br>**Kempton Park**†<br>Plumpton | Exeter<br>**Redcar**<br>**Southwell**†<br>*Fairyhouse* | Chepstow<br>Musselburgh<br>**Nottingham**<br>*Dundalk (AW)* | Ludlow<br>Newbury<br>Sedgefield<br>*Thules* | Fontwell Park<br>Hexham<br>Warwick<br>*Dundalk* †★ | Aintree<br>**Doncaster**<br>Kelso<br>Wincanton<br>*Naas* |
| | Goffs Sale | Goffs Sale | Goffs Sale | | Tattersalls<br>Ireland Sale | Tattersalls<br>Ireland Sale |
| **7** | **8** | **9** | **10** | **11** | **12** | **13** |
| Ffos Las<br>Sandown Park<br>*Navan* | Carlisle<br>Kempton Park<br>**Wolverhampton**† | Hereford<br>Huntingdon<br>Lingfield Park<br>*Fairyhouse* | Bangor-On-Dee<br>Exeter<br>*Dundalk (AW)* | Market Rasen<br>Sedgefield<br>Taunton<br>*Clonmel* | Cheltenham<br>**Newcastle**†<br>Southwell<br>*Dundalk* †★ | Cheltenham<br>**Lingfield Park**†<br>Uttoxeter<br>Wetherby<br>**Wolverhampton**†★<br>*Punchestown* |
| Tattersalls<br>Ireland Sale | Tattersalls<br>Ireland Sale | Tattersalls<br>Ireland Sale | Tattersalls<br>Ireland Sale | Tattersalls<br>Ireland Sale | Tattersalls<br>Ireland Sale | Arqana Sale<br>Tattersalls<br>Ireland Sale |
| **14** | **15** | **16** | **17** | **18** | **19** | **20** |
| Cheltenham<br>Fontwell Park<br>*Punchestown*<br>*Cork* | Leicester<br>Plumpton | Ayr<br>Fakenham<br>Lingfield Park<br>*Limerick* | Ffos Las<br>Hexham<br>Warwick<br>*Dundalk (AW)* | Market Rasen<br>Newcastle<br>Wincanton<br>*Thules* | Ascot<br>Catterick Bridge<br>Chepstow<br>*Dundalk* †★ | Ascot<br>Haydock Park<br>Huntingdon<br>**Lingfield Park**†<br>**Wolverhampton**†★<br>*Gowran Park* |
| Tattersalls<br>Ireland Sale<br>Goffs Sale<br>Arqana Sale | Arqana Sale<br>Goffs Sale | Arqana Sale<br>Goffs Sale | Arqana Sale<br>Goffs Sale | Goffs Sale | Goffs Sale | Goffs Sale |
| **21** | **22** | **23** | **24** | **25** | **26** | **27** |
| Exeter<br>Uttoxeter<br>*Navan* | Kempton Park<br>Ludlow<br>Musselburgh | Sedgefield<br>Southwell<br>**Wolverhampton**†★<br>*Punchestown* | Hereford<br>Wetherby<br>*Dundalk (AW)* | Lingfield Park<br>Taunton<br>**Wolverhampton**†<br>*Thules* | Doncaster<br>Newbury<br>**Southwell**†<br>*Dundalk* †★ | Bangor-On-Dee<br>Doncaster<br>Newbury<br>Newcastle<br>**Wolverhampton**†★<br>*Fairyhouse* |
| Goffs Sale | Tattersalls Sale | | Tattersalls Sale | Tattersalls Sale | Tattersalls Sale | Tattersalls Sale |
| **28** | **29** | **30** | | | | |
| Carlisle<br>Leicester<br>*Fairyhouse* | **Wolverhampton**†★ | **Lingfield Park**†<br>Southwell | | | | |
| | Tattersalls Sale | Tattersalls Sale | | | | |

# DECEMBER

| Sun | Mon | Tue | Wed | Thu | Fri | Sat |
|-----|-----|-----|-----|-----|-----|-----|
| | | | **1** Haydock Park **Lingfield Park†** *Dundalk (AW)* | **2** Leicester Market Rasen Wincanton *Clonmel* | **3** Exeter Sandown Park Sedgefield *Dundalk †★* | **4** Aintree Chepstow Sandown Park Wetherby **Wolverhampton†★** *Navan* |
| | | | Tattersalls Sale | Tattersalls Sale | Goffs UK Sale | Arqana Sale |
| **5** Huntingdon Kelso *Cork* *Punchestown* | **6** Lingfield Park Ludlow Musselburgh | **7** Fontwell Park **Southwell†★** Uttoxeter *Tramore* | **8** Hexham Leicester **Lingfield Park†** *Dundalk †* | **9** Newcastle Taunton Warwick | **10** Bangor-On-Dee Cheltenham Doncaster *Dundalk †★* | **11** Cheltenham Doncaster Hereford **Newcastle†** **Wolverhampton†★** *Fairyhouse* |
| Arqana Sale | Arqana Sale | Arqana Sale | Goffs Sale | Goffs Sale | | |
| **12** Carlisle Southwell | **13** Plumpton **Wolverhampton†★** | **14** Catterick Bridge Wincanton **Wolverhampton†★** | **15** **Lingfield Park†** Newbury *Dundalk †★* | **16** Exeter Ffos Las **Southwell†** *Naas* | **17** Ascot **Southwell†** Uttoxeter *Dundalk †★* | **18** Ascot Haydock Park **Lingfield Park†** Newcastle *Navan* |
| **19** Fakenham *Thurles* | **20** Lingfield Park Musselburgh | **21** Ayr Plumpton | **22** Ludlow **Southwell†** | **23** | **24** | **25** |
| **26** Fontwell Park Huntingdon Kempton Park Market Rasen Sedgefield Wetherby Wincanton **Wolverhampton†** *Down Royal* *Leopardstown* *Limerick* | **27** Chepstow Kempton Park Wetherby **Wolverhampton†** *Leopardstown* *Limerick* | **28** Catterick Bridge Leicester **Lingfield Park†** *Leopardstown* *Limerick* | **29** Doncaster Kelso Newbury **Southwell†** *Leopardstown* *Limerick* | **30** Haydock Park **Lingfield Park†** Taunton | **31** **Lingfield Park†** Uttoxeter Warwick *Punchestown* | |

# DATES OF PRINCIPAL RACES

(SUBJECT TO ALTERATION)

## JANUARY

| | | |
|---|---|---|
| Paddy Power Millionaire Handicap Chase | CHELTENHAM | 1st |
| Dornan Engineering Relkeel Hurdle | CHELTENHAM | 1st |
| Paddy Power Novices' Chase (registered as the Dipper Novices' Chase) | CHELTENHAM | 1st |
| Ballymore Novices' Hurdle | CHELTENHAM | 1st |
| Cheltenham Pony Club 'Junior' National Hunt Flat Race | CHELTENHAM | 1st |
| Savills New Year's Day Chase | TRAMORE | 1st |
| Unibet Tolworth Novices' Hurdle | SANDOWN PARK | 2nd |
| Unibet Mares Hurdle | SANDOWN PARK | 2nd |
| John & Chich Fowler Memorial EBF Mares' Chase | FAIRYHOUSE | 3rd |
| Ladbrokes Silviniaco Conti Chase | KEMPTON PARK | 9th |
| Ladbrokes Lanzarote Handicap Hurdle | KEMPTON PARK | 9th |
| Lawlors Of Naas Novices' Hurdle | NAAS | 10th |
| Pertemps Network Mares' Steeple Chase | LEICESTER | 13th |
| Alan Swinbank Mares' Standard Open National Hunt Flat Race | MARKET RASEN | 16th |
| McCoy Contractors Civil Engineering Classic Handicap Chase | WARWICK | 16th |
| McCoy Contractors Civils And Infrastructure Hampton Novices' Chase | WARWICK | 16th |
| Ballymore Leamington Novices' Hurdle | WARWICK | 16th |
| Dan & Joan Moore Memorial Handicap Chase | FAIRYHOUSE | 16th |
| Sky Bet Moscow Flyer Novices' Hurdle | PUNCHESTOWN | 17th |
| Sky Bet Killiney Novices' Chase | PUNCHESTOWN | 17th |
| Matchbook Betting Exchange Clarence House Chase | ASCOT | 23rd |
| Matchbook Betting Podcast Mares' Hurdle (registered as the Warfield Mares' Hurdle) | ASCOT | 23rd |
| Matchbook Better Way To Bet Holloway's Handicap Hurdle | ASCOT | 23rd |
| Peter Marsh Handicap Chase | HAYDOCK PARK | 23rd |
| The New One Unibet Hurdle (registered as the Champion Hurdle Trial) | HAYDOCK PARK | 23rd |
| Unibet Novices' Chase (registered as the Altcar Novices' Chase) | HAYDOCK PARK | 23rd |
| Sky Bet Supreme Trial Rossington Main Novices' Hurdle | HAYDOCK PARK | 23rd |
| Navan Handicap Hurdle | NAVAN | 23rd |
| Horse & Jockey Hotel Chase | THULES | 24th |
| Coolmore N.H. Sires Kew Gardens Irish EBF Mares Novices' Chase | THULES | 24th |
| Goffs Thyestes Handicap Chase | GOWRAN PARK | 28th |
| Galmoy Hurdle | GOWRAN PARK | 28th |
| Sky Bet Fillies' Juvenile Hurdle | DONCASTER | 29th |
| Pertemps Lady Protectress Mares' Chase | HUNTINGDON | 29th |
| Paddy Power Cotswold Chase | CHELTENHAM | 30th |
| Paddy Power Trophy Handicap Chase | CHELTENHAM | 30th |
| galliardhomes.com Cleeve Hurdle | CHELTENHAM | 30th |
| Ballymore Novices' Hurdle (registered as the Classic Novices' Hurdle) | CHELTENHAM | 30th |
| JCB Triumph Trial Juvenile Hurdle (registered as the Finesse Juvenile Hurdle) | CHELTENHAM | 30th |
| Sky Bet Handicap Chase | DONCASTER | 30th |
| Yorkshire Rose Mares' Hurdle | DONCASTER | 30th |
| Lightning Novices' Chase | DONCASTER | 30th |
| Albert Bartlett River Don Novices' Hurdle | DONCASTER | 30th |
| Solerina Mares' Novices' Hurdle | FAIRYHOUSE | 30th |
| Woodlands Novices' Chase | NAAS | 31st |
| Limestone Lad Hurdle | NAAS | 31st |

## FEBRUARY

| | | |
|---|---|---|
| Betway Winter Derby Trial Stakes | LINGFIELD PARK | 6th |
| Betway Kachy Stakes | LINGFIELD PARK | 6th |
| Virgin Bet Heroes Handicap Hurdle | SANDOWN PARK | 6th |
| Virgin Bet Scilly Isles Novices' Chase | SANDOWN PARK | 6th |
| Virgin Bet Contenders Hurdle | SANDOWN PARK | 6th |
| William Hill Towton Novices' Chase | WETHERBY | 6th |
| Chanelle Pharma Irish Champion Hurdle | LEOPARDSTOWN | 6th |
| Ladbrokes Dublin Chase | LEOPARDSTOWN | 6th |
| Ladbrokes Handicap Chase | LEOPARDSTOWN | 6th |
| Patrick Ward & Company Solicitors Arkle Novice Chase | LEOPARDSTOWN | 6th |
| Goffs Future Stars INH Flat Race | LEOPARDSTOWN | 6th |
| Matheson Handicap Chase | LEOPARDSTOWN | 6th |
| The Nathaniel Lacy & Partners Solicitors Novice Hurdle | LEOPARDSTOWN | 6th |
| bet365 Scottish Triumph Hurdle | MUSSELBURGH | 7th |
| Gaelic Plant Hire Leopardstown Chase | LEOPARDSTOWN | 7th |
| Chanelle Pharma Novice Hurdle | LEOPARDSTOWN | 7th |
| Irish Stallion Farms EBF Paddy Mullins Mares Handicap Hurdle | LEOPARDSTOWN | 7th |
| Flogas Novice Chase | LEOPARDSTOWN | 7th |
| William Fry Handicap Hurdle | LEOPARDSTOWN | 7th |

| | | |
|---|---|---|
| Coolmore Stud NH Sires Kew Gardens Mares INH Flat Race | LEOPARDSTOWN | 7th |
| Tattersalls Ireland Spring 4yo Hurdle | LEOPARDSTOWN | 7th |
| Paddy Power Irish Gold Cup | LEOPARDSTOWN | 7th |
| Betway Sidney Banks Memorial Novices' Hurdle | HUNTINGDON | 11th |
| Betfair Hurdle | NEWBURY | 13th |
| Betfair Denman Chase | NEWBURY | 13th |
| Betfair Exchange Chase (registered as the Game Spirit) | NEWBURY | 13th |
| Racing… Only Bettor Podcast Bumper | NEWBURY | 13th |
| Kingmaker Novices' Chase | WARWICK | 13th |
| St Mary's Lands Warwick Mares' Hurdle | WARWICK | 13th |
| Opera Hat Mares' Chase | NAAS | 13th |
| Racing TV Novices' Hurdle | EXETER | 14th |
| Racing TV Mares' Chase | EXETER | 14th |
| EBF Novices' Hurdle | PUNCHESTOWN | 14th |
| Grand National Trial Handicap Chase | PUNCHESTOWN | 14th |
| Jane Seymour Mares' Novices' Hurdle | SANDOWN PARK | 18th |
| Powerstown Novices' Hurdle | CLONMEL | 18th |
| Betfair Ascot Chase | ASCOT | 20th |
| Ascot Swinley Chase | ASCOT | 20th |
| Sodexo Reynoldstown Novices' Chase | ASCOT | 20th |
| William Hill Grand National Trial Handicap Chase | HAYDOCK PARK | 20th |
| William Hill Rendlesham Hurdle | HAYDOCK PARK | 20th |
| Albert Bartlett Prestige Novices' Hurdle | HAYDOCK PARK | 20th |
| Betway Kingwell Hurdle | WINCANTON | 20th |
| Red Mills Trial Hurdle | GOWRAN PARK | 20th |
| Red Mills Chase | GOWRAN PARK | 20th |
| Saudi Cup | RIYADH | 20th |
| Ten Up Novice Chase | NAVAN | 21st |
| Boyne Hurdle | NAVAN | 21st |
| Quevega Mares Hurdle | PUNCHESTOWN | 24th |
| Michael Purcell Novice Hurdle | ThuLES | 25th |
| Close Brothers Handicap Chase | KEMPTON PARK | 27th |
| Close Brothers Pendil Novices' Chase | KEMPTON PARK | 27th |
| Sky Bet Dovecote Novices' Hurdle | KEMPTON PARK | 27th |
| Close Brothers Adonis Juvenile Hurdle | KEMPTON PARK | 27th |
| Betway Winter Derby Stakes | LINGFIELD PARK | 27th |
| Betway Hever Sprint Stakes | LINGFIELD PARK | 27th |
| Winning Fair Juvenile Hurdle | FAIRYHOUSE | 27th |
| At The Races Bobbyjo Chase | FAIRYHOUSE | 27th |
| Paddy Power Newlands Chase | FONTWELL PARK | 28th |
| Stella Artois National Spirit Hurdle | NAAS | 28th |
| Nas na Riogh Novices' Handicap Chase | NAAS | 28th |
| Paddy Power Johnstown Novices' Hurdle | NAAS | 28th |

# MARCH

| | | |
|---|---|---|
| Patton Stakes | DUNDALK | 5th |
| Sky Sports Racing Mares' Novices' Hurdle | DONCASTER | 6th |
| Premier Chase | KELSO | 6th |
| bet365 Premier Hurdle | KELSO | 6th |
| Ladbrokes Spring Cup Stakes | LINGFIELD PARK | 6th |
| William Hill Supporting Greatwood Gold Cup Handicap Chase | NEWBURY | 6th |
| Flyingbolt Novices' Chase | NAVAN | 6th |
| TRI Equestrian Carrickmines Handicap Chase | LEOPARDSTOWN | 7th |
| Paddy Power EBF 'National Hunt' Novices' Handicap Hurdle Final | SANDOWN PARK | 13th |
| Paddy Power Imperial Cup Handicap Hurdle | SANDOWN PARK | 13th |
| Paddy Power Novices' Handicap Chase | SANDOWN PARK | 13th |
| EBF Mares' Standard Open National Hunt Flat Race | WOLVERHAMPTON | 13th |
| Bombardier Lady Wulfruna Stakes | GOWRAN PARK | 13th |
| Shamrock Handicap Chase | NAVAN | 13th |
| EBF Novice Final Handicap Chase | NAVAN | 13th |
| Leinster National | NAAS | 14th |
| An Uaimh Chase | NAAS | 14th |
| Irish Racing Writes Kingsfurze Novice Hurdle | NAAS | 14th |
| Directors Plate Novice Chase | LIMERICK | 14th |
| Shannon Spray EBF Mares Novice Hurdle | LIMERICK | 14th |
| Dawn Run EBF Mares Novice Chase | CHELTENHAM | 16th |
| Sky Bet Supreme Novices' Hurdle | CHELTENHAM | 16th |
| Sporting Life Arkle Challenge Trophy Novices' Chase | CHELTENHAM | 16th |
| Ultima Handicap Chase | CHELTENHAM | 16th |
| Unibet Champion Hurdle | CHELTENHAM | 16th |
| Close Brothers Mares' Hurdle (registered as the David Nicholson Mares' Hurdle) | CHELTENHAM | 16th |
| Boodles Juvenile Handicap Hurdle (registered as the Fred Winter Juvenile Handicap Hurdle) | CHELTENHAM | 16th |
| National Hunt Challenge Cup Amateur Jockeys' Novices' Steeple Chase | CHELTENHAM | 16th |
| Ballymore Novices' Hurdle (registered as the Baring Bingham Novices' Hurdle) | CHELTENHAM | 17th |

| | | |
|---|---|---|
| Brown Advisory Novices' Chase (registered as The Broadway Novices' Chase) | CHELTENHAM | 17th |
| Coral Cup Handicap Hurdle | CHELTENHAM | 17th |
| Betway Queen Mother Champion Chase | CHELTENHAM | 17th |
| Glenfarclas Cross Country Chase | CHELTENHAM | 17th |
| Johnny Henderson Grand Annual Challenge Cup Handicap Chase | CHELTENHAM | 17th |
| Weatherbys Champion Bumper | CHELTENHAM | 17th |
| Marsh Novices' Chase (registered as the Golden Miller Novices' Chase) | CHELTENHAM | 18th |
| Pertemps Network Final Handicap Hurdle | CHELTENHAM | 18th |
| Ryanair Chase (registered as the Festival Trophy Chase) | CHELTENHAM | 18th |
| Paddy Power Stayers' Hurdle | CHELTENHAM | 18th |
| Plate Handicap Chase | CHELTENHAM | 18th |
| Daylesford Mares' Novices' Hurdle (registered as the Dawn Run Mares' Novices' Hurdle) | CHELTENHAM | 18th |
| Fulke Walwyn Kim Muir Challenge Cup Handicap Chase | CHELTENHAM | 18th |
| JCB Triumph Hurdle | CHELTENHAM | 19th |
| Randox Health County Handicap Hurdle | CHELTENHAM | 19th |
| Albert Bartlett Novices' Hurdle (registered as the Spa Novices' Hurdle) | CHELTENHAM | 19th |
| WellChild Cheltenham Gold Cup | CHELTENHAM | 19th |
| St James's Place Festival Challenge Cup Open Hunters' Steeple Chase | CHELTENHAM | 19th |
| Mrs Paddy Power Mares' Chase (registered as the Liberthine Mares' Chase) | CHELTENHAM | 19th |
| Martin Pipe Conditional Jockeys' Handicap Hurdle | CHELTENHAM | 19th |
| Marston's 61 Deep Midlands Grand National Handicap Chase | UTTOXETER | 20th |
| Native Upmanship Novice Chase | THULES | 20th |
| Irish Lincolnshire | CURRAGH | 21st |
| Unibet Doncaster Mile Stakes | DONCASTER | 27th |
| Unibet Cammidge Trophy Stakes | DONCASTER | 27th |
| Unibet Lincoln (Heritage Handicap) | DONCASTER | 27th |
| Racing TV Magnolia Stakes | KEMPTON PARK | 27th |
| EBF 'National Hunt' Novices' Mares' Handicap Hurdle | NEWBURY | 27th |
| Dubai World Cup | MEYDAN | 27th |
| Al Quoz Sprint | MEYDAN | 27th |
| Dubai Golden Shaheen | MEYDAN | 27th |
| Dubai Turf | MEYDAN | 27th |
| Dubai Sheema Classic | MEYDAN | 27th |
| Devoy Stakes | NAAS | 28th |
| EBF Park Express Stakes | NAAS | 28th |
| Kevin McManus Bumper | LIMERICK | 28th |
| Hugh McMahon Memorial Novice Chase | LIMERICK | 28th |

## APRIL

| | | |
|---|---|---|
| Betway All-Weather Sprint Championships Conditions Stakes | LINGFIELD PARK | 2nd |
| Bombardier All-Weather Mile Championships Conditions Stakes | LINGFIELD PARK | 2nd |
| Betway Easter Classic All-Weather Middle Distance Championships Conditions Stakes | LINGFIELD PARK | 2nd |
| Betway All-Weather Marathon Championships Conditions Stakes | LINGFIELD PARK | 2nd |
| Ladbrokes All-Weather Fillies and Mares' Championships Conditions Stakes | LINGFIELD PARK | 2nd |
| Ladbrokes 3-Year-Old All-Weather Championships Conditions Stakes | LINGFIELD PARK | 2nd |
| Ladbrokes Burradon Stakes | NEWCASTLE | 2nd |
| Betway Challenger Middle Distance Chase Series Final Handicap Chase | HAYDOCK PARK | 3rd |
| Betway Challenger Two Mile Hurdle Series Final Handicap Hurdle | HAYDOCK PARK | 3rd |
| Betway Challenger Stayers Hurdle Series Final Handicap Hurdle | HAYDOCK PARK | 3rd |
| Betway Challenger Mares' Hurdle Series Final Handicap Hurdle | HAYDOCK PARK | 3rd |
| Betway Challenger Staying Chase Series Final Handicap Chase | HAYDOCK PARK | 3rd |
| Betway Challenger Series Mares' Chase Final Handicap Chase | HAYDOCK PARK | 3rd |
| Racing TV Snowdrop Fillies Stakes | KEMPTON PARK | 3rd |
| Noblesse Stakes | CORK | 3rd |
| Cork Sprint Stakes | CORK | 3rd |
| Glasscarn Handicap Hurdle | FAIRYHOUSE | 3rd |
| Total Enjoyment Mares Bumper | FAIRYHOUSE | 3rd |
| INHSO Final Novice Handicap Hurdle | FAIRYHOUSE | 3rd |
| Easter Handicap Hurdle | CORK | 4th |
| Imperial Call Chase | CORK | 4th |
| EBF Mares Novice Hurdle Final | FAIRYHOUSE | 4th |
| Ryanair Gold Cup | FAIRYHOUSE | 4th |
| Coolmore NH Sires Festival Novice Hurdle | FAIRYHOUSE | 4th |
| Rathbarry Novice Hurdle | FAIRYHOUSE | 4th |
| Greenogue Novice Handicap Chase | FAIRYHOUSE | 4th |
| Boylesports Irish Grand National | FAIRYHOUSE | 5th |
| Keelings Hurdle | FAIRYHOUSE | 5th |
| Percy Maynard 4YO Hurdle | FAIRYHOUSE | 5th |
| Fairyhouse Chase | FAIRYHOUSE | 5th |
| Barry Hills Further Flight Stakes | NOTTINGHAM | 7th |
| Betway Aintree Hurdle | AINTREE | 8th |
| Betway Bowl Chase | AINTREE | 8th |
| Manifesto Novices' Chase | AINTREE | 8th |
| Close Brothers Red Rum Handicap Chase | AINTREE | 8th |

| | | |
|---|---|---|
| Doom Bar Anniversary 4YO Juvenile Hurdle | AINTREE | 8th |
| Goffs UK Nickel Coin Mares' Standard Open National Hunt Flat Race | AINTREE | 8th |
| Randox Health Topham Handicap Chase | AINTREE | 9th |
| Marsh Chase | AINTREE | 9th |
| Betway Mildmay Novices' Chase | AINTREE | 9th |
| Doom Bar Sefton Novices' Hurdle | AINTREE | 9th |
| Betway Top Novices' Hurdle | AINTREE | 9th |
| Orrell Park Handicap Hurdle | AINTREE | 9th |
| Randox Health Grand National | AINTREE | 10th |
| Ryanair Stayers' Hurdle (registered as the Liverpool Hurdle) | AINTREE | 10th |
| Doom Bar Maghull Novices' Chase | AINTREE | 10th |
| Betway Mersey Novices' Hurdle | AINTREE | 10th |
| Bridle Road Handicap Hurdle | AINTREE | 10th |
| Weatherbys Racing Bank Standard Open National Hunt Flat Race | AINTREE | 10th |
| Ballysax Stakes | LEOPARDSTOWN | 11th |
| Leopardstown 2000 Guineas Trial | LEOPARDSTOWN | 11th |
| Leopardstown 1000 Guineas Trial | LEOPARDSTOWN | 11th |
| bet365 Feilden Stakes | NEWMARKET | 13th |
| Cure Parkinson's And Hambo Foundation Silver Trophy Handicap Chase | CHELTENHAM | 14th |
| bet365 Earl Of Sefton Stakes | NEWMARKET | 14th |
| Lanwades Stud Nell Gwyn Stakes | NEWMARKET | 14th |
| bet365 European Free Handicap Stakes | NEWMARKET | 14th |
| Heritage Stakes | LEOPARDSTOWN | 14th |
| April Fillies' Juvenile Handicap Hurdle | CHELTENHAM | 15th |
| EBF Mares' Novices' Handicap Chase Final | CHELTENHAM | 15th |
| Catesby Estates PLC Mares' Handicap Hurdle | CHELTENHAM | 15th |
| Glide Mares' Novices' Hurdle | CHELTENHAM | 15th |
| bet365 Craven Stakes | NEWMARKET | 15th |
| Connaught Access Flooring Abernant Stakes | NEWMARKET | 15th |
| Hillhouse Quarry Handicap Chase | AYR | 16th |
| Whitsbury Manor Stud/British EBF Lansdown Stakes | BATH | 16th |
| Coral Scottish Grand National | AYR | 17th |
| Coral Scottish Champion Hurdle | AYR | 17th |
| Jordan Electrics Ltd Future Champion Novices' Chase | AYR | 17th |
| Scotty Brand Handicap Chase | AYR | 17th |
| Dubai Duty Free Finest Surprise Stakes (registered as the John Porter Stakes) | NEWBURY | 17th |
| Watership Down Too Darn Hot Greenham Stakes | NEWBURY | 17th |
| Dubai Duty Free Stakes (registered as the Fred Darling) | NEWBURY | 17th |
| Alleged Stakes | CURRAGH | 17th |
| Gladness Stakes | CURRAGH | 17th |
| Blue Riband Trial Stakes | EPSOM DOWNS | 20th |
| EBF Stallions Gold Castle 'National Hunt' Novices' Hurdle | PERTH | 21st |
| TBA Fair Maid Of Perth Mares' Steeple Chase | PERTH | 23rd |
| bet365 Mile | SANDOWN PARK | 23rd |
| bet365 Gordon Richards Stakes | SANDOWN PARK | 23rd |
| bet365 Classic Trial | SANDOWN PARK | 23rd |
| EBF Stallions King Richard III Stakes | LEICESTER | 24th |
| bet365 Gold Cup Handicap Chase | SANDOWN PARK | 24th |
| bet365 Celebration Chase | SANDOWN PARK | 24th |
| bet365 Oaksey Chase | SANDOWN PARK | 24th |
| bet365 Select Hurdle | SANDOWN PARK | 24th |
| Salsabil Stakes | NAVAN | 24th |
| Committed Stakes | NAVAN | 24th |
| Vintage Crop | NAVAN | 24th |
| Woodlands Sprint Stakes | NAAS | 25th |
| Prix Ganay | PARISLONGCHAMP | 25th |
| British Stallion Studs EBF Nottinghamshire Oaks | NOTTINGHAM | 27th |
| Boylesports Champion Chase | PUNCHESTOWN | 27th |
| Evening Herald Champion Novice Hurdle | PUNCHESTOWN | 27th |
| Growise Novice Chase | PUNCHESTOWN | 27th |
| Kilashee Handicap Hurdle | PUNCHESTOWN | 27th |
| Longines Sagaro Stakes | ASCOT | 28th |
| Merriebelle Stable Commonwealth Cup Trial Stakes (registered as the Pavilion Stakes) | ASCOT | 28th |
| Queen Anne Trial Stakes | ASCOT | 28th |
| Attheraces Champion Bumper | PUNCHESTOWN | 28th |
| Bibby Financial Punchestown Gold Cup | PUNCHESTOWN | 28th |
| Guinness Handicap Chase | PUNCHESTOWN | 28th |
| Irish Daily Mirror War Of Attrition Novice Hurdle | PUNCHESTOWN | 28th |
| Liss A Paoraigh Mares Bumper | PUNCHESTOWN | 28th |
| Chelmer Fillies' Stakes | CHELMSFORD CITY | 29th |
| Rallymore Eustace Handicap Hurdle | PUNCHESTOWN | 29th |
| Ladbrokes World Series Hurdle | PUNCHESTOWN | 29th |
| Shawiya Mares Novice Hurdle | PUNCHESTOWN | 29th |

Ryanair Novice Chase ..................................................................................................... PUNCHESTOWN ...................... 29th
Three.ie Handicap Steeplechase ........................................................................................ PUNCHESTOWN ...................... 29th
EBF Daisy Warwick Fillies' Stakes .................................................................................... GOODWOOD ........................... 30th
Glencarraig Lady Mares Handicap Chase ........................................................................... PUNCHESTOWN ...................... 30th
Punchestown Champion Hurdle .......................................................................................... PUNCHESTOWN ...................... 30th
Punchestown Novice Handicap Chase ................................................................................ PUNCHESTOWN ...................... 30th
Tattersalls Ireland Champion Novice Hurdle ....................................................................... PUNCHESTOWN ...................... 30th

# MAY

Conqueror Fillies' Stakes .................................................................................................. GOODWOOD ........................... 1st
Palace House Stakes ........................................................................................................ NEWMARKET ......................... 1st
Newmarket Stakes ............................................................................................................ NEWMARKET ......................... 1st
Jockey Club Stakes ........................................................................................................... NEWMARKET ......................... 1st
QIPCO 2000 Guineas Stakes ............................................................................................. NEWMARKET ......................... 1st
Aes Champion 4yo Hurdle .................................................................................................. PUNCHESTOWN ...................... 1st
Ballymore Handicap Hurdle ............................................................................................... PUNCHESTOWN ...................... 1st
EBF Mares Champion Hurdle ............................................................................................. PUNCHESTOWN ...................... 1st
Pretty Polly Stakes ............................................................................................................ NEWMARKET ......................... 2nd
Betfair Dahlia Stakes ......................................................................................................... NEWMARKET ......................... 2nd
QIPCO 1000 Guineas Stakes ............................................................................................. NEWMARKET ......................... 2nd
Athasi Stakes .................................................................................................................... CURRAGH .............................. 3rd
Mooresbridge Stakes ........................................................................................................ CURRAGH .............................. 3rd
Tetrarch Stakes ................................................................................................................. CURRAGH .............................. 3rd
First Flier Stakes ............................................................................................................... CURRAGH .............................. 3rd
Vintage Tipple Stakes ........................................................................................................ GOWRAN PARK ..................... 4th
Arkle Finance Cheshire Oaks ............................................................................................. CHESTER .............................. 5th
MBNA Chester Vase Stakes ............................................................................................... CHESTER .............................. 5th
Victor McCalmont Stakes ................................................................................................... GOWRAN PARK ..................... 5th
Boodles Diamond Ormonde Stakes ..................................................................................... CHESTER .............................. 6th
Homeserve Dee Stakes ..................................................................................................... CHESTER .............................. 6th
Homeserve Huxley Stakes ................................................................................................. CHESTER .............................. 6th
Polonia Stakes .................................................................................................................. CORK ................................... 7th
Carey Group Buckhounds Stakes ....................................................................................... ASCOT ................................. 8th
Pertemps Network Spring Trophy Stakes ............................................................................ HAYDOCK PARK .................... 8th
Pertemps Network Swinton Handicap Hurdle ...................................................................... HAYDOCK PARK .................... 8th
RaceBets Derby Trial Stakes .............................................................................................. LINGFIELD PARK ................... 8th
RaceBets Million Chartwell Fillies' Stakes .......................................................................... LINGFIELD PARK ................... 8th
RaceBets Oaks Trial Fillies' Stakes .................................................................................... LINGFIELD PARK ................... 8th
EBF Weatherbys General Stud Book Kilvington Stakes ......................................................... NOTTINGHAM ........................ 8th
Blue Wind Stakes .............................................................................................................. NAAS ................................... 8th
Sole Power Stakes ............................................................................................................ NAAS ................................... 8th
Killarney Handicap Hurdle ................................................................................................. KILLARNEY ........................... 9th
Tourist Attraction Mares Hurdle .......................................................................................... KILLARNEY ........................... 9th
Derrinstown Derby Trial ..................................................................................................... LEOPARDSTOWN .................. 9th
Amethyst Stakes ............................................................................................................... LEOPARDSTOWN .................. 9th
Derrinstown 1000 Guineas Trial ......................................................................................... LEOPARDSTOWN .................. 9th
Emirates Poule d'Essai des Poulains ................................................................................... PARISLONGCHAMP ............... 9th
Emirates Poule d'Essai des Pouliches ................................................................................. PARISLONGCHAMP ............... 9th
Tori Global Supports The Samaritans Stakes (registered as the Royal Windsor Stakes) .......... WINDSOR ............................. 10th
An Riocht Chase ................................................................................................................ KILLARNEY ........................... 10th
Tattersalls Musidora Stakes ............................................................................................... YORK ................................... 12th
Duke Of York Clipper Logistics Stakes ............................................................................... YORK ................................... 12th
British Stallion Studs EBF Westow Stakes .......................................................................... YORK ................................... 13th
Al Basti Equiworld Dubai Middleton Fillies' Stakes ............................................................. YORK ................................... 13th
Al Basti Equiworld Dubai Dante Stakes .............................................................................. YORK ................................... 13th
Oaks Farm Stables Fillies' Stakes (registered as the Michael Seely Memorial Stakes) ........... YORK ................................... 14th
Langleys Solicitors EBF Marygate Fillies' Stakes ................................................................ YORK ................................... 14th
Matchbook Yorkshire Cup Stakes ....................................................................................... YORK ................................... 14th
Savel Beg Stakes .............................................................................................................. LEOPARDSTOWN .................. 14th
Al Rayyan Stakes (registered as the Aston Park) .................................................................. NEWBURY ............................ 15th
Haras De Bouquetot Fillies' Trial Stakes ............................................................................. NEWBURY ............................ 15th
Carnarvon Stakes .............................................................................................................. NEWBURY ............................ 15th
Al Shaqab Lockinge Stakes ............................................................................................... NEWBURY ............................ 15th
Betway Fairway Stakes ...................................................................................................... NEWMARKET ......................... 15th
Betway King Charles II Stakes ............................................................................................ NEWMARKET ......................... 15th
Yeats Stakes ..................................................................................................................... NAVAN .................................. 15th
Lacken Stakes ................................................................................................................... NAAS ................................... 16th
Whitehead Memorial Stakes ............................................................................................... NAAS ................................... 16th
Coolmore Stud Juvenile Fillies ........................................................................................... NAAS ................................... 16th
Weatherbys Hamilton Stakes ............................................................................................. WINDSOR ............................. 17th
Tennent's Lager British Stallion Studs EBF Rothesay Stakes ................................................ AYR ..................................... 19th
Heron Stakes .................................................................................................................... SANDOWN PARK ................... 20th
British Stallion Studs EBF Cocked Hat Stakes ..................................................................... GOODWOOD ......................... 21st
Height Of Fashion Stakes ................................................................................................... GOODWOOD ......................... 21st

EBF British Stallion Studs Cecil Frail Stakes .................................................. HAYDOCK PARK ........................ 21st
Betfair Tapster Stakes ........................................................................................ GOODWOOD ............................. 22nd
Betfair Festival Stakes ....................................................................................... GOODWOOD ............................. 22nd
Sandy Lane Stakes .............................................................................................. HAYDOCK PARK ........................ 22nd
Betway Pinnacle Stakes ...................................................................................... HAYDOCK PARK ........................ 22nd
Temple Stakes ..................................................................................................... HAYDOCK PARK ........................ 22nd
William Hill Bronte Cup Fillies' Stakes ............................................................ YORK ........................................ 22nd
Tattersalls Irish 2000 Guineas .......................................................................... CURRAGH ................................ 22nd
Weatherbys Greenlands Stakes .......................................................................... CURRAGH ................................ 22nd
Marble Hill Stakes .............................................................................................. CURRAGH ................................ 22nd
Lanwades Stud Stakes ......................................................................................... CURRAGH ................................ 22nd
Grande Course de Haies d'Auteuil .................................................................... AUTEUIL ................................... 22nd
Tattersalls Gold Cup .......................................................................................... CURRAGH ................................ 23rd
Tattersalls Irish 1000 Guineas .......................................................................... CURRAGH ................................ 23rd
Gallinule Stakes .................................................................................................. CURRAGH ................................ 23rd
Saxon Warrior Coolmore Prix Saint-Alary ...................................................... PARISLONGCHAMP ............... 23rd
Prix d'Ispahan ..................................................................................................... PARISLONGCHAMP ............... 23rd
Grand Steeple-Chase de Paris ............................................................................ AUTEUIL ................................... 23rd
Mayo Grand National .......................................................................................... BALLINROBE ............................ 25th
Henry II Stakes ................................................................................................... SANDOWN PARK ..................... 27th
Brigadier Gerard Stakes ..................................................................................... SANDOWN PARK ..................... 27th
National Stakes .................................................................................................... SANDOWN PARK ..................... 27th
John Of Gaunt Stakes .......................................................................................... HAYDOCK PARK ........................ 29th
Achilles Stakes .................................................................................................... HAYDOCK PARK ........................ 29th
Prix du Jockey Club ............................................................................................ CHANTILLY ............................... 30th

# JUNE

Silver Stakes ....................................................................................................... CURRAGH ................................ 2nd
Ballyogan Stakes ................................................................................................. CURRAGH ................................ 2nd
Glencairn Stakes .................................................................................................. LEOPARDSTOWN .................... 3rd
Njinsky Stakes ..................................................................................................... LEOPARDSTOWN .................... 3rd
Surrey Stakes ...................................................................................................... EPSOM DOWNS ...................... 4th
Coronation Cup .................................................................................................... EPSOM DOWNS ...................... 4th
The Oaks .............................................................................................................. EPSOM DOWNS ...................... 4th
The Derby ............................................................................................................. EPSOM DOWNS ...................... 5th
Princess Elizabeth Stakes ................................................................................... EPSOM DOWNS ...................... 5th
Diomed Stakes ..................................................................................................... EPSOM DOWNS ...................... 5th
'Dash' Stakes (Heritage Handicap) .................................................................... EPSOM DOWNS ...................... 5th
Stobo Castle Ladies' Day Gold Cup Fillies' Stakes (registered as the Maggie Dickson Stakes) ........ MUSSELBURGH ..................... 5th
Midsummer Sprint Stakes .................................................................................. CORK ....................................... 9th
Munster Oaks ....................................................................................................... CORK ....................................... 9th
Johnnie Lewis Memorial British EBF Stakes (registered as the Abingdon Stakes) ........ NEWBURY ................................ 10th
Ballycorus Stakes ................................................................................................ LEOPARDSTOWN .................... 10th
equinITy Technology Ganton Stakes .................................................................. YORK ........................................ 11th
Randox Health Scurry Stakes .............................................................................. SANDOWN PARK ..................... 12th
Sky Bet Race To The Ebor Grand Cup Stakes .................................................... YORK ........................................ 12th
British Stallion Studs EBF Cathedral Stakes ................................................... SALISBURY .............................. 13th
Longines Prix de Diane ....................................................................................... CHANTILLY ............................... 14th
Queen Anne Stakes .............................................................................................. ROYAL ASCOT ......................... 15th
Coventry Stakes ................................................................................................... ROYAL ASCOT ......................... 15th
King's Stand Stakes ............................................................................................. ROYAL ASCOT ......................... 15th
St James's Palace Stakes ..................................................................................... ROYAL ASCOT ......................... 15th
Ascot Stakes (Handicap) ..................................................................................... ROYAL ASCOT ......................... 15th
Wolferton Stakes ................................................................................................. ROYAL ASCOT ......................... 15th
Copper Horse Stakes (Handicap) ........................................................................ ROYAL ASCOT ......................... 15th
Queen Mary Stakes .............................................................................................. ROYAL ASCOT ......................... 16th
Queen's Vase ........................................................................................................ ROYAL ASCOT ......................... 16th
Duke Of Cambridge Stakes .................................................................................. ROYAL ASCOT ......................... 16th
Prince Of Wales's Stakes ..................................................................................... ROYAL ASCOT ......................... 16th
Royal Hunt Cup (Heritage Handicap) ................................................................ ROYAL ASCOT ......................... 16th
Windsor Castle Stakes ......................................................................................... ROYAL ASCOT ......................... 16th
Kensington Palace Stakes (Handicap) ............................................................... ROYAL ASCOT ......................... 16th
totepool Queen Charlotte Fillies' Stakes .......................................................... CHELMSFORD CITY ................. 16th
Norfolk Stakes ..................................................................................................... ROYAL ASCOT ......................... 17th
Hampton Court Stakes ......................................................................................... ROYAL ASCOT ......................... 17th
Ribblesdale Stakes .............................................................................................. ROYAL ASCOT ......................... 17th
Gold Cup ............................................................................................................... ROYAL ASCOT ......................... 17th
Britannia Stakes (Heritage Handicap) ............................................................... ROYAL ASCOT ......................... 17th
King George V Stakes (Handicap) ....................................................................... ROYAL ASCOT ......................... 17th
Buckingham Palace Stakes (Handicap) .............................................................. ROYAL ASCOT ......................... 17th
Albany Stakes ...................................................................................................... ROYAL ASCOT ......................... 18th
King Edward VII Stakes ....................................................................................... ROYAL ASCOT ......................... 18th
Commonwealth Cup ............................................................................................. ROYAL ASCOT ......................... 18th
Coronation Stakes ............................................................................................... ROYAL ASCOT ......................... 18th

| | | |
|---|---|---|
| Sandringham Stakes (Handicap) | ROYAL ASCOT | 18th |
| Duke Of Edinburgh Stakes (Handicap) | ROYAL ASCOT | 18th |
| Palace Of Holyroodhouse Stakes (Handicap) | ROYAL ASCOT | 18th |
| Martin Molony Stakes | LIMERICK | 18th |
| Chesham Stakes | ROYAL ASCOT | 19th |
| Jersey Stakes | ROYAL ASCOT | 19th |
| Hardwicke Stakes | ROYAL ASCOT | 19th |
| Diamond Jubilee Stakes | ROYAL ASCOT | 19th |
| Wokingham Stakes (Heritage Handicap) | ROYAL ASCOT | 19th |
| Golden Gates Stakes (Handicap) | ROYAL ASCOT | 19th |
| Queen Alexandra Stakes | ROYAL ASCOT | 19th |
| British Stallion Studs Land O'Burns Fillies' Stakes | AYR | 19th |
| Pontefract Castle Fillies' Stakes | PONTEFRACT | 20th |
| British Stallion Studs Eternal Fillies' Stakes | CARLISLE | 23rd |
| Naas Oaks Trial | NAAS | 23rd |
| Betfair Casion Hoppings Fillies' Stakes | NEWCASTLE | 25th |
| Betfair Exchange Chipchase Stakes | NEWCASTLE | 26th |
| Betfair Exchange Northumberland Plate (Heritage Handicap) | NEWCASTLE | 26th |
| Randox Health Criterion Stakes | NEWMARKET | 26th |
| Randox Health Fred Archer Stakes | NEWMARKET | 26th |
| Randox Health Empress Fillies' Stakes | NEWMARKET | 26th |
| GentingBet Midsummer Stakes | WINDSOR | 26th |
| Dubai Duty Free Irish Derby | CURRAGH | 26th |
| Dubai Duty Free Belgrave Stakes | CURRAGH | 26th |
| Dubai Duty Free Celebration Stakes | CURRAGH | 26th |
| Gain Railway Stakes | CURRAGH | 26th |
| bet365 Summer Cup | UTTOXETER | 27th |
| Comer International Curragh Cup | CURRAGH | 27th |
| Juddmonte Pretty Polly Stakes | CURRAGH | 27th |
| Grangecon Stud Balanchine Stakes | CURRAGH | 27th |
| International Stakes | CURRAGH | 27th |
| Lenebane Stakes | ROSCOMMON | 29th |

# JULY

| | | |
|---|---|---|
| Tipperary Stakes | TIPPERARY | 1st |
| Grimes Hurdle | TIPPERARY | 1st |
| Davies Insurance Services Gala Stakes | SANDOWN PARK | 2nd |
| Chasemore Farm Dragon Stakes | SANDOWN PARK | 2nd |
| bet365 Lancashire Oaks | HAYDOCK PARK | 3rd |
| Coral Charge (registered as the Sprint Stakes) | SANDOWN PARK | 3rd |
| Coral Marathon (registered as the Esher Stakes) | SANDOWN PARK | 3rd |
| Coral Distaff | SANDOWN PARK | 3rd |
| Coral-Eclipse | SANDOWN PARK | 3rd |
| Grand Prix de Saint-Cloud | SAINT-CLOUD | 4th |
| Weatherbys TBA Pipalong Stakes | PONTEFRACT | 6th |
| Princess Of Wales's Tattersalls Stakes | NEWMARKET | 8th |
| Bahrain Trophy Stakes | NEWMARKET | 8th |
| Tattersalls July Stakes | NEWMARKET | 8th |
| Bahrain International Sir Henry Cecil Stakes | NEWMARKET | 8th |
| bet365 Handicap Stakes (Heritage Handicap) | NEWMARKET | 8th |
| Tattersalls Falmouth Stakes | NEWMARKET | 9th |
| Duchess Of Cambridge Stakes | NEWMARKET | 9th |
| bet365 Trophy (Heritage Handicap) | NEWMARKET | 9th |
| bet365 Handicap Stakes (Heritage Handicap) | NEWMARKET | 9th |
| William Hill Summer Stakes | YORK | 9th |
| Midlands Grand National | KILBEGGAN | 9th |
| Betfred Summer Mile Stakes | ASCOT | 10th |
| Sportpesa City Plate Stakes | CHESTER | 10th |
| Darley July Cup Stakes | NEWMARKET | 10th |
| bet365 Superlative Stakes | NEWMARKET | 10th |
| bet365 Bunbury Cup (Heritage Handicap) | NEWMARKET | 10th |
| John Smith's Silver Cup Stakes | YORK | 10th |
| John Smith's City Walls Stakes | YORK | 10th |
| John Smith's Cup (Heritage Handicap) | YORK | 10th |
| Brownstown Stakes | FAIRYHOUSE | 11th |
| Qatar Prix Jean Prat | DEAUVILLE | 11th |
| Cairn Rouge Stakes | KILLARNEY | 12th |
| Bourn Vincent Memorial Handicap Steeplechase | KILLARNEY | 13th |
| Juddmonte Grand Prix de Paris | PARISLONGCHAMP | 13th |
| Green Room Meld Stakes | LEOPARDSTOWN | 15th |
| Irish Stallion Farms EBF Glasgow Stakes | HAMILTON PARK | 16th |
| bet365 Rose Bowl Stakes | NEWBURY | 16th |
| Betway Summer Plate Handicap Chase | MARKET RASEN | 17th |
| bet365 Stakes (registered as the Steventon Stakes) | NEWBURY | 17th |

| | | |
|---|---|---|
| bet365 Hackwood Stakes | NEWBURY | 17th |
| Ric And Mary Hambro Aphrodite Fillies' Stakes | NEWMARKET | 17th |
| Juddmonte Irish Oaks | CURRAGH | 17th |
| Jebel Ali Anglesey Stakes | CURRAGH | 17th |
| Minstrel Stakes | CURRAGH | 17th |
| Sapphire Stakes | CURRAGH | 18th |
| Kilboy Estate Stakes | CURRAGH | 18th |
| Sweet Mimosa Stakes | NAAS | 21st |
| Marwell Stakes | NAAS | 21st |
| British Stallion Studs EBF Star Stakes | SANDOWN PARK | 22nd |
| Silver Flash Stakes | LEOPARDSTOWN | 22nd |
| Vinnie Roe Stakes | LEOPARDSTOWN | 22nd |
| Tyros Stakes | LEOPARDSTOWN | 22nd |
| Acorn Insurance Valiant Stakes | ASCOT | 23rd |
| British Stallion Studs EBF Lyric Fillies' Stakes | YORK | 23rd |
| Her Majesty's Plate | DOWN ROYAL | 23rd |
| King George VI and Queen Elizabeth QIPCO Stakes | ASCOT | 24th |
| Princess Margaret Keeneland Stakes | ASCOT | 24th |
| BetfredTV Pat Eddery Stakes | ASCOT | 24th |
| Moet & Chandon international Stakes (Heritage Handicap) | ASCOT | 24th |
| Sky Bet York Stakes | YORK | 24th |
| Sky Bet Go Racing In Yorkshire Summer Festival Pomfret Stakes | PONTEFRACT | 25th |
| Al Shaqab Goodwood Cup Stakes | GOODWOOD | 27th |
| Qatar Lennox Stakes | GOODWOOD | 27th |
| Veuve Clicquot Vintage Stakes | GOODWOOD | 27th |
| Castlegar Novice Hurdle | GALWAY | 27th |
| Qatar Sussex Stakes | GOODWOOD | 28th |
| Markel Insurance Molecomb Stakes | GOODWOOD | 28th |
| thetote.com Galway Plate | GALWAY | 28th |
| Qatar Nassau Stakes | GOODWOOD | 29th |
| John Pearce Racing Gordon Stakes | GOODWOOD | 29th |
| Qatar Richmond Stakes | GOODWOOD | 29th |
| Corrib EBF Fillies Stakes | GALWAY | 29th |
| Guinness Galway Hurdle | GALWAY | 29th |
| Ballybrit Novice Chase | GALWAY | 29th |
| King George Qatar Stakes | GOODWOOD | 30th |
| L'Ormarins Queen's Plate Glorious Stakes | GOODWOOD | 30th |
| Bonhams Thoroughbred Stakes | GOODWOOD | 30th |
| Saint Clair Oak Tree Stakes | GOODWOOD | 30th |
| Qatar Lillie Langtry Stakes | GOODWOOD | 31st |
| Unibet Stewards' Cup (Heritage Handicap) | GOODWOOD | 31st |
| British Stallion Studs EBF Challice Stakes | NEWMARKET | 31st |
| Mervue Handicap Hurdle | GALWAY | 31st |

# AUGUST

| | | |
|---|---|---|
| MBNA Queensferry Stakes | CHESTER | 1st |
| Prix Rothschild | DEAUVILLE | 1st |
| Irish EBF Ballyhane Stud Median Sires Stakes | NAAS | 2nd |
| Ballyroan Stakes | LEOPARDSTOWN | 5th |
| El Gran Senor Stakes | TIPPERARY | 6th |
| Rose Of Lancaster Stakes | HAYDOCK PARK | 7th |
| British Stallion Studs EBF Dick Hern Stakes | HAYDOCK PARK | 7th |
| German-Thoroughbred.com Sweet Solera Stakes | NEWMARKET | 7th |
| Give Thanks Stakes | CORK | 7th |
| Platinum Stakes | CORK | 7th |
| Keeneland Phoenix Stakes | CURRAGH | 8th |
| QREC Phoenix Sprint | CURRAGH | 8th |
| LARC Prix Maurice de Gheest | DEAUVILLE | 8th |
| British Stallion Studs EBF Upavon Fillies' Stakes | SALISBURY | 11th |
| Hurry Harriet Stakes | GOWRAN PARK | 11th |
| Sovereign Stakes | SALISBURY | 12th |
| Invesco Desmond Stakes | LEOPARDSTOWN | 12th |
| Byerley Stud Stakes (registered as the St Hugh's Stakes) | NEWBURY | 13th |
| Ballycullen Stakes | CURRAGH | 13th |
| Curragh Stakes | CURRAGH | 13th |
| Royal Whip | CURRAGH | 13th |
| Unibet Hungerford Stakes | NEWBURY | 14th |
| Unibet Geoffrey Freer Stakes | NEWBURY | 14th |
| Denford Stakes | NEWBURY | 14th |
| EBF Stallions Highfield Farm Flying Fillies' Stakes | PONTEFRACT | 15th |
| Prix du Haras de Fresnay-Le-Buffard Jacques La Marois | DEAUVILLE | 15th |
| Juddmonte International Stakes | YORK | 18th |
| Sky Bet Great Voltigeur Stakes | YORK | 18th |
| Tattersalls Acomb Stakes | YORK | 18th |

| | | |
|---|---|---|
| Darley Yorkshire Oaks | YORK | 19th |
| Sky Bet Lowther Stakes | YORK | 19th |
| British EBF & Sir Henry Cecil Galtres Stakes | YORK | 19th |
| Clipper Logistics Handicap Stakes (Heritage Handicap) | YORK | 19th |
| Longines Irish Champions Weekend EBF Stonehenge Stakes | SALISBURY | 20th |
| Coolmore Nunthorpe Stakes | YORK | 20th |
| Weatherbys Hamilton Lonsdale Stakes | YORK | 20th |
| Al Basti Equiworld Dubai Gimcrack Stakes | YORK | 20th |
| Ruby Stakes | KILLARNEY | 20th |
| Chelmsford City Cup (Heritage Handicap) | CHELMSFORD CITY | 21st |
| Sportpesa Chester Stakes | CHESTER | 21st |
| Betway Atalanta Stakes | SANDOWN PARK | 21st |
| Betway Solario Stakes | SANDOWN PARK | 21st |
| Sky Bet City Of York Stakes | YORK | 21st |
| Sky Bet And Symphony Group Strensall Stakes | YORK | 21st |
| Julia Graves Roses Stakes | YORK | 21st |
| Sky Bet Ebor (Heritage Handicap) | YORK | 21st |
| Sky Bet Melrose (Heritage Handicap) | YORK | 21st |
| Debutante Stakes | CURRAGH | 21st |
| Futurity | CURRAGH | 21st |
| Lough Leane Handicap Chase | KILLARNEY | 21st |
| Mount Brandon Handicap Hurdle | KILLARNEY | 21st |
| Darley Prix Morny | DEAUVILLE | 22nd |
| Darley Prix Jean Romanet | DEAUVILLE | 22nd |
| Abergwaun Stakes | TIPPERARY | 26th |
| Fairy Bridge Stakes | TIPPERARY | 26th |
| Round Tower Stakes | CURRAGH | 27th |
| Snow Fairy Stakes | CURRAGH | 27th |
| Flame Of Tara Stakes | CURRAGH | 27th |
| William Hill Beverley Bullet Sprint Stakes | BEVERLEY | 28th |
| Ladbrokes Celebration Mile Stakes | GOODWOOD | 28th |
| Ladbrokes March Stakes | GOODWOOD | 28th |
| Ladbrokes Prestige Stakes | GOODWOOD | 28th |
| Price Bailey Chartered Accountants Hopeful Stakes | NEWMARKET | 28th |
| Sky Sports Racing Winter Hill Stakes | WINDSOR | 28th |
| Sri Lanka August Stakes | WINDSOR | 28th |
| Weatherbys Racing Bank Supreme Stakes | GOODWOOD | 29th |
| EBF Ripon Champion 2YO Trophy Stakes | RIPON | 30th |

# SEPTEMBER

| | | |
|---|---|---|
| Shadwell Dick Poole Fillies' Stakes | SALISBURY | 2nd |
| Lavazza Stakes (Heritage Handicap) | ASCOT | 4th |
| Betfair Sprint Cup Stakes | HAYDOCK PARK | 4th |
| Betfair Superior Mile Stakes | HAYDOCK PARK | 4th |
| Betfair Exchange Ascendant Stakes | HAYDOCK PARK | 4th |
| Unibet September Stakes | KEMPTON PARK | 4th |
| Unibet Sirenia Stakes | KEMPTON PARK | 4th |
| Al Basti Equiworld Dubai Garrowby Stakes | YORK | 5th |
| Prix du Moulin | PARISLONGCHAMP | 5th |
| Oyster Stakes | GALWAY | 7th |
| bet365 Scarbrough Stakes | DONCASTER | 8th |
| bet365 May Hill Stakes | DONCASTER | 9th |
| bet365 Park Hill Stakes | DONCASTER | 9th |
| bet365 Doncaster Cup Stakes | DONCASTER | 10th |
| Bombardier Flying Childers Stakes | DONCASTER | 10th |
| bet365 Sceptre Fillies' Stakes | DONCASTER | 10th |
| bet365 Flying Scotsman Stakes | DONCASTER | 10th |
| #ChesterRaces Supports The Injured Jockeys' Fund Stand Cup Stakes | CHESTER | 11th |
| Pertemps St Leger Stakes | DONCASTER | 11th |
| bet365 Park Stakes | DONCASTER | 11th |
| bet365 Champagne Stakes | DONCASTER | 11th |
| QIPCO Irish Champion Stakes | LEOPARDSTOWN | 11th |
| Coolmore Matron Stakes | LEOPARDSTOWN | 11th |
| Clipper Logistics Solonoway Stakes | LEOPARDSTOWN | 11th |
| KPMG Golden Fleece | LEOPARDSTOWN | 11th |
| Ingabelle Stakes | LEOPARDSTOWN | 11th |
| Kilternan Stakes | LEOPARDSTOWN | 11th |
| Moyglare Stud Blandford Stakes | CURRAGH | 12th |
| Goffs Vincent O'Brien National Stakes | CURRAGH | 12th |
| Comer Group International St Leger Stakes | CURRAGH | 12th |
| Moyglare Stud Stakes | CURRAGH | 12th |
| Derrinstown Stud Flying Five Stakes | CURRAGH | 12th |
| Qatar Prix Vermeille | PARISLONGCHAMP | 12th |
| Chasemore Farm Fortune Stakes | SANDOWN PARK | 15th |

EBF Stallions John Musker Fillies' Stakes................................................YARMOUTH................................15th
Jordan Electrics Doonside Cup Stakes.....................................................AYR..........................................16th
Arran Scottish Sprint EBF Fillies' Stakes.................................................AYR..........................................17th
Shadwell Stud/EBF Stallions Harry Rosebery Stakes...............................AYR..........................................17th
Dubai Duty Free Cup Stakes....................................................................NEWBURY.................................17th
Scotty Brand Firth Of Clyde Fillies' Stakes..............................................AYR..........................................18th
QTS Ayr Gold Cup (Heritage Handicap)....................................................AYR..........................................18th
Dubai Duty Free Mill Reef Stakes............................................................NEWBURY.................................18th
Dubai Duty Free Legacy Cup Stakes........................................................NEWBURY.................................18th
Dubai International Airport World Trophy Stakes.......................................NEWBURY.................................18th
Cordell Lavarack Stakes...........................................................................GOWRAN PARK.........................18th
Blenheim Stakes......................................................................................FAIRYHOUSE............................20th
Listowel Stakes........................................................................................LISTOWEL.................................20th
Latrigue 4YO Handicap Hurdle..................................................................LISTOWEL.................................21st
Tote Foundation Stakes............................................................................GOODWOOD..............................22nd
Guinness Kerry National............................................................................LISTOWEL.................................22nd
Tattersalls Stakes (registered as the Somerville Tattersall Stakes).............NEWMARKET.............................23rd
The Jockey Club Rose Bowl Stakes...........................................................NEWMARKET.............................23rd
Ladbrokes Handicap Hurdle.......................................................................LISTOWEL.................................23rd
Shadwell Joel Stakes................................................................................NEWMARKET.............................24th
Shadwell Rockfel Stakes...........................................................................NEWMARKET.............................24th
Princess Royal Muhaarar Stakes...............................................................NEWMARKET.............................24th
Tasleet British EBF Rosemary Stakes........................................................NEWMARKET.............................24th
Eqtidaar Godolphin Stakes........................................................................NEWMARKET.............................24th
Diamond Stakes.........................................................................................DUNDALK.................................24th
Thank You Rand Farm Park Prelude Handicap Hurdle..................................MARKET RASEN.......................25th
Juddmonte Middle Park Stakes..................................................................NEWMARKET.............................25th
Juddmonte Cheveley Park Stakes...............................................................NEWMARKET.............................25th
Juddmonte Royal Lodge Stakes..................................................................NEWMARKET.............................25th
bet365 Cambridgeshire Handicap Stakes (Heritage Handicap)....................NEWMARKET.............................25th
Beresford Stakes........................................................................................CURRAGH.................................26th
Loughbrown Stakes....................................................................................CURRAGH.................................26th
Renaissance Stakes....................................................................................CURRAGH.................................26th
CL & MF Weld Park Stakes.........................................................................CURRAGH.................................26th
Kilbegnet Novice Chase..............................................................................ROSCOMMON...........................27th
Navigation Stakes.......................................................................................CORK......................................28th

# OCTOBER

Teentech Noel Murless Stakes.....................................................................ASCOT....................................1st
Star Appeal Stakes......................................................................................DUNDALK.................................1st
Mucklemeg Mares Bumper...........................................................................GOWRAN PARK.........................1st
Pat Walsh Memorial Mares Hurdle...............................................................GOWRAN PARK.........................1st
tote.co.uk Cumberland Lodge Stakes...........................................................ASCOT....................................2nd
John Guest Racing Bengough Stakes............................................................ASCOT....................................2nd
John Guest Racing British EBF Stakes (registered as the October Stakes).....ASCOT....................................2nd
tote.co.uk Rous Stakes................................................................................ASCOT....................................2nd
Kingdom Of Bahrain Sun Chariot Stakes......................................................NEWMARKET.............................2nd
William Hill Two-Year-Old Trophy.................................................................REDCAR...................................2nd
Racing TV EBF Stallions Guisborough Stakes................................................REDCAR...................................2nd
Gowran Champion Chase..............................................................................GOWRAN PARK.........................2nd
Qatar Prix du Cadran....................................................................................PARISLONGCHAMP...................2nd
Qatar Prix de Royallieu.................................................................................PARISLONGCHAMP...................2nd
Concorde Stakes..........................................................................................TIPPERARY...............................3rd
Tipperary Hurdle..........................................................................................TIPPERARY...............................3rd
Like A Butterfly Novice Chase......................................................................TIPPERARY...............................3rd
Joe Mac Novice Hurdle.................................................................................TIPPERARY...............................3rd
Qatar Prix de l'Arc de Triomphe...................................................................PARISLONGCHAMP...................3rd
Qatar Prix de La Foret..................................................................................PARISLONGCHAMP...................3rd
Prix de L'Abbaye..........................................................................................PARISLONGCHAMP...................3rd
Qatar Prix Jean Luc Lagardere (Grand Criterium)..........................................PARISLONGCHAMP...................3rd
Qatar Prix Marcel Boussac...........................................................................PARISLONGCHAMP...................3rd
Longines Prix de l'Opera...............................................................................PARISLONGCHAMP...................3rd
Unibet Persian War Novices' Hurdle..............................................................CHEPSTOW..............................8th
bet365 Fillies' Mile......................................................................................NEWMARKET.............................8th
Godolphin Stud & Stable Staff Awards Challenge Stakes...............................NEWMARKET.............................8th
Darley Pride Stakes......................................................................................NEWMARKET.............................8th
Godolphin Lifetime Care Oh So Sharp Stakes................................................NEWMARKET.............................8th
Newmarket Academy Godolphin Beacon Project Cornwallis Stakes.................NEWMARKET.............................8th
bet365 Old Rowley Cup (Heritage Handicap).................................................NEWMARKET.............................8th
BetSafe Handicap Stakes (Heritage Handicap)...............................................YORK.......................................8th
Wasdell Group Silver Trophy Handicap Hurdle...............................................CHEPSTOW..............................9th
Dunraven Windows Novices' Chase...............................................................CHEPSTOW..............................9th
Darley Dewhurst Stakes................................................................................NEWMARKET.............................9th
Darley Stakes...............................................................................................NEWMARKET.............................9th

| | | |
|---|---|---|
| Godolphin Flying Start Zetland Stakes | NEWMARKET | 9th |
| Emirates Autumn Stakes | NEWMARKET | 9th |
| Dubai British BEF Boadicea Stakes | NEWMARKET | 9th |
| Together For Racing International Cesarewitch Handicap Stakes (Heritage Handicap) | NEWMARKET | 9th |
| coral.co.uk Rockingham Stakes | YORK | 9th |
| Coral Sprint Trophy (Heritage Handicap) | YORK | 9th |
| Lanwades and Staffordstown Studs Silken Glider Stakes | CURRAGH | 10th |
| Legacy Stakes | CURRAGH | 10th |
| Waterford Testimonial Stakes | CURRAGH | 10th |
| Greenmount Park Novice Hurdle | LIMERICK | 10th |
| Cailain Alainn Mares Hurdle | LIMERICK | 10th |
| Ladbrokes Munster National | LIMERICK | 10th |
| British Stallion Studs EBF Beckford Stakes | BATH | 13th |
| Carvills Hill Chase | PUNCHESTOWN | 13th |
| Buck House Novice Chase | PUNCHESTOWN | 13th |
| Mercury Stakes | DUNDALK | 13th |
| QIPCO Champion Stakes | ASCOT | 16th |
| Queen Elizabeth II Stakes | ASCOT | 16th |
| QIPCO British Champions Sprint Stakes | ASCOT | 16th |
| QIPCO British Champions Fillies & Mares Stakes | ASCOT | 16th |
| QIPCO British Champions Long Distance Stakes | ASCOT | 16th |
| Trigo Stakes | LEOPARDSTOWN | 16th |
| Killavullan Stakes | LEOPARDSTOWN | 16th |
| Racing TV Novices' Hurdle | KEMPTON PARK | 17th |
| Racing TV Hurdle | KEMPTON PARK | 17th |
| Kinsale Handicap Chase | CORK | 17th |
| Bluebell Stakes | NAAS | 17th |
| Garnet Stakes | NAAS | 17th |
| ebfstallions.com Silver Tankard Stakes | PONTEFRACT | 18th |
| Vertem Futurity Trophy Stakes | DONCASTER | 23rd |
| vertem.co.uk Doncaster Stakes | DONCASTER | 23rd |
| Pravha Stakes (registered as the St Simon Stakes) | NEWBURY | 23rd |
| Molson Coors Beverage Company Stakes (registered as the Horris Hill Stakes) | NEWBURY | 23rd |
| Racing TV Stakes (registered as the Radley Stakes) | NEWBURY | 23rd |
| Knockaire Stakes | LEOPARDSTOWN | 23rd |
| Eyrefield Stakes | LEOPARDSTOWN | 23rd |
| Criterium de Saint-Cloud | SAINT-CLOUD | 23rd |
| Criterium International | SAINT-CLOUD | 23rd |
| Monet's Garden Old Roan Limited Handicap Chase | AINTREE | 24th |
| Bettyville Steeplechase | WEXFORD | 24th |
| Prix Royal-Oak | PARISLONGCHAMP | 24th |
| Ladbrokes EBF River Eden Fillies' Stakes | LINGFIELD PARK | 28th |
| Ladbrokes EBF Fleur De Lys Fillies' Stakes | LINGFIELD PARK | 28th |
| Irish Stallion Farms EBF 'Bosra Sham' Fillies' Stakes | NEWMARKET | 29th |
| bet365 Handicap Chase | WETHERBY | 29th |
| Weatherbys Hamilton Wensleydale Juvenile Hurdle | WETHERBY | 29th |
| Cooley Stakes | DUNDALK | 29th |
| WKD Hurdle | DOWN ROYAL | 29th |
| Hamptons EBF Mares Novice Hurdle | DOWN ROYAL | 29th |
| Sodexo Gold Cup Handicap Chase | ASCOT | 30th |
| tote.co.uk Handicap Chase | ASCOT | 30th |
| Sodexo Handicap Hurdle | ASCOT | 30th |
| British Stallion Studs EBF Montrose Fillies' Stakes | NEWMARKET | 30th |
| MansionBet James Seymour Stakes | NEWMARKET | 30th |
| MansionBet Ben Marshall Stakes | NEWMARKET | 30th |
| bet365 Charlie Hall Chase | WETHERBY | 30th |
| bet365 Hurdle (registered as the West Yorkshire Hurdle) | WETHERBY | 30th |
| bet365 Mares' Hurdle | WETHERBY | 30th |
| Kauto Star Chase | DOWN ROYAL | 30th |
| Mac's Jou Handicap Hurdle | DOWN ROYAL | 30th |
| Skymas Chase | DOWN ROYAL | 30th |
| Colin Parker Memorial Intermediate Chase | CARLISLE | 31st |
| Paddy Power Cork Grand National Handicap Chase | CORK | 31st |
| Paddy Power EBF Novice Hurdle | CORK | 31st |
| Paddy Power EBF Novice Chase | CORK | 31st |
| Finale Stakes | NAAS | 31st |

# NOVEMBER

| | | |
|---|---|---|
| Unibet Floodlit Stakes | KEMPTON PARK | 1st |
| Haldon Gold Cup | EXETER | 2nd |
| Lexus Melbourne Cup | FLEMINGTON | 2nd |
| TVG Breeders' Cup Juvenile Presented by Thoroughbred Aftercare | DEL MAR | 5th |
| Breeders' Cup Juvenile Fillies' Turf | DEL MAR | 5th |
| Breeders' Cup Juvenile Fillies | DEL MAR | 5th |

| | | |
|---|---|---|
| Breeders' Cup Juvenile Turf Presented by Coolmore America | DEL MAR | 5th |
| Breeders' Cup Juvenile Turf Sprint | DEL MAR | 5th |
| Betfair Exchange British EBF Gillies Fillies' Stakes | DONCASTER | 6th |
| Betfair Wentworth Stakes | DONCASTER | 6th |
| Badger Beers Silver Trophy Handicap Chase | WINCANTON | 6th |
| Unibet Elite Hurdle | WINCANTON | 6th |
| Rising Stars Novices' Chase | WINCANTON | 6th |
| Poplar Square Chase | NAAS | 6th |
| Brown Lad Handicap Hurdle | NAAS | 6th |
| Fishery Lane 4YO Hurdle | NAAS | 6th |
| Longines Breeders' Cup Classic | DEL MAR | 6th |
| Longines Breeders' Cup Turf | DEL MAR | 6th |
| Longines Breeders' Cup Distaff | DEL MAR | 6th |
| FanDuel Breeders' Cup Mile Presented by PJDF | DEL MAR | 6th |
| Breeders' Cup Sprint | DEL MAR | 6th |
| Maker's Mark Breeders' Cup Filly & Mare Turf | DEL MAR | 6th |
| Big Ass Fans Breeders' Cup Dirt Mile | DEL MAR | 6th |
| Breeders' Cup Turf Sprint | DEL MAR | 6th |
| Breeders' Cup Filly & Mare Sprint | DEL MAR | 6th |
| Future Stars Intermediate Chase | SANDOWN PARK | 7th |
| Lismullen Hurdle | NAVAN | 7th |
| Fortria Chase | NAVAN | 7th |
| For Auction Novice Hurdle | NAVAN | 7th |
| Bangor-On-Dee Racecourse Mares' Novices' Chase | BANGOR-ON-DEE | 10th |
| British Stallion Studs EBF Hyde Stakes | KEMPTON PARK | 10th |
| MansionBet Bud Booth Mares' Chase | MARKET RASEN | 11th |
| Clonmel Oil Chase | CLONMEL | 11th |
| EBF TA Morris Memorial Mares Chase | CLONMEL | 11th |
| Ballymore Novices' Hurdle (registered as the Hyde Novices' Hurdle) | CHELTENHAM | 12th |
| Paddy Power Gold Cup Handicap Chase | CHELTENHAM | 13th |
| Planteur At Chapel Stud Handicap Chase | CHELTENHAM | 13th |
| JCB Triumph Hurdle Trial Juvenile Hurdle (registered as the Prestbury Juvenile Hurdle) | CHELTENHAM | 13th |
| Paddy Power Games Handicap Hurdle | CHELTENHAM | 13th |
| Karndean Designflooring Mares' Standard Open National Hunt Flat Race | CHELTENHAM | 13th |
| Betway Churchill Stakes | LINGFIELD PARK | 13th |
| Betway Golden Rose Stakes | LINGFIELD PARK | 13th |
| Morgiana Hurdle | PUNCHESTOWN | 13th |
| Craddockstown Novice Chase | PUNCHESTOWN | 13th |
| Unibet Greatwood Handicap Hurdle | CHELTENHAM | 14th |
| Shloer Chase (registered as the Cheltenham Chase) | CHELTENHAM | 14th |
| From The Horse's Mouth Podcast Novices' Chase (registered as the November Novices' Chase) | CHELTENHAM | 14th |
| Sky Bet Supreme Trial Novices' Hurdle (registered as the Sharp Novices' Hurdle) | CHELTENHAM | 14th |
| High Sheriff Of Gloucestershire Standard Open National Hunt Flat Race | CHELTENHAM | 14th |
| Grabel Mares Hurdle | PUNCHESTOWN | 14th |
| Florida Pearl Novice Chase | PUNCHESTOWN | 14th |
| Thules Chase | ThuLES | 18th |
| Chanelle Pharma 19th65 Chase | ASCOT | 20th |
| Coral Hurdle (registered as the Ascot Hurdle) | ASCOT | 20th |
| Betfair Chase (registered as the Lancashire Chase) | HAYDOCK PARK | 20th |
| Betfair Exchange Stayers' Handicap Hurdle | HAYDOCK PARK | 20th |
| Betfair Newton Novices' Hurdle | HAYDOCK PARK | 20th |
| Aries Girl Mares Bumper | NAVAN | 21st |
| Ladbrokes Troytown Handicap Chase | NAVAN | 21th |
| Monksfield Novice Hurdle | NAVAN | 21th |
| Racing TV Mares' Hurdle | KEMPTON PARK | 22nd |
| Ladbrokes Long Distance Hurdle | NEWBURY | 26th |
| Ladbrokes Committed To Safer Gambling Novices' Chase (registered as the Berkshire Novices' Chase) | NEWBURY | 26th |
| Ladbrokes Trophy Chase | NEWBURY | 27th |
| Ladbrokes John Francome Novices' Chase | NEWBURY | 27th |
| Ladbrokes Committed To Safer Gambling Intermediate Hurdle (registered as the Gerry Fielden Hurdle) | NEWBURY | 27th |
| Ladbrokes Mares' Novices' Hurdle | NEWBURY | 27th |
| Betfair Fighting Fifth Hurdle | NEWCASTLE | 27th |
| Betfair Exchange Rehearsal Handicap Chase | NEWCASTLE | 27th |
| Ballyhack Handicap Chase | FAIRYHOUSE | 27th |
| Houghton Mares' Chase | CARLISLE | 28th |
| Bar One Drinmore Novice Chase | FAIRYHOUSE | 28th |
| Bar One Hattons Grace Hurdle | FAIRYHOUSE | 28th |
| Bar One Royal Bond Novice Hurdle | FAIRYHOUSE | 28th |
| New Stand Handicap Hurdle | FAIRYHOUSE | 28th |
| Porterstown Handicap Chase | FAIRYHOUSE | 28th |
| Winter Festival Juvenile Hurdle | FAIRYHOUSE | 28th |

# DECEMBER

| | | |
|---|---|---|
| Unibet Wild Flower Stakes | KEMPTON PARK | 1st |
| Ballymore Winter Novices' Hurdle | SANDOWN PARK | 3rd |
| William Hill Becher Handicap Chase | AINTREE | 4th |
| William Hill Many Clouds Chase | AINTREE | 4th |
| williamhill.com Best Odds Guaranteed Fillies' Juvenile Hurdle | AINTREE | 4th |
| Betfair Tingle Creek | SANDOWN PARK | 4th |
| Planteur At Chapel Stud Henry VIII Novices' Chase | SANDOWN PARK | 4th |
| Betfair Exchange December Handicap Hurdle | SANDOWN PARK | 4th |
| Navan Novice Hurdle | NAVAN | 4th |
| Klairon Davis EBF Novice Chase | NAVAN | 4th |
| Foxrock Handicap Chase | NAVAN | 4th |
| Proudstown Handicap Hurdle | NAVAN | 4th |
| Fitzdares Club Loves The Peterborough Chase | HUNTINGDON | 5th |
| Fitzdares Club Salutes Henrietta Knight Mares' Standard Open National Hunt Flat Race | HUNTINGDON | 5th |
| Lombardstown EBF Mares Novice Chase | CORK | 5th |
| Kerry Group Hilly Way Chase | CORK | 5th |
| Kerry Group Cork Stayers Novice Hurdle | CORK | 5th |
| Voler La Vedette Mares Novice Hurdle | PUNCHESTOWN | 5th |
| John Durkan Memorial Chase | PUNCHESTOWN | 5th |
| Wigley Group Lady Godiva Mares' Novices' Steeple Chase | WARWICK | 9th |
| Unibet Handicap Chase | CHELTENHAM | 10th |
| Caspian Caviar Gold Cup Handicap Chase | CHELTENHAM | 11th |
| Unibet International Chase | CHELTENHAM | 11th |
| Albert Bartlett Novices' Hurdle (registered as the Bristol Novices' Hurdle) | CHELTENHAM | 11th |
| bet365 Summit Juvenile Hurdle | DONCASTER | 11th |
| bet365 December Novices' Chase | DONCASTER | 11th |
| Pertemps Network Mares' Chase | NEWBURY | 15th |
| Sky Bet Noel Novices' Chase | ASCOT | 17th |
| Sky Bet Supreme Trial Novices' Hurdle (registered as the Kennel Gate Novices' Hurdle) | ASCOT | 17th |
| Enter ITV7 Tonight Standard Open National Hunt Flat Race | ASCOT | 17th |
| Betfair Exchange Trophy | ASCOT | 18th |
| Porsche Long Walk Hurdle | ASCOT | 18th |
| Silver Cup Handicap Chase | ASCOT | 18th |
| Betfair Exchange Abram Mares' Novices' Hurdle | HAYDOCK PARK | 18th |
| Betway Quebec Stakes | LINGFIELD PARK | 18th |
| Future Champions Bumper | NAVAN | 18th |
| Tara Handicap Hurdle | NAVAN | 18th |
| Boreen Belle EBF Mares Novice Hurdle | ThuLES | 19th |
| Ladbrokes King George VI Chase | KEMPTON PARK | 26th |
| Ladbrokes Christmas Hurdle | KEMPTON PARK | 26th |
| Ladbrokes Kauto Star Novices' Chase | KEMPTON PARK | 26th |
| William Hill Rowland Meyrick Handicap Chase | WETHERBY | 26th |
| Racing Post Novice Chase | LEOPARDSTOWN | 26th |
| Knight Frank Juvenile Hurdle | LEOPARDSTOWN | 26th |
| Greenmount Park Novice Chase | LIMERICK | 26th |
| Coral Welsh Grand National Handicap Chase | CHEPSTOW | 27th |
| Coral Finale Juvenile Hurdle | CHEPSTOW | 27th |
| Ladbrokes Desert Orchid Chase | KEMPTON PARK | 27th |
| Ladbrokes Wayward Lad Novices' Chase | KEMPTON PARK | 27th |
| Paddy Power Future Champions Novice Hurdle | LEOPARDSTOWN | 27th |
| Paddy Power Dial A Bet Chase | LEOPARDSTOWN | 27th |
| Paddy Power Handicap Chase | LEOPARDSTOWN | 27th |
| Dorans Pride Novice Hurdle | LIMERICK | 27th |
| Savills Christmas Chase | LEOPARDSTOWN | 28th |
| Christmas Hurdle | LEOPARDSTOWN | 28th |
| Tim Duggan Memorial Handicap Chase | LIMERICK | 28th |
| Yorkshire Silver Vase Mares' Chase | DONCASTER | 29th |
| MansionBet Challow Novices' Hurdle | NEWBURY | 29th |
| Sporting Limerick 4yo Hurdle | LIMERICK | 29th |
| EBF Mares Hurdle | LEOPARDSTOWN | 29th |
| Matheson December Hurdle | LEOPARDSTOWN | 29th |
| Fort Leney Novice Chase | LEOPARDSTOWN | 29th |
| Byerley Stud Mares' Novices' Hurdle | TAUNTON | 30th |

The list of Principal Races has been supplied by the BHA and Horse Racing Ireland and is provisional.
In all cases, the dates, venues, and names of sponsors are correct at time of going to press, but also subject to possible alteration.

# INDEX TO TRAINERS
## †denotes Permit to train under N.H. Rules only

| Name | Team No. | Name | Team No. |
|---|---|---|---|
| BROTHERTON, MR ROY | 067 | CLOVER, MR TOM | 108 |
| BROWN, MR ALAN | 068 | COAKLEY, MR DENIS | 109 |
| BROWN, MR ANDI | 069 | COLE, PAUL & OLIVER | 110 |
| BROWN, MR DAVID | 070 | COLLIER, MR TJADE | 111 |
| BROWN, MR GARY | 071 | COLLINS, MR PAUL | 112 |
| †BRYANT, MISS MICHELLE | 072 | COLTHERD, MR STUART | 113 |
| BUCKLER, MR BOB | 073 | †CONWAY, MR SEAN | 114 |
| BULGIN, MR TOBY | 074 | CORBETT, MRS SUSAN | 115 |
| BURCHELL, MR DAI | 075 | †CORNWALL, MR JOHN | 116 |
| BURKE, MR KARL | 076 | COULSON, MR JAKE | 117 |
| BURKE, MR KEIRAN | 077 | COWARD, MISS JACQUELINE | 118 |
| †BURNS, MR HUGH | 078 | COWELL, MR ROBERT | 119 |
| BURROWS, MR OWEN | 079 | COX, MR CLIVE | 120 |
| BUTLER, MR JOHN | 080 | COYLE, MR TONY | 121 |
| BUTLER, MR PADDY | 081 | CRAGGS, MR RAY | 122 |
| †BUTTERWORTH, MRS BARBARA | 082 | CRISFORD, SIMON & ED | 123 |
| **C** | | CROOK, MR ANDREW | 124 |
| †CABBLE, MISS LOUISE | 083 | CURRAN, MR SEAN | 125 |
| CAMACHO, MISS JULIE | 084 | CURTIS, MISS REBECCA | 126 |
| CAMPION, MR MARK | 085 | **D** | |
| CANDLISH, MS JENNIE | 086 | DACE, MR LUKE | 127 |
| CANDY, MR HENRY | 087 | DALGLEISH, MR KEITH | 128 |
| CANN, MR GRANT | 088 | DALY, MR HENRY | 129 |
| CANTILLON, MR DON | 089 | DANDO, MR PHILLIP | 130 |
| CARBERRY, MRS LOUISA | 090 | DARTNALL, MR VICTOR | 131 |
| CARR, MRS RUTH | 091 | DASCOMBE, MR TOM | 132 |
| CARROLL, MR DECLAN | 092 | DAVIDSON, MR TRISTAN | 133 |
| CARROLL, MR TONY | 093 | DAVIES, MR JOHN | 134 |
| CARSON, MR TONY | 094 | DAVIES, MISS SARAH-JAYNE | 135 |
| CARTER, MR LEE | 095 | DAVIS, MISS JO | 136 |
| CASE, MR BEN | 096 | †DAVIS, MISS KATHARINE | 137 |
| CHAMINGS, MR PATRICK | 097 | †DAY, MR ANTHONY | 138 |
| CHANNON, MR MICK | 098 | DE BEST-TURNER, MR WILLIAM | 139 |
| CHAPMAN, MR MICHAEL | 099 | DE GILES, MR ED | 140 |
| †CHAPMAN, MR RYAN | 100 | DEACON, MR GEOFFREY | 141 |
| CHAPPET, MR FABRICE | 101 | †DENNIS, MR TIM | 142 |
| CHAPPLE-HYAM, MRS JANE | 102 | DICKIN, MR ROBIN | 143 |
| CHAPPLE-HYAM, MR PETER | 103 | †DIXON, MR JOHN | 144 |
| CHARALAMBOUS, MR PETER | 104 | DIXON, MR SCOTT | 145 |
| CHARLTON, MR ROGER | 105 | DOBBIN, MRS ROSE | 146 |
| CHISMAN, MR HARRY | 106 | †DODGSON, MR ASHLEY | 147 |
| CLEMENT, MR NICOLAS | 107 | DODS, MR MICHAEL | 148 |

| Name | Team No. |
|------|----------|
| DOW, MR SIMON | 149 |
| DOWN, MR CHRIS | 150 |
| DREW, MR CLIVE | 151 |
| DRINKWATER, MR DAVID | 152 |
| DRINKWATER, MR SAMUEL | 153 |
| DU PLESSIS, MISS JACKIE | 154 |
| DUFFIELD, MRS ANN | 155 |
| DUKE, MR BRENDAN W | 156 |
| DUNCAN, MR IAN | 157 |
| †DUNGER, MR NIGEL | 158 |
| DUNLOP, MR ED | 159 |
| DUNLOP, MR HARRY | 160 |
| DUNN, MRS ALEXANDRA | 161 |
| DUNNETT, MRS CHRISTINE | 162 |
| DURACK, MR SEAMUS | 163 |
| DWYER, MR CHRIS | 164 |
| DYSON, MISS CLAIRE | 165 |

**E**

| Name | Team No. |
|------|----------|
| EARLE, MR SIMON | 166 |
| EASTERBY, MR MICHAEL | 167 |
| EASTERBY, MR TIM | 168 |
| †ECKLEY, MR BRIAN | 169 |
| EDDERY, MR ROBERT | 170 |
| EDMUNDS, MR STUART | 171 |
| †EDWARDS, MR GORDON | 172 |
| EGERTON, MISS LUCINDA | 173 |
| ELLAM, MISS CLARE | 174 |
| ELLISON, MR BRIAN | 175 |
| ELSWORTH, MR DAVID | 176 |
| ENDER, MISS SARA | 177 |
| ENGLAND, MRS SAM | 178 |
| EUSTACE, MR JAMES | 179 |
| EVANS, MR DAVID | 180 |
| EVANS, MR JAMES | 181 |
| †EVANS, MRS MARY | 182 |
| EVANS, MRS NIKKI | 183 |
| †EVANS, MR RICHARD RHYS | 184 |
| EWART, MR JAMES | 185 |
| EYRE, MR LES | 186 |

**F**

| Name | Team No. |
|------|----------|
| FAHEY, MR RICHARD | 187 |
| FAIRHURST, MR CHRIS | 188 |

| Name | Team No. |
|------|----------|
| FANSHAWE, MR JAMES | 189 |
| FARRELLY, MR JOHNNY | 190 |
| FEILDEN, MISS JULIA | 191 |
| FELL, MR ROGER | 192 |
| FELLOWES, MR CHARLIE | 193 |
| FERGUSON, MR JAMES | 194 |
| FFRENCH DAVIS, MR DOMINIC | 195 |
| FIERRO, MR GUISEPPE | 196 |
| FIFE, MRS MARJORIE | 197 |
| FITZGERALD, MR TIM | 198 |
| FLINT, MR JOHN | 199 |
| FLOOD, MR DAVID | 200 |
| FORBES, MR TONY | 201 |
| FORD, MRS RICHENDA | 202 |
| FORSEY, MR BRIAN | 203 |
| FORSTER, MISS SANDY | 204 |
| FOSTER, MISS JO | 205 |
| FOX, MR JIMMY | 206 |
| FRANCE, MISS SUZZANNE | 207 |
| †FRANKLAND, MR DEREK | 208 |
| FRENCH, MR ALEX | 209 |
| FROST, MR JAMES | 210 |
| FROST, MR KEVIN | 211 |
| FRY, MR HARRY | 212 |
| FRYER, MS CAROLINE | 213 |
| FURTADO, MR IVAN | 214 |

**G**

| Name | Team No. |
|------|----------|
| GALLAGHER, MR JOHN | 215 |
| GALLAGHER, MR THOMAS | 216 |
| GANSERA-LEVEQUE, MRS ILKA | 217 |
| GARDNER, MRS SUSAN | 218 |
| †GASSON, MRS ROSEMARY | 219 |
| †GATES, MR MICHAEL | 220 |
| GEORGE, MR PAUL | 221 |
| GEORGE, MR TOM | 222 |
| GIFFORD, MR NICK | 223 |
| GILLARD, MR MARK | 224 |
| GOLDIE, MR JIM | 225 |
| GOLLINGS, MR STEVE | 226 |
| GORDON, MR CHRIS | 227 |
| GOSDEN, JOHN & THADY | 228 |
| GRAHAM, MRS HARRIET | 229 |

| Name | Team No. | Name | Team No. |
|------|----------|------|----------|
| GRANT, MR CHRIS | 230 | HENDERSON, MR PAUL | 271 |
| GRASSICK, MR JAMES | 231 | HERRINGTON, MR MICHAEL | 272 |
| GRASSICK, MR MICHAEL | 232 | HILL, MRS LAWNEY | 273 |
| GRAY, MR CARROLL | 233 | HILLS, MR CHARLES | 274 |
| GREATREX, MR WARREN | 234 | HOAD, MR MARK | 275 |
| GREENALL, MR OLIVER | 235 | HOBBS, MR PHILIP | 276 |
| GRETTON, MR TOM | 236 | HOBSON, MISS CLARE | 277 |
| GRIFFITHS, MR DAVID | 237 | HOBSON, MR RICHARD | 278 |
| GRISSELL, MRS DIANA | 238 | HODGES, MR RON | 279 |
| GROUCOTT, MR JOHN | 239 | HODGSON, MR SIMON | 280 |
| GUEST, MR RAE | 240 | †HOGARTH, MR HENRY | 281 |
| GUEST, MR RICHARD | 241 | HOLLINSHEAD, MISS SARAH | 282 |
| GUNDRY, MS POLLY | 242 | HOLLINSHEAD, STEPH | 283 |
| **H** | | HOLT, MR JOHN | 284 |
| HAGGAS, MR WILLIAM | 243 | HONEYBALL, MR ANTHONY | 285 |
| HALES, MR ALEX | 244 | HONOUR, MR CHRIS | 286 |
| HALFORD, MR MICHAEL | 245 | HORSFALL, MISS LAURA | 287 |
| HAMER, MRS DEBRA | 246 | †HOWELL, MS GEORGIE | 288 |
| HAMILTON, MRS ALISON | 247 | HUGHES, MRS DEBBIE | 289 |
| †HAMILTON, MR ANDREW | 248 | HUGHES, MR RICHARD | 290 |
| †HAMILTON, MRS ANN | 249 | HUMPHREY, MRS SARAH | 291 |
| HAMMOND, MR MICKY | 250 | †HUNTER, MR KEVIN | 292 |
| HANLON, MR STEPHEN | 251 | HURLEY, MISS LAURA | 293 |
| HANMER, MR GARY | 252 | **I** | |
| HANNON, MR RICHARD | 253 | INGRAM, MR ROGER | 294 |
| HARKER, MR GEOFFREY | 254 | IRVINE, MR ANDY | 295 |
| †HARPER, MR RICHARD | 255 | IVORY, MR DEAN | 296 |
| HARRINGTON, MRS JESSICA | 256 | **J** | |
| HARRIS, MISS GRACE | 257 | JACKSON, MISS TINA | 297 |
| HARRIS, MR MILTON | 258 | †JAMES, MISS HANNAH | 298 |
| HARRIS, MR RONALD | 259 | JAMES, MR LEE | 299 |
| HARRIS, MR SHAUN | 260 | JARDINE, MR IAIN | 300 |
| HARRISON, MISS LISA | 261 | JARVIS, MR WILLIAM | 301 |
| HARRISON, MR WILLIAM | 262 | JEFFERSON, MISS RUTH | 302 |
| HASLAM, MR BEN | 263 | JEFFREYS, MR DAVID | 303 |
| HAWKE, MR NIGEL | 264 | JENKINS, MR JOHN | 304 |
| †HAWKER, MR MICHAEL | 265 | JEWELL, MRS LINDA | 305 |
| HAWKER, MR RICHARD | 266 | JOHNSON, MR BRETT | 306 |
| †HAYNES, MR JONATHAN | 267 | JOHNSON, MR KENNY | 307 |
| HAYWOOD, MISS GAIL | 268 | JOHNSON HOUGHTON, MISS EVE | 308 |
| †HEARD, MR COLIN | 269 | JOHNSTON, MR MARK | 309 |
| HENDERSON, MR NICKY | 270 | JONES, MR ALAN | 310 |

| Name | Team No. |
|---|---|
| **K** | |
| KEATLEY, MR ADRIAN PAUL | 311 |
| †KEHOE, MRS FIONA | 312 |
| KEIGHLEY, MR MARTIN | 313 |
| KEIGHTLEY, MR SHAUN | 314 |
| KELLETT, MR CHRISTOPHER | 315 |
| KELLEWAY, MISS GAY | 316 |
| KENIRY, MRS STEF | 317 |
| KENT, MR NICK | 318 |
| KENT, MR TERRY | 319 |
| †KERR, MR LEONARD | 320 |
| KING, MR ALAN | 321 |
| KING, MR NEIL | 322 |
| KIRBY, MR PHILIP | 323 |
| KIRK, MR SYLVESTER | 324 |
| KITTOW, MR STUART | 325 |
| KNIGHT, MR WILLIAM | 326 |
| KOBEISSI, MR HILAL | 327 |
| KUBLER, DANIEL & CLAIRE | 328 |
| **L** | |
| LACEY, MR TOM | 329 |
| LAFFON-PARIAS, MR CARLOS | 330 |
| †LAMPARD, MR NICK | 331 |
| †LANDY, MR JUSTIN | 332 |
| LAVELLE, MISS EMMA | 333 |
| LAWES, MR TOBY | 334 |
| LEAVY, MR BARRY | 335 |
| LEE, MISS KERRY | 336 |
| LEECH, MRS SOPHIE | 337 |
| LEESON, MISS TRACEY | 338 |
| LEWIS, MRS SHEILA | 339 |
| LITTMODEN, MR NICK | 340 |
| LLEWELLYN, MR BERNARD | 341 |
| LONG, MR JOHN E. | 342 |
| LONGSDON, MR CHARLIE | 343 |
| LOUGHNANE, MR DAVID | 344 |
| LOUGHNANE, MR MARK | 345 |
| LYCETT, MR SHAUN | 346 |
| **M** | |
| MACEY, MISS JESSICA | 347 |
| MACKIE, MR JOHN | 348 |
| †MADDISON, MR PETER | 349 |
| MADGWICK, MR MICHAEL | 350 |
| MAIN, MRS HEATHER | 351 |
| †MAKIN, MRS JANE VICTORIA | 352 |
| MAKIN, MR PHILLIP | 353 |
| MALZARD, MRS ALYSON | 354 |
| MANN, MR CHARLIE | 355 |
| MARGARSON, MR GEORGE | 356 |
| MARTIN, MR ANDREW | 357 |
| †MARTIN, MISS NICKY | 358 |
| MASON, MR CHRISTOPHER | 359 |
| MASON, MRS JENNIFER | 360 |
| †MATHIAS, MISS JANE | 361 |
| MCBRIDE, MR PHILIP | 362 |
| MCCAIN, MR DONALD | 363 |
| MCCARTHY, MR TIM | 364 |
| MCENTEE, MR PHIL | 365 |
| MCGRATH, MR MURTY | 366 |
| MCGREGOR, MRS JEAN | 367 |
| MCJANNET, MR LUKE | 368 |
| MCPHERSON, MR GRAEME | 369 |
| †MCSHARRY, MR CHRISTOPHER | 370 |
| MEADE, MR MARTYN | 371 |
| MEADE, MR NOEL | 372 |
| MECHIE, MR NEIL | 373 |
| MEEHAN, MR BRIAN | 374 |
| MENUISIER, MR DAVID | 375 |
| MENZIES, MISS REBECCA | 376 |
| MIDDLETON, MR PHIL | 377 |
| MIDGLEY, MR PAUL | 378 |
| MILLMAN, MR ROD | 379 |
| MITCHELL, MR NICK | 380 |
| MITCHELL, MR RICHARD | 381 |
| MITFORD-SLADE, MR RICHARD | 382 |
| MOFFATT, MR JAMES | 383 |
| MOHAMMED, MR ISMAIL | 384 |
| MONGAN, MRS LAURA | 385 |
| MOORE, MR GARY | 386 |
| MOORE, MR J. S. | 387 |
| MORGAN, MISS LAURA | 388 |
| MORRIS, MR MOUSE | 389 |
| MORRIS, MR PATRICK | 390 |
| MORRISON, MR HUGHIE | 391 |

| Name | Team No. |
|---|---|
| MOUBARAK, MR MOHAMED | 392 |
| MUIR, MR WILLIAM | 393 |
| MULHALL, MR CLIVE | 394 |
| MULHOLLAND, MR NEIL | 395 |
| MULLANEY, MR LAWRENCE | 396 |
| MULLINEAUX, MR MICHAEL | 397 |
| MULLINS, MR SEAMUS | 398 |
| MULLINS, MR WILLIAM P. | 399 |
| MURPHY, MISS AMY | 400 |
| MURPHY, MR MIKE | 401 |
| MURPHY, MR OLLY | 402 |
| MURPHY, MR PAT | 403 |
| MURTAGH, MR BARRY | 404 |

**N**

| Name | Team No. |
|---|---|
| NAYLOR, DR JEREMY | 405 |
| NELMES, MRS HELEN | 406 |
| NEWCOMBE, MR TONY | 407 |
| NEWLAND, DR RICHARD | 408 |
| NEWTON-SMITH, MISS ANNA | 409 |
| NICHOLLS, MR ADRIAN | 410 |
| NICHOLLS, MR PAUL | 411 |
| NICOL, MR ADAM DAVID | 412 |
| NIVEN, MR PETER | 413 |
| NORTON, MR JOHN | 414 |

**O**

| Name | Team No. |
|---|---|
| O'BRIEN, MR A. P. | 415 |
| O'BRIEN, MR DANIEL | 416 |
| O'BRIEN, MR DONNACHA | 417 |
| O'BRIEN, MR FERGAL | 418 |
| O'BRIEN, MR JOSEPH | 419 |
| O'KEEFFE, MR JEDD | 420 |
| O'MEARA, MR DAVID | 421 |
| †O'NEILL, MRS DANIELLE | 422 |
| O'NEILL, MR JOHN | 423 |
| O'NEILL, MR JONJO | 424 |
| O'SHEA, MR JOHN | 425 |
| OLDROYD, MR GEOFFREY | 426 |
| OLIVER, MR HENRY | 427 |
| OSBORNE, MR JAMIE | 428 |
| OWEN, MISS EMMA | 429 |
| OWENS, MR PATRICK | 430 |

**P**

| Name | Team No. |
|---|---|
| PALMER, MR HUGO | 431 |
| PARR, MR JOSEPH | 432 |
| PATTINSON, MR MARK | 433 |
| PAULING, MR BEN | 434 |
| PEARCE, MR SIMON | 435 |
| PEARS, MR OLLIE | 436 |
| PERRATT, MISS LINDA | 437 |
| PERRETT, MRS AMANDA | 438 |
| PHELAN, MR PAT | 439 |
| PHILIPPART DE FOY, MR KEVIN | 440 |
| PHILLIPS, MR ALAN | 441 |
| PHILLIPS, MR RICHARD | 442 |
| PICKARD, MISS ELLA | 443 |
| PIPE, MR DAVID | 444 |
| POGSON, CHARLES & ADAM | 445 |
| PORTMAN, MR JONATHAN | 446 |
| POTTER, MR RYAN DAVID | 447 |
| POULTON, MRS CAMILLA | 448 |
| PRESCOTT BT, SIR MARK | 449 |
| PRICE, MISS KATY | 450 |
| PRICE, MR RICHARD | 451 |
| PRITCHARD, MR PETER | 452 |

**Q**

| Name | Team No. |
|---|---|
| QUINN, MR DENIS | 453 |
| QUINN, MR JOHN | 454 |
| QUINN, MR MICK | 455 |

**R**

| Name | Team No. |
|---|---|
| RALPH, MR ALASTAIR | 456 |
| REED, MR TIM | 457 |
| REES, MR DAVID | 458 |
| †REES, MRS HELEN | 459 |
| RICHARDS, MRS LYDIA | 460 |
| RICHARDS, MR NICKY | 461 |
| RICHES, MR JOHN DAVID | 462 |
| RIMELL, MR MARK | 463 |
| ROBERTS, MR DAVE | 464 |
| ROBERTS, MR MIKE | 465 |
| ROBINSON, MISS SARAH | 466 |
| †ROBSON, MR ADAM | 467 |
| ROBSON, MISS PAULINE | 468 |
| †ROSS, MR RUSSELL | 469 |

## W

| Name | Team No. |
|------|----------|
| WADHAM, MRS LUCY | 548 |
| WAGGOTT, MISS TRACY | 549 |
| WAINWRIGHT, MR JOHN | 550 |
| †WALEY-COHEN, MR ROBERT | 551 |
| WALFORD, MR MARK | 552 |
| WALFORD, MR ROBERT | 553 |
| WALKER, MR ED | 554 |
| WALL, MR CHRIS | 555 |
| WALL, MR TREVOR | 556 |
| WALLIS, MR CHARLIE | 557 |
| WALTON, MRS JANE | 558 |
| †WALTON, MR JIMMY | 559 |
| †WALTON, MRS SHEENA | 560 |
| WARD, MR TOM | 562 |
| WATSON, MR ARCHIE | 563 |
| WATSON, MR FRED | 564 |
| WATT, MRS SHARON | 565 |
| WAUGH, MR SIMON | 566 |
| WEATHERER, MR MARK | 567 |
| WEBBER, MR PAUL | 568 |
| WEST, MR ADAM | 569 |
| WEST, MISS SHEENA | 570 |
| WEST, MR SIMON | 571 |
| WESTON, MR DAVID | 572 |
| WESTON, MR TOM | 573 |
| WHILLANS, MR ALISTAIR | 574 |
| WHILLANS, MR DONALD | 575 |
| WHITAKER, MR RICHARD | 576 |
| WHITTINGTON, MR HARRY | 577 |
| WIGHAM, MR MICHAEL | 578 |
| †WILESMITH, MR MARTIN | 579 |
| WILLIAMS, MR CHRISTIAN | 580 |
| WILLIAMS, MR EVAN | 581 |
| WILLIAMS, MR IAN | 582 |
| WILLIAMS, MRS JANE | 583 |
| WILLIAMS, MR NICK | 584 |
| WILLIAMS, MR NOEL | 585 |
| WILLIAMS, MR OLLY | 586 |
| WILLIAMS, MR STUART | 587 |
| WILLIAMS, MISS VENETIA | 588 |
| WILLIAMSON, MRS LISA | 589 |

| Name | Team No. |
|------|----------|
| WILSON, MR ANDREW | 590 |
| WINGROVE, MR KEN | 591 |
| WINKS, MR PETER | 592 |
| WINTLE, MR ADRIAN | 593 |
| WOODMAN, MISS REBECCA | 594 |
| WOODMAN, MR STEVE | 595 |
| WOODS, MRS CYNTHIA | 596 |
| WOODS, MR SEAN | 597 |
| WOOLLACOTT, MRS KAYLEY | 598 |

## Y

| Name | Team No. |
|------|----------|
| †YORK, MR PHILLIP | 599 |
| YOUNG, MRS LAURA | 600 |
| YOUNG, MR MAXWELL | 601 |
| †YOUNG, MR WILLIAM | 602 |

## PROPERTY OF HER MAJESTY
# The Queen

Colours: Purple, gold braid, scarlet sleeves, black velvet cap with gold fringe

Trained by **Sir Michael Stoute**, Newmarket

### THREE-YEAR-OLDS

1   **EVALUATION,** b g Dubawi (IRE) - Estimate (IRE)
2   **GEOMETRIST,** b f Kingman - Hypoteneuse (IRE)
3   **JUST FINE (IRE),** b g Sea The Stars (IRE) - Bint Almatar (USA)
4   **PORTFOLIO (JPN),** b f Deep Impact (JPN) - Diploma

### TWO-YEAR-OLDS

5   **KITEFLYER,** b c 21/1 Iffraaj - Star Value (IRE) (Danehill Dancer (IRE))
6   **TRANSPIRE (FR),** b c 27/2 Frankel - Estimate (IRE) (Monsun (GER))

Trained by **William Haggas**, Newmarket

### THREE-YEAR-OLDS

7    **CHALK STREAM,** b g Sea The Stars (IRE) - Golden Stream (IRE)
8    **COMPANIONSHIP,** b f Galileo (IRE) - Sweet Idea (AUS)
9    **LIGHT REFRAIN,** b f Frankel - Light Music
10   **SECRET HAUNT,** b f Dubawi (IRE) - Enticement
11   **WINK OF AN EYE,** b g Dubawi (IRE) - Momentary

### TWO-YEAR-OLDS

12   **CLEAR DAY (FR),** b c 19/1 Camelot - Dawn Glory (Oasis Dream)
13   **EDUCATOR,** br c 4/2 Deep Impact (JPN) - Diploma (Dubawi (IRE))
14   **PERFECT ALIBI,** b f 23/2 Le Havre (IRE) - Daphne (Duke of Marmalade (IRE))
15   b c 14/4 Galileo (IRE) - Sweet Idea (AUS) (Snitzel (AUS))
16   b f 22/2 Dubawi (IRE) - Yellow Rosebud (IRE) (Jeremy (USA))

Trained by **Richard Hannon**, Marlborough

### THREE-YEAR-OLDS

17   **SERGEANT MAJOR,** b c Siyouni (FR) - Aurore (IRE)

### TWO-YEAR-OLDS

18   **EVERYDAY,** b c 29/4 Cable Bay (IRE) - Humdrum (Dr Fong (USA))

## PROPERTY OF HER MAJESTY
# The Queen

Trained by **Roger Charlton**, Beckhampton

### THREE-YEAR-OLDS

19  **ENCOURAGE,** b g Iffraaj - Good Hope
20  **ORDEROFSUCCESSION,** b f Siyouni (FR) - Sequence (IRE)

### TWO-YEAR-OLDS

21  **FRESH FANCY (IRE),** b f 15/2 New Approach (IRE) - Pure Fantasy (Fastnet Rock (AUS))

Trained by **Michael Bell**, Newmarket

### THREE-YEAR-OLDS

22  **BOOKMARK,** b f New Approach (IRE) - Free Verse
23  **CLOSENESS,** b f Iffraaj - Pack Together
24  **INVEIGLE,** b g Dark Angel (IRE) - Sand Vixen
25  **REALIST,** b g Camelot - Silver Mirage
26  **STIMULATE,** b f Motivator - Shama (IRE)
27  **SUN FESTIVAL,** b g Toronado - Raymi Coya (CAN)

### TWO-YEAR-OLDS

28  **IMPROVISE (FR),** b f 3/4 Iffraaj - Set To Music (IRE) (Danehill Dancer (IRE))
29  **SPRING IS SPRUNG (FR),** b c 21/2 Oasis Dream - Kinematic (Kyllachy)

Trained by **Andrew Balding**, Kingsclere

30  **KING'S LYNN,** 4 b g Cable Bay (IRE) - Kinematic

### THREE-YEAR-OLDS

31  **PINEAPPLE RING,** b f Kingman - Ananas
32  **TACTICAL,** b c Toronado (IRE) - Make Fast
33  **THOUGHT PROCESS,** b f Galileo (IRE) - Memory (IRE)

### TWO-YEAR-OLDS

34  **TACK (FR),** b c 15/2 Iffraaj - Make Fast (Makfi)
35  **IMMINENT,** b f 10/5 Dubawi (IRE) - Enticement (Montjeu (IRE))

## PROPERTY OF HER MAJESTY
# The Queen

Trained by **John & Thady Gosden**, Newmarket

### THREE-YEAR-OLDS

36 **PIED PIPER**, ch g New Approach (IRE) - Pure Fantasy
37 **VITAL FORCE (IRE)**, b f Invincible Spirit (IRE) - Bergamask (USA)
38 **WAKENING (IRE)**, br f Dark Angel (IRE) - Dancing Sands (IRE)
39 **WELL SPENT**, b f Siyouni (FR) - Pleasemetoo (IRE)

### TWO-YEAR-OLDS

40 **DUKEDOM (IRE)**, b c 27/1 Dubawi (IRE) - Nathra (IRE) (Iffraaj)
41 **REACH FOR THE MOON**, b c 15/2 Sea The Stars (IRE) - Golden Stream (IRE) (Sadler's Wells (USA))
42 **PARK STREET**, b c 4/5 New Approach (IRE) - City Chic (USA) (Street Cry (IRE))
43 **SAGA**, b gr c 25/3 Invincible Spirit (IRE) - Emily Bronte (Machiavellian (USA))

Trained by **Richard Hughes**, Upper Lambourn

### THREE-YEAR-OLDS

44 **TYNWALD**, b g Toronado (IRE) - Queen's Prize

### TWO-YEAR-OLDS

45 **LIGHT TRAVELLER (IRE)**, ch f 23/2 Siyouni (FR) - Shimmering Light (Dubawi (IRE))

### To be allocated

46 **DISCRETION**, b f 29/1 Dubawi (IRE) - Momentary (Nayef (USA))
47 **DISTANT LIGHT**, b f 12/3 Fastnet Rock (AUS) - Light Music (Elusive Quality (USA))
48 **DUTY BOUND**, b c 18/2 Kingman - Key Point (IRE) (Galileo (IRE))
49 **INTELLIGENTSIA (IRE)**, ch f 20/5 Exceed And Excel (AUS) - Discernable (Elusive Quality (USA))
50 **LINE OF DEFENCE**, ch c 19/1 Ulysses (IRE) - Touchline (Exceed And Excel (AUS))
51 **LOUDSPEAKER**, b g 27/4 Recorder - Daring Aim (Daylami (IRE))
52 **NAVAL COLLEGE**, b g 29/3 Dartmouth - Sequence (IRE) (Selkirk (USA))

Trained by **Nicky Henderson**, Lambourn

53 **BLUE HEAVEN**, 4 b f Blue Bresil (FR) - Spring Flight
54 **HAMILTON'S FANTASY**, 6 b m Mount Nelson - Romantic Dream
55 **ITALIAN SUMMER**, 6 br m Milan - Midsummer Magic
56 **KEEN ON**, 7 b g Kayf Tara - Romantic Dream
57 **KINCARDINE**, 4 b g Kayf Tara - Side Step
58 **RAPID FLIGHT**, 5 b g Midnight Legend - Spring Flight
59 **STEAL A MARCH**, 6 b g Mount Nelson - Side Step
60 **WAVE THE WAND**, 4 b g Gentlewave (IRE) - Magic Score

Trained by **Charlie Longsdon**, Chipping Norton

61 **HIGH YIELD**, 4 b g Yeats (IRE) - Midsummer Magic

**SOME TRAINERS' STRINGS ARE TAKEN FROM THE BHA RACING ADMINISTRATION WEBSITE AND INCLUDE HORSES LISTED ON THERE AS IN 'PRE-TRAINING', 'AT GRASS' OR 'RESTING'**

---

**1**   **MR NICK ALEXANDER, Kinneston**
Postal: Kinneston, Leslie, Glenrothes, Fife, KY6 3JJ
Contacts: **PHONE** 01592 840774 **MOBILE** 07831 488210
**EMAIL** nicholasalexander@kinneston.com **WEBSITE** www.kinneston.com

1 **ARNICA**, 8, b ch g Champs Elysees—Cordoba  **Mr J. K. McGarrity**
2 **ARTIC MANN**, 7, b g Sulamani (IRE)—Line Artic (FR)  **Alexander, Baxter & Jardine-Paterson**
3 **BALLYNANTY (IRE)**, 9, gr g Yeats (IRE)—Reina Blanca  **J Douglas Miller & Ken McGarrity**
4 **BENNY'S SECRET (IRE)**, 11, b g Beneficial—Greenhall Rambler (IRE)  **Katie & Brian Castle**
5 **BIBLICAL (FR)**, 6, ch g Harbour Watch (IRE)—Prophecie (FR)  **Mr John J Murray & Mrs Lynne MacLennan**
6 **BLAZING PORT (IRE)**, 6, b g Yeats (IRE)—Despute (IRE)  **Turcan, Borwick, Dunning & McGarrity**
7 **BROADWAY JOE (IRE)**, 7, b g Milan—Greenhall Rambler (IRE)  **Clan Gathering**
8 **CALIVIGNY (IRE)**, 12, b g Gold Well—Summer Holiday (IRE)  **Alexander Family**
9 **CANCAN (FR)**, 5, b m Al Namix (FR)—Kestrel Mail (FR)  **The Dregs Of Humanity**
10 **CENTENIER (FR)**, 5, b g Rail Link—Calling Grace (FR)  **Mrs J. A. Morris**
11 **CHANTING HILL (IRE)**, 7, b m Milan—Kitty Dillon (IRE)  **Quandt & Cochrane**
12 **CHARM OFFENSIVE (FR)**, 7, b m Le Triton (USA)—Go Lison (FR)  **The Nags to Riches Partnership**
13 **CHRISTMAS IN USA (FR)**, 9, b g Shaanmer (IRE)—Diamond of Diana (FR)  **Bowen & Nicol**
14 **CLAN LEGEND**, 11, ch g Midnight Legend—Harrietfield  **Clan Gathering**
15 **COUNTERMAND**, 9, b g Authorized (IRE)—Answered Prayer  **Mr N. W. Alexander**
16 **CRAIGANBOY (IRE)**, 12, b g Zagreb (USA)—Barnish River (IRE)  **Quandt, Cochrane, Lysaght**
17 **CREAM OF THE WEST (IRE)**, 5, b g Westerner—Clare Hogan (IRE)  **Quandt & Cochrane**
18 **DUBAI DAYS (IRE)**, 7, b g Dubai Destination (USA)—Comeragh Girl (IRE)  **Alexander, Morris & Parker**
19 **EAGLE RIDGE (IRE)**, 10, b g Oscar (IRE)—Azaban (IRE)  **Ken McGarrity and Murray Cameron**
20 **EBONY JEWEL (IRE)**, 7, b g Westerner—Lady Roania (IRE)  **Mrs L. Maclennan**
21 **ELVIS MAIL (FR)**, 7, gr g Great Pretender (IRE)—Queenly Mail (FR)  **The Ladies Who**
22 **ETOILE D'ECOSSE (FR)**, 7, gr m Martaline—Etoile de Mogador (FR)  **Mrs S. M. Irwin**
23 **FERNHILL LAD (IRE)**, 6, b g Dylan Thomas (IRE)—Sarahall (IRE)  **Coltman Cundall Matterson & Stephenson**
24 **FINAL REMINDER (IRE)**, 9, b m Gold Well—Olde Kilcormac (IRE)  **Katie & Brian Castle**
25 **FORTESCUE WOOD (IRE)**, 6, b g Westerner—Primrose Time  **Bowen & Nicol**
26 **GINGER MAIL (FR)**, 5, gr g Sinndar (IRE)—Queenly Mail (FR)  **Mrs J. Douglas Miller**
27 **GIPSY LEE ROSE (FR)**, 7, gr m Walk In The Park (IRE)—Vanoo d'Orthe (FR)  **Mrs S. M. Irwin**
28 **LAKE VIEW LAD (IRE)**, 11, gr g Oscar (IRE)—Missy O'Brien (IRE)  **Mr T. J. Hemmings**
29 **LANDECKER (IRE)**, 13, br g Craigsteel—Winsome Breeze (IRE)  **Mr N. W. Alexander**
30 **LET THERE BE LOVE (IRE)**, 6, b g Shantou (USA)—Zolotaya  **Katie & Brian Castle**
31 **LEWA HOUSE**, 5, b g Yeats (IRE)—Primrose Time  **Bissett Racing**
32 **MANETTI (IRE)**, 9, b g Westerner—Mrs Wallensky (IRE)  **Sandy's Angels**
33 **MARYLINE TRITT (FR)**, 5, b m Kap Rock (FR)—Tritone Crick (FR)  **Mr N. W. Alexander**
34 **MCGINTY'S DREAM (IRE)**, 10, b g Flemensfirth (USA)—Laboc  **Kinneston Racing**
35 **MEMOIRS (IRE)**, 6, b m Shirocco (GER)—Mtpockets (IRE)  **Miss A. R. Harper**
36 **MINUIT CIEL**, 5, b m Midnight Legend—Gaspaisielle  **The Nicole Racing Syndicate**
37 **MORE MADNESS (IRE)**, 14, b g Dr Massini (IRE)—Angelic Angel (IRE)  **J. F. Alexander**
38 **NAUTICAL MISS (IRE)**, 6, b br m Imperial Monarch (IRE)—
                                        Yourfinalanswer (IRE)  **Mr HW Turcan & Sir Simon Dunning**
39 **NED TANNER (IRE)**, 5, b g Milan—Rose Tanner (IRE)  **Hands and Heels**
40 **NICEANDEASY (IRE)**, 8, b g Kalanisi (IRE)—High Priestess (IRE)  **Katie & Brian Castle**
41 **NOT THE CHABLIS (IRE)**, 7, b g Scorpion (IRE)—De Street (IRE)  **Turcan, Dunning, Price, Stewart, Burnham**
42 **PEAK OF BEAUTY (IRE)**, 8, b m Mountain High (IRE)—Minoras Return (IRE)  **Mr D. Walker**
43 **PENNY RIVER**, 6, b m Kayf Tara—River Alder  **Katie & Brian Castle**
44 **RACING PULSE (IRE)**, 12, b g Garuda (IRE)—Jacks Sister (IRE)  **J. F. Alexander**
45 **RYEDALE RACER**, 10, b g Indian Danehill (IRE)—Jontys'lass  **Bissett Racing**
46 **SHAKA THE KING (IRE)**, 7, b g Yeats (IRE)—Kissantell (IRE)  **SprayClad UK**
47 **SILK OR SCARLET (IRE)**, 9, ch g Mahler—Scents of Clanagh (IRE)  **Ken McGarrity & Dudgeon, Cundall, Liddle**
48 4, B f Gentlewave (IRE)—Spinning Away  **Mr N. W. Alexander**
49 **STEVIE SMITH**, 5, b m Roderic O'Connor (IRE)—Poem (IRE)  **Mr R. J. C. Wilmot-Smith**
50 **TED VEALE (IRE)**, 14, b g Revoque (IRE)—Rose Tanner (IRE)  **Alexander Family**
51 **TRAVAIL D'ORFEVRE (FR)**, 5, gr g Martaline—Lady Needles (IRE)  **Bowen & Nicol**

# MR NICK ALEXANDER - continued

52 **UP HELLY AA KING**, 10, ch g And Beyond (IRE)—Gretton **Jean Matterson & J Douglas Miller**
53 **UPANDATIT (IRE)**, 6, b g Winged Love (IRE)—Betty Beck (IRE) **Miss J. G. K. Matterson**
54 **WAKOOL (FR)**, 5, gr g Motivator—Symba's Dream (USA) **Turcan, Borwick, Dunning & Fleming**

## THREE-YEAR-OLDS

55 B f Blue Bresil (FR)—Little Glenshee (IRE) **Mr N. W. Alexander**
56 B f Clovis du Berlais (FR)—Swift Getaway (IRE) **Mr N. W. Alexander**

**Other Owners:** Mr N. W. Alexander, Alexander Family, Mr L. Borwick, Mr A. J. Bowen, Lady Burnham, Mr M. Cameron, Mr B. C. Castle, Mrs C. Castle, The Hon T. H. V. Cochrane, Mrs M. C. Coltman, Mr R. H. Cundall, Mrs J. Douglas Miller, Dudgeon, Cundall, Liddle, Sir Simon Dunning, Miss D. F. Fleming, C. Lysaght, Mrs L. Maclennan, Miss J. G. K. Matterson, Mr J. K. McGarrity, Mr J. J. Murray, Mr A. G. Nicol, Mrs D. C. S. Price, Miss S. Quandt, Mr O. G. Stephenson, A. D. Stewart, H. W. Turcan.

**Assistant Trainer:** Catriona Bissett.

**NH Jockey:** Lucy Alexander. **NH Jockey:** Grant Cockburn. **Amateur Jockey:** Mr Kit Alexander.

---

**2**  **MISS LOUISE ALLAN, Newmarket**
Postal: **2 London Road, Newmarket, Suffolk, CB8 0TW**
Contacts: **MOBILE 07703 355878**
**EMAIL louiseallan1@hotmail.co.uk**

1 **EXMOOR BEAST**, 5, ch g Sepoy (AUS)—Junket **Mr R. P. Holley**
2 **HARD TOFFEE (IRE)**, 10, b g Teofilo (IRE)—Speciale (USA) **Miss V. L. Allan**
3 **PIPERS DREAM**, 4, b f Beat All (USA)—High Meadow Rose **Mr R. Moore**
4 **POETIC DEED**, 4, b f Dylan Thomas (IRE)—Late Night Deed

## THREE-YEAR-OLDS

5 **ALL THAT JAZZ (SAF)**, b f Trippi (USA)—Val de Ra (SAF)
6 **CALTON HILL (IRE)**, b g No Nay Never (USA)—Aljumar (IRE) **Mr R. P. Holley**
7 **RED BOULEVARD (SAF)**, b f Visionaire (USA)—Strawberry Lane (SAF)

**Other Owners:** Miss V. L. Allan.

---

**3**  **MR CONRAD ALLEN, Newmarket**
Postal: Trainer did not wish details of their string to appear

---

**4**  **MR SAM ALLWOOD, Whitchurch**
Postal: **Church Farm, Church Lane, Ash Magna, Whitchurch, Shropshire, SY13 4EA**
Contacts: **PHONE 07738 413579**
**EMAIL office@samallwood.co.uk**

1 **ALRIGHT CHIEF (IRE)**, 9, b br g Daylami (IRE)—Lee Valley Native (IRE) **Beverley & Steve Evason**
2 **ALTUMANINA**, 6, b m Helmet (AUS)—Tanwir **Mr P. J. Harney**
3 **AQUILA SKY (IRE)**, 6, b g Arcadio (GER)—Starventure (IRE) **The Lygon Lot**
4 **BEMPTON CLIFFS (IRE)**, 6, gr g Canford Cliffs (IRE)—Grand Lili **Mr M Dunlevy & Mrs H McGuinness**

## MR SAM ALLWOOD - continued

   5 **BITASWEETSYMPHONY (IRE)**, 6, b g Mahler—Libertango (IRE) **Bostock Dunlevy McGuinness Bradshaw**
   6 **BIZERTA (FR)**, 5, ch g Le Havre (IRE)—Blue Blue Sea **Mr H. Taylor**
   7 **GUILDHALL**, 5, b g Cityscape—Ecstasy **S. J. Allwood**
   8 **HOWYOUPLAYTHEGAME (FR)**, 5, b g Montmartre (FR)—Maille Asie (FR) **R. B. Francis**
   9 **JOBSONFIRE**, 9, b g Sulamani (IRE)—Seviot **Paul Clifton & Sarah Thomas**
10 **KITEINAHURRICANE (IRE)**, 6, b g Court Cave (IRE)—Katsura **Sam Allwood Racing Club**
11 4, Ch c Gentlewave (IRE)—Materiality **S. J. Allwood**
12 **NOTHING MAN (IRE)**, 7, b g Ask—Holly Gaga (IRE) **Allwood Ashton Gittins**
13 **OUT ON THE TEAR (IRE)**, 7, b g Arcadio (GER)—Madame Coco (IRE) **Sam Allwood Racing Club**
14 **R BERNARD**, 5, b g Norse Dancer (IRE)—Channel Treat **Mr R. J. W. Broadley**
15 **ROB THE GETAWAY (IRE)**, 8, b g Getaway (GER)—Kinard True (IRE) **Mr C. H. Gittins**
16 **SCRIPTED DESTINY**, 6, b m Shantou (USA)—Lemon Queen (IRE) **S. J. Allwood**
17 **SECRET COURT (IRE)**, 7, b m Court Cave (IRE)—Tasanak (IRE) **Mr P. J. Harney**
18 **SHENEEDEDTHERUN (IRE)**, 11, b m Kayf Tara—Lady Moon (FR) **Sam Allwood Racing Club**

### THREE-YEAR-OLDS

19 B g Pether's Moon (IRE)—Queen's Law (IRE) **S. J. Allwood**

**Other Owners:** S. J. Allwood, Mr G. J. Ashton, Mrs B. A. Bostock, Mr P. E. Bradshaw, Mr P. Clifton, Mr M. Dunlevy, Mr S. Evason, Mr C. H. Gittins, Mrs H. A. McGuinness, Miss S. M. Thomas.

---

## 5    MR ERIC ALSTON, Preston
Postal: **Edges Farm Stables, Chapel Lane, Longton, Preston, Lancashire, PR4 5NA**
Contacts: **PHONE 01772 612120 MOBILE 07879 641660 FAX 01772 619600**
**EMAIL eric1943@supanet.com**

   1 **ARKLOW GEORGE**, 4, b g Intrinsic—Brer Rabbit **Mr G. Caldwell**
   2 **BOUDICA BAY (IRE)**, 6, b m Rip Van Winkle (IRE)—White Shift (IRE) **The Grumpy Old Geezers**
   3 **CAPTAIN CORCORAN (IRE)**, 4, b g Anjaal—Hms Pinafore (IRE) **Whitehills Racing Syndicate 2**
   4 **DEAL DUN (IRE)**, 4, b f Free Eagle (IRE)—Dundel'S Spirit (IRE) **Mr C. F. Harrington**
   5 **FOX HILL**, 5, b m Foxwedge (AUS)—Siryena **Whitehills Racing Syndicate**
   6 **HARRY'S RIDGE (IRE)**, 6, b g Acclamation—Dani Ridge (IRE) **Mr L. Carlisle**
   7 **JABBAROCKIE**, 8, b g Showcasing—Canina **M Balmer, K Sheedy, P Copple, C Dingwall**
   8 **NIAGARA (IRE)**, 4, b g Power—Damalis (IRE) **Liam & Tony Ferguson**
   9 **REDROSEZORRO**, 7, b g Foxwedge (AUS)—Garter Star **Red Rose Partnership**
10 **SPIRIT POWER**, 6, b g Swiss Spirit—Verasina (USA) **The Selebians**

### THREE-YEAR-OLDS

11 **DESERT CAT**, b f Bobby's Kitten (USA)—Wonderful Desert **The Horses Mouth Racing Club**
12 **STORM DREAMER**, b c Oasis Dream—Ombre **Whitehills Racing Syndicate 3**

### TWO-YEAR-OLDS

13 B g 24/02 Free Eagle (IRE)—Elusive Ellen (IRE) (Elusive City (USA)) (9524) **Mr C. F. Harrington**
14 Ch g 23/04 Territories (IRE)—Jacaranda Ridge (Indian Ridge) (10000) **Mr P. Harrington**

**Other Owners:** Mr C. A. Ferguson, M. L. Ferguson.

**Assistant Trainer:** Mrs Sue Alston.

## 6 | MR CHARLIE APPLEBY, Newmarket
Postal: **Godolphin Management Co Ltd, Moulton Paddocks, Newmarket, Suffolk, CB8 7PJ**
WEBSITE www.godolphin.com

1 **AL SUHAIL**, 4, b c Dubawi (IRE)—Shirocco Star
2 **ALTHIQA**, 4, gr f Dark Angel (IRE)—Mistrusting (IRE)
3 **ART DU VAL**, 5, b g No Nay Never (USA)—Aquarelle Rare
4 **CIGOLI (IRE)**, 4, b c Galileo (IRE)—Posset
5 **D'BAI (IRE)**, 7, b g Dubawi (IRE)—Savannah Belle
6 **DESERT PEACE (USA)**, 4, b g Curlin (USA)—Stoweshoe (USA)
7 **EASTERN WORLD (IRE)**, 4, ch g Dubawi (IRE)—Eastern Joy
8 **GHOSTWATCH (IRE)**, 6, b g Dubawi (IRE)—Nature Spirits (FR)
9 **GLOBAL STORM (IRE)**, 4, b g Night of Thunder (IRE)—Travel (USA)
10 **GLORIOUS JOURNEY**, 6, b g Dubawi (IRE)—Fallen For You
11 **ISPOLINI**, 6, b g Dubawi (IRE)—Giants Play (USA)
12 **KINGSWEAR**, 4, b g Dubawi (IRE)—Galatee (FR)
13 **LAZULI (IRE)**, 4, b g Dubawi (IRE)—Floristry
14 **LOXLEY (IRE)**, 6, b g New Approach (IRE)—Lady Marian (GER)
15 **MAN OF PROMISE (USA)**, 4, b g Into Mischief (USA)—Involved (USA)
16 **ON THE WARPATH**, 6, ch g Declaration of War (USA)—Elusive Pearl (USA)
17 **PATH OF THUNDER (IRE)**, 4, ch g Night of Thunder (IRE)—Sunset Avenue (USA)
18 **RENAISSANCE QUEEN**, 4, ch f Pivotal—Indian Petal
19 **ROYAL CRUSADE**, 4, b c Shamardal (USA)—Zibelina (IRE)
20 **SAKURA PETAL**, 4, ch f Dubawi (IRE)—Dancing Rain (IRE)
21 **SAQQARA KING (USA)**, 4, gr ro g American Pharoah (USA)—Joyful Victory (CAN)
22 **SECRET ADVISOR (FR)**, 7, b g Dubawi (IRE)—Sub Rose (IRE)
23 **SECRET VICTORY**, 4, ch g Dubawi (IRE)—Hidden Gold (IRE)
24 **SPACE BLUES (IRE)**, 5, ch h Dubawi (IRE)—Miss Lucifer (FR)
25 **STAR SAFARI**, 5, b g Sea The Stars (IRE)—Intimhir (IRE)
26 **SUMMER ROMANCE (IRE)**, 4, gr f Kingman—Serena's Storm (IRE)
27 **VELORUM (IRE)**, 5, b g Sea The Stars (IRE)—Lily's Angel (IRE)
28 **WALTON STREET**, 7, b g Cape Cross (IRE)—Brom Felinity (AUS)
29 **WELL OF WISDOM**, 4, b g Oasis Dream—Alessandria
30 **ZAKOUSKI**, 5, b h Shamardal (USA)—O'Giselle (AUS)

### THREE-YEAR-OLDS

31 **A'SHAARI**, ch f Dubawi (IRE)—Hibaayeb
32 **ACT OF WISDOM (IRE)**, ch c Galileo (IRE)—Jacqueline Quest (IRE)
33 **ADAYAR (IRE)**, b c Frankel—Anna Salai (USA)
34 **AL NAYYIR**, b g Dubawi (IRE)—Bright Beacon
35 **AL NEFUD**, b g Dubawi (IRE)—Albasharah (USA)
36 **AL WAQIDI**, b c Dubawi (IRE)—Kazziana
37 **ALSEPHINA (IRE)**, b f Sea The Stars (IRE)—Pabouche (IRE)
38 **BANDINELLI**, ch c Dubawi (IRE)—Indian Petal
39 **BEAUTIFUL FUTURE (IRE)**, b f Night of Thunder (IRE)—Miss Lucifer (FR)
40 **CLOUDBRIDGE (USA)**, b g Hard Spun (USA)—Peace Camp (USA)
41 **COLOUR OF LIGHT (IRE)**, b f Shamardal (USA)—Violante (USA)
42 **CREATIVE FLAIR (IRE)**, b f Dubawi (IRE)—Hidden Gold (IRE)
43 **CREATIVE FORCE (IRE)**, ch g Dubawi (IRE)—Choose Me (IRE)
44 **DANILOVA**, b f Dubawi (IRE)—Princesse Dansante (IRE)
45 **DAZZLING BEAUTY**, b f Dubawi (IRE)—Be Fabulous (GER)
46 **DESERT WISDOM**, ch c Dubawi (IRE)—Tulips (IRE)
47 **DHAHABI (IRE)**, b c Frankel—Fleche d'Or
48 **DIVINE LIGHT (IRE)**, b f Kingman—Blue Angel (IRE)
49 **DUBAI VISION (USA)**, b c Medaglia d'Oro (USA)—Velvety (USA)
50 **ECHO POINT (IRE)**, ch g Dubawi (IRE)—Yodelling (USA)
51 **FABRIZIO**, b g Frankel—La Mortola
52 **FANCIFUL TALE (IRE)**, b f Dark Angel (IRE)—Beatrix Potter (IRE)
53 **FINAL APPLAUSE**, b f Dubawi (IRE)—Panegyric
54 **GOOD GRACE**, b f Dubawi (IRE)—Discourse (USA)

## MR CHARLIE APPLEBY - continued

55 **HIGHLAND AVENUE (IRE)**, gr c Dubawi (IRE)—Lumiere
56 **HURRICANE LANE (IRE)**, ch c Frankel—Gale Force
57 **KEMARI**, b g Dubawi (IRE)—Koora
58 **KING OF TOMORROW**, b g Dubawi (IRE)—Gallipot
59 **KNIGHT'S TOWN (IRE)**, b g Dansili—Knocknagree (IRE)
60 **KOMACHI (IRE)**, b c Kingman—Kamakura (USA)
61 **LA BARROSA (IRE)**, b c Lope de Vega (IRE)—Bikini Babe (IRE)
62 **LIGHT BEAM**, b g Dubawi (IRE)—Dalkova
63 **LIGHT SYMPHONY**, b f Dubawi (IRE)—Entertainment
64 **MAGICAL LAND (IRE)**, b c Frankel—Mistrusting (IRE)
65 **MANOBO (IRE)**, b c Sea The Stars (IRE)—Tasaday (USA)
66 **MASTER OF THE SEAS (IRE)**, b c Dubawi (IRE)—Firth of Lorne (IRE)
67 **MAWENZI**, b f Dubawi (IRE)—Tanzania (USA)
68 **MISS JINGLES (IRE)**, b f Exceed And Excel (AUS)—Veil of Silence (IRE)
69 **MODERN NEWS**, ch g Shamardal (USA)—Modern Ideals
70 **MOON SHIMMER**, b f Shamardal (USA)—Sound Reflection (USA)
71 **MYSTICAL DAWN (IRE)**, b c Sea The Stars (IRE)—My Spirit (IRE)
72 **NASH NASHA**, b f Dubawi (IRE)—Just The Judge (IRE)
73 **NAVAL CROWN**, b c Dubawi (IRE)—Come Alive
74 **NEPTUNE SEAS (IRE)**, b c Sea The Stars (IRE)—Emreliya (IRE)
75 **NEW EXCEED (IRE)**, ch f New Approach (IRE)—La Arenosa (IRE)
76 **NEW KINGDOM (IRE)**, b c Dubawi (IRE)—Nightime (IRE)
77 **NOBLE DYNASTY**, b c Dubawi (IRE)—Alina (IRE)
78 **ONE RULER (IRE)**, b c Dubawi (IRE)—Fintry (IRE)
79 **PERSIAN EMPIRE (IRE)**, b c Shamardal (USA)—Important Time (IRE)
80 **QUINTILLUS**, ch c Dubawi (IRE)—Epitome (IRE)
81 **REBEL'S ROMANCE (IRE)**, br g Dubawi (IRE)—Minidress
82 **RENAISSANCE ROSE (IRE)**, b f Shamardal (USA)—Sahraah (USA)
83 **ROYAL FLEET**, b c Dubawi (IRE)—Zibelina (IRE)
84 **ROYAL TOUCH**, b g Dubawi (IRE)—Gonbarda (GER)
85 **SASAKIA (IRE)**, b f Dubawi (IRE)—Eastern Joy
86 **SAYYIDA**, ch f Dubawi (IRE)—Khawlah (IRE)
87 **SECRET PROTECTOR (USA)**, b c War Front (USA)—Eternal Bounty (IRE)
88 **SILENT FILM**, ch g New Approach (IRE)—Dibajj (FR)
89 **SISKANY**, b c Dubawi (IRE)—Halay
90 **SYMBOLIC GESTURE**, b g New Approach (IRE)—Token of Love
91 **TABAQAT (IRE)**, b c Dubawi (IRE)—Karenine
92 **TAMBORRADA**, b g Dubawi (IRE)—Elle Shade
93 **TOROMONA (IRE)**, b c Shamardal (USA)—Tashelka (FR)
94 **VALIANT PRINCE (IRE)**, b c Dubawi (IRE)—Chachamaidee (IRE)
95 **VASILAKOS**, b c Dubawi (IRE)—First Victory (IRE)
96 **VISIONARY RULER**, b g Dubawi (IRE)—Alessandria
97 **WEDDING DANCE (IRE)**, b br f Invincible Spirit (IRE)—Wadaa (USA)
98 **WESTERN SYMPHONY (IRE)**, b c Shamardal (USA)—Balsamine (USA)
99 **WIRKO (GER)**, b c Kingman—Weltmacht
100 **YIBIR**, ch c Dubawi (IRE)—Rumh (GER)

## TWO-YEAR-OLDS

101 B f 20/03 Shamardal (USA)—All Clear (Dubawi (IRE))
102 B c 03/03 Lope de Vega (IRE)—Alta Lilea (IRE) (Galileo (IRE)) (209847)
103 B f 19/04 Shamardal (USA)—Anjaz (USA) (Street Cry (IRE))
104 B f 04/04 Teofilo (IRE)—Anna Salai (USA) (Dubawi (IRE))
105 B gr f 13/05 Invincible Spirit (USA)—Antiquities (Kaldounevees (FR))
106 B c 21/02 Frankel—As Good As Gold (IRE) (Oasis Dream) (480000)
107 Ch f 06/03 Shamardal (USA)—Asi Siempre (USA) (El Prado (IRE))
108 B c 13/04 Frankel—Attraction (Efisio) (1100000)
109 B c 04/04 Invincible Spirit (USA)—Autumn Lily (USA) (Street Cry (IRE))
110 B br c 19/02 Sea The Stars (IRE)—Awareness (USA) (Distorted Humor (USA)) (260000)
111 B f 04/04 Dubawi (IRE)—Be My Gal (Galileo (IRE)) (520000)

## MR CHARLIE APPLEBY - continued

**112** B c 07/02 Dark Angel (IRE)—Bean Feasa (Dubawi (IRE))
**113** B f 03/03 Dubawi (IRE)—Beautiful Romance (New Approach (IRE))
**114 BEFORE DAWN (IRE),** gr f 18/03 Dark Angel (IRE)—Mistrusting (IRE) (Shamardal (USA))
**115** B c 07/03 Invincible Spirit (IRE)—Belonging (Raven's Pass (USA))
**116** B c 11/02 Oasis Dream—Besotted (IRE) (Dutch Art)
**117** Ch c 03/03 Sea The Stars (IRE)—Bint Almatar (USA) (Kingmambo (USA))
**118** B c 16/02 Dubawi (IRE)—Black Cherry (Mount Nelson) (480000)
**119** B c 23/04 New Approach (IRE)—Blossomtime (Shamardal (USA))
**120** Br c 16/03 Shamardal (USA)—Blue Bunting (USA) (Dynaformer (USA))
**121** B c 10/02 Invincible Spirit (IRE)—Boldarra (USA) (Giant's Causeway (USA))
**122** B c 23/03 Dubawi (IRE)—Bright Beacon (Manduro (GER))
**123** B c 09/04 Frankel—Calare (IRE) (Dubawi (IRE))
**124** B c 18/04 Frankel—Concordia (Pivotal)
**125** B c 22/02 Dubawi (IRE)—Cushion (Galileo (IRE)) (2100000)
**126** Ch c 30/01 Galileo (IRE)—Dancing Rain (IRE) (Danehill Dancer (IRE))
**127** Ch c 11/01 New Approach (IRE)—Desert Blossom (IRE) (Shamardal (USA))
**128** B f 15/03 Sea The Stars (IRE)—Devonshire (IRE) (Fast Company (IRE))
**129** B c 11/05 Dubawi (IRE)—Discourse (USA) (Street Cry (IRE))
**130** Ch f 19/03 Frankel—Discursus (Dubawi (IRE))
**131** B c 23/04 Shamardal (USA)—Dubai Sunrise (USA) (Seeking The Gold (USA))
**132** B f 22/03 Teofilo (IRE)—Dufay (IRE) (Dubawi (IRE))
**133** B c 14/05 Galileo (IRE)—Eastern Joy (Dubai Destination (USA))
**134** B c 03/02 Oasis Dream—Easy Victory (Dubawi (IRE))
**135** B c 17/02 Shamardal (USA)—Emirates Rewards (Dubawi (IRE))
**136** Ch f 26/02 Dubawi (IRE)—Entertainment (Halling (USA))
**137** Ch f 09/04 Shamardal (USA)—Entertains (AUS) (Street Cry (IRE))
**138** Ch c 15/03 Shamardal (USA)—Epitome (IRE) (Nashwan (USA))
**139** Ch c 07/02 Dubawi (IRE)—Falls of Lora (IRE) (Street Cry (IRE))
**140** Ch c 06/02 Frankel—Final Stage (Street Cry (IRE))
**141** B c 19/03 Dubawi (IRE) —First Victory (IRE) (Teofilo (IRE))
**142** B f 08/03 Ribchester (IRE)—Firth of Lorne (IRE) (Danehill (USA))
**143** B f 07/04 Frankel—Fleche d'Or (Dubai Destination (USA)) (2000000)
**144** B c 17/03 Dubawi (IRE)—Galatee (FR) (Galileo (IRE))
**145** B c 20/02 Dubawi (IRE)—Gamilati (Bernardini (USA))
**146** B c 28/02 Dubawi (IRE)—Gaterie (USA) (Dubai Destination (USA))
**147** B f 15/02 Dubawi (IRE)—Gonbarda (GER) (Lando (GER))
**148** Ch c 16/03 Night of Thunder (IRE)—Good Place (USA) (Street Cry (IRE))
**149** B c 27/03 Dubawi (IRE)—Great And Small (Galileo (IRE)) (800000)
**150** B f 23/05 Dubawi (IRE)—Halay (Dansili)
**151** B c 25/02 Dubawi (IRE)—Hand Puppet (IRE) (Manduro (GER))
**152** Ch c 04/04 Teofilo (IRE)—Hawsa (USA) (Rahy (USA))
**153** Ch c 15/01 Dubawi (IRE)—Hertford Dancer (Foxwedge (AUS)) (300000)
**154** B c 28/04 Teofilo (IRE)—Important Time (IRE) (Oasis Dream)
**155** Ch c 12/04 Night of Thunder (IRE)—Indian Petal (Singspiel (IRE))
**156** Ch c 05/05 Dubawi (IRE)—Inner Secret (USA) (Singspiel (IRE))
**157** B c 03/02 Sea The Stars (IRE)—Innevera (FR) (Motivator) (425000)
**158** Br c 30/01 Dubawi (IRE)—Intricately (IRE) (Fastnet Rock (AUS)) (1100000)
**159** B c 30/04 Sea The Stars (IRE)—Irish History (IRE) (Dubawi (IRE))
**160** Ch c 09/04 Dubawi (IRE)—Jacqueline Quest (IRE) (Rock of Gibraltar (IRE)) (525000)
**161** B c 08/04 Shamardal (USA)—Kazimiera (Dubawi (IRE))
**162** B c 21/03 Dubawi (IRE)—Kazziana (Shamardal (USA))
**163** B f 24/03 New Approach (IRE)—Kenspeckle (Dubawi (IRE))
**164** B c 19/04 Shamardal (USA)—La Arenosa (IRE) (Exceed And Excel (AUS))
**165** B f 14/03 Teofilo (IRE)—Lava Flow (IRE) (Dalakhani (IRE))
**166 LIFE OF DREAMS,** b f 13/02 Dubawi (IRE)—Endless Time (IRE) (Sea The Stars (IRE))
**167** B c 08/02 Dubawi (IRE)—Linda Radlett (IRE) (Manduro (GER))
**168** B f 10/02 Dubawi (IRE)—Local Time (Invincible Spirit (IRE))
**169** B c 01/04 Kingman—Lombatina (FR) (King's Best (USA)) (475000)
**170** B f 02/02 Galileo (IRE)—Lumiere (Shamardal (USA))
**171** B f 22/05 Shamardal (USA)—Lyric of Light (Street Cry (IRE))

## MR CHARLIE APPLEBY - continued

**172** B f 01/03 Dubawi (IRE)—Majestic Queen (IRE) (Kheleyf (USA))
**173** B c 07/05 Sea The Stars (IRE)—Measured Tempo (Sadler's Wells (USA))
**174** Ch c 17/04 Dubawi (IRE)—Modern Ideals (New Approach (IRE))
**175** B c 10/02 Lope de Vega (IRE)—Moi Meme (Teofilo (IRE)) (900000)
**176** B c 25/02 Dubawi (IRE)—Monday Show (USA) (Maria's Mon (USA))
**177** B c 11/02 Kodiac—Montefino (IRE) (Shamardal (USA)) (255000)
**178** B c 11/04 Iffraaj—Mujarah (IRE) (Marju (IRE))
**179** B c 06/02 Postponed (IRE)—Najoum (USA) (Giant's Causeway (USA))
**180** Ch c 14/03 Dubawi (IRE)—Nightime (IRE) (Galileo (IRE))
**181** Ch f 22/04 Dubawi (IRE)—Opera Comique (FR) (Singspiel (IRE))
**182** Ch c 08/03 New Approach (IRE)—Panegyric (Monsun (GER))
**183** B c 09/03 Farhh—Patroness (Dubawi (IRE))
**184** B f 30/04 Frankel—Pearly Steph (FR) (Oasis Dream) (700000)
**185** B c 27/04 Teofilo (IRE)—Pietrafiore (IRE) (Dubawi (IRE))
**186** B c 24/04 Dark Angel (IRE)—Pimpernel (IRE) (Invincible Spirit (IRE))
**187** B f 22/05 Shamardal (USA)—Placidia (IRE) (Sea The Stars (IRE))
**188** B c 16/04 Dubawi (IRE)—Pleascach (IRE) (Teofilo (IRE))
**189** B f 03/03 Invincible Spirit (IRE)—Policoro (IRE) (Pivotal)
**190** B c 24/04 Dubawi (IRE)—Pomology (USA) (Arch (USA))
**191** Ch f 31/01 Sea The Stars (IRE)—Powder Snow (USA) (Dubawi (IRE))
**192** Ch f 31/01 Dubawi (IRE)—Priceless (Exceed And Excel (AUS)) (420000)
**193** Ch c 18/02 Dubawi (IRE)—Provenance (Galileo (IRE)) (800000)
**194** B f 30/04 New Approach (IRE)—Punctilious (Danehill (USA))
**195** B c 12/02 Shamardal (USA)—Pure Diamond (Street Cry (IRE))
**196** B f 21/01 Dubawi (IRE)—Qualify (Fastnet Rock (AUS))
**197** Ch f 27/02 Dubawi (IRE)—Really Special (Shamardal (USA))
**198** Gr f 06/03 Dark Angel (IRE)—Rock Opera (SAF) (Lecture (USA))
**199** B c 14/04 Dubawi (IRE)—Rumh (GER) (Monsun (GER))
**200** B f 05/03 Kingman—Sante (IRE) (Dream Ahead (USA)) (1450000)
**201** Ch c 06/02 Night of Thunder (IRE)—Scatter Dice (IRE) (Manduro (GER))
**202** B f 18/03 Dubawi (IRE)—Secret Gesture (Galileo (IRE))
**203** B c 25/03 Shamardal (USA)—Sense of Fun (USA) (Distorted Humor (USA))
**204** B c 13/04 Invincible Spirit (IRE)—Serene Beauty (USA) (Street Cry (IRE))
**205** B c 12/03 Dubawi (IRE)—Shawanda (IRE) (Sinndar (IRE))
**206** B f 10/03 Dubawi (IRE)—Show Day (IRE) (Shamardal (USA))
**207** B br f 20/02 Sea The Stars (IRE)—Silk Words (Dubawi (IRE))
**208** B c 08/02 Frankel—Skiffle (Dubawi (IRE))
**209** B c 16/03 Sea The Stars (IRE)—Smoulder (Redoute's Choice (AUS)) (680000)
**210** B f 19/03 Galileo (IRE)—Sobetsu (Dubawi (IRE))
**211** B c 03/05 Dubawi (IRE)—Soon (IRE) (Galileo (IRE)) (380000)
**212** B c 29/03 Dubawi (IRE)—Sound Reflection (USA) (Street Cry (IRE))
**213** B c 27/03 Kingman—Speralita (FR) (Frankel) (887813)
**214** Ch f 13/02 Dubawi (IRE)—Strathspey (New Approach (IRE))
**215** B c 16/02 Shamardal (USA)—Switching (USA) (Street Cry (IRE))
**216** B c 28/02 Shamardal (USA)—Tajriba (IRE) (Teofilo (IRE))
**217** B f 03/03 Dubawi (IRE)—Taranto (Machiavellian (USA))
**218** Ch c 29/04 Shamardal (USA)—Tasaday (Nayef (USA))
**219** B c 20/05 Shamardal (USA)—Tashelka (FR) (Mujahid (USA))
**220** B c 16/03 Sea The Stars (IRE)—Tearless (Street Cry (IRE))
**221** B f 11/03 Frankel—Tulips (IRE) (Pivotal)
**222** B f 19/02 Galileo (IRE)—Usherette (Shamardal (USA))
**223** Ch f 08/02 Dubawi (IRE)—Very Special (IRE) (Lope de Vega (IRE))
**224** Ch c 05/03 Dubawi (IRE)—Villarrica (USA) (Selkirk (USA))
**225** Ch f 13/03 Shamardal (USA)—Violante (USA) (Kingmambo (USA))
**226** B c 16/05 Exceed And Excel (AUS)—Windsor County (USA) (Elusive Quality (USA))
**227** B c 02/03 Oasis Dream—Winter Queen (Dubawi (IRE))
**228** Ch f 26/03 Shamardal (USA)—Winters Moon (IRE) (New Approach (IRE))
**229** **WITH THE MOONLIGHT (IRE),** b f 17/02 Frankel—Sand Vixen (Dubawi (IRE))
**230** B c 03/04 Shamardal (USA)—Yodelling (USA) (Medaglia d'Oro (USA))
**231** B c 01/02 Dubawi (IRE)—Zhukova (IRE) (Fastnet Rock (AUS))

## MR CHARLIE APPLEBY - continued

**232** B c 06/05 Dubawi (IRE)—Zibelina (IRE) (Dansili)
**233** Ch c 24/02 Frankel—Zindaya (USA) (More Than Ready (USA)) (280000)

**Assistant Trainer:** Alex Merriam, Marie Murphy, **Racing Secretary:** Hannah Pollard.

**Flat Jockey:** William Buick, James Doyle.

---

| 7 | **MR MICHAEL APPLEBY, Oakham** |
|---|---|

Postal: **The Homestead, Langham, Oakham, Leicestershire, LE15 7EJ**
Contacts: **PHONE 01572 722772 MOBILE 07884 366421**
EMAIL mickappleby@icloud.com WEBSITE www.mickappleby.com

1 **ACHILL QUEEN**, 4, ch f Nayef (USA)—Reveal The Light  **Mrs E. Cash**
2 **AEGEUS (USA)**, 5, b g First Defence (USA)—Supposition  **Mr W. M. Brackstone**
3 **AFRO BLUE (IRE)**, 4, b g Oasis Dream—Najraan  **The Lads From Leicester**
4 **ASAD (IRE)**, 5, ch g Lope de Vega (IRE)—Venus de Milo (IRE)  **The Weston Super Mares**
5 **AYR HARBOUR**, 4, b c Harbour Watch (IRE)—Sorella Bella (IRE)  **JP's Racing Syndicate**
6 **BAMBIRAPTOR**, 7, b m Royal Applause—Sharp Dresser (USA)  **Howdale Bloodstock**
7 **BANCNUANAHEIREANN (IRE)**, 14, b g Chevalier (IRE)—Alamanta (IRE)  **Mr W. Sewell & Mr Michael Appleby**
8 **BARRINGTON (IRE)**, 7, b g Casamento (IRE)—Mia Divina  **Mr Frank McAleavy & Mr Ian McAleavy**
9 **BLUELLA**, 6, b m Equiano (FR)—Mata Hari Blue  **Mr M. J. Golding**
10 **BRINGING GLORY (IRE)**, 4, b g Bated Breath—Roseraie (IRE)  **Mr S. G. Morris**
11 **BY JOVE**, 4, b g Nathaniel (IRE)—Calima Breeze  **M. Appleby**
12 **CASARUAN**, 4, b c Casamento (IRE)—Aruan  **B. D. Cantle**
13 **CASE KEY**, 8, gr g Showcasing—Fluttering Rose  **T. R. Pryke**
14 **CASH N CARRIE (IRE)**, 7, b m Casamento (IRE)—Tales of Erin (IRE)  **Mick Appleby Racing**
15 **CASHEL (IRE)**, 6, b g Sepoy (AUS)—Snow Dust  **Mr L. A. Bellman**
16 **CASPIAN PRINCE (IRE)**, 12, ch g Dylan Thomas (IRE)—Crystal Gaze (IRE)  **Mr S Louch & Mr M Appleby**
17 **CASTLE QUARTER (IRE)**, 5, b g Zoffany (IRE)—Queen's Pudding (IRE)  **Diamond Racing Ltd**
18 **CHANNEL PACKET**, 7, b h Champs Elysees—Etarre (IRE)  **Howdale Bloodstock**
19 **CLIPSHAM TIGER (IRE)**, 5, b g Bungle Inthejungle—Texas Queen  **Mr F. Morley**
20 **COME ON GIRL**, 4, gr f Outstrip—Floating  **Mrs D. Hopkins**
21 **COMPETITION**, 9, b g Multiplex—Compolina  **ValueRacingClub.co.uk**
22 **CRIMSON KING (IRE)**, 5, b g Kingman—Toi Et Moi (IRE)  **T. R. Pryke**
23 **DANZENO**, 10, b g Denounce—Danzanora  **Mr W. C. Wragg**
24 **DEINONYCHUS**, 10, b g Authorized (IRE)—Sharp Dresser (USA)  **Howdale Bloodstock**
25 **DOUBLE REFLECTION**, 6, b m Showcasing—Green And Bleue  **Mr C. Bacon**
26 **DREADNOUGHTUS**, 5, ch g Americain (USA)—Sharp Dresser (USA)  **Howdale Bloodstock**
27 **DREAM WORLD (IRE)**, 6, b m Dream Ahead (USA)—Tetard (IRE)  **Rod In Pickle Partnership**
28 **EDRAAK (IRE)**, 5, b g Elzaam (AUS)—So Blissful (IRE)  **Michael & Tommy Wickins**
29 **EPONINA (IRE)**, 7, b m Zoffany (IRE)—Dame Rochelle (IRE)  **Mrs E. Cash**
30 **FANTASY KEEPER**, 7, b g Mayson—Expressive  **The Fantasy Fellowship B**
31 **FANTASY LOVER (IRE)**, 4, b f Due Diligence (USA)—Jollification (IRE)  **The Fantasy Fellowship**
32 **FASHION FREE**, 4, b f Muhaarar—Ighraa (IRE)  **Mr L. J. M. J. Vaessen**
33 **FENIX**, 4, ch f Lope de Vega (IRE)—Stylishly  **The Horse Watchers**
34 **FINERY**, 4, b f Al Kazeem—Elysian  **Mr M. O. Ward**
35 **FIRST VOYAGE (IRE)**, 8, ch g Dubawi (IRE)—Concordia  **Mr D. G. Skelton**
36 **FISCAL PRUDENCE (IRE)**, 4, b g Fracas (IRE)—Airgead Nua (USA)  **ValueRacingClub.co.uk**
37 **FREE LOVE**, 5, b m Equiano (FR)—Peace And Love (IRE)  **The North South Syndicate**
38 **GO ON GAL (IRE)**, 8, b m Approve—Jeritza
39 **GOLD BROCADE (IRE)**, 4, ch f Dragon Pulse (IRE)—Primal Snow (USA)  **Mr R. Oliver**
40 **GRACIE'S GIRL**, 4, b f Heeraat (IRE)—Queens Revenge  **Mr R. Oliver**
41 **GRIMSTHORPE CASTLE**, 4, b g Dawn Approach (IRE)—Willoughby (IRE)  **Mr M. J. Taylor**
42 **HE'S A LEGEND**, 6, b g Schiaparelli (GER)—Midnight Fun  **M. Appleby**
43 **HELMET HOUSE**, 4, ch f Helmet (AUS)—Wentworth House  **B. D. Cantle**
44 **IT MUST BE FAITH**, 11, b g Mount Nelson—Purple Rain (IRE)  **Mick Appleby Racing**

# MR MICHAEL APPLEBY - continued

45 **JORVIK PRINCE**, 7, br g Kheleyf (USA)—Wotatomboy  **The Farming Boys**
46 **KATTANI (IRE)**, 5, b g Tamayuz—Katiola (IRE)  **Kaizen Racing**
47 **KELLS (IRE)**, 4, b c Galileo (IRE)—Christmas Kid (USA)  **Lycett Racing Ltd**
48 **KHAAN**, 6, ch g Kheleyf (USA)—Sharp Dresser (USA)  **Howdale Bloodstock**
49 **KING OF STARS (IRE)**, 4, gr g Starspangledbanner (AUS)—Glowing Star (IRE)  **Mr William Esdaile**
50 **KYBOSH (IRE)**, 5, b g Dansili—Super Sleuth (IRE)  **Mr L. A. Bellman**
51 **LACAN (IRE)**, 10, b g New Approach (IRE)—Invincible Isle (IRE)  **Mick Appleby Racing**
52 **LIAMBA**, 6, b m Equiano (FR)—Hisaronu (IRE)  **Diamond Racing Ltd**
53 **LIBERATION POINT (IRE)**, 4, b g Iffraaj—Botanique (IRE)  **The Horse Watchers**
54 **LOCH NESS MONSTER (IRE)**, 5, b g War Command (USA)—Celestial Dream (IRE)  **Mr M. J. Taylor**
55 **LOCKDOWN DREAM**, 4, b c Cityscape—Makindi  **M. Appleby**
56 **LORNA COLE (IRE)**, 5, gr m Lethal Force (IRE)—Suedehead  **M. Appleby**
57 **MICHELE STROGOFF**, 8, b g Aqlaam—Maschera d'Oro  **M. Appleby**
58 **MOHAREB**, 5, b g Delegator—Irrational  **Mr I. Lawrence**
59 **MOONRAKER**, 9, ch g Starspangledbanner (AUS)—Licence To Thrill  **The Kettlelites**
60 **MOSTALLIM**, 4, b g Bated Breath—Lifting Me Higher (IRE)  **The Hobbits**
61 **MOTAWAAFEQ (FR)**, 5, b g Wootton Bassett—Crossed Fingers (IRE)  **Middleham Park Racing II**
62 **N OVER J**, 6, b g Kodiac—Risk A Look  **Mrs D. R. Brotherton**
63 **NARJES**, 7, b m Sepoy (AUS)—Dubai Sea (USA)  **Mr N Hassan, Mr J Stevens & Mr J Chapman**
64 **NIGEL NOTT**, 5, ch g Dutch Art—Baileys Jubilee  **Mr N. Brereton**
65 **NIKOLAYEVA**, 4, b f Archipenko (USA)—Nezhenka  **ValueRacingClub.co.uk**
66 **OSLO**, 4, b g Gleneagles (IRE)—Intercontinental  **Mr N. Brereton**
67 **OUT FOR A DUCK**, 4, b f Due Diligence (USA)—Three Ducks  **MIDEST 1**
68 **RAADEA**, 4, ch g Showcasing—Dream Melody  **Mr C. Bacon**
69 **RAASEL**, 4, ch g Showcasing—Dubai Affair  **The Horse Watchers**
70 **RED JASPER**, 4, ch g Showcasing—Spate (IRE)  **Mr C. Bacon**
71 **RHYME SCHEME (IRE)**, 4, b f Poet's Voice—Tidal Moon  **Honestly Racing**
72 **ROCK ON RANI**, 4, ch g Sakhee (USA)—Krikket  **Mr N. C. Hoare**
73 **RULER RYDE**, 6, br g Alqaahir (USA)—Bobbies Ryde  **Mr T. F. G. Marks**
74 **SALATEEN**, 9, ch g Dutch Art—Amanda Carter  **ValueRacingClub.co.uk**
75 **SAMPERS SEVEN**, 4, b f Anjaal—Sampers (IRE)  **ValueRacingClub.co.uk**
76 **SEA OF MYSTERY (IRE)**, 8, b g Sea The Stars (IRE)—Sassenach (IRE)  **Mr Frank McAleavy & Mr Ian McAleavy**
77 **SPIDERSTEVE**, 6, b g Schiaparelli (GER)—Di's Dilemma  **Mr & Mrs T. W. Readett-Bayley**
78 **SPRING ROMANCE (IRE)**, 6, gr g Zebedee—Love And Devotion  **Mr N. Hassan**
79 **STRICT (IRE)**, 5, b g Slade Power (IRE)—Thawrah (IRE)  **Honestly Racing**
80 **SZARRATU (IRE)**, 5, ch m Mukhadram—Shena's Dream (IRE)  **Mr D. N. Skelton**
81 **TAN ARABIQ**, 8, b g Sir Percy—Tanning  **Sarnian Racing**
82 **THRAVE**, 6, b g Sir Percy—Feis Ceoil (IRE)  **M. Appleby**
83 **TRIPLE SPEAR**, 4, br g Showcasing—Secret Romance  **Mr P. Drinkwater**
84 **UNITED FRONT (USA)**, 4, b c War Front (USA)—Shell House (IRE)  **Mr C. Bacon**
85 **VIOLET PRINCESS**, 6, b m Native Ruler—Red To Violet  **Mr P. A. Jarvis**
86 **VOCATUS (IRE)**, 5, b g Vocalised (USA)—Beyond Intensity (IRE)  **ValueRacingClub.co.uk**
87 **WRATH OF HECTOR**, 4, b g Mayson—Dutch Mistress  **Central Racing Ltd**
88 **YOUR CHOICE**, 6, ch m Foxwedge (AUS)—Mildoura (FR)  **Mr J. Stevens**
89 **ZAPPER CASS (FR)**, 8, b g Elusive City (USA)—Moonlight Cass (IRE)  **M. Appleby**
90 **ZIM BABY**, 4, b f Roderic O'Connor (IRE)—Kenyan Cat  **Fosnic Racing**
91 **ZOOM ZOOM BABE**, 4, b f Footstepsinthesand—Blues In Cee (IRE)  **Mrs L. White**

## THREE-YEAR-OLDS

92 **APATITE**, b f Gleneagles (IRE)—Rainfall Radar (USA)  **Lycett Racing Ltd**
93 **BLUE HERO (CAN)**, b g Air Force Blue (USA)—Pomarine (USA)  **The Horse Watchers**
94 **BRECKLAND**, ch c Helmet (AUS)—Cherry Orchard (IRE)  **Stapleford Racing Ltd**
95 **EAGLE EYED FREDDIE**, b c Gleneagles (IRE)—Spice Trail  **Mr E. Foster**
96 **FANTASY MASTER**, ch c Sepoy (AUS)—Dinvar Diva  **The Fantasy Fellowship B**
97 **FOR PEAT'S SAKE**, b g Showcasing—Peacehaven (IRE)  **Mr I. Lawrence**
98 **GOTTA FEELING (IRE)**, b f Gutaifan (IRE)—Taaluf (IRE)  **Mr R Oliver & Mr M Appleby**
99 **HEADSHOT**, b c Awtaad (IRE)—Kesara  **Lycett Racing Ltd**
100 **HELMORA**, ch f Helmet (AUS)—Demora  **Mr W. C. Wragg**
101 **KABUTO**, b g Helmet (AUS)—Bochafina (FR)  **M. Appleby**

## MR MICHAEL APPLEBY - continued

102 **KATIE'S KITTEN,** ch f Bobby's Kitten (USA)—Freedom Reigns (IRE) **Fosnic Racing**
103 **MEHMO (IRE),** ch g Mehmas (IRE)—Baltic Belle (IRE) **Mr T. O. Bownes**
104 **MEONSTOKE,** b f Cable Bay (IRE)—Wentworth House **B. D. Cantle**
105 **MERRY SECRET (IRE),** b g Elzaam (AUS)—Secret Liaison (IRE) **Mr M. J. Taylor**
106 **MOPS GEM,** b f Equiano (FR)—Mops Angel **Mick Appleby Racing**
107 **PALOISE (FR),** b f Dabirsim (FR)—Snowbright **Mrs J. Burns**
108 **SNOW BERRY (IRE),** b f Dragon Pulse (IRE)—Primal Snow (USA) **J & A Young (Leicester) Ltd**
109 **SOBERTON,** b f Cable Bay (IRE)—Guishan **B. D. Cantle**
110 **SWINTON NOON,** b c Sepoy (AUS)—Marasil (IRE) **Mr L. J. M. J. Vaessen**
111 **TASHBEEH,** b c Siyouni (FR)—Aristotelicienne (IRE) **Mr C. Bacon**
112 **TWILLEY,** b f Nathaniel (IRE)—Poppy Bond **North Cheshire Trading & Storage Ltd**
113 **WARRIOR BRAVE,** b g Twilight Son—Gladiatrix **The Horse Watchers**

### TWO-YEAR-OLDS
114 **LADYMAC,** b f 31/01 Camacho—Prim (USA) (Elusive Quality (USA)) **Central Racing Ltd**

**Other Owners:** M. Appleby, Mr J. Chapman, Mr A. J. T. D'Arcy, Mr C. Dixon, Mr D. J. Greaves, Mr M. Harris, Mr N. Hassan, Mr R. Hoiles, Mr S. Louch, Mr F. McAleavy, Mr I. McAleavy, Mr R. Oliver, Rod In Pickle Partnership, Mr K. Roe, Exors of the Late Mr W. J. Sewell, Mr S. A. Sowray, Mr J. Stevens, Mr S. Sutton, Mr K. S. Ward, Mr T. Wickins.

**Assistant Trainer:** Jonathan Clayton.

**Flat Jockey:** Silvestre De Sousa, Luke Morris, Andrew Mullen, Alistair Rawlinson. **NH Jockey:** Richard Johnson, Jack Quinlan.
**Amateur Jockey:** Miss Serena Brotherton.

---

**8** **MR RICHARD ARMSON, Melbourne**
Postal: **Scotlands Farm, Burney Lane, Staunton-Harold, Melbourne, Derbyshire, DE73 8BH**

1 **ALBURN,** 11, b g Alflora (IRE)—Burn Brook **R. J. Armson**
2 **EL'AZAR (IRE),** 6, b g Imperial Monarch (IRE)—Presenting Lazarus (IRE) **R. J. Armson**
3 **HURRICANE VIC,** 11, b g Mount Nelson—Fountains Abbey (USA) **R. J. Armson**
4 **KEYNOTE (IRE),** 6, b g Dragon Pulse (IRE)—Taalluf (USA) **R. J. Armson**
5 **KILCARAGH BOY (IRE),** 12, b g King's Theatre (IRE)—Histologie (FR) **R. J. Armson**
6 **MACKIE DEE (IRE),** 9, b g Westerner—Whatdoyouthinkmac (IRE) **R. J. Armson**

---

**9** **MR PETER ATKINSON, Northallerton**
Postal: **Yafforth Hill Farm, Yafforth, Northallerton, North Yorkshire, DL7 0LT**
Contacts: **PHONE 01609 772598 MOBILE 07751 131215**

1 **BLACK MINSTER,** 6, bl g Trans Island—Mini Minster **Mr P. G. Atkinson**
2 **FINGAL'S HILL (IRE),** 5, b g Shirocco (GER)—Fingal's Sister (IRE) **Mr P. G. Atkinson**
3 **IRISH ROE (IRE),** 10, b m Vinnie Roe (IRE)—Betty's The Best (IRE) **Mrs L. Atkinson**
4 **PRIDE PARK (IRE),** 5, b g Yeats (IRE)—Ballyallia Pride (IRE) **Mr P. G. Atkinson**

## 10 MR MICHAEL ATTWATER, Epsom

Postal: Tattenham Corner Stables, Tattenham Corner Road, Epsom Downs, Surrey, KT18 5PP
Contacts: **PHONE** 01737 360066 **MOBILE** 07725 423633
**EMAIL** Attwaterracing@hotmail.co.uk **WEBSITE** www.attwaterracing.com

1 **ACCLAIM THE NATION (IRE)**, 8, b g Acclamation—Dani Ridge (IRE) **The Attwater Partnership**
2 **APRON STRINGS**, 5, b m Mayson—Royal Ivy **Canisbay Bloodstock**
3 **ASK THE GURU**, 11, b g Ishiguru (USA)—Tharwa (IRE) **Canisbay Bloodstock**
4 **BIG TIME MAYBE (IRE)**, 6, b g Dandy Man (IRE)—Divine Design (IRE) **Lamprell Roofing Ltd**
5 **BLUE CABLE**, 4, b f Cable Bay (IRE)—Bahama Blue **Mr R. Murphy**
6 **CAPPANANTY CON**, 7, gr g Zebedee—Fairmont (IRE) **Dare To Dream Racing**
7 **CHROMIUM**, 4, gr f Cable Bay (IRE)—Ghedi (IRE) **Dare To Dream Racing**
8 **CONCIERGE (IRE)**, 5, br g Society Rock (IRE)—Warm Welcome **Dare To Dream Racing**
9 **DELAGATE THE LADY**, 5, b m Delegator—Lady Phill **Mrs M. S. Teversham**
10 **DELAGATE THIS LORD**, 7, b g Delegator—Lady Filly **Mrs M. S. Teversham**
11 **DILIGENT LADY**, 4, b f Due Diligence (USA)—Lady Filly **Mrs M. S. Teversham**
12 **EPSOM DREAMER (IRE)**, 4, b f Raven's Pass (USA)—Saxon Princess (IRE) **Dare To Dream Racing**
13 **EZZRAH**, 5, b g Garswood—Tessie **Dare To Dream Racing**
14 **FOUR MILE BRIDGE (IRE)**, 5, b g Acclamation—Agent Allison **Mrs C. E. Peck**
15 **FUJAIRA KING (USA)**, 5, b g Kitten's Joy (USA)—Cat On a Tin Roof (USA) **Dare To Dream Racing**
16 **GAVLAR**, 10, b g Gentlewave (IRE)—Shawhill **Canisbay Bloodstock**
17 **HORNBY**, 6, b g Equiano (FR)—Kindia (IRE) **Canisbay Bloodstock**
18 **JOEY'S GIFT**, 4, b g War Command (USA)—Cadeau Speciale **The Attwater Partnership**
19 **JUST THAT LORD**, 8, ch g Avonbridge—Lady Filly **Mrs M. S. Teversham**
20 **KINGSTON KURRAJONG**, 8, b g Authorized (IRE)—Kingston Acacia **Canisbay Bloodstock**
21 **LAWN RANGER**, 6, b g Cityscape—Baylini **Canisbay Bloodstock**
22 **LEP**, 5, b g Nathaniel (IRE)—Liel **Dare To Dream Racing**
23 **MINHAAJ (IRE)**, 4, b f Invincible Spirit (IRE)—Sharqeyih **Dare To Dream Racing**
24 **MONTAQEM (FR)**, 4, b g Muhaarar—African Skies **Mrs C. E. Peck**
25 **MR FOX**, 5, b g Foxwedge (AUS)—Shared Moment (IRE) **The Attwater Partnership**
26 **MUSIC MAJOR**, 8, br g Bertolini (USA)—Music Maid (IRE) **The Attwater Partnership**
27 **NOBLE DEED**, 11, ch g Kyllachy—Noble One **Canisbay Bloodstock**
28 **PASSING CLOUDS**, 6, b g Kheleyf (USA)—Steppin Out **Canisbay Bloodstock**
29 **PINK FLAMINGO**, 5, b m Dream Ahead (USA)—Naivasha **Dare To Dream Racing**
30 **PRISMATIC (IRE)**, 4, b f Golden Horn—Teeky **The Attwater Partnership**
31 **REAL ESTATE (IRE)**, 6, b g Dansili—Maskunah (IRE) **Mr A. C. D. Main**
32 **SAVOY BROWN**, 5, b g Epaulette (AUS)—Kindia (IRE) **Canisbay Bloodstock**
33 **SILVER IMPERIAL**, 4, b f Anjaal—Silver Miss (FR) **BG Racing Partnership**
34 **SOLAR PARK (IRE)**, 5, ch g Kendargent (FR)—Solandia (IRE) **Haxted Racing**
35 **SOMETHING LUCKY (IRE)**, 9, gr g Clodovil (IRE)—Lucky Leigh **Dare To Dream Racing**
36 **STREET PARADE**, 5, b g Swiss Spirit—Jollification (IRE) **Dare To Dream Racing**
37 **THE CRUISING LORD**, 5, b g Coach House (IRE)—Lady Filly **Mrs M. S. Teversham**
38 **URTZI (IRE)**, 4, b f Due Diligence (USA)—Yankee Belle (USA) **The Attwater Partnership**

### THREE-YEAR-OLDS

39 **LOTHIAN**, b g Coach House (IRE)—Gracilia (FR) **Haxted Racing**
40 **MAAHI VE (IRE)**, ch f Havana Gold (IRE)—Elsa T (IRE) **The Attwater Partnership**
41 **MR MONEYPENNY**, b g Monsieur Bond (IRE)—Normandy Maid **Haxted Racing**
42 **SWISS FLAMINGO**, b f Swiss Spirit—Naivasha **Dare To Dream Racing**

### TWO-YEAR-OLDS

43 **ARD UP**, b g 09/02 Ardad (IRE)—Oriental Romance (IRE) (Elusive City (USA)) (5000) **The Attwater Partnership**
44 Ch f 02/02 Postponed (IRE)—Bowstar (Oasis Dream) **Canisbay Bloodstock**
45 Ch f 10/02 Cityscape—Cajun Moon (Showcasing) **Canisbay Bloodstock**
46 B f 09/02 Captain Gerrard (IRE)—Golden Amber (IRE) (Holy Roman Emperor (IRE))
47 B c 25/04 Brazen Beau (AUS)—Kindia (IRE) (Cape Cross (IRE)) **Canisbay Bloodstock**
48 B f 20/03 Heeraat (IRE)—Lady Suesanne (IRE) (Cape Cross (IRE)) **Attwater Hunt Partnership**
49 **MARY OF MODENA**, b f 21/01 Bated Breath—Miss Chicane (Refuse To Bend (IRE)) (6000) **Haxted Racing**
50 Ch g 07/03 Cotai Glory—Norwegian Highness (FR) (Kendargent (FR)) (4500) **Dare To Dream Racing**
51 B c 05/05 Showcasing—Reedanjas (IRE) (Sir Prancealot (IRE)) (13000) **The Attwater Partnership**
52 B f 23/03 Mayson—Strawberry Sorbet (Street Cry (IRE)) (2000)

## MR MICHAEL ATTWATER - continued

**Other Owners:** Mr B. M. Attwater, Mr M. J. Attwater, Mrs N. Hunt, Mr R. A. Hunt, R. F. Kilby, Mr A. C. D. Main, Mrs L. Main, Richard and Nicola Hunt, Miss M. E. Stopher, The Attwater Partnership.

**Assistant Trainer:** S. Sawyer.

---

**11** **MR JEAN-RENE AUVRAY, Calne**
Postal: **West Nolands Farm, Nolands Road, Yatesbury, Calne, Wiltshire, SN11 8YD**
Contacts: **MOBILE 07798 645796**
EMAIL jr.auvray@outlook.com WEBSITE www.jrauvrayracing.co.uk

1 BRIGHT VIEW (IRE), 4, b f Siyouni (FR)—Quilting (USA) **Nigel Kelly & Stuart McPhee**
2 HYACINTH (IRE), 4, b f New Approach (IRE)—Haughtily (IRE) **Nigel Kelly & Stuart McPhee**
3 STREETS OF FIRE (IRE), 7, br m Milan—Flaming Brandy (IRE) **Lady E. Mays-Smith**
4 TRIGGER HAPPY (IRE), 4, b g Gutaifan (IRE)—Boom And Bloom (IRE) **N. R. Kelly**

### THREE-YEAR-OLDS

5 MOSTAR MISS (IRE), b f Vadamos (FR)—Star Waves (IRE) **Nigel Kelly & Stuart McPhee**

**Other Owners:** N. R. Kelly, Mr S. K. McPhee.

---

**12** **MRS CAROLINE BAILEY, Holdenby**
Postal: **Holdenby Lodge, Spratton, Northants, NN6 8LG**
Contacts: **HOME 01604 883729 PHONE 01604 770234 MOBILE 07831 373340 FAX 01604 770423**
EMAIL caroline.bailey66@yahoo.com WEBSITE www.carolinebaileyracing.co.uk

1 ANOTHER NIGHTCAP (IRE), 5, gr ro g Dylan Thomas (IRE)—Silver Proverb
                                              **A Lofts K Nicholson P Proctor B Robinson**
2 BEGIN THE LUCK (IRE), 5, b g Le Fou (IRE)—Bobsyourdad (IRE) **Vaughan-Jones, Bailey & Mellor**
3 BOLDMERE, 8, b g Multiplex—Pugnacious Lady **W. J. Odell**
4 COBRA DE MAI (FR), 9, b g Great Pretender (IRE)—Miria Galanda (FR) **Mrs S. Carsberg**
5 COOLE LION (IRE), 7, br g Presenting—Kayanti (IRE) **Mrs W. M. Wesley**
6 CROSSPARK, 11, b g Midnight Legend—Blue Shannon (IRE) **Mrs W. M. Wesley**
7 DAINTY DORIS (IRE), 6, b m Oscar (IRE)—Asian Alliance (IRE) **Mr J. H. Chatfeild-Roberts**
8 ELKSTONE, 10, b g Midnight Legend—Samandara (FR) **Tredwell, Robinson, Proctor & Nicholson**
9 GIBBES BAY (FR), 9, gr g Al Namix (FR)—Nouvelle Donne (FR) **Mrs M. E. Moody**
10 HOWYA HUN (IRE), 7, b m Stowaway—Glencree Rose (IRE) **Mrs J. M. Dixon Smith**
11 HUNKY (FR), 4, b g Tirwanako (FR)—Funkia (FR) **G. T. H. Bailey**
12 JUST A DEAL, 6, b g Arvico (FR)—Monte Mayor Golf (IRE) **G. T. H. Bailey**
13 LADY MASTER, 8, b m Native Ruler—Elmside Katie **Mr P. Dixon Smith**
14 LORD SPARKY, 7, ch g Sulamani (IRE)—Braybrooke Lady (IRE) **The On The Bridle Partnership**
15 MALAPIE (IRE), 13, b g Westerner—Victorian Lady
16 MATCHMAKING (GER), 6, ch g Mastercraftsman (IRE)—Monami (GER) **J. B. Wallwin**
17 THOMAS SHELBY (IRE), 10, b g Witness Box (USA)—Deemiss (IRE) **Mrs A. Vaughan-Jones**

**Other Owners:** G. T. H. Bailey, Mrs A. L. Lofts, Mrs S. Mellor, Mr K. M. Nicholson, Mr P. S.C. Proctor, Mrs B. D. Robinson, J. Tredwell, Mrs A. Vaughan-Jones.

**NH Jockey:** Sean Bowen, Harry Skelton. **Amateur Jockey:** Mr Thomas McClorey.

| **13** | **MR KIM BAILEY, Cheltenham** |

Postal: **Thorndale Farm, Withington Road, Andoversford, Cheltenham, Gloucestershire, GL54 4LL**
Contacts: **PHONE 01242 890241 MOBILE 07831 416859 FAX 01242 890193**
EMAIL **info@kimbaileyracing.com** WEBSITE **www.kimbaileyracing.com**

1 **ADJOURNED**, 6, gr g Rip Van Winkle (IRE)—Bite of The Cherry **The Jury**
2 **AJERO (IRE)**, 6, b g Red Jazz (USA)—Eoz **Julie & David R Martin & Dan Hall**
3 **ALIANDY (IRE)**, 10, b g Presenting—Water Rock **A & S Enterprises Ltd**
4 **ANOTHER VENTURE (IRE)**, 10, ch g Stowaway—Hard Luck (IRE) **Racing For Maggie's Partnership**
5 **ARTHUR'S SIXPENCE**, 7, b g Vinnie Roe (IRE)—Loose Change (IRE) **Stillmoremoneythan**
6 **BALLETICON (IRE)**, 7, br g Arakan (USA)—Miss Garbo (IRE) **Inn For A Penny**
7 **BLAZON**, 8, b g Dansili—Zante **The Blazing Optimists**
8 **BOBHOPEORNOHOPE (IRE)**, 6, b g Westerner—Bandelaro (IRE) **Mr J. F. Perriss**
9 **CHAZZA (IRE)**, 7, b g Mahler—Presenting Proform (IRE) **The Azza Chance Syndicate**
10 **COMMODORE BARRY (IRE)**, 8, br g Presenting—Specifiedrisk (IRE) **The Commodores**
11 **DANDY DAN (IRE)**, 8, b g Midnight Legend—Playing Around **Mr P. J. Andrews**
12 **DESIGN ICON**, 5, ch g Schiaparelli (GER)—Bisaat (USA) **It's Only Money**
13 **DIAMOND GAIT**, 8, b m Passing Glance—Milliegait **Mr N. Carter**
14 **DOES HE KNOW**, 6, b g Alkaased (USA)—Diavoleria **Yes He Does Syndicate**
15 **DONNIE BRASCO (FR)**, 8, b g Buck's Boum (FR)—Parislatino (FR) **Thefiftyshadesofneigh Syndicate**
16 **DRUMREAGH (FR)**, 7, b m Court Cave (IRE)—Mollyash (IRE) **Bucks Fizz**
17 **DUKE OF EARL (FR)**, 5, br g Noroit (GER)—Visiorienne (FR) **Mr P. J. Andrews**
18 **EL PRESENTE**, 8, b g Presenting—Raitera (FR) **Davies Pilkington Yarborough Brooke**
19 **EQUUS DREAMER (IRE)**, 6, ch g Getaway (IRE)—
                              Thornleigh Blossom (IRE) **Mr & Mrs M Laws & Mr & Mrs P Woodhall**
20 **ESPOIR DE ROMAY (FR)**, 7, b g Kap Rock (FR)—Miss du Seuil (FR) **The Midgelets**
21 **FIRST FLOW (IRE)**, 9, b g Primary (USA)—Clonroche Wells (IRE) **A. N. Solomons**
22 **FLIRTATIOUS GIRL (IRE)**, 5, b m Flemensfirth (USA)—
                              Another Gaye (IRE) **Mrs I. C. Sellars & Major & Mrs P. Arkwright**
23 **GALANTE DE ROMAY (FR)**, 5, gr m Lord du Sud (FR)—Miss du Seuil (FR) **The Galante Gallopers**
24 **GERARD MENTOR (FR)**, 5, b g Policy Maker (IRE)—Trephine du Sulon (FR) **Garrett, Meacham & Woodhall**
25 **GETAWEAPON (IRE)**, 6, b m Getaway (GER)—Milan Serenade (IRE) **Mr J. F. Perriss**
26 **HAMILTON DICI (FR)**, 4, b g Coastal Path—Umbria Dici (FR) **Lady Dulverton**
27 **HAPPYGOLUCKY (IRE)**, 7, br g Jeremy (USA)—Mydadsabishop (IRE) **Lady Dulverton**
28 **HENDRA HOUSE (IRE)**, 5, b g Yeats (IRE)—Gold Strike (IRE) **Colourful Drinkers**
29 **HES NO TROUBLE (IRE)**, 8, b g Scorpion (IRE)—
                              She's No Trouble (IRE) **Jockey Club Ownership (SW 2020) Limited**
30 **HOLLYMOUNT HOLLY (IRE)**, 7, ch m Doyen (IRE)—Parsee (IRE) **Mr J. F. Perriss**
31 **I CAN'T EXPLAIN (IRE)**, 8, b g Getaway (GER)—Dr Sandra (IRE) **Julie & David R Martin & Dan Hall**
32 **I SPY A DIVA**, 4, b f Telescope (IRE)—Molly's A Diva **Mr J. F. Perriss**
33 **IMPERIAL AURA (IRE)**, 8, b g Kalanisi (IRE)—Missindependence (IRE) **Imperial Racing Partnership 2016**
34 **IMPERIAL ICON (IRE)**, 6, ch g Shantou (USA)—Bobomy (IRE) **Imperial Racing Partnership**
35 **INFLAGRANTE (IRE)**, 5, ch g Getaway (GER)—Maggie Connolly (IRE) **Mrs V. W. H. Johnson**
36 **JAVA POINT (IRE)**, 6, b g Stowaway—Classic Sun (GER) **Fanning, Griffith, Haddock**
37 **KYNTARA**, 5, b g Kayf Tara—Speed Bonnie Boat **Lady Dulverton**
38 **LADY OF THE NIGHT**, 8, b m Midnight Legend—Even Flo **Mr J. F. Perriss**
39 **LORD APPARELLI**, 6, ch g Schiaparelli (GER)—La Marette **The Schiaparellis**
40 **LOTS OF LUCK (IRE)**, 7, b g Millenary—Lovely Hand (IRE) **Mr J. F. Perriss**
41 **MINELLA WARRIOR (IRE)**, 9, b g King's Theatre (IRE)—Bobbi's Venture (IRE) **Mrs Julie Martin & David R. Martin**
42 **MISS GEMSTONE**, 7, ch m Midnight Legend—Real Treasure **The Real Partnership**
43 **MON PALOIS (FR)**, 9, b g Muhaymin (USA)—Gastinaise (FR) **Mrs E. A. Kellar**
44 **MR GREY SKY (IRE)**, 7, gr g Fame And Glory—Lakil Princess (IRE) **Mr P. J. Andrews**
45 **NEWTIDE (IRE)**, 8, br g Getaway (GER)—C'Est Fantastique (IRE) **Lady Dulverton**
46 **PARC D'AMOUR (IRE)**, 4, b g Walk In The Park (IRE)—Mal d'Amour (IRE) **The Strollers**
47 **PARTY FUZZ**, 6, b g Great Pretender (IRE)—Very Special One (IRE) **Mr P. J. Andrews**
48 **PRINCE LLYWELYN (IRE)**, 7, ch g Schiaparelli (GER)—La Marette **Mr P. Bennett-Jones**
49 **ROCKY'S TREASURE (IRE)**, 10, b g Westerner—Fiddlers Bar (IRE) **Mr J. F. Perriss**
50 **ROSMUC RELAY (IRE)**, 9, br g Presenting—Aughrim Vic (IRE) **Mr J. F. Perriss**
51 **SAMATIAN (IRE)**, 4, bl g Sageburg (IRE)—Bodhran Davis (IRE) **Mr N. Carter**
52 **SAMMEO (FR)**, 4, b br g Diamond Green (FR)—Goldnella (FR) **Lady Dulverton**

## MR KIM BAILEY - continued

53 **SAYADAM (FR)**, 4, b g Saint des Saints (FR)—Catmoves (FR) **Lady Dulverton**
54 **SHANACOOLE PRINCE (IRE)**, 8, ch g Primary (USA)—Shanacoole Rose (IRE) **Mr & Mrs Mark Laws**
55 **SHANTOU EXPRESS (IRE)**, 6, ch g Shantou (USA)—Spanker **The Second Chancers**
56 **SHINOBI (IRE)**, 5, ch g Iffraaj—Ninja Lady **Shinobithemoney**
57 **STARVOSKI (IRE)**, 6, b m Aizavoski (IRE)—Telstar (IRE) **The Grapevine Syndicate**
58 **STATION MASTER (IRE)**, 10, b g Scorpion (IRE)—Gastounette (IRE) **Mrs P. A. Perriss**
59 **SUBWAY SURF (IRE)**, 7, b m Milan—Dante Rouge (IRE) **Surf On The Turf**
60 **TALK OF FAME**, 6, b g Fame And Glory—Princess Oriane (IRE) **Lady Dulverton**
61 **TALK OF THE MOON**, 4, b f Pether's Moon (IRE)—Tara The Gossip (IRE) **Mr E. J. Hawkings**
62 **TANTOLI**, 4, ch g Norse Dancer (IRE)—Aoninch **99 problems but the horse ain't 1**
63 **THE BULL MCCABE (IRE)**, 7, b g Yeats (IRE)—Twilight View (IRE) **Park View**
64 **THE EDGAR WALLACE (IRE)**, 6, b g Flemensfirth (USA)—Annalecky (IRE) **Mr P. J. Andrews**
65 **THOSE TIGER FEET (IRE)**, 7, b g Shantou (USA)—Luca Lite (IRE) **Mr P. J. Andrews**
66 **TIME FOR HOLLIE**, 5, b m Black Sam Bellamy (IRE)—Any Pearl **Roy & Louise Swinburne**
67 **TRELAWNE**, 5, b g Geordieland (FR)—Black Collar **The Real Partnership**
68 **TRWYN DU (IRE)**, 5, b g Valirann (FR)—Broken Thought (IRE) **Julie & David R Martin & Dan Hall**
69 **TWO FOR GOLD (IRE)**, 8, b g Gold Well—Two of Each (IRE) **May We Never Be Found Out Partnership 2**
70 **VINNDICATION (IRE)**, 8, b g Vinnie Roe (IRE)—Pawnee Trail (IRE) **Moremoneythan**
71 **VOYBURG (IRE)**, 5, br g Sageburg (IRE)—Slevoy Ahoy (IRE) **The Ten Sages**
72 **WANDRIN STAR (IRE)**, 10, b g Flemensfirth (USA)—Keralba (USA) **Mrs P. A. Perriss**
73 **YEAVERING BELLE**, 7, ch m Midnight Legend—Fruit Yoghurt **The Belle Stars**
74 **YOUNEVERCALL (IRE)**, 10, b g Yeats (IRE)—Afarka (IRE) **Youneverknow Partnership**

**Other Owners:** Major P. W. F. Arkwright, Mrs Sandra G. E. Arkwright, Mrs C. Bailey, Mr K. C. Bailey, Mr O. S. W. Bell, Mrs C. Bevan, Mr Q. Bevan, Sir F. Brooke, Mr S. R. Cannon, Mr K. T. Clancy, Mrs V. Clancy, M. E. T. Davies, Mr O. Fanning, Mr N. Griffith, Mrs H. M. Haddock, D. A. Hall, Lady M. P. Hatch, Mrs J. M. Laws, Mr M. J. Laws, D. R. Martin, Mrs J. M. T. Martin, Mr R. A. Pilkington, Mrs N. P. Sellars, Mrs F. M. Woodhall, Mr P. W. Woodhall, The Earl Of Yarborough.

**Assistant Trainer:** Matthew Nicholls.

**NH Jockey:** David Bass. **Conditional Jockey:** Chester Williams.

---

**14** **MR LIAM BAILEY, Middleham**
Postal: **2 Little Spigot, Coverham, Middleham, Leyburn, North Yorkshire, DL8 4TL**
Contacts: PHONE **07807 519220**
EMAIL liambailey_foulricefarm@hotmail.com

1 **ABEL HANDY (IRE)**, 6, b g Arcano (IRE)—Belle Isle **Mrs C M Clarke, Foulrice Park Racing Ltd**
2 **BUYER BEWARE (IRE)**, 9, br g Big Bad Bob (IRE)—Adoring (IRE) **Mr C. R. Stirling**
3 **CANFORD'S JOY (IRE)**, 6, b g Canford Cliffs (IRE)—Joyful (IRE) **Mrs C M Clarke, Foulrice Park Racing Ltd**
4 **DE LATOUR**, 5, b g Epaulette (AUS)—Zerka **Oakfield Racing**
5 **FANZONE (IRE)**, 4, b g Gutaifan (IRE)—Dame Alicia (IRE) **Foulrice Park Racing Limited**
6 **FRAMLEY GARTH (IRE)**, 9, b g Clodovil (IRE)—Two Marks (USA) **FPR Yorkshire Syndicate**
7 **HAJJAM**, 7, b g Paco Boy (IRE)—Amanda Carter **Mrs C M Clarke, Foulrice Park Racing Ltd**
8 **HOW BIZARRE**, 6, ch m Society Rock (IRE)—Amanda Carter **Harswell Thoroughbred Racing, Fpr Ltd**
9 **INSIDE INTEL (IRE)**, 4, b f Intello (GER)—Polar Eyes **Mrs C M Clarke, Foulrice Park Racing Ltd**
10 **JUNGLE BOOK (GER)**, 4, ch g Sea The Moon (GER)—Josefine (GER) **Mrs C M Clarke, Foulrice Park Racing Ltd**
11 **LAGENDA**, 8, b g Dick Turpin (IRE)—Whirly Dancer **Oakfield Racing**
12 **LIFE KNOWLEDGE (IRE)**, 9, ch g Thewayyouare (USA)—
                                          Rosa Bellini (IRE) **Mrs C M Clarke, Foulrice Park Racing Ltd**
13 **MAGREVIO (IRE)**, 5, b g Helmet (AUS)—Queen Althea (IRE) **Mrs C. M. Clarke**
14 **MARKAZI (FR)**, 7, gr g Dark Angel (IRE)—Marasima (IRE) **Foulrice Park Racing Limited**
15 **PRINCESS NEARCO (IRE)**, 7, b m Elzaam (AUS)—Royal Jubilee (IRE) **Mrs C M Clarke, Foulrice Park Racing Ltd**
16 **QUANAH (IRE)**, 5, ch g Dandy Man (IRE)—Boucheron **Mrs A. M. Stirling**
17 **STRONSAY (IRE)**, 5, b g Gale Force Ten—Perfect Blossom **Mrs C M Clarke, Foulrice Park Racing Ltd**
18 **THREE SAINTS BAY (IRE)**, 6, b g Kodiac—Fiuise (IRE) **Mr C. R. Stirling**
19 **TYRELL (IRE)**, 8, b g Teofilo (IRE)—Sleeveless (USA) **Mr R Boswell & Colin Stirling**

## MR LIAM BAILEY - continued

### THREE-YEAR-OLDS
20 **HARSWELL DUCHESS (IRE),** b f Dragon Pulse (IRE)—Maiden Approach **Harswell Thoroughbred Racing, Fpr Ltd**
21 **HARSWELL DUKE (IRE),** b c Garswood—Grafitti **Harswell Thoroughbred Racing**
22 **HARSWELL PRINCE,** b c Cable Bay (IRE)—Agrippina **Harswell Thoroughbred Racing**

**Other Owners:** Mr R. Boswell, Mrs C. M. Clarke, Foulrice Park Racing Limited, Harswell Thoroughbred Racing, Mr M. Kirby, Mr C. R. Stirling, Miss M. A. Stirling, Mr R. J. Stirling.

---

## 15  MR GEORGE BAKER, Chiddingfold
Postal: **Robins Farm, Fisher Lane, Chiddingfold, Godalming, Surrey, GU8 4TB**
Contacts: **PHONE 01428 682059 MOBILE 07889 514881**
EMAIL gbakerracing@gmail.com WEBSITE www.georgebakerracing.com

1 **AMISI,** 5, ch m Nayef (USA)—Amicella **Mrs P. A. Scott-Dunn**
2 **ATOMIC JACK,** 6, b g Nathaniel (IRE)—
   Indigo River (IRE) **George Baker and Partners - Super Six, Mr G. Baker, Mr A. N. Cheyne, Turf Club 2020, Col A. J. E. Malcolm**
3 **AZOR AHAI,** 5, ch g Sixties Icon—Good Morning Lady **Let's Be Lucky Racing 25**
4 **BOWLING RUSSIAN (IRE),** 4, b g Lope de Vega (IRE)—Minute Limit (IRE) **Mr P. Bowden**
5 **CEMHAAN,** 4, b g Muhaarar—Shalwa **PJL Racing**
6 **CONFAB (USA),** 5, gr g Exchange Rate (USA)—Callmenancy (USA) **Confidence Partnership**
7 **CONFILS (FR),** 5, b m Olympic Glory (IRE)—Mambo Mistress (USA) **Confidence Partnership**
8 **CONFRERIE (IRE),** 6, b g Society Rock (IRE)—Intellibet One **New Confidence Partnership**
9 **DANTE'S VIEW (IRE),** 5, ch g Galileo (IRE)—Daivika (USA) **Mr J. G. N. Head**
10 **DYAMI (FR),** 4, b br g Bated Breath—Zaltana (USA) **Mark & Lavinia Sherwood**
11 **FAME N FORTUNE,** 5, b g Thewayyouare (USA)—Acapella Star (IRE) **Fame n Fortune Syndicate**
12 **FEAR NAUGHT,** 4, gr g Brazen Beau (AUS)—Tanda Tula (IRE) **Seaton Partnership**
13 **GEORGE BAKER (IRE),** 14, b g Camacho—Petite Maxine **George Baker & Partners**
14 **HIERONYMUS,** 5, b g Dutch Art—Sleek **Mrs Pao, Mr Stafford & Mr Tucker**
15 **HIGHWAY ONE (USA),** 7, b m Quality Road (USA)—Kinda Wonderful (USA) **Mr G. Baker**
16 **HONEYSUCKLE MOON,** 4, b f Make Believe—Zerka **Lady S. K. Marchwood**
17 **KAYARNAH,** 5, b m Mount Nelson—Sparkling Montjeu (IRE) **Christine Cone & Ursa Major Racing**
18 **KYLLISHI,** 4, ch f Kyllachy—Ishiamber **Mrs P. A. Scott-Dunn**
19 **LA MAQUINA,** 6, b g Dutch Art—Miss Meltemi (IRE) **George Baker and Partners - Super Six**
20 **MAMILLIUS,** 8, b g Exceed And Excel (AUS)—Laika Lane (USA) **The Mamillius Partnership**
21 **MARJORAM (IRE),** 4, b f Kodiac—Marywell **Jasper, Baker, McCaughey, Williams**
22 **MAY REMAIN,** 6, b g Mayson—Ultimate Best **Guards Club Racing Limited**
23 **MONTYS INN (IRE),** 5, b g Kodiac—Bailonguera (ARG) **The Montague Inn Syndicate**
24 **THE LAMPLIGHTER (FR),** 6, b g Elusive City (USA)—Plume Rouge **The Lamplighter Syndicate**
25 **WARGRAVE (IRE),** 5, b g Galileo (IRE)—Scream Blue Murder (IRE) **Mr P. Bowden**
26 **WATER'S EDGE (IRE),** 5, b g Footstepsinthesand—Sommer Queen (IRE) **Carbine of London Racing**
27 **WESTERN DAWN (IRE),** 5, b g Dawn Approach (IRE)—Yes Oh Yes (USA) **Let's Be Lucky Racing 24**

### THREE-YEAR-OLDS
28 **AMAZALI (IRE),** b f Elzaam (AUS)—Taffetta **Mr G. Baker**
29 **BONNET,** ch f Helmet (AUS)—Tanda Tula (IRE) **Seaton Partnership**
30 **CHLOHOLTEEN,** gr f Clodovil (IRE)—Shemissa (IRE) **C Wright, C Forsyth, H Wright, T Stinnes**
31 **DEVORGILLA,** ch f Mukhadram—Sweetheart Abbey **Miss S. Bannatyne**
32 **ETON BLUE (IRE),** b g Starspangledbanner (AUS)—Naturotopia (FR) **The Eton Ramblers**
33 **JACARANDA LADY (USA),** b f Gio Ponti (USA)—High Heeled Hope (USA) **Cornthrop Bloodstock Limited**
34 **PASSIONOVA (IRE),** b f Bated Breath—Passionable **John P & Baker Baker**
35 **RUN FORREST RUN (IRE),** b g Bobby's Kitten (USA)—Minute Limit (IRE) **Mr J R Wallis & Partners**
36 **SURREY PRINCESS,** b f Kingman—Terre du Vent (FR) **Surrey Racing (SPR)**

# MR GEORGE BAKER - continued

## TWO-YEAR-OLDS

37 **AWESOME DANCER (IRE)**, ch c 02/02 Highland Reel (IRE)—
Adutchgirl (GER) (Dutch Art) (28000) **Carbine of London Racing (2)**
38 **DESTINY QUEEN**, b c 08/02 Al Wukair (IRE)—Trissa (FR) (Anabaa (USA)) (46005) **The Wise Old Al Partnership**
39 Gr f 20/01 Fast Company (IRE)—Honorlina (FR) (Linamix (FR)) **Major-Gen G. H. Watkins**
40 **KENCARLOU (FR)**, gr c 21/02 Kendargent (FR)—
Kindly Dismiss (FR) (Excellent Art) (24213) **Surrey Racing (sm) & Partner**
41 Br c 22/02 Bated Breath—Metal Precious (FR) (Kendargent (FR)) (11000)
42 B f 24/04 Postponed (IRE)—Singuliere (IRE) (Singspiel (IRE)) (18000)
43 B c 22/03 Bated Breath—Sunflower (Dutch Art) (48000) **Highclere ThoroughbredRacing-Dream Again**
44 B g 14/03 Sixties Icon—Sweetheart Abbey (Dancing Spree (USA)) **Miss S. Bannatyne**
45 B f 17/02 Churchill (IRE)—Tobacco Bay (IRE) (Dark Angel (IRE)) (52000)

**Other Owners:** The Earl Of Brecknock, Mr G. Baker, Mr P.Bowden, Bowden & Baker, Mrs C. E. Cone, CreditIncome Investments 3 & Baker, Creditincome Investments (No 3) Limited, Sir Alex Ferguson, Mr A. Flintoff, Ms C. Forsyth, Mr S. Grubb, Mr C. R. Hadingham, Mr Alan Halsall, Miss L Hurley, E.L. James, Mr Peter Jensen, Mr B Kantor, Kirkwood and Friends, Mr Nick Mustoe, Mrs A. Pao, Mr G. Pariente, Lord Christopher Rathcreedan, Mr Don Shanks, Mrs L. M. Sherwood, Mr M. A. Sherwood, Earl Spencer, Mr N. J. Stafford, Miss T. Stinnes, Surrey Racing (SM), Mr C. Talbot, Mr Mark Tracey, S. P. Tucker, Turf Club 2020 & Co, URSA Major Racing, Mrs G. B. Walford, J. R. Wallis, Mr C. N. Wright, Miss H. E. Wright.

**Assistant Trainer:** Patrick Murphy, Valerie Murphy.

**Flat Jockey:** Pat Cosgrave, Nicola Currie, Cieren Fallon. **NH Jockey:** Marc Goldstein.

---

## 16 MR ANDREW BALDING, Kingsclere
Postal: **Park House Stables, Kingsclere, Newbury, Berkshire, RG20 5PY**
Contacts: **PHONE 01635 298210**
EMAIL **admin@kingsclere.com** WEBSITE **www.kingsclere.com**

1 **ALOUNAK (FR)**, 6, b g Camelot—Awe Struck **King Power Racing Co Ltd**
2 **BANGKOK (IRE)**, 5, b h Australia—Tanaghum **King Power Racing Co Ltd**
3 **BELL ROCK**, 5, b g Kingman—Liberally (IRE) **Mrs F. H. Hay**
4 **BERKSHIRE ROCCO (FR)**, 4, ch c Sir Percy—Sunny Again **Berkshire Parts & Panels Ltd**
5 **BOUNCE THE BLUES (IRE)**, 4, ch f Excelebration (IRE)—Jazz Up **Mrs B. M. Keller**
6 **CADEAU D'OR (FR)**, 4, ch g Le Havre (IRE)—Hill of Grace **John & Anne Soul**
7 **CHIL CHIL**, 5, b m Exceed And Excel (AUS)—Tiana **King Power Racing Co Ltd**
8 **CLEONTE (IRE)**, 8, ch g Sir Percy—Key Figure **King Power Racing Co Ltd**
9 **COLTRANE (IRE)**, 4, b c Mastercraftsman (IRE)—Promise Me (IRE) **Mick and Janice Mariscotti**
10 **DIOCLETIAN GIRL**, 6, b g Camelot—Saturday Girl **Mr R. J. C. Wilmot-Smith**
11 **FIESTA DE VEGA**, 4, ch g Lope de Vega (IRE)—Party (IRE) **PDR Properties**
12 **FOX CHAIRMAN (IRE)**, 5, b g Kingman—Starfish (IRE) **King Power Racing Co Ltd**
13 **FOX PREMIER (IRE)**, 5, b g Frankel—Fann (USA) **King Power Racing Co Ltd**
14 **FOX TAL**, 5, b g Sea The Stars (IRE)—Maskunah (IRE) **King Power Racing Co Ltd**
15 **GOOD BIRTHDAY (IRE)**, 5, b g Dabirsim (FR)—Chica Loca (FR) **King Power Racing Co Ltd**
16 **GROUP ONE POWER**, 4, b g Lope de Vega (IRE)—Lady Aquitaine (USA) **King Power Racing Co Ltd**
17 **GROVE FERRY (IRE)**, 4, b g Excelebration (IRE)—Rebelline (IRE) **Martin & Valerie Slade & Partner**
18 **HAPPY POWER (IRE)**, 5, gr h Dark Angel (IRE)—Tamarisk (GER) **King Power Racing Co Ltd**
19 **HORN OF PLENTY**, 4, b f Golden Horn—Gaze **Mildmay Racing**
20 **JOHNNY DRAMA (IRE)**, 6, b g Lilbourne Lad (IRE)—Quelle Histoire (IRE) **King Power Racing Co Ltd**
21 **KHALIFA SAT (IRE)**, 4, b c Free Eagle (IRE)—Thermopylae **A. Al Shaikh**
22 **KING'S LYNN**, 4, b c Cable Bay (IRE)—Kinematic **Her Majesty The Queen**
23 **LA HULOTTE (IRE)**, 4, ch f Lope de Vega (IRE)—Vakiyla (FR) **Mrs M. E. Wates**
24 **MONTANARI**, 4, ch g Sea The Moon (GER)—Pax Aeterna (USA) **Mick and Janice Mariscotti**
25 **MORANDO (FR)**, 8, gr g Kendargent (FR)—Moranda (FR) **King Power Racing Co Ltd**
26 **NATE THE GREAT**, 5, b g Nathaniel (IRE)—Theladyinquestion **Mildmay Racing & D. H. Caslon**

# MR ANDREW BALDING - continued

27 **OPERA GIFT**, 4, b g Nathaniel (IRE)—Opera Glass **J. C. Smith**
28 **PAPA POWER**, 4, b g Nathaniel (IRE)—Mosqueras Romance **King Power Racing Co Ltd**
29 **PIVOINE (IRE)**, 7, b g Redoute's Choice (AUS)—Fleur de Cactus (IRE) **King Power Racing Co Ltd**
30 **QUICKSTEP LADY**, 4, b f Australia—Strictly Dancing (IRE) **J. C. Smith**
31 **RANCH HAND**, 5, b g Dunaden (FR)—Victoria Montoya **Kingsclere Racing Club**
32 **RODIN**, 4, b g Mayson—Moon Goddess **The Pink Hat Racing Partnership**
33 **ROMAN KNOWS**, 4, b g Holy Roman Emperor (IRE)—Entre Nous (IRE) **Greenwood/Tolhurst**
34 **SHINE SO BRIGHT**, 5, gr h Oasis Dream—Alla Speranza **King Power Racing Co Ltd**
35 **SPANISH MISSION (USA)**, 5, b h Noble Mission—Limonar (IRE) **Team Valor Llc & Gary Barber**
36 **SPIRIT WARNING**, 5, b g Charm Spirit (IRE)—Averami **Kingsclere Racing Club**
37 **SPRING GLOW**, 4, gr f Mukhadram—Spring Dream (IRE) **Rainbow Racing**
38 **STONE OF DESTINY**, 6, b g Acclamation—Irishstone (IRE) **King Power Racing Co Ltd**
39 **SYMBOLIZE (IRE)**, 4, ch g Starspangledbanner (AUS)—French Flirt **Sheikh J. D. Al Maktoum**
40 **TEX AUSTRALIA (IRE)**, 4, b f Australia—Tech Exceed (GER) **Windmill Racing III**
41 **TRIBAL CRAFT**, 5, ch m Mastercraftsman (IRE)—Snoqualmie Star **J. C. Smith**
42 **VIA DE VEGA (FR)**, 4, ch g Lope de Vega (IRE)—Via Milano (FR) **PDR Properties**
43 **ZWAYYAN**, 8, ch g Pivotal—Mail The Desert (IRE) **King Power Racing Co Ltd**

## THREE-YEAR-OLDS

44 **ABRAG (IRE)**, b c Acclamation—By Jupiter **Mr M. Almahmoud**
45 **ACHELOIS (IRE)**, b f Zoffany (IRE)—Fontley **Thurloe for Royal Marsden Cancer Charity**
46 **ALCOHOL FREE (IRE)**, b f No Nay Never (USA)—Plying (USA) **J. C. Smith**
47 **ASAMOSA (USA)**, b f American Pharoah (USA)—Renee's Titan (USA) **Promenade Bloodstock Limited**
48 **AURIA**, b f Muhaarar—Tiana **Mrs F. Denniff**
49 **AURIFEROUS (IRE)**, b g Golden Horn—Sequester **Mick and Janice Mariscotti**
50 **BASHFUL**, b c Manduro (GER)—Inhibition **Kingsclere Racing Club**
51 **BEYOND BOUNDARIES (IRE)**, ch c Australia—What A Treasure (IRE) **King Power Racing Co Ltd**
52 **BONNYRIGG (IRE)**, b g Zoffany (IRE)—Impressionist Art (USA) **Mrs F. H. Hay**
53 **CALCUTTA CUP (FR)**, ch g Territories (IRE)—Lorient **Mrs F. H. Hay**
54 **CAROLUS MAGNUS (IRE)**, b g Holy Roman Emperor (IRE)—Izola **Kennet Valley Thoroughbreds III**
55 **CLASSIC LORD (GER)**, ch c Lord of England (GER)—Classic Diva (GER) **Park House Partnership**
56 **COVER DRIVE**, b c Mukhadram—Perfect Cover (IRE) **Park House Partnership**
57 **DAISY WARWICK**, b f Kingman—Our Poppet (IRE) **Hot To Trot Racing**
58 **DEJAME PASO (IRE)**, b c The Gurkha (IRE)—Bergamot Orange (USA) **N. M. Watts**
59 **DESERT RAVINE**, b g Tamayuz—Hidden Valley **Kingsclere Racing Club**
60 **DISCOMATIC (IRE)**, b c Estidhkaar (IRE)—Alltherightmoves (IRE) **Park House Partnership**
61 **EAGLE SPRINGS (IRE)**, ch g Free Eagle (IRE)—Set Fire (IRE) **Mr D J Burke & Mrs Susan Roy**
62 **EIKONIX**, b c Paco Boy (IRE)—Slide Show **Mr Daniel Hunt & Mrs Eileen Markham**
63 **EXPERT OPINION**, b g Worthadd (IRE)—Calypso Choir **J. C. Smith**
64 **FANTALOPE**, b f Lope de Vega (IRE)—Fantasia **G. Strawbridge**
65 **FIVETHOUSANDTOONE (IRE)**, b c Frankel—Promised Money (IRE) **King Power Racing Co Ltd**
66 **FLORENCE STREET**, b f Iffraaj—Queen's Dream (GER) **Sir A. Ferguson**
67 **FLYIN' HIGH**, b c Siyouni (FR)—Zee Zee Top **Castle Down Racing**
68 **FOXES TALES (IRE)**, b c Zoffany (IRE)—Starfish (IRE) **King Power Racing Co Ltd**
69 **GOLDEN CRUSADER (FR)**, b g Golden Horn—Ihsas (USA) **Relentless Dreamers Racing & Partner**
70 **GOOLWA (IRE)**, b f Australia—Pivotalia (IRE) **Sheikh J. D. Al Maktoum**
71 **GRANULEUX**, b c Bobby's Kitten (USA)—Grain Only **Miss K. Rausing**
72 **GYENYAME**, b g Nathaniel (IRE)—Lizzie Tudor **Ms K. Gough**
73 **HENRIK (IRE)**, br c Gutaifan (IRE)—Ibecke **Park House Partnership**
74 **HEY TEACHER**, b g Fascinating Rock (IRE)—See Emily Play (IRE) **Park House Partnership**
75 **HIMYAN (IRE)**, b f Muhaarar—Fort Del Oro (IRE) **Al Rabban Racing & Ballylinch Stud**
76 **IMPERIAL FORCE (IRE)**, b g Camacho—Cafetiere **Mr M. A. R. Blencowe**
77 **JUAN DE MONTALBAN (IRE)**, ch c Lope de Vega (IRE)—Abilene **Mick and Janice Mariscotti**
78 **KING VEGA**, ch c Lope de Vega (IRE)—Moi Meme **Apollo Racing & DTA Racing**
79 **KINGSOFTHEMIDLANDS (FR)**, b c Kingman—Spin (IRE) **King Power Racing Co Ltd**
80 **KNIGHT SALUTE**, b g Sir Percy—Shadow Dancing **Sheikh J. D. Al Maktoum**
81 **LANDING SYSTEM (IRE)**, b c Dornardini (USA)—Shamarbelle (IRE) **M M Stables**
82 **LION HUNTER (AUT)**, ch g Hunter's Light (IRE)—Lightning Debut **Mr B McGuire & Partner**
83 **LORCA (GER)**, b c Lucky Lion—Livia's Wake (IRE) **Highclero Thoroughbred Racing - Lion**

# MR ANDREW BALDING - continued

84  MARINE (IRE), b c Sea The Stars (IRE)—Ignis Away (FR)  **Qatar Racing Limited**
85  MAY NIGHT, ch g Mayson—Dream Melody  **M. Payton**
86  MELLOW MAGIC, b f Nathaniel (IRE)—Lady Brora  **Kingsclere Racing Club**
87  MELODY OF LIFE (IRE), b c Dark Angel (IRE)—Tamarisk (GER)  **King Power Racing Co Ltd**
88  MERCURIUS POWER (IRE), b c Awtaad (IRE)—Dame Hester (IRE)  **King Power Racing Co Ltd**
89  MONEYKENNY (IRE), gr ro g Kendargent (FR)—Divine Touch  **Park House Partnership**
90  MYSTERY SMILES (IRE), b c Mehmas (IRE)—Alexander Alliance (IRE)  **King Power Racing Co Ltd**
91  NAPPER TANDY, b c Mukhadram—Diktalina  **Lisahully Investments Ltd**
92  NEBULOSA, b f Archipenko (USA)—Nimiety  **Miss K. Rausing**
93  NEENEE'S CHOICE, b g Paco Boy (IRE)—Galaxy Highflyer  **Mick and Janice Mariscotti**
94  OO DE LALLY (IRE), b c Vadamos (FR)—In Dubai (USA)  **J. Palmer-Brown & Partner 2**
95  PINEAPPLE RING, b f Kingman—Ananas  **Her Majesty The Queen**
96  POLITICS (IRE), b c Muhaarar—Wrong Answer  **Qatar Racing Limited**
97  RECOVERY RUN, b c Nathaniel (IRE)—Regal Splendour  **Another Bottle Racing 2**
98  REGAL VEGA (IRE), ch c Lope de Vega (IRE)—Queen of Power (IRE)  **PDR Properties & Apollo Racing**
99  RIVAL, b c Iffraaj—Pamona (IRE)  **Highclere Tbred Racing-Peter Curling**
100  ROSCIOLI, b c Territories (IRE)—Never Lose  **Mr Philip Fox & Partner**
101  RUSHMORE, b c Lope de Vega (IRE)—Qushchi  **Qatar Racing Limited**
102  SCAMPI, b g Nayef (USA)—Preveza (FR)  **Mr M. W. Pendarves**
103  SEA FERN, b f Acclamation—Scots Fern  **Mrs P I Veenbaas & Partner**
104  SEB'S WELCOME (FR), b g Rajsaman (FR)—Invitee  **Mr L. L. Register**
105  SECRET SHADOW (IRE), b f Camelot—Secret Pursuit (IRE)  **Mr G. C. B. Brook**
106  SHE IS FIERCE, ch f New Approach (IRE)—She Is Great (IRE)  **Sheikh I. S. Al Khalifa**
107  SKIBO CASTLE (FR), b g Shalaa (IRE)—Noelani (IRE)  **Mrs F. H. Hay**
108  SPICE STORE, gr f Mastercraftsman (IRE)—Night Carnation  **G. Strawbridge**
109  SPIRIT LEVEL, b c Cable Bay (IRE)—Cape Spirit (IRE)  **Kingsclere Racing Club**
110  SPIRIT MIXER, ch g Frankel—Arabian Queen (IRE)  **J. C. Smith**
111  STAR CALIBER, b br c Golden Horn—Lombatina (FR)  **King Power Racing Co Ltd**
112  B c Vadamos (FR)—Strawberry Martini  **M M Stables**
113  SUNSET SALUTE, b c Twilight Son—Hill Welcome  **Park House Partnership**
114  SWIVELSTICK, ch g Pivotal—Gosbeck  **Park House Partnership**
115  TACTICAL, b c Toronado (IRE)—Make Fast  **Her Majesty The Queen**
116  TANGLEWOOD TALES, ch g Nathaniel (IRE)—Camdora (IRE)  **Geoff Blyth**
117  THE KODI KID (IRE), b g Kodi Bear (IRE)—Dat Il Do  **Park House Partnership**
118  TOUCHET BERET, b f Helmet (AUS)—Perfect Blessings (IRE)  **Dr Bridget Drew & Mr Ian Brown**
119  TWILIGHT TROUBLE, b g Twilight Son—Poly Pomona  **Relentless Dreamers Racing & Partner**
120  VALLEY FORGE, b c Dansili—Lixirova (FR)  **G. Strawbridge**
121  WALLEM, b c Sea The Moon (GER)—A L'Anglaise  **Al Rabban Racing & Partner**
122  WE'LL MEET AGAIN, b f Cityscape—Sweet Mandolin  **J. C. & S. R. Hitchins**
123  WINTERWATCH (GER), b g Lord of England (GER)—Wildlife Lodge (GER)  **Park House Partnership**
124  WITHOUT ENVY, b c Lope de Vega (IRE)—Purple Pearl (IRE)  **Mr & Mrs R Gorell/N Botica**
125  YOUTH SPIRIT (IRE), b c Camelot—Rocana  **A. Al Shaikh**
126  ZOOM TIGER, b c Zoffany (IRE)—Tiger Lilly (IRE)  **Cornthrop Bloodstock & David Redvers**
127  ZURAIG, gr c Teofilo (IRE)—Dakatari (FR)  **Noora Racing Ltd**

## TWO-YEAR-OLDS

128  ALDBOURNE, b c 19/02 Awtaad (IRE)—Always Gentle (IRE) (Redback) (38095)  **Hillwood Racing**
129  ALL GO, b f 07/03 Bobby's Kitten (USA)—Alboretta (Hernando (FR))  **Miss K. Rausing**
130  Ch c 26/04 Postponed (IRE)—Ana Shababiya (IRE) (Teofilo (IRE))  **A. Al Shaikh**
131  Ch f 17/02 Australia—Angel Terrace (USA) (Ghostzapper (USA))  **G. Strawbridge**
132  B f 14/02 New Bay—Arabescatta (Monsun (GER)) (30476)  **Thomas Green Syndicate**
133  B f 03/03 Frankel—Aricia (IRE) (Nashwan (USA))  **G. Strawbridge**
134  Ch c 27/01 Galileo Gold—Ashwaq (Sepoy (AUS))  **Al Rabban Racing**
135  ATTACHE, b c 26/02 Declaration of War (USA)—
                         Go Kart (IRE) (Intense Focus (USA)) (40000)  **Kennet Valley Thoroughbreds VII**
136  B c 26/02 Sea The Stars (IRE)—Azanara (IRE) (Hurricane Run (IRE)) (210000)  **Sheikh I. S. Al Khalifa**
137  BELLPORT (IRE), b f 29/03 Bated Breath—Burning Rules (IRE) (Aussie Rules (USA))  **Mrs Anita Wigan**
138  BERKSHIRE BREEZE (IRE), b c 21/01 Mastercraftsman (IRE)—
                         Bright And Shining (IRE) (Camelot) (47619)  **Berkshire Parts & Panels Ltd**

# MR ANDREW BALDING - continued

**139 BERKSHIRE PHOENIX (IRE),** b c 25/03 Bungle Inthejungle—
Scarlet Wings (Sir Percy) (17143) **Berkshire Parts & Panels Ltd**
**140 BERKSHIRE REBEL (IRE),** b c 26/04 Sir Percy—
Silicon Star (FR) (Starborough) (50000) **Berkshire Parts & Panels Ltd**
**141 BERKSHIRE SHADOW,** gr c 12/03 Dark Angel (IRE)—
Angel Vision (IRE) (Oasis Dream) (40000) **Berkshire Parts & Panels Ltd**
**142** B f 06/04 No Nay Never (USA)—Bewitchment (Pivotal) (185000) **St Albans Bloodstock Limited**
**143** B c 12/02 Lawman (FR)—Bizzaria (Lemon Drop Kid (USA)) (150000) **Apollo Racing**
**144** B c 14/02 Exceed And Excel (AUS)—Burma Sun (IRE) (Rip Van Winkle (IRE)) (50000) **Mr M. A. R. Blencowe**
**145 CADMUS (IRE),** b c 20/04 Gleneagles (IRE)—Allegrezza (Sir Percy) (57000) **Ellipsis & Partner**
**146** Ch c 04/04 Night of Thunder (IRE)—Candleberry (Shamardal (USA)) (175000) **King Power Racing Co Ltd**
**147 CAPTAIN SQUARE,** ch c 17/02 Sir Percy—Primobella (Duke of Marmalade (IRE)) **Mrs L E Ramsden & Partner**
**148 CITY SPIRIT,** b f 05/04 Cityscape—Cape Spirit (Cape Cross (IRE)) **Kingsclere Racing Club**
**149** B c 19/02 Harzand (IRE)—Clarinda (FR) (Montjeu (IRE)) (13317) **A. Al Shaikh**
**150** B c 19/04 Churchill (IRE)—Cochabamba (IRE) (Hurricane Run (IRE)) (70000) **Mrs F. H. Hay**
**151** B c 03/04 Estidhkaar (IRE)—Cute (Diktat) (38095) **Mr M. A. R. Blencowe**
**152** Ch c 18/04 Sea The Stars (IRE)—Daivika (USA) (Dynaformer (USA)) (66667) **Mr M. A. R. Blencowe**
**153** Gr f 31/01 Dark Angel (IRE)—Delevingne (Redoute's Choice (AUS)) (350000) **King Power Racing Co Ltd**
**154** B f 27/03 Dunaden (FR)—Diary (IRE) (Green Desert (USA)) **Qatar Racing Limited**
**155 DUCAL CROWN,** b f 23/01 Duke of Marmalade (IRE)—Ebony Flyer (SAF) (Jet Master (SAF)) **Cayton Park Stud Ltd**
**156 ELOGIO (IRE),** b c 17/03 Aclaim (IRE)—Scholarly (Authorized (IRE)) (42000) **J. Palmer-Brown & Partner 2**
**157 EMULATION,** b f 22/01 Ulysses (IRE)—My Hope (USA) (Afleet Alex (USA)) (175000) **King Power Racing Co Ltd**
**158** B c 31/01 The Gurkha (IRE)—Endure (IRE) (Green Desert (USA)) (28571) **Mr M. A. R. Blencowe**
**159 FLAG HIGH (IRE),** b c 05/03 Starspangledbanner (AUS)—Acid (Clodovil (IRE)) (20952) **J Maldonado/P Elson & Partner**
**160 FRANCHEMENT (IRE),** b c 26/02 Frankel—Dolled Up (IRE) (Whipper (USA)) **Mrs A. M. Hayes**
**161 FRANKELLA,** ch f 03/03 Frankel—Arabian Queen (IRE) (Dubawi (IRE)) **J. C. Smith**
**162** Br c 29/04 Kodiac—Fraulein (Acatenango) (140000) **Al Shaqab Racing UK Limited**
**163** B c 08/02 Kodiac—Freedom's Light (Galileo (IRE)) **G. Strawbridge**
**164** Ch c 26/02 Mehmas (IRE)—Gilded Truffle (IRE) (Peintre Celebre (USA)) (30000) **Sheikh J. D. Al Maktoum**
**165 GRIFFIN PARK,** b c 26/02 Elm Park—Know The Truth (Lawman (FR)) **Kingsclere Racing Club**
**166 HARROW (IRE),** gr c 19/03 El Kabeir (USA)—
School Run (IRE) (Invincible Spirit (IRE)) (85000) **Highclere Thoroughbred Racing - Wisteria**
**167 HAYNES,** b c 12/02 Postponed (IRE)—Pure Song (Singspiel (IRE)) (28000) **Ellipsis**
**168 HIGHLAND MONARCH,** b c 17/03 Highland Reel (IRE)—Australian Queen (Fastnet Rock (AUS)) **J. C. Smith**
**169 HOO YA MAL,** b c 16/04 Territories (IRE)—Sensationally (Montjeu (IRE)) (40000) **A. Al Shaikh**
**170 I'LL BE THERE,** ch f 07/03 Starspangledbanner (AUS)—Hanella (IRE) (Galileo (IRE)) (20000) **Abdulla Ali Al-Thani**
**171 ICY LADY,** ch f 06/03 Norse Dancer (IRE)—Celestial Secret (Sakhee's Secret) **J. C. Smith**
**172** B br c 09/03 Kitten's Joy (USA)—Justaroundmidnight (IRE) (Danehill Dancer (IRE)) (196921) **Qatar Racing Limited**
**173 KAREEM,** ch c 22/02 Gleneagles (IRE)—Wordless (IRE) (Rock of Gibraltar (IRE)) **Denford Stud**
**174** B c 24/04 Frankel—Kiyoshi (Dubawi (IRE)) **Qatar Racing Limited**
**175** B br c 02/03 Havana Gold (IRE)—Lady Perignon (Poet's Voice) **Mrs F. H. Hay**
**176** B f 27/02 Holy Roman Emperor (IRE)—Landela (Alhaarth (IRE)) (125000) **Sheikh J. D. Al Maktoum**
**177** Ch f 19/02 Nathaniel (IRE)—Le Badie (IRE) (Spectrum (IRE)) **Farleigh Court Racing Partnership**
**178 LITTLE HUSTLE,** b c 25/01 Fastnet Rock (AUS)—Amser (Frankel) (5000) **Mrs E. A. M. Balding**
**179** B f 01/05 Sea The Moon (GER)—Lixirova (FR) (Slickly (FR)) **G. Strawbridge**
**180** Ch c 10/04 Nathaniel (IRE)—
Long Face (USA) (Whywhywhy (USA)) (115000) **The Bermuda, Salman, Morris Partnership**
**181 LUNAR GAZE,** b f 08/04 Sea The Moon (GER)—Lady Brora (Dashing Blade) **Kingsclere Racing Club**
**182** B c 07/03 Acclamation—Lynique (IRE) (Dylan Thomas (IRE)) (58000) **Abdulla Ali Al-Thani**
**183 MASEKELA,** b c 07/04 El Kabeir (USA)—Lady's Purse (Doyen (IRE)) (30000) **Mick and Janice Mariscotti**
**184** B c 23/01 Frankel—Mix And Mingle (IRE) (Exceed And Excel (AUS)) (300000) **King Power Racing Co Ltd**
**185 MOMENT DE REVE,** b f 01/05 Equiano (FR)—Dreamily (IRE) (New Approach (IRE)) **Suzi Prichard-Jones**
**186 MR ZIPPI,** b c 28/04 Intello (GER)—Izzi Top (Pivotal) (100000) **Castle Down Racing**
**187 NEANDRA (GER),** b f 26/02 Jukebox Jury (IRE)—Noble Rose (GER) (Areion (GER)) (11299) **D J T Racing & Partner**
**188** B f 07/03 Time Test—Night Carnation (Sleeping Indian) **G. Strawbridge**
**189 NOBLE RUN (USA),** b c 13/04 Noble Mission—Toxis (USA) (Street Sense (USA)) (36190) **Another Bottle Racing 2**
**190** B c 14/04 New Bay—Nordkappe (GER) (High Chaparral (IRE)) (29523) **The Yippees & Partner**
**191** B f 16/02 No Nay Never (USA)—Novantae (Pivotal) (119047) **Cornthrop Bloodstock Limited**
**192 OASIS GIFT,** b c 16/02 Oasis Dream—Siren's Gift (Cadeaux Genereux) **J. C. Smith**

# MR ANDREW BALDING - continued

**193** B f 30/03 Gleneagles (IRE)—On Location (USA) (Street Cry (IRE)) (26000) **Mrs F. H. Hay**
**194** B c 11/05 Rock of Gibraltar (IRE)—Peppermint Green (Green Desert (USA)) (30000)
**195** Ch c 10/04 Lope de Vega (IRE)—
                          Princess Serena (USA) (Unbridled's Song (USA)) (230000) **King Power Racing Co Ltd**
**196** B f 11/01 Almanzor (FR)—Queen of The Stars (Sea The Stars (IRE)) **Mr Sultan Ali**
**197 RADIOACTIVE (FR),** b f 24/04 Elm Park—Masina City (Soul City (IRE)) (13720) **D J T Racing & Partner**
**198 RENDITION (IRE),** ch f 11/04 Ulysses (IRE)—Penny Lane Forever (Pivotal) **Cheveley Park Stud**
**199 RETICENT,** b f 02/05 Sixties Icon—Inhibition (Nayef (USA)) **Kingsclere Racing Club**
**200 RING FENCED,** b f 13/04 Haafhd—Victoria Pollard (Sir Percy) **Kingsclere Racing Club**
**201** B c 21/03 Nathaniel (IRE)—Robema (Cadeaux Genereux) (200000) **King Power Racing Co Ltd**
**202** Ch f 22/02 Nathaniel (IRE)—Rosie Briar (Mayson) **Dr J A E Hobby**
**203 SAORLA,** ch f 11/04 Charming Thought—Lizzie Tudor (Tamayuz) **Ms K. Gough**
**204 SCHMILSSON,** b c 22/04 Muhaarar—Zee Zee Top (Zafonic (USA)) (75000) **Mick and Janice Mariscotti**
**205 SEA GREY,** gr c 03/04 Ulysses (IRE)—Sensory (IRE) (Dream Ahead (USA)) (30000) **Abdulla Ali Al-Thani**
**206 SENORITA,** ch f 08/05 Farhh—Hala Madrid (Nayef (USA)) **Kingsclere Racing Club**
**207** B c 09/03 Frankel—Sharp Susan (USA) (Touch Gold (USA)) **Cayton Park Stud Ltd**
**208** Ch c 21/02 Elm Park—Sienna Bella (Anabaa (USA)) (6860) **Qatar Racing Ltd & Partner**
**209** B c 28/02 Galileo Gold—Silk Fan (IRE) (Unfuwain (USA)) (80000) **Al Shaqab Racing UK Limited**
**210 SILVER DAWN,** gr f 07/05 Dark Angel (IRE)—Strictly Dancing (IRE) (Danehill Dancer (IRE)) **J. C. Smith**
**211 SIXTIES LOOK,** b c 17/03 Sixties Icon—Averami (Averti (IRE)) **Kingsclere Racing Club**
**212** B c 06/02 Holy Roman Emperor (IRE)—Soprana (GER) (Cadeaux Genereux) (16142) **Sheikh J. D. Al Maktoum**
**213 SOUTHERLY STORM,** b c 19/02 Fastnet Rock (AUS)—Opera Gal (IRE) (Galileo (IRE)) **J. C. Smith**
**214 SPORTING ICON,** b c 18/02 Recorder—Rebecca Romero (Exceed And Excel (AUS)) **Kingsclere Racing Club**
**215** C c 03/02 Lope de Vega (IRE)—Starlet (IRE) (Sea The Stars (IRE)) (825000) **Qatar Racing Limited**
**216** Ch c 23/01 Lope de Vega (IRE)—Stone Roses (FR (Rip Van Winkle (IRE)) (130000) **Apollo Racing & SRB Equine**
**217** B f 07/05 Nayef (USA)—Sweet Mandolin (Soviet Star (USA)) **J. C. & S. R. Hitchins**
**218 SWILCAN BRIDGE,** b c 11/04 Helmet (AUS)—Avon Lady (Avonbridge) (14000) **Mick and Janice Mariscotti**
**219 TACK (FR),** b c 15/02 Iffraaj—Make Fast (Makfi) **Her Majesty The Queen**
**220** B f 05/03 Farhh—Tears of The Sun (Mastercraftsman (IRE)) (55000) **Dr Bridget Drew & Partners**
**221 VIRTUOSO,** b f 21/03 Passing Glance—Make Music (Acclamation) **Kingsclere Racing Club**
**222** B c 12/04 Storm The Stars (USA)—War Effort (USA) (War Front (USA)) **Sheikh J. D. Al Maktoum**
**223 WHIMSY,** ch f 05/05 Charming Thought—Cape Victoria (Mount Nelson) **Kingsclere Racing Club**
**224** B f 04/02 Churchill (IRE)—Wind Fire (USA) (Distorted Humor (USA)) **Qatar Racing Limited**

**Other Owners:** Mr H. A. Al Jehani, Al Rabban Racing, Mr Sultan Ali, Apollo Racing, I. A. Balding, Bermuda Racing, Mr J. Bridgman, Mr D. J. Burke, D. H. Caslon, Cliveden Stud Ltd, Cornthrop Bloodstock Limited, Mr B. J. C. Cullen, Mr D. Cullen, Dr Bridget Drew & Partners, N. R. R. Drew, Miss P. B. Drew, Dr S. B. Drew, P. E. Felton, Mr P. G. Fox, Mr G. Gill, Mr & Mrs R. M. Gorell, B. J. R. Greenwood, Mr N. G. R. Harris, Mr S. Hill, B. E. Holland, Mrs E. A. Ireland, G. R. Ireland, Mr G. M. C. Johnson, Mildmay Racing, Mr N. D. Morris, PDR Properties, Apollo Racing & Dta Racing, Mr D. Redvers, Mr L. L. Register, St Albans Bloodstock Limited, Mr A. M. Tolhurst, Mrs P I. Veenbaas.

**Assistant Trainer:** Nigel Walker.

**Flat Jockey:** Rob Hornby, Oisin Murphy, David Probert. **Apprentice Jockey:** Josh Bryan, William Carver, William Cox, Bradley Harris, Callum Hutchinson, Marie Perrault.

---

## 17 MR RICHARD BANDEY, Kingsclere
Postal: **Plantation House, Wolverton, Tadley, Hampshire, RG26 5RP**
Contacts: **MOBILE 07887 535615**

**1 ALL THE FAME (IRE),** 6, b g Fame And Glory—Abhainn Ri (IRE) **Miss A. M. Reed**
**2 DELTA RUN (IRE),** 4, b g Ocovango—Curragheen (IRE) **Wendy & Malcolm Hezel**
**3 ECLAIR MAG (FR),** 7, b h Network (GER)—Katerinette (FR) **Mr R. J. Bandey**
**4 ELYAQIM (FR),** 7, b g Spider Flight (FR)—Sinceres (FR) **Mr C. J. Boreham**
**5 FIRST ASSEMBLY (IRE),** 7, b g Arcadio (GER)—Presenting Katie (IRE) **Mr S. R. Cross**

# MR RICHARD BANDEY - continued

6 **FLECK IVY (IRE)**, 8, b g Mustameet (USA)—Just Like Ivy (CAN) **Mrs S. J. Maxse**
7 **FLINTARA**, 6, b m Kayf Tara—Flinders **Leith Hill Chasers**
8 **GODREVY POINT (FR)**, 5, b g Coastal Path—Quetzalya (FR) **Mr T. D. J. Syder**
9 **HORS GUARD (FR)**, 4, br g Kitkou (FR)—Soulte (FR) **Mr C. J. Boreham**
10 **LEITH HILL LAD**, 11, b g Kayf Tara—Leith Hill Star **Mr & Mrs N. F. Maltby**
11 **MOVE OVER DARLIN**, 4, b f Helmet (AUS)—Mystery Code **J. C. Sillett**
12 **SAINT PALAIS (FR)**, 4, b g Saint des Saints (FR)—Ladies Choice (FR) **Mr T. D. J. Syder**
13 **THE BOLSHOI BANDIT (IRE)**, 5, b g Sholokhov (IRE)—Milleners Gem (IRE) **Wendy & Malcolm Hezel**

## THREE-YEAR-OLDS

14 **EXTRACURICULAR**, b f Coach House (IRE)—First Term **The Plantation Picnic Club**

**Other Owners:** Mr M. W. Hezel, Mrs W. M. Hezel, Mr R Kirkland, Mrs J. Maltby, Mr N. F. Maltby.

---

## 18 MISS CHELSEA BANHAM, Newmarket
Postal: **Mulligans Cottage, Cowlinge, Newmarket, Suffolk, CB8 9HP**
Contacts: **PHONE 07387 169781**

1 **AL BATAL**, 8, b g Pastoral Pursuits—Flam **Mr M. J. Goggin**
2 **AT YOUR SERVICE**, 7, b g Frankel—Crystal Gaze (IRE) **Chelsea Banham Pre Training ltd**
3 **AXEL JACKLIN**, 5, b g Iffraaj—Reroute (IRE) **Mr A. Searle**
4 **CAFE ESPRESSO**, 5, b m Sir Percy—Forest Express (AUS) **Chelsea Banham Pre Training ltd**
5 **CHOCCO STAR (IRE)**, 5, b m Lawman (FR)—Sharplaw Star **Mr J. Edwards**
6 **HOLY TIBER (IRE)**, 6, b m Holy Roman Emperor (IRE)—Quiet Waters (USA) **Mr M. Bartram**
7 **INDEPENDENCE DAY (IRE)**, 8, b h Dansili—Damson (IRE) **Chelsea Banham Pre Training ltd**
8 **KALOOR**, 5, b g Nathaniel (IRE)—Blinking **Mr J. L. Day**
9 **KIT'S ALLANAH (IRE)**, 4, b f Dragon Pulse (IRE)—Jenny's Dancer **Mulligans Racing club**
10 **LADY OF YORK**, 7, b m Sir Percy—Parsonagehotelyork (IRE) **Chelsea Banham Pre Training ltd**
11 **MAKAMBE (IRE)**, 6, gr g Dark Angel (IRE)—Pink Diva (IRE) **Patrick, Sellars & Murphy**
12 **MIAELLA**, 6, b m Captain Gerrard (IRE)—Sweet Applause (IRE) **Mr M. Bartram**
13 **NYMPH SPIRIT**, 4, b f Swiss Spirit—Who Splashed Me **Mr M. Bartram**
14 **SUPER JULIUS**, 7, ch g Bated Breath—Paradise Isle **Mulligans Racing club**

## THREE-YEAR-OLDS

15 **ADMIRABLE LAD**, ch g Bated Breath—Admirable Spirit **Longview Stud & Bloodstock Ltd**
16 **AMAL (IRE)**, b f No Nay Never (USA)—Lundy Island **Mr Q. Khan**
17 B g Anodin (IRE)—Atacama Sunrise **Chelsea Banham Pre Training ltd**
18 **CAPRICIOUS**, b f Harzand (IRE)—Adaptability **Longview Stud & Bloodstock Ltd**
19 **KAWAALEES**, gr c Havana Gold (IRE)—Blanc de Chine (IRE) **Mulligans Racing club**
20 **KODI KUB (IRE)**, b g Kodi Bear (IRE)—Hint of Glas (FR) **Rockingham Reins Limited**
21 **PLASTIC PADDY**, b g Buratino (IRE)—Bereka **Mr M. J. Goggin**
22 **TOKYO CHIC**, b f Sir Percy—Lady Bling **Mulligans Racing club**
23 **TOPLIGHT**, b g Bated Breath—Operettist **Longview Stud & Bloodstock Ltd**

## TWO-YEAR-OLDS

24 **ACLAIMED LADY**, b f 12/02 Aclaim (IRE)—Doddinel (Dansili) **Longview Stud & Bloodstock Ltd**
25 **ATHENIAN STAR**, ch f 10/01 Intello (GER)—Adaptability (Mastercraftsman (IRE)) **Longview Stud & Bloodstock Ltd**
26 **NIGHT TRAVELLER**, ch f 28/02 Night of Thunder (IRE)—
Travelling (Dubai Destination (USA)) (40000) **Longview Stud & Bloodstock Ltd**

**Other Owners:** Mr R. Murphy, D. C. Patrick, Mr M. W. Sellars.

## 19 MR JACK BARBER, Crewkerne

Postal: Higher Peckmoor, Henley, Crewkerne, Somerset, TA18 8FF
Contacts: PHONE 01460 76555 MOBILE 07904 185720
EMAIL info@jackbarberracing.co.uk WEBSITE www.jackbarberracing.co.uk

1 **AMZAC MAGIC**, 9, b g Milan—Queen's Banquet **Mr J. Barber**
2 **BALLYKNOCK CLOUD (IRE)**, 10, gr g Cloudings (IRE)—Ballyknock Present (IRE) **Ballyknock Cloud Syndicate**
3 **BLACKJACK MAGIC**, 6, b g Black Sam Bellamy (IRE)—One Wild Night **Tony Hayward & Jack Barber**
4 **DARCY WARD (FR)**, 8, b g Doctor Dino (FR)—Alzasca (FR) **Mr J. Barber**
5 **DOYANNIE (IRE)**, 7, ch m Doyen (IRE)—Annie May (IRE) **Barber, Donlan-abrahams & Shortland**
6 **EARTH KING (IRE)**, 5, b g Shirocco (GER)—Beach Beauty (IRE) **Mrs C. E. Penny**
7 **EARTH STAR (IRE)**, 5, br g Presenting—Madam Bovary (IRE) **R. M. Penny**
8 **FLYING SARA**, 6, b m Malinas (GER)—Samandara (FR) **Peckmoor Flyers**
9 **GULSHANIGANS**, 9, b g Sakhee (USA)—Gulshan **F Newton, J J Barber & J Barber**
10 **LAMANVER BEL AMI**, 7, b g Black Sam Bellamy (IRE)—Lamanver Homerun **Wessex Racing Club**
11 **MIDNIGHT MALIN**, 5, b m Malinas (GER)—Dancingtilmidnight **Mrs S. J. Maltby**
12 **NORTON HILL (IRE)**, 5, b g Fame And Glory—Charming Leader (IRE) **Mr & Mrs J. J. Barber & Mr A. Norman**
13 5, B m Black Sam Bellamy (IRE)—One Wild Night **Mr J. Barber**
14 **ONEUPMANSHIP (IRE)**, 6, ch g Mahler—Letthisbetheone (IRE) **Charlie Walker & Phil Fry**
15 **RIDGEWAY FLYER**, 10, b g Tobougg (IRE)—Running For Annie **A. J. Norman**
16 **SHINTORI (FR)**, 9, b g Enrique—La Masai (FR) **Mrs R. E. Vicary**
17 **WHAT'LLBEWILLBE (IRE)**, 7, b g Mahler—Letterwoman (IRE) **C. C. Walker**

Other Owners: Mr J. Barber, Mr J. J. Barber, Mr E. J. Dolan-Abrahams, R. P. Fry, A. A. Hayward, A. J. Norman, Mr J. Shortland, C. C. Walker.

## 20 MRS STELLA BARCLAY, Garstang

Postal: Lancashire Racing Stables, The Paddocks, Strickens Lane, Barnacre, Garstang, Lancashire, PR3 1UD
Contacts: PHONE 01995 605790 MOBILE 07802 764094
EMAIL paul@lancashireracingstables.co.uk

1 **AUSSIE BREEZE**, 5, ch m Australia—Terre du Vent (FR) **Lancashire Racing Stables Ltd.**
2 **BENNY IN MILAN (IRE)**, 10, b g Milan—Chaparral Lady (IRE) **Keith Dodd & Network Racing**
3 **DARE TO BEGIN (IRE)**, 6, b br g Recital (IRE)—Everybodys Dream (IRE) **Winks Racing**
4 **DEOLALI**, 7, b g Sleeping Indian—Dulally **Matt Watkinson Racing Club**
5 **ELSPETH ROSE**, 4, b f Coach House (IRE)—Ella Rosie **Village Racing**
6 **GIANT STEPS (IRE)**, 4, b g Footstepsinthesand—Saysim West (IRE) **Mrs S. E. Barclay**
7 **GLENRUA (IRE)**, 8, b g Stowaway—Ceol Rua (IRE) **Keith Dodd & Matt Watkinson Racing Club**
8 **GLORIOUS RIO (IRE)**, 4, b g Gutaifan (IRE)—Renaissance Rio (IRE) **Matt Watkinson Racing Club**
9 **LATINO FLING (IRE)**, 6, b m Milan—Five of Spades (IRE) **Colin Taylor & Miss Kay Wilding**
10 **LITTLE STEVIE**, 9, b g Overbury (IRE)—Candy's Room (IRE) **Keith Dodd & Network Racing**
11 **MANSFIELD**, 8, b g Exceed And Excel (AUS)—Jane Austen (IRE) **The Style Council**
12 **MAURICIO (IRE)**, 7, ch g Helmet (AUS)—Essexford (IRE) **The Haydock Badgeholders**
13 **MELABI (IRE)**, 8, b g Oasis Dream—Briolette (IRE) **Matt Watkinson Racing Club**
14 **MISS MAWATHEEQ**, 5, b m Mawatheeq (USA)—Silver Miss (FR) **The Cataractonium Racing Syndicate**
15 **MISSESGEEJAY**, 11, br m Beat All (USA)—Riverbank Rainbow **The Coz Syndicate**
16 **PABLOBAR**, 5, b g Nayef (USA)—Calico Moon (USA) **Mr J. W. Hall**
17 **RIVERS END (IRE)**, 8, ch g Watar (IRE)—Crann River (IRE) **Matt Watkinson Racing Club**
18 **SHARRABANG**, 5, b g Coach House (IRE)—Dulally **Matt Watkinson Racing Club**
19 **STORM TIGER**, 5, b g Shirocco (GER)—Lucys Pet **Mr G. Seward**
20 **WILDMOUNTAINTHYME**, 5, b m Doncaster Rover (USA)—Awaywithefairies **Mr P. J. Metcalfe**

## MRS STELLA BARCLAY - continued

### THREE-YEAR-OLDS
21 **DANDY'S MAX (IRE)**, b g Dandy Man (IRE)—Fonnie (IRE) **Colin Taylor & Miss Kay Wilding**
22 **GHOSTLY**, gr g Outstrip—Alpha Spirit **Stella Barclay Racing Club**
23 **GO GO LUNA**, b f Heeraat (IRE)—Princess of Rock **Mr P. Sedgwick**
24 B f Heeraat (IRE)—Kallithea (IRE) **The Most Wanted Partnership**
25 **LANCASHIRE LIFE**, b f Coach House (IRE)—Betty's Pride **Betty's Brigade**
26 **ROSE OF LANCASHIRE**, b f Coach House (IRE)—Ella Rosie **CCCNLP**
27 **ROSESATHENDOFTIME**, b f Coach House (IRE)—China Lily (USA) **Mr P. J. Metcalfe**
28 **THE NEW NORMAL (IRE)**, b br g Estidhkaar (IRE)—Sparks (IRE) **Stella Barclay Racing Club**
29 **TOPFLIGHTSUPERFLY**, b f Heeraat (IRE)—Making Waves (IRE) **Mr P Bamford**

### TWO-YEAR-OLDS
30 B g 18/04 Coach House—Ella Rosie (Common Grounds) **Mrs S. E. Barclay**
31 Ch f 20/02 Pastoral Pursuits—Venus Rising (Observatory) **Mr J. W. Hall**

**Other Owners:** Alan Appleton, Steve & Eve Atkinson, John Ball, Tony Ball, Philip Bamford, Stella Barclay, Jim & Judy Barnes, Paul Bushell, John Calderbank, Dan Chappell, Andy Clarke, Paul Clarkson, Keith Dodd, Jeff Hall, Craig Harrison, Steve  Hicks, Ian Holt, Linda Holt, Shirley Hurst, Dave Kay, David & Trish Maitland-Price, Frank Martindale, Geoff & Jan Metcalfe, Philip & Christine Metcalfe, David Price, Peter Sedgwick, Graham Seward, Jeremy Simm, Chris Smith, Colin Taylor, Matt Watkinson, Josh Whittaker, Miss Kay Wilding, Trevor Willis.

---

### MRS TRACEY BARFOOT-SAUNT, Wotton-under-Edge
Postal: **Cosy Farm, Huntingford, Charfield, Wotton-under-Edge, Gloucestershire, GL12 8EY**
Contacts: **PHONE 01453 520312 MOBILE 07976 360626 FAX 01453 520312**

1 **BOMBAY BASIL (IRE)**, 7, b g Artan (IRE)—Taipan Sue (IRE) **Mrs T. M. Barfoot-Saunt**
2 **EARTH SPIRIT**, 8, b g Black Sam Bellamy (IRE)—Samandara (FR) **Mrs T. M. Barfoot-Saunt**
3 **MUNSTEAD MOONSHINE**, 5, ch m Sir Percy—Royal Patron **P. J. Ponting**
4 **TENSION TIME (IRE)**, 7, b g Dubai Destination (USA)—Leader's Hall (IRE) **BS Racing**
5 **TROTTER**, 7, b g Piccolo—Vintage Steps (IRE) **A Good Days Racing**
6 **TWICE THE MUSTARD**, 8, ch g Haafhd—Molly Pitcher (IRE) **Mr G. C. Barfoot-Saunt**

### THREE-YEAR-OLDS
7 **VIVIAN GREY (IRE)**, b g Dandy Man (IRE)—Zaaqya **P. J. Ponting**

**Other Owners:** Mr G. C. Barfoot-Saunt, Mrs T. M. Barfoot-Saunt.

---

### MR MAURICE BARNES, Brampton
Postal: **Tarnside, Farlam, Brampton, Cumbria, CA8 1LA**
Contacts: **PHONE 016977 46675 MOBILE 07760 433191**
**EMAIL anne.barnes1@btinternet.com**

1 **APACHE PILOT**, 13, br g Indian Danehill (IRE)—Anniejo **Farlam Flights Racing Club**
2 **ARGENT ET OR (FR)**, 8, br g Saint des Saints (FR)—Gold Or Silver (FR) **Mr M. A. Barnes**
3 **BAFANA BLUE**, 10, b g Blueprint (IRE)—Anniejo **Hogarth, Morris, Percival & Irving**
4 **BALKALIN (FR)**, 9, ch g Balko (FR)—Rose Caline (FR) **Mr M. A. Barnes**
5 **BOA ISLAND (IRE)**, 11, b g Trans Island—Eskimo Kiss (IRE) **Mr R. A. Clarke**
6 **DAPPER DAISY**, 5, ch m Dapper—Overpriced **Mr M. A. Barnes**
7 **DEERFOOT**, 5, ch g Archipenko (USA)—Danceatdusk **Mr M. A. Barnes**
8 **DOLLY DANCER (IRE)**, 7, b m Yeats (IRE)—Scrapper Jack (IRE) **Mr E. Cassie**

## MR MAURICE BARNES - continued

9 **FAIR LADY,** 7, b m Fair Mix (IRE)—Lady Sambury **J. R. Wills**
10 **FARLAM KING,** 8, br g Crosspeace (IRE)—Second Bite **Castle Racing & Partner**
11 **FAROCCO (GER),** 8, b g Shirocco (GER)—Fantasmatic (GER) **Miss A. P. Lee**
12 **FISHER GREEN (IRE),** 8, b g Rip Van Winkle (IRE)—Prealpina (IRE) **D. Carr**
13 **INDIAN VOYAGE (IRE),** 13, b g Indian Haven—Voyage of Dreams (USA) **D. Carr**
14 **ITSNOTYOUITSME,** 8, b g Milan—Brochrua (IRE) **J. Wade**
15 **KNOCKOURA (IRE),** 9, b g Westerner—Lisselton Thatch (IRE) **Mr M. A. Barnes**
16 **LOULOUMILLS,** 11, b m Rob Roy (USA)—Etching (USA) **Mr G. R. S. Nixon & Mr M. Barnes**
17 **MABLEABLE,** 5, b m Black Sam Bellamy (IRE)—Lady Jinks **Miss A. P. Lee**
18 **MY MACHO MAN (IRE),** 4, ch g Camacho—Mypreciousblue **Mr E. Cassie**
19 **OH NO,** 9, b g Indian Danehill (IRE)—See My Girl **Farlam Flights Racing Club**
20 **OISHIN,** 9, b g Paco Boy (IRE)—Roshina (IRE) **The Whisperers & Partner**
21 **PEAK TIME,** 8, ch g Distant Peak—Ruby Redwing
22 **PLACEDELA CONCORDE,** 8, b g Champs Elysees—Kasakiya (IRE) **Hogarth, Morris & Percival Racing**
23 **QUICK BREW,** 13, b g Denounce—Darjeeling (IRE) **The Wizards**
24 **ROLLERRULER,** 7, b g Native Ruler—Roll Over Rose (IRE) **Mr R. W. Powell**
25 **ROMA BANGKOK,** 5, b g Mount Nelson—Magika **Mr M. A. Barnes**
26 **SAINT ARVANS (FR),** 7, b g Motivator—Castellina (USA) **D. Carr**
27 **SMART PACO,** 7, ch g Paco Boy (IRE)—La Gifted **Mr M. A. Barnes**
28 **TOO WISE MAN (IRE),** 9, b g Dansant—Screen Idol (IRE) **Hazel & Racing**
29 **VICTORY ECHO (IRE),** 8, b g Cloudings (IRE)—Serendipity (IRE) **Mr M. A. Barnes**

**Other Owners:** Mr M. A. Barnes, Castle Racing, Miss H. M. Crichton, Mr J. G. Graham, K. Greenwell, Mr G. R. Hogarth, Mr K. Irving, Mr S. G. Johnston, Mr R. N. J. Lane, Mr A. J. Morris, Mr S. Nightingale, G. R. S. Nixon, Mr V. A. Percival, The Whisperers, Mr R. N. Towler.

**Assistant Trainer:** Dale Irving.

---

**23**
## MR BRIAN BARR, Sherborne
Postal: **Tall Trees Stud, Longburton, Sherborne, Dorset, DT9 5PH**
Contacts: **PHONE 01963 210173 MOBILE 07826 867881**
EMAIL brianbarrracing@hotmail.com WEBSITE www.brianbarrracing.co.uk TWITTER @brianbarrracing

1 **ANNIEMATION (IRE),** 4, b g Acclamation—Cafetiere **Mr W. Buckley**
2 **BELLA AMOURA,** 5, b m Nathaniel (IRE)—Dream Wild **Hitchins & Partners**
3 **BENANDGONE,** 4, b g Hallowed Crown (AUS)—Peaceful Soul (USA) **Mr G. Hitchins**
4 **DAN MCGRUE (IRE),** 9, b g Dansant—Aahsaypasty (IRE) **Miss D. Hitchins**
5 4, Gr g Born To Sea (IRE)—Danealla (IRE) **Mr P. Bona**
6 **DOLCIANO DICI (FR),** 8, b g Assessor (IRE)—Louve Rina (FR) **Miss D. Hitchins**
7 **GATES PASS,** 6, b br g Showcasing—Molly Mello (GER) **Chris Clark & Daisy Hitchins**
8 **GROUP STAGE (GER),** 5, b g Maxios—Good Hope (GER) **Troika Racing**
9 **INDEPENDENCE (USA),** 5, br g More Than Ready (USA)—Frivolous Alex (USA) **Mr G. Hitchins**
10 **INGENUITY,** 6, b g Slickly (FR)—Onlyyouknowme (IRE) **Miss D. Hitchins**
11 **JOHNI BOXIT,** 6, ch g Sakhee's Secret—Pink Supreme **Brian Barr Racing Club**
12 **JUPITER RISING (FR),** 5, b g Masterstroke (USA)—Dionea (IRE) **Brian Barr Racing Club**
13 **MADALLI (IRE),** 7, ch m Sans Frontieres (IRE)—Parkality (IRE) **Allison Family & Partner**
14 **MANOR PARK,** 6, b g Medicean—Jadeel **A L Barnes & Partner**
15 **MISTER MORETTI (IRE),** 6, b g Masterofthehorse (IRE)—Lost It (IRE) **Troika Racing**
16 **PARKER'S BOY,** 4, b g Hot Streak (IRE)—Shannon Spree **Mr T. Parker**
17 **SIRBOWTIEMAN (GER),** 4, b g Gale Force Ten—Sabaidee (IRE) **Bow Tie Racegoers & Partners**
18 **TOOLATETODELEGATE,** 7, b m Delegator—Little Caroline (IRE) **Brian Barr Racing Club**
19 **TRISTAN DE GANE (FR),** 6, br g Sinndar (IRE)—Adamise (FR) **Mr G. Hitchins**

## MR BRIAN BARR - continued

### THREE-YEAR-OLDS
20 **CALECO (IRE)**, b f Fast Company (IRE)—Caledonia Princess **Troika Racing**
21 **MADAME BIJOUX**, b f Geordieland (FR)—Madam Be **Brian Barr Racing Club**

### TWO-YEAR-OLDS
22 B f 15/02 Heeraat (IRE)—Fairmont (IRE) (Kingmambo (USA))

**Other Owners:** Mr I. Allison, Mr A. L. Barnes, Brian Barr Racing Club, Mr C. J. Clark, Miss D. Hitchins, Exors of the Late Mrs K. Hitchins, Mr P C. McGann, Mrs G. Morgan, The Bow Tie Racegoers.

**Assistant Trainer:** Daisy Hitchins.

**NH Jockey:** Paul O'Brien. **Amateur Jockey:** Mr A Butterfield.

---

**24** **MR RON BARR, Middlesbrough**
Postal: **Carr House Farm, Seamer, Stokesley, Middlesbrough, Cleveland, TS9 5LL**
Contacts: **PHONE 01642 710687 MOBILE 07711 895309**
EMAIL christinebarr1@aol.com

1 **COLLETTE (IRE)**, 4, ch f New Approach (IRE)—Shallow Lake (USA) **D Thomson & C Barr**
2 **DOMINNANNIE (IRE)**, 8, b m Paco Boy (IRE)—English Rose (USA) **Mrs V. G. Davies**
3 **GRACEFUL ACT**, 13, b m Royal Applause—Minnina (IRE) **Mr D. Thomson & Mrs R. E. Barr**
4 **MIGHTASWELLSMILE**, 7, b m Elnadim (USA)—Intishaar (IRE) **Mr K. Trimble**
5 **MITCHUM**, 12, b g Elnadim (USA)—Maid To Matter **S Haykin & R Barr**
6 **PEARL'S CALLING (IRE)**, 6, ch m Dandy Man (IRE)—Celtic Heroine (IRE) **Mrs V. G. Davies**

### THREE-YEAR-OLDS
7 B g Eagle Top—Karate Queen **Mrs C. Barr**
8 Ch g Eagle Top—Pay Time **Mrs V. G. Davies**

**Other Owners:** Mrs C. Barr, R. E. Barr, Miss S. Haykin, D. Thomson.

**Assistant Trainer:** Mrs C. Barr.

**Amateur Jockey:** Miss V. Barr.

---

**25** **MR DAVID BARRON, Thirsk**
Postal: **Maunby House, Maunby, Thirsk, North Yorkshire, YO7 4HD**
Contacts: **PHONE 01845 587435 FAX 01845 587331**
EMAIL david.barron@maunbyhouse.com

1 **ABOVE THE REST (IRE)**, 10, b g Excellent Art—Aspasias Tizzy (USA) **L. G. O'Kane**
2 **ANOTHER BATT (IRE)**, 6, ch g Windsor Knot (IRE)—Mrs Batt (IRE) **L. G. O'Kane**
3 **BARYSHNIKOV**, 5, ch g Mastercraftsman (IRE)—Tara Moon **Mr John Knotts & Partner**
4 **CLASS CLOWN (IRE)**, 4, ch g Intense Focus (USA)—Joli Elegant (IRE) **Dr N. J. Barron**
5 **CLON COULIS (IRE)**, 7, b m Vale of York (IRE)—Cloneden (IRE) **Ms Colette Twomey**
6 **DEEVIOUS BEAU**, 4, b g Brazen Beau (AUS)—Vespasia **Harrowgate Bloodstock Ltd**
7 **EDNA TALE**, 4, b f Casamento (IRE)—Sheezastorm (IRE) **Harrowgate Bloodstock Ltd**
8 **GREYFIRE**, 4, gr g Shooting To Win (AUS)—Ancestral Way **Mr D Ellis & Syps Ltd**
9 **GUNMETAL (IRE)**, 8, gr g Clodovil (IRE)—March Star (IRE) **Mrlaurenceo'Kane/Harrowgatebloodstockltd**
10 **JOSHUA R (IRE)**, 4, b g Canford Cliffs (IRE)—Khobaraa **Mrm.Rozenbroek/Harrowgatebloodstockltd**
11 **KYNREN (IRE)**, 7, b g Clodovil (IRE)—Art of Gold **Elliott Brothers & Peacock & Partner**

## MR DAVID BARRON - continued

12 **LOFTY**, 5, b g Harbour Watch (IRE)—Curly Come Home  **Mrh.D.Atkinson/Harrowgatebloodstockltd**
13 **MODULAR MAGIC**, 4, b g Swiss Spirit—Lucy Parsons (IRE)  **Mr P McKenna, Mr L O Kane & Partner**
14 **MOSSBAWN**, 4, b g Brazen Beau (AUS)—Maziona  **Mrlaurenceo'Kane/Harrowgatebloodstockltd**
15 **MR COCO BEAN (USA)**, 7, b g Gio Ponti (USA)—Ing Ing (FR)  **Mr S. G. Raines**
16 **NORTH WIND (IRE)**, 5, b g No Nay Never (USA)—Kawn  **Penton Hill Racing Limited**
17 **ON A SESSION (USA)**, 5, b g No Nay Never (USA)—Destiny Calls (USA)  **Penton Hill Racing Limited & Mr L O'Kane**
18 **POET'S LADY**, 4, gr f Farhh—La Gessa  **L. G. O'Kane**
19 **RECKLESS ENDEAVOUR (IRE)**, 8, b g Kodiac—Red Fanfare  **L. G. O'Kane**
20 **SORBONNE**, 5, ch g Cityscape—Sorcellerie  **Mr D Ellis & Partner**
21 **TEESCOMPONENTSFLY**, 4, ch g Shirocco (GER)—Hula Ballew  **Tees Components Ltd**
22 **VENTUROUS (IRE)**, 8, ch g Raven's Pass (USA)—Bold Desire  **Mrlaurenceo'Kane/Harrowgatebloodstockltd**
23 **VIVA VOCE (IRE)**, 4, b g Intense Focus (USA)—Moonbi Haven (IRE)  **Dr N. J. Barron**
24 **WILLING TO PLEASE**, 4, b f Iffraaj—Tebee's Oasis  **Minster Stud**
25 **ZARZYNI (IRE)**, 4, b g Siyouni (FR)—Zunera (IRE)  **L. G. O'Kane**

## THREE-YEAR-OLDS

26 **ANNIE ROSE**, b f Equiano (FR)—Tebee's Oasis  **Minster Stud & Partner**
27 **ARTHUR NORSE (IRE)**, ch g Anjaal—She's Neat (IRE)  **Mrs Anne Atkinson & Partner**
28 **ATIYAH**, br f Swiss Spirit—Jofranka  **Mrs Anne Atkinson & Partner**
29 **ATTABOY ROY (IRE)**, b g Prince of Lir (IRE)—Harmony Bay (IRE)  **Mr P Savill & Mr T Savill**
30 **BAZZY**, gr f Mukhadram—Perfect Haven  **Mr M. J. Rozenbroek**
31 **BERT KIBBLER (IRE)**, b g Fountain of Youth (IRE)—Annie Beach (IRE)  **Mrs D. Dalby & Harrowgate Bloodstock Ltd**
32 **CONTACT (IRE)**, gr c Gutaifan (IRE)—La Tulipe (IRE)  **Mr H. D. Atkinson**
33 **ESTICKY END (IRE)**, b g Estidhkaar (IRE)—Hay Now (IRE)  **Dr N. J. Barron**
34 **LILIKOI (IRE)**, b f Alhebayeb (IRE)—Passion Fruit  **Harrowgate Bloodstock Ltd**
35 B c Fountain of Youth (IRE)—Lucy Parsons (IRE)  **Harrowgate Bloodstock Ltd & Associate**
36 **MERESIDE MAGIC (IRE)**, b g Gutaifan (IRE)—Mary Thomas (IRE)  **Mereside Racing Limited & Partner**
37 **MERESIDE PEARL (IRE)**, ch f Pearl Secret—Setting Forth (IRE)  **Mereside Racing Limited & Partner**
38 **OTTO OYL**, br g Mayson—Olive Mary  **Dr N. J. Barron**
39 **POLAM LANE**, b g Swiss Spirit—La Zamora
40 B br g Pride of Dubai (AUS)—Princess Patsky (USA)  **Mr M. J. Rozenbroek**
41 **RITA R (IRE)**, b f Tagula (IRE)—Ashtaroute (USA)  **Mrm.Rozenbroek/Harrowgatebloodstockltd**
42 **TIME HAS WINGS (IRE)**, b f Moohaajim (IRE)—Rozene (IRE)  **Mrm.Rozenbroek/Harrowgatebloodstockltd**
43 **WESTERN MUSIC (IRE)**, b f Epaulette (AUS)—Western Tune (IRE)  **Harrowgate Bloodstock Ltd**
44 **WHERE'S BOBBY**, b f Bobby's Kitten (USA)—Kashoof  **Mr A. C. Cook**
45 Br g Havana Gold (IRE)—Zaaneh (IRE)

## TWO-YEAR-OLDS

46 B f 28/04 Bungle Inthejungle—Art of Gold (Excellent Art)
47 Ch g 22/04 Sixties Icon—Lucy Parsons (IRE) (Thousand Words)
48 B c 09/04 Gutaifan (IRE)—Mary Thomas (IRE) (Zoffany (IRE)) (4762)  **Mereside Racing Limited & Partner**
49 Ch g 15/04 Cityscape—Maziona (Dansili)
50 B c 28/03 Buratino (IRE)—Queen Athena (IRE) (Royal Applause) (3500)
51 B c 02/03 Heeraat (IRE)—Rosecomb (IRE) (Rip Van Winkle (IRE)) (2500)
52 **SUNDAY JUSTICE (IRE)**, b c 05/02 Gutaifan (IRE)—Knapton Hill (Zamindar (USA)) (4762)  **Dr N. J. Barron**
53 **THUNDER CHAP**, b c 11/04 Night of Thunder (IRE)—Percys Princess (Sir Percy) (8500)  **Penton Hill Racing Limited**

**Other Owners:** Mrs A. Atkinson, Mr H. D. Atkinson, Mrs S. C. Barron, Exors of the Late E. Carson, W. F. H. Carson, Mrs D. Dalby, C. R. Elliott, J. M. Elliott, Elliott Brothers And Peacock, Mr D. B. Ellis, Harrowgate Bloodstock Ltd, Mr J. Knotts, Mr P McKenna, Mereside Racing Limited, Minster Stud, L. G. O'Kane, Penton Hill Racing Limited, Mr M. J. Rozenbroek, SYPS (UK) Ltd, P. D. Savill, Mr T. H. Savill, Mr J. Wells.

**Assistant Trainer:** Nicola-Jo Barron.

## 26 MISS REBECCA BASTIMAN, Wetherby
Postal: **Goosemoor Farm, Warfield Lane, Wetherby, West Yorkshire, LS22 5EU**
Contacts: **PHONE 01423 359397, 01423 359783 MOBILE 07818 181313**
EMAIL rebeccabastiman@hotmail.co.uk

1 **AFTER JOHN**, 5, b g Dutch Art—Rosacara **Lady Jouse Partnership**
2 **DARK DEFENDER**, 8, b g Pastoral Pursuits—Oh So Saucy **Rebecca Bastiman Racing**
3 **DONNELLY'S RAINBOW (IRE)**, 8, b g Lilbourne Lad (IRE)—Donnelly's Hollow (IRE) **Mrs P. Bastiman**
4 **EDGAR ALLAN POE (IRE)**, 7, b g Zoffany (IRE)—Swingsky (IRE) **I B Barker / P Bastiman**
5 **HAYADH**, 8, gr g Oasis Dream—Warling (IRE) **Mrs P. Bastiman**
6 **HIGHLIGHT REEL (IRE)**, 6, b g Big Bad Bob (IRE)—Dance Hall Girl (IRE) **Grange Park Racing Club & Partner**
7 **JOSIEBOND**, 4, ch m Monsieur Bond (IRE)—Smiddy Hill **I. B. Barker**
8 **MAJESTE**, 7, b g Acclamation—Winged Valkyrie (IRE) **Let's Be Lucky Racing 17 & Partner**
9 **MILIANAPOWER**, 4, br f Power—Miliana (IRE) **Mrs P. Bastiman**
10 **SHINE ON BRENDAN (IRE)**, 4, b g Society Rock (IRE)—Something Magic **Lets Be Lucky 29 & Partner**
11 **STAYCATION (IRE)**, 5, b g Acclamation—Staceymac (IRE) **Mrs P. Bastiman**
12 **VICTORY ANGEL (IRE)**, 7, b g Acclamation—Golden Shadow (IRE) **Mrs P. Bastiman**
13 **WENSLEY**, 6, b g Poet's Voice—Keladora (USA) **Mr John Smith & Mrs P. Bastiman**
14 **WRITTEN BROADCAST (IRE)**, 4, gr g Gutaifan (IRE)—Teeline (IRE) **Mrs P. Bastiman**

**Other Owners:** I. B. Barker, Mrs P. Bastiman, Miss R. Bastiman, Mr A. D. Crombie, Mr G. G. Friel, Mr R. A. Gorrie, Mr S. T. Gorrie, Grange Park Racing Club, Mr I. C. Jones, Let's Be Lucky Racing 17, Let's Be Lucky Racing 26, Mr J. McAvoy, Mr J. Smith.

**Assistant Trainer:** Harvey Bastiman.

**Flat Jockey:** Phil Dennis.

## 27 MR RALPH BECKETT, Kimpton
Postal: **Kimpton Down Stables, Kimpton, Andover, Hampshire, SP11 8QQ**
Contacts: **PHONE 01264 772278 MOBILE 07802 219022**
EMAIL trainer@rbeckett.com

1 **ALBAFLORA**, 4, gr f Muhaarar—Almiranta **Miss K. Rausing**
2 **APOLLINAIRE**, 4, b g Poet's Voice—Affaire de Coeur **ADC Bloodstock**
3 **BIGGLES**, 4, b c Zoffany (IRE)—At A Clip **Lady N. F. Cobham**
4 **BRASCA**, 5, ch g Nathaniel (IRE)—Regalline (IRE) **Frank Brady & Brian Scanlon**
5 **BREATH CAUGHT**, 6, b g Bated Breath—Double Crossed **Amo Racing Limited**
6 **BURIRAM (IRE)**, 5, b g Reliable Man—Wild Step (GER) **King Power Racing Co Ltd**
7 **CHAMADE**, 4, b f Sepoy (AUS)—Colima (IRE) **Mr & Mrs David Aykroyd**
8 **DECLARED INTEREST**, 4, b f Declaration of War (USA)—Wiener Valkyrie **The Eclipse Partnership**
9 **DIOCLES OF ROME (IRE)**, 6, b g Holy Roman Emperor (IRE)—Serisia (FR) **Mrs Philip Snow & Partners**
10 **FOX DUTY FREE (IRE)**, 4, b g Kingman—Bugie d'Amore **King Power Racing Co Ltd**
11 **FUTURE INVESTMENT**, 5, b g Mount Nelson—Shenir **R.N.J.Partnership**
12 **GRAIN OF SENSE (IRE)**, 4, ch g Teofilo (IRE)—Grain of Truth **Clarendon Partnership**
13 **HELVEZIA (IRE)**, 4, b f Holy Roman Emperor (IRE)—Dame d'Honneur (IRE) **Westerberg**
14 **ICE STATION ZEBRA**, 4, b f Showcasing—Moretta Blanche **P. K. Gardner T/A Springcombe Park Stud**
15 **KINROSS**, 4, b c Kingman—Ceilidh House **Mr M. Chan**
16 **LUCANDER (IRE)**, 4, b g Footstepsinthesand—Lady Sefton **Mrs M. E. Slade & Mr B. Ohlsson**
17 **MASCAT**, 4, ch g Zoffany (IRE)—Critical Acclaim **Mr Y. M. Nasib**
18 **MAX VEGA (IRE)**, 4, b g Lope de Vega (IRE)—Paraphernalia (IRE) **The Pickford Hill Partnership**
19 **NEWBOLT (IRE)**, 4, gr g Bated Breath—Nirva (IRE) **Manor Farm Partnership**
20 **PRINCE ALEX (IRE)**, 4, b g Excelebration (IRE)—Interchange (IRE) **Amo Racing Limited**
21 **ROCK EAGLE**, 6, ch g Teofilo (IRE)—Highland Shot **J. C. Smith**
22 **SAM COOKE (IRE)**, 5, b g Pour Moi (IRE)—Saturday Girl **Chelsea Thoroughbreds - Wonderful World**
23 **TIGERSKIN**, 5, ch g Nathaniel (IRE)—Jamboretta (IRE) **Mr A. D. G. Oldrey & Mr G. C. Hartigan**
24 **TOMFRE**, 4, b g Cable Bay (IRE)—Kurtanella **Mrs Philip Snow & Partners**

## MR RALPH BECKETT - continued

25 **TRES SPECIALE**, 4, ch f Siyouni (FR)—Special Gift (IRE) **Ballylinch Stud**
26 **VICTORY CHIME (IRE)**, 6, b g Campanologist (USA)—Patuca **Mr A. Nevin**

### THREE-YEAR-OLDS

27 **A LEGACY**, b f Archipenko (USA)—All At Sea **Miss K. Rausing**
28 **ABSTINENCE**, ch f Lope de Vega (IRE)—Stone Roses (FR) **SRB Equine**
29 **AESTHETE**, b g Muhaarar—Miss Brown To You (IRE) **Mr R. A. Pegum**
30 **ALEAS**, ch g Archipenko (USA)—Alea Iacta **Miss K. Rausing**
31 **ATHEREA**, b f Heeraat (IRE)—Venus Grace **Mr G.C. Hartigan & Mr A.D.G.Oldrey**
32 **AVETA (FR)**, b f Gleneagles (IRE)—Embiyra (IRE) **Mrs Lynn Turner & Mr Guy Brook**
33 **BLUEBIRD DAY**, b f Hot Streak (IRE)—Moretta Blanche **Absolute Solvents Ltd**
34 **BULLACE**, b c Toronado (IRE)—Redstart **Mr A. D. G. Oldrey & Mr G. C. Hartigan**
35 **CASUARINA**, b f Sea The Moon (GER)—Caribana **Miss K. Rausing**
36 **CHERCHEZ**, b f Nathaniel (IRE)—Regardez **J. H. Richmond-Watson**
37 **DARK MOTIVE**, b f Motivator—Dark Swan (IRE) **The Prince of Wales & The Duchess of Cornwall**
38 **DEVILWALA (IRE)**, b c Kodiac—Najraan **Amo Racing Limited & Arjun Waney**
39 **ENTENDUE**, ch f Frankel—Evita Peron **Newsells Park Stud Limited**
40 **ENVEGA**, b f Lope de Vega (IRE)—Ennaya (FR) **Regents Consulting**
41 **ESCAPEMENT**, b f Invincible Spirit (IRE)—Mechanism **Exors of the late Mr K.Abdullah**
42 **FABILIS**, b c Frankel—Mirabilis (USA) **Exors of the late Mr K.Abdullah**
43 **FLEURMAN (IRE)**, gr g Mastercraftsman (IRE)—Fleur de Nuit (IRE) **The Lucra Partnership**
44 **FREE WILL**, b f Lope de Vega (IRE)—Free Rein **The Eclipse Partnership**
45 **GALAH**, b f Australia—Lunar Spirit **Mr & Mrs David Aykroyd**
46 **HOLLYWOOD LADY**, b f Sea The Stars (IRE)—Opera Gal (IRE) **J. C. Smith**
47 **ICONIC QUEEN**, b f Invincible Spirit (IRE)—Barshiba (IRE) **J. C. Smith**
48 **LORD PROTECTOR (GER)**, b g Pastorius (GER)—Lady Jacamira (GER) **Quantum Leap Racing X & Partner**
49 **LULLABY MOON**, b f Belardo (IRE)—Bold Bidder **Amo Racing Limited & Mr Charles Obank**
50 **MEU AMOR (FR)**, b f Siyouni (FR)—Enraptured (IRE) **Amo Racing Limited**
51 **NATURE (IRE)**, b f Nathaniel (IRE)—Chantrea (IRE) **Celbridge Estates Partnership**
52 **NEW MANDATE (IRE)**, b g New Bay—Mishhar (IRE) **Mr M. Chan**
53 **OMAN (IRE)**, ch g Australia—Awohaam (IRE) **Mr Y. M. Nasib**
54 **ORGETORIX**, b g Archipenko (USA)—Helvetia (USA) **Quantum Leap Racing Iv & Partner**
55 **OUR NEW BUDDY (IRE)**, br f New Approach (IRE)—Dream On Buddy (IRE) **Mrs H. J. E. Egan**
56 **PATIENT DREAM (FR)**, b g Al Kazeem—Parnell's Dream **Mr & Mrs David Aykroyd**
57 **POMELO (IRE)**, b f Dubawi (IRE)—Emulous **Exors of the late Mr K.Abdullah**
58 **RHEBUS ROAD (IRE)**, ch g Champs Elysees—Red Riddle (IRE) **The Lucra Partnership**
59 **SAMMY SUNSHINE (GER)**, ch f Sea The Moon (GER)—Summertime (GER) **The Sunshine Partnership**
60 **SCOPE (IRE)**, b c Teofilo (IRE)—Look So **J. H. Richmond-Watson**
61 **SERENA'S QUEEN**, gr f Iffraaj—Serena's Storm (IRE) **Kaniz Bloodstock Investments Ltd**
62 **SHRARA (IRE)**, b f Dandy Man (IRE)—Mitzi Winks (USA) **Al Rabban Racing**
63 **SIR MAXI**, b g Adaay (IRE)—Winifred Jo **Amo Racing Limited & Arjun Waney**
64 **SPY LEGEND**, b gr g Mastercraftsman (IRE)—Colima (IRE) **Mr & Mrs David Aykroyd**
65 **STAR OF ORION (IRE)**, b g Footstepsinthesand—Harpist (IRE) **Miss T. A. Ashbee**
66 **STATE OCCASION**, b f Iffraaj—Forest Crown **The Eclipse Partnership**
67 **SUREFIRE**, b c Fastnet Rock (AUS)—Modesta (IRE) **Exors of the late Mr K.Abdullah**
68 **TWISTED REALITY**, b f Fastnet Rock (AUS)—Lady Dragon (IRE) **Qatar Racing Limited**
69 **VELVET AND STEEL (USA)**, ch f Union Rags (USA)—Beyond Our Reach (IRE) **Mr J. D. Gunther**
70 **VESELA**, b f Frankel—Arabesque **Exors of the late Mr K.Abdullah**
71 **ZARTAJ (USA)**, b f Karakontie (JPN)—Lateen (USA) **K. A. Dasmal**
72 **ZINC WHITE (IRE)**, gr g Vadamos (FR)—Chinese White (IRE) **The Lucra Partnership**
73 **ZOFFARELLI (IRE)**, b g Zoffany (IRE)—Genuine Quality (USA) **Mrs M.E.Slade, Mr B.Ohlsson & Partner**

### TWO-YEAR-OLDS

74 B br f 12/02 Decorated Knight—Affaire de Coeur (Dalakhani (IRE)) **ADC Bloodstock**
75 **ALLEMANDE**, gr f 04/05 Sea The Moon (GER)—Almiranta (Galileo (IRE)) **Miss K. Rausing**
76 **ALTERNATIVA**, b f 14/03 Invincible Spirit (IRE)—Alyssa (Sir Percy) **Miss K. Rausing**
77 **AMAAZE**, b c 22/02 Adaay (IRE)—Birch Cove (IRE) (Shamardal (USA)) **Absolute Solvents Ltd**
78 **AMBER DEW**, b f 11/02 Showcasing—Roxy Star (IRE) (Fastnet Rock (AUS)) **Mrs D. J. James**
79 B f 21/02 Zarak (FR)—Around The Cape (IRE) (Cape Cross (IRE)) **Al Rabban Racing**

## MR RALPH BECKETT - continued

**80** Gr c 07/05 Champs Elysees—Artistica (IRE) (Spectrum (IRE)) (45000) **Quantum Leap Racing VI**
**81** B f 14/02 Nathaniel (IRE)—Assembly (USA) (Candy Ride (ARG)) **Qatar Racing Limited**
**82** BE LUCKY MY SON (IRE), b c 12/03 Dandy Man (IRE)—Ceol Loch Aoidh (IRE) (Medecis) (62000) **Mr P. Mellett**
**83** C b 08/05 Lope de Vega (IRE)—Bibury (Royal Applause) (170000) **Mr M. Chan**
**84** B c 01/02 Wootton Bassett—Born Cross (IRE) (Dubawi (IRE)) (44390) **The Lucra Partnership II**
**85** CARDINAL ROUGE (IRE), br c 19/03 Holy Roman Emperor (IRE)—
                         Flawless Pink (More Than Ready (USA)) (70000) **The Audax Partnership**
**86** B f 04/04 Dubawi (IRE)—Cocktail Queen (IRE) (Motivator) **J. C. Smith**
**87** B f 12/04 Nathaniel (IRE)—Coquette Noire (IRE) (Holy Roman Emperor (IRE)) (90000) **Qatar Racing Limited**
**88** DAIQUIRI FRANCAIS, b f 02/04 Havana Gold (IRE)—Moretta Blanche (Dansili) **Absolute Solvents Ltd**
**89** Br f 01/03 Kingman—Dark Swan (IRE) (Zamindar (USA)) **The Prince of Wales & The Duchess of Cornwall**
**90** DAYMAN (GER), b c 23/05 Oasis Dream—Daytona (GER) (Lando (GER)) (60533) **Amo Racing Limited**
**91** DELOREAN (IRE), b c 07/02 Time Test—
                         Dawn of Empire (USA) (Empire Maker (USA)) (50000) **The Lucra Partnership II**
**92** EDINBURGH ROCK (IRE), b c 30/04 Highland Reel (IRE)—
                         Sixpenny Sweets (IRE) (Dalakhani (IRE)) (50000) **The Lucra Partnership II**
**93** ELENA'S GIFT, ch f 14/02 Frankel—Sant Elena (Efisio) **The Eclipse Partnership**
**94** B f 27/03 Nathaniel (IRE)—Elizabelle (IRE) (Westerner) (48000) **Clarendon Partnership**
**95** ETERNAL LOVE, b f 25/03 Caravaggio (USA)—Embroidered Silk (IRE) (Galileo (IRE)) (45000) **Mr T.Stewart**
**96** B c 11/03 Highland Reel (IRE)—Examinee (GER) (Monsun (GER)) (32000) **Quantum Leap Racing XIV & Partner**
**97** FASHION LOVE, b f 24/02 Fastnet Rock (AUS)—Felicity (GER) (Inchinor) (129136) **Cornthrop Bloodstock Limited**
**98** B c 26/01 Profitable (IRE)—Gift of Music (IRE) (Cadeaux Genereux) **J. C. Smith**
**99** HELVETIQUE, b f 30/03 Bobby's Kitten (USA)—Helvetia (USA) (Blame) **Miss K. Rausing**
**100** HIGH FIBRE (IRE), b c 10/04 Vadamos (FR)—Multi Grain (Sir Percy) (25714) **The Lucra Partnership II**
**101** HITHER, b f 25/02 New Approach (IRE)—Hereawi (Dubawi (IRE)) **J. H. Richmond-Watson**
**102** JIMI HENDRIX (IRE), ch c 13/02 New Bay—
                       Planchart (Gio Ponti (USA)) (82000) **Chelsea Thoroughbreds Ltd**
**103** B f 08/03 Galileo (IRE)—Just The Judge (IRE) (Lawman (FR)) **Qatar Racing Limited**
**104** B g 11/02 Jack Hobbs (IRE)—Kallisha (Whipper (USA)) **D & J Newell**
**105** C f 23/04 Havana Gold (IRE)—Lady Dragon (IRE) (Galileo (IRE)) **Qatar Racing Limited**
**106** LADY SKYE, b f 14/02 Sea The Stars (IRE)—Memoria (Teofilo (IRE)) (165000) **Amo Racing Limited**
**107** Ch f 21/02 Lope de Vega (IRE)—Lipstick Rose (IRE) (Dream Ahead (USA)) **SRB Equine**
**108** LOVELY MANA (IRE), b f 15/04 Dabirsim (FR)—Enraptured (IRE) (Green Desert) (115000) **Amo Racing Limited**
**109** B f 01/03 Invincible Spirit (IRE)—Lucrece (Pivotal) (282486) **Amo Racing Limited**
**110** LUNA DORADA (IRE), b f 03/03 Golden Horn—Lunar Spirit (Invincible Spirit (IRE)) **Mr & Mrs David Aykroyd**
**111** B f 11/03 Lope de Vega (IRE)—Lunesque (Azamour (IRE)) **Regents Consulting**
**112** MALEX, b c 28/02 Kodiac—Trois Lunes (FR) (Manduro (GER)) (420000) **Amo Racing Limited**
**113** Ch c 18/02 Al Kazeem—Midnight Dance (IRE) (Danehill Dancer (IRE)) **J. C. Smith**
**114** B f 30/04 Siyouni (FR)—Oh Goodness Me (Galileo (IRE)) (255000) **Mr M. Chan**
**115** B f 17/04 American Pharoah (USA)—Parvaneh (IRE) (Holy Roman Emperor (IRE)) (125000) **Mr Andrew Rosen**
**116** PERCOLATE (IRE), ch c 12/03 Sir Percy—Rubileo (Galileo (IRE)) (80000) **The Audax Partnership**
**117** C f 06/05 Cityscape—Pivotal Drive (IRE) (Pivotal) (20000) **Melody Racing**
**118** POSTMARK, b c 20/04 Postponed (IRE)—Dream Wild (Oasis Dream) (52000) **The Audax Partnership**
**119** PROSPEROUS VOYAGE, b f 25/03 Zoffany (IRE)—
                       Seatone (USA) (Mizzen Mast (USA)) (61905) **Mr P Stokes & Mr S Krase**
**120** PUFFING (IRE), b f 24/01 Kingman—Puff (IRE) (Camacho) **Mr & Mrs David Aykroyd**
**121** QUAVERING (IRE), b c 13/03 Vocalised (USA)—
                       Halla Na Saoire (IRE) (Teofilo (IRE)) (47619) **The Lucra Partnership II**
**122** RECHERCHER, b f 11/03 Nathaniel (IRE)—Regardez (Champs Elysees) **J. H. Richmond-Watson**
**123** SHABANO (GER), ch c 16/04 Amaron—Summertime (GER) (Sholokhov (IRE)) (12913)
**124** B f 27/03 Night of Thunder (IRE)—She Is No Lady (Lope de Vega (IRE)) **D & J Newell**
**125** SIRAJO, b c 17/03 Showcasing—Bereka (Firebreak) (110000) **Amo Racing Limited & Arjun Waney**
**126** SKY BLUE PINK, ch f 10/02 Showcasing—Miss Work of Art (Dutch Art) **Absolute Solvents Ltd**
**127** B c 03/03 Kingman—Snoqualmie Star (Galileo (IRE)) **J. C. Smith**
**128** SWEET FANTASY, b f 24/02 Wootton Bassett—Parnell's Dream (Oasis Dream) **Mr & Mrs David Aykroyd**
**129** TAMRA'S ROCK (IRE), b c 19/04 Fascinating Rock (IRE)—
                       Ajaadat (Shamardal (USA)) (15238) **The Obank Partnership**
**130** UMAX (IRE), b c 08/03 Kingman—
                       Bella Nostalgia (IRE) (Raven's Pass (USA)) (300000) **Amo Racing Limited & Arjun Waney**

# MR RALPH BECKETT - continued

131 **UNSPOKEN (IRE)**, b c 19/02 Territories (IRE)—
                        Silent Secret (IRE) (Dubai Destination (USA)) (65000) **The Audax Partnership**
132 **VEE SIGHT**, b c 10/05 Churchill (IRE)—Look So (Efisio) **J. H. Richmond-Watson**
133 B f 28/01 Postponed (IRE)—Wall of Sound (Singspiel (IRE)) **Chasemore Farm**
134 B f 23/04 Nathaniel (IRE)—White Cay (Dalakhani (IRE)) (58111) **Qatar Racing Limited**
135 B f 12/03 Lope de Vega (IRE)—
                        Witches Brew (IRE) (Duke of Marmalade (IRE)) (142857) **Apollo Racing & Waverley Racing**
136 B c 18/03 Kodiac—You Dare To Dream (IRE) (Royal Applause) (30476) **Miss T. A. Ashbee**

**Assistant Trainer:** Adam Kite, Emma Wilkinson.

**Flat Jockey:** Rob Hornby, Richard Kingscote, Rossa Ryan.

---

## 28 MISS JESSICA BEDI, Yarm
Postal: **Hill House Farm, Kirklevington, Yarm, Cleveland, TS15 9PY**
Contacts: **PHONE 01642 780202**

1 **BUCK DANCING (IRE)**, 12, b g King's Theatre (IRE)—Polly Anthus **Mrs S. M. Barker**
2 **CHROI OLD GIRL (IRE)**, 7, b m Vinnie Roe (IRE)—Bathwick Lucy (IRE) **Mrs S. M. Barker**
3 **DERRICK D'ANJOU (IRE)**, 10, b g Double Eclipse (IRE)—Belle d'Anjou (FR) **Hill House Racing Club**
4 **LUCA BRASI'S BOY (IRE)**, 7, b g Court Cave (IRE)—Luca Brasio (IRE) **Hill House Racing Club**
5 **THAT SHIPS SAILED (IRE)**, 6, b g Califet (FR)—Mill Lady (IRE) **Capt M. Anderson**
6 **TUFF MCCOOL (IRE)**, 7, gr g Arcadio (GER)—Mrs Wallensky (IRE) **Hill House Racing Club**

---

## 29 MR MICHAEL BELL, Newmarket
Postal: **Fitzroy House, Newmarket, Suffolk, CB8 0JT**
Contacts: **PHONE 01638 666567 MOBILE 07802 264514**
**EMAIL office@fitzroyhouse.co.uk WEBSITE www.michaelbellracing.co.uk**

1 **BRACKISH**, 4, b g Golden Horn—Delizia (IRE) **Middleham Park Racing XXIV & Partner**
2 **HEARTBREAKER**, 4, b br f Cable Bay (IRE)—Intishaar (IRE) **M. L. W. Bell Racing Limited**
3 **HEAVEN FORFEND**, 4, b g Frankel—Heaven Sent **Ahmad Al Shaikh & Co**
4 **LETHAL LUNCH**, 6, gr g Lethal Force (IRE)—Pin Cushion **Middleham Park Racing XXXIII & Partner**
5 **MAXI BOY**, 4, b c Oasis Dream—Lavender And Lace **Amo Racing Limited**
6 **MISTER BLUE**, 4, b gr g Dark Angel (IRE)—Sarita **Lady Bamford**
7 **PLATFORM NINETEEN (IRE)**, 5, ch g Australia—Susan Stroman **The Royal Ascot Racing Club**
8 **STONE CIRCLE (IRE)**, 4, ch g No Nay Never (USA)—Candlehill Girl (IRE) **The Fitzrovians 3**

### THREE-YEAR-OLDS

9 **ACE ROTHSTEIN**, b g More Than Ready—A.P. Cindy **Kulbir Sohi and Sarah O'Connell**
10 **BARENBOIM**, b c Golden Horn—Labise (IRE) **W. J. & T. C. O. Gredley**
11 **BIG KITTY**, b f Bobby's Kitten (USA)—Bipartisan (IRE) **Mr M. E. Perlman**
12 **BOBBY ON THE BEAT (IRE)**, b g Bobby's Kitten (USA)—Late Night Movie (IRE) **The Fitzrovians 4**
13 **BOOKMARK**, b f New Approach (IRE)—Free Verse **Her Majesty The Queen**
14 **CLOSENESS**, b f Iffraaj—Pack Together **Her Majesty The Queen**
15 **COPAKE (IRE)**, b g Kodiac—Allegation (FR) **Patrick & Scott Bryceland**
16 **CRANE (IRE)**, b c Oasis Dream—Coconut Kreek **Lady Bamford**
17 **CREAM OF THE CROP (IRE)**, b f Shalaa (IRE)—I'm So Glad **Gone To Ground Partnership**
18 **CRYSTAL GUARD (IRE)**, b c Lope de Vega (IRE)—Crystal Melody **Mr Barnes Mrs Breitmeyer & Mrs Corbani**
19 **DIAMONDS AT DUSK**, b f Twilight Son—Diamond Run **Mascalls Stud**
20 **FAST EMMA (IRE)**, ch f Fast Company (IRE)—Emma Dora (IRE) **The Fitzrovians 4**

# MR MICHAEL BELL - continued

21 **GENEVA DIVA**, br f Frankel—Swiss Diva **Lordship Stud**
22 **HEATHERDOWN MATRON**, b f Equiano (FR)—Ile Deserte **The Heatherdonians**
23 **HOLY BEE (IRE)**, ch f Declaration of War (USA)—Scarlet Honey (FR) **Mrs I. Corbani**
24 **HORSEFLY (IRE)**, b f Camelot—Forthefirstime **Mrs G Rowland-Clark & Partner**
25 **INVEIGLE**, b g Dark Angel (IRE)—Sand Vixen **Her Majesty The Queen**
26 B g Kingman—Lady Alienor (IRE) **Mascalls Stud**
27 **LOCHANTHEM**, b f Fast Company (IRE)—Locharia **Mrs B Green Mr H Bethell & Mrs I Corbani**
28 **MASTERMAN (FR)**, ch g Reliable Man—Quenching (IRE) **Amo Racing Limited & Mr S Hanson**
29 **OLYMPIC THEATRE**, b g Mayson—Madame Vestris (IRE) **The Fitzrovians 3**
30 **REALIST**, b g Camelot—Silver Mirage **Her Majesty The Queen**
31 **SANTIKI**, b f Nathaniel (IRE)—Behkara (IRE) **Lady Bamford**
32 **SAVEASEA**, b c Sea the Moon—Crystal Mountain **W. J. & T. C. O. Gredley**
33 **SIM CARD (FR)**, b g Dabirsim (FR)—Rindiseyda (IRE) **The Fitzrovians 4**
34 **STIMULATE**, b f Motivator—Shama (IRE) **Her Majesty The Queen**
35 **SUN FESTIVAL**, b g Toronado (IRE)—Raymi Coya (CAN) **Her Majesty The Queen**
36 **TALL ORDER (IRE)**, b c Muhaarar—Fate (FR) **Mr S. Hanson**
37 **THE LIR JET (IRE)**, b c Prince of Lir (IRE)—Paper Dreams (IRE) **Qatar Racing Limited**
38 **THE VEGAS RAIDER (IRE)**, gr c Kendargent (FR)—Matorio (FR) **Middleham Park Racing CXIII & Partner**
39 **TRUE COURAGE**, b g Le Havre (IRE)—Pearly Steph (FR) **Mr S. Mizon**
40 **TWILIGHT HEIR**, b g Twilight Son—Xtrasensory **Qatar Racing Limited**

## TWO-YEAR-OLDS

41 **ADJUVANT (IRE)**, b c 25/04 New Bay—Levanto (IRE) (Lawman (FR)) (15238) **Mr A. Bound**
42 B f 30/04 Gleneagles (IRE)—All's Forgotten (USA) (Darshaan) **Lady Bamford**
43 **AT LIBERTY (IRE)**, b c 06/04 Muhaarar—Federation (Motivator) (50000) **Mr David Fish & Partner**
44 **BETWEEN THE SHEETS (IRE)**, gr f 25/04 El Kabeir (USA)—
                Shena's Dream (IRE) (Oasis Dream) (45000) **Mr C. N. Wright**
45 B c 20/04 Starspangledbanner (AUS)—Biaraafa (IRE) (Araafa (IRE)) (80952) **The Hawtin Family and Mrs I Corbani**
46 **BOLTHOLE (IRE)**, b c 06/03 Free Eagle (IRE)—
                Weekend Getaway (IRE) (Acclamation) (19000) **Mr Michael Buckley and Mrs Fiona Mahony**
47 Ch f 24/03 Lope de Vega (IRE)—Bristol Bay (IRE) (Montjeu) (60000) **The Hawtin Family and Partners**
48 Ch c 29/03 Sea The Moon (GER)—
                Claiomh Solais (IRE) (Galileo (IRE)) (26667) **Sarah & Wayne Dale & Mr David Fish**
49 B f 09/05 No Nay Never (USA)—
                Danehill's Dream (IRE) (Danehill (USA)) (100000) **Mrs Magnier, Mrs Sangster & Mrs Shanahan**
50 **DILLIAN (IRE)**, b c 12/03 Camelot—Debdebdeb (Teofilo (IRE)) **Mr D. Hanafin**
51 **FIFTY SENT**, b c 02/03 Dabirsim—Sentaril (Danehill Dancer (IRE)) (20000) **Mr Kulbir Sohi & Partner**
52 B f 03/04 Zoffany—Gypsy Eyes (High Chaparral) **Mrs B. V. Sangster**
53 **HAARAR**, b c 30/03 Muhaarar—
                Interchange (IRE) (Montjeu (IRE)) (50000) **D.W. & L.Y. Payne and G. & T. Blackiston**
54 **HEATHERDOWN HERO**, b c 11/02 Sea The Moon (GER)—
                Mariee (Archipenko (USA)) (22000) **The Heatherdonians 1**
55 **IMPROVISE (FR)**, b f 03/04 Iffraaj—Set To Music (IRE) (Danehill Dancer (IRE)) **Her Majesty The Queen**
56 **JOHN O'GROATS (FR)**, b c 28/02 Dabirsim (FR)—Ecume du Jour (FR) (Hawk Wing (USA)) (8071) **Mr David Fish**
   and Sarah and Wayne Dale
57 B c 07/02 Kodi Bear (IRE)—Liel (Pivotal) (55000) **Amo Racing Limited**
58 B f 27/01 Galileo—Lightning Thunder (Dutch Art) **Qatar Racing Limited**
59 **LILA GIRL (IRE)**, b f 01/02 Pride of Dubai (AUS)—The Shrew (Dansili) (43810) **Amo Racing Limited & Mrs**
   Patricia Burns
60 B f 24/04 Sir Percy—Mambo Gold (Medaglia D'oro) **Lady Bamford**
61 **MISS HARMONY**, ch f 25/04 Tamayuz—
                Muaamara (Bahamian Bounty) (47000) **Mr C Philipps Mr T Redman & Mr T Trotter**
62 **OH GREAT**, b c 06/03 Wootton Bassett—Teeslemee (Youmzain) **Amo Racing Limited**
63 **PUB CRAWL (IRE)**, b c 29/01 Noble Mission—
                Water Hole (IRE) (Oasis Dream) (90000) **Mrs I. Corbani and Mrs E O'Leary**
64 B br c 13/02 Dabirsim (FR)—Rich Legacy (IRE) (Holy Roman Emperor (IRE)) **Qatar Racing Limited**
65 B c 02/04 Invincible Spirit (IRE)—Sariska (Pivotal) **Lady Bamford**
66 **SPLENDID ISOLATION (IRE)**, b c 04/04 Bungle Inthejungle—
                Lavender List (IRE) (Pivotal) (8000) **Mr David Kilburn & Partner**

# MR MICHAEL BELL - continued

67 **SPRING IS SPRUNG (FR)**, b c 21/02 Oasis Dream—Kinematic (Kyllachy) **Her Majesty The Queen**
68 B c 27/04 Frankel—The Lark (Pivotal) **Lady Bamford**
69 B c 22/03 Almanzor (FR)—Timepecker (IRE) (Dansili) (61905) **Middleham Park Racing XLIII & Partner**
70 **USER KINDLY**, b c 09/03 Golden Horn—Round Midnight (Paco Boy) **W. J. & T. C. O. Gredley**
71 B c 05/05 Dark Angel—Venus De Milo (Duke of Marmalade) **Mrs Paul Shanahan**
72 **WARREN ROAD**, b c 11/02 Garswood—Fleur De Lis (Nayef) **W. J. & T. C. O. Gredley**

**Assistant Trainer:** Nick Bell.

**Flat Jockey:** Cieren Fallon. **Apprentice Jockey:** Joe Bradnam, Alex Jary.

---

## 30  MR JAMES BENNETT, Wantage
Postal: **2 Filley Alley, Letcombe Bassett, Wantage, Oxfordshire, OX12 9LT**
Contacts: **PHONE 01235 762163 MOBILE 07771 523076**
EMAIL jbennett345@btinternet.com

1 **GONZAGA**, 6, b g Oasis Dream—Symposia
2 **MOOD FOR MISCHIEF**, 6, b g Nathaniel (IRE)—Tina's Spirit (IRE)
3 **THE LAST MELON**, 9, ch g Sir Percy—Step Fast (USA)

**Owners:** Miss J. C. Blackwell.

**Assistant Trainer:** Jackie Blackwell.

**Flat Jockey:** Racheal Kneller. **NH Jockey:** David Bass, Jerry McGrath. **Amateur Jockey:** Miss Harriet Tucker.

---

## 31  MR ALAN BERRY, Cockerham
Postal: **Moss Side Racing Stables, Crimbles Lane, Cockerham, Lancashire, LA2 0ES**
Contacts: **PHONE 01524 791179 MOBILE 07880 553515**
EMAIL berryracing@hotmail.com

1 **ARTHUR WALSH (IRE)**, 4, b g Zebedee—Peach Bloom **Mr R. P. Quinn**
2 **BOB'S OSS (IRE)**, 4, b g Anjaal—Prisca **A Parr & A Berry**
3 **ECONOMIC CRISIS (IRE)**, 12, ch m Excellent Art—Try The Air (IRE) **William Burns & Alan Berry**
4 **I'LL BE GOOD**, 12, b g Red Clubs (IRE)—Willisa **Mr A. Berry**
5 **JUSTICE SHALLOW (FR)**, 5, ch g Shakespearean (IRE)—Try The Air (IRE) **Mr A. Berry**
6 **LEANNES LADY (IRE)**, 9, b m Ask—Wizzy (IRE) **Mr A. Berry**
7 **NOTWHATIAM (IRE)**, 11, b g Morozov (USA)—Riverfort (IRE) **Sureness Limited**
8 **ONE FOR BRAD (IRE)**, 6, b m Watar (IRE)—Our Jaffa (IRE) **Mr A. Berry**
9 **UNAUTHORISED ACT (IRE)**, 4, b f Elzaam (AUS)—Forest Delight (IRE) **Mr A. Berry**

### THREE-YEAR-OLDS

10 B f Helmet (AUS)—King's Guest (IRE) **Mr A. Berry**
11 **NAGASAKI DREAM**, b g Bated Breath—Calakanga **Mr R. P. Quinn**
12 B g Prince of Lir (IRE)—Zvezda (USA) **Mr A. Berry**

### TWO-YEAR-OLDS

13 B c 06/03 Bobby's Kitten (USA)—Akranti (Pivotal) **Mr R. P. Quinn**
14 B f 08/05 Elzaam (AUS)—Atlantic Cycle (IRE) (Stormy Atlantic (USA)) **Mr A. Berry**
15 Ch g 15/03 Bated Breath—Bounty Box (Bahamian Bounty) (4500) **Mr A. Berry**
16 B f 07/03 Battle of Marengo (IRE)—Cliff Walk (IRE) (Footstepsinthesand) **Mr R. P. Quinn**
17 Gr g 06/03 Lethal Force (IRE)—Poetic Dancer (Byron) (20000) **Mr A. Berry**

**Assistant Trainer:** John A. Quinn.

## 32   MR JOHN BERRY, Newmarket
Postal: **Beverley House Stables, Exeter Road, Newmarket, Suffolk, CB8 8LR**
Contacts: **PHONE 01638 660663**
**EMAIL johnwathenberry@yahoo.co.uk WEBSITE www.johnberryracing.com**

1 **BIG PETE**, 4, b g Nayef (USA)—Sweet Child O'Mine  **Mr J. A. Byrne**
2 **DAS KAPITAL**, 6, b g Cityscape—Narla  **J. C. De P. Berry**
3 **DEAR ALIX**, 6, b g Schiaparelli (GER)—Desiree (IRE)  **McArthur, Nastanovich E Berry**
4 **DEREHAM**, 5, b g Sir Percy—Desiree (IRE)  **Mrs E. L. Berry**
5 **HIDDEN PEARL**, 5, ch m Dunaden (FR)—Volkovkha  **The Sisters of Mercy & John Berry**
6 **KRYPTOS**, 7, b g Cacique (IRE)—Posteritas (USA)  **Mr A. W. Fordham**
7 **LOVING PEARL**, 5, b m Dunaden (FR)—Forever Loved  **Mr A. W. Fordham**
8 **ROY ROCKET (FR)**, 11, gr g Layman (USA)—Minnie's Mystery (FR)  **McCarthy & Berry**
9 **SO LOVED**, 4, b f Gregorian (IRE)—Forever Loved
10 **SUROOJ**, 4, br f Mukhadram—Eldalil  **J. C. De P. Berry**
11 **SYLVIA PLATH (IRE)**, 4, ch f Poet's Voice—Speak Softly (JPN)  **J. C. De P. Berry**
12 **THE ROCKET PARK (IRE)**, 8, b g Rock of Gibraltar (IRE)—Snowpalm  **L. C. Wadey**
13 **THE SIMPLE TRUTH (FR)**, 4, gr g Rajsaman (FR)—Minnie's Mystery (FR)  **Mr A. W. Fordham**
14 **TURN OF PHRASE**, 4, ch f Kitten's Joy (USA)—Gotcha Good (USA)  **J. C. De P. Berry**

### THREE-YEAR-OLDS
15 **CLOUDY ROSE**, ch f Proconsul—Zarosa (IRE)  **Runfortheroses**
16 Br g Rock of Gibraltar (IRE)—Yukon Girl (IRE)  **Mr D. Tunmore**

### TWO-YEAR-OLDS
17 **MRS MAISEL**, b f 24/04 Dunaden (FR)—Minnie's Mystery (FR) (Highest Honor (FR))  **J. C. De P. Berry**
18 **TARBAT NESS**, br gr g 20/03 Reliable Man—Ethics Girl (IRE) (Hernando (FR))
19 **TRUMPER**, b g 20/02 Jack Hobbs—Indira (Sleeping Indian)  **J. C. De P. Berry**

**Other Owners:** Mrs E. L. Berry, J. C. De P. Berry, Mr J. McArthur, Miss L. I. McCarthy, Mr R. A. Nastanovich, The Sisters Of Mercy.

**Flat Jockey:** Nicola Currie, John Egan, Josephine Gordon. **NH Jockey:** Will Kennedy, Jack Quinlan. **Amateur Jockey:** Mr R. Birkett.

## 33   MR JOHN A. BERRY, Blackwater
Postal: **Ballyroe, Blackwater, Enniscorthy, Co. Wexford, Ireland**
Contacts: **PHONE +353 53 912 7205 MOBILE +353 86 255 7537**
**EMAIL johnaberry24@gmail.com**

1 4, Ch g Watar (IRE)—Buslane (IRE)  **Not For Friends Syndicate**
2 **CADDY SHACK (IRE)**, 7, br m Arcadio (GER)—Hot Or What (IRE)  **Mrs J. Berry**
3 **EAGLE ROQUE (FR)**, 7, b g Youmzain (IRE)—Viola de La Roque (FR)  **M. Kavanagh**
4 **FUZZBUSTER (IRE)**, 7, b g Sans Frontieres (IRE)—Five Trix  **P. Laffin**
5 **GAME BIRD (IRE)**, 7, ch m Teofilo (IRE)—Rare Tern (IRE)  **H. Cleary**
6 **MISS MEMORIES (IRE)**, 5, b m Mahler—Try It Again (IRE)  **Fire & Ice Syndicate**
7 **NOW WE KNOW (IRE)**, 5, br g Ask—Saipan Storm (IRE)  **Mrs A. Berry**
8 **PULL THE OTHER ONE (IRE)**, 7, b g Scorpion (IRE)—Penny's Dream (IRE)  **J. P. McManus**
9 **SHE'S A CRACKER (IRE)**, 6, b m Arcadio (GER)—Hot Or What (IRE)  **Mrs J. Berry**
10 **TAXI RANK (IRE)**, 6, b m Arcadio (GER)—Buslane (IRE)  **Mrs A. Berry**
11 4, B g Ask—Try It Again (IRE)  **Fire & Ice Syndicate**

### THREE-YEAR-OLDS
12 Ch f Dansant—Golan River (IRE)  **M. J. Culleton**
13 B f Sageburg (IRE)—Primrose Lady (IRE)  **P. Byrne**
14 B f Sageburg (IRE)—Righty Rue (IRE)  **J. Berry**

## MR JOHN A. BERRY - continued

**Assistant Trainer:** Mr J. P. Berry.

**Conditional Jockey:** Ms S. Kavanagh. **Amateur Jockey:** Mr J. P. Berry, Mr R. A. Berry.

---

**34**

### MR JOHN BEST, Sittingbourne
Postal: **Eyehorn Farm, Munsgore Lane, Borden, Sittingbourne, Kent, ME9 8JU**
Contacts: **MOBILE 07889 362154**
EMAIL john.best@johnbestracing.com WEBSITE www.johnbestracing.com

1  **BERRAHRI (IRE)**, 10, b g Bahri (USA)—Band of Colour (IRE)  **White Turf Racing UK**
2  **BOBS LAD**, 4, b g Casamento (IRE)—Foxie Girl  **Mrs J. O. Jones**
3  **CASAVOLA**, 4, b f Casamento (IRE)—Queen Ranavola (USA)  **Lingfield Park Owners Group19 & Partners**
4  **EDDYSTONE ROCK (IRE)**, 9, ch g Rock of Gibraltar (IRE)—Bayberry (UAE)  **Mrs J. O. Jones**
5  **ELMEJOR (IRE)**, 5, b g Xtension (IRE)—Lyca Ballerina  **T & B Partnership**
6  **FEARLESS LAD (IRE)**, 11, b g Excellent Art—Souffle  **Mrs J. O. Jones**
7  **FOR RICHARD**, 5, b g Muhtathir—Retainage (USA)  **Mrs J. Coleman**
8  **HIORNE TOWER (FR)**, 10, b g Poliglote—Hierarchie (FR)  **Mrs J. O. Jones**
9  **MOLIVALIENTE (USA)**, 5, ro g The Factor (USA)—Bee Brave  **Curtis Bloodstock**
10  **PENTIMENTO**, 5, b g Garswood—M'Selle (IRE)  **Walter & Geraldine Paine**
11  **PLANTADREAM**, 6, b g Planteur (IRE)—Phantom Ridge (IRE)  **Mr H J Jarvis & Mrs P Jarvis**
12  **PRINCESS CARLY**, 4, b f Swiss Spirit—Amary (IRE)  **Rockingham Reins Limited**
13  **RODNEY LE ROC**, 4, b g Garswood—French Accent  **TMS & Beckett**
14  **TEBAY (IRE)**, 6, b g Elzaam (AUS)—Maid of Ale (IRE)  **Mr J. R. Best**
15  **TIPPERARY JACK (USA)**, 5, b g Violence (USA)—Indian Miss (USA)  **Curtis & Tomkins**
16  **TORBELLINO**, 5, b m Maxios—Tiny Smile (IRE)  **Ballantine Curtis Jenkins & Malt**
17  **TOROCHICA**, 5, ch m Toronado (IRE)—Biased  **Mr M. Admans**
18  **TREGURRIAN**, 4, ch g Equiano (FR)—Hvasavi (IRE)  **Mr H J Jarvis & Mrs P Jarvis**

### THREE-YEAR-OLDS

19  B gr g Outstrip—French Accent  **Mr M. Admans**
20  B f Style Vendome (FR)—Louya (IRE)
21  B f Garswood—Princess Spirit
22  **SANTIBURI SPIRIT**, gr ro f Outstrip—Santiburi Spring  **Hill Paine & Partners**

### TWO-YEAR-OLDS

23  **DOERR MARQUIS (IRE)**, b f 25/03 Kodiac—Rose of Africa (IRE) (Cape Cross (IRE)) (13000)  **Mr M. Admans**
24  Gr c 19/03 Lethal Force (IRE)—Elounta (Dubawi (IRE))
25  B c 14/04 Mayson—Ruby Wednesday (Mullionmileanhour (IRE))

**Other Owners:** Mr P. I. Beckett, Mr J. R. Best, H. J. Jarvis, Mrs P. Jarvis, Mr J. Miller, Miss H. J. Williams.

**Assistant Trainer:** Michelle Brister.

---

**35**

### MRS SUZI BEST, Lewes
Postal: **The Bungalow, Grandstand Stables, The Old Racecourse, Lewes, East Sussex, BN7 1UR**
Contacts: **MOBILE 07804 487296**
EMAIL sbestracing@yahoo.com

1  **BASHFUL BOY (IRE)**, 5, b g Magician (IRE)—Bacheliere (USA)  **Milldean Racing Syndicate**
2  **CORRIE LAKE (IRE)**, 8, ch m Stowaway—Corrie Hall (IRE)  **Miss F. O'Sullivan**
3  **DEREK DUVAL (USA)**, 7, b g Lope de Vega (IRE)—Lady Raj (USA)  **C. & Leon Best**

## MRS SUZI BEST - continued

4 **EVENTFUL**, 4, b f Oasis Dream—Spectacle **Guy Dunphy, Chris Dillon, Mr C Seeney**
5 **GLOBAL WONDER (IRE)**, 6, b g Kodiac—Traveller's Tales **The Global Wonder Partnership**
6 **GOOD TIME AHEAD (IRE)**, 7, b g Iffraaj—Good Time Sue (IRE) **Mark & Guy Dunphy**
7 **GRANDEE (IRE)**, 7, b g Lope de Vega (IRE)—Caravan of Dreams (IRE) **B Hepburn, A C Dillon**
8 **GRANGECLARE NORTH (IRE)**, 4, ch f Presenting—Hayabusa **Mr M. J. Benton**
9 **MAJOR REWARD (IRE)**, 5, b g Dawn Approach (IRE)—
                                    Zanzibar Girl (USA) **Guy Dunphy, Chris Dillon, Mr C Seeney**
10 **MATEWAN (IRE)**, 6, b g Epaulette (AUS)—Cochin (USA) **The Tuesday Syndicate & Roy David**
11 **NAUTICAL HAVEN**, 7, b g Harbour Watch (IRE)—Mania (IRE) **Mr Chris Dillon & Mr D G Edmonston**
12 **OFFICER DRIVEL (IRE)**, 10, b g Captain Rio—Spiritville (IRE) **John Collins & Cheam Marketing Consultan**
13 **POUR ME A DRINK**, 5, ch g Nathaniel (IRE)—Euroceleb (IRE) **Mr A. R. Coupland**
14 **PROMISES (IRE)**, 4, b f Bated Breath—Symposia **Milan Racing Club**
15 **RED CHARMER (IRE)**, 11, b g Red Clubs (IRE)—Golden Charm (IRE) **Cheam Marketing & Jim Smith**
16 **RETURNING GLORY**, 6, b g Exceed And Excel (AUS)—Tanzania (USA) **F. A. O'Sullivan & John Collins**
17 **SHOW OF FORCE**, 6, gr m Lethal Force (IRE)—Craighall **Mr A. R. Coupland**
18 **SIX GUN SERENADE (IRE)**, 10, b g Kalanisi (IRE)—Zenaide (IRE) **Mr J. J. Callaghan**
19 **THE TRAMPOLINIST (IRE)**, 6, b m Flemensfirth (USA)—D'Gigi **Mr M. J. Benton**
20 **WELLS GLORY (IRE)**, 5, b g Fame And Glory—Annas Theatre **Milldean Racing Syndicate**

**Other Owners:** Mr M. J. Benton, Mr L. Best, Cheam Marketing Consultants Limited, Mr J. Collins, Mr R. David, Mr C. J. Dillon, Mr G. Dunphy, Mr D. Edmonston, Mr B. Hepburn, Mr N. Mandry, Miss F. O'Sullivan, Mr C. A. Seeney, Mr J. D. A. Smith, The Tuesday Syndicate and Michael Watt, M. H. Watt.

**Assistant Trainer:** Mr Tom Best.

---

**36**   **MR EDWARD BETHELL, Middleham**
Postal: **Thorngill House, Middleham, Leyburn, Yorkshire, DL8 4TJ**
Contacts: **PHONE** 07767 622921
**EMAIL** edward@bethellracing.co.uk

1 **ARTISTIC RIFLES (IRE)**, 5, b g War Command (USA)—Chatham Islands (USA) **Zaro Srl**
2 **BRIARDALE (IRE)**, 9, b g Arcano—Marine City (JPN) **J. Carrick&Clarendon Thoroughbred Racing**
3 **EAGLE'S FOOT (IRE)**, 4, b g Free Eagle (IRE)—Carmens Fate **The Eagle's Foot Syndicate**
4 , Ch f Archipenko (USA)—Fittonia (FR)
5 **IDOAPOLOGISE (IRE)**, 4, b g Havana Gold (IRE)—Shiba (FR) **Clarendon Thoroughbred Racing**
6 **MOSS GILL (IRE)**, 5, b g No Nay Never (USA)—Sharaarah (IRE) **G Van Cutsem, J & S Bethell**
7 **MUDAWWAN (IRE)**, 7, b g Invincible Spirit (IRE)—Louve Sacree (USA) **Clarendon Thoroughbred Racing**
8 **STOCKBRIDGE TAP**, 4, ch g Nayef (USA)—Last Supper **R. F. Gibbons**
9 **STRAWBERRYANDCREAM**, 6, ch m Cityscape—Miss Apricot **Mrs S. Bethell**
10 **ULSHAW BRIDGE (IRE)**, 6, b g High Chaparral (IRE)—Sharaarah (IRE) **J. Carrick&Clarendon Thoroughbred Racing**
11 **ZEIMAAM (IRE)**, 4, ch g Slade Power (IRE)—Jathaabeh **Mr M. J. Dawson**

### THREE-YEAR-OLDS

12 **BLU BOY (IRE)**, b g Muhaarar—Ventura Mist **Mr J. E. Lund**
13 **DANIEL (IRE)**, b g Nathaniel (IRE)—Liel
14 **EXALTED LEADER**, b g Acclamation—Authoritarian **Geoffrey van Cutsem & Partners**
15 **FLIQUET**, b f Outstrip—True Pleasure (IRE) **Clarendon Thoroughbred Racing**
16 **GAERWEN**, b g Muhaarar—Royal Eloquence (IRE) **Mr J. A. Tabet**
17 **GAINSBOURG**, b c Sixties Icon—Aromatherapy
18 **GRANTLEY (IRE)**, b g Charm Spirit (IRE)—Peig (IRE) **Clarendon Thoroughbred Racing**
19 **GUSTAV GRAVES**, b c Bobby's Kitten (USA)—Bondesire **Mr & Mrs G. Turnbull**
20 **RICH DREAM (IRE)**, b g Make Believe—Poppet's Lovein **The Vickers & Clark Racing Partnership**
21 **ST CLEMENT**, ch g Cityscape—Miss Apricot **Clarendon Thoroughbred Racing**
22 **THE QUEENS LADIES**, b f Heeraat (IRE)—Blades Princess **NE1 Racing Club**

## MR EDWARD BETHELL - continued

### TWO-YEAR-OLDS

**23 CHICANERY,** b f 17/01 Aclaim (IRE)—Feint (Teofilo (IRE)) (5000) **P. G. Jacobs**
**24 CHILLINGHAM (IRE),** b c 24/02 Ulysses (IRE)—
Last Jewel (IRE) (Invincible Spirit (IRE)) (40000) **Mr J. Carrick, J & S Taylor**
**25 EXMINSTER (IRE),** b c 24/04 Ribchester (IRE)—
Surface of Earth (USA) (Empire Maker (USA)) (20952) **Clarendon Thoroughbred Racing**
**26 FEARBY (IRE),** b c 09/02 Havana Gold (IRE)—
Coolminx (IRE) (One Cool Cat (USA)) (21000) **Clarendon Thoroughbred Racing**
**27** Ch f 19/04 Garswood—Highleaf (Pivotal) **Mr D. W. Armstrong**
**28 KHURUMBI (IRE),** b f 12/03 The Gurkha (IRE)—
Sharaarah (IRE) (Oasis Dream) (23810) **Geoffrey van Cutsem & Partners**
**29 RICH KING,** b c 11/03 Gleneagles (IRE)—Hairspray (Bahamian Bounty) (45000) **Vickers Racing**
**30 THEWAYTOTHESTARS,** b f 29/01 Due Diligence (USA)—Last Supper (Echo of Light) (762) **R. F. Gibbons**
**31** Ch f 03/04 Garswood—Winter's Night (IRE) (Night Shift (USA)) **Mr D. W. Armstrong**
**32 YOUNG WINSTON,** b c 14/02 Churchill (IRE)—Come With Me (Dansili) (32000) **Geoffrey van Cutsem & Partners**

**Other Owners:** Mrs S. Bethell, Mr J. Carrick, Mr W. Carson, Clarendon Thoroughbred Racing, Mr M. Clark, Hototrot Racing, Mr S. Taylor, Mr D. Y. Vickers, R. T. Vickers, Mr Julian Wilson, Mr Christopher Wright.

---

**37** **MR WILLIAM BETHELL, Arnold**
Postal: **Arnold Manor, Arnold, Hull, North Humberside, HU11 5JA**
Contacts: **PHONE 01964 562996**
**EMAIL wabethell@btinternet.com**

1 **DHARAN (FR),** 8, b g Slickly Royal (FR)—Kelle Home (FR) **W. A. Bethell**
2 **FITSAOHA (FR),** 6, b m Barastraight—Kelle Home (FR) **W. A. Bethell**
3 **GALIDERMES (FR),** 4, b g Hunter's Light (IRE)—Angie Eria (FR) **W. A. Bethell**
4 **ISLE OF WOLVES,** 5, b g Nathaniel (IRE)—L'Ile Aux Loups (IRE) **W. A. Bethell**
5 **LOPES DANCER (IRE),** 9, b g Lope de Vega (IRE)—Ballet Dancer (IRE) **W. A. Bethell**
6 **MIAMI PRESENT (IRE),** 11, b br g Presenting—Miami Nights (GER) **W. A. Bethell**
7 **NEWBERRY NEW (IRE),** 9, b g Kodiac—Sunblush (UAE) **W. A. Bethell**
8 **STEEL HELMET (IRE),** 7, ch g Helmet (AUS)—Marine City (JPN) **W. A. Bethell**

---

**38** **MR ROBERT BEVIS, Duckington**
Postal: **The White House, Old Coach Road, Duckington, Cheshire, SY14 8LH**
**EMAIL robertjbevis66@aol.com**

1 **ACH CAPTAIN (IRE),** 8, b g Milan—Quinnsboro Ice (IRE) **R. J. Bevis**
2 **DANILO D'AIRY (FR),** 8, ch g Anzillero (GER)—Monita d'Airy (FR) **R. J. Bevis**
3 **SARTENE'S SON (FR),** 8, ch g Linda's Lad—Sartene (FR) **R. J. Bevis**
4 **TURNING GOLD,** 7, ch g Pivotal—Illusion **R. J. Bevis**
5 **UNBLINKING,** 8, b g Cacique (IRE)—Deliberate **R. Bevis**

## 39 MR GEORGE BEWLEY, Appleby-In-Westmorland
Postal: Jerusalem Farm, Colby, Appleby-In-Westmorland, Cumbria, CA16 6BB
Contacts: PHONE 017683 53003 MOBILE 07704 924783
EMAIL bewleyracing@outlook.com WEBSITE www.georgebewleyracing.co.uk

1 ARTICLE FIFTY (IRE), 8, b g Doyen (IRE)—Annie Go (IRE) Jgs,Richardson, Davidson & Mandle
2 BACKPACKER (IRE), 6, ch g Tobougg (IRE)—Oscars Vision (IRE) J. Wade
3 BASK IN THE GLORY (IRE), 8, ch g Beneficial—Shamrock Miss (IRE) Mr D H & E Montgomerie
4 BREAKING THE ICE (IRE), 6, b g Frozen Power (IRE)—Specific (IRE) Mr R Fisher & Bewley
5 CLONDAW FIXER (IRE), 9, b g Court Cave (IRE)—The Millers Tale (IRE) Mrs C. J. Todd
6 5, B g Black Sam Bellamy (IRE)—Dutch Star G. T. Bewley
7 FAMOUS RESPONSE (IRE), 7, b g Fame And Glory (IRE)—Any Response (IRE) G. T. Bewley
8 INNIS SHANNON (IRE), 11, br m Stowaway—Put On Hold (IRE) Mrs Lesley Bewley & Mr John Gibson
9 KENNEDYS FIELD, 8, b g Multiplex—Supreme Lady (IRE) Victoria Bewley & Lizzy Annett
10 MAH MATE BOB (IRE), 9, b g Mahler—Bobset Leader (IRE) J. Wade
11 MINNIMO, 6, ch g Motivator—Alessandra Mrs E. Annett
12 OUR MORRIS (IRE), 10, b g Milan—Broken Gale (IRE) Mr R Fisher & Bewley
13 PASS RUSHER (IRE), 6, b g Doyen (IRE)—Coolrush (IRE) Mr A. Udale
14 RAISE YOUR HAND (IRE), 6, br g Imperial Monarch (IRE)—Midnight Dasie (IRE) Mrs E. Annett
15 4, Ch g Getaway (GER)—Rathleek Mr A. Udale
16 RUSSELL'S QUARTER (IRE), 6, b g Imperial Monarch (IRE)—Native Bev (IRE) Southdean Racing Club
17 SAVOY COURT (IRE), 5, b g Robin des Champs (IRE)—North Star Poly (IRE) Eales, Brown & Lloyd
18 WAR AT SEA (IRE), 7, gr g Mastercraftsman (IRE)—Swirling (IRE) Mrs Lesley Bewley & Mr John Gibson

Other Owners: Mrs E. Annett, Mr S. J. Baird, G. T. Bewley, Mrs L. Bewley, Miss V. F. Bewley, Mr E. R. Brown, Mr L. J. Davidson, Mr K. F. Eales, Mr R. A. Fisher, Mr J. H. Gibson, Mr J. H. Graham, Mrs J. Lloyd, Mrs R. J. Mandle, D. H. Montgomerie, Mrs E. Montgomerie, Mr W. Richardson.

NH Jockey: Jonathon Bewley, Colm McCormack, Craig Nichol.

## 40 MR SAEED BIN SUROOR, Newmarket
Postal: Godolphin Office, Snailwell Road, Newmarket, Suffolk, CB8 7YE
Contacts: PHONE 01638 569956
WEBSITE www.godolphin.com

1 ARABIAN WARRIOR, 4, b g Dubawi (IRE)—Siyaadah
2 ARABIC CHARM (IRE), 4, b f Exceed And Excel (AUS)—Fond Words (IRE)
3 BASIC BEAUTY, 4, ch f Dubawi (IRE)—West Wind
4 BEAUTIFUL SCENERY (IRE), 4, b f Shamardal (USA)—Mont Etoile (IRE)
5 BEDOUIN'S STORY, 6, b g Farhh—Time Crystal (IRE)
6 BENBATL, 7, b h Dubawi (IRE)—Nahrain
7 BIG MEETING (IRE), 4, b br g Shamardal (USA)—Beta
8 BIG TEAM (USA), 4, b br c Speightstown (USA)—Kotuku
9 BIN BATTUTA, 7, ch g Dubawi (IRE)—Land of Dreams
10 BRIGHT START (USA), 4, b br g Medaglia d'Oro (USA)—Blue Petrel (USA)
11 BRILLIANT LIGHT, 4, b g Sea The Stars (IRE)—Flame of Gibraltar (IRE)
12 CITY WALK (IRE), 4, b c Brazen Beau (AUS)—My Lucky Liz (IRE)
13 COLOUR IMAGE (IRE), 4, b g Kodiac—Chroussa (IRE)
14 DEEP SNOW, 4, b f Bated Breath—Polar Circle (USA)
15 DESERT FIRE (IRE), 6, b g Cape Cross (IRE)—Crystal House (CHI)
16 DISCOVER DUBAI (IRE), 4, b c Teofilo (IRE)—Emboss (IRE)
17 DREAM CASTLE, 7, b g Frankel—Sand Vixen
18 DUBAI FUTURE, 5, b g Dubawi (IRE)—Anjaz (USA)
19 DUBAI HORIZON (IRE), 7, b g Poet's Voice—Chibola (ARG)
20 DUBAI ICON, 5, b g New Approach (IRE)—Arabian Beauty (IRE)
21 DUBAI LEGACY (USA), 5, b g Discreet Cat (USA)—Afsana (USA)

## MR SAEED BIN SUROOR - continued

22 **DUBAI LOVE**, 4, b f Night of Thunder (IRE)—Devotion (IRE)
23 **DUBAI MIRAGE (IRE)**, 4, ch g Dubawi (IRE)—Calipatria
24 **DUBAI SOUQ (IRE)**, 4, b g Dubawi (IRE)—Balsamine (USA)
25 **DUBAI TRADITION (USA)**, 5, b g Medaglia d'Oro (USA)—Wavering (IRE)
26 **DUBAI WELCOME**, 4, gr ro g Dubawi (IRE)—Emily Bronte
27 **ELECTRICAL STORM**, 4, b g Dubawi (IRE)—Mujarah (IRE)
28 **FESTIVAL OF COLOUR (IRE)**, 4, b g Kodiac—Redmaven (IRE)
29 **FINAL SONG (IRE)**, 4, b f Dark Angel (IRE)—Rahiyah (USA)
30 **FINAL STORY (USA)**, 4, b c Into Mischief (USA)—Katherine'skadence (USA)
31 **FIRST SNOWFALL**, 4, b f Dubawi (IRE)—Flying Cloud (IRE)
32 **FIRST VIEW (IRE)**, 4, b g Exceed And Excel (AUS)—Love Charm
33 **FUTURE KING (IRE)**, 4, b c Dark Angel (IRE)—Relation Alexander (IRE)
34 **GHALY**, 5, ch g Dubawi (IRE)—Hanky Panky (IRE)
35 **GIFTS OF GOLD (IRE)**, 6, b g Invincible Spirit (IRE)—Sanna Bay (IRE)
36 **GLOBAL HEAT (IRE)**, 5, b g Toronado (IRE)—Raskutani
37 **GLOBAL HUNTER (IRE)**, 5, b h Kodiac—Romie's Kastett (GER)
38 **GLOBAL WALK (IRE)**, 4, b g Society Rock (IRE)—Shehila (IRE)
39 **HIGH END**, 7, b br g Dubawi (IRE)—Crystal Music (USA)
40 **LAND OF LEGENDS (IRE)**, 5, b g Iffraaj—Homily
41 **LASER SHOW (IRE)**, 4, ch g New Approach (IRE)—Entertains (AUS)
42 **LAST LOOK (IRE)**, 5, b m Pivotal—Gonbarda (GER)
43 **LIGHT AND DARK**, 5, b g Shamardal (USA)—Colour (AUS)
44 **LIVE YOUR DREAM (IRE)**, 4, b g Iffraaj—Dream Book
45 **LONG TRADITION (IRE)**, 4, b c Shamardal (USA)—Irish History (IRE)
46 **LOST IN TIME**, 4, b g Dubawi (IRE)—Reunite (IRE)
47 **MAJOR PARTNERSHIP (IRE)**, 6, gr g Iffraaj—Roystonea
48 **MILITARY MARCH**, 4, b c New Approach (IRE)—Punctilious
49 **MOUNTAIN HUNTER (USA)**, 7, b g Lonhro (AUS)—Tamarillo
50 **MOVING LIGHT (IRE)**, 4, ch c Night of Thunder (IRE)—North East Bay (USA)
51 **MUTAFAWWIG**, 5, b h Oasis Dream—Reunite (IRE)
52 **NIGHT HUNTER (USA)**, 4, gr c Tapit (USA)—Wickedly Wise (USA)
53 **PASSION AND GLORY (IRE)**, 5, b g Cape Cross (IRE)—Potent Embrace (USA)
54 **PERFECT WINTER (IRE)**, 5, b m Invincible Spirit (IRE)—Heartily (IRE)
55 **PIECE OF HISTORY (IRE)**, 6, b g Iffraaj—Moonlife (IRE)
56 **QUIET EVENING (IRE)**, 4, b f Teofilo (IRE)—Prussian
57 **RAAEB (IRE)**, 4, ch c Raven's Pass (USA)—Kalaatah (USA)
58 **REAL WORLD (IRE)**, 4, b c Dark Angel (IRE)—Nafura
59 **ROYAL MARINE (IRE)**, 5, b g Raven's Pass (USA)—Inner Secret (USA)
60 **ROYAL PARTNERSHIP**, 4, b g Shamardal (USA)—Adoringly (IRE)
61 **SECRET MOMENT (IRE)**, 4, b g Exceed And Excel (AUS)—Devotee (USA)
62 **SHINING EXAMPLE (IRE)**, 4, b c Shamardal (USA)—Kailani
63 **SILENT ESCAPE (IRE)**, 4, ch f New Approach (IRE)—Rosewater (IRE)
64 **SILENT HUNTER**, 5, b h Dutch Art—Yellow Rosebud (IRE)
65 **SILVER LINE (IRE)**, 7, gr g Dark Angel (IRE)—Admire The View (IRE)
66 **STUNNING BEAUTY (IRE)**, 4, ch f Shamardal (USA)—Short Skirt
67 **TOMOUH (IRE)**, 4, b f Dubawi (IRE)—Sundrop (JPN)
68 **UNTOLD STORY (IRE)**, 4, ch c Teofilo (IRE)—Tanzania (USA)
69 **VOLCANIC SKY**, 6, b g Street Cry (IRE)—Short Skirt
70 **WARNING SHOT (IRE)**, 4, ch g Exceed And Excel (AUS)—Margravine (USA)
71 **WHITE MOONLIGHT (USA)**, 4, b f Medaglia d'Oro (USA)—Fitful Skies (IRE)

### THREE-YEAR-OLDS

72 **ALKHATTAAF**, b c Mukhadram—Rewaaya (IRE)
73 **BRIGHT MOONLIGHT (IRE)**, ch f Night of Thunder (IRE)—Utrecht
74 **CHIEF OF STAFF**, b c Dark Angel (IRE)—Patroness
75 **DUBAI HOPE (IRE)**, b br f Invincible Spirit (IRE)—City Glam (ARG)
76 **DUBAI LADY (IRE)**, b f Invincible Spirit (IRE)—Long Lashes (USA)
77 **DUBAI TREASURE (IRE)**, b f Sea The Stars (IRE)—Measured Tempo
78 **FINAL THOUGHT (IRE)**, b f Sea The Stars (IRE)—Anjaz (USA)

## MR SAEED BIN SUROOR - continued

79 **FIRST SMILE (IRE)**, gr f Dark Angel (IRE)—Jealous Again (USA)
80 **FROZEN PATH**, ch c Dubawi (IRE)—Flying Cloud (IRE)
81 **GOLD WING**, b f Golden Horn—Aviacion (BRZ)
82 **GREAT HUNTER (IRE)**, gr c Dark Angel (IRE)—Floristry
83 **GREAT NEWS**, gr c Shamardal (USA)—Nahoodh (IRE)
84 **KARUOKA**, br f Awtaad (IRE)—Dubai Fashion (IRE)
85 **LAST LIGHT (IRE)**, b g Teofilo (IRE)—Lea Valley
86 **LAST SUNSET (IRE)**, b br f Teofilo (IRE)—Dufay (IRE)
87 **LINE OF ATTACK**, b c Dawn Approach (IRE)—Huma Bird
88 **LONE FIGHTER (IRE)**, b c Dawn Approach (IRE)—Pulcinella (IRE)
89 **LOST GOLD (IRE)**, b br c Dark Angel (IRE)—Windsor County (USA)
90 **LUBNA**, b f Mustajeeb—Muwakleh
91 **MARCHING ARMY**, ch c Iffraaj—Show Day (IRE)
92 **MASQOOL (IRE)**, br c Invincible Spirit (IRE)—Eshaadeh (USA)
93 **MOMENT OF BEAUTY**, b f Teofilo (IRE)—Praia
94 **MOTATAABEQ (IRE)**, b c Kodiac—Jabhaat (USA)
95 **MUSIC WRITER (IRE)**, b c Belardo (IRE)—Music Chart (USA)
96 **NAJM KABIR (IRE)**, ch c Pivotal—Hush Money (CHI)
97 **NATION'S HISTORY (IRE)**, gr g Dark Angel (IRE)—Raphinae
98 **NATURAL COLOUR**, b f Exceed And Excel (AUS)—Safiyna (FR)
99 **OPENING SCENE**, b f Territories (IRE)—Beautiful Ending
100 **PERFECT BALANCE (IRE)**, b c Invincible Spirit (IRE)—Winter Queen
101 **RAAJIL (IRE)**, br c Awtaad (IRE)—Qaadira (USA)
102 **ROYAL INVITATION**, ch c New Approach (IRE)—Nadia
103 **SHINING BLUE (IRE)**, b c Exceed And Excel (AUS)—Braided (USA)
104 **SMART START (IRE)**, b c Teofilo (IRE)—Haughtily (IRE)
105 **SOFT WHISPER (IRE)**, b f Dubawi (IRE)—Placidia (IRE)
106 **SOLDIER'S SECRET (IRE)**, ch c Fast Company (IRE)—Beautiful Forest
107 **STEADY HAND (IRE)**, br c Golden Horn—Silk Words
108 **STORM DAMAGE**, b c Night of Thunder (IRE)—Sundrop (JPN)
109 **STORM FRONT**, ch c Helmet (AUS)—Vituisa
110 **SYMPHONY SOUND (IRE)**, b f Shamardal (USA)—Country Music
111 **WARM SMILE**, ch f New Approach (IRE)—Adoringly (IRE)
112 **WILD HURRICANE (IRE)**, b c Dubawi (IRE)—Wavering (IRE)
113 **WILD RHYTHM (IRE)**, ch c Dubawi (IRE)—Mandinga (BRZ)

## TWO-YEAR-OLDS

114 B br c 20/03 Iffraaj—Adoringly (IRE) (Dubawi (IRE))
115 Ch c 18/02 Giant's Causeway (USA)—Almusafa (USA) (Haafhd)
116 B c 19/04 Frankel—Antara (GER) (Platini (GER))
117 B f 17/02 Invincible Spirit (IRE)—Beautiful Forest (Nayef (USA))
118 B c 25/03 Profitable (IRE)—Betimes (New Approach (IRE))
119 B f 10/02 Teofilo (IRE)—Blue Illusion (Dubawi (IRE))
120 Ch f 18/04 Teofilo (IRE)—Bluefire (Distorted Humor (USA))
121 Br c 18/02 Cable Bay (IRE)—Bonhomie (Shamardal (USA)) (150000)
122 Ch f 17/02 Profitable (IRE)—Calipatria (Shamardal (USA))
123 B f 21/04 Invincible Spirit (IRE)—Country Music (Street Cry (IRE))
124 B c 09/04 Awtaad (IRE)—Elraazy (Dubawi (IRE))
125 Ch c 01/02 New Bay (FR)—Ever Love (BRZ) (Nedawi) (180000)
126 Ch c 20/04 Ribchester (IRE)—Farthing (IRE) (Mujadil (USA)) (125000)
127 B f 15/03 The Gurkha (IRE)—First Blush (IRE) (Pivotal)
128 Ch c 01/03 Iffraaj—Forte (New Approach (IRE)) (52000)
129 Ch f 15/05 Ribchester (IRE)—Kalaatah (USA) (Dynaformer (USA))
130 B f 15/04 Dark Angel (IRE)—Karenine (High Chaparral (IRE))
131 B c 22/04 Invincible Spirit (IRE)—Long Lashes (USA) (Rock Hard Ten (USA))
132 B c 07/04 Iffraaj—Manaboo (Hard Spun (USA))
133 B f 22/04 Iffraaj—Mar Mar (IRE) (Invincible Spirit (IRE))
134 B f 26/04 Dubawi (IRE)—Mise En Rose (USA) (War Front (USA))
135 B c 04/03 Postponed (IRE)—Moonlife (IRE) (Invincible Spirit (IRE))

## MR SAEED BIN SUROOR - continued

**136** Ch c 27/01 Exceed And Excel (AUS)—My Call (Shamardal (USA))
**137** B c 08/04 Profitable (IRE)—Nafura (Dubawi (IRE))
**138** B c 03/02 Fast Company (IRE)—Patent Joy (IRE) (Pivotal)
**139** B c 17/05 Invincible Spirit (IRE)—Qaadira (USA) (Mr Greeley (USA))
**140** B c 20/04 Tamayuz—Shaarfa (USA) (Dynaformer (USA))
**141** B f 07/04 Teofilo (IRE)—Snow Powder (IRE) (Raven's Pass (USA))
**142** B f 10/05 Teofilo (IRE)—Snow Rose (USA) (Elusive Quality (USA))
**143** B c 21/04 Postponed (IRE)—Sundrop (JPN) (Sunday Silence (USA))
**144** B br c 03/03 Kitten's Joy (USA)—Tafaneen (USA) (Dynaformer (USA))
**145** B f 01/03 Teofilo (IRE)—Trieste (Dubawi (IRE))
**146** B f 25/01 Mehmas (IRE)—Turuqaat (Fantastic Light (USA)) (180000)
**147** B c 19/02 Starspangledbanner (AUS)—Violet's Gift (IRE) (Cadeaux Genereux) (360000)
**148** Ch c 27/02 Iffraaj—Voice of Truth (USA) (Dubawi (IRE))
**149** B f 06/05 Night of Thunder (IRE)—Wedding March (IRE) (Dalakhani (IRE))

**Assistant Trainer:** Anthony Paul Howarth.

---

### MRS EMMA-JANE BISHOP, Cheltenham
Postal: **Brockhill, Naunton, Cheltenham, Gloucestershire, GL54 3BA**
Contacts: **MOBILE 07887 845970 FAX 01451 850199**
EMAIL emmabishopracing@hotmail.com WEBSITE www.emmabishopracing.com

**1 ANOTHER GLANCE**, 5, br m Passing Glance—Roberta Back (IRE)  **Mrs J. Arnold**
**2 ARQUEBUSIER (FR)**, 11, br g Discover d'Auteuil (FR)—Djurjura (FR)  **Mr R. Foulquies**
**3 BAJARDO (IRE)**, 13, b g Jammaal—Bit of Peace (IRE)  **Mrs J. Arnold**
**4 GLANCE BACK**, 5, b g Passing Glance—Roberta Back (IRE)  **Select Racing Club & Mrs M J Arnold**
**5 LUMINATION**, 5, b g Toronado (IRE)—Sparkling Eyes  **Manton Park Racing**
**6 MACKSVILLE (IRE)**, 8, gr g Mastercraftsman (IRE)—Fairest of All (IRE)  **Mrs J. Arnold**
**7 MASTER MALCOLM**, 4, ch g Mastercraftsman (IRE)—Desert Sage  **Mrs C. Richmond-Watson**
**8 MAX DYNAMO**, 11, b g Midnight Legend—Vivante (IRE)  **Mrs M. J. Wilson**
**9 MIDNIGHT TROUBLE**, 9, b g Midnight Legend—Friendly Request  **Mrs J. Organ**
**10 PAST MASTER**, 8, gr g Mastercraftsman (IRE)—Millestan (IRE)  **Mrs E. J. Bishop**
**11 SHEEZA LEGEND**, 7, b m Midnight Legend—Roberta Back (IRE)  **Emma Bishop Racing Club**
**12 STAAR (IRE)**, 7, b g Sea The Stars (IRE)—Bitooh  **Mrs J. Arnold**
**13 THEOULE (FR)**, 5, b br g Le Havre (IRE)—Santa Louisia  **Manton Park Racing**

**Other Owners:** Mrs J. Arnold, The Select Racing Club Limited.

---

### MR FRANK BISHOP, Kidderminster
Postal: **Parkside, Blakeshall, Wolverley, Kidderminster, Worcestershire, DY11 5XW**
Contacts: **MOBILE 07900 407647**

**1 AFRICAN QUEST**, 7, b m Air Quest—Pursuit of Purpose  **Mr M. R. Baldry**
**2 CHANDON ELYSEES**, 8, b m Champs Elysees—Upstream  **Mr M. R. Baldry**
**3 DIAMONDS DREAM**, 4, b f Captain Gerrard (IRE)—Blakeshall Diamond  **Mr F. A. Bishop**
**4 HURRICANE ALERT**, 9, b g Showcasing—Raggle Taggle (IRE)  **Mr M. R. Baldry**
**5 LADYGERRARD**, 4, b f Captain Gerrard (IRE)—Sarlat  **Mr M. P. Bishop**
**6** 4, B g Mazameer (IRE)—Porthwidden Beach (USA)  **Mr M. R. Baldry**
**7 WILLSY**, 8, b g Sakhee's Secret—Blakeshall Rose  **Mr F. A. Bishop**

## MR FRANK BISHOP - continued

### THREE-YEAR-OLDS

**8** MARGARETS MEMORY, ch f Mazameer (IRE)—Old Peg  **Mr F. A. Bishop**

### TWO-YEAR-OLDS

**9** B f 04/05 Equiano (FR)—Broughtons Charm (IRE) (Invincible Spirit (IRE)) (800)  **Mr F. A. Bishop**
**10** B c 16/05 Garswood—Miss Toldyaso (IRE) (Barathea (IRE)) (1500)  **Mr F. A. Bishop**
**11** B c 10/04 Epaulette (AUS)—Twilight Belle (IRE) (Fasliyev (USA)) (2000)  **Mr F. A. Bishop**

**Assistant Trainer:** Mr Martin Bishop.

---

**43**    **MR KEVIN BISHOP, Bridgwater**
Postal: **Barford Park Stables, Spaxton, Bridgwater, Somerset, TA5 1AF**
Contacts: **PHONE 01278 671437 MOBILE 07816 837610**
**EMAIL** hevbishop@hotmail.com

**1** ALBERTS MONARCH (IRE), 6, b g Imperial Monarch (IRE)—Baby Goose (IRE)  **Mr B. V. Lund**
**2** BIG DATA (IRE), 7, br g Oscar (IRE)—Nolagh Supreme (IRE)  **Familia Venari Syndicate**
**3** CHAMPAGNE VINTAGE (IRE), 8, b g Stowaway—Ask My Granny (IRE)  **Barry Silkman & Gary Pascoe**
**4** CHANKAYA, 4, ch g Dubawi (IRE)—Splashdown  **Barry Silkman & Gary Pascoe**
**5** FLOW WITH EVE, 12, b m With The Flow (USA)—Vercheny  **Michael & Will Potter**
**6** HANAFY (USA), 4, ch g Animal Kingdom (USA)—Uroobah (USA)  **Barry Silkman & Gary Pascoe**
**7** HANDFUL OF GOLD (IRE), 4, ch f No Nay Never (USA)—Golden Passion (IRE)  **Mr B. V. Lund**
**8** JUST GO FOR IT, 8, b m Passing Glance—Just Jasmine  **Mr S. G. Atkinson**
**9** LETS GO DUTCHESS, 11, b m Helissio (FR)—Lets Go Dutch  **K. Bishop**
**10** OWENRIFF ANNA (IRE), 6, gr m Tikkanen (USA)—La Cyborg (FR)  **Mr B. V. Lund**
**11** OWENRIFF PEARL (IRE), 6, b br m Stowaway—Tizzy Frizzy  **Mr B. V. Lund**
**12** PRECIOUS GROUND, 11, b g Helissio (FR)—Wild Ground (IRE)  **Mr K. Jones**
**13** RAAJIHAH, 4, ch f Tamayuz—Muthabara (USA)  **Mrs C. E. Peck**
**14** ROSSERK ABBEY (IRE), 8, ch g Fruits of Love (USA)—Here Comes Alli (IRE)  **Mr B. V. Lund**
**15** 4, Ch c Tamayuz—Shaddeya (IRE)  **Mr B. V. Lund**
**16** SOMERSET JEM, 12, b g Sir Harry Lewis (USA)—Monger Lane  **Slabs & Lucan**
**17** THE GREAT RAYMONDO, 9, b g Passing Glance—Fantasy Parkes  **Slabs & Lucan**
**18** THESTOPPERDUNNE (IRE), 8, b g Craigsteel—Island Heron (IRE)  **Mr B. V. Lund**

### TWO-YEAR-OLDS

**19** Gr f 07/02 El Kabeir (USA)—Purple Velvet (IRE) (Dark Angel (IRE))  **Mr B. V. Lund**
**20** B f 30/05 Buratino (IRE)—Square Pants (USA) (King of Kings (IRE))  **Mr B. V. Lund**

**Other Owners:** G. J. Pascoe, B. Silkman.

**Assistant Trainer:** Heather Bishop.

**Amateur Jockey:** Mr Conor Smith.

---

**44**    **MISS LINDA BLACKFORD, Tiverton**
Postal: **Shortlane Stables, Rackenford, Tiverton, Devon, EX16 8EH**
Contacts: **PHONE 01884 881589 MOBILE 07887 947832**
**EMAIL** overthelast@outlook.com **WEBSITE** www.overthelast.com

**1** ACROSS THE PARK (IRE), 7, b g Presenting—Miss Baresi (IRE)  **Easylife Partnership**
**2** ALKADEMON (IRE), 7, br g Alkaadhem—Cats Concert (IRE)  **Over The Last Racing**
**3** LAWSONS THORNS (IRE), 12, b g Presenting—Ardnurcher (IRE)  **Mr N. Mackenzie**

## MISS LINDA BLACKFORD - continued

4 **LURE DES PRES (IRE)**, 9, b g Robin des Pres (FR)—Pinkeen Lady (IRE)  **Mr M. J. Vanstone**
5 **MONARCH O THE GLEN (IRE)**, 6, b g Imperial Monarch (IRE)—Good Thyne Lisa (IRE)  **Over The Last Racing**
6 **POET'S REFLECTION (IRE)**, 6, b m Dylan Thomas (IRE)—
Lola's Reflection  **Mr D. Cocks & Mrs S. Livesey-van Dorst**
7 **STEEL EXPRESS (IRE)**, 9, b g Craigsteel—Assidua (IRE)  **Nerves of Steel Partnership**

**Other Owners:** Miss L. A. Blackford, Mr D. J. Cocks, Mrs S. H. Livesey-Van Dorst, Mrs Susan Quick.

**Assistant Trainer:** M. J. Vanstone.

**NH Jockey:** James Best, Micheal Nolan, Nick Scholfield. **Conditional Jockey:** Sean Houlihan.

---

**45**

### MR MICHAEL BLAKE, Trowbridge
Postal: Staverton Farm, Trowbridge, Wiltshire, BA14 6PE
Contacts: PHONE 01225 782327 MOBILE 07971 675180
EMAIL mblakestavertonfarm@btinternet.com WEBSITE www.michaelblakeracing.co.uk

1 **BOUNTY PURSUIT**, 9, b g Pastoral Pursuits—Poyle Dee Dee  **Racing For A Cause**
2 **CHAMPS DE REVES**, 6, b g Champs Elysees—Joyeaux  **Staverton Owners Group**
3 **FARD**, 6, b g Dutch Art—Rose Blossom  **Mrs J. M. Gould**
4 **FREEDOM AND WHEAT (IRE)**, 5, b g Fast Company (IRE)—Rustam  **Racing For A Cause**
5 **HIGH CLASS AFFAIR (IRE)**, 4, ch f Zebedee—Acushladear (IRE)  **In the Mix Racing**
6 **HURRICANE ARCADIO (IRE)**, 7, b g Arcadio (GER)—Back To Favour (IRE)  **Staverton Owners Group**
7 **LOVE DREAMS (IRE)**, 7, b g Dream Ahead (USA)—Kimola (IRE)  **Mr A. D. Potts**
8 **MR ZEE (IRE)**, 4, b g Zebedee—Monsusu (IRE)  **Staverton Owners Group**
9 **SMOKE ON THE WATER**, 5, ch g Iffraaj—Fullaah (IRE)  **Michael & Sharon Blake**
10 **TIS FANTASTIC (FR)**, 6, gr g Montmartre (FR)—Anadara (FR)  **The Moonlighters**
11 **TRIO D'ECAJEUL (FR)**, 7, b g Diamond Boy (FR)—Daresta (FR)  **West Wilts Hockey Lads**
12 **WAITINONASUNNYDAY (IRE)**, 8, gr g Tikkanen (USA)—Coppenagh Lady (IRE)  **West Wilts Hockey Lads**

**Other Owners:** M. J. Blake, Mrs S. E. Blake, Mr R. C. Butcher, Mrs V. A. Butcher, Ms E. C. Chivers, Mr P. J. Gadsden.

**Assistant Trainer:** Sharon Blake.

---

**46**

### MR MICHAEL BLANSHARD, Upper Lambourn
Postal: Lethornes Stables, Upper Lambourn, Hungerford, Berkshire, RG17 8QP
Contacts: PHONE 01488 71091 MOBILE 07785 370093 FAX 01488 73497
EMAIL blanshard.racing@btconnect.com WEBSITE www.michaelblanshard.com

1 **ACCOMPLICE**, 7, b m Sakhee's Secret—Witness  **The Reignmakers**
2 **FAMOUS DYNASTY (IRE)**, 7, b g Famous Name—Daffodil Walk (IRE)  **Lady E Mays-Smith & Partners**
3 **MRS BENSON (IRE)**, 6, ch m Rip Van Winkle (IRE)—Ebble  **The Reignmakers**

### THREE-YEAR-OLDS

4 **LADYROC**, b f Charm Spirit (IRE)—Craighall  **Vincent Ward**
5 Ch f Coach House—Nimble Kimble
6 **SUPREMO**, b f Outstrip—Thiel  **Brian Oakley**
7 **WISPER (IRE)**, ch f Belardo (IRE)—Whisp (GER)  **The Reignmakers**

## MR MICHAEL BLANSHARD - continued

### TWO-YEAR-OLDS

**8** B f 20/04 Bobby's Kitten—Kaminari (IRE) (Sea The Stars (IRE))
**9** Gr f 16/03 Pearl Secret—Skiing (Sakhee's Secret)

**Other Owners:** S. Beccle, M. T. W. Blanshard, D. Cannings, M. Else, J. Gale, B. Mitchell.

**Yard Sponsor:** Oakley Coachbuilders Ltd.

**Flat Jockey:** David Probert.

---

### 47 MISS GILLIAN BOANAS, Saltburn
Postal: **Groundhill Farm, Lingdale, Saltburn-By-The-Sea, Cleveland, TS12 3HD**
Contacts: **MOBILE 07976 280154**
EMAIL gillianboanas@aol.com

**1 BABY JANE (IRE)**, 6, b m Oscar (IRE)—Young Lady (IRE) **Miss G Boanas & Mr M Foxton**
**2 BESTIARIUS (IRE)**, 9, b g Vinnie Roe (IRE)—Chione (IRE) **Miss G. L. Boanas**
**3 BROCTUNE RED**, 6, ch g Haafhd—Fairlie **Mrs M. B. Thwaites**
**4 CIMETTA**, 6, b m Lucarno (USA)—Nobratinetta (FR) **Mr T. C. Dawson**
**5 CRIXUS'S ESCAPE (IRE)**, 8, ch g Beneficial—Tierneys Choice (IRE) **Mr R. Collins**
**6 FAME AND HOPE (IRE)**, 6, b m Fame And Glory—Kaituna (IRE) **Mr John Coates Mr Richard Smith**
**7 FLEXI FURLOUGH (IRE)**, 5, gr m Milan—Young Lady (IRE) **D. C. Renton**
**8 GENERALISATION (IRE)**, 8, b g Arcadio (GER)—Will She Smile (IRE) **Miss G. L. Boanas**
**9 GREAT COLACI**, 8, b g Sulamani (IRE)—Fairlie **Rug, Grub & Pub Partnership**
**10 JACK OF ALL SHAPES (IRE)**, 5, b g Arcadio (GER)—Arequipa (IRE) **Miss G. L. Boanas**
**11 JUST CALL ME AL (IRE)**, 8, br g Presenting—Tonaphuca Girl (IRE) **M.B.Thwaites G Boanas G Halder**
**12** 5, Ch g Schiaparelli (GER)—La Calinda **Tees Components Ltd**
**13 LADY VINETTA**, 6, b m Sulamani (IRE)—Vinetta **The Thoughtful Partnership**
**14 LOCH LINNHE**, 9, b g Tobougg (IRE)—Quistaquay **Miss G Boanas & Mr M Foxton**
**15 OLIVER'S BETTY**, 6, br m Dick Turpin (IRE)—Luck Will Come (IRE) **Miss G. L. Boanas**
**16 POUND OFF YOU**, 5, ch m Haafhd—Let It Be **Miss G. L. Boanas**
**17 SULTANS PRIDE**, 9, b g Sulamani (IRE)—Pennys Pride (IRE) **Reveley Racing 1**
**18 SWEET VINETTA**, 7, gr m Fair Mix (IRE)—Vinetta **The Supreme Partnership**
**19 TEESCOMPONENTS LAD**, 8, b g Midnight Legend—Northern Native (IRE) **Tees Components Ltd**
**20 TEESCOMPONENTSTRIG**, 6, ch g Black Sam Bellamy (IRE)—La Calinda **Tees Components Ltd**

**Other Owners:** Miss G. L. Boanas, J. W. Coates, M. E. Foxton, Mr G. S. Halder, Rug, Grub & Pub Partnership, R. V. Smith, Mrs M. B. Thwaites.

---

### 48 MRS MYRIAM BOLLACK-BADEL, Chantilly-Lamorlaye
Postal: **20 Rue Blanche, 60260 Lamorlaye, France**
Contacts: **HOME +33 3 44 21 33 67 MOBILE +33 6 10 80 93 47 FAX +33 3 44 21 33 67**
EMAIL myriam.bollack@gmail.com

**1 ARGENTINE (FR)**, 4, ch f Rio de La Plata (USA)—Albicocca (FR) **Mr Patrick Fellous**
**2 AVEC LAURA**, 8, ch h Manduro (GER)—Sign of Life **Mme M. Bollack-Badel**
**3 BOUMMA DREAM**, 4, b f Charm Spirit (IRE)—Holy Moly (USA) **Oscar Ortmans**
**4 DARE**, 4, b f Bated Breath—Heronetta **Oscar Ortmans**
**5 GREEN SIREN (FR)**, 5, ch m Siyouni (FR)—Green Speed (FR) **Mr J. C. Smith**
**6 GREEN SPIRIT (FR)**, 4, b g Charm Spirit (IRE)—Green Speed (FR) **Mr J. C. Smith**
**7 NI CHAUD NI FROID (FR)**, 5, ch m Norse Dancer (IRE)—Numerologie (FR) **Alain Badel**

## MRS MYRIAM BOLLACK-BADEL - continued

8 **PASSEFONTAINE (FR)**, 4, b f Wootton Bassett—Perpetual Glory  **Ecurie Noel Forgeard**
9 **SINGSTREET (FR)**, 5, b g Evasive—Sinnderelle (FR)  **Ecurie Noel Forgeard**

### THREE-YEAR-OLDS

10 **COGOLIN (FR)**, ch c Goken (FR)—Albicocca (FR)  **Mr Patrick Fellous**
11 **GREEN GLORY (FR)**, b c Olympic Glory (FR)—Green Speed (FR)  **Mr J. C. Smith**
12 **MARCIE (IRE)**, b f Marcel (IRE)—Ayun (USA)  **Oscar Ortmans**
13 **PHEDRE (FR)**, b f Myboycharlie—Perpetual Glory  **Ecurie Noel Forgeard**
14 **ZYGFRYD (FR)**, ch c Literato (FR)—Zython (FR)  **Zygfryd Partnership**

### TWO-YEAR-OLDS

15 **ACREGATE**, ch c 04/05 Ribchester (IRE)—Green Speed (FR) (Green Tune (USA))
16 **LUNE DE RIO (FR)**, ch f 30/03 Rio de La Plata (USA)—Rocheville (FR) (Air Chief Marshal (IRE))
17 **NUMERO (FR)**, b f 25/01 Myboycharlie (IRE)—Numerologie (IRE) (Numerous (USA))
18 **PENTAOUR (FR)**, ch c 28/03 Toronado (IRE)—Perpetual Glory (Dansili))
19 **SINNDARILLO (FR)**, b c 19/02 Amarillo (IRE)—Sinnderelle (FR) (Sinndar (IRE))
20 **WELCOME SIGHT**, br f 21/02 Aclaim (IRE)—Loch Mirage (Elusive City (USA))
21 **ZINNIA (FR)**, ch c 24/04 Waldpark (GER)—Zython (FR) (Kabool))

**Other Owners:** Mr Anthony Bolis, Mr J. C. Smith, Mr Henri d'Aillieres

**Assistant Trainer:** Alain Badel, **Head Girl:** Mrs Laura Martaud, **Travelling Head:** Mr Philippe Celier.

**Flat Jockey:** Stephane Pasquier.

---

## 49  MR MARTIN BOSLEY, Chalfont St. Giles
Postal: **Bowstridge Farm, Bowstridge Lane, Chalfont St. Giles, Buckinghamshire, HP8 4RF**
Contacts: **PHONE 01494 875533 MOBILE 07778 938040**
EMAIL **martin@martinbosley.com** WEBSITE **www.martinbosleyracing.com**

1 **ASSEMBLED**, 5, gr g Iffraaj—Bezique  **Ms J. Williams**
2 **CATHEADANS FURY**, 7, ch m Firebreak—Dualagi  **M.A.S.A.**
3 **CHAMPION CHASE (FR)**, 9, b g Voix du Nord (FR)—Darling Frisco (FR)  **Mr M. R. Bosley**
4 **DRUNKEN PIRATE**, 8, b g Black Sam Bellamy (IRE)—Peel Me A Grape  **Mrs E. A. Prowting**
5 **HURCLE (IRE)**, 4, b g Exceed And Excel (AUS)—Switcher (IRE)  **Quartet Racing**
6 **KARALIUS (NZ)**, 6, b h Cape Blanco (IRE)—Imbudo (AUS)  **Mr D. Stenning**
7 **NAWAR**, 6, b g Henrythenavigator (USA)—Nouriya  **Quartet Racing**
8 **NORSE CASTLE**, 8, b g Norse Dancer (IRE)—Hursley Hope (IRE)  **M.A.S.A.**
9 **ROUNDEL**, 5, b g Dawn Approach (IRE)—Revered  **Bayard Racing**
10 **ZEFFERINO**, 7, ch g Frankel—Turama  **J. Carey**

### THREE-YEAR-OLDS

11 **SENNEN**, gr ro g Outstrip—Makara  **Mr M. J. Watson**

**50**  **MR MARCO BOTTI, Newmarket**
Postal: **Prestige Place, Snailwell Road, Newmarket, Suffolk, CB8 7DP**
Contacts: **PHONE 01638 662416 MOBILE 07775 803007 FAX 01638 662417**
**EMAIL office@marcobotti.co.uk WEBSITE www.marcobotti.co.uk**

1 **ALJARI**, 5, b h Quality Road (USA)—Rhagori  **Mr R. El Youssef**
2 **ARABIC WELCOME (IRE)**, 4, b br g Shamardal (USA)—Bint Almatar (USA)  **Mrs L. Botti**
3 **CASINA DI NOTTE (IRE)**, 7, ch g Casamento (IRE)—Nightswimmer (IRE)  **Mrs L. Botti**
4 **COUNT OF AMAZONIA (IRE)**, 4, b c Lope de Vega (IRE)—Queen Myrine (IRE)  **K Sohi & Partner**
5 **DARK SCIMITAR (USA)**, 4, b br g Verrazano (USA)—Don't Stop to Shop (USA)  **Marrone de Bianco Partnership 1**
6 **FELIX**, 5, ch g Lope de Vega (IRE)—Luminance (IRE)  **K Sohi & Partner**
7 **FUTURISTIC (IRE)**, 5, b g Shamardal (USA)—Aqlaam Vision  **Mr Manfredini & Partner**
8 **GIUSEPPE CASSIOLI**, 4, b c Bated Breath—Olympic Medal  **What A Time To Be Alive 2 & Partner**
9 **GUROOR**, 5, ch m Lope de Vega (IRE)—Shalwa  **Milan Racing Club**
10 **HABIT ROUGE**, 4, b g Helmet (AUS)—Hurricane Harriet  **Ambrosiana Racing & Partner**
11 **MADE IN ITALY (IRE)**, 4, b f Mukhadram—Delicatezza  **Ambrosiana Racing & Les Boyer**
12 **MISSION BOY**, 5, b g Paco Boy (IRE)—Miss Mission (IRE)  **Mr R Bruni & Partner**
13 **NO NAY BELLA (IRE)**, 4, b f No Nay Never (USA)—
                                                        Illuminating Dream (IRE)  **Middleham Park Racing CXXI & Partners**
14 **PRETENDING (ITY)**, 8, b g Librettist (USA)—Brumeux (IRE)  **Mrs L. Botti**
15 **PRETTY IN GREY**, 4, gr f Brazen Beau (AUS)—Maglietta Fina (IRE)  **Mrs B. M. Keller**
16 **PROSILI (IRE)**, 4, b f Dansili—Propaganda (IRE)  **Mr W. Moraes**
17 **ROME IMPERIAL (IRE)**, 4, b f Siyouni (FR)—Ascot Lady (IRE)  **Archi & Boyer**
18 **SILVER SAMURAI**, 4, gr g Cable Bay (IRE)—High Tan  **What A Time To Be Alive 1**
19 **SKY LAKE (GER)**, 4, b f Dabirsim (FR)—Salona (GER)  **Scuderia Archi Romani & Partner**
20 **SWEET CELEBRATION (IRE)**, 5, b m Excelebration (IRE)—Snow Dust  **MPR, Ventura Racing 5 & Partner**
21 **THOWQ (IRE)**, 4, b f Invincible Spirit (IRE)—Alaata (USA)  **Mamba Racing & Partner**
22 **TRULY TOGETHER (IRE)**, 4, b f Mastercraftsman (IRE)—Belly To Belly (IRE)  **Les Boyer Partnership**
23 **WAIT FOREVER (IRE)**, 6, b h Camelot—Mount McLeod (IRE)  **Mr R Bruni & Partner**

## THREE-YEAR-OLDS

24 **AMALFI SALSA (IRE)**, b f Mastercraftsman (IRE)—Lemon Rock  **Middleham Park Racing LXXIV**
25 **ANGELS WILL RISE**, b f Dark Angel (IRE)—Loaves And Fishes  **Milan Racing Club**
26 **APRES DARK (IRE)**, b g Estidhkaar (IRE)—Luvmedo (IRE)  **Scuderia Archi Romani & Partner**
27 **ATALIS BAY**, b c Cable Bay (IRE)—Atalis  **Scuderia Blueberry SRL**
28 **BIGSALONSUNTOWN (USA)**, ch c Speightstown (USA)—Salonsun (GER)  **Mr E. Elhrari**
30 **BLUENOSE BELLE (USA)**, b f Noble Mission—Poster Girl (USA)  **Middleham Park Racing CXXVI & Les Boyer**
30 **BROWN DELIVERS (USA)**, b c Mshawish (USA)—Alpaca Fina (CAN)  **Team Valor LLC**
31 **CAPTAIN HELMET**, ch c Helmet (AUS)—Captain Secret  **Scuderia Blueberry SRL**
32 **CASSOWARY (IRE)**, ch f Australia—Arose  **Saveall Green & James 1**
33 **CLEARLY CRYSTAL**, ch f Exceed And Excel (AUS)—Sky Crystal (GER)  **London Calling Syndicate**
34 **COLORANDO**, ch f Territories (IRE)—Mail Express (IRE)  **Scuderia Archi Romani**
35 **COSMIC GEORGE (IRE)**, b c Dawn Approach (IRE)—Badalona  **Middleham Park Racing XCVIII & Partner**
36 **DAMA BIANCA**, b f Adaay (IRE)—Letterfromamerica (USA)  **Heart of the South Racing 112 & Partner**
37 **DIVINE MAGIC**, b f Farhh—Magika  **Les Boyer Partnership**
38 **EARTH WAY**, b f Power—Heavenly Verse  **Milan Racing Club**
39 **EVENING SONG**, b f Twilight Son—Zerka  **Saveall Green & James 1**
40 **FIRE IN THE RAIN**, b f Starspangledbanner (AUS)—Downhill Dancer (IRE)  **Mr I. Alsagar**
41 **GEREMIA (IRE)**, b g Fastnet Rock (AUS)—Gerika (FR)  **La Tesa SPA**
42 **HEAVENLY ROSE**, b f Showcasing—Heavenly Scent  **Mrs L. Botti**
43 **HIGHEST AMBITION (FR)**, b c Siyouni (FR)—High Story (FR)  **Mr S. R. Chua**
44 **INVINCIBLE LASS (IRE)**, b br f Invincible Spirit (IRE)—Polygon (USA)  **Heart of the South Racing 124**
45 **INVITE (IRE)**, b f The Gurkha (IRE)—Katiyra (IRE)  **Team Valor LLC**
46 **JURY PICO (IRE)**, b f Night of Thunder (IRE)—Think (FR)  **Mr E. Elhrari**
47 **KING TIGER**, b c Swiss Spirit—Dubawi's Spirit (IRE)  **Mamba Racing & Partner**
48 **LADY ARGENTO (IRE)**, b f Australia—Cronsa (GER)  **La Tesa SPA**
49 **MAJOR J**, b g Siyouni (FR)—My Special J's (USA)  **Newsells Park Stud Limited**
50 **MENDENHALL**, b c Dansili—Brandybend (IRE)  **A J Suited Partnership**
51 **MILLION REASONS (IRE)**, ch g Mehmas (IRE)—Yasmeena (USA)  **Milan Racing Club 1**
52 **MOLIWOOD**, b c Fastnet Rock (AUS)—Shalwa  **Les Boyer Partnership 1**

## MR MARCO BOTTI - continued

53 **NIGHT FORCE (IRE)**, gr c Dark Angel (IRE)—Sleeping Beauty (IRE)  **Mr Abbas Alalawi & Partner**
54 **NUSHAFREEN**, b f Holy Roman Emperor (IRE)—Day Away (IRE)  **Mr I. Alsagar**
55 **POP YA COLLAR (IRE)**, b g Pride of Dubai (AUS)—Yeah Baby (IRE)  **K Sohi & Partner**
56 **PRAISE OF SHADOWS (IRE)**, b c Exceed And Excel (AUS)—Moon Over Water (IRE)  **& al Kamda**
57 **RISING STAR**, b f Fast Company (IRE)—Ile Flottante  **Mamba Racing & Partner**
58 **ROCAMBOLE**, b f Farhh—Sadaharu (FR)  **Les Boyer Partnership**
59 **SILVER GUNN (IRE)**, gr c Lope de Vega (IRE)—Claba di San Jore (IRE)  **Mr P. Hunt**
60 **SIMPLE STAR (IRE)**, b c Sea The Stars (IRE)—Simple Elegance (USA)  **K Sohi & Partner**
61 **SMART QIBILI (USA)**, ch c Speightster (USA)—Allerton (USA)  **Prestige Five**
62 **SUMMERTIME ROMANCE**, b f Declaration of War (USA)—Montjess (IRE)  **Middleham Park XXII & Steven Rocco 1**
63 **TAMIGI**, b f Due Diligence (USA)—Cheeky Girl  **Milan Racing Club**
64 **THE THUNDERER (IRE)**, b c Gleneagles (IRE)—Purple Sage (IRE)  **E. I. Mack**
65 **TRICOLORE (ITY)**, b c Twilight Son—Tribulina
66 **VALENTINKA**, ch f Helmet (AUS)—Pantile  **Mrs L. Botti**
67 **ZAURAK**, b f Zoffany (IRE)—Pursuitofthestars (IRE)  **Grundy Bloodstock Limited 1**

### TWO-YEAR-OLDS

68 B f 20/04 Belardo (IRE)—Alexandrite (Oasis Dream) (20000)  **Nick Bradley Racing 30 & Sohi & Partner**
69 B c 18/02 Belardo (IRE)—Alpine (Rail Link) (22857)  **Mrs L. Botti**
70 Ch f 02/03 Decorated Knight—Aniarnota (IRE) (Dalakhani (IRE))  **Mr I. Alsagar**
71 **ARAMCO (IRE)**, b c 10/04 Sea The Moon (GER)—Her Honour (IRE) (Shamardal (USA)) (90000)  **Mr S. R. Chua**
72 Ch c 27/04 Ulysses (IRE)—Atalis (Holy Roman Emperor (IRE)) (26000)  **Blueberry R. & Boyer Boyer**
73 B f 19/03 Galileo Gold—Boadicee (Aqlaam)  **Mr C. J. Murfitt & Partner**
74 **CAPLA FEVER (IRE)**, b f 26/04 Fast Company (IRE)—
                    Full Moon Fever (IRE) (Azamour (IRE)) (4286)  **Capla Developments & Milan Racing Club**
75 **ENCOUNTERED (IRE)**, b c 18/03 Churchill (IRE)—Enrol (Pivotal) (160000)  **Mr B. C. M. Wong**
76 B c 20/03 Flintshire—Endless Light (Pivotal) (11000)
77 B c 16/04 Dabirsim (FR)—Everglow (FR) (Dawn Approach (IRE)) (9684)
78 Gr c 15/03 Gutaifan (IRE)—Fanciful Dancer (Groom Dancer (USA)) (35000)
79 B f 25/01 Churchill (IRE)—Ghurfah (Tamayuz) (16190)
80 **GIAVELLOTTO (IRE)**, ch c 09/04 Mastercraftsman (IRE)—Gerika (FR) (Galileo (IRE))
81 B c 17/03 Outstrip—Ile Flottante (Duke of Marmalade (IRE))
82 **JUSTJAMIE**, b c 04/03 Sir Percy—Slewtoo (Three Valleys (USA))  **Dachel Stud**
83 Ch c 19/03 Charming Thought—Kasumi (Inchinor) (16000)  **Ahmed Bintooq & Partner**
84 B f 02/04 Time Test—Kelowna (IRE) (Pivotal) (21000)
85 **LA DUCHESSE (GER)**, b f 13/03 Iffraaj—La Reine Noir (GER) (Rainbow Quest (USA)) (13000)
86 Gr c 08/05 Muhaarar—Maglietta Fina (IRE) (Verglas (IRE))
87 B f 27/03 Havana Gold (IRE)—Moma Lee (Duke of Marmalade (IRE)) (6000)
88 B f 10/04 Farhh—Nota Bene (GER) (Slickly (FR)) (12000)
89 B c 12/03 Awtaad (IRE)—Passionable (New Approach (IRE)) (28571)
90 B c 25/01 Bated Breath—Respondez (Oasis Dream) (42000)
91 B c 05/04 Postponed (IRE)—Ruffled (Harlan's Holiday (USA))
92 B c 27/01 Sea The Stars (IRE)—Santa Anabaa (Exceed And Excel (AUS)) (45000)  **E. I. Mack**
93 B c 05/04 The Gurkha (IRE)—Siesta Time (Oasis Dream) (8571)  **Mr Ahmad Alrashidi & Partner**

**Other Owners:** Mrs E. Adamski, Mrs E. Agostini, Mr P. Agostini, Mr A. Al Alawi, Mr A. Al Kamda, Mr R. Al Kamda, Mr A. M. M. H. A. Alrashidi, Ambrosiana Racing, Mr A. Baragiola, Miss E. M. Baragiola, Mr L. Biffi, Mr A. Bintooq, Mrs L. Botti, Mr N. Bradley, Mr R. Bruni, Mr T. Denham, Mr A. J. Driver, Grundy Bloodstock Ltd, Heart of the South Racing 112, Miss S. Holden, Mr J. G. James, O. H. Kingsley, Les Boyer Partnership, Mamba Racing, Mr G. Manfredini, Marrone de Bianco Partnership, Middleham Park Racing CXXI, Middleham Park Racing CXXVI, Middleham Park Racing XCVIII, Middleham Park XXII & Steven Rocco, Middleham Park and Ventura Racing 5, Milan Racing Club, Mr C. J. Murfitt, Nick Bradley Racing 30, Mrs R. J. Norman, Mr M. A. O'Connell, T. S. Palin, Mr R. B. Patel, Mr J. R. Penny, M. Prince, Mr G. Saveall-Green, Saveall-Green & James, Scuderia Archi Romani, Scuderia Blueberry SRL, Mr K. Sohi, Mr P. Stubbins, What A Time To Be Alive, What A Time To Be Alive 2.

**Assistant Trainer:** Alberto Baragiola, Lucie Botti.

**Apprentice Jockey:** Stefano Cherchi, Morgan Cole, Christian Howarth, Ellie Norris.

## 51 MR GEORGE BOUGHEY, Newmarket

Postal: **Saffron House Stables, Hamilton Road, Newmarket, Suffolk, CB8 0NY**
Contacts: **PHONE 07765 132508**
EMAIL george@georgeboughey.com

1 **ALIX JAMES**, 4, b g Acclamation—Tout Va Bien (IRE)
2 **ARCTIC VICTORY (IRE)**, 4, b f Ivawood (IRE)—Impressive Victory (USA)
3 **ATHEEB**, 4, b g Muhaarar—Lady Francesca
4 **BATCHELOR BOY (IRE)**, 4, ch g Footstepsinthesand—Kathoe (IRE)
5 **DIRTY RASCAL (IRE)**, 5, b g Acclamation—Refusetolisten (IRE)
6 **EVERKYLLACHY (IRE)**, 7, br m Kyllachy—Superfonic (FR)
7 **JEAN BAPTISTE (IRE)**, 4, b g Invincible Spirit (IRE)—Pioneer Bride (USA)
8 **KHATM**, 4, b g Dubawi (IRE)—Hawaafez
9 **LOSTWITHIEL (IRE)**, 4, b g Camelot—Hespera
10 **PHOLAS**, 4, b f Iffraaj—Scallop
11 **ROCK SOUND (IRE)**, 6, ch g Lope de Vega (IRE)—Thoughtless Moment (IRE)
12 **RUBY RED EMPRESS (IRE)**, 4, b f Holy Roman Emperor (IRE)—Rougette
13 **SCHOOL OF THOUGHT**, 4, ch g Sir Percy—Lady Sylvia
14 **SONGKRAN (IRE)**, 5, b g Slade Power (IRE)—Choose Me (IRE)
15 **THREE C'S (IRE)**, 7, b g Kodiac—Ms Mary C (IRE)
16 **WIDAAD**, 4, b f Muhaarar—Mudaaraah

## THREE-YEAR-OLDS

17 **AIR TO AIR**, ch c Toronado (IRE)—Blossom Mills
18 B f Toronado (IRE)—Aldayha (IRE)
19 **ALMADRINA**, ch f Australia—Queens Park (FR)
20 **ANOTHER DAWN**, b f Exceed And Excel (AUS)—Queen Philippa (USA)
21 **BELLA B**, b f Requinto (IRE)—Angie And Liz (IRE)
22 **EPIDEMIC (IRE)**, b g Exceed And Excel (AUS)—Symposia
23 **FREAK OUT (IRE)**, b g Kodiac—Herridge (IRE)
24 **GAELIC LAW**, b c Mayson—Lawyers Choice
25 **HIDING DAVE (IRE)**, b g Ivawood (IRE)—Lady Lizabeth (IRE)
26 **MIRAGE MAC**, ch f Bobby's Kitten (USA)—Megachurch (USA)
27 **MYSTERY ANGEL (IRE)**, b br f Kodi Bear (IRE)—Angel Grace (IRE)
28 **SILENT QUEEN (IRE)**, b f Gutaifan (IRE)—Gold Hush (USA)

## TWO-YEAR-OLDS

29 **BELACQUA (IRE)**, b f 26/02 Havana Gold (IRE)—Chatting (IRE) (Intikhab (USA)) (10500)
30 B f 15/02 Showcasing—Bird Key (Cadeaux Genereux) (140000)
31 **BOLTON ABBEY (IRE)**, b c 30/04 Holy Roman Emperor (IRE)—In The Lurch (Mount Nelson) (20000)
32 B c 17/02 Ivawood (IRE)—Caprella (Kheleyf (USA))
33 **CASHEW (IRE)**, b f 06/02 Bated Breath—Taste The Salt (IRE) (Born To Sea (IRE)) (28571)
34 B c 27/01 Ribchester (IRE)—Dew Line (IRE) (Vale of York (IRE)) (26667)
35 B f 03/02 Markaz (IRE)—Disko (IRE) (Kodiac) (10476)
36 B f 28/03 Havana Gold (IRE)—Divine Grace (IRE) (Definite Article) (33000)
37 **DOVES CRY (IRE)**, b f 03/02 Footstepsinthesand—Fickle Feelings (IRE) (Nayef (USA)) (9524)
38 B f 18/04 Tamayuz—Duchesse (IRE) (Duke of Marmalade (IRE)) (23809)
39 Ch f 13/02 Galileo Gold—Elshamms (Zafonic (USA)) (27000)
40 B f 16/02 Gutaifan (IRE)—Fast Pick (IRE) (Fastnet Rock (AUS)) (17000)
41 **GOLDEN MAC (IRE)**, b c 28/03 Galileo Gold—Tara Celeb (Excelebration (IRE)) (14285)
42 B f 10/03 Camacho—Mary Pekan (IRE) (Sri Pekan (USA)) (18000)
43 B f 06/02 Bobby's Kitten (USA)—Phantasmagoric (IRE) (Dansili) (20000)
44 B f 28/04 Muhaarar—Pickle (Piccolo) (25000)
45 Ch f 12/04 Equiano (FR)—Psychic's Dream (Oasis Dream) (11000)
46 Br c 20/02 Bated Breath—Queen of Mean (Pivotal) (18000)
47 B f 10/03 No Nay Never (USA)—Reverent (IRE) (Teofilo (IRE)) (50000)
48 B c 20/03 Bated Breath—Saniyaat (Galileo (IRE))
49 B f 08/02 Acclamation—Scent Of Roses (IRE) (Invincible Spirit)
50 B c 28/03 Adaay (IRE)—Selkirk Sky (Selkirk (USA)) (20000)
51 **SIMPLY SONDHEIM**, b c 09/05 Pivotal—Finishingthehat (Sixties Icon)

## MR GEORGE BOUGHEY - continued

52 B c 08/05 No Nay Never (USA)—Tadris (USA) (Red Ransom (USA)) (70000)
53 **WAVE FAREWELL**, b f 14/02 Bobby's Kitten (USA)—Wavelet (Archipenko (USA))
54 Ch f 12/02 Galileo Gold—Wee Jean (Captain Gerrard (IRE)) (11000)
55 **WHITE JASMINE (IRE)**, gr f 04/03 Dark Angel (IRE)—White Daffodil (IRE) (Footstepsinthesand) (230000)

---

**52**
### MR DARAGH BOURKE, Lockerbie
Postal: **Cherrybank, Waterbeck, Lockerbie, Dumfries and Galloway, DG11 3EY**
Contacts: **MOBILE 07495 948493**

1 **ALLTHATGLISTENS (IRE)**, 8, b m Gold Well—Avenging Angel (IRE) **Mrs L. J. McLeod**
2 **DIXIELAND SWING (IRE)**, 6, b g Red Jazz (USA)—Kathleen Rafferty (IRE) **Mr D. F. Bourke**
3 **EVER READY EDDIE (IRE)**, 5, b h Ocovango—Youngvicky (IRE) **Mr S. Lowther**
4 **EVITA DU MESNIL (FR)**, 7, gr m Gris de Gris (IRE)—Perle du Mesnil (FR) **Mrs L. J. McLeod**
5 **FIRE AWAY (IRE)**, 8, b g Getaway (GER)—Joan's Girl (IRE) **Mr D. F. Bourke**
6 **GALLAHERS CROSS (IRE)**, 9, b g Getaway (GER)—Raheen Lady (IRE) **Mr D. F. Bourke**
7 **GOLDEN CHANCER**, 7, b g Gold Well—Princess Oriane (IRE) **Mr S. Lowther**
8 **LOSTOCK HALL (IRE)**, 9, b g Lord Shanakill (USA)—Cannikin (IRE) **Mrs L. J. McLeod**
9 **MASTER OF THE MALT**, 5, b g Yeats (IRE)—Mrs Malt (IRE) **Mr S. Lowther**
10 **METRO BOULOT DODO**, 8, br g Robin des Champs (FR)—Lizzy Langtry (IRE) **Mr D. F. Bourke**
11 **OLD JEWRY (IRE)**, 7, b g Le Fou (IRE)—Clerken Bridge (IRE) **Cherrybank Crusaders**
12 **PADDY THE PANDA (IRE)**, 6, b g Flemensfirth (USA)—Pandorama Lady (IRE) **Mr S. Lowther**
13 **PADS (IRE)**, 11, b br g Luso—Augusta Victoria **Mr S. Lowther**

---

**53**
### MR PETER BOWEN, Haverfordwest
Postal: **Yet-Y-Rhug, Letterston, Haverfordwest, Pembrokeshire, SA62 5TB**
Contacts: **PHONE 01348 840486 MOBILE 07811 111234 FAX 01348 840486**
**EMAIL info@peterbowenracing.co.uk WEBSITE www.peterbowenracing.co.uk**

1 **BRIEF ACQUAINTANCE (IRE)**, 5, br g Yeats (IRE)—Daisy's Sister **Mrs K. Bowen**
2 **CANDY BURG (FR)**, 8, b g Sageburg (IRE)—Candinie (USA) **Miss R. R. I. Howells**
3 **COLBY (IRE)**, 8, b g Witness Box (USA)—Wet And Dry (IRE) **Patrick Unsworth**
4 **COUGAR'S GOLD (IRE)**, 10, b g Oscar (IRE)—Top Her Up (IRE) **Mr W. E. V. Harries**
5 **COURTLAND (IRE)**, 6, b g Court Cave (IRE)—Media View (IRE) **Miss Jayne Brace & Mr Gwyn Brace**
6 **DALKINGSTOWN (IRE)**, 7, ch g Malinas (GER)—True Rose (IRE) **R. R. Owen**
7 **DR ROBIN (IRE)**, 11, b g Robin des Pres (FR)—Inter Alia (IRE) **Peter Bowen Racing Club**
8 **DRIFT ROCK (IRE)**, 7, ch g Malinas (GER)—Araucaria (IRE) **Amanda & Patrick Bancroft**
9 **EASY BUCKS (IRE)**, 6, b g Getaway (GER)—Tushana (IRE) **Mr M. B. Bowen**
10 **EQUUS DANCER (IRE)**, 7, b g Jeremy (USA)—Celtic Cailin (IRE) **R. R. Owen**
11 **FRANCKY DU BERLAIS (FR)**, 8, b g Saint des Saints (FR)—Legende du Luy (FR) **R. R. Owen**
12 **GAME LINE (IRE)**, 7, ch g Sandmason—Superline (IRE) **Roggie Crew**
13 **GET AN OSCAR (IRE)**, 7, ch m Getaway (GER)—Lady Perspex (IRE) **Peter Bowen Racing Club**
14 **GETASTAR (IRE)**, 5, ch g Getaway (GER)—Metro Star (IRE) **Amanda & Patrick Bancroft**
15 **HENRI MORGAN PARRY (IRE)**, 5, b g Ballingarry (IRE)—
                                         Milutonga Has (FR) **Mr Ednyfed & Mrs Elizabeth Morgan**
16 **LANDOFSMILES (IRE)**, 8, b g Beneficial—Sadie Supreme (IRE) **Miss Jayne Brace & Mr Gwyn Brace**
17 **LE TUEUR (IRE)**, 6, ch g Flemensfirth (USA)—Golden Odyssey (IRE) **Peter Bowen Racing Club**
18 **LERMOOS LEGEND (IRE)**, 6, b g Midnight Legend—Absalom's Girl **Mr J. A. Martin**
19 **LORD BRYAN (IRE)**, 10, b g Brian Boru—Run Cat (IRE) **Miss Jayne Brace & Mr Gwyn Brace**
20 **LORD NAPIER (IRE)**, 8, b g Galileo (IRE)—Jacqueline (IND) **F. Lloyd**
21 **MAC TOTTIE (IRE)**, 8, b g Midnight Legend—Tot of The Knar **Steve & Jackie Fleetham**

## MR PETER BOWEN - continued

22 **MINELLA DADDY (IRE),** 11, b g Flemensfirth (USA)—Old Moon (IRE) **Roddy Owen & The Late Paul Fullagar**
23 **MO TOTTIE,** 7, b m Midnight Legend—Tot of The Knar **Steve & Jackie Fleetham**
24 **MON RAY (IRE),** 4, b f Montmartre (FR)—Seven Even (FR) **Carl & Emma Pyne**
25 **MONTANNA,** 7, ch g Notnowcato—Asi (USA) **F. Lloyd**
26 **MORE BUCK'S (IRE),** 11, ch g Presenting—Buck's Blue (FR) **Mr M. B. Bowen**
27 **NO QUARTER ASKED (IRE),** 6, b g Jeremy (USA)—Louis's Teffia (IRE) **R. R. Owen**
28 **ORSINO (IRE),** 7, b g Galileo (IRE)—Birmanie (USA) **Peter Bowen Racing Club**
29 **PADDY'S RETURN (IRE),** 5, b g Ocovango—Witneses Daughter (IRE) **Miss Jayne Brace & Mr Gwyn Brace**
30 **PILGRIMS KING (IRE),** 5, b g Sholokhov (IRE)—So You Said (IRE) **Mr W. E. V. Harries**
31 **SHAREEF STAR,** 6, b g Sea The Stars (IRE)—Gotlandia (FR) **F. Lloyd**
32 **STAPLE HEAD (IRE),** 9, b g Morozov (USA)—Undesperado View (IRE) **W. D. Lewis**
33 **STATUARIO,** 6, b g Helmet (AUS)—Cat Hunter **Mrs N. Unsworth**
34 6, B m Getaway (GER)—Top Nurse (IRE) **Mrs K. Bowen**
35 **TRUMPS BENEFIT (IRE),** 8, b g Beneficial—Balla Brack (IRE) **C P Civil Engineering UK Ltd**
36 **WINGED DREAM,** 7, b m Winged Love (IRE)—Deploys Dream (IRE) **Mickey Bowen & Will Harman**

**Other Owners:** Mrs A. Bancroft, P. A. Bancroft, Mrs K. Bowen, Mr M. B. Bowen, D. G. Brace, Miss M. J. Brace, Exors of the Late Mr P. G. Fullagar, Mr W. Harman, Mrs E. Morgan, Mr E. O. Morgan, R. R. Owen, Mrs V. J. Patrick, Mr C. Pyne, Mrs E. R. Pyne, Mrs N. Unsworth.

**Assistant Trainer:** Karen Bowen, Michael Bowen.

**NH Jockey:** James Bowen, Sean Bowen.

---

**54**
## MISS SARAH BOWEN, Bromsgrove
Postal: **New House, Forest Farm, Forest Lane, Hanbury, Bromsgrove, Worcestershire, B60 4HP**
Contacts: **PHONE 07718 069485**
EMAIL **sarah.bowen25@hotmail.com**

1 **KING FRANK,** 8, b g Fantastic Spain (USA)—Elegant Accord (IRE) **Mrs S. A. Bowen**
2 **UPTON BEAT,** 6, b g Beat All (USA)—Upton Cliche **Miss S. L. Bowen**

---

**55**
## MR ROY BOWRING, Edwinstowe
Postal: **Fir Tree Farm, Edwinstowe, Mansfield, Nottinghamshire, NG21 9JG**
Contacts: **PHONE 01623 822451 MOBILE 07973 712942**
EMAIL **srbowring@outlook.com**

1 **ABOUT GLORY,** 7, b g Nayef (USA)—Lemon Rock **S. R. Bowring**
2 **ARTILLERY,** 4, b g Brazen Beau (AUS)—Malpas Missile (IRE) **S. R. Bowring**
3 **BACK FROM DUBAI (IRE),** 4, b g Exceed And Excel (AUS)—Emirates Rewards **Mr K. Nicholls**
4 **DECISION MAKER (IRE),** 7, b g Iffraaj—Consensus (IRE) **Mr K. Nicholls**
5 **DYLAN'S LAD (IRE),** 4, b g G Force (IRE)—Chizzler (IRE) **S.R. & Malc Hancock**
6 **FIRST EXCEL,** 9, ch g First Trump—Exceedingly Good (IRE) **S. R. Bowring**
7 **JEANS MAITE,** 5, b m Burwaaz—Misu's Maite **S. R. Bowring**
8 **NINE ELMS (USA),** 6, ch g Street Cry (IRE)—Nawaiet (USA) **Mr K. Nicholls**

### THREE-YEAR-OLDS

9 **BETTER BY FAR (IRE),** b f Exceed And Excel (AUS)—Silkwood **S. R. Bowring**
10 **HIYA MAITE,** b g Heerat (IRE)—Misu's Maite **S. R. Bowring**
11 **TRULIE GOOD,** b f Heerat (IRE)—Exceedingly Good (IRE) **S. R. Bowring**

**Other Owners:** S. R. Bowring, Mr M. Hancock.

**56**

## MR JIM BOYLE, Epsom

Postal: **South Hatch Stables, Burgh Heath Road, Epsom, Surrey, KT17 4LX**
Contacts: **WORK 07719 554147 MOBILE 07719 554147**
**WORK EMAIL info@jamesboyle.co.uk HOME EMAIL Jimboyle17@hotmail.com EMAIL pippaboyle@
hotmail.com WEBSITE www.jamesboyle.co.uk**

1 **AMARETTO**, 6, b g Kyllachy—Dan Loose Daughter **A. B. Pope**
2 **ANGELS ROC**, 4, b g Roderic O'Connor (IRE)—Divine Pamina (IRE) **Lady R. M. Prosser**
3 **BAD COMPANY**, 4, b g Fast Company (IRE)—Clearing **The Clean Sweep Partnership**
4 **BEAT THE HEAT**, 4, b g Hot Streak (IRE)—Touriga **Inside Track Racing Club**
5 **BONUS**, 4, b g Roderic O'Connor (IRE)—Spring Clean (FR) **The Clean Sweep Partnership**
6 **CRISTAL SPIRIT**, 6, b g Nathaniel (IRE)—Celestial Girl **The Waterboys**
7 **DESERT LAND (IRE)**, 5, b g Kodiac—La Chicana (IRE) **R S Matharu & Harry Wigan**
8 **DOLPHIN VISTA (IRE)**, 8, b g Zoffany (IRE)—Fiordiligi **The BeeGeeZ**
9 **GIBRALTARIAN (IRE)**, 5, b m War Command (USA)—Star of Gibraltar **Mr D. A. Poole**
10 **LEROY LEROY**, 5, b g Compton Place—Small Fortune **The Reserve Tankers**
11 **OTAGO**, 4, b g Cable Bay (IRE)—Spinning Top **Mr P and Mrs L Rowe and Mr John Turner**
12 **PEACE PREVAILS**, 6, ch m Declaration of War (USA)—Miss Mediator (USA) **Mr M. Aljoe**
13 **PURE PURFECTION (IRE)**, 4, b f Dream Ahead (USA)—Rose of Africa (IRE) **Maid In Heaven Partnership**
14 **QUITA**, 5, b m Footstepsinthesand—Quiania (IRE) **Mr D. Buckell**
15 **SHINING**, 5, b m Lethal Force (IRE)—Spring Clean (FR) **The Clean Sweep Partnership**
16 **SPREADSHEET**, 4, b g Exceed And Excel (AUS)—Mundana (IRE) **Reynolds Farm Syndicate**

### THREE-YEAR-OLDS

17 **AVENTURINA**, b f Charming Thought—Clearing **Dr Pamela Wilson & Partners**
18 **DOWNSMAN (IRE)**, b g Fast Company (IRE)—Hawk Dance (IRE) **The Paddock Space Partnership 2**
19 **GOING GONE (IRE)**, b g Le Havre (IRE)—Sea The Sun (GER) **Taylor & O'Dwyer**
20 **HOPE SPRINGS**, b f Mukhadram—Spring Clean (FR) **The Clean Sweep Partnership**
21 **LADY SUSIE (IRE)**, b f Equiano (FR)—Seduct (IRE) **Epsom Equine Spa Partnership**
22 **MARLAY PARK**, b br g Cable Bay (IRE)—Lovers' Vows **Inside Track Racing Club**

### TWO-YEAR-OLDS

23 B f 04/04 Night of Thunder (IRE)—Clearing (Sleeping Indian)
24 **HEN HARRIER (IRE)**, ch f 01/03 Profitable (IRE)—Ventura Falcon (IRE) (Excellent Art) (14286) **Taylor & O'Dwyer**
25 B f 15/03 Equiano (FR)—Inke (IRE) (Intikhab (USA))
26 Ch f 12/02 Fast Company (IRE)—Interlacing (Oasis Dream)
27 **MELERI**, b f 21/02 Nathaniel (IRE)—Divine Pamina (IRE) (Dark Angel (IRE)) **Lady R. M. Prosser**
28 Ch c 05/02 Tamayuz—Solandia (IRE) (Teofilo (IRE)) (8000)
29 Ch c 16/02 Nathaniel (IRE)—Sonnetation (IRE) (Dylan Thomas (IRE))
30 Gr f 16/04 El Kabeir (USA)—Trading Places (Dansili) (6053)

**Other Owners:** Mr J. R. Boyle, Mrs P. Boyle, M. C. Cook, Mr A. C. Elliott, Ms J. E. Harrison, Mr J. Hillier, Mr R. S. Matharu, Mr A. J. R. Moseley, Mr H. E. Wigan, Dr P. Wilson.

---

**57**

## MR RICHARD BRABAZON, Curragh

Postal: **Rangers Lodge, The Curragh, Co. Kildare, R56 Y443, Ireland**
Contacts: **MOBILE +353 87 251 5626**
**EMAIL Brabazonrichard@gmail.com WEBSITE www.richardbrabazon.ie**

1 **HAYYEL (IRE)**, 6, b m Dark Angel (IRE)—Ravissante (IRE) **Celbridge Estates**
2 **PIRATE LASS (IRE)**, 4, b f Born To Sea (IRE)—Grand Treasure (IRE) **Cafe Du Journal Syndicate**

### THREE-YEAR-OLDS

3 **FAIR DAMSEL (IRE)**, ch f Dragon Pulse (IRE)—Placere (IRE)
4 **GORDON BENNETT (IRE)**, b c Prince of Lir (IRE)—Laureldean Lady (IRE)

## MR RICHARD BRABAZON - continued

### TWO-YEAR-OLDS

5 GOD KNOWS (IRE), b f 08/05 Divine Prophet (AUS)—Placere (IRE) (Noverre (USA))

**Assistant Trainer:** Heidi Brabazon.

---

**58**
### MR DAVID BRACE, Bridgend
Postal: **Llanmihangel Farm, Pyle, Bridgend, Mid Glamorgan, CF33 6RL**
Contacts: **PHONE 01656 742313**

1 BRACHO, 9, b g Dr Massini (IRE)—Branston Lily **Mr D. Brace**
2 COLORADO DOC, 10, b g Dr Massini (IRE)—First Royal (GER) **Mr D. Brace**
3 DAN GUN (IRE), 7, b g Intikhab (USA)—Lady Magdalena (IRE) **Mr D. Brace**
4 DELKANTRA (IRE), 11, b g Putra Pekan—Delheim (IRE) **Mr D. Brace**
5 DON'T LAUGH AT ME, 6, b g Schiaparelli (GER)—Nurse Brace **Mr D. Brace**
6 GATS AND CO, 6, b g Dr Massini (IRE)—Vineuil (FR) **Mr D. Brace**
7 GETAWAY FLYER (IRE), 8, b m Getaway (GER)—No Moore Bills **Mr D. Brace**
8 ISOSCELES (IRE), 5, b g Rulership (JPN)—Triple Pirouette (USA) **Mr D. Brace**
9 PATSIO (IRE), 13, b g Moscow Society (USA)—Supreme Favour (IRE) **Mr D. Brace**
10 PINK EYED PEDRO, 10, b g Dr Massini (IRE)—Poacher's Paddy (IRE) **Mr D. Brace**
11 RIVER LLYNFI (IRE), 5, b g Ocovango—La Lambertine (FR) **Mr D. Brace**
12 ROBIN DES PEOPLE (IRE), 11, br g Robin des Pres (FR)—Zelea (IRE) **Mr D. Brace**
13 SHANANDOA, 10, b m Shamardal (USA)—Divisa (GER) **Mr D. Brace**
14 WATCHING BRIEF (IRE), 8, b g Rudimentary (USA)—Miss Tsigalko (IRE) **Mr D. Brace**
15 WILLIAM MONEY (IRE), 14, b g Cloudings (IRE)—All of A Kind (IRE) **Mr D. Brace**

**Assistant Trainer:** Robbie Llewellyn.

**Conditional Jockey:** Connor Brace.

---

**59**
### MR MARK BRADSTOCK, Wantage
Postal: **Old Manor Stables, Foresters Lane, Letcombe Bassett, Wantage, Oxfordshire, OX12 9NB**
Contacts: **WORK 01235 760780 HOME 01235 760780 PHONE 01235 760754 MOBILE 07887 686697**
**EMAIL mark.bradstock@btconnect.com WEBSITE www.markbradstockracing.co.uk**

1 BENDY BOW, 6, br g Malinas (GER)—Maid of Oaksey **The BB Partnership**
2 CRAWFORD, 5, b g Kayf Tara—Maid of Oaksey **The Billy Partnership**
3 EGLANTIER (FR), 7, b g Bonbon Rose (FR)—Kyalami (FR) **UK Gunite Ltd**
4 FLINTHAM, 12, b g Kayf Tara—Plaid Maid (IRE) **The Rasher Partnership**
5 I'M HERE (IRE), 8, ch g Hurricane Run (IRE)—Is It Here (IRE) **The Hooch Partnership**
6 IDOLS'S EYE (FR), 6, b g Diamond Boy (FR)—Rose Caline (FR) **M. F. Bradstock**
7 JAISALMER (IRE), 9, b g Jeremy (USA)—Shara (IRE) **The Jeremy Partnership**
8 JAKAMANI, 7, b g Sulamani (IRE)—Kentford Grebe **Miss C Fordham & Mr C Vernon**
9 SOUTHFIELD LILY, 5, b m Yeats (IRE)—Chamoss Royale (FR) **Mrs A. B. Yeoman**
10 SOUTHFIELD MEGAN, 5, b m Dylan Thomas (IRE)—Southfield Etoile **Mrs A. B. Yeoman**
11 SOUTHFIELD TORR, 8, gr ro g Fair Mix (IRE)—Chamoss Royale (FR) **Mrs Angela Hart & Mrs Angela Yeoman**
12 STEP BACK (IRE), 11, ch g Indian River (FR)—Stepitoutmary (IRE) **Cracker and Smodge Partnership**
13 STOOP LEAD (IRE), 7, b g Jeremy (USA)—The Only Girl (IRE) **Lord P. Oaksey**

**Other Owners:** M. F. Bradstock, C. Elgram, Miss C. Fordham, Mrs A. R. Hart, Mr J. B. G. Macleod, Mr J. Reilly, Mr J. R. Rowlands, Mr R. W. Tyrrell, C. A. Vernon, Mrs A. B. Yooman.

**Assistant Trainer:** Sara Bradstock, **Head Girl:** Lily Bradstock, **Racing Secretary:** Samantha Partridge.

**NH Jockey:** Nico De Boinville.

## 60 MR BARRY BRENNAN, Lambourn
Postal: **2 Rockfel Road, Lambourn, Hungerford, Berkshire, RG17 8NG**
Contacts: **MOBILE 07907 529780**
EMAIL barrybrennan2@hotmail.co.uk WEBSITE www.barrybrennanracing.co.uk

1 BLUE SLATE (IRE), 4, gr g Alhebayeb (IRE)—Hallbeck **F. J. Brennan**
2 CREM FRESH, 7, b m Malinas (GER)—Clotted Cream (USA) **D. R. T. Gibbons**
3 DARAZ LEGACY, 7, ch m Schiaparelli (GER)—Daraz Rose (IRE) **F. J. Brennan**
4 DEBBONAIR (IRE), 5, b g Slade Power (IRE)—Bryanstown Girl (IRE) **D. R. T. Gibbons**
5 FINE INVESTMENT, 6, b br g Beat All (USA)—Pretty Lady Rose **Mrs L. Osborne**
6 KALAYA (IRE), 5, b m Thewayyouare (USA)—Kalabaya (IRE) **D. R. T. Gibbons**
7 LADY VERA (IRE), 6, b m Shirocco (GER)—Kayf Vera (IRE) **M. J. Hills**
8 PARA MIO (IRE), 6, b g Pour Moi (IRE)—Malaspina (IRE) **Three Dads Syndicate**
9 SNUG AS A BUG (IRE), 6, b m Shirocco (GER)—More Equity **Mrs L. Osborne**
10 TRANQUIL DAWN (IRE), 7, gr m Oscar (IRE)—Young Lady (IRE) **Mrs L. Osborne**

### THREE-YEAR-OLDS

11 HIGH HOPES LADY, b f Linda's Lad—Lady Arbella **F. J. Brennan**

## 61 MR JOHN BRIDGER, Liphook
Postal: **Upper Hatch Farm, Liphook, Hampshire, GU30 7EL**
Contacts: **PHONE 01428 722528 MOBILE 07785 716614**
EMAIL jbridger@sky.com

1 ALKA STEP (IRE), 10, gr g Alkaadheem—D'Bibbys Step (IRE) **Mr J E Burrows & Mrs V C Burrows**
2 AMNAA, 4, b f Bungle Inthejungle—She Mystifies **Watts & Spooner**
3 BE PREPARED, 4, b g Due Diligence (USA)—Chicklade **Mr P. Cook**
4 CHAIRMANIC (IRE), 4, b g G Force (IRE)—Beauty of The Sea **Mr J. E. Burrows**
5 DELICATE KISS, 7, b m Delegator—Desert Kiss **DBD Partnership**
6 FIRENZE ROSA (IRE), 6, b m Zebedee—Our Nana Rose (IRE) **Mr & Mrs K. Finch**
7 LETHAL BLAST, 4, b f Lethal Force (IRE)—Having A Blast (USA)
8 PETTOCHSIDE, 12, b g Refuse To Bend (IRE)—Clear Impression (IRE) **Mr P. Cook**
9 PORTO FERRO (IRE), 7, b m Arcano (IRE)—Sassari (IRE) **Mr J. J. Bridger**
10 RUBEE FORTY, 4, b f Lethal Force (IRE)—Desert Kiss **Mrs D. J. Ellison**
11 SANTORINI SAL, 4, b c Gregorian (IRE)—Aegean Mystery **Mystery Partnership**
12 SHANI, 4, b f Heeraat (IRE)—Limegrove **China Racing Club**
13 SIXTIES HERO, 4, b g Sixties Icon—Waraqa (USA) **T. M. Jones**
14 STARCHANT, 5, b m Gregorian (IRE)—Aegean Mystery **Double-R-Racing**
15 TIME MASTER, 6, b g Olden Times—She Wont Tell **T. M. Jones**

### THREE-YEAR-OLDS

16 ESSME, b c Twilight Son—Desert Kiss
17 MATIRA BAY (IRE), b f Vadamos (FR)—Blue Holly (IRE) **Mr & Mrs K. Finch**
18 PIAZOLLA (IRE), b c Outstrip—Kilakey (IRE) **Mr & Mrs K. Finch**
19 SILVER REFLECTION, gr f Gutaifan (IRE)—Pivotal Bride **Mr & Mrs K. Finch**
20 VERRE DORE, b f Heeraat (IRE)—Nairobi (FR) **Mr M J Evans & Mr T M Jones**

**Other Owners:** Mr J. J. Bridger, Mr J. E. Burrows, Mrs V. C. Burrows, Mr P. Cook, Mrs D. A. Ellison, Mrs D. J. Ellison, Mr M. J. Evans, Mrs D. Finch, K. Finch, T. M. Jones, Mr B. Olkowicz, Exors of the Late Mr G. K. Panos, Mr W. J. Spooner, Mr M. Watts.

**Assistant Trainer:** Rachel Cook.

## 62   MR DAVID BRIDGWATER, Stow-on-the-Wold
Postal: Wyck Hill Farm, Wyck Hill, Stow-on-the-Wold, Cheltenham, Gloucestershire, GL54 1HT
Contacts: PHONE 01451 830349 MOBILE 07831 635817 FAX 01451 830349
EMAIL sales@bridgwaterracing.co.uk WEBSITE www.bridgwaterracing.co.uk

1  4, B g Authorized (IRE)—Ahdaaf (USA)  **Mr S. Hunt**
2  5, B g Midnight Legend—Aster (IRE)  **P. J. Cave**
3  **BARNAVIDDAUN (IRE)**, 8, b g Scorpion (IRE)—Lucy Murphy (IRE)  **Graham Clarkson & Andrew Smelt**
4  **BOLD RED**, 5, ch g Dunaden (FR)—Bold Tara  **Mrs Anne Lee-Warner**
5  **COBY NINE (IRE)**, 8, b g Arcadio (GER)—Timing  **The Roworth Family Syndicate**
6  **DAME DU SOIR (FR)**, 8, br m Axxos (GER)—Kassing (FR)  **Graham Clarkson & Andrew Smelt**
7  **DRAKES WELL (IRE)**, 8, b g Mustameet (USA)—Clare Belle (IRE)  **Mr S. R. L. Corbett**
8  **DUTCH ADMIRAL (IRE)**, 4, ch g Dutch Art—Apasionata Sonata (USA)  **P. J. Cave**
9  **ENRICHISSANT (FR)**, 7, b br g Speedmaster (GER)—Quibble (FR)  **Simon & Liz Hunt**
10  **EPPLETON COLLIER (FR)**, 5, b g Balko (FR)—Golden Firebird (IRE)  **Mr S. Hunt**
11  **EXTRAORDINARY MAN (FR)**, 5, b g No Risk At All (FR)—Argovie (FR)  **Mr S. Hunt**
12  **GAIA VALLIS (FR)**, 5, b m Saint des Saints (FR)—Toccata Vallis (FR)  **David Bridgwater Racing**
13  4, B g Diamond Boy (FR)—Lazoukine (FR)  **Mr S. Hunt**
14  **OAKLEY HALL (IRE)**, 9, b g Milan—Rockwell College (IRE)  **Taymar Racing**
15  **ON THE METER (IRE)**, 7, b br g Eastern Anthem (IRE)—Party Belle  **Premier Plastering (UK) Limited**
16  **PICTURESQUE VIEW (IRE)**, 5, b g Camelot—Magic Peak (IRE)  **Constructive Equine**
17  **PIRATE SAM**, 6, b g Black Sam Bellamy (IRE)—Teenero  **JA & RJ Chenery & Partners**
18  4, B g War Command (USA)—Precious Gem (IRE)
19  **SA ALORS (FR)**, 5, b m Nicaron (GER)—Line Tzigane (FR)  **Terry & Sarah Amos**
20  **SALTY BOY (IRE)**, 8, b g Stowaway—Ballons Oscar (IRE)  **Premier Plastering (UK) Limited**
21  **SAQUEBOUTE (FR)**, 4, b f Slickly Royal (FR)—Grande Cavale (FR)  **Mr S. Hunt**
22  **SPECTACULARDISPLAY (IRE)**, 5, b g Camelot—Asteya (IRE)  **Deauville Daze Partnership**
23  **THE CONDITIONAL (IRE)**, 9, b g Kalanisi (IRE)—Gorrie Vale (IRE)  **P. J. Cave**
24  **URANUS DES BORDES (FR)**, 5, b g Kapgarde (FR)—Queen des Bordes (FR)  **Mr S. Hunt**
25  **VAN MEEGEREN (IRE)**, 5, ch g Gale Force Ten—Ashdali (IRE)  **Mrs J. A. Chenery & Mr R. J. Chenery**
26  **WENCESLAUS (GER)**, 9, b g Tiger Hill (GER)—Warrior Czarina (USA)  **Deauville Daze Partnership**
27  **ZAMANI (GER)**, 5, ch g Mamool (IRE)—Zuccarella (GER)  **Mr R. Wilson**

### THREE-YEAR-OLDS

28  Bl g Great Pretender (IRE)—Athinea (FR)  **Mr S. Hunt**
29  **CARPE DIEM (FR)**, b g Walzertakt (GER)—Chance Bleue (FR)  **Terry & Sarah Amos**
30  **IT'S FOR YOU MUM (FR)**, gr f Lord du Sud (FR)—Odile (FR)  **Mr S. Hunt**
31  **PASDATTENTES (FR)**, b f Walzertakt (GER)—Line Tzigane (FR)  **Terry & Sarah Amos**
32  **TELLAIRSUE (GER)**, ch g Zoffany (IRE)—Tiangua  **Mr R. Wilson**

**Other Owners:** Mrs S. P. Amos, T. P. Amos, D. G. Bridgwater, Mrs J. A. Chenery, Mr R. J. Chenery, Mrs J. A. Chenery & Mr R. J. Chenery, David Bridgwater Racing, Mr A. Gunn, Miss L. M. Haywood, Mrs E. A. Hunt, Mr S. Hunt, Mr M. Kempley, Mr T. J. Payton.

**Assistant Trainer:** Mrs Lucy K. Bridgwater.

**NH Jockey:** Tom Scudamore. **Conditional Jockey:** Daniel Hiskett, Callum McKinnes. **Apprentice Jockey:** Poppy Bridgwater.

## 63   MR ROBYN BRISLAND, Stockbridge
Postal: Stud House, Danebury, Stockbridge, Hampshire, SO20 6JX
Contacts: MOBILE 07771 656081
EMAIL robbris@me.com

1  4, Ch g Anjaal—Abbotsfield (IRE)
2  **ALBA DEL SOLE (IRE)**, 6, b m Dandy Man (IRE)—Winterwell (USA)  **Mr M. Seedel**
3  **ANDRE AMAR (IRE)**, 5, b g Dandy Man (IRE)—Heaven's Vault (IRE)  **Mr M. Seedel**

## MR ROBYN BRISLAND - continued

4 **BIG IMPACT**, 4, b g Lethal Force (IRE)—Valandraud (IRE) **Mr D. R. J. Freeman**
5 **BLACK BOX**, 4, b f Iffraaj—Perfect Story (IRE) **Cross Channel Racing Club**
6 **BRASS CLANKERS**, 4, b g Helmet (AUS)—Millsini **Mrs J. Brisland**
7 **BUTCHEROFSTOCKHOLM**, 4, b g Toronado (IRE)—Anna's Vision (IRE) **Cross Channel Racing & Partner**
8 **COLD HARBOUR**, 6, b g North Light (IRE)—Pilcomayo (IRE) **Mrs J. Brisland**
9 **COMPASS POINT**, 6, b h Helmet (AUS)—Takarna (IRE) **Cross Channel Racing & Partner**
10 **CONSTABLE (IRE)**, 4, b g Lawman (FR)—Pinacotheque (IRE) **Mrs J. A. Cornwell**
11 **DEEDS NOT WORDS (IRE)**, 10, b g Royal Applause—Wars (IRE) **Cross Channel Racing & Partner**
12 **ESSGEE NICS (IRE)**, 8, b g Fairly Ransom (USA)—Vannuccis Daughter (IRE) **Wackey Racers Harefield**
13 **EVASIVE POWER (USA)**, 5, b g Elusive Quality (USA)—Casting Director (USA) **Mrs J. Brisland**
14 **FAREWELL KISS (IRE)**, 4, ch f Exceed And Excel (AUS)—Kiss Me Goodbye **Cross Channel Racing Club**
15 **GINGER BOX**, 4, gr ro f Mastercraftsman (IRE)—Ellbeedee (IRE) **Cross Channel Racing Club**
16 **HARBOUR STORM**, 6, br g Sayif (IRE)—Minette **Mr C. J. Harding**
17 **KINDLY**, 8, b m Kyllachy—Touching (IRE) **Mrs A. L. Heayns**
18 **KODIAC HARBOUR (IRE)**, 6, b g Kodiac—Operissimo **Cross Channel Racing Club**
19 **LUA DE MEL (IRE)**, 4, b f Casamento (IRE)—Selfara **Cross Channel Racing Club**
20 **MARBLES ARE BLUE**, 4, b c Sidestep (AUS)—Cheap N Chic **Cross Channel Racing Club**
21 **MONSIEUR PATAT**, 4, b g Coach House (IRE)—Miss Trish (IRE) **Wackey Racers Harefield**
22 **NAVAJO DAWN (IRE)**, 4, b f Dawn Approach (IRE)—Patience Alexander (IRE) **Ferrybank Properties Limited**
23 **NAVAL COMMANDER**, 4, b br c French Navy—Quail Landing **Mrs Jackie Cornwell & Partner**
24 **NICK VEDDER**, 7, b g Rip Van Winkle (IRE)—Devotion (IRE) **Wackey Racers Harefield**
25 **NINETEENRBO'MALLEY**, 9, b g Beat All (USA)—My Nora (IRE) **Mr E. G. O'Malley**
26 **NORWEGIAN RED**, 4, b g Sayif (IRE)—Bahie **Cross Channel Racing & Partner**
27 **OCEAN BEYOND**, 4, b c Al Kazeem—Fuschia **Mrs J. A. Cornwell**
28 **OCEAN RUMOUR**, 4, ch f Mayson—Sea Whisper **The Foxford House Partnership**
29 **POWER ABOVE (IRE)**, 4, ch f Power—Moynsha Lady (IRE) **Mrs J. Brisland**
30 **POWER OVER ME (IRE)**, 4, b g Ivawood (IRE)—Bridge Note (USA) **Mrs J. Brisland**
31 **PULL HARDER CON**, 4, b c Mayson—Cut The Cackle **Mr C. J. Harding**
32 **PURPLE SANDPIPER**, 4, b g Mayson—The Lady Lapwing **Mrs F A Veasey & Mrs Jo Brisland**
33 **SECRET RETURN (IRE)**, 8, ch m Roderic O'Connor (IRE)—Quick Return **Cross Channel Racing Club**
34 **SETTLE PETAL**, 7, b m Peintre Celebre (USA)—Shall We Dance **Mr M. Seedel**
35 **SIX TIL TWELVE (IRE)**, 5, b g Bungle Inthejungle—Cuiseach (IRE) **Mrs J. Brisland**
36 **SOLENT SCENE**, 4, b g Footstepsinthesand—Stravie (IRE) **Mrs J. A. Cornwell**
37 **TACKLESLIKEAFERRET (IRE)**, 4, b g Alhebayeb (IRE)—Regal Kiss **Cross Channel Racing & Partner**
38 **THE BULL (IRE)**, 6, ch g Camacho—Zarara (USA) **Mrs J. Degnan**
39 **WHISTLING SANDS**, 5, b g Gregorian (IRE)—Sea Whisper **Mrs J. Brisland**

### THREE-YEAR-OLDS

40 B f Outstrip—Absent Amy (IRE)
41 B g Sinndar (IRE)—Amba
42 **APACHE CHARM**, b f Swiss Spirit—Nizhoni (USA) **Ferrybank Properties Limited**
43 **APACHE JEWEL (IRE)**, b f Teofilo (IRE)—Floating Along (IRE) **Ferrybank Properties Limited**
44 **APACHE MIST**, b f Adaay (IRE)—Mutoon (IRE) **Ferrybank Properties Limited**
45 **CAMPACHOOCHOO (IRE)**, b f Kodi Bear (IRE)—Divert (IRE) **Cross Channel Racing & Partner**
46 Gr f Vadamos (FR)—Chiara Wells (IRE) **Ferrybank Properties Limited**
47 B g Marcel (IRE)—Eleanor Eloise (USA)
48 **ELLIE PIPER**, b f Acclamation—Corncockle **Luther Lives On**
49 **HONG KONG FURY (IRE)**, b g Pride of Dubai (AUS)—Spanish Doll **Cross Channel Racing Club**
50 **HOWZAK**, b c Sepoy (AUS)—Alys Love
51 **HUNDON**, b c Brazen Beau (AUS)—Darwinia (GER) **Stapleford Racing Houghton Bloodstock**
52 **JUSCOMINPASTY**, b f Bobby's Kitten (USA)—Chatalong (IRE) **Mrs A. L. Heayns**
53 **MANDM**, b c Haafhd—Bonne de Fleur
54 B f Morpheus—Oriental Romance (IRE)
55 **RIVERS LAD**, b g Adaay (IRE)—Siena Gold **From The Front Racing**
56 B g Famous Name—Sea Regatta (IRE)
57 **SERGEANT TIBBS**, b c Bobby's Kitten (USA)—Beautiful View **Nick Andersen & Partner**
58 Ch f French Navy—Straviethirteen **Mrs J. A. Cornwell**

## MR ROBYN BRISLAND - continued

### TWO-YEAR-OLDS
59 B c 05/04 Hot Streak (IRE)—Jasmine Royale (Royal Applause) (2000) **Mrs J. Brisland**

**Other Owners:** Mr N. Andersen, Mrs J. Brisland, M. Bryson, Mrs J. A. Cornwell, Cross Channel Racing Club, Mr P. D. Ebdon, Miss M. Hancox, Mr M. J. Hocking, Houghton Bloodstock, Mr M. Seedel, R. W. Sharp, Stapleford Racing Ltd, Mrs F. A. Veasey.

**Flat Jockey:** Martin Harley, Luke Morris.

---

|  | **MR ANTONY BRITTAIN, Warthill** |
|---|---|
| **64** | Postal: **Northgate Lodge, Warthill, York, YO19 5XR**<br>Contacts: **PHONE 01759 371472 FAX 01759 372915**<br>**EMAIL email@antonybrittain.co.uk WEBSITE www.antonybrittain.co.uk** |

1 ABNAA, 4, b g Dark Angel (IRE)—Along Came Casey (IRE) **John & Tony Jarvis & Partner**
2 ANOTHER ANGEL (IRE), 7, b g Dark Angel (IRE)—Kermana (IRE) **Mr Antony Brittain**
3 BEATBYBEATBYBEAT, 8, ch m Poet's Voice—Beat As One **Mr Antony Brittain**
4 CANFORD BAY (IRE), 7, b g Canford Cliffs (IRE)—Maundays Bay (IRE) **Northgate Racing**
5 DAAFR (IRE), 5, b g Invincible Spirit (IRE)—Kitty Love (USA) **Mrs C. Brittain**
6 DIYARI (IRE), 4, b g Dubawi (IRE)—Mutebah (IRE) **Made Profiles Ltd & Partner**
7 DRAKEFELL (IRE), 6, b h Canford Cliffs (IRE)—Cake (IRE) **Northgate Racing**
8 INEXPLICABLE (IRE), 4, b g Dark Angel (IRE)—Bikini Babe (IRE) **R Wherritt & Partner**
9 INTERNATIONAL LAW, 7, gr g Exceed And Excel (AUS)—Cruel Sea (USA) **John & Tony Jarvis & Partner**
10 KLOPP, 5, b m Monsieur Bond (IRE)—Caranbola **Mr Antony Brittain**
11 LUCKY LODGE, 11, b g Lucky Story (USA)—Melandre **Mr Antony Brittain**
12 MONDAMMEJ, 4, b g Lope de Vega (IRE)—Lamps of Heaven (IRE) **Mrs C. Brittain**
13 MUTABAAHY (IRE), 6, b g Oasis Dream—Habaayib **King For A Day & Antony Brittain**
14 ONE ONE SEVEN (IRE), 5, b g Arcano (IRE)—Maany (USA) **John & Tony Jarvis & Partner**
15 PUCHITA (IRE), 6, b m Acclamation—Violet Ballerina (IRE) **Mr Antony Brittain**
16 QAARAAT, 6, b g Acclamation—Ladyship **Mr Antony Brittain**
17 RAABEH, 4, b g Showcasing—Twinkle Twinkle **John & Tony Jarvis & Partner**
18 ROOT SIXTY SIX, 4, ch g Monsieur Bond (IRE)—Mozayada (USA) **Mr Antony Brittain**
19 SLOWMO (IRE), 5, b g Kodiac—Motion Lass **Mr Antony Brittain**
20 SPARTAN FIGHTER, 4, b g Dutch Art—Survived **John & Tony Jarvis & Partner**
21 TATHMEEN (IRE), 6, b g Exceed And Excel (AUS)—Deyaar (USA) **Mr Antony Brittain**
22 THAWRY, 6, b g Iffraaj—Salacia (IRE) **Mr Antony Brittain**
23 TRAVELLER (FR), 7, b g Henrythenavigator (USA)—Nantes (GER) **John & Tony Jarvis & Partner**
24 VAN DIJK, 4, b g Cable Bay (IRE)—Stresa **Mr Antony Brittain**

### THREE-YEAR-OLDS
25 ALL ABOUT CHARLEY, b f Music Master—Lorimer's Lot (IRE) **Mr S Lorimer**
26 MABDAA, b g Oasis Dream—Darajaat (USA) **Tykes & Terriers Racing Club**
27 STAMFORD BRIDGE, b g Albaasil (IRE)—Caranbola **Mr Antony Brittain**
28 UPSIDE DOWN, b f Albaasil (IRE)—Melandre **Mr Antony Brittain**

**Other Owners:** Mr Antony Brittain, Mr I. Harle, Mr A. Jarvis, Mr J. Jarvis, King For A Day Club, Made Profiles Ltd, Mr B Totty, Mr J R Wherritt.

**Flat Jockey:** Cam Hardie.

**65** **MR DANIEL BROOKE, Middleham**
Postal: **Brough Farm, Middleham, LEYBURN, North Yorkshire, DL8 4SG**
Contacts: **PHONE 01969 625259**
EMAIL danny.brooke@yahoo.com

1 **COSMIC LAW (IRE)**, 5, b g No Nay Never (USA)—Dhamma (USA) **Mrs J. A. Brooke**
2 **DERWENT DEALER (IRE)**, 5, gr g Cloudings (IRE)—Feenakilmeedy (IRE) **D & S Barker**
3 **DIABOLEO (FR)**, 5, ch g Galileo (IRE)—Beautifix (GER) **Mrs J. A. Brooke**
4 **EMMA BEAG (IRE)**, 10, b m Westerner—Emma Jane (IRE) **Maurice Friel, Mrs Mary Sadler & Partner**
5 **FAHAD**, 4, b g Farhh—Radhaadh (IRE) **Mr S. C. Foster**
6 **FIDDLERS BOW (IRE)**, 12, b g Whitmore's Conn (USA)—
Soraleda (IRE) **MT Buckley & Brough Farm Racing Partners**
7 **FLAVIUS TITUS**, 6, ch g Lethal Force (IRE)—Furbelow **Mr Foster & Partner**
8 **FREQUENCY CODE (FR)**, 5, ch g Le Havre (IRE)—Stylish **Mrs J. A. Brooke**
9 **GET THE FACTS (IRE)**, 7, b g Publisher (USA)—Ollar Rose **Mrs M. Hatfield & Mrs S. Kramer**
10 **GLENGARRY**, 8, b g Monsieur Bond (IRE)—Lady McBeth (IRE) **The Glengarry Partnership**
11 **GLOBETROTTER (IRE)**, 7, ch g Helmet (AUS)—Shimna **Sowray Brothers, Brooke & Platts**
12 **LONGTIMESINCEJASPR (IRE)**, 7, b m Stowaway—A Tanner Rate (IRE) **Exors of the Late J. D. Gordon**
13 **LORD OF THE ROCK (IRE)**, 9, b g Rock of Gibraltar (IRE)—La Sylphide **Mrs J. A. Brooke**
14 **MELGATE MAJEURE**, 5, br g Lethal Force (IRE)—Ambrix (IRE) **MT Buckley & Brough Farm Racing Partners**
15 **MELVICH BAY**, 4, b f Telescope (IRE)—Douryna **Mr A. Grant**
16 **NORTHERN LYTE**, 5, b m Sir Percy—Phoenix Clubs (IRE) **Mr A. Grant**
17 **PIAZON**, 10, br g Striking Ambition—Colonel's Daughter **The Body Warmers**
18 **REASSURANCE**, 6, b m Champs Elysees—Timely Words **Mr J. Platts**
19 **REVERANT CUST (IRE)**, 10, gr g Daylami (IRE)—Flame Supreme (IRE) **The Three Eejits**
20 **SAUCHIEHALL STREET (IRE)**, 6, b g Mastercraftsman—Top Trail (USA) **The Dalby Family**
21 **STARLYTE (IRE)**, 4, b f Sir Percy—Virevolte (FR) **Mr A. Grant**
22 **SWEET MARMALADE (IRE)**, 6, b m Duke of Marmalade (IRE)—Lady Chaparral **Mr & Mrs G. Turnbull**
23 **TRUE ROMANCE (IRE)**, 7, gr g Mastercraftsman (IRE)—Full of Love (IRE) **Mr K. S. Ward**
24 **WESTDANTE (IRE)**, 6, b g Westerner—Mydante (IRE) **Mrs J. A. Brooke**

**THREE-YEAR-OLDS**

25 **GEORGE SQUARE (IRE)**, b g Epaulette (AUS)—Corsage (IRE) **Alan Court & Brough Farm Racing Partners**

**TWO-YEAR-OLDS**

26 B g 02/05 Due Diligence (USA)—Triveni (FR) (Lando (GER)) (7619) **D & S Barker**

**Other Owners:** Mr D. Barker, Mrs S. J. Barker, Mrs J. A. Brooke, Brough Farm Racing Partnership, Mr M. T. Buckley, Mr A. Court, Mrs J. A. Dalby, Mr P.N. Dalby, Mr S. C. Foster, Mr M. Friel, Mrs M. Hatfield, Mrs S. Kramer, Mr J. McInerney, Mr J. Platts, Mrs M. Sadler, Mr S. A. Sowray.

**66** **LADY SUSAN BROOKE, Llandrindod Wells**
Postal: **Tyn-y-Berth Farm, Dolau, Llandrindod Wells, Powys, LD1 5TW**
Contacts: **PHONE 01597 851190 MOBILE 07977 114834**
EMAIL suebrooke@live.co.uk

1 **ORCHESTRATED (IRE)**, 10, b g Mahler—Rose Island **Lady Brooke**
2 **OXFORD BLU**, 7, b g Aqlaam—Blue Zealot (IRE) **Lady Brooke**
3 **SNOWPIERCER (FR)**, 7, b g Astarabad (USA)—My Darling Rose (FR) **Lady Brooke**
4 **SPOCK (FR)**, 16, b g Lost World (IRE)—Quark Top (FR) **Lady Brooke**
5 **STARCROSSED**, 9, b g Cape Cross (IRE)—Gretna **Lady Brooke**
6 **THREE COUNTY'S (IRE)**, 10, b br g Beneficial—Pattern Queen (IRE) **Lady Brooke**
7 **VINNIE RED (IRE)**, 12, ch g Vinnie Roe (IRE)—Conzara (IRE) **Lady Brooke**
8 **YOURHOLIDAYISOVER (IRE)**, 14, ch g Sulamani (IRE)—Whitehaven **Lady Brooke**

**Assistant Trainer:** Lorna Brooke.

**Amateur Jockey:** Miss Lorna Brooke.

## MR ROY BROTHERTON, Pershore
**67** Postal: Mill End Racing Stables, Netherton Road, Elmley Castle, Pershore, Worcestershire, WR10 3JF
Contacts: **PHONE 01386 710772 MOBILE 07973 877280**

1 **AUNTIE JUNE**, 5, ch m Piccolo—Basle **Mr M. A. Geobey**
2 **CNOC SION (IRE)**, 11, b g Gold Well—Bondi Babe (IRE) **Exors of the Late C. A. Newman**
3 **DEISE VU (IRE)**, 13, b g Brian Boru—Deise Dreamer (IRE) **Elmley Queen**
4 **DUN BAY CREEK**, 10, b g Dubai Destination (USA)—Over It **Elmley Queen 2**
5 **FILBERT STREET**, 6, ch g Poet's Voice—Tinnarinka **R. Brotherton**
6 **LANZAROTE SUNSHINE**, 4, b f Music Master—Basle **Mr M. A. Geobey**
7 **MIRACLE GARDEN**, 9, ch g Exceed And Excel (AUS)—Sharp Terms **Mr M. A. Geobey**
8 **PRESENTING BEARA (IRE)**, 13, b g Presenting—Ginger Bar (IRE) **R. Brotherton**

**Other Owners:** R. Brotherton, Mr N. A. Lavender Jones, Mr M. A. Savage.

**Assistant Trainer:** Justin Brotherton.

**NH Jockey:** Jamie Moore.


## MR ALAN BROWN, Malton
**68** Postal: Lilac Farm, Yedingham, Malton, North Yorkshire, YO17 8SS
Contacts: **PHONE 01944 728090 MOBILE 07970 672845**
**EMAIL** ad.brown@hotmail.co.uk **WEBSITE** www.alanbrownracing.co.uk

1 **ATRAFAN (IRE)**, 7, b g Atraf—Up Front (IRE) **Mr F. E. Reay**
2 **BLACKCURRENT**, 5, b g Kuroshio (AUS)—Mamounia (IRE) **Max Europe Limited**
3 **BLACKJACK**, 4, b g Sleeping Indian—Medam **The Hon Mrs E. S. Cunliffe-Lister**
4 **GUARDIA SVIZZERA (IRE)**, 7, b g Holy Roman Emperor (IRE)—Winged Harriet (IRE) **Rangers Racing Syndicate**
5 **JEMS BOND**, 4, ch g Monsieur Bond (IRE)—Saphire **Mr S. Pedersen & Mr Frank Reay**
6 **THOMAS HAWK**, 4, b g Gregorian (IRE)—Miss Mohawk (IRE) **Mrs M. A. Doherty**

### THREE-YEAR-OLDS
7 **EMBLA**, b f Albaasil (IRE)—Medam **The Hon Mrs E. S. Cunliffe-Lister**
8 **LILY'S GIFT**, b f Poet's Voice—Nefetari **Mr Frank Reay & Mr A. D. Brown**
9 **SHEILA'S LEGACY**, ch f Medicean—Fairy Shoes **The Odd Partnership**

### TWO-YEAR-OLDS
10 B g 21/03 Albaasil (IRE)—Medam (Medicean) **The Hon Mrs E. S. Cunliffe-Lister**
11 B f 10/04 Night of Thunder (IRE)—Nefetari (Kodiac) **Mr F. E. Reay**
12 B c 11/04 Peace Envoy (FR)—Redalani (IRE) (Redback) **S. E. Pedersen**
13 **URBAN ROAD**, ch c 24/03 Monsieur Bond (IRE)—Normandy Maid (American Post) **Max Europe Limited**

**Other Owners:** A. D. Brown, Mr D. D. Oakes, S. E. Pedersen, Mr F. E. Reay.

**69**
## MR ANDI BROWN, Newmarket
Postal: **Southfields Stables, Hamilton Road, Newmarket, Suffolk, CB8 7JQ**
Contacts: **PHONE 01638 669652 MOBILE 07980 393263 FAX 01638 669652**
EMAIL southfieldsstables@btinternet.com WEBSITE www.southfieldsstables.co.uk

1 **BROUGHTONS RUBY**, 5, b m Harbour Watch (IRE)—Broughtons Jewel (IRE)  **Broughton Thermal Insulations**
2 **KIRTLING**, 10, gr g Araafa (IRE)—Cape Maya  **Faith Hope and Charity**

### THREE-YEAR-OLDS
3 **CAMASSIA (IRE)**, b f Holy Roman Emperor (IRE)—Duna (GER)  **A. S. Brown**

**Assistant Trainer:** Miss Linsey Knocker.

---

**70**
## MR DAVID BROWN, Whitby
Postal: **6 Linden Lane, Newholm, Whitby, North Yorkshire, YO21 3QX**
Contacts: **PHONE 01636 613793 MOBILE 07889 132931**
EMAIL david@davidbrownracing.com

1 **BEN LILLY (IRE)**, 4, b g Gleneagles (IRE)—Aristocratic Lady (USA)  **Jack Thomas & Ben Thomas**
2 **CRUISING**, 4, b g Helmet (AUS)—Lanai (IRE)  **Mr R. Hull**
3 **FROW (IRE)**, 5, b g Swiss Spirit—Royal Arruhan  **Mr A. Cosias**
4 **FUTURE INVESTMENT**, 5, b g Mount Nelson—Shenir  **R.N.J. Partnership**
5 **HARBOUR VISION**, 6, gr g Harbour Watch (IRE)—Holy Nola (USA)  **New Vision Bloodstock**
6 **NORTHERN CHARM**, 4, b f Equiano (FR)—Grace Hull  **Mr R. Hull**
7 **TRUE HERO**, 5, b g Charm Spirit (IRE)—Beldale Memory (IRE)  **Mr R. Hull**

### THREE-YEAR-OLDS
8 **CAN CAN GIRL (IRE)**, b f Champs Elysees—Osthurry (IRE)  **Bratwa**
9 **HARWORTH (IRE)**, b g Showcasing—Kiyra Wells (IRE)  **Mr R. Hull**
10 **LADY ZIANA**, b f Dawn Approach (IRE)—Heartlines (USA)  **Mount Pleasant Farm Syndicate**
11 **MAGIC GEM**, ch c Garswood—Thorntoun Piccolo  **Mr R. Hull**
12 **PIPS TUNE**, ch g Helmet (AUS)—Paquerettza (FR)  **Mrs S. Brown**
13 **ROADRUNNER (IRE)**, b g Make Believe—Flanders (IRE)  **Bratwa**
14 **SOVEREIGN MOON**, b f Swiss Spirit—Rivas Rhapsody (IRE)  **Mr R. Hull**
15 **VIVIENS GIRL**, gr f Brazen Beau (AUS)—Grace Hull  **Mr R. Hull**

### TWO-YEAR-OLDS
16 B g 30/01 Gutaifan (IRE)—Elfine (IRE) (Invincible Spirit (IRE)) (7619)  **Mr R. Hull**
17 B f 05/03 Red Jazz (USA)—Gypsy Style (Desert Style (IRE))
18 B f 23/03 Helmet (AUS)—Lanai (IRE) (Camacho)  **Mr R. Hull**
19 **LETHAL VISION**, b f 22/03 Lethal Force (IRE)—Pigeon Point (Harbour Watch (IRE)) (1000)  **New Vision Bloodstock**
20 **SUN RISING (IRE)**, ch f 17/04 Dawn Approach (IRE)—
                              Beauty Pageant (IRE) (Bahamian Bounty)  **D H Brown, Mr Clive Watson & Mr J. R. Atherton**

**Other Owners:** Mr J. R. Atherton, Mr D. H. Brown, Mr R. Hull, N. Skinner, Mr B. M. Thomas, Mr J. F. Thomas, Mr C. Watson.

**Assistant Trainer:** Dushyant Dooyea.

**Flat Jockey:** Tom Eaves.

## 71 MR GARY BROWN, Compton
Postal: **East Yard, Hamilton Stables, Hockham Road, Compton, Berkshire, RG20 6QJ**
Contacts: **PHONE 07545 915253**
**EMAIL gbrownracing@hotmail.co.uk**

1 **ALIOSKI**, 4, b g Kodiac—Luluti (IRE) **G. Cheshire**
2 **CLOSE FRIEND (IRE)**, 5, b g Ocovango—Apterous (IRE) **Mr S. Doyle**
3 **HE IS A CRACKER (FR)**, 5, b g Califet (FR)—She Is A Cracker (FR) **Mr N. Byrne**
4 **KEEP BELIEVING (IRE)**, 7, b g Zoffany (IRE)—What About Me (IRE) **Mr J. Buckland**
5 **MAKE A DEAL (IRE)**, 5, b g Shantou (USA)—Miss Denman (IRE) **Mr S. Doyle**
6 **SATURDAY SONG**, 5, b g Kayf Tara—Fernello **Mr S. Doyle**
7 **SHALOTT (IRE)**, 4, b g Camelot—Nasanice (IRE) **Mr G. Costelloe**

## 72 MISS MICHELLE BRYANT, Lewes
Postal: **Bevern Bridge Farm Cottage, South Chailey, Lewes, East Sussex, BN8 4QH**
Contacts: **PHONE 01273 400638 MOBILE 07976 217542**
**EMAIL bear_2009@live.co.uk**

1 **CHURCHTOWN GLEN (IRE)**, 8, b g Getaway (GER)—Annagh Lady (IRE) **Miss M P Bryant, David & Eileen Bryant**
2 **CORLOUGH MOUNTAIN**, 17, ch g Inchinor—Two Step **Miss M. P. Bryant**
3 **FITZY**, 5, b g Epaulette (AUS)—Zagarock **Miss M. P. Bryant**
4 **HAWK GOLD (IRE)**, 17, ch g Tendulkar (USA)—Heiress of Meath (IRE) **Miss M. P. Bryant**
5 **KILLABRAHER CROSS (IRE)**, 14, gr g Kasmayo—Enoughrose (IRE) **Miss M. P. Bryant**

**Other Owners:** Mr D. Bryant, Mrs E. Bryant, Miss M. P. Bryant.

**Amateur Jockey:** Miss M. P. Bryant.

## 73 MR BOB BUCKLER, Bridgwater
Postal: **Gibb Hill, Courtway, Spaxton, Bridgwater, Somerset, TA5 1DR**
Contacts: **PHONE 01278 671268 MOBILE 07785 773957**
**EMAIL rbuckler@btconnect.com WEBSITE www.robertbucklerracing.co.uk**

1 **ALL KINGS (IRE)**, 12, b g Milan—Rilmount (IRE) **R. H. Buckler**
2 **ARCTIC POET**, 5, b g Dylan Thomas (IRE)—Arctic Flow **Mrs H. R. Dunn**
3 **BALLYEGAN (IRE)**, 16, b g Saddlers' Hall (IRE)—Knapping Princess (IRE) **R. H. Buckler**
4 **BARBARIAN**, 5, b g Black Sam Bellamy (IRE)—Mizzurka **Golden Cap**
5 **CUSHUISH**, 8, b m Yeats (IRE)—My Petra **Cushuish Syndicate**
6 **FLOWING CADENZA**, 7, b m Yeats (IRE)—Over The Flow **Mrs H. R. Dunn**
7 **GIBB HILL**, 7, ch g Frozen Fire (GER)—River Reine (IRE) **Mrs D Gamble & R H Buckler**
8 **MIZZ MOONDANCE**, 6, b m Yeats (IRE)—Mizzurka **R. H. Buckler**
9 **REGAL FLOW**, 14, b g Erhaab (USA)—Flow **Mrs H. R. Dunn**
10 **SAKANDI**, 6, b m Frozen Fire (GER)—River Reine (IRE) **4 Gals and a filly**
11 **UNWIN VC**, 7, b g Black Sam Bellamy (IRE)—Becky B **Golden Cap**

**Other Owners:** R. H. Buckler, Mrs D. R. Gamble.

**Head Lad:** Giles Scott.

**Conditional Jockey:** Sean Houlihan.

**74** **MR TOBY BULGIN, Thetford**
Postal: **High Fen, Thornham Road, Methwold, Thetford, Norfolk, IP26 4PJ**
EMAIL toby@beatbushfarm.co.uk

1 **DARLING ALKO (FR)**, 8, b g Al Namix (FR)—Padalko Tatou (FR) **Mrs N. H. Bulgin**
2 **GERRITZEN**, 6, ch m Geordieland (FR)—Wibble Wobble **Mrs N. H. Bulgin**
3 6, B m Librettist (USA)—Jessie May (IRE) **Mrs N. H. Bulgin**
4 **RAPAPORT**, 9, b m Dr Massini (IRE)—Seemarye **Mrs N. H. Bulgin**
5 **SOLAR SOVEREIGN (IRE)**, 6, b g Multiplex—Royal Roxy (IRE) **Mrs N. H. Bulgin**
6 **TRICOMI**, 6, b br m Getaway (GER)—Annaghbrack (IRE) **Mrs N. H. Bulgin**

**THREE-YEAR-OLDS**

7 B f Clovis du Berlais (FR)—Mere Detail (IRE) **Mrs N. H. Bulgin**
8 **WAIKIKI SOL**, b g Brazen Beau (AUS)—Wiki Tiki **Mr M. Bartram**

**TWO-YEAR-OLDS**

9 B f 08/05 Kayf Tara—Mere Detail (IRE) (Definite Article) **Mrs N. H. Bulgin**


**75** **MR DAI BURCHELL, Ebbw Vale**
Postal: **Drysiog Farm, Briery Hill, Ebbw Vale, Gwent, NP23 6BU**
Contacts: **PHONE 01495 302551 MOBILE 07980 482860**

1 **BENTLEY WOOD**, 4, b g Sixties Icon—Dozen (FR) **The Bill & Ben Partnership**
2 **CROPLEY (IRE)**, 12, gr g Galileo (IRE)—Niyla (IRE) **Miss S. Carter**
3 **DAWNSLITTLEDIAMOND**, 4, b f Pether's Moon (IRE)—Gallimaufry **Mr L. Davies**
4 **FACT FLOW (IRE)**, 12, br g Whitmore's Conn (USA)—Beaver Run (IRE) **The Bill & Ben Partnership**
5 **FURIOUSLY FAST (IRE)**, 9, b g Fast Company (IRE)—Agouti **B. M. G. Group**
6 **GOOD IMPRESSION**, 6, b g Showcasing—Daintily Done **B. M. G. Group**
7 **WINGED ISLE**, 6, b g Winged Love (IRE)—Zaffaranni (IRE) **Mrs G. A. Davies**

**Assistant Trainer:** Ruth Burchell.

**Flat Jockey:** Hollie Doyle. **NH Jockey:** Robert Dunne, Alan Johns. **Conditional Jockey:** Jordan Nailor. **Amateur Jockey:**
Miss Jodie Hughes.


**76** **MR KARL BURKE, Leyburn**
Postal: **Spigot Lodge, Middleham, Leyburn, North Yorkshire, DL8 4TL**
Contacts: **PHONE 01969 625088 MOBILE 07778 458777 FAX 01969 625099**
EMAIL karl@karlburke.co.uk WEBSITE www.karlburke.co.uk

1 **AINSDALE**, 4, b c Mayson—Bruni Heinke (IRE) **Mr D. W. Armstrong**
2 **ANGEL OF THE GLEN (FR)**, 4, b f Gleneagles (IRE)—Archangel Gabriel (USA) **Hunscote Stud Limited**
3 **ASTRO JAKK (IRE)**, 5, b g Zoffany (IRE)—By The Edge (IRE) **Titanium Racing Club**
4 **BARON RUN**, 11, ch g Bertolini (USA)—Bhima **Mr Eric Burke & Partner**
5 **BORN TO BE ALIVE (IRE)**, 7, b g Born To Sea (IRE)—Yaria (IRE) **Mr T Dykes & Mrs E Burke**
6 **DULCIMA (IRE)**, 4, ch f Australia—Boast **Mr M Smith & Mr D Kilpatrick**
7 **EXALTED ANGEL (FR)**, 5, b g Dark Angel (IRE)—Hurryupharriet (IRE) **Pau-perth Partnership & Mrs E Burke**
8 **FRONTLINE PHANTOM (IRE)**, 14, b g Noverre (USA)—Daisy Hill **Mr Eric Burke & Partner**
9 **KELLY'S DINO (FR)**, 8, b g Doctor Dino (FR)—Sabolienne (FR) **Mr Liam Kelly & Mrs E Burke**
10 **LADY IN FRANCE**, 5, b m Showcasing—Sacre Coeur **Clipper Group Holdings Ltd**
11 **LITTLE RED SOCKS (IRE)**, 4, b f Acclamation—Wild Academy (IRE) **Mrs E. M. Burke**

## MR KARL BURKE - continued

12 **LORD OBERON**, 6, b g Mayson—Fairy Shoes  **Mr D J MacKay & Mrs E Burke**
13 **LORD OF THE LODGE (IRE)**, 4, b c Dandy Man (IRE)—Archetypal (IRE)  **Mrs E. M. Burke**
14 **MOONBOOTZ (IRE)**, 4, ch g No Nay Never (USA)—Orange Pip  **Titanium Racing Club**
15 **NEVER IN PARIS (IRE)**, 4, b f No Nay Never (USA)—Meeting In Paris (IRE)  **Ontoawinner, A Marsh & E Burke**
16 **PARALLEL WORLD (IRE)**, 5, b g Morpheus—Miss Glitters (IRE)  **Ontoawinner 14 & Mrs E Burke**
17 **RAYONG**, 4, b g Mayson—Lydiate (IRE)  **King Power Racing Co Ltd**
18 **RAYYAN**, 4, b g Siyouni (FR)—Hurryapharriet (IRE)  **Al Shaqab Racing UK Limited**
19 **SALINE BAY (IRE)**, 4, b f Maxios—Breathe (FR)  **Miss I. Keogh**
20 **SHALLOW HAL**, 5, b g Mayson—Bazelle  **Ontoawinner 14 & Mrs E Burke**
21 **SOCIALLY SHADY**, 4, ch g Zoffany (IRE)—Executrix  **Mr Liam Kelly & Mrs E Burke**
22 **SUPERIORITY (IRE)**, 4, b f Exceed And Excel (AUS)—Janina  **Mr J Laughton & Mrs E Burke**
23 **TELE RED**, 4, b g Telescope (IRE)—Hardy Blue (IRE)  **Mr J. Kenny**
24 **WOKE (IRE)**, 4, b br f Showcasing—Analysis  **Mrs E. M. Burke**
25 **YES ALWAYS (IRE)**, 4, b f No Nay Never (USA)—Flavia Tatiana (IRE)  **The Cool Silk Partnership**
26 **YOU'RE FIRED (IRE)**, 10, b g Firebreak—My Sweet Georgia (IRE)  **Mrs E. M. Burke**

## THREE-YEAR-OLDS

27 **ALBA DE TORMES (IRE)**, gr c Lope de Vega (IRE)—Danaskaya (IRE)  **Ballylinch Stud**
28 **ALYARA**, b f Cable Bay (IRE)—Norway Cross  **Mr M. S. Al Shahi**
29 Br c Garswood—Anglezarke (IRE)  **Mr D. W. Armstrong**
30 **BAMBULE (FR)**, b f Dabirsim (FR)—Bleu Nil (IRE)  **Ecurie Normandie Pur Sang**
31 **BICKERSTAFFE**, b c Mayson—Ocean Boulevard  **Mr D. W. Armstrong**
32 **BLUEWATER LADY (USA)**, b f Noble Mission—Water Hole (IRE)  **Morera Partnership**
33 **BOOGIE TIME (IRE)**, b g Kodiac—Get Up And Dance  **Mr Carl Waters & Mrs E Burke**
34 **BRIGHT APPARITION**, b g Charm Spirit (IRE)—Katie's Diamond (FR)  **Mr D J MacKay & Mrs E Burke**
35 **CELESTIAL QUEEN**, b f Dark Angel (IRE)—Agnes Stewart (IRE)  **Clipper Group Holdings Ltd**
36 **CUBANO (IRE)**, ch g Havana Gold (IRE)—Special Miss  **Mr T. J. Dykes**
37 **DABIRSTAR (FR)**, b f Dabirsim (FR)—Aster Nox (USA)  **Hold Your Horses Racing & Mrs E Burke**
38 **DANDALLA (IRE)**, b f Dandy Man (IRE)—Chellalla  **Nick Bradley Racing 28 & E Burke**
39 **DISTINCTION (IRE)**, b g Kodiac—Tajbell (IRE)  **Mr Carl Waters & Mrs E Burke**
40 **ELAKAZAAM (IRE)**, b g Elzaam (AUS)—Adaptation  **More Turf Racing & Mrs E Burke**
41 **FAE THE PORT (FR)**, b g French Navy—Gipsy Doll  **Men Fae the Clyde**
42 **HIGHTOWN HEIGHTS (IRE)**, b f Teofilo (IRE)—Wedding Wish (IRE)  **Mr C. R. Hirst**
43 **INFLUENCE IS POWER (IRE)**, b g Kodi Bear (IRE)—Siesta Time  **Hj Racing & Mrs E Burke**
44 **INVINCIBLY (IRE)**, b g Invincible Spirit (IRE)—Recite (JPN)  **Apple Tree Stud**
45 **JACATTACK (IRE)**, ch g Anjaal—Onomatomania (USA)  **Mrs E. M. Burke**
46 **KEVIN THE MINION (IRE)**, bl g Brazen Beau (AUS)—Dark Opal (IRE)  **Mr G. White**
47 **KORNFLAKE (IRE)**, ch f Night of Thunder (IRE)—Muccia (IRE)  **Mr C. R. Hirst**
48 **LEAD STORY (IRE)**, b f New Bay—Newsletter (IRE)  **Ballylinch Stud**
49 **MILLIONS**, ch c Pivotal—Sugar Mill  **Mr Carl Waters & Mrs E Burke**
50 **MINEANDYOURS**, b g Garswood—Celestial Dawn  **Heaton, Buckle & Burke**
51 **MISS SEAFIRE (IRE)**, b f Dandy Man (IRE)—Solstice  **Mr Carl Waters & Mrs E Burke**
52 **NIGHT OF ROMANCE**, ch f Night of Thunder (IRE)—Shohrah (IRE)  **Mr J Laughton & Mrs E Burke**
53 **NORTH OF AMAZING**, b g Havana Gold (IRE)—Princess Guest (IRE)  **Mrs B Keller & Mrs E Burke**
54 **OMANY AMBER**, gr f Gregorian (IRE)—Londonnetdotcom (IRE)  **K. A. Dasmal**
55 **OPEN MYSTERY**, ch g Garswood—Mysterious Girl (IRE)  **Hambleton Racing Ltd XXXV & E Burke**
56 **READMAN**, b g Showcasing—Blue Aegean  **Clipper Group Holdings Ltd**
57 **REBEL AT DAWN (IRE)**, b g Dandy Man (IRE)—Ragtime Dancer  **Mr Carl Waters & Mrs E Burke**
58 **RED FASCINATOR**, b f Kodiac—Red Turban  **Cheveley Park Stud Limited**
59 **RED RIGHT SAND (IRE)**, gr g Footstepsinthesand—Artistica (IRE)  **More Turf Racing & Mrs E Burke**
60 Ch g Garswood—Robin Park  **Mr D. W. Armstrong**
61 **SEEKING PERFECTION**, b f Twilight Son—Arabian Music (IRE)  **Mr Carl Waters & Mrs E Burke**
62 **SHAABASH (IRE)**, b g Poet's Voice—Vanity's Girl (IRE)  **Mr B Chatwal & Mrs E Burke**
63 **SHE'S NO ANGEL (IRE)**, ch f Libertarian—Angel Voices (IRE)  **Mrs E. M. Burke**
64 **SHE'S SO NICE (IRE)**, b f Mehmas (IRE)—Elkimatt  **Mr Carl Waters & Mrs E Burke**
65 **SIGNIFICANTLY**, ch c Garswood—Rosebride  **Mr J Laughton & Mrs E Burke**
66 **SIMONS KING (IRE)**, b c Kingman—Sanaya (IRE)  **Ecurie Normandie Pur Sang**
67 **SONDERBAR**, b c Siyouni (FR)—Sandbar  **Ecurie Normandie Pur Sang**
68 **SPYCATCHER (IRE)**, b c Vadamos (FR)—Damask (IRE)  **Highclere T'BredRacing-Adriana Zaefferer**

## MR KARL BURKE - continued

69 **STAR ACT (IRE)**, b f Acclamation—Sign From Heaven (IRE) **Mrs E. M. Burke**
70 **STONEGARTH (IRE)**, b g Gutaifan (IRE)—Mayorstone (IRE) **Hope Eden Racing Ltd & Mrs E Burke**
71 **STYLISH PERFORMER (IRE)**, ch g Dandy Man (IRE)—Va Pensiero (IRE) **Pau - Perth Partnership**
72 **SURF (FR)**, b f Oasis Dream—Eleona (GER) **David Redvers & Sarah O'Connell**
73 **TAPETEN TONI (FR)**, ch g Mehmas (IRE)—Takara Girl (FR) **Ecurie Normandie Pur Sang**
74 **TARNEEMAT**, b f War Command (USA)—Sounds of April (IRE) **Mr A. Mohamdi**
75 **TERRICHANG**, b f Dandy Man (IRE)—Fleur de Sel **Nick Bradley Racing 2 & Mrs E Burke**
76 **TIKI FIRE (IRE)**, b f Awtaad (IRE)—Debuetantin **& Dance**
77 **TIPPERARY TIGER (IRE)**, b g Mayson—Tipperary Boutique (IRE) **Get & E Lets Get Racing & Mrs E Burke**
78 **TRICKY SOLDIER (FR)**, b c Soldier Hollow—Totsiyah (IRE) **Ecurie Normandie Pur Sang**
79 **UCCELLO (IRE)**, b c Frankel—Apsara (FR) **Clipper Group Holdings Ltd**
80 **WEST WAY NEVER (IRE)**, b f No Nay Never (USA)—Western Mystic (GER) **Ecurie Normandie Pur Sang**
81 **WIZARD D'AMOUR**, gr ro c Dutch Art—Holistic **Mr Carl Waters & Mrs E Burke**
82 **YEMENI AMBER**, b f Territories (IRE)—Varnish **K. A. Dasmal**

## TWO-YEAR-OLDS

83 B c 19/03 Dandy Man (IRE)—Adaptation (Spectrum (IRE)) (47619) **Claret & Racing**
84 **ALMOHANDESAH**, b f 22/03 Postponed (IRE)—Chocolate Hills (FR) (Exceed And Excel (AUS)) (16500) **A. Al Shaikh**
85 Ch f 03/03 Bated Breath—Amber Queen (IRE) (Cadeaux Genereux) (20952) **Nick Bradley Racing 15 & Mrs E Burke**
86 Ch c 29/04 Monsieur Bond (IRE)—Arculinge (Paris House) (25000) **Mrs E. M. Burke**
87 B c 09/04 Intello (GER)—Augusta Ada (Byron)
88 Ch f 16/02 Garswood—Bahia Emerald (IRE) (Bahamian Bounty) (13333)
89 Gr c 28/03 El Kabeir (USA)—Ballet Move (Oasis Dream) (10000)
90 B c 08/02 Invincible Spirit (IRE)—Bruni Heinke (IRE) (Dutch Art) **Mr D. W. Armstrong**
91 Ch c 05/03 Profitable (IRE)—By The Edge (IRE) (Shinko Forest (IRE)) (37000) **Mrs E. M. Burke**
92 B c 08/04 Dandy Man (IRE)—Chicago Fall (IRE) (Dark Angel (IRE)) (38095) **K. A. Dasmal**
93 B f 03/03 Adaay (IRE)—Clouds Rest (Showcasing) (14000) **Ontoawinner, Mr & Mrs Bainbridge & Burke**
94 B c 21/03 Aclaim (IRE)—Czarna Roza (Polish Precedent (USA)) (5000) **J. C. Fretwell**
95 Gr f 25/01 Highland Reel (IRE)—Diamond Fever (IRE) (Fasliyev (USA)) (25827) **Ecurie Normandie Pur Sang**
96 B c 13/02 Vadamos (FR)—Fashionable Spirit (IRE) (Invincible Spirit (IRE)) (38095)
97 **FAVOURITE CHILD**, b f 07/03 Mattmu—Today's The Day (Alhaarth (IRE)) (4500) **Bearstone Stud Limited**
99 **FILLE DE LA LUNE**, b f 06/02 Sea The Moon (GER)—
　　　　　　　　　　　　　Tickle Me (GER) (Halling (USA)) (10476) **Nick Bradley Racing 33 + Burke**
99 **FRISKY**, ch f 18/03 Bated Breath—Thrill (Pivotal) **Cheveley Park Stud Limited**
100 **GIFTED GOLD (IRE)**, ch f 24/03 Profitable Gold—
　　　　　　　　　　　　　Flare of Firelight (USA) (Birdstone (USA)) (82000) **Mr Carl Waters & Mrs E Burke**
101 **GUILDED (IRE)**, b f 04/02 Mastercraftsman (IRE)—
　　　　　　　　　　　　　Lajatico (Equiano (FR)) (17000) **Nick Bradley Racing 1 & Mrs E Burke**
102 B c 22/01 Oasis Dream—Heavenly Verse (Poet's Voice) (27000) **Mr Liam Kelly & Mrs E Burke**
103 B c 28/04 Ardad (IRE)—High Tan (High Chaparral (IRE)) (12381)
104 **HONEY SWEET (IRE)**, b f 16/02 Adaay (IRE)—
　　　　　　　　　　　　　Sweet Sienna (Harbour Watch (IRE)) (50000) **Nick Bradley Racing 14 & Mrs E Burke**
105 B c 13/02 Mayson—Idealist (Rip Van Winkle (IRE)) (44762) **C & E Burke**
106 B l c 19/02 Dabirsim (FR)—Iffraja (IRE) (Iffraaj) (28249) **Mr M. S. Al Shahi**
107 B c 20/04 Es Que Love (IRE)—In Seconds (USA) (Giant's Causeway (USA)) **Mrs T. Burns**
108 B f 24/04 Showcasing—Infamous Angel (Exceed And Excel (AUS)) (33000) **Hj Racing & Mrs E Burke**
109 Gr c 18/01 El Kabeir (USA)—Katrine (IRE) (Kodiac) (25714) **G & E Burke**
110 B c 01/03 Elzaam (AUS)—Kiralik (Efisio) (9000) **Miss K. Buckle**
111 B c 06/02 Profitable (IRE)—
　　　　　　　　　　　　　La Roumegue (USA) (Henrythenavigator (USA)) (55238) **Almohamediya Racing & Mrs E Burke**
112 **LETHAL LEVI**, b c 27/03 Lethal Force (IRE)—Dartrix (Dutch Art) **Mr J. A. Knox and Mrs M. A. Knox**
113 **LIGHTENING GESTURE**, b c 03/02 Estidhkaar (IRE)—
　　　　　　　　　　　　　Cornlaw (Lawman (FR)) **Nick Bradley Racing 12 & Mrs E Burke**
114 Gr f 18/02 El Kabeir (USA)—Little Audio (IRE) (Shamardal (USA)) (26667) **More Turf Racing & Mrs E Burke**
115 **LULLABY BAY**, b f 31/01 Profitable (IRE)—Dubai Affair (Dubawi (IRE)) (35000) **Bearstone Stud Limited**
116 B c 06/04 Twilight Son—Madame Mere (IRE) (Dalakhani (IRE)) (9524) **Heaton, Buckle & Burke**
117 B f 24/04 Showcasing—Modesty's Way (USA) (Giant's Causeway (USA)) (15000) **Mr T Dykes & Mrs E Burke**
118 B c 01/03 Gregorian (IRE)—Mordoree (IRE) (Mayson) (10000) **Mrs T. Burns**
119 B c 01/04 Profitable (IRE)—Newsroom (IRE) (Manduro (GER)) (37000) **C & E Burke**

## MR KARL BURKE - continued

120 **OPPRESSIVE,** ch f 19/02 Ulysses (IRE)—Sultry (Pivotal) **Cheveley Park Stud Limited**
121 B f 02/03 Cotai Glory—Overheard (IRE) (Lope de Vega (IRE)) **Nick Bradley Racing 5 & E Burke**
122 **PINK STORM,** b f 20/02 Aclaim (IRE)—Rowan Brae (Haafhd) (35000) **Mr B Chatwal & Mrs E Burke**
123 B f 12/03 Time Test—Pure Joy (Zamindar (USA)) (31428) **Nick Bradley Racing 34, Redvers & Burke**
124 **QUICK CHANGE,** b f 15/01 New Approach (IRE)—Ensemble (FR) (Iron Mask (USA)) **The All About York Partnership**
125 B f 12/03 Brazen Beau (AUS)—Raggle Taggle (IRE) (Tagula (IRE)) (7143) **Hold Your Horses Racing & Mrs E Burke**
126 B c 19/04 Bungle Inthejungle—Regrette Rien (IRE) (Chevalier (IRE)) (13810)
127 **RHINOPLASTY (IRE),** ch f 23/04 Buratino (IRE)—
                    Alta Definizione (IRE) (Hawk Wing (USA)) (8571) **Nick Bradley Racing 16 + Burke**
128 B f 22/02 Ardad (IRE)—Shifting Moon (Kheleyf (USA)) (30000) **Nick Bradley Racing 17 + Burke**
129 B c 04/03 Havana Gold (IRE)—Showstoppa (Showcasing) (28571) **Mr E. J. Hughes**
130 Ch f 13/03 Exceed And Excel (AUS)—Silent Confession (Mr Greeley (USA)) **AlMohamediya Racing**
131 **SKY WATCHER (IRE),** b f 04/03 Galileo Gold—
                    Ballet of Doha (IRE) (Zebedee) (14285) **Nick Bradley Racing 35 & E Burke**
132 **SNOOZE N YOU LOSE (FR),** b f 09/04 Ribchester (IRE)—Wake Up Call (Noverre (USA)) (57143) **Mrs M. Bryce**
133 **TOTHENINES (IRE),** br gr c 18/02 Dandy Man (IRE)—
                    Ultimate Best (King's Best (USA)) (38095) **Middleham Park Racing Ci & Mrs E Burke**
134 **TRUE JEM (FR),** b f 21/02 Dabirsim (FR)—Vally Jem (FR) (Dylan Thomas (IRE)) (40355) **Nick Bradley Racing 47**
135 Ch f 28/02 Recorder—Urban Art (FR) (Siyouni (FR)) (6000) **R & B Barker**
136 B f 19/03 Estidhkaar (IRE)—Wishyouwerehere (IRE) (Footstepsinthesand) (4761) **Nick Bradley Racing 25 & E Burke**

**Other Owners:** Sheikh N. Al Khalifa, Sheikh N. M. H. Al Khalifa, AlMohamediya Racing, Miss J. K. Allison, Mr B. L. Barker, Mr
N. Bradley, Mr S. Bridge, C. Bryce, Mr P. Bryceland, Mr S. Bryceland, Miss K. Buckle, Mr E. J. Burke, Mrs E. M. Burke, Mr B. S.
Chatwal, Mrs F. H. B. Cork, Mr J. F. P. Cork, Mrs J. Dance, Mr J. E. Dance, Mr P. Doughty, Mr T. J. Dykes, Mr J. J. Fildes, Free
Claret Racing, H/J Racing, Hambleton Racing Ltd, Hambleton Racing Ltd XXXV, Mr P. Harper, Mrs R. L. Heaton, Mr C. R. Hirst,
Hold Your Horses Racing, Miss S. Holden, Mr S. G. Hope, Hope Eden Racing Limited, G. Horsford, Mr K. W. Jarvis, Mrs B. M.
Keller, Mr L. Kelly, Mr R. Kent, Mr D. F. Kilpatrick, Mr J. Laughton, Let's Get Racing Ltd, Mr D. J. MacKay, Mr A. R. W. Marsh,
Mr R. C. McKeown, Mr H. J. Merry, Middleham Park Racing Cl, More Turf Racing, Nick Bradley Racing 1, Nick Bradley Racing
12, Nick Bradley Racing 14, Nick Bradley Racing 15, Nick Bradley Racing 16, Nick Bradley Racing 17, Nick Bradley Racing 2,
Nick Bradley Racing 25 & Sohi, Nick Bradley Racing 28, Nick Bradley Racing 33, Nick Bradley Racing 34, Nick Bradley Racing
35, Nick Bradley Racing 5, Mr N. J. O'Brien, Ms S. O'Connell, Ontoawinner, Ontoawinner 14, Ontoawinner, Mr&Mrs Bainbridge,
T. S. Palin, Pau - Perth Partnership, M. Prince, Mr D. Redvers, Mr M. Smith, Mr S. R. H. Turner, Mr C. J. Waters.

**Assistant Trainer:** Mrs Elaine Burke, Kelly Burke, Lucy Burke, Joe O'Gorman, **Pupil Assistant:** Ian Hickey.

**Flat Jockey:** Ben Curtis, Clifford Lee. **Apprentice Jockey:** Rhona Pindar, Harrison Shaw.

---

**77**    **MR KEIRAN BURKE,** Sturminster Newton
         Postal: **Rudge Hill Farm, Rivers Corner, Sturminster Newton, Dorset**
         Contacts: **MOBILE 07855 860993**

1 **EVERLANES,** 8, br m Shirocco (GER)—Good Thinking **Barrow Hill**
2 **GOLDEN POET (IRE),** 9, b g Urban Poet (USA)—Little Linnet **K B Racing**
3 4, B f Fame And Glory—Good Thinking **Barrow Hill**
4 **KALABEE (IRE),** 6, b g Kalanisi (IRE)—American Honey (IRE) **K B Racing**
5 **LADY WILBERRY,** 4, br f Montmartre (FR)—Lady Willa (IRE) **Balham Hill Racing**
6 **LAST ROYAL,** 6, b g Sulamani (IRE)—First Royal (IRE) **Glanvilles Stud Partners**
7 **MINE'S A PINT,** 9, b g Network (GER)—Ryme Bere (FR) **Goodfellers Racing**
8 **MR MAGILL (FR),** 9, b g Hamairi (IRE)—Marie Cuddy (IRE) **K B Racing**
9 **PUTDECASHONTHEDASH (IRE),** 8, b g Doyen (IRE)—Be My Adelina (IRE) **Goodfellers Racing**
10 **SCRUMPY BOY,** 9, b g Apple Tree (FR)—Presuming **SMLC Racing**
11 **SOUL ICON,** 4, b g Sixties Icon—Solitairy Girl **Glanvilles Stud Partners**
12 **SPIRIT OF ROME (IRE),** 7, ch m Mastercraftsman (IRE)—Zagreb Flyer **K B Racing**

**Other Owners:** Mr K. M. F. Burke, Dr G. W. Guy, Mr W. D. Procter, Miss E. Rogers.

**78** **MR HUGH BURNS, Alnwick**
Postal: **Rose Cottage, Hedgeley Hall, Powburn, Alnwick, Northumberland, NE66 4HZ**
Contacts: **PHONE 01665 578647 MOBILE 07503 539571**
EMAIL hughburns123@hotmail.co.uk

1 **CLABARE,** 10, b g Proclamation (IRE)—Choral Singer **Mr H. Burns**
2 **COUNTRY DELIGHTS (IRE),** 8, b m Mahler—Nadwell (IRE) **Mr H. Burns**
3 **COURT TYCOON (IRE),** 9, b g Court Cave (IRE)—Tycooness (IRE) **Mr H. Burns**
4 **J POWERS FORGE (IRE),** 8, b g Bushranger (IRE)—Tillan Fuwain (FR) **Mr H. Burns**
5 **MASH POTATO (IRE),** 11, b g Whipper (USA)—Salva **Mr H. Burns**
6 **MAUREEN'S STAR (IRE),** 8, b m Gold Well—Serpentine Mine (IRE) **Mr H. Burns**
7 **MYLITTLEOULBUDDY (IRE),** 8, b m Darsi (FR)—She Will Return (IRE) **Mr H. Burns**
8 **SHANTOU CITY (IRE),** 6, ch g Shantou (USA)—Zuleika (IRE) **Mr H. Burns**
9 **SPIRIT OF DREAMS (IRE),** 6, b m Dream Ahead (USA)—Easy To Thrill **Mr H. Burns**

**79** **MR OWEN BURROWS, Lambourn**
Postal: **Kingwood House Stables Ltd, Lambourn Woodlands, Hungerford, Berkshire, RG17 7RS**
Contacts: **PHONE 01488 73144**
WORK EMAIL enquiries@kingwoodhousestables.co.uk

1 **AL FAYYAAFY,** 4, ch c Le Havre (IRE)—Adjudicate **Hamdan bin Rashid Al Maktoum**
2 **AL NAMIR (IRE),** 4, b g Shamardal (USA)—Rayaheen **Hamdan bin Rashid Al Maktoum**
3 **DANYAH (IRE),** 4, b g Invincible Spirit (IRE)—Cuis Ghaire (IRE) **Hamdan bin Rashid Al Maktoum**
4 **DAWAAM (USA),** 5, b g Kitten's Joy (USA)—Nereid (USA) **Hamdan bin Rashid Al Maktoum**
5 **FAKHOOR (IRE),** 6, b g Oasis Dream—Darajaat (USA) **Hamdan bin Rashid Al Maktoum**
6 **HUKUM (IRE),** 4, b c Sea The Stars (IRE)—Aghareed (USA) **Hamdan bin Rashid Al Maktoum**
7 **ITKAANN (IRE),** 4, b g Gutaifan (IRE)—Mimisel **Sheikh Ahmed Al Maktoum**
8 **MURAAD (IRE),** 5, gr g Dark Angel (IRE)—Hidden Girl (IRE) **Hamdan bin Rashid Al Maktoum**
9 **TAAWFAN (IRE),** 4, b f Night of Thunder (IRE)—Ameerat **Sheikh Ahmed Al Maktoum**
10 **TABDEED,** 6, ch g Havana Gold (IRE)—Puzzled (IRE) **Hamdan bin Rashid Al Maktoum**
11 **THUMUR (USA),** 4, b br g Golden Horn—Time Being **Hamdan bin Rashid Al Maktoum**

**THREE-YEAR-OLDS**
12 **ALBASHEER (IRE),** ch c Shamardal (USA)—Muteba (IRE) **Hamdan bin Rashid Al Maktoum**
13 **ALGHADEER (IRE),** b c Lope de Vega (IRE)—Dark Crusader (IRE) **Hamdan bin Rashid Al Maktoum**
14 **ALJARYAAL (FR),** b g Siyouni (FR)—Jane Eyre **Hamdan bin Rashid Al Maktoum**
15 **ANMAAT (IRE),** b g Awtaad (IRE)—African Moonlight (UAE) **Hamdan bin Rashid Al Maktoum**
16 **ASADJUMEIRAH,** b c Adaay (IRE)—Place In My Heart **Hamdan bin Rashid Al Maktoum**
17 B f Muhaarar—Bulbul (IRE) **Hadi Al-Tajir**
18 **GHAZAALY (IRE),** b f Kodiac—Airfield **Hamdan bin Rashid Al Maktoum**
19 **HASANAAT,** b f Oasis Dream—Hedaaya (IRE) **Hamdan bin Rashid Al Maktoum**
20 **JAWHARY,** b g Cable Bay (IRE)—Conservatory **Hamdan bin Rashid Al Maktoum**
21 **KHATWAH (IRE),** ch f Lope de Vega (IRE)—Accipiter **Hamdan bin Rashid Al Maktoum**
22 **LAMUTANAAHY (IRE),** b f Exceed And Excel (AUS)—Dispel **Hamdan bin Rashid Al Maktoum**
23 **MAAARKAH (IRE),** gr g Markaz (IRE)—Bunditten (IRE) **Hamdan bin Rashid Al Maktoum**
24 **MAREERA,** b f Elusive Quality (USA)—Nasmatt **Sheikh Ahmed Al Maktoum**
25 **MAWKEB (USA),** b c Kitten's Joy (USA)—Illegal Search (USA) **Hamdan bin Rashid Al Maktoum**
26 **MINZAAL (IRE),** b c Mehmas (IRE)—Pardoven (IRE) **Hamdan bin Rashid Al Maktoum**
27 **MOHASSANA (USA),** b f More Than Ready (USA)—Safarjal (IRE) **Hamdan bin Rashid Al Maktoum**
28 **MOKTASAAB,** ch c Lope de Vega (IRE)—Dash To The Front **Hamdan bin Rashid Al Maktoum**
29 **MONAAJEZ (USA),** gr c Speightstown (USA)—Broadway Show (USA) **Hamdan bin Rashid Al Maktoum**
30 **MONJAZAAT,** b f Dark Angel (IRE)—Fatanah (IRE) **Hamdan bin Rashid Al Maktoum**
31 **MOSABAQA (IRE),** b f Muhaarar—Estidraaj (USA) **Hamdan bin Rashid Al Maktoum**
32 **MUJASSID (USA),** b f Dark Angel (IRE)—Hatheer (USA) **Hamdan bin Rashid Al Maktoum**
33 **QASAAYED,** b f Lope de Vega (IRE)—Gile Na Greine (IRE) **Hamdan bin Rashid Al Maktoum**

## MR OWEN BURROWS - continued

34 **RASHEED (IRE)**, b g Oasis Dream—Raaqy (IRE)  **Hamdan bin Rashid Al Maktoum**
35 **TALBEYAH (IRE)**, b f Lope de Vega (IRE)—Thai Haku (IRE)  **Hamdan bin Rashid Al Maktoum**
36 **TAWAAZON (IRE)**, b g Invincible Spirit (IRE)—Tamadhor (IRE)  **Hamdan bin Rashid Al Maktoum**
37 **TWAASOL**, b g Adaay (IRE)—Dolly Colman (IRE)  **Sheikh Ahmed Al Maktoum**
38 **WALEYFA**, b f Awtaad (IRE)—Sweet Secret  **Sheikh Ahmed Al Maktoum**
39 **WISHAAH**, b c Oasis Dream—Mia Diletta  **Hamdan bin Rashid Al Maktoum**
40 **ZAAMMIT**, b c Muhaarar—Path of Peace  **Sheikh Ahmed Al Maktoum**

## TWO-YEAR-OLDS

41 B c 02/04 Dark Angel (IRE)—Adhwaa (Oasis Dream)  **Hamdan bin Rashid Al Maktoum**
42 B f 05/04 Intello (GER)—Aghareed (USA) (Kingmambo (USA))  **Hamdan bin Rashid Al Maktoum**
43 B f 08/03 Ribchester (IRE)—Aneedah (IRE) (Invincible Spirit (IRE)) (110000)  **Sheikh Ahmed Al Maktoum**
44 Ch f 08/02 Kitten's Joy (USA)—Aroosah (IRE) (Dansili)  **Hamdan bin Rashid Al Maktoum**
45 Ch c 17/02 Lope de Vega (IRE)—Ashaaqah (IRE) (Dansili)  **Hamdan bin Rashid Al Maktoum**
46 B f 01/03 War Front (USA)—Ausus (USA) (Invasor (ARG))  **Hamdan bin Rashid Al Maktoum**
47 B f 18/03 Exceed And Excel (AUS)—Bahjtee (Pivotal)  **Sheikh Ahmed Al Maktoum**
48 Ch f 24/02 Profitable (IRE)—Bold Assumption (Observatory (USA)) (150000)  **Hamdan bin Rashid Al Maktoum**
49 B f 12/03 Exceed And Excel (AUS)—Cool Thunder (IRE) (Shamardal (USA)) (8571)  **Hadi Al-Tajir**
50 B c 22/02 Kodiac—Eavesdrop (IRE) (Galileo (IRE)) (110000)  **Hamdan bin Rashid Al Maktoum**
51 Ch f 02/04 Speightstown (USA)—Elraazy (USA) (Malibu Moon (USA))  **Hamdan bin Rashid Al Maktoum**
52 B c 10/03 Nathaniel (IRE)—Fawaayed (IRE) (Singspiel (IRE))  **Hamdan bin Rashid Al Maktoum**
53 Ch c 06/03 Kitten's Joy (USA)—Fly Past (Zamindar (USA))  **Hamdan bin Rashid Al Maktoum**
54 B c 17/04 Muhaarar—Hedaaya (IRE) (Indian Ridge)  **Hamdan bin Rashid Al Maktoum**
55 B br c 28/03 Aclaim (IRE)—Kendal Mint (Kyllachy) (145000)  **Hamdan bin Rashid Al Maktoum**
56 B c 10/03 Acclamation—Marisol (IRE) (Teofilo (IRE)) (95000)  **Hamdan bin Rashid Al Maktoum**
57 B c 23/05 Invincible Spirit (IRE)—Mejala (IRE) (Red Ransom (USA))  **Hamdan bin Rashid Al Maktoum**
58 Gr ro f 20/04 Golden Horn—Mooakada (IRE) (Montjeu (IRE))  **Hamdan bin Rashid Al Maktoum**
59 B f 16/04 Muhaarar—Moonlit Garden (IRE) (Exceed And Excel (AUS)) (110000)  **Sheikh Ahmed Al Maktoum**
60 B c 05/02 Awtaad (IRE)—Mudawanah (Dansili)  **Hamdan bin Rashid Al Maktoum**
61 Ch f 07/03 Lope de Vega (IRE)—Mutebah (IRE) (Marju (IRE))  **Hamdan bin Rashid Al Maktoum**
62 B f 01/03 Muhaarar—Nasmatt (Danehill (USA))  **Sheikh Ahmed Al Maktoum**
63 Ch c 19/03 Sea The Stars (IRE)—Natagora (FR) (Divine Light (JPN))  **Hamdan bin Rashid Al Maktoum**
64 B c 16/03 Invincible Spirit (IRE)—Raaqy (IRE) (Dubawi (IRE))  **Hamdan bin Rashid Al Maktoum**
65 Br c 22/05 Muhaarar—Shimah (USA) (Storm Cat (USA))  **Hamdan bin Rashid Al Maktoum**
66 B c 20/04 Dark Angel (IRE)—Soraaya (IRE) (Elnadim (USA))  **Sheikh Ahmed Al Maktoum**

**Assistant Trainer:** Robert McDowall.

---

| 80 | **MR JOHN BUTLER, Newmarket**<br>Postal: **The Cottage, Charnwood Stables, Hamilton Road, Newmarket, Suffolk, CB8 7JQ**<br>Contacts: **MOBILE 07764 999743**<br>EMAIL johnbutler1@btinternet.com |
|---|---|

1 **ADMODUM (USA)**, 8, ch g Majestic Warrior (USA)—Unbridled Treasure (USA)  **Mr A. Campbell**
2 **AVARICE (IRE)**, 4, b g Zoffany (IRE)—Spirit Watch (IRE)  **L. M. Power**
3 **CASTLE KING (IRE)**, 6, b g Milan—Daneva (IRE)  **Mr J. Butler**
4 **CONNEMERA QUEEN**, 8, ch m Major Cadeaux—Cashleen (USA)  **Power Geneva Ltd**
5 **DELEYLL**, 7, ch g Sepoy (AUS)—Strings  **Power Geneva Ltd**
6 **DIVINE CONSENT**, 4, b g Muhaarar—Cozy Maria (USA)  **Mr J. Butler**
7 **DUBAI PARADISE (IRE)**, 4, ch f Exceed And Excel (AUS)—Good Place (USA)  **Mr D. James**
8 **EFFRONTE**, 4, b c Brazen Beau (AUS)—Wigan Lane  **Mr J. Butler**
9 **EGOTISTIC**, 4, ch f Sepoy (AUS)—Self Centred  **Mr J. Butler**
10 **ENZO (IRE)**, 6, b g Exceed And Excel (AUS)—Zamhrear  **Mr J. Butler**
11 **FAIR POWER (IRE)**, 7, b g Power—Pitrizza  **Mr N. Holmes**
12 **FALCAO (IRE)**, 9, b g Majestic Missile (IRE)—Cafe Lassere (USA)  **Mr J. Butler**

# MR JOHN BUTLER - continued

13 **GENUINE APPROVAL (IRE)**, 8, ch m Approve (IRE)—Genuinely (IRE) **Madeira Racing**
14 **HAVEONEYERSELF (IRE)**, 6, b g Requinto (IRE)—Charismas Birthday (IRE) **Mr J. Butler**
15 **HERONS NEST (IRE)**, 4, ch f Starspangledbanner (AUS)—Fataawy (IRE) **Mr J. Butler**
16 **INAAM (IRE)**, 8, b g Camacho—Duckmore Bay (IRE) **Power Geneva Ltd**
17 **JOYFUL DREAM (IRE)**, 7, ch m Dream Ahead (USA)—Tearsforjoy (USA) **Mr G. Dolan**
18 **KATALAN (GER)**, 8, b g Adlerflug (GER)—Kalla **Miss A. Haynes**
19 **KINGSLEY KLARION (IRE)**, 8, b g Arcano (IRE)—May Day Queen (IRE) **Madeira Racing**
20 **LOVELY LOU LOU**, 5, b m Sir Percy—Silver Linnet (IRE) **Miss E. D. Dent**
21 **MARTINEO**, 6, b g Declaration of War (USA)—Woodland Scene (IRE) **Power Geneva Ltd**
22 **MIME DANCE**, 10, b g Notnowcato—Encore My Love **Mr J. Butler**
23 **MUSTAQQIR (IRE)**, 5, b br h Shamardal (USA)—Albaraah (IRE) **Mr N. Buresli**
24 **MUTARABBY (IRE)**, 7, ch g Tamayuz—Shaarfa (USA) **White Gold**
25 **MYSTICAL CLOUDS (IRE)**, 8, gr g Cloudings (IRE)—Silent Valley **Mr A. Campbell**
26 **NEVER SURRENDER (IRE)**, 7, b g High Chaparral (IRE)—Meiosis (USA) **Mr A. Campbell**
27 **NEVER TO FORGET**, 6, b g Medicean—Fontaine House **Mr K. W. Sneath**
28 **OUT THE GATE**, 4, b g Sayif (IRE)—Aneesah **Mr J. Butler**
29 **PRECISELY**, 4, b f Al Kazeem—Easter Diva (IRE) **C Benham/ D Whitford/ L Quinn/ K Quinn**
30 **PUSHKIN MUSEUM (IRE)**, 10, gr g Soviet Star (USA)—Chaste **Power Geneva Ltd**
31 **RIVER NORE (IRE)**, 6, b br g Stowaway—I'm Grand (IRE) **Mr J. Hutchinson**
32 **RUBY GATES (IRE)**, 8, b m Avonbridge—Wild Academy (IRE) **Mr D. James**
33 **SOAR ABOVE**, 6, gr ro g Lethal Force (IRE)—Soar **Mr J. Butler**
34 **TIME TO SEA (IRE)**, 7, b g Born To Sea (IRE)—Eastern Glow **C Benham/ D Whitford/ L Quinn/ K Quinn**
35 **TOOFI (FR)**, 10, b g Henrythenavigator (USA)—Silver Bark **Northumbria Leisure Ltd**
36 **UZINCSO**, 5, b g Mayson—Capacious **Recycled Products Limited**
37 **WARRIOR GODDESS**, 6, b m Henrythenavigator (USA)—Azenzar **Mr J. Butler**
38 **WELOOF (FR)**, 7, b g Redoute's Choice (AUS)—Peinted Song (USA) **L. M. Power**
39 **WINDRUSH SONG**, 4, b f Gentlewave (IRE)—Dayia (IRE) **Lady J. Green**

## THREE-YEAR-OLDS

40 **FARHAN (IRE)**, b c Zoffany (IRE)—Market Forces **Mr N. Buresli**
41 **GREYED FIRST (IRE)**, gr f Fascinating Rock (IRE)—Grey Thou Art (IRE) **Mr J. Butler**
42 **IVASECRET (IRE)**, b c Ivawood (IRE)—Ziggy's Secret **C Benham/ D Whitford/ L Quinn/ K Quinn**
43 **KINDERDIJK**, b f Dutch Art—Winds of Time (IRE) **Mr A. L. Al Zeer**
44 **LASTING BEAUTY (FR)**, gr f Dark Angel (IRE)—War Effort (USA) **Mr J. Butler**
45 **LIMITED EDITION**, b c Al Kazeem—Hope And Fortune (IRE) **K. J. Quinn**
46 **MAP (IRE)**, b f Vadamos (FR)—Artesana **Mr J. Butler**
47 **RHYTHM N ROCK (IRE)**, b c Fascinating Rock (IRE)—Rythmic **Mr J. Butler**
48 **SPLIT ELEVENS**, b g Ajaya—Woodland Scene (IRE) **Mr D. James**

## TWO-YEAR-OLDS

49 B c 02/04 Zoffany (IRE)—Red Stars (IRE) (Manduro (GER)) (6667) **Mr J. Butler**
50 B c 10/03 National Defense—Starbright (IRE) (Duke of Marmalade (IRE)) (5714) **Mr J. Butler**

**Other Owners:** Mr C. F. Benham, Mr J. Butler, Gold scaffolding Ltd, Mrs S. Horne, K. J. Quinn, Mr L. M. Quinn, K. Quinn/ C. Benham, Whiterok Ltd, Mr D. L. Whitford.

**Assistant Trainer:** Alice Haynes.

## 81  MR PADDY BUTLER, Lewes
Postal: **Homewood Gate Racing Stables, Novington Lane, East Chiltington, Lewes, East Sussex, BN7 3AU**
Contacts: **PHONE 01273 890124 MOBILE 07973 873846**
EMAIL **homewoodgate@aol.com**

1 **ART OF AMERICA**, 6, br g American Post—Marigay's Magic **Mrs E. A. Elliott**
2 **ENGAGING SAM**, 4, ch g Casamento (IRE)—Engaging **Mrs E. Lucey-Butler**
3 **ESTIBDAAD (IRE)**, 11, b g Haatef (USA)—Star of Siligo (USA) **Miss M. P. Bryant**
4 **FLOWERS ON VENUS (IRE)**, 9, ch g Raven's Pass (USA)—Chelsea Rose (IRE) **Miss M. P. Bryant**
5 **FRANZI FURY (IRE)**, 6, b m Carlo Bank (IRE)—Sara Cara (IRE) **Mrs E. Lucey-Butler**
6 **HARAZ (IRE)**, 8, b g Acclamation—Hanakiyya (IRE) **Christopher W Wilson & Partner**
7 **JUMPING JACK (IRE)**, 7, b g Sir Prancealot (IRE)—She's A Character **Miss M P Bryant, David & Eileen Bryant**
8 **MERCERS**, 7, b m Piccolo—Ivory's Joy **Homewoodgate Racing Club**
9 **REMEMBERTHETITANS**, 5, ch g Bated Breath—Summers Lease **Homewoodgate Racing Club**
10 **UAE SOLDIER (USA)**, 6, b g Dansili—Time On **Mrs E. Lucey-Butler**

### THREE-YEAR-OLDS

11 **SHESSWEET (IRE)**, b f Epaulette (AUS)—Aweebounce (IRE) **Mrs E. Lucey-Butler**

**Other Owners:** Mr D. Bryant, Mrs E. Bryant, Miss M. P. Bryant, Mrs E. Lucey-Butler, C. W. Wilson.

**Assistant Trainer:** Mrs E Lucey-Butler.

**Amateur Jockey:** Miss M. Bryant, Miss J. Oliver.

## 82  MRS BARBARA BUTTERWORTH, Appleby
Postal: **Bolton Mill, Bolton, Appleby-in-Westmorland, Cumbria, CA16 6AL**
Contacts: **PHONE 017683 61363 MOBILE 07778 104118**

1 **BLACK LABEL**, 10, b g Medicean—Black Belt Shopper (IRE) **Miss E. Butterworth**
2 **COEUR AIMANT (FR)**, 6, b g Maresca Sorrento (FR)—Babet (IRE) **Mrs B. Butterworth**
3 **IBN AL EMARAT (IRE)**, 6, b g Excelebration (IRE)—Grace of Dubai (FR) **Miss E. Butterworth**
4 **SNOWED IN (IRE)**, 12, gr g Dark Angel (IRE)—Spinning Gold **Miss E. Butterworth**

**Assistant Trainer:** Miss Elizabeth Butterworth.

**NH Jockey:** Sean Quinlan.

## 83  MISS LOUISE CABBLE, Bridgwater
Postal: **Rowden Farm, Spaxton, Bridgwater, Somerset, TA5 1DF**
Contacts: **MOBILE 07703 045260**

1 **JUST DEEGEETEEBEE**, 5, b g Malinas (GER)—Rising Bell **A. G. Fear**
2 **SPICY FRUITY (IRE)**, 11, b g Fruits of Love (USA)—Rocksham (IRE) **A. G. Fear**
3 **WONDERFUL DREAMER (IRE)**, 8, b g Vocalised (USA)—Go Hiontach (USA) **A. G. Fear**

## 84 MISS JULIE CAMACHO, Malton
Postal: **Star Cottage, Welham Road, Norton, Malton, North Yorkshire, YO17 9QE**
Contacts: **PHONE 01653 696205 MOBILE 07950 356440, 07779 318135 FAX 01653 696205**
**EMAIL julie@jacracing.co.uk WEBSITE www.juliecamacho.com**

1 **ADMIRAL PERCY**, 4, ch g Sir Percy—Oceans Apart **Owners Group 003**
2 **BIG LES (IRE)**, 6, b g Big Bad Bob (IRE)—Love Match **Stockdale Racing**
3 **BILL CODY (IRE)**, 6, b g Declaration of War (USA)—Call This Cat (IRE) **Judy & Richard Peck**
4 **BORSDANE WOOD**, 4, b g Invincible Spirit (IRE)—Highleaf **Mr D. W. Armstrong**
5 **BURTONWOOD**, 9, b g Acclamation—Green Poppy **Judy & Richard Peck & Partner**
6 **CAPTAIN CORELLI (IRE)**, 4, ch g Anjaal—Disprove (IRE) **Judy & Richard Peck**
7 **CHOSEN WORLD**, 7, b g Intikhab (USA)—Panoptic **The Kirkham Partnership**
8 **DELUXE MUSIC**, 4, b f Lope de Vega (IRE)—Divergence (IRE) **G. B. Turnbull Ltd**
9 **EDGEWOOD**, 5, b g Garswood—Heskin (IRE) **Mr D. W. Armstrong**
10 **I KNOW HOW (IRE)**, 6, b g Epaulette (AUS)—Blue Crystal (IRE) **Judy & Richard Peck & Partner**
11 **JUDICIAL (IRE)**, 9, b g Iffraaj—Marlinka **Elite Racing Club**
12 **KAYEWHYKELLY (IRE)**, 4, ch f Dragon Pulse (IRE)—Meduse Bleu **Cliff Stud Limited**
13 **KODIKOVA (IRE)**, 4, b f Speightstown (USA)—Kodiva (IRE)
14 **LATTERHEAD (IRE)**, 4, b f Raven's Pass (USA)—Sequined (USA) **G B Turnbull Ltd & Julie Camacho**
15 **LOOK OUT LOUIS**, 5, b g Harbour Watch (IRE)—Perfect Act **Graeme Howard & Partner**
16 **LORTON**, 5, b m Sepoy (AUS)—Oilinda **G. B. Turnbull Ltd**
17 **MAKANAH**, 6, b g Mayson—Diane's Choice **Axom LXXI**
18 **MARVEL**, 5, b g Poet's Voice—Baralinka (IRE) **Owners Group 010**
19 **MAURICE DANCER**, 4, b g Kodiac—Kind of Hush (IRE) **Elite Racing Club**
20 **MY FRIEND STAN (IRE)**, 4, b g Slade Power (IRE)—Tributary **Owners Group 059**
21 **PROCLAIMER**, 4, b g Free Eagle (IRE)—Pious **Owners Group 033**
22 **SECRET EQUITY**, 4, ch f Equiano (FR)—Secret Charge **Mr B. A. McGarrigle**
23 **SHEPHERDS WAY (IRE)**, 4, gr f Dark Angel (IRE)—Strait Power (IRE) **Mr D. W. Armstrong**
24 **TAMBOURINE GIRL**, 4, b f Cable Bay (IRE)—Triton Dance (IRE) **Owners Group 041**
25 **THE GREY BAY (IRE)**, 4, gr g Gutaifan (IRE)—Coursing **Judy & Richard Peck**
26 **URBAN SPIRIT (IRE)**, 7, b g Born To Sea (IRE)—Rose of Mooncoin (IRE) **Mr I. R. Clements & Dr L. G. Parry**
27 **WAITANGI (IRE)**, 4, b g Dawn Approach (IRE)—Thinking Spirit **Miss J. A. Camacho**
28 **WETHER FELL**, 4, b g Due Diligence (USA)—Triveni (FR) **Miss J. A. Camacho**

## THREE-YEAR-OLDS
29 **BHAJI**, b g Sepoy (AUS)—Luna Mission (IRE) **Mr J. Allison**
30 **BRIDGETOWN**, br c Mayson—Marigot Bay **Owners Group 069**
31 **FORT MCHENRY**, b g Starspangledbanner (AUS)—Winter Bloom (USA) **Mr & Mrs G. Turnbull**
32 **GLITTERBOX GIRL (IRE)**, b f Kodiac—Silca Boo **Cliff Stud Limited**
33 **LAZYITIS**, b f Swiss Spirit—Horsforth **Morecool Racing**
34 **LOWESWATER**, b f Adaay (IRE)—Oilinda **Miss J. A. Camacho**
35 **MAPLE JACK**, ch c Mayson—Porcelain (IRE)
36 **OH SO QUIET**, b f Dutch Art—Kind of Hush (IRE) **Elite Racing Club**
37 **QUEST FOR FUN**, ch g Lope de Vega (IRE)—Craic Agus Spraoi (IRE) **Mr & Mrs G. Turnbull**
38 **THACKTHWAITE**, b g Brazen Beau (AUS)—L'Eglise **G. B. Turnbull Ltd**

## TWO-YEAR-OLDS
39 Ch f 18/04 Dandy Man (IRE)—Bahamian Wishes (IRE) (Bahamian Bounty) (9000) **Judy & Richard Peck**
40 **ENRAGED**, b f 01/03 Adaay (IRE)—Little Lady Katie (IRE) (Lord Shanakill (USA)) (27619) **A. R. Barnes**
41 **HARRIS CHOICE**, b c 12/03 Estidhkaar (IRE)—Anamarka (Mark of Esteem (IRE)) (22857) **Cliff Stud Limited**
42 **MISTER FALSETTO**, b c 10/04 Twilight Son—Bint Arcano (FR) (Arcano (IRE)) (11500) **Miss J. A. Camacho**
43 B f 02/04 Tamayuz—Vassaria (IRE) (Rock of Gibraltar (IRE)) (2000) **Miss J. A. Camacho**

**Other Owners:** Mr Martin Brown, Miss J. A. Camacho, Mr I. R. Clements, G. B. Turnbull Ltd, Mr G. P. Howard, Dr Exors of the Late L. G. Parry, Mrs J. M. Peck, Judy & Richard Peck, Mr R. S. Peck, Mrs R. E. Pritchard, Mr C. Verity, Miss V. Watt.

**Assistant Trainer:** Steve Brown.

**Flat Jockey:** Paul Mulrennan, Callum Rodriguez.

**85** **MR MARK CAMPION, Malton**
Postal: **Whitewell House Stables, Whitewall, Malton, North Yorkshire, YO17 9EH**
Contacts: **PHONE 01653 692729 MOBILE 07973 178311 FAX 01653 600066**
EMAIL info@markcampion-racing.com WEBSITE www.markcampion-racing.com

1 CIVIL ENSIGN (FR), 7, b g Rob Roy (USA)—Petillante Royale (FR) **Whitewell Racing**
2 DINONS (FR), 8, b g Balko (FR)—Beni Abbes (FR) **Whitewell Racing**
3 LAXEY (IRE), 7, b g Yeats (IRE)—Nerissa (IRE) **Whitewell Racing**
4 LORD WARBURTON (IRE), 4, ch g Zoffany (IRE)—Portrait Of A Lady (IRE) **Whitewell Racing**
5 MELDRUM WAY (IRE), 8, b g Getaway (GER)—Meldrum Hall (IRE) **Mark Campion Racing Club**
6 MOUNTAIN RAPID (IRE), 9, ch m Getaway (GER)—Founding Daughter (IRE) **Whitewell Racing**
7 SE YOU, 6, b g Sepoy (AUS)—Lady Hestia (USA) **Mark Campion Racing Club**
8 TROIS BON AMIS (IRE), 7, gr g Lilbourne Lad (IRE)—Vanozza (FR) **Whitewell Racing**

**Assistant Trainer:** Mrs F. Campion.

**86** **MS JENNIE CANDLISH, Leek**
Postal: **Basford Grange Farm, Basford, Leek, Staffordshire, ST13 7ET**
Contacts: **PHONE 07976 825134, 07889 413639 FAX 01538 360324**
EMAIL jenniecandlish@yahoo.co.uk WEBSITE www.jenniecandlishracing.co.uk

1 ANNEBELLE (IRE), 6, b m Jeremy (USA)—Garryduff Eile (IRE) **Mr B. J. Hall**
2 ANNIES PRAYER (IRE), 4, b g Sageburg (IRE)—Slate Lady (IRE) **Brian Verinder & Alan Baxter**
3 BARNAY, 6, b g Nayef (USA)—Barnezet (GR) **D. Ashbrook**
4 BOWSER (IRE), 6, ch g Tobougg (IRE)—Welsh Rhapsody (IRE) **Ms J. Candlish**
5 BREADCRUMBS (FR), 4, b br f Dabirsim (FR)—Sister Agnes (IRE) **J. L. Marriott**
6 BRYDEN BOY (IRE), 11, b g Craigsteel—Cailin Vic Mo Cri (IRE) **Alan Baxter & Brian Hall**
7 CAMACHO MAN (IRE), 4, ch g Camacho—Ezilii (IRE) **Whites Property Limited**
8 CATCHMEIFYOUCAN (IRE), 7, b m Touch of Land (FR)—Irish Honey (IRE) **A Baxter, C Burke & N Sobreperez**
9 CHEDDLETON, 6, br g Shirocco (GER)—Over Sixty **Mr P. & Mrs G. A. Clarke**
10 CLICK AND COLLECT, 9, b g Humbel (USA)—Galena (GER) **D. Ashbrook**
11 CONFRONTATIONAL (IRE), 7, b g Footstepsinthesand—Chevanah (IRE) **Mr B. W. Verinder**
12 COSHESTON, 8, ch g Black Sam Bellamy (IRE)—Rare Ruby (IRE) **Mrs J. M. Ratcliff**
13 CRACK DU NINIAN (FR), 6, b g Le Houssais (FR)—Syphaline (FR) **Mr P. & Mrs G. A. Clarke**
14 DIVA DE VASSY (FR), 5, b m Blue Bresil (FR)—Daniety (FR) **J. L. Marriott**
15 FOLLOW YOUR FIRE (IRE), 6, b g Le Fou (IRE)—Jollie Bollie (IRE) **Pam Beardmore & Jennie Candlish**
16 FOR JIM (IRE), 9, gr g Milan—Dromhale Lady (IRE) **Ms J. Candlish**
17 FORTIFIED BAY (IRE), 9, b g Makfi—Divergence (USA) **Alan Baxter & Terry Hastie**
18 GLENAMOY LAD, 7, b g Royal Applause—Suzy Alexander **Ms J. Candlish**
19 GOLAN CLOUD (IRE), 8, b g Golan (IRE)—Mite Be Cloudy (IRE) **Ms J. Candlish**
20 HACHERT, 4, b g Lope de Vega (IRE)—Sense of Joy **Jonathan & Catherine Williams**
21 HAPPY HOLLOW, 9, b g Beat Hollow—Dombeya (IRE) **Mr A. J. Baxter**
22 LEESWOOD LILY, 8, b m Aflora (IRE)—Showtime Annie **Mr M. M. Allen**
23 MARTHA YEATS (IRE), 6, b m Yeats (IRE)—Stratosphere **Mrs F. M. Draper**
24 MINT CONDITION, 7, b g Black Sam Bellamy (IRE)—Winning Counsel (IRE) **Whites Property Limited**
25 MUTAABEQ (IRE), 6, ch g Teofilo (IRE)—Khulood (USA) **Glen's Fools 2**
26 OSCARS LEADER (IRE), 8, b g Oscar (IRE)—Lead'er Inn (IRE) **J. L. Marriott**
27 OUTCROP (IRE), 7, b g Rock of Gibraltar (IRE)—Desert Sage **Alan Baxter & Brian Hall**
28 PAKIE'S DREAM (IRE), 7, b g Arcadio (GER)—Emily's Princess (IRE) **Mr A. J. Baxter**
29 QUICK PICK (IRE), 10, b g Vinnie Roe (IRE)—Oscars Arrow (IRE) **4 Left Footers & A Blewnose**
30 RED GIANT (IRE), 10, ch g Beneficial—Barrack Star (IRE) **Mr V. A. Healy**
31 SHOW PALACE, 8, ch g Showcasing—Palais Polaire **Paul Wright Bevans & Jennie Candlish**
32 SPECIAL BRUTE (GER), 6, br g Maxios—Secrets **Brian Verinder & Alan Baxter**
33 SPIRIT OF HALE (IRE), 10, ch g Stowaway—Roseboreen (IRE) **Mrs A. V. Hall**
34 SPLASH THE CASH (IRE), 8, b m Scorpion (IRE)—Goldfeather (IRE) **Alan Baxter & Terry Hastie**
35 STAR ASCENDING (IRE), 9, ch g Thousand Words—Sakaka **Mr P. Wright-Bevans**

# MS JENNIE CANDLISH - continued

36 **STOP TALKING (IRE)**, 9, b m Gamut (IRE)—Miss Snapdragon (IRE) **Anthony,Barrett,Baxter,Corbett,Deane,Lloyd**
37 **SURE I'M YOUR MAN (IRE)**, 4, b g Sea The Moon (GER)—All Hallows (IRE) **Mr A. J. Baxter**
38 **TANARPINO**, 10, ch g Tobougg (IRE)—Got Tune (FR) **Mr P. & Mrs G. A. Clarke**
39 **THEFLYINGPORTRAIT (IRE)**, 12, gr g Portrait Gallery (IRE)—Skule Hill Lass (IRE) **The Mere Partnership**
40 **TOO MUCH TO ASK (IRE)**, 8, b g Ask—Chinara (IRE) **Whites Property Limited**
41 **ULVERSTON (IRE)**, 6, b g Yeats (IRE)—So Supreme (IRE) **Mr P. & Mrs G. A. Clarke**
42 **ZOLFO (IRE)**, 9, gr g Cloudings (IRE)—Hardy Lamb (IRE) **Matt Barrett & Alan Baxter**
43 **ZUCKERBERG (GER)**, 5, b g Kamsin (GER)—Zazera (FR) **J. L. Marriott**

**Other Owners:** Mr M. Barrett, Mr A. J. Baxter, Mrs P.M. Beardmore, Mr C. Burke, Ms J. Candlish, Mrs G. A. Clarke, Mr P. Clarke, Mr B. J. Hall, Mr T. Hastie, Mr N. Sobreperez, Mr B. W. Verinder, Mrs C. Williams, Mr J. Williams, Mr P. Wright-Bevans.

**Assistant Trainer:** Alan O'Keeffe.

**Flat Jockey:** Joe Fanning. **NH Jockey:** Sean Quinlan.

---

## 87 MR HENRY CANDY, Wantage
Postal: **Kingstone Warren, Wantage, Oxfordshire, OX12 9QF**
Contacts: **PHONE 01367 820276 MOBILE 07836 211264**
EMAIL henrycandy@btconnect.com

1 **ALFRED BOUCHER**, 5, gr g Aussie Rules (USA)—Policy Term (IRE) **Mr R. Allcock**
2 **BIMBLE (IRE)**, 4, b f Acclamation—Cape Violet (IRE) **Mr A. Davis**
3 **BLESSED (IRE)**, 4, b g Canford Cliffs (IRE)—Bless You **Mr A. S. F. Frost, T. A. F. Frost**
4 **BY STARLIGHT (IRE)**, 4, b f Sea The Stars (IRE)—Step Lightly (IRE) **Mr A. Davis**
5 **CANDLEMAS**, 4, b f Mukhadram—Candoluminescence **Henry D. N. B. Candy**
6 **FOUR FEET (IRE)**, 5, b g Harbour Watch (IRE)—Royal Connection **Henry D. N. B. Candy**
7 **GREENSIDE**, 10, b g Dubawi (IRE)—Katrina (IRE) **Clayton, Frost, Kebell & Turner**
8 **HOORAY HENRY**, 4, gr g Brazen Beau (AUS)—All That Jas (IRE) **Henry D. N. B. Candy**
9 **JOUSKA**, 4, b f Cable Bay (IRE)—Quiet Protest (USA) **Mr A. Davis**
10 **LA LUNE**, 5, ch m Champs Elysees—Moonlight Mystery **Alizeti Partners, Clive & Pamela Brandon**
11 **MAIDEN CASTLE**, 5, b g Nayef (USA)—Danae **Girsonfield Ltd**
12 **MARIETTY**, 4, b f Music Master—Bikini **Mrs S. Lidsey**
13 **SCEPTRED ISLE**, 4, b f Cityscape—Danae **Girsonfield Ltd**
14 **SOLDIER'S SON**, 5, b g Epaulette (AUS)—Elsie's Orphan **Henry D. N. B. Candy**
15 **TWILIGHTING**, 5, b m Kyllachy—Night Affair **Six Too Many**
16 **WOODCOCK (IRE)**, 4, gr g Gutaifan (IRE)—Tooley Woods (IRE) **Henry D. N. B. Candy**

## THREE-YEAR-OLDS

17 **ALLERBY**, b f Iffraaj—Alice Alleyne (IRE) **Major M. G. Wyatt**
18 **BIBULOUS (IRE)**, b c Camacho—Cant Hurry Love **Mr A. Davis**
19 **COLOMBE (IRE)**, b f Mehmas (IRE)—Symbol of Peace (IRE) **Acloque, Benson and Frost**
20 **GEORGE MORLAND**, b c Camacho—Baharah (USA) **Mr R. Allcock**
21 **KINGSTON STAR (IRE)**, b f Gutaifan (IRE)—Star of Malta **Mr C. M. Humber, Henry D. N. B. Candy**
22 **LUCKY BAY**, b f Beat Hollow—Free Offer **Earl Cadogan**
23 **PEARL BAY**, b f Cable Bay (IRE)—Pavonine **Henry Candy & Partners V**
24 **POLLINATE**, b f Oasis Dream—Spring Fling **Six Too Many**
25 **PORNSTAR MARTINI (IRE)**, b f Bungle Inthejungle—Misplace (IRE) **Mr C. J. Haughey**
26 **RING OF LIGHT**, gr g Mayson—Silver Halo **T A Frost & Simon Broke & Partners**
27 **ROSA BONHEUR**, ch f Camacho—Fire Line **Mr R. Allcock**
28 **RUN TO FREEDOM**, b c Muhaarar—Twilight Mistress **Mr G. A. Wilson**
29 **SANCTIFIED**, b f Equiano (FR)—Bookiesindexdotnet **Mr A. Davis**
30 **SOVEREIGN SLIPPER**, b c Charm Spirit (IRE)—Last Slipper **Mr D B Clark & Mr H Candy**
31 **TWILIGHT CALLS**, b c Twilight Son—Zawiyah **Cheveley Park Stud Limited**
32 **UNFOOLISH (IRE)**, b f Fastnet Rock (AUS)—Foolish Act (IRE) **Mr A. Davis**
33 **VIGNONI**, b g Helmet (AUS)—Mondovi **P. G. Jacobs**

# MR HENRY CANDY - continued

## TWO-YEAR-OLDS

34 **BRUSH CREEK**, b f 19/02 Twilight Son—Resort (Oasis Dream) **Cheveley Park Stud Limited**
35 **BUSSELTON**, b c 09/04 Dark Angel (IRE)—Pirouette (Pivotal) (48000) **Earl Cadogan**
36 **CENTRE DRIVE**, b f 14/04 Iffraaj—Upper Street (IRE) (Dansili) **Major M. G. Wyatt**
37 **CLOUD CUCKOO**, b g 21/03 Mayson—Crimson Cloud (Kyllachy) (24000) **Henry D. N. B. Candy**
38 B c 14/03 Nayef (USA)—Danae (Dansili) **Girsonfield Ltd**
39 **HEARTBREAK LASS**, b f 24/03 Cotai Glory—Motion Lass (Motivator) (142857) **Mr A. Davis**
40 B f 08/03 The Gurkha (IRE)—In Secret (Dalakhani (IRE)) **Earl Cadogan**
41 **JACK LESLIE**, b c 06/04 Twilight Son—Fenella Rose (Compton Place) (34000) **P. G. Jacobs**
42 Gr f 06/03 Mastercraftsman (IRE)—
    La Chapelle (IRE) (Holy Roman Emperor (IRE)) (12000) **T. Frost, Mrs Candy, Jill Lamb Bloodstock & S. Clayton**
43 **NIVELLE'S MAGIC**, b f 08/04 Hellvelyn—Nihal (IRE) (Singspiel (IRE)) **Mr Michael Aram, Henry D. N. B. Candy**
44 Ch c 05/02 Nathaniel (IRE)—Patching (Foxwedge (AUS)) (22000) **Mr D B Clark & Mr H Candy**
45 **RAVELLO SUNSET**, b c 16/03 Twilight Son—Amalfi (IRE) (Acclamation) (5000) **Henry D. N. B. Candy**
46 **RENOIR**, b c 26/02 Nathaniel (IRE)—Feis Ceoil (IRE) (Key of Luck (USA)) **Mr R. Allcock**
47 B c 12/04 Cable Bay (IRE)—Rock Follies (Rock of Gibraltar (IRE)) (9000) **Mr A. Davis**
48 B c 07/03 Heeraat (IRE)—Sea of Hope (IRE) (Rock of Gibraltar (IRE)) (762) **Mr A. Davis**
49 Ch c 14/03 Pearl Secret—Speed Princess (Fast Company (IRE)) (17143) **Mr A. Davis**
50 **TWILIGHT MISCHIEF**, b f 10/01 Twilight Son—Cardrona (Selkirk (USA)) (5000) **Candy, Pritchard & Thomas**

**Assistant Trainer:** Amy Scott.

---

## 88 | MR GRANT CANN, Lower Hamswell
Postal: Park Field, Hall Lane, Lower Hamswell, Bath, Gloucestershire, BA1 9DE
Contacts: **PHONE** 01225 891674 **MOBILE** 07968 271118

1 **CADEAU DU BRESIL (FR)**, 9, b g Blue Bresil (FR)—Melanie du Chenet (FR) **J. G. Cann**
2 **DISTANT VIEW**, 4, b f Telescope (IRE)—Ruby Crown **J. G. Cann**
3 **GET ON JEREMY (IRE)**, 6, b g Jeremy (USA)—Sitetanic (IRE) **J. G. Cann**
4 **LADY STANHOW**, 6, br m Getaway (GER)—Loxhill Lady **J. G. Cann**
5 **QUEEN OF THE COURT (IRE)**, 8, b m Court Cave (IRE)—Waydale Hill **J. G. Cann**

---

## 89 | MR DON CANTILLON, Newmarket
Postal: 63 Exeter Road, Newmarket, Suffolk, CB8 8LP
Contacts: **PHONE** 01638 668507 **MOBILE** 07709 377601

1 **ADMIRING GLANCE (IRE)**, 4, b f Shantou (USA)—As I Am (IRE) **D. E. Cantillon**
2 **BOLD VISION (IRE)**, 5, b g Shirocco (GER)—As I Am (IRE) **D. E. Cantillon**
3 **NAVARRA PRINCESS (IRE)**, 6, b m Intense Focus (USA)—Navarra Queen **D. E. Cantillon**

**90**

**MRS LOUISA CARBERRY, Senonnes**
Postal: **Les Fosses, Senonnes, Pays de la Loire, 53390, France**
Contacts: **WORK +33 6 24 86 63 69**
**WORK EMAIL louisacarberryracing@gmail.com**

1 **ADORABLE DE BALLON (FR)**, 5, ch m Barastraight—Nile Breeze (FR)
2 **ALEXANDER (FR)**, 5, ch g Motivator—Little Tinka
3 **BRIGHT LIGHTS (FR)**, 4, b f Pour Moi (IRE)—Lights On Me
4 **CANICHETTE (FR)**, 4, b f Prince Gibraltar (FR)—Noanoa (FR)
5 **CESAR DE BALLON (FR)**, 4, b c Doctor Dino (FR)—Nile Altesse (FR)
6 **CHARMEUR DE BALLON (FR)**, 5, b g Barastraight—Nile Altesse (FR)
7 **DINETTE DE BALLON (FR)**, 9, b m Doctor Dino—Nile Altesse (FR)
8 **DOCTEUR DE BALLON (FR)**, 9, ch g Doctor Dino (FR)—Nile Breeze (FR)
9 **DOURDOUR (FR)**, 9, b g Redback—La Bezizais (FR)
10 **GRAN DIOSE (FR)**, 5, b g Planteur (IRE)—Noanoa (FR)
11 **GRANDISSIMA (FR)**, 5, b m Turgeon (USA)—Magnolia de Toury (FR)
12 **HIGGY (FR)**, 4, b g Kitkou (FR)—Raidfolle d'Airy (FR)
13 **JAMMY RUGGER**, 5, ch g Yorgunnabelucky (USA)—Shanxi Girl
14 **KALINSKI (IRE)**, 7, b g Kalanisi (IRE)—Blonde Ambition (IRE)
15 **KINCSEM PARK (FR)**, 4, b f Turgeon (USA)—Baracoa
16 **LADY LIZZY**, 5, ch m Rio de La Plata (USA)—Elzebieta (FR)
17 **LADY SCATTERLEY (FR)**, 5, ch m No Nay Never (USA)—Camdara (FR)
18 **LINCEAU (FR)**, 5, b g Fuisse (FR)—La Bezizais (FR)
19 **SOME OPERATOR (IRE)**, 7, b g September Storm (GER)—Emilies Pearl (IRE)
20 **SPIRIT OF THE BAY (FR)**, 6, b m Spirit One (FR)—Persian Bay (FR)
21 **SURDOUE DE BALLON (FR)**, 8, b g Turgeon (USA)—Nile Breeze (FR)
22 **TOP ROCK TALULA (IRE)**, 6, b m Lord Shanakill (USA)—Spirit Watch (IRE)

**THREE-YEAR-OLDS**

23 **AMANHA (FR)**, b f Authorized (IRE)—My Glitters (FR)
24 **DIBAMBA PASSION (FR)**, b f Konig Turf (GER)—Popirone (FR)
25 **GILOU JAGUEN (FR)**, b g Bathyrhon (GER)—Don'aristarque (FR)
26 **INVITED (FR)**, b f Nidor (FR)—Baracoa
27 **IRIS DE GRUGY (FR)**, b f Masterstroke (USA)—Diane de Grugy (FR)
28 **MALAYAN STYLE (FR)**, b g Style Vendome (FR)—Malacca Straits
29 **PARFAITE SURPRISE (FR)**, b f Elliptique (IRE)—Princesse Fiona (FR)

**91**

**MRS RUTH CARR, Stillington**
Postal: **Mowbray House Farm, Easingwold Road, Stillington, York, North Yorkshire, YO61 1LT**
Contacts: **WORK 01347 823776 MOBILE 07721 926772**
**EMAIL ruth@ruthcarrracing.co.uk, chrissie@ruthcarrracing.co.uk WEBSITE www.ruthcarrracing.co.uk**

1 **ALQAAB**, 6, gr g Swiss Spirit—Skiing **J Greaves, R Willcock & Ruth Carr**
2 **ATHMAD (IRE)**, 5, b g Olympic Glory (IRE)—Black Mascara (IRE) **R J H Limited & Ruth Carr**
3 **BOBBY JOE LEG**, 7, ch g Pastoral Pursuits—China Cherub **Mrs A. Clark**
4 **CITY WANDERER (IRE)**, 5, b g Kodiac—Viletta (GER) **Mrs S Hibbert & Mrs R Carr**
5 **COPPER AND FIVE**, 5, ch g Paco Boy (IRE)—Peachez
6 **DON'T JOKE**, 4, ch g Slade Power (IRE)—Lady Frances **Grange Park Racing XIV & Ruth Carr**
7 **EMBOUR (IRE)**, 6, b g Acclamation—Carpet Lady (IRE) **Formulated Polymer Products Ltd**
8 **FINAL FRONTIER (IRE)**, 8, b g Dream Ahead (USA)—Polly Perkins (IRE) **V. Khosla**
9 **FORESEEABLE FUTURE (FR)**, 6, b g Harbour Watch (IRE)—Russian Spirit **RHD & Ruth Carr**
10 **FREEDOM FLYER (IRE)**, 4, b g Invincible Spirit (IRE)—Liberating **Mr Michael Hill**
11 **HIGHLAND ACCLAIM (IRE)**, 10, b g Acclamation—Emma's Star (ITY) **Grange Park Racing Club & Ruth Carr**
12 **HOSTELRY**, 4, ch f Coach House—Queens Jubilee
13 **KATHEEFA (USA)**, 7, gr g Street Cry (IRE)—Wid (USA) **Mr Michael Hill**

## MRS RUTH CARR - continued

14 **KHAZAF**, 6, b g Dawn Approach (IRE)—Winds of Time (IRE)  **Mrs R. A. Carr**
15 **KYLIE RULES**, 6, br m Aussie Rules (USA)—Africa's Star (IRE)
16 **LOULIN**, 6, ch g Exceed And Excel (AUS)—Wimple (USA)  **G. Murray**
17 **MAC MCCARTHY (IRE)**, 4, ch g Anjaal—Kitty Softpaws (IRE)  **The Venturers & Mrs R Carr**
18 **MAGICAL EFFECT (IRE)**, 9, ch g New Approach (IRE)—Purple Glow (IRE)  **Miss Vanessa Church**
19 **MONAADHIL (IRE)**, 7, b g Dark Angel (IRE)—Urban Daydream (USA)  **Mr Michael Hill**
20 **MUTAMADED (IRE)**, 8, b g Arcano (IRE)—Sahaayeb (IRE)  **The Bottom Liners & Mrs R. Carr**
21 **MUTANAASEQ (IRE)**, 6, ch g Red Jazz (USA)—Indaba (IRE)  **Grange Park Racing VIII & Mrs R Carr**
22 **O'REILLY'S PASS**, 4, b g Australia—Dynaglow (USA)  **Mr J. A. Swinburne & Mrs Ruth A. Carr**
23 **OUTTAKE**, 4, br g Outstrip—Cambridge Duchess  **The Hollinbridge Partnership & Ruth Carr**
24 **POWER PLAYER**, 5, b g Slade Power (IRE)—Varnish  **Grange Park Racing XIII & Ruth Carr**
25 **SANDY B**, 4, ch f Monsieur Bond (IRE)—China Cherub  **Mrs A. Clark**
26 **SHARP EXHIBIT (IRE)**, 4, ch f Showcasing—Sharp Relief (IRE)  **Mrs R. A. Carr**
27 **SPANISH ANGEL (IRE)**, 4, br g Gutaifan (IRE)—City Dazzler (IRE)  **The Beer Stalkers & Ruth Carr**
28 **SUPERSEDED (IRE)**, 5, gr g Exceed And Excel (AUS)—Satwa Ruby (FR)  **Northumbria Leisure Ltd**
29 **SUWAAN (IRE)**, 7, ch g Exceed And Excel (AUS)—Janina  **Mr J. A. Swinburne & Mrs Ruth A. Carr**
30 **TAMKEEN**, 6, ch g Kyllachy—Regatta (USA)  **Mrs R. A. Carr**
31 **TREVIE FOUNTAIN**, 4, b g Fountain of Youth (IRE)—Fantacise  **Grange Park Racing Vii & Ruth Carr**
32 **UPSTAGING**, 9, b g Mount Nelson—Corndavon (USA)
33 **ZEBULON (IRE)**, 7, gr g Zebedee—Novelina (IRE)  **Bruce Jamieson, Barbara Dean, Ruth Carr**

### THREE-YEAR-OLDS

34 **LOQUACIOUS BOY (IRE)**, b g Camacho—Talkative  **Mrs Marion Chapman & Mrs Ruth A. Carr**
35 B g Due Diligence (USA)—Royal Blossom (IRE)  **Mrs R. A. Carr**
36 Gr g Hellvelyn—Sas (IRE)  **Mrs R. A. Carr**
37 **SUGAR ANGEL**, gr f Lethal Force (IRE)—Sugar Mountain (IRE)  **Dennis Clayton & Ruth Carr**
38 **THE FAST LION (IRE)**, b g The Last Lion (IRE)—Wizz Up (IRE)  **Miss B Houlston, Mrs M Chapman & Mrs R Carr**

### TWO-YEAR-OLDS

39 **MIDAS (IRE)**, ch g 07/05 Galileo Gold—
                        Keeper's Ring (USA) (Street Cry (IRE)) (12000)  **The Beer Stalkers & Ruth Carr**
40 **VAN ZANT**, b g 29/03 Lethal Force (IRE)—Emmuska (Sir Percy) (13333)  **Ged Martin Nick & Mrs R Carr**

**Other Owners:** T. J. E. Brereton, Mrs R. A. Carr, Mrs M. Chapman, Miss V. A. Church, Mr D. G. Clayton, Mr A. D. Crombie, Mr T. W. Deadman, Mrs B. I. Dean, Mr C. Dufferwiel, Mr F. H. Eales, Ged Martin Nick, Grange Park Racing Club, Grange Park Racing VII, Grange Park Racing VIII, Grange Park Racing X1V, Grange Park Racing XIII, Mr J. A. Greaves, J. P. Hames, Mrs S. Hibbert, Michael Hill, Hollinbridge Partnership, Miss B. J. Houlston, Mr A. B. Jamieson, Mr D. R. Kelly, Mr P. Newell, R J H Limited, RHD Research Limited, Mr G. A. Shields, Mr E. T. Surr, Mr J. A. Swinburne, The Beer Stalkers, The Bottom Liners, Mr R. Willcock, Mr R. W. Wilson.

**Assistant Trainer:** Mrs M. Chapman, **Racing Secretary:** Mrs Chrissie Skyes.

**Flat Jockey:** Jack Garritty, Andrew Mullen, James Sullivan. **Amateur Jockey:** Miss Emily Bullock.

---

**92**  **MR DECLAN CARROLL, Malton**
Postal: **Santry Stables, Langton Road, Norton, Malton, North Yorkshire, YO17 9PZ**
Contacts: **MOBILE 07801 553779**
**EMAIL declancarrollracing@gmail.com**

1 **ASMUND (IRE)**, 4, b g Zebedee—Suffer Her (IRE)  **Mrs S. A. Bryan**
2 **CHICKENFORTEA (IRE)**, 7, gr g Clodovil (IRE)—Kardyls Hope (IRE)  **Mr Brian Chambers**
3 **EMIYN (FR)**, 4, b g Invincible Spirit (IRE)—Edelmira (IRE)  **Fab Five**
4 **JACKAMUNDO (FR)**, 5, b g Fast Company (IRE)—Luxie (IRE)  **Danny Fantom Racing Ltd**
5 **MACHREE (IRE)**, 6, b m Lord Shanakill (USA)—Faleena (IRE)  **Mr B. Cooney**
6 **MOTAHASSEN (IRE)**, 7, br g Lonhro (AUS)—Journalist (IRE)  **Mrs S. A. Bryan**

## MR DECLAN CARROLL - continued

7 **MUSIC SEEKER (IRE)**, 7, b g Henrythenavigator (USA)—Danehill Music (IRE) **Mrs S. A. Bryan**
8 **NATCHEZ TRACE**, 4, b g Invincible Spirit (IRE)—Passage of Time **Second Chancers**
9 **PHOTOGRAPH (IRE)**, 4, b g Kodiac—Supreme Occasion (IRE) **Ray Flegg & John Bousfield**
10 **QUITEACATCH**, 4, b g Due Diligence (USA)—Teggiano (IRE) **Yenilecas Syndicate**
11 **SHAWAAMEKH**, 7, b g Born To Sea (IRE)—Frances Stuart (IRE) **Highgreen Partnership**
12 **TRINITY LAKE**, 5, b g Dansili—Mirror Lake **Dreams**

### THREE-YEAR-OLDS

13 **BALLYCOMMON (IRE)**, b g Dabirsim (FR)—Luxie (IRE) **B&E Partnership**
14 **FIRST COMPANY (IRE)**, b c Fast Company (IRE)—Pira Palace (IRE) **Northern Marking Ltd**
15 **IRELAND'S EYE (IRE)**, b g Canford Cliffs (IRE)—Sofi's Spirit (IRE) **Dreams**
16 **JACK DANIEL (IRE)**, b c Equiano (FR)—Mirdhak **Danny Fantom Racing Ltd**
17 **JAKACAN (IRE)**, b g Acclamation—Masonbrook Lady (IRE) **Ray Flegg & John Bousfield**
18 **LE CHEVAL RAPIDE (IRE)**, b g Estidhkaar (IRE)—Greek Spirit (IRE) **Dreams**
19 **LOUBY LOU (IRE)**, b f Awtaad (IRE)—Na Zdorovie **Danny Fantom Racing Ltd**
20 **LOVE SENSATION**, b f Exceed And Excel (AUS)—Super Saturday (IRE) **John & Jess Dance**
21 B f Acclamation—Martina Franca **Yenilecas Syndicate**
22 **TWEET TWEET**, ch f Twilight Son—Tweety Pie (IRE) **Mrs P A Johnson & Mr C H Stephenson**
23 **ZAHRISA**, b f Harzand (IRE)—Isa **Mrs P. A. Johnson**

### TWO-YEAR-OLDS

24 Br c 25/04 Fast Company (IRE)—All In Green (IRE) (Diamond Green (FR)) (4286)
25 Gr c 23/03 Mehmas (IRE)—Bo Bridget (IRE) (Mastercraftsman (IRE)) (807) **The Indecisive 8**
26 Ch c 13/03 Mayson—Brockholes (Equiano (FR)) **Mr D. W. Armstrong**
27 **GANNON GLORY (IRE)**, b c 13/05 Cotai Glory—
                                  Folegandros Island (FR) (Red Rocks (IRE)) (64000) **Northern Marking Ltd**
28 B c 10/04 Garswood—Mis Chicaf (IRE) (Prince Sabo)
29 Ch c 03/02 Poet's Voice—Roman Holiday (IRE) (Holy Roman Emperor (IRE)) (14000)
30 B f 19/04 Garswood—Sirenuse (IRE) (Exceed And Excel (AUS)) **Mr Andy Turton, Mr Terry Johnston**
31 B c 26/04 Mayson—Skipton (IRE) (Dark Angel (IRE)) **Mr D. W. Armstrong**
32 B c 04/04 Bated Breath—Songseeker (IRE) (Oasis Dream) (5000) **Mr Brian Chambers**

**Other Owners:** Mr John Blackburn, Mr H. J. Bousfield, Mr Neil Carlyle, Mrs D. Carroll, D. Carroll, Mr J. E. Dance, R. J. Flegg, Mr E. H. M. Frost, Mr W. Griffin, Mr George Jackson, Mrs P.A. Johnson, Mr Mick Larkin, Mrs Y. Lavin, Faisal Maassarani, Mrs L. Maher, Mrs N. McDonnell, Ms C. Mulrennan, Mr E. G. Murray, Ms S. O'Dowd, C. H. Stephenson, The Indecisive 8, Mr H. E. Wigan, Mr Derek Wilson, Mr J Wilson.

**Assistant Trainer:** Kym Dee.

**Apprentice Jockey:** Zak Wheatley. **Amateur Jockey:** Donovan Goucher.

---

**93**    **MR TONY CARROLL, Cropthorne**
Postal: **Mill House Racing, Cropthorne, Pershore, Worcs**
Contacts: **PHONE 01386 861020 MOBILE 07770 472431 FAX 01386 861628**
**EMAIL a.w.carroll@btconnect.com WEBSITE www.awcarroll.co.uk**

1 4, B g Due Diligence (USA)—Audrey Brown **Mr A. W. Carroll**
2 **BALTIC PRINCE (IRE)**, 11, b g Baltic King—Brunswick **Mr A. Mills**
3 **BE FAIR**, 5, b g Kyllachy—Going For Gold **Surefire Racing & Partner**
4 **BE MY SEA (IRE)**, 10, b g Sea The Stars (IRE)—Bitooh **L. T. Cheshire**
5 **BEAU GESTE (IRE)**, 5, b g Lilbourne Lad (IRE)—Valbonne (IRE) **The Bbc Partnership**
6 **BEZZAS LAD (IRE)**, 4, b g Society Rock (IRE)—Red Rosanna **Mr P. J. Sumner**
7 **BLACK BUBLE (FR)**, 8, b g Valanour (IRE)—Miss Bubble Rose (FR) **Northway Lodge Racing**
8 **BLUE VENTURE**, 4, b f Bated Breath—Blue Goddess (IRE) **G. A. Wilson**
9 **BOLD DECISION**, 5, b g Zoffany (IRE)—Poly Pomona **Shropshire Wolves & Partner**

## MR TONY CARROLL - continued

10 **BOOM THE GROOM (IRE)**, 10, b g Kodiac—Ecco Mi (IRE) **Mr B. J. Millen**
11 **BROTHER IN ARMS (IRE)**, 7, b g Kodiac—Cool Cousin (IRE) **Cover Point Racing**
12 **CAFE SYDNEY (IRE)**, 5, ch m Foxwedge (AUS)—Carafe **Contubernium Racing**
13 **CALIN'S LAD (IRE)**, 6, ch g Equiano (FR)—Lalina (GER) **Lycett Racing Ltd**
14 **CHASMA**, 11, b m Kayf Tara—Luneray (FR) **China Racing Club**
15 **CHERISH (FR)**, 4, b f Hunter's Light (IRE)—Agent Kensington **Wedgewood Estates**
16 **CHETAN**, 9, b g Alfred Nobel (IRE)—Island Music (IRE) **L Judd T Stamp J Hardcastle R Miles**
17 **CHIEF SITTINGBULL**, 8, ch g Indian Haven—Saharan Song (IRE) **Mrs S. A. Bowen**
18 **CLASHANISKA (IRE)**, 5, b g Dark Angel (IRE)—Spirit Watch (IRE) **Mr A. W. Carroll**
19 **CLEARLY CAPABLE (IRE)**, 12, b g Bienamado (USA)—Spout Road (IRE) **Mr A. W. Carroll**
20 **DE VEGAS KID (IRE)**, 7, ch g Lope de Vega (IRE)—Fravolina (USA) **The Rebelle Boys**
21 **DELLA MARE**, 5, b m Delegator—Golbelini **The Fine Gild Racing Partnership**
22 **DOC SPORTELLO (IRE)**, 9, b g Majestic Missile (IRE)—Queen of Silk (IRE) **Mr W. G. Nixon**
23 **DOCTOR NUNO**, 4, b g Due Diligence (USA)—Aubrietia **Shropshire Wolves**
24 **DRAGOON SPRINGS (IRE)**, 5, br g Arcadio (GER)—Lunar Star (IRE) **Mr I. Slatter**
25 **EASTERN STAR (IRE)**, 5, b m Dylan Thomas (IRE)—Sweet Surprise (IRE) **The Fruit Flow Partners**
26 **ELEGANT LOVE**, 5, b m Delegator—Lovellian **H. M. W. Clifford**
27 **ESSAKA (IRE)**, 9, b g Equiano (FR)—Dream Vision (USA) **Mrs J. Carrington**
28 **FIELDSMAN (USA)**, 9, b g Hard Spun (USA)—R Charlie's Angel (USA) **SF Racing Club**
29 **FLY THE NEST (IRE)**, 5, b g Kodiac—Queen Wasp (IRE) **Mr B. J. Millen**
30 **FORESEE (GER)**, 8, b g Sea The Stars (IRE)—Four Roses (IRE) **Millen & Cooke**
31 **FORTUITOUS**, 4, b g Camelot—Operettist **Longview Stud & Bloodstock Ltd**
32 **FRENCH KISS (IRE)**, 6, b g French Fifteen (FR)—Ms Cordelia (USA) **CCCP Syndicate**
33 **FUME (IRE)**, 5, b g Frankel—Puff (IRE) **Surefire Racing**
34 **GLOBAL STYLE (IRE)**, 6, b g Nathaniel (IRE)—Danaskaya (IRE) **Curry House Corner & Partner**
35 **GOLD STANDARD (IRE)**, 5, ch g Casamento (IRE)—Goldplated (IRE) **Mr J. M. Wall**
36 **HARBOUR PROJECT**, 4, b g Harbour Watch (IRE)—Quelle Affaire **Mrs Y. T. Wallace**
37 **HE'S OUR STAR (IRE)**, 4, b g Lord Shanakill (USA)—Afilia **Mrs S. R. Keable**
38 **HEART OF A HUNTER (FR)**, 4, b g Hunter's Light (IRE)—Kiss My Heart **Wedgewood Estates**
39 **HENRY CROFT**, 8, b g Dubawi (IRE)—Karen's Caper (USA) **Mr B. J. Millen**
40 **HOT HOT HOT**, 4, ch f Hot Streak (IRE)—Just Emma **Mr A. W. Carroll**
41 **ILHABELA FACT**, 7, b gr h High Chaparral (IRE)—Ilhabela (IRE) **Cooke & Millen**
42 **IT'S WONDERFUL (FR)**, 4, b f Orpen (USA)—Heaven **Wedgewood Estates**
43 **KNOCKABOUT QUEEN**, 5, b m Sixties Icon—Rough Courte (IRE) **Mr J. Tucker**
44 **KONDRATIEV WAVE (IRE)**, 4, ch g Dragon Pulse (IRE)—Right Reason (IRE) **Mr B. J. Millen**
45 **LAST PAGE**, 6, b g Pastoral Pursuits—No Page (IRE) **Harvey Lawrence Ltd**
46 **LATENT HEAT (IRE)**, 5, b g Papal Bull—Taziria (SWI) **Mr J. M. Wall**
47 **LEQUINTO (IRE)**, 4, b g Requinto (IRE)—Moss Nation **Mrs Y. T. Wallace**
48 **LIGHT UP OUR STARS (IRE)**, 5, b g Rip Van Winkle (IRE)—Shine Like A Star **Mr D. Boocock**
49 **LONG CALL**, 4, b g Authorized (IRE)—Gacequita (URU) **Northway Lodge Racing**
50 **LUSCIFER**, 4, b g Heeraat (IRE)—Nut (IRE) **Mr Tony K Singh & Mr S Doocey**
51 **MADRINHO (IRE)**, 8, ch g Frozen Power (IRE)—Perfectly Clear (USA) **Mr A. Mills**
52 **MAN OF THE NORTH**, 8, b g And Beyond (IRE)—Latin Beauty (IRE) **Last Day Racing Partnership**
53 **MUSEE D'ORSAY (IRE)**, 5, b g Showcasing—Da's Wish (IRE) **The Rebelle Boys**
54 **NELSON RIVER**, 6, b g Mount Nelson—I Say (IRE) **CCCP Syndicate**
55 **NIGHT BEAR**, 4, ch g Dragon Pulse (IRE)—Contenance (IRE) **Mr R. Bellamy**
56 **OEIL DE TIGRE (FR)**, 10, b g Footstepsinthesand—Suerte **Mr A. W. Carroll**
57 **OH SO NICE**, 5, b m Kyllachy—Femme de Fer **Wedgewood Estates**
58 **OKAIDI (USA)**, 4, ch g Anodin (IRE)—Oceanique (USA)
59 **ONEBABA (IRE)**, 5, ch g No Nay Never (USA)—Enharmonic (USA) **Shropshire Wolves**
60 **OUR MAN IN HAVANA**, 6, b g Havana Gold (IRE)—Auntie Kathryn (IRE) **D. J. Oseman**
61 **PILOT WINGS (IRE)**, 6, b g Epaulette (AUS)—Intaglia (GER) **Green lighting Ltd**
62 **POETIC FORCE (IRE)**, 7, ch g Lope de Vega (IRE)—Obligada (IRE) **Mr S. Barton**
63 **POP DANCER (IRE)**, 4, b g Kodiac—Pop Art (IRE) **Mr B. J. Millen**
64 **POPPLE**, 6, b g Mayson—Fit To Burst **J. C. S. Wilson**
65 **POUR LA VICTOIRE (IRE)**, 11, b g Antonius Pius (USA)—Lady Lucia (IRE) **Curry House Corner & Partner**
66 **PRAIRIE TOWN (IRE)**, 10, b g High Chaparral (IRE)—Lake Baino **Cooke & Millen**
67 **PROTON (IRE)**, 5, b g Slade Power (IRE)—Singing Bird (IRE) **The Risk Takers Partnership**
68 **RECON MISSION (IRE)**, 5, b h Kodiac—Ermine Ruby **Mr B. J. Millen**
69 **RED ALERT**, 7, b g Sleeping Indian—Red Sovereign **Mr A. W. Carroll**

## MR TONY CARROLL - continued

70 **ROSE HIP,** 6, b m Acclamation—Poppy Seed **Lady Whent**
71 **SECOND COLLECTION,** 5, b m Delegator—Quelle Affaire **Mr Ian Furlong & Partner**
72 **SEND IN THE CLOUDS,** 4, b g Delegator—Saharan Song (IRE) **Mrs Y. T. Wallace**
73 **SILENT ATTACK,** 8, b g Dream Ahead (USA)—Chanterelle (FR) **South Yorkshire Racing**
74 **SIR TITAN,** 7, b g Aqlaam—Femme de Fer **Wedgewood Estates**
75 **SNOW LEOPARD (IRE),** 5, gr g Mount Nelson—La Gandilie (FR) **CCCP Syndicate**
76 **SOCIAL CITY,** 5, b g Cityscape—Society Rose **H. M. W. Clifford**
77 **SONG OF BEAUTY (FR),** 4, gr f Authorized (IRE)—Song of India **Wedgewood Estates**
78 **SONG OF SUMMER (FR),** 5, gr m Sommerabend—Song of India **Wedgewood Estates**
79 **TAYLORS THREE ROCK (IRE),** 5, ch m Roderic O'Connor (IRE)—Miss Me **Ms K. J. Austin**
80 **TELEKINETIC,** 6, b m Champs Elysees—Kinetix **Six Pack**
81 **TEMUR KHAN,** 6, br g Dansili—Slink **Mrs H. Hogben**
82 **THUNDEROAD,** 5, b g Street Sense (USA)—Royal Crystal (USA) **Mrs L. Hunt**
83 **TONI'S A STAR,** 9, b m Avonbridge—Canina **A Star Recruitment Limited**
84 **TOP BOY,** 11, b g Exceed And Excel (AUS)—Injaaz **Mrs S. A. Bowen**
85 **UNDER CURFEW,** 5, ch g Stimulation (IRE)—Thicket **Mr M. J. Wellbelove**
86 **URBAN HIGHWAY (IRE),** 5, b g Kodiac—Viking Fair **Millen & Partner**
87 **VAPE,** 4, gr g Dark Angel (IRE)—Puff (IRE) **Mr A. W. Carroll**
88 **VIVE LE ROI (IRE),** 10, b g Robin des Pres (FR)—Cappard View (IRE) **Surefire Racing**
89 **WILEY POST,** 8, b g Kyllachy—Orange Pip **Lady Whent**
90 **WINDSORLOT (IRE),** 8, ch g Windsor Knot (IRE)—Majestic Jenny (IRE) **SF Racing Club**
91 **WINNETKA (IRE),** 4, ch g Camacho—Little Audio (IRE) **Mr A. W. Carroll**
92 **WREN IN THE HOUSE,** 4, b f Coach House (IRE)—Farmers Dream (IRE) **D. J. Oseman**

### THREE-YEAR-OLDS

93 **BRANSTON PIKKLE,** b c Farhh—Triveni (FR) **Mr S. P. Barry**
94 Gr c Hot Streak (IRE)—Cool Angel (IRE) **Mr A. W. Carroll**
95 B g Epaulette (AUS)—Dunbrody (FR) **Mr A. W. Carroll**
96 B c Mayson—Eleodora
97 **HOLBACHE,** b g Coach House (IRE)—By Rights **Day & & Dewhurst**
98 **HOOVES LIKE JAGGER (IRE),** b g Sir Prancealot (IRE)—Roseisarose (IRE) **Mr A. Mills**
99 **IRON WOLF,** br g Fountain of Youth (IRE)—Vilnius **Mr A. W. Carroll**
100 B f Hunter's Light (USA)—Katya Kabanova **Wedgewood Estates**
101 **MID DAY RUSH (IRE),** ch f Dandy Man (IRE)—Que Sera Sera **Andrew Griffiths & Charles Tristram**
102 **NUTS IN MAY,** b f Mayson—Poppy Seed **Lady Whent**
103 **PAYMASTER,** ch c Hot Streak (IRE)—High 'n Dry (IRE) **Mr A. W. Carroll**
104 **QUEEN SARABI (IRE),** b f The Last Lion (IRE)—Tango Tonic (IRE) **Ms E. A. Judd**
105 Ch c Hot Streak (IRE)—Saharan Song (IRE) **Cole, Green & Wellbelove**
106 **TEDDY B,** ch g Sepoy (AUS)—Effie B **Univit Ltd**

**Other Owners:** Mr J. Babb, Mr J. A. Barber, Mr D. R. Blake, Mr R. Buckland, Mr A. W. Carroll, Mr M. S. Cooke, Curry House Corner, Mr J. R. Daniell, Mrs D. S. Dewhurst, J. A. Dewhurst, Mr S. Doocey, Mr I. Furlong, Mr A. S. Griffiths, Mr I. Johnson, Last Day Racing Partnership, Mr J. Lawrence, Mr B. J. Millen, Mr R. J. Millen, Dr A. D. Rogers, Shropshire Wolves, R. Simpson, Mr K. Singh, Surefire Racing, Mr L. C. Thomas, Mr V. Thompson, Mr C. Tristram, Mr A. N. Waters.

---

## 94 MR TONY CARSON, Newmarket
Postal: **Cedar Lodge Racing Stables, Hamilton Road, Newmarket, Suffolk, CB8 0NQ**
Contacts: **MOBILE 07837 601867**
**WORK EMAIL tcarsonracing@gmail.com INSTAGRAM tcarsonracing**

1 **BURNING SUN (IRE),** 4, ch f Slade Power (IRE)—Crimson Year (USA) **Mr C. Butler**
2 **DAME DENALI,** 4, b f Casamento (IRE)—Doric Lady **Dennett Cameron Francis Hart**
3 **DENABLE,** 5, b g Champs Elysees—Surprise (IRE) **Mr C. T. Dennett**
4 **DISTANT UNIVERSE,** 6, b m Universal—Distant Florin **Mr C. T. Dennett**
5 **FLAMINGO ROSE,** 4, gr f Casamento (IRE)—Distant Waters **Mrs J. O'Neill**

## MR TONY CARSON - continued

6 **FRICKA**, 8, b m Sulamani (IRE)—Distant Florin  **Mr C. T. Dennett**
7 **GULLAND ROCK**, 10, b g Exceed And Excel (AUS)—Sacre Coeur  **Mr A. T. Carson**
8 **PIANISSIMO**, 5, b g Teofilo (IRE)—Perfect Note  **Mr C. Butler**
9 **RASAASY (IRE)**, 5, b g Cape Cross (IRE)—Drops (IRE)  **Mr C. Butler**
10 **SHE'S ON THE EDGE (IRE)**, 4, b f Canford Cliffs (IRE)—Tea Cup  **Mr A. T. Carson**

### THREE-YEAR-OLDS

11 **CAHORS**, gr f Lethal Force (IRE)—Surprise (IRE)  **Mr C. T. Dennett**
12 **FIAMETTE**, ch f Free Eagle (IRE)—High Reserve  **Mr C. Butler**
13 **NEEDWOOD BLOSSOM**, b f Garswood—Fangfoss Girls  **Mr C. Butler**
14 **NOZIERES**, b f Mayson—Cool Catena  **Mr C. T. Dennett**
15 **POY**, b c Sepoy (AUS)—Sail Home

### TWO-YEAR-OLDS

16 B f 09/03 Bobby's Kitten (USA)—Bright Girl (IRE) (Invincible Spirit (IRE))
17 **NITRO NEMO**, b c 27/02 Marcel (IRE)—Believe In Dreams (Equiano (FR))
18 Ch f 14/04 Garswood—Roslea Lady (IRE) (Alhaarth (IRE)) (800)

**Other Owners:** Mr Peter Foster, Mr Jason Walsh.

**Flat Jockey:** William Carson. **NH Jockey:** Mr Graham Carson. **Amateur Jockey:** Kerryanne Alexander.

---

### 95 MR LEE CARTER, Epsom
Postal: **The Old Yard, Clear Height Stables, Epsom, Surrey, KT18 5LB**
Contacts: **PHONE 01372 740878 MOBILE 07539 354819 FAX 01372 740898**
EMAIL leecarterracing@aol.co.uk WEBSITE www.leecarterracing.com

1 **BRAZEN POINT**, 4, b c Brazen Beau (AUS)—Point of Control  **Kestonracingclub**
2 **CELESTIAL BLISS**, 4, b g Oasis Dream—La Pomme d'Amour  **Mr J. J. Smith**
3 **CLIFF FACE (IRE)**, 8, b m Canford Cliffs (IRE)—Kotdiji  **Mr J. J. Smith**
4 **COME ON TIER (FR)**, 6, b g Kendargent (FR)—Milwaukee (FR)  **Mr J. J. Smith**
5 **COMEONFEELTHEFORCE (IRE)**, 5, b m Slade Power (IRE)—Balladiene (IRE)  **Ewell Never Know**
6 **CUBAN SPIRIT**, 6, b g Harbour Watch (IRE)—Madam Mojito (USA)  **Mr J. J. Smith**
7 **DOVE DIVINE (FR)**, 5, b m Le Havre (IRE)—Numerieus (FR)  **Peter Clarke Racing Partners**
8 **ENOUGH ALREADY**, 5, b g Coach House (IRE)—Funny Enough  **Mr R. M. C. Barney**
9 **FAIRY FAST (IRE)**, 5, b m Requinto (IRE)—Fairy Trader (IRE)  **Only One Bid Partnership**
10 **FORTISSIMO (IRE)**, 5, b g Dream Ahead (USA)—Double Diamond (FR)  **Mr J. J. Smith**
11 **GOLD CLUB**, 10, b g Multiplex—Oceana Blue  **Tattenham Corner Racing IV**
12 **MAAZEL (IRE)**, 7, b g Elzaam (AUS)—Laylati (IRE)  **Mr J. J. Smith**
13 **MANZIL (IRE)**, 6, ch g Bated Breath—Pointed Arch (IRE)  **Mr R. M. C. Barney**
14 **MISS ELSA**, 5, b m Frozen Power (IRE)—Support Fund (IRE)  **Mr J. J. Smith**
15 **SALEH (IRE)**, 8, b g Iffraaj—Pellinore (USA)  **Only One Bid Partnership**
16 **SAVITAR (IRE)**, 6, b g Shamardal (USA)—Foofaraw (USA)  **Tattenham Corner Racing IV**
17 **SHYRON**, 10, b g Byron—Coconut Shy  **Mr J. J. Smith**
18 **THE WARRIOR (IRE)**, 9, b g Exceed And Excel (AUS)—Aymara  **Peter Clarke Racing Partners**
19 **TREBLE CLEF**, 6, b g Helmet (AUS)—Musical Key  **Mrs K. T. Carter**
20 **VIVENCY (USA)**, 4, b f Noble Mission—Hint of Joy (USA)  **Kestonracingclub**

### THREE-YEAR-OLDS

21 **HEAVEN'S BILL (IRE)**, b br c Red Jazz (USA)—Hawaiian Storm  **Kestonracingclub**

**96**
### MR BEN CASE, Banbury
Postal: **Wardington Gate Farm, Edgcote, Banbury, Oxfordshire, OX17 1AG**
Contacts: **PHONE 01295 750959 MOBILE 07808 061223 FAX 01295 758840**
**EMAIL** info@bencaseracing.com **WEBSITE** www.bencaseracing.com

1  **BATTLE OF PAVIA (IRE)**, 5, b g Milan—First Battle (IRE)  **Lady Jane Grosvenor**
2  **CHARYN CANYON (IRE)**, 5, b m Leading Light (IRE)—Nechtan (IRE)  **Mr A. H. Harvey**
3  **CLEVER GIRL (IRE)**, 4, ch f Intello (GER)—Bertie's Best  **Mr B. I. Case**
4  **CODED MESSAGE**, 8, b m Oscar (IRE)—Ring Back (IRE)  **Wardington Hopefuls**
5  **CONCEROE (IRE)**, 5, br g Kalanisi (IRE)—Made In Kk (IRE)  **Lady Jane Grosvenor**
6  **DASH OF BLUE**, 6, b g Great Pretender (IRE)—Madame Bleue  **Bluebuyu**
7  **DORADO DOLLAR (IRE)**, 7, ch g Golden Lariat (USA)—Stability Treaty (IRE)  **Miss P. Murray**
8  **FADE AND DIE**, 5, ch g Gentlewave (IRE)—Ring Back (IRE)  **Mr D P Walsh & Mr A Barry**
9  **FELTON BELLEVUE (FR)**, 6, b g Kap Rock (FR)—Sister du Berlais (FR)  **Mrs H Munn, Mr R E Good, Mr B Case**
10 **FERN HILL (IRE)**, 6, b g Dylan Thomas (IRE)—Water Rock  **Cross Foran Harrison**
11 **FOURTOUT (FR)**, 6, b g Honolulu (FR)—Madisone Fool (FR)  **Wardington Hopefuls**
12 **GAZETTE BOURGEOISE (FR)**, 5, b m Spanish Moon (USA)—Jasmine (FR)  **Mr A. H. Harvey**
13 **HUGO'S REFLECTION (FR)**, 9, b g Robin des Champs (FR)—Dawn Court  **Case Racing Partnership**
14 **KASABA BAY**, 4, ch g Universal (IRE)—Emmaslegend  **Mrs L. R. Lovell**
15 **KILBREW BOY (IRE)**, 8, b g Stowaway—Bean Ki Moon (IRE)  **Mr B. I. Case**
16 **KINGS TEMPTATION**, 9, b g King's Theatre (IRE)—Temptation (IRE)  **Lady Jane Grosvenor**
17 **MIDNIGHTREFLECTION**, 6, b m Midnight Legend—Hymn To Love (FR)  **Case Racing Partnership & Anita J Lush**
18 **NANNY MAY**, 4, b f Nayef (USA)—Plaisterer  **David Andrews Partnership**
19 **NORVICS REFLECTION (IRE)**, 6, b g Mahler—Finallyfree (IRE)  **Mrs S. R. Bailey**
20 **PRINCESS ROXY**, 8, ch m Midnight Legend—Royal Roxy (IRE)  **Mr A. H. Harvey**
21 **SHANTY ALLEY**, 7, b g Shantou (USA)—Alexander Road (IRE)  **Jerry Wright Adam Lucock Patricia Murray**
22 **SHEILA TANIST (IRE)**, 8, b m Court Cave (IRE)—Douglas Park (IRE)  **Case Racing Partnership**
23 **SILENT ENCORE (IRE)**, 9, ch g Curtain Time (IRE)—What Can I Say (IRE)  **North & South Racing Partnership**
24 **THE GOLDEN REBEL (IRE)**, 7, b g Gold Well—Good Thought (IRE)  **The Golden Rebels**
25 **TROUVILLE LADY**, 4, b f Boris de Deauville (IRE)—Artofmen (IRE)  **Foran Lovell Moore**
26 **WELSH'S CASTLE (IRE)**, 9, b g Mahler—Kyle Again (IRE)  **M. A. Kemp**
27 **WISECRACKER**, 8, br g Sageburg (IRE)—Folie Lointaine (FR)  **Lady Jane Grosvenor**

**Other Owners:** Mr A. K. Barry, Mr B. I. Case, Mrs S. L. Case, Case Racing Partnership, Mr R. Cross, David Andrews Partnership, Mrs S. P. Foran, Mr R. E. Good, Mr J. E. Harrison, Mrs M. A. Howlett, Mrs L. R. Lovell, Mr A. W. Lucock, Miss A. J. Lush, Mr T. W. Moore, Mrs H. M. Munn, Miss P. Murray, The Golden Rebels, J. Wright.

**Amateur Jockey:** Charlie Case.

**97**
### MR PATRICK CHAMINGS, Basingstoke
Postal: **Inhurst Farm Stables, Baughurst, Tadley, Hampshire, RG26 5JS**
Contacts: **PHONE 0118 981 4494 MOBILE 07831 360970 FAX 0118 982 0454**
**EMAIL** chamingsracing@talk21.com

1  **AMATHUS (IRE)**, 4, b g Anjaal—Effige (IRE)  **Mr D. F. Henery**
2  **CHARLES MOLSON**, 10, b g Monsieur Bond (IRE)—Arculinge  **Trolley Action**
3  **DOURADO (IRE)**, 7, b h Dark Angel (IRE)—Skehana (IRE)  **Mrs B. C. Wickens**
4  **DREAMING OF PARIS**, 6, b m Oasis Dream—Parisi  **The Foxford House Partnership**
5  **EMERALD FOX**, 6, b m Foxwedge (AUS)—Roshina  **Mr P. R. Chamings**
6  **GHEPARDO**, 6, b m Havana Gold (IRE)—Clincher  **The Foxford House Partnership**
7  **GLOBAL ACCLAMATION**, 5, b g Acclamation—High Luminosity (USA)  **Inhurst Players**
8  **GUILTY PARTY (IRE)**, 4, b f Lawman (FR)—Coolree Marj (IRE)  **Mrs R. Lyon & Mr P. R. Chamings**
9  **HARLEQUIN ROSE (IRE)**, 7, ch m Dutch Art—Miss Chaussini (IRE)  **G E Bassett & P R Chamings**
10 **LONDON CALLING (IRE)**, 4, b g Requinto—Bellechance  **Symonds, Camis & Fitchett**
11 **MAGICAL DRAGON (IRE)**, 4, b g Dragon Pulse (IRE)—Place That Face  **& Symonds**
12 **MISTER FREEZE (IRE)**, 7, ch g Frozen Power (IRE)—Beacon of Hope (IRE)  **G N Hunt, G E Bassett**

## MR PATRICK CHAMINGS - continued

13 **MY LADY CLAIRE**, 5, ch m Cityscape—Lady Sylvia  **Mr D. J. Keast**
14 **PERFECT OUTING**, 4, gr f Outstrip—Makara  **Mildmay Racing**
15 **PITCHCOMBE**, 4, b g Lethal Force (IRE)—Emmuska  **Mr D. F. Henery**
16 **RINTY MAGINTY (IRE)**, 5, b g Camacho—Peanut Butter (IRE)  **Mr P. R. Chamings**
17 **SPANISH STAR (IRE)**, 6, b g Requinto (IRE)—Rancho Star (IRE)  **Shirley Symonds & Fred Camis**
18 **TAWTHEEF (IRE)**, 4, b g Muhaarar—Miss Beatrix (IRE)  **Trolley Action**
19 **TOP CLASS ANGEL (IRE)**, 4, b f Dark Angel (IRE)—Expensive Date  **Mr S. Thompson**
20 **VINCENZO COCCOTTI (USA)**, 9, gr ro g Speightstown (USA)—Ocean Colors (USA)  **Mr D. F. Henery**

## THREE-YEAR-OLDS

21 **ABADESSA (IRE)**, b f The Gurkha (IRE)—Abbasharjah (GER)  **Mrs R. Lyon**

**Other Owners:** Mr G. E. Bassett, F. D. Camis, Mr P. R. Chamings, Mr D. P. Fitchett, Mr G. N. Hunt, Mrs R. Lyon, Mr H. R. Symonds, Mrs S. A. Symonds.

**Assistant Trainer:** Phillippa Chamings.

---

## 98    MR MICK CHANNON, West Ilsley
Postal: **West Ilsley Stables, West Ilsley, Newbury, Berkshire, RG20 7AE**
Contacts: **PHONE 01635 281166 FAX 01635 281177**
**EMAIL mick@mick-channon.co.uk WEBSITE www.mickchannon.tv**

1 4, B f Gleneagles (IRE)—Al Manaal
2 **ALENH**, 4, b g gr Al Kazeem—Enaitch (IRE)  **Mr & Mrs D. D. Clee**
3 **AWEEMAWEH (IRE)**, 4, ch g Bungle Inthejungle—Grotta Del Fauno (IRE)  **Six or Sticks**
4 **BARBILL (IRE)**, 5, b g Zebedee—Fiuise (IRE)  **Mrs S. G. Bunney**
5 **BAREST OF MARGINS (IRE)**, 5, b g Shirocco (GER)—Holly Baloo (IRE)  **The Tailenders**
6 **BRING THE MONEY (IRE)**, 4, b g Anjaal—Princess Banu  **M. R. Channon**
7 **CERTAIN LAD**, 5, b g Clodovil (IRE)—Chelsey Jayne (IRE)  **Mr C. R. Hirst**
8 **CHAIRMANOFTHEBOARD (IRE)**, 5, b g Slade Power (IRE)—
                                          Bound Copy (USA)  **David Kilburn, David Hudd & Chris Wright**
9 **DALANIJUJO (IRE)**, 4, ch f Night of Thunder (IRE)—Kiss From A Rose  **Mr C. R. Hirst**
10 **DANCING JO**, 5, b g Mazameer (IRE)—Remix (IRE)  **R.E.F.TEN**
11 **DARK ICON**, 4, br f Sixties Icon—Dark Raider (IRE)  **Recycled Products Limited**
12 **DECEPTION VALLEY (IRE)**, 4, b g Slade Power (IRE)—Sahaayef (IRE)  **M. R. Channon**
13 **GALAHAD THREEPWOOD**, 4, b g Nathaniel (IRE)—Tesary  **The Megsons & Partner**
14 **GLEN FORSA (IRE)**, 9, b g Mahler—Outback Ivy (IRE)  **Mr T. P. Radford**
15 **HOLD THE NOTE (IRE)**, 7, b g Jeremy (USA)—Keys Hope (IRE)  **Mr T. P. Radford**
16 **HUNDRED ISLES (IRE)**, 4, b g Fastnet Rock (AUS)—Gallic Star (IRE)  **Jon & Julia Aisbitt**
17 **INDIAN CREAK (IRE)**, 4, b g Camacho—Ushindi (IRE)  **Peter Taplin & Susan Bunney**
18 **KALEIDOSCOPIC**, 4, b f Le Havre (IRE)—Riot of Colour  **Hunscote Stud Limited & Partner**
19 **KOEMAN**, 7, b g Dutch Art—Angelic Note (IRE)  **Peter Taplin & Susan Bunney**
20 **MILLTOWN STAR**, 4, b g Roderic O'Connor (IRE)—Hail Shower (IRE)  **Hunscote Stud Limited & Partner**
21 **MISTER WHITAKER (IRE)**, 9, b g Court Cave (IRE)—Benbradagh Vard (IRE)  **Mr T. P. Radford**
22 **RAINS OF CASTAMERE (IRE)**, 4, ch g Harbour Watch (IRE)—Shrimpton  **M. R. Channon**
23 **SEAGULLS NEST**, 4, b f Camelot—Mare Imbrium (USA)  **Barry Walters Farms**
24 **SHE STRIDES ON**, 4, ch f Paco Boy (IRE)—Pose (IRE)  **M. R. Channon**
25 **SINGLE (IRE)**, 4, ch f Nathaniel (IRE)—Solita (USA)  **The Sweet Partnership**
26 **STEEL AN ICON**, 4, b f Sixties Icon—Steel Free (IRE)  **Recycled Products Limited**
27 **STORTING**, 5, b g Iffraaj—Stella Point (IRE)  **Jon & Julia Aisbitt**
28 **TRAIS FLUORS**, 7, b br g Dansili—Trois Lunes (FR)  **Mr L. Harris**
29 **WIGHTMAN (IRE)**, 4, b g Anjaal—Defensive Boast (USA)  **M. R. Channon**

## MR MICK CHANNON - continued

### THREE-YEAR-OLDS
30 **AMY BEACH (IRE)**, b f New Approach (IRE)—Isabella Bird **Jon & Julia Aisbitt**
31 **AONACH MOR**, b c Twilight Son—Royal Ffanci **Hunscote Stud Limited**
32 **ARCADIAN NIGHTS**, b c Exceed And Excel (AUS)—Lady Lahar **John & Zoe Webster & Partner**
33 Ch f Captain Gerrard (IRE)—Blakeshall Rose **Bastian Family**
34 **CAIRN GORM**, ch c Bated Breath—In Your Time **Hunscote Stud Limited & Partner**
35 **DANNY BLEU (IRE)**, br c Clodovil (IRE)—Casual Remark (IRE) **Mrs T. Burns**
36 **DANZART (IRE)**, b g Dandy Man (IRE)—Surava **The Bexley Boys**
37 **DIAMONDS DANCING**, b f Swiss Spirit—Crazee Diamond **M. R. Channon**
38 **EEL PIE ISLAND**, b f Sixties Icon—Ificaniwill (IRE)
39 **EVA ICON**, gr f Sixties Icon—El Che **Mr Peter Taplin & Partner**
40 **FANGORN**, b c Bungle Inthejungle—Inffiraaj (IRE) **Ann Black & Partner**
41 B f Sixties Icon—Follow The Faith
42 **FOLLY BEACH**, b f Golden Horn—Vive Ma Fille (GER) **Mr J. M. Mitchell**
43 **FRED BEAR (IRE)**, b g Kodi Bear (IRE)—Subtle Affair (IRE) **Tom & Ann Black, Sean Coleman & Partner**
44 **GEARING'S POINT**, b f Harbour Watch (IRE)—Amahoro **Dave & Gill Hedley**
45 **GONE MOD**, b f Sixties Icon—Bridie Ffrench
46 **GREYSTOKE**, b c Sixties Icon—Siri **Dave & Gill Hedley**
47 **HIROMICHI (FR)**, gr c Dabirsim (FR)—Pachelbelle (FR) **Jon & Julia Aisbitt**
48 **ILLYKATO (IRE)**, b f Toronado (IRE)—Key Light (IRE) **Mr C. R. Hirst**
49 **JANIE JONES**, ch f Le Havre (IRE)—Coquet **The Megsons**
50 **JESSOP**, b f Sixties Icon—Zaatar (IRE) **M. R. Channon**
51 **KNIGHTOFPENTACLES (IRE)**, b gr g Sir Prancealot (IRE)—Danamight (IRE) **Six Or Sticks 2020**
52 **LAETOLI**, b f Footstepsinthesand—Exentricity **Barry Walters Farms & Partner**
53 **MAHALE**, b f Kodiac—Zarafa **Dave & Gill Hedley**
54 **MAJESTIC (IRE)**, b g Conduit (IRE)—Grevillea (IRE) **Mr N. J. Hitchins**
55 **MIRROR KISSES**, b f Requinto (IRE)—Sandy Times (IRE) **M. R. Channon**
56 **NODSASGOODASAWINK**, ch f Sixties Icon—Winkaway **P. Taplin**
57 **SAULIRE STAR (IRE)**, b f Awtaad (IRE)—Gallic Star (IRE) **Jon & Julia Aisbitt**
58 **SLY MADAM**, b f Sixties Icon—Tanojin (IRE) **Stoneham Park Stud**
59 **SMEATON'S LIGHT (IRE)**, b gr g Dragon Pulse (IRE)—Clenaghcastle Lady (IRE) **Mr Rory O'Rourke & Partner**
60 **SOPHIGGLIA**, gr f Sixties Icon—Myladyjane (IRE) **Nick & Olga Dhandsa & John & Zoe Webster**
61 B f Cityscape—Symboline
62 **URBAN VIOLET**, b f Cityscape—Just Violet **Eternal Folly Partnership I**

### TWO-YEAR-OLDS
63 Gr c 02/04 Gregorian (IRE)—Amahoro (Sixties Icon) **Dave & Gill Hedley**
64 B c 10/05 Gregorian (IRE)—Anazah (USA) (Diesis) **Mrs T. Burns**
65 B c 15/04 Sixties Icon—Ann Without An E (Rip Van Winkle (IRE))
66 **BAROQUE STAR (IRE)**, ch f 26/04 Lope de Vega (IRE)—Gallic Star (IRE) (Galileo (IRE)) **Jon & Julia Aisbitt**
67 **BASS STRAIT**, b f 29/03 Cityscape—Rough Courte (IRE) (Clodovil (IRE)) **Aston Bloodstock**
68 B f 18/03 Gregorian (IRE)—Bridie Ffrench (Bahamian Bounty)
69 B c 14/03 Territories (IRE)—Bright Flash (Dutch Art) (28000)
70 B c 13/03 Showcasing—Carpe Diem Lady (IRE) (Acclamation) (38095) **Mr C. R. Hirst**
71 **CHELMS PRINCE**, b c 26/04 Heeraat (IRE)—Mistic Magic (IRE) (Orpen (USA)) **Lee Harris & Partner**
72 **CHELMS PRINCESS**, b gr f 24/04 Gregorian (IRE)—Alpha Spirit (Sixties Icon) **Lee Harris & Partner**
73 B c 28/01 Churchill (IRE)—Chicago Star (Exceed And Excel (AUS))
74 **CLIFFORD (IRE)**, ch c 19/03 Ruler of The World (IRE)—Grevillea (IRE) (Admiralofthefleet (USA)) **Mr N. J. Hitchins**
75 Ch f 29/04 Profitable (IRE)—Dayrose (Daylami (IRE)) (15000)
76 B f 04/04 Sixties Icon—Dozen (FR) (Mastercraftsman (IRE))
77 B f 07/04 Oasis Dream—Effie B (Sixties Icon) **Bastian Family**
78 B f 19/02 Gregorian (IRE)—El Che (Winker Watson) **Mr Peter Taplin & Partner**
79 B f 09/02 Sixties Icon—Estrellada (Oasis Dream)
80 B f 02/03 Gregorian (IRE)—Ettie Hart (IRE) (Bushranger (IRE)) (762)
81 B f 20/02 Churchill (IRE)—Fiumicino (Danehill Dancer (IRE))
82 Ch c 03/03 Sixties Icon—Flashyfrances (Franklins Gardens)
83 B c 02/05 Havana Gold (IRE)—In Your Time (Dalakhani (IRE))
84 **INGRA TOR (IRE)**, b c 05/03 Churchill (IRE)—Kassia (IRE) (Acclamation) **Jon & Julia Aisbitt**
85 Br gr c 29/03 Clodovil (IRE)—Irene Adler (IRE) (Born To Sea (IRE)) **Mr Rory O'Rourke & Partner**

## MR MICK CHANNON - continued

86  B gr f 25/02 Al Kazeem—Jersey Breeze (IRE) (Dark Angel (IRE)) **Mrs S. G. Bunney**
87  B f 16/03 Bungle Inthejungle—Katevan (IRE) (Heliostatic (IRE)) (6000) **Mrs T Burns & Partner**
88  B f 26/02 Anjaal—Loveisallaroundyou (IRE) (Clodovil (IRE)) **Mrs T. Burns**
89  B f 21/03 Anjaal—Lucky Leigh (Piccolo)
90  B f 22/03 Australia—Miss Lahar (Clodovil (IRE)) (30000) **Barry Walters Farms**
91  B gr f 05/04 Caravaggio (USA)—Novalina (IRE) (Galileo (IRE)) (37000) **David Kilburn, David Hudd & Chris Wright**
92  B c 29/04 Sixties Icon—Outside Art (Excellent Art) **Mrs Janet Evans & Partners**
93  B br f 04/02 Gutaifan (IRE)—Sahafh (USA) (Rock Hard Ten (USA))
94  B f 27/02 Sixties Icon—Shadows Ofthenight (IRE) (Fastnet Rock (AUS))
95  B f 23/01 Sixties Icon—Shrimpton (Cadeaux Genereux)
96  B c 05/04 Sixties Icon—Siri (Atlantic Sport (USA)) **Dave & Gill Hedley**
97  B c 11/02 Vadamos (FR)—Society Gal (IRE) (Galileo (IRE)) (27000)
98  B gr c 27/04 Garswood—Tigrilla (IRE) (Clodovil (IRE)) (10000)
99  B c 18/04 Clodovil (IRE)—Top Act (FR) (Fantastic Light (USA)) (50000)
100  B c 08/04 Sixties Icon—Unbeaten (Bahamian Bounty)
101  B c 04/04 Belardo (IRE)—Vincita (IRE) (Lawman (FR)) (5000)
102  Ch gr c 21/04 Sixties Icon—Vive Ma Fille (GER) (Doyen (IRE)) **Mr J. M. Mitchell**
103  B c 19/04 Sixties Icon—Waitingforachance (Sayif (IRE)) (762)
104  B gr f 11/02 Sixties Icon—Whiteley (IRE) (Dark Angel (IRE)) **Peter Taplin & Susan Bunney**
105  **WONDERFUL WORLD,** b c 20/04 Bungle Inthejungle—
                                              La Gifted (Fraam) (13333) **George Materna & Roger Badley**
106  B f 27/02 Sixties Icon—Zaatar (IRE) (Fast Company (IRE)) (762)
107  B c 29/04 Churchill (IRE)—Zarafa (Fraam)

**Other Owners:** Mr Stuart Bell, Mr W H Carson, Mr  Peter Fekete, Mr Garry Gilroy, Mr David  Hall, Insignia Racing, John Guest Racing Ltd, M Al-Qatami & K M Al-Mudhaf, Mr J. L. Marsden, Mr & Mrs G Blackwell, Mr & Mrs M Jones, Mr W Parish, Tails Partnership, Mr C. N. Wright.

**Assistant Trainer:** Jack Channon, Allana  Mason.

---

**99**

**MR MICHAEL CHAPMAN, Market Rasen**
Postal: **Woodlands Racing Stables, Woodlands Lane, Willingham Road, Market Rasen, Lincolnshire, LN8 3RE**
Contacts: **PHONE 01673 843663 MOBILE 07971 940087**
**EMAIL woodlands.stables@btconnect.com WEBSITE www.woodlandsracingstables.co.uk**

1  **FAST DEAL,** 4, ch g Fast Company (IRE)—Maven **Mrs M. M. Chapman**
2  **GLACIER FOX,** 6, ch g Foxwedge (AUS)—Beat Seven **Mrs M. M. Chapman**
3  **L'ES FREMANTLE (FR),** 10, b g Orpen (USA)—Grand Design **Mr G. Nolan**
4  **LUDUAMF (IRE),** 7, ch g Tamayuz—Aphorism **Mrs M. M. Chapman**
5  **NOLANS HOTSPUR (IRE),** 9, b g Bushranger (IRE)—Cayambe (IRE) **Mr G. Nolan**
6  **PORT LAIRGE,** 11, b g Pastoral Pursuits—Stylish Clare (IRE) **Mrs M. M. Chapman**

**Assistant Trainer:** Mrs M. Chapman.

---

**100**

**MR RYAN CHAPMAN, St Mawgan**
Postal: **Trevenna Forge, St Mawgan , Newquay , Cornwall, TR8 4EZ**

1  **AWESOME TUNES (IRE),** 11, b g Milan—Europet (IRE) **Mr R. G. Chapman**
2  **COMERAGH LAD (IRE),** 7, b g Morozov (USA)—Fox Glacier (IRE) **Mr R. G. Chapman**
3  **DOYEN EXPRESS (IRE),** 7, b m Doyen (IRE)—Crimson Bow (GER) **Mr R. G. Chapman**
4  **PERUVIEN BLEU (FR),** 9, b br g Fuisse (FR)—Edelmira (FR) **Mr R. G. Chapman**
5  **THE RIGHT PROFILE (IRE),** 8, b g Milan—Bonnie And Bright (IRE) **Mr R. G. Chapman**

**101** **MR FABRICE CHAPPET, Chantilly**
Postal: **29 Avenue de Joinville, 60500 Chantilly, France**
Contacts: PHONE **+33 3 44 21 03 00**
EMAIL chappet.office@chappetracing.fr WEBSITE www.chappetracing.com

1 ALBA POWER (IRE), 6, b g Fast Company (IRE)—Shehila (IRE) **F. J. Carmichael**
2 AQUASTAR (IRE), 5, b g Sea The Stars (IRE)—Chiosina (IRE) **F. J. Carmichael**
3 BARDO (FR), 4, b g Siyouni (FR)—Dilag **C.N. Wright**
4 BAVARIA BABY (FR), 4, b f Dabirsim (FR)—Baiadera (GER) **Ecurie Normandie Pur Sang**
5 CELESTIN (FR), 4, b c Dabirsim (FR)—Celesteville (IRE) **Ecurie Normandie Pur Sang**
6 DREAM WORKS, 4, gr c Wootton Bassett—Sablionniere (FR) **Ecurie J. L. Bouchard**
7 FRANKEL'S MAGIC (FR), 4, b f Frankel—Global Magic **R. Shaykhutdinov**
8 GOLD TRIP (FR), 4, b c Outstrip—Sarvana (FR) **Ecurie J. L. Bouchard**
9 INSTRUIT, 4, b c Intello (GER)—Stumpy **A. Gilibert**
10 INTELLOGENT (IRE), 6, ch h Intello (GER)—Nuit Polaire (IRE) **F. J. Carmichael**
11 JAMILYA (FR), 4, gr f Kingman—Jane Eyre **R. Shaykhutdinov**
12 KEN COLT (IRE), 6, b g Kendargent (FR)—Velvet Revolver (IRE) **Roy Racing Ltd**
13 KILFRUSH MEMORIES (FR), 5, b h Shakespearean (IRE)—Elusive Lily **S. Vidal**
14 LIGHT IN THE DARK (FR), 4, b f Dark Angel (IRE)—Wonderous Light (IRE) **R. Shaykhutdinov**
15 MOON DREAM (IRE), 4, b c Dream Ahead (USA)—Lune Rose **Ecurie Vivaldi**
16 PISANELLO (IRE), 4, b c Raven's Pass (USA)—Painting (IRE) **Haras d'Etreham**
17 REY PELAYO (FR), 5, b h Wootton Bassett—Darkova (USA) **Ecurie J. L. Bouchard**
18 ROC ANGEL (FR), 7, ch g Rock of Gibraltar (IRE)—Forewarned (IRE) **A. Gilibert**
19 ROLLEVILLE (FR), 4, ch f Rock of Gibraltar (IRE)—Racemate **G. Augustin-Normand**
20 ROYAUMONT (FR), 4, b g Dabirsim (FR)—Rosie Thomas (IRE) **A. Gilibert**
21 SPEAK OF THE DEVIL (FR), 4, b f Wootton Bassett—Moranda (FR) **R. Shaykhutdinov**
22 VAL FEX (FR), 4, b f Elvstroem—Val d'Hiver **Haras de Saint Julien**
23 WATCHMEN (FR), 4, b g Elvstroem—Watchful **Antoinette Tamagni**
24 WIND SPIRIT (FR), 4, b c Charm Spirit (IRE)—Alpine Rose **C. Marzocco**
25 YSSINGEAUX (FR), 5, b g Dabirsim (FR)—Lovely Best (FR) **A. Gilibert**

## THREE-YEAR-OLDS

26 ACAPULCO GOLD (FR), b f Bungle Inthejungle—Velvet Revolver **C.N. Wright**
27 AL NAYEBA, b f Siyouni (FR)—Changing Skies (IRE) **Al Shaqab Racing**
28 ALL THE KING'S MEN (FR), b c Kingman—Gooseley Chope (FR) **F. J. Carmichael**
29 AMEERA, ch f Tamayuz—Ocean Talent **Elbashir Elhrari**
30 ANGEL, b c Fastnet Rock—Engage (IRE) **Ecurie Ades Hazan**
31 BAVARIA EXPRESS (FR), b f Dabirsim (FR)—Baiadera (GER) **Ecurie Normandie Pur Sang**
32 BEL ARISTO (FR), b c New Approach (IRE)—Baroness Daniela **A. Gilibert**
33 COMPLICATION, b br f No Nay Never (USA)—Sleek Gold **K. M. Al Attiyah**
34 COVADONGA, b f Scissor Kick (AUS)—Minza (FR) **Haras d'Etreham**
35 EARLY LIGHT (FR), b c Wootton Bassett—Accalmie **H. Saito**
36 EASTER, b c Exosphere (AUS)—Excellent Girl **Aleyrion Bloodstock**
37 FOREST OF WISDOM, b c Ifraaj—Wiesenlerche **R. Shaykhutdinov**
38 FRONT LINE, b f War Front (USA)—Fresh Air (IRE) **Haras d'Etreham**
39 GAGARIN'S MOON, b c Sea The Moon (GER)—Gagarina (IRE) **R. Shaykhutdinov**
40 GALACTICA (FR), b c Dabirsim (FR)—Garmerita **Ecurie Normandie Pur Sang**
41 GIRL ON THE MOON (FR), b f Wootton Bassett—Tempera Noire (FR) **J.E. Dubois**
42 GLORY LIGHT, b f Olympic Glory (IRE)—Sandy Light (IRE) **D. Malingue**
43 KAPANI (FR), bl g Soldier Hollow—Oceanie **Hubert Meraud**
44 KARAMBASIM (FR), b c Dabirsim (FR)—Khandaat **Ecurie Normandie Pur Sang**
45 LAURA MARS (IRE), b f Elusive Quality—Earth Goddess **A. Gilibert**
46 LEO VEGA (FR), b f Wootton Bassett—Vega Sicilia (FR) **Elbashir Elhrari**
47 LUCKY SIM (FR), b c Dabirsim (FR)—Lady Zinaad **Ecurie Normandie Pur Sang**
48 MANDOLINE, b f Muhaarar—Attractive Lady **A. Gilibert**
49 MON AMOUR (IRE), b f Kodi Bear (IRE)—Monspa **Ecurie Normandie Pur Sang**
50 MORE JOY (FR), b f Mont Jeu—La Joie **H. de Pracomtal**
51 MY SYMBOL, b c Quality Road (USA)—Russian Symbol (IRE) **A. Gilibert**
52 NEPALAIS, b c The Gurkha—Daltiana (FR) **A. Gilibert**
53 OK BOOMER (IRE), b f Slade Power (IRE)—Pinaruh (IRE)

## MR FABRICE CHAPPET - continued

54  **OMNIA MUNDA MUNDIS**, b f Australia—Regina Mundi (IRE)  **San Paolo Agri Stud**
55  **PRINCE LANCELOT**, b c Sir Prancealot (IRE)—Rainbow Vale (FR)  **A. Gilibert**
56  **PULSING**, b c Dragon Pulse—Kingdome Come  **H. de Pracomtal**
57  **SECOND TO NONE (IRE)**, b c Zoffany (IRE)—Magic America  **Ecurie J. L. Bouchard**
58  **SHABANDOZ**, b c Wootton Bassett—Shabyt  **Nurlan Bizakov**
59  **SHALIMA (FR)**, ch f Sinndar—Shanaza  **Haras de Beauvoir**
60  **SILENCE**, b c Olympic Glory (IRE)—Sailor Moon  **Ecurie des Monceaux**
61  **SILVER HORN**, b f Golden Horn—Magnificient Style  **Haras d'Etreham**
62  **SIYOUNOW (IRE)**, ch f Siyouni (FR)—Alta Lilea (IRE)  **F. Bianco**
63  **SMALL FIRES (FR)**, b c Dabirsim (FR)—Silent Sunday (IRE)  **Ecurie Normandie Pur Sang**
64  **STONETAIL**, b c Frankel—Dubai Rose  **H. Saito**
65  **TAN TAMASHA**, ch f Ifraaj—Tamasha  **Nurlan Bizakov**
66  **TAZMANIAN DEVIL**, b c New Bay—High Limits (IRE)  **C. Marzocco**
67  B c The Gurkha—Texaloula  **NBH Racing**
68  **THIS KISS**, b f Siyouni (FR)—This Time  **Antoinette Tamagni**
69  **TOMBECKA (IRE)**, b f Kingman—Totally Devoted  **Nurlan Bizakov**
70  **TOURBE (FR)**, b c Wootton Bassett—Pestagua  **Ecurie des Dragons**
71  **TRULY GLORIOUS**, b f Intello (GER)—Trully Blessed  **Haras de Saint Julien**
72  **VAL BASSETT (FR)**, b g Wootton Bassett—Val d'Hiver  **Haras de Saint Julien**
73  **WATCH HIM (FR)**, b c Elvstroem (AUS)—Watchful (IRE)  **A. Gilibert**
74  **WHITE WHISKY**, b c Kodiac—Mambo Light (USA)  **Ecurie J. L. Bouchard**

Trainer did not supply details of their two-year-olds.

**Other Owners:** K. M. Al Attiyah, F. Chappet, A. Curty, Meridian International, P. Nataf, M. Al Attiya, Hubert Meraud, J. Messara.

---

**102**
## MRS JANE CHAPPLE-HYAM, Newmarket
Postal: **Abington Place Racing Stables, 44 Bury Road, Newmarket, Suffolk, CB8 7BT**
Contacts: PHONE **07899 000555** MOBILE **07899 000555** FAX **01638 661335**
EMAIL **janechapplehyam@hotmail.co.uk, janechapplehyamracing@outlook.com**

1   **AMBASSADORIAL (USA)**, 7, b g Elusive Quality (USA)—Tactfully (IRE)  **Ms J. F. Chapple-Hyam**
2   **APLOMB (IRE)**, 5, b g Lope de Vega (IRE)—Mickleberry (IRE)  **Mrs F. J. Carmichael**
3   **AZETS**, 5, b g Dubawi (IRE)—Nashmiah (IRE)  **Johnstone Partnership**
4   **CIRCUS COUTURE (IRE)**, 9, ch g Intikhab (USA)—Bois Joli (IRE)  **Ms J. F. Chapple-Hyam**
5   **DALGARNO (FR)**, 8, b g Sea The Stars (IRE)—Jakonda (USA)  **Mrs F. J. Carmichael**
6   **EMOJIE**, 7, b g Captain Gerrard (IRE)—Striking Pose (IRE)  **Jakes Family**
7   **EXTRODINAIR**, 6, b g Captain Gerrard (IRE)—Mindfulness  **Jakes Family**
8   **FLIGHT PATH**, 4, gr g Mukhadram—Tipping Over (IRE)  **Tipping Over**
9   **GATILLO**, 8, gr g Showcasing—Crystal Gale (IRE)  **Jakes Family**
10  **GOLDEN LOVE**, 4, b f Dubawi (IRE)—Belle d'Or (USA)  **Mr A. E. Oppenheimer**
11  **I AM THE SECRET (SAF)**, 5, gr g Querari (SAF)—Secret of Victoria (SAF)  **Mr M. Harniman**
12  **LETHAL ANGEL**, 6, gr m Lethal Force (IRE)—Heliograph  **Billy And The Boys**
13  **MAID MILLIE**, 5, b m Dream Ahead (USA)—Maid A Million  **Ms J. F. Chapple-Hyam**
14  **STAMFORD RAFFLES**, 8, b g Champs Elysees—Romantic Retreat  **Ms J. F. Chapple-Hyam**
15  **SUZI'S CONNOISSEUR**, 10, b g Art Connoisseur (IRE)—Suzi Spends (IRE)  **Ms J. F. Chapple-Hyam**
16  **SWEET CANDY DALE**, 6, b m Captain Gerrard (IRE)—Sweet Seville (FR)  **T. G. Price**
17  **TO BE WILD (IRE)**, 8, br g Big Bad Bob (IRE)—Fire Up  **Mrs F. J. Carmichael**
18  **UBER COOL (IRE)**, 7, b g Born To Sea (IRE)—My Uptown Girl  **Fiona Carmichael & Jane Chapple-Hyam**
19  **WAR LEADER (USA)**, 4, b c War Front (USA)—Sun Shower (IRE)  **Ms J. F. Chapple-Hyam**

### THREE-YEAR-OLDS

20  **ALBADRI (IRE)**, b c Dandy Man (IRE)—Miss Legal Eagle (IRE)  **Alsharq racing**
21  **BELLOSA (IRE)**, b f Awtaad (IRE)—Poole Belle (IRE)  **Sir E. J. Loder**
22  **EX GRATIA**, b f Exceed And Excel (AUS)—Beta  **Miss K. Rausing**

## MRS JANE CHAPPLE-HYAM - continued

23 **LADY AMALTHEA (IRE)**, b f Prince of Lir (IRE)—Erbonne Girl (IRE) **Ms J. F. Chapple-Hyam**
24 **MANDARIN DUCK (IRE)**, b g Fascinating Rock (IRE)—Foreign Language (USA) **Ms J. F. Chapple-Hyam**
25 **PRINCE OF ABINGTON (IRE)**, b g Prince of Lir (IRE)—Greatest Dancer (IRE) **Morriss, Harrison, Chapple-Hyam**
26 **SAFFRON BEACH (IRE)**, ch f New Bay—Falling Petals (IRE) **Mrs B. V. Sangster, J Wigan & O Sangster**
27 **SOLOMONS JUDGEMENT (IRE)**, gr g Outstrip—Full Bloom **Ms J. F. Chapple-Hyam**

### TWO-YEAR-OLDS

28 **HEAT OF THE MOMENT**, ch f 14/02 Bobby's Kitten (USA)—

Heat of The Night (Lear Fan (USA)) **Miss K. Rausing**

29 **ROCKET YOGI (IRE)**, ch c 07/04 Fast Company (IRE)—

Yogi's Girl (IRE) (Harbour Watch (IRE)) (40000) **Mr G. W. Y. Li**

**Other Owners:** Mrs A. J. Brudenell, Mrs F. J. Carmichael, Ms J. F. Chapple-Hyam, Ms A. Harrison, Mr J. C. Jakes, Mrs T. M. A. Jakes, Mr H. A. Johnstone, Mr J. W. Johnstone, Mrs Zara Johnstone, Ms E. Kennedy, Mrs M. D. Morriss, B. V. Sangster, Mrs L. O. Sangster, Mr O. R. J. Sangster, J. Wigan.

**Assistant Trainer:** Abi Harrison.

**Flat Jockey:** Tim Clark. **Apprentice Jockey:** Jay Mackay, Levi Williams.

---

## 103  MR PETER CHAPPLE-HYAM, Newmarket
Postal: St Gatien Stables, All Saints Road, Newmarket, Suffolk, CB8 8HJ

1 **BHARANI STAR (GER)**, 4, ch f Sea The Stars (IRE)—Bay of Islands (FR) **Phoenix Thoroughbred Limited**
2 **DEJA (FR)**, 6, b g Youmzain (IRE)—Atarfe (IRE) **Phoenix Thoroughbred Limited**
3 **MARTINENGO (IRE)**, 6, b g Elusive Pimpernel (USA)—Albiatra (USA) **Ms S. E. Wall**
4 **MDINA**, 4, b f Mukhadram—Inchberry **Star Pointe Ltd**
5 **UNION SPIRIT**, 4, b br g Outstrip—Nouvelle Lune **Miss Sally Wall & Star Pointe Ltd**

### THREE-YEAR-OLDS

6 Ch f Mastercraftsman (IRE)—Arosa (IRE) **Phoenix Thoroughbred Limited**
7 B c Frankel—Attraction **Phoenix Thoroughbred Limited**
8 B c Galileo (IRE)—Convocate (USA) **Phoenix Thoroughbred Limited**
9 **FAST MEDICINE (IRE)**, b c Iffraaj—Annie The Doc **Phoenix Ladies Syndicate Limited**
10 **ISLE OF LIGHT**, b g Twilight Son—Belle Isle
11 **MASTER OF SOULS (IRE)**, b c Kodiac—Soul Searcher (IRE) **Phoenix Thoroughbred Limited**
12 **MISSED ILLUSION (IRE)**, b f Zoffany (IRE)—Thought Is Free **Mrs F. H. Hay**
13 B c Frankel—Oakley Girl **Phoenix Thoroughbred Limited**
14 **STOLEN SPOTLIGHT**, b c Showcasing—Overturned **Phoenix Thoroughbred Limited**
15 B f Marcel (IRE)—Waterways (IRE)

**Other Owners:** Star Pointe Ltd, Ms S. E. Wall.

## 104 MR PETER CHARALAMBOUS, Newmarket
Postal: **30 Newmarket Road, Cheveley, Suffolk, CB8 9EQ**
Contacts: PHONE 07921 858421
EMAIL camalotracing@btinternet.com

1 **THEYDON SPIRIT**, 6, ch g Piccolo—Ela Gorrie Mou **pcracing.co.uk**

### THREE-YEAR-OLDS

2 **APOLLO ONE**, ch c Equiano (FR)—Boonga Roogeta **pcracing.co.uk**
3 B c Toronado (IRE)—Ela Goog La Mou **pcracing.co.uk**
4 B c Toronado (IRE)—Ela Gorrie Mou **pcracing.co.uk**

## 105 MR ROGER CHARLTON, Beckhampton
Postal: **Beckhampton House, Marlborough, Wiltshire, SN8 1QR**
Contacts: PHONE 01672 539533 MOBILE 07710 784511
EMAIL office@beckhamptonstables.com WEBSITE www.rogercharlton.com

1 **AMIR KABIR**, 4, b g Mukhadram—Victory Garden **Dr Jamal Ahmadzadeh & Mrs D Swinburn**
2 **BLUE MIST**, 6, ch g Makfi—Namaskar **Exors of the late Mr K. Abdullah**
3 **COCHISE**, 5, b g Intello (GER)—Ship's Biscuit **P. Newton**
4 **DANCING HARRY (IRE)**, 4, b g Camelot—Poisson d'Or **Fishdance Ltd**
5 **EXTRA ELUSIVE**, 6, ch g Mastercraftsman (IRE)—Nessina (USA) **Mr I. Alsagar**
6 **IMPERIUM (IRE)**, 5, ch g Frankel—Ramruma (USA) **Weston Brook Farm & Bromfield**
7 **IVADREAM**, 4, b g Ivawood (IRE)—Midnight Fling **Mr S. Emmet & Miss R. Emmet**
8 **LOUGANINI**, 4, ch g Zoffany (IRE)—Princess Loulou (IRE) **Mr I. Alsagar**
9 **MAKRAM (IRE)**, 4, b g Make Believe—Spontaneous (IRE) **Mr M. Al-Qatami & Mr K. M. Al-Mudhaf**
10 **MINISTERIAL**, 4, b g Sea The Stars (IRE)—Rainbow Dancing **Clipper Group Holdings Ltd**
11 **SINJAARI (IRE)**, 5, b g Camelot—Heavenly Song (IRE) **Mohammed Jaber**
12 **SLEEPING LION (USA)**, 6, ch g Teofilo (IRE)—Flame of Hestia (IRE) **Merry Fox Stud Limited**
13 **TEMPUS**, 5, b g Kingman—Passage of Time **Exors of the late Mr K. Abdullah**
14 **TRUE DESTINY**, 4, b g Mastercraftsman (IRE)—Holy Dazzle **Exors of the Late Sultan Ahmad Shah**
15 **WIN O'CLOCK**, 4, ch c Australia—Gee Kel (IRE) **Kingwood Stud Management Co Ltd**
16 **WITHHOLD**, 8, b g Champs Elysees—Coming Back **Mr A. G. Bloom**

### THREE-YEAR-OLDS

17 **AMALFI BAY**, b g Lope de Vega (IRE)—Affinity **Elite Racing Club**
18 **BARN OWL**, b c Frankel—Thistle Bird **Nat Rothschild**
19 **BEAUTIFUL BERTIE**, br g Charm Spirit (IRE)—Really Lovely (IRE) **Mr & Mrs Paul & Clare Rooney**
20 **BEHELD**, ch f Frankel—Tendu **Exors of the late Mr K. Abdullah**
21 **BIG BOY BOBBY (IRE)**, b g Vadamos (FR)—Duchess of Foxland (IRE) **Mr & Mrs Paul & Clare Rooney**
22 **BIG DREAM (IRE)**, b g Oasis Dream—Piccola Sissi (IRE) **Mohammed Jaber**
23 **BOLTAWAY**, ch c Dubawi (IRE)—Proviso **Exors of the late Mr K. Abdullah**
24 **DALMA**, b f Frankel—Royal Secrets (IRE) **Mohammed Jaber**
25 **DOLPHIN**, b f Sea The Stars (IRE)—Dolma (IRE) **Lady Bamford**
26 **DORTE (IRE)**, b f Dubawi (IRE)—Gretchen **Normandie Stud Ltd**
27 **DREAMBIRD (IRE)**, b f Oasis Dream—Pocket Watch **Mr S. A. Stuckey**
28 **ELEVATE**, b f Paco Boy (IRE)—Telescopic **Hugo Hunt Racing**
29 **ELVIC**, b f Siyouni (FR)—Magical Romance (IRE) **Nat Rothschild**
30 **ENCOURAGE**, b g Iffraaj—Good Hope **Her Majesty The Queen**
31 B f Galileo (IRE)—Hazariya (IRE) **Allison , Merry and Rosen**
32 **HER WAY**, ch f Charming Thought—On Her Way **Beckhampton Stables Ltd**
33 **IN THE BREEZE (IRE)**, b g Harzand (IRE)—Its In The Air (IRE) **P Inglett, S de Zoete and C Milln**
34 **JUMBY BREEZE**, b f Dubawi (IRE)—Annabelle's Charm (IRE) **Merry Fox Stud Limited**
35 **KEEPER**, b c Frankel—Portodora (USA) **Exors of the late Mr K. Abdullah**
36 **KING OF TSAVO**, b c Dubawi (IRE)—Royal Decree (USA) **Mr A. Rosen**

# MR ROGER CHARLTON - continued

37 **LION FACE (IRE)**, b g Animal Kingdom (USA)—Blue Enzian (USA) **Mr D. Bannon**
38 **LOVE IS YOU (IRE)**, b f Kingman—Fallen For You **Normandie Stud Ltd**
39 **LUCID DREAMER**, gr f Dansili—Sleep Walk **Exors of the late Mr K. Abdullah**
40 **NADEIN**, b f Golden Horn—Oud Metha **Mohammed Jaber**
41 **NAJEEBA**, gr f Dansili—Rose of Miracles **Mr I. Alsagar**
42 **ONE JOURNEY**, b f Mastercraftsman (IRE)—Estrela **Mrs S. A. J. Kinsella**
43 **ORDEROFSUCCESSION**, b f Siyouni (FR)—Sequence (IRE) **Her Majesty The Queen**
44 **PLEASANT MAN**, b c Galileo (IRE)—Melito (AUS) **Brook Farm Bloodstock**
45 **QUILTED**, b f Frankel—Nimble Thimble (USA) **Exors of the late Mr K. Abdullah**
46 **RUMI**, br g Harzand (IRE)—Donatia **Dr J Ahmadzadeh**
47 **SALIGO BAY (IRE)**, b g New Bay—Glorification **Ballylinch Stud, P Inglett & N Jones**
48 **SAND IN MY SHOES (FR)**, b g Mastercraftsman (IRE)—Suquia (GER) **Beckhampton Stables Ltd**
49 **TIME INTERVAL**, b g Adaay (IRE)—Kuriosa (IRE) **P Inglett, S de Zoete and C Milln**
50 **UMM HURAIR (IRE)**, br f Awtaad (IRE)—Oasis Sunset (IRE) **Mohammed Jaber**
51 **VALORANT**, b f Showcasing—Comeback Queen **Kingwood Stud Management Co Ltd**
52 **WANNABE DONALD (IRE)**, b g Oasis Dream—Wannabe Loved **Normandie Stud Ltd**
53 **WITHOUT REVENGE**, b g Muhaarar—La Dorotea (IRE) **Carter, Dean, Gerber, Inglett**

## TWO-YEAR-OLDS

54 **ALBERT**, b c 18/04 Fastnet Rock—Fallen In Love (Galileo) **Normandie Stud Ltd**
55 **ANNIE'S SONG**, b f 09/04 Camacho—Dutch Treaty (Dutch Art) (47619) **Philip and Libby Newton**
56 Ch f 02/04 Exceed And Excel—Areyaam (Elusive Quality) **Ahmed Jaber**
57 B c 28/02 Almanzor—Between Us (Galileo) **Mohammed Jaber**
58 B c 14/03 Acclamation—Buying Trouble (Hat Trick) **Hot To Trot**
59 Ch c 04/03 Mastercraftsman—Champagne Ceri (Montjeu) **Seasons Holidays**
60 B f 03/02 Kingman—Choumicha (Paco Boy) **Mohammed Jaber**
61 B c 23/03 New Approach—Comeback Queen (Nayef) **Kingwood Stud Management Co Ltd**
62 B f 04/03 Gleneagles (IRE)—Crystal Morning (Cape Cross (IRE)) (65000) **Middleham Park Racing**
63 **DANCING EAGLE**, b f 18/04 Gleneagles (IRE)—Maid To Dream (Oasis Dream) (150000) **Fishdance Ltd**
64 **DANCING EMPRESS (IRE)**, b f 13/03 Holy Roman Emperor (IRE)—
Aspasias Tizzy (USA) (Tiznow (USA)) (52000) **Fishdance Ltd**
65 **DANCING TANGO (IRE)**, b f 04/02 Camelot—Dream Approach (IRE) (New Approach (IRE)) **Fishdance Ltd**
66 B f 06/02 Oasis Dream—Dhan Dhana (Dubawi) **Mohammed Jaber**
67 **FOZZIE BEAR (IRE)**, b c 01/03 Kodiac—Dabtiyra (IRE) (Dr Devious (IRE)) (75000) **de Zoete, Inglett & Jones**
68 Ch f 21/04 Slade Power—Go Angellica (Kheleyf) **Ahmed Jaber**
69 **GOLDEN SHEEN**, ch f 03/03 Frankel—Yellow Band (USA) (Dalakhani (IRE)) (100000) **Merry Fox Stud Limited**
70 B c 07/03 Frankel—Hana Lina (Oasis Dream) **Saeed Jaber**
71 B c 20/03 Kodiac—Homily (Singspiel) **Kingwood Stud Management Co Ltd**
72 **HONKY TONK MAN (IRE)**, b c 22/01 Tamayuz—Dance Hall Girl (IRE) (Dansili) (68000) **de Zoete, Inglett & Jones**
73 **JUDITH**, b f 02/04 Almanzor—Stella Bellissima (Sea The Stars) **Normandie Stud Ltd**
74 **JUMBLY**, b f 23/04 Gleneagles (IRE)—Thistle Bird (Selkirk (USA)) **Emmy Rothschild**
75 B gr f 22/03 Mastercraftsman—Kinni (Dansili) **Seasons Holidays**
76 B f 17/03 Kingman—Langlauf (Raven's Pass) **Mr A. G. Bloom**
77 Ch f 15/02 Decorated Knight—Lost Icon (Intikhab) **Mr I. Alsagar**
78 **LOVING CARE**, b c 07/03 Fastnet Rock—Loving Things (Pivotal) **Normandie Stud Ltd**
79 B c 28/03 Dabirism—Lunearia (Galileo) **Mohammed Jaber**
80 B f 25/03 Kingman—Lustrous (Champs Elysees) (310000) **St Albans Bloodstock Limited**
81 Ch c 02/02 Teofilo (IRE)—Majestic Manner (Dubawi (IRE)) **Saeed Jaber**
82 **MARS MAGIC**, b c 28/04 Magician—Celerina (Choisir) **Linda Mars**
83 B c 22/02 Churchill—Materialistic (Oasis Dream) **Mohammed Jaber**
84 B c 10/04 Siyouni (FR)—Nessina (USA) (Hennessy (USA)) (95000) **Brook Farm Bloodstock**
85 **NEXT SECOND**, b f 11/03 Hot Streak (IRE)—
Millisecond (Royal Applause) (21000) **Andrew Bengough and Partners**
86 B c 02/04 Kodiac—Nijah (Pivotal) **Mohammed Jaber**
87 **OUT FROM UNDER**, b c 20/03 Dubawi (IRE)—Koora (Pivotal) (120000) **White Birch Farm and Fittocks Stud**
88 Gr f 29/01 Caravaggio—Pannonia (Street Cry) **Mohammed Jaber**
89 B f 22/04 Shalaa (IRE)—Paradise Sea (USA) (Stormy Atlantic (USA)) **Mr I. Alsagar**
90 Ch c 31/01 Le Havre—Paris Winds (Galileo) **Sangster and Inglett**
91 B g 06/03 Vadamos—Pearly Spirit (Invincible Spirit) **Mr & Mrs Paul & Clare Rooney**

## MR ROGER CHARLTON - continued

92 **PIROUZ**, b c 27/03 El Kabeir (USA)—President's Seal (Aqlaam) (30000) **Dr J Ahmadzadeh**
93 B c 09/05 Al Kazeem—Poplin (Medicean) **D. J. Deer**
94 **PRINCESS LAVINIA**, b f 14/03 Bated Breath—Lavinia's Grace (Green Desert) **Mr James Stewart**
95 Ch f 11/04 Twilight Son—Retake (Reset) **Kingwood Stud Management Co Ltd**
96 Gr f 21/04 Time Test—Sell Out (Act One) **Mr & Mrs Paul & Clare Rooney**
97 B c 05/05 Frankel—September Stars (Sea The Stars) **Mr A. Rosen**
98 Ch c 08/02 Decorated Knight—Shaden (Kodiac) **Mr I. Alsagar**
99 B f 02/05 Night Of Thunder—Sharaakah (Roderic O'Connor) **Mohammed Jaber**
100 B f 02/05 Cityscape—Slide Show (Galileo) **Daniel Hunt**
101 Ch c 28/02 Night Of Thunder—Something Exciting (Halling) **Kingwood Stud Management Co Ltd**
102 B f 24/02 Shamardal—Soorah (Dubawi) **Mohammed Jaber**
103 B f 15/03 Muhaarar—Spring Fling (Assertive) (15000) **Too Many Partners**
104 Ch f 26/02 Postponed—Starscape (Cape Cross) **Mohammed Jaber**
105 **SWEET WILLIAM**, b c 24/03 Sea The Stars (IRE)—Gale Force (Shirocco) **Normandie Stud Ltd**
106 **TEMPTATION**, b f 08/03 Dabirism—Temptress (Shirocco) **Andrew Bengough and Partners**
107 B c 10/05 Camacho—That's My Style (Dalakhani) **Mohammed Jaber**
108 **VALSAD**, b c 15/05 INTELLO (GER)—Vuela (Duke Of Marmalade) **Mr S. A. Stuckey**
109 **WONDERFUL TIMES**, b f 11/03 Golden Horn—Wonderfully (Galileo) **Normandie Stud Ltd**
110 B c 26/02 Night Of Thunder (IRE)—Ya Hajar (Lycius (USA)) **Saeed Jaber**
111 B f 22/03 Golden Horn—Zamoura (Azamour) **D. J. Deer**

**Assistant Trainer:** Harry Charlton, **Pupil Assistant:** Matt Fielding.

**Flat Jockey:** Jason Watson. **Apprentice Jockey:** Thomas Greatrex.

---

**106** **MR HARRY CHISMAN, Stow-on-the-Wold**
Postal: **25 Coachmans Court, Station Road, Moreton-In-Marsh, Gloucestershire, GL56 0DE**
Contacts: **PHONE 07787 516723**
**WEBSITE www.harrychisman.co.uk**

1 **ALL RILED UP**, 13, b m Dr Massini (IRE)—Martha Reilly (IRE)
2 **FOYLESIDEVIEW (IRE)**, 9, b g Dark Angel (IRE)—Showerproof **Paul Baker Wendy Summers Duncan Wood**
3 **LEGENDOIRE (IRE)**, 7, b g Fast Company (IRE)—Last Shaambles (IRE) **Mr P. M. Baker**

**Other Owners:** Mr P. M. Baker, Miss W. Summers, D. C. Wood.

**Assistant Trainer:** G. Charles-Jones.

**Flat Jockey:** Robert Havlin. **NH Jockey:** Tom O'Brien, Sean Quinlan. **Conditional Jockey:** Daniel Hiskett. **Amateur Jockey:** Mr Paddy Berkins.

---

**107** **MR NICOLAS CLEMENT, Chantilly**
Postal: **37, Avenue de Joinville, 60500 Chantilly, France**
Contacts: **PHONE +33 3 44 57 59 60 MOBILE +33 6 07 23 46 40**
**EMAIL office@nicolasclement.com WEBSITE www.nicolasclement.com**

1 **AIGUIERE D'ARGENT (FR)**, 4, b g Exceleration (IRE)—Plaisanciere (FR)
2 **ASSIGNED (IRE)**, 4, b f Camelot—Entrust (NZ)
3 **CONTROL TOWER**, 4, b f Youmzain (IRE)—La Tour Rouge
4 **FITZCARRALDO**, 4, ch c Makfi—Sapfo (FR)
5 **GYPSY WHISPER**, 4, b f Helmet (AUS)—Secret Insider (USA)
6 **HAVANA BOUND**, 4, ch f Havana Gold (IRE)—Exceedingly Rare (IRE)

## MR NICOLAS CLEMENT - continued

7 **HIGH TECH (FR)**, 4, b g Intello (GER)—Highborne (FR)
8 **KALANI**, 4, b f Wootton Bassett—On The Line (FR)
9 **NOW WE KNOW (FR)**, 4, gr c Kendargent (FR)—Now Forever (GER)
10 **PERHAPS (FR)**, 4, b f Lope de Vega (IRE)—Reprint (IRE)
11 **STAKING (FR)**, 6, b g Stormy River (FR)—Shaking
12 **TIGER TOUCH (USA)**, 4, b c American Pharoah (USA)—Osaila (IRE)
13 **WHISKEY LULLABY**, 4, b f Intello (GER)—Colonialiste (IRE)

## THREE-YEAR-OLDS

14 **ADHBA (FR)**, b f Style Vendome (FR)—Zalal
15 **BENI KHIAR (FR)**, ch c Amaron—Elea (GER)
16 **BLLUSHING**, ch c Sepoy (AUS)—Convention
17 **CAPRICE DES DIEUX (FR)**, b c Declaration of War—Neko (FR)
18 **FENELON (FR)**, b c Fastnet Rock (AUS)—Aigue Marine
19 **HOPISSIME (FR)**, b f Camelot—Baino Hope (FR)
20 **IMAGE INEXPLICABLE**, ch f Sixties Icon—Puzzling
21 **JANULIS (FR)**, b c Toronado (IRE)—Leen (FR)
22 **KING'S HARLEQUIN (IRE)**, b f Camelot—Swift Action (IRE)
23 **LA VIE (FR)**, b f Shalaa (IRE)—Twyla Tharp (FR)
24 **LAKE PLACID (FR)**, b c Olympic Glory (IRE)—Lathah (IRE)
25 **LAZY (GER)**, b c Siyouni (FR)—Larella (GER)
26 **LILY FOR EVER (FR)**, b f Dariyan (FR)—Golden Lily (FR)
27 **MAGIC CARPET (FR)**, b f Pomellato (GER)—Mantissa
28 **MAJORETTE (FR)**, ch f Showcasing—Idle Tears
29 **MERCIELAGO (FR)**, b c Teofilo (IRE)—Mondalay
30 **NOW LE HAVRE (FR)**, b c Le Havre (IRE)—Now Forever (GER)
31 **PLAY ALL DAY (USA)**, b f Kitten's Joy (USA)—Nominative (USA)
32 **POWHATAN (FR)**, b g The Wow Signal (IRE)—Feelin Foxy
33 **SCHOONER RIDGE (IRE)**, b f Siyouni (FR)—Surprisingly (IRE)
34 **SCILIAR (IRE)**, ch c Raven's Pass (USA)—Snake Dancer (IRE)
35 **SPORT COUPE (FR)**, ch c Toronado (IRE)—Ideechic (FR)
36 **TAMBOOTIE (IRE)**, ch f Siyouni (FR)—Extreme Green
37 **WARNING AT SEA (IRE)**, b f Sea The Moon (GER)—Forewarned (IRE)
38 **WILDWOOD (FR)**, b br f Maxios—Walayta (FR)

## TWO-YEAR-OLDS

39 B f 15/03 Ectot—Across The Sky (IRE) (Cape Cross (IRE))
40 **ADAM'S RIB**, b f 06/02 Ribchester (IRE)—Megan Lily (IRE) (Dragon Pulse (IRE)) (80000)
41 B c 19/02 Zelzal (FR)—Al Wathna (Nayef (USA))
42 **CAP SAN ROMAN (FR)**, b f 25/03 Muhaarar—Cap Verite (IRE) (Cape Cross (IRE))
43 **COMMANDER BUZZKILL**, b f 10/05 Lope de Vega (IRE)—Centime (Royal Applause) (65000)
44 B f 17/02 Iffraaj—Diamond Bangle (IRE) (Galileo (IRE)) (25000)
45 B c 01/05 Shalaa (IRE)—Dynamite (FR) (Dynaformer (USA))
46 Ch f 01/02 Almanzor (FR)—Glowing Cloud (Dylan Thomas (IRE))
47 **LA TOUR DES REVES (FR)**, b f 19/03 Oasis Dream—La Tour Rouge (Monsun (GER))
48 **LADY ARIELLA (FR)**, ch f 08/03 Ruler of The World (IRE)—Sea The Future (IRE) (Sea The Stars (IRE))
49 Ch f 03/04 New Bay—Morgenlicht (GER) (Sholokhov (IRE))
50 B f 24/03 Kendargent (FR)—Now Forever (GER) (Tiger Hill (IRE))
51 B f 26/02 Sir Percy—Odense (USA) (Medaglia d'Oro (USA))
52 B f 29/03 Shalaa (IRE)—Peaceful Love (GER) (Dashing Blade)
53 Ch f 21/03 Brametot (IRE)—Pepite Noire (FR) (Redback)
54 Ch f 19/03 Mastercraftsman (IRE)—Peppermint (IRE) (Elusive City (USA))
55 **PRINCESS GLITTERS (FR)**, b f 21/03 Zarak (FR)—Lady Glitters (FR) (Homme de Loi (FR))
56 Ch c 11/04 Almanzor (FR)—Private Eye (FR) (American Post)
57 **QUEEN'S HARLEQUIN (FR)**, b f 24/04 Camelot—Chicago May (FR) (Numerous (FR))
58 B c 07/05 Zoffany (IRE)—Rock My World (GER) (Sholokhov (IRE))
59 **ROSETTA STONE (FR)**, ch c 26/04 Rock of Gibraltar (IRE)—Forewarned (IRE) (Grand Lodge (USA))
60 **ROYAL RIVER (FR)**, b c 22/04 Holy Roman Emperor (IRE)—Rambert (Acclamation)
61 **SOUTHWEST HARBOR (IRE)**, b f 15/02 Churchill (IRE)—Squeeze (IRE) (Danehill Dancer (IRE)) (95238)

## MR NICOLAS CLEMENT - continued

**62 SUNRAY (IRE),** ch f 24/04 Dawn Approach (IRE)—Snake Dancer (IRE) (Golden Snake (USA))
**63** B f 24/03 Camelot—Tasharowa (FR) (Linamix (FR))
**64** B f 11/02 Curlin (USA)—Taste of Heaven (AUS) (Encosta de Lago (AUS))
**65 THEORETICAL (FR),** ch f 06/04 Tamayuz—Game Theory (IRE) (Aussie Rules (USA))
**66 TOURNICOTON (FR),** b c 29/05 Myboycharlie (IRE)—Winshine (FR) (Chineur (FR))
**67** B c 02/03 Kendargent (FR)—Vefa (FR) (Siyouni (FR))
**68 WINGS OF FIRE (FR),** b c 10/02 Wings of Eagles (FR)—Sajida (FR) (Medicean)
**69 YOU'VE GOT SAIL (FR),** b c 21/03 Pomellato (GER)—Yachtclubgenoa (IRE) (Teofilo (IRE))

**Flat Jockey:** Sebastien Maillot, Stephane Pasquier, Thomas Truillier. **Apprentice Jockey:** Aaron Mackay.

---

| 108 | **MR TOM CLOVER, Newmarket**<br>Postal: **Kremlin House Stables, Fordham Road, Newmarket, Suffolk, CB8 7AQ**<br>Contacts: **PHONE 07795 834960, 01638 660055**<br>**EMAIL thomaspwclover@gmail.com WEBSITE www.tomcloverracing.com** |
|---|---|

**1 AQUASCAPE (IRE),** 4, br g Montmartre (FR)—Water Feature **Mr M. J. Bringloe**
**2 BALGAIR,** 7, ch g Foxwedge (AUS)—Glencal **Newmarket Racing Club HQi**
**3 CELSIUS (IRE),** 5, ch g Dragon Pulse (IRE)—Grecian Artisan (IRE) **J. Collins, C. Fahy & S. Piper**
**4 CRIMEWAVE (IRE),** 5, b g Teofilo (IRE)—Crossover **The Rogues Gallery**
**5 EAGLESGLEN,** 4, b g Gleneagles (IRE)—Coquet **The Rogues Gallery**
**6 GIFT OF KINGS,** 4, b g Kingman—Indian Love Bird **Newmarket Racing Club HQ**
**7 GRAND CANAL (IRE),** 4, b g Australia—Loreto (IRE) **Mr P. Chau**
**8 HUNNI,** 6, b m Captain Gerrard—Lady O Malley (IRE) **The Hunni Partnership**
**9 JACK'S POINT,** 5, b g Slade Power (IRE)—Electra Star **Ben Spiers & Adam Signy**
**10 MONSIEUR LAMBRAYS,** 5, b g Champs Elysees—Windermere Island **K. A. Dasmal**
**11 RITCHIE VALENS (IRE),** 5, ch g Helmet (AUS)—Miss Cape (IRE) **Dr O. Rangabashyam**
**12 ROGUE ASSASSIN (IRE),** 4, ch g Iffraaj—Zahrat Narjis **The Rogues Gallery**
**13 RUE DE LA GAITE (IRE),** 4, b f No Nay Never (USA)—Rhiannon (IRE) **Bringloe & Clarke**

### THREE-YEAR-OLDS

**14 ADELITA (IRE),** b f Territories (IRE)—Sibling Honour **Mr M E & Mrs G J Davey**
**15 APPRECIATE (IRE),** ch c Australia—Became (USA) **H Moorhead, C Fahy & J Collins**
**16 CASH MACHINE (IRE),** b c Twilight Son—Puzzled (IRE) **The Rogues Gallery**
**17 EL PICARO (IRE),** b c Dragon Pulse (IRE)—Ice On Fire **The Rogues Gallery**
**18 FAIRY DUST (IRE),** b f Gregorian (IRE)—Dreaming Lady (IRE) **The Fairy Dust Partnership**
**19 MARIENPLATZ,** b f New Bay—Mia San Triple **Gute Freunde Partnership**
**20 RAJMEISTER,** b c Showcasing—Brilliant Sunshine **Mr R. S. Matharu**
**21 ROCKETT MAN,** ch c Equiano (FR)—Flamenco Dancer **The Rogues Gallery**
**22 ROGUE BEAR (IRE),** br c Kodiac—Rancho Montoya (IRE) **The Rogues Gallery**
**23 ROGUE FORCE (IRE),** b c Iffraaj—Lonely Rock **The Rogues Gallery**
**24 ROGUE MISSILE (IRE),** b f Dandy Man (IRE)—Confusing **The Rogues Gallery**
**25 ROGUE POWER,** b c Pivotal—Strawberry Sorbet **The Rogues Gallery**
**26 ROMAN POWER (IRE),** b f Holy Roman Emperor (IRE)—Cool Power (IRE) **The Cool Powers**
**27 SUGAULI (IRE),** b g The Gurkha (IRE)—Wood Chorus **The Rogues Gallery**
**28 THE GUVNOR (IRE),** b c Frankel—Eva's Request (IRE) **The Rogues Gallery**
**29 THOMAS COCHRANE (IRE),** b g War Command (USA)—La Conquerante **The Thomas Cochrane Partnership**

### TWO-YEAR-OLDS

**30** Ch f 27/02 Dandy Man (IRE)—Ai Chan (IRE) (Dream Ahead (USA)) (14286) **Carroll House Racing**
**31 ALANINE,** gr ro f 02/05 Bobby's Kitten (USA)—Albacocca (With Approval (CAN)) **Miss K. Rausing**
**32 ANGEL OF TRAFALGAR,** b c 25/03 Dark Angel (IRE)—
                         Learned Friend (GER) (Seeking The Gold (USA)) (45000) **& John Alston**
**33** B f 26/02 Holy Roman Emperor (IRE)—Ape Attack (Nayef (USA)) **Chasemore Farm LLP**
**34** B c 29/04 Zoffany (IRE)—Atlantic Isle (GER) (Tamayuz) (30000) **Carroll House Racing**

## MR TOM CLOVER - continued

**35** B c 03/02 Fastnet Rock (AUS)—Banzari (Motivator) (20000) **Carroll House Racing**
**36** Ch c 06/05 Bobby's Kitten (USA)—Caribana (Hernando (FR)) (21000) **Carroll House Racing**
**37** Ch f 28/04 Anjaal—Dreaming Lady (IRE) (Dream Ahead (USA)) **Carroll House Racing**
**38** B f 01/03 Slade Power (IRE)—Imasumaq (IRE) (Teofilo (IRE)) (20000) **The Tripletto Partnership & Partner**
**39** **MR BEAUFORT,** b c 24/04 Cable Bay (IRE)—Tan Tan (King's Best (USA)) (12000) **The Mr Beaufort Syndicate**
**40** B f 25/02 Adaay (IRE)—Mrs Penny (AUS) (Planchet (AUS)) (5000) **Nick Bradley 41 & Partners**
**41** **PAPA COCKTAIL (IRE),** b c 12/03 Churchill (IRE)—Anklet (IRE) (Acclamation) (40000) **K. A. Dasmal**
**42** B c 04/04 Muhaarar—Primo Lady (Lucky Story (USA)) (28000) **Carroll House Racing**
**43** **SANFELICE (IRE),** b f 03/03 Acclamation—Mickleberry (IRE) (Desert Style (IRE)) (30000) **Halcyon Thoroughbreds**
**44** B c 18/02 Churchill (IRE)—Sarinda (Dubawi (IRE)) (62000) **Mr E. Elhrari**
**45** B c 28/03 New Approach (IRE)—Sharnberry (Shamardal (USA)) (35000) **Carroll House Racing**
**46** Gr c 25/04 Mastercraftsman (IRE)—Wood Chorus (Singspiel (IRE)) (20000) **Carroll House Racing**

**Other Owners:** Mrs J. A. Alston, Mr J. P. Alston, J. Barton, Mr N. Bradley, Mr M. J. Bringloe, Mr R. A. Clarke, Mrs J. I. Clover, Mr T. P. Clover, Mrs G. J. Davey, Mr M. E. Davey, Mr A. J. Driver, El Catorce, Mr A. R. Elliott, Mr P Green, Dowager Countess of Harrington, Miss S. Holden, Mrs G. A. S. Jarvis, Mrs A. H. Jordan, Ms G. F. Khosla, Mr R. P. Marchant, Mr S. Marchant, Mr T. Muller, Nick Bradley Racing 41, Mr R. Nunn, Mr R. B. Patel, Mr C. Pizarro, Mrs K. Pizarro, Mr A. Signy, Mr B. P. J. Spiers, Tripletto Partnership.

---

## 109 MR DENIS COAKLEY, West Ilsley
Postal: Keeper's Stables, West Ilsley, Newbury, Berkshire, RG20 7AH
Contacts: PHONE 01635 281622 MOBILE 07768 658056
EMAIL racing@deniscoakley.com WEBSITE www.deniscoakley.com

**1** **CARMENERE,** 4, ch f Dawn Approach (IRE)—Sacred Aspect (IRE) **Sparkling Partners**
**2** **GIVEPEACEACHANCE,** 6, b m Declaration of War (USA)—Mount Crystal (IRE) **Chris van Hoorn Racing**
**3** **PARTY ISLAND (IRE),** 4, ch g Tagula (IRE)—Pretty Demanding (IRE) **Mr T. A. Killoran**
**4** **POWER HOME (IRE),** 7, ch m Power—Ascendancy **Poachers' Dozen**
**5** **RUSKIN RED (IRE),** 4, ch g Mastercraftsman (IRE)—Firey Red (IRE) **Mrs B. Coakley**
**6** **SHEILA'S SPIRIT,** 5, b g Swiss Spirit—Velma Kelly **Mrs B. Coakley**
**7** **SONNETINA,** 5, b m Poet's Voice—Tebee's Oasis **The Good Mixers**

### THREE-YEAR-OLDS

**8** **BOBBY KENNEDY,** b g Bobby's Kitten (USA)—All Annalena (IRE) **Ms I. Coakley**
**9** **CARIBOU,** b c Adaay (IRE)—Blue Lyric **Mr N. Y. O. Askar**
**10** **EAGLES DARE,** b g Free Eagle (IRE)—Fasten Up **Keeper's 12**
**11** **LISDARRAGH (USA),** b g Hit It A Bomb (USA)—Thewholeshebang (USA) **Mrs U. M. Loughrey**
**12** **NELL QUICKLY (IRE),** b f The Gurkha (IRE)—Burke's Rock **Chris van Hoorn Racing**
**13** **PATROON (USA),** b g Blame (USA)—Inventing Paradise (USA) **Chris van Hoorn Racing**
**14** **SUPERSONIQUE,** b f Cable Bay (IRE)—La Concorde (FR) **Mrs B. Coakley**
**15** **WATERLOO SUNSET,** b c Adaay (IRE)—Atwix **Mrs B. Coakley**

### TWO-YEAR-OLDS

**16** B f 06/02 Time Test—Goodnightsuzy (IRE) (Azamour (IRE)) (10000) **West Ilsley Racing**
**17** **HOORNBLOWER,** ch c 24/02 Ulysses (IRE)—Tulip Dress (Dutch Art) (42000) **Chris van Hoorn Racing**
**18** **ISKAHEEN (IRE),** b c 17/03 Profitable (IRE)—Scarlet Rosefinch (Cockney Rebel (IRE)) (17000) **Mrs U. M. Loughrey**
**19** B f 02/04 Adaay (IRE)—Kip (Rip Van Winkle (IRE)) (9000) **Mrs B. Coakley**

**Other Owners:** Miss A. D. Swift, Mr C. T. Van Hoorn.

**110** **PAUL & OLIVER COLE, Whatcombe**
Postal: **Whatcombe Racing Stables, Whatcombe, WANTAGE, Oxfordshire, OX12 9NW**
Contacts: **PHONE 01488 638433**
EMAIL admin@paulcole.co.uk

1 **ARCTIC SEA**, 7, b br g Oasis Dream—Rainbow Dancing **P. F. I. Cole Ltd**
2 **CELTIC ART (FR)**, 4, ch c Mastercraftsman (IRE)—Irish Song (FR) **Mrs F. H. Hay**
3 **CELTIC CLASSIC (IRE)**, 5, b g Cacique (IRE)—Dabtiyra (IRE) **P. F. I. Cole Ltd**
4 **DARK PHOENIX (IRE)**, 4, gr g Camacho—Alba Verde **P. F. I. Cole Ltd**
5 **DUKE OF HAZZARD (FR)**, 5, b h Lope de Vega (IRE)—With Your Spirit (FR) **Mrs F. H. Hay**
6 **GLENGOWAN (IRE)**, 4, b f Kingman—Pink Damsel (IRE) **Mrs F. H. Hay**
7 **HIGH COMMISSIONER (IRE)**, 5, ch g Australia—Winesong (IRE) **P. F. I. Cole Ltd**
8 **HIGHLAND CHIEF (IRE)**, 4, b c Gleneagles (IRE)—Pink Symphony **Mrs F. H. Hay**
9 **IVATHEENGINE (IRE)**, 4, br g Ivawood (IRE)—Sharp Applause (IRE) **Mr F. P. Stella**
10 **JAZZ PARTY**, 4, b g New Approach (IRE)—Harlem Dancer **C. Shiacolas**
11 **LIN CHONG**, 4, b g Muhaarar—Reroute (IRE) **Hurun Racing**
12 **MAJESTIC DAWN (IRE)**, 5, ch h Dawn Approach (IRE)—Jolie Chanson (FR) **Green & Norman**
13 **MEDIEVAL (IRE)**, 7, b g Kodiac—Quickstyx **P. F. I. Cole Ltd**
14 **QUEMONDA**, 5, ch m Mount Nelson—Quesada (IRE) **Mrs E. A. Bass**
15 **RIVER DAWN**, 5, ch g Dawn Approach (IRE)—Echo River (USA) **P. F. I. Cole Ltd**
16 **SANDYMAN**, 5, ch g Footstepsinthesand—Quiz Mistress **The Fairy Story Partnership**
17 **THE FIRST KING (IRE)**, 4, b g War Command (USA)—Rochitta (USA) **P. F. I. Cole Ltd**

## THREE-YEAR-OLDS

18 **ARIZONA GOLD**, b g Bated Breath—Poulaine Bleue **P. F. I. Cole Ltd**
19 **BALEARIC (IRE)**, b g Gleneagles (IRE)—Ballybacka Lady (IRE) **Mrs F. H. Hay**
20 **BLUE LILY (USA)**, b f American Pharoah (USA)—Winnie Dixie (USA) **Mrs F. H. Hay**
21 **CHAPPAQUIDDICK**, b f Camelot—Lilac (IRE) **Mr C. N. Wright**
22 **DURABELLA (IRE)**, b f Manduro (GER)—Aztec Queen **The Fairy Story Partnership**
23 **GENERAL LEE (IRE)**, b c Lope de Vega (IRE)—Hall Hee (IRE) **Mrs F. H. Hay**
24 **GORDONSTOUN (IRE)**, b c Gleneagles (IRE)—Elusive Girl (IRE) **L.Cole, B. Williams, Flm Ltd, C. Vincent**
25 **IMPERIAL DAWN**, b c Dawn Approach (IRE)—Miss Lahar **C S Norman, Max W-jones, J. Edgedale**
26 **MUNIFICENT**, b c Pearl Secret—Hulcote Rose (IRE) **C. & Hassiakos**
27 **RAW HIDE (IRE)**, b c War Command (USA)—Tioga Pass **The Fairy Story Partnership**
28 **RODEO DRIVE (IRE)**, br f Kodi Bear (IRE)—Hflah (IRE) **Christopher Wright & David Kilburn**
29 **SERENHILL**, gr f Kingston Hill—Seramindar **The Fairy Story Partnership**
30 **STRICTLY SPICY**, b c Nathaniel (IRE)—Spicy Dal **M. Arbib**
31 **SUBTLE BEAUTY**, b f Gleneagles (IRE)—Mirage (IRE) **Mrs F. H. Hay**
32 **WANTAGE (IRE)**, b c Camelot—Lucy Cavendish (USA) **Mr C S Norman & the Wantage Syndicate**
33 **ZHANG FEI (FR)**, b c Camelot—Mambomiss (FR) **Hurun Racing, C. S. Norman, S. Magnier**

## TWO-YEAR-OLDS

34 B f 23/04 Fast Company (IRE)—Antillia (Red Ransom (USA)) (6000) **Mr F. P. Stella**
35 **DEACS DELIGHT**, ch c 14/04 Tamayuz—Keene Dancer (Danehill Dancer (IRE)) (10000) **Cole, Deacon, & Vincent**
36 Gr c 04/04 Havana Gold (IRE)—Eastern Destiny (Dubai Destination (USA)) **Mr P. F. I. Cole**
37 B f 17/02 Frankel—Household Name (Zamindar (USA)) (95000) **Mrs F. H. Hay**
38 **JACK DARCY (IRE)**, b c 30/04 Gleneagles (IRE)—Pretty Face (Rainbow Quest (USA)) (24000)
39 B c 18/02 Aclaim (IRE)—Rochitta (USA) (Arch (USA)) (70000) **Mrs F. H. Hay**
40 **SANITISER**, b c 08/04 The Gurkha (IRE)—Spicy Dal (Dalakhani (IRE)) **M. Arbib**
41 **TARTAN CHIEF**, br c 25/02 Dark Angel (IRE)—Pink Symphony (Montjeu (IRE)) **Mrs F. H. Hay**
42 **WARHOL (IRE)**, b c 17/03 Belardo (IRE)—Darsan (IRE) (Iffraaj) (57143) **C & F McKay**

**Other Owners:** Mrs L. Cole, Mr R. H. Deacon, Mr J. W. Edgedale, Financial Lifestyle Management Limited, Mrs J. Green, S. Hassiakos, Hurun Racing, D. Kilburn, Mrs S. C. Magnier, Mr F. McKay, Mr C. S. Norman, Mr J. Piggott, C. Shiacolas, The Wantage Syndicate, Mr C. Vincent, Mr L. Vincent, Mr M. Wallace-Jones, Mrs R. L. Williams, Mr C. N. Wright.

## 111 MR TJADE COLLIER, Wilsden
Postal: **Salter Royd House, Shay Lane, Wilsden, Bradford, West Yorkshire, BD15 0DJ**
Contacts: **PHONE 01535 271445**
**EMAIL tjade331@icloud.com**

1 5, B m Kayf Tara—Alflora's Girl (IRE)  **T. Collier**
2 **BLUE HAWAII (IRE),** 6, b m Jeremy (USA)—Luanna (IRE)  **R. Banks & J. Sheard**
3 4, Ch f Schiaparelli (GER)—Brukirk Lass  **T. Collier**
4 **CALL ME JEZZA (IRE),** 6, b g Jeremy (USA)—Fair Astronomer (IRE)  **Mr J. N. Sheard**
5 **CHEMICAL WARFARE (IRE),** 4, b g Fame And Glory—Blazing Sky (IRE)  **T. Collier**
6 4, B g Black Sam Bellamy (IRE)—Damascena (GER)  **T. Collier**
7 4, B g Hillstar—Definite Grey (IRE)  **T. Collier**
8 **DOORS BREAKER (FR),** 4, b g American Post—Polyandry (IRE)  **T. Collier**
9 4, Gr g Recharge (IRE)—Inthesettlement  **T. Collier**
10 **LADRONNE (FR),** 7, b g Linda's Lad—Worldeta (FR)  **T C Racing Syndicate**
11 **MIDNIGHT ANTICS (IRE),** 7, b m Midnight Legend—Toungara (FR)  **T C Racing Syndicate**
12 4, Ch f Schiaparelli (GER)—Miss Hollybell  **T. Collier**
13 4, B g Kayf Tara—Molly Flight (FR)  **T. Collier**
14 **QUEEN OF THE ROAD,** 4, b f Kingston Hill—Lily Rules (IRE)  **T. Collier**
15 **RAYTHEHANDYMAN (IRE),** 5, br g Westerner—La Femme Blanche (IRE)  **T C Racing Syndicate**
16 **SHANTOU BOUDICCA,** 5, ch m Shantou (USA)—Toubeera  **T C Racing Syndicate**
17 4, B f Valirann (FR)—Sharps Express (IRE)  **T. Collier**

Other Owners: Mr R. Banks, Mr J. N. Sheard.

## 112 MR PAUL COLLINS, Saltburn-By-The-Sea
Postal: **Trainer did not wish details of their string to appear**

## 113 MR STUART COLTHERD, Selkirk
Postal: **Clarilawmuir Farm, Selkirk, Selkirkshire, TD7 4QA**
Contacts: **PHONE 01750 21251 MOBILE 07801 398199 FAX 01750 21251**
**EMAIL wscoltherd@gmail.com**

1 **ACHILL ROAD BOY (IRE),** 12, b g Morozov (USA)—
Presenting Katie (IRE)  **Farming Army Newitt Flannigan Findlater**
2 **ANNIES REGATTA,** 5, b m Flemensfirth (USA)—Queens Regatta (IRE)  **Mercer Campbell Stanners**
3 **ARCHI'S AFFAIRE,** 7, ch g Archipenko (USA)—Affaire d'Amour  **Coltherd Racing Club**
4 **ARD CHROS (IRE),** 9, b g Publisher (USA)—Threecrossmammies (IRE)  **Coltherd McDougal**
5 **CAPTAIN REDBEARD (IRE),** 12, ch g Bach (IRE)—Diesel Dancer (IRE)  **W. S. Coltherd**
6 **CASIMIR DU CLOS (FR),** 9, b g Blue Bresil (FR)—Cyrienne du Maine (FR)  **Newitt Flannigan Scott Gillie Swinton**
7 **CHANCEANOTHERFIVE (IRE),** 9, b g Dubai Destination (USA)—Ryhall (IRE)  **Mr Richard & Mrs Lisa McCulloch**
8 **COOPER'S CROSS (IRE),** 6, b g Getaway (GER)—Rocella (GER)  **The Vacuum Pouch Company Limited**
9 **DAMIENS DILEMMA (IRE),** 13, b g Wareed (IRE)—Olympos Belle (IRE)  **R. L. Miller-Bakewell**
10 **DEEP CHARM,** 7, b g Kayf Tara—Reel Charmer  **Mr Richard & Mrs Lisa McCulloch**
11 **DEQUALL,** 5, ch g Zoffany (IRE)—Bark (IRE)  **W. S. Coltherd**
12 **DUTCH CANYON (IRE),** 11, b g Craigsteel—Chitabe (IRE)  **Mr J. Muir**
13 **FELIX MENDELSSOHN (IRE),** 10, b g Galileo (IRE)—Ice Queen (IRE)
14 **GET HELP (IRE),** 8, b g Gold Well—Present Abbey (IRE)  **Robertson,Gillie,Tawse,Knaggs,Ferguson**
15 **GRAND VOYAGE (FR),** 5, b g Network (GER)—Qape Noir (FR)  **Shire Dreamers**
16 **GRAYSTOWN (IRE),** 9, b g Well Chosen—Temple Girl (IRE)  **The Farming Army**
17 **JACK YEATS (IRE),** 5, b g Galileo (IRE)—Fire Lily (IRE)  **Harelaw Racing**

## MR STUART COLTHERD - continued

18 **JIMMY RABBITTE (IRE)**, 8, b g Dubai Destination (USA)—Time To Act **Coltherd Racing Club**
19 **LOCKER ROOM TALK (IRE)**, 8, b g Beneficial—Whistling Gypse (IRE) **The Vacuum Pouch Company Limited**
20 **LONGTYMEGONE (IRE)**, 11, b g Portrait Gallery (IRE)—Katie O'Toole (IRE) **W. S. Coltherd**
21 **MAID O'MALLEY**, 8, b m Black Sam Bellamy (IRE)—Jolie (IRE) **W. S. Coltherd**
22 4, B g Notnowcato—Meldrum Hall (IRE)
23 **MILLY ON AIR**, 5, ro m Proclamation (IRE)—Lady Counsellor **Mr R. J. Perryman**
24 **MISS MISTRAL (IRE)**, 5, gr m War Command (USA)—Drifting Mist **Coltherd Racing Club**
25 **MRS VONN (IRE)**, 9, b m Scorpion (IRE)—Mrs Ritchie **Mercer Campbell Stanners**
26 **POOKIE PEKAN (IRE)**, 8, b g Putra Pekan—Shii-Take's Girl **Mr J. Muir**
27 4, b f Yorgunnabelucky (USA)—Pugnacious Lady
28 **RIDETHEWAVES**, 5, b m Gentlewave (IRE)—Julia Too
29 **SILKEN MOONLIGHT**, 7, b m Aqlaam—Silk (IRE) **Coltherd Racing Club**
30 **ST BASIL**, 8, gr g Geordieland (FR)—Wibble Wobble **Mr J L & Mrs H R Gledson**
31 **TO THE LIMIT (IRE)**, 6, gr g Carlotamix (FR)—Miss Kilkeel (IRE) **Border Eagles**
32 **WARENDORF (FR)**, 8, b g Speedmaster (GER)—Hyllisia (FR) **Howard Coltherd Flannigan Newitt**
33 **WHEELBAHRI**, 7, b g Bahri (USA)—Midlem Melody **W. S. Coltherd**

**Other Owners:** Mr D. T. Campbell, W. S. Coltherd, Mr T. Ferguson, Mr G. Findlater, Mr I. R. Flannigan, Mr R. Flannigan, Mr E. Gillie, Mrs H. R. Gledson, J. L. Gledson, Mr D. A. Gray, Mr G. P Howard, Mr D. Knaggs, Mrs L. J. McCulloch, Mr R. McCulloch, Mr G. McDougal, Mr K. Mercer, Mrs S. C. Newitt, Mr D. Reive, Mr B. A. Robertson, Mr M. J. Scott, Mr M. Stanners, Mr S. Swinton, Mrs S. Tawse, The Farming Army.

**Conditional Jockey:** Sam Coltherd.

---

| 114 | **MR SEAN CONWAY, Lutterworth**<br>Postal: Home Farm, Shawell Lane, Cotesbach, Lutterworth, Leicestershire, LE17 4HR<br>Contacts: MOBILE 07879 066901 |
|---|---|

1 **BEFOREYPUSHDACHAIR (IRE)**, 7, b g Garuda (IRE)—No Ones Oscar (IRE) **Mr S. Conway**
2 **CALYPSO STORM (IRE)**, 10, b g Trans Island—Valin Thyne (IRE) **Mr S. Conway**
3 **CREGGAN WHITE HARE (IRE)**, 6, b br g Arcadio (GER)—Mia Zia (FR) **Mr S. Conway**
4 **DEFINITE WARRIOR (IRE)**, 8, b g Definite Article—Waist Deep (IRE) **Mr S. Conway**
5 **KYMATA**, 7, b m Sulamani (IRE)—Miss Annabell (IRE) **Mr S. Conway**
6 **LITTLE SAINT (IRE)**, 6, b g Morozov (USA)—Matinee Show (IRE) **Mr S. Conway**
7 **MOUNT HANOVER**, 10, b g Kayf Tara—Via Ferrata (FR) **Mr S. Conway**
8 **NIGHTVISITINGSONG**, 5, b m Kayf Tara—Box of Trix (IRE) **Mr S. Conway**
9 **OLIVER'S ISLAND (IRE)**, 9, b g Milan—Leading Rank (IRE) **Mr S. Conway**
10 **PUNTER PAT**, 5, b g Sakhee (USA)—Narima (GER) **Mr S. Conway**
11 **THE GIRL THAT SANG (IRE)**, 7, b m Flemensfirth (USA)—Soul Mate (IRE) **Mr S. Conway**
12 **WHERE'S THE TAPE**, 4, b f Coach House (IRE)—Atlantide (USA) **Mr S. Conway**

**Amateur Jockey:** Mr Philip Armson.

---

| 115 | **MRS SUSAN CORBETT, Otterburn**<br>Postal: Girsonfield, Otterburn, Newcastle upon Tyne, Tyne and Wear, NE19 1NT<br>Contacts: PHONE 01830 520771 MOBILE 07713 651215 FAX 01830 520771<br>EMAIL girsonfield@outlook.com WEBSITE www.girsonfield.co.uk |
|---|---|

1 **ANDANTE (IRE)**, 4, b g Califet (FR)—Court Over **Mr W. F. Corbett**
2 **ATOMIC ANGEL**, 6, gr m Geordieland (FR)—Sovereignoftheseas **Castle View Racing**
3 **DEVOUR (IRE)**, 8, b g Milan—Marble Desire (IRE) **Girsonfield Racing Club**

## MRS SUSAN CORBETT - continued

4 **GORGEOUS GOBOLINA**, 5, b m Captain Gerrard (IRE)—
Gorgeous Goblin (IRE) **Mr & Mrs Shaun & Leanne Humphries**
5 **GOWANBUSTER**, 6, b g Bahri (USA)—Aahgowangowan (IRE) **Gowan Racing**
6 **GOWANLASSIE**, 4, ch f Mayson—Gowanharry (IRE) **Gowan Racing**
7 **GREY EXPECTATIONS**, 5, gr m Proclamation (IRE)—Linns Heir
8 **HARLEYS MAX**, 12, b g Winged Love (IRE)—Researcher **Girsonfield Racing Club**
9 **HARRISONS PROMISE**, 9, b m Westerner—Hello My Lovely
10 **HILLS OF CONNEMARA (IRE)**, 9, gr m Tikkanen (USA)—Desirable Rhythm (IRE) **Mrs F. W. W. Chapman**
11 **JODY**, 8, ch m Kheleyf (USA)—Canis Star
12 **LES'S LEGACY**, 4, b g Kutub—Morning With Ivan (IRE) **Mr L. P. Richards**
13 **LET'S SWAY**, 7, b m Authorized (IRE)—Let's Dance (IRE) **Castle View Racing**
14 **MACARDLE (IRE)**, 8, b g Beneficial—Monavale (IRE) **Mr L. P. Richards**
15 **MAGIC OF MILAN (IRE)**, 8, b m Milan—Laughing Lesa (IRE) **Mr W. F. Corbett**
16 **ORLAS' ABBEY**, 6, b m Multiplex—Evelith Abbey **Girsonfield Racing Club**
17 **PENTELITUBBY**, 6, ch g Kutub (IRE)—Penteli **Mr W. F. Corbett**
18 **PRINCESS AVERY (IRE)**, 7, b m Yeats (IRE)—Bobs Article (IRE) **Mrs F. W. W. Chapman**
19 **REDESDALE REBEL**, 5, ch g Mayson—Jubilee **Castle View Racing**
20 **REIVERS LODGE**, 9, b m Black Sam Bellamy (IRE)—Crystal Princess (IRE)
21 **SKIPTHESCALES (IRE)**, 9, b g Winged Love (IRE)—Waterland Gale (IRE) **Mr L. P. Richards**
22 **SPIT IT OUT (IRE)**, 4, b g Swiss Spirit—Seriously (FR) **Girsonfield Racing Club**
23 4, B f Califet (FR)—Strike An Ark (IRE)
24 **SUTTON WAY**, 9, b m Bahri (USA)—Kates Own
25 **TOOYOU**, 6, gr m Proclamation (IRE)—Lady Counsellor **The Nelson Racing Partnership**
26 **VISION DE DAME (FR)**, 5, b m Vision d'Etat (FR)—Belle Dame (GER) **Ms J. E. Maggs**
27 **WOR VERGE**, 8, b g Virtual—Hanover Gate **The Goodfellow Partnership**

### THREE-YEAR-OLDS

28 Ch f Cityscape—First Harmony **Castle View Racing**
29 Ch f Ruler of The World (IRE)—Ogaritmo **Ms J. E. Maggs**

**Other Owners:** Mrs F. W. W. Chapman, Mr D. J. Clarke, Mr W. F. Corbett, Mr M. D. Foden, Mrs L. Humphries, Mr S. Humphries, The Nelson Racing Partnership, Mr L. Waugh, Mrs V. M. Waugh.

**Assistant Trainer:** Mr James Corbett, **Travelling Head:** Emma Tully, **Yard Sponsor:** Finnies Heavy Haulage.

---

**116** **MR JOHN CORNWALL, Melton Mowbray**
Postal: **April Cottage, Pasture Lane, Hose, Melton Mowbray, Leicestershire, LE14 4LB**
Contacts: **PHONE 01664 444453 MOBILE 07939 557091 FAX 01664 444754**
EMAIL johncornwall7@gmail.com

1 **LESKINFERE (IRE)**, 8, b g Darsi (FR)—Taipans Girl (IRE) **Mr J. R. Cornwall**
2 **TORRENT DES MOTTES (FR)**, 10, gr g Montmartre (FR)—Wavy (FR) **Mr J. R. Cornwall**

**117**
**MR JAKE COULSON, Heaton**
Postal: Bent End Farm, Bearda Hill Racing, Heaton, Macclesfield, Cheshire, SK11 0SJ
Contacts: MOBILE 07460 471492
EMAIL beardahillracing@gmail.com

1 **CHAPATI (FR)**, 7, gr g Fragrant Mix (IRE)—Bessouba (FR) **Mr N. Carter**
2 5, B g Sir Percy—Clifton Encore (USA) **Mr K. Dove**
3 **COOK THE BOOKS (IRE)**, 8, b g Stowaway—Greenhill Millie (IRE) **Cathedral Plastics Limited**
4 **CURRABEHA HILL (IRE)**, 9, b g Beneficial—Our Deadly (IRE) **Mr N. Carter**
5 **FALBERTO (FR)**, 6, b g Alberto Giacometti (IRE)—Valrina (FR) **Mr N. Carter**
6 **FARM THE ROCK (IRE)**, 10, b g Yeats (IRE)—Shades of Lavender (IRE) **Mr N. Carter**
7 **GIBBERWELL (IRE)**, 5, b g Getaway (GER)—Unique Snoopy (IRE) **All Or Nothing Racing Club**
8 **MON PORT (IRE)**, 9, b g Scorpion (IRE)—Sounds Charming (IRE) **Mr N. Carter**
9 4, B f Sir Percy—Moonlight Babe (USA) **Mrs N. Naylor**
10 **PADDY THE CHAMP (IRE)**, 5, b g Ocovango—Glass Curtain (IRE) **Mr N. Carter**
11 **QUIVVY LOUGH (IRE)**, 7, b m Court Cave (IRE)—Quivvy Bridge (IRE) **Mr K. Dove**
12 **ROB ROYAL (FR)**, 9, gr g Rob Roy (USA)—Royale Trophy (FR) **Mr N. Carter**

**Assistant Trainer:** Sarah Carter.

**118**
**MISS JACQUELINE COWARD, Sheriff Hutton**
Postal: Low Moor Farm, Dalby, Dalby, Yorkshire, YO60 6PF
Contacts: PHONE 01653 628995

1 **ALRIGHT MARLENE (IRE)**, 8, b m Stowaway—One Theatre (IRE) **Mr J. W. Nellis**
2 **EDEN COLLONGES (FR)**, 7, ch g Lucarno (USA)—Regence Collonges (FR) **Mr I. Robinson**
3 **IT'S YOUR MOVE (IRE)**, 9, b g Flemensfirth (USA)—Jeruflo (IRE) **Mr I. C. Wilson**
4 **PATH TO FREEDOM (IRE)**, 9, b g Mr Dinos (IRE)—Old Kentucky (IRE) **Mrs J. Nellis**
5 **TOM CODY (IRE)**, 5, b g Morozov (USA)—Smiths Lady (IRE) **Mr I. C. Wilson**

**119**
**MR ROBERT COWELL, Newmarket**
Postal: Bottisham Heath Stud, Six Mile Bottom, Newmarket, Suffolk, CB8 0TT
Contacts: PHONE 01638 570330 MOBILE 07785 512463
EMAIL robert@robertcowellracing.co.uk WEBSITE www.robertcowellracing.co.uk

1 **ALJADY (FR)**, 6, b g Bated Breath—No Truth (IRE) **Mrs M. J. Morley**
2 **ARAIFJAN**, 4, ch g Kyllachy—Light Hearted **Mr T. W. Morley**
3 **ARECIBO (FR)**, 6, b g Invincible Spirit (IRE)—Oceanique (USA) **Mr T. W. Morley**
4 **AUTUMN FLIGHT (IRE)**, 5, b g Dandy Man (IRE)—Swallow Falls (IRE) **Mrs Morley, R Penney & A Rix**
5 **BENEFIT STREET (IRE)**, 4, b g Zebedee—Sweet'n Sassy (IRE) **Mrs M. J. Morley**
6 **BLUE DE VEGA (GER)**, 8, b g Lope de Vega (IRE)—Burning Heights (GER) **Mrs M. J. Morley**
7 **DIAMOND DOUGAL (IRE)**, 6, b g Zebedee—Blue Saphire **Mrs M. J. Morley**
8 **DUBAI STATION**, 4, b c Brazen Beau (AUS)—Princess Guest (IRE) **Park M & Dasmal Dasmal**
9 **GOLDEN AGE (FR)**, 4, b g Golden Horn—Farnesina (FR) **Mr C Humphris & Partner**
10 **GRANDFATHER TOM**, 6, b g Kheleyf (USA)—Kassuta **Mr J. Sargeant**
11 **GREEN DOOR (IRE)**, 10, b g Camacho—Inourhearts (IRE) **Bottisham Heath Stud**
12 **HYBA**, 4, b f Muhaarar—Jellwa (IRE) **Bottisham Heath Stud**
13 **ISHVARA**, 4, b f Dutch Art—Cloud's End **Manor Farm Stud & Mr J. E. Rose**
14 **LIPSINK (IRE)**, 4, b c Kodiac—Iron Lips **Mr J. Sargeant**
15 **MANUMISSION (IRE)**, 4, b c Muhaarar—Passion Overflow (USA) **The Cool Silk Partnership**
16 **MOMENTUM SWING**, 4, br g Dark Angel (IRE)—Winning Express (IRE) **Mr R. Ng**

# MR ROBERT COWELL - continued

17 **ROCKET ACTION**, 5, gr g Toronado (IRE)—Winning Express (IRE)  **Mr R. Ng**
18 **SWELL SONG**, 5, ch m Kyllachy—Racina  **Mr I. A. Southcott**
19 **TOMSHALFBROTHER**, 5, b g Sir Percy—Kassuta  **Mr J. Sargeant**

## THREE-YEAR-OLDS

20 **AISH**, b f Twilight Son—Chandresh  **Manor Farm Stud & Partner**
21 **BARBAROMA (IRE)**, b c Prince of Lir (IRE)—Little Italy (USA)  **The Cool Silk Partnership**
22 **BUSINESS FLIGHT (USA)**, b br c Fed Biz (USA)—The Right Bird (USA)  **Mr T. W. Morley**
23 **CARBON POSITIVE (USA)**, ch g Distorted Humor (USA)—Everything Sweet (USA)  **Mrs F. H. Hay**
24 **FAUSTUS**, b c Mayson—Israfel  **Mrs J. Hadida**
25 **ISLE OF LISMORE (IRE)**, b g Zebedee—Spring Bouquet (IRE)  **Mr P. S. Ryan**
26 **JAZZY SOCKS**, b g Showcasing—Weisse Socken (IRE)  **K. A. Dasmal**
27 **K REX (USA)**, b br g Speightster (USA)—Chasing Lightning (USA)  **K. A. Dasmal**
28 **NAVY DRUMS (USA)**, b br g Super Saver (USA)—Beat to Quarters (USA)  **K. A. Dasmal**
29 **RAZOR GLASS (USA)**, b br f Congrats (USA)—Lemon Splash (CAN)  **Mr T. W. Morley**
30 **SICILIAN BELLE**, b f Brazen Beau (AUS)—Sciacca (IRE)  **Bottisham Heath Stud**
31 B f Brazen Beau (AUS)—Slewtoo  **Dachel Stud**
32 **SUGAR DUMPLING (IRE)**, b f Brazen Beau (AUS)—Falsify  **Bottisham Heath Stud**
33 **SWOOPER**, b g Brazen Beau (AUS)—Most Tempting  **Bottisham Heath Stud**
34 **TAKE UP ARMS (USA)**, b br g Violence (USA)—Battle Axe (USA)  **Mr T. W. Morley**

## TWO-YEAR-OLDS

35 B f 20/02 Kodiac—Alchemilla (Dubai Destination (USA)) (95238)
36 **ANGLE LAND**, b f 19/04 Mayson—Jumeirah Star (USA) (Street Boss (USA))  **K Dasmal, A Rix, R Penney**
37 B f 27/01 Intrinsic—Chantilly Jewel (USA) (Century City (IRE))  **Bottisham Heath Stud**
38 B c 23/04 Prince of Lir (IRE)—Falsify (Compton Place)  **Bottisham Heath Stud**
39 B f 01/03 Farhh—Hot Reply (Notnowcato)
40 **KING OF SPEED (IRE)**, b c 24/02 Acclamation—Music And Dance (Galileo (IRE)) (45000)  **K. A. Dasmal**
41 B c 25/03 Havana Gold (IRE)—Majestic Alexander (IRE) (Bushranger (IRE)) (109524)  **Mrs F. H. Hay**
42 B f 23/03 Mayson—Most Tempting (Showcasing)  **Bottisham Heath Stud**
43 B f 01/03 Havana Gold (IRE)—Out of The Dark (IRE) (Kyllachy) (7500)  **The Tigers Racing Syndicate & D Tunmore**
44 **PRINCE OF SPEED**, b c 10/03 Havana Gold (IRE)—Liberty Chery (Statue of Liberty (USA)) (50000)  **K. A. Dasmal**
45 B f 16/01 Charming Thought—Sciacca (IRE) (Royal Applause)  **Bottisham Heath Stud**

**Other Owners:** Bottisham Heath Stud, Mr R. M. H. Cowell, K. A. Dasmal, C. Humphris, O. H. Kingsley, Manor Farm Stud (Rutland), Middleham Park Racing XCIV, Mrs M. J. Morley, Mrs R. J. Norman, T. S. Palin, Mr R. C. Penney, M. Prince, Mr A. J. Rix, J. E. Rose, The Tigers Racing Syndicate, Mr D. Tunmore, M. H. Watt.

**Assistant Trainer:** Mr Ross Studholme.

---

**120** | **MR CLIVE COX, Hungerford**
Postal: **Beechdown Farm, Sheepdrove Road, Lambourn, Hungerford, Berkshire, RG17 7UN**
Contacts: **WORK 01488 73072 MOBILE 07740 630521**
EMAIL **clive@clivecox.com** WEBSITE **www.clivecox.com**

1 **ABLE GRACE (IRE)**, 4, b f No Nay Never (USA)—Sanadaat  **Ms C. LI**
2 **DANCE FEVER (IRE)**, 4, b g Sir Prancealot (IRE)—Silk Fan (IRE)  **Kennet Valley Thoroughbreds VIII**
3 **LITTLE PALAVER**, 9, b g Showcasing—Little Nymph  **Mr T. H. S. Fox**
4 **LOUIE DE PALMA**, 9, b g Pastoral Pursuits—Tahirah  **Mr P. N. Ridgers**
5 **MIDNIGHT DRIFT**, 4, b gr f Lethal Force (IRE)—Malilla (IRE)  **Clive Cox Racing Ltd**
6 **NOTFORALONGTIME**, 4, b g Paco Boy (IRE)—Punchy Lady  **Mr & Mrs Paul & Clare Rooney**
7 **POSITIVE**, 4, b c Dutch Art—Osipova  **Mr Alan Spence**
8 **PRIZE FIGHTING**, 4, b g Sepoy (AUS)—Street Fire (IRE)  **Mr & Mrs P Hargreaves & Mr A D Spence**
9 **RIVER NYMPH**, 4, b c Cable Bay (IRE)—Little Nymph  **Mr T. H. S. Fox**

## MR CLIVE COX - continued

10 **STREAMLINE**, 4, b c Due Diligence (USA)—Ahwahnee **Mainline Racing**
11 **TIS MARVELLOUS**, 7, b g Harbour Watch (IRE)—Mythicism **Miss J. Deadman & Mr S. Barrow**
12 **TOMMY ROCK (IRE)**, 4, gr g Society Rock (IRE)—Chiara Wells (IRE) **Mr P. N. Ridgers**

## THREE-YEAR-OLDS

13 **ARATUS (IRE)**, b c Free Eagle (IRE)—Shauna's Princess (IRE) **A. Butler**
14 **ASCOT ADVENTURE**, ch c Mayson—Kasumi **Woodhurst Ltd & Withernsea**
15 **BERTIE'S WISH (IRE)**, b g Fast Company (IRE)—Dance Bid **Mr & Mrs Paul & Clare Rooney**
16 **BREAKAWAY**, b f Muhaarar—Cloud's End **Mr Alan Spence**
17 **BREATH OF SUN**, b c Bated Breath—Heliograph **Mr T. H. S. Fox**
18 **CHEERS STEVE**, ch g Lethal Force (IRE)—Dartrix **Clive Cox Racing Ltd**
19 **CHURCHILL BAY**, b g The Last Lion (IRE)—Cape Cay **J. C. Smith**
20 **COBH (IRE)**, br c Kodi Bear (IRE)—Arbeel **China Horse Club International Limited**
21 **DILIGENT HARRY**, b c Due Diligence (USA)—Harryana To **The Dilinquents**
22 Ch f Night of Thunder (IRE)—Exempt **Sheikh R. D. Al Maktoum**
23 **FERNANDO RAH**, b c Lethal Force (IRE)—Lacing **Mr P. N. Ridgers**
24 **FIRST EDITION (IRE)**, b br c Invincible Spirit (IRE)—Remember **Mrs A. O'Callaghan**
25 **FOREVER FORWARD (IRE)**, b c Exceed And Excel (AUS)—
Teofilo's Princess (IRE) **Mr Simon Munir & Mr Isaac Souede**
26 **FUNKY BEAR (IRE)**, b g Kodi Bear (IRE)—Ice Haven (IRE) **Mrs O. A. Shaw**
27 **GET IT**, b c Twilight Son—Pine Ridge **Mr A. L. Cohen**
28 **GLOBAL ACCLAIM**, b f Acclamation—Oeuvre d'Art (IRE) **P. J. Gleeson**
29 **IMPRESSIONS DREAM**, gr f Lethal Force (IRE)—Silken Skies (IRE) **Clive Cox Racing Ltd**
30 **INVINCIBLE SOLDIER (IRE)**, b g The Gurkha (IRE)—Guessing (USA) **Ms A. E. Bilton**
31 **ISABELLA GILES (IRE)**, b f Belardo (IRE)—Majestic Dubawi **Mr & Mrs Paul & Clare Rooney**
32 **ISABELLA SWAN**, b f Twilight Son—First Eclipse (IRE) **Redgate Bloodstock**
33 **JUST AMBER**, b c Lethal Force (IRE)—Milly's Gift **Ken Lock Racing**
34 **KOHINOOR**, b f Adaay (IRE)—Satsuma **AlMohamediya Racing**
35 **MILLE MIGLIA**, b f Pride of Dubai (AUS)—Millestan (IRE) **Hot To Trot Racing & D B Clark**
36 **MINE'S A DOUBLE**, b c Mukhadram—Mosa Mine **Maywood Stud**
37 **MOMENT CRITIQUE**, ch f Bated Breath—Tarqua (IRE) **Earl of Carnarvon**
38 **NANDO PARRADO**, b c Kodiac—Chibola (ARG) **Mrs M. McCartan**
39 **NIGHT NARCISSUS (IRE)**, b f Kodi Bear (IRE)—Midnight Martini **AlMohamediya Racing**
40 **PILGRIM'S LIGHT (IRE)**, b f Dark Angel (IRE)—Tariysha (IRE) **J. M. Egan**
41 **PINBALL WIZARD (IRE)**, b g Dark Angel (IRE)—Alsalwa (IRE) **Mr Alan Spence**
42 **PRIDE OF ENGLAND (AUS)**, b g Pride of Dubai (AUS)—Weetles **D B Clark & A R Bentall**
43 **PROP FORWARD**, b c Iffraaj—My Propeller (IRE) **J. C. Smith**
44 **ROSE ALL DAY**, b f Oasis Dream—May Rose (IRE) **Mr A D Spence & Mr M B Spence**
45 **ROYAL SCIMITAR (IRE)**, b c Territories (IRE)—Prequel (IRE) **AlMohamediya Racing**
46 **SADIQAA (IRE)**, b g Estidhkaar (IRE)—Tatiana Romanova (USA) **Amigos Partnership**
47 **SHIMLA ROLANN**, gr f Lethal Force (IRE)—Fanrouge (IRE) **Mr A. G. Craddock**
48 **SKY BLUE THINKING**, b f Charming Thought—Powder Blue **Cavendish Bloodstock & Star Pointe**
49 **SOVEREIGN LEADER (IRE)**, gr g Dark Angel (IRE)—Havin' A Good Time (IRE) **Mr J. Goddard**
50 **SPIRIT OF THE BAY (IRE)**, b f Cable Bay (IRE)—Decorative (IRE) **The Baywatchers**
51 **SUPREMACY (IRE)**, b c Mehmas (IRE)—Triggers Broom (IRE) **Mr J. Goddard**
52 **TARAVARA (IRE)**, b g The Gurkha (IRE)—Red Blossom **China Horse Club International Limited**
53 **TELL'EM NOWT**, b c Belardo (IRE)—Taleteller (USA) **Mrs O. A. Shaw**
54 **TITLE TRACK**, br f Pivotal—Lyricist **Quantum Leap Racing Ii & Partner**
55 **TOP OF THE SHOP (IRE)**, b c Mehmas (IRE)—Oh Simple Thing (IRE) **Miss J. Deadman & Mr S. Barrow**
56 **TREGONY**, ch f New Bay—Timarwa (IRE) **S R Hope & S W Barrow**
57 **WESTERN ALLIANCE (IRE)**, b c Kingman—Cruck Realta **Clipper Group Holdings Ltd**
58 **WHISKEY 'N' CHIPS**, gr f Dark Angel (IRE)—Ensemble (FR) **Mr P Stokes & Mr S Krase**

## TWO-YEAR-OLDS

59 **ADATORIO**, br c 24/03 Adaay (IRE)—Belatorio (IRE) (Oratorio (IRE)) (20952) **Belatorio Syndicate**
60 Ch f 29/04 Showcasing—Ahwahnee (Compton Place) (35000) **Mrs M. McCartan**
61 Ch c 16/01 Territories (IRE)—Analytical (Lethal Force (IRE)) (35000) **AlMohamediya Racing**
62 **APPLAUD NOW**, b c 25/02 Acclamation—Straight Away (Dubawi (IRE)) **J. C. Smith**
63 **AUTUMN MAGIC**, b f 16/02 Brazen Beau (AUS)—Heliograph (Ishiguru (USA)) **Mr P. N. Ridgers**

## MR CLIVE COX - continued

64 **AWESOME LAWSON (IRE),** ch c 08/03 Prince of Lir (IRE)—
Joyous (Assertive) (22857) **Miss J. Deadman & Mr S. Barrow**
65 Gr c 04/03 Dark Angel (IRE)—Barroche (IRE) (Kodiac) (80000) **Mr A. L. Cohen**
66 B c 30/04 Lawman (FR)—Bayja (IRE) (Giant's Causeway (USA)) (95000) **Mr J. Goddard**
67 B f 06/03 Muhaarar—Bella Lulu (Iffraaj) (100000) **Mr I. Alsagar**
68 **BENEFIT,** b f 08/02 Acclamation—Boost (Pivotal) **Cheveley Park Stud Limited**
69 **BERMUDA,** b f 01/02 Kodiac—Poana (FR) (New Approach (IRE)) **Cheveley Park Stud Limited**
70 B c 21/04 Aclaim (IRE)—Cadeaux Power (Major Cadeaux) (28571) **AlMohamediya Racing**
71 **CAVE DIVER,** b f 07/02 Ulysses (IRE)—Fellbeck (Cacique (IRE)) **Cheveley Park Stud Limited**
72 Br c 16/04 Due Diligence (USA)—Chicklade (Firebreak) (76190) **Mr & Mrs Paul & Clare Rooney**
73 **CRAZYLAND,** b f 08/05 Kodiac—Imperialistic Diva (IRE) (Haafhd) (57000) **Mr P Stokes & Mr S Krase**
74 **DARK SWANSONG (IRE),** b c 27/02 Dark Angel (IRE)—Pixeleen (Pastoral Pursuits) (100000) **Mr A. G. Craddock**
75 B c 12/02 Due Diligence (USA)—Endow (IRE) (Shamardal (USA)) (38000) **AlMohamediya Racing**
76 **FAITHFUL SPIRIT,** b f 09/04 Cable Bay (IRE)—
Don't Forget Faith (USA) (Victory Gallop (CAN)) (5714) **Don't Forget Faith Syndicate**
77 B c 16/01 Showcasing—Foxcatcher (Foxwedge (AUS)) (65000)
78 Ch c 29/03 Profitable (IRE)—Frabjous (Pivotal) (68571) **Mr & Mrs Paul & Clare Rooney**
79 B c 31/01 Adaay (IRE)—Glacier Point (Foxwedge (AUS)) (30000) **B Allen, G Hill & N Wagland**
80 B c 25/01 Cotai Glory—Global Alexander (IRE) (Dark Angel (IRE)) (64762) **AlMohamediya Racing**
81 B c 28/03 Footstepsinthesand—Harpist (IRE) (Danehill Dancer (IRE)) (47619) **Mr & Mrs Paul & Clare Rooney**
82 B c 14/04 Adaay (IRE)—Harryana To (Compton Place)
83 Ch c 16/04 Churchill (IRE)—Ighraa (IRE) (Tamayuz) (32381)
84 **INCUMBENT,** b c 23/01 Ulysses (IRE)—Executrix (Oasis Dream) (60000) **Cheveley Park Stud Limited**
85 **INSTINCTIVE MOVE,** b c 18/03 Showcasing—Peach Melba (Dream Ahead (USA)) (90000) **Sheikh I. S. Al Khalifa**
86 B f 19/04 Profitable (IRE)—Intimacy (IRE) (Teofilo (IRE)) (48000)
87 **ISAKOVA,** ch f 16/03 Pivotal—Russian Heroine (Invincible Spirit (IRE)) **Cheveley Park Stud Limited**
88 B c 09/04 Mehmas (IRE)—Keukenhof (IRE) (Dutch Art) (62000) **Mr S. R. Bin Ghadayer**
89 **LET'S FLY AGAIN,** b c 06/04 Kodiac—
Kinnaird (IRE) (Dr Devious (IRE)) (125000) **Mr Simon Munir & Mr Isaac Souede**
90 B f 26/02 Kodi Bear (IRE)—Malila (IRE) (Red Clubs (IRE)) **Clive Cox Racing Ltd**
91 **MAMBO BEAT (IRE),** ch c 10/03 Red Jazz (USA)—Bulrushes (Byron) (71429) **Middleham Park Racing CXIV**
92 B c 07/02 Awtaad (IRE)—Midnight Martini (Night Shift (USA)) (75000) **Mr J. Goddard**
93 **MIDNIGHT TRAIN,** b c 28/03 Iffraaj—Amarysia (FR) (Medicean) (50000) **A.D. & A.J. Pearson**
94 B c 03/02 Acclamation—Minalisa (Oasis Dream) (60000) **AlMohamediya Racing**
95 **OLYMPIC EAGLE,** b c 28/02 Gleneagles (IRE)—Olympic Runner (Exceed And Excel (AUS)) **J. C. Smith**
96 B c 13/04 Frankel—One Last Dance (AUS) (Encosta de Lago (AUS)) **Fairway Thoroughbreds Pty Ltd**
97 **PAVLODAR (FR),** ch c 10/04 Recorder—Sampaquita (FR) (Poet's Voice) (12913) **N. Bizakov**
98 **REGAL ENVOY,** b c 01/04 Ardad (IRE)—Regina (Green Desert (USA)) (52381) **Kennet Valley Thoroughbreds I**
99 **RETURN VOYAGE (USA),** b f 07/03 Street Boss (USA)—Sail Away Home (USA) (Kingmambo (USA)) (68000) **Mr P Stokes & Mr S Krase**
100 **RUM COCKTAIL,** b f 30/04 Muhaarar—Tropical Treat (Bahamian Bounty) **J. C. Smith**
101 **SAFETY FIRST,** b f 13/04 New Bay—Soteria (IRE) (Acclamation) (95238) **China Horse Club International Limited**
102 Ch f 06/05 Profitable (IRE)—Sassy Gal (IRE) (King's Best (USA)) (58000) **Mr & Mrs Paul & Clare Rooney**
103 **SATELLITE CALL (IRE),** b c 12/01 Kodiac—Ball Girl (IRE) (Tagula (IRE)) (74285) **Mr S. Davies**
104 B f 13/02 Zoffany (IRE)—Savannah Belle (Green Desert (USA)) **Mrs Patricia J. Burns**
105 **SHIMMERING SKY,** b c 01/03 Galileo Gold—
Oh Simple Thing (IRE) (Compton Place) (15238) **Miss J. Deadman & Mr S. Barrow**
106 B c 11/04 Mehmas (IRE)—Shoshoni Wind (Sleeping Indian) (110000) **Mr Saeed Bin Mohammed Al Qassimi**
107 Gr ro c 13/04 Lethal Force (IRE)—Silken Skies (IRE) (Zoffany (IRE)) **Clive Cox Racing Ltd**
108 **SPECIAL TIMES,** b f 29/03 Time Test—Salonmare (GER) (Manduro (GER)) (34000) **Windmill Racing**
109 Ch f 27/04 Showcasing—Suelita (Dutch Art) (200000)
110 **SURAC (IRE),** b c 25/01 Frankel—Belesta (Xaar) (123810) **Mr Simon Munir & Mr Isaac Souede**
111 B c 17/02 Profitable (IRE)—Throne (Royal Applause) (49524) **AlMohamediya Racing**
112 **TRANS MONTANA,** b f 22/03 Mondialiste (IRE)—Tarqua (IRE) (King Charlemagne (USA)) **Earl of Carnarvon**
113 **UBERRIMA FIDES,** b c 09/04 Exceed And Excel (AUS)—
Baileys Showgirl (FR) (Sepoy (AUS)) (62000) **Mr Simon Munir & Mr Isaac Souede**
114 **VAUNTED,** b f 24/02 Ardad (IRE)—Vallila (Dunkerque (FR)) (15000) **Keep Kicking Racing**
115 **WINGS OF WAR,** gr c 04/03 Dark Angel (IRE)—Futoon (IRE) (Kodiac) (133333) **Sheikh I. S. Al Khalifa**

## MR CLIVE COX - continued

**Other Owners:** Mr S. W. Barrow, Clive Cox Racing Ltd, Miss J. Deadman, Mrs R. J. Hargreaves, C. J. Harper, Mr R. S. Hoskins, Hot To Trot Racing 2, Mr A. Pearson, Mr Alan Spence.

**Flat Jockey:** Hector Crouch, Liam Keniry, Adam Kirby. **Apprentice Jockey:** Amelia Glass.

---

## 121 MR TONY COYLE, Norton
Postal: **Long Row Stables, Beverley Road, Norton, Malton, North Yorkshire, YO17 9PJ**
Contacts: **MOBILE 07976 621425**
EMAIL tonycoyleracing@hotmail.co.uk

1 **BORIS THE BRAVE**, 4, b g Universal (IRE)—Newgate Queen  **Mrs A. M. Johnson**
2 **BROKEN SPEAR**, 5, b g Pastoral Pursuits—My Pretty Girl  **Morecool Racing**
3 **EY UP ITS MICK**, 5, b g Milk It Mick—Silky Silence  **Mrs M. Lingwood**
4 **FLOWER POWER**, 10, br m Bollin Eric—Floral Rhapsody  **Mr A. C. Coyle**
5 **FULL CIRCLE**, 4, b g Finsceal Fior (IRE)—Full Bloom  **Shoreham Stud & Tony Coyle**
6 4, B f Kodiac—Geht Fasteur (IRE)  **Mr A. C. Coyle**
7 **LITTLE PIPPIN**, 8, b m Sir Percy—Lady Le Quesne (IRE)  **Mr A. C. Coyle**
8 **NEWGATE ANGEL**, 5, b m Heeraat (IRE)—Rio's Girl  **Mrs A. M. Johnson**
9 **NEWGATE SQUAL**, 4, ch f Sleeping Indian—Rio's Girl  **Mrs A. M. Johnson**
10 **WALTON THORNS (IRE)**, 4, b g Zebedee—Bishop's Lake  **C. R. Green**
11 **WOTS THE WIFI CODE**, 4, b g Fast Company (IRE)—Velvet Jaguar  **Mrs M. Lingwood**

### THREE-YEAR-OLDS

12 **EY UP IT'S MAGGIE**, b f Equiano (FR)—Velvet Jaguar  **Mrs M. Lingwood**
13 **FLEETING BLUE (FR)**, ch f French Navy—My Pretty Girl  **David Bishop & Tony Coyle**

**Other Owners:** Mr D. F. L. Bishop, Mr A. C. Coyle, Mrs H. B. Raw, Exors of the Late J. Raw, Mr J. Walsh.

**Flat Jockey:** Barry McHugh.

---

## 122 MR RAY CRAGGS, Sedgefield
Postal: **East Close Farm, Sedgefield, Stockton-On-Tees, Cleveland, TS21 3HW**
Contacts: **PHONE 01740 620239 FAX 01740 623476**

1 **AMELIA R (IRE)**, 5, b m Zoffany (IRE)—Xaloc (IRE)  **R. Craggs**
2 **AMOURI CHIEF**, 7, b g Sleeping Indian—Tour d'Amour (IRE)  **R. Craggs**
3 **AMOURI GLEAM**, 6, b m Arabian Gleam—Tour d'Amour (IRE)  **R. Craggs**
4 **AMOURIE**, 5, ch m Haafhd—Tour d'Amour (IRE)  **R. Craggs**
5 **CORAL QUEEN**, 10, b m Desideratum—Queen's Lodge (IRE)  **R. Craggs**
6 **QUAY QUEST**, 7, ch g Shami—Quay Four (IRE)  **R. Craggs**
7 **SPYCRACKER**, 4, b g Monsieur Bond (IRE)—Tour d'Amour (IRE)  **R. Craggs**
8 **TARA TIARA**, 9, b m Kayf Tara—Royal Roxy (IRE)  **R. Craggs**
9 **WELL I NEVER**, 9, b g Josr Algarhoud (IRE)—Tour d'Amour (IRE)  **R. Craggs**

### THREE-YEAR-OLDS

10 **KHABIB (IRE)**, b br g Mehmas (IRE)—Lady Mega (IRE)  **R. Craggs**

**Assistant Trainer:** Miss J N Craggs.

## 123 SIMON & ED CRISFORD, Newmarket

Postal: **Gainsborough Thoroughbreds Limited, Gainsborough Stables, Hamilton Road, Newmarket, Suffolk, CB8 0TE**
Contacts: **PHONE 01638 662661**
**EMAIL** info@gainsboroughoffice.com **WEBSITE** www.gainsboroughthoroughbreds.com
**TWITTER** @gainsboroughhq **INSTAGRAM** @gainsboroughhq

1 **A'ALI (IRE),** 4, b br c Society Rock (IRE)—Motion Lass
2 **AADDEEY (IRE),** 4, b g New Approach (IRE)—Feedyah (USA)
3 **CENTURY DREAM (IRE),** 7, b h Cape Cross (IRE)—Salacia (IRE)
4 **EPIC HERO (FR),** 5, b g Siyouni (FR)—Grace Lady (FR)
5 **FINEST SOUND (IRE),** 4, b g Exceed And Excel (AUS)—Amplifier
6 **INTUITIVE (IRE),** 5, b g Haatef (USA)—Majraa (FR)
7 **JASH (IRE),** 5, b h Kodiac—Miss Azeza
8 **LABEEBB (IRE),** 4, b g Exceed And Excel (AUS)—Tazffin (IRE)
9 **MAAMORA (IRE),** 5, b m Dubawi (IRE)—Zoowraa
10 **OCEANS MEET (IRE),** 4, b f Sea The Stars (IRE)—Elision (IRE)
11 **ROULSTON SCAR (IRE),** 5, b g Lope de Vega (IRE)—Pussycat Lips (IRE)
12 **WITHOUT A FIGHT (IRE),** 4, b g Teofilo (IRE)—Khor Sheed

## THREE-YEAR-OLDS

13 **AL SAARIYAH (IRE),** b f Acclamation—Marsh Daisy
14 **ALHAMMAAM (IRE),** b g Lope de Vega (IRE)—Jadhwah
15 **ATACAMENA (IRE),** b f Fast Company (IRE)—Emboss (IRE)
16 **BAHRAIN PRIDE,** b c Kodiac—Life of Pi
17 **BARSHAA,** b f Dubawi (IRE)—Sajjhaa
18 **CAMELOT TALES (FR),** b c Camelot—Temptress (IRE)
19 **CHINOOK,** b f Sea The Stars (IRE)—Papaya (IRE)
20 **CREDENCE STAR (USA),** b c American Pharoah (USA)—Harlan's Honor (USA)
21 **DARK CHARM (USA),** b br f More Than Ready (USA)—Rosalie Road (USA)
22 **FIGHT FOR IT (IRE),** b c Camelot—Dorothy B (IRE)
23 **FIGURES,** b f Fastnet Rock (AUS)—Gadfly
24 **ILZA'EEM (FR),** b c Olympic Glory (IRE)—Money Time (IRE)
25 **IMMELMANN (GER),** b g Adlerflug (GER)—Irika (GER)
26 **JADOOMI (FR),** b c Holy Roman Emperor (IRE)—South Sister
27 **JARWAH (IRE),** b f Muhaarar—Daymooma
28 **LATEST GENERATION,** b c Frankel—Rizeena (IRE)
29 **LEGAL ATTACK,** b c Shalaa (IRE)—Lauren Louise
30 **LINE OF DESCENT (IRE),** b g Nathaniel (IRE)—Joys of Spring (IRE)
31 **MANKHOOL,** ch g New Approach (IRE)—Majestic Manner
32 **MASTER OF COMBAT (IRE),** b c Invincible Spirit (IRE)—Sharja Queen
33 **MATAMUA,** b gr f Lope de Vega (IRE)—Iromea (IRE)
34 **MISS MARBLE,** b f Iffraaj—Lottie Dod (IRE)
35 **NOORJIHAN,** b f Kingman—Comic (IRE)
36 **NUMOOR,** b g Siyouni (FR)—Nabaraat (USA)
37 **OPERATIC (IRE),** ch f Showcasing—Dream Dana (IRE)
38 **PATINA,** b f New Approach (IRE)—Mazuna (IRE)
39 **PRETTY FAIR (IRE),** ch f Dubawi (IRE)—Talent
40 **PRINCESS ANOUSCHKA,** b f Kingman—Lustrous
41 **RIKNNAH (IRE),** b f Shamardal (USA)—Red Dune (IRE)
42 **ROYAL AIR FORCE (IRE),** b c Fastnet Rock (AUS)—Private Paradise (IRE)
43 **ROYAL HARMONY (IRE),** b f Shamardal (USA)—Lady Of Dubai
44 **SALEYMM (IRE),** b c Dubawi (IRE)—Talmada (USA)
45 **SHIELDED (IRE),** b g Buratino (IRE)—Shambolique
46 **SO IMPRESSED (IRE),** b f Exceed And Excel (AUS)—Mundana (IRE)
47 **STAR JEWEL,** b f Territories (IRE)—Dubai Affair
48 **STRIKEBACK (FR),** b g Intello (GER)—Serisia (FR)
49 **TORRKEE (FR),** b c Myboycharlie (IRE)—Fontaine Margot (FR)
50 **UNIQUE CUT (IRE),** b f Kodiac—Intaglia
51 **VOICE OF WISDOM (IRE),** b f Invincible Spirit (IRE)—Greatest Virtue

## SIMON & ED CRISFORD - continued

52 **WELSH GOLD,** ch f Night of Thunder (IRE)—Linet (IRE)
53 **ZAMAANI (IRE),** ch c Night of Thunder (IRE)—Alice Rose (IRE)

## TWO-YEAR-OLDS

54 B c 14/04 Invincible Spirit (IRE)—Aaraamm (USA) (Street Cry (IRE)) (100000)
55 **AL AGAILA (IRE),** b f 12/02 Lope de Vega (IRE)—L'Amour de Ma Vie (USA) (Dansili) (193705)
56 **AL BAHIA (IRE),** b f 17/04 Zoffany (IRE)—Straw Hat (IRE) (Galileo (IRE)) (76190)
57 **AMMOLITE (IRE),** ch f 02/03 Profitable (IRE)—Romie's Kastett (GER) (Halling (USA)) (95000)
58 B c 09/04 Gleneagles (IRE)—Anaamil (IRE) (Darshaan)
59 **ANTHEM NATIONAL (IRE),** b c 27/03 Dark Angel (IRE)—
Anthem Alexander (IRE) (Starspangledbanner (AUS)) (95000)
60 **ARTAOIS,** b c 23/03 Kodiac—La Patria (Dubawi (IRE)) (170000)
61 Gr f 24/04 Caravaggio (USA)—Atlantic Drift (Oasis Dream) (150000)
62 B f 30/03 Shamardal (USA)—Baheeja (Dubawi (IRE))
63 **BOLD PRESENCE,** b c 10/02 Siyouni (FR)—Appearance (Galileo (IRE))
64 **CAESAR'S PALACE,** b c 13/02 Holy Roman Emperor (IRE)—Return Ace (Zamindar (USA)) (50000)
65 B c 22/03 Shamardal (USA)—Dark Liberty (IRE) (Dark Angel (IRE))
66 **DESERT TEAM (IRE),** b f 16/04 Invincible Spirit (IRE)—Kilmah (Sepoy (AUS))
67 B c 19/04 Zoffany (IRE)—Dewdrop (IRE) (Galileo (IRE)) (60000)
68 B c 05/04 Tamayuz—Dheyaa (IRE) (Dream Ahead (USA))
69 **DUKEMAN (IRE),** b c 06/05 Kingman—She's Mine (IRE) (Sea The Stars (IRE)) (500000)
70 B f 25/01 Awtaad (IRE)—Ejadah (IRE) (Clodovil (IRE))
71 **ELITE ARTIST,** b f 18/02 Shamardal (USA)—Aquatinta (GER) (Samum (GER))
72 B c 25/02 Iffraaj—Feedyah (USA) (Street Cry (IRE))
73 **FINE BALANCE (IRE),** b f 11/02 Siyouni (FR)—Cash In The Hand (USA) (Exchange Rate (USA)) (220000)
74 B f 14/04 Kingman—Fine Time (Dansili) (475000)
75 B f 25/02 Starspangledbanner (AUS)—Floriade (IRE) (Invincible Spirit (IRE)) (125000)
76 B f 10/02 Kodiac—Fort Del Oro (IRE) (Lope de Vega (IRE)) (210000)
77 **GOLDEN GLANCE,** b f 28/01 Golden Horn—Zeeba (IRE) (Barathea (IRE))
78 B f 21/02 Exceed And Excel (AUS)—Hushing (Pivotal)
79 B f 09/02 Tamarkuz (USA)—Jannattan (USA) (Street Cry (IRE))
80 B f 11/03 Iffraaj—Lady of Persia (JPN) (Shamardal (USA))
81 Ch f 24/03 Night of Thunder (IRE)—Late Romance (USA) (Storm Cat (USA))
82 **LEGGYDAISY (FR),** ch f 16/02 The Grey Gatsby (IRE)—Leggy Lizzy (FR) (Le Havre (IRE))
83 **LUCKY SHAKE (FR),** bl f 09/02 Zelzal (FR)—Lucky Lot (Exceed And Excel (AUS))
84 Br gr c 11/05 Dark Angel (IRE)—Majeyda (USA) (Street Cry (IRE))
85 B c 18/03 Dubawi (IRE)—Megaron (Dansili)
86 **MISS FEDORA (IRE),** b f 23/02 Helmet (AUS)—Shahabad (Shamardal (USA))
87 **NEW NATION (IRE),** b c 13/03 Starspangledbanner (AUS)—Intermittent (Cacique (IRE)) (140000)
88 **NIGHT SPARKLE (IRE),** b f 06/05 Postponed (IRE)—Rose Diamond (IRE) (Daylami (IRE))
89 Ch c 12/05 Sea The Stars (IRE)—October Queen (IRE) (Iffraaj)
90 B f 18/03 Fastnet Rock (AUS)—Pivotal Mission (Pivotal)
91 B f 08/02 Kodiac—Pizzarra (Shamardal (USA))
92 Ch c 15/02 Night of Thunder (IRE)—Populist (IRE) (Shamardal (USA)) (100000)
93 **PROFIT GIVEN (IRE),** ch f 15/03 Profitable (IRE)—Kitty Softpaws (IRE) (Royal Applause) (100000)
94 **QUEEN OF CHANGE (IRE),** b f 09/03 Sea The Stars (IRE)—Salacia (IRE) (Echo of Light)
95 B f 26/03 Churchill (IRE)—Pussycat Lips (IRE) (Holy Roman Emperor (IRE)) (340000)
96 Ch c 08/04 Sea The Moon (GER)—Proserpine (Hat Trick (JPN))
97 **READY TO SHINE (IRE),** b f 26/04 Camelot—Matorio (FR) (Oratorio (IRE)) (340000)
98 B c 23/03 Australia—Reset In Blue (IRE) (Fastnet Rock (AUS)) (85000)
99 B f 14/02 Dubawi (IRE)—Rizeena (IRE) (Iffraaj)
100 B f 28/03 Churchill (IRE)—South Bay (Exceed And Excel (AUS)) (42000)
101 B c 06/04 Lope de Vega (IRE)—Special Gal (FR) (Galileo (IRE)) (170000)
102 B c 03/04 Caravaggio (USA)—Spring Garden (IRE) (Fastnet Rock (AUS)) (95238)
103 **SPRINGTIME,** b c 10/03 Postponed (IRE)—Frangipanni (IRE) (Dansili)
104 B c 15/01 Fastnet Rock (AUS)—Stars At Night (IRE) (Galileo (IRE)) (95000)
105 Gr ro f 30/04 Dubawi (IRE)—Summer Fete (IRE) (Pivotal)
106 B c 05/02 Iffraaj—Taqdees (IRE) (Sea The Stars (IRE))
107 Br c 31/03 Kodiac—Terhaab (USA) (Elusive Quality (USA))

## SIMON & ED CRISFORD - continued

**108** THE PRESERVER, b c 23/03 Sea The Stars (IRE)—Willoughby (IRE) (Oasis Dream) (280000)
**109** B br c 02/02 Zarak (FR)—Three Cards (Mastercraftsman (IRE)) (90395)
**110** B c 16/04 Wootton Bassett—Vega Sicilia (FR) (Elusive City (USA)) (84745)

---

**124** **MR ANDREW CROOK, Leyburn**
Postal: **Ashgill Stables (Yard 2), Tupgill Park, Coverham, Middleham, North Yorkshire, DL8 4TJ**
Contacts: **PHONE 01969 640303 MOBILE 07764 158899**
**EMAIL** andycrookracing@gmail.com **WEBSITE** www.andrewcrookracing.co.uk

**1** CRAKEHALL LAD (IRE), 10, ch g Manduro (GER)—My Uptown Girl **Mrs K. M. Savage**
**2** CYRANO STAR (FR), 9, gr g Martaline—Quezac du Boulay (FR) **Leeds Plywood & Doors Ltd**
**3** DONALD DUX (IRE), 7, b g Sholokhov (IRE)—Good Shine (IRE) **Mr D. Carter**
**4** EARLY BOY (FR), 10, b g Early March—Eclat de Rose (FR) **R. P. E. Berry**
**5** EMPORTEPARLAFOULE (FR), 7, gr g Smadoun (FR)—Sempiternelle (FR) **Mr D. Carter**
**6** HAUT BERRY (FR), 4, bl g My Risk (FR)—Bonjour Madame (FR) **R. P. E. Berry**
**7** 4, B f Flemensfirth (USA)—Jontys'lass **Mr D. Carter**
**8** LADY BABS, 7, br m Malinas (GER)—Jontys'lass **Ashgill Stud**
**9** MISS PLYMWICK, 4, ch f Monsieur Bond (IRE)—Bezant (IRE) **The 100 Club**
**10** OUR CILLA, 7, gr m Sixties Icon—Kinetix **Mr D. Carter**
**11** RACEMAKER, 7, b g Stimulation (IRE)—Sophies Heart **Mrs H. Sinclair**
**12** TILTILYS ROCK (IRE), 4, ch g Society Rock (IRE)—Tiltili (IRE) **Mr D. Carter**
**13** VESHENSKAYA (IRE), 6, b m Sholokhov (IRE)—Manorville (IRE) **Signify Partnership**
**14** ZARA'S UNIVERSE, 5, b m Universal (IRE)—Jontys'lass **Mrs C Hopper & David Carter**

### THREE-YEAR-OLDS

**15** ABLE LOVE, ch f Bated Breath—Loveable **Mrs C. Hopper**
**16** ORCHID ROSE (IRE), b f Mehmas (IRE)—Pale Orchid (IRE) **Mr D. Carter**
**17** B c Sea The Stars (IRE)—Rich Jade (USA) **Mr D. Carter**

**Other Owners:** R. P. E. Berry, Mr D. Carter, Miss A. M. Crook, Miss M. Hodgson, Mrs C. Hopper, Mrs K. M. Savage, Mr J. A. Saxby, Mr E. Skeels, O. R. Weeks.

**Assistant Trainer:** Amy Crook.

**Flat Jockey:** Jason Hart, Kevin Stott. **NH Jockey:** Will Kennedy.

---

**125** **MR SEAN CURRAN, Swindon**
Postal: **Twelve Oaks, Lechlade Road, Highworth, Swindon, Wiltshire, SN6 7QR**
Contacts: **MOBILE 07774 146169**

**1** ALL YOURS (FR), 10, ch g Halling (USA)—Fontaine Riant (FR) **Power Geneva Ltd**
**2** ALMUFEED (IRE), 4, b g Mukhadram—Anqooda (USA) **Power Geneva Ltd**
**3** ARTHUR'S REUBEN, 8, b g Malinas (GER)—Ambitious Annie **Mr A. J. White**
**4** BUCKLAND BOY (IRE), 6, b g Bated Breath—Rancho Montoya (USA) **Mr P. S. McNally**
**5** DAPA LAD (IRE), 6, b g Yeats (IRE)—Flame of Dixie (IRE) **Mr A. J. White**
**6** DOMAINE DE L'ISLE (FR), 8, b g Network (GER)—Gratiene de L'Isle (FR) **Oaks & Ian Hutchins**
**7** DOUKAROV (FR), 6, b g Le Havre (IRE)—Landskia (FR) **Mr A. J. White**
**8** GRIGGY (IRE), 5, b g Dandy Man—Joint Destiny (IRE) **Power Geneva Ltd**
**9** LIONEL ROAD, 4, b g Lethal Force (IRE)—Fanrouge (IRE) **Ron Smith Recycling Ltd**
**10** OBLATE, 5, b m Epaulette (AUS)—Lady Benedicte (IRE) **12 Oaks Racing**
**11** PINK JAZZ (IRE), 4, b g Red Jazz (USA)—Marvelofthelodge (IRE) **Power Geneva Ltd**

## MR SEAN CURRAN - continued

12 **REVOLUTIONARY MAN (IRE)**, 6, b g Exceed And Excel (AUS)—Bint Almukhtar (IRE) **Power Geneva Ltd**
13 **TALKING ABOUT YOU**, 4, b f Sixties Icon—Ificaniwill (IRE) **I. M. McGready**
14 **TREATY OF DINGLE**, 4, b f Roderic O'Connor (IRE)—Josefa Goya **Power Geneva Ltd**
15 **UNFORGIVING MINUTE**, 10, b g Cape Cross (IRE)—Ada River **Power Geneva Ltd**
16 **WORD OF HONOUR**, 5, b g Showcasing—Veiled Intrigue **Mr N. Byrne**

### THREE-YEAR-OLDS

17 Ch f French Navy—Costa Del Fortune (IRE)

**Other Owners:** 12 Oaks Racing, Mr J. M. S. Curran, Mr I Hutchins, L. M. Power.

---

| 126 | **MISS REBECCA CURTIS, Newport** |
|---|---|

Postal: **Fforest Farm, Newport, Pembrokeshire, SA42 0UG**
Contacts: **PHONE 01348 811489 MOBILE 07970 710690**
EMAIL rebcurtis@hotmail.com

1 **ABSOLUTE POWER**, 10, b g Flemensfirth (USA)—Crystal Ballerina (IRE) **M Sherwood & S Gammond**
2 **ANAX (IRE)**, 7, b g Oscar (IRE)—Limetree Leader (IRE) **Mr N. D. Morris**
3 **BARNARD CASTLE (IRE)**, 6, b g Oscar (IRE)—Rambling Liss (IRE) **Conyers, O'Reilly, Roddis, Zeffman**
4 **BEATTHEBULLET (IRE)**, 7, br g Flemensfirth (USA)—Top Quality **Miss R. Curtis**
5 **BLACK SAM MELODY**, 5, b m Black Sam Bellamy (IRE)—Moonlight Music (IRE) **Mr M. A. Sherwood**
6 **BOLEY BAY (IRE)**, 6, b g Yeats (IRE)—Print It On Lips (IRE) **Fforest Star Racing Ltd**
7 **CABOT HILLS (IRE)**, 4, b g Gleneagles (IRE)—Peeping Fawn (USA) **The Brizzle Boys**
8 **CUBAO (IRE)**, 7, b g Fame And Glory—Rematch (IRE) **Primus Partners**
9 **DALAMAN (IRE)**, 10, b g Duke of Marmalade (IRE)—Crimphill (IRE) **Diamond Racing Ltd**
10 **EASY WOOD (FR)**, 7, gr g Martaline—Ball of Wood (FR) **Miss R. Curtis**
11 **FACT CHECKER**, 4, b g Teofilo (IRE)—Disavow **Fforest Star Racing Ltd**
12 **FIDDLERS TRACKER (IRE)**, 6, b g Pour Moi (IRE)—Tracker **Mr R. Hyde**
13 **FINANCIAL OUTCOME (IRE)**, 8, b g Financial Reward (IRE)—Catriona's Mare (IRE) **Ccorz Partners**
14 **GEORDIE DES CHAMPS (IRE)**, 10, br g Robin des Champs (FR)—Kilcoleman Lady (IRE) **Mr J. P. McManus**
15 **HARD GROUND**, 7, b g Malinas (GER)—Poppy Come Running (IRE) **Mrs C. M. Lockett**
16 **HIS OSCAR (IRE)**, 6, b g Oscar (IRE)—St Helans Bay (IRE) **Got There In the End Partnership**
17 **JOE FARRELL (IRE)**, 12, b g Presenting—Luck of The Deise (IRE) **M Sherwood, N Morris & J Turner**
18 **JOUEUR BRESILIEN (FR)**, 9, b g Fuisse (FR)—Fille du Bresil (FR) **Inthewayboy Group**
19 **JUST A THOUGHT (IRE)**, 9, ch m Stowaway—Carrig Lucy (IRE) **Hyde, Outhart, Moran & Hill**
20 **LEGENDS GOLD (IRE)**, 7, b m Gold Well—Fu's Legend (IRE) **Lockett,Hyde,Mountford,Bishop&Outhart**
21 **LISNAGAR OSCAR (IRE)**, 8, b g Oscar (IRE)—Asta Belle (FR) **Racing For Fun**
22 **LISSITZKY (IRE)**, 6, b g Declaration of War (USA)—Tarfshi **Mr N. D. Morris**
23 **MINELLA BOBO (IRE)**, 8, gr g Oscar (IRE)—Line Kendie (FR) **Moran, Outhart, McDermott, Hyde & Hill**
24 **OSCAR ASCHE (IRE)**, 7, b g Oscar (IRE)—Boro Supreme (IRE) **Spencer Gammond,Jackie Rymer&rob Farnham**
25 **PATS FANCY (IRE)**, 6, b g Oscar (IRE)—Pat's Darling (IRE) **Hydes,McDermott,Spencer,Frobisher & Lee**
26 **PENNYFORAPOUND (IRE)**, 7, b g Winged Love (IRE)—
                                                Recession Lass (IRE) **R & J Farnham,P Burns,S Gammond,F Street**
27 5, B g Frozen Power (IRE)—Perovskia (USA) **Miss R. Curtis**
28 **RANIERI (IRE)**, 6, b g Westerner—Carrigmoorna Storm (IRE) **The Brizzle Boys**
29 **RELENTLESS DREAMER (IRE)**, 12, br g Kayf Tara—Full of Elegance (FR) **Mr N. D. Morris**
30 **RUTHLESS ARTICLE (IRE)**, 8, b g Definite Article—Lady Kamando **J Rymer R Farnham C Rymer J Farnham**
31 **SUMMER NAME (IRE)**, 9, b g Duke of Marmalade (IRE)—Summer's Eve **Relentless Dreamers Racing**
32 **SUNSET SHOWDOWN (IRE)**, 8, b g Flemensfirth (USA)—Sunset Queen (IRE) **Mr J. P. McManus**
33 **TIME TO FOLLOW (IRE)**, 5, b g Flemensfirth (USA)—Supreme Beneficial (IRE) **Fforest Star Racing Ltd**
34 **TINKERS HILL TOMMY (IRE)**, 10, b g King's Theatre (IRE)—Satco Street (IRE) **W. D. Lewis**
35 **UNIVERSAL BROOK**, 5, b m Universal (IRE)—Alfies Gift **Mrs G. A. Davies**
36 **WAYFINDER (IRE)**, 7, br g Shantou (USA)—Sibury (IRE) **The Wayfinders**

## MISS REBECCA CURTIS - continued

**Other Owners:** Mr D. J. Bishop, Mr P. Burns, Mr A. R. Clerkson, Mr J. Conyers, Miss R. Curtis, Mr M. Davis, Mrs J. L. Farnham, Mr R. A. Farnham, Fishlake Commercial Motors Ltd, Mr S. Frobisher, Mr G. S. Gammond, Mr L. Gardner, Mr I. Glendenning, Mr N. Goulden, Mr N. J. Guttridge, M. Hill, Mr K. Hopgood, Mr M. Hyde, Mr R. Hyde, Mr R. J. Line, Mrs C. M. Lockett, Mr D. P. McDermott, Mr B. Merrett, Ms J. A. Moran, Mr N. D. Morris, Mrs K. M. Mountford, Mr J. P. O'Reilly, Mr W. J. O'Reilly, A. J. Outhart, Mr S. Palmer, Mr S. C. Prowting, Mr N. M. Roddis, Mr C. A. Rymer, Mr J. Rymer, Mrs J. Rymer, Mr M. A. Sherwood, Mr A. Spencer, Mrs F. Street, Mr C. R. Trembath, Mr J. Turner, D. C. Zeffman.

**Assistant Trainer:** Paul Sheldrake.

---

**127**
### MR LUKE DACE, Billingshurst
Postal: Copped Hall Farm and Stud, Okehurst House, Okehurst Lane, Billingshurst, West Sussex, RH14 9HR
Contacts: **MOBILE 07949 401085 FAX 01403 612176**
**EMAIL lukedace@yahoo.co.uk WEBSITE www.lukedace.co.uk**

1 **HARLEQUIN,** 4, b g Swiss Spirit—Falcon In Flight **Mr R. L. Page**
2 **TAUREAN STAR (IRE),** 8, b g Elnadim (USA)—Marhaba **The Sussex Partnership**

### THREE-YEAR-OLDS

3 **EXECUTIVE,** b f Swiss Spirit—Stylistik **Mr R. L. Page**
4 **FRIDAY,** b f Swiss Spirit—Falcon In Flight **Mr R. L. Page**
5 **INTRUSIVE,** b c Fountain of Youth (IRE)—Intrusion **Surrey Hills Racing**

**Other Owners:** Mr M. Giles, Mr T. F. Giles, Mr J. McGuinness, Mr L. McGuinness, Mr S. Mitchell, Mr K. J. Nichols, Mr M. Wenman.

**Assistant Trainer:** Mrs L Dace.

---

**128**
### MR KEITH DALGLEISH, Carluke
Postal: Belstane Racing Stables, Carluke, Lanarkshire, ML8 5HN
Contacts: **PHONE 01555 773335**
**EMAIL dalgleish.racing@outlook.com**

1 **ABERAMA GOLD,** 4, b c Heeraat (IRE)—Nigella **M & I I**
2 **AIN'T NO SUNSHINE (IRE),** 5, b g Shantou (USA)—Screaming Witness (IRE) **Straightline Bloodstock**
3 **ALRIGHT SUNSHINE (IRE),** 6, b g Casamento (IRE)—Miss Gibraltar **Straightline Bloodstock**
4 **AMALFI DOUG (FR),** 11, gr g Network (GER)—Queissa (FR) **The County Set (seven) & Partner**
5 **ARTHUR'S SEAT (IRE),** 4, b g Champs Elysees—Sojitzen (FR) **Mr & Mrs Paul & Clare Rooney**
6 **BALRANALD (FR),** 5, b g Mastercraftsman (IRE)—Shining Glory (GER) **Mr J. Fyffe**
7 **BEECHWOOD JUDE (FR),** 5, b g War Command (USA)—Ponte Sanangelo (FR) **Middleham Park Racing LXXXIV**
8 **BIG JIM DWYER (IRE),** 5, b g Born To Sea (IRE)—Cape Joy (IRE) **Campbell, Cull, Gilbert & Mackenzie**
9 **BLUESKYANDSUNSHINE (IRE),** 6, b g Fame And Glory—Printing Polly (IRE) **Straightline Bloodstock**
10 **BREGUET BOY (IRE),** 4, br g Requinto (IRE)—Holly Hawk (IRE) **Straightline Bloodstock**
11 **BRINGITONBORIS (USA),** 4, gr g Distorted Humor (USA)—Miss Fontana (USA) **Mr J S Morrison & Partner**
12 **CABALLERO (IRE),** 5, ch g Camacho—Dame d'Honneur (IRE) **Equus I**
13 **CHICHESTER,** 4, b g Dansili—Havant **Sir Ian & Ms Catriona Good**
14 **CHOOKIE DUNEDIN,** 6, b g Epaulette (AUS)—Lady of Windsor (IRE) **Raeburn Brick Limited**
15 **CLAY REGAZZONI,** 4, b g Due Diligence (USA)—Shifting Moon **Middleham Park Racing XXXVIII & Partner**
16 **CORTON LASS,** 6, gr m Showcasing—Elbow Beach **Mr J. J. Hutton**
17 **DARK LOCHNAGAR (USA),** 5, b g Australia—Virginia Waters (USA) **Weldspec Glasgow Limited**
18 **DEMOCRATIC OATH (IRE),** 6, b g Stowaway—Reina Reed (IRE) **Mr J. Fyffe**

## MR KEITH DALGLEISH - continued

19 **EL PICADOR (IRE)**, 5, b g Dansili—West of Venus (USA) **Sir Ian & Ms Catriona Good**
20 **EURO IMPLOSION (IRE)**, 5, b g Battle of Marengo (IRE)—Mikes Baby (IRE) **Mr J S Morrison**
21 **FASHION ADVICE**, 4, ch f Dandy Man (IRE)—Secret Advice **A. R. M. Galbraith**
22 **FELDSPAR**, 4, b g Champs Elysees—Novellara **Straightline Bloodstock**
23 **FINALLY MINE (USA)**, 4, ch f Animal Kingdom (USA)—Midnight Music (IRE) **Weldspec Glasgow Limited**
24 **FIRST ACCOUNT**, 7, b br g Malinas (GER)—Kind Nell **Straightline Bloodstock**
25 **FONZERELLI (IRE)**, 5, b m Schiaparelli (GER)—Cadoutene (FR) **Straightline Bloodstock**
26 **FRIENDLY ADVICE (IRE)**, 5, ch g Orientor—Secret Advice **A. R. M. Galbraith**
27 **GET ON JOHN (IRE)**, 6, b g Getaway (GER)—Opera Season (IRE) **Campbell, Cull, Gilbert & Mackenzie**
28 **GLORIOUS LADY (IRE)**, 7, b m Fame And Glory—Lady Secret (FR) **Straightline Bloodstock**
29 **GOMETRA GINTY (IRE)**, 5, b m Morpheus—Silver Cache (USA) **Ken McGarrity & Partner**
30 **GOODTIMES BADTIMES (IRE)**, 6, b g Doyen (IRE)—One Love (IRE) **Mr J. Fyffe**
31 **GRUMPY MCGRUMPFACE (IRE)**, 6, b g Arctic Cosmos (USA)—Celestial Spirit (IRE) **The Gilbert's & Mr Campbell**
32 **HEAR ME OUT (IRE)**, 4, b g Kingston Hill—Waha (IRE) **Straightline Bloodstock**
33 **HIGH MOON**, 6, b g Midnight Legend—Dizzy Frizzy **Straightline Bloodstock**
34 **HIGHWAY COMPANION (IRE)**, 7, b g Milan—Niffyrann (FR) **Weldspec Glasgow Limited**
35 **HOME BEFORE DUSK**, 6, b g Medicean—Flylowflylong (IRE) **Mr G. R. Leckie**
36 **HOOPMALASSIE (USA)**, 4, b f Honor Code (USA)—Casual Smile **Weldspec Glasgow Limited**
37 **HOWZER BLACK (IRE)**, 5, br g Requinto (IRE)—Mattinata **Middleham Park Racing LXXVI**
38 **I CAN'T REMEMBER (IRE)**, 4, b g Dragon Pulse (IRE)—Time Signal **Campbell, Cull, Gilbert & Mackenzie**
39 **I'M TO BLAME (IRE)**, 8, b g Winged Love (IRE)—Swap Shop (IRE) **The Gilbert's & Mr Campbell**
40 **KALYPTRA (FR)**, 5, b g Fair Mix (IRE)—Lovely Origny (FR) **Straightline Bloodstock**
41 **KILBARRY LEADER (IRE)**, 5, b m Leading Light (IRE)—Eternal Lady (IRE) **Straightline Bloodstock**
42 **LE MAGNIFIQUE (GER)**, 4, ch g Kamsin (GER)—La Poesie (GER) **Straightline Bloodstock**
43 **LET ME BE (IRE)**, 5, b g Gale Force Ten—Peryzat (IRE) **Straightline Bloodstock**
44 **MACHIOS**, 4, br g Maxios—Astragal **Sir Ian & Ms Catriona Good**
45 **MI CAPRICHO (IRE)**, 6, b g Elzaam (AUS)—Mavemacullen (IRE) **Mr C. Jones**
46 **MONSIEUR CO (FR)**, 8, b g Turgeon (USA)—Cayras Style (FR) **Ken McGarrity & Partner**
47 **MURPHY'S LAW (IRE)**, 7, b g Gold Well—Balleen Rose (IRE) **Straightline Bloodstock**
48 **NAME OF FAME (IRE)**, 6, b g Fame And Glory—Outo'theblue (IRE) **Straightline Bloodstock**
49 **NEWTOWN BOY (IRE)**, 8, b g Beneficial—Tanit Lady (IRE) **The County Set Eight**
50 **ON A PROMISE (IRE)**, 9, gr g Definite Article—Silvers Knowe (IRE) **Straightline Bloodstock**
51 **ONE NIGHT IN MILAN (IRE)**, 8, b g Milan—Native Mo (IRE) **The Gilbert's & Mr Campbell**
52 **OSCAR CLOUDS (IRE)**, 6, b g Oscar (IRE)—Bobbing Back (IRE) **Straightline Bloodstock**
53 **PADDYPLEX**, 8, b g Multiplex—Turtle Bay **G & J Park**
54 **PLATINUMCARD (IRE)**, 6, b g Golden Lariat (USA)—Flemensfirth Lady (IRE) **Straightline Bloodstock**
55 **POUGNE BOBBI (FR)**, 10, b br g Protektor (GER)—Amicus **Straightline Bloodstock**
56 **PRINCE KAYF**, 7, b g Kayf Tara—Annie's Answer (IRE) **Straightline Bloodstock**
57 **RAYMOND (IRE)**, 6, b g Tobougg (IRE)—Crack The Kicker (IRE) **Straightline Bloodstock**
58 **RED BOND (IRE)**, 5, b g Red Jazz (USA)—Faithfulbond (IRE) **Middleham Park Racing XXVII**
59 **ROMAN STONE (USA)**, 5, b g Noble Mission—Winendynme (USA) **Weldspec Glasgow Limited**
60 **SEXTANT**, 6, b g Sea The Stars (IRE)—Hypoteneuse (IRE) **Straightline Bloodstock**
61 **SHAWS BRIDGE (IRE)**, 4, b g Kalanisi (IRE)—Zaffarella (IRE) **The Gilbert's & Mr Campbell**
62 **SIDI ISMAEL (FR)**, 7, b g Great Pretender (IRE)—Tetouane (FR) **Straightline Bloodstock**
63 **SOLDIER'S MINUTE**, 6, b g Raven's Pass (USA)—Hadba (IRE) **Weldspec Glasgow Limited**
64 **TARQUIN STARDUST (FR)**, 5, gr g Great Pretender (IRE)—Turgotine (FR) **Mrs K. E. Gilbert**
65 **TAXMEIFYOUCAN (IRE)**, 7, b g Beat Hollow—Accounting **Straightline Bloodstock**
66 **TEFNUT (USA)**, 4, b f American Pharoah (USA)—Virginia Waters (USA) **Weldspec Glasgow Limited**
67 **THREE CASTLES**, 5, b g Zoffany (IRE)—Fountain of Honour (IRE) **Mr J. K. McGarrity**
68 **TIP TOP TONTO (IRE)**, 5, b g Milan—Sarahs Quay (IRE) **The Gilbert's & Mr Campbell**
69 **UNIVERSAL GLEAM (IRE)**, 5, b g Sir Percy—Mookhlesa **Straightline Bloodstock**
70 **VENTURA FLAME (IRE)**, 4, b f Dandy Man (IRE)—Kramer Drive (IRE) **Middleham Park Racing LXXXIII & Partner**
71 **VOLATILE ANALYST (USA)**, 4, b g Distorted Humor (USA)—Gentle Caroline (USA) **Mr K. W. Dalgleish**
72 **WARRIORS STORY**, 5, b g Midnight Legend—Samandara (FR) **Straightline Bloodstock**
73 **WHAT'S THE STORY**, 7, b g Harbour Watch (IRE)—Spring Fashion (IRE) **Weldspec Glasgow Limited**
74 **YOU BIG DOSSER (IRE)**, 5, b g Getaway (GER)—Sharifa (GER) **Straightline Bloodstock**
75 **YOUNEVERLETMEDOWN (IRE)**, 4, br f Footstepsinthesand—Calorie **Mr K. W. Dalgleish**

## MR KEITH DALGLEISH - continued

### THREE-YEAR-OLDS

76 **AYR EMPRESS (IRE)**, b f Holy Roman Emperor (IRE)—Miss Anneliese (IRE) **W. M. Johnstone**
77 **BEECHWOOD EMILY**, b f Holy Roman Emperor (IRE)—Gale Green **Middleham Park Racing XXV & Partner**
78 **CARN A CHLAMAIN (USA)**, b g Fed Biz (USA)—Chalonitka (USA) **Weldspec Glasgow Limited**
79 **COOL DANDY (IRE)**, b f Dandy Man (IRE)—Cool Express (IRE) **Mr F. Brady**
80 **CORRA LINN (IRE)**, b f Footstepsinthesand—Miss Corinne **Weldspec Glasgow Limited**
81 **CULLY**, b f Havana Gold (IRE)—Tell The Wind (IRE) **Mrs J. M. MacPherson**
82 **DENZIL'S LAUGHING (IRE)**, b g Mehmas (IRE)—Question (USA) **Ontoawinner 8 & Partner**
83 **DONIZETTI**, b g Twilight Son—Modern Art **Weldspec Glasgow Limited**
84 B g Fast Company (IRE)—Dubai's Success **Straightline Bloodstock**
85 **GAELIC SECRET**, b br c Pearl Secret—Ceilidh Band **& Dance**
86 **GIOIA CIECA (USA)**, b c Kitten's Joy (USA)—Dynacielo (USA) **Weldspec Glasgow Limited**
87 **HEIGHTS OF ABRAHAM (IRE)**, b c Starspangledbanner (AUS)—High Vintage (IRE) **Two Goldfish & A Balloon 1**
88 **HIPSWAY (IRE)**, ch f The Gurkha (IRE)—Clodovina (IRE) **Weldspec Glasgow Limited**
89 **INAHOOP (IRE)**, b f Camacho—La Estatua **Mr K. W. Dalgleish**
90 **KRAKEN FILLY (IRE)**, b f Camacho—Tip It On The Top (IRE) **Mr J. Fyffe**
91 **NOBLE CRUSADE (USA)**, b c Noble Mission—Hint of Joy (USA) **Weldspec Glasgow Limited**
92 **ROYAL ADVICE (IRE)**, ch g Anjaal—Tamara Love (IRE) **Mr G. R. Leckie**
93 **SOAPYS SISTER**, b f Hot Streak (IRE)—Littlemisssunshine (IRE) **Mrs J. M. MacPherson**
94 **SUMMA PETO (USA)**, gr ro c Dialed In (USA)—Unbridled Gem (USA) **Weldspec Glasgow Limited**
95 **TATSTHEWAYTODOIT**, b c Mayson—Resist **Middleham Park Racing CXIX & Partner**
96 **THE THIN BLUE LINE (IRE)**, b br c Mehmas (IRE)—Rahlah **Middleham Park Racing LI & Partner**
97 **TRISTAN DA CUNHA (IRE)**, br f Slade Power (IRE)—Wild Academy (IRE) **Mr K. W. Dalgleish**

**Other Owners:** Mr S. Bridge, Mr J. J. Campbell, County Set Seven, Mr R. Cull, Mr K. W. Dalgleish, Mrs J. Dance, Mr J. E. Dance, Equus I, Mrs K. E. Gilbert, Mr R. P. Gilbert, Richard & Katherine Gilbert, G. Godsman, Ms C. Good, Sir Ian Good, Keith Dalgleish Racing Limited, Robert Macgregor, Mrs P.M. Mackenzie, Mr J. K. McGarrity, Middleham Park Racing CXIX, Middleham Park Racing LI, Middleham Park Racing LXXXIII, Middleham Park Racing XXV, Middleham Park Racing XXXVIII, Mr J S Morrison, Mr N. J. O'Brien, Ontoawinner 8, T. S. Palin, Mr G. Park, Miss J. Park, M. Prince, Mr S. C. Reay, Mr E. M. Sutherland, Mr D. A. Walker.

**Assistant Trainer:** Kevin Dalgleish.

**NH Jockey:** Callum Bewley. **Flat Jockey:** Rowan Scott.

---

**129** **MR HENRY DALY, Ludlow**
Postal: **Trainer did not wish details of their string to appear**

---

**130** **MR PHILLIP DANDO, Peterston-Super-Ely**
Postal: **Springfield Court, Peterston-Super-Ely, Cardiff, South Glamorgan, CF5 6LG**
Contacts: PHONE 01446 760012 MOBILE 07872 965395

1 **BEAU HAZE**, 8, b g Black Sam Bellamy (IRE)—Bella Haze **P. C. Dando**
2 **CHANTILLY HAZE**, 6, b m Black Sam Bellamy (IRE)—Bella Haze **P. C. Dando**
3 **HARRY HAZE**, 9, b g Dr Massini (IRE)—Gypsy Haze **Mr Phillip Dando & Mr Anthony Brown**
4 **IFANDABUT (IRE)**, 9, b g Scorpion (IRE)—Native Wonder (IRE) **The Gambling Cousins**
5 **SAM HAZE**, 7, b g Black Sam Bellamy (IRE)—Bella Haze **P. C. Dando**

**Other Owners:** Mr H. A. Brown, P. C. Dando.

**Assistant Trainer:** Mrs Rebecca Davies.

## 131 MR VICTOR DARTNALL, Barnstaple
Postal: **Higher Shutscombe Farm, Charles, Brayford, Barnstaple, Devon, EX32 7PU**
Contacts: **PHONE 01598 710280 MOBILE 07974 374272 FAX 01598 710708**
**EMAIL victordartnall@gmail.com WEBSITE www.victordartnallracing.com**

1 **ADMIRAL'S SECRET,** 10, b g Kayf Tara—Bobs Bay (IRE) **The Whacko Partnership**
2 **ATJIMA (IRE),** 6, b m Mahler—Qui Plus Est (FR) **Mr N. Viney**
3 **BINDON LANE,** 7, b g Arvico (FR)—Cuckoo Lane (IRE) **Mrs E. S. Weld**
4 **BOLVING (IRE),** 10, b g Stowaway—Kiniohio (FR) **Mrs C. M. Barber**
5 **DANCING SHADOW (IRE),** 12, br g Craigsteel—Be My Shadow (IRE) **The Dancing Shadows**
6 **EXMOOR EXPRESS (IRE),** 8, b g Sans Frontieres (IRE)—Blue Article (IRE) **The First Shutscombe Syndicate**
7 **FISHERMANS COVE (IRE),** 7, b g Getaway (GER)—Toscar (IRE) **G. D. Hake**
8 **GET WISHING (IRE),** 9, b g Getaway (GER)—Third Wish (IRE) **Edge Of Exmoor**
9 **HALDON HILL (IRE),** 8, b g Mahler—Qui Plus Est (FR) **Mr J. P. McManus**
10 **HARTNOLL HERO (IRE),** 5, br g Sageburg (IRE)—Skyra (IRE) **Mrs.S.De Wilde,Mr.B.Dallyn,Mrs.C.Carter**
11 **HOOPER'S LEGEND,** 10, b g Midnight Legend—Norton Sapphire **Mr R. Harding**
12 **HOWARDIAN HILLS (IRE),** 8, b g Vale of York (IRE)—Handsome Anna (IRE) **Mr V. R. A. Dartnall**
13 **MAHLER'S FIRST (IRE),** 9, b g Mahler—Fridays Folly (IRE) **First Brayford Partnership**
14 **MIDNIGHT SAPPHIRE,** 11, ch m Midnight Legend—Norton Sapphire **Mr R. Harding**
15 **MINNIE ESCAPE,** 9, b m Getaway (GER)—Minnie Hill (IRE) **The Second Brayford Partnership**
16 **RIVER BRAY (IRE),** 8, ch g Arakan (USA)—Cill Fhearga (IRE) **The River Bray Syndicate**
17 **RUN TO MILAN (IRE),** 9, b g Milan—Run Supreme (IRE) **Barber, Birchenhough, De Wilde**
18 **SOCKEYE (IRE),** 5, ch g Mahler—Another Present (IRE) **Mrs C. M. Barber**
19 **SWEET ADARE (IRE),** 8, b m Getaway (GER)—The Adare Woman (IRE) **G. D. Hake**

### THREE-YEAR-OLDS

20 B g Cannock Chase (USA)—Dance A Daydream **Edge Of Exmoor**
21 **MELODOR,** ch f Cannock Chase (USA)—Legal Art **Edge Of Exmoor**

**Other Owners:** Mrs C. M. Barber, Mrs K. Birchenhough, Ms C. Carter, Mr B. C. Dallyn, Mr V. R. A. Dartnall, Mrs S. De Wilde, Mr J. Edelman, Mrs S. M. Hall, Mr M. E. Nicholls, Mr M. W. Richards, Mr L. Singleton, A. P. Staple.

**Assistant Trainer:** G. A. Dartnall.

## 132 MR TOM DASCOMBE, Malpas
Postal: **Manor House Stables, Malpas, Cheshire, SY14 8AD**
Contacts: **PHONE 01948 820485 MOBILE 07973 511664 FAX 01948 820495**
**EMAIL tom@manorhousestables.com WEBSITE www.manorhousestables.com**

1 **ANGEL ALEXANDER (IRE),** 5, ro g Dark Angel (IRE)—
Majestic Alexander (IRE) **Birbeck Mound Trowbridge & Owen**
2 **BRAD THE BRIEF,** 4, b g Dutch Art—Kenzadargent (FR) **Chasemore Farm LLP**
3 **CHARLIE D (USA),** 6, b g Animal Kingdom (USA)—Ocicat (USA) **Mr D. R. Passant & Mr T. Dascombe**
4 **DANA FOREVER (IRE),** 4, b f Requinto (IRE)—Positive Step (IRE) **Miss S. Y. D. Goh**
5 **FINOAH (IRE),** 5, b g Kodiac—Burstingdalak (IRE) **Alan & Sue Cronshaw & Partner**
6 **GIFTED RULER,** 4, b g Muhaarar—Dubai Bounty **Mr D. R. Passant**
7 **HE'S A KEEPER (IRE),** 4, gr g Brazen Beau (AUS)—Silver Grey (IRE) **Mr N. Canning**
8 **ICONIC CHOICE,** 5, ch m Sixties Icon—Adorable Choice (IRE) **Mr J. D. Brown**
9 **LINCOLN PARK,** 5, b g Kyllachy—Twilight Pearl **Gary Dewhurst & Manor House Stables**
10 **MISTY GREY (IRE),** 4, gr g Dark Angel (IRE)—Chinese White (IRE) **Barbara & Alick Richmond**
11 **MORISCO (IRE),** 4, b g Requinto (IRE)—Mattinata **Mrs C. L. Ingram**
12 **PHUKET POWER (IRE),** 4, b g Kodiac—Brazilian Bride (IRE) **King Power Racing Co Ltd**
13 **POT OF PAINT,** 4, b g New Approach (IRE)—Regency (JPN) **Mr D. R. Passant**
14 **RAJINSKY (IRE),** 5, b g Zoffany (IRE)—Pink Moon (IRE) **Mr R. S. Matharu**
15 **SHA LA LA LA LEE,** 6, b g Helmet (AUS)—Shamara (IRE) **Nigel and Sharon Mather & Charles Ledigo**
16 **SHE'S ALL IN GOLD (IRE),** 4, b f Golden Horn—Simonetta (IRE) **Mr D. Ward**

# MR TOM DASCOMBE - continued

17 **WELSH WAYNE (IRE)**, 4, ch g Dragon Pulse (IRE)—Balaagha (USA) **Manor House Stables LLP**
18 **WILLIE JOHN**, 6, b g Dansili—Izzi Top

## THREE-YEAR-OLDS

19 **ADAAY DREAM**, b g Adaay (IRE)—Virtuality (USA) **Faulkner, Joynson, Morris & Simpson**
20 **ANDRONICUS BEAU (IRE)**, b g Gutaifan (IRE)—Bella Ophelia (IRE) **Nolan Pritchard Rutherford Witheridge**
21 **ARTORIOUS (IRE)**, ch c New Bay—Sudu Queen (GER) **Mr D. R. Passant**
22 **ASTRONOMIC CHOICE**, b g Havana Gold (IRE)—Adorable Choice (IRE) **Mr J. D. Brown**
23 **AUROCH**, b f Iffraaj—The Gold Cheongsam (IRE) **Michael Owen Racing Club I**
24 **BAKERSBOY**, b c Oasis Dream—Dubai Bounty **David Lowe & Partner**
25 **CAPO BAY (IRE)**, b c Fast Company (IRE)—Satin Cape (IRE) **Deva Racing Chester**
26 **COMMONSENSICAL**, b g Bated Breath—Critical Path (IRE) **More Turf Racing**
27 **FALCON BROOK**, b c Heeraat (IRE)—Sitting Pretty (IRE) **Owen Promotions & Dooley Thoroughbreds**
28 **FIRST LOTT**, b f Harbour Watch (IRE)—Don't Tell Mary (IRE) **Keith & Mary Trowbridge**
29 **FOOLS RUSH IN (IRE)**, br g Mehmas (IRE)—Faddwa (IRE) **Calling the Shots**
30 **GET FUNKY (IRE)**, ch c Pearl Secret—Voom Voom (IRE) **& Dance**
31 **HARMONY LIL (IRE)**, b f Kodi Bear (IRE)—Lil's Joy (IRE) **Sue Cronshaw & Karen Bennett**
32 **KAYFAST WARRIOR (IRE)**, b g No Nay Never (USA)—Stranded **Middleham Park Racing XXXVI**
33 **LADY MORGANA (IRE)**, b f Camelot—Silent Act (USA) **Mr & Mrs R. Scott**
34 **LAXTON LADD (IRE)**, gr g Iffraaj—Morning Frost (IRE) **More Turf Racing**
35 **MIRAMICHI (IRE)**, b g Markaz (IRE)—Mattinata **Mrs C. L. Ingram**
36 **PAWS FOR THOUGHT (IRE)**, b g Requinto (IRE)—Kitty Softpaws (IRE) **Mrs C. A. Shaw**
37 **POOL BAR LADY**, ch f Proconsul—Raktina **Steven Packham & Owen Promotions Ltd**
38 **RATTLING ROSIE**, gr f Lethal Force (IRE)—Lady Red Oak **Mr D. R. Passant**
39 **ROBUSTLY**, b f Dandy Man (IRE)—Veiled Beauty (USA) **Chasemore Farm LLP**
40 **ROCKETS RED GLARE (IRE)**, ch c Starspangledbanner (AUS)—Spirit of Paris (IRE) **Mr D. J. Lowe**
41 **SCOTS GOLD (IRE)**, gr g Dark Angel (IRE)—Duchess Andorra (IRE) **Barry, Trowbridge & Empire State Racing**
42 **SOLENT GATEWAY (IRE)**, b g Awtaad (IRE)—Aoife Alainn (IRE) **Mr D. R. Passant & Hefin Williams**
43 **SPIRIT OF SISRA (IRE)**, b f Zoffany (IRE)—Tadris (USA) **Mr T. Graham**
44 **THE NU FORM WAY (FR)**, b c Le Havre (IRE)—Jamboree (IRE) **Carswell Racing**

## TWO-YEAR-OLDS

45 B c 06/03 Kodiac—Alyaafel (Cape Cross (IRE)) (47619)
46 B c 25/01 El Kabeir (USA)—Areyaam Rose (IRE) (Teofilo (IRE)) (43810) **Gary Dewhurst & Manor House Stables**
47 B f 18/03 Dandy Man (IRE)—Britain's Pride (Royal Applause) (36190) **Dandy Boys**
48 B g 13/02 Slade Power—Brogan (Pivotal) **Chasemore Farm LLP**
49 B c 02/04 Prince of Lir (IRE)—Conjuring (IRE) (Showcasing) (23810) **Manor House Racing & Owen**
50 **COSTA ADEJE (IRE)**, b c 09/03 Cotai Glory—Penny Rouge (IRE) (Pennekamp (USA)) (28571) **Deva Racing Cotai**
51 B c 10/04 Dark Angel (IRE)—Cut No Ice (IRE) (Verglas (IRE)) (100000) **Owen Rothwell Studholme**
52 B c 09/03 Showcasing—Daring Day (Acclamation) (85000) **& Dance**
53 **DEVIOUS ANGEL (IRE)**, b f 08/04 Cotai Glory—Angel Meadow (Mayson) (15238) **Roudee Racing**
54 B c 12/04 Caravaggio (USA)—Dress Rehearsal (IRE) (Galileo (IRE)) (28571) **Mr R. Jones**
55 B c 08/02 Acclamation—Duchess Power (IRE) (Dutch Art) (114286) **Done Ferguson Mason Owen**
56 Ch g 09/02 Territories (IRE)—Dynaglow (USA) (Dynaformer (USA)) (7143) **Chasemore Farm LLP**
57 B f 12/03 Kodiac—Easy Times (Nayef (USA)) (47619) **Bouch Dawson Witheridge**
58 **GLITTERING CHOICE**, b f 14/02 Havana Gold (IRE)—Adorable Choice (IRE) (Choisir (AUS)) **Mr J. D. Brown**
59 B f 22/03 Dandy Man (IRE)—Imelda Mayhem (Byron) (41905) **Mr F. A. A. Nass**
60 Ch f 19/04 Profitable (IRE)—Jenny Lind (Singspiel (IRE)) (50000) **Manor House Racing & Owen**
61 B c 25/01 Starspangledbanner (AUS)—Joquina (IRE) (Big Bad Bob (IRE)) (46000)
62 **LADY VALENTINE (IRE)**, b f 14/02 No Nay Never (USA)—
Mais Si (Montjeu (IRE)) (38095) **Manor House Racing & Partner**
63 **LARKIN (IRE)**, gr c 18/03 Dark Angel (IRE)—Plagiarism (USA) (Lonhro (AUS)) (83810) **Mrs C. L. Ingram**
64 B c 17/01 Kodi Bear (IRE)—Lil's Joy (IRE) (Lilbourne Lad (IRE)) (38095) **Dandy Boys**
65 B c 21/02 Holy Roman Emperor (IRE)—Lisa Gherardini (IRE) (Barathea (IRE)) (38095) **More Turf Racing**
66 **LITTLE MISS DYNAMO (IRE)**, b f 24/03 Starspangledbanner (AUS)—
Frankly So (IRE) (Frankel) (12000) **Mr D. R. Passant**
67 **LORDMAN (IRE)**, b c 14/04 El Kabeir (USA)—
Lady Marita (IRE) (Dandy Man (IRE)) (17143) **Roudee Racing Lordman**
68 B f 03/03 Olympic Glory (IRE)—Maleficent (Azamour (IRE)) **Chasemore Farm LLP**

## MR TOM DASCOMBE - continued

69 **MONKMOOR (IRE)**, b c 14/04 Australia—Spontaneous (IRE) (Sinndar (IRE)) (9524) **Mr D. R. Passant**
70 B c 23/01 Footstepsinthesand—Nonetheless (IRE) (Fastnet Rock (AUS)) (33333)
71 Ch f 09/04 Bungle Inthejungle—Princess Banu (Oasis Dream) (24000) **Dandy Boys**
72 B c 02/03 Galileo Gold—Race In Focus (IRE) (Vocalised (USA)) (28000) **Deva Racing Galileo Gold**
73 **RICKENBACKER (IRE)**, b c 29/03 Requinto (IRE)—
        Mattinata (Tiger Hill (IRE)) (17143) **Roudee Racing Rickenbacker & Partner**
74 B f 04/04 Kingman—Roedean (IRE) (Oratorio (IRE)) (135000) **Miss S. Y. D. Goh**
75 B c 24/03 Cable Bay (IRE)—Royal Whisper (Royal Applause) (28571) **Mike Nolan & John Abbey**
76 **SO SMART (IRE)**, b c 08/04 Dandy Man (IRE)—
        Model Looks (IRE) (Majestic Missile (IRE)) (66667) **Manor House Racing & Partner**
77 B c 24/03 Cotai Glory—Sommorell (IRE) (Fast Company (IRE)) (45714) **Mr R. Jones**
78 B c 11/02 Ribchester (IRE)—Suddenly (GER) (Excelebration (IRE)) (35000)
79 B f 01/05 Slade Power (IRE)—Summer In February (Sixties Icon) **Chasemore Farm LLP**
80 B c 20/04 Dark Angel (IRE)—Swiss Dream (Oasis Dream) (95238) **Turf & Promotions**
81 **TAA LAA**, b f 31/03 Heeraat (IRE)—Kirrin Island (USA) (Arch (USA)) **O'Halloran Owen Satchell**
82 B c 20/04 Heeraat (IRE)—Trixie Malone (Ishiguru (USA)) **Nick Hughes & Owen Promotions Ltd**
83 B f 17/04 Profitable (IRE)—Up At Dawn (Inchinor) (45000)
84 **VICTORIA FALLS (IRE)**, b f 22/03 Heeraat (IRE)—Lady Red Oak (Medicean) (952) **Mr D. R. Passant**

**Other Owners:** J. E. Abbey, Mr N. B. Attenborough, Mr D. J. Barry, Mrs K. V. Bennett, Mr P. G. Birbeck, A. W. Black, Mrs J. E. Black, Mr G. Bouch, Mr A. Brown, Mr D. J. E. Carswell, Mr E. Carswell, Chasemore Farm LLP, Clipper Group Holdings Ltd, Mr N. Clyne, Mrs F. H. B. Cork, Mr J. F. P. Cork, Mr A. Cronshaw, Alan & Sue Cronshaw, Mrs S. P. Cronshaw, Mrs J. Dance, Mr J. E. Dance, Mr T. G. Dascombe, Mrs R. L. Dawson, Mr G. Dewhurst, Mr P. E. Done, Done Ferguson Mason, Mr J. Dooley, Mr M. Edwards, Empire State Racing Partnership, Mr J. A. Faulkner, Sir A. Ferguson, Mr J. J. Fildes, Mr N. J. Hughes, Mr D. W. Jenkins, Mr R. Jones, Mr R. K. Joynson, Mr C. Ledigo, Mr D. J. Lowe, Manor House Racing, Manor House Stables LLP, G. A. Mason, Mr N. P. Mather, Mrs S. E. Mather, Michael Owen Racing Club, More Turf Racing, Mr R. G. Morris, Mr S. N. Mound, Mr F. Nolan, Mr M. O'Halloran, Mr M.J Owen, Owen Promotions Limited, Mr S. Packham, Mr D. R. Passant, Mr C. D. Pritchard, Mr J. Rothwell, Roudee Racing Rickenbacker, L. M. Rutherford, Mr M. Satchell, Mr P. Simpson, Mr D. Studholme, The Edinburgh Woollen Mill Ltd, K. P. Trowbridge, Keith & Mary Trowbridge, Mrs M. C. Trowbridge, Mr H. Williams, Mr R. L. K. Witheridge.

**Assistant Trainer:** Colin Gorman.

**Flat Jockey:** Richard Kingscote. **Apprentice Jockey:** Elisha Whittington. **Amateur Jockey:** Miss Alyson Deniel.

---

## 133 MR TRISTAN DAVIDSON, Carlisle
Postal: **Bellmount, Laversdale, Irthington, Carlisle, Cumbria, CA6 4PS**
Contacts: **MOBILE 07789 684290**

1 **ASK PADDINGTON (IRE)**, 7, ch g Ask—Dual Obsession **SprayClad UK**
2 **ASKGARMOR (IRE)**, 9, b g Ask—Karmafair (IRE) **Mr E. G. Tunstall**
3 **BIG TIME DANCER (IRE)**, 8, b g Zoffany (IRE)—Final Opinion (IRE) **Andy Bell Anna Noble Arnie Flower**
4 **BOOTLEGGER (IRE)**, 8, b g Kayf Tara—Sweetbitter (FR) **The Risk Takers Partnership**
5 **CARISBROOK (IRE)**, 6, ch g Stowaway—Happy Fleet **Mr E. G. Tunstall**
6 **COLINTHECATERPILAR (IRE)**, 7, br g Robin des Pres (FR)—Salsita (FR) **Mr J. Jeromson**
7 **CRESSWELL QUEEN**, 6, b m Brian Boru—Cresswell Willow (IRE) **J. T. Davidson**
8 **DIODORUS (IRE)**, 7, b g Galileo (IRE)—Divine Proportions (USA) **Mr T. Kindleyside**
9 **GRAN PARADISO (IRE)**, 9, ch g Galileo (IRE)—Looking Lovely (IRE) **N. Sanderson**
10 **GREENGAGE (IRE)**, 6, b m Choisir (AUS)—Empowermentofwomen (IRE) **J. T. Davidson**
11 **HEAVENLY TALE (IRE)**, 5, b m Shamardal (USA)—Angels Story (IRE) **Toby Noble & Andy Bell**
12 **JUSTATENNER**, 10, b g Northern Legend—Shelayly (IRE) **The Whartons**
13 **NELSON ROAD (IRE)**, 8, b g Mount Nelson—Merciful (IRE) **J. T. Davidson**
14 **PEARL OF QATAR**, 5, gr m Footstepsinthesand—Musical Molly (IRE) **Border Raiders & T Davidson**
15 **RUBENESQUE (IRE)**, 9, b m Getaway (GER)—Shouette (IRE) **Toby Noble & Andy Bell**
16 **STYLE IT OUT**, 7, b m Gold Well—Caitlin Rose (IRE) **The Good the Bad the Ugly**
17 **THE DUTCHMAN (IRE)**, 11, b g King's Theatre (IRE)—Shivermetimber (IRE) **SprayClad UK**

## MR TRISTAN DAVIDSON - continued

18 **TOMORROW'S ANGEL**, 6, ch m Teofilo (IRE)—Funday **Adamson, Etheridge & Jardine**
19 **UGO DU MISSELOT (FR)**, 7, b g Irish Wells (FR)—Princesse Pauline (FR) **Graeme Curnow & T Davidson**

### THREE-YEAR-OLDS

20 **DEIRA CHAMPION**, b g Golden Horn—Handana (IRE) **Mr J. Jeromson**

**Other Owners:** Mr G. G. Adamson, Mr A. Bell, Border Raiders, Mr G. Curnow, J. T. Davidson, Mr Gary Etheridge, Mr S. A. Flower, Mr I. Jardine, Mrs A. M. Noble, Mr T. Noble, Mr E. G. Tunstall, Mrs J. H. Wharton, Mr R. E. Wharton, Mr T. R. Wharton.

---

**134**
**MR JOHN DAVIES, Darlington**
Postal: **Denton Grange, Piercebridge, Darlington, County Durham, DL2 3TZ**
Contacts: **PHONE 01325 374366 MOBILE 07746 292782**
EMAIL johndavieshorses@live.co.uk WEBSITE www.johndaviesracing.com

1 **ALFRED RICHARDSON**, 7, ch g Dapper—Vera Richardson (IRE) **K Kirkup & J Davies**
2 **BIRDIE BOWERS (IRE)**, 4, b g Bungle Inthejungle—Shamiya (IRE) **K. Kirkup**
3 **BLUETECH**, 4, ch g Casamento (IRE)—Tamara Bay **Mr & Mrs R Scott & J Davies**
4 **HIGHJACKED**, 5, b g Dick Turpin (IRE)—Vera Richardson (IRE) **K Kirkup & J Davies**
5 **KOLOSSUS**, 5, ch g Assertive—Bikini **K. Kirkup**
6 **OOH LA LAH**, 4, b f Champs Elysees—Cameo Tiara (IRE) **Mr C. W. Davies**
7 **PETITIONER (IRE)**, 7, b g Dansili—Reflective (USA) **Mr C. J. Mooney**
8 **SEXYFISH (FR)**, 6, b g Authorized (IRE)—Honorable Love **The Sexy Fish Partnership**

### THREE-YEAR-OLDS

9 **CORNELL**, b g Cannock Chase (USA)—Tsarina Louise **Ms D. Nicholson**
10 Br f Cannock Chase (USA)—Floradorado **J. J. Davies**
11 **TYKENWEAR**, b f Cannock Chase (USA)—La Hoofon **J. J. Davies**
12 B c Heeraat (IRE)—Vera Richardson (IRE) **K. Kirkup**
13 Ch f Monsieur Bond (IRE)—Wedgewood Star **Mr C. W. Davies**

**Other Owners:** Mr K. Borrett, J. J. Davies, Mr P. Dunnill, K. Kirkup, Mrs P. M. Scott, Mr & Mrs R. Scott, R. Scott, Mr P. Taylor.

---

**135**
**MISS SARAH-JAYNE DAVIES, Leominster**
Postal: **The Upper Withers, Hundred Lane, Kimbolton, Leominster, Herefordshire, HR6 0HZ**
Contacts: **PHONE 01584 711138 MOBILE 07779 797079**
EMAIL amy@sjdracing.co.uk WEBSITE www.sjdracing.co.uk

1 **ABSOLUTE ALTITUDE**, 4, b g Cacique (IRE)—Nougaboo (USA) **Miss N. Thompson**
2 **ACCESSALLAREAS (IRE)**, 16, ch g Swift Gulliver (IRE)—Arushofgold (IRE) **Miss S. J. Davies**
3 **BLUE BEIRUT (IRE)**, 5, b g Lilbourne Lad (IRE)—Ornellaia (IRE) **Mr A. J. Gough**
4 **CELESTIAL LIGHT**, 5, b m Universal (IRE)—Miss Lightning **Pipannsue Partnership**
5 5, Ch m Black Sam Bellamy (IRE)—Clever Liz **Mr A. J. Gough**
6 **DUSTIN DES MOTTES (FR)**, 8, b g Kapgarde (FR)—
                                    Puszta des Mottes (FR) **Steve Mace, Paul Whilock & Mark Hammond**
7 **EST ILLIC (IRE)**, 7, b br g Court Cave (IRE)—Ten Friends (IRE) **Mr A. J. Gough**
8 **FAIR TO DREAM**, 8, b g Fair Mix (IRE)—Sahara's Dream **K. E. Stait**
9 **HUME LOUGH**, 10, b g Teofilo (IRE)—Pink Cristal **Withers Winners**
10 **INVINCIBLE WISH (IRE)**, 9, b g Vale of York (IRE)—Moonlight Wish (IRE) **Michael & Lesley Wilkes**
11 **LAST ENCOUNTER (IRE)**, 11, b g Beneficial—Last Campaign (IRE) **Michael & Lesley Wilkes**

## MISS SARAH-JAYNE DAVIES - continued

12 **LUIS VAN ZANDT (IRE)**, 7, b g Scorpion (IRE)—Banrion Na Boinne **Moorland Racing**
13 **MALVOLIO (IRE)**, 5, ch g Farhh—Philae (USA) **Moorland Racing**
14 **MOUNT OLIVER (IRE)**, 11, b g Mountain High (IRE)—Little Nancy (IRE) **Miss S. J. Davies**
15 **PEMBROKE HOUSE**, 14, gr g Terimon—Bon Coeur **Sarah-jayne Davies & Steve Mace**
16 **ROYAL ACT**, 9, br g Royal Anthem (USA)—Native's Return (IRE) **Moorland Racing & Mark Hammond**
17 **SALAZAR (IRE)**, 6, ch g Raven's Pass (USA)—Queen Padme (IRE) **Mr R. D. Bradford**
18 **SECRET MELODY**, 8, b g Sakhee's Secret—Montjeu's Melody (IRE) **Moorland Racing & Mark Hammond**
19 **SHARP REPLY (IRE)**, 7, b g Holy Roman Emperor (IRE)—Sabindra **Miss N. Thompson**
20 **STORM GIRL**, 5, b m Paco Boy (IRE)—Evenstorm (USA) **Mr A. J. Gough**
21 **THEQUEENBEE (IRE)**, 6, b m Stowaway—Accordeon Royale (IRE) **Michael & Lesley Wilkes**
22 5, Ch h Norse Dancer (IRE)—Toffeepot **Moorland Racing**
23 **VOLATORE**, 5, b g Lucarno (USA)—Rocking Robin **Quadriga Racing**
24 **YOU OWE ME**, 4, ch g Champs Elysees—Elpida (USA) **Michael & Lesley Wilkes**

**Other Owners:** Miss S. J. Davies, Mrs S. M. Davies, Mr M. J. Hammond, Mrs A. M. Mace, S. A. Mace, Moorland Racing, Mrs C. Tucker, Mr M. J. F. Tucker, Mrs P. Vaughan, Mrs B. Vincent, Mr J. F. Vincent, Mr P. R. Whilock, Mrs L. Wilkes, Mr M. H. A. Wilkes.

**Racing Secretary:** Amy Watkins.

**NH Jockey:** Lee Edwards. **Conditional Jockey:** Charlie Hammond.

---

**136**  **MISS JO DAVIS, Highworth**
Postal: Eastrop, Highworth, Wiltshire, SN6 7PP
Contacts: PHONE 01793 762232 MOBILE 07879 811535 FAX 01793 762232
EMAIL jo@jodavisracing.com WEBSITE www.jodavisracing.com

1 **BECCACCINO**, 5, b g Schiaparelli (GER)—Sea Snipe
2 **CAPELLIAN CRUSADER (IRE)**, 12, b g Cape Cross (IRE)—Llia **Mrs P. M. Brown**
3 **CATLOW (IRE)**, 8, b g Let The Lion Roar—Jon Jon's Grace (IRE) **Maggie Davis & Jo Davis**
4 **DREAMINGOFASONG**, 5, b m Epalpette (AUS)—No Frills (IRE) **Mrs P. M. Brown**
5 **FLYING RISK (IRE)**, 6, b m Shirocco (GER)—Sunynshare (IRE) **The Ab Fab Patsy Partnership**
6 **GALLIC DESTINY (IRE)**, 10, b g Champs Elysees—Cross Your Fingers (USA) **Mrs P. M. Brown**
7 **HOLLYWOOD BLACK (FR)**, 4, b g Fuisse (FR)—Belle Sauvage (FR) **Miss J. S. Davis**
8 **IT'S FOR ALAN**, 8, b g Multiplex—Miss Keck **Tony Worth & Vic Bedley**
9 **JOHN BISCUIT**, 13, ch g Hawk Wing (USA)—Princess Magdalena **Mrs P. M. Brown**
10 **MR FITZROY (IRE)**, 11, ch g Kyllachy—Reputable **Mrs P. M. Brown**
11 **PASSING EVE**, 5, b m Passing Glance—Eveon (IRE) **Jo Davis & Chris Butler**
12 **SAGGAZZA**, 7, b g Schiaparelli (GER)—Wee Dinns (IRE) **Mrs P. M. Brown**
13 **THE BIG YIN**, 7, ch g Malinas (GER)—Bright Spangle (IRE) **TheseGirlsCan Racing Club**

**Other Owners:** Mr R. C. C. Baker, V. R. Bedley, Mr C. Butler, Miss J. S. Davis, Mrs M. A. Davis, Mr A. G. Worth.

**Assistant Trainer:** Gregg Whitehead.

---

**137**  **MISS KATHARINE DAVIS, Reading**
Postal: Brewery Fields Farm, Southend, Reading, Berkshire, RG7 6JP
EMAIL katharinedavisracing@gmail.com

1 **CHANTECLER**, 10, b g Authorized (IRE)—Snow Goose **Mr D. White**
2 **GIVEHIMHISDEW (IRE)**, 6, b g Shirocco (GER)—Tarantella Lady **Mr D. White**
3 **KING LEWLEW**, 4, b g Swiss Spirit—Aura **Mr D. White**

## MISS KATHARINE DAVIS - continued

4 **POLLYAMOROUS (IRE),** 6, b m Califet (FR)—Our Polly (IRE) **Mr D. White**
5 **TELLEROFTALES (IRE),** 6, b g Yeats (IRE)—Sweetbitter (FR) **Mr D. White**
6 **WHISKEY TIMES (IRE),** 8, br m Olden Times—Tomcoole Oscar (IRE) **Mr D. White**
7 **WORTH KNOWING (IRE),** 6, b g Stowaway—Duclair Duck (IRE) **Mr D. White**

---

**138**
### MR ANTHONY DAY, Hinckley
Postal: **Wolvey Fields Farm, Coalpit Lane, Wolvey, Hinckley, Leicestershire, LE10 3HD**

1 **GETTYSBURGH (IRE),** 6, b m Presenting—Rhapsody In Blue (GER) **Mrs K. D. Day**
2 **LAVERTEEN (FR),** 10, b g Laveron—Manson Teene (FR) **Mrs K. D. Day**
3 **MY ANCHOR,** 10, b g Mount Nelson—War Shanty **Mrs K. D. Day**
4 **STRIPE OF HONOUR (IRE),** 8, b g Court Cave (IRE)—Miss Top (IRE) **Mrs K. D. Day**

---

**139**
### MR WILLIAM DE BEST-TURNER, Marlborough
Postal: **Browns Farm, Marlborough , Wiltshire, SN8 4nD**
Contacts: **HOME 01249 813850 PHONE 01249 811944 MOBILE 07977 910779**
EMAIL debestracing@hotmail.co.uk

1 **CALGARY TIGER,** 6, b g Tiger Groom—Sachiko **W. de Best-Turner**
2 **MOLLY'S ANGEL,** 4, ch f Arvico (FR)—Sterling Moll **Debestracing**
3 **NELSON'S HILL,** 11, b g Mount Nelson—Regal Step **Debestracing**
4 **PIXELATIT,** 6, b m Dream Eater (IRE)—Spartaculous **Debestracing**
5 **RUBY RUBLES,** 4, b f Phenomena—Spartaculous **W. de Best-Turner**
6 **TIGER PRINT,** 6, b m Tiger Groom—Maylan (IRE) **Debestracing**

**Assistant Trainer:** Mrs I. de Best.

---

**140**
### MR ED DE GILES, Ledbury
Postal: **Lilly Hall Farm, Little Marcle, Ledbury, Herefordshire, HR8 2LD**
Contacts: **PHONE 01531 637369 MOBILE 07811 388345**
EMAIL ed@eddegilesracing.com WEBSITE www.eddegilesracing.com

1 **BOMBERO (IRE),** 7, b g Dragon Pulse (IRE)—Mathool (IRE) **Woodham Walter Partnership**
2 **BORN TO FINISH (IRE),** 8, b g Dark Angel (IRE)—Music Pearl (IRE) **Crowd Racing & R Christison**
3 **CHIFA (IRE),** 4, br g Gutaifan (IRE)—Inca Trail (USA) **Mr J. P. Carrington**
4 **CORRIDA DE TOROS (IRE),** 5, b g Lope de Vega (IRE)—The Shrew **Mr Ali Mortazavi & Ms Sirma Dogan**
5 **FAITQUE DE L'ISLE (FR),** 6, ch g Secret Singer (FR)—
                                        Naiade de L'Isle (FR) **DFA Racing (Donaldson, Currie, Edwards)**
6 **FITZROVIA,** 6, br g Poet's Voice—Pompey Girl **Simon Treacher & Clarissa Casdagali**
7 **FRANCISCO BAY,** 5, b g Paco Boy (IRE)—Lucky Breeze (IRE) **Mr C. C. Shand Kydd & Partner**
8 **HOUI CHERIE (FR),** 4, gr f Cima de Triomphe (IRE)—Joslaine (FR) **Mr A. J. Edwards**
9 **LUCKY DRAW,** 4, b f Roderic O'Connor (IRE)—Lucky Breeze (IRE) **Mr C. C. Shand Kydd & Partner**
10 **OVERHAUGH STREET,** 8, b g Bahri (USA)—Bom Chicka Wah Wah (USA) **Sharron & Robert Colvin**
11 **ROAR (IRE),** 7, b g Pour Moi (IRE)—Evening Rushour (IRE) **Mr P. Inglett**
12 **SOBRIQUET (IRE),** 4, ch f Night of Thunder (IRE)—Broadway Duchess (IRE) **The LAM Partnership**

# MR ED DE GILES - continued

13 **SWANTON BLUE (IRE)**, 8, b g Kodiac—Cabopino (IRE) **Crowd Racing & Partner**
14 **TIZIO (IRE)**, 4, b g Intello (GER)—Tiziana (FR) **N. J. Allen**
15 **TREACHEROUS**, 7, b g Paco Boy (IRE)—Black Baroness **Woodham Walter Partnership**
16 **WIND IN MY SAILS**, 9, b g Footstepsinthesand—Dylanesque **Mr P. J. Manser**
17 **ZLATAN (IRE)**, 8, b g Dark Angel (IRE)—Guard Hill (USA) **Casdagli & Partners**

## THREE-YEAR-OLDS

18 **ALPINE STROLL**, b c Nathaniel (IRE)—Kammaan **The LAM Partnership**
19 **INSPIRING LOVE**, ch f Cityscape—Miss Meticulous **The LAM Partnership**
20 **KALAMITY KITTY**, b f Cityscape—Lucky Breeze (IRE) **Fair Wind Partnership & Partner**
21 **RUN RED RUN**, ch f Kutub (IRE)—Chalosse **Sharron & Robert Colvin**
22 **URBAN FOREST**, ch g Cityscape—Tijuca (IRE) **Carrington & Cunningham**

## TWO-YEAR-OLDS

23 B f 17/04 Time Test—Aurora Gray (Rip Van Winkle (IRE)) (7000) **Simon Treacher, Robert Colvin & Partner**
24 B f 14/04 Helmet (AUS)—Cloudchaser (IRE) (Red Ransom (USA)) **Mr E. B. de Giles**
25 B c 26/03 Helmet (AUS)—Lucky Breeze (IRE) (Key of Luck (USA)) **Mr E. B. de Giles**
26 **MACON BELLE**, b f 28/03 Due Diligence (USA)—
Disco Ball (Fantastic Light (USA)) (8000) **Woodham Walter Partnership**
27 B c 22/01 Ulysses (IRE)—Verity (Redoute's Choice (AUS)) (35000) **Woodham Walter Partnership**

**Other Owners:** Mr J. P. Carrington, Mrs C. R. Casdagli, Mr R. Christison, R. Colvin, Mrs S. Colvin, Crowd Racing Partnership, Ms A. P. M. Cunningham, Ms S. Dogan, Fair Wind Partnership, Dr M. F. Ford, Mr C. McKenna, Mr A. Mortazavi, Ms L. M. Mulcahy, C. C. Shand Kydd, Mr S. Treacher, A. J. Viall, Mr E. B. de Giles.

---

## 141 MR GEOFFREY DEACON, Compton
Postal: **Hamilton Stables, Hockham Road, Compton, Newbury, Berkshire, RG20 6QJ**
Contacts: **MOBILE 07967 626757**
**EMAIL** geoffdeacon5@gmail.com **WEBSITE** www.geoffreydeacontraining.com

1 **APRICOT STAR (IRE)**, 4, ch f Anjaal—Allegrissimo (IRE) **Allinc Property Services**
2 **CAPTAIN RYAN**, 10, b g Captain Gerrard (IRE)—Ryan's Quest (IRE) **Geoffrey Deacon Racing Crew**
3 **DARK CROCODILE (IRE)**, 6, b g Dark Angel (IRE)—Heaven's Vault (IRE) **Mr M. D. Drake**
4 4, Gr f Heeraat (IRE)—Elderberry **Geoffrey Deacon Racing Crew**
5 4, Gr f Fast Company (IRE)—Glastonberry **Mr A. Altazi**
6 **HONEY BOO**, 8, ch m Tobougg (IRE)—Queen of The Bees (IRE) **Mrs S. A. Roe**
7 **JUST ALBERT**, 4, gr ro g Toronado (IRE)—Deire Na Sli (IRE) **Mr and Mrs Duckett**
8 5, B m Born To Sea (IRE)—Khajool (IRE) **Geoffrey Deacon Racing Crew**
9 **LA ROCA DEL FUEGO (IRE)**, 5, br g Rock of Gibraltar (IRE)—Reign (IRE) **Mr M. D. Drake**
10 **MISREAD**, 5, ch m Nayef (USA)—Widescreen (USA) **Geoffrey Deacon Racing Club**
11 **NIGHT N GALE (IRE)**, 5, b m Gale Force Ten—Hadya (IRE) **Geoffrey Deacon Racing Crew**
12 **RAHMAH (IRE)**, 9, b g Vale of York (IRE)—Sweet Home Alabama (IRE) **Mr P. D. Cundell and Partner**
13 **SAHHAB (USA)**, 4, b f Declaration of War (USA)—Princess Consort (USA) **Mr A. Altazi**
14 **WOGGLE (IRE)**, 6, ch m Camacho—Radio Wave **Hearty Racing**

## THREE-YEAR-OLDS

15 **DOLLY DRAKE**, b f Havana Gold (IRE)—Farletti **Mr M. D. Drake**
16 **HAVANA LADY**, ch f Havana Gold (IRE)—Victrix Ludorum (IRE) **Mr J. Kelly**
17 **OXFORD HIGH (IRE)**, b f Kodiac—Morinda **Mr P. D. Cundell and Partner**

## TWO-YEAR-OLDS

18 Gr g 05/04 Heeraat (IRE)—Glastonberry (Piccolo) **Mr G. Deacon**

**Other Owners:** P. D. Cundell, Mr G. Deacon.

**Assistant Trainer:** Sally Duckett.

**142** **MR TIM DENNIS, Bude**
Postal: Thorne Farm, Bude, Cornwall, EX23 0LU

1 NEETSIDE (IRE), 9, b m Getaway (GER)—Lady Wagtail (IRE) **Mrs J. E. Dennis**

**143** **MR ROBIN DICKIN, Alcester**
Postal: Hill Farm, Park Lane, Great Alne, Alcester, Warwickshire, B49 6HS
Contacts: MOBILE 07979 518594, 07979 518593
EMAIL claire@robindickinracing.org.uk WEBSITE www.robindickinracing.org.uk

1 ANTI COOL (IRE), 12, b g Heron Island (IRE)—Youngborogal (IRE) **Robin Dickin Racing Club**
2 BLACK KALAROSA (IRE), 7, br m Kalanisi (IRE)—Blackthorne Winter (IRE) **NHRE Racing Club**
3 CHEER'S DELBOY (IRE), 8, ch g Golan (IRE)—Lindy Lou **Just 4 Fun**
4 DONTMINDDBOYS (IRE), 12, gr g Portrait Gallery (IRE)—Native Ocean (IRE) **Medbourne Racing**
5 FITZ WELL (IRE), 6, b g Milan—La Sentinelle (FR) **The Fitz Well Songsters**
6 GALACTIC POWER (IRE), 11, ch g Gamut (IRE)—Celtic Peace (IRE) **Robin Dickin Racing Club**
7 GLEN MOOAR (IRE), 7, br g Presenting—Supreme Serenade (IRE) **Mrs C. M. Dickin, Mr C. J. Dickin, The
   Tricksters, Mr H. Brown, The Goodies & The Tricksters, D. J. Hern, The Goodies**
8 IT FITZ, 4, gr g Havana Gold (IRE)—Crocus Rose **Cahill FitzGerald Bloodstock Ltd**
9 LARA TROT (IRE), 9, b m Scorpion (IRE)—Honour Own (IRE) **The Trotters**
10 MR PALMTREE (IRE), 8, gr g Robin des Pres (FR)—
   Mattys Joy (IRE) **Mrs C. M. Dickin, The Cocoa Nuts & the Tricksters, Mr C. J. Dickin, Mr T. P. Poulson, The Tricksters, Mr H. Brown, The Cocoa Nuts**
11 ONEIDA TRIBE (IRE), 12, b g Turtle Island (IRE)—Glory Queen (IRE) **Robin Dickin Racing Club**
12 OVER THINKING (IRE), 5, b g Gamut (IRE)—Keep Thinking (IRE) **Mrs C. M. Dickin**
13 ROYAL BASSETT (FR), 4, b g Wootton Bassett—Donna Roberta (GER) **The Bertie Allsorts**
14 SCORCHED EARTH (IRE), 5, ch g Zoffany (IRE)—How's She Cuttin' (IRE) **The Bertie Allsorts**
15 SOME FINISH (IRE), 12, b g Kayf Tara—Kylie Kaprice (GER) **Mrs C Dickin & The Some Finish Partners**
16 SPEEDY CHOICE (IRE), 6, b m Stowaway—Shinrock Jackie (IRE) **The Trotters**
17 5, B m Fame And Glory—Talk To The Missus (IRE) **Mrs C. M. Dickin**
18 THREE BULLET GATE (IRE), 8, b g Touch of Land (FR)—Brave Hope (IRE) **The Point Of Attack Partnership**
19 TWYCROSS WARRIOR, 9, b g Cockney Rebel (IRE)—Gaelic Roulette (IRE) **Graham & Lynn Knight**
20 WILLIAMDECONQUEROR, 5, b g Native Ruler—Dancing Daffodil **Mrs C. M. Dickin**
21 WRYNNER (IRE), 5, ch m Imperial Monarch (IRE)—Annabaskey (IRE) **Miss H. Dickin**

**THREE-YEAR-OLDS**

22 B g Swiss Spirit—Shilpa (IRE) **Mrs C. M. Dickin**

**Assistant Trainer:** Claire Dickin.

**NH Jockey:** Jack Quinlan. **Conditional Jockey:** Tabitha Worsley.

## 144 MR JOHN DIXON, Carlisle
Postal: **Moorend, Thursby, Carlisle, Cumbria, CA5 6QP**
Contacts: **PHONE 01228 711019**

1 **BALLELA'S DREAM**, 7, b m Josr Algarhoud (IRE)—Ballela Road (IRE) **Mrs S. F. Dixon**
2 **CAPTAIN ZEBO (IRE)**, 9, b g Brian Boru—Waydale Hill **Mrs S. F. Dixon**
3 **PISTOL (IRE)**, 12, b g High Chaparral (IRE)—Alinea (USA) **Mrs S. F. Dixon**
4 **PRESENCE FELT (IRE)**, 13, br g Heron Island (IRE)—Faeroe Isle (IRE) **Mrs S. F. Dixon**
5 **ROAD TO ROSLEY**, 4, b g Millenary—Ballela Road (IRE) **Mrs S. F. Dixon**

**Amateur Jockey:** Mr J. J. Dixon.

## 145 MR SCOTT DIXON, Retford
Postal: **Haygarth House Stud, Haygarth House, Babworth, Retford, Nottinghamshire, DN22 8ES**
Contacts: **PHONE 01777 869079, 01777 701818, 01777 869300 MOBILE 07976 267019 FAX 01777 869326**
**EMAIL scottdixon1987@hotmail.com, mrsyvettedixon@gmail.com WEBSITE www.scottdixonracing.com**

1 **ALEX GRACIE**, 4, b f Fountain of Youth (IRE)—Kyllarney **Middleham Park Racing LXIV**
2 **BEST TAMAYUZ**, 10, ch g Tamayuz—Pink Ivory **Winning Connections Racing**
3 **BLUE STREAK**, 4, ch f Hot Streak (IRE)—Vivid Blue **The Cool Silk Partnership**
4 **BOND ANGEL**, 6, gr m Monsieur Bond (IRE)—Angel Grigio **B. W. Parren**
5 **BREAK THE SILENCE**, 7, b g Rip Van Winkle (IRE)—In A Silent Way (IRE) **Winning Connections Racing**
6 **CAPRICIOUS MADAM**, 4, ch f Monsieur Bond (IRE)—La Capriosa **ARC Racing Club**
7 **CATESBY**, 4, b g Slade Power (IRE)—Bonfire Heart **The Scott Dixon Racing Partnership**
8 **COBH KID**, 4, b g Kyllachy—Never A Quarrel (IRE) **Anglo Irish Partners**
9 **CROSSE FIRE**, 9, b g Monsieur Bond (IRE)—Watersilk (IRE) **Dixon, Brennan, Lucas, Mahony, Sweeting**
10 **DARK SHOT**, 8, b g Acclamation—Dark Missile **Chappell Rose & Radford**
11 **EBURY**, 5, ch g Iffraaj—Alabelle **Mr S. E. Chappell**
12 **FEEL THE THUNDER**, 5, b h Milk It Mick—Totally Trusted **The Scott Dixon Racing Partnership**
13 **FINE WINE (FR)**, 4, b g Dream Ahead (USA)—Mulled Wine (FR) **The Scott Dixon Racing Partnership**
14 **GENTLY SPOKEN (IRE)**, 4, b gr f Gutaifan (IRE)—Always Gentle (IRE) **The Scott Dixon Racing Partnership**
15 **GIOGIOBBO**, 8, b h Bahamian Bounty—Legnani **ARC Racing Syndicate**
16 **GOSSIP**, 4, b f Exceed And Excel (AUS)—Al Sharood **The Scott Dixon Racing Partnership**
17 **HARMONIOUS**, 4, b br g New Approach (IRE)—Clear Voice (USA) **P. J. Dixon**
18 **HEADLAND**, 5, b g Harbour Watch (IRE)—Bazzana **ARC Racing Club**
19 **HENRY THE SIXTH**, 5, b h Milk It Mick—Six Wives **Sexy Six Partnership**
20 **KRYSTALLITE**, 8, ch m Kheleyf (USA)—Chrystal Venture (IRE) **Paul J Dixon & The Chrystal Maze Ptn**
21 **MARNIE JAMES**, 6, b g Camacho—Privy Garden (IRE) **P. J. Dixon**
22 **MAY THE SIXTH**, 4, b f Mayson—Six Wives **Sexy Six Partnership**
23 **OPPORTUNIST**, 5, b h Cape Cross (IRE)—Argent du Bois (USA) **The Scott Dixon Racing Partnership**
24 **PERTEMPS SIA (IRE)**, 4, b f Canford Cliffs (IRE)—Sentimental (IRE) **Pertemps Ltd**
25 **PILGRIMS PURSUIT**, 5, b g Pastoral Pursuits—Scrooby Baby **Winning Connections Racing**
26 **SAMOVAR**, 6, b g Finjaan—Chrystal Venture (IRE) **P J Dixon,Chrystal Maze & Ashley Severn**
27 **SHACKABOOAH**, 4, b g Swiss Spirit—Ginger Cookie **John & Paul Dixon**
28 **SOCIOLOGIST (FR)**, 6, ch g Society Rock (IRE)—Fabiola (GER) **Rob Massheder, A J Turton & Partners**
29 **SOLO HUNTER**, 10, b g Sleeping Indian—Night Owl **Rob Massheder, A J Turton & Partners**
30 **THUNDERCLOUD**, 6, gr m Aussie Rules (USA)—Trustthunder **Winning Connections Racing**
31 **TILLY DEVINE**, 7, gr m Aussie Rules (USA)—Cora Pearl **Winning Connections Racing**
32 **VIADUCT**, 4, b g Showcasing—Folly Bridge **The Scott Dixon Racing Partnership**
33 **VISIBILITY (IRE)**, 4, b g Raven's Pass (USA)—Cry Pearl (USA) **Mr B. W. Parren & Partner**
34 **ZARGUN (GER)**, 6, b h Rock of Gibraltar (IRE)—Zenaat **The Scott Dixon Racing Partnership**

### THREE-YEAR-OLDS
35 **A PINT OF BEAR (IRE)**, gr g Kodi Bear (IRE)—Heart of An Angel **The Bear Partnership**
36 **ARFINN ROSE**, br g Swiss Spirit—Ginger Cookie **Ne-chance Racing, Rose, Kirkham & Dixon**

## MR SCOTT DIXON - continued

**37** B f Epaulette (AUS)—Chrystal Venture (IRE) **P J Dixon,Chrystal Maze & Ashley Severn**
**38 DRIFTWOOD,** b f Footstepsinthesand—Bonfire Heart **Rob Massheder, A J Turton & Partners**
**39** B f Fountain of Youth (IRE)—Kyllarney
**40** Ch c Monsieur Bond (IRE)—La Capriosa **The Scott Dixon Racing Partnership**
**41 TORQUE,** b f Belardo (IRE)—Semaral (IRE) **The Scott Dixon Racing Partnership**
**42 WALTZING (IRE),** b g Kodiac—Dancing Jest (IRE) **The Scott Dixon Racing Partnership**

### TWO-YEAR-OLDS

**43** B c 11/02 Twirling Candy (USA)—Costume (Danehill (USA)) (38000) **The Scott Dixon Racing Partnership**

**Other Owners:** Mr A. D. Baker, Mr J. N. Blackburn, Mr K. Brennan, P.J. Dixon, Mr M. Hilton, Mr N. N. Kane, Mr A. Kirkham, Mr D. R. Lucas, Mr M. J. Mahony, Mr R. Massheder, Ne-Chance, B. W. Parren, Mr D. Rose, Mr A. Severn, J & Severn, Mr P. Sweeting, The Chrystal Maze Partnership, Mr A. C. Timms, Mr A. Turton.

**Assistant Trainer:** Mr K. Locking.

**Amateur Jockey:** Mr Kevin Locking.

---

## 146 MRS ROSE DOBBIN, Alnwick
Postal: **South Hazelrigg Farm, Chatton, Alnwick, Northumberland, NE66 5RZ**
Contacts: **PHONE 01668 215151, 01668 215395 MOBILE 07969 993563 FAX 01668 215114**
**EMAIL** hazelriggracing1@btconnect.com **WEBSITE** www.rosedobbinracing.co.uk

**1 ARDGLASS STAR (IRE),** 7, b g Arctic Cosmos (USA)—Verney Roe (IRE) **Mrs R. Dobbin**
**2 BAKO DE LA SAULAIE (FR),** 10, b g Balko (FR)—Krickette (FR) **Mr & Mrs Duncan Davidson**
**3 BIGIRONONHISHIP (IRE),** 10, b g Beneficial—Portobello Lady (IRE) **Mr & Mrs Duncan Davidson**
**4 BROADSTRUTHER (IRE),** 6, b g Shantou (USA)—Accardi (IRE) **Mr & Mrs Duncan Davidson**
**5 CHOSEN FLAME (IRE),** 9, b g Well Chosen—Flaming Misty (IRE) **S & G Soils Limited**
**6 CLASSICAL SOUND (IRE),** 9, b g Mahler—Sovienne (IRE) **Hunter, Matterson & Dobbin**
**7 COOLE HALL (IRE),** 9, b g Flemensfirth (USA)—Coole Assembly (IRE) **Mr & Mrs Duncan Davidson**
**8 DEFINITE WISDOM (IRE),** 8, b g Definite Article—
                                    Wisdom And Light (IRE) **M & M Edwardson, M Hunter & J Matterson**
**9 DO NOT DISTURB (IRE),** 8, b g Mahler—Galbertstown Run (IRE) **Mr & Mrs Duncan Davidson**
**10 DOKTOR GLAZ (FR),** 11, b g Mount Nelson—Deviolina (IRE) **Mr & Mrs D Davidson & The Friday Lions**
**11 EAGLE DE GUYE (FR),** 7, b g Buck's Boum (FR)—Balibirds (FR) **Mr & Mrs Duncan Davidson**
**12 ESPOIR MORIVIERE (FR),** 7, ch g Saddex—Sagesse Moriviere (FR) **Dunkley, Ray & Roberts**
**13 FAMOUS MOMENT (IRE),** 6, b g Fame And Glory—Endless Moments (IRE) **Mr & Mrs Duncan Davidson**
**14 FETE CHAMPETRE (IRE),** 6, b g Robin des Champs (FR)—John's Eliza (IRE) **Mr & Mrs Duncan Davidson**
**15 FINAL FLING (IRE),** 10, b g Milan—Supreme Singer (IRE) **J. M. & Mrs M. R. Edwardson**
**16 GEORDIELANDGANGSTA,** 8, br g Geordieland (FR)—Dunsfold Duchess (IRE) **Mrs R. Dobbin**
**17 GET WITH IT (IRE),** 6, b g Getaway (GER)—Listening (IRE) **Mr & Mrs Duncan Davidson**
**18 HITMAN FRED (IRE),** 8, b g Getaway (GER)—Garravagh Lass (IRE) **Mr & Mrs Duncan Davidson**
**19 HONOURABLE GENT,** 13, b g Gentleman's Deal (IRE)—Gudasmum (IRE) **Mr & Mrs Duncan Davidson**
**20 JACK DEVINE (IRE),** 9, b g Kalanisi (IRE)—Sybil Says (IRE) **Mr & Mrs Duncan Davidson**
**21 JONNIESOFA (IRE),** 11, b g Well Made (GER)—
                                    Lucky Sarah (IRE) **Mr R & Mrs A The Late Mr A.Houghton & Partners**
**22 LAST ONE TO SHOW (IRE),** 6, b g Arcadio (GER)—Garravagh Lass (IRE) **Mrs R. Dobbin**
**23 LE CHEVAL NOIR (IRE),** 7, b g Le Fou (IRE)—Bonny Lass **Mr & Mrs Duncan Davidson**
**24 MISTER DON (IRE),** 11, br g Presenting—Spring Flower (IRE) **Mr Ronnie Jacobs & Mrs Rose Dobbin**
**25 MONFASS (IRE),** 10, b g Trans Island—Ajo Green (IRE) **Mrs Dobbin & The Dimhorns**
**26 OKAVANGO DELTA (IRE),** 5, b g Ocovango—Court My Eye **One For the Road Flower**
**27 PERMISSION GRANTED (IRE),** 9, b g Oscar (IRE)—Ask The Misses (IRE) **Jacobs, Dickson, Ray R Tebay**
**28 PLANET NINE (IRE),** 9, b g Flemensfirth (USA)—Old Moon (IRE) **Mr & Mrs Duncan Davidson**
**29 PURCELL'S BRIDGE (FR),** 14, b g Trempolino (USA)—Theatrical Lady (USA) **Mrs R. Dobbin**
**30 RATH AN IUIR (IRE),** 8, b g Flemensfirth (USA)—Amathea (FR) **Mr & Mrs Duncan Davidson**
**31 ROMULUS DU DONJON (IRE),** 10, gr g Stormy River (FR)—Spring Stroll (USA) **Jacobs, Ray & Roberts**

## MRS ROSE DOBBIN - continued

32 **SEVEN EYE BRIDGE (IRE)**, 6, b g Sans Frontieres (IRE)—Woodland Path (IRE)  **Mr J. A. F. Filmer-Wilson**
33 **SHANBALLY ROSE (IRE)**, 7, b m Court Cave (IRE)—Amy's Song (IRE)  **Mrs C Hunter & Mr & Mrs M Edwardson**
34 **SLANELOUGH (IRE)**, 9, b g Westerner—Tango Lady (IRE)  **Miss J. Matterson & Mrs D. Davidson**
35 **SMUGGLER'S STASH (IRE)**, 11, ch g Stowaway—Sweetasanu (IRE)  **The Friday Lions 2**
36 **SOME REIGN (IRE)**, 10, b g Kayf Tara—Bridge Love (FR)  **Mr & Mrs Duncan Davidson**
37 **STYLE NELSON (FR)**, 6, b g Mount Nelson—Ana Style (FR)  **Mr & Mrs Duncan Davidson**
38 **SWEET AS CANDY (IRE)**, 9, b g Morozov (USA)—Sweet Nancy (IRE)  **Mr & Mrs Duncan Davidson**
39 **TAILSPIN (IRE)**, 11, b g Scorpion (IRE)—Gospellianne (FR)  **Mrs R. Dobbin**
40 **TROOPER TURNBULL (IRE)**, 7, b g Arcadio (GER)—Clover Pearl (IRE)  **Hunter & McKie**
41 **VINTAGE GLEN (IRE)**, 9, b g Ask—Rare Vintage (IRE)  **Jacobs & Macconnachie**
42 **WILD POLLY (IRE)**, 7, ch m Mahler—Dalzenia (FR)  **Mr & Mrs Duncan Davidson**
43 **WORCESTER PEARMAIN**, 11, b m Beat All (USA)—Granoski Gala  **Mr & Mrs Duncan Davidson**

**Other Owners:** D. H. Davidson, Mr & Mrs Duncan Davidson, Mrs S. K. Davidson, Mr J. L. Dickson, Mr L. Dimsdale, Mrs R. Dobbin, Miss E. Dunkley, J. M. Edwardson, J. M. & Mrs M. R. Edwardson, Mrs M. R. Edwardson, Mrs S. Helmont, Mr A. Houghton, Mrs A. M. Houghton, Mr R. Houghton, Mrs C. H. C. Hunter, M. S. Hunter, Mr R. A. Jacobs, J. R. Jeffreys, Miss C. L. Jones, Mr I. G. Macconnachie, Miss J. G. K. Matterson, Mrs V. J. McKie, Mrs M. H. Ray, Mr R. Roberts, Mr D. A. C. Spencer-Churchill, Mr R. Tebay.

**Assistant Trainer:** Tony Dobbin.

**NH Jockey:** Craig Nichol.

---

**147** **MR ASHLEY DODGSON, Thirsk**
Postal: **Southerby House, Catton, Thirsk, North Yorkshire, YO7 4SQ**

1 **MR DEALER (IRE)**, 9, b g Mr Dinos (IRE)—Vera Glynn (IRE)  **Mrs F. M. G. Dodgson**

---

**148** **MR MICHAEL DODS, Darlington**
Postal: **Denton Hall Farm, Piercebridge, Darlington, County Durham, DL2 3TY**
Contacts: **PHONE 01325 374270 MOBILE 07860 411590, 07773 290830 FAX 01325 374020**
**EMAIL dods@michaeldodsracing.co.uk WEBSITE www.michaeldodsracing.co.uk**

1 **ANTICO LADY (IRE)**, 5, b m Dandy Man (IRE)—Former Drama (USA)  **Julie & Keith Hanson**
2 **ARCAVALLO (IRE)**, 6, ch g Arcano (IRE)—Pashmina (IRE)  **Mr P Appleton & Mrs Anne Elliott**
3 **ARCH MOON**, 4, b g Sea The Moon (GER)—Archduchess  **Mr Allan Mcluckie & Mr M. J. K. Dods**
4 **BILLY NO MATES (IRE)**, 5, b g Clodovil (IRE)—Sabaidee (IRE)  **Mr J Sagar & Mr M Dods**
5 **BLACKHEATH**, 6, b g Excelebration (IRE)—Da's Wish (IRE)  **Game on Racing**
6 **BYRON'S CHOICE**, 6, b g Poet's Voice—Byrony (IRE)  **Mr Doug Graham & Mrs M Wynn-williams**
7 **CAMACHO CHIEF (IRE)**, 6, b g Camacho—Passage To India (IRE)  **Davison & Drysdale**
8 **COMMANCHE FALLS**, 4, br g Lethal Force (IRE)—Joyeaux  **Mr Doug Graham, Davison & Drysdale**
9 **DAKOTA GOLD**, 7, b g Equiano (FR)—Joyeaux  **Doug Graham, Ian Davison, Alan Drysdale 1**
10 **DANCIN BOY**, 5, br g Gregorian (IRE)—La Gifted  **Mr R. R. D. Saunders**
11 **DANIELSFLYER (IRE)**, 7, b g Dandy Man (IRE)—Warm Welcome  **Elliott Brothers And Peacock**
12 **FIRBY (IRE)**, 6, b g Rock of Gibraltar (IRE)—Huffoof (IRE)  **Mrs Angela Taylor & M Dods**
13 **FOUR JACKS (IRE)**, 4, b g Camacho—Taaluf (IRE)  **Mr G Thompson & Mr M Dods**
14 **GALE FORCE MAYA**, 5, ch m Gale Force Ten—Parabola  **Mr F. Lowe**
15 **GET KNOTTED (IRE)**, 9, ch g Windsor Knot (IRE)—Genuinely (IRE)  **D. Neale**
16 **GIGI'S BEACH**, 4, b g Oasis Dream—Clenor (IRE)  **Denton Hall Racing Ltd**
17 **JAWWAAL**, 6, ch g Bahamian Bounty—Avenbury  **Sekura Trade Frames Ltd**
18 **JOHN KIRKUP**, 6, ch g Assertive—Bikini  **Mrs Suzanne Kirkup & Mr Kevin Kirkup**

## MR MICHAEL DODS - continued

19 **JOMONT (FR)**, 4, b g Motivator—Sea Life (FR) **Mrs Teresa Blackett & M Dods**
20 **LANGHOLM (IRE)**, 5, b g Dark Angel (IRE)—Pindrop **Mrs C. E. Dods**
21 **MECCA'S HOT STEPS**, 4, ch f Hot Streak (IRE)—Vintage Steps (IRE) **Mr David T J Metcalfe & Mr M J K Dods**
22 **MUSTAQBAL (IRE)**, 9, b g Invincible Spirit (IRE)—Alshamatry (USA) **Denton Hall Racing Ltd**
23 **PEERLESS PERCY (IRE)**, 4, b g Sir Percy—Victoria Montoya **D. Neale**
24 **PENDLETON**, 5, b g Garswood—Anglezarke (IRE) **Mr D. W. Armstrong**
25 **PROUD ARCHI (IRE)**, 7, b g Archipenko (USA)—Baharah (USA) **Eagle Racing**
26 **QUE AMORO (IRE)**, 5, b m Es Que Love (IRE)—Onomatomania (USA) **Mr P Appleton & Mrs Anne Elliott**
27 **SIN E SHEKELLS**, 4, ch g Bated Breath—Meddling **Mrs C. E. Dods**
28 **STALLONE (IRE)**, 5, b g Dandy Man (IRE)—Titian Queen **Dods Racing Club**
29 **TROUBADOR (IRE)**, 4, gr g Poet's Voice—Eastern Destiny **Mr J Sagar & Mr S Lowthian**
30 **TWIST OF HAY**, 4, b f Showcasing—Spinatrix **Mr J. A. Knox and Mrs M. A. Knox**
31 **WAHOO**, 6, b g Stimulation (IRE)—Shohrah (IRE) **Mr J Blackburn & Mr A Turton**
32 **WOVEN**, 5, ch g Dutch Art—Regal Silk **Mr J. Sagar**

### THREE-YEAR-OLDS

33 **BERRY EDGE (IRE)**, b g Mukhadram—Amaany **Elliott Brothers And Peacock**
34 **BLACKROD**, b c Mayson—Hilldale **Mr D. W. Armstrong**
35 **BLOWING WIND (IRE)**, b g Markaz (IRE)—Wojha (IRE) **Denton Hall Racing Ltd**
36 **BOLD TERRITORIES (IRE)**, ch g Territories (IRE)—Amberley Heights (IRE) **Tg Racing**
37 **BRYANWOOD (IRE)**, b g Garswood—Amary (IRE) **Mr V Spinks & Partner**
38 **BURSCOUGH**, b g Garswood—Heskin (IRE) **Mr D. W. Armstrong**
39 **CLARISSA**, b f Equiano (FR)—Lady Clair (IRE) **White Rose Racing**
40 **CLEVELEYS**, b g Mayson—Soapy Delight **Mr D. W. Armstrong**
41 **DIAMOND HAZE (IRE)**, b g Coulsty (IRE)—Cannot Give (USA) **John Burns & Michael Dods**
42 **DIAMONDONTHEHILL**, b g Al Kazeem—It's My Time **Sekura Group & John Burns**
43 **EQUIEM (IRE)**, b g Equiano (FR)—Emeralds Spirit (IRE) **T. A. Scothern**
44 **FIRST GREYED (IRE)**, gr g Gutaifan (IRE)—Hidden Girl (IRE) **The Gorijeb Partnership**
45 **FURY NIGHT (IRE)**, br g Dragon Pulse (IRE)—Highly Exclusive (IRE) **Mr J. N. Blackburn**
46 **HAVAGOMECCA**, ch f Havana Gold (IRE)—Bikini **Mr David T J Metcalfe & Mr M J K Dods**
47 **HEAR ME ROAR (IRE)**, b g The Last Lion (IRE)—Dutch Heiress **Mr P Appleton & Mrs Anne Elliott**
48 **LOUIS THE WARRIOR**, ch g Cityscape—Muara **Mr W. R. Arblaster**
49 **MADRESELVA**, ch f Equiano (FR)—Mosqueras Romance **Mrs T Burns, Mr M D Pearson & M Dods**
50 **MECCA'S DIAMOND (IRE)**, gr f Gregorian (IRE)—Blue Bahia (IRE) **D. T. J. Metcalfe**
51 **NAVAJO SPRING (IRE)**, b f Charm Spirit (IRE)—Clifton Dancer **Mr D. R. Graham**
52 **NEON CITY**, b g Territories (IRE)—Alkadi (IRE) **J Blackburn & M Dods**
53 **NORTHERN EXPRESS (IRE)**, ch g Zoffany (IRE)—Hint of A Tint (IRE) **Sekura Trade Frames Ltd**
54 **NOSEY ROSIE POSEY**, ch f Power—Vicky Valentine **Mr F. Lowe**
55 **PACHA PRINCE (IRE)**, b g Sir Prancealot (IRE)—Fainleog (IRE) **Mrs C. E. Dods**
56 **POSITIVE MENTALITY (IRE)**, b f Acclamation—Mikandy (IRE) **Mr D. Vere Hunt**
57 **SANDERLIN (IRE)**, ch g Footstepsinthesand—Coppertop (IRE) **Mr D. Richardson**
58 **SCARBOROUGHDEBUT**, b f Acclamation—Scarborough (IRE) **Taylor's Bloodstock Ltd**
59 **SECRET EAGLE**, ch g Pearl Secret—Piste **Mrs C. E. Dods**
60 **TIME FOR A GOOD UN**, b g Adaay—Anna Barkova (IRE) **Foster & Barry Watson**
61 **WHITTLE LE WOODS**, b c Lethal Force (IRE)—Lady Loch **Mr D. W. Armstrong**
62 **WOR WILLIE**, b g Mukhadram—Caterina de Medici (FR) **D. Neale**

### TWO-YEAR-OLDS

63 **ALETHIOMETER (FR)**, b f 14/04 Aclaim (IRE)—
                           Live Love Laugh (FR) (Redoute's Choice (AUS)) (12914) **Mrs C. Dods & Mr D Stone**
64 **AUDIT (IRE)**, b g 07/04 Footstepsinthesand—Bayan Kasirga (IRE) (Aussie Rules (USA)) (32381) **The Bottom Liners**
65 **CAMACHO KING (IRE)**, b c 25/04 Camacho—St Athan (Authorized (IRE)) (12000) **Mr F. Lowe**
66 B f 23/04 Adaay (IRE)—Cheeky Girl (College Chapel) (4000) **Dods Racing Club**
67 **CLARETS GLORY (IRE)**, b c 28/03 Cotai Glory—Puddles (FR) (Holy Roman Emperor (IRE)) (30000) **D & M Dods**
68 **JOEYREMY (IRE)**, b g 06/04 Gutaifan (IRE)—School Holidays (USA) (Harlan's Holiday (USA)) (17143) **Top House 4**
69 **PURPLE ICE (IRE)**, gr g 11/01 El Kabeir (USA)—
                        Maybe Now Baby (IRE) (Kodiac) (20952) **High Hopes Partnership & Partner**
70 Gr g 19/03 El Kabeir (USA)—Red Savina (Exceed And Excel (AUS)) (22857) **J Blackburn & M Dods**

## MR MICHAEL DODS - continued

71 **RED WARNING (IRE)**, ch c 14/03 Bungle Inthejungle—
Red Red Rose (Piccolo) (13333) **Ian Davison & Geoff Thompson**
72 Gr f 14/03 El Kabeir (USA)—Sea of Dreams (IRE) (Oasis Dream) (47000) **Mr P Appleton & Mrs Anne Elliott**
73 Gr c 08/02 Elzaam (AUS)—Sesmen (Inchinor) (23810) **Dunham Trading & Carole Dods**
74 B f 21/01 Mehmas (IRE)—Special Focus (IRE) (Intense Focus (USA)) (34000) **Mrs C. Dods & Mr D Stone**
75 **TWILIGHT FALLS**, b f 14/05 Twilight Son—Aunt Nicola (Reel Buddy (USA)) (5000) **Bearstone Stud Limited**
76 **VACCINE (IRE)**, b c 01/02 Vadamos (FR)—Strike A Light (Dutch Art) (35238) **Rjh Ltd & D Stone**

**Other Owners:** Mr P. Appleton, Mr D. A. Bardsley, Mr J. N. Blackburn, Mrs T. Blackett, Mr J. Burns, Mrs T. Burns, Mr L. H. Christie, Mr Ian Davison, Mrs C. E. Dods, M. J. K. Dods, Mr A. Drysdale, Dunham Trading Ltd, Mrs A. E. Elliott, Mr M. P. Glass, Mr D. R. Graham, Mrs J. Hanson, Mr K. Hanson, Mr J. B. Hart, High Hopes Partnership, Mr R. Homburg, Mr A. S. Kelvin, K. Kirkup, Mrs S. Kirkup, Mr R. A. Little, Mr S. R. Lowthian, Mr A. McLuckie, D. T. J. Metcalfe, Mr R. I. Moffatt, Mr S. Peacock, Mr M. D. Pearson, R J H Limited, Mr J. Sagar, Sekura Trade Frames Ltd, Mr S. R. Skinns, V. J. Spinks, Mr D. Stone, Mr M. W. Syme, Mrs A. Taylor, Mr N. H. Taylor-Garthwaite, Mr P. E. Taylor-Garthwaite, Mr S. A. Taylor-Garthwaite, Mr G. C. Thompson, Mr A. Turton, Mr B. Watson, F. Watson, D. Watts, Mrs M. Wynn-Williams.

**Assistant Trainer:** Carole Dods, **Head Lad:** Steve Alderson, David Dickenson.

**Flat Jockey:** Connor Beasley, Paul Mulrennan, Callum Rodriguez. **Apprentice Jockey:** Aidan Redpath. **Amateur Jockey:** Miss Chloe Dods, Miss Sophie Dods, Miss Rachel Taylor.

---

## 149 | MR SIMON DOW, Epsom
Postal: **Clear Height Stable, Derby Stables Road, Epsom, Surrey, KT18 5LB**
Contacts: PHONE **01372 721490** MOBILE **07860 800109**
EMAIL simon@simondow.co.uk WEBSITE www.simondow.co.uk TWITTER @SimonDowRacing

1 **APOLLINARIS (IRE)**, 4, b g Dandy Man (IRE)—Source of Life (IRE) **Mr M. J. Convey**
2 **BEAT THE BREEZE**, 4, gr g Outstrip—Tranquil Flight **Mr S. A. Caunce**
3 **BUSTED ICE (IRE)**, 6, b g Falco (USA)—Sansiwa (IRE) **Mr M. J. Convey**
4 **CAFE MILANO**, 4, b g Al Kazeem—Selka (FR) **Stoney's Bloodstock**
5 **CHICA DE LA NOCHE**, 7, b m Teofilo (IRE)—Welsh Cake **Mr R. J. Moss**
6 **CHICA DEL DIA**, 4, b f Toronado (IRE)—Vezere (USA) **Mr R. J. Moss**
7 **CORAZON ESPINADO (IRE)**, 6, b h Iffraaj—Three Decades (IRE) **Mr R. J. Moss**
8 **DELCIA**, 5, b m Delegator—Fiducia **S. L. Dow**
9 **HEADLEY GEORGE (IRE)**, 4, b g Due Diligence (USA)—Silent Secret (IRE) **Mr M. J. Convey**
10 **HECTOR LOZA**, 4, b g Kodiac—Queen Sarra **Mr R. J. Moss**
11 **IVAQUESTION (IRE)**, 4, b g Ivawood (IRE)—Parlour **R. A. Murray-Obodynski**
12 **MONT KIARA (FR)**, 8, b g Kendargent (FR)—Xaarienne **Mr C. G. J. Chua**
13 **MOOSMEE (IRE)**, 4, br g Society Rock (IRE)—Tara Too (IRE) **Miss S. D. Groves**
14 **MR SCARAMANGA**, 7, b h Sir Percy—Lulla **Mr R. J. Moss**
15 **MUNGO'S QUEST (IRE)**, 4, ch g Sir Prancealot (IRE)—Sheila Blige **David Sorrell & Simon Dow**
16 **NEFARIOUS (IRE)**, 5, ro g Zebedee—Tellelle (IRE) **R Moss, H Redknapp**
17 **PRINCE ROCK (IRE)**, 6, ch g Society Rock (IRE)—She's A Queen (IRE) **Mr M. McAllister**
18 **PRINCES DES SABLES**, 5, ch m Monsieur Bond (IRE)—Hopes N Dreams (IRE) **JCG Chua & CK Ong**
19 **QUE QUIERES (USA)**, 5, b g Bernardini (USA)—Christine Daae (USA) **Mr R. J. Moss**
20 **RECUERDAME (USA)**, 5, b g The Factor (USA)—B R's Girl (USA) **Mr R. J. Moss**
21 **ROUNDABOUT MAGIC (IRE)**, 7, ch h Zebedee—Cayo Largo (IRE) **Six Mile Hill Racing**
22 **SHERPA TRAIL (USA)**, 5, gr ro g Gio Ponti (USA)—Vapour Musing **S. L. Dow**
23 **SUBLIMINAL**, 6, b g Arcano (IRE)—Rare Virtue (USA) **Mr M. McAllister**
24 **THE GAME IS ON**, 5, b g Garswood—Paquerettza (FR) **Mr B. R. Lindley**

### THREE-YEAR-OLDS
25 **ARENAS DEL TIEMPO**, 3, br f Footstepsinthesand—Vezere (USA) **Mr R. J. Moss**
26 **BLUE BERET**, ch f Helmet (AUS)—Vivid Blue **Bantry Boy's Partnership**
27 **JEREMIAH JOHNSON (IRE)**, b c Camacho—Lady Lassie (IRE) **J J's Syndicate & Simon Dow**

## MR SIMON DOW - continued

28 **PABLO DEL PUEBLO (IRE),** b g Kodiac—Solar Event  **Mr R. J. Moss**
29 **PETESORSE (IRE),** b g Morpheus—Cayo Largo (IRE)  **Peter Sheldon & Simon Dow**
30 **SOYUZ,** b c Sea The Moon (GER)—Inchberry  **Hawkins Family & Star Pointe Ltd**
31 **TWENTYSHARESOFGREY,** bl gr f Markaz (IRE)—Carsulae (IRE)  **The Fat Jockey Partnership**
32 **WAKE UP HARRY,** b c Le Havre (IRE)—Regatta (FR)  **Mr H. Redknapp**

### TWO-YEAR-OLDS

33 **CABLE MOUNTAIN,** b c 16/03 Cable Bay (IRE)—
                                 Esteemed Lady (IRE) (Mark of Esteem (IRE)) (12000)  **The Fat Jockey Partnership**
34 B f 30/03 Havana Gold (IRE)—Dainty Dandy (IRE) (Dandy Man (IRE)) (13000)  **The Fat Jockey Partnership**
35 **EDDY MAY (IRE),** b f 26/03 Profitable (IRE)—
                                 Hollow Green (IRE) (Beat Hollow (IRE)) (11000)  **Eddy May Racing Partnership**

**Other Owners:** Mr S. Buy, S. L. Dow, Mr D. L. Galway, Mr N. J. Hawkins, J J's Syndicate, M. G. Mackenzie, Mr R. J. Moss, Mr B Phillpott, Mr H. Redknapp, Mr N. S. Scandrett, Mr P. J. Sheldon, Mr D. G. Sorrell, Star Pointe Ltd, Mr I. R. Steadman, Mr A. Webb, Mr N. White.

---

## 150  MR CHRIS DOWN, Cullompton
Postal: **Upton, Cullompton, Devon, EX15 1RA**
Contacts: **PHONE 01884 33097 MOBILE 07828 021232 FAX 01884 33097**
EMAIL cjdownracing@gmail.com

1 **ARCTIC FOOTPRINT,** 7, br m Blueprint (IRE)—Arctic Flow  **Mrs H. R. Dunn**
2 **BATTLE MARCH (USA),** 4, b g War Front (USA)—Lahinch Classics (IRE)  **Chris Down Racing**
3 **BROADCLYST (IRE),** 9, b g Ask—Broadcast  **Mrs S. M. Trump**
4 **BRYHER,** 4, b g Dream Eater (IRE)—Angel Sprints  **Miss V. M. Halloran**
5 **CHAMPAGNE IDEAS (IRE),** 8, b g Acambaro (GER)—Charannah (IRE)  **Upton Racing 2**
6 **COBRA ANGEL (IRE),** 7, br m Flemensfirth (USA)—Lemon Cello (IRE)  **Upton Racing 1**
7 **FANFAN LA COLMINE (FR),** 6, b g No Risk At All (FR)—Union Leto (FR)  **Mr P. R. Carter**
8 **FAT SAM,** 7, ch g Denham Red (FR)—Emergence (FR)  **Mr D. Lockwood**
9 **FRANKINCENSE (IRE),** 6, b g Galileo (IRE)—Anna Karenina (IRE)  **The Almost Hopeful Partnership**
10 **HAZY DREAM,** 5, gr m Dream Eater (IRE)—Lily Potts  **C. J. Down**
11 **JOHNNY B (IRE),** 7, b g Famous Name—Zoudie  **Mrs P. Roffe-Silvester**
12 **MIDNIGHT ANNIE,** 7, b m Arvico (FR)—Miss Midnight  **J. Norman**
13 **MINELLA MOJO (IRE),** 9, b g King's Theatre (IRE)—On The Horizon (IRE)  **Cilla Partnership**
14 **MISS MARETTE,** 5, b m Passing Glance—La Marette  **Culm Valley Racing**
15 **MOTTS CROSS (IRE),** 10, b g Scorpion (IRE)—Rainy Season (IRE)  **Mrs S. M. Trump**
16 **MR SOCIABLE,** 6, b g Geordieland (FR)—Secret Queen  **Kittymore Racing**
17 **NOSTALGICA,** 4, b f Sea The Moon (GER)—Neige d'Antan  **C. J. Down**
18 **PAHASKA (GER),** 8, b m Saddex—Pacific Sun (GER)  **P Holland,JT Measures,MA Kerr,V Holland**
19 **PUZZLE CACHE,** 7, b m Phoenix Reach (IRE)—Secret Queen  **Kittymore Racing**
20 **RUSSIES DREAM,** 5, b g Dream Eater (IRE)—Russie With Love
21 **WHAT A PLEASURE,** 5, b gr m Al Namix (FR)—Emergence (FR)  **Mr D. Lockwood**

**Other Owners:** R. A. Davies, Mrs J. Elliott, P. D. Holland, Mrs V. Holland, Ms M. A. Kerr, Mr J. T. Measures, Miss E. M. Pearse, Mrs P. Roffe-Silvester, Ms K. H. Smith.

**NH Jockey:** James Davies.

## 151 MR CLIVE DREW, Rampton
Postal: **Fox End Stables, 83 King Street, Rampton, Cambridgeshire, CB24 8QD**
Contacts: **PHONE 01954 250772 MOBILE 07917 718127**
EMAIL polly.drew@googlemail.com

1 MAISON BRILLET (IRE), 14, b g Pyrus (USA)—Stormchaser (IRE) **C. Drew**
2 MONSIEUR ROYALE, 11, ch g Monsieur Bond (IRE)—Bond Royale **C. Drew**

### THREE-YEAR-OLDS
3 HALLO SIXTIES, b c Sixties Icon—Hallo Sexy **C. Drew**
4 B c Alhebayeb (IRE)—Ur Secret Is Safe (IRE)

**Assistant Trainer:** Miss Polly Drew.

## 152 MR DAVID DRINKWATER, Redmarley
Postal: **Chapel Farm, Chapel Lane, Redmarley, Gloucester, Gloucestershire, GL19 3JF**
Contacts: **PHONE 07766 011007, 07973 193771**
EMAIL drinkys35@outlook.com

1 ASHPAN SAM, 12, b g Firebreak—Sweet Patoopie **R Tudor Holdings Limited**
2 DLTRIPLESEVEN (IRE), 8, gr g Dark Angel (IRE)—Namu **R Tudor Holdings Limited**
3 MAHNA MAHNA (IRE), 7, b g Kodiac—Namu **R Tudor Holdings Limited**
4 MISS DUSKY DIVA (IRE), 9, gr m Verglas (IRE)—Dispol Veleta **R Tudor Holdings Limited**
5 SPIRIT OR WINE, 5, b m Swiss Spirit—Namu **R Tudor Holdings Limited**
6 TABLE BLUFF (IRE), 12, ch g Indian Haven—Double Deal **R Tudor Holdings Limited**

**Assistant Trainer:** Rachel Tudor.

## 153 MR SAMUEL DRINKWATER, Strensham
Postal: **The Granary, Twyning Road, Strensham, Worcester, Worcestershire, WR8 9LH**
Contacts: **MOBILE 07747 444633**
EMAIL samdrinkwater@gmail.com

1 BALLYBREEZE, 5, b g Schiaparelli (GER)—Cottstown Gold (IRE) **Mr K. J. Price**
2 BUZZ DE TURCOING (FR), 7, b g Maresca Sorrento (FR)—Panora Night (FR) **Prestbury Thoroughbreds**
3 CAPTAIN JACK, 8, b g Mount Nelson—Court Princess **Mr & Mrs D. C. Holder**
4 COACHELLA GREEN (IRE), 9, b m Westerner—Turquoise Green (IRE) **Mr D. A. Hunt**
5 4, B g Mount Nelson—Court Princess
6 COURTEVA, 6, b m Multiplex—Court Princess **Mr & Mrs D. C. Holder**
7 CUP OF COFFEE (FR), 7, b m Dragon Dancer—Danser Sur La Lune (FR) **Mr D. A. Hunt**
8 FENRIR BINDING, 6, b g Norse Dancer (IRE)—Bethany Lewis **The Wolfpack**
9 FLIGHT COMMAND (IRE), 4, br g War Command (USA)—Regency Girl (IRE) **Prestbury Thoroughbreds**
10 GALLIC GEORDIE, 8, b g Geordieland (FR)—Je Ne Sais Plus (FR) **Glastonburys & On the Gallops 1**
11 GENERAL CONSENSUS, 9, br g Black Sam Bellamy (IRE)—Charlottes Webb (IRE) **Mrs K. Drinkwater**
12 GENTLE FIRE, 5, b m Phoenix Reach (IRE)—Pugnacious Lady **Court Reclamation & Salvage Ltd**
13 HAPPY AND CONTENT (IRE), 5, b m Fame And Glory—Happy Reunion (IRE) **P. Drinkwater**
14 HAPPY B (IRE), 6, b g Lord Shanakill (USA)—Happy Reunion (IRE) **P. Drinkwater**
15 HELLO BOB, 6, ch m Cityscape—Maid of Perth **Mrs J. Drinkwater**
16 HOWLING MILAN (IRE), 7, b g Milan—Fantasia Filly (FR) **Strensham Stragglers**
17 JEN'S GEORGIE, 6, gr m Geordieland (FR)—Je Ne Sais Plus (FR) **Glastonburys & On the Gallops 2**
18 KICKONMYSON, 5, b g Schiaparelli (GER)—Madam Min **The Cheltenham Boys Racing Club**

## MR SAMUEL DRINKWATER - continued

19 **LA FILLE FRANCAISE (FR)**, 8, b m Kapgarde (FR)—Pondimari (FR) **Mrs J. C. Venvell**
20 **NIGHTBOATTOCLYRO**, 7, ch g Sulamani (IRE)—Wychwoods Legend **Glastonburys & On the Gallops 1**
21 **RUSSIAN SERVICE**, 9, b g Robin des Champs (FR)—Just Kate **Stephen Mattick & Mr D.P. Drinkwater**
22 **SAMSON'S REACH**, 8, b g Phoenix Reach (IRE)—Court Wing (IRE) **Court Reclamation & Salvage Ltd**
23 **SAWPIT SIENNA**, 6, b m Dylan Thomas (IRE)—Sawpit Supreme **Mr D. A. Hunt**
24 **SERGEANT BRODY**, 10, ch g Black Sam Bellamy (IRE)—Ardent Bride **Mrs K. Drinkwater**
25 **SOME CAN DANCE (IRE)**, 8, b g Gold Well—Rocella (GER) **Richard Bailey & Mr D P Drinkwater**
26 **STORMING CARLOS (IRE)**, 4, b g Carlotamix (FR)—Storming Run (IRE) **Mick Coulson, Karen Drinkwater**
27 **STRENSHAM COURT**, 6, b g Great Pretender (IRE)—Diktalina **P. Drinkwater**
28 **SWIFT CRUSADOR**, 10, b g Kayf Tara—Goldenswift (IRE) **All Bar None Racing**
29 **TALK OF A STORM**, 6, b m Yorgunnabelucky (USA)—Taken By Storm **Mrs M. Finch**
30 **TOP DECISION (IRE)**, 8, ch g Beneficial—Great Decision (IRE) **Prestbury Thoroughbreds**

**Other Owners:** Mr R. E. Bailey, R. J. Clarke, Mr M. D. Coulson, Mr D. P. Drinkwater, Mrs K. Drinkwater, P. Drinkwater, Mrs A. J. Glastonbury, Mr K. J. Glastonbury, Kevin & Anne Glastonbury, Mr M. Glastonbury, Mr R. Glastonbury, Mrs C. R. Holder, D. C. Holder, Mr S. J. Mattick, On The Gallops Racing Club.

---

## 154 MISS JACKIE DU PLESSIS, Saltash
Postal: **Burell Farm, Longlands, Saltash, Cornwall, PL12 4QH**
Contacts: **PHONE 01752 842362 MOBILE 07970 871505**
**EMAIL** ziggerson@aol.com

1 **ASKRUMOR (IRE)**, 8, b m Ask—Star of Hope (IRE) **Miss J. M. du Plessis**
2 **BOTUS FLEMING**, 6, ch g Tiger Groom—Chelsea Express **Miss J. M. du Plessis**
3 **CORNELIUS SOCKS (IRE)**, 11, b g Asian Heights—Delightful Choice (IRE) **Miss J. M. du Plessis**
4 **ERICAS LAD**, 9, b g Mutazayid (IRE)—Kingsmill Quay **Miss J. M. du Plessis**
5 **KINGSMILL GIN**, 8, b m Fair Mix (IRE)—Kingsmill Lake **Miss J. M. du Plessis**
6 6, B m Lucarno (USA)—Kingsmill Lake **Miss J. M. du Plessis**
7 **LIBERTY ROCK (IRE)**, 5, ch g Libertarian—Star Seventeen **Mr N. R. Banks**
8 **LINGUINE (FR)**, 11, ch g Linngari (IRE)—Amerissage (USA) **Mr A. M. Rennison**
9 **LITTLE PEACHEY (IRE)**, 5, b m September Storm (GER)—Mrs Peachey (IRE) **The Boom Syndicate**
10 **MOLLYVICO**, 6, b m Arvico (FR)—Magic Valentine **V & J Plessis**
11 **PORT O'CLOCK (IRE)**, 6, ch g Sans Frontieres (IRE)—Rever Up (IRE) **Mr J. E. Gardener**
12 **RUSSIAN INVASION (IRE)**, 6, b g Aizavoski (IRE)—Kerso (IRE) **Mr D. P. Summersby**
13 **SEA DESTINATION (IRE)**, 10, b m Dubai Destination (USA)—Nautical Lady (IRE) **The Cornish Barmies**
14 **ST ERNEY**, 10, ch g Kadastrof (FR)—Ticket To The Moon **Miss J. M. du Plessis**
15 **STAGE SUMMIT (IRE)**, 9, gr g Tikkanen (USA)—Summittotalkabout (IRE) **The Lanson Lads**
16 **THEATRE MIX**, 8, gr m Fair Mix (IRE)—Theatre Diva (IRE) **The Cornish Barmies**
17 **VALENTINO**, 6, b g Sulamani (IRE)—Romance Dance **Mr Shane O Sullivan & Miss J Du Plessis**

**Other Owners:** Mr S. M. O'Sullivan, Mrs V. West, Miss J. M. du Plessis.

---

## 155 MRS ANN DUFFIELD, Leyburn
Postal: **Sun Hill Racing Ltd, Sun Hill Farm, Constable Burton, Leyburn, North Yorkshire, DL8 5RL**
Contacts: **PHONE 01677 450303 MOBILE 07802 496332 FAX 01677 450993**
**EMAIL** ann@annduffield.co.uk **WEBSITE** www.annduffield.co.uk

1 **ALLAYNE B**, 4, b f Swiss Spirit—Annie Kenney **Mr David Barker & Partner**
2 **ARNOLD**, 7, b g Equiano (FR)—Azurinta (IRE) **DJ & SA Shewring & Partner**
3 **BIBBIDIBOBBIDIBOO (IRE)**, 6, b m Red Jazz (USA)—Provence **Mr T. S. Ingham & Mrs Liz Ingham**
4 **CLOTHERHOLME (IRE)**, 4, b g Sir Prancealot (IRE)—Giorgi (IRE) **Mr T. S. Ingham & Mrs Liz Ingham**

## MRS ANN DUFFIELD - continued

5 **CUPPACOCO**, 6, b m Stimulation (IRE)—Glen Molly (IRE)  **Mrs C. A. Gledhill**
6 **LADY NECTAR (IRE)**, 4, b f Zebedee—Mitchelton (FR)  **Mr T. S. Ingham & Mrs Liz Ingham**
7 **QUERCUS (IRE)**, 4, b g Nayef (USA)—Dufoof (IRE)  **Mrs C. A. Gledhill**
8 **ROYAL RESIDENCE**, 6, b g Epaulette (AUS)—Jubilant Queen  **Mr T. S. Ingham & Mrs Liz Ingham**

### THREE-YEAR-OLDS

9 **CATHERINE'S GIRL**, b f Fountain of Youth (IRE)—Say A Prayer  **Mr T. S. Ingham & Mrs Liz Ingham**
10 **CORAL STONE**, b f Fountain of Youth (IRE)—Seaperle
11 B g Fountain of Youth (IRE)—Dont Tell Nan
12 **FAVOURITE NIECE**, b f Fountain of Youth (IRE)—Ambella (IRE)  **Mr T. S. Ingham & Mrs Liz Ingham**
13 **FOUNTAIN'S FLYER**, b g Fountain of Youth (IRE)—Bravo  **Mr David Barker & Partner**
14 **LOCH LONG (IRE)**, b g Awtaad (IRE)—Scatina (IRE)  **Mr J. A. Kay**
15 **MISS BEHAVING**, b f Showcasing—Granola  **Mr P Bamford & Ms J Bianco**
16 **MR TREVOR (IRE)**, b c Kodi Bear (IRE)—Muscadelle  **Mr T. S. Ingham & Mrs Liz Ingham**
17 **SHESAHEART**, b f Brazen Beau (AUS)—Shesastar  **J Bianco & S Hardy**
18 **WALTER**, b g Prince of Lir (IRE)—Queen of The Nile  **DJ & SA Shewring, L Patterson & Partner**

**Other Owners:** P. Bamford, D. K. Barker, Ms J. F. Bianco, Mrs A. Duffield, Miss S. E. Hardy, Mrs M. E. Ingham, Mr T. S. Ingham, Mr L. S. Patterson, Mr D. J. Shewring, Mrs S. A. Shewring.

---

**156**
## MR BRENDAN W. DUKE, The Curragh
Postal: **Fenway House, Pollardstown, Curragh, Co. Kildare, Ireland**
Contacts: **MOBILE +353 85 818 9724**
EMAIL brendanwduke@hotmail.com

1 5, B h So You Think (NZ)—I'm Sheikra (IRE)  **Brendan W. Duke Racing**
2 **JOAN OF PIMLICO (IRE)**, 4, b f Free Eagle (IRE)—Poplar Close (IRE)  **Martin Hayes, Peter Slezak**
3 **LEAGAN GAEILGE (IRE)**, 5, b m Vocalised (USA)—Feile Bride (IRE)  **Mrs Jackie Bolger**
4 **LISTENING MODE (IRE)**, 5, b g Vocalised (USA)—Teoirim (IRE)  **Mrs Jackie Bolger**
5 **MADE IN PIMLICO (IRE)**, 4, ch c Dragon Pulse (IRE)—Runway Giant (USA)  **The Fenway Syndicate**
6 **PRIDE OF PIMLICO (IRE)**, 5, ch g Casamento (IRE)—Casina Valadier (IRE)  **Martin Hayes & Peter Slezak**
7 **PUNCH BAG (IRE)**, 10, ch g Teofilo (IRE)—Heir Today (IRE)  **Martin Hayes, Peter Slezak**
8 **SOUTH BOSTON (IRE)**, 4, b g Fracas (IRE)—Foofaraw (USA)  **Mrs Jackie Bolger, Mr Joseph Joyce**
9 **SPEAK NOW (IRE)**, 4, b g Vocalised (USA)—Heir Today (IRE)  **Mrs Jackie Bolger**
10 **VOCAL QUEEN (IRE)**, 6, b m Vocalised (USA)—Silver Queen  **Mrs Jackie Bolger**

### THREE-YEAR-OLDS

11 **DOCTOR BROWN BEAR (IRE)**, b c Estidhkaar (IRE)—All In Clover (IRE)  **Brendan W. Duke Racing**
12 **ENYA VA (IRE)**, b f Vadamos (FR)—Red Blanche (IRE)  **Enya Va Syndicate**
13 **MARKETTA**, b f Markaz (IRE)—Liscoa (IRE)  **Brendan W. Duke Racing**
14 B c Parish Hall (IRE)—Odisha (USA)  **Mrs Jackie Bolger**
15 **THE BLUE GARTER (IRE)**, b f Kodi Bear—You're My Cracker  **Joseph Duke**

### TWO-YEAR-OLDS

16 B c 05/04 Dragon Pulse—I'm Sheikra (IRE) (Captain Rio)
17 Ch c 05/04 Dawn Approach (IRE)—Introibo (IRE) (Intense Focus (USA))  **Mrs Jackie Bolger**
18 Br c 04/03 Danon Ballade (JPN)—Patronne (Domedriver (IRE))
19 B f 06/05 Peace Envoy—Testing (FR) (New Approach)  **Mrs Jackie Bolger**

**Other Owners:** Mrs Jackie Bolger.

**Flat Jockey:** Rory Cleary, Kevin Manning, Ronan Whelan. **NH Jockey:** Sean Flanagan. **Apprentice Jockey:** Luke McAteer.

**157** **MR IAN DUNCAN, Coylton**
Postal: **Sandhill Farm, Coylton, Ayr, Ayrshire, KA6 6HE**
Contacts: **PHONE 01292 571118 MOBILE 07731 473668 FAX 01292 571118**
**EMAIL idracing@outlook.com**

1 **ABRACH ROAD**, 6, ch g Supreme Sound—Belfast Central (IRE) **Mr A. J. R. Lilley**
2 **CYPRUS AVENUE**, 9, b m Kayf Tara—Za Beau (IRE) **Dr S. Sinclair**
3 4, B f Kayf Tara—French Fashion (IRE)
4 **IMPERIAL PRINCE (IRE)**, 12, b g Subtle Power (IRE)—Satco Rose (IRE) **Stephen Sinclair & Ian Duncan**
5 **JESSIEMAC (IRE)**, 7, br m Sholokhov (IRE)—All Our Blessings (IRE) **Alan & Barry Macdonald**
6 **KING OF FASHION (IRE)**, 11, ch g Desert King (IRE)—French Fashion (IRE) **Dr S. Sinclair**
7 **LARGY PROSPECT (IRE)**, 9, b g Stowaway—Thrilling Prospect (IRE) **Sinclair, Hammersley & Davidson**
8 **NO NO MAC (IRE)**, 12, b g Oscar (IRE)—Whatdoyouthinkmac (IRE) **Alan & Barry Macdonald**
9 **NORDIC EXPRESS**, 4, ch f Norse Dancer (IRE)—Belfast Central (IRE) **Stephen Sinclair & Ian Duncan**
10 **ORIENT SUNSET**, 7, ch m Orientor—Watch Closely Now (IRE) **I. A. Duncan**
11 **PORTSTORM**, 6, b g Shirocco (GER)—Viva Victoria **Gregg, Lilley, Davidson, Hammersley**
12 **ROYAL RANK**, 5, b g Epaulette (AUS)—Deserted **R Lilley & I A Duncan**
13 **STRONG ECONOMY (IRE)**, 9, ch g Sandmason—Odd Decision (IRE) **Alan & Barry Macdonald**
14 4, Ch f Sulamani (IRE)—Watch Closely Now (IRE) **Mr A. J. R. Lilley**

**Other Owners:** Mr C. Davidson, I. A. Duncan, Mr A. L. Gregg, Mr G. Hammersley, Mr A. J. R. Lilley, Dr S. Sinclair.

**158** **MR NIGEL DUNGER, Pulborough**
Postal: **17 Allfrey Plat, Pulborough, West Sussex, RH20 2BU**
Contacts: **PHONE 07494 344167 MOBILE 07790 631962**
**EMAIL debdunger05@gmail.com**

1 **HIER ENCORE (FR)**, 9, ch g Kentucky Dynamite (USA)—Hierarchie (FR) **N. A. Dunger**
2 **PRIDE OF PEMBERLEY (IRE)**, 9, ch g Flemensfirth (USA)—On Galley Head (IRE) **N. A. Dunger**

**Assistant Trainer:** Mrs D Dunger.

**159** **MR ED DUNLOP, Newmarket**
Postal: **La Grange Stables, Fordham Road, Newmarket, Suffolk, CB8 7AA**
Contacts: **PHONE 01638 661998 MOBILE 07785 328537 FAX 01638 667394**
**EMAIL edunlop@eddunloppracing.co.uk WEBSITE www.edunlop.com**

1 **AHDAB (IRE)**, 4, b g Shamardal (USA)—Habaayib
2 **ALTERNATIVE FACT**, 6, b g Dalakhani (IRE)—O Fourlunda
3 **DELAQUINN**, 4, b g Roderic O'Connor (IRE)—Hector's Girl
4 **GLOBAL ART**, 6, b g Dutch Art—Constant Dream
5 **GLOBAL DESTINATION (IRE)**, 5, b g Slade Power (IRE)—Silk Trail
6 **JUAN LES PINS**, 4, b g Invincible Spirit (IRE)—Miss Cap Ferrat
7 **MASTER THE STARS (GER)**, 4, b g Sea The Stars (IRE)—Magma (GER)
8 **MAYSONG**, 4, ch g Mayson—Aldeburgh Music (IRE)
9 **PARIKARMA (IRE)**, 4, b f Canford Cliffs (IRE)—Pushkar
10 **RED VERDON (USA)**, 8, ch g Lemon Drop Kid (USA)—Porto Marmay (IRE)
11 **ROCA MAGICA**, 5, b m Garswood—Marigay's Magic
12 **SOCIETY LION**, 4, b g Invincible Spirit (IRE)—Pavlosk (USA)
13 **TORO DORADO**, 5, b g Toronado (IRE)—Rawoof (IRE)
14 **VIRGIN SNOW**, 4, b f Gleneagles (IRE)—Snow Fairy (IRE)

## MR ED DUNLOP - continued

### THREE-YEAR-OLDS

**15 AJRAD**, ch g New Approach (IRE)—Princess Cammie (IRE)
**16 ALABLAQ (IRE)**, ch g Lope de Vega (IRE)—Tributary
**17 ARTHUR'S REALM (IRE)**, b c Camelot—Morning Line (FR)
**18 BELLA LUCE (IRE)**, b f Invincible Spirit (IRE)—Prima Luce (IRE)
**19 BELLAGIO**, b g Fountain of Youth (IRE)—Koharu
**20 BILLIE'S GIRL (IRE)**, b f Lope de Vega (IRE)—Horse Sense (IRE)
**21 DANSING BEAR (IRE)**, b g Kodi Bear (IRE)—Atlas Silk
**22 DEW YOU BELIEVE (IRE)**, b g Make Believe—Dew (IRE)
**23 HARRIER HAWK**, b f Harzand (IRE)—The Madding Crowd
**24 IN THE GENES**, b f Iffraaj—Synergy (FR)
**25 JOHN LEEPER (IRE)**, b c Frankel—Snow Fairy (IRE)
**26 KRANK IT (FR)**, b br g Dabirsim (FR)—Vallota
**27 LENNY'S SPIRIT (FR)**, b br c Intello (GER)—Moonee Valley (FR)
**28 MAIDEN'S TOWER (IRE)**, b br f Golden Horn—Harlem Dancer
**29 MUTAWAARID**, br g Dawn Approach (IRE)—Murahana (IRE)
**30 RED GLORY (IRE)**, b g Harzand (IRE)—Perfect Touch (USA)
**31 ROYAL HEART (FR)**, b g Wootton Bassett—Gift of Life (USA)
**32 SAMBORA GIRL**, b f Farhh—Elis Eliz (IRE)
**33 TARA ITI**, ch g Sixties Icon—Royal Warranty
**34 THREE TREES (FR)**, b br c Shalaa (IRE)—Mistress Greeley (USA)
**35 URAIB**, b f Shalaa (IRE)—Social Media
**36 VERREAUX EAGLE (IRE)**, gr f Free Eagle (IRE)—Evening Frost (IRE)
**37 ZANKALA (IRE)**, b f Zoffany (IRE)—Sannkala (FR)

### TWO-YEAR-OLDS

**38** B f 09/03 Dark Angel (IRE)—A Huge Dream (IRE) (Refuse To Bend (IRE))
**39** Ch c 17/03 Australia—Aegean Girl (IRE) (Henrythenavigator (USA)) (57000)
**40** Ch f 30/03 Mehmas (IRE)—Araajmh (USA) (Street Cry (IRE)) (130000)
**41** Ch f 26/03 New Approach (IRE)—Autumn Leaves (FR) (Muhtathir) (40000)
**42** B g 23/03 Harzand (IRE)—Bantam (IRE) (Teofilo (IRE))
**43 BELLARENA LADY**, b f 26/02 Due Diligence (USA)—Eshq (IRE) (Oasis Dream) (12000)
**44** B c 30/01 Camelot—Button Up (IRE) (So You Think (NZ)) (30000)
**45 CAPRICIOUS CAITLIN**, b f 09/03 Iffraaj—Capricious Cantor (IRE) (Cape Cross (IRE))
**46** B c 01/03 Camelot—Capriole (Noverre (USA)) (150000)
**47** B f 06/02 Fast Company (IRE)—Club Prive (IRE) (Acclamation) (35238)
**48 CRAFTY MISTRESS**, b gr f 02/03 Mastercraftsman (IRE)—Alsium (IRE) (Invincible Spirit (IRE)) (6000)
**49** B c 28/04 Sea The Stars (IRE)—Dolce Strega (IRE) (Zoffany (IRE)) (40000)
**50** B f 17/04 Dark Angel (IRE)—Dreamlike (Oasis Dream) (90000)
**51 FESTIVAL OF LIGHT**, b f 11/03 Time Test—Luminda (IRE) (Danehill (USA))
**52** Ch c 25/03 Ribchester (IRE)—Gheedaa (USA) (Tamayuz)
**53** B c 24/04 Lope de Vega (IRE)—Great Heavens (Galileo (IRE)) (200000)
**54** Ch f 05/03 Night of Thunder (IRE)—Harlequin Girl (Where Or When (IRE)) (110000)
**55** B f 03/02 Lawman (FR)—Hidden Girl (IRE) (Tamayuz) (42857)
**56** B c 21/03 Belardo (IRE)—Illico (Dansili) (14285)
**57** B f 21/04 Churchill (IRE)—Indigo Lady (Sir Percy) (90000)
**58** B c 27/03 Lope de Vega (IRE)—Indiscreet (FR) (Siyouni (FR)) (52000)
**59** Ch f 04/05 Ulysses (IRE)—Last Echo (IRE) (Whipper (USA)) (20000)
**60** Ch c 19/02 New Bay—Louve Rare (IRE) (Rock of Gibraltar (IRE)) (205000)
**61** B c 31/03 Time Test—Lynnwood Chase (USA) (Horse Chestnut (SAF)) (150000)
**62 MANHATTANVILLE (IRE)**, ch c 06/02 Tamayuz—Carol (IRE) (Acclamation) (4843)
**63** B c 03/03 Siyouni (FR)—Monroe Bay (IRE) (Makfi) (230000)
**64** B f 12/01 Mastercraftsman (IRE)—Music In My Heart (Galileo (IRE)) (115000)
**65** B c 20/03 Buratino (IRE)—Musical Review (UAE) (Jade Robbery (USA)) (11904)
**66** B c 16/04 Fulbright—Practicallyperfect (IRE) (King Charlemagne (USA)) (4439)
**67** B c 17/01 New Approach (IRE)—Radhaadh (IRE) (Nayef (USA)) (50000)
**68** Gr c 15/02 Oasis Dream—Red Halo (IRE) (Galileo (IRE)) (35000)
**69** B f 14/04 Nathaniel (IRE)—Rondine (FR) (Makfi) (55000)
**70** B c 10/04 Make Believe—Sapphire Waters (IRE) (Six Sense (JPN)) (65000)

## MR ED DUNLOP - continued

71 **SARKHA (IRE)**, b c 26/02 The Gurkha (IRE)—Saga Celebre (FR) (Peintre Celebre (USA)) (22000)
72 B f 13/02 Havana Gold (IRE)—Shafafya (Shamardal (USA))
73 B c 19/03 Muhaarar—Shurfah (IRE) (Sea The Stars (IRE))
74 B f 09/04 Postponed (IRE)—Sky Crystal (GER) (Galileo (IRE)) (85000)
75 B c 02/04 Camelot—Sterling Sound (USA) (Street Cry (IRE)) (90000)
76 B f 15/02 Siyouni (IRE)—Twitch (IRE) (Azamour (IRE)) (90000)
77 B c 06/03 Lope de Vega (IRE)—Wild Irish Rose (IRE) (Galileo (IRE)) (130000)

**Owners:** Hamdan bin Rashid Al Maktoum, & Allison, Mrs J. Allison, S. A. Allison, Anamoine Ltd, Mr R. J. Arculli, Mrs J. E. Ball, Sir Francis Brooke, Cayton Park Stud Limited, Mr A. N. Cheyne, W. Cox, The Earl Of Derby, Mr E. A. L. Dunlop, R. P. Foden, Mrs N. M. Horswell, Horswell, Phillipps, Robinson & Rodgers, La Grange Partnership, Mr A. Leopold, Mr A. Leopold & Ms L. Norman, Lord Derby & Ors, Col A. J. E. Malcolm, Miltil Consortium, A. M. Mitchell, Ms L. C. Norman, Old Road Securities Plc, P Deals & H-Bs, Mr G. P. A. Philipps, Mr Richard Pilkington, Mr D. B. Plows, R Foden, M Mitchell & Plows, Mr P. J. Robinson, Mr P. J. Rodgers, Mrs S. M. Roy, The Alternative Lot, The EDR Partnership, The Sambora Partnership, Turf Club 2020, Turf Club 2020 Racing, Mr P. Turner, Windflower Overseas Holdings Inc.

**Assistant Trainer:** Jack Morland, **Head Lad:** Gordon Storrie.

---

**160**

## MR HARRY DUNLOP, Lambourn
Postal: Frenchmans Lodge Stables, Upper Lambourn, Hungerford, Berkshire, RG17 8QW
Contacts: **PHONE** 01488 73584 **MOBILE** 07880 791895
**EMAIL** info@harrydunlopracing.com **WEBSITE** www.harrydunlopracing.com

1 **ANGEL ON HIGH (IRE)**, 4, b c Dark Angel (IRE)—Angel of The Gwaun (IRE) **Mr L. N. Jones**
2 **GENTLEMAN AT ARMS (IRE)**, 4, gr g Reliable Man—Sworn Sold (GER) **Be Hopeful (2) & Fair Salinia Ltd**
3 **JACKFINBAR (FR)**, 6, b h Whipper (USA)—Anna Simona (GER) **Haven't A Pot**
4 **PRIDE OF AMERICA (FR)**, 4, b g American Post—Atarfe (IRE) **Haven't A Pot, D. Macauliffe & Anoj Don**
5 **QUARRY BEACH**, 5, b m Dutch Art—Free Offer **The Gehrings & Partners**
6 **TRIXIE WATERBURY (IRE)**, 4, b f Baltic King—Smart Bounty **The Megsons & Partner**

### THREE-YEAR-OLDS

7 **DREAM CHASER (FR)**, b g Dream Ahead (USA)—Avodale (IRE) **Kirby, Gehring & Woodley**
8 **HONOURS**, b f Exceed And Excel (AUS)—Roses For The Lady (IRE) **Mr L. N. Jones**
9 **LAWMANS BLIS (IRE)**, b c Lawman (FR)—Megec Blis (IRE) **Mr J. R. Dwyer**
10 **MAKETH BELIEVETH (IRE)**, b c Make Believe—Lady Penko (FR) **Haven't A Pot & Ballylinch Stud**
11 **MAXINE (IRE)**, b f Maxios—Saltita (IRE) **Friends of John Dunlop**
12 **MISS ZENLINGUS (IRE)**, b f Kodiac—Orpha **Haven't A Pot**
13 **ONENIGHTINMIAMI (FR)**, b g Motivator—Highborne (FR) **Mrs S. M. Roy**
14 **POINT LOUISE**, b f Free Eagle (IRE)—Cape Mystery **Velocity Racing & Mr S. Birdseye**
15 **QUELLE VITESSE (GER)**, b f Golden Horn—Queensberry (GER) **Mr Erik Penser & Bloomsbury Stud**
16 **SEA OF CHARM (FR)**, b f Charm Spirit (IRE)—Sea Meets Sky (FR) **Elwes, Cooper, Bailey & Deal**
17 **THUNDER AHEAD**, b c Dark Angel (IRE)—Champagne Time (IRE) **Mr L. N. Jones**
18 **TURACO**, b g Kodi Bear (IRE)—Hobby **Larksborough Stud Limited & Partner**

### TWO-YEAR-OLDS

19 **ADAAY IN ASIA**, b f 15/03 Adaay (IRE)—Asia Minor (IRE) (Pivotal) (10500) **The 2 Under Partnership**
20 **GRENADA**, b c 04/03 Oasis Dream—Pina (Dansili)
21 **MIRIQUE (IRE)**, b f 09/02 Ribchester (IRE)—Magique (IRE) (Jeremy (USA)) (35000) **Frenchmans Lodge Stables Partnership**

**Other Owners:** Mrs S. Abbott, Mrs S. Bailey, Ballylinch Stud, Be Hopeful (2), Mr S. C. Birdseye, Bloomsbury Stud, Mr A. K. Cooper, Mr A. R. Culumbarapitiyage Don, Mr P. A. Deal, Mrs C. A. M. Dunlop, H. J. L. Dunlop, Mr N. R. Elwes, Mr G. Freeman, Mr K. C. Freeman, S. A. Hanson, Haven't A Pot, Larksborough Stud Limited, Mr D. P. MacAuliffe, Daniel MacAuliffe & Anoj Don, Mr A. P. Megson, Mrs J. Megson, E. Penser, Mr L. C. Reed, Mrs S. M. Roy, The Megsons, Velocity Racing, Mr D. A. Woodley.

**161** **MRS ALEXANDRA DUNN, Wellington**
Postal: **The Gallops, West Buckland, Wellington, Somerset, TA21 9LE**
Contacts: **MOBILE 07738 512924**
WEBSITE www.alexandradunnracing.com

1 **ARGUS (IRE)**, 9, b g Rip Van Winkle (IRE)—Steel Princess (IRE) **Helium Racing LTD**
2 **BALLARD DOWN (IRE)**, 8, b g Canford Cliffs (IRE)—Mackenzie's Friend **Mr S. Bean**
3 **BLACKWATER BRAMBLE (IRE)**, 10, b g King's Theatre (IRE)—Don't Be Upset (IRE) **Mrs K. R. Smith-Maxwell**
4 **BORN TO REASON (IRE)**, 7, b g Born To Sea (IRE)—Laureldean Lady (IRE) **West Buckland Bloodstock Ltd**
5 **BROKE AWAY (IRE)**, 9, br m Stowaway—Not Broke Yet (IRE) **Mr D. R. Arthur**
6 **CHIAVARI (IRE)**, 7, b m Born To Sea (IRE)—Chiarezza (AUS) **Dave Arthur & W.B.B.**
7 **CITY FLAME**, 5, b m Cityscape—High Drama (IRE) **Mr M. Vaughan**
8 **CRY WOLF**, 8, ch g Street Cry (IRE)—Love Charm **W.B.B. & G.J. Daly**
9 **DE LITTLE ENGINE (IRE)**, 7, ch g Power—Reveuse de Jour (IRE) **West Buckland Bloodstock Ltd**
10 **DIDO**, 11, b g Killer Instinct—Bowdlane Barb **Mr R. H. Fox**
11 **ENMESHING**, 8, ch g Mastercraftsman (IRE)—Yacht Club (USA) **The Crafty Six & W. B. B.**
12 **ESTATE ITALIANA (USA)**, 4, b br g Elusive Quality (USA)—Unaccompanied (IRE) **Team Dunn**
13 **FRENCH MIX (USA)**, 7, b m Dalakhani (IRE)—Alharmina **Lycett Racing Ltd**
14 **GANG WARFARE**, 10, b g Medicean—Light Impact (IRE) **Gangbusters & Partner**
15 **HOLY GUNNER**, 7, b g Malinas (GER)—Holy Smoke **Miss R. J. Smith-Maxwell**
16 **JERSEY GREY (FR)**, 4, gr g Rajsaman (FR)—Akoyama **Mr S. Bean**
17 **JERSEY MASTER (IRE)**, 4, ch g Mastercraftsman (IRE)—Banquise (IRE) **West Buckland Bloodstock Ltd**
18 **KAPITALISTE (FR)**, 5, b g Intello (GER)—Kapitale (GER) **The Profile Partnership 2**
19 **MASTER MEAD**, 6, b g Malinas (GER)—Double Mead **Mrs K. R. Smith-Maxwell**
20 **MINELLA VOUCHER**, 10, b g King's Theatre (IRE)—All Rise (GER) **Team Dunn & W.B.B.**
21 **MOLAAHETH**, 5, b g Heeraat (IRE)—All Fur Coat **West Buckland Bloodstock Ltd**
22 **MR MINERALS**, 7, ch g Poet's Voice—River Song (USA) **Helium Racing LTD**
23 **MYFANWY'S JEWEL**, 6, b m Arvico (FR)—Lady Myfanwy **Best by Miles**
24 **NOW CHILDREN (IRE)**, 7, ch g Dragon Pulse (IRE)—Toberanthawn (IRE) **West Buckland Bloodstock Ltd**
25 **PANATOS (FR)**, 6, b g Denon (USA)—Prairie Scilla (GER) **Helium Racing LTD**
26 **PINSON DU RHEU (FR)**, 10, b g Al Namix (FR)—Venus du Rheu (FR) **Mr S. Bean**
27 **PUNKAWALLAH**, 7, b g Sepoy (AUS)—Max One Two Three (IRE) **Mr S. Bean**
28 **REGULATOR (IRE)**, 6, b g Acclamation—Rasana **S. Towens & W.B.B.**
29 **ROCK OF STAR (FR)**, 4, b g Nom de d'La (FR)—Rolie de Vindecy (FR) **Mr S. Bean**
30 **SARCEAUX (FR)**, 4, gr f Rajsaman (FR)—Sainte Adresse **Mr S. Bean**
31 **SAUSALITO SUNRISE (IRE)**, 13, b g Gold Well—Villaflor (IRE) **Mrs K. R. Smith-Maxwell**
32 **SHINGHARI (IRE)**, 9, br g Cape Cross (IRE)—Sindiyma (IRE) **West Buckland Bloodstock Ltd**
33 **SILVERGROVE**, 13, b g Old Vic—Classic Gale (USA) **Mrs K. R. Smith-Maxwell**
35 **SOLOIST (IRE)**, 5, b m Camelot—Ayshea **Ms L. L. Clune**
36 **THAHAB IFRAJ (IRE)**, 8, ch g Frozen Power (IRE)—Penny Rouge (IRE) **The Dunnitalls & Partner**
36 **THE BRITISH LION (IRE)**, 6, b g Power—Mala Mala (IRE) **Helium Racing LTD**
37 **THE EAGLE'S NEST (IRE)**, 7, ch g Lope de Vega (IRE)—Follow My Lead **Helium Racing LTD**
38 **THE RAIN KING (IRE)**, 4, b g No Nay Never (USA)—Brigids Cross (IRE) **West Buckland Bloodstock Ltd**
39 **TOAD OF TOAD HALL**, 5, b g Universal (IRE)—Double Mead **Mrs K. R. Smith-Maxwell**
40 **ZEYZOUN (FR)**, 7, b g Excelebration (IRE)—Zayanida (IRE) **West Buckland Bloodstock Ltd**

## THREE-YEAR-OLDS

41 B f Haathd—Holy Veil
42 **SENTILLY (FR)**, b f Air Chief Marshal (IRE)—Sainte Adresse **Mr S. Bean**

**Other Owners:** Mr D. R. Arthur, G. J. Daly, Mrs A. Dunn, Mr T. Dunn, Mr D. J. Fitzgerald, Gangbusters, Team Dunn, The Crafty Six, The Dunnitalls, The Profile Partnership, Mr N. Towens, West Buckland Bloodstock Ltd, Mrs C. M. Wheatley, Mr T. Wheatley.

## 162 MRS CHRISTINE DUNNETT, Norwich
Postal: **College Farm, Hingham, Norwich, Norfolk, NR9 4PP**
Contacts: **PHONE 01953 851364 MOBILE 07775 793523**
EMAIL christine@christinedunnett.com WEBSITE www.christinedunnett.com

1 5, B g Mazameer (IRE)—Bongoali **Christine Dunnett Racing (Arryzona)**
2 FAREGAAN, 4, b f Muhaarar—Al Fareej (IRE) **Team Kraka**
3 FLOWER OF THUNDER (IRE), 4, b f Night of Thunder (IRE)—Flower Fairy (USA) **Mrs C. A. Dunnett**
4 KRAKA (IRE), 6, b g Dark Angel (IRE)—Manuelita Rose (ITY) **Team Kraka**
5 MOMENT OF PEACE, 4, b g Gregorian (IRE)—Penny's Pearl (IRE) **Machin, Milner, Sparkes & Dunnett**
6 PERCY TOPLIS, 7, b g Kheleyf (USA)—West Lorne (USA) **Christine Dunnett Racing (Arryzona)**
7 QUEEN OF BURGUNDY, 5, b m Lethal Force (IRE)—Empress Adelaide **Trevor & Ruth Milner**
8 SECRET TREATIES, 5, b m Heeraat (IRE)—Honky Tonk Queen (USA) **Mr A. Machin & Mrs C. Dunnett**
9 SHYJACK, 6, ch g Archipenko (USA)—Coconut Shy **Christine Dunnett Racing (Arryzona)**

### THREE-YEAR-OLDS
10 B c Lethal Force (IRE)—Barathea Dancer (IRE) **Mr P. D. West**
11 BRAZEN ARROW, b g Brazen Beau (AUS)—Patience **Mr P. D. West**
12 B g Estidhkaar (IRE)—Hot Property (USA) **Mrs C. A. Dunnett**
13 INSPECTOR BLAKE, ch g Helmet (AUS)—Shamara (IRE) **Mr P. Eggett**
14 KODI GOLD (IRE), b g Kodi Bear (IRE)—Labisa (IRE) **Mr J. A. Alsabah**
15 LUCAYAN, gr f Belardo (IRE)—Sandy Cay (USA) **Trevor & Ruth Milner**
16 MAGNA OF ILLUSION, b f Estidhkaar (IRE)—Enterprising **Mr A. S. Machin**
17 B c Bobby's Kitten (USA)—Marigay's Magic **Mr E. N. Sparkes**
18 B f Epaulette (AUS)—No Nightmare (USA) **Jonathan Butcher & Christine Dunnett**
19 ROSETINTEDGLASSES (IRE), b f Gutaifan (IRE)—

Manuelita Rose (ITY) **Christine Dunnett & Alan & Barbara Brown**

### TWO-YEAR-OLDS
20 B f 03/04 Mehmas (IRE)—Enterprising (Dansili) (2000) **Mr A. S. Machin**
21 SONNY BROWN, b c 17/02 Mayson—Sand And Deliver (Royal Applause) (2000)

**Other Owners:** Mr A. Brown, Mrs B. I. Brown, Mr J. G. Butcher, Mr F. G. Butler, Mrs C. A. Dunnett, Mr A. S. Machin, Mrs R. L. Milner, Mr T. Milner, Mr G. R. Price, Mr A. P. Scriggins, Mr E. N. Sparkes, R. C. Spore, Mr P. D. West.

---

## 163 MR SEAMUS DURACK, Upper Lambourn
Postal: **The Croft Stables, Upper Lambourn, Hungerford, Berkshire, RG17 8QH**
Contacts: **PHONE 01488 491480 MOBILE 07770 537971**
EMAIL sd.111@btinternet.com WEBSITE www.seamusdurack.com

1 ALFREDO (IRE), 9, ch g Arcano (IRE)—Western Sky **Mr Stephen Tucker & Mr Keith Mcintosh**
2 CANIMAR, 6, b m Havana Gold (IRE)—Acquifer **Miss J. V. Pahlman**
3 CAYIRLI (FR), 9, b g Medicean—Clarinda (FR) **S. P. Tucker**
4 EXCELINTHEJUNGLE (IRE), 5, b g Bungle Inthejungle—Kannon **Egan Waste & Beddoes**
5 FAST ART (IRE), 5, b g Fast Company (IRE)—Poulkovo (IRE) **Mr & Mrs A Archer & Mr & Mrs M Leonard**
6 PHOENIX AQUILUS (IRE), 4, b g Slade Power (IRE)—Permsiri (IRE) **Mr S. E. Durack**
7 THE SWAGMAN (USA), 7, ch g Galileo (IRE)—Ventura (IRE) **Clan McNeil**

### THREE-YEAR-OLDS
8 THUNDER LILY (IRE), b f Night of Thunder (IRE)—Permsiri (IRE) **Mr Stephen Tucker and Mr S Durack**

**Other Owners:** Mr A. Archer, Mrs J. Archer, Miss S. J. Beddoes, Mr S. E. Durack, Egan Waste Services Ltd, Mr M. A. Leonard, Mrs M. E. Leonard, Mr K. R. McIntosh, Mr J. McNeil, Mr P. J. McNeil, S. P. Tucker.

**Assistant Trainer:** Sam Beddoes.

**164**
**MR CHRIS DWYER, Newmarket**
Postal: Paddocks View, Brickfield Stud, Exning Road, Newmarket, Suffolk, CB8 7JH
EMAIL getadwyer@aol.com

1 **CAPLA CRUSADER,** 5, b g Archipenko (USA)—Desert Berry **Strawberry Fields Stud**
2 **GLOBAL ESTEEM (IRE),** 4, b g Kodiac—Baltic Belle (IRE) **Dr J. Hon**
3 **GLOBAL PROSPECTOR (USA),** 5, b br g Scat Daddy (USA)—Alegendinmyownmind **Dr J. Hon**
4 **GLOBAL WARNING,** 5, b g Poet's Voice—Persario **Dr J. Hon**
5 **HELIAN (IRE),** 5, b h Shamardal (USA)—Amathia (IRE) **Ms Helian Jianru & Mr Yin Yue**
6 **LONDON EYE (USA),** 5, ch g Australia—Circle of Life (USA) **Dr J. Hon**
7 **SIR OLIVER (IRE),** 4, b g Dark Angel (IRE)—Folga **Dr J. Hon**

## TWO-YEAR-OLDS

8 **GLOBAL FLIGHT,** b f 07/02 Mayson—Global Spring (IRE) (Kodiac) **Global Group Lifestyle and Sports Club**
9 **GLOBAL GRANDEUR,** b f 23/02 Fastnet Rock (AUS)—Raggety Ann (IRE) (Galileo (IRE)) (40000) **Dr J. Hon**
10 **GLOBAL MIRAGE,** b f 12/03 Mayson—Jeanie Johnston (IRE) (One Cool Cat (USA)) (20000) **Dr J. Hon**
11 **GLOBAL ROMANCE (IRE),** ch f 30/03 Iffraaj—Katawi (Dubawi (IRE)) (52000) **Dr J. Hon**
12 **GLOBAL TYCOON (IRE),** br gr c 28/02 Caravaggio (USA)—Much Faster (IRE) (Fasliyev (USA)) (50000) **Dr J. Hon**
13 B c 25/04 Harzand (IRE)—Juno Moneta (IRE) (Holy Roman Emperor (IRE)) (6000) **Strawberry Fields Stud**
14 B c 17/04 No Nay Never (USA)—Shahinda (FR) (Sea The Stars (IRE)) (64568) **Dr J. Hon**

**Other Owners:** Ms J. Helian, Mr Y. Yin.

**165**
**MISS CLAIRE DYSON, Evesham**
Postal: Froglands Stud Farm, Froglands Lane, Cleeve Prior, Evesham, Worcestershire, WR11 8LB
Contacts: PHONE 01789 774000, 07803 720183 FAX 01789 774000
EMAIL cdyson@live.co.uk WEBSITE www.clairedysonracing.co.uk

1 **CHARLIE MON (IRE),** 12, ch g Presenting—Prowler (IRE) **Mr R. M. Evans**
2 **CLASSIC TUNE,** 11, b g Scorpion (IRE)—Classic Fantasy **D. J. Dyson**
3 4, B c Lope de Vega (IRE)—Dazzle Dancer (IRE) **Miss C. Dyson**
4 **DONE DEAL (IRE),** 6, b g Azamour (IRE)—Dundel'S Spirit (IRE) **Miss C. Dyson**
5 **GREGARIOUS (IRE),** 8, gr g Big Bad Bob (IRE)—Sense of Greeting (IRE) **Mr J. Summers**
6 **HY BRASIL (IRE),** 4, b g Fastnet Rock (AUS)—Kahyasi Moll (IRE) **DYDB Marketing Limited**
7 **LINGER (IRE),** 8, b g Cape Cross (IRE)—Await So **Dyadb Marketing & C Dyson**
8 **MIDNIGHT OWLE,** 11, ch g Midnight Legend—Owlesbury Dream (IRE) **FSF Racing**
9 **MIND'S EYE (IRE),** 9, b g Stowaway—Joleen (IRE) **DYDB Marketing Limited**
10 **MINELLA STYLE (IRE),** 11, b g King's Theatre (IRE)—Rose of The Erne (IRE) **Mr G. T. Sainsbury**
11 **PASSAM,** 9, b g Black Sam Bellamy (IRE)—One Wild Night **FSF Racing**
12 5, B g Harbour Watch (IRE)—Pigeon Pie **D. J. Dyson**
13 **SNEAKY FEELING (IRE),** 9, b g Oscar (IRE)—Shuil Aris (IRE) **Mr G. T. Sainsbury**
14 **STILL A DREAM,** 8, b g Sulamani (IRE)—Owlesbury Dream (IRE) **FSF Racing**
15 **THE COME BACK DUDE (IRE),** 7, ch g Stowaway—Bells Glory (IRE) **FSF Racing**
16 5, B g Frozen Fire (GER)—Wrensboro (IRE) **Miss C. Dyson**

**Other Owners:** DYDB Marketing Limited, Miss C. Dyson.

**NH Jockey:** David Noonan. **Conditional Jockey:** Charlie Hammond.

## 166 MR SIMON EARLE, Sutton Veny
Postal: The Lower Barn, The Beeches Farm, Deverill Road, Sutton Veny, Wiltshire, BA12 7BY
Contacts: PHONE 01985 840450 MOBILE 07850 350116 FAX 01985 840450
EMAIL simonearleracing@btinternet.com WEBSITE www.simonearleracing.co.uk

1 ASHTON COURT (IRE), 7, b g Court Cave (IRE)—Hayabusa **Mr R. H. J. Martin**
2 BIG TREE (IRE), 8, b g Scorpion (IRE)—Montecateno (IRE) **Mr K. M. Harris**
3 KILKEASKIN MOLLY (IRE), 7, b br m Mountain High (IRE)—
Nicola's Girl (IRE) **Mr S. A. Earle, Mr C. V. Marment, Mrs P. L. Bridel, Mr C. Church**
4 RARE CLOUDS, 7, b g Cloudings (IRE)—Rare Vintage (IRE) **Mr R. H. J. Martin**
5 WITCH FROM ROME, 10, b g Holy Roman Emperor (IRE)—Spangle **Mr S. A. Earle**

### THREE-YEAR-OLDS
6 MR SUNDANCER, b c Paco Boy (IRE)—Trumpet Lily

Other Owners: Mrs P Bridel, Mr C Marment, Mr C Church, Mr Peter Goodwin.

## 167 MR MICHAEL EASTERBY, Sheriff Hutton
Postal: New House Farm, Sheriff Hutton, York, North Yorkshire, YO60 6TN
Contacts: PHONE 01347 878368 MOBILE 07831 347481 FAX 01347 878204
EMAIL enquiries@mickeasterby.co.uk WEBSITE www.mickeasterby-racing.co.uk

1 A DAY IN DONOSTIA (IRE), 4, b g Nathaniel (IRE)—Dreaming of Stella (IRE) **Golden Equinox Racing 1**
2 4, B f Iffraaj—Aetna **Mr B. Padgett**
3 ALBERT'S BACK, 7, b g Champs Elysees—Neath **Golden Ratio & J Blackburn**
4 APOLLO KNIGHT, 4, b g Telescope (IRE)—Laetitia (IRE) **Mr J Blackburn Racing**
5 ART OF DIPLOMACY, 5, b g Archipenko (USA)—Rowlestone Express **Imperial Racing, J Blackburn & P Scott**
6 AU JUS, 5, ch m Nayef (USA)—Serraval (FR) **J. T. Brown**
7 BANKAWI, 4, b f Coach House (IRE)—Whitby **South Bank Racing 2**
8 BAVARDAGES (IRE), 4, b g Dream Ahead (USA)—Petits Potins (IRE) **Laura Mason Syndicate Racing**
9 BREAKING RECORDS (IRE), 6, b g Kodiac—Querulous (USA) **Gay & Peter Hartley & Mr Ryan Chapman**
10 CASILLI, 4, b f Cacique (IRE)—Lilli Marlane **Tinning, Wallis, Hollings & Hull**
11 CASTLEHILL LAD, 4, ch g New Approach (IRE)—Sudfah (USA) **Mr A Stott & Mrs J Lukas**
12 CHOOSEY (IRE), 6, ch g Choisir (AUS)—Petit Chou (IRE) **K. Wreglesworth**
13 COME ON LINDA, 4, gr f Alhebayeb (IRE)—Friendship Is Love **Mrs L Folwell & Southbank Racing**
14 CONTRAST (IRE), 7, ch g Dutch Art—Israar **Mr A Saha Racing**
15 COVIGLIA, 7, gr g Invincible Spirit (IRE)—Bright Snow (USA) **Mr John Blackburn Racing**
16 DREAMS AND VISIONS (IRE), 5, b g Archipenko (USA)—Kibini **Imperial Racing, J Blackburn & P Scott**
17 DUBAI INSTINCT, 5, b g Le Havre (IRE)—Riotous Applause **Mr J Goodrick Racing**
18 ELIGIBLE (IRE), 5, b g Dark Angel (IRE)—Secrets Away (IRE) **Mr M Grayson & Mr L Westwood**
19 ELYSIAN FLAME, 5, ch g Champs Elysees—Combustible (IRE) **Mr J Blackburn & Imperial Racing P'ship**
20 EN COULEUR, 4, b g Archipenko (USA)—Medaille d'Or **Mr J Blackburn & Imperial Racing P'ship**
21 ENLIGHTEN, 7, b g Kayf Tara—Rapturous **The Laura Mason Syndicate**
22 FLYMETOTHESTARS, 8, b g Sea The Stars (IRE)—Precious Gem (IRE) **Middleham Park Racing, Mrs H Abbott**
23 GAOLBREAKER (IRE), 5, ch g Getaway (GER)—Glaisdale **Mr N Wrigley, Mrs J Lukas & Mr B Guerin**
24 GEORGE RIDSDALE, 5, ch g Ruler of The World (IRE)—
Cape Rising (IRE) **Mr J Blackburn & Imperial Racing P'ship**
25 GULF OF POETS, 9, b g Oasis Dream—Sandglass **Mr J Blackburn Mr A Pollock Mr A Turton**
26 HARVEST DAY, 6, b m Harbour Watch (IRE)—Miss Wells (IRE) **Mrs C E Mason & Partner**
27 IRISH EILEEN, 4, b f Coach House (IRE)—El Molino Blanco **David Scott Ltd, Mr P Cram & Mr H Cram**
28 ITOJEH, 4, ch g Cityscape—Croeso Cariad **Mr J Blackburn Racing**
29 JESMOND, 4, b f Telescope (IRE)—Jaunty Flight **Mr M Grayson & Imperial Racing**
30 LA RAV (IRE), 7, b g Footstepsinthesand—Swift Acclaim (IRE) **Mr B Hoggarth, Mr S Hull & Mr S Davis**
31 LATE ARRIVAL (IRE), 4, b g Night of Thunder (IRE)—Powdermill **Mr A. G. Pollock, Mr S. A. Windle**

## MR MICHAEL EASTERBY - continued

32 **LUKE**, 4, b c Lucarno (USA)—More Ballet Money **Falcon's Line Ltd**
33 **MARWARI (IRE)**, 5, b g Exceed And Excel (AUS)—Miss Polaris **Mr J Blackburn & Imperial Racing P'ship**
34 **QAWAMEES (IRE)**, 6, b g Exceed And Excel (AUS)—Jabhaat (USA) **The Irrational Group & Mr J Blackburn**
35 **QUICK LOOK**, 8, b g Kheleyf (USA)—Weqaar (USA) **Golden Ratio, Hull, Hollings & Lms**
36 **REFUGE**, 4, b g Harbour Watch (IRE)—Beldale Memory (IRE) **J Blackburn & Julia Lukas**
37 **RESTIVE (IRE)**, 8, b g Rip Van Winkle (IRE)—I Hearyou Knocking (IRE) **M. W. Easterby**
38 **RING OF GOLD**, 4, b g Havana Gold (IRE)—Pitter Patter **Gay & Peter Hartley Racing**
39 4, B c Saddler Maker (IRE)—Ringaround **Imperial Racing Partnership 2016**
40 **ROCKET DANCER**, 4, b g Toronado (IRE)—Opera Dancer **Southbank Racing, S Hull & S Hollings**
41 **SAM'S CALL**, 4, b g Finjaan—Winner's Call **Westy Partnership**
42 **SAM'S GUNNER**, 4, ch g Black Sam Bellamy (IRE)—Falcon's Gunner **Falcon's Line Ltd**
43 **SKYE DREAMING (FR)**, 4, b g Dabirsim (FR)—Madonna Incognito (USA) **Skye Dreaming Partnership**
44 **SWISS KNIGHT**, 6, b g Oasis Dream—Swiss Diva **Mr A Pollock & Mr H Jones**
45 **TAPIS LIBRE**, 13, b g Librettist (USA)—Stella Manuela (FR) **The Laura Mason Syndicate**
46 **UNPLUGGED (IRE)**, 5, b g Alhebayeb (IRE)—Crown Light **Pellon Racing**
47 **WHERE'S JEFF**, 6, b g Haafhd—Piece of Magic **A G Pollock & Golden Ratio Partnership**
48 **WHITWELL**, 4, b g Cable Bay (IRE)—Blissamore **W. H. & Mrs J. A. Tinning & Mrs C Wallis**
49 **WILD THUNDER (IRE)**, 4, b g Night of Thunder (IRE)—Shama's Song (IRE) **Mr B. Padgett**

## THREE-YEAR-OLDS

50 **ALSITHEE**, b g Summer Front (USA)—Secret Dream (IRE) **Mr Andrew Stott Racing**
51 **AUSSIE STORMER (IRE)**, b g Mehmas (IRE)—Stormy Clouds (IRE) **Mr A. G. Pollock**
52 **CAPLA LASS**, b f Garswood—Sarah Berry **Capla Developments Racing**
53 **COME ON JACK**, b g War Command (USA)—Zari **Mr J Blackburn & Imperial Racing P'ship**
54 B c Bobby's Kitten (USA)—Eminencia **Mr J Blackburn & Imperial Racing P'ship**
55 **HOOFS HAPPY NOW**, gr f Outstrip—Hoof's So Lucky **Laura Mason Syndicate Racing**
56 **KEEP THE FAITH (IRE)**, ch g Al Kazeem—Selka (FR) **Mr J Blackburn & Imperial Racing P'ship**
57 **LOCKDOWN LATCHICO**, b g Swiss Spirit—Chicklade **Caroline Cooper Racing**
58 **MAYELF**, ch g Mayson—Delft **Mrs L Folwell & Mr D Scott**
59 **MELGATE MONTY**, gr g Lethal Force—Sacred Aspect (IRE) **Bernard Hoggarth Racing**
60 **MELGATE MYSTIC**, b grg Lethal Force (IRE)—Thrill **Mr B Hoggarth & Mr J Blackburn**
61 **ONE FOR THE LADIES**, b f Swiss Spirit—Spritzeria **Southbank Racing, S Hull & S Hollings**
62 Ch f Eagle Top—Poetic Verse **Mr J. N. Blackburn**
63 **RHYTHMIC BLUES**, ch g Bobby's Kitten (USA)—
                                    Medium of Exchange (USA) **J Blackburn, Imperial Racing & M Grayson**
64 Ch c Doyen (IRE)—Ringaround **Imperial Racing Partnership 2016**
65 **SARAS CALL**, b f Monsieur Bond (IRE)—Winner's Call **Mrs Linda Folwell Racing**
66 B g Iffraaj—Short Affair **Mr A Saha Racing**
67 **SO GRATEFUL**, b g Swiss Spirit—Bow Bridge **Mrs A. Jarvis**
68 **SUBTLE INNUENDO (IRE)**, gr g Lawman (FR)—Whistling Straits (FR) **Imperial Racing & Mr J Blackburn**
69 **TWO BROTHERS**, b g Sir Percy—Blandish (USA) **Thompson Brothers**
70 **VON MELAS (IRE)**, b g Battle of Marengo (IRE)—Rock Magic (IRE) **Mr J Blackburn & Imperial Racing P'ship**
71 **WESTERN BEAT (IRE)**, ch f Mehmas (IRE)—Western Sky **Altitude Racing 3 & Partner**
72 **WHERE'S STEPH**, b f Eagle Top—Piece of Magic **Mr A Pollock & Mr H Jones**
73 **WILLIEWINAMILLION**, b g Charm Spirit (IRE)—Mrs Greeley **The Whc Syndicate**
74 **YORKSHIRE LADY**, gr f Mukhadram—Brave Mave **Mrs L Folwell & Mr J Munroe**

## TWO-YEAR-OLDS

75 B f 09/05 Sir Percy—Aetna (Indesatchel (IRE)) **Mr B. Padgett**
76 B f 14/01 Ardad (IRE)—Amitola (IRE) (Choisir (AUS)) **Mr J. N. Blackburn, Mr B. Padgett**
77 C c 17/03 Divine Prophet (AUS)—Amodio (IRE) (Cape Cross (IRE)) (9524) **Mr B. Padgett**
78 B f 08/02 Al Kazeem—Avessia (Averti (IRE)) (14286) **Mrs C E Mason & Partner**
79 Ro f 27/04 Outstrip—Be Lucky (Kyllachy) **The Lee Westwood Partnership**
80 Br c 25/03 Outstrip—Bow Bridge (Bertolini (USA)) **Mrs A. Jarvis**
81 Gr f 06/05 Pastoral Pursuits—Brave Mave (Daylami (IRE)) **The Laura Mason Syndicate**
82 Gr g 24/04 El Kabeir (USA)—Cesca (Fastnet Rock (AUS)) (3810) **J Blackburn, Imperial Racing & M Grayson**
83 B g 25/01 Sir Percy—Charity (Azamour (IRE)) (7500) **J Blackburn, Imperial Racing & M Grayson**
84 B f 28/01 Ardad (IRE)—Combustible (IRE) (Halling (USA)) **Mr J Blackburn & Imperial Racing P'ship**
85 B f 26/02 Nathaniel (IRE)—Danvina (IRE) (Dansili) (3810) **J Blackburn, Imperial Racing & M Grayson**

## MR MICHAEL EASTERBY - continued

**86** B c 22/04 Muhaarar—Deccan Queen (Rail Link) (4762)  **Mr Chris Stubbs**
**87** DECONTRACTE, b c 23/03 Ardad (IRE)—Natural Appeal (IRE) (Dark Angel (IRE)) (14286)  **Mr B. Hoggarth**
**88** B f 08/03 Forever Now—Diavoleria (Slip Anchor)
**89** B g 28/04 Camacho—Drifting Mist (Muhtathir) (15000)  **The Lee Westwood Partnership**
**90** Br gr g 09/03 Outstrip—Dusty Blue (Medicean)
**91** B f 11/04 Pastoral Pursuits—El Molino Blanco (Royal Applause)  **David Scott & Co (Pattern Makers) Ltd**
**92** B c 20/03 Coach House (IRE)—Elegant Pursuit (Pastoral Pursuits)
**93** Br c 22/03 Galileo Gold—Empress Rock (IRE) (Fastnet Rock (AUS))  **Mr B. Padgett**
**94** B c 11/03 Mastercraftsman (IRE)—Eneryda (FR) (Sinndar (IRE)) (8095)  **J Blackburn, Imperial Racing & M Grayson**
**95** B g 11/04 Ulysses (IRE)—Force One (Dansili)  **J Blackburn, Imperial Racing & M Grayson**
**96** B g 15/02 Ardad (IRE)—High Cross (IRE) (Cape Cross (IRE))  **The Lee Westwood Partnership**
**97** B g 31/01 Nathaniel (IRE)—Island Magic (Oasis Dream)  **Mr J Blackburn & Imperial Racing P'ship**
**98** LE BEAU GARCON, b c 10/04 Brazen Beau (AUS)—Bacall (Paco Boy (IRE)) (1714)  **Bernard Hoggarth Racing**
**99** B g 16/03 Lawman (FR)—Maidin Maith (IRE) (Montjeu (IRE)) (15000)  **J Blackburn, Imperial Racing & M Grayson**
**100** B f 10/02 Nathaniel (IRE)—
Malmesbury (IRE) (Holy Roman Emperor (IRE))  **Mr J Blackburn & Imperial Racing P'ship**
**101** B g 27/01 Teofilo (IRE)—Milady (Shamardal (USA)) (5000)  **J Blackburn, Imperial Racing & M Grayson**
**102** B f 28/02 Holy Roman Emperor (IRE)—
Modern Art (New Approach (IRE)) (7619)  **J Blackburn, Imperial Racing & M Grayson**
**103** Gr g 27/04 Sea The Moon (GER)—
Neige d'Antan (Aussie Rules (USA)) (22000)  **J Blackburn, Imperial Racing & M Grayson**
**104** B f 11/05 Forever Now—Piece of Magic (Alflora (IRE))
**105** B g 08/02 Heeraat (IRE)—Piranha (IRE) (Exceed And Excel (AUS))  **Mr  Malc Hancock**
**106** B g 17/03 Ulysses (IRE)—
Portraitofmylove (IRE) (Azamour (IRE)) (12381)  **J Blackburn, Imperial Racing & M Grayson**
**107** B c 08/02 Pivotal—Queen's Castle (Dansili)  **J Blackburn, Imperial Racing & M Grayson**
**108** B g 10/04 Free Eagle (IRE)—
Rebel Force (IRE) (Dalakhani (IRE)) (9524)  **J Blackburn, Imperial Racing & M Grayson**
**109** B f 01/05 Sir Percy—Ringaround (Karinga Bay)  **Imperial Racing Partnership 2016**
**110** B f 31/01 Havana Gold (IRE)—Rocking The Boat (IRE) (Zebedee)  **Mr J Blackburn & Imperial Racing P'ship**
**111** B f 15/02 El Kabeir (USA)—
Sensational Samba (IRE) (Exceed And Excel (AUS)) (9524)  **Mr S. A. Hollings, Southbank Racing**
**112** Gr g 12/03 Lawman (FR)—Skyline Dancer (Dalakhani (IRE)) (16000)  **J Blackburn, Imperial Racing & M Grayson**
**113** B f 07/02 Caravaggio (USA)—
Spirit of Cuba (IRE) (Invincible Spirit (IRE)) (28571)  **Mr S. A. Hollings, Southbank Racing**
**114** B g 02/02 Dabirsim (FR)—Spirit of India (Galileo (IRE))  **Mr J Blackburn & Imperial Racing P'ship**
**115** Ch f 09/02 Havana Gold (IRE)—
Strawberry Martini (Mount Nelson) (20000)  **Imperial Racing Partnership 2016, Mr R. H. Cooper**
**116** B c 12/02 Estidhkaar (IRE)—Viva Diva (Hurricane Run (IRE)) (2857)  **Southbank Racing**

**Other Owners:** Altitude Racing, Mr C. Bennett, Mr J. N. Blackburn, Mr J Blackburn & Imperial Racing P'ship, Mr J. E. Bray, Mr R. Chapman, Mr R. Connolly, Mr R. H. Cooper, Mr H. Cram, Mr P. D. Cram, David Scott & Co (Pattern Makers) Ltd, Mr S. G. Davis, M. W. Easterby, Mrs L. S. Folwell, Golden Equinox Racing, Mr J. Goodrick, Mr M. Grayson, Mr B. M. P. R. Guerin, Gay & Peter Hartley, P. A. H. Hartley, Mrs R. C. Hartley, Mr B. Hoggarth, Mr S. A. Hollings, S. Hull, Imperial Racing Partnership 2016, Mr H. Jones, The Laura Mason Syndicate, Mrs J. K. Lukas, Mrs C. E. Mason, Mr J Goodrick Racing, Mr S Hull & Laura Mason Syndicate, Mr J. Munroe, Mr A. G. Pollock, Mr I. Robinson, Mr A. Saha, D. Scott, Mr P. G. Scott, Southbank Racing, Stittenham Racing, Mr A. F. Stott, Mr P. Stubbins, Miss M. L. Taylor, Mr G. Thompson, Mr O. Thompson, Mrs J. A. Tinning, W. H. Tinning, Mr A. Turton, Mr L. J. Vincent, Mrs C. M. Wallis, Mr L. J. Westwood, Mr S. A. Windle, Mr S. J. Winter, Mr C. J. Woods, N. H. T. Wrigley, Mr A. H. L. Zheng.

**Assistant Trainer:** Miss Caroline  Bartram, D. M. Easterby.

**Flat Jockey:** Nathan Evans, Paul Mulrennan, James Sullivan. **NH Jockey:** Harry Bannister. **Apprentice Jockey:** Miss Joanna Mason, William Pyle. **Amateur Jockey:** Miss S. Brotherton.

**168**

**MR TIM EASTERBY, Malton**
Postal: **Habton Grange, Great Habton, Malton, North Yorkshire, YO17 6TY**
Contacts: **PHONE 01653 668566 FAX 01653 668621**
EMAIL easterby@habtonfarms.co.uk WEBSITE www.timeasterby.co.uk

1 **AASHEQ (IRE)**, 8, b g Dubawi (IRE)—Beach Bunny (IRE) **Ryedale Partners No1**
2 **AFANDEM (IRE)**, 7, b g Vale of York (IRE)—Al Mahmeyah **Reality Partnerships XI**
3 **AL ERAYG (IRE)**, 8, b g Oasis Dream—Vallee des Reves (USA) **Reality Partnerships III**
4 **AMADEUS GREY (IRE)**, 5, gr g Zebedee—Benedicte (IRE) **Ontoawinner 10 & Partner**
5 **APPOINTED**, 7, b m Delegator—Celestial Harmony **Habton Racing**
6 **ART POWER (IRE)**, 4, gr c Dark Angel (IRE)—Evening Time (IRE) **King Power Racing Co Ltd**
7 **ASYLO (IRE)**, 9, b g Flemensfirth (USA)—Escrea (IRE) **Mr I. P. Crane**
8 **BOARDMAN**, 5, b g Kingman—Nimble Thimble (USA) **Mr Ball, Mr Hodkinson, Mr Malley & Ptr**
9 **BOLLIN ACE**, 10, b g Bollin Eric—Bollin Annabel **Ryedale Partners No 3**
10 **BOLLIN JOAN**, 6, b m Mount Nelson—Bollin Greta **N Arton, P Hebdon, R Taylor & Prtnr**
11 **BOLLIN MARGARET**, 4, b f Fountain of Youth (IRE)—Bollin Greta **Mr D B & Mrs C Lamplough & Partner**
12 **BOLLIN NEIL**, 5, ch g Haafhd—Bollin Nellie **Habton Racing**
13 **BOLLIN PHOENIX**, 4, b g Phoenix Reach (IRE)—Bollin Annabel **Habton Racing**
14 **BOLLIN TED**, 7, b g Haafhd—Bollin Greta **Mr Neil Arton & Partner**
15 **BOSSIPOP**, 8, ch g Assertive—Opopmil (IRE) **A. R. Turnbull**
16 **BROTHER MCGONAGALL**, 7, b r Equiano (FR)—Anatase **Reality Partnerships VI**
17 4, B g Mazameer (IRE)—Cassique Lady (IRE) **Habton Racing**
18 **CASSY O (IRE)**, 4, b g Camacho—Hawaajib (FR) **R. Taylor & Mr P. Hebdon**
19 **CHIEF CRAFTSMAN**, 7, gr ro g Mastercraftsman (IRE)—Eurolink Raindance (IRE) **Mr & Mrs J. D. Cotton**
20 **CILLUIRID (IRE)**, 7, b g Arcadio (GER)—Garw Valley **Reality Partnerships IV**
21 **CONTREBASSE**, 6, b g Champs Elysees—Viola da Braccio (IRE) **The Harmonious Lot & Partner**
22 **COPPER KNIGHT (IRE)**, 7, b g Sir Prancealot (IRE)—Mystic Dream **Middleham Park, Ventura Racing 6&partner**
23 **COUNT D'ORSAY (IRE)**, 5, b g Dandy Man (IRE)—Deira (USA) **Mr Ambrose Turnbull & John Cruces**
24 **CRUYFF TURN**, 4, ch g Dutch Art—Provenance **Aberdeen Park & Partner**
25 **DANCE KING**, 11, ch g Danehill Dancer (IRE)—One So Wonderful **Habton Racing**
26 **DANZAN (IRE)**, 6, b g Lawman (FR)—Charanga **Reality Partnerships XVII**
27 **DARK JEDI (IRE)**, 5, b g Kodiac—Whitefall (USA) **Mr Evan M Sutherland & Partner**
28 **DELGREY BOY**, 4, b g Delegator—Maybeagrey **Reality Partnerships XIV**
29 **DREAMSELLER (IRE)**, 5, b g Dream Ahead (USA)—Picture of Lily **Ryedale Partners No. 2**
30 **DUKE OF YORKSHIRE**, 11, b g Duke of Marmalade (IRE)—Dame Edith (FR) **Habton Racing**
31 **EAST STREET REVUE**, 8, ch g Pastoral Pursuits—Revue Princess (IRE) **Mr S. A. Heley & Partner**
32 **EEH BAH GUM (IRE)**, 6, b g Dandy Man (IRE)—Moonline Dancer (FR) **Mr N. A. Rhodes**
33 **EURO FOU (IRE)**, 6, ch g Le Fou (IRE)—Euro Joy (IRE) **Habton Racing**
34 **EXCESSABLE**, 8, ch g Sakhee's Secret—Kummel Excess (IRE) **Mr B Guerin & Habton Racing**
35 **FARHH TO GO**, 4, b g Farhh—Queen Aggie (IRE) **Habton Racing**
36 **FISHABLE**, 4, b g Dutch Art—Sweet Stream (ITY) **Mr B Guerin & Habton Racing**
37 **GARDEN OASIS**, 6, b g Excelebration (IRE)—Queen Arabella **Mr T. A. Scothern & Partner**
38 **GLENCADAM GLORY**, 7, b g Nathaniel (IRE)—Lady Grace (IRE) **MPR, Ventura Racing 15 & Partner**
39 **GOLDEN APOLLO**, 7, ch g Pivotal—Elan **Mr David Scott & Partner**
40 **GRAND PIANOLA**, 4, b g Firebreak—Grand Liaison **Mr J. C. Mowat**
41 **HIGHWAYGREY**, 5, b g Dick Turpin (IRE)—Maybeagrey **Reality Partnerships VII**
42 **HILDENLEY**, 4, ch g Teofilo (IRE)—Alpine Storm (IRE) **Elsa Crankshaw, Gordon Allan & Partner**
43 **HYPERFOCUS (IRE)**, 7, b g Intense Focus (USA)—Jouel (FR) **Ryedale Partners No 14**
44 **IWASTHEFUTUREONCE (IRE)**, 8, b g Fruits of Love (USA)—Ruthy Lukey (IRE) **Ryedale Partners No 11**
45 **JEWEL MAKER (IRE)**, 6, b g Invincible Spirit (IRE)—Sapphire (IRE) **Reality Partnerships I**
46 **JUST HISS**, 8, b g Lawman (FR)—Feather Boa (IRE) **The Sandmoor Partnership**
47 **JUST MAGIC**, 5, ch g Sepoy (AUS)—Magic Music (IRE) **R. Bailey**
48 **KYOTO STAR (FR)**, 7, b g Oasis Dream—Hanami **Mr I. P. Crane**
49 **LAMPANG (IRE)**, 4, b c Dandy Man (IRE)—Black Mascara (IRE) **King Power Racing Co Ltd**
50 **LITTLE TED**, 4, ch g Cityscape—Speedy Utmost Meg **Mr M. J. Macleod**
51 **MAC AILEY**, 5, ch g Firebreak—Rosabee (IRE) **Dubelem (racing) Limited & Partner**
52 **MANIGORDO (USA)**, 4, b br g Kitten's Joy (USA)—Cutting Edge (USA) **Mr M. J. Macleod**
53 **MIKMAK**, 3, b g Makfi—Rakata (USA) **K J Racing**
54 **MILL RACE KING**, 8, b g Scorpion (IRE)—Oso Special **Reality Partnerships IX**
55 **MISCHIEF MANAGED (IRE)**, 7, ch g Tagula (IRE)—Cape Clear **Dubelem (Racing) Limited**

# MR TIM EASTERBY - continued

56 **MOROZOV COCKTAIL (IRE)**, 5, b g Morozov (USA)—Gold Platinum (IRE)  **Mr & Mrs N Wrigley & Partner**
57 **MOTARAJEL**, 4, b g Camacho—Vereri Senes  **Reality Partnerships XVIII**
58 **MR CARPENTER (IRE)**, 5, gr ro g Mastercraftsman (IRE)—Satwa Pearl  **Mr B Valentine & Partner**
59 **MUKHAYYAM**, 9, b g Dark Angel (IRE)—Caster Sugar (USA)  **Mr T. A. Scothern & Partner**
60 **MULTELLIE**, 9, b g Multiplex—Bollin Nellie  **Mr David Scott & Partner**
61 **MUSIC SOCIETY (IRE)**, 6, gr g Society Rock (IRE)—Absolutely Cool (IRE)  **R. Taylor & Mr P. Hebdon**
62 **MY THOUGHT (IRE)**, 4, b g Kodiac—Aricia (IRE)  **Mr Evan M Sutherland & Partner**
63 **NEARLY A GONNA**, 4, ro g Helmet (AUS)—Clodova (IRE)  **E. A. Brook**
64 **NED'S ESCAPE (IRE)**, 6, b g Getaway (GER)—Ned's Joy (IRE)  **Mr T. J. Hemmings**
65 **NODDYOLDER**, 4, b g Slade Power (IRE)—Shamardal Phantom (IRE)  **Reality Partnerships**
66 **OBEE JO (IRE)**, 5, b g Kodiac—Maleha (IRE)  **Mrs Joanne Boxcer & Partner**
67 **ORION'S BOW**, 10, ch g Pivotal—Heavenly Ray (USA)  **Mr T. J. Swiers**
68 **PARYS MOUNTAIN (IRE)**, 7, gr g Dark Angel (IRE)—Muzdaan (IRE)  **Reality Partnerships XII**
69 **PERFECT SWISS**, 5, b g Swiss Spirit—Perfect Practice  **Mr Craig Wilson & Partner**
70 **PHOENIX APPROACH (IRE)**, 4, b g Dawn Approach (IRE)—Purple Warrior (USA)  **Mr Lee Bond & Partner**
71 **POET'S DAWN**, 6, ch g Poet's Voice—Dudley Queen (IRE)  **Mr Timothy O'Gram & Partner**
72 **PUPPETONASTRING**, 6, b m Sixties Icon—Valbuena (IRE)  **David Lumley & Prtnr**
73 **REGAL MIRAGE (IRE)**, 7, ch g Aqlaam—Alzaroof (USA)  **Ryedale Partners No 7**
74 **RELKADAM (FR)**, 7, ch g Muhtathir—Gloirez (FR)  **Ryedale Partners No 12**
75 4, B g Norse Dancer (IRE)—Rule Britannia  **Mr E. A. Brook & Partner**
76 **SAMEEM (IRE)**, 5, b g New Approach (IRE)—Ahla Wasahl  **The Sandmoor Partnership**
77 **SAN ROCH (FR)**, 4, ch g Le Havre (IRE)—Four Green (FR)  **Ryedale Partners No 13**
78 **SECRETARIAL (IRE)**, 5, b m Kingman—Wadaat  **Habton Racing**
79 **SHERIFF GARRETT (IRE)**, 7, b g Lawman (FR)—Few Are Chosen (IRE)  **Ontoawinner 10 & Partner 4**
80 **SILVER SNIPER**, 4, gr g Zebedee—Velvet Kiss (IRE)  **David Lumley & Prtnr**
81 **SIR CHARLES PUNCH**, 4, b g Sir Percy—Russian Punch  **Ryedale Partners No. 10**
82 **SKIPNESS**, 6, b g Desideratum—Gwyre (IRE)  **Habton Racing**
83 **STAXTON**, 6, b g Equiano (FR)—Snake's Head  **Ontoawinner 10 & Partner**
84 **STRONGBOWE (FR)**, 5, b g Siyouni (FR)—Landing Site (FR)  **Ryedale Partners No 6**
85 **STROXX (IRE)**, 4, b g Camacho—Labisa (IRE)  **Stroxx Partnership**
86 **SUNDAY SOVEREIGN**, 4, b g Equiano (FR)—Red Sovereign  **King Power Racing Co Ltd**
87 **TEMPER TRAP**, 4, br g Slade Power (IRE)—Sloane Square  **Ontoawinner 10 & Partner**
88 **TEMPLEPOINT**, 10, gr g Fair Mix (IRE)—Flamebird (IRE)  **Mr J. W. E. Bevin**
89 **TRUE BLUE MOON (IRE)**, 6, gr g Holy Roman Emperor (IRE)—Fancy Intense  **Mr B Valentine & Partner**
90 **UGO GREGORY**, 5, gr g Gregorian (IRE)—Raajis (IRE)  **Mr F. Gillespie**
91 4, B f Fountain of Youth (IRE)—Upton Seas  **Mr E. A. Brook & Partner**
92 **VIVE LA DIFFERENCE (IRE)**, 7, b g Holy Roman Emperor (IRE)—Galaxie Sud (USA)  **Ryedale Partners No 5**
93 **WADE'S MAGIC**, 4, gr g Lethal Force (IRE)—Miliika  **Reality Partnerships XVI**
94 **WALK WITH KINGS (IRE)**, 5, b g Ruler of The World (IRE)—Shakeeba (IRE)  **Habton Racing**
95 **WAR DEFENDER**, 4, b g War Command (USA)—Never Lose  **Ryedale Partners No.15**
96 **WELLS FARHH GO (IRE)**, 6, b h Farhh—Mowazana (IRE)  **Mr S A Heley & Partner**
97 **WILDBEAUTIFULTHING**, 4, b f Cityscape—Beautifulwildthing  **Mr M. J. Macleod**
98 **XCELENTE**, 4, b g Exceed And Excel (AUS)—Vanity Rules  **Ontoawinner, Ckw Engineering & Partner**

## THREE-YEAR-OLDS

99 **ALBEGONE**, b g Alhebayeb (IRE)—Pacngo  **Mr D B & Mrs C Lamplough & Partner**
100 **AVA GO JOE (IRE)**, b g Dragon Pulse (IRE)—Elusive Ellen (IRE)  **Mr B Valentine & Partner**
101 **BARNEY'S BAY**, b g Cable Bay (IRE)—Fisadara  **Mr J. R. Saville**
102 B g Brazen Beau (AUS)—Bexandella  **Mr T. A. Scothern & Partner**
103 **BITE YA LEGS**, b g Pastoral Pursuits—Cheers For Thea (IRE)  **ALAW**
104 **BRANDY BAY**, b f Cable Bay (IRE)—Shaken And Stirred  **Mr D. A. West & Partner**
105 **CANARIA PRINCE**, bl g Alhebayeb (IRE)—Gran Canaria Queen  **The Senators**
106 **CAPE HORN**, b g Gleneagles (IRE)—Amazonas (IRE)  **Sir Robert Ogden**
107 **CARRIGILLIHY**, gr g New Bay—Spectacle  **The Harmonious Lot & Partner**
108 **CRAGSIDE**, b g Pride of Dubai (AUS)—Umneeyetae (AUS)  **Elsa Crankshaw, Gordon Allan & Partner**
109 B g Mayson—Crimson Cloud  **Habton Racing**
110 **DAN DE LIGHT (IRE)**, ch g Twilight Son—Nancy Astor  **Reality Partnerships X**
111 **DEREKSSON (IRE)**, b g Mayson—Sampleur (FR)  **Ontoawinner 10 & Partner**
112 **DUE LOOK**, b f Due Diligence (USA)—Look Here's Dee  **S. L. Edwards**

# MR TIM EASTERBY - continued

113 **ECLIPSE DE LUNAR (IRE)**, b g Sea The Moon (GER)—Scoville (GER)  **Bulmer, Hebdon R Taylor**
114 **ELEGANT ELLEN (FR)**, b f Shalaa (IRE)—Lily of The Lake (FR)  **Mr L. Mulryan**
115 **EYE KNEE**, b c Territories (IRE)—Western Pearl  **A. Ali**
116 **FOSSOS (IRE)**, b c Dandy Man (IRE)—Beguiler  **FOSSOS**
117 **GOLDEN DOVE**, b f Golden Horn—Laughing Dove (IRE)  **Mr & Mrs J. D. Cotton**
118 **HARD TO FAULT**, b c Harzand (IRE)—Polly Floyer  **Habton Racing**
119 **IMPELLER**, b g Pivotal—Musical Beat (IRE)  **D Scott & Co (pattern makers) Ltd & Ptr**
120 **INTELLO BOY**, ch g Intello (GER)—New Romantic  **Mr & Mrs J. D. Cotton**
121 B g Fountain of Youth (IRE)—Katie Boo (IRE)  **Habton Racing**
122 **KENTUCKY KITTEN (IRE)**, b g Bobby's Kitten (USA)—Galistic (IRE)  **Mrs T. Whatley**
123 **KIDYOUNOT (IRE)**, b g Mehmas (IRE)—Jenlen (USA)  **Mr E. A. Brook & Partner**
124 **LA VIE JOLIE (IRE)**, ch f Mastercraftsman (IRE)—Aurora Borealis (IRE)  **Sir Robert Ogden**
125 **LADY BOND**, b f Fastnet Rock (AUS)—Liberally (IRE)  **Mr Lee Bond & Partner**
126 **LISTEN AGAIN (IRE)**, b f Make Believe—Though (IRE)  **Ryedale Partners No 8**
127 **LOST MY SOCK (IRE)**, ch g Bungle Inthejungle—Changari (USA)  **Ptners & O Rourke**
128 **MAKE A SPARK (IRE)**, b f Flintshire—Imalwayshotforyou (USA)  **Habton Racing**
129 B f Nathaniel (IRE)—Maven  **Habton Racing**
130 **MAXIMUM RISK (IRE)**, b g Twilight Son—Hasty (IRE)  **Abbas Alalawi & Partner**
131 **MIDNIGHT STRIPPER**, gr ro f Outstrip—Midnight Mojito  **Mr D. A. West & Partner**
132 **MOORLAND QUEEN (IRE)**, b f Kodiac—Qalahari (IRE)  **Hp Racing Moorland Queen & Ptnr**
133 **MOZAMBIQUE (IRE)**, ch g Australia—Song of My Heart (IRE)  **Sir Robert Ogden**
134 **MYRISTICA (IRE)**, br f Harzand (IRE)—Black Mascara (IRE)  **King Power Racing Co Ltd**
135 **NAUGHTY ANA (IRE)**, b f Anodin (IRE)—Boldarra (USA)  **A. R. Turnbull**
136 B g Poet's Voice—No Poppy (IRE)  **Mr J Musgrave & Partner**
137 **OLYMPUS (IRE)**, b g Kingman—Carpe Vita (IRE)  **Sir Robert Ogden**
138 B f Fountain of Youth (IRE)—Penny Garcia  **Mr J. F. Bowers**
139 **PIVOTING**, b g Charming Thought—Poppy Pivot (IRE)  **A. R. Turnbull**
140 **PORTENO**, b g Cityscape—Speedy Utmost Meg  **Mr M. J. Macleod**
141 **SHOWALONG**, ch c Showcasing—Muaamara  **The Showalong Partnership**
142 **SOLLER BAY (IRE)**, b f Iffraaj—Ahazeej (IRE)  **Mrs Joanne Boxcer & Partner**
143 **SUMMER POWER (FR)**, b g Pivotal—Belle Josephine  **King Power Racing Co Ltd**
144 **SYMBOL OF HOPE**, b g Dandy Man (IRE)—Catalina Bay (IRE)  **Clipper Group Holdings Ltd**
145 **TEQUILA ROYALE**, b f Equiano (FR)—Traditionelle  **Lovely Bubbly Racing**
146 **TOM'S REIGN BEAU**, b g Brazen Beau (AUS)—Miaplacidus (IRE)  **Mr S A Heley & Partner**
147 **TRIPLE JAYE**, b f Charming Thought—Carpe Vita (IRE)  **Ontoawinner 10, Saxtead Livestock & Prtr**
148 **UNDER FOX (IRE)**, b g Dandy Man (IRE)—Lily's Rainbow (IRE)  **King Power Racing Co Ltd**
149 B f Casamento (IRE)—Upton Seas  **Habton Racing**
150 **WILDCITYDIVA**, ch f Cityscape—Beautifulwildthing  **Mr M. J. Macleod**
151 **WINTER POWER (IRE)**, b f Bungle Inthejungle—Titian Saga (IRE)  **King Power Racing Co Ltd**

## TWO-YEAR-OLDS

152 B c 08/04 Sea The Moon (GER)—Bracing Breeze (Dansili) (23810)  **Ashfield Caravan Park**
153 B c 30/04 Strath Burn—Dakota Two (IRE) (Frenchmans Bay (FR)) (11000)  **Habton Racing**
154 B c 07/04 Brazen Beau (AUS)—Delta Diva (USA) (Victory Gallop (CAN)) (6000)  **Habton Racing**
155 Ch f 23/02 Mehmas (IRE)—Fayreway (IRE) (Strategic Prince) (10000)  **Ontoawinner 10 & Partner**
156 **FLIPPIN' ECK (IRE)**, b c 08/02 Gleneagles (IRE)—
Sweet Serendipity (Stimulation (IRE)) (22857)  **Nick Rhodes & Partner**
157 B f 09/04 Kodiac—Fusion (IRE) (Cape Cross (IRE)) (29524)  **Reality Partnerships II**
158 **GIGGLE BAND (IRE)**, b f 25/04 Bungle Inthejungle—
Perle de La Mer (IRE) (Born To Sea (IRE)) (15238)  **Mr John Davies & Partner**
159 **GNAT ALLEY (IRE)**, gr f 12/03 Caravaggio (USA)—Winter Snow (IRE) (Raven's Pass (USA)) (30000)  **Mr J. C. Davies**
160 B c 16/02 Mattmu—Ice Mayden (Major Cadeaux) (6190)  **Mr B Valentine & Partner**
161 B f 01/03 Ardad (IRE)—Love Action (IRE) (Motivator) (8000)  **Grange Park Racing Club & Hr**
162 **MANILA SCOUSE**, b c 28/02 Aclaim (IRE)—
Forever Excel (IRE) (Excelebration (IRE)) (8571)  **Mr Ambrose Turnbull & John Cruces**
163 B c 05/02 Buratino (IRE)—Midnight Mojito (Azamour (IRE)) (5000)  **Habton Racing**
164 B f 02/04 Bungle Inthejungle—Milly's Secret (IRE) (Sakhee's Secret) (8000)  **Habton Racing**
165 **PERLA**, b f 04/05 Twilight Son—Seaperle (Firebreak) (1000)  **Bearstone Stud Limited**
166 Ch f 25/02 Territories (IRE)—Present Day (Cadeaux Genereux) (9000)  **Habton Racing**

## MR TIM EASTERBY - continued

**167** RED ASTAIRE, ch c 16/02 Intello (GER)—Barynya (Pivotal) (7000) **The Wolf Pack 2 & Partner**
**168** Ch c 10/02 Buratino (IRE)—Silent Serenade (Bertolini (USA)) (4762) **Mr B Valentine & Partner**
**169** B f 05/03 Iffraaj—Stella Point (IRE) (Pivotal) (16190) **Habton Racing**
**170** THE GREY WOLF (IRE), gr c 22/03 Dark Angel (IRE)—
Penny Pepper (Fast Company (IRE)) (60000) **The Wolf Pack 2 & Partner**
**171** B f 14/02 Territories (IRE)—Weisse Socken (IRE) (Acclamation) (13333) **N. A. Jackson**
**172** B f 03/03 Territories (IRE)—Xylophone (Medicean) (20952) **Habton Racing**
**173** ZIMMERMAN, ch c 15/02 Poet's Voice—Cresta Gold (Halling (USA)) (20000) **Linkenholt Racing & Partner**

**Other Owners:** Mr A. Al Alawi, Mr G. Allan, Mr N. F. Arton, Mr J. Ball, Mr L. Bond, Mrs J. Boxcer, Mr S. Bridge, E. A. Brook, Mr S. N. Bulmer, Miss E. Crankshaw, Mr A. D. Crombie, Mr J. Cruces, David Scott & Co (Pattern Makers) Ltd, Mr J. C. Davies, Mr A. Denham, Mr T. Denham, Dubelem (Racing) Limited, Mr T. D. Easterby, Mr G. Fox, Mr A. Gemmell, A. J. J. Gompertz, Grange Park Racing Club, Mr J. H. Green, Mrs K. E. Green, Mr B. M. P. R. Guerin, HP Racing Moorland Queen, Habton Racing, Mr P. F. Hebdon, S. A. Heley, Mr A. S. Hodkinson, Mr M. Kershaw, Mrs D. Lamplough, D. B. Lamplough, Linkenholt Racing, Mr David John Lumley, Mrs S. Magnier, Mr P. Malley, Middleham Park and Ventura Racing 15, Middleham Park and Ventura Racing 6, Mr P. H. Milmo, Mr J. E. Mott, Mrs J. M. Mott, Mr J. C. Musgrave, Mr N. J. O'Brien, T. J. O'Gram, Mrs M. O'Rourke, Sir R. Ogden C.B.E., LLD, Ontoawinner 10, Ontoawinner, CKW Engineering, Mr W. M. Oxley, T. S. Palin, W. H. Ponsonby, M. Prince, Mr A. H. Raby, Mr N. A. Rhodes, Ryedale Partners No 4, Saxtead Livestock Ltd, T. A. Scothern, D. Scott, Mr J. F. Strain, Mr T. J. Strain, Mr E. M. Sutherland, Mr R. Taylor, The Harmonious Lot, A. R. Turnbull, Mr B. Valentine, D. A. West, Mr C. Wilson, N. H. T. Wrigley, Mrs V. A. Wrigley.

---

**169** **MR BRIAN ECKLEY, Brecon**
Postal: **Closcedi Farm, Llanspyddid, Brecon, Powys, LD3 8NS**
Contacts: **PHONE 01874 622422 MOBILE 07891 445409**
**EMAIL brian.eckley@live.co.uk**

**1** JAUNTY EXPRESS, 5, b g Yorgunnabelucky (USA)—Jaunty Spirit **B. J. Eckley**
**2** JAUNTY FREYJA, 6, b m Norse Dancer (IRE)—Jaunty Walk **B. J. Eckley**
**3** JAUNTY VIKING, 6, b g Norse Dancer (IRE)—Jaunty Spirit **B. J. Eckley**
**4** 4, B f Yorgunnabelucky (USA)—Jaunty Walk **B. J. Eckley**
**5** LIBBERTY HUNTER, 5, b g Yorgunnabelucky (USA)—Classy Crewella **B. J. Eckley**
**6** LIBERTY BELLA, 7, b m Librettist (USA)—Classy Crewella **B. J. Eckley**
**7** TIMEFORADANCE, 6, b g Norse Dancer (IRE)—Timeforagin **B. J. Eckley**
**8** TIMEFORATUNE, 5, b g Yorgunnabelucky (USA)—Timeforagin **B. J. Eckley**

---

**170** **MR ROBERT EDDERY, Newmarket**
Postal: **Robert Eddery Racing Limited, Heyward Place Stables, Hamilton Road, Newmarket, Suffolk, CB8 7JQ**
Contacts: **PHONE 01638 428001 MOBILE 07938 898455**
**EMAIL info@robertedderyracing.com WEBSITE www.robertedderyracing.com**

**1** COLWOOD, 7, ch g Champs Elysees—La Colline (GER) **R. J. Creese**
**2** COUNTRY'N'WESTERN (FR), 9, b g Samum (GER)—Cracking Melody **Mr C. R. Eddery**
**3** EEVILYNN DREW, 4, b g Epaulette (AUS)—Halicardia **Graham & Lynn Knight**
**4** ELSIE VIOLET (IRE), 5, ch m Gale Force Ten—Kuaicoss (IRE) **E. S. Phillips**
**5** GEORGE THOMAS, 5, b g Heerraat (IRE)—Lexington Rose **Mr C. R. Eddery**
**6** HOTSPUR HARRY (IRE), 4, b g Zoffany (IRE)—Dark Crusader (IRE) **R. J. Creese**
**7** MANZO DURO (IRE), 4, b g Slade Power (IRE)—Miss Cape (IRE) **Mr C. R. Eddery**
**8** NATIVE SILVER, 5, gr g Olympic Glory (IRE)—Kendorova (IRE) **Pamela Aitken & Julia Rayment**
**9** SPRING BLOOM, 4, ch g Power—Almond Branches **Mrs P. Aitken**

## MR ROBERT EDDERY - continued

10 TYNECASTLE PARK, 8, b g Sea The Stars (IRE)—So Silk  Mr C. R. Eddery

### THREE-YEAR-OLDS
11 CLASSY DAME (IRE), b f Belardo (IRE)—Scholarly  Graham & Lynn Knight & R J Creese
12 VINO SANTO, b g Cable Bay (IRE)—Sugar Free (IRE)  Julia Rayment & Robert Eddery

**Other Owners:** Mrs P. Aitken, R. J. Creese, Mr C. R. Eddery, G. Knight, Graham & Lynn Knight, Mrs L. C. Knight, Mrs J. M. Rayment.

**Flat Jockey:** Andrea Atzeni. **Apprentice Jockey:** Selma Grage. **Amateur Jockey:** Mr George Eddery.

---

**171**  **MR STUART EDMUNDS, Newport Pagnell**
Postal: **6 Fences Farm, Tyringham, Newport Pagnell, Buckinghamshire, MK16 9EN**
Contacts: **PHONE 01908 611369, 01908 611406 MOBILE 07778 782591 FAX 01908 611255**
EMAIL Trishandstu@aol.com

1 A LITTLE CHAOS (IRE), 7, b m Yeats (IRE)—Marias Dream (IRE)  The Garratt Family
2 AIRGEAD SUAS (IRE), 8, b m Gold Well—Emmas' House (IRE)  The Holryale Partnership
3 BLACKFINCH, 6, ch g Black Sam Bellamy (IRE)—Grassfinch  The Long Hop Syndicate
4 BLUE BIKINI, 5, b m Winged Love (IRE)—Bleu d'Avril (FR)  Nick Brown Racing
5 BLUE CATO (IRE), 4, b g Notnowcato—Heart of Love (IRE)  The Horwoods Partnership
6 BRAN, 6, b g Sakhee (USA)—Cup of Love (USA)  M. Kehoe
7 CLASSIC BEN (IRE), 8, b g Beneficial—Dark Daisy (IRE)  The Lavendon Partnership
8 DEPUTY'S OSCAR (IRE), 8, b m Oscar (IRE)—Shesourpresent (IRE)  Horwood Harriers Partnership
9 DRUMLEE GETAWAY (IRE), 6, b m Getaway (GER)—The Vicars Lady (IRE)  Mr P. D. Wells
10 DUNEFINCH, 5, b g Dunaden (FR)—Grassfinch  Far Bihoue Partnership
11 GO MILLIE GO (IRE), 8, b m Milan—Another Present (IRE)  The Chicheley Partnership
12 GRAND LORD (FR), 5, gr g Lord du Sud (FR)—Toscane des Fleurs (FR)  Mr D. Mitson
13 HAVANA HERMANO (IRE), 7, b g Flemensfirth (USA)—Senorita Rumbalita  The Golf Victor Charlie Syndicate
14 HI HO SILVA LINING (IRE), 5, b br g Flemensfirth (USA)—Madame McGoldrick (IRE)  The Ivo Partnership
15 HILLFINCH, 4, ch f Hillstar—Grassfinch  Exors of the Late Mr P. D. Robeson
16 HOMETOWN BOY (IRE), 6, ch g Curtain Time (IRE)—Mercy Mission  The Garratt Family
17 LARUSSO (IRE), 4, ch g Doyen (IRE)—Muckle Flugga (IRE)  The Larusso Partnership
18 MANDOCELLO (FR), 5, b g Motivator—Serenada (FR)  Mrs R. L. Banks
19 MARSH WREN, 5, b m Schiaparelli (GER)—Carolina Wren  Far Bihoue Partnership
20 MASKADA (FR), 5, b m Masked Marvel—Mandina (FR)  M. Kehoe
21 MEGAN (GER), 4, ch f Lord of England (GER)—Mrs Summersby (IRE)  The Danum Partnership
22 MEXICO (GER), 5, b g Sea The Moon (GER)—Mexicali (IRE)  Mr D. Mitson
23 MIDNIGHT MARY, 5, b m Midnight Legend—Epee Celeste (FR)  Mr S A Richards & Louise Kemble
24 MY GIRL LOLLIPOP (IRE), 5, b m Mahler—Pop Princess  Mrs N. C. Kappler
25 NOW MCGINTY (IRE), 10, b g Stowaway—Western Whisper (IRE)  The Garratt Family
26 ONE EYE ON VEGAS, 4, b g Blue Bresil (FR)—Savingforvegas (IRE)  Mr B. H. Turner
27 OUR BUBBA (IRE), 7, b g Scorpion (IRE)—Lady Marnay (IRE)  The Sharnbrook Partnership
28 QUEENOHEARTS (IRE), 8, ch m Flemensfirth (USA)—Chars (IRE)  The Sherington Partnership
29 RED ROYALIST, 7, b g Royal Applause—Scarlet Royal  Mrs R. L. Banks
30 ROWLAND WARD, 5, b g Sea The Stars (IRE)—Honor Bound  Mr D. Mitson
31 SOME CAN SING (IRE), 6, b g Recital (FR)—Our Fair Lady (IRE)  Woodhall Kenward Fuller
32 VELVET VOICE, 7, b m Azamour (IRE)—Battery Power  Sarabex
33 WHO'S THE BOSS (IRE), 6, b br m Oscar (IRE)—Final Episode (IRE)  Mr D. Mitson
34 WOLF OF WINDLESHAM (IRE), 9, ch g Mastercraftsman (IRE)—Al Amlah (USA)  M. W. Lawrence
35 YOUNG OFFENDER (IRE), 6, b g Rule of Law (USA)—Cayetina  Mr D. Mitson

## MR STUART EDMUNDS - continued

### THREE-YEAR-OLDS

36  **SEDGE WREN,** b f Blue Bresil (FR)—Carolina Wren **Exors of the Late Mr P. D. Robeson**
37  **TREEFINCH,** b f Telescope (IRE)—Grassfinch **Exors of the Late Mr P. D. Robeson**

**Other Owners:** Ms L. M. Kemble, Mr K. J. Orchard, Mr S. A. Richards, Mr D. A. M. R. Shuttle, Mr J. A. Tabb, Mr B. H. Turner.

**Assistant Trainer:** Miss Harriet Edmunds.

---

**172**  **MR GORDON EDWARDS, Minehead**
Postal: **Summering, Wheddon Cross, Minehead, Somerset, TA24 7AT**
Contacts: **PHONE 01643 831549 MOBILE 07970 059297 FAX 01643 831549**
**EMAIL angelaedwards549@gmail.com**

1  **IN ARREARS (IRE),** 9, b m Beneficial—Gullet Dawn (IRE) **G. F. Edwards**
2  **SHANANN STAR (IRE),** 15, br m Anshan—Baile An Droichid (IRE) **G. F. Edwards**

**Amateur Jockey:** Mr D. Edwards.

---

**173**  **MISS LUCINDA EGERTON, Malton**
Postal: **Flint Hall, Brawby, Malton, North Yorkshire, YO17 6PZ**
Contacts: **PHONE 01944 768233 MOBILE 07900 458666**
**EMAIL lucy@legertonracing.co.uk WEBSITE www.legertonracing.co.uk**

1  **BEAUTY DRAGON (IRE),** 9, b g Rip Van Winkle (IRE)—Turning Light (GER) **Miss S. J. Perry**
2  **CALCULUS (IRE),** 4, b c Frankel—Vital Statistics **Miss L. Egerton**
3  **KING FAN,** 4, b c Kingman—Forever Times **Miss L. Egerton**
4  **MIDDLESCENCE (IRE),** 7, ch g Lope de Vega (IRE)—Silesian (IRE) **Reassuringly Racy Club**
5  **NAKED LASS,** 4, b f Champs Elysees—Undress (IRE) **Miss L. Egerton**
6  4, B f Flemensfirth (USA)—Nivalf **Miss L. Egerton**
7  **OPECHEE (IRE),** 10, b g Robin des Champs (FR)—Falcons Gift (IRE) **Northern Belles**
8  **OROBAS (IRE),** 9, b g Dark Angel (IRE)—Miss Mujadil (IRE) **Northern Belles**
9  **PRISSY MISSY (IRE),** 4, b f Gutaifan (IRE)—Maracuja **Miss L. Egerton**
10  **RIPPLET,** 6, b m Rip Van Winkle (IRE)—Seradim **Flint Hall Racing**
11  **SIGNORE PICCOLO,** 10, b g Piccolo—Piccolo Cativo **Mike and Eileen Newbould**
12  **SMART LIVING,** 6, b g Teofilo (IRE)—Ard Fheis (IRE) **Northern Belles**
13  **TRUE COMPANION (IRE),** 8, b g Fast Company (IRE)—Panglossian (IRE) **Mr H. Beggs**
14  **TRUMPETS CALL (IRE),** 4, ch g Anjaal—Yellow Trumpet **Miss L. Egerton**
15  **WELSH RAREBIT,** 8, b g Dylan Thomas (IRE)—Chelsey Jayne (IRE) **Flint Hall Racing**
16  **WYNFORD (IRE),** 8, ch g Dylan Thomas (IRE)—Wishing Chair (USA) **Mike and Eileen Newbould**

### THREE-YEAR-OLDS

17  B f Hallowed Crown (AUS)—Gold Tobougg **Flint Hall Racing**

### TWO-YEAR-OLDS

18  B f 29/03 Ardad (IRE)—Alnawiyah (Dalakhani (IRE))
19  Gr c 22/04 Gutaifan (IRE)—Flame of Ireland (IRE) (Fasliyev (USA))
20  Gr f 25/01 El Kabeir (USA)—Gold Tobougg (Tobougg (IRE)) **Mr J. M. Newbould**

**Other Owners:** Miss L. Egerton, Mrs E. E. Newbould, Mr J. M. Newbould.

**174** **MISS CLARE ELLAM, Market Drayton**
Postal: **Lostford Manor Stables, Mickley, Tern Hill, Market Drayton, Shropshire, TF9 3QW**
Contacts: **MOBILE 07974 075042**
EMAIL clareellam@btinternet.com WEBSITE www.clareellamracing.com

1 **ARCHIE STEVENS**, 11, b g Pastoral Pursuits—Miss Wells (IRE) **Miss Clare L. Ellam**
2 **BADREPUTATION**, 4, b g Iffraaj—Cats Eyes **Mr D. T. Carder**
3 **FRIENDS DON'T TELL**, 5, b g Mount Nelson—The Blue Dog (IRE) **Mr R. P. Clarke**
4 **KHELEYF'S GIRL**, 6, br m Kheleyf (USA)—Handsome Molly **Miss Clare L. Ellam**
5 **LUNAR MIST**, 7, b m Bated Breath—Time Will Show (FR) **Mr R. P. Clarke**
6 **PADDOCKS LOUNGE (IRE)**, 14, b g Oscar (IRE)—Sister Rosza (IRE) **Chrissy's Passion Racing**
7 **ROCK UP IN STYLE**, 5, b g Showcasing—Flora Trevelyan **The Double Six Racing Partnership**
8 **SAW THE SEA**, 5, b g Sea The Moon (GER)—Frances Stuart (IRE) **Mr R. P. Clarke**
9 **SIMAFAR (IRE)**, 7, b g Makfi—Simawa (IRE) **Mr R. P. Clarke**

**Assistant Trainer:** Amy Myatt.

**175** **MR BRIAN ELLISON, Malton**
Postal: **Spring Cottage Stables, Langton Road, Norton, Malton, North Yorkshire, YO17 9PY**
Contacts: **PHONE 01653 690004 MOBILE 07785 747426 FAX 01653 690008**
EMAIL office@brianellisonracing.co.uk WEBSITE www.brianellisonracing.co.uk

1 **ASHINGTON**, 6, b g Canford Cliffs (IRE)—Kadoma **Mr T. Alderson**
2 **BALLYVIC BORU (IRE)**, 9, b g Brian Boru—Thedoublede (IRE) **Mr P J Martin & Partner**
3 **BARON DE MIDLETON (IRE)**, 8, b g Brian Boru—Present Climate (IRE) **Phil & Julie Martin**
4 **BORDEAUX BILL (IRE)**, 10, b g Craigsteel—Laura Croft (IRE) **Julie & Phil Martin**
5 **BRANCASTER (IRE)**, 7, ch g Casamento (IRE)—Makheelah **Brian Ellison Racing Club**
6 **BURN SOME DUST (IRE)**, 6, b g Shirocco (GER)—Chilly Filly (IRE) **Mr D. R. Gilbert**
7 **CHATEAU MARMONT (IRE)**, 8, b g Flemensfirth (USA)—Sliabh Geal Gcua (IRE) **Brian Ellison Racing Club**
8 **CIVIL LAW (IRE)**, 4, gr g Dark Angel (IRE)—Tribune (FR)
9 **CONSTANTINE BAY**, 10, b g Kayf Tara—Alina Rheinberg (GER) **D Gilbert, M Lawrence, A Bruce**
10 **CORMIER (IRE)**, 5, b g Born To Sea (IRE)—Scotch Bonnet (IRE) **Mr D. R. Gilbert**
11 **DEFINITLY RED (IRE)**, 12, ch g Definite Article—The Red Wench (IRE) **Phil & Julie Martin**
12 **DUKE DEBARRY (IRE)**, 10, b g Presenting—Blue Dante (IRE) **Middleham Park Racing CIX**
13 **EL JEFE (IRE)**, 4, b g Born To Sea (IRE)—Ros Mountain (IRE) **Roxholme Racing**
14 **ELEVEN SEVEN TEN (IRE)**, 5, b g Gale Force Ten—Faanan Aldaar (IRE) **Mrs C. L. Ellison**
15 **FAIR STAR (IRE)**, 5, b g Sea The Stars (IRE)—Night Fairy (IRE) **D Gilbert, M Lawrence, A Bruce**
16 **FOREST BIHAN (FR)**, 10, ch g Forestier (FR)—Katell Bihan (FR) **Phil & Julie Martin**
17 **GHADBBAAN**, 5, ch g Intello (GER)—Rock Choir **Mr K. J. Strangeway**
18 **GOLD MINER**, 8, b g Goldmark (USA)—Sly Empress (IRE) **Mr M. M. Allen**
19 **GRANDMA**, 4, b f Mayson—Livia Drusilla (IRE) **Brian Ellison Racing Club**
20 **HACKBERRY**, 4, b g Nathaniel (IRE)—Dumfriesshire **J Blackburn, Imperial Racing & B Ellison**
21 **HIGHEST MOUNTAIN (FR)**, 5, b g Siyouni (FR)—Chanson Celeste **B. Dunn**
22 **HIGHLAND SKY (IRE)**, 6, b g Camelot—Healing Music (FR) **Mr P Boyle & Mr Brian Ellison**
23 **INSTANT REPLAY (IRE)**, 9, ch g Fruits of Love (USA)—Ding Dong Belle **Phil & Julie Martin**
24 **JEAN MARY**, 4, ch f Cityscape—Ananda Kanda (USA) **Mr K. J. Strangeway**
25 **KATSONIS (IRE)**, 4, b g Ivawood (IRE)—Livadiya (IRE) **S & S Racing & Partner**
26 **KEARNEY HILL (IRE)**, 6, b g Dylan Thomas (IRE)—Sunny Glen (IRE) **Julie & Phil Martin**
27 **KISS MY FACE (IRE)**, 4, b g Nathaniel (IRE)—Bridle Belle **D Gilbert, M Lawrence, A Bruce**
28 **LARGY MOUTH**, 6, b g Court Cave (IRE)—Leblon (IRE) **Mr D. J. Burke & Mr P Alderson**
29 **LUCKY ROBIN (IRE)**, 9, ch g Mister Fotis (USA)—Bewilderment (IRE) **Brian Ellison Racing Club**
30 **MAIFALKI (FR)**, 8, b g Falco (USA)—Makila (IRE) **Lamont Racing**
31 **MEDAKI ROC (IRE)**, 5, b g Shirocco (GER)—Sliabh Geal Gcua (IRE) **Mr P. Boyle**
32 **MING DYNASTY (FR)**, 9, b g King's Best (USA)—Memoire (FR) **Mr P. Boyle**
33 **MR WHIPPED (IRE)**, 8, br g Beneficial—Dyrick Daybreak (IRE) **Phil & Julie Martin**
34 **MRS HYDE (IRE)**, 8, b m Flemensfirth (USA)—Funny Times **The Jekyll**

## MR BRIAN ELLISON - continued

35 **NANS GIFT (IRE)**, 6, b m Presenting—Easter Bonnie (IRE) **Roxholme Racing**
36 **NIETZSCHE**, 8, ch g Poet's Voice—Ganga (IRE) **D Gilbert, M Lawrence, A. Bruce, G. Wills**
37 **NIGHT RANGER**, 4, br g Dansili—Sleep Walk **Ellison, Lyons and Thompson**
38 **OSCAR CEREMONY (IRE)**, 10, b g Oscar (IRE)—Native Singer (IRE) **Ms J. Matthews**
39 **PALLAS DANCER**, 4, b g War Command (USA)—Dance Card **Spring Cottage Syndicate 3**
40 **PISTOL PARK (FR)**, 10, b g Poliglote—Pistolera (GER) **Brian's Mates**
41 **PRUSSIA WITH LOVE**, 7, br m Presenting—Ruby Royale **Roxholme Racing**
42 **PUNXSUTAWNEY PHIL (IRE)**, 4, b g Shirocco (GER)—Chilly Filly (IRE) **Mr D. R. Gilbert**
43 **QUICKLY DOES IT**, 5, b m Havana Gold (IRE)—Mylington Maid **Quickly Group Holdings Limited**
44 **RECLAIM VICTORY (IRE)**, 4, b f Helmet (AUS)—Doctor's Note **Quickly Group Holdings Ltd & Partner**
45 **ROBEAM (IRE)**, 5, b g Helmet (AUS)—Secret Flame **Brian Ellison Racing Club**
46 **SAM'S ADVENTURE**, 9, b g Black Sam Bellamy (IRE)—My Adventure (IRE) **Julie & Phil Martin**
47 **SEZINA**, 4, ch f Cityscape—Sorcellerie **Mr K. J. Strangeway**
48 **SHARP SUITED**, 6, b g Dansili—Appearance **D Gilbert, M Lawrence, A Bruce**
49 **SNOOKERED (IRE)**, 7, b g Born To Sea (IRE)—Secret Quest **Brian Ellison Racing Club**
50 **STONE PRINCESS (IRE)**, 4, gr f Camacho—Stone Roses (IRE) **S & S Racing & Partner**
51 **SWAFFHAM BULBECK (IRE)**, 7, b g Jeremy (USA)—Ballygologue (IRE) **Roxholme Racing**
52 **THE DANCING POET**, 5, ch g Poet's Voice—Caldy Dancer (IRE) **Spring Cottage Syndicate**
53 **THE KING OF MAY (FR)**, 7, b g High Rock (IRE)—Waltzing (IRE) **Phil & Julie Martin**
54 **THE MACKEM MISSILE (IRE)**, 4, ch f Society Rock (IRE)—Southern Barfly (USA) **Mrs L. Pallas**
55 **THE MACKEM TORPEDO**, 5, b g Multiplex—Gagajulu **Ian & Thomas Pallas**
56 **TUPELO MISSISSIPPI (IRE)**, 6, b g Yeats (IRE)—Mislean (IRE) **Phil & Julie Martin**
57 **TYCHE**, 4, b f Due Diligence (USA)—Szabo's Art **Spring Cottage Syndicate 3**
58 **URBAN LEGEND (IRE)**, 7, b g Pasternak—Da Das Delight (IRE) **Mr P Boyle & Mr Brian Ellison**
59 **VICTORIANO (IRE)**, 5, b g Teofilo (IRE)—Victorian Beauty (USA) **Mr Brian Ellison**
60 **WEAKFIELD (IRE)**, 8, b g Court Cave (IRE)—Thats The Lot (IRE) **Phil & Julie Martin**
61 **WHISKEY AND WATER**, 5, b g Harbour Watch (IRE)—Bahamamia **D Gilbert, M Lawrence, A Bruce**
62 **WINDSOR AVENUE (IRE)**, 9, b g Winged Love (IRE)—Zaffarella (IRE) **Phil & Julie Martin**

### THREE-YEAR-OLDS

63 **KING VIKTOR**, ch g Cityscape—Ananda Kanda (USA) **Mr K. J. Strangeway**
64 **LOCOMOTIVE BRETH (IRE)**, b g Exceed And Excel (AUS)—Perfect Fun **Mr T. Alderson**
65 **PALLAS LORD (IRE)**, b c Dandy Man (IRE)—Nutshell **Mrs L. Pallas**
66 **SHAMROCK WINE (IRE)**, b f Epaulette (AUS)—Sakaka **Mr K. Brown**
67 B f Pride of Dubai (AUS)—Sugarformyhoney (IRE)
68 **TANTASTIC**, b g Mayson—Love Island **Spring Cottage Syndicate 2**
69 **THE MOUSEN CHAMP**, b g Buratino (IRE)—Show Willing (IRE) **Spring Cottage Syndicate 2**
70 **TIBERIUS AUGUSTUS**, b g Adaay (IRE)—Livia Drusilla (IRE) **Brian Ellison Racing Club**
71 **TOMMY TITTLEMOUSE (IRE)**, b g Sir Prancealot (IRE)—French Doll (IRE) **Mrs L. Pallas**

### TWO-YEAR-OLDS

72 **CIANCIANA**, ch f 31/01 Cityscape—Golden Valley (Three Valleys (USA)) (762) **Mrs C. L. Ellison**
73 B f 19/02 Mondialiste (IRE)—Kaiulani (IRE) (Danehill Dancer (IRE)) **Geoff & Sandra Turnbull**
74 **LITTLE EMMA LOULOU**, ch f 04/02 Jack Hobbs—Reaf (In The Wings) (14286) **Ian & Thomas Pallas**
75 B g 17/05 Brazen Beau (AUS)—Mexican Milly (IRE) (Noverre (USA)) **Hughes Bros Construction LTD**
76 **MYTHICAL MOLLY (IRE)**, b f 17/02 Profitable (IRE)—The Tempest (Mastercraftsman (IRE)) (28571) **Mrs L. Pallas**
77 B f 01/04 Helmet (AUS)—Xtrasensory (Royal Applause) (5238) **Mr K. Brown**

**Other Owners:** P.S. Alderson, Mr J. N. Blackburn, Mr P. Boyle, Mr A. Bruce, Mr D. J. Burke, Mr Brian Ellison, Mrs C. L. Ellison, Mr D. R. Gilbert, Mr S. T. Hoare, Imperial Racing Partnership 2016, Mr M. Lawrence, Mr N. P. Lyons, Mrs J. A. Martin, Mr P. J. Martin, Quickly Group Holdings Limited, Mr I. Robinson, Mr R. J. T. Smillie, Mr P.M. Stacey, Miss M. L. Taylor, Mr D. Thompson, Mr G. Wills.

**Assistant Trainer:** Jessica Bell.

**Flat Jockey:** Ben Robinson, Kieran Schofield. **NH Jockey:** Henry Brooke, Brian Hughes, Sean Quinlan. **Apprentice Jockey:** Harry Russell.

## 176  MR DAVID ELSWORTH, Newmarket
Postal: **Kings Yard, Egerton House Stables, Cambridge Road, Newmarket, Suffolk, CB8 0TH**
Contacts: **PHONE 01638 665511 MOBILE 07540 750424**
**EMAIL office@drcelsworth.com**

1 **BLUE SKYLINE (IRE)**, 4, ch g Footstepsinthesand—
Ballerina Blue (IRE)  **K. J. Quinn, Mr C. F. Benham, Mr L. M. Quinn, Mr D. L. Whitford**
2 **DESERT SKYLINE (IRE)**, 7, ch g Tamayuz—
Diamond Tango (FR)  **K. J. Quinn, Mr C. F. Benham, Mr L. M. Quinn, Mr D. L. Whitford**
3 **DOGGED**, 4, b g Due Diligence (USA)—Bling Bling (IRE)  **Mr D. R. C. Elsworth, Mr M. D. Elliott**
4 **END RESULT**, 4, b f Nathaniel (IRE)—Daniella  **Mr Brian Cooper, Mrs Elaine Cooper**
5 **GLENCORA (IRE)**, 4, b f Gleneagles (IRE)—Eleanora Duse (IRE)  **Mr Brian Cooper, Mrs Elaine Cooper**
6 **NO NONSENSE**, 5, b g Acclamation—Gift of Music (IRE)  **J. C. Smith**
7 **OZGOOD (IRE)**, 4, b g Australia—
Anna Karenina (USA)  **K. J. Quinn, Mr C. F. Benham, Mr L. M. Quinn, Mr D. L. Whitford**
8 **RIPP ORF (IRE)**, 7, b g Rip Van Winkle (IRE)—
Barzah (IRE)  **K. J. Quinn, Mr C. F. Benham, Mr L. M. Quinn, Mr D. L. Whitford**
9 **SIR DANCEALOT (IRE)**, 7, b g Sir Prancealot (IRE)—
Majesty's Dancer (USA)  **K. J. Quinn, Mr C. F. Benham, Mr L. M. Quinn, Mr D. L. Whitford**
10 **STARSHIBA**, 4, b g Acclamation—Dashiba  **J. C. Smith**
11 **WAIT FOR THE LORD**, 5, b m Bated Breath—
Miss Moses (USA)  **G. B. Partnership, M. G. H. Heald, Mr A. M. H. Heald**

### THREE-YEAR-OLDS
12 **PIROUETTE QUEEN**, ch f Pivotal—Something Exciting  **Quinn,Quinn, Benham, Whitford & Elsworth, Mr D. R. C. Elsworth, K. J. Quinn, Mr C. F. Benham, Mr L. M. Quinn, Mr D. L. Whitford**
13 **SKEDADDLE (IRE)**, b f Fast Company (IRE)—Knock Twice (USA)  **Mr D. R. C. Elsworth**
14 **SOMETHING ENTICING (IRE)**, b f Fascinating Rock (IRE)—La Chapelle (IRE)  **Trebles Holford Thoroughbreds**

### TWO-YEAR-OLDS
15 B c 09/04 Ribchester (IRE)—Bonnie Brae (Mujahid (USA)) (13000)  **Rosyground Stud**
16 Ch c 03/03 Sixties Icon—Flashyfrances (Franklins Gardens)  **Mr D. R. C. Elsworth**

**Other Owners:** Mr Brian Cooper, David Elsworth & Michael Elliott.

**Assistant Trainer:** Mr Andrew Morris.

## 177  MISS SARA ENDER, Malton
Postal: **Swallows Barn, East Heslerton, Malton, North Yorkshire, YO17 8RN**
Contacts: **MOBILE 07983 462314**
**EMAIL seequineservices@hotmail.com WEBSITE www.nevilleender.wix.com/enderracing**

1 **ACCOMPANIED (USA)**, 5, b g Distorted Humor (USA)—Unaccompanied (IRE)  **Mr N. P. Ender**
2 **DURLINGTON (FR)**, 8, ch g Montmartre (FR)—Dalyonne (FR)  **Mr N. P. Ender**
3 **EVISCERATING (IRE)**, 9, gr g Court Cave (IRE)—Titanic Quarter (IRE)  **Mr N. P. Ender**
4 **INDIAN SUNBIRD (IRE)**, 4, b g Hillstar—Mausin (IRE)  **Mr N. P. Ender**
5 **KING ATHELSTAN (IRE)**, 6, b g Mayson—Ashtaroute (USA)  **Mr N. P. Ender**
6 **LORD SPRINGFIELD (IRE)**, 8, ch g Well Chosen—Super Thyne (IRE)  **Mr N. P. Ender**
7 4, B g Morozov (USA)—Ms Jilly Maaye (IRE)
8 **MURCHISON RIVER**, 7, b g Medicean—Free Offer  **Mr N. P. Ender**
9 **ROGAN'S FANCY (IRE)**, 5, b g Frozen Power (IRE)—Kanuri (IRE)  **Mr L. Murray**
10 **WELLS GOLD (IRE)**, 10, b g Gold Well—Exit Baby (IRE)  **Mr I. Ender**
11 **WHEREWOULDUGETIT (IRE)**, 7, b g Morozov (USA)—Matinee Show (IRE)  **Mr N. P. Ender**

**Assistant Trainer:** Mr Neville Ender.

## 178   MRS SAM ENGLAND, Guiseley
Postal: **Brentwood, Manor Farm, Guiseley, Leeds, West Yorkshire, LS20 8EW**
Contacts: **MOBILE 07921 003155**

1 **ASK PADDY (IRE)**, 9, ch g Ask—Dalzenia (FR) **Gremot Racing 2**
2 **BILLY RAY**, 6, b g Sixties Icon—Fiumicino **Bonnet de Douche**
3 **BORODIN (IRE)**, 6, b g High Chaparral (IRE)—Songbird (IRE) **The Flat Cappers**
4 **CHEF D'OEUVRE (FR)**, 10, b g Martaline—Kostroma (FR) **The Sandmoor Partnership 2**
5 **CYBALKO (FR)**, 8, b g Balko (FR)—Cybertina (FR) **The Atkin Partnership**
6 **DRUMOCHTER**, 7, br m Bated Breath—Dixey **Mowbray Park**
7 **GENNADY (IRE)**, 7, b g Arakan (USA)—Topathistle (IRE) **Cragg Wood Racing**
8 **GOING MOBILE (IRE)**, 6, b g Arcano (IRE)—Next To The Top **Cragg Wood Racing**
9 **GOLD RUNNER (IRE)**, 9, b m Gold Well—Copper Coast (IRE) **Itsnotabadlife**
10 **LANVAL (IRE)**, 4, b g Camelot—Flamingo Sea (USA) **Crowd Racing & Sam England**
11 **LAST GOODBYE (IRE)**, 10, b g Millenary—Welsh Ana (IRE) **The Sandmoor Partnership 2**
12 **LIFFEYDALE DREAMER (IRE)**, 6, b m Azamour (IRE)—Owega Dale (IRE) **Worcester Racing Club & Partner**
13 **MAMOO**, 8, ch g Sir Percy—Meredith **Nmus**
14 **MANWELL (IRE)**, 11, b g Gold Well—Roborette (FR) **Sam England Racing Club**
15 **MARK'S CHOICE (IRE)**, 5, b g Bungle Inthejungle—Ramamara (IRE) **Cragg Wood Racing**
16 **MY RENAISSANCE**, 11, b br g Medicean—Lebenstanz **Mrs J. E. Drake**
17 **NEAR KETTERING**, 7, ch g Medicean—Where's Broughton **Redivivus Racing**
18 **OKSANA**, 8, b m Midnight Legend—La Harde (FR) **Sam England Racing Club**
19 **PALIXANDRE (FR)**, 7, b g Kapgarde (FR)—Palmeriade (FR) **Cragg Wood Racing**
20 **PEPPER STREET (IRE)**, 6, b m Born To Sea (IRE)—Mindy (IRE) **Pepper Street Partnership**
21 **RUKWA (FR)**, 7, b g Soldier Hollow—So Oder So (FR) **John Birtles, Gary Ellis , Gary Smith**
22 **SPOT ON SOPH (IRE)**, 5, b m Walk In The Park (IRE)—Gwenadu (FR) **Mowbray Park**
23 **TARA MILL (IRE)**, 8, b g Kalanisi (IRE)—Eileens Dream (IRE) **Simon & Angela Gillie**
24 **WELL SMITTEN (IRE)**, 9, b g Gold Well—The Dark One (IRE) **Gunalt Partnership**
25 **WISHFULL DREAMING**, 10, ch g Alflora (IRE)—Poussetiere Deux (FR) **Mr J C England and Valerie Beattie**

**Other Owners:** Mr M. V. Atkinson, Mr P. H. Ayre, Mrs V. A. Beattie, Mr J. Birtles, Mr A. J. Cooper, Mr T. K. Davis, Mrs J. E. Drake, Mr R. Drye, Mr G. G. Edwards, Mr G. Ellis, Mr J. C. England, Mrs S. A. England, Mrs S. Fawcett, Mr G. Fox, Mrs A. Gillie, Mr S. P. Gillie, Mr J. H. Green, M. P. Hill, Mrs J. Holgate, Mr S. A. Hollings, Dr K. Howard, Mrs P. Howard, Mr I. Janotta, Mr C. McKenna, Mr J. E. Mott, Mr G. Smith, Miss H. Webster, Worcester Racing Club.

## 179   MR JAMES EUSTACE, Newmarket
Postal: **Park Lodge Stables, Park Lane, Newmarket, Suffolk, CB8 8AX**
Contacts: **PHONE 01638 664277 MOBILE 07802 243764, 07733 413771**
EMAIL **jameseustace@tiscali.co.uk, harry@harryeustaceracing.com** WEBSITE **www.jameseustace.com**

1 **AMSBY**, 4, b g Sir Percy—Astrodiva **Judi Dench, Bryan Agar & Mystic Meg Ltd.**
2 **ASTROGEM**, 4, b f Equiano (FR)—Astromancer (USA) **Mystic Meg Limited**
3 **ASTROMAN**, 4, b g Garswood—Mega (IRE) **Mystic Meg Limited**
4 **BAY BELLE**, 5, b m Major Cadeaux—Belle Boleyn **Mr P. T. M. Kingston**
5 **COVERHAM (IRE)**, 7, b g Bated Breath—Mark Too (IRE) **Blue Peter Racing 15**
6 **FORT NELSON**, 4, b g Mount Nelson—Iron Butterfly **Mr. Harold Nass & Partners**
7 **GLENDUN (USA)**, 7, b g First Defence (USA)—La Mina (USA) **The MacDougall Two**
8 **HIGHFALUTING (IRE)**, 7, b g High Chaparral (IRE)—Walk On Water **Mr D. H. Batten**
9 **POSTIE**, 5, b m Medicean—Postage Stampe **Mr Andrew McGladdery & Mrs James Eustace**
10 **POTENZA (IRE)**, 5, b g Born To Sea (IRE)—Cranky Spanky (IRE) **The MacDougall Two**
11 **TOPANTICIPATION**, 4, b f Mount Nelson—Topatoo **M. P. Bowring & R. Smith**
12 **WITH CAUTION (IRE)**, 5, ch m Dandy Man (IRE)—Kitty Softpaws (IRE) **Harold Nass & Partners**

## MR JAMES EUSTACE - continued

### THREE-YEAR-OLDS
13 **ANCIENT TIMES,** b g Exceed And Excel (AUS)—Oriental Step (IRE) **The MacDougall Two**
14 **FANTASISING,** ch f Pivotal—Fantasy In Blue **Park Lodge Racing**
15 **HARSTON,** b f Harzand (IRE)—Time Crystal (IRE) **Major M. G. Wyatt**
16 **NORDIC DASH,** b f Norse Dancer (IRE)—Dashiba **J. C. Smith**
17 **SOURIRE SECRET,** b g Monsieur Bond (IRE)—Smile That Smile **D. G. Tompkins**
18 **ZIGGY,** b g Sixties Icon—Brushing **Sarabex & Aragon Racing**

### TWO-YEAR-OLDS
19 **ALNWICK CASTLE,** b f 01/02 Sir Percy—Iron Butterfly (Shirocco (GER)) **H. D. Nass**
20 **ALNWICK ROSE,** b f 21/03 Sir Percy—Juniper Girl (IRE) (Revoque (IRE)) **Mr A. J. McGladdery**
21 **ASTROBRIO,** ch f 26/01 Garswood—Astrosecret (Halling (USA)) **Mystic Meg Limited**
22 **BE GLORIOUS,** b f 04/01 Kodiac—Spirit Raiser (IRE) (Invincible Spirit (IRE)) (80000) **Glentree Pastoral Pty Ltd,**
     **Russell and Lesley Jones and Families**
23 **BELHAVEN (IRE),** ch f 09/03 Belardo (IRE)—Park Haven (IRE) (Marju (IRE)) (17000) **A. M. Mitchell**
24 B c 23/04 Starspangledbanner (AUS)—Blue Dahlia (IRE) (Shamardal (USA)) (20000) **Candour House and Partner**
25 **CHASING APHRODITE,** b c 15/02 Profitable (IRE)—Tutti Frutti (Teofilo (IRE)) (60000) **Gullwing Enterprises W.L.L.**
26 B c 23/02 The Last Lion (IRE)—China In My Hands (Dark Angel (IRE)) (30000) **The MacDougall Two**
27 **CLARITUDO,** b c 20/03 Nathaniel (IRE)—Clarentine (Dalakhani (IRE)) (21000) **Jackson XV**
28 B c 21/04 Decorated Knight—Desert Lily (IRE) (Redoute's Choice (AUS)) (15000) **Mrs G. R. Eustace**
29 **FIRST VIOLIN,** b c 10/03 Norse Dancer (IRE)—Opera Queen (Nathaniel (IRE)) **J. C. Smith**
30 **FLAMING LORD,** ch c 04/03 Zarak (FR)—Elusive Flame (Elusive City (USA)) **J. C. Smith**
31 **FULL OF BEANS,** b f 28/03 Spill The Beans (AUS)—Naivasha (Captain Gerrard (IRE)) (8000) **Chief Singer Racing**
32 **J'ADORE (IRE),** b f 03/03 Australia—
                              Dillydallydo (IRE) (Holy Roman Emperor (IRE)) (64762) **Gullwing Enterprises W.L.L.**
33 **LUMLEY (IRE),** b f 03/03 The Gurkha (IRE)—Anestasia (IRE) (Anabaa (USA)) (26667) **Thunder From Down Under**
34 **REGIMENTAL GENT,** b c 20/03 The Gurkha (IRE)—City Girl (IRE) (Elusive City (USA)) **J. C. Smith**
35 Bl g 13/03 Postponed (IRE)—Sated (Manduro (GER)) **Major M. G. Wyatt**
36 **TIMES TWO,** b f 03/02 Time Test—Time Crystal (IRE) (Sadler's Wells (USA)) **Major M. G. Wyatt**

**Other Owners:** Mr R. P. Abel, B. R. Agar, Aragon Racing, Mr D. F. Ballheimer, M. P. Bowring, Mrs B. J. Carter, C. Z. Curtis, Dame J. O. Dench, Mrs G. R. Eustace, Mr A. C. Frost, Mrs J. A. Gibson, Mr S. J. Gibson, Mr R. D. E. Marriott, Mrs W. L. Marriott, Mr A. J. McGladdery, Mystic Meg Limited, H. D. Nass, Sarabex, Mr P. H. Skinner, Mrs K. J. Smith, Mr R. Smith, Mr R. J. Uzupris.

**Assistant Trainer:** Harry Eustace.

---

| 180 | **MR DAVID EVANS, Abergavenny** |
|---|---|

Postal: Ty Derlwyn Farm, Pandy, Abergavenny, Monmouthshire, NP7 8DR
Contacts: **PHONE** 07834 834775, 01873 890837 **MOBILE** 07860 668499 **FAX** 01873 890837
**EMAIL** pdevansracing@btinternet.com **WEBSITE** www.pdevansracing.co.uk

1 **A GO GO,** 4, b f Heeraat (IRE)—Gagajulu **R & 11**
2 **ALL YOU WISH,** 4, b g Showcasing—Moment of Time **Mr Z. Austin**
3 **AMOR FATI (IRE),** 6, b g Zoffany (IRE)—Roman Love (IRE) **Mr Stuart Morgan & Partner**
4 **BOMBASTIC (IRE),** 6, ch g Raven's Pass (USA)—Star of The West **Mr Z. Austin**
5 **GLASVEGAS (IRE),** 4, gr g Zebedee—Rejuvenation (IRE) **T. H. Gallienne**
6 **GLOBE THEATRE (USA),** 5, b h War Front (USA)—Was (IRE) **Rob Emmanuelle, Lynn Cullimore & Partner**
7 **HAMARON (GER),** 4, ch g Amaron—Hungry Heidi **Dave & Emma Evans**
8 **HEER WE GO AGAIN,** 4, b g Heeraat (IRE)—Madam Mojito (USA) **Dave & Emma Evans**
9 **HERM (IRE),** 7, b g Bushranger (IRE)—School Holidays (USA) **T. H. Gallienne**
10 **JUNGLE BELLS (IRE),** 4, b f Bungle Inthejungle—Ela Tina (IRE) **P. D. Evans**
11 **LIHOU,** 5, ch g Mayson—Kodiac Island **T. H. Gallienne**
12 **MABRE (IRE),** 4, gr g Make Believe—Slope **Mr K. McCabe**
13 **PLUNGER,** 6, ch g Helmet (AUS)—Percolator **Mr Z. Austin**
14 **REGAL EAGLE (IRE),** 4, b g Free Eagle (IRE)—Spinamix **Mr E. R. Griffiths**

## MR DAVID EVANS - continued

15 **SIAVASH (FR)**, 4, b g Prince Gibraltar (FR)—Sizal (FR)  **Mr K. McCabe**
16 **SNOW OCEAN (IRE)**, 5, b g Exceed And Excel (AUS)—Callistan (IRE)  **Shropshire Wolves 3**
17 **STORMY NIGHT (GER)**, 4, b c Charm Spirit (IRE)—Seven Shares (IRE)  **Mr B Mould & Partner**
18 **TEN CHANTS**, 4, gr g Gregorian (IRE)—Tenbridge  **John Abbey & Emma Evans**
19 **TUNDRA (GER)**, 5, b m Nathaniel (IRE)—Tuiga (IRE)  **Spiers & Hartwell Ltd & Mrs E. Evans**
20 **TWPSYN (IRE)**, 5, b g Es Que Love (IRE)—Gold Blended (IRE)  **Rob Emmanuelle, T Burns & P D Evans**
21 **ZULU ZANDER (IRE)**, 4, b g Bungle Inthejungle—Fig Digliani (IRE)  **Mr John Wilcox & P D Evans**

### THREE-YEAR-OLDS

22 **ALMOST AN ANGEL**, b g Heeraat (IRE)—Broughtons Mystery  **Mr G. E. P. Dudfield**
23 **BANOFFEE (IRE)**, b f Anjaal—Princess Banu  **D. E. Edwards**
24 **BARONESS RACHAEL**, b f Poet's Voice—Queen Aggie (IRE)  **Shropshire Wolves**
25 **BLUE MOONRISE**, gr f Gutaifan (IRE)—Song To The Moon (IRE)  **R. Kent**
26 **COUL QUEEN (IRE)**, b f Coulsty (IRE)—Lady Spangles (IRE)  **T & Evans**
27 **DACESA (IRE)**, ch f Tamayuz—Duchesse (IRE)  **R. Kent**
28 **DOCTOR CHURCHILL (IRE)**, b g Mukhadram—Salhooda (IRE)  **Mr P. G. Molony**
29 **HOTALENA**, b f Hot Streak (IRE)—Ya Halla (IRE)  **Dave & Emma Evans**
30 **ISLA VISTA**, b f Muhaarar—Ripples Maid  **R. Kent**
31 **IT'S A LOVE THING**, b g Intrinsic—Lady Kyllar  **P. D. Evans**
32 B f Proconsul—Justazippy  **M. W. Lawrence**
33 **MARTA BOY**, ch g Sepoy (AUS)—Perfect Story (IRE)  **Mr Francis Maghery & Partner**
34 **NAYON**, b c Nayef (USA)—Freedom Song  **Mr M. J. Pearce**
35 **OBTUSE (IRE)**, gr g Clodovil (IRE)—Leading Actress (IRE)  **Mr K. McCabe**
36 **OOH IS IT**, ch g Es Que Love (IRE)—Candleberry  **P. D. Evans**
37 **PLUM RUN (IRE)**, b f Fulbright—Pearly Brooks  **Dave & Emma Evans**
38 **PORTELET BAY**, b g Mayson—Fenella Rose  **T. H. Gallienne**
39 **ROHAAN (IRE)**, b g Mayson—Vive Les Rouges  **Mr K. McCabe**
40 **SAY IT AS IT IS (IRE)**, b g Buratino (IRE)—Annellis (UAE)  **Mrs I. M. Folkes**
41 **SILK TIE**, b g Intrinsic—Silken Express (IRE)  **P. D. Evans**
42 **TATABOQ (IRE)**, gr g Markaz (IRE)—Walayef (USA)  **Dave & Emma Evans**
43 **THE PRETTY WAY**, b f Garswood—Wenden Belle (IRE)  **Mrs I. M. Folkes**

### TWO-YEAR-OLDS

44 B f 16/04 Heeraat (IRE)—Aquasulis (IRE) (Titus Livius (FR))  **R. Kent**
45 B f 08/02 Mayson—Aubrietia (Dutch Art) (6667)  **Shropshire Wolves**
46 B gr c 05/04 Outstrip—Camp Fire (IRE) (Lahib (USA)) (18000)  **T. H. Gallienne**
47 B f 12/03 Havana Gold (IRE)—Delizia (IRE) (Dark Angel (IRE))
48 B f 31/03 Heeraat (IRE)—Dutch Cat (Dutch Art)
49 B c 02/03 Heeraat (IRE)—Erica Bing (Captain Gerrard (IRE))  **Mr S. W. Banks**
50 B f 10/04 Coulsty (IRE)—Piccelina (Piccolo)  **T & Evans**
51 B f 24/02 Fountain of Youth (IRE)—Shamardal Phantom (IRE) (Shamardal (USA))
52 B f 11/04 Heeraat (IRE)—Skylla (Kyllachy)
53 B f 05/04 Heeraat (IRE)—Song To The Moon (IRE) (Oratorio (IRE))
54 B f 08/05 Aclaim (IRE)—Street Chic (USA) (Street Cry (IRE)) (4000)  **Amazing Racing**
55 B c 06/04 Holy Roman Emperor (IRE)—Wavebreak (Tiger Hill (IRE))
56 B f 09/05 Equiano (FR)—Wenden Belle (IRE) (Brave Act)  **Mrs I. M. Folkes**

**Other Owners:** J. E. Abbey, Mr J. Babb, Mrs T. Burns, Mrs L. A. Cullimore, Mr R. Emmanuel, Mrs E. Evans, Miss M. L. Evans, P.D. Evans, R. Kent, Mr F. P. Maghery, Mr S. Morgan, Mr B. J. Mould, Shropshire Wolves, R. Simpson, Spiers & Hartwell Ltd, Mr J. A. Wilcox.

**Assistant Trainer:** Emma Evans.

## 181 MR JAMES EVANS, Worcester
Postal: 14-16 Kinnersley Severn Stoke, Worcester, Worcestershire
Contacts: MOBILE 07813 166430
EMAIL herbie_evans@hotmail.com WEBSITE www.hjamesevans.co.uk

1  COMPADRE (IRE), 10, b g Yeats (IRE)—Jolivia (FR)  **Mrs J. Evans**
2  CONNETABLE (FR), 9, b g Saint des Saints (FR)—Montbresia (FR)  **Elegant Clutter Ltd**
3  CROESO CYMRAEG, 7, b g Dick Turpin (IRE)—Croeso Cusan  **Richard Evans Bloodstock**
4  FRENCH DE GUYE (FR), 6, gr g Lord du Sud (FR)—Kasibelle de Guye (FR)  **Elegant Clutter & Mr S D Faiers**
5  FUWAIRT (IRE), 9, b g Arcano (IRE)—Safiya Song (IRE)  **Peter Clarke Racing Partners**
6  GALACTIC SPIRIT, 6, ch g Dutch Art—Gino's Spirits  **Mr B. W. Preece**
7  HOLIDAY MAGIC (IRE), 10, gr g Dark Angel (IRE)—Win Cash (IRE)  **The Emily Charlotte Partnership**
8  KENTUCKY KINGDOM (IRE), 5, b g Camacho—Venetian Rhapsody (IRE)  **The Cheltenham Flyers**
9  LORD GETAWAY (IRE), 9, b g Getaway (GER)—Terre d'Orient (FR)  **Mrs J. Evans**
10 MOSSING, 9, b m Passing Glance—Missy Moscow (IRE)  **Mrs J. Evans**
11 NOBEL LEADER (IRE), 11, b g Alflora (IRE)—Ben Roseler (IRE)  **Mr S. D. Faiers**
12 OPTIMISTIC BIAS (IRE), 12, b g Sayarshan (FR)—Dashers Folly (IRE)  **Elegant Clutter Ltd**
13 SANDS COVE (IRE), 14, b g Flemensfirth (USA)—Lillies Bordello (IRE)  **Mrs J. Evans**

### THREE-YEAR-OLDS
14 BUNGLEDUPINBLUE (IRE), b f Bungle Inthejungle—Generous Heart  **Mr Q. Khan**
15 DOONBEG FARMER (IRE), br g Vadamos (FR)—Risk A Look  **Peter Clarke Racing Partners**
16 DREAM COMPOSER (FR), b c Dream Ahead (USA)—High Spice (USA)  **Peter Clarke Racing Partners**

### TWO-YEAR-OLDS
17 B c 19/04 Bated Breath—Firenze (Efisio) (35000)  **Peter Clarke Racing Partners**

**Other Owners:** Elegant Clutter & Mr S D Faiers, Elegant Clutter Ltd, Mr S. D. Faiers.

**Assistant Trainer:** Mrs Jane Evans.

## 182 MRS MARY EVANS, Haverfordwest
Postal: Hengoed, Clabeston Road, Haverfordwest, Dyfed, SA63 4QL
Contacts: PHONE 01437 731336

1  ADIMELO (FR), 11, b br g Honolulu (IRE)—Meliflo (FR)  **Mary & Billy Evans**
2  HOLD COURT (IRE), 14, br g Court Cave (IRE)—Tipsy Miss (IRE)  **Mary & Billy Evans**

**Other Owners:** Mrs M. Evans, W. J. Evans.

**Assistant Trainer:** W J Evans.

## 183 MRS NIKKI EVANS, Abergavenny
Postal: Penbiddle Farm, Penbidwal, Pandy, Abergavenny, Gwent, NP7 8EA
Contacts: MOBILE 07977 753437
EMAIL penbiddleracing@gmail.com WEBSITE NikkiEvansRacing.Net FACEBOOK NikkiEvansRacing
TWITTER @PenbiddleRacing WHATSAPP 07977753437

1  AASLEAGH DAWN (IRE), 8, b m Milan—Aasleagh Lady (IRE)  **P. T. Evans**
2  CARNAGE, 6, b g Holy Roman Emperor (IRE)—Sylvestris (IRE)  **Mr J. Berry**
3  GLOBAL FRONTIER (IRE), 7, b g Sans Frontieres (IRE)—Avoca Star (IRE)  **Mr M Donlin and Partner**
4  JAGANORY (IRE), 9, b g Dylan Thomas (IRE)—Jacquelin Jag (IRE)  **Evans & Donlin**

## MRS NIKKI EVANS - continued

5 **JUKEBOX JUNIOR**, 5, gr g Jukebox Jury (IRE)—Street Fire (IRE) **Mrs M. E. Gittings-Watts**
6 **LATE SHIPMENT**, 10, b g Authorized (IRE)—Time Over **Mrs M. E. Gittings-Watts**
7 **ORANGE GINA**, 5, ch m Schiaparelli (GER)—Bobs Present **Martin Donlin & Lynne Bodman**
8 **PEDRO DE STYLES (FR)**, 6, b g Pedro The Great (USA)—Toscabella (FR) **Mrs N. S. Evans**
9 **SPIRITUS MUNDI (IRE)**, 6, b g Yeats (IRE)—Maiden City (IRE) **P. T. Evans**
10 **SUE BE IT (IRE)**, 10, b m Presenting—Runaround Sue (IRE) **Hanford's Chemist Ltd**
11 **TAKBEER (IRE)**, 9, b g Aqlaam—Precious Secret (IRE) **Mrs M. E. Gittings-Watts**
12 **TIME FOR CHAMPERS (IRE)**, 11, b m Robin des Champs (FR)—Someone Told Me (IRE) **Hanford's Chemist Ltd**
13 **WATCHMAN (IRE)**, 7, b g Oasis Dream—Caphene **Tip of the Sword Racing**
14 **YORKSHIRE GOLD**, 4, b g Muhaarar—Swift Campaign (IRE) **Tip of the Sword Racing**

## TWO-YEAR-OLDS

15 Ch f 01/04 Sixties Icon—Section Onesixsix (IRE) (Dandy Man (IRE))

**Other Owners:** Miss M. Barlow, Mrs L. Bodman, Mr M. S. Donlin, Mrs N. S. Evans, P. T. Evans, Mrs M. E. Gittings-Watts, Mr M. Huntington, Mr J. Knight, Nikki Evans Racing.

**Assistant Trainer:** Mr P. T. Evans.

---

**184**
## MR RICHARD RHYS EVANS, Stratford-on-Avon
Postal: **Oxstalls Farm, Warwick Road, Stratford-Upon-Avon, Warwickshire, CV37 0NS**
Contacts: **PHONE 01789 205277**
EMAIL oxstallsfarm@gmail.com

1 **A MIDNIGHT KISS**, 6, b m Midnight Legend—Wise Little Girl **Mr R. R. Evans**

---

**185**
## MR JAMES EWART, Langholm
Postal: **James Ewart Racing Limited, Craig Farm, Westerkirk, Langholm, Dumfriesshire, DG13 0NZ**
Contacts: **PHONE 013873 70707 MOBILE 07786 995073**
EMAIL office@jeracing.co.uk WEBSITE www.jamesewartracing.com

1 **AQUITAINE BOY (FR)**, 6, b g Walk In The Park (IRE)—Dolce Vita Yug
2 **ARISTO DU PLESSIS (FR)**, 11, b g Voix du Nord (FR)—J'Aime (FR)
3 **ASCOT DE BRUYERE (FR)**, 11, b br g Kapgarde (FR)—Quid de Neuville (FR)
4 **BEAT BOX (FR)**, 5, b g Cokoriko (FR)—Niemen (FR)
5 **BINGO D'OLIVATE (FR)**, 10, b g Laverock (IRE)—Ombrelle de L'Orme (FR)
6 **BLACK PIRATE**, 9, b g Black Sam Bellamy (IRE)—Proper Posh
7 **BLUEFORTYTWO**, 8, gr g Overbury (IRE)—Celine Message
8 **BRAYHILL (IRE)**, 6, b g Sholokhov (IRE)—Definite Love (IRE)
9 **BULLION (FR)**, 8, ch g Full of Gold (FR)—Ryde (FR)
10 **CALIX DELAFAYETTE (FR)**, 9, b g Caballo Raptor (CAN)—Obepinedelafayette (FR)
11 **CELLAR VIE**, 7, gr g Tikkanen (USA)—Branceilles (FR)
12 **CHARMANT (FR)**, 9, b g Balko (FR)—Ravissante (FR)
13 **COCHISEE**, 7, gr g Tikkanen (USA)—Pocahontas (FR)
14 **DUNLY (FR)**, 8, b g Gris de Gris (IRE)—Octavine du Meix (FR)
15 **EMPIRE DE MAULDE (FR)**, 7, b g Spanish Moon (USA)—Ondine de Brejoux (FR)
16 **ETTILA DE SIVOLA (FR)**, 7, gr g Noroit (GER)—Wild Rose Bloom (FR)
17 **FAST SCENIC (FR)**, 6, b g Brave Mansonnien (FR)—Scenaria (IRE)
18 **FEETRONIE DE KERVI (FR)**, 6, b m No Risk At All (FR)—Malandra
19 **FOR THREE (IRE)**, 7, b g Pour Moi (IRE)—Asmaa (USA)
20 **FOSTERED PHIL (IRE)**, 7, b g Arcadio (GER)—Knock Na Shee (IRE)

## MR JAMES EWART - continued

21 **FOXEY,** 6, b g Foxwedge (AUS)—Blue Lyric
22 **HONOURARY GIFT (IRE),** 8, b g City Honours (USA)—Zaffalong (IRE)
23 **JASSAS (FR),** 9, ch g Fuisse (FR)—Sylverina (FR)
24 **KARISMATIK (FR),** 5, b g Kap Rock (FR)—Crack d'Emble (FR)
25 **LAKE TAKAPUNA (IRE),** 10, b g Shantou (USA)—Close To Shore (IRE)
26 **LORD ROCO,** 5, b g Rocamadour—Dolly Penrose
27 **MUHTAMAR (FR),** 6, ch g Muhtathir—Martalina (FR)
28 **NIKGARDE (FR),** 6, b g Kapgarde (FR)—Nikoline (FR)
29 4, Ch g Ocovango—Nora's Flame (IRE)
30 **RINGO KID,** 8, b g Bushranger (IRE)—Clincher
31 **SAO MAXENCE (FR),** 8, b g Saint des Saints (FR)—Primadona (FR)
32 **THE BLAME GAME (IRE),** 7, b g Getaway (GER)—Tribal Princess (IRE)
33 **THE CARETAKER,** 5, b g Mukhadram—Perfect Story (IRE)
34 **TORTUGA BAY,** 7, b m Sulamani (IRE)—Empress of Light
35 **WESTLAND ROW (IRE),** 9, br g Oscar (IRE)—Presenting Proform (IRE)

## THREE-YEAR-OLDS

36 **ERIMITIES,** b f Black Sam Bellamy (IRE)—Think Green
37 **SCARLET N' BLACK,** b g Black Sam Bellamy (IRE)—Overlady

## TWO-YEAR-OLDS

38 Ch f 24/05 Black Sam Bellamy (IRE)—Overlady (Overbury (IRE))
39 B g 11/04 Black Sam Bellamy (IRE)—Think Green (Montjeu (IRE))

**Owners:** Exors of the Late Mr J. D. Allen, Mr R. Carruthers, Craig Farm Syndicate,Percy,Palmer,Graham, Mrs J. E. Dodd, Mrs L. J. Drew, Mr J. J. Elliot, Mrs B. J. Ewart, Mr J. Ewart, N. M. L. Ewart, Ewart, Carruthers, Graham, Ewart, Murrills, Ewart, Palmer & Percy, Mrs Hugh Fraser, Exors of the Late Mr J. D. Gordon, W. Graham, Grahamcarruthersdrewhugheskessonhiggins, Mrs M. Higgins, Mr D. M. C. Hughes, Mrs A. G. Humbert, Mr M. J. James, Dr C. M. Kesson, Kesson,Phillips,Humbert,Ogilvie,Graham, Leeds Plywood & Doors Ltd, Mr S. A. Murrills, Mr P. M. Ogilvie, Dr R. A. Palmer, Mrs J. D. Percy, Mr A. M. Phillips, Mr A Phillips & Mrs N Sperling, Phillips,Elliot,Carruthers,Drew,Palmer, Mr D. I. Rolinson, Mr R. E. Smith, Mrs J. Sperling, Mr D. R. Stanhope, The Craig Farm Syndicate, The Steel Bonnets.

**Assistant Trainer:** Briony Ewart.

**NH Jockey:** Rachael McDonald.

---

**186**  ## MR LES EYRE, Beverley
Postal: **Ivy House Stables, Main Street, Catwick, Beverley, North Humberside, HU17 5PJ**
Contacts: **MOBILE 07864 677444**
**EMAIL leseyreracing@hotmail.co.uk**

1 **AMBER ROCK (USA),** 5, b g Australia—Amber Isle (USA)  **RP Racing Ltd**
2 **BIRKENHEAD,** 4, b g Captain Gerrard (IRE)—Vilnius  **Sunpak Racing**
3 **COTE D'AZUR,** 8, ch g Champs Elysees—Florentia  **Billy Parker & Steven Parker**
4 **DAWAALEEB (USA),** 7, b g Invincible Spirit (IRE)—Plaza (USA)  **Billy Parker & Steven Parker**
5 **HIGHLY SPRUNG (IRE),** 8, b g Zebedee—Miss Donovan  **Mr A Turton & Dr V Webb**
6 **LE BAYOU (FR),** 4, b g Dabirsim (FR)—Kastiya (FR)  **RP Racing Ltd**
7 **MORETTI (IRE),** 6, b m Requinto (IRE)—Hassaya (IRE)  **Mr G. Parkinson & Mr J. L. Eyre**
8 **QUEEN OF KALAHARI,** 6, b m Lethal Force (IRE)—Aromatherapy  **Les Eyre Racing Partnership I**
9 **YORKSHIRE FLYER (IRE),** 5, b g Cape Cross (IRE)—Moonlight Wish (IRE)  **Mr J. L. Eyre**

## THREE-YEAR-OLDS

10 **BEDFORD FLYER (IRE),** b c Clodovil (IRE)—Nafa (IRE)  **RP Racing Ltd**
11 **COSMIC STAR,** b gr f Charm Spirit (IRE)—Reaching Ahead (USA)  **Melissa Cooke & Val Webb**
12 **JUST FRANK,** b g Epaulette (AUS)—Mabinia (IRE)  **Billy Parker & Steven Parker**

## MR LES EYRE - continued

13 **RON O,** ch c Toronado (IRE)—Xaloc (IRE) **Mr M. J. Rozenbroek**
14 B g Brazen Beau (AUS)—Sweetnessandlight **Mr P. Ward**

### TWO-YEAR-OLDS
15 **ARKID,** b c 11/03 Ardad (IRE)—Lady Vermeer (Dutch Art) (6500) **Mr G. Parkinson & Mr J. L. Eyre**
16 **JUST ANOTHER (IRE),** ch c 28/04 Bungle Inthejungle—Labyrinthine (IRE) (Pivotal) (22000) **B Parker, S Parker J Blackburn**
17 B c 03/02 Lethal Force (IRE)—Mitigate (Lawman (FR)) **RP Racing Ltd**
18 B g 12/04 Kodi Bear (IRE)—Mojita (IRE) (Montjeu (IRE)) (19048) **RP Racing Ltd**
19 Gr f 24/02 Gutaifan (IRE)—Proudofyou (USA) (Tizway (USA)) **Mr J. L. Eyre**
20 **REEL TIMBA (IRE),** b c 03/03 Highland Reel (IRE)—Timba (Oasis Dream) (20000) **Mr M. J. Rozenbroek**
21 Ch f 20/03 Excelebration (IRE)—Rozene (IRE) (Sleeping Indian) **M Rozenbroek & J L Eyre**

**Other Owners:** Mr J. N. Blackburn, Mrs M. A. Cooke, Mr J. L. Eyre, Mr B. Parker, Mr S. Parker, Mr G. Parkinson, Mr M. J. Rozenbroek, Mr A. Turton, Dr V. Webb.

**Assistant Trainer:** Tracy Johnson.

---

**187** **MR RICHARD FAHEY, Malton**
Postal: Trainer did not wish details of their string to appear

---

**188** **MR CHRIS FAIRHURST, Middleham**
Postal: Glasgow House, Middleham, Leyburn, North Yorkshire, DL8 4QG
Contacts: PHONE 01969 622039 MOBILE 07889 410840
EMAIL cfairhurst@tiscali.co.uk

1 **BENADALID,** 6, b g Assertive—Gambatte **Mrs S. France**
2 **FEEBI,** 5, b m Pour Moi (IRE)—Scorn (USA) **Mr A. Davies**
3 **FLORENZA,** 8, b m Haafhd—Danzatrice **980 Racing**
4 **LASTING LEGACY,** 4, gr f Lethal Force (IRE)—Araminte **Exors of the Late Mrs L. Peacock**
5 **MASHAM MOOR,** 4, b g Music Master—Jane's Payoff (IRE) **Mrs C. Arnold**
6 **RED TORNADO (FR),** 9, ch g Dr Fong (USA)—Encircle (USA) **Richard III Partnership**
7 **SIXTIES STAR,** 7, b g Sixties Icon—Songbook **Mrs A. M. Leggett**
8 **THE ARMED MAN,** 8, b g Misu Bond (IRE)—Accamelia **Mrs C. Arnold**
9 **TOP ATTRACTION,** 4, b g Fountain of Youth (IRE)—Symphonic Dancer (USA) **The PQD Partnership**
10 **VELMA,** 4, b f Fast Company (IRE)—Valoria **Mr A. Davies**

### THREE-YEAR-OLDS
11 **JUST FOR CYNTH,** b f Sepoy (AUS)—Muzhil (IRE) **Hugh T. Redhead**
12 **KAYLYN,** b f Charm Spirit (IRE)—Dark Quest **Mr A. Davies**

**Other Owners:** Mr J. M. Tozer, Mr M. D. Tozer.

**189** **MR JAMES FANSHAWE, Newmarket**
Postal: **Pegasus Stables, Snailwell Road, Newmarket, Suffolk, CB8 7DJ**
Contacts: **PHONE 01638 664525 FAX 01638 664523**
EMAIL james@jamesfanshawe.com WEBSITE www.jamesfanshawe.com, www.fredarcherracing.com

1 **AUDARYA (FR)**, 5, b m Wootton Bassett—Green Bananas (FR) **Mrs A. M. Swinburn**
2 **BINT AUSTRALIA (IRE)**, 4, ch f Australia—Healing Music (FR) **Mr Nabil Mourad**
3 **BOMB PROOF (IRE)**, 4, br g Society Rock (IRE)—Chantaleen (FR) **Fred Archer Racing - Skylark**
4 **BONNEVAL**, 4, b g Siyouni (FR)—Dreamlike **Fittocks Booth Boorer Bengo Silver Steed**
5 **CASUAL REPLY**, 5, b m Frankel—Passing Parade **Merry Fox Stud Limited**
6 **CROWN POWER (IRE)**, 4, b f Camelot—Causeway Queen (IRE) **King Power Racing Co Ltd**
7 **ENVISAGING (IRE)**, 7, b g Zoffany (IRE)—Star of Stars (IRE) **Fred Archer Racing - Ormonde**
8 **ESTATE HOUSE (FR)**, 4, b g Oasis Dream—Alsace Lorraine (IRE) **Merry Fox Stud Limited**
9 **FLOWER OF SCOTLAND**, 4, b f Gleneagles (IRE)—Seal of Approval **T. R. G. Vestey**
10 **FLYING WEST**, 4, b f Free Eagle (IRE)—West of The Moon **Cheveley Park Stud Limited**
11 **FRESH**, 4, b g Bated Breath—Kendal Mint **Clipper Group Holdings Ltd**
12 **GOING UNDERGROUND**, 4, ch g Lope de Vega (IRE)—Jam Jar **Mrs A. M. Swinburn**
13 **HI WAY**, 4, b f Intrinsic—Sensible Way (USA) **Mrs J. M. J. Fanshawe**
14 **KINGSHOLM (IRE)**, 4, b g Tagula (IRE)—Fixed Gaze (USA) **D Redvers, D Howden & J Fanshawe**
15 **KNOWING**, 5, b g Pour Moi (IRE)—Wedding Speech (IRE) **Mr Gary Marney**
16 **PRAISE THE LORD**, 4, b c Bated Breath—Hallelujah **Mr T. Wells**
17 **RED HOT RADISH**, 4, ch g Helmet (AUS)—Chetwynd (IRE) **John and Trish Shropshire**
18 **SECOND SLIP (IRE)**, 4, b g Lope de Vega (IRE)—Arkadina (IRE) **Merry Fox Stud Limited**
19 **SERENADING**, 5, br m Iffraaj—Constant Dream **Mr John E Rose & Manor Farm Stud**
20 **SHOW ME A SUNSET**, 5, b g Showcasing—Sunrise Star **The Cool Silk Partnership**
21 **SPANISH ARCHER (FR)**, 6, b g Lope de Vega (IRE)—Parcelle Perdue (FR) **Fred Archer Racing - Iroquois**
22 **THE TIN MAN**, 9, b g Equiano (FR)—Persario **Fred Archer Racing - Ormonde**
23 **TURN ON THE CHARM (FR)**, 4, b g Charm Spirit (IRE)—Shendaya (FR) **Fred Archer Racing - Paradox**
24 **VIBRANCE**, 5, b m Nathaniel (IRE)—Park Crystal (IRE) **Cheveley Park Stud Limited**
25 **VIOLA (IRE)**, 4, ch f Lope de Vega (IRE)—Sistine **Elite Racing Club**

**THREE-YEAR-OLDS**

26 **ARADENA (IRE)**, b f Helmet (AUS)—Air Kiss **Dr Catherine Wills**
27 **BLUE ARTEMIS**, b f Showcasing—Azure Amour (IRE) **Fred Archer Racing - Dutch Oven**
28 **CEDAR'S STARS**, b f Sea The Stars (IRE)—Instance **Mr C. Fox & Mr B. Wilson**
29 **CRATHES CASTLE**, b g Oasis Dream—Allyday **Mr A. R. Boyd-Rochfort**
30 **DEVILRY**, b f Sea The Moon (GER)—Diablerette **Miss K. Rausing**
31 **EMERGING (IRE)**, b g The Gurkha (IRE)—Don't Cry For Me (USA) **Mr B. C. M. Wong**
32 **ENSURED (IRE)**, ch g Sea The Stars (IRE)—Brazilian Bride (IRE) **Mr B. C. M. Wong**
33 **ETERNAL LIGHT (IRE)**, ch f New Approach (IRE)—Scribonia (IRE) **Qatar Racing Limited**
34 **GEMINGA**, b f Awtaad—Starlet (IRE) **The Earl Of Halifax**
35 **GRANNY MELBA**, b f Australia—Spirit Raiser (IRE) **The Hon William Vestey**
36 **GREEK FLAME (FR)**, ch f Siyouni (FR)—Flame of Hestia (IRE) **Merry Fox Stud Limited**
37 **HANDSOME (IRE)**, b g Kodiac—Victoria Montoya **Cornthrop Bloodstock & Qatar Racing**
38 **HEAR THE MUSIC (IRE)**, b f Muhaarar—Split Trois (FR) **Mr Mohamed Obaida**
39 **HICKORY (IRE)**, b c Free Eagle (IRE)—Badr Al Badoor (IRE) **Fred Archer Racing - Galliard**
40 **ISOLA ROSSA**, b f Iffraaj—Isola Verde **Jan & Peter Hopper & Michelle Morris**
41 **IT GIRL**, b f Ito (GER)—Baltic Best (IRE) **Fittocks Stud**
42 **JASMINE JOY (IRE)**, b f Lope de Vega (IRE)—Pecking Order (IRE) **Merry Fox Stud Limited**
43 **KARTVELIAN (IRE)**, ch f Tamayuz—Petite Georgia (IRE) **Andrew & Julia Turner**
44 **KINGDOM FOUND (IRE)**, b f Kingman—Lonely Ahead (USA) **Mr Mohamed Obaida**
45 **LOVING DASH**, b f Lope de Vega (IRE)—Miss Dashwood **Helena Springfield Ltd**
46 B f Lope de Vega (IRE)—Missed Call (IRE) **Mr Malcolm C. Denmark**
47 **MURAU**, b g Mukhadram—Entitlement **Dr Catherine Wills**
48 **PERSARIA**, b f Equiano (FR)—Persario **Hot To Trot Racing V**
49 **POOKY**, ch f Twilight Son—Firenze **Sheikh Juma Dalmook Al Maktoum**
50 **SEASTAR**, ch f Sea The Moon (GER)—Lady Stardust **Mrs Martin Armstrong**
51 **TWO TWO TIME**, ch f Al Kazeem—Alla Breve **Cheveley Park Stud Limited**
52 **UPROAR**, b f Sepoy (AUS)—Isis (USA) **Dr Catherine Wills**

## MR JAMES FANSHAWE - continued

### TWO-YEAR-OLDS

53 **ANNIE GALE (IRE)**, b f 26/04 No Nay Never (USA)—
Double Fantasy (GER) (Indian Ridge) (30476) **Fred Archer Racing - Minting**
54 B f 24/02 Dubawi (IRE)—Biz Bar (Tobougg (IRE)) (96852) **Qatar Racing Limited**
55 **BLUEBIRD**, b f 17/03 Acclamation—Blues Sister (Compton Place) **Jan & Peter Hopper & Michelle Morris**
56 B f 13/05 Kitten's Joy (USA)—Cat's Claw (USA) (Dynaformer (USA)) **Qatar Racing Limited**
57 **CITRUS GROVE (IRE)**, b f 11/03 Oasis Dream—Zest (IRE) (Duke of Marmalade (IRE)) **Elite Racing Club**
58 **COMPLIANT**, b f 14/03 Pivotal—Royal Seal (Dansili) **Cheveley Park Stud Limited**
59 B f 15/03 Storm The Stars (USA)—Daintily Done (Cacique (IRE)) **Sheikh Juma Dalmook Al Maktoum**
60 B c 05/04 Iffraaj—Dash To The Front (Diktat) **Castle Down Racing**
61 **EURAQUILO**, b c 30/03 Raven's Pass (USA)—Air Kiss (Red Ransom (USA)) **Dr Catherine Wills**
62 **ISCHIA**, ch f 10/05 Equiano (FR)—Isola Verde (Oasis Dream) (29000) **Fred Archer Racing - Lady Golightly**
63 **LAILAH**, b f 12/04 Australia—Wedding Speech (IRE) (Acclamation) **Mr Gary Marney**
64 **LIBERTUS**, b c 21/03 Equiano (FR)—
Italian Connection (Cadeaux Genereux) (42000) **Fred Archer Racing - Peeping Tom**
65 B f 06/04 Golden Horn—Moonlight Sonata (Galileo (IRE)) **Mrs Mary Slack**
66 B c 29/04 Ribchester (IRE)—Pauline (Royal Applause) (37000) **Chris van Hoorn Racing**
67 **ROYAL SCANDAL**, ch f 28/02 Dubawi (IRE)—Seal of Approval (Authorized (IRE)) (120000) **T. R. G. Vestey**
68 B f 17/03 Frankel—Speedy Boarding (Shamardal (USA)) **Helena Springfield Ltd**
69 Ch c 27/03 Farhh—Strictly Lambada (Red Ransom (USA)) **Castle Down Racing**
70 **TAYCAN**, b f 04/02 Postponed (IRE)—Act Fast (Shamardal (USA)) (13000) **Mrs Michelle Morris**
71 **TELEMACHUS**, b c 05/03 Ulysses (IRE)—
Tallulah Rose (Exceed And Excel (AUS)) (50000) **Cheveley Park Stud Limited**
72 **VESTMENT**, b f 27/03 Ulysses (IRE)—Postulant (Kyllachy) **Cheveley Park Stud Limited**
73 **WANDERING ROCKS**, ch c 16/02 Ulysses (IRE)—West of The Moon (Pivotal) (90000) **Cheveley Park Stud Limited**
74 **WANNABE BRAVE (IRE)**, b c 27/02 Fastnet Rock (AUS)—
Wannabe Special (Galileo (IRE)) (78000) **Michael and Gloria Davey**

**Other Owners:** Mr Geoffrey Baber, Mrs Denise Beetles, Mr Graham Beetles, Mr John Bodie, Sheikh J. D. Al Maktoum, Mr Paul Arlotte, Mrs S. R. Armstrong, Mr A. N. C. Bengough, D. Boorer, Mr P. Booth, Mr Isidore Carivalis, Mr Robert Cooper, Cornthrop Bloodstock Limited, Mrs G. J. Davey, Mr M. E. Davey, Mr M E & Mrs G J Davey, Mr Alex Davidson, M. C. Denmark, Mr Roy Eady, Mr Nigel Elwes, Mrs Georgia Fanshawe, Fittocks Stud, Mr C. E. S. Fox, Mr Tony Francis, Mr Colin Gilbert, Mr Haydn Gott, Mr Robert Grove, C. J. Harper, Helena Springfield Ltd, Mrs J. P. Hopper, Mr P. Hopper, Mr R. S. Hoskins, Hot To Trot Racing 1, Mr Dave King, Mr Mike King, Mrs Sarah King, Mr Arne Korsbakken, Mr Tim Lane, Mr Bill Lemon, Mr Niall Lynch, Manor Farm Stud (Rutland), Mr G. Marney, Mrs Lee Masters, Mrs Liz Meads, Mrs Joan Mitchell, Mr John Mitchell, Mrs M. L. Morris, N. Mourad, Mrs Christine Munday, Mr Colin Munday, Mrs Tam Murray Thriepland, M. Obaida, Mr Gordon Papworth, Mr Andrew Peffers, Mr Ian Pittaway, Mr Peter Prynn, Qatar Racing Limited, Mr Bill Rogerson, J. E. Rose, Mrs Pat Rowley, Mr David Russell, Mr William Russell, Mr Ulf Ryden, Miss Hermione Scrope, Mrs Sue Sheldon-Law, Mr P. G. S. Silver, Mrs M. Slack, Mr Nigel Smith, Mr G. Steed, Mr Richard Stephens, Mr Bob Stevens, Hilary Sunman, Miss A. D. Swift, Mr David Tarrant, Mr Peter Tarrant, Mr Adam Tjolle, Mr Valere Nikolas Frederick Tjolle, Mr A. R. Turner, Mrs J. J. Turner, Mr C. T. Van Hoorn, The Hon W. G. Vestey, Mrs Janet Walker, Mr Michael Whatley, Dr C. M. H. Wills, Mr B. Wilson, Mr Peter Young.

**Assistant Trainer:** Tom Fanshawe.

---

 **190**

**MR JOHNNY FARRELLY**, Midford
Postal: **Upper Twinhoe Farm, Midford, Bath, Avon, BA2 8QX**
Contacts: PHONE 01278 671782 MOBILE 07811 113363

1 **ADDIS ABABA (IRE)**, 6, ch g Declaration of War (USA)—Song of My Heart (IRE) **Manhole Covers Ltd**
2 **ALI THE HUNTER (IRE)**, 8, ch m Papal Bull—Polish Spring (IRE) **Monday Boys Partnership**
3 **AND THE NEW (IRE)**, 10, b g Kalanisi (IRE)—Wheredidthemoneygo (IRE) **Mr P. A. Randall**
4 **AUTUMN GOLD**, 8, ch m Apple Tree (FR)—Present Love (IRE) **Mr D. J. Adams**
5 **BATHWICK BRAVE (IRE)**, 14, b g Westerner—Dorans Grove **Mr J. Farrelly**
6 **BERMEO (IRE)**, 10, b g Definite Article—Miss Blueyes (IRE) **Manhole Covers Ltd**
7 **BIG PICTURE**, 9, b g Recharge (IRE)—Just Jenny (IRE) **Donegal Mayo Association**

## MR JOHNNY FARRELLY - continued

8 **BLACK NOAH**, 6, br g Big Bad Bob (IRE)—Frequently **Mr P. M. Tosh**
9 **BLACKTHORN WINTER**, 7, b g Morozov (USA)—Presenting Gayle (IRE) **Mr D. J. Adams**
10 **BREFFNIBOY (FR)**, 7, b g Sageburg (IRE)—Dawn Cat (USA) **F. A. Clegg**
11 **CAPTAIN IVAN (IRE)**, 7, ch g Stowaway—Western Starlight (IRE) **Mr P. A. Randall**
12 **CAPTAINS RUN (IRE)**, 9, ch g Curtain Time (IRE)—Sailors Run (IRE) **Mr P. M. Tosh**
13 **CHANCE IT (IRE)**, 11, b g Tajraasi (USA)—Lafanta (IRE) **F. A. Clegg**
14 **CROWN HILL (IRE)**, 11, b g Definite Article—Silver Prayer (IRE) **Hanford's Chemist Ltd**
15 **DRUIM SAMHRAIDH (IRE)**, 8, b g Pushkin (IRE)—Lady Rene (IRE) **Mr C. McNally**
16 **EGGESFORD**, 7, b g Foxwedge (AUS)—Elegant Pride **Mrs L. J. Young**
17 **ERICA ROSE**, 6, b m Bollin Eric—Eccentricity **Mrs B. C. Tucker**
18 **FARCEUR DE MAULNE (FR)**, 6, b g Doctor Dino (FR)—Alize de La Prise (FR) **Landowners, Penwill, Skuse**
19 **FOOL TO CRY (IRE)**, 8, ch m Fast Company (IRE)—Islandagore (IRE) **Mr J. Farrelly**
20 **GASTARA**, 6, b g Kayf Tara—Gaspaisie (FR) **Ms Gillian Metherell**
21 **GINGILI**, 11, b g Beat All (USA)—Gentian **Mr J. Farrelly**
22 **GOLD MAN (IRE)**, 12, ch g Presenting—Mama Jaffa (IRE) **Mr Greenfingers Syndicate**
23 **HAVANA RIVER (IRE)**, 8, b m Mahler—Dancingonthemoon (IRE) **Mr J. Folan**
24 **HOW'S THE CRICKET (IRE)**, 6, b g Doyen—Hayley Cometh (IRE) **Manhole Covers Ltd**
25 **KALASKADESEMILLEY**, 10, b g Myboycharlie (IRE)—Congressional (IRE) **Mr J. Farrelly**
26 **KRUJERS GIRL (IRE)**, 9, b m Definite Article—Lady Rene (IRE) **Mr C. McNally**
27 **LADY MAKFI (IRE)**, 9, b m Makfi—Dulcet Tones (IRE) **Mr J. McMahon**
28 **LAKE SHORE DRIVE (IRE)**, 9, b g Thewayyouare (USA)—Labrusca **Mr Greenfingers Syndicate**
29 **LOVE THE LEADER (IRE)**, 13, b g Fruits of Love (USA)—Suelena (IRE) **Mr J. Farrelly**
30 **MEGAUDAIS SPEED (FR)**, 9, b g Puit d'Or (IRE)—La Rouadiere (FR) **The Isle Of Frogs Partnership**
31 **MR LANDO**, 12, b g Shirocco (GER)—Capitana (GER) **The Lansdowners**
32 **NUMBERONEBEAUBOW**, 6, ch m Norse Dancer (IRE)—Pull The Wool (IRE) **Mr P. M. Tosh**
33 **ORMSKIRK**, 8, gr g Hellvelyn—River Song (USA) **Mrs G. Morgan**
34 **OUTLAW JACK (IRE)**, 9, b g Mr Dinos (IRE)—Bonus Issue (IRE) **Mr P. M. Tosh**
35 **SANDFORD CASTLE (IRE)**, 11, b g Norwich—Pegs Polly (IRE) **Live The Life**
36 **SATOSHI (IRE)**, 7, b g Shirocco (GER)—Morar **Mr J. Farrelly**
37 **SCARAMUCCI (IRE)**, 7, b g Sholokhov (GER)—Toppolesa (IRE) **Mr P. M. Tosh**
38 **SEHAYLI (IRE)**, 8, b g Iffraaj—Quaich **Mr P. M. Tosh**
39 **SPARKLING DAWN**, 9, gr m Sulamani (USA)—Clotted Cream (USA) **Live The Life - Atlas**
40 **THEDANCINGMAN**, 8, b g Jeremy (USA)—Broadway Dancer **Mrs L. J. Young**
41 **TRUE THOUGHTS (IRE)**, 6, b g So You Think (NZ)—True Joy (IRE) **Mrs L. J. Young**
42 **VALSE AU TAILLONS (FR)**, 8, b m Montmartre (FR)—Eyaelle (FR) **Hanford's Chemist Ltd**
43 **WESTERN SUNRISE (IRE)**, 12, b m Westerner—Presenting Gayle (IRE) **Mr D. J. Adams**
44 **WINTER SPICE (IRE)**, 10, gr g Verglas (IRE)—Summer Spice (IRE) **Mrs E. A. Heal**

**Other Owners:** J. F. Baldwin, Mr N. Penwill, Mr B. Skuse, The Lansdowners, Mr C. V. Vining, Mr G. C. Vining, R. T. Wilkins.

---

**191** | **MISS JULIA FEILDEN, Newmarket**
Postal: **Harraton Stud, Laceys Lane, Exning, Newmarket, Suffolk, CB8 7HW**
Contacts: **MOBILE 07974 817694**
EMAIL **juliafeilden@gmail.com** WEBSITE **www.juliafeildenracing.com**

1 **ALIBABA**, 4, b g Lawman (FR)—Fantasy In Blue **Ahamed Farook & Julia Feilden**
2 **ENGRAVE**, 5, gr m Dark Angel (IRE)—Hot Wired **Newmarket Equine Tours Racing Club**
3 **MRS MEADER**, 5, b m Cityscape—Bavarica **Nj Bloodstock**
4 **OUD METHA BRIDGE (IRE)**, 7, ch g Helmet (AUS)—Central Force **In It To Win Partnership**
5 **PAINTBALL WIZARD (IRE)**, 5, ch g Mastercraftsman (IRE)—Dance Avenue (IRE) **Carol Bushnell & Partners**
6 **PARTY PLANNER**, 4, gr f Mastercraftsman—Sweet Sixteen (IRE) **Colomane Racing**
7 **PRODUCTIVE (IRE)**, 4, b g Dark Angel (IRE)—Thawrah (IRE) **Ahamed Farook & Partners**
8 **RAHA**, 5, b m Mukhadram—Cefira (USA) **Ahamed Farook & Julia Feilden**
9 **SPANISH MANE (IRE)**, 6, b m Havana Gold (IRE)—Kiva **Stowstowquickquickstow Partnership**
10 **VALLETTA SUNSET**, 4, b g Casamento (IRE)—Sunset Kitty (USA) **Steve Clarke & Partners 3**
11 **WINTER SNOWDROP (IRE)**, 5, gr m War Command (USA)—Morning Jewel (IRE) **Mrs C. T. Bushnell**

## MISS JULIA FEILDEN - continued

### THREE-YEAR-OLDS

12 **CABRINI**, b f Charm Spirit (IRE)—Under The Rainbow **Adrian Sparks & Partner**
13 **DILLY ROSA**, b f Due Diligence (USA)—Rosa Luxemburg **Newmarket Equine Tours Racing Club**
14 **FEN TIGER (IRE)**, b g Vadamos (FRE)—Three Knots (IRE) **Mrs C. T. Bushnell**
15 **PIRANHADRAMA**, b f Heeraat (IRE)—Piranha (IRE) **Colomane Racing**
16 **SARAY PRINCE (IRE)**, ch g Exceed And Excel (AUS)—Zabeel Princess **Chris Cleevely & Partners**
17 **SMOKEY MALONE**, gr g Outstrip—Trixie Malone **The Sultans of Speed**

### TWO-YEAR-OLDS

18 **SCOTCH MIST**, gr f 12/02 Time Test—Positive Spin (Dalakhani (IRE) (12000) **Carol Bushnell & Partners**
19 **THE MOUSE KING (IRE)**, gr c 06/04 El Kabeir (USA)—
　　　　　　　　　　　　　　　　　　　　　　Empress Anna (IRE) (Imperial Ballet (IRE)) (11000) **Mrs C. T. Bushnell**

**Other Owners:** Mr N. Child, Mr S. J. Clarke, Mr C. R. Cleevely, Mr A. R. Farook, Miss J. D. Feilden, Mr M. Hancock, Mr Neil Hormann, Mr N. J. Johnston, Mr C. M. Page, Mr A. K. Sparks, Mr O. A. Wideson.

**Assistant Trainer:** Ross Birkett.

**Flat Jockey:** Dylan Hogan. **Amateur Jockey:** Mr R. Birkett, Mr Sam Feilden.

---

**192** **MR ROGER FELL, Nawton**
Postal: **Arthington Barn House, Highfield Lane, Nawton, York, North Yorkshire, YO62 7TU**
Contacts: **PHONE** 01439 770184
**EMAIL** rogerfellracing@gmail.com **WEBSITE** www.rogerfell.co.uk

1 **AD LIBITUM**, 6, b g Elusive Quality (USA)—Sarmad (USA) **Colne Valley Racing & Partner**
2 **ADMIRALITY**, 7, b g Mount Nelson—Dialma (USA) **Middleham Park Ventura Racing& Salthouse**
3 **AL OZZDI**, 6, b g Acclamation—Zibeling (IRE) **Northern Marking Ltd & Partner**
4 **ANYTHINGTODAY (IRE)**, 7, b g Zoffany (IRE)—Corking (IRE) **Woodhurst Construction Ltd**
5 **CAPTAINOFTHEBOUNTY (USA)**, 5, b g War Front (USA)—Drifting Cube (AUS) **Mr R. G. Fell**
6 **CLUB WEXFORD (IRE)**, 10, b g Lawman (FR)—Masnada (IRE) **Mr R. G. Fell**
7 **COCKALORUM (IRE)**, 6, b g Cape Cross (IRE)—Opinionated (IRE) **H Dean & R Fell**
8 **COWBOY SOLDIER (IRE)**, 6, b g Kodiac—Urgele (FR) **Ebor Racing Club V111**
9 **DAAWY (IRE)**, 7, ch g Teofilo (IRE)—Juno Marlowe (IRE) **Henry Dean, Jane & Victoria Greetham**
10 **DANDYS GOLD (IRE)**, 7, b m Dandy Man (IRE)—Proud Penny (IRE) **Nick Bradley Racing 8 & Partner**
11 **DAPPER MAN (IRE)**, 7, b g Dandy Man (IRE)—Gist (IRE) **Colne Valley Racing & Partner**
12 **DAVE DEXTER**, 5, b g Stimulation (IRE)—Blue Crest (FR) **The Wolf Pack & Partner**
13 **DRAMATISTA (IRE)**, 4, ch f Lope de Vega (IRE)—Aoife Alainn (IRE) **Nick Bradley & Ballylinch Stud**
14 **END ZONE**, 4, b g Dark Angel (IRE)—Brown Eyed Honey **Middleham Park Racing XIX & Salthouse**
15 **ERICH BLOCH (IRE)**, 5, b g Dandy Man (IRE)—Star Bonita (IRE) **Swales & Fell**
16 **GLOBAL SPIRIT**, 6, b g Invincible Spirit (IRE)—Centime **Arthington Barn Racing**
17 **HAROME (IRE)**, 7, ch g Bahamian Bounty—Clytha **Middleham Park Racing LXXI & Partner**
18 **HUMBERT (IRE)**, 7, b g Kodiac—Fee Eria (FR) **Woodhurst Construction Ltd**
19 **KAPONO**, 5, b g Kuroshio (AUS)—Fair Maiden (JPN) **Mr S. M. Al Sabah**
20 **KUPA RIVER (IRE)**, 7, b g Big Bad Bob (IRE)—Lamanka Lass (USA) **Middleham Park Racing LXXII & Partner**
21 **LA TRINIDAD**, 4, b g Bated Breath—High Drama (IRE) **Mrs D. W. Davenport**
22 **MEDICINE JACK**, 7, ch g Equiano (FR)—Agony Aunt **Fell & Salthouse**
23 **MONTALVAN (IRE)**, 5, ch g Lope de Vega (IRE)—Shermeen (IRE) **Swales & Fell**
24 **MUNTADAB (IRE)**, 9, b g Invincible Spirit (IRE)—Chibola (ARG) **Swales & Fell**
25 **MY BOY LEWIS (IRE)**, 5, b g Dandy Man (IRE)—Flamelet (USA) **Fell & Salthouse**
26 **NORDIC FIRE**, 5, b g Dream Ahead (USA)—Nordic Spruce (USA) **Withernsea & Woodhurst Ltd**
27 **OSO RAPIDO (IRE)**, 4, b g Kodiac—Burke's Rock **Woodhurst Construction & G Chrysanthou**
28 **PRESIDENTIAL (IRE)**, 7, b g Invincible Spirit (IRE)—Poetical (IRE) **Nick Bradley Racing 3,Ian White &partner**
29 **SPANTIK**, 4, b g Canford Cliffs (IRE)—Syrdarya **Mount Pleasant Racing & Partner**
30 **THORNTOUN CARE**, 10, b g Rail Link—Thorntoun Piccolo **Irvine Lynch & David Collier**
31 **USTATH**, 5, ch g Exceed And Excel (AUS)—Adorn **Middleham Park Racing LXXXII & Partner**
32 **ZIHAAM**, 7, ch g Dutch Art—Hymnsheet **Nick Bradley Racing 29 & Partner**
33 **ZYLAN (IRE)**, 9, ch g Kyllachy—Belgique (IRE) **Mr R. G. Fell**

## MR ROGER FELL - continued

### THREE-YEAR-OLDS
34 **HARSWELL PRINCESS (IRE)**, b f Kodiac—Silque **Harswell Thoroughbred Racing**
35 **POCKLEY**, b g Shalaa (IRE)—Wanting (IRE) **Nick Bradley Racing 37 & Partners**
36 **THE FLYING GINGER (IRE)**, ch f Showcasing—Law of The Range **Mr S. M. Al Sabah**

### TWO-YEAR-OLDS
37 Br f 08/05 Aclaim (IRE)—Billowing (IRE) (Candy Ride (ARG)) **Mr S. M. Al Sabah**
38 Ch f 29/04 Decorated Knight—Ellbeedee (IRE) (Dalakhani (IRE)) (28000) **Nick Bradley Racing 6 & Partner**
39 Ch f 03/02 Galileo Gold—Eponastone (IRE) (Footstepsinthesand) (8000)
40 **JONNY BOXER**, b c 24/03 Profitable (IRE)—Gala Style (IRE) (Elnadim (USA)) (22000) **Fell & Salthouse**
41 B f 23/03 Brazen Beau (AUS)—Last Frontier (FR) (Kendargent (FR)) (9500) **Nick Bradley Racing 12 & Partners**
42 B c 18/01 Vadamos (FR)—Last Hooray (Royal Applause) (7500)
43 B f 26/02 Markaz (IRE)—Maid In Heaven (IRE) (Clodovil (IRE)) (2857) **Mr R. G. Fell**

**Other Owners:** Armstrong Richardson & Co Ltd, Ballylinch Stud, Mr N. Bradley, Mr G. Chrysanthou, Mr D. Collier, Colne Valley Racing, Mr H. T. H. Dean, Mr A. Denham, Mr T. Denham, Mr R. G. Fell, Mr A. Franks, S. Franks, Mrs J. Greetham, Miss V. Greetham, Miss S. Holden, Mr N. E. M. Jones, Mr P. M. Lockwood, I. M. Lynch, Middleham Park Racing LXXI, Middleham Park Racing LXXII, Middleham Park Racing LXXXII, Middleham Park Racing XIX, Middleham Park and Ventura Racing 6, Mount Pleasant Racing, Nick Bradley Racing 12, Nick Bradley Racing 2, Nick Bradley Racing 29, Nick Bradley Racing 3, Nick Bradley Racing 37, Nick Bradley Racing 6, Nick Bradley Racing 8, Northern Marking Ltd, A. F. O'Callaghan, T. S. Palin, M. Prince, Mr W. J. Salthouse, Mr D. A. Swales, Mr M. Taylor, Mr I. K. White, Withernsea Thoroughbred Limited, Woodhurst Construction Ltd.

**Assistant Trainer:** Sean Murray.

---

**193** **MR CHARLIE FELLOWES, Newmarket**
Postal: **Bedford House Stables, 7 Bury Road, Newmarket, Suffolk, CB8 7BX**
Contacts: **PHONE 01638 666948 MOBILE 07968 499596**
**EMAIL charlie@charliefellowesracing.co.uk WEBSITE www.charliefellowesracing.co.uk**

1 **AMARILLO STAR (IRE)**, 4, ch g Society Rock (IRE)—Neutrina (IRE) **Lady De Ramsey**
2 **BEAUTY CHOICE**, 4, b g Bated Breath—Modesty's Way (USA) **Mr S. M. Kwok**
3 **BILLHILLY (GER)**, 4, b g Sea The Stars (IRE)—Boccassini (GER) **K Sohi & C Fellowes**
4 **BLOW YOUR HORN (IRE)**, 4, b g Golden Horn—She's Complete (IRE) **Mr J. Soiza**
5 **BOMA GREEN**, 4, b g Iffraaj—Dubai Cyclone (USA) **Mrs S. M. Roy**
6 **BYRON HILL (IRE)**, 4, b g Kingston Hill—Gwen Lady Byron (IRE) **The St Gatien Stables Partnership**
7 **BYZANTIA**, 4, b f Golden Horn—Hoyam **A. E. Oppenheimer**
8 **CARNWENNAN (IRE)**, 6, b g Cacique (IRE)—Slieve **Mr K. F. V. Kong**
9 **CHIEFOFCHIEFS**, 8, b g Royal Applause—Danvers **M. L. Ayers**
10 **DUBIOUS AFFAIR (IRE)**, 5, b m Frankel—Dubian To (IRE) **M. Obaida**
11 **DUEL IN THE SUN (IRE)**, 4, ch c Sea The Stars (IRE)—Queen's Conquer **Mrs S. M. Roy**
12 **GOLDEN DRAGON (IRE)**, 4, b c Starspangledbanner (USA)—
                                   Emerald Cutter (USA) **Happy Valley Racing & Breeding Limited**
13 **GOLDEN FORCE**, 5, b g Lethal Force (IRE)—Malilla (IRE) **A. M. Mitchell**
14 **JEREMIAH**, 6, ch g Kheleyf (USA)—Tessie **M. L. Ayers**
15 **KING CARNEY**, 4, ch g Australia—Petit Trianon **Mrs S. M. Roy**
16 **KING OTTOKAR (FR)**, 5, b g Motivator—Treasure (FR) **Mrs S. M. Roy**
17 **LADY OF ARAN (IRE)**, 6, b m Sir Prancealot (IRE)—
                               Tipperary Boutique (IRE) **Bengough, Fellowes, Horsford & Soiza**
18 **LONDON ARCH**, 4, b g Fastnet Rock (AUS)—Mount Crystal (IRE) **Mr P Hickman, Mr G Johns & Mr D King**
19 **LORD HALIFAX (IRE)**, 5, b g Famous Name—Neutral **Never So Bold - Aquino**
20 **MADAME PELTIER (IRE)**, 4, b f Exceed And Excel (AUS)—
                                   Airline Hostess (IRE) **Mr P Hickman, Mr G Johns & Mr D King**
21 **MAYFAIR POMPETTE (FR)**, 5, ch m Toronado (IRE)—Tipsy Me
22 **MR CURIOSITY**, 4, b g Frankel—Our Obsession (IRE) **A. E. Oppenheimer**

## MR CHARLIE FELLOWES - continued

23 **NAWAFETH (USA)**, 4, gr f The Factor (USA)—Safarjal (IRE) **Macauliffe Don Darivas Frost & Fellowes**
24 **PERFECT INCH**, 4, ro f Dark Angel (IRE)—Inchina **Mr A E Oppenheimer & Ms A Oppenheimer**
25 **PIRATE KING**, 6, br g Farhh—Generous Diana **Daniel MacAuliffe & Anoj Don**
26 **PRINCE OF ARRAN**, 8, b g Shirocco (GER)—Storming Sioux **Mr S. M. bel Obaida**
27 **RED POPPY**, 4, ch f Declaration of War (USA)—Valiant Girl **Mrs L. Barry**
28 **SOROS**, 4, b g Teofilo (IRE)—Hana Lina **Mr P Hickman, Mr G Johns & Mr D King**
29 **STAR DREAMER**, 4, b f Nathaniel (IRE)—Queen's Dream (IRE) **Mr A Simpson & Mrs S Roy**
30 **VANITY AFFAIR (IRE)**, 4, b g Mayson—Height of Vanity (IRE) **Dun Lee & Charlie Fellowes**
31 **VIA SERENDIPITY**, 7, b g Invincible Spirit (IRE)—Mambo Light (USA) **Happy Valley Racing & Breeding Limited**

## THREE-YEAR-OLDS

32 B f Flintshire—Bajan (USA) **Mr C. Johnsen**
33 B g Sea The Stars (IRE)—Bibury **Dahab Racing**
34 **CABLE GUY**, b c Cable Bay (IRE)—Diane's Choice **Owners Group 055**
35 **CELERIA**, b f Golden Horn—Hoyam **A. E. Oppenheimer**
36 **DEPUTY (IRE)**, b g Lawman (FR)—Finagle (IRE) **Highclere T'Bred Racing - Philip Blacker**
37 **DESERT MARATHON**, b f Pride of Dubai (AUS)—Run of The Day **Mr D. R. J. King**
38 **FIRST CONNECTION (FR)**, ch c Gleneagles (IRE)—Vendetta (IRE) **Mrs S. M. Roy**
39 **GEORGE SCOTT (IRE)**, b g Zoffany (IRE)—African Plains **Offthebridle Podcast**
40 **GLENEAGLET**, b f Gleneagles (IRE)—Seolan (IRE) **Mr D. Pearson**
41 **ICONIQUE**, b gr f Sixties Icon—Rose Cheval (USA) **Newmarket Racing Club HQ**
42 **INJAZATI (IRE)**, ch c Night of Thunder (IRE)—Mathanora (IRE) **M. Obaida**
43 **IVYNATOR (IRE)**, b g Muhaarar—Venturous Spirit (FR) **The Accession Partners**
44 **JOHNNY ESTELLA (IRE)**, b g No Nay Never (USA)—Sapphire Diva (IRE) **Mr J. Soiza**
45 **JUSTICIALISM (IRE)**, b c Vadamos (FR)—Peronism (USA) **M. Obaida**
46 **KATYUSHA**, b f Siyouni (FR)—Akhmatova **Mr D. S. Lee**
47 **LITTLE GEM**, b f Bobby's Kitten (USA)—Harlequin Twist **Mr E. E. A. Buddle**
48 **MARIEGOLD**, b f Golden Horn—Sinnamary **A. E. Oppenheimer**
49 **MONTE CARLO BAY (CAN)**, b g Noble Mission—Snow Lady (USA) **Mr Graham Smith-Bernal & Mr Alan Dee**
50 **PURPLE RIBBON**, b f Gleneagles (IRE)—Crimson Ribbon (USA) **A. E. Oppenheimer**
51 B c Free Eagle (IRE)—Silirisa (FR) **The Staying Syndicate**
52 **SONG TWO (IRE)**, b g Twilight Son—Meydan Princess (IRE) **Yeomanstown Stud & Charlie Fellowes**
53 **STAR OF SCREEN (FR)**, ch f Australia—Stage Queen (IRE) **Lady Bamford**
54 **TALLULAH (IRE)**, ch f Sea The Stars (IRE)—Ninas Terz (GER) **Mrs S. M. Roy**
55 B c Charming Thought—Tessie **M. L. Ayers**
56 **THE FIRST HURRAH (FR)**, b f Muhaarar—Sweet Cecily (IRE) **Mr Graham Smith-Bernal & Mr Alan Dee**
57 **UNCLE JOHNNY**, b c No Nay Never (USA)—Found You (USA) **Joe Soiza & Charlie Fellowes**
58 **VADREAM**, b f Brazen Beau (AUS)—Her Honour (IRE) **Mr D. R. J. King**
59 B g Awtaad (IRE)—Ziria (IRE) **Mr C. H. Fellowes**

## TWO-YEAR-OLDS

60 **ATRIUM**, b c 21/04 Holy Roman Emperor (IRE)—
Hail Shower (IRE) (Red Clubs (IRE)) (60000) **Highclere Thoroughbred Racing - Pergola**
61 **COOKIES AND CREME**, ch f 25/03 Siyouni (FR)—Coconut Creme (Cape Cross (IRE)) **Normandie Stud Ltd**
62 B f 18/04 Ardad (IRE)—Eolith (Pastoral Pursuits) (13000) **Miranda Beaufort**
63 **FRESH HOPE**, b f 25/03 New Approach (IRE)—Wiener Valkyrie (Shamardal (USA)) **The Eclipse Partnership**
64 **GRAND ALLIANCE (IRE)**, b c 31/03 Churchill (IRE)—Endless Love (IRE) (Dubai Destination (USA)) **Mrs S. M. Roy**
65 B c 19/04 Dark Angel (IRE)—Masaya (Dansili) (38000) **Dahab Racing**
66 B c 12/04 Kodiac—Night Queen (IRE) (Rip Van Winkle (IRE)) (61905) **Dahab Racing**
67 B f 03/05 Equiano (FR)—Persario (Bishop of Cashel) **Mrs Elizabeth Grundy, Hot to Trot Racing 2**
68 **PROSPECTING**, ch f 27/01 Spill The Beans (AUS)—Elvira Delight (Desert Style (IRE)) **Mr F. J. Perry**
69 B f 14/04 Dabirsim (FR)—Puzzler (IRE) (New Approach (IRE)) (20000) **Mrs S. M. Roy**
70 **SAN FRANCISCO BAY (IRE)**, b c 10/02 Muhaarar—
Stor Mo Chroi (IRE) (Montjeu (IRE)) (9523) **Mr Graham Smith-Bernal & Mr Alan Dee**
71 B f 18/04 Ardad (IRE)—Sandy Times (IRE) (Footstepsinthesand) (12500) **Offthebridle Podcast II**
72 B f 18/04 Kodiac—Sona (Dansili) **Lady Bamford**
73 B f 02/03 Postponed (IRE)—Strathnaver (Oasis Dream) **St Albans Bloodstock**
74 **SURREY KNIGHT (FR)**, b c 15/05 Le Havre (IRE)—
Millionaia (IRE) (Peintre Celebre (USA)) (30669) **Surrey Racing (SK)**

## MR CHARLIE FELLOWES - continued

75 B f 03/04 Intello (GER)—Tempest Fugit (IRE) (High Chaparral (IRE)) (38000)  **Middleham Park Racing LXXV**
76 **YOUNG ENDLESS,** b c 12/05 Champs Elysees—Eternity Ring (Alzao (USA))  **The Endless Acres Five**
77 **ZLOTY,** b c 22/04 Telescope (IRE)—Pound Sterling (Champs Elysees)  **Marshall Farms (Ashton) Ltd**

**Other Owners:** Mr A. N. C. Bengough, Mr A. Darivas, Mr A. Dee, Mr A. R. Don, Mr C. H. Fellowes, Mr E. H. M. Frost, Mr P. J. Hickman, G. Horsford, Mr G. Johns, Mr D. R. J. King, Mr D. S. Lee, Mr D. P. MacAuliffe, Daniel MacAuliffe & Anoj Don, Mr D. O'Callaghan, Ms A. Oppenheimer, A. E. Oppenheimer, Mrs S. M. Roy, Alasdair Simpson, Mr G. F. Smith-Bernal, Mr K. Sohi, Mr J. Soiza, Mr M. R. Soiza, Joe Soiza & Mason Soiza.

**Flat Jockey:** Stevie Donohoe. **Apprentice Jockey:** Aled Beech.

---

**194**
### MR JAMES FERGUSON, Newmarket
Postal: **Saville House Stables, St Mary's Square, Newmarket, Suffolk, CB8 0HZ**
Contacts: **WORK 01638 599581 MOBILE 07826 889571**
**WORK EMAIL james@jamesfergusonracing.com**

1 **ANGEL OF DELIGHT (IRE),** 4, gr f Dark Angel (IRE)—Ventura Mist  **Rathordan Partnership**
2 **ARABIAN KING,** 5, ch g New Approach (IRE)—Barshiba (IRE)  **The Gem Set**
3 **BADRAH (USA),** 4, ch f Kitten's Joy (USA)—Aqsaam (USA)  **Mr J. P. Ferguson**
4 **COZONE,** 4, b g Pour Moi (IRE)—Bella Nouf  **Middleham Park Racing & Theawesomededudes**
5 **EDITH PIAF (IRE),** 4, b f Le Havre (IRE)—Blissful Beat  **Mr J. P. Ferguson**
6 **JOHNNY REB,** 5, b g Showcasing—Specific Dream  **North Farm Stud Limited**
7 **LEADER WRITER (FR),** 9, b g Pivotal—Miss Emma May (IRE)  **The Leader Writer Group**
8 **MACK THE KNIFE (IRE),** 4, b g Australia—Kitty Matcham (IRE)  **Mr J. J. Ferguson**
9 **ONE HART (IRE),** 4, br g Gutaifan (IRE)—Crystal Morning (IRE)  **Mr J. J. Ferguson**
10 **SNOWALOT (IRE),** 4, b g Camelot—Bright Snow (USA)  **Mr K. K. B. Ho**

## THREE-YEAR-OLDS

11 **ACROSS THE NILE,** b f Iffraaj—Meeting Waters  **The Saville House Syndicate**
12 **BAKR,** b f Kodiac—Qawaasem (IRE)  **Gow Equine Ltd**
13 **COPINET,** b f Mehmas (IRE)—Dominatrix  **A Cantillon & R Ryan**
14 **CURRENCY EXCHANGE (IRE),** ch g Night of Thunder (IRE)—Mon Bijou (IRE)  **John Ferguson & Walkuptrotback**
15 **EPIC EXPRESS,** ch g Twilight Son—Keep The Secret  **Mrs S. Dwyer**
16 **FIORDLAND (IRE),** b g Invincible Spirit (IRE)—Cascading  **The 4letterfirstnames Partnership**
17 **FRANCESCO GUARDI (IRE),** b c Frankel—Trophee (FR)  **The 4letterfirstnames & Ballylinch Stud**
18 **HEMSWORTH (IRE),** b g New Approach (IRE)—Vetlana (IRE)  **Mr D. R. Seldon**
19 **LAZENBY (IRE),** b c Vadamos (FR)—Good For Her  **Mr D. R. Seldon**
20 **PREY FOR GLORY,** b g Free Eagle (IRE)—Mama Rocco  **Mrs A. Cantillon**
21 **RIDGEWAY AVENUE (USA),** ch c Kitten's Joy (USA)—Trensa (USA)  **Mr L. J. Williams**
22 **SMOOTH SPIRIT,** b g Charm Spirit—Valonia  **The Free Spirits**
23 **WHATITIZZ,** br f Cable Bay (IRE)—Wosaita  **Blackrock Racing Uk & Mr G Bishop**
24 **ZOETIC,** b f Kodiac—Zallerina  **Glentree Pastoral Pty Ltd**

## TWO-YEAR-OLDS

25 B c 26/04 Kodiac—Al Andalyya (USA) (Kingmambo (USA)) (70000)
26 Ch c 12/04 Ulysses (IRE)—Arwaah (IRE) (Dalakhani (IRE)) (40000)
27 **DEAUVILLE LEGEND (IRE),** b c 16/03 Sea The Stars (IRE)—
                                   Soho Rose (IRE) (Hernando (FR)) (161421)  **Mr K. K. B. Ho**
28 B f 19/02 Siyouni (FR)—Gadfly (Galileo (IRE))  **Qatar Racing Limited**
29 B c 14/03 Havana Gold—Gertrude Versed (Manduro (GER))  **Qatar Racing Limited**
30 B c 31/01 Starspangledbanner (AUS)—Jazz Cat (IRE) (Tamayuz) (32000)  **Mr G. S. Bishop**
31 B c 21/04 New Bay—Lady Penko (FR) (Archipenko (USA)) (75000)  **The 4letterfirstnames & Ballylinch Stud**
32 B c 16/03 Invincible Spirit (IRE)—Lulawin (Kyllachy) (205000)  **Mrs S. M. Roy**
33 B c 30/01 Lope de Vega (IRE)—Miss Celie (IRE) (Galileo (IRE)) (60000)
34 **OCEANIA LEGEND (IRE),** ch c 03/03 Australia—Ame Bleue (Dubawi (IRE)) (64568)  **Mr K. K. B. Ho**

## MR JAMES FERGUSON - continued

35 B c 14/04 Adaay (IRE)—Salome (FR) (Fuisse (FR)) (11000) **John Ferguson & Walkuptrotback**
36 B f 10/02 Territories (IRE)—Satsuma (Compton Place) (18000)
37 B c 05/03 Iffraaj—Sloane Square (Teofilo (IRE)) (130000) **M. A. C. Buckley**
38 Ch f 02/03 Free Eagle (IRE)—Tonle Sap (Manduro (GER)) (2000)
39 Ch c 29/03 Frankel—Ventura (IRE) (Spectrum (IRE)) (138095)

**Head Girl:** Aideen Marshall, **Travelling Head:** Alyson West.

---

| 195 | **MR DOMINIC FFRENCH DAVIS, Lambourn** |
|---|---|

Postal: **College House, 3 Oxford Street, Lambourn, Hungerford, Berkshire, RG17 8XP**
Contacts: **HOME 01488 72342 PHONE 01488 73675 MOBILE 07831 118764 FAX 01488 73675
EMAIL ffrenchdavis@btinternet.com WEBSITE www.ffrenchdavis.com**

1 **ANONYMOUS JOHN (IRE)**, 9, gr g Baltic King—Helibel (IRE) **Mr R. F. Haynes**
2 **BOY GEORGE**, 4, b g Equiano (FR)—If I Were A Boy (IRE) **Mr R. F. Haynes**
3 **CALL MY BLUFF (IRE)**, 4, b g Make Believe—Ocean Bluff (IRE) **The Ffrench Connection**
4 **EGYPSYAN CRACKAJAK**, 4, b g Kutub (IRE)—Three Scoops **G. King Haulage Ltd**
5 **FORKED LIGHTNING**, 4, b g Night of Thunder (IRE)—Darrfonah (IRE) **Gary & Paul Townend**
6 **HEATON CHAPEL (IRE)**, 4, b g Requinto (IRE)—Coastal Storm **Mr T. Gibbons**
7 **INDEED**, 6, b g Showcasing—Argumentative **Marchwood Aggregates**
8 **JAMES PARK WOODS (IRE)**, 5, b g Australia—Happy Holly (IRE) **Philip Banfield & Dominic Ffrench Davis**
9 **NELL 'N' FLO (IRE)**, 5, b m Leading Light (IRE)—Bella's Bury **D. J. S. Ffrench Davis**
10 **SNOWBIRD (IRE)**, 10, ch m Presenting—Blueanna (IRE) **The roll a silver dollar syndicate**
11 **THEMATIC (USA)**, 5, b g Noble Mission—Gateway (USA) **Marchwood Aggregates**
12 **WHATTHEBUTLERSAW (IRE)**, 12, br g Arcadio (GER)—
Phar From Men (IRE) **Mrs P Ffrench Davis & Mr D Ffrench Davis**

### THREE-YEAR-OLDS

13 **GOINGTOCALIFORNIA (IRE)**, b c Bungle Inthejungle—Her Red Devil (IRE) **D. J. S. Ffrench Davis**
14 **JUST A JEROBOAM**, b g Bobby's Kitten (USA)—Isostatic **Jeroboam syndicate**

**Other Owners:** P. Banfield, Mr G. H. Black, D. J. S. Ffrench Davis, Mrs P. Ffrench Davis, Mrs G. Townend.

**Assistant Trainer:** Ben Ffrench Davis.

**NH Jockey:** Mark Grant.

---

| 196 | **MR GUISEPPE FIERRO, Hednesford** |
|---|---|

Postal: **Brook House, Rawnsley Road, Hednesford, Cannock, Staffordshire, WS12 1RB**
Contacts: **PHONE 01543 879611 MOBILE 07976 321468**

1 **JUST LIKE BETH**, 13, b m Proclamation (IRE)—Just Beth **G. Fierro**
2 **LAFILIA (GER)**, 6, b m Teofilo (IRE)—Labrice **G. Fierro**
3 **LITTLE DOTTY**, 12, br m Erhaab (USA)—Marsh Marigold **G. Fierro**
4 **RAMBLING RIVER**, 10, b g Revoque (IRE)—Just Beth **G. Fierro**
5 **SUNDANCE BOY**, 12, gr g Proclamation (IRE)—Just Beth **G. Fierro**

**Assistant Trainer:** M Fierro.

**197**

**MRS MARJORIE FIFE, Stillington**
Postal: White Thorn Farm, Stillington, Easingwold, York, YO61 1LT
Contacts: PHONE 01347 822012 MOBILE 07890 075217
EMAIL wfife10416@aol.com

1 **B FIFTY TWO (IRE)**, 12, br g Dark Angel (IRE)—Petite Maxine **Thorpe Farm Rehab & Fitness**
2 **MISTER UNIVERSUM (GER)**, 9, b g Cape Cross (IRE)—Miss Europa (IRE) **Thorpe Farm Rehab & Fitness**
3 **MOUNTAIN RESCUE (IRE)**, 9, b g High Chaparral (IRE)—Amber Queen (IRE) **Thorpe Farm Rehab & Fitness**
4 **PANZERTANK (IRE)**, 4, b g Exceed And Excel (AUS)—Falling Petals (IRE) **Mrs M. Turner**

**Other Owners:** Mrs A. Fife, Mrs M. Fife, Mr T. W. Fife.

**198**

**MR TIM FITZGERALD, Malton**
Postal: Norton Grange, Norton, Malton, North Yorkshire, YO17 9EA
Contacts: PHONE 01653 228456 MOBILE 07950 356437
EMAIL fitzgeraldracing@hotmail.com

1 **DARKEST DREAM**, 5, b m Albaasil (IRE)—Rare Ruby (IRE) **Mr R. S. Fiddes**
2 **HE'S MAGIC**, 10, b g Court Masterpiece—Lady Magician **Mrs M. Lingwood**
3 **KINGI COMPTON**, 5, b g Compton Place—Missprint **The Jolly Racing**
4 **MISSTIFY**, 5, bl m Albaasil (IRE)—Miss Holly **Mr R. S. Fiddes**
5 **MORE BEER (IRE)**, 6, b br g Westerner—Whites Cross (IRE) **Mr M. Pimlott**
6 **MURITZ**, 4, ch f Free Eagle (IRE)—Super Gitana (IRE) **The Jolly Racing**
7 **PROPHECY**, 5, b g Albaasil (IRE)—Littlemoor Lass **Mr R. S. Fiddes**
8 **SAME OPINION (IRE)**, 6, b g Flemensfirth (USA)—Rosa Rugosa (IRE) **Crowd Racing Partnership**
9 **TOUT PARIS (FR)**, 6, b g Kapgarde (FR)—Parice de La Borie (FR) **Mr M. Pimlott**

**THREE-YEAR-OLDS**

10 **LOCKDOWN**, b g Charm Spirit (IRE)—Bounty Box **Mr M. Pimlott**
11 **THE SEDBERGHIAN (IRE)**, b f Kodi Bear (IRE)—Shirley Blake (IRE) **sedbergh lads club**

**199**

**MR JOHN FLINT, Bridgend**
Postal: Woodland Lodge, Waunbant Road, Kenfig Hill, Bridgend, Mid Glamorgan, CF33 6FF
Contacts: MOBILE 07581 428173 FAX 01656 744347
EMAIL johnflint900@gmail.com WEBSITE www.johnflintracing.com

1 **AMATEUR (IRE)**, 8, ch g Giant's Causeway (USA)—Adja (IRE) **Burnham Plastering & Drylining Ltd**
2 **CANFORD STAR (IRE)**, 8, b m Canford Cliffs (IRE)—Alexander Alliance (IRE) **Mrs S. M. Farr**
3 **CARP KID (IRE)**, 6, b g Lope de Vega (IRE)—Homegrown (IRE) **JACK Racing**
4 **CHAMPAGNE HIGHLIFE (GER)**, 4, b g Holy Roman Emperor (IRE)—Casanga (IRE) **The Highlife Racing Club**
5 **COURT DUTY (IRE)**, 9, b g Court Cave (IRE)—Easter Duties (IRE) **Davies & Price**
6 **DIAMOND SHOWER (IRE)**, 5, b m Clodovil (IRE)—Star Lodge **Mr D. A. Poole**
7 **EDDIEMAURICE (IRE)**, 10, ch g Captain Rio—Annals **J. L. Flint**
8 **GRAVITY WAVE (IRE)**, 7, br g Rip Van Winkle (IRE)—Phrase **J. L. Flint**
9 **I AM PLASTERED**, 6, b g Midnight Legend—One For Joules (IRE) **Burnham Plastering & Drylining Ltd**
10 **ISLA DI MILANO (IRE)**, 10, b g Milan—Monagea Island (IRE) **Mr J. M. H. Hearne**
11 **ITSALLABOUTLUCK (IRE)**, 4, b g Kodiac—Lucky (IRE) **E. R. Clough**
12 **JUST RIGHT**, 6, ch m Medicean—Rightside **J. L. Flint**
13 **LAC SACRE (FR)**, 12, b g Bering—Lady Glorieuse (FR) **Mr L. H. & Mrs T. Evans**
14 **LAMBS LANE (IRE)**, 9, b g Mahler—Ilikeyou (IRE) **Miss S. D. Redpath**
15 **LOVE AND BE LOVED**, 7, b m Lawman (FR)—Rightside **J. L. Flint**

## MR JOHN FLINT - continued

16 **LYNDON B (IRE)**, 5, b g Charm Spirit (IRE)—Kelsey Rose **P.DuffyD.SemmensVWilliamsRHarperMLoveday**
17 **MAMA AFRICA (IRE)**, 7, br m Big Bad Bob (IRE)—Colourpoint (USA) **J. L. Flint**
18 **MONTY MASSINI**, 10, b g Dr Massini (IRE)—Miss Montgomery (IRE) **Mrs S. M. Farr**
19 **OUTER SPACE**, 10, b g Acclamation—Venoge (IRE) **Mr D. A. Poole**
20 5, B g Monsieur Bond (IRE)—Sea Crest **Aled Evans & Tommy Williams**
21 **THE WIRE FLYER**, 6, b g Champs Elysees—Good Morning Star (IRE) **Aled Evans & Tommy Williams**
22 **WINKLEMANN (IRE)**, 9, br g Rip Van Winkle (IRE)—Kykuit (USA) **J. L. Flint**
23 **WITH PLEASURE**, 8, b g Poet's Voice—With Fascination (USA) **Burnham Plastering & Drylining Ltd**

**Other Owners:** Mr A. Evans, Mr L. H. Evans, Mrs T. Evans, Mr T. Williams.

**Assistant Trainer:** Mrs Martine Louise Flint, Rhys Flint.

---

**200** **MR DAVID FLOOD, Hungerford**
Postal: **15 High Street, Chiseldon, Swindon, Wiltshire, SN4 0NG**
Contacts: PHONE 07919 340619
EMAIL davidflood1@hotmail.co.uk

1 **BAZOOKA (IRE)**, 10, b g Camacho—Janadam (IRE) **Mrs A. Cowley**
2 **GLENCOE BOY (IRE)**, 4, b g Gleneagles (IRE)—Eastern Appeal (IRE) **Mrs A. Cowley**
3 **KENDERGARTEN KOP (IRE)**, 6, ch g Kendargent (FR)—Elsa T (IRE) **Royal Wootton Bassett Racing Limited**
4 **LEO'S LUCKYMAN**, 4, b g Cable Bay (IRE)—Atalis **Royal Wootton Bassett Racing Limited**
5 **MAJESTYK FIRE (IRE)**, 4, ch g Ivawood (IRE)—Dream Impossible (IRE) **Mrs A. Cowley**
6 **PEDESTAL (IRE)**, 7, b g Invincible Spirit (IRE)—Ashley Hall (USA) **Mrs A. Cowley**
7 **STOPDWORLDNLETMEOF**, 7, b g Piccolo—Dilli Dancer **Royal Wootton Bassett Racing Limited**
8 **TOOLMAKER**, 4, b g Harbour Watch (IRE)—Calypso Dream (IRE) **Royal Wootton Bassett Racing Limited**

---

**201** **MR TONY FORBES, Uttoxeter**
Postal: **Hill House Farm, Poppits Lane, Stramshall, Uttoxeter, Staffordshire, ST14 5EX**
Contacts: PHONE 01889 562722 MOBILE 07967 246571
EMAIL tony@thimble.net

1 **BARCA (USA)**, 7, b g War Front (USA)—Magnificent Honour (USA) **Mr A. L. Forbes**
2 **NO ALARM (IRE)**, 9, b g Getaway (GER)—Chapanga (IRE) **Mr A. L. Forbes**
3 **TINGO IN THE TALE (IRE)**, 12, b g Oratorio (IRE)—Sunlit Skies **Mr A. L. Forbes**

**Assistant Trainer:** Mr Tim Eley.

---

**202** **MRS RICHENDA FORD, Blandford Forum**
Postal: **Garlands Farm, The Common, Okeford Fitzpaine, Blandford Forum, Dorset, DT11 0RT**
Contacts: MOBILE 07800 634846
WORK EMAIL Richendaford@gmail.com WEBSITE www.richendafordracing.co.uk
FACEBOOK RichendaFordRacing INSTAGRAM RichendaFordRacing

1 **ALVAREZ (IRE)**, 5, ch g Notnowcato—Golden Memories (IRE) **Richenda Ford Racing Club**
2 **DONT BE ROBIN (IRE)**, 9, b g Robin des Pres (FR)—Rainbow Times (IRE) **Mr & Mrs K. B. Snook**
3 **FLAMENCO DE KERSER (FR)**, 6, b g Vendangeur (IRE)—Nouba de Kerser (FR)
4 **HENZO DES BOULLATS (FR)**, 4, b g Saddler Maker (IRE)—Becky des Boulats (FR) **Mr & Mrs K. B. Snook**

## MRS RICHENDA FORD - continued

  5 **LEAVE MY ALONE (IRE)**, 8, br m Getaway (GER)—Glenda King (IRE)  **Mr & Mrs K. B. Snook**
  6 **MONKEY HARRIS (IRE)**, 9, b g Oscar (IRE)—Benefit Ball (IRE)  **Mr & Mrs K. B. Snook**
  7 **SHANROE SMOOCH (IRE)**, 8, b g Ask—Lady Quesada (IRE)  **Mr & Mrs K. B. Snook**
  8 4, B f Pether's Moon (IRE)—Sovereignsflagship (IRE)  **Mr & Mrs K. B. Snook**

**Other Owners:** K. B. Snook, Mrs M. Snook.

---

| | |
|---|---|
| **203** | **MR BRIAN FORSEY, Taunton**<br>Postal: **Three Oaks, Ash Priors, Taunton, Somerset, TA4 3NQ**<br>Contacts: **PHONE 01823 433914 MOBILE 07747 392760**<br>EMAIL forsey2001@yahoo.com |

  1 **BARISTA (IRE)**, 13, b g Titus Livius (FR)—Cappuccino (IRE)  **Three Oaks Racing & Mrs P Bosley**
  2 **BUTTERFIELD (IRE)**, 8, b g Fastnet Rock (AUS)—Cozzene's Angel (USA)  **Mr Alan Stevens & Mr Brian Forsey**
  3 **DROPZONE (USA)**, 12, b g Smart Strike (CAN)—Dalisay (IRE)  **Mr Alan Stevens & Mr Brian Forsey**
  4 **KERRY'S BOY (IRE)**, 8, b g Oscar (IRE)—Kerry's Girl (IRE)  **Mr M. P. Ardley**

**Other Owners:** Mrs P. M. Bosley, B. Forsey, A. G. Stevens.

**Assistant Trainer:** Mrs Elizabeth Chatfield.

---

| | |
|---|---|
| **204** | **MISS SANDY FORSTER, Kelso**<br>Postal: **Halterburn Head, Yetholm, Kelso, Roxburghshire, TD5 8PP**<br>Contacts: **PHONE 01573 420615 MOBILE 07976 587315, 07880 727877 FAX 01573 420615**<br>EMAIL clivestorey@btinternet.com |

  1 **ASHJAN**, 8, b g Medicean—Violet (IRE)  **Dave Skeldon & Sandy Forster**
  2 **BALLYTOBIN (IRE)**, 6, ch g Salutino (GER)—Restless Dreams (IRE)  **Dave Skeldon & Sandy Forster**
  3 **CHARLIE SNOW ANGEL (IRE)**, 12, b g Overbury (IRE)—Sister Seven (IRE)  **C. Storey**
  4 **CLAUD AND GOLDIE (IRE)**, 12, ch g Portrait Gallery (IRE)—Glacial Jewel (IRE)  **The Border Racers**
  5 **GYPSEY'S SECRET (IRE)**, 6, b m Dylan Thomas (IRE)—Lady Howe  **Mr M. H. Walton**
  6 **KITTY FISHER (IRE)**, 11, b m Scorpion (IRE)—Luck of The Deise (IRE)  **Ms Allison Grant Long & Partner**
  7 **LASTIN' MEMORIES**, 9, b g Overbury (IRE)—Dusky Dante (IRE)  **Dave Skeldon & Sandy Forster**
  8 **LISSEN TO THE LADY (IRE)**, 7, b m Fame And Glory (IRE)—Liss Rua (IRE)  **Mr M. H. Walton**
  9 **MORNINGSIDE**, 8, b g Kayf Tara—Bouncing Bean  **I I F T F**
 10 **NETTLEBUSH (IRE)**, 11, br g Kalanisi (IRE)—Amber Gale (IRE)  **Mrs I Thomson & Miss S Forster**
 11 **STOWAWAY JOHN (IRE)**, 7, b g Stowaway—Figlette  **Dave Skeldon & Clive Storey**

**Other Owners:** Miss S. E. Forster, Ms A. G. Long, Mrs M. A. H. Shanks, Mr D. A. Skeldon, C. Storey, Mrs I. H. Thomson.

**Assistant Trainer:** C. Storey.

**Amateur Jockey:** Miss J. Walton.

## 205 MISS JO FOSTER, Ilkley
Postal: **The Old Mistal, Brookleigh Farm, Burley Road, Menston, Ilkley, West Yorkshire, LS29 6NS**
Contacts: PHONE 07980 301808 MOBILE 07980 301808
EMAIL info@jofosterracing.co.uk WEBSITE www.jofosterracing.co.uk

1 CHASE THE WIND (IRE), 12, ch g Spadoun (FR)—Asfreeasthewind (IRE) **Mr J. Nixon**
2 DA VINCI HAND (IRE), 6, b g Champs Elysees—Thousandkissesdeep (IRE) **Mr J. Nixon**
3 FRANKIE BALLOU (IRE), 12, br g Norwich—One Up (IRE) **The Yorkshire Racing Partnership**
4 GO TO COURT (IRE), 8, b m Court Cave (IRE)—Go Franky (IRE) **Miss J. E. Foster**
5 LAMMTURNER (IRE), 9, b m Brian Boru—Deploy Or Die (IRE) **Mr E. C. Wilkin**
6 ONE STEP TOO FAR (IRE), 4, br g Footstepsinthesand—High Society Girl (IRE) **The Golden Syndicate**
7 PANIC OVER (IRE), 5, b g Mahler—Vinnes Friend (IRE) **The Golden Syndicate**
8 SEAPOINT (IRE), 7, b m Footstepsinthesand—Genuinely (IRE) **Give It A Go Partners**
9 SIGURD (GER), 9, ch g Sholokhov (IRE)—Sky News (GER) **Mrs E. A. Verity**
10 TWO HOOTS (IRE), 10, gr g Tikkanen (USA)—Supreme Beneficial (IRE) **Reign It In 2**
11 WONDERFUL WOMAN (IRE), 7, ch m Ask—Green Sea **Greenwood, Collins & Foster**

**Other Owners:** J. Berry, Ms J. Clark, Mr M. Collins, Mr W. M. Curtis, Mrs C. Finn, Miss J. E. Foster, P. Foster, Mrs J. Greenwood, Mr S. A. Hollings, Mr D. Liddle, Mr A. P. Moncaster, Mr L. S. Musson, Mrs C. Potter, Mr M. J. Roche, Mr C. J. Teal, Mr P. Thompson.

**Assistant Trainer:** P. Foster.

**NH Jockey:** Henry Brooke.

## 206 MR JIMMY FOX, Marlborough
Postal: **Highlands Farm Stables, Herridge, Collingbourne Ducis, Marlborough, Wiltshire, SN8 3EG**
Contacts: PHONE 01264 850218, 07931 724358 MOBILE 07702 880010
EMAIL jcfoxtrainer@aol.com

1 ACT ACCORDINGLY, 8, gr g Sagamix (FR)—Anns Girl **Mrs J. A. Cleary**
2 GRACEFUL JAMES (IRE), 8, ch g Rock of Gibraltar (IRE)—Little Miss Gracie **Abacus Employment Services Ltd**
3 GRACIOUS GEORGE (IRE), 11, b g Oratorio (IRE)—Little Miss Gracie **Highlands Farm Racing Partnership**
4 PURPLE PADDY, 6, b g Swiss Spirit—Stunning In Purple (IRE) **Mr A. Lucas**
5 4, B g Music Master—Stunning In Purple (IRE)

### THREE-YEAR-OLDS

6 DUE DILLY, b br f Due Diligence (USA)—Star Pursuits **Mrs S. J. Fox**
7 PURPLE POPPY, b f Swiss Spirit—Stunning In Purple (IRE) **Mrs B. A. Fuller**

**Other Owners:** Mrs S. J. Fox, Mrs B. A. Fuller.

**Assistant Trainer:** Sarah-Jane Fox.

**207**
## MISS SUZZANNE FRANCE, Norton on Derwent
Postal: **Cheesecake Hill House, Highfield, Beverley Road, Norton on Derwent, North Yorkshire, YO17 9PJ**
Contacts: **PHONE 07904 117531 MOBILE 07904 117531 FAX 01653 691947**
EMAIL **suzzanne@newstartracing.co.uk** WEBSITE **www.suzzannefranceracing.com, www. newstartracing.co.uk**

1 **ARCHIVE (FR),** 11, b g Sulamani (IRE)—Royale Dorothy (FR)  **Newstart Partnership & Co**
2 **BILLY DYLAN (IRE),** 6, b g Exceleration (IRE)—It's True (IRE)  **Newstart Partnership**
3 **HE'S GUILTY (USA),** 5, b br g Blame (USA)—She's Smashing (USA)  **Miss Kate Dobb & Mr Stuart Dobb**
4 **STAND FREE,** 4, b f Helmet (AUS)—Ivory Silk  **Miss Kate Dobb & Mr Stuart Dobb**

**Other Owners:** Miss K. M. Dobb, Mr S. Dobb, Mrs P. France, Newstart Partnership.

**Assistant Trainer:** Mr Aaron James.

---

**208**
## MR DEREK FRANKLAND, Brackley
Postal: **Springfields, Mixbury, Brackley, Northamptonshire, NN13 5RR**
Contacts: **MOBILE 07763 020406 FAX 01280 847334**
EMAIL **dsfrankland@aol.com**

1 **CANNY TOM (IRE),** 11, b g Jimble (FR)—Tombazaan (IRE)  **Mr D. S. Frankland & Mr D. J. Trott**
2 **JOINT ACCOUNT (IRE),** 8, b g Jimble (FR)—Late Back (IRE)  **Mr D. S. Frankland & Mr D. J. Trott**

**Other Owners:** D. S. Frankland, Mr D. J. Trott.

---

**209**
## MR ALEX FRENCH, Newmarket
Postal: **Phantom House, Fordham Road, Newmarket, Suffolk, CB8 7AA**
Contacts: **PHONE 07776 306588**
EMAIL **a.french@outlook.com**

1 **NAVAL OFFICER,** 6, b g Helmet (AUS)—Ariyfa (IRE)  **Ms J. A. French**
2 **SEA THE GIRL,** 4, b f Sea The Moon (GER)—Bountiful Girl  **Jam Tomorrow Partnership**
3 **SWEET AND INNOCENT,** 5, br m Lethal Force (IRE)—Zainda (IRE)  **Jam Tomorrow Partnership**

### THREE-YEAR-OLDS
4 **FLYING INSTRUCTOR (IRE),** b g Nayef (USA)—Devonelli (IRE)  **Ms J. A. French**
5 Gr g Charm Spirit (IRE)—Frosty Berry
6 **OUT OF SIGHT (IRE),** b c Outstrip—Bountiful Girl  **Ms J. A. French**

### TWO-YEAR-OLDS
7 B c 05/05 Muhaarar—Muajiza (Pivotal)
8 B c 17/03 Dawn Approach (IRE)—Spellcraft (Dubawi (IRE))

**Other Owners:** Ms J. A. French, Mrs S. E. L. Rigby.

## 210 MR JAMES FROST, Buckfastleigh
Postal: **Hawson Stables, Buckfastleigh, Devon, TQ11 0HP**
Contacts: **HOME** 01364 642332 **PHONE** 01364 642267 **MOBILE** 07860 220229 **FAX** 01364 643182
**EMAIL** info@frostracingclub.co.uk

1 **ANTIDOTE (IRE)**, 5, gr g Dark Angel (IRE)—Mood Indigo (IRE) **Frost Racing Club**
2 **BOGOSS DU PERRET (FR)**, 10, b br g Malinas (GER)—Lady Paques (FR) **Mrs J. Bury**
3 **FINDUSATGORCOMBE**, 9, b g Tobougg (IRE)—Seemma **Mr P. R. Meaden**
4 **FOILLMORE (IRE)**, 6, gr g Carlotamix (FR)—Beale Native (IRE) **Frost Racing Club**
5 **FS LOLA**, 7, ch m Arvico (FR)—Semi Colon (FR) **Martin Hill and Partners**
6 **GORCOMBE'S RASCAL**, 8, b g Fantastic View (USA)—Seem of Gold **Mr P. R. Meaden**
7 **LEGEND OF ZORRO (IRE)**, 8, ch g Touch of Land (FR)—Wotaglen (IRE) **G. D. Thompson**
8 **LITTLE MISS ALICE**, 5, b m Alqaahir (USA)—Miss Grace **J. D. Frost**
9 **MINIMALISTIC (IRE)**, 9, b g Definite Article—Grangeclare Star (IRE) **& Darke**
10 **OTTER LYNN**, 6, b m Alqaahir (USA)—Definite Lynn (IRE) **Frost Racing Club**
11 **PRESGRAVE (IRE)**, 4, b g Camelot—Alamouna (IRE) **N. W. Lake**
12 **SAINTEMILION (FR)**, 8, b g Diamond Green (FR)—Matakana (FR) **J. D. Frost**
13 **SILVER QUAY (IRE)**, 9, gr g Dark Angel (IRE)—She Runs (FR) **C & Mrs A Jones**
14 **SIMPLE WORDS (IRE)**, 5, gr m Dark Angel (IRE)—Fascination (IRE) **Gaskell Coward Russell &smith**
15 **THIS BREAC (IRE)**, 10, br g Carlo Bank (IRE)—De Breac (IRE) **Mr. Andrew Shepherd & Mr. Jimmy Frost**
16 **TREACYS JIM (IRE)**, 7, b g Milan—Bridge Hotel Lilly (IRE) **Frost Racing Club**
17 **TRIPLE CHIEF (IRE)**, 10, b br g High Chaparral (IRE)—Trebles (IRE) **G. D. Thompson**
18 **WHAT A BALOO (IRE)**, 6, b g Jeremy (USA)—Luca Lite (IRE) **Share My Dream**

**Other Owners:** Mr C. Coward, Mr E. A. Darke, Mrs S. L. Darke, J. D. Frost, Ms F. A. Gaskell, Mr C. Jones, Mrs J. A. Jones, Mr T. G. Russell, Mr A. J. Shepherd, Mr A. D. Smith.

**Assistant Trainer:** G. Frost.

**NH Jockey:** Bryony Frost.

## 211 MR KEVIN FROST, Newark
Postal: **Hill Top Equestrian Centre, Danethorpe Lane, Danethorpe Hill, Newark, Nottinghamshire, NG24 2PD**
Contacts: **PHONE** 07748 873092 **MOBILE** 07919 370081
**EMAIL** info@kevinfrostracing.co.uk **WEBSITE** www.kevinfrostracing.co.uk

1 **ALEEF (IRE)**, 8, b g Kodiac—Okba (USA) **Mr D Orr & Mr M Humphreys**
2 **ARRANMORE**, 4, b g Oasis Dream—Ceisteach (IRE) **D & M Lynch**
3 **AWEEDRAM (IRE)**, 5, ch g Mukhadram—Invitee **Curzon House Partnership**
4 **BILLIEBROOKEDIT (IRE)**, 6, ch g Dragon Pulse (IRE)—Klang (IRE)
5 **CANZONE**, 4, ch g Siyouni (FR)—Stirring Ballad **Rocky Canzone Partnership**
6 **CHIEFTAIN'S CHOICE (IRE)**, 12, b g King's Theatre (IRE)—Fairy Native (IRE) **Curzon House Partnership & Friends**
7 **DOCUMENTING**, 8, b g Zamindar (USA)—Namaskar **Kevin Frost Racing Club & M.A. Humphreys**
8 **EPANEEMA (IRE)**, 6, b m Epaulette (AUS)—Taqqara (IRE) **R & A Frost**
9 **ETOILE DU MATIN (IRE)**, 8, b g Millenary—Dey Like Me (IRE) **K Frost & W Smith**
10 **FRANCIS XAVIER (IRE)**, 7, b g High Chaparral (IRE)—Missionary Hymn (USA) **Curzon House Partnership**
11 **GEOGRAPHY TEACHER (IRE)**, 5, b g Bungle Inthejungle—Magical Bupers (IRE) **B & A Frost**
12 **GLEN VINE**, 7, ch g Robin des Champs (FR)—Gaspara (FR) **Rocky Canzone Partnership & Mr K Frost**
13 **HART FELL**, 5, b g Nayef (USA)—Dumfriesshire **Total Asbestos Solutions Limiited**
14 **HELVETIAN**, 6, b g Swiss Spirit—Lucky Dip **Ms T. Keane**
15 **ICE CANYON**, 7, b g Raven's Pass (USA)—Picture Hat (USA) **Mr Derek & Mrs Marie Dean**
16 **KEY LOOK (IRE)**, 4, ch f Dawn Approach (IRE)—Fashion Line (IRE) **Holmfirth Racing**
17 **MANFADH (IRE)**, 6, b g Iffraaj—Asiya (USA) **Mr Derek & Mrs Marie Dean**
18 **MOONSHINE MO**, 4, b g Pastoral Pursuits—Topflight Princess **Dallas Racing & Partners**
19 **PERFECT GRACE (IRE)**, 5, b m Bated Breath—Bassinet (USA) **Mr S. Petty**
20 **POPPY JAG (IRE)**, 6, b m Kodiac—Jacquelin Jag (IRE) **Curzon House Partnership**

## MR KEVIN FROST - continued

21 **REACTION TIME**, 6, b g Dubawi (IRE)—Cloudspin (USA) **Mrs F. Fox**
22 **STEAL THE SCENE (IRE)**, 9, b g Lord Shanakill (USA)—Namoos (USA) **Curzon House Partnership & Friends**
23 **THE THROSTLES**, 6, b g Poet's Voice—Stylish Dream (USA) **Kevin Frost Racing Club & Trisha Keane**
24 **WHITE MOCHA (USA)**, 6, ch g Lope de Vega (IRE)—Lastroseofsummer (IRE) **Curzon House Partnership**

### THREE-YEAR-OLDS
25 **OWENS LAD**, b g Harbour Watch (IRE)—Dancing Primo **L. R. Owen**

### TWO-YEAR-OLDS
26 **FERRO D'ORR (IRE)**, b c 02/04 Dawn Approach (IRE)—Miss Cogent (IRE) (Clodovil (IRE)) (5500) **D & A Frost**
27 **SWIFT REMARK**, ch c 03/03 Bated Breath—Kite Mark (Mark of Esteem (IRE)) (1500) **P & K Frost**

**Other Owners:** Mr M. Aniol, Curzon House Partnership, Dallas Racing, D. Dean, Mrs M. Dean, Mrs A. Frost, Mr K. Frost, Mr D. Gallagher, Mr M. A. Glassett, Mr M. A. Humphreys, Mr H. Jones, Miss J. Jones, Ms T. Keane, Mr R. Krzywicki, Mr M. J. Lynch, Mr D. Orr, B. W. Parren, Mr M. G. Roberts, Rocky Canzone Partnership, Mr W. L. B. Smith, Mr P. Swift, The Kevin Frost Racing Club, Mr S. W. Turner.

**Assistant Trainer:** William Frost.

---

## 212    MR HARRY FRY, Dorchester
Postal: Corscombe, Dorchester, Dorset, DT2 0PD
Contacts: WORK 01935 350330 PHONE 01935 350330
EMAIL info@harryfryracing.com WEBSITE www.harryfryracing.com

1 **ACTING LASS (IRE)**, 10, b g King's Theatre (IRE)—Darrens Lass (IRE) **Nigel & Barbara Collison**
2 **APERITIVO (IRE)**, 5, b g Milan—Dubai Glory **C. C. Walker**
3 **AS I SEE IT**, 9, b g King's Theatre (IRE)—Chomba Womba (IRE) **Mrs D. J. Goodall**
4 **ASK ME EARLY (IRE)**, 7, gr g Ask—Cotton Ali (IRE) **The Dare Family**
5 **BLACK MISCHIEF**, 9, b g Black Sam Bellamy (IRE)—Miss Mitch (IRE) **Tom Chadney and Friends**
6 **BOOTHILL (IRE)**, 6, b br g Presenting—Oyster Pipit (IRE) **Brian & Sandy Lambert**
7 **BULLIONAIRE (IRE)**, 8, b g Gold Well—Dontcallerthat (IRE) **Phil Fry & Charlie Walker -Osborne House**
8 **BURROWS TREAT (IRE)**, 5, b m Muhtathir—La Vie de Boitron (FR) **Mr M. Stenning**
9 **CAPTAIN DRAKE (IRE)**, 8, b g Getaway (GER)—Julika (GER) **Gary Stevens & Brian & Sandy Lambert**
10 **DAYTIME AHEAD (IRE)**, 10, gr m Daylami (IRE)—Bright Times Ahead (IRE) **Mrs J. M. Dare**
11 **DEEPER BLUE (FR)**, 5, ch g Muhtathir—Divine Cayras (FR) **C. C. Walker**
12 **DRUMCLIFF (IRE)**, 10, b g Presenting—Dusty Too **Mr J. P. McManus**
13 **FISHKHOV (FR)**, 6, ch g Sholokhov (IRE)—Kavalle (FR) **Masterson Holdings Limited**
14 **FLOWN THE NEST**, 5, ch m Iffraaj—Go Angellica (IRE) **Mrs C. Fry**
15 **FORTUNES MELODY**, 4, b f Yorgunnabelucky (USA)—Fulgora **Mr Simon Munir & Mr Isaac Souede**
16 **FREDDIE DARLING (IRE)**, 6, b g Shantou (USA)—Baby Lenson (IRE) **Rhapsody Racing**
17 **GALLANT COMMANDER (FR)**, 5, gr g Lord du Sud (FR)—Rockbelle (FR) **N. G. Cooper**
18 **GENTLEMAN KAP (FR)**, 5, b g Kapgarde (FR)—Sabubelle (FR) **Mr M. Stenning**
19 **GET BACK GET BACK (IRE)**, 6, b g Lord Shanakill (USA)—Bawaakeer (USA) **Get Back Get Back**
20 **GOLD IN DOHA (FR)**, 5, b g Spanish Moon (USA)—Utah Bald (FR) **Mrs C. Fry**
21 **GOUDHURST STAR (IRE)**, 5, b g Yeats (IRE)—Baliya (IRE) **Nigel & Barbara Collison**
22 **HE'S GOT THE LOT (FR)**, 5, b g Maxios—Aujiang (GER) **Lough Derg Syndicate**
23 **HURRICANE MITCH (IRE)**, 6, b g Shirocco (GER)—Miss Mitch (IRE) **Tom Chadney and Friends**
24 **IF THE CAP FITS (IRE)**, 9, b g Milan—Derravaragh Sayra (IRE) **Mr Simon Munir & Mr Isaac Souede**
25 **IMPERIAL ESPRIT (IRE)**, 7, b g Scorpion (IRE)—Shesourpresent (IRE) **Imperial Racing Partnership 2016**
26 **INISHBIGGLE (IRE)**, 6, b g Asian Heights—Leahs Joy (IRE) **Masterson Holdings Limited**
27 **ISHKHARA LADY**, 7, b m Scorpion (IRE)—Loxhill Lady **The Horse Flys Partnership**
28 **JOLLY'S CRACKED IT (FR)**, 12, b g Astarabad—Jolly Harbour **GDM Partnership**
29 5, Ch g Cityscape—Juno Mint **Sandie & David Newton**
30 **JUST A STING (IRE)**, 9, b g Scorpion (IRE)—Shanann Lady (IRE) **Nigel & Barbara Collison**
31 **KING ROLAND (IRE)**, 7, br g Stowaway—Kiltiernan Robin (IRE) **Masterson Holdings Limited**
32 **LAST OF A LEGEND (IRE)**, 4, b f Midnight Legend—Blue Buttons (IRE) **Hot To Trot Jumping**

# MR HARRY FRY - continued

33 **LIGHTLY SQUEEZE**, 7, b g Poet's Voice—Zuleika Dobson  **J Davies & Govier & Brown**
34 **LITTERALE CI (FR)**, 8, b m Soldier of Fortune (IRE)—Cigalia  **Mr J. P. McManus**
35 **MA BELLE NOIRE**, 4, br f Soldier of Fortune (IRE)—Loxhill Lady  **The Zoomers**
36 **METIER (IRE)**, 5, b g Mastercraftsman (IRE)—We'll Go Walking (IRE)  **G. C. Stevens**
37 **MIGHT I (IRE)**, 5, b g Fame And Glory—Our Honey (IRE)  **Brian & Sandy Lambert**
38 **MILLBANK FLYER (IRE)**, 6, b g Milan—The Last Bank (IRE)  **The Jago Family Partnership**
39 **MILLE SUSSURRI (IRE)**, 6, b g Milan—Silent Whisper (IRE)  **The Jago Family Partnership**
40 **MISTY WHISKY**, 7, gr m Stowaway—Whisky Rose (IRE)  **Distillery Stud**
41 **MOMELLA (IRE)**, 9, ch m Sholokhov (IRE)—Missing Link (IRE)  **Holt, Clark, Macnabb, Nugent & Robinson**
42 **MR ONE MORE (IRE)**, 9, b g Asian Heights—Norah's Quay (IRE)  **Mr J. P. McManus**
43 **MUY BIEN (IRE)**, 5, b g Cloudings (IRE)—Sari Rose (FR)  **Mrs C. Fry**
44 **ON MY COMMAND (IRE)**, 5, b m War Command (USA)—Highindi  **Mr I. Neocleous**
45 **ONEFORTHEROADTOM**, 8, gr g Fair Mix (IRE)—Ifni du Luc (FR)  **Mr J. P. McManus**
46 **OUR SURPRISE (IRE)**, 6, b br g Jeremy (USA)—Cadia's Lady (IRE)  **Mr Simon Munir & Mr Isaac Souede**
47 **P T BARNUM (IRE)**, 6, b g Fame And Glory—Trabrega Bay (IRE)  **Mrs C. Fry**
48 **PADSTOW HARBOUR**, 6, ch m Malinas (GER)—Cherry Pie (FR)  **Mr T. J. Hemmings**
49 **PHOENIX WAY (IRE)**, 8, b g Stowaway—Arcuate  **Mr J. P. McManus**
50 **POGO I AM**, 7, b m Passing Glance—Orbital Orchid  **Sandie & David Newton**
51 **PURE BLISS**, 6, ch m Mount Nelson—Burton Ash  **Jago & Allhusen**
52 **REVELS HILL (IRE)**, 6, b g Mahler—Chlolo Supreme (IRE)  **Noel Fehily Racing Syndicates-Revels Hil**
53 **RUFIO**, 7, b g Schiaparelli (GER)—Mole End  **The Lost Boys**
54 **SAMARQUAND**, 7, b g Malinas (GER)—Samandara (FR)  **R. P. Fry**
55 **SANDY MARASCHINO (IRE)**, 5, b g Milan—Diamond Smiles  **Mrs C. Fry**
56 **SANGUINAIRE (IRE)**, 5, ch m Sans Frontieres (IRE)—Mhuire Na Gale (IRE)  **Somerset Racing**
57 **SHALL WE GO NOW**, 8, b g Midnight Legend—Suave Shot  **Noel Fehily Racing Syndicate - Shall We**
58 **SIR IVAN**, 11, b g Midnight Legend—Tisho  **The Eyre Family**
59 **SKYLARK NINETEEN (IRE)**, 5, b br g Mahler—Florafern  **Mrs C. Fry**
60 **THE BIG STING (IRE)**, 6, b g Scorpion (IRE)—Glory Queen (IRE)  **Charlie Walker & Phil Fry -osborne House**
61 **THE SCIENTIST (FR)**, 4, gr g Al Namix (FR)—Lady of Good Hope (FR)  **Somerset Racing**
62 **UNOWHATIMEANHARRY**, 13, b g Sir Harry Lewis (USA)—Red Nose Lady  **Mr J. P. McManus**
63 **WALK ON HIGH**, 4, b g Walk In The Park (IRE)—Highland Retreat  **The Highland Walkers**
64 **WHISKY EXPRESS**, 5, ch m Imperial Monarch (IRE)—Loxhill Lady  **Lorna Squire, R Metherell, D German**
65 **WHITE HART LADY (IRE)**, 7, b m Doyen (IRE)—Hats And Heels (IRE)  **Chasing Gold Limited**
66 **WHITEHOTCHILLIFILI (IRE)**, 7, b m Milan—Mhuire Na Gale (IRE)  **Chasing Gold Limited**
67 **WINNINGSEVERYTHING (IRE)**, 7, b g Flemensfirth (USA)—Baliya (IRE)  **Jago & Allhusen**

## THREE-YEAR-OLDS

68 **BO KAAP (IRE)**, b g Mount Nelson—Vizean (IRE)  **Bo Kaap Partnership**
69 **FOREVER BLESSED (IRE)**, b g Zoffany (IRE)—Yet Again  **Thornton, Gibbs, Davies & Fry**

**Other Owners:** Mr N. C. Allhusen, G. S. Brown, Mrs S. Cameron, Mr C. N. Clark, Mrs B. Collison, Mr N. Collison, Mr J. M. Dare, Mrs J. M. Dare, Mr J. Davies, Mr M. R. Dentten, Viscountess S. J. Dilhorne, Mrs C. A. Eyre, Mr C. G. S. Eyre, Mr H. Eyre, Mrs C. Fry, Dr C. E. Fry, R. P. Fry, Mr D. S. J. German, Mr R. Gibbs, Mrs D. J. Goodall, Mr P. Govier, Govier & Brown, Mr A. G. Hipgrave, Mr A. Holt, Mr F. C. A. Jago, Mr J. L. Jago, Miss M. L. A. Jago, Mr P. J. A. Jago, Mr I. N. Kingham, Mr B. Lambert, Mr I. Macnabb, Mr R. F. Magrath, Mr T. F. McGowan, R. J. Metherell, S. E. Munir, Mr D. Newton, Mrs J. S. Newton, Mr J. O. Nugent, Mrs R. Philipps, Mr J. D. Robinson, Mr I. Souede, Mrs L. Squire, G. C. Stevens, Mr G. M. Thornton, Mr J. P. G. Turner, C. C. Walker, Mr J. D. Wallen, Mrs R. E. Young.

**Assistant Trainer:** Ciara Fry.

**NH Jockey:** Sean Bowen. **Conditional Jockey:** Lorcan Murtagh. **Amateur Jockey:** Miss A. B. O'Connor.

## 213 MS CAROLINE FRYER, Wymondham
Postal: **Browick Hall Cottage, Browick Road, Wymondham, Norfolk, NR18 9RB**
Contacts: PHONE **07768 056076** MOBILE **07768 056076**
EMAIL **caroline@carolinefryerracing.co.uk, c.fryer528@btinternet.com**
WEBSITE **www.carolinefryerracing.co.uk**

1 **AMETHEA (IRE)**, 7, b m Yeats (IRE)—Moricana (GER) **C J Underwood & Caroline Fryer**
2 **DARIUS DES BOIS (FR)**, 8, b g Great Pretender (IRE)—Palafixe (FR) **Mark Flinton and Caroline Fryer**
3 **DONTCOUNTURCHIKENS (IRE)**, 7, b g Getaway (GER)—Stormy Breeze (IRE)
4 **GOODNIGHT CHARLIE**, 11, gr m Midnight Legend—Over To Charlie **Miss C. Fryer**
5 **LORD TOPPER**, 8, b g Sir Percy—Fugnina **Mark Flinton and Caroline Fryer**
6 **RATOUTE YUTTY**, 8, b m Midnight Legend—Easibrok Jane **C J Underwood & Caroline Fryer**

**Other Owners:** Miss C. Fryer, C. J. Underwood.

## 214 MR IVAN FURTADO, Newark
Postal: **The Old Stables, Averham Park Farm, Averham, Newark, Nottinghamshire, NG23 5RU**
Contacts: MOBILE **07783 520746**
EMAIL **ivan.furtado@hotmail.co.uk**

1 **AD DAHNA**, 4, b f Invincible Spirit (IRE)—Albasharah (USA) **Mr C. Hodgson**
2 **AL SAKEET**, 4, b g Cable Bay (IRE)—Coin A Phrase **Gary White & the Giggle Factor**
3 **ALMINOOR (IRE)**, 4, b g Kodiac—Aravonian **Mr C. Hodgson**
4 **ATYAAF**, 6, b g Invincible Spirit (IRE)—Eshaadeh (USA) **GB Civil Engineering (Leicester) LTD**
5 **BROKEN RIFLE**, 4, b g Havana Gold (IRE)—Peace Concluded **J. C. Fretwell**
6 **BUSBY (IRE)**, 6, b g Kodiac—Arabian Pearl (IRE) **The Giggle Factor Partnership**
7 **BYFORD (FR)**, 4, b g Toronado (IRE)—Verba (FR) **Mr C. Hodgson**
8 **CALIFORNIA LAD**, 8, b g Aussie Rules (USA)—Medaille d'Or **Daniel MacAuliffe & Anoj Don**
9 **CAPTAIN ST LUCIFER**, 4, b g Casamento (IRE)—Delaware Dancer (IRE) **Stuart Dobb & Kate Dobb**
10 **CHANTREYS**, 4, gr ro f Mayson—Raajis (IRE) **The Giggle Factor Partnership**
11 **CHIPIRON (FR)**, 5, ch g Rio de La Plata (USA)—Chicago May (FR) **Mr D. Croot**
12 **CRAZY SPIN**, 5, b m Epaulette (AUS)—George's Gift **The Giggle Factor Partnership**
13 **DARALIMI (FR)**, 5, b g Siyouni (FR)—Daryaba (IRE) **J. L. Marriott**
14 **DESERT EMPEROR**, 4, b g Camelot—Praia (GER) **J. L. Marriott**
15 **DREW BREEZE (IRE)**, 4, ch g Camacho—Three Cheers (IRE) **Mr R. Tedstone**
16 **DUBLIN BLUE**, 6, ch g Sixties Icon—Mistic Magic (IRE) **Daniel MacAuliffe & Anoj Don**
17 **EAGLEWAY (FR)**, 5, b g Sakhee's Secret—Tearsforjoy (USA) **J. L. Marriott**
18 **EPIC CHALLENGE**, 6, b g Mastercraftsman (IRE)—Keep Dancing (IRE) **Robert Greenwood Racing**
19 **FLASH TO BANG**, 4, b g Telescope (IRE)—Fangfoss Girls **Central Racing Ltd**
20 **FLY TRUE**, 8, b m Raven's Pass (USA)—Have Faith (IRE) **Stuart Dobb & Kate Dobb**
21 **FOLLOWTHESTARS (IRE)**, 5, b g Sea The Stars (IRE)—Penny Post (IRE) **J. L. Marriott**
22 **HEALING POWER**, 5, b g Kodiac—Loch Ma Naire (IRE) **Mr C. Hodgson**
23 **HECTOR'S HERE**, 5, b g Cityscape—L'Addition **John Marriott & Giggle Factor**
24 **JUNGLE SPEED (FR)**, 5, b g Bungle Inthejungle—Velvet Revolver (IRE) **J. L. Marriott**
25 **KENYX (FR)**, 4, b g Kendargent (FR)—Onyx (FR) **Mr G. White**
26 **LAST DATE**, 4, br g Music Master—Tanning **Mr E. P. Spain**
27 **LEGAL REFORM (IRE)**, 4, b g Lawman (FR)—Amhrasach (IRE) **GB Civil Engineering (Leicester) LTD**
28 **LOCO DEMPSEY (FR)**, 4, b f Cityscape—L'Addition **The Giggle Factor Partnership**
29 **LOOSE CHIPPINGS (IRE)**, 7, b g Rock of Gibraltar (IRE)—Karjera (IRE) **The Giggle Factor Partnership**
30 **MEMORY DREAM (FR)**, 4, b g Motivator—Ascot Memory (IRE) **Daniel MacAuliffe & Anoj Don**
31 **MENINA ATREVIDA**, 5, ch m Nayef (USA)—Delaware Dancer (IRE) **Stuart Dobb & Kate Dobb**
32 **MOMTALIK (USA)**, 6, b g Point of Entry (USA)—Sacred Feather (USA) **GB Civil Engineering (Leicester) LTD**
33 **MOUNT MAYON (IRE)**, 4, b g Kodiac—Nisrinya (IRE) **Mr C. Hodgson**
34 **NOBLE DAWN (GER)**, 4, ch f Dawn Approach (IRE)—Neuquen (IRE) **J. L. Marriott**
35 **PACT OF STEEL**, 6, ch g Declaration of War (USA)—She's My Dandy (IRE) **Daniel MacAuliffe & Anoj Don**
36 **QUEEN LAGERTHA**, 4, ch f Starspangledbanner (AUS)—Milton of Campsie **Ten in a Row**

## MR IVAN FURTADO - continued

37 **RECALL IT ALL,** 4, b g Toronado (IRE)—Rotunda **The Giggle Factor Partnership**
38 **SCUDAMORE (FR),** 4, ch g Dawn Approach (IRE)—Emirates Comfort (IRE) **Mr C. Hodgson**
39 **STARTER FOR TEN,** 4, b g Bated Breath—Scariff Hornet (IRE) **Mr R. Tedstone**
40 **STRAITOUTTACOMPTON,** 5, b g Compton Place—Red Mischief (IRE) **Golden Equinox Racing**
41 **SWEET ANGEL,** 4, b f Heeraat (IRE)—Sweet Lily Pea (USA) **Supreme Bloodstock**
42 **SWORD EXCEED (GER),** 7, b g Exceed And Excel (AUS)—

Sword Roche (GER) **21st Century Racing & Nigel Sennett**
43 **TESTON (FR),** 6, ch g Rio de La Plata (USA)—Tianshan (FR) **Daniel MacAuliffe & Anoj Don**
44 **TILSITT (FR),** 4, b g Charm Spirit (IRE)—Azores (IRE) **J. C. Fretwell**
45 **TOSCAN GENIUS (FR),** 4, b g Deep Impact (JPN)—Shagah (IRE) **The Giggle Factor Partnership**
46 **XAAROS (FR),** 4, gr g Kendargent (FR)—Xaarina (FR) **J. L. Marriott**
47 **ZUCKERBERG (FR),** 4, ch g Camacho—Queenie Keen (IRE) **Mr R. Tedstone**

### THREE-YEAR-OLDS

48 **ELEVEN ELEVEN (FR),** b g Olympic Glory (IRE)—Pretty Panther (FR) **The Giggle Factor Partnership**
49 **GEMS JEWEL,** b f Charming Thought—Blissamore **Mr A. C. Cook**
50 **HAVANA QUEEN,** b f Havana Gold (IRE)—Coeurafinfluence **21st Century Racing**
51 **JAZPER,** b g Heeraat (IRE)—Dharwa **Richard Kent & Giggle Factor**
52 **JUST BEAUTIFUL,** br f Pride of Dubai (AUS)—Astrelle (IRE) **Gary White & the Giggle Factor**
53 **MISTY AWANA,** b f Paco Boy (IRE)—Permaisuri (IRE) **Mr T. R. B. T. A. Shah**
54 **PRIDE DAY,** b f Adaay (IRE)—Transvaal Sky **The Giggle Factor Partnership**
55 **ROAD TO RINGLET,** b g Cameron Highland (IRE)—Tiga Tuan (FR) **Mr T. R. B. T. A. Shah**
56 **ROHAYS,** b f Pride of Dubai (AUS)—Shegotloose (USA) **The Giggle Factor Partnership**
57 B c Showcasing—Sahara Sunshine
58 **SHEHARZ,** b f Harzand (IRE)—O'Connor's Girl
59 **SILVER SCREEN STAR,** gr f Havana Gold (IRE)—Daheeya **The Giggle Factor & Alan Fenn**
60 B g Assertive—Tanning
61 **THE NAIL GUNNER (IRE),** b g Tough As Nails (IRE)—Remediate (USA) **Mr W. P. Flynn**
62 **TOM MIX,** ch g Sepoy (AUS)—Golden Dirham **Mrs S Nicholls Mrs R J Mitchell**
63 **TORTURE (IRE),** b c Pride of Dubai (AUS)—Michael's Song (IRE) **J. C. Fretwell**

### TWO-YEAR-OLDS

64 B gr c 11/02 Lethal Force (IRE)—Camposanto (Pivotal) (3333)
65 B f 14/04 Belardo (IRE)—Circleofinfluence (USA) (Eurosilver (USA)) (3333)
66 Gr f 13/02 Johnny Barnes (IRE)—Coldgirl (FR) (Verglas (IRE)) (16949) **Daniel MacAuliffe & Anoj Don**
67 B f 08/02 Buratino (IRE)—Heart's Desire (IRE) (Royal Applause) (4761)
68 Br f 25/01 Vadamos (FR)—Listen Alexander (IRE) (Kodiac) (14000)
69 B f 12/03 Free Eagle (IRE)—Maggie Lou (IRE) (Red Ransom (USA)) (8000)
70 B f 31/03 Sun Central (IRE)—Maggie Pink (Beat All (USA))
71 B f 09/04 Nathaniel (IRE)—Mensoora (SAF) (Jet Master (SAF)) (5000)

**Other Owners:** 21st Century Racing, A. W. Catterall, Mrs B. Catterall, Miss K. M. Dobb, Mr S. Dobb, Mr A. Fenn, Mr J. R. Holt, R. Kent, Mr A. T. Larkin, J. L. Marriott, Mrs R. J. Mitchell, Mrs S. E. Nicholls, Mr N. P. Sennett, The Giggle Factor Partnership, Mr G. White.

---

**215** **MR JOHN GALLAGHER, Moreton-In-Marsh**
Postal: **Grove Farm**, Chastleton, Moreton-In-Marsh, Gloucestershire, GL56 0SZ
Contacts: **PHONE** 01608 674492 **MOBILE** 07780 972663
**EMAIL** gallagherracing@phonecoop.coop **WEBSITE** www.gallagherracing.com

1 **FOXY FEMME,** 5, ch m Foxwedge (AUS)—Pusey Street Vale **Mrs C. R. Clifford**
2 **GREEN POWER,** 6, b g Kheleyf (USA)—Hakuraa (IRE) **Nino's Partnership**
3 **INTERCESSOR,** 4, b g Due Diligence (USA)—Miss Meticulous **The LAM Partnership**
4 **JUNOESQUE,** 7, b m Virtual—Snake Skin **Ford Associated Racing Team**
5 **LADY ILEY,** 4, b f Equiano (FR)—Hollybell **C. R. Marks (Banbury)**

## MR JOHN GALLAGHER - continued

6 **PURBECK HILLS (IRE)**, 5, b g Oasis Dream—Albisola (IRE)  **Mr J. N. Greenley**
7 **QUAINT (IRE)**, 4, b f Dandy Man (IRE)—Destiny's Kitten (IRE)  **Caveat Emptor Partnership**
8 **QUENCH DOLLY**, 7, gr m Hellvelyn—Hollybell  **John Gallagher**
9 **RIVAS ROB ROY**, 6, ch g Archipenko (USA)—Rivas Rhapsody (IRE)  **Mr T. J. F. Smith**
10 **SARAS HOPE**, 4, b g Swiss Spirit—Rivas Rhapsody (IRE)  **Max Europe Limited**
11 **THORN**, 5, b g Dansili—Thistle Bird  **Mr R G Robinson & Mr R D Robinson**
12 **TOMAHAWK RIDGE (IRE)**, 5, gr g Alhebayeb (IRE)—Low Cut Affair (IRE)  **Max Europe Limited**
13 **WILDOMAR**, 12, b g Kyllachy—Murrieta  **John Gallagher**
14 **WILLCOLLINS (IRE)**, 7, b g Superior Premium—Macs Belle (IRE)  **Mr J. Evans**

### THREE-YEAR-OLDS

15 **FORZA DEL DESTINO**, ch f Lethal Force (IRE)—Danehill Destiny  **The LAM Partnership**
16 **PUSEY STREET**, ch f Equiano (FR)—Pusey Street Lady  **John Gallagher**
17 **SILVER DIVA**, gr f Hellvelyn—Heartsong (IRE)  **J & L Wetherald - M & M Glover**
18 **SWIFT PUSEY**, gr f Hellvelyn—Pusey Street Vale  **C. R. Marks (Banbury)**

### TWO-YEAR-OLDS

19 B c 30/03 Ardad (IRE)—Bella Catalina (Acclamation) (5714)  **Andrew Bell & Michael Wright**
20 **GRAND BOBBY**, gr c 15/04 Bobby's Kitten (USA)—Grand Myla (IRE) (Dark Angel (IRE)) (1905)  **Mr R. Little**
21 B f 25/03 Garswood—Princess Luna (GER) (Grand Lodge (USA))  **Andrew Bell & Michael Wright**
22 **RUNNER BEAN**, b f 25/02 Heeraat (IRE)—Miss Meticulous (Bahamian Bounty)  **The LAM Partnership**

**Other Owners:** Mr A. Bell, Dr M. F. Ford, Ms M. E. Glover, M. P. Glover, Mrs B. A. Long, J. F. Long, Ms L. M. Mulcahy, Mr R. D. Robinson, Mr R. G. Robinson, Mr J. A. Wetherald, Mrs L. T. Wetherald, Mr M. F. Wright.

**Assistant Trainer:** Mr B Denvir.

---

## 216  MR THOMAS GALLAGHER, Borehamwood
Postal: **5 Old Priory Park, Old London Road, St. Albans, Hertfordshire, AL1 1QF**

1 **AH WELL (IRE)**, 9, b g Gold Well—Valentina Gaye (IRE)  **Mr J. J. Reddington**
2 **BEEPEECEE**, 7, b g Henrythenavigator (USA)—Roedean (IRE)  **Mr J. J. Reddington**
3 **CAPITOLE (FR)**, 5, b g Born To Sea (IRE)—Capitale (FR)  **Mr J. J. Reddington**
4 **CARTRON (IRE)**, 5, b g Acclamation—Like A Dream (FR)  **Mr J. J. Reddington**
5 **FERN ARABLE**, 7, b m Fair Mix (IRE)—Charlottes Webb (IRE)  **Mr J. J. Reddington**
6 **GLENDEVON (USA)**, 6, ch g Scat Daddy (USA)—Flip Flop (FR)  **Mr J. J. Reddington**
7 **GREAT UNIVERSE**, 5, b g Universal (IRE)—As Was  **Mr J. J. Reddington**
8 **HELLO MR BRUNO (FR)**, 5, gr ro m Mastercraftsman (IRE)—Onega Lake (IRE)  **Mr J. J. Reddington**
9 **I'M DIGBY (IRE)**, 4, gr ro g Gutaifan (IRE)—Lathaat  **Mr J. J. Reddington**
10 **LOHANS CROSS (IRE)**, 6, gr g Carlotamix (FR)—Whisky (IRE)  **Mr J. J. Reddington**
11 **LOST IN THE MIST (IRE)**, 5, ch g Shirocco (GER)—Spirit Rock (IRE)  **Mr J. J. Reddington**
12 **MOMENTO (FR)**, 4, b g Casamento (IRE)—Mooizo (IRE)  **Mr J. J. Reddington**
13 **MR HARP (IRE)**, 8, b g Court Cave (IRE)—Chapel Wood Lady (IRE)  **Mr J. J. Reddington**
14 **SECOND SUBALTERN (USA)**, 5, b g Declaration of War (USA)—Queen of The Night  **Mr J. J. Reddington**
15 6, B g Multiplex—Sudden Beat  **Mr J. J. Reddington**

## 217 MRS ILKA GANSERA-LEVEQUE, Newmarket

Postal: **Saint Wendreds, Hamilton Road, Newmarket, Suffolk, CB8 7JQ**
Contacts: **PHONE 01638 454973 MOBILE 07855 532072**
EMAIL office@gansera-leveque.com WEBSITE www.gansera-leveque.com

1 4, B g Exceed And Excel (AUS)—Ice Palace
2 **IKIGAI**, 4, b f Sayif (IRE)—Usem **Mrs I. Gansera-Leveque**
3 **JUST ONCE**, 5, b m Holy Roman Emperor (IRE)—Nur Jahan (IRE) **Mrs I. Gansera-Leveque**
4 **MELODIC THUNDER (FR)**, 4, b f Night of Thunder (IRE)—Mystic Melody (IRE) **Joe Saumarez Smith & Partners**
5 **MYSTIC DRAGON**, 5, ch m Intello (GER)—Portrait **Mr S. P. Hussain**
6 **RISING SEAS**, 6, b g Mount Nelson—Puya **Mrs I. Gansera-Leveque**
7 **WENDREDA**, 4, b f Casamento (IRE)—Zagarock **Mrs I. Gansera-Leveque**

### THREE-YEAR-OLDS

8 **BECKENBAUER**, br c Slade Power (IRE)—La Pieta (AUS) **Phoenix Ladies Syndicate Limited**
9 **EDENS LAWN**, b f Ruler of The World (IRE)—Jewelled **M & M Franklin**
10 **MERCI PERCY (FR)**, b f Sir Percy—Acacalia (GER)
11 **RABAT (IRE)**, b f Mehmas (IRE)—Refuse To Give Up (IRE) **Phoenix Ladies Syndicate Limited**
12 **RETROUVAILLES**, b br f Iffraaj—Badweia (USA) **Phoenix Ladies Syndicate Limited**

### TWO-YEAR-OLDS

13 B c 01/03 Kingman—Frenzified (Yeats (IRE))
14 B c 14/02 Showcasing—Glade (Bertolini (USA)) (38095)
15 B c 16/03 Aclaim (IRE)—La Pieta (AUS) (Redoute's Choice (AUS))
16 B f 14/04 Aclaim (IRE)—Linet (IRE) (Oasis Dream)

**Other Owners:** Fergus Anstock, Mr J. J. Brummitt, Mr P. G. Buist, Mr M. Edwards, Mr M. Franklin, Mrs M. G. Franklin, Mr J. W. Saumarez Smith.

**Assistant Trainer:** Stephane Leveque.

## 218 MRS SUSAN GARDNER, Longdown

Postal: **Woodhayes Farm, Longdown, Exeter**
Contacts: **PHONE 01392 811213 MOBILE 07936 380492**
EMAIL woodhayesstudfarm@btinternet.com WEBSITE www.suegardnerracing.co.uk

1 **ALRAMZ**, 5, b g Intello (GER)—Rewaaya (IRE) **Clear Racing**
2 **BLUFFMEIFYOUCAN**, 4, br g Yorgunnabelucky (USA)—Cita Verda (FR) **Mr D. V. Gardner**
3 **BREDON HILL LEO**, 9, b g Sulamani (IRE)—Persian Clover **Mr & Mrs R W & Mrs J M Mitchell**
4 **DOCTOR LOOK HERE (IRE)**, 11, b g Dr Massini (IRE)—Eye Vision (IRE) **Mr P. A. Tylor & Mr D V Gardner**
5 **EMMPRESSIVE LADY (IRE)**, 6, b m Jeremy (USA)—Court Lexi (IRE) **Clear Racing**
6 **ENDLESS FLIGHT (IRE)**, 7, b g Winged Love (IRE)—Lady Oakwell (IRE) **Mr D. V. Gardner**
7 **HAVACUPPA**, 7, b m Dream Eater (IRE)—Darjeeling (IRE) **Mr D. V. Gardner**
8 **HERE'S HERBIE**, 13, b g Classic Cliche (IRE)—Tyre Hill Lilly **Mr P. A. Tylor & Mr D V Gardner**
9 **INDIAN HARBOUR**, 8, b g Indian Haven—Hawait Al Barr **Harris,Wheeler &,Gardner**
10 **KING ORRY (IRE)**, 6, b g Oscar (IRE)—Deer Island Peg (IRE) **Gardner Wheeler**
11 **LIGHTONTHEWING (IRE)**, 6, b g Winged Love (IRE)—Neat 'n Nimble **Mr D. V. Gardner**
12 **ONLY GORGEOUS**, 12, b g Vertical Speed (FR)—Pure Beautiful **Miss Jane Edgar & Mr D. V. Gardner**
13 **SIROP DE MENTHE (FR)**, 11, ch g Discover d'Auteuil (FR)—Jolie Menthe (FR) **Clear Racing & Partner**
14 **TEA TIME FRED**, 12, b g Kayf Tara—Darjeeling (IRE) **Mr D. V. Gardner**
15 **TEA TIME ON MARS**, 9, ch g Schiaparelli (GER)—Darjeeling (IRE) **Mrs B. Russell & Mr D. V. Gardner**
16 **THEBUDINPUNDIT**, 5, b g Multiplex—Buddug **Mr D. V. Gardner**
17 **TRANS EXPRESS (IRE)**, 11, br g Trans Island—Hazel Fastrack **Mr D. V. Gardner**
18 **TRUE SPICE (IRE)**, 6, b m Scorpion (IRE)—Miss Pepperpot (IRE) **Mr D. V. Gardner**
19 **WOULDUADAMANDEVEIT (IRE)**, 8, b g Stowaway—Figlette **Keith Harris & Tom Gardner**
20 **ZILLION (IRE)**, 7, b g Zebedee—Redelusion (IRE) **Miss Jane Edgar & Mr D. V. Gardner**

## MRS SUSAN GARDNER - continued

**Other Owners:** Miss J. E. Edgar, Mr D. V. Gardner, Mr T. A. Gardner, Mr B. J. Greening, Mrs M. M. Greening, Mr K. T. Harris, Mrs J. M. Mitchell, R. W. Mitchell, Mrs B. A. Russell, P. A. Tylor, Mr N. J. Wheeler.

**Assistant Trainer:** D. V. Gardner.

**NH Jockey:** Lucy Gardner, Micheal Nolan.

---

## 219 MRS ROSEMARY GASSON, Banbury
Postal: **Alkerton Grounds, Balscote, Banbury, Oxfordshire, OX15 6JS**
Contacts: **PHONE 01295 730248 MOBILE 07769 798430**
EMAIL arb@agf.myzen.co.uk

1 **BIGNORM (IRE)**, 9, b g Mahler—Merry Heart (IRE) **Mrs R. Gasson**
2 **DESERT DE BRUYERE (FR)**, 8, b g Great Pretender (IRE)—Quid de Neuville (FR) **Mrs R. Gasson**
3 **DRAGON KHAN (IRE)**, 12, b g Dr Fong (USA)—Desert Magic (IRE) **Mrs R. Gasson**
4 **FREEDOM CHIMES**, 7, b g Champs Elysees—Ombre **Mrs R. Gasson**
5 **IRISH OCTAVE (IRE)**, 11, b g Gamut (IRE)—Fairytaleofnewyork (IRE) **Mrs R. Gasson**
6 **MR MCGUINESS (IRE)**, 11, b g Kalanisi (IRE)—Maig Mandy (IRE) **Mrs R. Gasson**
7 **SCARTARE (IRE)**, 10, br g Trans Island—La Speziana (IRE) **Mrs R. Gasson**
8 **SIDEWAYSINMILAN (IRE)**, 6, b g Milan—Erins Love (IRE) **Mrs R. Gasson**

**NH Jockey:** Ben Poste.

---

## 220 MR MICHAEL GATES, Stratford-Upon-Avon
Postal: **Comfort Park Stud & Racing Stables, Campden Road, Clifford Chambers, Stratford-Upon-Avon, Warwickshire, CV37 8LW**
Contacts: **PHONE 07581 246070**
EMAIL comfortparkstud@hotmail.co.uk

1 **DAYBREAK BOY (IRE)**, 8, b br g Kingsalsa (USA)—Aloisi
2 **DOVER THE MOON (IRE)**, 10, b g Bushranger (IRE)—Gold Script (FR) **Mr M. Gates**
3 **DRUMNAGREAGH (IRE)**, 8, b m September Storm (GER)—Saffron Pride (IRE) **Mr M. Gates**
4 **SIR WARRIOR**, 10, b g Mawjud—Soramic (FR) **Mr M. Gates**

---

## 221 MR PAUL GEORGE, Crediton
Postal: **Higher Eastington, Lapford, Crediton, Devon, EX17 6NE**
Contacts: **MOBILE 07733 171112**
EMAIL paul.george1@icloud.com WEBSITE www.paulgeorgeracing.co.uk

1 **ARTHALOT (IRE)**, 4, b g Camelot—Annina (IRE) **Thethrillofitall**
2 **BILINGUAL**, 4, b f Le Havre (IRE)—Downhill Dancer (IRE) **Miss K. M. George**
3 **LITTLE JESSTURE (IRE)**, 5, b m Dylan Thomas (IRE)—The Legislator (IRE) **Bob Butler & Karen George**
4 **RATHAGAN**, 4, b g Kyllachy—Ardessie **Miss K. M. George**
5 **SHERWOOD FORRESTER**, 5, b g Nayef (USA)—Panoptic **P. J. H. George**

## MR PAUL GEORGE - continued

### THREE-YEAR-OLDS

6 **LHEBAYEB (GER),** b f Alhebayeb (IRE)—Lady Gabrielle (IRE) **Miss K. M. George**
7 B g Captain Gerrard (IRE)—Sober Up
8 **SOPHIE,** ch f Farhh—Poyle Sophie **Miss K. M. George**
9 Ch g Proconsul—Spiraea
10 **SURPASSING (IRE),** b f Outstrip—Another Name (USA) **Miss K. M. George**
11 **SYMPATHISE (IRE),** b f Kodi Bear (IRE)—Starfly (IRE) **Miss K. M. George**
12 **UP BEFORE DAWN (IRE),** ch f Buratino (IRE)—Up At Dawn **Boddy, O Sullivan & George**

### TWO-YEAR-OLDS

13 **ARBOY WILL,** b g 14/04 Ardad (IRE)—High 'n Dry (IRE) (Halling (USA))
14 Bl f 25/01 Brazen Beau (AUS)—Be Joyful (IRE) (Teofilo (IRE)) (800)
15 B f 19/03 Kodi Bear (IRE)—Heart of An Angel (Dark Angel (IRE)) (2500)
16 B br f 16/02 Slade Power (IRE)—Piccola Sissi (IRE) (Footstepsinthesand) (1500)
17 B f 05/02 Ardad (IRE)—Powerfulstorm (Bertolini (USA)) (3500)

**Other Owners:** Mr D. Boddy, Mr R. Butler, Miss K. M. George, Mr M. Masters, S. O'Sullivan, Mr R. Paver, Mr C. Perrin, Mr C. A. Poulter, Mr G. Stead.

**Assistant Trainer:** Cassie Haughton.

**Apprentice Jockey:** Rhiain Ingram.

---

**222**　**MR TOM GEORGE, Slad**
Postal: Down Farm, Slad, Stroud, Gloucestershire, GL6 7QE
Contacts: **PHONE** 01452 814267 **MOBILE** 07850 793483
**EMAIL** tom@trgeorge.com **WEBSITE** www.tomgeorgeracing.co.uk

1 **ABOVE SUSPICION (IRE),** 6, b g Oscar (IRE)—The Sailors Bonnet (IRE) **O'Donohoe, Cavanagh, Robinson, Nelson**
2 **ACTIVIAL (FR),** 11, gr g Lord du Sud (FR)—Kissmirial (FR) **R. S. Brookhouse**
3 4, B g Soldier of Fortune (IRE)—Afaraka (IRE) **R. S. Brookhouse**
4 **AIR NAVIGATOR,** 10, b g Yeats (IRE)—Lox Lane (IRE) **Lady N. F. Cobham**
5 **ANOTHER STOWAWAY (IRE),** 9, b g Stowaway—Another Pet (IRE) **H Stephen Smith & Family Gabbertas**
6 **BABY KING (IRE),** 12, b g Ivan Denisovich (IRE)—Burn Baby Burn (IRE) **About Two Weeks**
7 **BALLON ONABUDGET (IRE),** 8, b g Arcadio (GER)—Little Present (IRE) **The Little Faith Syndicate**
8 **BANISH (USA),** 8, b g Smart Strike (CAN)—Beyond Our Reach (IRE) **Mr H. F. Birtles**
9 **BANNISTER (FR),** 4, gr g Olympic Glory (IRE)—Amou Daria (FR) **Crossed Fingers Partnership**
10 **BIG BRESIL (IRE),** 6, b g Blue Bresil (FR)—Cutielilou (FR) **R. S. Brookhouse**
11 **BLACK OP (IRE),** 10, br g Sandmason—Afar Story (IRE) **R. S. Brookhouse**
12 **BOAGRIUS (IRE),** 9, ch g Beneficial—Greenhall Rambler (IRE) **The MerseyClyde Partnership**
13 **BOYHOOD (IRE),** 10, b g Oscar (IRE)—Glen Dubh (IRE) **H Stephen Smith & The Gabbertas Family**
14 **BRANDON HILL (IRE),** 13, b g Beneficial—Annesbanker (IRE) **Mr T. George**
15 **BUCK'S BIN'S (FR),** 7, b g Khalkevi (IRE)—Buck's Bravo (FR) **R. S. Brookhouse**
16 **BUCK'S BOGGLE (FR),** 5, b g Tiger Groom—Buck's Bravo (FR) **R. S. Brookhouse**
17 **BUN DORAN (IRE),** 10, b g Shantou (USA)—Village Queen (IRE) **Crossed Fingers Partnership**
18 **CALL ME RAFA (IRE),** 4, b g Mahler—Annie Grit (IRE) **Mr C. B. Compton**
19 **CAPTAIN BLACKPEARL,** 7, ch g Black Sam Bellamy (IRE)—
　　　　　　　　　　　　　　Bonne Anniversaire **R Foden T Keelan J Moynihan I Woodward**
20 **CASA TALL (FR),** 7, b g No Risk At All (FR)—Gribouille Parcs (FR) **Tony, Judith, Sharon, Dermot & David**
21 **CHAMPAGNE CITY,** 8, ch g Tobougg (IRE)—City of Angels **R. S. Brookhouse**
22 **CLEAR ON TOP (IRE),** 5, b g Robin des Champs (FR)—Homelander (IRE) **Nelson, Bovington, Taylor, Delarocha**
23 **CLONDAW CASTLE (IRE),** 9, b g Oscar (IRE)—Lohort Castle (IRE) **J French, D McDermott, S Nelson, T Syder**
24 **COME ON GRUFF (IRE),** 5, b g Mahler—Annie Grit (IRE) **Mr N T Griffith & H M Haddock**
25 **COME ON TEDDY (IRE),** 7, b g Fame And Glory—Theatre View (IRE) **Noel Fehily Racing Syndicates-Teddy**
26 **COTTUN (FR),** 5, b g Le Havre (FR)—Montebella (FR) **Sharon Nelson & Katya Taylor Delarocha**

## MR TOM GEORGE - continued

27 **COUPDEBOL (FR)**, 6, gr g Rajsaman (FR)—Chance Bleue (FR) **Terry Warner & Tim Syder**
28 **CREALION (FR)**, 5, b g Creachadoir (IRE)—Lady La Lionne (FR) **S Nelson, T Keelan, H Polito, C Compton**
29 **DARLING DU LARGE (FR)**, 8, b m Kapgarde (FR)—Dissidente (FR) **Mr S. W. Clarke**
30 **DOCTOR DEX (IRE)**, 8, b g Oscar (IRE)—Larnalee (IRE) **Crossed Fingers Partnership**
31 **DOM BOSCO**, 4, b g Blue Bresil (FR)—Definitely Better (IRE) **Miss J. A. Hoskins**
32 **DOUBLE SHUFFLE (IRE)**, 11, b g Milan—Fiddlers Bar (IRE) **Crossed Fingers Partnership**
33 **DRUMLEE SUNSET (IRE)**, 11, br g Royal Anthem (USA)—Be My Sunset (IRE) **R. S. Brookhouse**
34 **ESPOIR DE TEILLEE (FR)**, 9, b g Martaline—Belle de Lyphard (FR) **R. S. Brookhouse**
35 **FANFAN DU SEUIL (FR)**, 6, b g Racinger (FR)—Nina du Seuil (FR) **Crossed Fingers Partnership**
36 **FARO DE KERSER (FR)**, 6, b g Ungaro (GER)—Nuit de Kerser (FR) **The Twenty One Partnership**
37 **FEARLESS FRACAS (IRE)**, 7, b g Fracas (IRE)—Mayo Mystique (IRE) **R. S. Brookhouse**
38 **FONTLEY HOUSE (IRE)**, 6, b g Ask—Down Town Cork (IRE) **Colin Perry, Alan Waller & John Lawson**
39 **FORGOT TO ASK (IRE)**, 9, b g Ask—Lady Transcend (IRE) **Miss J. A. Hoskins**
40 **GET BYE (IRE)**, 6, b g Getaway (GER)—Cappa Or (IRE) **Mr C. B. Compton**
41 **GLOBAL EFFECT (IRE)**, 6, b br g Presenting—Ella Watson (IRE) **S Nelson, R Blunt, K Delarocha, D Savell**
42 **GLOCKENSPIEL (IRE)**, 6, b g Teofilo (IRE)—Morning Bell **Mr D. W. Fox**
43 **GO ON BRYCEY LAD (FR)**, 5, b g Saddler Maker (IRE)—Lonita d'Airy (FR) **The MerseyClyde Partnership**
44 **HOOLIGAN (IRE)**, 6, b g Aizavoski (IRE)—Victory Run (IRE) **O'Donohoe, Cavanagh, Robinson, Nelson**
45 **JOBESGREEN LAD**, 6, b g Passing Glance—Overnight Fame (IRE) **Mr R. T. Cornock**
46 **KAKAMORA**, 6, b g Great Pretender (IRE)—Roche d'Or **Mr T. D. J. Syder**
47 **KK LEXION (IRE)**, 10, b g Flemensfirth (USA)—Kiloradante (IRE) **Perry, Lawson, Waller, McDermott**
48 **LETS GO CHAMP (IRE)**, 6, b g Jeremy (USA)—Dark Mimosa (IRE) **R. S. Brookhouse**
49 **LYDIA VIOLET (IRE)**, 6, br m Kalanisi (IRE)—Anne Hathaway (IRE) **Chasing Gold Limited**
50 **MANOFTHEMOMENT (IRE)**, 7, b g Jeremy (USA)—Endless Ambition (IRE) **James Longley & Charles Tatnall**
51 **MASSINI MAN**, 8, b g Dr Massini (IRE)—Alleged To Rhyme (IRE) **Mrs E. A. Fletcher**
52 **MAXIMUM DEX (IRE)**, 4, b g Westerner—Parsons Hall (IRE) **Crossed Fingers Partnership**
53 **MILLIE ROUND (IRE)**, 5, b m Fame And Glory—Molly Round (IRE) **The Borris Partnership**
54 **MINELLA FOR ME (IRE)**, 11, b g King's Theatre (IRE)—Irish Mystics (IRE) **Mr S. W. Clarke**
55 **MISS CHANTELLE**, 4, b f Yorgunnabelucky (USA)—Miss Estela (IRE) **R. S. Brookhouse**
56 **MOSAMBO (IRE)**, 6, b m Fame And Glory—Similan (IRE) **Somerset Racing**
57 **OLD DUKE (IRE)**, 4, br g Shirocco (GER)—Sunlight (IRE) **Aniol & Burslem**
58 **OSCAR ROBERTSON (IRE)**, 7, b g Oscar (IRE)—Beaus Polly (IRE) **Crossed Fingers Partnership**
59 **OVERALL MAJORITY (IRE)**, 5, b g Sholokhov (IRE)—
　　　　　　　　　　　　　　　　　　　　　Liss Alainn (IRE) **S Nelson K Delarocha T Keelan J Edgedale**
60 4, B f Passing Glance—Overnight Fame (IRE) **Mr R. T. Cornock**
61 5, B g Fame And Glory—Queen's Leader **Mr N T Griffith & H M Haddock**
62 **RABBLE ROUSER (IRE)**, 4, b g Aizavoski (IRE)—
　　　　　　　　　　　　　　　　　The Flaming Matron (IRE) **O'Donohoe, Cavanagh, Robinson, Nelson**
63 **ROCK ON ROCCO (IRE)**, 7, b g Shirocco (GER)—Katalina **R. S. Brookhouse**
64 **SAY THE WORD**, 5, b g Authorized (IRE)—Soryah (IRE) **Silkword Racing Partnership**
65 **SEPTEMBER DAISY**, 6, b m September Storm (GER)—Alleged To Rhyme (IRE) **Mrs E. A. Fletcher**
66 **SMUGGLER'S BLUES (IRE)**, 9, b g Yeats (IRE)—Rosy de Cyborg (FR) **D Rea & K Bebbington**
67 **SPRINGFIELD FOX**, 8, gr g Sagamix (FR)—Marlbrook Fox **O'Donohoe, Cavanagh, Robinson, Nelson**
68 **STRIKE IN MILAN (IRE)**, 9, b g Milan—Great Days (IRE) **R. S. Brookhouse**
69 **SUMKINDOFKING (IRE)**, 10, br g King's Theatre (IRE)—Shannon Rose (IRE) **Mr K. M. Bebbington**
70 **SUMMERVILLE BOY (IRE)**, 9, b g Sandmason—Suny House **R. S. Brookhouse**
71 **THE BRASS MAN (IRE)**, 7, b g Milan—The Brass Lady (IRE) **S Nelson G Birrell K Delarocha D Savell**
72 4, B f Walk In The Park (IRE)—Toungara (FR) **Mr S. W. Clarke**
73 **TRIBESMANS GLORY (IRE)**, 7, b g Jeremy (USA)—Benecash (IRE) **T Keelan,J Moynihan,S Nelson,D O'Donohoe**
74 **VALSEUR DU GRANVAL (FR)**, 12, b g Della Francesca (USA)—
　　　　　　　　　　　　　　　　　　　　　　La Grande Vallee (FR) **D Thompson & The Magic Ten**
75 **WHAT (IRE)**, 7, b g Oscar (IRE)—Fuel Queen (IRE) **Mrs S. George**
76 **WHAT A STEAL (IRE)**, 4, b g Flemensfirth (USA)—Misty Heather (IRE) **O'Donohoe, Delchar, Jack, Nelson**
77 **WRITTENINTHESAND (IRE)**, 7, b g Milan—Sommer Sonnet (IRE) **Wilkin, Orr, Boileau & Douglas**
78 **ZOUTOISE (FR)**, 6, b m Enrique—Belle Yepa (FR) **Mr S. W. Clarke**

## MR TOM GEORGE - continued

### THREE-YEAR-OLDS
79 **ROYAL REGARD (FR)**, b c Shalaa (IRE)—Royal Highness (GER) **Mr T. George**
80 B c Walk In The Park (IRE)—Toungara (FR) **Mr S. W. Clarke**

### TWO-YEAR-OLDS
81 B br c 13/02 Manduro (GER)—Triceps (IRE) (Excelebration (IRE)) (20984)

**Other Owners:** Mr M. Aniol, Mr K. M. Bebbington, Mrs E. G. A. Birrell, Mr R. J. Blunt, Mrs H. L. Boileau, Mr D. A. Bovington, Mr P. R. Burslem, Mr J. P. Cavanagh, Mr S. W. Clarke, Mr C. B. Compton, Mrs J. C. E. Crichton, Mr S. M. Delchar, Mr J. S. A. Douglas, Mr J. W. Edgedale, Mr J. M. Fawbert, Mr C. P. L. Francklin, Mr J. A. R. R. French, Mr J. M. Gabbertas, Mr R. K. Gabbertas, Mrs S. P. Gabbertas, Mrs V. Gabbertas, Mr N. Griffith, Mrs H. M. Haddock, Mr P. Jack, Mrs A. J. Jamieson, Mr T. J. Keelan, Lady A. J. Kiszely, Mr J. B. Lawson, Mr J. T. C. Longley, Mr D. P. McDermott, Mr A. McMorrough Kavanagh, Ms J. A. Moran, Mr J. Moynihan, Mrs S. C. Nelson, Mr D. J. O'Donohoe, Mrs S. Orr, Mr D. Osullivan, A. J. Outhart, Mr C. H. Perry, Mrs H. W. Polito, Sir C. A. Ponsonby, Mr David Rea, Ms V. Robinson, Mr D. A. Savell, H. S. Smith, Mr T. D. J. Syder, Mr C. R. S. Tatnall, Mr J. Taylor, Mrs K. Torres de la Rocha, A. M. Waller, J. T. Warner, Mr R. C. Wilkin, Mr N. Williamson.

**Assistant Trainer:** John Cullinan, Darren O'Dwyer, **Travelling Head:** Sarah Peacock, **Secretary:** Lauren Thompson.

**NH Jockey:** Jonathan Burke, Ciaran Gethings. **Conditional Jockey:** Thomas Doggrell. **Amateur Jockey:** Noel George.

---

**223** | **MR NICK GIFFORD, Findon**
Postal: **The Downs, Stable Lane, Findon, West Sussex, BN14 0RT**
Contacts: **PHONE 01903 872226 MOBILE 07940 518077**
**EMAIL downs.stables@btconnect.com WEBSITE www.nickgiffordracing.co.uk**

1 **BELARGUS (FR)**, 6, b g Authorized (IRE)—Belga Wood (USA) **Mr J. P. McManus**
2 **CASTLEDHEM (IRE)**, 6, b g Alkaadhem—Castle Hope (IRE) **Paul & Louise Bowtell**
3 **COBBS CORNER (IRE)**, 5, b g Ocovango—A Long Way **Mr M. P. Jones**
4 **CORAL LAD (IRE)**, 6, b g Shirocco (GER)—Gli Gli (IRE) **Project Mars Racing Partnership**
5 **DELTA ROSE (IRE)**, 7, br m Robin des Champs (FR)—Cruising Katie (IRE) **J. R. Hulme**
6 **DIDTHEYLEAVEUOUTTO (IRE)**, 8, ch g Presenting—Pretty Puttens (IRE) **Mr J. P. McManus**
7 **EL TORNADO (IRE)**, 7, gr g Martaline—Okawanga Royale (FR) **develeco group ltd**
8 **FAIRWAY FREDDY (IRE)**, 8, b g Elusive Pimpernel (USA)—Silent Supreme (IRE) **New Gold Dream**
9 **FLY NUMBER ONE (IRE)**, 7, b g Oscar (IRE)—Kahysera **Mr The Brooks Family and J Kyle**
10 **FOLLOW INTELLO (IRE)**, 6, b g Intello (GER)—Sauvage (FR) **Mrs R. E. Gifford**
11 **GLEN ROCCO**, 10, ch g Shirocco (GER)—Adees Dancer **Kyle, Mason, Brooks, Ferguson & Stevens**
12 **ITSNOTWHATYOUTHINK (IRE)**, 6, b br g Westerner—Baladiva (IRE) **Mrs L Bowtell & Mrs S Cotty**
13 **JUNGLE PROSE (IRE)**, 6, b br m Yeats (IRE)—Spring Baloo (IRE) **Nick Gifford Racing Club**
14 **KADIYAMA (IRE)**, 4, b f Born To Sea (IRE)—Kadayna (IRE) **The Lavender Chickens**
15 **KINGS KRACKERTARA**, 6, b m Kayf Tara—Firecracker Lady (IRE) **J.C.Harrison Lee & T.Howard Partnership**
16 **LEGENDARY GRACE**, 4, b f Multiplex—Fairyinthewind (IRE) **Mr R. J. Delnevo**
17 4, b f Finsceal Fior (IRE)—Lounaos (FR) **Mrs R. E. Gifford**
18 **MARINE JAG (FR)**, 4, b f Saint des Saints (FR)—Soif d'Aimer (FR) **Paul & Louise Bowtell**
19 **MY BAD LUCY**, 5, b g Kayf Tara—Luci di Mezzanotte **Mr M. K. O'Shea**
20 **MYSTIC DREAMER (IRE)**, 7, b m Sans Frontieres (IRE)—Free Dreamer (IRE) **Nick Gifford Racing Club**
21 **NORTHERN POET (IRE)**, 6, b g Yeats (IRE)—Crowning Virtue (IRE) **The Hope Springs Syndicate**
22 **PADDY'S POEM**, 10, b g Proclamation (IRE)—Ashleys Petale (IRE) **Mrs T. J. Stone-Brown**
23 **ROSE OF AGHABOE (IRE)**, 8, b m Gold Well—Shillinglee Spring **The Rose Tinted Partnership**
24 **SIMPLY SUPREME (IRE)**, 6, b m Robin des Champs (FR)—Old Dreams (IRE) **Ledwardian Legacy Partnership**
25 **THE MIGHTY DON (IRE)**, 9, ch g Shantou (USA)—Flying Answer (IRE) **Golden Rose Partnership**
26 4, B br g Getaway (GER)—Total Gossip (IRE)
27 **WEE RUPERT**, 5, b g Shirocco (GER)—Arctic Actress **The Blows Hot and Cold Syndicate**
28 **ZUBA**, 5, b g Dubawi (IRE)—Purr Along **The South Downs Partnership**

## MR NICK GIFFORD - continued

Other Owners: Mr J. P. M. Bowtell, Mrs L. Bowtell, Mr G. F. Brooks, Mrs S. Cotty, Sir A. Ferguson, Mr J. Kyle, G. A. Mason, Mr D. J. Stevens, Mrs L. Wolfe.

NH Jockey: James Davies.

---

**224** **MR MARK GILLARD, Sherborne**
Postal: **Hawkes Field Farm, Hilton, Blandford Forum, Dorset, DT11 0DN**
Contacts: **PHONE 01258 881111 MOBILE 07970 700605**
**EMAIL office@markgillardracing.com WEBSITE www.markgillardracing.com**

1 AVITHOS, 11, b m Kayf Tara—Digyourheelsin (IRE) **Mr N J McMullan & Mr T Winzer**
2 DON'T JUMP GEORGE (IRE), 6, b g Canford Cliffs (IRE)—My Sweet Georgia (IRE) **Mr J. Searchfield**
3 FINISHER (USA), 6, br g Street Cry (IRE)—Morena (PER) **Mrs P. M. R. Gillard**
4 JOHN BETJEMAN, 5, b g Poet's Voice—A Great Beauty **Gillard, Gillard, Seegar**
5 KINGSTON MIMOSA, 9, b g Kheleyf (USA)—Derartu (AUS) **Mr S. J. Garnett**
6 NO NO CARDINAL (IRE), 12, ch g Touch of Land (FR)—Four Moons (IRE) **T. J. C. Seegar**
7 NO NO TONIC, 7, b m Sulamani (IRE)—Karinga Madame **N. J. McMullan**
8 TOUCH SCREEN (IRE), 11, b g Touch of Land (FR)—Capard Lady (IRE) **M. C. Denning**
9 VANDERBILT (IRE), 7, ch g Intense Focus (USA)—Star of The West **T. J. C. Seegar**
10 ZELLERATE (IRE), 4, b g Gutaifan (IRE)—Ride For Roses (IRE) **Miss Kay Russell**

### THREE-YEAR-OLDS
11 BANNERGIRL (IRE), ch f Starspangledbanner (AUS)—Scarlet Belle **Mr R. M. Rivers**
12 HAZMAT (IRE), br f Harzand (IRE)—Suite (IRE) **Mr R. M. Rivers**

Other Owners: Mr R. Gillard, Mr R. Gillard, N. J. McMullan, T. J. C. Seegar, T. O. Winzer.

Assistant Trainer: Mrs Pippa Gillard, Yard Sponsor: Ascot Park Polo Club.

Conditional Jockey: Fergus Gillard.

---

**225** **MR JIM GOLDIE, Glasgow**
Postal: **Libo Hill Farm, Uplawmoor, Glasgow, Lanarkshire, G78 4BA**
Contacts: **PHONE 01505 850212 MOBILE 07778 241522**
**WEBSITE www.jimgoldieracing.com**

1 AYR POET, 6, b g Poet's Voice—Jabbara (IRE) **The Reluctant Suitor's**
2 BE PROUD (IRE), 5, b g Roderic O'Connor (IRE)—Agnista (IRE) **Whitestonecliffe Racing Partnership**
3 CALL ME GINGER, 5, ch g Orientor—Primo Heights **Johnnie Delta Racing**
4 CASTLE VIEW (IRE), 4, ch g Casamento (IRE)—Spirit of The Sea (IRE) **Mrs A. E. Giles**
5 EUCHEN GLEN, 8, b g Authorized (IRE)—Jabbara (IRE) **W. M. Johnstone**
6 FIRLINFEU, 6, b g New Approach (IRE)—Antara (GER) **Johnnie Delta Racing**
7 4, B g Sulamani (IRE)—Gargoyle Girl
8 5, B g Orientor—Gargoyle Girl
9 GLENIFFER, 5, b g Orientor—Glenlini **Johnnie Delta Racing**
10 GLOBAL HUMOR (USA), 6, b g Distorted Humor (USA)—In Bloom (USA) **Flash Figs Racing**
11 JESSIE ALLAN (IRE), 10, b m Bushranger (IRE)—Ishimagic **Mr R. W. C. McLachlan**
12 JORGIE (FR), 4, ch g George Vancouver (USA)—Capannacce (IRE) **Mr J Fyffe & Mr D Pryde**
13 LORD OF THE GLEN, 6, b g Orientor—Glenlini **Johnnie Delta Racing**
14 MAZAMIX, 4, br f Mazameer (IRE)—Crosby Millie **The Vital Sparks**
15 ONE LAST HUG, 6, b g Orientor—Gargoyle Girl **Mr James Callow & Mr J. S. Goldie**

## MR JIM GOLDIE - continued

16 **ORIENTAL LILLY**, 7, ch m Orientor—Eternal Instinct  **Johnnie Delta Racing**
17 **PAMMI**, 6, b m Poet's Voice—Bright Girl (IRE)  **Ayrshire Racing & Partner**
18 **PRIMO'S COMET**, 6, b g Orientor—Primo Heights  **Whitestonecliffe Racing Partnership**
19 **RAINY CITY (IRE)**, 11, b g Kalanisi (IRE)—Erintante (IRE)  **Mr James Callow & Mr J. S. Goldie**
20 **RIOJA DAY (IRE)**, 11, b g Red Clubs (IRE)—Dai E Dai (USA)  **Mr J. S. Goldie**
21 **ROCK REBEL (IRE)**, 6, ch g Rock of Gibraltar (IRE)—Belle Rebelle (IRE)  **The Reluctant Suitor's**
22 **SARVI**, 6, br m Intello (GER)—Crystal Swan (IRE)  **Johnnie Delta Racing**
23 **SCOTS SONNET**, 7, b g Poet's Voice—Jabbara (IRE)  **Mr W. M. Johnstone & Mr J. S. Goldie**
24 **SIR CHAUVELIN**, 9, b g Authorized (IRE)—Jabbara (IRE)  **J. & G. Thomson**
25 **SOUND OF IONA**, 5, ch m Orientor—Eternal Instinct  **Mr & Mrs G Grant & the Reluctant Suitors**
26 **STAR CRACKER (IRE)**, 9, ch g Starspangledbanner (AUS)—Champagne Cracker  **Mr G E Adams & Mr J S Goldie**
27 **SUMMER HEIGHTS**, 4, b f Orientor—Primo Heights  **Mr Paul Stewart & Mr Jim S Goldie**
28 **TANASOQ (IRE)**, 8, b g Acclamation—Alexander Youth (IRE)  **Mr F Brady & Mr J S Morrison**
29 **TANNADICE PARK (IRE)**, 6, b m Shirocco (GER)—Catcherinscratcher (IRE)  **Johnnie Delta Racing**
30 **TARA KAY**, 5, b m Kayf Tara—La Vecchia Scuola (IRE)  **The Reluctant Suitor's**
31 **TOMMY G**, 8, ch g Makfi—Primo Heights  **Johnnie Delta Racing**
32 **WILLSHEWONTSHE**, 4, ch f Mazameer (IRE)—Rathlin Sound  **Mr James Callow & Mr J. S. Goldie**

### THREE-YEAR-OLDS

33 Ch g Orientor—Glenlini  **The Reluctant Suitor's**
34 **RORY**, ch g Orientor—Eternal Instinct  **The Reluctant Suitor's**
35 **WATER OF LEITH (IRE)**, b g Kodiac—Zakhrafa (IRE)  **Flash Figs Racing**

**Other Owners:** Mr G. Adams, Ayrshire Racing, Mr N. Boyle, Mr F. Brady, Mr J. R. Callow, Mr J. Fyffe, Mrs D. I. Goldie, Mr J. S. Goldie, Mrs C. H. Grant, Mr G. R. Grant, W. M. Johnstone, Mr D. W. McIntyre, Mr J S Morrison, D. G. Pryde, Mr P. Stewart, The Reluctant Suitor's, G. M. Thomson.

**Assistant Trainer:** George Goldie, James Goldie.

---

## MR STEVE GOLLINGS, Louth
Postal: **Highfield House, Scamblesby, Louth, Lincolnshire, LN11 9XT**
Contacts: **PHONE** 01507 343213, 01507 343204 **MOBILE** 07860 218910
**EMAIL** stevegollings@aol.com **WEBSITE** www.stevegollings.com

1 **COLONY QUEEN**, 5, b m Gregorian (IRE)—Queen Margrethe  **David & Ros Chapman**
2 **DR RIO (FR)**, 5, b g Rio de La Plata (USA)—Dr Wintringham (IRE)  **Northern Bloodstock Racing**
3 **MOLTEN LAVA (IRE)**, 9, b g Rock of Gibraltar (IRE)—Skehana (IRE)  **Mrs Jayne M. Gollings**
4 **NAT LOVE (IRE)**, 4, b g Gregorian (IRE)—Chaguaramas (IRE)  **David & Ros Chapman**
5 **NEVADA**, 8, gr g Proclamation (IRE)—La Columbina  **Northern Bloodstock Racing**
6 **VENTURA GOLD (IRE)**, 6, b g Red Jazz (USA)—Desert Shine (IRE)  **Mr R. C. Key**

### THREE-YEAR-OLDS

7 **EXCUISITE**, gr f Gregorian (IRE)—Amour Fou (IRE)  **Mrs Jayne M. Gollings**

**Other Owners:** Mr D. O. Chapman, Mrs R. M. H. Chapman.

**Assistant Trainer:** Mrs J M Gollings.

## 227 MR CHRIS GORDON, Winchester
Postal: **Morestead Farm Stables, Morestead, Winchester, Hampshire, SO21 1JD**
Contacts: **PHONE 01962 712774 MOBILE 07713 082392**
**EMAIL chrisgordon68@hotmail.co.uk WEBSITE www.chrisgordonracing.com**

1 ALBERT HUCKLEBUCK (IRE), 5, b g Leading Light (IRE)—Queen of Cool (IRE) **Ms E. J. Southall**
2 ALKETIOS (GR), 10, b g Kavafi (IRE)—Mazea (IRE) **Chris Gordon Racing Club**
3 AMERICAN GERRY (IRE), 5, b g Americain (USA)—Hurricane Society (IRE) **Geake Family**
4 ANNUAL INVICTUS (IRE), 6, b g Mahler (IRE)—Shantou Rose (IRE) **Mr T. M. Smith**
5 BADDESLEY (IRE), 6, b g Presenting—Fox Theatre (IRE) **Mr Richard & Mrs Carol Cheshire**
6 BADDESLEY KNIGHT (IRE), 8, b g Doyen (IRE)—Grangeclare Rhythm (IRE) **Mr Richard & Mrs Carol Cheshire**
7 BADDESLEY PRINCE (IRE), 7, b g Doyen (IRE)—Norabella (IRE) **Mr Richard & Mrs Carol Cheshire**
8 BLACK CENTAUR (IRE), 8, b g Oscar (IRE)—Arcanum (IRE) **Davies King Selway Wavish**
9 BLAME THE GAME (IRE), 6, b g Darsi (FR)—Lucy Walters (IRE) **Redz Together**
10 BROTHER WINDSOR (IRE), 5, b g Valirann (FR)—Mrs Bukay (IRE) **Party People 2**
11 CADMAR, 7, b g Shirocco (GER)—Raitera (FR) **Mr Richard & Mrs Carol Cheshire**
12 CAN'T STOP NOW (IRE), 4, ch g Starspangledbanner (AUS)—Sorry Woman (IRE) **Let's Be Lucky Racing 30**
13 4, B g Diamond Boy (FR)—Clochette de Sou (FR) **Mrs J. L. Gordon**
14 COMMANCHE RED (IRE), 8, ch g Mahler—Auntie Bob **Mr Richard & Mrs Carol Cheshire**
15 COMMANDANT (IRE), 8, br g Presenting—Miss Nomer (IRE) **Mrs B. I. Chantler**
16 CORONADO JOE, 5, ch g Norse Dancer (IRE)—Hopatina (IRE) **Mr E. J. Hawkings**
17 4, b g Mahler—Deianira (IRE) **Mrs N. Morris**
18 FIZZLESTIX (FR), 9, b g Bonbon Rose (FR)—Skipnight **Mrs C. New**
19 GO UNIVERSAL (IRE), 7, b g Gold Well—And Whatever Else (IRE) **A. C. Ward-Thomas**
20 GRANGECLARE KNIGHT (IRE), 5, b m Doyen (IRE)—Grangeclare Rhythm (IRE) **Gordon & Cheshire**
21 HAREFIELD (IRE), 8, b g Doyen (IRE)—Bobbi's Venture (IRE) **Mr A. Charity**
22 HIGHWAY ONE O ONE (IRE), 9, br g Stowaway—High Accord (IRE) **A. C. Ward-Thomas**
23 HIGHWAY ONE O TWO (IRE), 6, b br g Shirocco (GER)—Supreme Dreamer (IRE) **A. C. Ward-Thomas**
24 HIWAY ONE O THREE (IRE), 4, b g Sageburg (IRE)—Good Time In Milan (IRE) **Ward-thomas & Dennis**
25 INVINCIBLE CAVE (IRE), 8, b g Court Cave (IRE)—Bespoke Baby (IRE) **Mrs J. L. Gordon**
26 ITSONLYROCKNROLL (IRE), 9, ch g Shantou (USA)—Compelled (IRE) **The Select Syndicate**
27 JIMMY, 3, ch g Norse Dancer (IRE)—Isintshelovely (IRE) **Gilbert & Gordon**
28 LE FOU ROYAL (FR), 10, b g Le Fou (IRE)—Kalon Ced'a (FR) **Mrs B. M. Ansell**
29 LORD BADDESLEY (IRE), 6, b br g Doyen (IRE)—Tropical Ocean (IRE) **Mr Richard & Mrs Carol Cheshire**
30 MELLOW BEN (IRE), 8, b g Beneficial—Mellowthemoonlight (IRE) **Broadsword Group Ltd**
31 MOUNT WINDSOR (IRE), 6, br g Mountain High (IRE)—Mrs Bukay (IRE) **Party People**
32 NOT NOW INDIAN (FR), 5, b g Indian Danehill (USA)—Not Now Katie **Mr C. J. Edwards**
33 ON THE SLOPES, 7, b g Librettist (USA)—Dalriath **Skill Scaffolding Ltd**
34 ONLY MONEY (IRE), 7, ch g Getaway (GER)—Kings Diva (IRE) **Ward-thomas & Dennis**
35 PASVOLSKY (IRE), 6, ch g Aizavoski (IRE)—Snowlaw (IRE) **The Augean Stables Syndicate**
36 PRESS YOUR LUCK (IRE), 6, b g Doyen (IRE)—Merry Gladness (IRE) **Cox, Lloyd & Finden**
37 RAMORE WILL (IRE), 10, gr g Tikkanen (USA)—Gill Hall Lady **E. J. Farrant**
38 REALLYRADICAL (IRE), 8, b g Insatiable (IRE)—Glenogra Cailin (IRE) **Mrs B. I. Chantler**
39 ROCKOLLECTION (FR), 4, gr g Dragon Dancer—Dona Honoria (FR) **Tony O'Gorman**
40 SAMI BEAR, 5, b g Sulamani (IRE)—Dalriath **Team ABC**
41 SANDY BROOK (IRE), 6, ch g Sandmason—Lovely Lolly (IRE) **Goodwin Racing Ltd**
42 SHUT THE BOX (IRE), 7, ch g Doyen (IRE)—Bond Holder (IRE) **The Shut The Box Syndicate**
43 SLY MINX, 4, b f Sixties Icon—Tanojin (IRE) **7RUS**
44 SMURPHY ENKI (FR), 6, b g Blue Bresil (FR)—Creme Veloutee (IRE) **Miss J. A. Goddard**
45 STANLEY PINCOMBE (IRE), 4, b g Multiplex—Allez Zane **Ms E. J. Southall**
46 STORM DENNIS (IRE), 5, b g Libertarian—Lady Eile (IRE) **Mr D. S. Dennis**
47 STRAIGHT SWAP (IRE), 6, b br g Yeats (IRE)—Alittlebitofheaven **Ward-thomas & Dennis**
48 THE TIN MINER (IRE), 10, br g Presenting—Sidalcea (IRE) **Mrs B. M. Ansell**
49 TOP MAN (IRE), 7, b g Milan—Get In There (IRE) **Broadsword Group Ltd**
50 TWOMINUTES TURKISH (IRE), 6, ch g Mahler—Kilbarry Cliche (IRE) **The Cabal**
51 UNANSWERED PRAYERS (IRE), 5, b g Ocovango—Fitanga Speed (IRE) **The Pres Partnership**
52 VICENZO MIO (FR), 11, b g Corri Piano (FR)—Sweet Valrose (FR) **Chris Gordon Racing Club**
53 WHO IS THAT (IRE), 5, ch g Shirocco (GER)—Nodelay (IRE) **Mr D. S. Dennis**

## MR CHRIS GORDON - continued

### THREE-YEAR-OLDS
54 **INVICTUS DE BRION (FR)**, b g Vespone (IRE)—Assemblee A Brion (FR)
55 **SPANISH HUSTLE**, b g Pearl Secret—Dos Lunas (IRE) **Let's Be Lucky Racing 30**
56 **TECHNO VIKING (IRE)**, b g Australia—Danehill Music (IRE) **Mr R. A. Gorrie**

**Other Owners:** Mrs C. L. Cheshire, Mr R. Cheshire, Mr P. Cox, Mrs C. E. Davies, Mr D. S. Dennis, W. E. Enticknap, Mr A. P. Finden, L. Gilbert, C. E. Gordon, Mr S. C. Hobbs, Mr D. Horsman, Mrs L. M. King, Mr P. D. Lloyd, Mr B. Ralph, A. G. Selway, A. C. Ward-Thomas, Mr P. T. J. Wavish, Mr J. Williams.

**Assistant Trainer:** Jenny Gordon.

**NH Jockey:** Tom Cannon. **Conditional Jockey:** Nathan Brennan.

---

**228** | **JOHN & THADY GOSDEN, Newmarket**
Postal: **Clarehaven, Bury Road, Newmarket, Suffolk, CB8 7BY**
Contacts: **PHONE 01638 565400**

1 **AL RUFAA (FR)**, 4, b g Kingman—Clarmina (IRE)
2 **ALMIGHWAR**, 4, b c Dubawi (IRE)—Taghrooda
3 **AMTIYAZ**, 4, b c Frankel—Rose of Miracles
4 **ANASTARSIA (IRE)**, 4, b f Sea The Stars (IRE)—Aniseed (IRE)
5 **CAPE PALACE**, 4, b g Golden Horn—Mia Diletta
6 **DUBAI WARRIOR**, 5, b h Dansili—Mahbooba (AUS)
7 **FAISAL**, 4, b c Golden Horn—Bella Lulu
8 **FOREST OF DEAN**, 5, b g Iffraaj—Forest Crown
9 **GALLAGHER**, 4, b g Oasis Dream—Azanara (IRE)
10 **GLOBAL GIANT**, 6, b h Shamardal (USA)—Aniseed (IRE)
11 **GOLDEN RULES**, 4, b g Golden Horn—Sinnamary (IRE)
12 **GRAND BAZAAR**, 4, b g Golden Horn—Damaniyat Girl (USA)
13 **HAQEEQY (IRE)**, 4, b g Lope de Vega (IRE)—Legal Lyric (IRE)
14 **HARROVIAN**, 5, b g Leroidesanimaux (BRZ)—Alma Mater
15 **HUMANITARIAN (USA)**, 5, b g Noble Mission—Sharbat (USA)
16 **INDIE ANGEL (IRE)**, 4, gr f Dark Angel (IRE)—Indigo Lady
17 **KING LEONIDAS**, 4, b c Kingman—Reem (AUS)
18 **LEAFHOPPER (IRE)**, 4, gr f Dark Angel (IRE)—Layla Jamil (IRE)
19 **LOGICIAN**, 5, gr h Frankel—Scuffle
20 **LORD NORTH (IRE)**, 5, b g Dubawi (IRE)—Najoum (USA)
21 **MAGICAL MORNING**, 4, b g Muhaarar—The Lark
22 **MAJESTIC NOOR**, 4, b f Frankel—Nouriya
23 **MISHRIFF (IRE)**, 4, b c Make Believe—Contradict
24 **MOONLIGHT IN PARIS (IRE)**, 4, b f Camelot—Malayan Mist (IRE)
25 **MOSTLY**, 4, b f Makfi—Montare (IRE)
26 **PALACE PIER**, 4, b c Kingman—Beach Frolic
27 **PITCHER'S POINT (USA)**, 4, b g Medaglia d'Oro (USA)—Hungry Island (USA)
28 **PORTRUSH**, 4, b f Frankel—Concentric
29 **RIOT (IRE)**, 4, b g Kingman—Alexander Queen (IRE)
30 **ROYAL MEWS (FR)**, 4, ch g Siyouni (FR)—Queen Arabella
31 **STRADIVARIUS (IRE)**, 7, ch h Sea The Stars (IRE)—Private Life (FR)
32 **SUNRAY MAJOR**, 4, b c Dubawi (IRE)—Zenda
33 **TAQAREER (IRE)**, 4, b g Frankel—Bethrah (IRE)
34 **TENBURY WELLS (USA)**, 4, b g Medaglia d'Oro (USA)—Dayatthespa (USA)
35 **URSA MINOR (IRE)**, 4, b g Sea The Stars (IRE)—Kincob (USA)
36 **WALDFABEL**, 4, ch f Frankel—Waldmark (GER)
37 **WALDKONIG**, 4, b c Kingman—Waldlerche
38 **WORTHILY (USA)**, 4, b g Point of Entry (USA)—Vignette (USA)

## JOHN & THADY GOSDEN - continued

### THREE-YEAR-OLDS

39 **ALBERT CAMUS**, ch c Teofilo (IRE)—Petite Nymphe
40 **ALIOMAANA**, ch f Raven's Pass (USA)—Taqdees (IRE)
41 **ALPHA KING**, br g Kingman—Kilo Alpha
42 **ANGEL'S KISS**, b f Dark Angel (IRE)—Ardent
43 **AT A PINCH**, b f Lope de Vega (IRE)—Inchina
44 **BALLANTRUAN**, b c Harzand (IRE)—Chincoteague (IRE)
45 **BEAU NASH (IRE)**, b c Golden Horn—What Style (IRE)
46 **BEHOLDING**, b f Le Havre (IRE)—Lady Darshaan (IRE)
47 **BLUE DIAMOND (IRE)**, b f Galileo (IRE)—Pearling (USA)
48 **BRIDESMAN**, b g Exceed And Excel (AUS)—Love Charm
49 **BURNING SEA (IRE)**, b f Lope de Vega (IRE)—Burning Heights (GER)
50 **CHIASMA (IRE)**, b f Galileo (IRE)—Kind (IRE)
51 **CIVIL CODE**, b c Muhaarar—Helleborine
52 **CORDOUAN (FR)**, b c Shalaa (IRE)—Piler Lann (FR)
53 **COUNSEL**, ch c Frankel—Honorina
54 **DADDY FRANK**, b c Frankel—Smart Change (USA)
55 **DARAMETHOS (IRE)**, b c Sea The Stars (IRE)—Dark Orchid (USA)
56 **DARLECTABLE YOU**, b f Dubawi (IRE)—Dar Re Mi
57 **DARLING HEART (IRE)**, b f Muhaarar—Sarita
58 **DEFINED**, b c Golden Horn—Criteria (IRE)
59 **DELTA BAY**, b f Nathaniel (IRE)—Tropicana Bay
60 **DERAB**, b c Sea The Stars (IRE)—Concentric
61 **DISBELIEVE**, b f Golden Horn—Disavow
62 **EBNZAIDOON (USA)**, ch c Speightstown (USA)—Nereid (USA)
63 **EL JAD (IRE)**, ch c Shamardal (USA)—Doors To Manual (USA)
64 **EMPEROR SPIRIT (IRE)**, b c Holy Roman Emperor (IRE)—Aspasias Tizzy (USA)
65 **ETERNAL SUMMER**, b f Kingman—Rose Blossom
66 **EVANIA**, b f Golden Horn—Hanami
67 **EXISTENT**, b c Kingman—Entity
68 **FIRST LIGHT**, ch c Dubawi (IRE)—Anzhelika (IRE)
69 **FRANKLET**, b f Frankel—Martlet
70 **FREE WIND (IRE)**, b f Galileo (IRE)—Alive Alive Oh
71 **FUNDAMENTAL**, b gr c Dark Angel (IRE)—Integral
72 **GAL WONDER**, b f Galileo (IRE)—J Wonder (USA)
73 **GLEN SAVAGE (IRE)**, b c Gleneagles (IRE)—Rocksavage (IRE)
74 **GOLDEN ACE**, b f Golden Horn—Deuce Again
75 **GOLDEN BUGLE**, b br f Golden Horn—Belle d'Or (USA)
76 **GOLDEN DARLING (IRE)**, gr f Australia—Grey Lilas (IRE)
77 **GOONER BOY**, b c Sea The Stars (IRE)—Sharnberry
78 **GURU**, b c Kingman—Dream Peace (IRE)
79 **HAIJA (FR)**, b f Shalaa (IRE)—Rasmiya (IRE)
80 **HAMHAMA (IRE)**, ch f Slade Power (IRE)—Flare of Firelight (USA)
81 **HAYKAL**, b f Nathaniel (IRE)—Rhagori
82 **HIGHLAND ROCKER (FR)**, gr c Gleneagles (IRE)—Cay Dancer
83 **IMPERIAL SUN**, b c Sea The Stars (IRE)—Abunai
84 **INDIGO GIRL**, b f Dubawi (IRE)—Montare (IRE)
85 **IRONSIDE (IRE)**, b g Invincible Spirit (IRE)—Sagami (USA)
86 **JACK KENNEDY**, b c Galileo (IRE)—Jack Naylor
87 **KAAHIRA**, b f Kingman—Mahbooba (AUS)
88 **KESTENNA**, ch f Pride of Dubai (AUS)—Lamyaa
89 **KINDERFRAU**, b f Sea The Stars (IRE)—Prussian
90 **KUSNACHT**, b f Kingman—Kinnaird (IRE)
91 **LAW OF THE SEA**, b c Golden Horn—Leaderene
92 **LIVERPOOL KNIGHT**, b c Golden Horn—Nouriya
93 **LOVING DREAM**, b f Gleneagles (IRE)—Kissable (IRE)
94 **MAGNIFIQUE (FR)**, ro f Dansili—Classe Vendome (FR)
95 **MARRAKECH MOON**, b c No Nay Never (USA)—Morocco Moon
96 **MARSHALL PLAN**, b c Golden Horn—Manaboo (USA)

# JOHN & THADY GOSDEN - continued

97 **MEGALLAN,** b c Kingman—Eastern Belle
98 **MERITORIOUS,** b g Make Believe—Make Merry
99 **MISS FINLAND (IRE),** b f Invincible Spirit (IRE)—Marvada (IRE)
100 **MISSILE,** b f Dubawi (IRE)—Ribbons
101 **MITHRAS,** b c Dubawi (IRE)—Irish Rookie (IRE)
102 **MOHJATTY (IRE),** b f Awtaad (IRE)—Ezima (IRE)
103 **MONSOON MOON,** gr f Kingman—Scuffle
104 **MOSELLE VALLEY (GER),** b f Guiliani (IRE)—Montfleur
105 **MOSTAHDAF (IRE),** br c Frankel—Handassa
106 **MOTAJARRED,** b c Siyouni (FR)—Moonlit Garden (IRE)
107 **NETHERTON,** b f Frankel—Lynnwood Chase (USA)
108 **OTYRAR,** b c New Approach (IRE)—Ollie Olga (USA)
109 **PARLIAMENT,** b c Fastnet Rock (AUS)—Starlet's Sister (IRE)
110 **PENNYMOOR,** b f Frankel—Penelopa
111 **PETER THE GREAT,** b c New Approach (IRE)—Palitana (USA)
112 **PIED PIPER,** ch g New Approach (IRE)—Pure Fantasy
113 **POET OF LIFE (IRE),** b c Frankel—Blue Kimono (IRE)
114 **PRINCESS NADIA,** b f Sea The Stars (IRE)—Princess Noor (IRE)
115 **QUEEN CHARLOTTE,** gr f Zoffany (IRE)—Gala
116 **QUEEN OF ZABEEL (IRE),** b f Iffraaj—Music Show (IRE)
117 **QURTAJANA (FR),** b f Shalaa (IRE)—Shotgun Gulch (USA)
118 **RAINBOW FIRE (IRE),** b c Kodiac—Heroine Chic (IRE)
119 **RANCHERO (IRE),** b c Kodiac—Rajmahal (UAE)
120 **RED SQUARE (IRE),** b f Frankel—Stellar Glow (IRE)
121 **REGENT,** gr f Frankel—Approach
122 **RESTITUTION (FR),** b c Frankel—Restiana (FR)
123 **RIFLEMAN (IRE),** ch c The Gurkha (IRE)—Dietrich (USA)
124 **SECOND KINGDOM,** b c Make Believe—Simple Magic (IRE)
125 **SENITA,** br f Frankel—Atone
126 **SEVENAL,** b c Sea The Stars (IRE)—Latice (IRE)
127 **SHAIKHENA (USA),** b f More Than Ready (USA)—Tafaneen (USA)
128 **SIDE SHOT,** b g Frankel—Photographic
129 **SIR EDWARD ELGAR (IRE),** b c No Nay Never (USA)—Stroke of Six (IRE)
130 **SOCIAL STATUS,** b f Frankel—Household Name
131 **STAR OF EMARAATY (IRE),** ch f Pride of Dubai (AUS)—La Grande Elisa (IRE)
132 **TANGELO,** b f Nathaniel (IRE)—Colourful
133 **TASLIMA,** b f Golden Horn—Tamarind (IRE)
134 **TAWAHUB,** br f Kingman—Mawheba (IRE)
135 **TAWLEED (IRE),** b g Exceed And Excel (AUS)—Terhaab (USA)
136 **TEARDROP ROCK,** b f Fastnet Rock (AUS)—Map of Heaven
137 **THEYAZIN (FR),** b c Siyouni (FR)—Dalamar
138 **THIRD KINGDOM,** b c Make Believe—Spring In The Air (CAN)
139 **THOUSAND OAKS (IRE),** b f Kingman—Roheryn (IRE)
140 **TOP BRASS,** b c Gleneagles (IRE)—California (IRE)
141 **TOP TABLE,** b f War Front (USA)—Mesa Fresca (USA)
142 **TRAWLERMAN (IRE),** b c Golden Horn—Tidespring (IRE)
143 **UNCLE BRYN,** b c Sea The Stars (IRE)—Wall of Sound
144 **UNFORGOTTEN (IRE),** gr ro g Exceed And Excel (AUS)—Souviens Toi
145 **VITAL FORCE (IRE),** b f Invincible Spirit (IRE)—Bergamask (USA)
146 **VOICE OF GLORY,** b f Poet's Voice—Vanity Rules
147 **WAKENING (IRE),** b br f Dark Angel (IRE)—Dancing Sands (IRE)
148 **WELL SPENT,** b f Siyouni (FR)—Pleasemetoo (IRE)
149 **WILD IRIS (IRE),** b f No Nay Never (USA)—Aspasi
150 **YOUCOULDHAVESAIDNO,** b f Shalaa (IRE)—Tara's Force (IRE)
151 **ZAGATO,** b c Frankel—Izzi Top

Trainer did not supply details of their two-year-olds.

**Flat Jockey:** L. Dettori, Martin Harley, Robert Havlin, Nicky Mackay, Kieran O'Neill. **Apprentice Jockey:** Benoit De La Sayette.

## 229 MRS HARRIET GRAHAM, Jedburgh
Postal: Strip End, Jedburgh, Roxburghshire, TD8 6NE
Contacts: PHONE 01835 840354 MOBILE 07843 380401
EMAIL hgrahamracing@aol.com

1 AYE RIGHT (IRE), 8, b g Yeats (IRE)—Gaybric (IRE)  **& Adam**
2 BIG ARTHUR, 4, b g Passing Glance—Xpectations (IRE)  **The Potassium Partnership**
3 BOWDEREK, 6, b m Scorpion (IRE)—Blue Nymph  **& Adam**
4 CLARET DABBLER, 7, ch g Haafhd—Floreana (GER)  **Mrs A. J. Boswell**
5 4, B g Yeats (IRE)—Down Ace (IRE)  **Mr S. Townshend**
6 MILLARVILLE (IRE), 8, b m Court Cave (IRE)—Portavoe (IRE)  **& Adam**
7 SHOUGHALL'S BOY (IRE), 5, b g Watar (IRE)—Lady Shackleton (IRE)  **Mr R. Chapman**
8 VERAVERA, 5, b m Black Sam Bellamy (IRE)—Minimum  **H G Racing**

**Other Owners:** Mrs E. Adam, Mr G. F. Adam.

**Assistant Trainer:** R D Graham.

**NH Jockey:** Callum Bewley, Tommy Dowson.

## 230 MR CHRIS GRANT, Billingham
Postal: Low Burntoft Farm, Wolviston, Billingham, Cleveland, TS22 5PD
Contacts: PHONE 01740 644054 MOBILE 07860 577998
EMAIL chrisgrantracing@gmail.com WEBSITE www.chrisgrantracing.co.uk

1 ACDC (IRE), 11, b g King's Theatre (IRE)—Always Alert (IRE)  **D&D Armstrong Limited**
2 BALLINTOGHER BOY (IRE), 7, b g Flemensfirth (USA)—Room Seven (IRE)  **C. Grant**
3 CHEEKY CHES, 6, ch g Sulamani (IRE)—Youamazeme  **The Magic Circle**
4 DARIUS DES SOURCES (FR), 8, gr g Irish Wells (FR)—Lionata (FR)  **D & D Armstrong Ltd & Mr L Westwood**
5 DONNA'S DIAMOND (IRE), 12, gr g Cloudings (IRE)—Inish Bofin (IRE)  **D&D Armstrong Limited**
6 DONNA'S DIVA, 6, b m Oscar (IRE)—Micro Mission (IRE)  **D&D Armstrong Limited**
7 FITZ PARK (IRE), 5, b g Robin des Champs (FR)—Evening Rushour (IRE)  **D. Mossop**
8 FLAKARNA, 6, b m Lucarno (USA)—Flaybay  **Miss A. P. Lee**
9 FRANKS FANCY (IRE), 6, b g Stowaway—Palesa Accord (IRE)  **G. F. White**
10 GLORY HIGHTS, 5, b g Fame And Glory—Lady Hight (FR)  **John & Grant**
11 HEY BOB (IRE), 9, b g Big Bad Bob (IRE)—Bounty Star (IRE)  **Miss Alison P. Lee & Mr Chris Grant**
12 JACQANINA, 6, b m Fame And Glory—Ninna Nanna (FR)  **Mr J. Kenny**
13 JINKAMAN, 7, b g Black Sam Bellamy (IRE)—Lady Jinks  **Miss A. P. Lee**
14 LEAD THE PACK (IRE), 5, b g Leading Light (IRE)—Rudi Tuesday (IRE)  **D & D Armstrong Ltd & Mr L Westwood**
15 5, B g Califet (FR)—Louis's Teffia (IRE)  **D&D Armstrong Ltd & Mr Chris Grant**
16 LYNDALE, 6, gr g Mountain High (IRE)—Grey Clouds  **John & Grant**
17 MAGIC WAVE, 5, b g Gentlewave (IRE)—Annie's Gift (IRE)  **The Magic Circle**
18 5, Br g Cloudings (IRE)—Mayfly  **D&D Armstrong Limited**
19 MELONY, 6, b m Scorpion (IRE)—Bet Davis (IRE)  **Mrs H. N. Eubank**
20 RED OCHRE, 8, b g Virtual—Red Hibiscus  **Mrs M Nicholas & Chris Grant**
21 RED REMINDER, 7, b m Mount Nelson—Red Hibiscus  **Mrs H. N. Eubank**
22 SERGEANT STRIPPY, 5, ch g Proclamation—Forsters Plantin  **Mr Andrew W Robson & Chris Grant**
23 SIX ONE NINE (IRE), 6, b g Cloudings (IRE)—Indian Athlete (IRE)  **D&D Armstrong Limited**
24 SLANEMORE HILL (IRE), 9, br g Court Cave (IRE)—Goodonyou-Polly (IRE)  **The Hon Mrs D. J. Faulkner**
25 SOLSTICE TWILIGHT, 9, b m Milan—Twilight Eclipse (IRE)  **Mrs D. J. Ritzema**
26 STRONG TEAM (IRE), 8, b g Exceed And Excel (AUS)—Star Blossom (USA)  **C. Grant**
27 THEATRE LEGEND, 8, b g Midnight Legend—Theatre Belle  **Division Bell Partnership**
28 ZAKETY ZAK, 10, b g Overbury (IRE)—Jeanne d'Arc  **Mr D. M. Wordsworth**

## MR CHRIS GRANT - continued

**Other Owners:** D&D Armstrong Limited, C. Grant, Miss A. P. Lee, Mrs M. Nicholas, Mr A. W. Robson, J. Wade, Mr L. J. Westwood.

**Assistant Trainer:** Mrs S. Grant.

**NH Jockey:** Brian Hughes, Callum Bewley.

---

### 231 MR JAMES GRASSICK, Cheltenham
Postal: **Dryfield Farm, Cleeve Hill, Cheltenham, Gloucestershire, GL54 5AG**
Contacts: **MOBILE 07976 779623**

1 DOVER LIGHT, 4, ch g Sir Prancealot (IRE)—Miss Mediator (USA) **J. R. Grassick**
2 ISOBEL BLEU, 6, b m Arvico (FR)—Applepie Lady (IRE) **J. R. Grassick**
3 LADY NATASHA (IRE), 8, b m Alfred Nobel (IRE)—Hot To Rock (IRE) **J. R. Grassick**
4 MADAMES GIRL (IRE), 4, ch f Rock of Gibraltar (IRE)—Miss Madame (IRE) **J. R. Grassick**
5 VALENTINE MIST (IRE), 9, b m Vale of York (IRE)—Silvertine (IRE) **J. R. Grassick**

### THREE-YEAR-OLDS
6 LIVING ON A DREAM, b f Swiss Spirit—Khafayif (USA) **J. R. Grassick**

---

### 232 MR MICHAEL GRASSICK, Curragh
Postal: **Fenpark House, Pollardstown, Curragh, Co. Kildare, Ireland**
Contacts: **MOBILE +353 86 364 8829**
**EMAIL** michaelgrassick1@gmail.com **WEBSITE** www.michaelcgrassick.com

1 INDY SYSTEM (IRE), 5, gr m Raven's Pass (USA)—Perruche Grise (FR) **T. Geary**
2 LOINGSEOIR (IRE), 5, b g Henrythenavigator (USA)—Only Exception (IRE) **Roisin Walshe**
3 4, B f Elusive Pimpernel (USA)—Princess Nicole (IRE) **M. C. Grassick**
4 TEXAS ROCK (IRE), 10, b g Rock of Gibraltar (IRE)—Vestavia (IRE) **J. Keeling**
5 VERHOYEN, 6, b g Piccolo—Memory Lane **P. Cullen**

**Flat Jockey:** W J Lee.

---

### 233 MR CARROLL GRAY, Bridgwater
Postal: **The Little Glen, Peartwater Road, Spaxton, Bridgwater, Somerset, TA5 1DG**
Contacts: **MOBILE 07989 768163**

1 BELLAMY'S GREY, 9, gr g Black Sam Bellamy (IRE)—Lambrini Queen **Riverdance Consortium 2**
2 BET ON BETTY, 8, b m Flying Legend (USA)—Cadourova (FR) **Unity Farm Holiday Centre Ltd**
3 FRAME RATE, 6, b g Arcano (IRE)—Miss Quality (USA) **Mrs M. E. Gittings-Watts**
4 MORPET, 12, b g Morpeth—Kathies Pet **Mrs S. Hutchings**
5 PRINCESS ROANIA (IRE), 10, b m Dubai Destination (USA)—Lady Roania (IRE) **Mrs D. Cossey**
6 SEASEARCH, 6, b g Passing Glance—Seaflower Reef (IRE) **Riverdance Consortium 3**
7 VINNIE'S ICON (IRE), 7, b m Vinnie Roe (IRE)—Iconic Events (IRE) **Mr R. J. Napper & Mr S Reeves**

**Other Owners:** Mr R. J. Napper, Mr S. A. Reeves.

**Assistant Trainer:** Mrs C. M. L. Gray.

**NH Jockey:** Micheal Nolan.

## 234  MR WARREN GREATREX, Upper Lambourn

Postal: Uplands, Upper Lambourn, Hungerford, Berkshire, RG17 8QH
Contacts: PHONE 01488 670279 MOBILE 07920 039114 FAX 01488 72193
EMAIL info@wgreatrexracing.com WEBSITE www.wgreatrexracing.com

1   ABUFFALOSOLDIER (IRE), 4, br g Mahler—Adderstonlee (IRE) **& Wailers**
2   ALLANAH'S BOY (IRE), 4, b g Westerner—Countess Eileen (IRE) **Fitorfat Racing**
3   AMERICAN LEGACY, 5, ch g Shirocco (GER)—Karingas Legacy **Jim and Claire Limited**
4   ANOTHER EMOTION (FR), 9, gr g Turgeon (USA)—Line Perle (FR) **Fitorfat Racing**
5   ATAILOF TWO CITIES (IRE), 4, b f Champs Elysees—Chelsea Morning (USA) **Million in Mind Partnership**
6   AUDACITY, 5, ch g Pivotal—Carlanda (FR) **The Audacity Partnership**
7   BAILARICO (IRE), 8, b g Dubawi (IRE)—Baila Me (GER) **Fitorfat Racing**
8   BAMFORD EDGE (IRE), 4, b g Flemensfirth (USA)—Black Rock Lady (IRE) **Jim and Claire Limited**
9   BEAUFORT (IRE), 5, b g Zoffany (IRE)—Change Course **The Beaufort Partnership**
10  BILL BAXTER (IRE), 5, gr g Milan—Blossom Rose (IRE) **Glassex Holdings Ltd**
11  BOB MAHLER (IRE), 9, b g Mahler—Cooladurragh (IRE) **Bolingbroke, Bunch, Howard & Sutton**
12  BOLD SOLDIER, 6, b g Kayf Tara—Major Hoolihan **Alan & Andrew Turner**
13  BOLSOVER BILL (IRE), 4, b g Getaway (GER)—Peripheral Vision (IRE) **Jim and Claire Limited**
14  DANCINGWITH STORMS (IRE), 7, ch g New Approach (IRE)—Mad About You (IRE) **Jim and Claire Limited**
15  DHOWIN (IRE), 7, b g Yeats (IRE)—On The Way Home (IRE) **Mrs Jill Eynon & Mr Robin Eynon**
16  DORISA QUEEN, 5, b m Shirocco (GER)—Ellnando Queen **Mrs R. I. Vaughan**
17  DRUMLEE WATAR (IRE), 8, ch g Watar (IRE)—Dolly of Dublin (IRE) **Mr B. J. C. Drew**
18  ECTOR (FR), 7, b g Coastal Path—Evane (FR) **Fitorfat Racing**
19  ELLEON (FR), 6, b g Martaline—Ailette **The Spero & Batting Partnership**
20  EMITOM (IRE), 7, b g Gold Well—Avenging Angel (IRE) **The Spero Partnership Ltd**
21  FAMILIAR SPIRIT, 5, b m Fame And Glory—Sounds Familiar (IRE) **Hot To Trot Racing**
22  FRANKIE BABY (IRE), 6, b g Yeats (IRE)—Belsalsa (FR) **Jim and Claire Limited**
23  FRAUGHAN HILL (IRE), 5, b g Jet Away—Miss Foaley (IRE)
24  FULL SPES (FR), 5, gr g Al Namix (FR)—Full Passion (FR) **J & R Eynon, Majithia & Awr Consultancy**
25  GANGSTER (IRE), 11, ch g Green Tune (USA)—Dahlia's Krissy (USA) **Jim and Claire Limited**
26  GO PHARISEE FLYER (FR), 5, b g Cokoriko (FR)—Rosalie Malta (FR) **Glassex Holdings Ltd**
27  GOLDEN ROC (IRE), 6, b g Shirocco (GER)—Sovereign Lass (IRE) **Keith Hunter & Francis Ong**
28  HENSCHKE (IRE), 7, b g Mahler—Reserve The Right (IRE) **Mrs T. J. Stone-Brown**
29  HERAKLES (FR), 4, b g Saddler Maker (IRE)—Une Histoire (FR) **Mr W. J. Greatrex**
30  HERE HARE HERE (IRE), 4, b g Masterstroke (USA)—Valence (FR) **Mr A. Pegley**
31  HERMANI (FR), 4, b g Gris de Gris (IRE)—Lola Lolita (FR)
32  IRISH LION (IRE), 5, b g Leading Light (IRE)—Ask Sally (IRE) **Mr W. J. Greatrex**
33  ISLE OF RONA, 4, gr f Kayf Tara—Wassailing Queen **Jim and Claire Limited**
34  JUST A SIP, 6, b m Great Pretender (IRE)—One Gulp **Mrs T. Greatrex**
35  KEEPER HILL (IRE), 10, b g Westerner—You Take Care (IRE) **McNeill Family Ltd**
36  KEMBLE'S CASCADE (IRE), 6, b g Kalanisi (IRE)—Beauty Star (IRE) **Mr Awk Merriam & Mrs Henri Bayford**
37  KICKSAFTERSIX (IRE), 5, b g Scorpion (IRE)—Astalanda (FR) **The Spero Partnership Ltd**
38  LEXSMIDNIGHTRUNNER (FR), 4, b g Diamond Boy (FR)—Sainterose (FR) **Mr A. Pegley**
39  LOYALTY BINDS ME, 5, b g Schiaparelli (GER)—Mrs Fawlty **Mr N. C. Pullen, Miss K. Hannigan**
40  MAHLERVOUS (IRE), 8, b g Mahler—Brook Style (IRE) **The Marvellous Partnership**
41  MANDALAYAN (IRE), 6, b g Arakan (USA)—Danza Nera (IRE) **Alan & Andrew Turner**
42  MARTHA BRAE, 5, b m Shirocco (GER)—Harringay **Mrs R. I. Vaughan**
43  MILITAIRE, 4, b g Soldier of Fortune (IRE)—La Dame Brune (FR) **Jim and Claire Limited**
44  MINELLA EXAMINER, 8, b g Beat Hollow—Bold Fire **The Examiners**
45  MISS HONEY RYDER (IRE), 8, b m Stowaway—Seesea (IRE) **The Albatross Club**
46  MISSED VACATION (IRE), 4, b f Sholokhov (IRE)—Liss Na Piseoga (IRE) **Alan & Andrew Turner**
47  5, B g Shirocco (GER)—Molly's Case (IRE) **Mrs N. C. Turner**
48  MONSIEUR GINO (FR), 4, b g It's Gino (GER)—Nana Desir (FR) **Mr & Mrs Sandy Orr**
49  MOUSETRAP, 4, gr f Al Namix (FR)—Mickie
50  MULCAHYS HILL (IRE), 9, b g Brian Boru—Belsalsa (FR) **Jim and Claire Limited**
51  NORTH STAR OSCAR (IRE), 7, b g Oscar (IRE)—North Star Poly (IRE) **The North Star Oscar Partnership**
52  NOW LOOK AT ME (IRE), 7, ch g Shantou (USA)—Similan (IRE) **McNeill Family Ltd**
53  PICARA'S PROMISE, 5, ch m Gentlewave (IRE)—Ambrosia's Promise (IRE) **The Spero Partnership Ltd**
54  PORTRUSH TED (IRE), 9, b g Shantou (USA)—Village Queen (IRE) **McNeill Family Ltd**
55  PRINTING DOLLARS (IRE), 8, br m Doyen (IRE)—Printing Polly (IRE) **Mr R. B. Waley-Cohen**

## MR WARREN GREATREX - continued

56 **ROCCOWITHLOVE**, 7, b g Shirocco (GER)—Love Train (IRE) **Crimbourne Bloodstock**
57 **SALAMANCA SCHOOL (FR)**, 4, b g Rock of Gibraltar (IRE)—Princess Sofia (UAE) **As Sutch Partnership**
58 **SARIM (IRE)**, 6, b g Declaration of War (USA)—Silver Star **Fitorfat Racing**
59 **SILVER AND GOLD**, 5, gr g Martaline—Raitera (FR) **Jim and Claire Limited**
60 **SPEEDY CARGO (IRE)**, 8, b g Stowaway—Vics Miller (IRE) **N.W.A. Bannister & M.J.R. Bannister**
61 **STAR FLYER (IRE)**, 4, ch g Jet Away—Gaye Mercy **Jim and Claire Limited**
62 **SUNNY EXPRESS (IRE)**, 6, b g Jeremy (USA)—Golden Summer (IRE) **McNeill Family and Prodec Networks Ltd**
63 4, B f Kayf Tara—Supreme Present
64 **TALKTOMENOW**, 7, b g Shirocco (GER)—Sweet Stormy (IRE) **Fitorfat Racing**
65 **TIMELESS BEAUTY (IRE)**, 6, b m Yeats (IRE)—Love Divided (IRE) **McNeill Family & Patrick&scott Bryceland**
66 **WELLNTYNE**, 6, b g Multiplex—Captivating Tyna (IRE) **Mr W. Tilley**
67 **WESTERN STARLET (IRE)**, 6, b g Westerner—Pepsi Starlet (IRE) **Mrs J & Miss C Shipp & W Greatrex**
68 **WIND FROM THE WEST**, 4, b f Shirocco (GER)—Free Thinking **Mr R. B. Waley-Cohen**
69 **YOUNG LIEUTENANT (IRE)**, 7, b g Robin des Champs (FR)—Be My Gesture (IRE) **Mrs S. M. Drysdale**

**Other Owners:** AWR Consultancy Ltd, Mr M. J. R. Bannister, Mr N. W. A. Bannister, Mr M. Bartram, Mr T. J. Batting, Mr L. A. Bolingbroke, Mr P Bryceland, Mr S. Bryceland, Mrs P. M. Bunch, Mr B. W. Enright, Mrs J. M. Eynon, R. A. F. Eynon, Mrs Jill Eynon & Mr Robin Eynon, Mr T. R. Gittins, Glassex Holdings Ltd, Mr W. J. Greatrex, Mr M. W. Gregory, Mr M. Helyar, Mr G. P. Howard, K. L. Hunter, Mrs L. Majithia, Mr P. Martin, Mr M. McLoughlin, McNeill Family Ltd, A. W. K. Merriam, Ms H. J. Merriam, Mr P. Molony, Mr K. O'Brien, Odfloors Ltd, Mr F. Ong, Mrs C. R. Orr, Mr J. A. M. Orr, Mr C. M. Parker, Mr M. Parker, Prodec Networks Ltd, K & N Pullen, Mr D. A. Roberts, Mr M. N. Scott, Miss C. S. D. Shipp, Mrs J. Shipp, Mr C. J. Sutton, The Spero Partnership Ltd, Mr D. A. Turner, Mrs N. J. White, Mr S. Williams.

**Assistant Trainer:** Oliver Kozak, **Head Lad:** Trigger Plunkett, Ian Yeates.

**Flat Jockey:** Edward Greatrex. **NH Jockey:** Harry Bannister, Adrian Heskin, Gavin Sheehan. **Conditional Jockey:** Caoilin Quinn. **Apprentice Jockey:** Thomas Greatrex. **Amateur Jockey:** Mr Daniel Kyne.

---

**235**
## MR OLIVER GREENALL, Malpas
Postal: Stockton Hall Farm, Oldcastle, Malpas, Cheshire, SY14 7AE
Contacts: PHONE 01948 861207 MOBILE 07771 571000
EMAIL ocg@stocktonhall.co.uk WEBSITE www.olivergreenall.co.uk

1 **A LARGE ONE PLEASE (FR)**, 6, ch g Planteur (IRE)—Turtledove (FR) **Mr G. Dewhurst**
2 **ACE VENTURA**, 6, b g Mayson—Ventura Highway **Hardscrabble**
3 **ANNAHALLA REBEL (IRE)**, 6, b g Shirocco (GER)—Some Catch (IRE) **Miss N. Jones**
4 **ARCTIC ROAD**, 8, b g Flemensfirth (USA)—Arctic Actress **Mr J. F. Wilson**
5 **ASHARANN (FR)**, 4, b g Zoffany (IRE)—Ashalanda (FR) **E. A. Brook**
6 **AUTHORIZO (FR)**, 6, b g Authorized (IRE)—Street Lightning (FR) **The Deesiders**
7 **BLUE COLLAR GLORY (IRE)**, 4, b f Fame And Glory—Rosy de Cyborg (FR) **Bcc Racing Partnership**
8 **BOSSINEY BAY (IRE)**, 6, b m Camelot—Ursula Minor (IRE) **The Lucky Lovers Partnership II**
9 **CAPTAIN REVELATION**, 9, ch g Captain Rio—Agony Aunt **Cheshire Racing**
10 **CAVE TOP (IRE)**, 9, b g Court Cave—Cyrils Top Girl (IRE) **Lord Daresbury & Jocelyn Rosenburg**
11 **CAWTHORNE**, 7, b g Sulamani (IRE)—Kings Maiden (IRE) **Sheikh Muir, Cossins and Astbury**
12 **CHRIS COOL**, 5, b g Sulamani (IRE)—Cool Friend (IRE) **Evason, Harney & Greenall**
13 **CLONDAW PRETENDER**, 6, br g Great Pretender (IRE)—Shropshire Girl **Peavoy Emdells Daresbury Adams**
14 **CONUNDRUM**, 5, ch g Sir Percy—Famusa **The Conundrum Partnership**
15 **DIEU VIVANT (FR)**, 8, b g Network (GER)—Panique Pas (FR) **Lord Daresbury**
16 **DRAGONFRUIT**, 6, ch g Black Sam Bellamy (IRE)—Fruity Farm **Mrs B. A. Bostock**
17 **ECOSSAIS (FR)**, 7, b g Saddler Maker (IRE)—Sacade (FR) **Oliver Greenall Racing Club**
18 **EL BORRACHO (IRE)**, 6, br g Society Rock (IRE)—Flame of Hibernia (IRE) **El Borracho Syndicate**
19 **ESCALADE (IRE)**, 4, b f Canford Cliffs (IRE)—Sliding Scale **Bcc Racing Partnership**
20 **EVANDER (IRE)**, 6, b g Arcadio (GER)—Blazing Belle (IRE) **Highclere Tbracing Henry Moore & Partner**
21 **FIRST MAN (IRE)**, 6, b g Lilbourne Lad (IRE)—Dos Lunas (IRE) **The Haydock Park Racing Syndicate**
22 **FIVE BAR BRIAN (IRE)**, 7, br g Elusive Pimpernel (USA)—Vayenga (FR) **Deva Racing Five Bar Brian**
23 **FORT DE L'OCEAN (FR)**, 6, b g Racinger (FR)—Iconea (FR) **Hedgehoppers**

## MR OLIVER GREENALL - continued

24 **FRATERCULUS (IRE)**, 4, ch g Teofilo (IRE)—Sanaara (USA) **Coxon, Daresbury, Dewhurst & Macechern**
25 **FURIUS DE CIERGUES (FR)**, 6, gr g Lord du Sud (FR)—Java de Ciergues (FR) **Brook & Daresbury**
26 **GAMESTERS ICON**, 6, b m Sixties Icon—Gamesters Lady **Gamesters Partnership**
27 **GOLD DESERT**, 4, ch g Mastercraftsman (IRE)—Tendency (IRE) **Harbour Rose Partnership**
28 **GOUET DES BRUYERES (FR)**, 5, b g Policy Maker (IRE)—Innsbruck (FR) **Daresbury Buckley Greenall Walsh**
29 **GRAND COUREUR (FR)**, 9, b br g Grand Couturier—Iris du Berlais (FR) **Bostock & Chesters**
30 **GRIS DE PRON (FR)**, 8, b g Gris de Gris (FR)—Say Say (FR) **Mr G. W. Briscoe**
31 **HATS OFF TO LARRY**, 7, b g Sixties Icon—Highland Jig **Mr O. C. Greenall**
32 **HERBIERS (FR)**, 4, b g Waldpark (GER)—Qualanke (FR) **The Nevers Racing Partnership**
33 **HOMME PUBLIC (FR)**, 4, b g Cokoriko (FR)—Uddy (FR) **The Nevers Racing Partnership Ii**
34 **HORACIO APPLE'S (FR)**, 4, ch g Saddex—Apple's Noa (FR) **Highclere Thoroughbred Racing - Apple**
35 **JUST GOT TO GET ON**, 7, ch g Malinas (GER)—Just Cliquot **Mrs C. Swarbrick**
36 **KIMBERLEY**, 4, b f Oasis Dream—Millennium Star (IRE) **Stockton Hall Farm Racing**
37 **KING GYPSY (IRE)**, 6, b br g Court Cave (IRE)—Be My Gypsy (IRE) **Brook, Chesters & Guerriero**
38 **LATE ROMANTIC (IRE)**, 11, b g Mahler—Mere Gaye (IRE) **Spitalized Racing**
39 **LEX TALIONIS (IRE)**, 8, b g Thewayyouare (USA)—Dawn Air (USA) **The Lucky Lovers Partnership III**
40 **LORD COUNTY (FR)**, 7, gr g Lord du Sud (FR)—County County (FR) **E. A. Brook**
41 **LUCKY LOVER BOY (IRE)**, 6, b g Teofilo (IRE)—Mayonga (IRE) **The Lucky Lovers Partnership**
42 **MIDNIGHT MOSS**, 9, ch g Midnight Legend—Brackenmoss (IRE) **Midnight Moss Partnership**
43 **MIGHTY MARVEL (IRE)**, 6, b g Morozov (USA)—Alphablend (IRE) **The Marvel Partnership**
44 **MISS DELIGHTED (IRE)**, 8, b m Getaway (GER)—Abhainn Ri (IRE) **Arkwrightblummichaelsononionsdaresbury**
45 **MISS TARA MOSS**, 6, b m Kayf Tara—Brackenmoss (IRE) **Miss Tara Moss Syndicate**
46 **NORTH POINT**, 4, b g Norse Dancer (IRE)—Cascades (IRE) **Harbour Rose Partnership**
47 **NURIEL (GER)**, 4, b g Nutan (IRE)—Numero Uno (GER) **Adams, Brook, Daresbury & Rosenberg**
48 **OCEANS RED**, 5, ch g Yorgunnabelucky (USA)—Djess **Spitalized Racing**
49 **PHIL DE PAIL (FR)**, 4, gr g Silver Frost (IRE)—Dame de Pail (FR) **Stockton Hall Farm Racing**
50 **RAVING BONKERS**, 4, b g Notnowcato—Harriet's Girl **Oliver's Army**
51 **RED CENTRE (USA)**, 5, ch g Australia—Magical Steps (USA) **E. A. Brook**
52 **SAMBLUCKY**, 5, b g Black Sam Bellamy (IRE)—Jayjay Joules **Mr D. A. Malam**
53 **SHADY CHARACTER**, 8, b g Malinas (GER)—Shady Anne **Jocelyn Rosenberg & Roger Weatherby**
54 **SHAYMIN**, 7, b m Malinas (GER)—Shayzara (IRE) **Mr D. Sherlock**
55 **SOME SPIN (IRE)**, 6, b g Getaway (GER)—Princess Knapping (IRE) **AdamsClarkeCoxonDaresburyMinshawOnions**
56 **SOMEONE YOU LOVE**, 5, b m Schiaparelli (GER)—Perjury **Mr G. Malanga**
57 **STEEL YARD (IRE)**, 6, ch g Frozen Fire (GER)—Banphrionsa (IRE) **Mrs J. Smith**
58 5, B m Gentlewave (IRE)—Sting In The Gale **James and Jean Potter Ltd**
59 **STRONG RESEMBLANCE (IRE)**, 10, b g Tikkanen (USA)—Shenamar (USA) **Oliver's Army**
60 **SUCELLUS**, 5, b g Dansili—Primevere (IRE) **P. G. Evans**
61 **TOP OF THE ROCKS (FR)**, 8, b g Rock of Gibraltar (IRE)—Runaway Top **The Top of The Rocks Syndicate**
62 **TWOTWOTHREE (IRE)**, 8, b g Shantou (USA)—Sibury (IRE) **Evason, Hewitt, Michaelson & Walsh**
63 **VANDEMERE (IRE)**, 6, b g Jeremy (USA)—Victoria Bridge (IRE) **Mr S. Burns**
64 **VEREINA**, 6, b m Universal (IRE)—Lady de La Vega (FR) **Oliver Greenall Racing Club**
65 **WASASTYLEQUEEN**, 6, b m Schiaparelli (GER)—As Was **The Burling Family Ltd**
66 **ZALVADOS (FR)**, 8, ch g Soldier of Fortune (IRE)—Zariyana (IRE) **Mr D. C. Mercer**
67 **ZIP PEARL (IRE)**, 5, b m Milan—Pearl Buttons **Deva Racing Five Bar Brian**

## THREE-YEAR-OLDS

68 **BOUNDSY BOY**, b g Awtaad (IRE)—Wadaat **Mr O. C. Greenall**

**Other Owners:** Mr G. F. C. Adams, Mrs Sandra G. E. Arkwright, Mr M. Astbury, Mrs J. L. Baldwin, Mr W. B. B. Blum Gentilomo, Mrs B. A. Bostock, E. A. Brook, Mr K. J. Buckley, Mr P. J. Chesters, Mr S. A. Coxon, Lord Daresbury, Mr P. A. Davies, Mr G. Dewhurst, Mr K. J. Dodd, Mr B. H. Dolan, Mr S. Evason, Mr O. C. Greenall, Mr J. T. Guerriero, Mr P. J. Harney, Mr N. A. D. Hassall, R. J. Hewitt, Highclere TBred Racing -Henry Moore, Highclere Thoroughbred Racing Ltd, M. B. Jones, Mr M. H. Lampton, Gavin MacEchern, Mr J. McInerney, Exors of the Late Mr R. P. B. Michaelson, Mrs L. J. Midgley, Mr R. J. Nicholas, Mr J. D. Norbury, Mr A. W. Onions, Mr K. J. Roscoe, Mr J. P. Rosenberg, Mr M. Smyth, Steven James Project Management Ltd, Mr D. Studholme, Mr D. J. Walsh, Mr M. S. Walsh, Mr R. N. Weatherby.

**Assistant Trainer:** J. Guerriero.

## 236 MR TOM GRETTON, Inkberrow
Postal: C/o Gretton & Co Ltd, Middle Bouts Farm, Bouts Lane, Inkberrow, Worcester
Contacts: **PHONE 01386 792240 MOBILE 07866 116928 FAX 01386 792472**
**EMAIL** tomgretton@hotmail.co.uk **WEBSITE** www.tomgrettonracing.com

1 **BAGAN**, 7, ch g Sulamani (IRE)—Aunt Rita (IRE)  **Lewis Family & Tom Gretton Racing Club**
2 **BRING THE BACON**, 6, b g Sulamani (IRE)—Grainne Ni Maille  **Mr B. P. Keogh**
3 **COMMITTEE OF ONE**, 6, b m Universal (IRE)—Inkberrow Rose (IRE)  **Lewis Family & Tom Gretton Racing Club**
4 **JOHNNY MAC (IRE)**, 6, b g Imperial Monarch (IRE)—Killowen Pam (IRE)  **Mr M. Slingsby**
5 **KAUTO RIKO (FR)**, 10, b g Ballingarry (IRE)—Kauto Relstar (FR)  **Mr & Mrs J.Dale & Partners**
6 **LICKPENNY LARRY**, 10, gr g Sagamix (FR)—Myriah (IRE)  **Mr A. S. Clarke**
7 **LIGHTNING BLUE**, 4, b f Harbour Watch (IRE)—Blue Beacon  **Mr S. Barraclough**
8 **LINCOLN LYN**, 5, b m Universal (IRE)—Altesse de Sou (FR)  **Mr B. P. Keogh**
9 **ONE LAST GLANCE**, 4, b g Passing Glance—Lillie Lou  **Fred Camis & Ray Fielder**
10 **PASSING SECRETS**, 5, bl g Passing Glance—Tabora  **T. R. Gretton**
11 **PERSUER**, 5, ch m Intello (GER)—Chase The Lady (USA)  **G1 Racing Club Ltd**
12 **PRETTY FANTASY (IRE)**, 5, b m Casamento (IRE)—Pixie Belle (IRE)  **Mr B. P. Keogh**
13 **WILDKATZE (GER)**, 5, b m Kamsin (GER)—Zaynaat  **Tom Gretton Racing Club**
14 **ZORLU (IRE)**, 8, b g Invincible Spirit (IRE)—Special Assignment (USA)  **Didn't Cost A Lot Racing Club**

**Other Owners:** F. D. Camis, Mrs J. S. Dale, Mr J. W. Dale, Mr B. Dennehy, R. Fielder, Mrs L. Gretton, T. R. Gretton, Mr I. M. Lewis, Mr G. C. Parkins, Mr T. Rees, Tom Gretton Racing Club.

**Assistant Trainer:** Laura Gretton.

## 237 MR DAVID GRIFFITHS, Bawtry
Postal: **Martin Hall farm, Martin Common, Bawtry, Doncaster, South Yorkshire, DN10 6DA**
Contacts: **PHONE 01302 714247 MOBILE 07816 924621**
**EMAIL** davidgriffiths250@hotmail.com **WEBSITE** www.davidgriffithsracing.co.uk

1 **ARCHIMEDES (IRE)**, 8, b g Invincible Spirit (IRE)—Waveband  **Ladies & The Tramps**
2 **COOL SPIRIT**, 6, b g Swiss Spirit—Marmot Bay (IRE)  **Mr D. Milthorp**
3 **DE BRUYNE HORSE**, 6, b g Showcasing—Right Rave (IRE)  **A.Turton, Rob Massheder, A.Rhodes & 1**
4 **DUKE OF FIRENZE**, 12, ch g Pivotal—Nannina  **Adlam,Damary-Thompson,Wilson,Griffiths**
5 5, B h Epaulette (AUS)—Enchanted Dream
6 **FALSE ID**, 8, b g Aqlaam—Miss Dutee  **Michael Marsh & Griffiths**
7 **HALTWHISTLE**, 4, b g Phoenix Reach (IRE)—Lookalike  **Mrs S. E. Griffiths**
8 **LEO MINOR (USA)**, 7, b g War Front (USA)—Kissed (IRE)  **Eros Bloodstock**
9 **LUCKY BEGGAR (IRE)**, 11, gr g Verglas (IRE)—Lucky Clio (IRE)  **The Count On Arthur Racing Club & 1**
10 **ORNATE**, 8, b g Bahamian Bounty—Adorn  **Kings Road Racing Partnership**
11 **TERUNTUM STAR (FR)**, 9, ch g Dutch Art—Seralia  **Mrs E. Jepson**

### THREE-YEAR-OLDS

12 **SALSOUL**, b f Kodiac—Goldcrest

### TWO-YEAR-OLDS

13 B f 25/03 Profitable (IRE)—Rancho Montoya (IRE) (High Chaparral (IRE)) (13333)
14 B c 21/02 Iffraaj—White Rosa (IRE) (Galileo (IRE))

**Other Owners:** Mr J. P. Adlam, Mr M. Burton, Mrs S. E. Griffiths, Mr P. Lewis, Mr M. Marsh, Mr R. Massheder, Mr A. Rhodes, Mr J. Slater, Mr A. Turton.

**Assistant Trainer:** Mrs S. E. Griffiths.

**Flat Jockey:** David Allan, Phil Dennis.

## 238  MRS DIANA GRISSELL, Robertsbridge
Postal: Brightling Park, Robertsbridge, East Sussex, TN32 5HH
Contacts: PHONE 01424 838241 MOBILE 07950 312610
EMAIL digrissell@aol.com WEBSITE www.brightlingpark.com

1  BALLINTARA (IRE), 9, b g Getaway (GER)—Miltara (IRE)  Cockerell Cowing Racing
2  COOLADERRY KING (IRE), 13, b g King Cheetah (USA)—Daly Lady (IRE)  Mr C. J. D. Rawdon-Mogg
3  EOS (FR), 7, gr m Martaline—Oreli (FR)  Mrs D. M. Grissell
4  ISKRABOB, 11, ch g Tobougg (IRE)—Honour Bolton  Mrs S. B. Bolton
5  JAPPELOUP (IRE), 12, b br g Presenting—Crackin' Liss (IRE)  Mrs C. A. Bailey
6  MILTON, 9, br g Nomadic Way (USA)—Jesmund  Mrs C. A. Webber
7  WESTTARA, 6, b g Westerner—Miltara (IRE)  Cockerell Cowing Racing

Other Owners: B. J. Cockerell, A. Cowing.

Assistant Trainer: Paul Hacking, Head Girl: Donna French.

Amateur Jockey: Mr James Rawdon-Mogg.

## 239  MR JOHN GROUCOTT, Much Wenlock
Postal: Dairy Cottage, Bourton, Much Wenlock, Shropshire, TF13 6QD
Contacts: PHONE 01746 785603

1  AGAINN DUL AGHAIDH, 10, b g Black Sam Bellamy (IRE)—Star Ar Aghaidh (IRE)  The Wenlock Optimists
2  ALDERSON, 8, b g Zamindar (USA)—Claradotnet  Mr G. D. Kendrick
3  BATTLEFIELD (IRE), 9, b g Central Park (IRE)—Silly Mille (IRE)  Mrs B. Clarke
4  BATTLETANK (IRE), 8, b g Robin des Pres (FR)—Regal Brigade (IRE)  Mrs B. Clarke
5  EL SCORPIO (IRE), 9, b g Scorpion (IRE)—El Monica (IRE)  Mrs B. Clarke
6  HAPPY NEWS, 8, gr m Fair Mix (IRE)—Welcome News  Mrs C. L. Shaw
7  HEDGEBIRD, 7, b m Black Sam Bellamy (IRE)—Morville  Mrs B. Clarke
8  JESSIE LIGHTFOOT (IRE), 7, b m Yeats (IRE)—Needle Doll (IRE)  Mr E. C. Parkes
9  KAYF ANEDA, 6, b m Kayf Tara—Aneda Rose (IRE)
10  LADY MALARKEY (IRE), 6, b m Scorpion (IRE)—Heather Feather (IRE)  Mr E. C. Parkes
11  MUSE OF FIRE (IRE), 7, b g Getaway (GER)—Maria Sophia (IRE)  C. J. Tipton
12  NEWERA, 9, ch g Makfi—Coming Home  Mr D. R. Passant
13  ON THE PLATFORM (IRE), 5, b g Valirann (FR)—Coca's Lady (IRE)  Mrs B. Clarke
14  OVERAWED, 10, b m Overbury (IRE)—Alleged To Rhyme (IRE)  Mrs E. A. Fletcher
15  RICHARDSON, 6, ch g Kirkwall—Makeover  Mr G. D. Kendrick
16  SHININSTAR (IRE), 12, b g Westerner—Shiny Button  Mrs B. Clarke
17  STAR OF RORY (IRE), 7, b g Born To Sea (IRE)—Dame Alicia (IRE)  Mr D. R. Passant & Hefin Williams
18  THE TOOJUMPA, 8, b m Midnight Legend—Sunnyland  The Wenlock Optimists
19  TRUCKERS HIGHWAY (IRE), 12, b g Rudimentary (USA)—Countessdee (IRE)  C. J. Tipton

Other Owners: Mr D. R. Passant, Mr H. Williams.

## 240  MR RAE GUEST, Newmarket
Postal: Chestnut Tree Stables, Hamilton Road, Newmarket, Suffolk, CB8 0NY
Contacts: WORK 01638 661508 MOBILE 07711 301095
EMAIL raeguest@raeguest.com WEBSITE www.raeguest.com

1  ARAMIS GREY (IRE), 4, gr f Gutaifan (IRE)—Sveva (IRE)  The Musketeers
2  ARRIVISTE, 4, b f Sea The Moon (GER)—Apparatchika  Miss K. Rausing
3  CAPE SUNSET, 4, b g Gutaifan (IRE)—Cape Factor (IRE)  Mr D. J. Willis
4  CAPLA BERRY, 5, b m Roderic O'Connor (IRE)—Salsa Brava (IRE)  G. F. L. Robinson

## MR RAE GUEST - continued

5 **CRY HAVOC (IRE)**, 4, b f War Command (USA)—Na Zdorovie **The Musketeers**
6 **FAUVETTE (IRE)**, 4, gr f Dark Angel (IRE)—Falsafa **Mr R. Guest**
7 **GOOD REASON**, 4, gr f Dark Angel (IRE)—Sander Camillo (USA) **The Good Reason Partners**
8 **LAND OF WINTER (FR)**, 5, b g Camelot—Gaselee (USA) **Paul Smith & Rae Guest**
9 **MJOLNIR**, 4, b c Dark Angel (IRE)—Minalisa **C. J. Mills**
10 **ROSA GOLD**, 4, b f Havana Gold (IRE)—Rosa Grace **Top Hat & Tails**
11 **SHEMSA (FR)**, 4, b f Siyouni (FR)—Shemima **Miss K. Rausing**
12 **SQUELCH**, 5, b m Dark Angel (IRE)—Blancmange **Purple & Yellow**
13 **ZARRAR (IRE)**, 6, b g Thewayyouare (USA)—Featherlight **Miss V. Markowiak**

### THREE-YEAR-OLDS

14 **BAHIA STAR**, b f Twilight Son—Bahia Breeze **BB Bloodstock**
15 **CAPE COLUMBUS**, b c Acclamation—Cape Factor (IRE) **Mr D. J. Willis**
16 **COATOFMANYCOLOURS**, gr f Hellvelyn—Madame Lafite **Lady Cecil & Family & Rae Guest**
17 **EMPRESS MAKEDA (IRE)**, b f Sea The Stars (IRE)—Sheba Five (USA) **Mrs S. Rogers, Mr A. P. Rogers**
18 **HOLWAH**, b f Kingman—Shimah (USA) **Mr E. P. Babington**
19 **JEWEL IN MY CROWN**, gr f Mukhadram—Rosa Grace **Mr E. P. Duggan**
20 **MIKASA**, b f Exceed And Excel (AUS)—Minalisa **C. J. Mills**
21 **RITA THE CHEETAH**, b f Prince of Lir (IRE)—Munaawashat (IRE) **Lady Cecil & Family & Rae Guest**
22 **WALKILL (USA)**, b br f Kitten's Joy (USA)—Time Being **Reiko Baum & Michael Baum**
23 **WALTZING QUEEN (IRE)**, b f Helmet (AUS)—Alsaaden **BB Thoroughbreds**

### TWO-YEAR-OLDS

24 **BELLA VENETA**, b f 06/04 Belardo (IRE)—World Class (Galileo (IRE)) (12000) **The Chestnut Tree Syndicate**
25 **DAYS LIKE THIS**, b f 20/04 Iffraaj—Safiyna (FR) (Sinndar (IRE)) (6000) **Mr D. J. Willis**
26 B f 24/01 Outstrip—Glittering Prize (UAE) (Cadeaux Genereux) (800) **Mr R. Guest**
27 **LUNA BREEZE**, b f 03/02 Nathaniel (IRE)—Bahia Breeze (Mister Baileys) **BB Bloodstock**
28 **MELODRAMATICA**, b f 03/04 Bobby's Kitten (USA)—Memory Lane (With Approval (CAN)) **Miss K. Rausing**
29 **MIZZEN YOU**, gr f 12/04 Mizzen Mast (USA)—Preferential (Dansili) (24000) **The Chestnut Tree Syndicate**
30 **RIBTICKLER (IRE)**, b f 24/03 Ribchester (IRE)—
  Folk Singer (Cape Cross (IRE)) (20000) **The Storm Again Syndicate**
31 **ROSIDA**, ch f 09/04 Ribchester (IRE)—
  Chirkova (USA) (Sadler's Wells (USA)) (21000) **The Chestnut Tree Syndicate**
32 **WALTZING INTIME (IRE)**, b f 20/03 Australia—Alsaaden (Acclamation) **BB Thoroughbreds**

**Other Owners:** Mr Michael Baum, Mrs R. Baum, Mr E. P. Duggan, R. T. Goodes, Derek & Rae Guest, Mr R. Guest, Lady Cecil & Family, Sonia M. Rogers & Anthony Rogers, Mr P. J. Smith, Mr B. Stewart.

---

**241**  ## MR RICHARD GUEST, Ingmanthorpe
Postal: Ingmanthorpe Racing Stables, Loshpot Lane, Ingmanthorpe, Wetherby, West Yorkshire, LS22 5HL
Contacts: **PHONE** 07840 112303 **MOBILE** 07398 600270
**WORK EMAIL** enquiries@richardguestracing.co.uk **FACEBOOK** @richardguesthorseracing
**TWITTER** @GuestRacing

1 **AMBITIOUS ICARUS**, 12, b g Striking Ambition—Nesting Box **Mr C. J. Penney**
2 **BREATHOFFRESHAIR**, 7, b g Bated Breath—Stormy Weather **Mr C. J. Penney**
3 4, Pt c Angrove Spottedick—Charlemagne Diva **Mr C. J. Penney**
4 **EXCHEQUER (IRE)**, 10, ch g Exceed And Excel (AUS)—Tara's Force (IRE) **Mr J Toes & Mr J O'Loan**
5 **FAST LIGHT**, 4, b f Fast Company (IRE)—Mylington Light **Mrs A. Kenny**
6 **FOXRUSH TAKE TIME (FR)**, 6, b g Showcasing—Stranded **Mrs A. Kenny**
7 **ISNTSHESOMETHING**, 9, b m Assertive—Princess Almora **Mr C. J. Penney**
8 **LASTMANLASTROUND (IRE)**, 8, b g Azamour (IRE)—Lastroseofsummer (IRE) **Mrs A. Kenny**
9 **MY GIRL MAISIE (IRE)**, 7, b m Fast Company (IRE)—Queen Al Andalous (IRE) **Mrs A. Kenny**
10 **NO CIVIL JUSTICE**, 6, b g Milk It Mick—Flashing Floozie **Mrs A. Kenny**
11 **NOCIVILJUSTICEHERE**, 5, b m Lilbourne Lad (IRE)—Cameo Tiara (IRE) **Mrs A. Kenny**
12 **TELLOVOI (IRE)**, 13, b g Indian Haven—Kloonlara (IRE) **Mrs A. Kenny**

## MR RICHARD GUEST - continued

13 **TREASURED COMPANY (IRE)**, 5, b g Fast Company (IRE)—Lady's Locket (IRE)  **Mr C. J. Penney**
14 **WHATWOULDYOUKNOW (IRE)**, 6, b g Lope de Vega (IRE)—Holamo (IRE)  **Dearing Plastics Ltd & Partner**

### THREE-YEAR-OLDS

15 B g Garswood—Ailsa On My Mind (IRE)  **Mrs A. Kenny**
16 **CIVIL JUSTICE GONE**, b f Finjaan—Modern Lady  **Mrs A. Kenny**
17 **LIVVIE**, b f Ajaya—Fol O'Yasmine  **The Hands & Heels Partnership**
18 **RIGGSBY (IRE)**, b g Acclamation—Silk Affair (IRE)  **The Hands & Heels Partnership**
19 B g Scissor Kick (AUS)—Via Lazio  **Mr C. J. Penney**

### TWO-YEAR-OLDS

20 B f 03/05 Garswood—Ailsa On My Mind (IRE) (Dark Angel (IRE)) (762)  **Mr C. J. Penney**
21 B g 18/04 Intrinsic—Cthulhu (USA) (Henrythenavigator (USA)) (2381)

**Other Owners:** Mr S. Bland, Mr E. Cosgrove, Mr J. J. Cosgrove, Dearing Plastics Ltd, Mr John O'Loan, Mr C. J. Penney, Mr J. Toes.

**Assistant Trainer:** Mr Chris Penney.

---

| 242 | **MS POLLY GUNDRY, Ottery St Mary**<br>Postal: Holcombe Brook, Holcombe Lane, Ottery St Mary, Devon, EX11 1PH<br>Contacts: PHONE 01404 811181 MOBILE 07932 780621<br>EMAIL pollygundrytraining@live.co.uk WEBSITE www.pollygundrytraining.co.uk |
|---|---|

1 **BIG TIME FRANK (IRE)**, 10, b g Bienamado (USA)—Pure Spirit (IRE)  **N Allen & P Bowler**
2 **DANSEUR DU LARGE (FR)**, 8, gr g Martaline—Antagua (FR)  **M James & S Jarrett**
3 **DAWSON CITY**, 12, b g Midnight Legend—Running For Annie  **Kim Franklin & Polly Walker**
4 **DOCTOR DOTTY**, 6, b m Dr Massini (IRE)—Anadama (IRE)  **Mr P. Isaac**
5 **GERTIES GARTER**, 9, b m Getaway (GER)—Chasers Chic  **Mrs A. E. R. Goodwin**
6 **GIO'S GIRL**, 8, ch m Schiaparelli (GER)—Programme Girl (IRE)  **James, Pearn, Shires & Walker**
7 **HOLD ME TIGHT (IRE)**, 7, b g Zoffany (IRE)—All Embracing (IRE)  **Mrs W. J. Jarrett**
8 **MISS HARRIETT**, 5, b m Arvico (FR)—Ivorsagoodun  **Mr P. G. Gibbins**
9 **WEE FLY TOO**, 6, b m Native Ruler—Wee Fly (FR)  **T. R. Oliver**
10 **WHO TOLD YOU**, 8, b m Sulamani (IRE)—Thebelloftheball  **Mr J. P. Selby**
11 **WIND TOR**, 9, b m Midnight Legend—Flowing On  **Mr E. W. Walker**

### THREE-YEAR-OLDS

12 **THE YELLOW MINI**, b f Cannock Chase (USA)—Cheap N Chic  **Exors of the Late Mr M. James**
13 **TOBIE JONES**, b f Cannock Chase (USA)—Triplicity  **Exors of the Late Mr M. James**

**Other Owners:** Mr N. G. Allen, Mr P. O. Bowler, Miss K. M. Franklin, Exors of the Late Mr M. James, Mr S. H. Jarrett, John A. G. Pearn, Mr N. R. Shires, Mrs P. Walker.

**Assistant Trainer:** Edward Walker.

**NH Jockey:** James Best, Nick Schofield. **Amateur Jockey:** Mr Josh Newman.

## 243 MR WILLIAM HAGGAS, Newmarket

Postal: **Somerville Lodge, Fordham Road, Newmarket, Suffolk, CB8 7AA**
Contacts: **PHONE 01638 667013 MOBILE 07860 282281 FAX 01638 660534**
EMAIL **william@somerville-lodge.co.uk** WEBSITE **www.somerville-lodge.co.uk**

1 **A STAR ABOVE**, 4, b g Sea The Stars (IRE)—Loveisallyouneed (IRE) **Sheikh Juma Dalmook Al Maktoum**
2 **ADDEYBB (IRE)**, 7, ch g Pivotal—Bush Cat (USA) **Sheikh Ahmed Al Maktoum**
3 **AJYAALL (FR)**, 4, b g Kingman—Lucrece **Sheikh Ahmed Al Maktoum**
4 **AL AASY (IRE)**, 4, b c Sea The Stars (IRE)—Kitcara **Hamdan Al Maktoum**
5 **AL TARMAAH (IRE)**, 4, b g Muhaarar—How's She Cuttin' (IRE) **Hamdan Al Maktoum**
6 **AL ZARAQAAN**, 4, br c Golden Horn—Asheerah **Hamdan Al Maktoum**
7 **AMETIST**, 4, ch g Dutch Art—Zykina **Cheveley Park Stud**
8 **BOOSALA (IRE)**, 4, b c Dawn Approach—Zoowraa **Sheikh Ahmed Al Maktoum**
9 **BORN WITH PRIDE (IRE)**, 4, b f Born To Sea (IRE)—Jumooh **Sunderland Holding Inc.**
10 **CONVICT**, 4, ch g Australia—Tweed **Mr J. B. Haggas**
11 **CRAVED**, 4, b g Kodiac—Enticing (IRE) **Lael Stable**
12 **FAVORITE MOON (GER)**, 4, b g Sea The Moon (GER)—Favorite (GER) **Saeed Suhail**
13 **FAYLAQ**, 5, b g Dubawi (IRE)—Danedream (GER) **Hamdan Al Maktoum**
14 **HURRICANE IVOR (IRE)**, 4, b g Ivawood (IRE)—Quickstep Queen **Mrs F. J. Carmichael**
15 **ILARAAB (IRE)**, 4, b c Wootton Bassett—Belova (IRE) **Sheikh Ahmed Al Maktoum**
16 **IRISH ADMIRAL (IRE)**, 4, b g French Navy—Magadar (USA) **Sheikh Ahmed Al Maktoum**
17 **JOHAN**, 4, b g Zoffany (IRE)—Sandreamer (IRE) **Jon & Julia Aisbitt**
18 **KETTLE HILL**, 4, b g Gleneagles (IRE)—Sentaril **Lael Stable**
19 **MIDRARR (IRE)**, 4, b f Dubawi (IRE)—Oojooba **Sheikh Ahmed Al Maktoum**
20 **MONTATHAM**, 5, gr g Showcasing—Eastern Destiny **Hamdan Al Maktoum**
21 **MY OBERON (IRE)**, 4, b c Dubawi (IRE)—My Titania (IRE) **Sunderland Holding Inc.**
22 **NAHAARR (IRE)**, 5, b h Dark Angel (IRE)—Charlotte Rua (IRE) **Sheikh Ahmed Al Maktoum**
23 **OTI MA BOATI**, 4, b f Iffraaj—Mania (IRE) **Lael Stable**
24 **PABLO ESCOBARR (IRE)**, 5, b g Galileo (IRE)—Bewitched (IRE) **Mr Hussain Alabbas Lootah**
25 **ROBERTO ESCOBARR (IRE)**, 4, b c Galileo (IRE)—Bewitched (IRE) **Mr Hussain Alabbas Lootah**
26 **SARGASSO SEA**, 4, ch f Sea The Stars (IRE)—Sayyedati Storm (USA) **Bermuda Racing Ltd**
27 **TOM COLLINS**, 4, b g Dubawi (IRE)—Cocktail Queen (IRE) **Mr N. Jonsson**
28 **TOMORROW'S DREAM (FR)**, 4, b f Oasis Dream—Midnight Thoughts (USA) **Apple Tree Stud**
29 **WITH THANKS (IRE)**, 4, b f Camacho—Thanks (IRE) **Sheikh Rashid Dalmook Al Maktoum**

### THREE-YEAR-OLDS

30 **ALANMAR**, b c Siyouni (FR)—America Nova (FR) **Hamdan Al Maktoum**
31 **ALDAARY**, ch g Territories (IRE)—Broughtons Revival **Hamdan Al Maktoum**
32 **ALENQUER (FR)**, b c Adlerflug (GER)—Wild Blossom (GER) **M M Stables**
33 **ALTO VOLANTE**, b c Kingman—Disco Volante **A. E. Oppenheimer**
34 **ARAMAIC (IRE)**, b br c Le Havre (IRE)—Middle Persia **Sheikh Isa Salman**
35 **AROUSING**, b f Kodiac—Enticing (IRE) **Lael Stable**
36 **ARTEMISIA LOMI (IRE)**, b f Galileo (IRE)—Sharp Susan (USA) **Cayton Park Stud Limited**
37 **AUNTY BRIDY**, ch f Camacho—Benedicte (IRE) **Lael Stable**
38 **AWESOMEBYNATURE**, b f Kodiac—Janey Muddles (IRE) **Clarea Au**
39 **BAAEED**, b c Sea The Stars (IRE)—Aghareed (USA) **Hamdan Al Maktoum**
40 **BABINDI**, b br f Frankel—Bantu **Sir P Vela Hon J Broughton Hon P Stanley**
41 **BACHAU**, b g Kodiac—Margaret's Mission (IRE) **Julie & David R Martin & Dan Hall**
42 **BARTZELLA**, b f Golden Horn—Primevere (IRE) **A. E. Oppenheimer**
43 **BASHKIROVA**, b f Pivotal—Russian Finale **Cheveley Park Stud**
44 **BELIEF**, b f Le Havre (IRE)—Elysian **Cheveley Park Stud**
45 **BRECCIA**, b f Intello (GER)—Rock Choir **Cheveley Park Stud**
46 **CANDLEFORD**, b c Kingman—Dorcas Lane **Barnane Stud Ltd**
47 **CHALK STREAM**, b g Sea The Stars (IRE)—Golden Stream (IRE) **Her Majesty The Queen**
48 **CLOUDY DAWN (IRE)**, gr f Kodiac—In The Mist **Mr James Wigan**
49 **COMPANIONSHIP**, b f Galileo (IRE)—Sweet Idea (AUS) **Her Majesty The Queen**
50 **CONSERVATOIRE**, ch f Dutch Art—Piano **Cheveley Park Stud**
51 **CONSTANTA**, b f Camelot—Diala (IRE) **Sheikh Abdulla Al Khalifa**
52 **COOL NIKI (USA)**, gr ro f Flintshire—Mortgage the House (USA) **Qatar Racing Limited**
53 **CRISTAL CLERE (IRE)**, b g Harzand (IRE)—Lady Catherine **G&MRobertsGreenSavidgeWhittal-Williams**

## MR WILLIAM HAGGAS - continued

54 **DHUSHAN (IRE)**, gr c Sea The Stars (IRE)—Causa Proxima (FR)  **Sheikh Ahmed Al Maktoum**
55 **DIAMOND DROP (IRE)**, br f Dansili—El Manati (IRE)  **Sheikh Rashid Dalmook Al Maktoum**
56 **DUBAI HONOUR (IRE)**, b c Pride of Dubai (AUS)—Mondelice  **Mohammed Obaida**
57 **ELVRIKA (IRE)**, b f Kodiac—Villa Royale  **Mr & Mrs R. Scott**
58 **EVIDENT BEAUTY (IRE)**, br f Le Havre (IRE)—Selyl  **Sunderland Holding Inc.**
59 **FIREWORKS (FR)**, b c Kingman—Miss Plimsoll (USA)  **Mrs F. J. Carmichael**
60 **GAASSEE (IRE)**, b c Sea The Stars (IRE)—Oojooba  **Sheikh Ahmed Al Maktoum**
61 **IDOL**, ch f Pivotal—Hightime Heroine (IRE)  **Cheveley Park Stud**
62 **IMPULSIVE ONE (USA)**, b g Union Rags (USA)—Hokey Okey (USA)  **Mr Simon Munir & Mr Isaac Souede**
63 **INTO THE FIRE (FR)**, ch g Intello (GER)—Roman Ridge (FR)  **Mrs F. J. Carmichael**
64 **JUST JACOB (IRE)**, b g Charm Spirit (IRE)—Bari (IRE)  **Ian & Christine Beard & Family**
65 **KAHEALL**, b c Muhaarar—If So  **Sheikh Ahmed Al Maktoum**
66 **KOLISI (IRE)**, b g Harzand (IRE)—Wild Step (GER)  **Mr Graham  Smith-Bernal**
67 **LADY ROCKSTAR**, b f Frankel—Noozhah  **Clipper Group Holdings Ltd**
68 **LANCERO**, b c Iffraaj—Fashion Parade  **Sheikh Abdulla Al Khalifa**
69 **LIGHT REFRAIN**, b f Frankel—Light Music  **Her Majesty The Queen**
70 **LILAC ROAD (IRE)**, ch f Mastercraftsman (IRE)—Lavender Lane (IRE)  **Jon & Julia Aisbitt**
71 **LOCHNAVER**, b f Frankel—Strathnaver  **St Albans Bloodstock Limited**
72 **LOCKERBIE**, ch f New Approach (IRE)—Tweed  **Mr J. B. Haggas**
73 **MAAJDAH (IRE)**, b f Shamardal (USA)—Zoowraa  **Sheikh Ahmed Al Maktoum**
74 **MAHRAJAAN (USA)**, ch c Kitten's Joy (USA)—Lahudood  **Hamdan Al Maktoum**
75 **MAIN EVENT**, b g Frankel—Superstar Leo (IRE)  **Lael Stable**
76 **MARAAKIZ (IRE)**, b c Muhaarar—Entisaar (AUS)  **Hamdan Al Maktoum**
77 **MAYAAS**, gr g Dark Angel (IRE)—Best Terms  **Hamdan Al Maktoum**
78 **MOBAADEL (USA)**, b c Speightstown (USA)—Maggy's Melody (USA)  **Hamdan Al Maktoum**
79 **MOHAAFETH (IRE)**, ch c Frankel—French Dressing  **Hamdan Al Maktoum**
80 **MOJDDEE (IRE)**, ch c Teofilo (IRE)—Vine Street (IRE)  **Sheikh Ahmed Al Maktoum**
81 **MONHAMMER**, b g Awtaad (IRE)—Soviet Terms  **Hamdan Al Maktoum**
82 **MONTASSIB**, ch c Exceed And Excel (AUS)—Felwah  **Mr K. Al Sayegh**
83 **MOORBIK**, b c Iffraaj—Mamma Morton (IRE)  **Sheikh Ahmed Al Maktoum**
84 **MOTAWAAJED (IRE)**, gr g Dark Angel (IRE)—Alaata (USA)  **Hamdan Al Maktoum**
85 **MUHALHEL (IRE)**, b c Lope de Vega (IRE)—Abbagnato  **Mr Saeed Al Qassimi**
86 **MUJTABA**, b c Dubawi (IRE)—Majmu (AUS)  **Hamdan Al Maktoum**
87 **PAGAN (IRE)**, b c Sir Prancealot (IRE)—Style (IRE)  **Mr Graham  Smith-Bernal**
88 **PRIDE OF PRIORY**, b c Pivotal—Millennium Star (IRE)  **Mr T. J. W. Bridge**
89 **READY TO VENTURE**, b f Kingman—Wonderstruck (USA)  **Lael Stable**
90 **RESUMPTION**, ch g Nathaniel (IRE)—Pivotal Drive (IRE)  **Mohammed Obaida**
91 **SACRED**, b f Exceed And Excel (AUS)—Sacre Caroline (USA)  **Cheveley Park Stud**
92 **SAIGON**, b c Frankel—Silk Sari  **Fittocks Stud & Partners**
93 **SANS PRETENTION (IRE)**, b f Galileo (IRE)—Flippant (USA)  **Bernard Kantor & Partner**
94 **SEA EMPRESS (IRE)**, ch f Sea The Stars (IRE)—Tayma (IRE)  **Sunderland Holding Inc.**
95 **SEA IS GOLD (IRE)**, b f Sea The Stars (IRE)—Jumooh  **Sunderland Holding Inc.**
96 **SEA KARATS (IRE)**, b f Sea The Stars (IRE)—Kitcara  **Sunderland Holding Inc.**
97 **SEA LA ROSA (IRE)**, ch f Sea The Stars (IRE)—Soho Rose (IRE)  **Sunderland Holding Inc.**
98 **SEA OSCAR**, b f Sea The Stars (IRE)—Aktoria (FR)  **Sunderland Holding Inc.**
99 **SEA SPEEDWELL**, ch f Sea The Stars (IRE)—Flower Market  **Sunderland Holding Inc.**
100 **SEA SYLPH (IRE)**, ch f Sea The Stars (IRE)—Valais Girl  **Sunderland Holding Inc.**
101 **SECRET HAUNT**, b f Dubawi (IRE)—Enticement  **Her Majesty The Queen**
102 **SHAMARDALAH**, ch f Shamardal (USA)—Mardie Gras  **Sheikh Juma Dalmook Al Maktoum**
103 **SKULK**, b f Kingman—Slink  **Mr James Wigan**
104 **SKYRUNNER (IRE)**, b c Invincible Spirit (IRE)—Maidservant (USA)  **Mr Graham  Smith-Bernal**
105 **SKYTREE**, b f Dark Angel (IRE)—Tiptree (IRE)  **Mr & Mrs M. Morris**
106 **SPIRIT OF BERMUDA (IRE)**, b f Twilight Son—Laqataat (IRE)  **Bermuda Racing Ltd**
107 **SUBSTANTIAL**, b br c Siyouni (FR)—Sentaril  **Lael Stable**
108 **SWEET BELIEVER (IRE)**, b f Make Believe—Olivia Pope (IRE)  **Sheikh Rashid Dalmook Al Maktoum**
109 **TARAASHOQ (GER)**, b g Maxios—Tassina (GER)  **Hamdan Al Maktoum**
110 **TARHIB (IRE)**, b f Dark Angel (IRE)—Allez Alaia (IRE)  **Hamdan Al Maktoum**
111 **TITIAN (IRE)**, b g Iffraaj—Lucelle (IRE)  **Mr Michael Buckley**
112 **USLOOB (IRE)**, b c Invincible Spirit (IRE)—Thawaany (IRE)  **Hamdan Al Maktoum**
113 **VIOLET WARDA (IRE)**, b f Kodiac—Warda  **Sheikh Juma Dalmook Al Maktoum**

# MR WILLIAM HAGGAS - continued

114 **VISALA**, b f Exceed And Excel (AUS)—Visoliya (FR) **Miss Y. M. G. Jacques**
115 **YAZAMAN (IRE)**, b g Kodiac—Online Alexander (IRE) **Sheikh Ahmed Al Maktoum**
116 **YOJAARI**, b c Iffraaj—Khatiba (IRE) **Sheikh Ahmed Al Maktoum**
117 **ZENITH (IRE)**, gr c Invincible Spirit (IRE)—Freezy (IRE) **Highclere Tbred Racing-Charlie Langton**

## TWO-YEAR-OLDS

118 Ch f 11/03 Iffraaj—Adjudicate (Dansili) (45000) **Sheikh Rashid Dalmook Al Maktoum**
119 Ch c 30/05 Lope De Vega—Alaata (Smart Strike) **Hamdan Al Maktoum**
120 B c 26/02 Dubawi (IRE)—Alshadhia (Marju) **Hamdan Al Maktoum**
121 Gr br c 11/02 Dark Angel—Alwarga (Street Sense) (USA) **Sheikh Ahmed Al Maktoum**
122 **AMANZOE (IRE)**, b f 29/04 Fastnet Rock (AUS)—Starship (IRE) (Galileo) (IRE)) **The Starship Partnership Ii**
123 B f 29/04 Sea The Stars (IRE)—Angel of The Gwaun (IRE) (Sadler's Wells (USA)) **Mr Neil Jones**
124 B f 05/03 Kodiac—Areeda (IRE) (Refuse To Bend (IRE)) **Hamdan Al Maktoum**
125 B c 10/04 Kingman—Bargain Buy (Tamayuz) **Sheikh Rashid Dalmook Al Maktoum**
126 B f 10/03 Frankel—Besharah (Kodiac) **Sheikh Rashid Dalmook Al Maktoum**
127 **CANONIZED**, b f 10/02 Acclamation—Sainted (Dutch Art) **Cheveley Park Stud**
128 **CANTERBURY BELL (IRE)**, b f 01/04 Ribchester (IRE)—Lavender Lane (IRE) (Shamardal (USA)) **Jon & Julia Aisbitt**
129 **CARYATID**, b f 09/03 Intello (GER)—Spacious (Nayef (USA)) **Cheveley Park Stud**
130 **CLEAR DAY (FR)**, b c 19/01 Camelot—Dawn Glory (Oasis Dream) **Her Majesty The Queen**
131 B c 09/03 Showcasing—Cloud Line (Danehill Dancer) **Lael Stable**
132 Ch f 07/03 Shamardal (USA)—Cristal Fizz (IRE) (Power) **Sheikh Juma Dalmook Al Maktoum**
133 B f 12/02 Iffraaj—Dawn Horizons (New Approach (IRE)) (90000) **Sheikh Juma Dalmook Al Maktoum**
134 B f 06/03 Lawman—Debuetatin (Big Shuffle) **Sheikh Isa Salman**
135 B f 09/03 Kodiac—Deleyla (Acclamation) **Sheikh Ahmed Al Maktoum**
136 **EDUCATOR**, br c 04/02 Deep Impact (JPN)—Diploma (Dubawi (IRE)) **Her Majesty The Queen**
137 Ch c 25/02 Lope De Vega—Effervesce (Galileo) **Sheikh Isa Salman**
138 **ENSHRINE**, b f 03/04 Ulysses—Sacre Caroline (Blame) **Cheveley Park Stud**
139 B f 14/03 Dark Angel (IRE)—Entisaar (More Than Ready) **Hamdan Al Maktoum**
140 B f 23/01 Muhaarar—Etaab (Street Cry) **Hamdan Al Maktoum**
141 Ch f 27/02 Galileo (IRE)—Ferdoos (Dansili) **Sheikh Ahmed Al Maktoum**
142 **FOOTSY**, ch c 12/05 Siyouni (FR)—Barter (Daylami (IRE)) **Fittocks Stud & White Birch Farm**
143 B c 21/03 Muhaarar—Front House (IRE) (Sadler's Wells (USA)) (38000) **Mr J. B. Haggas**
144 **GLORY AND GOLD**, b f 20/02 Havana Gold—Grace And Glory (Montjeu) **Mr Nicholas Jones**
145 Ch c 18/03 Havana Gold (IRE)—Granola (Makfi) (70000) **Saeed Suhail**
146 **HAMAKI (IRE)**, b c 19/04 Churchill (IRE)—Sarawati (IRE) (Haafhd) (142857) **Mr Simon Munir & Mr Isaac Souede**
147 **HELLO SYDNEY (IRE)**, b c 26/02 Zoffany—Queen of Stars (Green Desert) **Mr Abdulla Belhabb**
148 **HOLOCENE**, ch f 04/04 Ulysses—Heaven Sent (Pivotal) **Cheveley Park Stud**
149 **HURRY UP HEDLEY (IRE)**, b c 26/03 Mehmas (IRE)—
    Forevertwentyone (IRE) (Approve (IRE)) (23810) **Ian & Christine Beard & Family**
150 **ICE HOUSE**, ch f 21/02 Ulysses (IRE)—Ice Palace (Polar Falcon) (USA) **Cheveley Park Stud**
151 **ICYKEL (IRE)**, ch f 22/02 Frankel—Cold As Ice (Western Winter) **Barnane Stud Ltd**
152 B f 12/03 Lope De Vega—Inchmarlow (Galileo) **Hamdan Al Maktoum**
153 **IRISH MILLIONS**, ch c 16/02 Profitable (IRE) (Halling (USA)) (60000) **Mr T. J. W. Bridge**
154 **IRRESISTABLE**, gr f 19/02 Dark Angel (IRE)—Sommesnil (King's Best (USA)) **Miss Y. M. G. Jacques**
155 **JUST A TAD**, b f 30/04 Intello (GER)—Tadpole (Sir Percy) (7000) **Ian & Christine Beard & Family**
156 **KING OF ICE**, ch c 25/03 Ulysses (IRE)—Queen of Ice (Selkirk (USA)) (60000) **Cheveley Park Stud**
157 B f 03/05 Farhh—Kitty For Me (Pour Moi (IRE)) (125000) **Sheikh Rashid Dalmook Al Maktoum**
158 Gr f 05/02 Dark Angel (IRE)—La Rioja (Hellvyln) **Qatar Racing Limited**
159 Ch c 22/03 Farhh—Local Spirit (USA) (Lion Cavern (USA)) (35000) **Sheikh Juma Dalmook Al Maktoum**
160 **LUIS FERNANDO**, gr c 19/02 Australia—Bewitched (IRE) (Dansili) (71429) **Mr Abdulla Hussain Lootah**
161 **LYSANDER**, br c 04/02 New Approach (IRE)—
    Darting (Shamardal (USA)) (120000) **Highclere Thoroughbred Racing - Beehives**
162 B br f 05/03 Showcasing—Margaret's Mission (IRE) (Shamardal (USA)) **St Albans Bloodstock Limited**
163 **MARMALASHES (IRE)**, ch f 04/04 Australia—Marmalady (Duke of Marmalade (IRE)) **Barnane Stud Ltd**
164 B f 25/03 Storm The Stars (USA)—Miss Carbonia (IRE) (Lilbourne Lad (IRE)) **Sheikh Juma Dalmook Al Maktoum**
165 B f 13/02 Nathaniel (IRE)—Miss Pinkerton (Danehill (USA)) (80000) **Mr Abdulla Belhabb**
166 Ch c 15/02 Frankel—Muffri'Ha (IRE) (Iffraaj) **Sheikh Juma Dalmook Al Maktoum**
167 B c 05/04 Siyouni—Musaanada (Sea The Stars) **Hamdan Al Maktoum**
168 B c 21/04 Nathaniel—My Special J's (Harlan's Holiday) **Sheikh Isa Salman**

## MR WILLIAM HAGGAS - continued

169 B c 23/02 Kodiac—Naafer (Oasis Dream) **Hamdan Al Maktoum**
170 B c 24/04 Kodiac—Nations Alexander (IRE) (Dark Angel (IRE)) (300000) **Hamdan Al Maktoum**
171 **NUANCE**, b c 25/01 Frankel—Intimation (Dubawi) **Cheveley Park Stud**
172 B c 09/04 Iffraaj—Oojooba (Monsun (GER)) **Sheikh Ahmed Al Maktoum**
173 **PERFECT ALIBI**, b f 23/02 Le Havre (IRE)—Daphne (Duke of Marmalade (IRE)) **Her Majesty The Queen**
174 **PERSIST**, b f 18/01 Frankel—Persuasive (IRE) (Dark Angel (IRE)) **Cheveley Park Stud**
175 B f 21/04 Almanzor (FR)—Plume Rose (Marchand de Sable (USA)) (95000) **St Albans Bloodstock Limited**
176 B c 09/03 Sea The Stars—Polly's Mark (Mark of Esteem) **Sheikh Isa Salman/M.Morris/S.Scupham**
177 B f 07/03 Kodiac—Qatar Power (FR) (Le Havre (IRE)) (193705) **Qatar Racing Limited**
178 **RAOUL DUFY**, b c 05/04 Havana Gold (IRE)—Lisiere (IRE) (Excellent Art) (15000) **Mr R. Green**
179 B f 24/02 Kingman—Rekdhat (Shamardal) **Sheikh Ahmed Al Maktoum**
180 Ch f 15/02 Frankel—Remember You (IRE) (Invincible Spirit (IRE)) (133333) **Sheikh Juma Dalmook Al Maktoum**
181 B f 21/03 Shamardal—Saraha (Dansili) **Hamdan Al Maktoum**
182 **SCATTERING**, b c 18/01 Showcasing—Seed Corn (Exceed And Excel (AUS)) **Mr Nicholas Jones**
183 **SEA THE SEVEN**, b f 01/02 Sea The Stars (IRE)—Nadia Glory (Oasis Dream) (85000) **Mr Graham Smith-Bernal**
184 B c 24/03 Shamardal (USA)—Sealife (IRE) (Sea The Stars (IRE)) **Sheikh Juma Dalmook Al Maktoum**
185 **SECOND WIND (IRE)**, b c 28/01 Kodiac—Princess Janie (USA) (Elusive Quality (USA)) (75000) **Wrigleys & Wyatts**
186 B f 01/02 Oasis—Sharqeyih (Shamardal) **Hamdan Al Maktoum**
187 B f 24/03 Oasis Dream—Shingwedzi (SAF) (Trippi (USA)) **Cayton Park Stud Limited**
188 B f 13/02 Frankel—Soundstrings (Oasis Dream) **Lael Stable**
189 **SPANISH (IRE)**, ch f 08/03 Lope de Vega (IRE)—Czabo (Sixties Icon) (135000) **Sheikh Isa Salman**
190 B c 22/03 Australia—Star Search (Zamindar (USA)) (60000) **Mr N. Jonsson**
191 B c 19/03 Havana Gold—Superstar Leo (College Chapel) **Lael Stable**
192 B c 14/04 Galileo (IRE)—Sweet Idea (AUS) (Snitzel (AUS)) **Her Majesty The Queen**
193 B c 07/02 Time Test—Tebee's Oasis (Oasis Dream) (120000) **Sheikh Ahmed Al Maktoum**
194 **TIBER FLOW (IRE)**, br gr c 16/04 Caravaggio (USA)—Malabar (Raven's Pass (USA)) **Jon & Julia Aisbitt**
195 B c 01/05 Invincible Spirit (IRE)—Tutu Nguru (USA) (Blame (USA)) **Sheikh Juma Dalmook Al Maktoum**
196 B f 10/05 Almanzor (FR)—Vivacity (Trempolino (USA)) (180000) **Bermuda Racing Ltd**
197 B c 31/03 Siyouni—Wonderstruck (Sea The Stars) **Lael Stable**

**Assistant Trainer:** Josh Hamer, Andy McIntyre, Isabella Paul.

---

## 244 MR ALEX HALES, Edgecote
Postal: **Trafford Bridge Stables, Edgecote, Banbury, Oxfordshire, OX17 1AG**
Contacts: PHONE **01295 660131** MOBILE **07771 511652** FAX **01295 660128**
EMAIL **alex@alexhalesracing.co.uk** WEBSITE **www.alexhalesracing.co.uk**

1 **BOURBON BEAUTY**, 6, b m Great Pretender (IRE)—It Doesn't Matter **Old Stoics Racing Club 2**
2 **CEARA BE (IRE)**, 8, b m Oscar (IRE)—Pearl's A Singer (IRE) **Mr P. J. Byrne**
3 **CRONK Y KNOX (IRE)**, 6, gr g Cloudings (IRE)—Exit Baby (IRE) **Mr D. L. Simkins**
4 **DIRTY DANCER (FR)**, 4, b f No Nay Never (USA)—Super Marmelade (IRE) **Westerberg**
5 **DON'T ASK (IRE)**, 8, b g Ask—Outback Ivy (IRE) **Gumbrills Racing Partnership**
6 **DOWNBYTHESTRAND (IRE)**, 12, b g Vertical Speed (FR)—Fancyfacia (IRE) **Mrs C. E. Osborne**
7 **FAGAN**, 11, gr g Fair Mix (IRE)—Northwood May **Mr B. E. Brackenbury**
8 **FLORRIE KNOX (IRE)**, 8, gr g Gold Well—Miss Orphan (FR) **The Fortune Hunters**
9 **FLOW AWAY (IRE)**, 7, br m Stowaway—Water Rock **Mr N Rodway & Partner**
10 **FOR PLEASURE (IRE)**, 6, ch g Excelebration (IRE)—Darsan (IRE) **Premier Plastering (UK) Limited**
11 **GET YOUR OWN (IRE)**, 6, b br g Getaway (GER)—Western Girl **The The Get Your Own Racing Partnership**
12 **GONE IN SIXTY**, 4, b g Sixties Icon—Gib (IRE) **Golden Equinox Racing**
13 **GOVERNOR GREEN (IRE)**, 4, b g Aiken—Little Green (IRE) **The Fortune Hunters**
14 **HAS TROKE (FR)**, 4, b g Masterstroke (USA)—Shifa (FR)
15 **HICONIC**, 4, b f Sixties Icon—Hi Note **Golden Equinox Racing & Partner**
16 **HUNTSMAN SON (IRE)**, 11, b g Milenary—Daly Lady (IRE) **Mrs W. M. Wesley**
17 **JIMMI CHEW (IRE)**, 8, br g Jimble (FR)—Katie Baby (IRE) **Mr B. E. Brackenbury**
18 **JONJOELA (IRE)**, 10, b m Great Exhibition (USA)—Yorkshire Blade (IRE) **In The Pink Partnership**

# MR ALEX HALES - continued

19 **JUST MARVIN (IRE)**, 8, b g Atraf—Gailybay Ellen (IRE)  **Mr S. Brown**
20 **KANKIN**, 5, ch g Archipenko (USA)—Touriga  **Mr A. L. Cohen**
21 **MARIA MAGDALENA (IRE)**, 5, b m Battle of Marengo (IRE)—Few Words  **The Problem Solvers**
22 **METHAG (FR)**, 8, b m Pour Moi (IRE)—Kyria  **The One For Us**
23 **MILLERS BANK**, 7, b g Passing Glance—It Doesn't Matter  **Millers Bank Partnership**
24 4, B f Presenting—Mtpockets (IRE)  **Edging Ahead**
25 **ONE IN ALL IN (IRE)**, 8, b g Lawman (FR)—Albaiyda (IRE)  **Edging Ahead**
26 **PETITE DAME (IRE)**, 5, b m Shantou (USA)—Offside Rule (IRE)  **Edging Ahead**
27 **ROUGH NIGHT (IRE)**, 8, b g Doyen (IRE)—Sunny Bob (IRE)  **Miss P. M. Morris**
28 **SAY NOTHING**, 5, b m Nathaniel (IRE)—I Say (IRE)  **The The Silent Partners**
29 **SEA PRINCE**, 5, b g Born To Sea (IRE)—Briery (IRE)  **The Sea Prince Racing Partnership**
30 **SHIROCCSMYWORLD (IRE)**, 6, ch m Shirocco (GER)—Phillis Hill  **Golden Equinox Racing**
31 **SMOOTH STEPPER**, 12, b g Alflora (IRE)—Jazzy Refrain (IRE)  **Mr B. E. Brackenbury**
32 **SPLINTER**, 4, b g Garswood—Cracking Lass (IRE)  **The Carpenters**
33 **STACEY SUE**, 8, b m Robin des Champs (FR)—Antonia Hall (IRE)  **The The Backburners**
34 **SUN RISING HILL (IRE)**, 5, b g Mahler—Mini Karinga  **Mr B. E. Brackenbury**
35 **SWILLY SUNSET**, 8, b g Kyllachy—Spanish Springs (IRE)  **In The Pink Partnership**
36 **TICKET TO L A (IRE)**, 6, b m Westerner—In Bloom (IRE)  **Golden Equinox Racing & Partner**
37 **TIME FOR TIMONE (IRE)**, 6, b g Mahler—Letterwoman (IRE)  **Mr B. E. Brackenbury**
38 **WUN WUN**, 4, b f Power—Elizabeth Coffee (IRE)

## THREE-YEAR-OLDS

39 **DI BELLO ROSA (IRE)**, b f Belardo (IRE)—Toolentidhaar (USA)  **Golden Equinox Racing**
40 **DRAGON'S FIRE**, b g Equiano (FR)—Annawi  **Millard Charter Chapman Pearce & Partner**
41 **FAMILY TIME**, b g Excelebration (IRE)—Porcini  **Mr B. E. Brackenbury**
42 **INCLEMENT WEATHER**, b f Bated Breath—Rapid Recruit (IRE)  **Golden Equinox Racing**

Other Owners: Mr C. Bennett, Mr S. Bocking, Mr S. Brown, Miss S. E. Burnell, Golden Equinox Racing, Mr A. M. Hales, Millard, Charter, Chapman, Mr N. Rodway, Mr C. J. Woods.

---

**245**

# MR MICHAEL HALFORD, Kildare
Postal: **Copper Beech Stables, Doneaney, Kildangan Road, Kildare, Co. Kildare, R51 TC79, Ireland**
Contacts: **WORK +353 45 526 119 MOBILE +353 87 257 9204 WORK FAX +353 45 526 157
WORK EMAIL info@michaelhalford.com WEBSITE www.michaelhalford.com**

1 **ANYONECANHAVEITALL**, 5, b g Nathaniel (IRE)—Floriade (IRE)  **Mr Garrett Freyne**
2 **ARCANEARS (IRE)**, 6, b g Arcano (IRE)—Ondeafears (IRE)  **Mrs Caroline Roper**
3 **ARDLA (IRE)**, 6, b g Delegator—Tamaletta (IRE)  **Ms Fiona Wentges**
4 **EAGLE'S FLIGHT (IRE)**, 4, b g Gleneagles (IRE)—Love Excelling (FR)  **Mr John Connaughton**
5 **EYE OF THE DRAGON (IRE)**, 5, b m Dragon Pulse (IRE)—Jiran (IRE)  **Mr Evan Newell, Ms Linda Pullman**
6 **FINANS BAY (IRE)**, 4, b c Kodiac—Wrood (USA)  **Mr N Hartery**
7 **GOLDEN TWILIGHT (IRE)**, 4, b g Dawn Approach (IRE)—Great Hope (IRE)  **Mr F W Lynch**
8 **GOUGANE BARRA (USA)**, 7, b br g First Defence (USA)—Beiramar (IRE)  **Mr P Rooney**
9 **HODD'S GIRL (IRE)**, 4, gr f Zebedee—Ms Inkonia Hodd (IRE)  **Rocky Horror Partnership**
10 **ILLUSORY (IRE)**, 4, b f Make Believe—Ezalli (IRE)  **Ballylinch Stud**
11 **KATIYMANN (IRE)**, 9, b g Shamardal (USA)—Katiyra (IRE)  **Mr P Rooney**
12 **LADY DE VESCI (IRE)**, 8, ch m Approve (IRE)—La Bandola (GER)  **Anita Soros & John Keogh**
13 **LORD PARK (IRE)**, 4, b c Tamayuz—Hammiya (IRE)  **Mr Garrett Freyne**
14 **MASSIF CENTRAL (IRE)**, 7, b g Arcano (IRE)—Melaaya (USA)  **Mr P Rooney**
15 **OVERTAKE**, 4, gr g Outstrip—Winterbourne  **Mrs L Halford**
16 **SENDMYLOVETOYOU (IRE)**, 5, b m Invincible Spirit (IRE)—Sendmylovetorose  **Mr M Enright**
17 **SHAMIYAN (IRE)**, 5, b g Lope de Vega (IRE)—Shamooda (IRE)  **Mr R. McNally**
18 **SHEDINI (IRE)**, 4, b g Siyouni (FR)—Shebella (IRE)  **Mr R. McNally**
19 **SIENNA LADY (IRE)**, 4, b f Lope de Vega (IRE)—Paimpolaise (IRE)  **Mr M Enright**
20 **SINDHIA (IRE)**, 4, b f Mastercraftsman (IRE)—Sinaniya (USA)  **H. H. Aga Khan**

## MR MICHAEL HALFORD - continued

21 **SLIEVE BEARNAGH (IRE)**, 4, b c Zoffany (IRE)—Angels Story (IRE) **Mr P Rooney**
22 **SPELGA**, 5, b g Sir Percy—Emma's Gift (IRE) **Mr P Rooney**
23 **SURROUNDING (IRE)**, 8, b m Lilbourne Lad (IRE)—Roundabout Girl (IRE) **Mr P E I Newell**
24 **TIRMIZI (FR)**, 8, b g Sea The Stars (IRE)—Timabiyra (IRE) **Mr P Rooney**
25 **TURBO COMMAND (IRE)**, 4, gr g War Command (USA)—The Tempest **Mr Sammy Hon Kit Ma**
26 **WAR DIARY**, 6, b g Declaration of War (USA)—Titivation **Mr P Rooney**
27 **WITHBATEDBREATH (IRE)**, 4, b c Bated Breath—Starlight Symphony (IRE) **Withbatedbreath Partnership**

## THREE-YEAR-OLDS

28 **BARON ZEE (IRE)**, gr c Zoffany (IRE)—Callistan (IRE) **Castle Beech Partnership**
29 **BEAR STORY (IRE)**, b c Kodiac—Angels Story (IRE) **Mr John Connaughton**
30 **BOOK OF VERSE (USA)**, ch c Curlin (USA)—Silvester Lady **Mrs W O'Leary**
31 **BRIGHT GLORY GB**, br c Starspangledbanner (AUS)—Luminance (IRE) **Castle Beech Partnership**
32 **CIAO NAW (IRE)**, b f Rock of Gibraltar (IRE)—High Society Girl (IRE) **Mr Nasir Askar**
33 **COLLEEN'S PRINCE (IRE)**, b g Prince of Lir (IRE)—Blondie's Esteem (IRE) **Mr Brian Gallivan**
34 **DIAMIL (IRE)**, b c Awtaad (IRE)—Diylawa (IRE) **H. H. Aga Khan**
35 **EBASARI (IRE)**, b c Lope de Vega (IRE)—Ebayya (IRE) **H. H. Aga Khan**
36 **ELZAAMSAN (IRE)**, b c Elzaam (AUS)—Lady Conway (USA) **Castle Beech Partnership**
37 **ETERNAL CLASSIC (IRE)**, gr c Free Eagle (IRE)—Kapera (FR) **Eternal Classic Partnership**
38 **FARAWAY DREAMS (IRE)**, ch f Pride of Dubai (AUS)—Airline Hostess (IRE) **Mr John Connaughton**
39 **HAKIMPOUR (IRE)**, b g Muhaarar—Hanakiyya (IRE) **H. H. Aga Khan**
40 **HAZIYA (IRE)**, br f Le Havre (IRE)—Hazaraba (IRE) **H. H. Aga Khan**
41 **INDIGO DESERT (IRE)**, b c Exceed And Excel (AUS)—Ghany (IRE) **Castle Beech Partnership**
42 **JE T'AI PORTE (IRE)**, b f Footstepsinthesand—Hasanza (USA) **Mrs L Halford**
43 **KALAROUN (IRE)**, b c Starspangledbanner (AUS)—Karalara (IRE) **H. H. Aga Khan**
44 **KARATAYKA (IRE)**, b f Dariyan (FR)—Karamaya (IRE) **H. H. Aga Khan**
45 **KARISSIA (IRE)**, b f Olympic Glory (IRE)—Kerisa (IRE) **H. H. Aga Khan**
46 **LET ME PASS (IRE)**, ch c Raven's Pass (USA)—City Vaults Girl (IRE) **Mr Nasir Askar**
47 **MAZYAD (IRE)**, b c Fastnet Rock (AUS)—Masiyma (IRE) **H. H. Aga Khan**
48 **OTAY (IRE)**, b c Elzaam (AUS)—Love Note (USA) **Ms Leah Halford**
49 **PRINCE ABAMA (IRE)**, ch c Tamayuz—Abama Lady (CAN) **Castle Beech Partnership**
50 **RAYADIYR (IRE)**, b c Gleneagles (IRE)—Raydiya (IRE) **H. H. Aga Khan**
51 **RAYAGARA (IRE)**, b f Dark Angel (IRE)—Raydara (IRE) **H. H. Aga Khan**
52 **ROSA DARTLE (IRE)**, ch f Territories (IRE)—Batiste **Mrs Kathleen Whelan**
53 **ROZIYNA (IRE)**, b f Sea The Stars (IRE)—Rayisa (IRE) **H. H. Aga Khan**
54 **SILAIYLI (IRE)**, b c Olympic Glory (IRE)—Sinaniya (USA) **H. H. Aga Khan**
55 B f Mount Nelson—Slipper Orchid (IRE) **Mrs Caroline Roper**
56 **SMART 'N' DANDY (IRE)**, ch g Dandy Man (IRE)—Musaadaqa (IRE) **Castle Beech Partnership**
57 **STELLAR SPIRIT (IRE)**, b g Charm Spirit (IRE)—Sharp Relief (IRE) **Castle Beech Partnership**
58 **TOO NICE (IRE)**, ch c Night of Thunder (IRE)—Pixie Belle (IRE) **Mr Nasir Askar**
59 **WYCHWOOD WHISPER (IRE)**, b f Belardo (IRE)—Paimpolaise (IRE) **Mr M Enright**
60 **ZAYNUDIN (IRE)**, b c Fastnet Rock (AUS)—Zanoubiya (IRE) **H. H. Aga Khan**
61 **ZURKHANA (IRE)**, b f Helmet (AUS)—Zunera (IRE) **H. H. Aga Khan**
62 **ZYRIANNA (IRE)**, b f Footstepsinthesand—Zariyna (IRE) **H. H. Aga Khan**

## TWO-YEAR-OLDS

63 **ASKARABAD (IRE)**, b c 30/01 Fast Company (IRE)—Askeria (IRE) (Sadler's Wells (USA)) **H. H. Aga Khan**
64 **CEALLACH (IRE)**, ch c 13/05 Lope de Vega (IRE)—Alvee (IRE) (Key of Luck (USA)) (25000) **Mr P Rooney**
65 Ch c 28/04 Profitable (IRE)—Dancing Years (IRE) (Iffraaj) (43810) **Castle Beech Partnership**
66 Ch c 06/04 No Nay Never (USA)—Duchessofflorence (Pivotal) **Mr M Enright**
67 B f 22/04 Camelot—Golden Pearl (Oasis Dream) **Mr M Enright**
68 **HEZAHUNK (IRE)**, b c 09/05 Fast Company (IRE)—Temecula (IRE) (High Chaparral (IRE)) **Mr M Enright**
69 **KAMPALA BEACH (IRE)**, b c 20/04 Belardo (IRE)—Translator (IRE) (Choisir (AUS)) **Mr M Phelan**
70 **LUV TURBO (IRE)**, b c 05/02 Decorated Knight—Katch Me Katie (Danehill (USA)) (10000) **Mr Sammy Hon Kit Ma**
71 B c 18/04 Charm Spirit (IRE)—Masiyma (IRE) (Dalakhani (IRE)) **H. H. Aga Khan**
72 Bl c 08/02 Le Havre (IRE)—Pirita (IRE) (Invincible Spirit (IRE)) **Mr N Hartery**
73 B c 17/02 Clodovil (IRE)—Queenie Keen (IRE) (Refuse To Bend (IRE)) **Mr N Hartery**
74 B c 26/02 Coulsty (IRE)—Ranallagh Rocket (IRE) (Acclamation) **Mr N Hartery**
75 B c 15/03 Churchill (IRE)—Raydiya (IRE) (Marju (IRE)) **H. H. Aga Khan**

## MR MICHAEL HALFORD - continued

76 **RIYAMI (IRE)**, b c 27/02 Fastnet Rock (AUS)—Riyaba (IRE) (Dalakhani (IRE)) **H. H. Aga Khan**
77 **SILVER TURBO (IRE)**, gr c 05/02 Gleneagles (IRE)—
Bright Snow (USA) (Gulch (USA)) (33333) **Mr Sammy Hon Kit Ma**
78 **TURBO TWO (IRE)**, b c 12/05 Holy Roman Emperor (IRE)—
Swish (GER) (Monsun (GER)) (57143) **Mr Sammy Hon Kit Ma**

**Assistant Trainer:** Fabian Burke.

**Flat Jockey:** Niall McCullagh, Ronan Whelan. **Apprentice Jockey:** Adam Farraghar, Ada Higgins Corrigan, Ciaran Moody.
**Amateur Jockey:** Mr Evan Halford.

---

**246** **MRS DEBRA HAMER, Carmarthen**
Postal: **Bryngors Uchaf, Nantycaws, Carmarthen, Dyfed, SA32 8EY**
Contacts: **HOME 01267 234585 MOBILE 07980 665274**
EMAIL hamerracing@hotmail.co.uk

1 **GLOI**, 10, b m Overbury (IRE)—Go Gwenni Go **Nick Youngman Nicola Cooper**
2 **JAC BROWN**, 7, b g Multiplex—Do It On Dani **The Hamers**
3 **LAYERTHORPE (IRE)**, 9, b bl g Vale of York (IRE)—Strobinia (IRE) **Mr C. A. Hanbury**
4 **LOOKS LIKE POWER (IRE)**, 11, ch g Spadoun (FR)—Martovic (IRE) **Mr C. A. Hanbury**
5 **OUT THE GLEN (IRE)**, 8, b g Millenary—Dicera (IRE) **Mrs J. M. Edmonds**
6 **SADDLERS QUEST**, 7, b m Dr Massini (IRE)—Lady Maranzi **Mrs D. A. Hamer**
7 **SKATING AWAY (IRE)**, 5, b m Bungle Inthejungle—She Runs (FR) **Mrs A. Sloyan**
8 **TOBEFAIR**, 11, b br g Central Park (IRE)—Nan **Down The Quay Club**

**Other Owners:** Miss N. Y. Cooper, Mr N. E. Youngman.

**Assistant Trainer:** Mr M. P. Hamer.

---

**247** **MRS ALISON HAMILTON, Denholm**
Postal: **Dykes Farm House, Denholm, Hawick, Roxburghshire, TD9 8TB**
Contacts: **PHONE 01450 870323 MOBILE 07885 477349**
EMAIL Alisonhamilton53@yahoo.com

1 **BUTTEVANT LADY (IRE)**, 8, b m Presenting—Off She Goes (IRE) **J. P. G. Hamilton**
2 **CHOIX DES ARMES (FR)**, 9, b g Saint des Saints (FR)—Kicka **J. P. G. Hamilton**
3 **EXPRESS DES MOTTES (FR)**, 7, b g Network (GER)—
Uzelle des Mottes (FR) **Mr & Mrs D S Byers & Jpg Hamilton**
4 **GETAWAY KID (IRE)**, 9, ch g Getaway (GER)—Bambootcha (IRE) **J. P. G. Hamilton**
5 **GUN MERCHANT**, 8, b g Kayf Tara—Pearly Legend **J. P. G. Hamilton**
6 **PAINTERS LAD (IRE)**, 10, b g Fruits of Love (USA)—Great Cullen (IRE) **J. P. G. Hamilton**
7 **SANDHURST LAD (IRE)**, 10, b g Shantou (USA)—Sudden Beat **J. P. G. Hamilton**
8 **SHAUGHNESSY**, 8, b g Shantou (USA)—Sudden Beat **J. P. G. Hamilton**
9 **SKYHILL (IRE)**, 8, b g Gold Well—Classic Mari (IRE) **Mr & Mrs D S Byers & Jpg Hamilton**
10 **TOWERBURN (IRE)**, 12, b g Cloudings (IRE)—Lady Newmill (IRE) **J. P. G. Hamilton**
11 **WAYUPINTHESKY (IRE)**, 14, gr g Cloudings (IRE)—Riancoir Alainn **J. P. G. Hamilton**

**Other Owners:** Mr & Mrs D. S. Byers, D. S. Byers, Mrs M. J. Byers, Mrs A. C. Hamilton, J. P. G. Hamilton.

**Assistant Trainer:** Mr G. Hamilton.

## 248 MR ANDREW HAMILTON, Carluke
Postal: Nellfield House, Braidwood, Carluke, Lanarkshire, ML8 4PP
Contacts: PHONE 01555 771502

1 CRACKDELOUST (FR), 9, b g Daramsar (FR)—Magic Rose (FR) Mr A. B. Hamilton
2 FLASH MORIVIERE (FR), 6, b g Maresca Sorrento (FR)—Fleur de Princesse (FR) Mr A. B. Hamilton
3 GOLDSLINGER (FR), 9, b g Gold Away (IRE)—Singaporette (FR) Mr A. B. Hamilton
4 ISTIMRAAR (IRE), 10, b g Dansili—Manayer (IRE) Mr A. B. Hamilton
5 MAJOR DAVIS (FR), 9, b g Vision d'Etat (FR)—Majorica Sancta (FR) Mr A. B. Hamilton
6 SQUIRE'S TALE (IRE), 7, b g Galileo (IRE)—Weekend Strike (USA) Mr A. B. Hamilton
7 TUATHA DE DANNAN (IRE), 6, ch g Imperial Monarch (IRE)—Glenasheen (IRE) Mr A. B. Hamilton

## 249 MRS ANN HAMILTON, Newcastle Upon Tyne
Postal: Claywalls Farm, Capheaton, Newcastle Upon Tyne, Tyne and Wear, NE19 2BP
Contacts: PHONE 01830 530219 MOBILE 07704 670704
EMAIL annhamilton1952@hotmail.com

1 BAVINGTON BOB (IRE), 6, br g Court Cave (IRE)—Chocolate Silk (IRE) Mr I. Hamilton
2 NUTS WELL, 10, b g Dylan Thomas (IRE)—Renada Mr I. Hamilton
3 PAY THE PIPER (IRE), 9, b g Court Cave (IRE)—Regal Holly Mr I. Hamilton
4 TOMMY'S OSCAR (IRE), 6, b g Oscar (IRE)—Glibin (IRE) Mr I. Hamilton
5 WHATS THE MATTER (IRE), 5, b g Golden Lariat (USA)—Gincell Lady (IRE) Mr I. Hamilton

Assistant Trainer: Ian Hamilton.

## 250 MR MICKY HAMMOND, Middleham
Postal: Oakwood Stables, East Witton Road, Middleham, Leyburn, North Yorkshire, DL8 4PT
Contacts: PHONE 01969 625223 MOBILE 07808 572777
EMAIL micky@mickyhammondracing.co.uk WEBSITE www.mickyhammondracing.co.uk

1 APPLAUS (GER), 9, b g Tiger Hill (IRE)—All About Love (GER) The Deckchair Syndicate
2 ARTIC QUEST (IRE), 9, ch g Trans Island—Back The Queen (IRE) Ian Barran & Oakwood
3 BALLYCRYSTAL (IRE), 10, b g Oscar (IRE)—Musical Madam (IRE) A & S Associates
4 BELLE O' THE DALES (FR), 5, b m Blue Bresil (FR)—Egery (FR) Mr S. M. & Mrs. D. S. Everard
5 BLACK KETTLE (IRE), 11, b g Robin des Pres (FR)—Whistful Suzie (IRE) Tasker-Brown & Partners
6 BLUE HUSSAR (IRE), 10, b g Montjeu (IRE)—Metaphor (USA) Mr Richard Howard & Mr Ben Howard
7 BRICKADANK (IRE), 5, b g Cape Cross (IRE)—Tralanza (IRE) A & S Associates
8 BURDIGALA (FR), 8, b g Way of Light (USA)—Tiara Rosemary Hetherington & Partner
9 BURNAGE BOY (IRE), 5, b g Footstepsinthesand—Speedi Mouse JFW Properties Limited
10 CIARABELLA (IRE), 8, b m Gold Well—Fancy Fashion (IRE) M.H.O.G.
11 CLEAR WHITE LIGHT, 5, b g Dubawi (IRE)—Dalkova Run For Home Racing
12 COCKNEY BEAU (FR), 6, gr g Cockney Rebel (IRE)—Salsa Melody (FR) Cheerleader Racing
13 COMMANDING SPIRIT (IRE), 9, ch g Presenting—Park Athlete (IRE) Mrs Jennifer Hill & Mrs Samantha Toomes
14 CORNERSTONE LAD, 7, b g Delegator—Chapel Corner (IRE) Mrs B. M. Lofthouse
15 COUNTESS OLIVIA (IRE), 4, ch f Ruler of The World (IRE)—Twelfth Night (IRE) John & Kate Sidebottom
16 DADDYJACKS SPECIAL (FR), 5, gr g Spirit One (FR)—Great Way (FR) Mr S. Nicols
17 DESARAY GIRL (FR), 6, gr m Montmartre (FR)—Feria To Bitch (FR) Resdev Ltd
18 DONTDELAY (IRE), 11, b g Indian Danehill (IRE)—Garden Heaven (IRE) The Golden Cuckoo
19 DRAGONS WILL RISE (IRE), 5, b g Dragon Pulse (IRE)—Jaldini (IRE) The Golden Cuckoo
20 ELYSEES (IRE), 6, ch g Champs Elysees—Queen of Tara (IRE) Craig & Laura Buckingham
21 ENFIN PHIL (FR), 7, ch g No Risk At All (FR)—Nheyranne (FR) Randall Orchard & Partners
22 ERAGONE (FR), 7, gr g Martaline—Sharonne (FR) Mr S. Sutton
23 EX S'ELANCE (FR), 7, b g Saddex—Pampa Brune (FR) The Fifty Fifty Partnership

## MR MICKY HAMMOND - continued

24 **EXCALIBUR (POL)**, 8, gr g Youmzain (IRE)—Electra Deelites **M.H.O.G.**
25 **FARSIDEOFTHEMOON (IRE)**, 6, b g Fame And Glory—Bean Ki Moon (IRE) **G. R. Orchard**
26 **FOSTER'SISLAND**, 6, b g Trans Island—Mrs Eff **The Oakwood Nobels**
27 **FRANKELIO (FR)**, 6, b g Frankel—Restiadargent (FR) **Forty Forty Twenty**
28 **FREDDIE'S FRONTIER (IRE)**, 5, b g Sans Frontieres (IRE)—Supreme Style (IRE) **Mrs J. E. Newett**
29 **FURAX (FR)**, 6, gr g Martaline—Veleha (FR)
30 **GETAWAY JEWEL (IRE)**, 7, b g Getaway (GER)—Fada's Jewel (IRE) **MKJP RACING**
31 **GLOBAL JACKPOT**, 8, b g Flying Legend (USA)—A Fistful of Euros **Mrs H. Sugden**
32 **GRAND DU NORD (FR)**, 5, b g Montmartre (FR)—Vanille d'Ainay (FR) **Middleham Park Racing & Mr S Nicols**
33 **GRANGE RANGER (IRE)**, 9, b g Kalanisi (IRE)—Grangeclare Flight **Oakwood Rainbow**
34 **GREAT RAFFLES (FR)**, 5, b g Kapgarde (FR)—Une Artiste (FR) **The Golden Cuckoo**
35 **HARRY GO (IRE)**, 5, b g Bahri (USA)—Waverbeck (IRE) **Mr J. B. Harrison**
36 **HIGH NOON (IRE)**, 9, b g Westerner—Seymourswift **Mr Nick Pietrzyk & Partner**
37 **HOWZAT HIRIS (FR)**, 4, gr f Al Namix (FR)—Une Dame d'Or (FR) **Sticky Wicket Racing**
38 **ICONIC HERO (IRE)**, 8, b g Oscar (IRE)—Classy Society (IRE) **The Rat Pack Racing Club**
39 **ILAYA (FR)**, 7, gr m Kapgarde (FR)—Tour Magic (FR) **The Golden Cuckoo**
40 **IRV (IRE)**, 5, ch g Zoffany (IRE)—Marion Antoinette (IRE) **I. M. Lynch**
41 **JUST JEAN (IRE)**, 4, b f Society Rock (IRE)—Yashila (IRE) **Mr & Mrs P. Chapman**
42 **JUST PADDY'S BAND (IRE)**, 5, ch g Sholokhov (IRE)—Tweedledrum
43 **JUSTFORJAMES (IRE)**, 12, b g Dr Massini (IRE)—Over The Road (IRE) **J4J Partnership**
44 **KAYF ADVENTURE**, 10, b g Kayf Tara—My Adventure (IRE) **Cheltenham Trail & Cleeve Racing Club**
45 **KILDRUM (IRE)**, 8, b g Milan—Close Flame (IRE) **Mr T. M. Clarke**
46 **KISUMU**, 9, b g High Chaparral (IRE)—Arum Lily (USA) **Tasker-Brown & Partners**
47 **KNOCKNAMONA (IRE)**, 10, b g Trans Island—Faraday Lady (IRE) **The Rat Pack Racing Club**
48 **LATE DATE (IRE)**, 10, b g Oscar (IRE)—Regents Ballerina (IRE) **County Set Six & Partner**
49 **LLEYTON (IRE)**, 9, b br g Kalanisi (IRE)—Bonnie Parker (IRE) **& Southerington**
50 **LUCOU (FR)**, 5, b g Axxos (GER)—Winnor (FR) **A Walsh, J Hill, S Toomes**
51 **MAC CENNETIG (IRE)**, 9, b g Brian Boru—Buslane (IRE) **Mrs B. M. Lofthouse**
52 **MAISON D'OR (IRE)**, 7, b g Galileo (IRE)—Thai Haku (IRE) **Mr D. Lees**
53 **MARVELLOUS JOE (IRE)**, 6, b g Mahler—Marvellous Dream (FR) **Mr Joe Buzzeo & Partner**
54 **MASTER GUSTAV**, 5, b g Mahler—Annaghbrack (IRE) **Mrs B. M. Lofthouse**
55 **MISTER MCARTHUR**, 5, ch g Phoenix Reach (IRE)—Arctic Queen **McGoldrick Racing**
56 **NOT WHAT IT SEEMS (IRE)**, 5, b g Robin des Pres (FR)—Kyle Ruby (IRE) **Stephen Sugden & Ryder Sugden**
57 **ONENIGHTINTOWN (IRE)**, 7, b g Robin des Pres (FR)—Snug Bunch (IRE) **M.H.O.G.**
58 **ONLYFOOLSOWNHORSES (IRE)**, 10, br g Presenting—
Lizzy Langtry (IRE) **The Cheltenham Trail & Proform Racing**
59 **PENPAL (FR)**, 6, ch g Muhtathir—Penkinella (FR) **The Golden Cuckoo**
60 **QUOTELINE DIRECT**, 8, ch g Sir Percy—Queen's Pudding (USA) **JFW Properties Limited**
61 **RADDLE AND HUM (IRE)**, 7, b m Milan—Gaybric (IRE) **Miss R. Dennis**
62 **RED SKYE DELIGHT (IRE)**, 5, gr m Clodovil (IRE)—Sole Bay **Miss R. Dennis**
63 **ROCKLIFFE**, 8, b g Notnowcato—Hope Island (IRE) **Rm&t, S Toomes, J Hill & Partners**
64 **RORY AND ME (FR)**, 6, b g Shamardal (USA)—Rosawa (FR) **Mr Richard Howard & Mr Ben Howard**
65 **ROXYFET (FR)**, 11, b g Califet (FR)—Roxalamour (FR) **Mr Samuel Sutton & Partners**
66 **ROYAL VILLAGE (IRE)**, 9, b g Scorpion (IRE)—Etoile Margot (FR) **Cheltenham Trail & Cleeve Racing Club**
67 **RUSSIAN ROYALE**, 11, b m Royal Applause—Russian Ruby (FR) **Raypasha**
68 **SAUCY SALLY (IRE)**, 6, b m Declaration of War (USA)—Ardere (USA) **Mr S & Mrs D Everard, A Smith & O Weeks**
69 **SCHIEHALLION MUNRO**, 8, ch g Schiaparelli (GER)—Mrs Fawlty **Tennant, Lynch,Sharpe and Boston**
70 **SHIGHNESS**, 4, b f Passing Glance—Sharwakom (IRE) **Keep The Faith Partnership**
71 **SILVER TASSIE (IRE)**, 13, b g Shantou (USA)—Silver Castor (IRE) **Mr R. M. Howard**
72 **SINCERELY RESDEV**, b g Rock of Gibraltar (IRE)—Sincerely **Resdev Ltd**
73 **SPARKLE IN HIS EYE**, 5, ch g Sea The Stars (IRE)—Nyarhini **M. D. Hammond**
74 **SQUARE VIVIANI (FR)**, 10, b g Satri (IRE)—Idria (GER) **Stephen Sugden & Ryder Sugden**
75 **STORMIN NORMAN**, 8, b g Sir Percy—Roses **The Monday Club**
76 **STRIKE WEST (IRE)**, 9, b g Westerner—Fuel Queen (IRE) **The Multi-Taskers**
77 **SWINTON DIAMOND (IRE)**, 10, b g Dubai Destination (USA)—Absent Beauty (IRE) **Mr & Mrs I P Earnshaw**
78 **THE PINE MARTIN (IRE)**, 11, br g Kalanisi (IRE)—Regal Holly **The Rat Pack Racing Club**
79 **THE RESDEV WAY**, 8, b g Multiplex—Lady Duxyana **Resdev Ltd**
80 **THE RETRIEVER (IRE)**, 6, ch g Shamardal (USA)—Silent Secret (IRE) **R M & T Holdings Limited & Partners**
81 **THE RUTLAND REBEL (IRE)**, 5, b g Delegator—Do Disturb (IRE) **Stephen Sugden & Ryder Sugden**
82 **THE VERY THING (IRE)**, 7, b g Getaway (GER)—Katie Quinn (IRE) **Mr D. Walpole**

## MR MICKY HAMMOND - continued

83 **TRIMMERS LANE (IRE)**, 11, b g Publisher (USA)—Kilcormac Glow (IRE) **Mr I. Ender**
84 **WALKONBY**, 4, ch f Sixties Icon—Shadows Ofthenight (IRE) **Cheltenham Trail & Cleeve Racing Club**
85 **WHO'S THE GUV'NOR (IRE)**, 7, b g Gold Well—Clamit Brook (IRE) **Mr & Mrs I P Earnshaw**
86 **WISHFUL THINKING (GER)**, 8, b g Sholokhov (IRE)—Wonderful Time (GER) **D H Lees & Sons Limited**
87 **WISTERIAROSE**, 5, b m Leading Light (IRE)—Mille Et Une (FR) **Mrs J. E. Newett**

### THREE-YEAR-OLDS

88 **CREATIVE MOJO (IRE)**, gr f Marcel (IRE)—Zebgrey (IRE)
89 **HERESMAX (IRE)**, b g Gutaifan (IRE)—Euroceleb (IRE) **Mr M. Andrews**
90 B f Garswood—Laughing Water (FR) **Mr S. Lockyer**
91 **MYBOYMAX (FR)**, b g Myboycharlie (IRE)—Plebeya (IRE)
92 **RED AMAPOLA**, b f Marcel (IRE)—Si Belle (IRE) **Miss R. Dennis**

### TWO-YEAR-OLDS

93 B g 29/04 Pearl Secret—Medicean Bliss (IRE) (Medicean) (1143)

**Other Owners:** I. J. Barran, R. P. E. Berry, Mr C. Buckingham, Mrs L. K. Buckingham, J. Buzzeo, Mr J. Cain, Mrs J. Chapman, Mr P. W. Chapman, Mr S. J. M. Cobb, Mr R. Doak, Mr I. P. Earnshaw, Mrs J. Earnshaw, Mrs D. S. Everard, Mr S. M. Everard, G. Godsman, M. D. Hammond, Mr D. A. Harrison, Mrs R. Hetherington, Mrs J. Hill, Mr J. A. Hill, Mrs G. Hogg, Mr B. R. Howard, Mr R. M. Howard, Mr R. Manners, Middleham Park Racing XXIII, Mr S. Nicols, G. R. Orchard, T. S. Palin, Mr N. Pietrzyk, M. Prince, R M & T Holdings Limited, Mr J. Reid, Mr A. Savage, Mr J. Sidebottom, Mrs K. Sidebottom, A. W. Sinclair, Mr A. Smith, Ms C. Southerington, Mrs P. Southerington, Mr R. Sugden, Mr S. Sugden, Mr S. Sutton, Mrs G. M. Swinglehurst, J. M. Swinglehurst, Mr J. E. Tennant, Lady S. Toomes, Mr A. Walsh, O. R. Weeks.

**Assistant Trainer:** Mrs G. Hogg.

**NH Jockey:** Alain Cawley, Joe Colliver. **Conditional Jockey:** Billy Garritty, Aidan Macdonald, Emma Smith-Chaston. **Apprentice Jockey:** Aiden Brookes. **Amateur Jockey:** Miss R. Smith, James Waggott.

---

## 251    MR STEPHEN HANLON, Butterton
Postal: Butterton Racing Stables, Park Road, Butterton, Newcastle, Staffordshire, ST5 4DZ
EMAIL smhanlonracing@hotmail.com

1 **AKUA (IRE)**, 6, b m Kodiac—Sava Sunset (IRE)
2 **ANCIENT ASTRONAUT**, 8, b g Kodiac—Tatora **Newgen Racing Group**
3 **CAPPADOCIA (IRE)**, 11, b g Mujadil (USA)—Green Vision (IRE) **Newgen Racing Group**
4 **DIVINE CONNECTION**, 4, b f Cable Bay (IRE)—Divine Power **Newgen Racing Group**
5 **MASQUE OF ANARCHY (IRE)**, 5, b g Sir Percy—Charming (IRE) **Newgen Racing Group**
6 **MERCURY**, 9, ch g Showcasing—Miss Rimex (IRE) **Newgen Racing Group**
7 4, B f Bungle Inthejungle—Miss Mauna Kea (IRE) **Newgen Racing Group**
8 **NANNY MAKFI**, 8, b m Makfi—Pan Galactic (USA) **Newgen Racing Group**
9 **ROSE BANDIT (IRE)**, 4, b f Requinto (IRE)—Poppy's Rose **The Strattonites**
10 **STRAFFAN (IRE)**, 6, b m Clodovil (IRE)—Laureldean Spirit (IRE) **Newgen Racing Group**
11 4, B f Anjaal—Vivacious Way **Newgen Racing Group**

### THREE-YEAR-OLDS

12 B c Excelebration (IRE)—Absolute Pleasure **Newgen Racing Group**
13 B f The Last Lion (IRE)—Billie Eria (IRE) **Newgen Racing Group**
14 B f Free Eagle (IRE)—Holy Norma **Newgen Racing Group**
15 B f Belardo (IRE)—Jolyne **Newgen Racing Group**

### TWO-YEAR-OLDS

16 Ch c 13/04 Outstrip—Touriga (Cape Cross (IRE)) **The Strattonites**

## 252  MR GARY HANMER, Tattenhall
Postal: **Church Farm, Harthill Lane, Harthill, Tattenhall, Chester, Cheshire, CH3 9LQ**
Contacts: **MOBILE 07737 181165**

1  **ARCTIC VALLEY (IRE)**, 7, b g Arctic Cosmos (USA)—Grangevalley Gold (IRE)  **The Ed-chester Partnership**
2  **CAPE FAIR**, 8, b m Fair Mix (IRE)—Capania (IRE)  **W. J. Swinnerton**
3  **CARLA KOALA**, 5, b m Kuroshio (AUS)—Bold Love  **Mr A. Bithell**
4  **COSTLY DIAMOND (IRE)**, 7, ch m Mahler—Sweet Ouzel (IRE)  **TGK Construction Co. Ltd**
5  **DAWN RAIDER (IRE)**, 9, b g Mahler—Woodview Dawn (IRE)  **Mr T. G. Kelly**
6  **DEE EIRE**, 4, bl f Gentlewave (USA)—Kahipiroska (FR)  **The Deeside Partnership**
7  **DEE LANE (IRE)**, 8, br g Oscar (IRE)—Royal Robin (IRE)  **The Deeside Partnership**
8  **DEE STAR (IRE)**, 8, b g Shantou (USA)—Alicias Lady (IRE)  **The Deeside Partnership**
9  **FUSIONFORCE (IRE)**, 14, b g Overbury (IRE)—Seviot  **Mr S. P. Edkins**
10  **HIGH COUNSEL (IRE)**, 12, br g Presenting—The Bench (IRE)  **Herongate Racers**
11  **HILLVIEW (IRE)**, 5, b g Fruits of Love (USA)—Da Das Delight (IRE)  **Mr D. O. Pickering**
12  **ISTHEBAROPEN**, 8, b m Grape Tree Road—Seviot  **Mr G. Evans**
13  **KNOCKNAGOSHEL (IRE)**, 8, b g Kalanisi (IRE)—Granny Clark (IRE)  **Knock Knock Syndicate**
14  **LEDHAM (IRE)**, 6, b g Shamardal (USA)—Pioneer Bride (USA)  **Mr G. Evans**
15  **LITTLE JACK**, 7, b g Malinas (GER)—Persian Forest  **Mr A. Bithell**
16  **LOCH GARMAN ARIS (IRE)**, 11, b g Jammaal—See Em Aime (IRE)  **The Brookes Family**
17  **LOU TREK (FR)**, 7, b g Linda's Lad—Nara Eria (FR)  **Mr T. G. Kelly**
18  **MALINA OCARINA**, 6, b m Malinas (GER)—Ocarina Davis (FR)  **M.H. Racing Malina**
19  **O CEALLAIGH (IRE)**, 12, b g Westerner—Hirayna  **Mr G. Evans**
20  **O'GRADY'S BOY (IRE)**, 10, b g Kalanisi (IRE)—Jemima Jay (IRE)  **The Deeside Partnership**
21  **OSCAR NOMINATION (IRE)**, 9, b g Getaway (GER)—Nightofthe Oscars (IRE)  **The Deeside Partnership**
22  **PACKETTOTHERAFTERS (IRE)**, 12, b g Craigsteel—Darazari River (IRE)  **The Tunstall Green Partnership**
23  **SIR TIVO (FR)**, 7, b g Deportivo—Miss Possibility (USA)  **Mrs J. A. Ashley**
24  **STEEL WAVE (IRE)**, 11, br g Craigsteel—Musical Waves (IRE)  **Mr S. Walker**
25  **WBEE (IRE)**, 6, b g Yeats (IRE)—Consultation (IRE)  **Mrs M. D. Ritson**
26  **WHAT A LAUGH**, 16, b g Kayf Tara—Just For A Laugh  **Mr S. P. Edkins**

**Other Owners:** Mr S. P. Edkins, M. E. Green, Mr N. P. Tunstall, Mr G. J. Winchester.

---

## 253  MR RICHARD HANNON, Marlborough
Postal: **Herridge Racing Stables, Herridge, Collingbourne Ducis, Wiltshire, SN8 3EG**
Contacts: **PHONE 01264 850254 FAX 01264 850076**
**EMAIL kevin@richardhannonracing.co.uk WEBSITE www.richardhannonracing.co.uk**

1  **ALWAYS FEARLESS (IRE)**, 4, ch g Camacho—Zenella
2  **ARAFI**, 4, ch f Farhh—Chocolate Hills (FR)
3  **BEAT LE BON (FR)**, 5, b g Wootton Bassett—Frida La Blonde (FR)
4  **BIG WING (IRE)**, 4, b g Free Eagle (IRE)—Orafinitis (IRE)
5  **CITYZEN SERG (IRE)**, 4, b g Raven's Pass (USA)—Summer Dream (IRE)
6  **ELEGANT ERIN (IRE)**, 4, b f Dandy Man (IRE)—Eriniya (IRE)
7  **FOX POWER (IRE)**, 5, gr g Dark Angel (IRE)—Zenella
8  **FROZEN WATERS (IRE)**, 4, ch c No Nay Never (USA)—Whitefall (USA)
9  **IN THE COVE (IRE)**, 5, b h Footstepsinthesand—Vatrouchka (USA)
10  **LEXINGTON DASH (FR)**, 4, b c Siyouni (FR)—Mythical Border (USA)
11  **LEXINGTON FORCE (FR)**, 4, b c Dabirsim (FR)—Fox Force Five (IRE)
12  **LOST EDEN (IRE)**, 4, b g Sea The Stars (IRE)—Ghostflower (IRE)
13  **LOVE LOVE**, 4, b f Kodiac—Perfect Blessings (IRE)
14  **MAFIA POWER**, 4, b g Gleneagles (IRE)—Rivara
15  **MAGICAL WISH (IRE)**, 5, br g Heeraat (IRE)—Tomintoul Magic (IRE)
16  **MAKEEN**, 4, b g Dubawi (IRE)—Estidraaj (USA)
17  **MALVERN**, 4, gr g Outstrip—Perfect Muse
18  **MAMBO NIGHTS (IRE)**, 4, b c Havana Gold (IRE)—Inez

## MR RICHARD HANNON - continued

19 **MAN OF THE NIGHT (FR)**, 4, b c Night of Thunder (IRE)—Mandheera (USA)
20 **MARK OF GOLD**, 4, b c Golden Horn—Polly's Mark (IRE)
21 **MUMS TIPPLE (IRE)**, 4, ch g Footstepsinthesand—Colomone Cross (IRE)
22 **NOONDAY GUN**, 4, gr g Dubawi (IRE)—Sky Lantern (IRE)
23 **NUGGET**, 4, b c Siyouni (FR)—Gemstone (IRE)
24 **OH THIS IS US (IRE)**, 8, b h Acclamation—Shamwari Lodge (IRE)
25 **OUZO**, 5, b g Charm Spirit (IRE)—Miss Meltemi (IRE)
26 **POSTED**, 5, b m Kingman—Time Away (IRE)
27 **QAYSAR (FR)**, 6, b g Choisir (AUS)—Coco Demure (IRE)
28 **SKY POWER (IRE)**, 4, b g Fastnet Rock (AUS)—Dame Blanche (IRE)
29 **TAHITIAN PRINCE (FR)**, 4, b g Siyouni (FR)—Tehamana (IRE)
30 **THEOTHERSIDE (IRE)**, 4, br f Dandy Man (IRE)—New Magic (IRE)
31 **TYPHOON TEN (IRE)**, 5, b g Slade Power (IRE)—Cake (IRE)
32 **WAR GLORY (IRE)**, 8, b g Canford Cliffs (IRE)—Attracted To You (IRE)
33 **WATAN**, 5, ch h Toronado (IRE)—Shotgun Gulch (IRE)
34 **WIN WIN POWER (IRE)**, 4, b g Exceed And Excel (AUS)—Spesialta

## THREE-YEAR-OLDS

35 **AL FAHDAA**, b f Toronado (IRE)—Sefaat
36 **ALAZWAR (IRE)**, b g Awtaad (IRE)—Venetian Beauty (USA)
37 **ALBERTVILLE (FR)**, b c Olympic Glory (IRE)—Mneerah (FR)
38 **ALJADEED**, b g Cable Bay (IRE)—Coin A Phrase
39 B f No Nay Never (USA)—Along The Shore (IRE)
40 **ANGHAAM (IRE)**, gr f Frankel—Natagora (FR)
41 **ARSONIST (GER)**, b c Sea The Moon (GER)—Amalie (GER)
42 **BABAJAN (IRE)**, b g Acclamation—Alerted (USA)
43 **BANNERMAN**, ch g Starspangledbanner (AUS)—Updated (FR)
44 **BEIJING BILLY (IRE)**, b c Shanghai Bobby (USA)—Rag And Bone (CAN)
45 **BELLA NOTTE**, ch f Twilight Son—Fair Value (IRE)
46 **BILLY MILL**, b c Adaay (IRE)—Phantom Spirit
47 **CARAMELISED**, b c Dansili—Caster Sugar (USA)
48 **CHINDIT (IRE)**, b c Wootton Bassett—Always A Dream
49 **CIRRUS**, ch f Starspangledbanner (AUS)—Callendula
50 **CLARENDON CROSS**, b c New Approach (IRE)—Meet Me Halfway
51 **CLARENDON HOUSE**, b c Mehmas (IRE)—Walaaa (IRE)
52 **CLAY**, b c Sixties Icon—Tamso (USA)
53 **CONIGER (IRE)**, b f Coulsty (IRE)—Macadamia (IRE)
54 **CRITICAL (FR)**, b f No Nay Never (USA)—Maid To Believe
55 **DAY TRADER (IRE)**, b c Estidhkaar (IRE)—Rocking Horse
56 **DEWEY ROAD (IRE)**, b c No Nay Never (USA)—Celestial Dream (IRE)
57 **DIAMOND OF DUBAI**, gr c Dubawi (IRE)—Rose Diamond (IRE)
58 **DILLYDINGDILLYDONG**, b g Territories (IRE)—Cephalonie (USA)
59 **DINGLE (IRE)**, b c Footstepsinthesand—Beal Ban (IRE)
60 **ELOQUENT ARTHUR**, b c Sir Prancealot (IRE)—Ambriel (IRE)
61 **EMINENT HIPSTER (IRE)**, b c Make Believe—Organza
62 **EMJAYTWENTYTHREE**, b c Adaay (IRE)—Cards
63 **ENOUGHISGOODENOUGH (IRE)**, b f Dark Angel (IRE)—The Hermitage (IRE)
64 **ESCOBEDO**, b c Nathaniel (IRE)—Notary
65 **ETONIAN (IRE)**, b c Olympic Glory (IRE)—Naan (IRE)
66 **FANCY MAN (IRE)**, b c Pride of Dubai (AUS)—Fancy (IRE)
67 **FASCINATING SHADOW (IRE)**, b c Fascinating Rock (IRE)—Golden Shadow (IRE)
68 **FAST STEPS (IRE)**, b c Footstepsinthesand—Inis Boffin
69 **FOUNTAIN CROSS**, b c Muhaarar—Infamous Angel
70 **GENUFLEX**, b c Holy Roman Emperor (IRE)—Gravitation
71 **GOOD LISTENER (IRE)**, b c Mehmas (IRE)—Looks Great
72 **GRAND SCHEME (IRE)**, b c Territories (IRE)—Antillia
73 **GUSTAV HOLST (IRE)**, b c Sea The Stars (IRE)—Scarlet And Gold (IRE)
74 **HAPPY ROMANCE (IRE)**, b f Dandy Man (IRE)—Rugged Up (IRE)
75 **HOST (IRE)**, b c Mehmas (IRE)—Mistress Makfi (IRE)

## MR RICHARD HANNON - continued

76 **KEEP RIGHT ON (IRE),** b c Acclamation—Khalice
77 **KOOL MOE DEE (IRE),** b g Mehmas (IRE)—Senadora (GER)
78 **LAFAN (IRE),** b c Dandy Man (IRE)—Light Glass (IRE)
79 **LEXINGTON FURY (IRE),** br c Footstepsinthesand—Majraa (FR)
80 **LEXINGTON KNIGHT (IRE),** ch c Night of Thunder (IRE)—Petit Adagio (IRE)
81 **LEXINGTON LIBERTY (IRE),** b f Dandy Man (IRE)—Warm Welcome
82 **MALATHAAT (IRE),** ch f Frankel—Sweepstake (IRE)
83 **MAMMASAIDKNOCKUOUT (IRE),** b f Vadamos (FR)—Open Verse (USA)
84 **MEADOW SPRITE (IRE),** ch f Slade Power (IRE)—Pivotique
85 **MICKYDEE,** b g Twilight Son—Spangle
86 **MIND HUNTER (IRE),** b c Gleneagles (IRE)—Gadwa
87 **MODEL ACTRESS (IRE),** b f Dansili—Top Model (IRE)
88 **MOJO STAR (IRE),** b c Sea The Stars (IRE)—Galley
89 **MR TRICK (IRE),** b g Kodiac—Alkhawarah (USA)
90 **MUAY THAI (IRE),** b g Acclamation—Myturn (IRE)
91 **MUMMY BEAR (IRE),** br f Kodi Bear (IRE)—Shortmile Lady (IRE)
92 **NAZAAHA (IRE),** b f Shamardal (USA)—Fleeting Smile (USA)
93 **NIGHT OF DREAMS,** gr ro c Dark Angel (IRE)—Bint Almukhtar (IRE)
94 **NIGHT OF HOPE (IRE),** b f Night of Thunder (IRE)—Zarabaya (IRE)
95 **OWER STARLIGHT,** b c Cityscape—Rebel Magic
96 **POWER STATION,** b c Footstepsinthesand—Juno Moneta (IRE)
97 **PROFESSOR CALCULUS,** b c Twilight Son—Roslea Lady (IRE)
98 **PURE DREAMER,** b c Oasis Dream—Pure Line
99 **QUEEN OF ASIA (IRE),** b f Exceed And Excel (AUS)—Alumni
100 **RAINBOW'S PONY (IRE),** b f Acclamation—Mirror Effect (IRE)
101 **REMEDIUM,** b g Adaay (IRE)—Lamentation
102 **REVEREND HUBERT (IRE),** ch c Zoffany (IRE)—Bright Sapphire (IRE)
103 **RHYTHM (IRE),** b f Acclamation—Strasbourg Place
104 **RIFFAA WONDER (IRE),** b c Kodiac—Zain Time
105 **RIVER ALWEN (IRE),** gr c Dark Angel (IRE)—Intense Pink
106 **ROYAL EVENT (IRE),** b f Golden Horn—Salacia (IRE)
107 **ROYAL TRIBUTE (IRE),** b c Kingman—Sweet Acclaim (IRE)
108 **SAFE PASSAGE,** b f Paco Boy (IRE)—Daring Aim
109 **SENTENCE,** b f Dubawi (IRE)—Caraboss
110 **SERGEANT MAJOR,** b c Siyouni (FR)—Aurore (IRE)
111 **SHALANEZ (IRE),** br f Shalaa (IRE)—Inez
112 **SHANGHAI ROCK,** b c Dark Angel (IRE)—Red Lady (IRE)
113 **SHINE FOR YOU,** b f Siyouni (FR)—Lady Viola
114 **SIAM FOX (IRE),** b g Prince of Lir (IRE)—Folegandros Island (FR)
115 **SILVER MELODY (IRE),** b c Muhaarar—Handbell (IRE)
116 **SIR RUMI (IRE),** ch c Gleneagles (IRE)—Reine des Plages (IRE)
117 **SNOW LANTERN,** gr f Frankel—Sky Lantern (IRE)
118 **SOUNDSLIKETHUNDER (IRE),** ch c Night of Thunder (IRE)—Dust Flicker
119 **STATE SECRETARY (IRE),** b g Muhaarar—Danetime Out (IRE)
120 **SUNSET,** b c Twilight Son—Mrs Mogg
121 **TAJDID (FR),** b c Toronado (IRE)—Anew
122 **TAMYEEZ (USA),** ch f Tamarkuz (USA)—Hijaab (USA)
123 **TEODOLINA (IRE),** b f Kodiac—Teodelight (IRE)
124 **THANK YOU NEXT (IRE),** b f No Nay Never (USA)—Two Pass (IRE)
125 **VENTURA TORMENTA (IRE),** b c Acclamation—Midnight Oasis
126 **VENTURA WIZARD,** ch g Pearl Secret—Concentration (IRE)
127 **VICTORIOUS NIGHT (IRE),** b c Night of Thunder (IRE)—Akuna Magic (IRE)
128 **VITRUVE (IRE),** gr c Toronado (IRE)—Strawberrydaiquiri
129 **ZION STAR (IRE),** b c Estidhkaar (IRE)—Yasmin Satine (IRE)
130 **ZWELELA (FR),** b f Toronado (IRE)—Umm Bab (IRE)

## MR RICHARD HANNON - continued

### TWO-YEAR-OLDS

**131** Ch c 12/02 Olympic Glory (IRE)—Al Anqa (Galileo (IRE))
**132** B c 03/03 Zelzal (FR)—Al Markhiya (IRE) (Arcano (IRE))
**133 ALAADEE,** b c 15/04 Night of Thunder (IRE)—Rose Season (Cape Cross (IRE)) (40000)
**134** B c 24/01 Garswood—Allegramente (Dansili) (9500)
**135** B f 10/02 Iffraaj—Alouja (IRE) (Raven's Pass (USA)) (24762)
**136** B f 27/04 Swiss Spirit—Amber Lane (Compton Place) (8000)
**137 AMERICAN KESTREL (IRE),** b f 25/03 Starspangledbanner (AUS)—Marsh Hawk (Invincible Spirit (IRE))
**138 ARDBRACCAN (IRE),** b f 28/04 Lawman (FR)—Bosphorus Queen (IRE) (Sri Pekan (USA)) (30476)
**139** B c 12/03 Mukhadram—Barnezet (GR) (Invincible Spirit (IRE))
**140** B c 13/03 Muhaarar—Bint Almukhtar (IRE) (Halling (USA))
**141** B c 15/03 Ribchester (IRE)—Black Pearl (IRE) (Lord Shanakill (USA)) (80000)
**142 BOSH (IRE),** b c 16/02 Profitable (IRE)—Tropical Mist (IRE) (Marju (IRE)) (62000)
**143** B c 06/04 Elzaam (AUS)—Brown Bee (IRE) (Camacho) (19048)
**144 BYKER (IRE),** b c 10/05 Le Havre (IRE)—Bridge of Peace (Anabaa (USA)) (57143)
**145** B c 15/03 Acclamation—Colour Blue (IRE) (Holy Roman Emperor (IRE)) (92000)
**146 CONDUCIVE (IRE),** b c 18/02 Profitable (IRE)—Amallna (Green Desert (USA)) (65000)
**147 DARK TULIP,** b f 31/03 Dark Angel (IRE)—Rimth (Oasis Dream)
**148 DAWN OF LIBERATION (IRE),** b c 06/02 Churchill (IRE)—Danetime Out (IRE) (Danetime (IRE)) (145000)
**149 DESERT (IRE),** b c 22/02 Havana Gold (IRE)—Jewel In The Sand (IRE) (Bluebird (USA)) (24762)
**150 DESERT ANGEL (IRE),** b gr c 22/04 Dark Angel (IRE)—Slieve Mish (IRE) (Cape Cross (IRE)) (51429)
**151** B c 26/01 Mehmas (IRE)—Diaminda (IRE) (Diamond Green (FR)) (160000)
**152** B c 05/02 Sea The Moon (GER)—Dubai Cyclone (USA) (Bernardini (USA)) (135000)
**153 DUELIST,** b c 13/02 Dubawi (IRE)—Coplow (Manduro (GER))
**154 DUKEBOX (IRE),** b c 22/03 Holy Roman Emperor (IRE)—Broadway Duchess (IRE) (New Approach (IRE)) (61905)
**155** Ch c 09/04 Footstepsinthesand—Duljanah (IRE) (Dream Ahead (USA))
**156** B c 27/02 Havana Gold (IRE)—Ejaazah (IRE) (Acclamation)
**157** B f 06/03 Dabirsim (FR)—Elite (Invincible Spirit (IRE)) (14286)
**158** B f 10/02 Mehmas (IRE)—Epatha (IRE) (Highest Honor (FR)) (60533)
**159 EVERYDAY,** b c 29/04 Cable Bay (IRE)—Humdrum (Dr Fong (USA))
**160 EXCELING (IRE),** b f 11/03 Exceed And Excel (AUS)—Jadaayil (Oasis Dream) (19048)
**161** B f 15/03 Fast Company (IRE)—Fairy Lights (Shamardal (USA))
**162** Ch c 18/02 Exceed And Excel (AUS)—Falling Petals (IRE) (Raven's Pass (USA)) (120000)
**163** B c 12/02 Shalaa (IRE)—Fazendera (IRE) (Elusive City (USA)) (100000)
**164** Ch c 22/02 Ribchester (IRE)—Fluvial (IRE) (Exceed And Excel (AUS)) (82000)
**165 FRUSTRATING,** b c 28/04 Ardad (IRE)—Miss Villefranche (Danehill Dancer (IRE)) (31429)
**166 GAIUS,** b c 13/02 Havana Gold (IRE)—Gemina (IRE) (Holy Roman Emperor (IRE))
**167** B f 14/04 Ribchester (IRE)—Galley (Zamindar (USA)) (95238)
**168 GISBURN (IRE),** ch c 15/01 Ribchester (IRE)—Disclose (Dansili) (83810)
**169 GOD OF THUNDER (IRE),** b c 28/03 Tagula (IRE)—Tawjeeh (Haafhd) (11000)
**170 GOLDILOCKS,** ch f 02/02 Havana Gold (IRE)—Life Is Golden (USA) (Giant's Causeway (USA)) (28000)
**171 GROOM,** br c 30/03 Aclaim (IRE)—Tohaveandtohold (Pivotal) (34286)
**172 GUBBASS (IRE),** b c 12/02 Mehmas (IRE)—Vida Amorosa (IRE) (Lope de Vega (IRE)) (24762)
**173 GUITAR,** b c 27/04 Mayson—Clapperboard (Royal Applause) (30000)
**174 HAPAP (IRE),** b c 24/02 Dark Angel (IRE)—Apphia (IRE) (High Chaparral (IRE)) (100000)
**175** B c 30/03 No Nay Never (USA)—Hestia (FR) (High Chaparral (IRE)) (44391)
**176** B c 14/02 Night of Thunder (IRE)—Hokkaido (Street Cry (IRE)) (240000)
**177 HOTLINE BLING (IRE),** b c 17/02 Cotai Glory—Kocna (IRE) (Aussie Rules (USA)) (42000)
**178 INDIAN GURU (IRE),** ch f 02/04 Ribchester (IRE)—Transcendence (IRE) (Arcano (IRE)) (57143)
**179** Ch f 11/03 The Gurkha (IRE)—Inez (Dai Jin) (67000)
**180 IRISA,** b f 12/04 Tamayuz—Aertex (IRE) (Exceed And Excel (AUS))
**181** B c 03/04 Aclaim (IRE)—Itsinthestars (Zoffany (IRE)) (75000)
**182** B c 05/04 Equiano (FR)—King's Guest (IRE) (King's Best (USA)) (12000)
**183 KINTBURY,** b f 03/04 Nathaniel (IRE)—Promising (IRE) (Invincible Spirit (IRE))
**184 KODIAS SANGARIUS (IRE),** b f 20/04 Kodiac—Oui Say Oui (IRE) (Royal Applause) (64762)
**185** B c 04/03 Sea The Stars (IRE)—Lady Of Dubai (Dubawi (IRE))
**186** B c 03/03 Dubawi (IRE)—Lilian Baylis (IRE) (Shamardal (USA))
**187 LOQUACE (IRE),** b f 06/02 Exceed And Excel (AUS)—Parle Moi (USA) (Giant's Causeway (USA)) (67000)
**188 MAGIC WARRIOR (IRE),** b c 27/03 Kodiac—Alkhawarah (USA) (Intidab (USA)) (145000)

## MR RICHARD HANNON - continued

**189 MARITIME RULES (IRE)**, b c 03/03 Mehmas (IRE)—Beauty of The Sea (Elusive Quality (USA)) (90476)
**190** B f 09/03 Camacho—Mia Madonna (Motivator) (32381)
**191** B f 27/01 No Nay Never (USA)—Miss Understood (IRE) (Excellent Art) (125000)
**192 MONET'S SUNRISE**, b c 05/03 Le Havre (IRE)—Distant (USA) (First Defence (USA)) (95000)
**193 MONITOR**, b c 25/01 Dabirsim (FR)—Discipline (Dansili) (34286)
**194 MOUNT KOSCIUSZKO**, br gr c 19/02 National Defense—Sans Equivoque (GER) (Stormy River (FR))
**195 MOUNT RAINIER (IRE)**, b f 25/04 Kodiac—Viz (IRE) (Darshaan)
**196 MOUNT SNOWDON (IRE)**, b c 18/03 War Front (USA)—Christmas Joy (IRE) (Galileo (IRE))
**197** B f 20/04 Fast Company (IRE)—Mundana (IRE) (King's Best (USA))
**198 NIGHT ARC**, b c 03/02 Twilight Son—Gymnaste (IRE) (Shamardal (USA)) (70000)
**199 NIGHT GLASS (IRE)**, b c 10/04 Galileo Gold—Hen Night (IRE) (Danehill Dancer (IRE)) (42857)
**200** B c 24/03 Mehmas (IRE)—Nina Bonita (IRE) (Danehill Dancer (IRE)) (90000)
**201 OH HERBERTS REIGN (IRE)**, b c 07/02 Acclamation—Western Safari (IRE) (High Chaparral (IRE)) (100000)
**202** B c 04/03 Zelzal (FR)—One River (FR) (Stormy River (FR)) (18563)
**203 OWER INDEPENDENCE**, b f 12/02 Adaay (IRE)—Mary's Pet (Where Or When (IRE))
**204** Ch f 01/05 Farhh—Petite Nymphe (Golan (IRE)) (60000)
**205 PETRILA (IRE)**, b c 03/04 Acclamation—Simply Awesome (IRE) (Awesome Again (CAN)) (92000)
**206** B c 30/04 Holy Roman Emperor (IRE)—Polka Dot (IRE) (Galileo (IRE)) (54286)
**207** B c 13/03 Time Test—Precious Angel (IRE) (Excelebration (IRE)) (3000)
**208 PRIDE ASIDE**, b f 12/02 Pride of Dubai (AUS)—Arabda (Elnadim (USA)) (47619)
**209 PRINCESS OLLY (IRE)**, b f 14/05 Invincible Spirit (IRE)—Cristal Fashion (IRE) (Jeremy (USA)) (220000)
**210 PYRRHIC DANCER (IRE)**, b c 21/02 Holy Roman Emperor (IRE)—Kirk's Dancer (USA) (Dunkirk (USA)) (38095)
**211 RADAD (IRE)**, ch c 14/02 Footstepsinthesand—Keyta Bonita (IRE) (Denon (USA)) (18095)
**212** B c 19/03 Shamardal (USA)—Rayaheen (Nayef (USA))
**213 RIVER PRIDE**, b f 15/02 Oasis Dream—Highest (Dynaformer (USA))
**214 SALITEH**, b f 27/02 Ardad (IRE)—Poesy (Poet's Voice) (43000)
**215 SANDY'S HOPE (IRE)**, ch f 19/04 Dream Ahead (USA)—Sandy's Charm (FR) (Footstepsinthesand) (60532)
**216 SIAMSA (IRE)**, b f 21/02 Starspangledbanner (AUS)—Sliabh Luachra (IRE) (High Chaparral (IRE)) (228571)
**217** B c 26/03 Kodiac—Sodashy (IRE) (Noverre (USA)) (130000)
**218 SOUTH AUDLEY**, b c 27/03 Aclaim (IRE)—Sefaat (Haafet (USA))
**219 SOWS (IRE)**, b f 09/02 Kodiac—Zvarkhova (FR) (Makfi) (95238)
**220 ST ELMO'S FIRE (IRE)**, b c 10/04 Mehmas (IRE)—El Morocco (USA) (El Prado (IRE)) (30000)
**221** B c 05/05 Night of Thunder (IRE)—Surprise (IRE) (Anabaa Blue) (250000)
**222 SYMPHONY PERFECT (IRE)**, b f 02/03 Fast Company (IRE)—Irish Romance (IRE) (Rip Van Winkle (IRE)) (28571)
**223 SYSTEM (IRE)**, b f 04/03 Galileo Gold—Spiritual Air (Royal Applause) (76190)
**224 TACARIB BAY**, b c 09/02 Night of Thunder (IRE)—Bassmah (Harbour Watch (IRE))
**225** B c 03/02 Adaay (IRE)—The Giving Tree (IRE) (Rock of Gibraltar (IRE)) (45000)
**226 THREE DONS (IRE)**, b c 10/03 Fast Company (IRE)—Avizare (IRE) (Lawman (FR)) (39048)
**227 THUNDER MAX**, ch c 11/02 Night of Thunder (IRE)—Tuolumne Meadows (High Chaparral (IRE)) (147619)
**228 THUNDER QUEEN**, b f 03/03 Night of Thunder (IRE)—Muzhil (IRE) (Manduro (GER)) (68571)
**229** B f 30/04 Cable Bay (IRE)—Todber (Cape Cross (IRE)) (15238)
**230** B f 18/02 Olympic Glory (IRE)—Travel Writer (IRE) (New Approach (IRE)) (9000)
**231 TRIQUETRA (IRE)**, b f 10/02 Dark Angel (IRE)—Button Down (Oasis Dream) (114286)
**232 TRUGANINI (IRE)**, b f 05/03 Lawman (FR)—Tazmania (IRE) (Helmet (AUS)) (38095)
**233 TYSON (IRE)**, gr c 26/02 Starspangledbanner (AUS)—Ach Alannah (IRE) (Marju (IRE)) (75000)
**234** B c 18/04 Cotai Glory—Warm Welcome (Motivator) (125000)
**235** B f 25/02 Acclamation—Westadora (IRE) (Le Havre (IRE)) (55238)
**236** B c 08/02 Olympic Glory (IRE)—Ysandre (Zamindar (USA))
**237 ZOLTAN STAR**, b c 09/05 Kodiac—Siralen (USA) (Majestic Warrior (USA)) (55000)

**Head Man:** Colin Bolger, Tony Gorman.

**Flat Jockey:** Pat Dobbs, Sean Levey, Rossa Ryan. **Apprentice Jockey:** Liam Browne, Luke Catton, Thore Hammer Hansen, Ed Rees.

## 254 MR GEOFFREY HARKER, Thirsk
Postal: **Stockhill Green, York Rd, Thirkelby, Thirsk, North Yorkshire, YO7 3AS**
Contacts: **PHONE 01845 501117 MOBILE 07803 116412, 07930 125544**
**EMAIL gandjhome@aol.com WEBSITE www.geoffharkerracing.com**

1 **CALONNE (IRE),** 5, gr g Alhebayeb (IRE)—Lady Pastrana (IRE) **P. I. Harker**
2 **ELDELBAR (SPA),** 7, ch g Footstepsinthesand—Malinche **The Twelve Minimum Racing Club**
3 **GETAWAY GUILLAUNE (IRE),** 6, b m Getaway (GER)—Corrie Hall (IRE) **The Twelve Minimum Racing Club**
4 **HAIL SEZER,** 4, b g Intrinsic—Nice One **The Twelve Minimum Racing Club**
5 **RANGEFIELD EXPRESS (IRE),** 5, b g Born To Sea (IRE)—Bogini (IRE) **Cloud 9 Racing & Phil Harker**
6 **ROCKET ROD (IRE),** 4, b g Australia—Tessa Reef (IRE) **The Twelve Minimum Racing Club**
7 **RUM RUNNER,** 6, b g Havana Gold (IRE)—Thermopylae **The Twelve Minimum Racing Club**
8 **SAVALAS (IRE),** 6, gr g Zebedee—Tap The Dot (IRE) **The Twelve Minimum Racing Club**
9 **SCOTTISH SUMMIT (IRE),** 8, b g Shamardal (USA)—
Scottish Stage (IRE) **T Banerjee,N Mather,P Downes & G Harker**
10 **WENTWORTH FALLS,** 9, gr g Dansili—Strawberry Morn (CAN) **The Fall Guys Club**
11 **WHITEHALL,** 6, b g Dansili—Majestic Roi (USA) **P. I. Harker**

**Other Owners:** Dr A. T. Banerjee, Cloud 9 Racing, Mr P. Downes, Mr G. A. Harker, P. I. Harker, Mr D. M. Mather.

**Assistant Trainer:** Jenny Harker.

**NH Jockey:** W. T. Kennedy.

## 255 MR RICHARD HARPER, Kings Sutton
Postal: **Home Farm, Kings Sutton, Banbury, Oxfordshire, OX17 3RS**
Contacts: **PHONE 01295 810997 MOBILE 07970 223481**
**EMAIL richard@harpersfarm.co.uk**

1 **THOMAS BLOSSOM (IRE),** 11, b g Dylan Thomas (IRE)—Woman Secret (IRE) **R. C. Harper**

**Assistant Trainer:** C. Harper.

## 256 MRS JESSICA HARRINGTON, Kildare
Postal: **Commonstown Stud, Moone, Co. Kildare, Ireland**
Contacts: **PHONE +353 59 862 4153 MOBILE +353 87 256 6129**
**EMAIL jessica@jessicaharringtonracing.com WEBSITE www.jessicaharringtonracing.com**

1 **AESOP (IRE),** 4, b g Make Believe—Sadima (IRE)
2 **ALPINE STAR (IRE),** 4, ch f Sea The Moon (GER)—Alpha Lupi (IRE)
3 **ANCIENT SPIRIT (GER),** 6, b h Invincible Spirit (IRE)—Assisi (GER)
4 **ASHDALE BOB (IRE),** 6, b g Shantou (USA)—Ceol Rua (IRE)
5 **ATHA SOLAS (IRE),** 4, b f Shirocco (GER)—Coonagh Cross (IRE)
6 **AUTUMN EVENING,** 4, ch g Tamayuz—Martagon Lily
7 **BARBADOS (IRE),** 5, b g Galileo (IRE)—Sumora (IRE)
8 **BARRINGTON COURT,** 7, ch m Mastercraftsman—Arabian Hideaway
9 4, B g Martaline—Beau Bridget (IRE)
10 **BOOLA BOOLA (IRE),** 4, b g Invincible Spirit (IRE)—We Can Say It Now (AUS)
11 **BOPEDRO (FR),** 5, b g Pedro The Great (USA)—Breizh Touch (FR)
12 **CALIFORNIA BREEZE (IRE),** 5, br m Shirocco (GER)—Taraval (IRE)
13 **CAMPHOR (IRE),** 5, b m Camelot—Paraphernalia
14 **CAYENNE PEPPER,** 4, ch f Australia—Muwakaba

## MRS JESSICA HARRINGTON - continued

15 **CLASSIC MOET (IRE)**, 5, b m Beat Hollow—Holloden (IRE)
16 **COMMANDER LADY (IRE)**, 6, b m Yeats (IRE)—Shuil Aris (IRE)
17 **CROSSHILL (IRE)**, 6, b g Sholokhov (IRE)—Rathvawn Belle (IRE)
18 **DAISY DUFRESNE (IRE)**, 5, b m Doyen (IRE)—Daytona Lily (IRE)
19 **DISCORDANTLY (IRE)**, 7, b g Salutino (GER)—Collinstown Queen (IRE)
20 **EDISON KENT (IRE)**, 5, b g Leading Light (IRE)—Kentish Town (IRE)
21 **EMILY MOON (IRE)**, 7, b m Beneficial—Wood Lily (IRE)
22 **EVER PRESENT**, 5, br g Elusive Pimpernel—Persian Memories
23 **EXIT POLL (IRE)**, 7, b g Elusive Pimpernel (USA)—Carolobrian (AUS)
24 **FLOR DE LA LUNA**, 4, b f Sea The Moon—Fresa
25 **FORBEARANCE (IRE)**, 4, b f Galileo (IRE)—Nechita (AUS)
26 **FREE SOLO (IRE)**, 4, ch c Showcasing—Amuser (IRE)
27 **GOT TRUMPED**, 6, ch g Thewayyouare (USA)—Madam President
28 **GUIRI (GER)**, 6, ch g Motivator—Guardia (GER)
29 **HARPOCRATES (IRE)**, 4, b c Invincible Spirit (IRE)—Ideal
30 **ILMIG (IRE)**, 4, b g Galileo (IRE)—Acoma (USA)
31 **IMPACT FACTOR (IRE)**, 9, b g Flemensfirth (USA)—Hello Kitty (IRE)
32 **INDIGO BALANCE (IRE)**, 5, b b r h Invincible Spirit (IRE)—Rose de France (IRE)
33 **JETT (IRE)**, 10, b g Flemensfirth (USA)—La Noire (IRE)
34 **JUNGLE JUNCTION (IRE)**, 6, br g Elusive Pimpernel (USA)—Consignia (IRE)
35 **KING OF COMEDY (IRE)**, 5, b h Kingman—Stage Presence (IRE)
36 **LADY ANNER (IRE)**, 4, b f Fastnet Rock (AUS)—Lady Bones (IRE)
37 **LADY TASMANIA**, 4, b f Australia—Nimboo (USA)
38 **LEO DE FURY (IRE)**, 5, ch h Australia—Attire
39 **LIFETIME AMBITION**, 6, b g Kapgarde—Jeanquiri
40 **LOBO ROJO**, 4, ch c Lope de Vega (IRE)—Louve Nationale (IRE)
41 **LYNWOOD GOLD (IRE)**, 6, gr ro g Mastercraftsman (IRE)—Witch of Fife (USA)
42 **MADISON TO MONROE (IRE)**, 8, ro g Presenting—Caltra Princess (IRE)
43 **MAGIC OF LIGHT (IRE)**, 10, b m Flemensfirth (USA)—Quest of Passion (FR)
44 **MAUD GONNE SPIRIT (IRE)**, 4, ch f Intello—Bari
45 **MIA MENTO (IRE)**, 5, b m Casamento (IRE)—Mia Divina
46 **MOROSINI (FR)**, 6, b g Martaline—Iris du Berlais (FR)
47 **MR HENDRICKS**, 7, b g Milan—Coming Home
48 **NEVERUSHACON (IRE)**, 10, b g Echo of Light—Lily Beth (IRE)
49 **NEWTOWN PERY (IRE)**, 6, b m Yeats (IRE)—Blooming Quick (IRE)
50 **NJORD (IRE)**, 5, b g Roderic O'Connor—Rosalind Franklin (IRE)
51 **NOT MANY LEFT (IRE)**, 8, b g Oscar (IRE)—Lasado (IRE)
52 **OH SO CHIC**, 4, b f Farhh—Lady Hen
53 **ONLYHUMAN (IRE)**, 8, b g Invincible Spirit (IRE)—Liscune (IRE)
54 **PEPPERONI PETE**, 5, b g Zoffany—Zaafran
55 **POLISHED STEEL (IRE)**, 7, b g Jeremy (USA)—Chaperoned (IRE)
56 **PORT STANLEY**, 7, b g Papal Bull—Prairie Moonlight
57 **PROTAGONIST (IRE)**, 4, b c Wootton Bassett—Sagariya
58 **RAPID RESPONSE (FR)**, 7, br m Network (GER)—La Grande Villez (FR)
59 **REAL APPEAL (GER)**, 4, b g Sidestep (AUS)—Runaway Sparkle
60 **SANDYMOUNT BABY (IRE)**, 4, b f Elusive Pimpernel (USA)—Joleah (IRE)
61 **SHONA MEA**, 4, b f Dragon Pulse—Weekend Getaway
62 **SILENCE PLEASE (IRE)**, 4, b f Gleneagles—Crazy Volume
63 **SILVER SHEEN (IRE)**, 7, b g Sulamani—Silver Gypsy
64 **SIZING POTTSIE**, 7, b g Kapgarde—Line Salsa
65 **TAURAN SHAMAN (IRE)**, 5, b h Shamardal—Danelissima
66 **THEGOAHEADMAN (IRE)**, 7, br g Jeremy (USA)—Little Luv (IRE)
67 **VALERIA MESSALINA (IRE)**, 4, b f Holy Roman Emperor—Arty Crafty
68 **WALK TO FREEDOM (IRE)**, 11, br g Arcadio (GER)—Carryonharriet (IRE)
69 **WHISPERINTHEBREEZE**, 8, gr ro g Kayf Tara—Silver Spinner
70 **WINGIN A PRAYER (IRE)**, 6, b g Winged Love—Toubliss
71 **YA YA BABY (IRE)**, 4, b f Hallowed Crown (AUS)—Standout (FR)

## MRS JESSICA HARRINGTON - continued

### THREE-YEAR-OLDS

72 **ACE AUSSIE (IRE)**, b c Australia—Queenscliff (IRE)
73 **ALEEN CUST (IRE)**, b f New Bay—Elltaaf (IRE)
74 **ALICE KITTY (IRE)**, ch f Bobby's Kitten (USA)—Classic Legend
75 **ANNA STRADA**, ch f Havana Gold (IRE)—Frequently
76 **ANNER CASTLE (IRE)**, b c Fastnet Rock (AUS)—Marigold Hotel (IRE)
77 **ANTHEM (IRE)**, ch c Australia—Sophie Germain (IRE)
78 **AURORA PRINCESS (IRE)**, b f The Gurkha (IRE)—Rub A Dub Dub
79 **BARON WILD (IRE)**, b g Zoffany (IRE)—Wild Child (IRE)
80 **BELL I AM (IRE)**, b f Belardo (IRE)—Adroit (IRE)
81 **BELL PEPPER (IRE)**, b f Iffraaj—Abend (IRE)
82 **BONTE MOI (FR)**, b f Le Havre (IRE)—Oh Goodness Me
83 **CADILLAC (IRE)**, b c Lope de Vega (IRE)—Seas of Wells (IRE)
84 **CASTLE STABLES (IRE)**, b g Australia—Invincible Cara (IRE)
85 **CITRONNADE**, b f Lemon Drop Kid (USA)—Bohemian Dance (IRE)
86 **CLEW BAY (IRE)**, b f New Bay—Kalandara (IRE)
87 **CLIMATE (IRE)**, b f Australia—Frappe (IRE)
88 **COLD STEEL (USA)**, br c Summer Front (USA)—Shotgun Persuasion (USA)
89 **COSMIC VEGA (IRE)**, b c Lope de Vega (IRE)—Pivotal Era
90 **CYCLADIC (IRE)**, b f Fastnet Rock (AUS)—Peloponnese (FR)
91 **DEPUTY SANDY (IRE)**, b c Footstepsinthesand—Bayan Kasirga (IRE)
92 **DICKIEDOODA (IRE)**, ch f Starspangledbanner (AUS)—So Dandy (IRE)
93 **ESPOUSE (IRE)**, b f Elusive Pimpernel (USA)—Sea of Dreams (IRE)
94 **FEELING TIP TOP (IRE)**, b c Elzaam (AUS)—Fickle Feelings (IRE)
95 **FERMOY (IRE)**, b f Kodiac—Ramone (IRE)
96 **FLY GIRL (IRE)**, b f The Gurkha (IRE)—Katchy Lady
97 **GIULIANA (GER)**, b f Muhaarar—Golden Whip
98 **GOLDEN LYRIC**, b br f Lope de Vega (IRE)—As Good As Gold (IRE)
99 **GOODNIGHT KISS (IRE)**, b f Fastnet Rock (AUS)—Sweet Dreams Baby (IRE)
100 **HAMWOOD FLIER (IRE)**, gr f Kodiac—Fonda (USA)
101 **HELL BENT (IRE)**, ch c Mastercraftsman (IRE)—Fikrah
102 **JUSTATUNE (IRE)**, b f Australia—Crafty (AUS)
103 **KOJIN (IRE)**, ch c Siyouni (FR)—Nebraas
104 **KOREA (IRE)**, b f Galileo (IRE)—Miss Childrey (IRE)
105 **LADY BARRINGTON (IRE)**, b f Camelot—Ceol An Ghra (IRE)
106 B c Rajj (IRE)—Lady Temptress (IRE)
107 **LAELAPS (IRE)**, b c Exceed And Excel (AUS)—Magen's Star (IRE)
108 **LIGHT OF MY EYES**, b f Frankel—Divine Proportions
109 **LOCH LEIN (IRE)**, b f Invincible Spirit (IRE)—Ashley Hall (USA)
110 **LOS ANDES**, b c Karakontie—Candy Kitty
111 **LUCKY VEGA (IRE)**, b c Lope de Vega (IRE)—Queen of Carthage (USA)
112 **MALAYSIAN (IRE)**, ch f Pride Of Dubai—Booker
113 **MALOJA**, b f Showcasing—Eyeshine
114 **MCPHERSON**, b c Golden Horn—Moonlight Sonata
115 **MUCKROSS (IRE)**, b c Zoffany (IRE)—Early Addition (IRE)
116 **MY MINERVINA (IRE)**, b f Holy Roman Emperor (IRE)—Are You Mine (IRE)
117 **NO SPEAK ALEXANDER (IRE)**, b f Shaala—Rapacity Alexander
118 **NOISE (IRE)**, b f Zoffany (IRE)—Girouette (IRE)
119 **O'REILLY (FR)**, b c Frankel—Fann (USA)
120 B c Epaulette (AUS)—Oasis Fire (IRE)
121 **OH SAY (IRE)**, b c Starspangledbanner (AUS)—Mysterious Burg (FR)
122 **ONLY SKY (IRE)**, b f Sea The Stars (IRE)—Star Mon Amie (IRE)
123 **OODNADATTA (IRE)**, b br f Australia—Bewitched (IRE)
124 **PALIFICO**, ch f Siyouni (FR)—Montalcino (IRE)
125 **PAPPINA (IRE)**, ch f Sea The Stars (IRE)—Padmini
126 **PRETTY'N'SMART (IRE)**, b f Iffraaj—Photophore (IRE)
127 **PRIVILEGE**, b g Holy Roman Emperor (IRE)—Two Days In Paris (FR)
128 **PROVOCATEUSE (IRE)**, b f Pride Of Dubai—Malicieuse
129 **ROSES BLUE (IRE)**, b f Kodiac—Sweet Irish

# MRS JESSICA HARRINGTON - continued

130 **ROSIE BASSETT**, b f Wootton Bassett—Lipstick Rose (IRE)
131 **SACRED RHYME (IRE)**, ch f Lope de Vega (IRE)—Singing Field (IRE)
132 **SAGAR LAKE (FR)**, ch f Sepoy (AUS)—Sablerose (IRE)
133 **SANTOSHA (IRE)**, b f Coulsty (IRE)—Princess Zoffany (IRE)
134 Gr f Lope de Vega (IRE)—Screen Star (IRE)
135 **SIGN FROM ABOVE (IRE)**, b c Sea The Stars (IRE)—Martine's Spirit (IRE)
136 **SIOFRA (IRE)**, b f Iffraaj—The Fairy (IRE)
137 **SOARING SKY (IRE)**, b f Free Eagle (IRE)—Allannah Abu
138 **SPANISH CLASS (IRE)**, b f Lope de Vega (IRE)—School Run (IRE)
139 **STARDAYZ (IRE)**, b f Camelot—Red Avis
140 **STAY SAFE (IRE)**, b f Showcasing—Boo Boo Bear (IRE)
141 B f Bobby's Kitten (USA)—Sularina (IRE)
142 **TAIPAN (FR)**, b c Frankel—Kenzadargent (FR)
143 **THE BLUE BRILLIANT (IRE)**, b f Fastnet Rock (AUS)—Butterfly Blue (IRE)
144 **THEORY OF MUSIC (IRE)**, b f Fastnet Rock (AUS)—Beyond Compare (IRE)
145 **VALLE DE LA LUNA**, b f Galileo—Fiesolana
146 **WINDSOR PASS (IRE)**, b f Lope de Vega (IRE)—Carte de Visite (USA)
147 **YOU OWE ME MONEY (IRE)**, b f Awtaad (IRE)—Magie Noire (IRE)
148 **YULONG DE LEGEND (IRE)**, b c Kodiac—Plum Sugar (IRE)
149 **ZAFFY'S PRIDE (IRE)**, b f Pride of Dubai (AUS)—Zaafran

## TWO-YEAR-OLDS

150 B c 03/03 Street Sense (USA)—Accusation (USA) (Royal Academy (USA))
151 **ADONIS (IRE)**, ch c 05/03 Siyouni (FR)—Rajaratna (IRE) (Galileo (IRE))
152 B f 19/02 Fastnet Rock (AUS)—Affability (IRE) (Dalakhani (IRE)) (55000)
153 **AIRGLOW (USA)**, b f 22/02 Kitten's Joy (USA)—Absolute Crackers (IRE) (Giant's Causeway (USA)) (93090)
154 **ALIZARINE**, b f 15/03 Sea The Moon (GER)—Alea Iacta (Invincible Spirit (IRE))
155 B c 28/02 Kodiac—Alonsoa (IRE) (Raven's Pass (USA)) (78000)
156 Ch c 28/02 Curlin (USA)—An Cailin Orga (IRE) (Galileo (IRE)) (240000)
157 B f 02/05 Sea The Moon (GER)—Angelic Air (Oasis Dream) (58000)
158 Gr f 26/03 Oasis Dream—Angelic Guest (IRE) (Dark Angel (IRE)) (23810)
159 B g 20/04 Holy Roman Emperor (IRE)—Apparatchika (Archipenko (USA)) (26000)
160 B c 18/02 Acclamation—Aristocratic (Exceed And Excel (AUS)) (55000)
161 **BLACK PEPPER (IRE)**, b br f 17/04 Caravaggio (USA)—Hug And A Kiss (USA) (Thewayyouare (USA)) (59048)
162 Gr c 12/02 Lope de Vega (IRE)—Claba di San Jore (IRE) (Barathea (IRE)) (115000)
163 **CORVIGLIA (USA)**, ch f 13/04 Karakontie (JPN)—Light Blow (USA) (Kingmambo (USA))
164 **DISCOVERIES (IRE)**, b f 29/04 Mastercraftsman (IRE)—Alpha Lupi (IRE) (Rahy (USA))
165 **ECOUTEZ (IRE)**, b f 09/04 Exceed And Excel (AUS)—Ecoutila (USA) (Rahy (USA))
166 B c 24/02 Acclamation—Exquisite Ruby (Exceed And Excel (AUS)) (147619)
167 B f 04/05 Belardo (IRE)—Fashion Line (IRE) (Cape Cross (IRE)) (26634)
168 B f 02/04 Sea The Stars (IRE)—Greenisland (IRE) (Fasliyev (USA))
169 **ILE DE CIRCE (IRE)**, ch f 30/03 Ulysses (USA)—Sea Chanter (USA) (War Chant (USA))
170 **IMPEACHD ALEXANDER (IRE)**, b f 05/02 Starspangledbanner (AUS)—Pious Alexander (IRE) (Acclamation) (9685)
171 **IRISH LULLABY**, gr f 30/01 Nathaniel (IRE)—Victoria Regina (IRE) (Mastercraftsman (IRE))
172 **IRISH VIRTUOSO**, gr f 10/03 Mastercraftsman (IRE)—Shenir (Mark of Esteem (IRE)) (128571)
173 B gr f 18/04 Caravaggio (USA)—Jasmine Blue (IRE) (Galileo (IRE)) (58000)
174 B f 03/05 Starspangledbanner (AUS)—Je T'Adore (IRE) (Montjeu (IRE)) (42857)
175 B f 25/02 Caravaggio (USA)—Just Joan (IRE) (Pour Moi (IRE)) (65000)
176 **KOMEDY KICKS (IRE)**, b f 14/03 Churchill (IRE)—Komedy (IRE) (Kodiac) (95238)
177 Ch c 17/02 Lope de Vega (IRE)—Kuna Yala (GER) (Manduro (GER))
178 Ch c 20/02 New Approach (IRE)—La Superba (IRE) (Medicean) (105000)
179 Ch f 12/03 Pride of Dubai (AUS)—Mighty Girl (FR) (Makfi) (16000)
180 B f 22/04 Galileo (IRE)—Night Lagoon (GER) (Lagunas) (305000)
181 **PANTELLERIA (USA)**, b f 06/04 Kitten's Joy (USA)—Kyllachy Queen (IRE) (Kyllachy)
182 **PARIS LIGHTS (IRE)**, b c 21/03 Siyouni (FR)—Cabaret (IRE) (Galileo (IRE)) (650000)
183 B f 18/03 Rajj (IRE)—Princess Aloof (IRE) (Big Bad Bob (IRE)) (1614)
184 Ch f 21/03 Air Force Blue (USA)—Princess Sinead (IRE) (Jeremy (USA)) (19048)
185 **SABLONNE**, b f 15/04 Dark Angel (IRE)—Starlit Sands (Oasis Dream)
186 B f 03/03 Gleneagles (IRE)—Sandstone (Dansili)

## MRS JESSICA HARRINGTON - continued

**187 SIERRA NEVADA (USA),** b f 13/02 American Pharoah (USA)—Visions of Clarity (IRE) (Sadler's Wells (USA))
**188** B c 28/02 Lope de Vega (IRE)—Starflower (Champs Elysees) (50000)
**189 STELLAROCK (IRE),** b f 01/03 Fastnet Rock (AUS)—Wild Child (IRE) (Galileo (IRE))
**190** B f 12/02 Oasis Dream—Street Marie (USA) (Street Cry (IRE)) (9524)
**191** B c 19/04 Pivotal—Tipping Over (IRE) (Aussie Rules (USA)) (85714)
**192 TREVAUNANCE (IRE),** b f 13/03 Muhaarar—Liber Nauticus (IRE) (Azamour (IRE))
**193** B f 02/02 Australia—True Verdict (IRE) (Danehill Dancer (IRE)) (38095)
**194** B f 04/05 Kodi Bear (IRE)—Tut (IRE) (Intikhab (USA)) (23000)
**195 UPBEAT,** b f 07/03 Invincible Spirit (IRE)—Blissful Beat (Beat Hollow)
**196 VERLINGA (IRE),** b f 08/02 Dubawi (IRE)—Bocca Baciata (IRE) (Big Bad Bob (IRE))
**197** B c 03/03 Zoffany (IRE)—What Say You (IRE) (Galileo (IRE)) (45000)
**198 WILLAMETTE VALLEY (IRE),** b f 06/03 Galileo (IRE)—Fire Lily (IRE) (Dansili)
**199 YASHIN (IRE),** b c 07/04 Churchill (IRE)—Mirdhak (Dansili)

**Assistant Trainer:** Miss Kate Harrington, Eamonn Leigh.

---

**257**
## MISS GRACE HARRIS, Shirenewton
Postal: **White House, Shirenewton, Chepstow, Gwent, NP16 6AQ**
Contacts: **MOBILE 07912 359425**
EMAIL gracebarris90@gmail.com WEBSITE www.graceharrisracing.com

**1 AIR OF YORK (IRE),** 9, b g Vale of York (IRE)—State Secret  **Mrs L. A. Cullimore**
**2 CHIEF BRODY,** 10, b g Phoenix Reach (IRE)—Cherry Plum  **Lucy Sandford & Richard Phillips**
**3 DEREK LE GRAND,** 4, b g Mukhadram—Duo de Choc (IRE)  **Mrs V. James**
**4 FAINT HOPE,** 9, ch g Midnight Legend—Rhinestone Ruby  **Mrs Elaine Tate & Partner**
**5 FINAL LIST (IRE),** 7, ch g Doyen (IRE)—Lady Goldilocks (IRE)  **Mr J. Thomas**
**6 HALF NELSON,** 6, ch g Mount Nelson—Maria Antonia (IRE)  **Jonathan Thomas & Partner**
**7 HAVANA SUNSET,** 5, b g Havana Gold (IRE)—Sunset Kitty (USA)  **Grace Harris Racing**
**8 ISLAND MEMORY,** 4, b f Exceed And Excel (AUS)—Ya Latif (IRE)  **Mr J. Knight**
**9 JACKE IS BACK (FR),** 6, b g Planteur (IRE)—Black Jack Lady (IRE)  **J. Thomas, D. Lawton & Associates**
**10 KARAKORAM,** 6, b g Exceleration (IRE)—Portrait  **Grace Harris Racing**
**11 NEARLY FAMOUS,** 8, b m Rip Van Winkle (IRE)—Ermena  **Brendon Sabin & Partner**
**12 ON CALL (IRE),** 8, b g Flemensfirth (USA)—Oscar's Reprieve (IRE)  **Red & Black Racing**
**13 PROFILE PICTURE (IRE),** 7, b g Sans Frontieres (IRE)—Sehoya (USA)  **R Matthews, D Matthews & Associates**
**14 RIVER SONG (IRE),** 4, b f Battle of Marengo (IRE)—Yurituni  **Riverwood Racing**
**15 TALLY'S SON,** 7, b g Assertive—Talamahana  **Paul & Ann de Weck**
**16 THE GARRISON (IRE),** 7, b g Arakan (USA)—Kerry Lily (IRE)  **Mrs V. James**

### THREE-YEAR-OLDS

**17 LUXY LOU (IRE),** ch f The Last Lion (IRE)—Dutch Courage  **Mr Ronald Davies & Mrs Candida Davies**

**Other Owners:** Mrs C. M. Davies, Mr R. I. D. Davies, Mrs A. De Weck, Grace Harris Racing, Miss G. Harris, Ms M. Harris, Mrs D. L. S. Lawton, Mr D. Matthews, Mr R. Matthews, Riverwood Racing, Mr B. Sabin, Mrs E. Tate, Mr J. Thomas, P. L. de Weck.

**Assistant Trainer:** Michelle Harris.

## 258 MR MILTON HARRIS, Warminster
Postal: **The Beeches, Deverill Road, Sutton Veny, Warminster, Wiltshire, BA12 7BY**
Contacts: **MOBILE 07879 634308**

1 **ACHY BREAKY HEART (IRE)**, 7, b m Milan—Hazy Outlook (IRE) **Mr M. Harris**
2 **AINTREE MY DREAM (FR)**, 11, b br g Saint des Saints (FR)—Pretty Melodie (FR) **Mrs S. E. Brown**
3 **ALCOCK AND BROWN (IRE)**, 9, b g Oasis Dream—Heart Stopping (USA) **Air-water Treatments Ltd**
4 **AWAY FOR SLATES (IRE)**, 11, b g Arcadio (GER)—Rumi **Mrs Anthea Williams & Partner**
5 **CANNIE LAD**, 6, b g Haafhd—So Cannie **Only Horses and Fools**
6 **DISCREET HERO (IRE)**, 8, ch g Siyouni (FR)—Alfaguara (USA) **Mr F. Tieman**
7 **ELECTRIC ANNIE (IRE)**, 6, b m Fame And Glory—Decent Dime (IRE) **Mr R. Sparks**
8 **GLOBAL AGREEMENT**, 4, ch g Mayson—Amicable Terms **Charlie Holding, Emdells & Partners**
9 **GOOD BYE (GER)**, 6, ch g Tertullian (USA)—Guantana (GER) **Mr M. Harris**
10 **GOODWOOD SHOWMAN**, 6, b g Showcasing—Polly Floyer **Mr M. Harris**
11 **IF KARL'S BERG DID**, 6, b g Fame And Glory—Mayberry **Air-water Treatments Ltd**
12 **JACAMAR (GER)**, 6, b g Maxios—Juvena (GER) **Pegasus Bloodstock Limited**
13 **JACKSON HILL (IRE)**, 7, b g Jeremy (USA)—Definite Leader (IRE) **The Jackson 8**
14 **JANUS (IRE)**, 6, b g Rock of Gibraltar (IRE)—Jardina (AUS) **Only Horses and Fools**
15 **KHAN (GER)**, 7, b h Santiago (GER)—Kapitol (GER) **Mr M. Adams**
16 **KING'S PROCTOR (IRE)**, 6, b g Cape Cross (IRE)—Alimony (IRE) **Air-water Treatments Ltd**
17 **KNOWWHENTOHOLDEM (IRE)**, 6, b br g Flemensfirth (USA)—Definite Design (IRE)
18 4, Br f Telescope (IRE)—Koala Bear
19 **MAGIC RIVER (IRE)**, 10, ch g Indian River (FR)—All Magic (IRE) **Emdells Limited**
20 **MASTEROFTHEHEIGHTS (IRE)**, 5, b g Masterofthehorse (IRE)—Martha's Way **Mr A. Harrison**
21 **MI LADDO (IRE)**, 5, gr g Lilbourne Lad (IRE)—Fritta Mista (IRE) **Emdells Limited**
22 **MILITARY DRESS (IRE)**, 6, b m Epaulette (AUS)—Dune Breeze (IRE) **Mr R. Sparks**
23 **MR YEATS (IRE)**, 4, b g Yeats (IRE)—Va'vite (IRE) **Emdells Limited**
24 **NOT GOING OUT (IRE)**, 7, ch g Doyen (IRE)—Alannico **Ruth Nelmes & Milton Harris**
25 **PANDA SEVEN (FR)**, 4, b g Wootton Bassett—Hermanville (IRE) **Mr M. Harris**
26 **PHILLIPSTOWN ELLEN (IRE)**, 4, b f Xtension (IRE)—Royal Bean (USA) **Mr C. J. Harding**
27 **PRESENTING YEATS (IRE)**, 5, b g Yeats (IRE)—Va'vite (IRE) **Mrs D. Dewbery**
28 **PYRAMID PLACE (IRE)**, 4, b g Authorized (IRE)—Attima **Mr M. Harris**
29 **RAASED (IRE)**, 4, b g Teofilo (IRE)—Yanabeeaa (USA) **Mr M. Harris**
30 **SERGEANT (FR)**, 4, b g Nutan (GER)—Stella Marina (IRE) **Mr M. Harris**
31 5, B m Heeraat (USA)—So Cannie
32 **SONGO (IRE)**, 5, b g Most Improved (IRE)—Sacre Fleur (IRE) **Pegasus Bloodstock Limited**
33 **STIMULATING SONG**, 6, ch g Stimulation (IRE)—Choral Singer **Pegasus Bloodstock & Mr A. Harrison**
34 **SUFI**, 7, ch g Pivotal—Basanti (USA) **Mr J. F. Pearl**
35 **SUPER SUPERJACK**, 4, ch g Harbour Watch (IRE)—La Palma **L. R. Turland**
36 **TECHNOLOGICAL**, 6, gr g Universal (IRE)—Qeethaara (USA) **Air-water Treatments Ltd**
37 **THE LACEMAKER**, 7, b m Dutch Art—Sospel **Mrs D. C. Scott**
38 **WASEEM FARIS (IRE)**, 12, b g Exceed And Excel (AUS)—Kissing Time **Mr M. Harris**
39 **WETANWINDY**, 6, br g Watar (IRE)—Tinkwood (IRE) **Mr M. Harris**
40 5, B m Milan—Zoeys Dream (IRE)

### THREE-YEAR-OLDS
41 **ABHAINN (FR)**, b g Youmzain (IRE)—Abaco Ridge **North East Racehorses**
42 B g Monsieur Bond (IRE)—Choral Singer **Pegasus Bloodstock Limited**
43 Ch f Pride of Dubai (AUS)—Diamond Duchess (IRE)
44 **HAVANA CABANA**, b f Havana Gold (IRE)—Word Perfect **The Original Gang**
45 B g Footstepsinthesand—Maontri (IRE)
46 **PULSATION (IRE)**, ch g Dragon Pulse (IRE)—Rouwaki (USA) **Mr M. Harris**
47 **TEMPAH**, b f Heeraat (IRE)—Amicable Terms **Sutton Veny Racing Syndicate**
48 Ch g Champs Elysees—Va'vite (IRE)

### TWO-YEAR-OLDS
49 B f 19/04 Dragon Pulse (IRE)—Blas Ceoil (USA) (Mr Greeley (USA))
50 Ch g 26/03 El Kabeir (USA)—Diamond Duchess (IRE) (Dubawi (IRE))
51 Gr f 14/05 Universal (IRE)—Qeethaara (USA) (Aljabr (USA))

## MR MILTON HARRIS - continued

**Other Owners:** Charlie Holding Limited, Emdells Limited, Mr J. G. Giddings, Mr M. Harris, Mr A. Harrison, Mrs R. E. Nelmes, Pegasus Bloodstock Limited, Mrs A. M. Williams.

---

**259** **MR RONALD HARRIS, Chepstow**
Postal: Ridge House Stables, Earlswood, Chepstow, Monmouthshire, NP16 6AN
Contacts: **PHONE 01291 641689 MOBILE 07831 770899 FAX 01291 641258**
**EMAIL** ridgehousestables.ltd@btinternet.com **WEBSITE** www.ronharrisracing.co.uk

1 **DEADLY ACCURATE**, 6, br g Lethal Force (IRE)—Riccoche (IRE) **Mr S. Bell**
2 **DIAMOND VINE (IRE)**, 13, b g Diamond Green (FR)—Glasnas Giant **Ridge House Stables Ltd**
3 **ELZAAM'S DREAM (IRE)**, 5, b m Elzaam (AUS)—Alinda (IRE) **Ridge House Stables Ltd**
4 **EQUALLY FAST**, 9, b g Equiano (FR)—Fabulously Fast (USA) **Mr S. Bell**
5 **EYE OF THE WATER (IRE)**, 5, b g Lilbourne Lad (IRE)—Desert Location **Mr M. E. Wright**
6 **FANTASY JUSTIFIER (IRE)**, 10, b g Arakan (USA)—Grandel **Ridge House Stables Ltd**
7 **GLAMOROUS FORCE**, 4, b g Lethal Force (IRE)—Glamorous Spirit (IRE) **M Doocey, S Doocey & P J Doocey**
8 **I'M WATCHING YOU**, 4, ch g Harbour Watch (IRE)—Victrix Ludorum (IRE) **Ridge House Stables Ltd**
9 **MAJESTIC HERO (IRE)**, 9, b g Majestic Missile (IRE)—Xena (IRE) **Mrs Jackie Jarrett & Ridge House Stables**
10 **MERWEB (IRE)**, 6, gr g Shamardal (USA)—Ashley Hall (USA) **J. A. Gent**
11 **POWERFUL DREAM (IRE)**, 8, b m Frozen Power (IRE)—Noble View (USA) **Ridge House Stables Ltd**
12 **RECTORY ROAD**, 5, b g Paco Boy (IRE)—Caerlonore (IRE) **Mr S. R. Middleton**
13 **SACRED LEGACY (IRE)**, 4, ch g Zebedee—Sacred Love (IRE) **Ridge House Stables Ltd**
14 **SARAH'S VERSE**, 4, b f Poet's Voice—Sancai (USA) **Ridge House Stables Ltd**
15 **SECRET POTION**, 7, b g Stimulation (IRE)—Fiancee (IRE) **RHS Ltd & Mr R. Fox**
16 **TEXAN NOMAD**, 9, ch g Nomadic Way (USA)—Texas Belle (IRE) **Mr J. W. Miles**
17 **THE DALEY EXPRESS (IRE)**, 7, b g Elzaam (AUS)—Seraphina (IRE) **The W.H.O. Society**
18 **THEGREYVTRAIN**, 5, gr m Coach House (IRE)—Debutante Blues (USA) **Ridge House Stables Ltd**
19 **TRUSTY RUSTY**, 4, ch f Roderic O'Connor (IRE)—Madame Rouge **H. M. W. Clifford**
20 **UNION ROSE**, 9, b g Stimulation (IRE)—Dot Hill **Exors of the Late Mr D. A. Evans**
21 **VIOLA PARK**, 7, b g Aqlaam—Violette **Margaret Hatherell & Rhs Ltd**
22 **WE'RE REUNITED (IRE)**, 4, b g Kodiac—Caelis **H. M. W. Clifford**

### THREE-YEAR-OLDS

23 Ch g Coach House (IRE)—Festival Dance
24 **GOLDEN RIDGE (IRE)**, ch g Buratino (IRE)—Picture of Lily **Ridge House Stables Ltd**
25 **MANGO TWITCHER**, b f Sayif (IRE)—Lady Mango (IRE) **Ridge House Stables Ltd**
26 **NOIR DAME (IRE)**, b f Slade Power (IRE)—Ascot Lady (IRE) **H. M. W. Clifford**

### TWO-YEAR-OLDS

27 B c 28/02 Gutaifan (IRE)—Glamorous Air (IRE) (Air Express (IRE)) (36190) **M Doocey, S Doocey & P J Doocey**

**Other Owners:** Mr M. A. Doocey, Mr P. J. Doocey, Mr S. Doocey, Mr R. S. Fox, Mrs M. E. Hatherell, Mrs J. Jarrett, Ridge House Stables Ltd.

**Flat Jockey:** Luke Morris.

**260** **MR SHAUN HARRIS, Worksop**
Postal: **Pinewood Stables, Carburton, Worksop, Nottinghamshire, S80 3BT**
Contacts: **PHONE 01909 470936 MOBILE 07761 395596**
**EMAIL shaunharrisracing@yahoo.com WEBSITE www.shaunharrisracing.co.uk**

1 **ALI STAR BERT**, 5, b g Phoenix Reach (IRE)—Clumber Pursuits **Notts Racing, S A Harris & Miss H Ward**
2 **BALLYVIL (IRE)**, 4, b g Clodovil (IRE)—Welsh Diva
3 **DETACHMENT**, 8, b g Motivator—Argumentative **J. Morris**
4 **DOLPHIN VILLAGE (IRE)**, 11, b g Cape Cross (IRE)—Reform Act (USA) **Nottinghamshire Racing**
5 **HEAR THE CHIMES**, 12, b g Midnight Legend—Severn Air **Miss G. H. Ward**
6 **ORBIT OF IOLITE**, 5, ch g Sun Central (IRE)—Blue Clumber **Miss G. H. Ward**
7 **QUICK MONET (IRE)**, 8, b g Excellent Art—Clinging Vine (USA) **J. Morris**

Other Owners: Miss G. H. Ward.

Assistant Trainer: Miss G. H. Ward.

**261** **MISS LISA HARRISON, Wigton**
Postal: **Cobble Hall, Aldoth, Nr Silloth, Cumbria, CA7 4NE**
Contacts: **PHONE 016973 61753 MOBILE 07725 535554 FAX 016973 42250**
**EMAIL lisa@daharrison.co.uk**

1 **A PLACE APART (IRE)**, 7, b g Power—Simadartha (USA) **D A Harrison Racing**
2 **GREEN ZONE (IRE)**, 10, b g Bushranger (IRE)—Incense **T Hunter & D A Harrison Racing**
3 **INSTINGTIVE (IRE)**, 10, b g Scorpion (IRE)—Fully Focused (IRE) **D A Harrison & Abbadis Racing & Thompson**
4 **MALANGEN (IRE)**, 6, b g Born To Sea (IRE)—Lady's Locket (IRE) **D A Harrison Racing**
5 **MILEVA ROLLER**, 9, b m Multiplex—Alikat (IRE) **D A Harrison Racing**
6 **MUWALLA**, 14, b g Bahri (USA)—Easy Sunshine (IRE) **Bell Bridge Racing**
7 **SOLWAY AVA**, 8, b m Overbury (IRE)—Solway Sunset
8 **SOLWAY BERRY**, 10, b m Overbury (IRE)—Solway Rose **D A Harrison Racing**
9 **SOLWAY LARK**, 10, b g Beat All (USA)—Solway Larkin (IRE) **F Crone& D A Harrison Racing**
10 **SOLWAY MOLLY**, 6, b m Trans Island—Solway Sunset **D A Harrison Racing**
11 **SOLWAY MOUSE**, 7, b m Multiplex—Notadandy **D A Harrison Racing**
12 **SOLWAY PRIMROSE**, 7, b m Overbury (IRE)—Solway Rose **D A Harrison Racing**
13 **SOLWAY SPIRIT**, 8, b g Overbury (IRE)—Notadandy
14 **SONG OF THE NIGHT (IRE)**, 10, b g Mahler—Pollys Attic (IRE) **Mr & Mrs Batey & D A Harrison Racing**

Other Owners: Abbadis Racing Club, Mrs A. E. Batey, Mr K. D. Batey, Mrs F. H. Crone, D A Harrison Racing, Mr D. Gillespie, Mr J. D. Graves, Miss L. Harrison, Mr R. A. Harrison, Mr W. H. Harrison, Mr T. Hunter, R. E. Jackson, Mr K. V. Thompson.

**262** **MR GARY HARRISON, Lanark**
Postal: **Highacre, New Trows Road, Lesmahagow, Lanark, Lanarkshire, ML11 0JS**
Contacts: **PHONE 07717 757162**
**EMAIL garyharrison1968@gmail.com**

1 **BELLA FEVER (URU)**, 5, b m Texas Fever (USA)—Passionbabypassion (USA) **Miss E. Johnston**
2 **BUILDING YEAR (IRE)**, 7, b g Intikhab (USA)—The Oldladysays No (IRE) **Miss S. K. Harrison**
3 **DAIJOOR**, 5, br g Cape Cross (IRE)—Angel Oak **Miss S. K. Harrison**
4 **FAIRYWORLD (USA)**, 4, b f City Zip (USA)—Looking Glass (USA)
5 **MAJOR PUSEY**, 9, ch g Major Cadeaux—Pusey Street Lady **Miss S. K. Harrison**
6 **NIGHT MOON**, 5, b g Dubawi (IRE)—Scatina (IRE) **Miss S. K. Harrison**
7 **ORIENTAL RELATION (IRE)**, 10, gr g Tagula (IRE)—Rofan (USA) **Miss E. Johnston**

## MR GARY HARRISON - continued

8 **SILVERBOOK**, 6, b g New Approach (IRE)—Sahraah (USA) **Miss E. Johnston**
9 **VENUSTA (IRE)**, 5, b m Medicean—Grevillea (IRE) **Miss S. K. Harrison**

---

| **263** | **MR BEN HASLAM, Middleham** |
|---|---|

Postal: Castle Hill Stables, Castle Hill, Middleham, Leyburn, North Yorkshire, DL8 4QW
Contacts: **PHONE 01969 624351 MOBILE 07764 411660**
**EMAIL** office@benhaslamracing.com **WEBSITE** www.benhaslamracing.com

1 **AIDEN'S REWARD (IRE)**, 4, b g Dandy Man (IRE)—Bonne **Mrs C Barclay & Mr D Wood**
2 **AUCKLAND LODGE (IRE)**, 4, ch f Dandy Man (IRE)—Proud Maria (IRE) **The Auckland Lodge Partnership**
3 **BLACK KRAKEN**, 5, b g Battle of Marengo (IRE)—Stereo Love (FR) **Mr D. Shapiro & Mr B. M. R. Haslam**
4 **BLAZING DREAMS (IRE)**, 5, b g Morpheus—Pure Folly (IRE) **Simon King & Partner**
5 **BLINDINGLY (GER)**, 6, br g Shamardal (USA)—Boccassini (GER) **Mrs C. Barclay**
6 **CALEVADE (IRE)**, 5, gr g Gregorian (IRE)—Avoidance (USA) **D Shapiro, Mrs Anne Haslam & Partners**
7 **CASH AGAIN (FR)**, 9, br g Great Pretender (FR)—Jeu de Lune (FR) **Mrs C. Barclay**
8 **CASTLEHILL RETREAT**, 4, ch g Casamento (IRE)—Ansina (USA) **Middleham Park Xx, Mrs C Barclay & J Pak**
9 **CHARLEMAINE (IRE)**, 4, b c War Command (USA)—Newyearresolution (USA) **Mr S. J. Robinson**
10 **COUNTISTER (FR)**, 9, b m Smadoun (FR)—Tistairly (FR) **Mr J. P. McManus**
11 **DEMI SANG (FR)**, 8, b g Gris de Gris (IRE)—Morvandelle (FR) **Mr J. P. McManus**
12 **EMILY'S DELIGHT (IRE)**, 4, ch f Anjaal—Masela (IRE) **Mrs C. Barclay**
13 **EPEIUS (IRE)**, 8, b g Arakan (USA)—Gilda Lilly (USA) **Ben Haslam Racing Syndicate**
14 **EVER SO MUCH (IRE)**, 12, b g Westerner—Beautiful World (IRE) **Mr J. P. McManus**
15 **FORTAMOUR (IRE)**, 5, b g Es Que Love (IRE)—Kathy Sun (IRE) **C Barclay, Racing Knights & C Cleevely**
16 **FRANCE DE REVE (FR)**, 6, gr m Lord du Sud (FR)—Kyrielle de Reve (FR) **Mr J. P. McManus**
17 **GAMEFACE (IRE)**, 7, b g Oscar (IRE)—Queensland Bay **Mr J. P. McManus**
18 **GELBOE DE CHANAY (FR)**, 5, b m Rail Link—Rose Celebre (FR) **Mr J. P. McManus**
19 **LADY SHANAWELL (IRE)**, 5, ch m Lord Shanakill (USA)—Lukes Well (IRE) **Blue Lion Racing IX**
20 **LASKADINE (FR)**, 6, b m Martaline—Laskadoun (FR) **Mr J. P. McManus**
21 **LORD CAPRIO (IRE)**, 6, b g Lord Shanakill (USA)—Azzurra du Caprio (IRE) **Blue Lion Racing IX**
22 **NATALEENA (IRE)**, 5, b m Nathaniel (IRE)—Hayyona **Shapiro,Milner,Rees,Nicol,Feeney & Adams**
23 **NATIONAL TREASURE (IRE)**, 4, b f Camelot—Flawless Beauty **Ms R G Hillen & Partner**
24 **PHOENIX STRIKE**, 4, b g Casamento (IRE)—Promise You **Mr D. Shapiro**
25 **PROTEK DES FLOS (FR)**, 9, b g Protektor (GER)—Flore de Chantenay (FR) **Mr J. P. McManus**
26 **RATHHILL (IRE)**, 8, b g Getaway (GER)—Bella Venezia (IRE) **Mr J. P. McManus**
27 **RITCHIE STAR (IRE)**, 5, b g Lilbourne Lad (IRE)—Array of Stars (IRE) **Mr R. Tocher**
28 **RIVER FROST**, 9, b g Silver Frost (IRE)—River Test **Mr J. P. McManus**
29 **ROCK ON FRUITY (IRE)**, 12, b g Fruits of Love (USA)—Sancta Miria (IRE) **Mr J. P. McManus**
30 **ROXBORO ROAD (IRE)**, 8, b g Oscar (IRE)—Pretty Neat (IRE) **Mr J. P. McManus**
31 **SANDRET (IRE)**, 5, b g Zebedee—Sava Sunset (IRE) **Mrs C Barclay & Ben Haslam Racing Synd**
32 **SASSOON**, 5, ch g Poet's Voice—Seradim **Mr S. J. Robinson**
33 **SCOOP THE POT (IRE)**, 11, b g Mahler—Miss Brecknell (IRE) **Mr J. P. McManus**
34 **SOLO SAXOPHONE (IRE)**, 7, b g Frankel—Society Hostess (USA) **Golden Equinox Racing**
35 **SPIDER PIG (IRE)**, 5, b br g Yeats (IRE)—Beaus Polly (IRE) **More Turf Racing**

### THREE-YEAR-OLDS

36 **BUMBLE BEEE (IRE)**, b f Kodiac—Emirates Challenge (IRE) **Brinkley, Farthing R Catling**
37 **CHADLINGTON LAD (IRE)**, b g Estidhkaar (IRE)—Fuaigh Mor (IRE) **Mr R Brinkley & Mr R Catling**
38 B c Nathaniel (IRE)—Duchess of Azeley **Exors of the Late Mr G. Turnbull**
39 **HOLY CHALICE (IRE)**, b f Helmet (AUS)—Holy Grail (IRE) **Mr C. R. Hirst**
40 **LIGHTENING COMPANY (IRE)**, b g Fast Company (IRE)—
                                 Shama's Song (IRE) **Middleham Park Racing Cxv & C Barclay**
41 **MACHO PRIDE (IRE)**, b g Camacho—Proud Maria (IRE) **The Auckland Lodge Partnership**
42 **MAEVE'S MEMORY (IRE)**, b f Kodiac—Startori **The Auckland Lodge Partnership**
43 **SERENA GRACE**, gr f Sir Percy—Serena Grae **Mr A. J. Kent**
44 **SUNTORY STAR (IRE)**, ch f Starspangledbanner (AUS)—Sunbula (USA) **Racing Knights & John Robinson**

## MR BEN HASLAM - continued

45 WE STILL BELIEVE (IRE), b br g Lawman (FR)—Curious Lashes (IRE)  **Sam Farthing, Linda McGarry & Ken Nicol**

### TWO-YEAR-OLDS
46 DO I DREAM (IRE), b f 08/01 Mondialiste (IRE)—Novita (FR) (American Post) (4285)  **Racing Knights**
47 B f 20/04 Profitable (IRE)—Ebtisama (USA) (Kingmambo (USA)) (25714)  **Mrs C. Barclay, Hope Eden Racing**
48 B c 21/04 Holy Roman Emperor (IRE)—
                                Euroceleb (IRE) (Peintre Celebre (USA)) (40000)  **Mrs C. Barclay, Hope Eden Racing**
49 B f 14/03 Ribchester (IRE)—Fresh Mint (IRE) (Sadler's Wells (USA)) (41000)  **Mrs C. Barclay, Hope Eden Racing**
50 B c 01/04 Holy Roman Emperor (IRE)—Hala Hala (IRE) (Invincible Spirit (IRE)) (55000)  **Mr D. Shapiro**
51 B c 29/04 Dabirsim (FR)—Hoku (IRE) (Holy Roman Emperor (IRE)) (66667)  **Mr D. Shapiro**
52 B f 04/04 Profitable (IRE)—Miss Azeza (Dutch Art) (145000)  **Mr D. Shapiro**
53 ON THE RIVER, b c 25/02 Heeraat (IRE)—Lady Lekki (IRE) (Champs Elysees)  **The Multifruit Syndicate**
54 Ch f 26/04 Air Force Blue (USA)—Rocktique (USA) (Rock Hard Ten (USA)) (9524)  **Mr S. Farthing, Mr R. R. Brinkley**
55 B c 28/01 Ribchester (IRE)—Sugar Free (GER) (Exceed And Excel (AUS)) (140000)  **Mr D. Shapiro**
56 SWEETEST COMPANY (IRE), b f 21/04 Fast Company (IRE)—
                                Florida City (IRE) (Pennekamp (USA)) (20952)  **Racing Knights**

**Other Owners:** Mr P. Adams, Mrs C. Barclay, Ben Haslam Racing Syndicate, Mr R. R. Brinkley, Mr R. J. Catling, Mr C. R. Cleevely, Mr S. Farthing, Mrs J. M. Feeney, Mr J. S. Feeney, Mrs A. M. C. Haslam, Mr B. M. R. Haslam, Mr S. P. King, Mrs L. McGarry, Middleham Park Racing CXV, Middleham Park Racing XX, Mrs S. V. Milner, Mr K. Nicol, T. S. Palin, M. Prince, Racing Knights, Mr M. Rees, Mr S. J. Robinson, Mr D. Shapiro, Mr D. Wood, Mr P. G. Wood.

**Assistant Trainer:** Alice Haslam.

---

**264** **MR NIGEL HAWKE, Tiverton**
Postal: **Thorne Farm, Stoodleigh, Tiverton, Devon, EX16 9QG**
Contacts: **PHONE 01884 881666 MOBILE 07769 295839**
**EMAIL nigel@thornefarmracingltd.co.uk WEBSITE www.nigelhawkethornefarmracing.co.uk**

1 A NEW SIEGE (IRE), 6, ch m New Approach (IRE)—Arminta (USA)  **Atlantic Friends Racing**
2 ALMINAR (IRE), 8, b g Arakan (USA)—Classic Magic (IRE)  **Mr M. J. Phillips**
3 BALLYMAGROARTY BOY (IRE), 8, b g Milan—Glazed Storm (IRE)  **The Nigel Hawke Racing Club**
4 BELLA BEAU (IRE), 6, b m Jeremy (USA)—Bella Patrice (IRE)  **Mr M. J. Phillips**
5 BIG CHIEF (IRE), 6, b g Westerner—Eastertide (IRE)
6 BLUE DAVIS, 4, b f Blue Bresil (FR)—Ocarina Davis (FR)  **Thorne Farm Racing Limited**
7 BRING THE ACTION (IRE), 5, b g Jet Away—Lady Firefly (IRE)  **Ms C. Holmes-Elliott**
8 CALIN DU BRIZAIS (FR), 10, b g Loup Solitaire (USA)—Caline du Brizais (FR)  **Meadvale Syndicate**
9 CALL ME SAINTE (FR), 4, b f Saint des Saints (FR)—Call Me Blue (FR)  **Simms, Capps**
10 CAMRON DE CHAILLAC (FR), 9, br g Laverock (IRE)—Hadeel (FR)  **Mr R. Lane**
11 CIDER KILT (IRE), 5, b g Yeats (IRE)—Royal Nora (IRE)  **Mr P. A. Willis**
12 CLONMONARCH (IRE), 6, b g Imperial Monarch (IRE)—Grancore Girl (IRE)  **Mr R. Lane**
13 CROSSFIREHURRICANE, 7, b m Malinas (GER)—Leroy's Sister (FR)  **Thorne Farm Racing Limited**
14 DAWN TROUPER (IRE), 6, b g Dawn Approach (IRE)—Dance Troupe  **Mr R. Lane**
15 DEVONGATE, 4, b g Delegator—Up And Running  **Miss J. S. Dorey**
16 EUROWORK (FR), 7, bl g Network (GER)—Nandina (FR)  **R. J. & Mrs J. A. Peake**
17 GALORE DESASSENCES (FR), 5, b g Rail Link—Villezbelle (FR)  **Mark Phillips & Partner**
18 GEORDIE WASHINGTON (IRE), 5, b br g Sageburg (IRE)—Rathturtin Brief (IRE)  **Atlantic Friends Racing**
19 GUARDIA TOP (FR), 5, b m Top Trip—Jour de Chance (FR)  **Terence Wood, Samuel Jefford & Partners**
20 GWENNOLINE (FR), 5, gr m Balko (FR)—Ugoline (FR)  **Thorne Farm Racing Limited**
21 HARTLAND QUAY (IRE), 6, b gr g Arcadio (GER)—Regents Ballerina (IRE)  **Mr Richard Weeks & Partner**
22 HEART OF KERNOW (IRE), 9, b g Fruits of Love (USA)—Rathturtin Brief (IRE)  **Mrs K. Hawke & Mr W. Simms**
23 HISTORIC HEART (IRE), 4, ch g Fracas (IRE)—Irish Question (IRE)  **Atlantic Friends Racing**
24 INNERPICKLE, 5, b g Pour Moi (IRE)—Bay Swallow (IRE)  **Ms C. Holmes-Elliott**
25 JOHANOS (FR), 10, ch g Limnos (JPN)—Madame Johann (FR)  **Mark Phillips, Mrs Pumphrey & Partners**
26 KAPITALL, 6, b m Kapgarde (FR)—Doubly Guest  **R. J. Weeks**

## MR NIGEL HAWKE - continued

27 **KENDELU (IRE)**, 6, b g Yeats (IRE)—Supreme Baloo (IRE) **Ken & Della Neilson & Partners**
28 **KINGCORMAC (IRE)**, 5, b g Shirocco (GER)—On The Up (IRE)
29 **LAZARINA (IRE)**, 6, b m Doyen (IRE)—Maid of Steel (IRE) **Mr N. J. Hawke**
30 **LE MUSEE (FR)**, 8, b g Galileo (IRE)—Delicieuse Lady **Mrs K Hawke,W Simms & Dragonfly Racing**
31 **LETTER AT DAWN (IRE)**, 4, b g Dawn Approach (IRE)—Christinas Letter (IRE) **Dare To Dream Racing**
32 **MEAD VALE**, 8, ch g Schiaparelli (GER)—Devon Peasant **Meadvale Syndicate**
33 **NACHI FALLS**, 8, ch g New Approach (IRE)—Lakuta (IRE) **R & Hawke Club**
34 **NIKAP (FR)**, 7, b m Kapgarde (FR)—Nika Glitters (FR) **Kapinhand**
35 **NOVUS ADITUS (IRE)**, 5, b g Teofilo (IRE)—Novel Approach (IRE) **Atlantic Friends Racing**
36 **OURO BRANCO (FR)**, 8, b g Kapgarde (FR)—Dolce Vita Yug **Pearce Bros & Partner**
37 **PEARL ROYALE (IRE)**, 9, b m Robin des Champs (FR)—Dartmeet (IRE) **Mr M. J. Phillips**
38 **PEAT MOSS (IRE)**, 4, b g Fracas (IRE)—Dancing On Turf (IRE) **Atlantic Friends Racing**
39 **POLA CHANCE (FR)**, 5, gr m Boris de Deauville (IRE)—

                             Take A Chance (FR) **Smith Evans Bevan Browne Thorne Farm**

40 **POMME**, 10, b m Observatory (USA)—Mirthful (USA)
41 **REPETITIO (IRE)**, 5, b g Pour Moi (IRE)—Fionnuar (IRE) **Mr N. J. Hawke**
42 **SINDABELLA (FR)**, 5, b m Sinndar (IRE)—Figarella Gaugain (FR) **Surefire Racing**
43 **SOME DETAIL (IRE)**, 7, b g Getaway (GER)—You Should Know Me (IRE) **Milltown Racing**
44 **SPEREDEK (FR)**, 10, b br g Kapgarde (FR)—Sendamagic (FR) **Kapinhand**
45 **TANGO DU ROY (IRE)**, 8, b g Court Cave (IRE)—Hamari Gold (IRE) **Mr I. G. Prichard**
46 **TANRUDY (FR)**, 7, b g Presenting—Come In Moscow (IRE) **Mark J Phillips & Mrs A B Walker**
47 **THE BOOLA BEE (IRE)**, 8, b m Arcadio (GER)—Hy Kate (IRE) **Mr R. Lane**
48 **THE IMPOSTER (FR)**, 4, b g Authorized (IRE)—Miss Dixie **Mark Philips & J H Gumbley**
49 **THEOCRAT (IRE)**, 4, b c Teofilo (IRE)—Novel Approach (IRE) **Atlantic Friends Racing**
50 **WISE GARDEN (FR)**, 6, b m Kapgarde (FR)—Fabulous Wisdom (FR) **Kapinhand**
51 **YES GOVERNOR (IRE)**, 6, b g Scorpion (IRE)—Golden Diva (IRE) **Mr S. C. Browne**
52 **YOUNG O'LEARY (IRE)**, 7, b g Scorpion (IRE)—Cantou (IRE) **Mr I. G. Prichard**

**Other Owners:** M. J. Bevan, Mrs K. M. Brain, Mr S. C. Browne, Mr M. G. Capps, Mr S. A. Evans, Mr F. G. Flanagan, Mr J. H. Gumbley, Mrs K. Hawke, Mr N. J. Hawke, Exors of the Late Mr T. B. James, Mrs H. M. Jefferies, Mr S. Jefford, Mr K. Neilson, Mrs J. Peake, Mr R. Peake, Mr D. A. Pearce, Mr M. J. Phillips, Mrs M. M. R. Pumphrey, Mr W. J. Simms, Mrs D. E. Smith, The Nigel Hawke Racing Club, Thorne Farm Racing Limited, Mrs A. B. Walker, R. J. Weeks, Mr S. W. H. Winfield, Mr T. Wood.

**Assistant Trainer:** Edward Buckley, Katherine Hawke.

**NH Jockey:** Sean Bowen, Tom Cannon, Danny Cook, David Noonan. **Conditional Jockey:** Tom Buckley. **Amateur Jockey:** Mr Kieran Buckley.

---

| 265 | **MR MICHAEL HAWKER, Chippenham**<br>Postal: **Battens Farm, Allington, Chippenham, Wiltshire, SN14 6LT** |
|---|---|

1 **MORTENS LEAM**, 9, b g Sulamani (IRE)—Bonnet's Pieces **Mr M. R. E. Hawker**
2 6, B g Scorpion (IRE)—Sheknowsyouknow
3 **SPOTTY DOG**, 6, ch g Sixties Icon—Where's My Slave (IRE) **Mr M. R. E. Hawker**

**266** **MR RICHARD HAWKER, Frome**
Postal: **Rode Farm, Rode, Bath, Somerset, BA11 6QQ**
Contacts: **PHONE 01373 831479**

1 BABY MOONBEAM, 6, bl gr m Passing Glance—Charliebob **R. G. B. Hawker**
2 BEES AND HONEY, 5, b m Black Sam Bellamy (IRE)—Pougatcheva (FR) **Miss B. E. Childs**
3 FIVE GOLD BARS (IRE), 8, b g Gold Well—Native Euro (IRE)
4 GENTLEMAN FARMER, 9, ch g Tobougg (IRE)—Sweet Shooter **R. G. B. Hawker**
5 HINTERLEITENWEG (IRE), 6, b m Stowaway—Youngborogal (IRE) **T. P. Eades**
6 JACK SNIPE, 12, b g Kirkwall—Sea Snipe **Mrs P. J. Pengelly**
7 JANESPRICELESS, 5, b gr m Jelani (IRE)—Jane's Budget **Miss J. Nicholls**
8 PARLOUR MAID, 10, gr m Dr Massini (IRE)—Charliebob **Rolling Aces**
9 PENGO'S BOY, 12, gr g Proclamation (IRE)—Homeoftheclassics **Mrs P. J. Pengelly**
10 RESTLESS BRIAN, 7, b g Brian Boru—Restless Native (IRE) **R. J. Francome**
11 SASTRUGA (IRE), 8, b g Masterofthehorse (IRE)—Crimson Blue (IRE) **Mr B. A. Hawker**
12 THIRSTY FARMER, 7, b g Sulamani (IRE)—Sweet Shooter **R. G. B. Hawker**

**267** **MR JONATHAN HAYNES, Brampton**
Postal: **Cleugh Head, Low Row, Brampton, Cumbria, CA8 2JB**
Contacts: **PHONE 016977 46253 MOBILE 07771 511471**

1 BERTIELICIOUS, 13, b g And Beyond (IRE)—Pennepoint **J. C. Haynes**
2 DOROTHY'S FLAME, 9, ch m Black Sam Bellamy (IRE)—Flame of Zara **J. C. Haynes**
3 GETONSAM, 9, ch g Black Sam Bellamy (IRE)—Pennepoint **J. C. Haynes**
4 HIDDEN CARGO (IRE), 9, b g Stowaway—All Heart **J. C. Haynes**
5 MR JV, 5, ch g And Beyond (IRE)—Flame of Zara **J. C. Haynes**

**268** **MISS GAIL HAYWOOD, Moretonhampstead**
Postal: **Stacombe Farm, Doccombe, Moretonhampstead, Newton Abbot, Devon, TQ13 8SS**
Contacts: **PHONE 01647 440826**
**EMAIL gail@gghracing.com WEBSITE www.gghracing.com**

1 HIJA, 10, b m Avonbridge—Pantita **Haywood's Heroes**
2 LADY WOLF, 5, b m Kuroshio (AUS)—Angry Bark (USA) **Devrain Partners**
3 POL MA CREE, 6, b g Arvico (FR)—Mere Salome (IRE) **Manhole Covers Ltd**
4 RICHARDOFDOCCOMBE (IRE), 15, b g Heron Island (IRE)—Strike Again (IRE) **Phillip & Mary Creese**
5 RUSSIAN'S LEGACY, 11, b m Kayf Tara—Ruby Star (IRE) **Phillip & Mary Creese**
6 SECRET PALACE, 9, ch m Pastoral Pursuits—Some Sunny Day **Phillip & Mary Creese**
7 ZULU, 7, b g Cockney Rebel (IRE)—Pantita **The Young Warriors**

**Other Owners:** Mr P. V. Creese, Mrs S. M. Creese, Miss G. G. Haywood, Ms V. O'Sullivan.

**NH Jockey:** David Noonan, Ben Poste. **Conditional Jockey:** Rex Dingle.

**269**

**MR COLIN HEARD, Boscastle**
Postal: **Lower Pennycrocker Farm, Boscastle, Cornwall, PL35 0BY**
Contacts: **PHONE** 01840 250613
**EMAIL** colin.heard@yahoo.com

1 **MAKETY**, 7, ch m Black Sam Bellamy (IRE)—Mi Money **Mrs K. Heard**

**270**

**MR NICKY HENDERSON, Lambourn**
Postal: **Seven Barrows, Lambourn, Hungerford, Berkshire, RG17 8UH**
Contacts: **PHONE** 01488 72259 **MOBILE** 07774 608168
**EMAIL** njh@njhenderson.com

1 **ADJALI (GER)**, 6, b g Kamsin (GER)—Anabasis (GER) **Mr Simon Munir & Mr Isaac Souede**
2 **AHORSEWITHNONAME**, 6, b m Cacique (IRE)—Sea of Galilee **Mr D. J. Burke & Mr P Alderson**
3 **ALLART (IRE)**, 7, b g Shantou (USA)—The Adare Woman (IRE) **R. A. Bartlett**
4 **ALTIOR (IRE)**, 11, b g High Chaparral (IRE)—Monte Solaro (IRE) **Mrs P. J. Pugh**
5 **AMAZING PRESENCE**, 5, b m Presenting—Tarla (FR) **Sharon Kinsella & Jane Allison**
6 4, B f Kapgarde (FR)—Anais Collonges (FR) **Middleham Park Racing XXI**
7 **ARCADIAN PEARL (IRE)**, 6, br g Arcadio (GER)—Grangeclare Pearl (IRE) **Biddestone Racing XVII**
8 **AT POETS CROSS (IRE)**, 5, b g Yeats (IRE)—At The Pound Cross (IRE) **HP Racing At Poets Cross**
9 **BALCO COASTAL (FR)**, 5, b g Coastal Path—Fliugika (FR) **Mr M. R. Blandford**
10 **BALLINGERS CORNER (IRE)**, 6, br m Jeremy (USA)—Dances With Waves (IRE) **Mr M. G. Roberts**
11 **BALLYCROSS**, 10, b g King's Theatre (IRE)—Ninna Nanna (FR) **Mr Oscar Singh & Miss Priya Purewal**
12 **BARBADOS BLUE (IRE)**, 7, b m Getaway (GER)—Buck's Blue (IRE) **Crimbourne Bloodstock**
13 **BARELY FAMOUS (IRE)**, 5, b m Fame And Glory—Cause Celebre (IRE)
14 **BARON NELSON (IRE)**, 5, b g Mount Nelson—Toolentidhaar (USA) **Mr M. A. R. Blencowe**
15 **BEWARE THE BEAR (IRE)**, 11, b g Shantou (USA)—Native Bid (IRE) **G. B. Barlow**
16 **BIRCHDALE (IRE)**, 7, b g Jeremy (USA)—Onewayortheother (IRE) **Mr J. P. McManus**
17 **BLAIRGOWRIE (IRE)**, 5, b g Yeats (IRE)—Gaye Preskina (IRE) **T. Barr**
18 **BLUE HEAVEN**, 4, b f Blue Bresil (FR)—Spring Flight **Her Majesty The Queen**
19 **BLUE STELLO (FR)**, 5, b g Spider Flight (FR)—Benina (FR)
20 **BOND'S LOVER (IRE)**, 7, gr m Flemensfirth (USA)—Courageuse (FR)
21 **BOTHWELL BRIDGE (IRE)**, 6, b g Stowaway—Raise The Issue (IRE) **T. Barr**
22 **BRAVE EAGLE (IRE)**, 9, b g Yeats (IRE)—Sinful Pleasure (IRE) **R. M. Kirkland**
23 **BRILLIANT PRESENT (IRE)**, 5, br m Presenting—Ouro Preto **Mr & Mrs J. D. Cotton**
24 **BROOMFIELD BURG (IRE)**, 5, br g Sageburg (IRE)—Somedaysomehow (IRE) **Mr J. P. McManus**
25 4, B g Walk In The Park (IRE)—Buck's Blue (IRE) **Mr M. A. R. Blencowe**
26 **BURROWS EDGE (FR)**, 8, b g Martaline—La Vie de Boitron (FR) **M. A. C. Buckley**
27 **BUTTSBURY LADY**, 6, b m Great Pretender (IRE)—Ceilidh Royal
28 **BUVEUR D'AIR (FR)**, 10, b g Crillon (FR)—History (FR) **Mr J. P. McManus**
29 **BUZZ (FR)**, 7, gr g Motivator—Tiysha (IRE) **Thurloe for Royal Marsden Cancer Charity**
30 **CALL ME LORD (FR)**, 8, b br g Slickly (FR)—Sosa (GER) **Mr Simon Munir & Mr Isaac Souede**
31 **CAPTAIN MORGS (IRE)**, 5, b g Milan—Gold Donn (IRE) **The Albatross Club**
32 **CARIBEAN BOY (FR)**, 7, gr g Myboycharlie (IRE)—Caribena (FR) **Mr Simon Munir & Mr Isaac Souede**
33 **CASABLANCA MIX (FR)**, 9, ch m Shirocco (GER)—Latitude (FR)
34 **CASCOVA (IRE)**, 6, b g Casamento—Sina Cova (FR) **Chelsea Thoroughbreds & Trull House Stud**
35 **CHAMP (IRE)**, 9, b g King's Theatre (IRE)—China Sky (IRE) **Mr J. P. McManus**
36 **CHAMPAGNE MYSTERY (IRE)**, 7, b g Shantou (USA)—Spanker **Mr T. J. Hemmings**
37 **CHAMPAGNE PLATINUM (IRE)**, 7, gr g Stowaway—Saffron Holly (IRE) **Mr J. P. McManus**
38 **CHANTRY HOUSE (IRE)**, 7, br g Yeats (IRE)—The Last Bank (IRE) **Mr J. P. McManus**
39 **CHASAMAX (IRE)**, 6, b g Jeremy (USA)—Peratus (IRE) **International Plywood (Importers) Ltd**
40 **CHIVES**, 7, b g Sulamani (IRE)—Ceilidh Royal
41 **CLAIMANTAKINFORGAN (FR)**, 9, b g Great Pretender (IRE)—Taquine d'Estrees (FR) **Lady Dulverton**
42 **CLEAN GETAWAY (IRE)**, 4, b g Getaway (GER)—Dee Two O Two (IRE) **Unique Financial Racing Partnership**
43 **COLONIAL DREAMS (IRE)**, 9, b g Westerner—Dochas Supreme (IRE) **C. N. Barnes**

# MR NICKY HENDERSON - continued

44 **COMMODORE MILLER**, 4, b g Blue Bresil (FR)—Milligait **HP Racing Commodore Miller**
45 **CORRANY (IRE)**, 7, br g Court Cave (IRE)—Time For An Audit **Mr T. J. Hemmings**
46 **CRAIGNEICHE (IRE)**, 7, br g Flemensfirth (USA)—Itsalark (IRE) **R. M. Kirkland**
47 **DAME DE COMPAGNIE (FR)**, 8, b m Lucarno (USA)—Programmee (FR) **Mr J. P. McManus**
48 **DIAMOND RIVER (IRE)**, 6, ch g Imperial Monarch (FR)—
                                                    River Clyde (IRE) **Jockey Club Ownership (SW 2020) Limited**
49 **DICKIE DIVER (IRE)**, 8, b g Gold Well—Merry Excuse (IRE) **Mr J. P. McManus**
50 **DIVA'S MIX**, 6, b m Fair Mix (IRE)—Divisa (GER)
51 **DOCTE DINA (FR)**, 7, ch m Doctor Dino (FR)—Artofmen (FR) **Walters Plant Hire & Potter Group**
52 **DODDIETHEGREAT (IRE)**, 5, b g Fame And Glory—Asturienne **Mr K. Alexander**
53 **DUKE OF BRONTE**, 7, b g Mount Nelson—Reaf **Harts Farm Stud**
54 **DUKE OF CHALFONT (FR)**, 5, b g Alianthus (GER)—Bonne Mere (FR) **Mr A. Speelman & Mr M. Speelman**
55 **DUSART (IRE)**, 6, b g Flemensfirth (USA)—Dusty Too **R. A. Bartlett**
56 **EL KALDOUN (FR)**, 7, b g Special Kaldoun (FR)—Kermesse d'Estruval (FR) **Middleham Park Racing CIV**
57 **ELUSIVE BELLE (IRE)**, 7, b m Elusive Pimpernel (USA)—Soviet Belle (IRE) **Annabel Waley-Cohen & Family**
58 **EMIR SACREE (FR)**, 7, b g Network (GER)—Altesse Sacree (FR) **G. L. Porter**
59 **EPATANTE (FR)**, 7, b m No Risk At All (FR)—Kadjara (FR) **Mr J. P. McManus**
60 **FABLE (FR)**, 6, b m Coastal Path—Toscane des Fleurs (FR) **Owners Group 078**
61 **FALCO BLITZ (FR)**, 7, b g Falco (USA)—Ignited **Axom LXXVII**
62 **FANTASTIC LADY (FR)**, 6, b m Network (GER)—Latitude (FR)
63 **FATHER JOHN (FR)**, 6, b g Secret Singer (FR)—Oudette (FR) **Middleham Park Racing XI**
64 **FIRESTEP (IRE)**, 5, b g Mahler—Springinherstep (IRE) **Charles Dingwall & the Infamous Five**
65 **FIX SUN (FR)**, 6, b g Al Namix (FR)—Quelly Bruere (FR) **Mr Simon Munir & Mr Isaac Souede**
66 **FLINTEUR SACRE (FR)**, 6, b g Network (GER)—Fatima III (FR) **Mr J. P. McManus**
67 **FLORESSA (FR)**, 6, b m Poliglote—Dona Rez (FR) **Just Four Men**
68 **FOLLOW THE BEAR (IRE)**, 9, b g King's Theatre (IRE)—Mrs Dempsey (IRE) **G. B. Barlow**
69 **FOX'S SOCKS (FR)**, 6, br g Crillon (FR)—Queva de Sarti (FR) **Mr J. Palmer-Brown**
70 **FRED (FR)**, 6, b br g Cokoriko (FR)—Veribelle (FR) **Mr Simon Munir & Mr Isaac Souede**
71 **FRENCH CRUSADER (FR)**, 8, b g Kapgarde—Largesse (FR) **R. M. Kirkland**
72 **FUGITIVES DRIFT (IRE)**, 6, b g Yeats (IRE)—Shebeganit (IRE) **HP Racing Fugitives Drift**
73 **FUSIL RAFFLES (FR)**, 6, b g Saint des Saints (FR)—Tali des Obeaux (FR) **Mr Simon Munir & Mr Isaac Souede**
74 **GALAN DES PLANCHES (FR)**, 5, b g Crillon (FR)—Quaty des Planches (FR) **The Ten From Seven**
75 **GALLYHILL (IRE)**, 6, b g Getaway—Tanit **Mr C. M. Grech**
76 **GIPSY DE CHOISEL (FR)**, 5, b br g Great Pretender (IRE)—
                                                    Beautiful Choisel (FR) **Mr Simon Munir & Mr Isaac Souede**
77 **GLOBAL SOCIETY**, 6, b g Shirocco—Oligarch Society (IRE) **Mr J. L. Lightfoot**
78 **GLYNN (IRE)**, 7, b g Winged Love (IRE)—Barnish River (IRE) **Owners Group 039**
79 **GO CHIQUE (FR)**, 5, b m Crillon (FR)—Similaresisoldofa (FR) **Middleham Park Racing CX**
80 **GO SACRE GO (FR)**, 5, b g Network (GER)—Altesse Sacree (FR) **G. L. Porter**
81 **GOLD PRESENT (IRE)**, 11, br g Presenting—Ouro Preto **Mr & Mrs J. D. Cotton**
82 **GOODBYE STRANGER (FR)**, 4, b g Kapgarde (FR)—Romaneda (FR) **Mr Simon Munir & Mr Isaac Souede**
83 **GRAN LUNA (FR)**, 5, b m Spanish Moon (USA)—Coppena (FR) **Surrey Racing (GL)**
84 **GRAND MOGUL (IRE)**, 7, b g Presenting—Oligarch Society (IRE)
85 **GUNNERY (IRE)**, 8, ch g Le Havre (IRE)—Loup The Loup (FR) **Mrs F. H. Hay**
86 **HAMILTON'S FANTASY**, 6, b m Mount Nelson—Romantic Dream **Her Majesty The Queen**
87 **HAUL AWAY (IRE)**, 8, b g Stowaway—Lisacul Queen (IRE) **R. M. Kirkland**
88 **HEROSS DU SEUIL (FR)**, 4, b g Rail Link—Tulipe du Seuil (FR) **Mrs M. Donnelly**
89 **HIGH WORTH (IRE)**, 4, b g Universal (IRE)—High Benefit (IRE)
90 **HIJACK (IRE)**, 6, b g Fame And Glory—Etoile Margot (FR) **Highclere Thoroughbred Racing - Fame**
91 **HOB HOUSE (FR)**, 4, b g Walk In The Park (IRE)—Tante Sissi (FR) **Mr J. P. McManus**
92 **HOOPER**, 5, b g Rip Van Winkle (IRE)—Earth Amber **Pump & Plant Services Ltd**
93 **HORN CAPE (FR)**, 4, gr g Fame And Glory—Capstone (FR) **Mr J. P. McManus**
94 **HURLING MAGIC (IRE)**, 7, b g Doyen (IRE)—Distelle (IRE) **Owners Group 035**
95 **HURRICANE LE DUN (FR)**, 4, b g Doctor Dino (FR)—Heviz (FR)
96 **HYLAND (FR)**, 4, gr g Turgeon (USA)—Medine (FR) **Mr A. Speelman & Mr M. Speelman**
97 **I AM MAXIMUS (FR)**, 5, b g Authorized (IRE)—Polysheba (FR) **Mr C. M. Grech**
98 **IGOR**, 8, b g Presenting—Stravinsky Dance **MHankin CNoell MenHolding RWaley-Cohen**
99 **INDIAN GLORY (IRE)**, 6, b m Fame And Glory—Real Papoose (IRE) **International Plywood (Importers) Ltd**
100 **IT SURE IS (IRE)**, 6, b g Shirocco (GER)—Stay At Home Mum (IRE) **Mrs M. Donnelly**
101 **ITALIAN LEGEND (IRE)**, 6, b br g Fame And Glory—Alannico **R. M. Kirkland**

# MR NICKY HENDERSON - continued

102 **ITALIAN SUMMER**, 6, br m Milan—Midsummer Magic  **Her Majesty The Queen**
103 **JANIKA (FR)**, 8, b g Saddler Maker (IRE)—Majaka (FR)  **Mr Simon Munir & Mr Isaac Souede**
104 **JEN'S BOY**, 7, b g Malinas (GER)—Friendly Craic (IRE)  **Middleham Park Racing CV**
105 **JONBON (FR)**, 5, b g Walk In The Park (IRE)—Star Face (FR)  **Mr J. P. McManus**
106 **KIMMINS**, 6, b m High Chaparral (IRE)—Tinagoodnight (FR)  **Mr J. P. McManus**
107 **KINCARDINE**, 4, b g Kayf Tara—Side Step  **Her Majesty The Queen**
108 **L'AMI SERGE (IRE)**, 11, b g King's Theatre (IRE)—La Zingarella (IRE)  **Mr Simon Munir & Mr Isaac Souede**
109 **LAUGHING LUIS**, 7, b g Authorized (IRE)—Leitzu (IRE)
110 **LE BATEAU**, 5, b g Le Havre (FR)—Bugie d'Amore
111 **LECALE'S ARTICLE (IRE)**, 7, b g Malinas (GER)—Brookville (IRE)  **Mrs M. Donnelly**
112 **LELANTOS (IRE)**, 5, br g Presenting—Western Focus (IRE)  **Middleham Park Racing XCI**
113 **LILLY PEDLAR**, 6, b m Yeats (IRE)—Mathine (FR)  **Hot To Trot Jumping**
114 **LOVEHERANDLEAVEHER (IRE)**, 9, b br m Winged Love (USA)—Rowdy Exit (IRE)  **Mr Alan Spence**
115 **LUST FOR GLORY (IRE)**, 8, b m Getaway (GER)—Maisie Presenting (IRE)  **Annabel Waley-Cohen & Family**
116 **MAJOR STING (IRE)**, 5, b g Scorpion (IRE)—Suzababe (IRE)  **The SMBs**
117 **MARIE'S ROCK (IRE)**, 6, b br m Milan—By The Hour (IRE)  **Middleham Park Racing XLII**
118 **MARMALAID**, gr f Martaline—Miracle Maid  **Mr D. J. Burke & Mr P Alderson**
119 4, Ch f Mahler—Martovic (IRE)
120 **MENGLI KHAN (IRE)**, 8, b g Lope de Vega (IRE)—Danielli (IRE)  **Mr M. A. R. Blencowe**
121 **MILL GREEN**, 9, b g Black Sam Bellamy (IRE)—Ceilidh Royal
122 **MIND SUNDAY (FR)**, 5, gr m Never On Sunday (FR)—Mind Master (USA)  **Walters Plant Hire Ltd**
123 **MISS FARAGE (IRE)**, 6, b m Sans Frontieres (IRE)—Maid of Might (IRE)  **Turf Club 2020**
124 **MISTER COFFEY (FR)**, 6, b g Authorized (IRE)—Mamit-tor  **Lady C. Bamford & Miss A. Bamford**
125 **MISTER FISHER (IRE)**, 7, b g Jeremy (USA)—That's Amazing (IRE)  **James & Jean Potter**
126 **MONTE CRISTO (FR)**, 5, b g Montmartre (FR)—Rylara des Brosses (FR)  **Mr Simon Munir & Mr Isaac Souede**
127 **MOONLIGHT FLIT (IRE)**, 5, b g Getaway (GER)—Dreaming On (IRE)  **Thurloe 57**
128 **MORNING VICAR**, 8, b g Beneficial—Mary's Little Vic (IRE)  **The Parishioners**
129 **MOT A MOT (FR)**, 5, gr g Martaline—Gaily Zest (USA)  **Walters Plant Hire & Potter Group**
130 **MOUNT PLEASANT**, 4, b g Mount Nelson—Polish Belle  **Mr M. A. R. Blencowe**
131 **MY WHIRLWIND (IRE)**, 6, b m Stowaway—Garranlea Maree (IRE)  **Mr J. P. McManus**
132 **NO ORDINARY JOE (IRE)**, 5, b g Getaway (GER)—Shadow Dearg (IRE)  **Mr J. P. McManus**
133 **OK CORRAL (IRE)**, 11, b g Mahler—Acoola (IRE)  **Mr J. P. McManus**
134 **ON THE BLIND SIDE (IRE)**, 9, b g Stowaway—Such A Set Up (IRE)  **Mr Alan Spence**
135 **ONE HANDSOME DUDE (IRE)**, 6, b g Canford Cliffs (IRE)—Allegrina (IRE)  **Steve & Jolene de'Lemos**
136 **OVERPRICED MIXER**, 4, b g Harbour Watch (IRE)—Chincoteague (IRE)  **Owners Group 051**
137 **PALLADIUM**, 5, ch g Champs Elysees—Galicuix  **A. Meade, G. Van Geest, E. Kelvin-hughes**
138 **PARIS DIXIE**, 6, b m Champs Elysees—Last of The Dixies  **Owners Group 037**
139 **PARISIAN BLUE**, 5, b br m Getaway (GER)—Another Evening (IRE)  **Crimbourne Bloodstock**
140 **PAROS (FR)**, 4, ch g Masterstroke (USA)—Soft Blue (FR)  **Middleham Park Racing CXXV**
141 **PATROCLUS (IRE)**, 5, b g Shirocco (GER)—King'sandqueen's (IRE)  **Walters Plant Hire & Potter Group**
142 **PIPESMOKER (FR)**, 6, b g Authorized (IRE)—Pisa (GER)  **Lady Dulverton**
143 **PISTOL WHIPPED (IRE)**, 7, b g Beneficial—Holiday Time (IRE)  **Mr A. Speelman & Mr M. Speelman**
144 4, B g Kapgarde (FR)—Polly Peachum (IRE)  **Middleham Park Racing LXI**
145 **PRECIOUS CARGO**, 8, b g Yeats (IRE)—Kilbarry Classic (IRE)  **T. Barr**
146 **PROGRESSIVE**, 4, b f Nathaniel (IRE)—Graduation  **A D Spence & John Connolly**
147 **PYM (IRE)**, 8, b g Stowaway—Liss Rua (IRE)  **Mrs P. J. Pugh**
148 **QUEENS RIVER**, 5, b m Kayf Tara—Follow My Leader (IRE)  **Mr J. P. McManus**
149 **RAPID FLIGHT**, 5, b g Midnight Legend—Spring Flight  **Her Majesty The Queen**
150 **RATHER BE (IRE)**, 10, b g Oscar (IRE)—Irish Wedding (IRE)  **Eventmasters Racing**
151 4, B g Walk In The Park (IRE)—Refinement (IRE)  **Mrs D. A. Tabor**
152 **RUSSIAN RULER (IRE)**, 4, b br g Sholokhov (IRE)—Hot Choice  **Unique Financial Racing Partnership**
153 **SANTINI**, 9, b g Milan—Tinagoodnight (FR)  **Mr & Mrs R. G. Kelvin-Hughes**
154 **SCARPIA (IRE)**, 7, ch g Sans Frontieres (IRE)—Bunglasha Lady (IRE)  **Mrs T. J. Stone-Brown**
155 **SETTIE HILL (USA)**, 8, b g Cape Blanco (IRE)—Claire Soleil (USA)  **Michael Buckley & Exors of the late Lord Vestey**
156 **SHISHKIN (IRE)**, 7, b g Sholokhov (IRE)—Labarynth (IRE)  **Mrs M. Donnelly**
157 **SON OF CAMAS (FR)**, 6, ch g Creachadoir (IRE)—Camas (FR)  **Sullivan Bloodstock Limited**
158 **STEAL A MARCH**, 6, b g Mount Nelson—Side Step  **Her Majesty The Queen**
159 **STORM OF INTRIGUE (IRE)**, 9, b g Oscar (IRE)—Storminoora (IRE)  **Mr Oscar Singh & Miss Priya Purewal**
160 **STYLE DE GARDE (FR)**, 7, b g Kapgarde (FR)—Anowe de Jelois (FR)  **Highclere Thoroughbred Racing - Style**
161 **SUNRISE RUBY (IRE)**, 7, ch m Sholokhov (IRE)—Maryota (FR)  **Blunt, Breslin, Duffy, Slattery**

# MR NICKY HENDERSON - continued

162 **SURREY QUEST (IRE)**, 4, b g Milan—Roztoc (IRE)  **Surrey Racing (SQ)**
163 **TERREFORT (FR)**, 8, gr g Martaline—Vie de Reine (FR)  **Mr Simon Munir & Mr Isaac Souede**
164 **THE BOMBER LISTON (IRE)**, 5, b g Yeats (IRE)—True Britannia  **Mr J. P. McManus**
165 **THE CASHEL MAN (IRE)**, 9, b g High Chaparral (IRE)—Hadarama (IRE)  **Mrs F. H. Hay**
166 **THEINVAL (FR)**, 11, b g Smadoun (FR)—Kinevees (IRE)  **Mr & Mrs Sandy Orr**
167 **TIME FLIES BY (IRE)**, 6, ch g Getaway (GER)—What A Mewsment (IRE)  **Mr J. P. McManus**
168 **TOP NOTCH (FR)**, 10, b g Poliglote—Topira (FR)  **Mr Simon Munir & Mr Isaac Souede**
169 **TWEED SKIRT**, 4, b f Martaline—Theatre Girl  **Just Four Men With Rose Tinted Glasses**
170 **VALSHEDA**, 6, b g Milan—Candy Creek (IRE)  **Mr & Mrs R. G. Kelvin-Hughes**
171 **VALTOR (FR)**, 12, b g Nidor (FR)—Jossca (FR)  **Mr Simon Munir & Mr Isaac Souede**
172 **VEGAS BLUE (IRE)**, 6, b m Getaway (GER)—Bella Venezia (IRE)  **Crimbourne Bloodstock**
173 **VERDANA BLUE (IRE)**, 9, b m Getaway (GER)—Blue Gallery (IRE)  **Mrs D. A. Tabor**
174 **VERSATILITY**, 7, b g Yeats (IRE)—Stravinsky Dance  **The Barrow Boys 2**
175 **WAVE THE WAND**, 4, b g Gentlewave (IRE)—Magic Score  **Her Majesty The Queen**
176 **WELSH SAINT (IRE)**, 7, b g Saint des Saints (FR)—Minirose (FR)  **Walters Plant Hire & Potter Group**
177 **WHATSWRONGWITHYOU (IRE)**, 10, ch g Bienamado (USA)—Greenfield Noora (IRE)  **Turf Club 2020**
178 **WHITLOCK**, 6, ch g Dutch Art—Barynya  **Lady Lloyd-Webber**
179 **WILL CARVER (IRE)**, 6, b g Califet (FR)—Rock Angel (IRE)  **Owners Group 064**
180 **WISEGUY (IRE)**, 5, b g Fame And Glory—Sunset Queen (IRE)  **Mrs John Magnier & Mrs Paul Shanahan**
181 **WRAYSFORD (IRE)**, 5, b g Presenting—Ballygalli Heights (IRE)  **Sullivan Bloodstock Ltd & Chris Giles**

**Other Owners:** Miss J. K. Allison, R. K. Aston, R. A. Bartlett, Bloomsbury Stud, M. A. C. Buckley, Chelsea Thoroughbreds Ltd, Just Four Men, Mr & Mrs R. G. Kelvin-Hughes, Dr J. P. C. Poupel, Rose Tinted Glasses, Mr Alan Spence, Sullivan Bloodstock Limited, Sundorne Products (Llanidloes) Ltd, The Infamous Five, Walters Plant Hire Ltd.

**NH Jockey:** James Bowen, Aidan Coleman, Nico De Boinville, Jeremiah McGrath. **Conditional Jockey:** Joe Anderson, Ben Ffrench Davis, Alfie Jordan.

---

**271**  **MR PAUL HENDERSON, Whitsbury**
Postal: **1 Manor Farm Cottage, Whitsbury, Fordingbridge, Hampshire, SP6 3QP**
Contacts: **PHONE 01725 518113 MOBILE 07958 482213 FAX 01725 518113**
**EMAIL phendersonracing@gmail.com**

1 **ABBEY STREET (IRE)**, 10, b g Asian Heights—Cnocbui Cailin (IRE)  **Mr and Mrs J Baigent**
2 **BALLYEGAN HERO (IRE)**, 10, b g Oscar (IRE)—Kelly Gales (IRE)
3 **BIG MAN CLARENCE (IRE)**, 10, b g Golden Tornado (IRE)—Glens Lady (IRE)  **Pittville Park**
4 **CROSSLEY TENDER**, 8, b g Sulamani (IRE)—Slow Starter (IRE)  **Hawkings Harding Pearson Pyatt Willis**
5 **DOITFORTHEVILLAGE (IRE)**, 12, b g Turtle Island (IRE)—Last Chance Lady (IRE)  **The Rockbourne Partnership**
6 **DOYEN QUEEN (IRE)**, 7, b m Doyen (IRE)—Panoora Queen (IRE)  **NHRE Racing Club**
7 **DUARIGLE (IRE)**, 9, ch g Dubai Destination (USA)—Silver Valley (IRE)  **A Pearson E Hawkings M Jenner P Scope**
8 **ENTRE DEUX (FR)**, 7, b g Khalkevi (FR)—Evitta (FR)  **Mr S. Tulk**
9 **FETHARD FLYER (IRE)**, 9, b g Brian Boru—Strylea (IRE)  **J. P. Duffy**
10 **GOOD MAN VINNIE (IRE)**, 10, ch g Vinnie Roe (IRE)—Pellerossa (IRE)  **Sarah Habib & Ed Hawkings**
11 **HATCHET JACK (IRE)**, 9, b g Black Sam Bellamy (IRE)—
                                                Identity Parade (IRE)  **A J Pearson, Mark Jenner, Ed Hawkings**
12 **LARCADIO (IRE)**, 8, b g Arcadio (GER)—Le Ciel (IRE)  **The Rockbourne Partnership**
13 **LISRONAGH STONE (IRE)**, 8, b g Arcadio (GER)—From Above (IRE)  **Table 8**
14 **MAASAI WARRIOR (IRE)**, 6, b g Lovelace—No Case (IRE)  **A Pearson E Hawkings M Jenner P Scope**
15 **MEGALODON (IRE)**, 8, b g Getaway (GER)—Fitzgrey (IRE)  **Hawkings Finch Harding Stubbs Willis**
16 **MR P (IRE)**, 6, br g Malinas (GER)—La Belle Sauvage  **Mr C. Pistasczuk**
17 **MR SCAFF (IRE)**, 7, br g Vocalised (USA)—Nancy Rock (IRE)  **M R Scaffolding Services Ltd**
18 **MR STUBBS (IRE)**, 10, b g Robin des Pres (FR)—Crystal Stream (IRE)  **Turbanators**
19 **NO DRAMA (IRE)**, 6, ch g Mahler—Calimesa (IRE)  **The Sundowners**
20 **OUR NEST EGG (IRE)**, 8, b m Scorpion (IRE)—Little Nest Egg (IRE)  **The Two Hats Syndicate**
21 **POLAR LIGHT**, 6, b m Norse Dancer (IRE)—Dimelight  **J. P. Duffy**

## MR PAUL HENDERSON - continued

22 **RING MINELLA (IRE)**, 10, b g King's Theatre (IRE)—Ring of Water (USA)  **NHRE Racing Club**
23 **SHAW'S CROSS (IRE)**, 9, b g Mr Dinos (IRE)—Capparoe Cross (IRE)  **Mareildar Racing Part 1**
24 **STALIN'S SCRIPT (IRE)**, 6, b g Sholokhov (IRE)—Sara's Girl (IRE)  **Mr M. Day**
25 **THE GRANSON (IRE)**, 9, b g Jeremy (USA)—Kimberely Bay (IRE)  **John Finch & Mike & Tracie Willis**
26 **TZUNAMI**, 5, ch g Gentlewave (IRE)—Kylenoe Fairy (IRE)  **Mr E. J. Hawkings**
27 **UN BEAU ROMAN (FR)**, 13, bl g Roman Saddle (IRE)—Koukie (FR)  **Mr J. H. W. Finch**

**Other Owners:** Mr J. H. W. Finch, Mrs S. J. Habib, Mr B. C. Harding, Mr E. J. Hawkings, Mr M. E. Jenner, Mr A. Pearson, Mr J. Pyatt, Mr P. T. Scope, Mr T. J. Stubbs, Mr M. R. Willis, Mrs T. J. Willis.

---

**272**  **MR MICHAEL HERRINGTON, Willoughton**
Postal: **Mount House Stables, Long Lane, Willoughton, Gainsborough, Lincolnshire, DN21 5SQ**
Contacts: **MOBILE 07855 396858**
**EMAIL info@michaelherringtonracing.co.uk WEBSITE www.michaelherringtonracing.co.uk**

1 **ANIF (IRE)**, 7, b g Cape Cross (IRE)—Cadenza (FR)  **Stuart Herrington & Peter Forster**
2 **ARCHIPPOS**, 8, b g Archipenko (USA)—Sparkling Clear  **Stuart Herrington & Peter Forster**
3 **AYYAAMY (IRE)**, 4, b g Sir Prancealot (IRE)—Araajmh (USA)  **Michael Herrington Racing Club**
4 **BAY OF NAPLES (IRE)**, 5, b g Exceed And Excel (AUS)—Copperbeech (IRE)  **Mrs S. E. Lloyd**
5 **BEYOND INFINITY**, 4, ch g Bated Breath—Lady Gloria  **Tara Moon Partnership**
6 **CHILLON CASTLE**, 5, br m Swiss Spirit—Positivity  **Michael Herrington Racing Club**
7 **DARWINA**, 5, gr m Dark Angel (IRE)—Anadolu (IRE)  **K & L Fitzsimons**
8 **EDESSANN (IRE)**, 5, ch g Lope de Vega (IRE)—Edelmira (IRE)  **Away Days Racing Club**
9 **GLORIOUS CHARMER**, 5, b g Charm Spirit (IRE)—Fantacise  **Flash Figs Racing**
10 **JAN VAN HOOF (IRE)**, 10, b g Dutch Art—Cosenza  **Mrs H. J. Lloyd-Herrington**
11 **JUST KATY**, 4, b f Mount Nelson—Katy Nowaitee  **Team Given 3**
12 **KOMMANDER KIRKUP**, 10, ch g Assertive—Bikini  **Mrs H. Lloyd-Herrington & S. Herrington**
13 **LADY ALAVESA**, 6, b m Westlake—Matilda Peace  **Mrs S. E. Lloyd**
14 **MAHARASHTRA**, 5, b g Schiaparelli (GER)—Khandala (IRE)  **Nicholas Baines & Mrs H Lloyd-Herrington**
15 **QUIET PRIDE (IRE)**, 5, b m Sholokhov (IRE)—Flemens Pride  **Mark Dunphy & David Frame**
16 **STEELRIVER (IRE)**, 11, b g Iffraaj—Numerus Clausus (FR)  **Mrs H. J. Lloyd-Herrington**
17 **STREET POET (IRE)**, 8, b g Poet's Voice—Street Star (USA)  **Nicholas Baines & Mrs H Lloyd-Herrington**
18 **THAAYER**, 6, b g Helmet (AUS)—Sakhya (IRE)  **Mrs H. Lloyd-Herrington & S. Herrington**
19 **THE GAME OF LIFE**, 6, b g Oasis Dream—Velvet Star (IRE)  **Mrs H. J. Lloyd-Herrington**

### THREE-YEAR-OLDS

20 **BATOCCHI**, b c Bated Breath—Tarocchi (USA)  **Team Given 4**
21 **DREAM FOUNTAIN**, b c Fountain of Youth (IRE)—Mania (IRE)  **Team Given 5**
22 **DUBAI JEANIUS (IRE)**, b g Pride of Dubai (AUS)—Tempura (GER)  **Mrs H. J. Lloyd-Herrington**
23 **RATAFIA**, b c Iffraaj—Aetna  **Ingram Racing**
24 **SPARKLING PERRY**, b f Fountain of Youth (IRE)—Bebe de Cham  **Lovely Bubbly Racing**

**Other Owners:** Mr N. J. Baines, Mr M. P. Dunphy, K. Fitzsimons, Mrs L. Fitzsimons, Mr P. D. Forster, Mr D. Frame, Mr J. S. Herrington, Mrs H. J. Lloyd-Herrington, Mr G. O. Tourle, Mr M. H. Tourle.

**Assistant Trainer:** Helen Lloyd-Herrington.

## 273 MRS LAWNEY HILL, Aston Rowant
Postal: Woodway Farm, Aston Rowant, Watlington, Oxford, OX49 5SJ
Contacts: PHONE 01844 353051 MOBILE 07769 862648
EMAIL lawney@lawneyhill.co.uk WEBSITE www.lawneyhill.co.uk

1 BUNNY BORU, 7, b m Brian Boru—Home By Midnight **Martin Redman & Maurice Thomas**
2 CLONDAW WESTIE (IRE), 10, b g Westerner—You're A Native (IRE) **For Fun Partnership**
3 EVERYTHING'SONTICK (IRE), 5, br g Scorpion (IRE)—Atomic Betty (IRE) **Martin Redman & Maurice Thomas**
4 GARS BAR DINE (FR), 10, b g Martaline—Treekle Toffee (FR) **N. R. A. Sutton**
5 LISHEEN PRINCE (IRE), 10, b g Oscar (IRE)—Dino's Monkey (IRE) **The Sunday Night Partnership**
6 MAN OF STEEL (IRE), 12, b br g Craigsteel—Knappogue Honey (IRE) **Mr A. Hill**
7 MYSPACENOTYOURS, 6, b m Dr Massini (IRE)—Home By Midnight **Martin Redman & Maurice Thomas**
8 SHIMBA HILLS, 10, b g Sixties Icon—Search Party **Mr A. Hill**
9 THE BRASSMOULDER (IRE), 11, b g Milan—Wyndham Bobbin (IRE) **Mr R. W. L. Cranfield**
10 VELVET COGNAC, 13, b g Grape Tree Road—Scandalous Affair **Mr A. Hill**
11 WESTBROOK BERTIE, 6, b g Sixties Icon—Evanesce **The Further Folly Partnership**

## 274 MR CHARLES HILLS, Lambourn
Postal: Wetherdown House, Lambourn, Hungerford, Berkshire, RG17 8UB
Contacts: PHONE 01488 71548 FAX 01488 72823
EMAIL info@charleshills.co.uk WEBSITE www.charleshills.com

1 AFAAK, 7, b g Oasis Dream—Ghanaati (USA) **Mr Hamdan Al Maktoum**
2 ALREHB (USA), 4, gr ro c War Front (USA)—Tahrir (IRE) **Mr Hamdan Al Maktoum**
3 BAASHIR (IRE), 4, b c Muhaarar—Eshaadeh (USA) **Mr Hamdan Al Maktoum**
4 BADRI, 4, b g Dark Angel (IRE)—Penny Drops **Mr Hamdan Al Maktoum**
5 BATTAASH (IRE), 7, b g Dark Angel (IRE)—Anna Law (IRE) **Mr Hamdan Al Maktoum**
6 CAESONIA, 5, ch m Garswood—Agrippina **Mrs Fiona Williams**
7 CARAUSIUS, 4, b g Cacique (IRE)—Domitia **Mrs Fiona Williams**
8 DULAS (IRE), 4, b g Raven's Pass (USA)—Petit Calva (FR) **Julie Martin & David R. Martin & Partner**
9 EQUILATERAL, 6, b g Equiano (FR)—Tarentaise **Mrs Fitri Hay**
10 FANTASY BELIEVER (IRE), 4, b g Make Believe—Avizare (IRE) **The Fantasy Believer Syndicate**
11 FLEETING PRINCE (IRE), 4, b c No Nay Never (USA)—My Sweet Georgia (IRE) **Mrs Susan Roy**
12 FLIPPA THE STRIPPA (IRE), 4, gr f Outstrip—Celsius Degre (IRE) **Mr Christopher Wright**
13 GARRUS (IRE), 5, gr g Acclamation—Queen of Power (IRE) **Mrs Susan Roy**
14 KHAADEM (IRE), 5, br h Dark Angel (IRE)—White Daffodil (IRE) **Mr Hamdan Al Maktoum**
15 KING'S KNIGHT (IRE), 4, b c Dark Angel (IRE)—Oatcake **Mr Ziad A Galadari**
16 MAY SONIC, 5, b g Mayson—Aromatherapy **Hills Angels**
17 MOTAGALLY, 5, b g Swiss Spirit—Gilt Linked **Mr Hamdan Al Maktoum**
18 MUMTAAZ (IRE), 4, b g Invincible Spirit (IRE)—Monzza **Faringdon Place 1 Partnership**
19 PERSUASION (IRE), 4, b c Acclamation—Effervesce (IRE) **Mrs Susan Roy**
20 POGO (IRE), 5, b h Zebedee—Cute **Gary & Linnet Woodward**
21 REWAAYAT (IRE), 6, br g Pivotal—Rufoof **Mr Hamdan Al Maktoum**
22 ROYAL COMMANDO (IRE), 4, b c No Nay Never (USA)—Online Alexander (IRE) **Mr Ziad A Galadari**
23 SHURAFFA (IRE), 4, b f Shamardal (USA)—Shamtari (IRE) **Mr C. B. Hills**
24 SPOOF, 6, b g Poet's Voice—Filona (IRE) **Gary & Linnet Woodward**
25 SPUROFTHEMOMENT, 4, b f Brazen Beau (AUS)—Royal Blush **One More Moment of Madness**
26 TILSIT (USA), 4, b c First Defence (USA)—Multilingual **Exors of the late Mr K. Abdullah**
27 TOMMY DE VITO, 4, b c Dandy Man (IRE)—Rohlindi **Chelsea Thoroughbreds - Goodfellas**
28 VINDOLANDA, 5, ch m Nathaniel (IRE)—Cartimandua **Mrs Fiona Williams**

### THREE-YEAR-OLDS

29 ALTAAYSHAH (IRE), b f Dark Angel (IRE)—Anna Law (IRE) **Mr Hamdan Al Maktoum**
30 AMLWCH (IRE), b gr g Muhaarar—Nations Alexander (IRE) **Mr Dan Hall**
31 ARIEL (IRE), b c Exceed And Excel (AUS)—Garra Molly (IRE) **Mr P. K. Siu**

## MR CHARLES HILLS - continued

32 **ARTHUR CONAN DOYLE**, b c Oasis Dream—Secret Keeper **Chelsea Thoroughbreds - Sherlock Holmes**
33 **BALQAA**, b f Cable Bay (IRE)—Angels Wings (IRE) **Mr Hamdan Al Maktoum**
34 **BURMA SKY**, b g Muhaarar—Heho **Mr P Winkworth**
35 **CROSSFORD (IRE)**, b c Dawn Approach (IRE)—Stylish One (IRE) **Mr R A Bartlett & Partners**
36 **DARK SHIFT**, gr c Dark Angel (IRE)—Mosuo (IRE) **Mr H. Frost**
37 **DIAMOND FIFE**, b f Excelebration (IRE)—Chelsea Morning (USA) **Mr Christopher Wright & Mr Robin Millar**
38 **EASY TO DREAM**, b f Muhaarar—Inyordreams **One More Moment of Madness**
39 **ENHIMAAR**, gr f Dark Angel (IRE)—Shawka **Mr Hamdan Al Maktoum**
40 **EQUALITY**, b c Equiano (FR)—Penny Drops **Kennet Valley Thoroughbreds II**
41 **GIVE 'EM THE SLIP**, b f Oasis Dream—Super Sleuth (IRE) **J Gompertz,Clivedenstud,S Roy,J Schroder**
42 **GREY SPARKLE (IRE)**, gr f Starspangledbanner (AUS)—
                                           Sparkling (IRE) **John C Grant,Mohammed Ali,Mrs B W Hills**
43 **IBIZA ROCKS**, gr c Dark Angel (IRE)—The Thrill Is Gone **Mr Christopher Wright**
44 **IL BANDITO (IRE)**, b g Acclamation—Molly Dolly (IRE) **Mrs Susan Roy**
45 **ILLIES MEMORIES (IRE)**, b f Hard Spun (USA)—Anne of Kiev (IRE) **Mr John C Grant & Mrs E O'Leary**
46 **JADWAL**, b g Mustajeeb—Atab (IRE) **Mr Hamdan Al Maktoum**
47 **LE ROI LION (ITY)**, b c Camacho—Delia Eria (IRE) **Mrs Annette O'Callaghan**
48 **MEJTHAAM (IRE)**, b f Exceed And Excel (AUS)—Adhwaa **Mr Hamdan Al Maktoum**
49 **MENAI BRIDGE**, b g Cable Bay (IRE)—Sonnellino **N N Browne & Paul McNamara**
50 **MOBARHIN (IRE)**, b c Muhaarar—Fadhayyil **Mr Hamdan Al Maktoum**
51 **MOQADAMA (IRE)**, b f Dark Angel (IRE)—White Daffodil (IRE) **Mr Hamdan Al Maktoum**
52 **MORAWETH (USA)**, ch c Speightstown (USA)—Istiraaha (USA) **Mr Hamdan Al Maktoum**
53 **MUJBAR**, b c Muhaarar—Madany (IRE) **Mr Hamdan Al Maktoum**
54 **MUMMY'S BOY**, b c Footstepsinthesand—Dance On The Hill (IRE) **Christopher Johnston & Partners**
55 **MUTALAAQY (IRE)**, b g Dark Angel (IRE)—Misdaqeya **Mr Hamdan Al Maktoum**
56 **MUTARAAFEQ (IRE)**, b g Estidhkaar (IRE)—Cumbree (IRE) **Mr Hamdan Al Maktoum**
57 **MUTARABES (IRE)**, b c Dark Angel (IRE)—Relation Alexander (IRE) **Mr Hamdan Al Maktoum**
58 **MUTASAABEQ (IRE)**, br c Invincible Spirit—Ghanaati (USA) **Mr Hamdan Al Maktoum**
59 **OUTCAST**, b f Outstrip—Jakarta Jade (IRE) **Mildmay Racing**
60 **PERFECT DREAM**, b f Oasis Dream—Jane's Memory (IRE) **Dr Bridget Drew  & Partners**
61 **PONTIUS (IRE)**, b c No Nay Never (USA)—Sacrament (IRE) **B W Hills, M Kerr-dineen & M Hughes**
62 **PRADO**, b f Iffraaj—Royal Empress (IRE) **Mrs Fitri Hay**
63 **PROPAGATION (IRE)**, b g Acclamation—Thakerah (IRE) **Mr B. W. Hills**
64 **RIVER TWEED (IRE)**, b g Starspangledbanner (AUS)—Sorry Woman (FR) **Mrs Fitri Hay**
65 **ROYAL MUSKETEER**, b c Acclamation—Queen's Pearl (IRE) **Mr Ziad A Galadari**
66 **SARATOGA GOLD**, ch c Mayson—Lady Sylvia **Mr David J. Keast**
67 **SARROOD (IRE)**, b f Mukhadram—Zaakhir (IRE) **Mr Hamdan Al Maktoum**
68 **SHOBIZ**, b g Showcasing—Royal Confidence **Mr D. M. James**
69 **SMOOTH CONNECTION (IRE)**, b c Gleneagles (IRE)—Endless Love (IRE) **Mrs Susan Roy**
70 **SNASH (IRE)**, b c Markaz (IRE)—Wardat Dubai **Mr N. Cowes, Mr B. W. Hills**
71 **TANMAWWY (IRE)**, b c Invincible Spirit (IRE)—Rufoof **Mr Hamdan Al Maktoum**
72 **THE ATTORNEY (IRE)**, b c Kodiac—Next Trial (IRE) **Mr Ziad A Galadari**
73 **TOUCHWOOD (IRE)**, b c Invincible Spirit (IRE)—Aaraamm (USA) **Mr H. Frost**
74 **WHITE LADY (IRE)**, b f Dark Angel (IRE)—Wiltshire Life (IRE) **A O'Callaghan, J Allison, P Hills**

## TWO-YEAR-OLDS

75 B c 29/04 Zoffany (IRE)—Aljumar (IRE) (Marju (IRE)) (45000)
76 B c 02/03 Cable Bay (IRE)—Angels Wings (IRE) (Dark Angel (IRE)) (11000)
77 B c 31/03 War Front (USA)—Aqsaam (USA) (Dynaformer (USA))
78 **BEACHES**, b c 29/03 Churchill (IRE)—Know Me Love Me (IRE) (Danehill Dancer (IRE)) (95238)
79 **CAESAR NERO**, b c 02/04 Territories (IRE)—Publilia (Makfi) (8000)
80 **DILIGENTLY DONE**, b f 15/03 Due Diligence (USA)—Quite A Story (Equiano (FR)) (8000)
81 B f 09/04 Profitable (IRE)—Emperors Pearl (IRE) (Holy Roman Emperor (IRE)) (34286)
82 B f 18/04 Dark Angel (IRE)—Fadhayyil (Tamayuz)
83 B f 26/02 Dark Angel (IRE)—Faraday Light (IRE) (Rainbow Quest (USA))
84 B c 26/01 Churchill (IRE)—Gertrude Gray (IRE) (Hurricane Run (IRE))
85 B c 01/05 Muhaarar—Ghanaati (USA) (Giant's Causeway (USA))
86 B c 16/04 Tamayuz—Got To Dream (Duke of Marmalade (IRE)) (50000)
87 **GREEN TEAM STATION (IRE)**, b c 28/03 Ribchester (IRE)—Indian Angel (Indian Ridge) (34000)

## MR CHARLES HILLS - continued

88  B c 12/04 Cotai Glory—Hasty (IRE) (Invincible Spirit (IRE)) (38095)
89  B f 01/02 Mastercraftsman (IRE)—Hyphaema (IRE) (Rock of Gibraltar (IRE)) (35000)
90  **IBN ALDAR,** br c 08/04 Twilight Son—Bint Aldar (Zoffany (IRE)) (47619)
91  **INVERNESS (IRE),** b c 23/04 Highland Reel (IRE)—Four Eleven (CAN) (Arch (USA)) (110000)
92  B c 04/05 Sea The Stars (IRE)—Kelly Nicole (IRE) (Rainbow Quest (USA)) (75000)
93  Ch f 07/04 Lethal Force (IRE)—Love On The Rocks (IRE) (Exceed And Excel (AUS))
94  B c 02/03 Acclamation—Lydia Becker (Sleeping Indian) (130000)
95  B f 17/05 Kingman—Maayaat (USA) (Jazil (USA))
96  B f 10/04 Frankel—Madany (IRE) (Acclamation)
97  **MAYFAIR STROLL (IRE),** b f 11/04 Gleneagles (IRE)—Zadalla (Zaha (CAN)) (15000)
98  B c 08/03 Dark Angel (IRE)—Merry Me (IRE) (Invincible Spirit (IRE))
99  Ch f 19/02 Dubawi (IRE)—Neshmeya (Lawman (FR))
100 **NO MORE TIERS,** b f 19/04 Hot Streak (IRE)—Aromatherapy (Oasis Dream)
101 B c 20/03 Kodiac—Online Alexander (Acclamation)
102 **ORAZIO (IRE),** br c 29/03 Caravaggio (USA)—Lady Fashion (Oasis Dream) (204762)
103 **PEACE NEGOTIATION (IRE),** b c 27/02 No Nay Never (USA)—Madeenaty (IRE) (Dansili) (110000)
104 **POINT LYNAS (IRE),** b c 14/03 Iffraaj—Initially (Dansili) (40000)
105 **PRINCESS ARIEL,** b f 05/02 Gleneagles (IRE)—Dutch Princess (Dutch Art)
106 Ch c 03/04 Belardo (IRE)—Ragtime Dancer (Medicean) (60000)
107 B f 12/02 Dark Angel (IRE)—Relation Alexander (IRE) (Dandy Man (IRE)) (145000)
108 Ch c 22/03 Dawn Approach (IRE)—Reyaadah (Tamayuz)
109 B f 03/05 Invincible Spirit (IRE)—Rufoof (Zamindar (USA))
110 Ro c 06/05 Mastercraftsman (IRE)—Sanaya (IRE) (Barathea (IRE)) (65000)
111 **SONNY LISTON (IRE),** b c 30/01 Lawman (FR)—Stars In Your Eyes (Galileo (IRE)) (60000)
112 **TAMARAMA,** b f 05/03 Muhaarar—Kalsa (IRE) (Whipper (USA))
113 B f 18/03 Dubawi (IRE)—Thafeera (USA) (War Front (USA))
114 **U A E FIFTY (IRE),** b c 06/04 Dandy Man (IRE)—Bounty'S Spirit (Bahamian Bounty) (17143)
115 B f 31/03 Adaay (IRE)—Vespasia (Medicean) (8000)
116 B c 24/02 Footstepsinthesand—Virginia Celeste (IRE) (Galileo (IRE)) (68000)
117 B c 25/02 Le Havre (IRE)—Waldnah (New Approach (IRE)) (325000)
118 Ch c 25/04 Galileo Gold—Zelie Martin (IRE) (Invincible Spirit (IRE)) (23810)

**Other Owners:** Ahmad Al Shaikh, Lady Bamford, Mr John E. Bodie, D. H. Caslon, Chelsea Thoroughbreds Ltd, Mr C.  Conroy, Guards Club Racing Limited, Mr M. V. Magnier, Mr James A. Oldham, PJL Racing, Amo  Racing LTD, Mr Steven Rocco, Mrs Paul Shanahan, The Chriselliam Partnership.

**Assistant Trainer:** Nicola  Dowell, Jamie Insole.

---

**275**

## MR MARK HOAD, Lewes
Postal: **Windmill Lodge Stables, Spital Road, Lewes, East Sussex, BN7 1LS**
Contacts: **PHONE 01273 480691, 01273 477124 MOBILE 07742 446168 FAX 01273 477124**
**EMAIL markhoad@aol.com**

1  **BROUGHTONS COMPASS,** 4, b g Henrythenavigator (USA)—Sayrianna  **Mr B Pay**
2  **COTEAUX DU LAYON,** 4, b g Gregorian (IRE)—Jocasta Dawn  **R. P. C. Hoad**
3  **HEY HO LET'S GO,** 5, b g Dream Ahead (USA)—Lookslikeanangel  **Mrs K. B. Tester**
4  **HIT THE BEAT,** 6, br m Fast Company (IRE)—Dance Express (IRE)  **Mrs K. B. Tester**
5  **I AM WILD,** 6, b m Lilbourne Lad (IRE)—Wild Sauce  **I Am Wild Syndicate**
6  **LUCKY FACE,** 4, b f Requinto (IRE)—Bit Windy  **Mr K. W. Sneath**

**276** **MR PHILIP HOBBS, Minehead**
Postal: **Sandhill, Bilbrook, Minehead, Somerset, TA24 6HA**
Contacts: **PHONE 01984 640366 MOBILE 07860 729795 FAX 01984 641124**
**EMAIL pjhobbs@pjhobbs.com WEBSITE www.pjhobbs.com**

1 **ACROSS THE CHANNEL (FR)**, 6, b g Dunkerque (FR)—Aulne River (FR) **Mr A. L. Cohen**
2 **ADVANTURA (IRE)**, 4, b g Watar (IRE)—Keys Hope (IRE) **A. P. Staple**
3 **ARIAN (IRE)**, 9, b m King's Theatre (IRE)—Brave Betsy (IRE) **Mr D. M. Mathias**
4 **AUBA ME YANG (IRE)**, 5, b g Fame And Glory—No Bodys Flame (IRE) **S & G Soils Limited**
5 **AULD SOD (IRE)**, 8, b g Court Cave (IRE)—Didn't You Know (FR) **Mr C. A. H. Tilley**
6 **AWAKE AT MIDNIGHT**, 9, b g Midnight Legend—Wakeful **Mrs S. L. Lloyd-Baker**
7 **BARBROOK STAR (IRE)**, 9, b g Getaway (GER)—Fille de Robin (FR) **Mrs B. A. Hitchcock**
8 **BEAU DU BRIZAIS (FR)**, 9, gr g Kapgarde (FR)—Belle du Brizais (FR) **Mrs C. Skan**
9 **BIG SHARK (IRE)**, 7, b g Vinnie Roe (IRE)—Castlelost (IRE) **Mrs C Walsh & Eden Valley Chancers**
10 **BROTHER TEDD**, 12, gr g Kayf Taro—Neltina **Scrase Farms**
11 **CAMPROND (FR)**, 5, b g Lope de Vega (IRE)—Bernieres (IRE) **Mr J. P. McManus**
12 **CANASTERO (IRE)**, 5, b g Getaway (GER)—Lucky Pigeon (IRE) **Mrs C. Skan**
13 **CAPE MILANO (IRE)**, 6, b br g Milan—Shatani (IRE) **Mrs J. A. S. Luff**
14 **CHALGROVE (FR)**, 5, b g Le Havre (FR)—Exit To Derawlin (FR) **Snowdrop Stud Company Ltd**
15 **CHEF D'EQUIPE (FR)**, 9, b g Presenting—Millesimee (FR) **David Maxwell Racing Limited**
16 **COTSWOLD WAY (IRE)**, 8, b g Stowaway—Rosies All The Way **Miss I. D. Du Pre**
17 **DAN'S CHOSEN**, 6, b g Well Chosen—Miss Audacious (IRE) **The Philip Hobbs Racing Partnership II**
18 **DANGAN DES CHAMPS (IRE)**, 6, b br m Robin des Champs (FR)—Our Lucky Venture (IRE) **Mr M. Hoare**
19 **DEFI DU SEUIL (FR)**, 8, b g Voix du Nord (FR)—Quarvine du Seuil (FR) **Mr J. P. McManus**
20 **DEISE ABA (IRE)**, 8, b g Mahler—Kit Massini (IRE) **Mr T. J. Hemmings**
21 **DEMOPOLIS (FR)**, 7, b g Poliglote—Princess Demut (GER) **Mr J. P. McManus**
22 **DOLPHIN SQUARE (IRE)**, 7, b g Shantou (USA)—Carrig Eden Lass (IRE) **David Maxwell Racing Limited**
23 **DOSTAL PHIL (FR)**, 8, b g Coastal Path—Quiphile (FR) **Mr J. P. McManus**
24 **EARTH COMPANY (IRE)**, 5, b br g Arcadio (GER)—Lady Rhinestone (IRE) **R. M. Penny**
25 **EARTH LORD (IRE)**, 5, ch g Mahler—Glebe Beauty (IRE) **R. M. Penny**
26 **EARTH MOOR (IRE)**, 7, ch g Ask—Merrylas (IRE) **Mrs C. E. Penny**
27 **EBONY GALE**, 7, b g Shiroccco (GER)—Glenora Gale (IRE) **Mrs J. A. S. Luff**
28 **ECU DE LA NOVERIE (FR)**, 7, b g Linda's Lad—Quat'sous d'Or (FR) **David Maxwell Racing Limited**
29 **ET APRES THOU (FR)**, 7, b g Network (GER)—Lady Thou (FR) **Dr V. M. G. Ferguson**
30 **EVERGLOW**, 6, b g Presenting—Cent Prime **Mr P. A. Munnelly**
31 **FESTIVAL DAWN**, 9, b m Kayf Taro—Keel Road (IRE) **N. R. A. Sutton**
32 **FEUILLE DE CHENE (FR)**, 6, b m Montmartre (FR)—Haldiana (FR) **Mr J. P. McManus**
33 **FLINCK (IRE)**, 7, b g Fame And Glory—Princess Supreme (IRE) **R. A. Bartlett**
34 **FOR LANGY (FR)**, 6, b g Day Flight—Jubilee II (FR) **David Maxwell Racing Limited**
35 **FOREVER DES LONG (FR)**, 6, b g Blue Bresil (FR)—
Fetuque Du Moulin (FR) **Noel Fehily Racing Syndicates-Forever De**
36 **GALA BALL (FR)**, 11, b g Flemensfirth (USA)—Nuit des Chartreux (FR) **R & Mrs J. E. Gibbs**
37 **GARDE LA VICTOIRE (FR)**, 12, b g Kapgarde (FR)—Next Victory (FR) **Mrs D. L. Whateley**
38 **GAVROCHEKA (FR)**, 5, b m Spanish Moon (USA)—Troika (FR) **Mr J. P. McManus**
39 **GLASHA'S PEAK**, 7, b m Flemensfirth (USA)—Peggies Run **Sir Christopher & Lady Wates**
40 **GOLDEN SOVEREIGN (IRE)**, 7, b g Gold Well—Fugal Maid (IRE) **Mr L. Quinn**
41 **GOSHEVEN (IRE)**, 8, b g Presenting—Fair Choice (IRE) **The Grocer Syndicate**
42 **GUERNESEY (IRE)**, 5, gr g Martaline—Myrtille Jersey (FR) **J. T. Warner**
43 **GUMBALL (FR)**, 7, gr g No Risk At All (FR)—Good Time Girl (FR) **J. T. Warner**
44 **HONORARY COLONEL (IRE)**, 5, b g Ocovango—Mushagak (IRE) **Mr A. E. Peterson**
45 **HOPE YOU DO (FR)**, 4, b g Boris de Deauville (IRE)—Une Tournee (FR) **Mr J. P. McManus**
46 **JERRYSBACK (IRE)**, 9, b g Jeremy (USA)—Get A Few Bob Back (IRE) **Mr J. P. McManus**
47 **KALOOKI (GER)**, 7, gr g Martaline—Karuma (GER) **Mr A. L. Cohen**
48 **KANUKANKAN (IRE)**, 6, ch g Arakan (USA)—Blow A Gasket (IRE) **Mrs L. R. Lovell**
49 **KATIES ESCAPE (IRE)**, 6, ch m Getaway (GER)—Katies Pet (IRE) **The Philip Hobbs Racing Partnership**
50 **KEEP MOVING (IRE)**, 9, b g Linda's Lad—Keeping Gold (FR) **The Country Side**
51 **KEEP ROLLING (IRE)**, 8, ch g Mahler—Kayles Castle (IRE) **Mick Fitzgerald Racing Club**
52 **KEPY BLANC (FR)**, 6, ch g Kapgarde (FR)—Villemanzie (FR) **David Maxwell Racing Limited**
53 **KIMARELLI**, 4, b f Schiaparelli (GER)—Kim Tian Road (IRE) **Knaves Ash Racing**
54 **LANGLEY HUNDRED (IRE)**, 4, b g Sholokhov (IRE)—Theregoesthetruth (IRE) **The Englands and Heywoods**

## MR PHILIP HOBBS - continued

55 **LARKBARROW LAD**, 8, b g Kayf Tara—Follow My Leader (IRE)  **The Englands and Heywoods**
56 **LE LIGERIEN (FR)**, 8, b g Turgeon (USA)—Etoile de Loir (FR)  **D. R. Churches**
57 **LITTLE RIVER BAY (IRE)**, 6, b m Shirocco (GER)—Penneyrose Bay  **Sir Christopher & Lady Wates**
58 **LONGSHANKS (IRE)**, 7, b g Scorpion (IRE)—Cash A Lawn (IRE)  **Unity Farm Holiday Centre Ltd**
59 **LUTTRELL LAD (IRE)**, 5, b g Beat Hollow—Fairly Definite (IRE)  **Owners for Owners Luttrell Lad**
60 **MAJESTIC MERLIN**, 6, b g Midnight Legend—Posh Emily  **J.L & P Frampton A.M Midgley R.J Hodges**
61 **MASTER WORK (FR)**, 8, b g Network (GER)—Mascarpone (FR)  **Mr B K Peppiatt & Mr D R Peppiatt**
62 **MASTERS LEGACY (IRE)**, 6, br g Getaway (GER)—Gently Go (IRE)  **Mrs P. M. Bosley**
63 **MCNAMARAS BAND (IRE)**, 8, b g Getaway (GER)—Katies Pet (IRE)  **Tim Syder & Dominic Burke**
64 **MELEKHOV (IRE)**, 7, b g Sholokhov (IRE)—Yorkshire Girl (IRE)  **Owners For Owners: Melekhov**
65 5, Ch m Black Sam Bellamy (IRE)—Miss Chinchilla  **The Philip Hobbs Racing Partnership II**
66 **MISTER MARBLES (IRE)**, 5, br g Doyen (IRE)—Presenting Marble (IRE)  **Mr A. E. Peterson**
67 **MISTER TIMMYTUCKS**, 8, b g Kayf Tara—No Need For Alarm  **A. G. Fear**
68 **MONEY SPINNER (IRE)**, 4, b g Soldier of Fortune (IRE)—Floral Spinner  **Mr A. E. Peterson**
69 **MOON TIGER (FR)**, 5, b g Le Havre (IRE)—Lune Orientale (FR)  **The Macaroni Beach Society**
70 **MUSICAL SLAVE (IRE)**, 8, b g Getaway (GER)—Inghwung  **Mr J. P. McManus**
71 **MY KEEPSAKE**, 5, br m Kalanisi (IRE)—Dudeen (IRE)  **The Vintage Hunters**
72 **NO COMMENT**, 10, br g Kayf Tara—Dizzy Frizzy  **Mr J. P. McManus**
73 **OAKLEY (IRE)**, 8, b g Oscar (IRE)—Tirolean Dance (IRE)  **Mr T. D. J. Syder**
74 **OFF THE PLANET (IRE)**, 6, ch g Presenting—Kings Diva (IRE)  **The Brushmakers**
75 **ONE FOR YOU (IRE)**, 6, b g Yeats (IRE)—Tempest Belle (IRE)  **Martin St. Quinton & Tim Syder**
76 **ORBYS LEGEND (IRE)**, 5, b g Milan—Morning Legend (IRE)  **Highclere Thoroughbred Racing - Milan**
77 **PILEON (IRE)**, 7, b g Yeats (IRE)—Heath Heaven  **Mr Tim Syder & Martin St Quinton**
78 **POINTED AND SHARP (IRE)**, 9, b g Scorpion (IRE)—Leamybe (IRE)  **Tony Staple & George Giles**
79 **POL CROCAN (IRE)**, 6, br g Shirocco (GER)—She's All That (IRE)  **Mrs C. Skan**
80 **POTTERS VENTURE (IRE)**, 7, b g Arcadio (GER)—Starventure (IRE)  **Mr A. E. Peterson**
81 **PRESUMING ED (IRE)**, 6, b g Westerner—Maracana (IRE)  **Louisville Syndicate II**
82 **RENWICK (IRE)**, 8, b g Milan—Come In Moscow (IRE)  **Mrs D. L. Whateley**
83 **ROCK THE KASBAH (IRE)**, 11, ch g Shirocco (GER)—Impudent (IRE)  **Mrs D. L. Whateley**
84 **ROCKHAMTOM (IRE)**, 5, b g Leading Light (IRE)—Glencree Rose (IRE)  **Mrs J. J. Peppiatt**
85 **RONDE DE NUIT (FR)**, 4, b f Doctor Dino (FR)—Nuit de Guerre (FR)  **Mr J. P. McManus**
86 **SAMBURU SHUJAA (FR)**, 8, b g Poliglote—Girelle (FR)  **R. & Mrs J. E. Gibbs**
87 **SANDY BOY (IRE)**, 7, b g Tajraasi (USA)—Annienoora (IRE)  **Mrs B. A. Hitchcock**
88 5, Ch m Midnight Legend—Setter's Princess  **R. J. Hodges**
89 **SHANTOU SUNSET**, 7, ch m Shantou (USA)—Kingara  **The Philip Hobbs Racing Partnership**
90 **SINGAPORE SAGA**, 6, b m Midnight Legend—Kim Tian Road (IRE)  **Taunton Racecourse Owners Club**
91 **SMARTY WILD**, 7, b g Fair Mix (IRE)—Blaeberry  **Mr Michael & Mrs Norma Tuckey**
92 **SPORTING JOHN (IRE)**, 6, b br g Getaway (GER)—Wild Spell (IRE)  **Mr J. P. McManus**
93 **SPRINGTOWN LAKE (IRE)**, 9, b g Gamut (IRE)—Sprightly Gal (IRE)  **Mr T. D. J. Syder**
94 **ST BARTS (IRE)**, 7, b g High Chaparral (IRE)—Lindeman (IRE)  **Mr & Mrs R. G. Kelvin-Hughes**
95 **STEELY ADDITION (IRE)**, 9, b g Craigsteel—Blond's Addition (IRE)  **Step By Step**
96 **STELLAR MAGIC (IRE)**, 6, b g Arctic Cosmos (USA)—Inter Alia (IRE)  **A. Stennett**
97 **STOKE PERO (IRE)**, 5, gr h Libertarian—Gallery Gale (IRE)  **The Englands and Heywoods**
98 **STORM FORCE BEN (IRE)**, 7, b g Fame And Glory—Torduff Storm (IRE)  **Dr V. M. G. Ferguson**
99 **STRONG PURSUIT (IRE)**, 11, ch g Flemensfirth (USA)—Loughaderra (IRE)  **Mr T. D. J. Syder**
100 **SURTITLE (IRE)**, 5, b g Presenting—Annabaloo (IRE)  **Mrs V. F. Burke**
101 5, B g Califet (FR)—Tasanak (IRE)  **F. R. Jarvey**
102 **TEN SIXTY (IRE)**, 11, br g Presenting—Senora Snoopy (IRE)  **Mr A. L. Cohen**
103 **THYME HILL**, 7, b g Kayf Tara—Rosita Bay  **The Englands and Heywoods**
104 **TIDAL FLOW**, 8, b g Black Sam Bellamy (IRE)—Mrs Philip  **Brocade Racing**
105 **TRES FRANCAIS**, 6, b g Great Pretender (IRE)—Cerise Bleue (FR)  **David Maxwell Racing Limited**
106 **TRUCKERS PASS (IRE)**, 7, br g Kalanisi (IRE)—Lady Knightess (IRE)  **Brocade Racing**
107 **TRUCKIN AWAY (IRE)**, 8, br g Getaway (GER)—Simons Girl (IRE)  **Brocade Racing**
108 **VANGO DE VAIGE (FR)**, 8, b g Great Pretender (IRE)—Yellow Park (FR)  **M. Short**
109 **WAIT FOR ME (FR)**, 11, b g Saint des Saints (FR)—Aulne River (FR)  **Mr A. L. Cohen**
110 **WESTEND STORY (IRE)**, 10, b g Westerner—Sarahall (IRE)  **Mick Fitzgerald Racing Club**
111 **WILDFIRE WARRIOR (IRE)**, 6, b g Flemensfirth (USA)—Lady of Fortune (IRE)  **Mrs D. L. Whateley**
112 **WINTER GETAWAY (IRE)**, 8, b m Getaway (GER)—Galzig (IRE)  **The Kingpins**
113 **YOUNG WILLIAM (IRE)**, 5, b g Yeats (IRE)—Full of Fruit (IRE)  **Mr T. D. J. Syder**
114 **ZAFAR (GER)**, 6, b g Kamsin (GER)—Zambuka (FR)  **Govier & Brown**

# MR PHILIP HOBBS - continued

**115 ZANZA (IRE)**, 7, b g Arcadio (GER)—What A Bleu (IRE)  **Louisville Syndicate Elite**
**116 ZOFFEE**, 5, b g Zoffany (IRE)—Mount Crystal (IRE)  **Mr A. E. Peterson**

**Other Owners:** Mrs A. E. M. Broom, Mr G. R. Broom, Mrs J. L. Buckingham, Mr K. Buckle, Mr D. J. Burke, C. J. Butler, Mr I. A. Collinson, Mr J. P Cooper, Miss I. D. Du Pre, Eden Valley Chancers, Mr A. D. England, Mrs E. England, J. L. Frampton, Mr P.S. Frampton, John Frampton & Paul Frampton, Exors of the Late H. R. Gibbs, Mrs J. E. Gibbs, Mr G. R. Giles, Mr A. H. Heywood, Mr A. S. Heywood, R. J. Hodges, A. M. Midgley, B. K. Peppiatt, D. R. Peppiatt, D. A. Rees, N. C. Savery, Exors of the Late Mrs J. E. Scrase, Mr J. M. Scrase, Mr N. D. Scrase, Mr M. G. St Quinton, A. P. Staple, Step By Step Supporting Independence Ltd, Mr T. D. J. Syder, M. J. Tuckey, Mrs N. Tuckey, C. J. M. Walker, Mrs C. J. Walsh, Sir Christopher Wates, Lady G. F. Wates.

**Assistant Trainer:** Ben Robarts, Johnson White.

**NH Jockey:** Richard Johnson, Micheal Nolan, Tom O'Brien. **Conditional Jockey:** Sean Houlihan, Ben Jones.
**Amateur Jockey:** Mr Isaac Buncle, Mr Tom Dixon, Mr Jack Martin, Mr David Maxwell.

---

## 277 MISS CLARE HOBSON, Royston
Postal: **The Woolpack, London Road, Reed, Royston, Hertfordshire, SG8 8BB**
Contacts: **MOBILE 07966 734889**
EMAIL clarehobsonracing@gmail.com

1 **BRIGHT SAFFRON**, 6, ch m Champs Elysees—Mercy Pecksniff  **Smith's Wapping Partnership**
2 **BULLSEMPIRE (IRE)**, 8, b g Papal Bull—Satanella (IRE)  **The Fox and Duck syndicate**
3 **DHARMA RAIN (IRE)**, 6, b m High Chaparral (IRE)—Crazy Volume (IRE)  **Mr B. White**
4 **FOXY SINGER (FR)**, 6, b m Secret Singer (FR)—Newport (FR)  **Mr H. R. Hobson**
5 **JIMMY MAC**, 5, b g Malinas (GER)—Flo The Machine (IRE)  **Mrs R. E. Hobson**
6 4, B g Universal (IRE)—Jump To The Beat
7 **KING CNUT (FR)**, 7, ch g Kentucky Dynamite (USA)—Makadane  **Mr H. R. Hobson**
8 **MR NICE GUY (IRE)**, 5, b g Nathaniel (IRE)—Three Choirs (IRE)  **Mr L. Brooks**
9 **OLDABBEY BRIDGE (IRE)**, 7, b g Morozov (USA)—Jacks Joy (IRE)  **Mrs R. E. Hobson**
10 **SEVERUS ALEXANDER (IRE)**, 5, b g Zoffany (IRE)—Sacrosanct (IRE)  **Mr L. Brooks**
11 **THE TURFACCOUNTANT (IRE)**, 5, b g Ask—Kayfs Fancy (IRE)  **Mr H. R. Hobson**
12 **TIGRAY (USA)**, 5, gr g Tapit (USA)—Daisy Devine (USA)  **Faces Partnership**
13 **TWO BIDS**, 5, gr g Dalakhani (IRE)—Echelon  **Outlaw Pro Limited**
14 **UNCLE O**, 7, gr g Fair Mix (IRE)—Clever Liz  **Mr H. R. Hobson**
15 **WOODFORD BRIDGE**, 5, b m Champs Elysees—A Lulu Ofa Menifee (USA)  **Mr G. Molen**

**Other Owners:** Mrs S. Kaur, Mr V. Singh, Miss H. D. Ward, Mrs J. A. Ward, Miss J. J. Ward.

**Assistant Trainer:** Harry Hobson.

---

## 278 MR RICHARD HOBSON, Little Rissington
Postal: **Bobble Barn Farm, Little Rissington, Cheltenham, Gloucestershire, GL54 2NE**
Contacts: **PHONE 01451 820535 MOBILE 07939 155843**
EMAIL hobson.r1@sky.com WEBSITE www.richardhobsonracing.co.uk

1 **CHIC NAME (FR)**, 9, b g Nickname (FR)—Vuelta Al Ruedo (FR)  **The Boom Syndicate**
2 **DE FORGOTTEN ONE**, 7, b g Malinas (GER)—As Was  **Mr D. W. Fox**
3 **DEFI SACRE (FR)**, 8, b g Network (GER)—Iowa Sacree (FR)  **Mr R. I. H. Wills**
4 **DISCKO DES PLAGES (FR)**, 8, b g Balko (FR)—Lady des Plages (FR)  **Mr G. C. Farr**
5 **ECHO WATT (FR)**, 7, gr g Fragrant Mix (IRE)—Roxane du Bois (FR)  **The Boom Syndicate**
6 **EUREU DU BOULAY (FR)**, 7, b g Della Francesca (USA)—Idole du Boulay (FR)  **J. & R. Hobson**
7 **FANZIO (FR)**, 6, b g Day Flight—Tu L'As Eu (FR)  **Ms S. A. Fox**

# MR RICHARD HOBSON - continued

  8 **FUGITIF (FR)**, 6, b g Ballingarry (IRE)—Turiane (FR)  **Carl & E. Hussain**
  9 **GRENADINE SAVE (FR)**, 5, b m Walk In The Park (IRE)—Mary Way (FR)  **Foxtrot NH Racing Partnership**
 10 **IBIS DU RHEU (FR)**, 10, b g Blue Bresil (FR)—Dona du Rheu (FR)  **Mr D. W. Fox**
 11 **LORD DU MESNIL (FR)**, 8, b g Saint des Saints (FR)—Ladies Choice (FR)  **Mr Paul Porter & Mike & Mandy Smith**
 12 **PARISIENNE GOLD (FR)**, 4, b f Network (GER)—Parthenia (IRE)  **The Boom Syndicate**
 13 **PETIT PALAIS**, 6, ch g Champs Elysees—Galicuix  **Stoneleigh Racing**
 14 **RAMONEX (GER)**, 10, b g Saddex—Ramondia (GER)  **Mr R. H. Hobson**
 15 **SAINT XAVIER (FR)**, 9, b g Saint des Saints (FR)—Princesse Lucie (FR)  **Mr D. W. Fox**
 16 **VALADOM (FR)**, 12, gr g Dadarissime (FR)—Laurana (FR)  **Mr R. H. Hobson**
 17 **WHO'S MY JOCKEY (IRE)**, 8, b g Yeats (IRE)—Scandisk (IRE)  **Carl Hinchy & Mark Scott**

**Other Owners:** Mr D. Abraham, Mrs J. Abraham, Mr C. S. Hinchy, Mr R. H. Hobson, Dr E. Hussain, Mr M. S. Scott, Mr J. Sheppard.

**Assistant Trainer:** Shirley Jane Becker, **Head Lad:** Dawson Lees.

**NH Jockey:** James Bowen, Danny Cook. **Conditional Jockey:** Jordan Nailor, Paul O'Brien.

---

**279**

## MR RON HODGES, Somerton
Postal: **Little Orchard, George Street, Charlton Adam, Somerton, Somerset, TA11 7AS**
Contacts: **PHONE 01458 223922 MOBILE 07770 625846**
EMAIL mandyhodges@btconnect.com

 1 **MET BY MOONLIGHT**, 7, b m Sakhee's Secret—Starlight Walk  **P. E. Axon**
 2 **MIDNIGHT MIDGE**, 7, b g Midnight Legend—Posh Emily  **A Midgley, R J Hodges**
 3 **MILES OF SUNSHINE**, 16, b g Thowra (FR)—Rainbow Nation
 4 **SWEET NIGHTINGALE**, 4, b f Excelebration (IRE)—Night Symphonie  **R. J. Hodges**

**Other Owners:** R. J. Hodges, A. M. Midgley.

---

**280**

## MR SIMON HODGSON, Hook
Postal: **12 Hei - Lin Way, Ludgershall, Andover, Hampshire, SP11 9QH**
Contacts: **PHONE 07786 730853**
EMAIL hodgsters@hotmail.co.uk

 1 **APPLETART (IRE)**, 4, b f Nathaniel (IRE)—Gertrude Gray (IRE)  **Mr P. T. Newell**
 2 **C'EST NO MOUR (GER)**, 8, b g Champs Elysees—C'Est L'Amour (GER)  **Mr P. R. Hedger & P C F Racing Ltd**
 3 **CONTINUUM**, 12, b br g Dansili—Clepsydra  **P C F Racing Ltd**
 4 **DEFINITE WINNER (IRE)**, 10, b m Definite Article—Sindabezi (IRE)  **Mr P. T. Newell**
 5 **FINAIR**, 4, b f Finjaan—Afro  **P C F Racing Ltd**
 6 **FLAT TO THE MAX (FR)**, 6, b g Maxios—Another Name (USA)  **Mr P. R. Hedger & P C F Racing Ltd**
 7 **HELETA**, 4, b f Helmet (AUS)—Juno Moneta (IRE)  **P C F Racing Ltd**
 8 **MR MAC**, 7, b g Makfi—Veronica Franco  **P C F Racing Ltd**
 9 **TOTAL COMMITMENT (IRE)**, 5, b g Exceed And Excel (AUS)—Crysdal  **P C F Racing Ltd**
10 **TRALEE HILLS**, 7, gr ro g Mount Nelson—Distant Waters  **P C F Racing Ltd**

### THREE-YEAR-OLDS
11 **TWILIGHT MADNESS**, ch c Twilight Son—Rhal (IRE)  **Mr P. R. Hedger & P C F Racing Ltd**

**Other Owners:** P. R. Hedger, P C F Racing Ltd.

## 281  MR HENRY HOGARTH, Stillington
Postal: **New Grange Farm, Stillington, York**
Contacts: **PHONE 01347 811168 MOBILE 07788 777044 FAX 01347 811168**
**EMAIL harryhogarth@ymail.com**

1 **ARCHIE BROWN (IRE)**, 7, b g Aizavoski (IRE)—Pure Beautiful (IRE) **Hogarth Racing**
2 **BOSS DES MOTTES (FR)**, 10, b g Califet (FR)—Puszta des Mottes (FR) **Hogarth Racing**
3 **GOLDRAPPER (IRE)**, 8, b g Gold Well—Mrs Bukay (IRE) **Hogarth Racing**
4 **GRAND ENTERPRISE**, 11, b g Fair Mix (IRE)—Miss Chinchilla **Hogarth Racing**
5 **JACK LAMB**, 9, gr g Sulamani (IRE)—Charlotte Lamb **Hogarth Racing**
6 **KAMIL (GER)**, 8, ch g Sholokhov (IRE)—Kastoria (GER) **Hogarth Racing**
7 **MANCE RAYDER (IRE)**, 8, b g Flemensfirth (USA)—J'Y Viens (FR) **Hogarth Racing**
8 **THE BLACK SQUIRREL (IRE)**, 8, br g Craigsteel—Terra Lucida (IRE) **Hogarth Racing**
9 **WOOD EMERY (FR)**, 9, b g Califet (FR)—Take Emery (FR) **Hogarth Racing**

**Other Owners:** Mr H. P. Hogarth, J. Hogarth, J. L. Hogarth, P. H. Hogarth.

**Assistant Trainer:** Russ Garritty.

**NH Jockey:** Jamie Hamilton. **Conditional Jockey:** Billy Garritty.

## 282  MISS SARAH HOLLINSHEAD, Upper Longdon
Postal: **Lodge Farm, Upper Longdon, Rugeley, Staffordshire, WS15 1QF**
Contacts: **PHONE 01543 490298**

1 **CALAJANI (FR)**, 8, b g Azamour (IRE)—Clarinda (FR) **N. Chapman**
2 **CAPPELLA FELLA (IRE)**, 4, b g Cappella Sansevero—Almatlaie (USA) **Mr R. Robinson & Ms S. Hollinshead**
3 **CASTLEREA TESS**, 8, ch m Pastoral Pursuits—Zartwyda (IRE) **Mr John Graham & Sarah Hollinshead**
4 **DIAMOND JILL (IRE)**, 4, b f Footstepsinthesand—Sindiyma (IRE) **Mr J. Gould**
5 **DIAMOND JOEL**, 9, b g Youmzain (IRE)—Miss Lacroix **Mrs N. S. Harris**
6 **FINAL ATTACK (IRE)**, 10, b g Cape Cross (IRE)—Northern Melody (IRE) **N. Chapman**
7 **GMS PRINCE**, 6, b g Kayf Tara—Zartwyda (IRE) **Graham Brothers Racing Partnership**
8 **GMS PRINCESS**, 5, b m Albaasil (IRE)—Zartwyda (IRE) **Graham Brothers Racing Partnership**
9 **GMS TEESSIDE**, 4, b g Heeraat (IRE)—Zartwyda (IRE) **Graham Brothers Racing Partnership**
10 **HEAD HIGH (IRE)**, 8, gr g Mastercraftsman (IRE)—Elisium **Mrs M Moore & Sarah Hollinshead**
11 **JENNY REN**, 6, b m Multiplex—Cherished Love (IRE) **Mr J. Gould**
12 **KATIE KILMINSTER**, 9, b m Kayf Tara—Norma Hill **Mr G. Lloyd**
13 **LETHAL LOOK**, 5, gr g Lethal Force (IRE)—Look Here's Dee **S. L. Edwards**
14 **LOOKFORARAINBOW**, 8, b g Rainbow High—Look Here's May **The Giddy Gang**
15 **PUSH AHEAD (IRE)**, 12, br g Flemensfirth (USA)—Candle Massini (IRE) **Miss S. A. Hollinshead**
16 **SINNDARELLA (IRE)**, 5, b m Fast Company (IRE)—Alafzara (IRE) **Exors of the Late Mr J. A. Ashley**
17 **UNCLE BERNIE (IRE)**, 11, gr g Aussie Rules (USA)—Alwiyda (USA) **Miss S. A. Hollinshead**
18 **ZENAFIRE**, 12, b g Firebreak—Zen Garden **Mr R. J. R. Moseley**

**Other Owners:** Mr J. R. Graham, Miss S. A. Hollinshead, Mr A. Lawrence, Mrs M. A. Moore, R. Robinson.

## 283 STEPH HOLLINSHEAD, Rugeley, Staffordshire
Postal: **Catmint Lodge, Bardy Lane, Upper Longdon, Rugeley, Staffordshire, WS15 4LJ**
Contacts: **HOME 01543 327609 PHONE 07554 008405 MOBILE 07791 385335**
EMAIL **steph_hollinshead@hotmail.co.uk** WEBSITE **www.stephhollinsheadracing.com**

1 **AL SIMMO,** 4, b f Al Kazeem—Magic Destiny **R. Bailey**
2 4, B f Albaasil (IRE)—Boa
3 **CARRIAGE CLOCK,** 4, b f Coach House (IRE)—Circadian Rhythm **M Johnson & S C Hawkins**
4 **HOTCITY,** 4, b f Cityscape—Even Hotter **Mrs V. C. Gilbert**
5 **I HAD A DREAM,** 4, b f Dream Ahead (USA)—Grandmas Dream **Maximum Racing 1**
6 **LOCALLINK (IRE),** 7, b g Sandmason—Suny House **The Captain On the Bridge Partnership**
7 **MISS MOCKTAIL (IRE),** 6, b m Getaway (GER)—Identity Parade (IRE) **Lysways Racing**
8 **PUSHOVER,** 4, gr f Hellvelyn—Soft Touch (IRE)
9 **RACY STACEY,** 4, ch f Fast Company (IRE)—Stilettoesinthemud (IRE) **Gray & hawkins**
10 **THE GOLDEN CUE,** 6, ch g Zebedee—Khafayif (USA) **The Golden Cue Partnership**
11 **THE RED WITCH,** 4, b f Cable Bay (IRE)—Lady Macduff (IRE) **Mrs D. A. Hodson**

### THREE-YEAR-OLDS
12 **ALICE KAZEEM,** ch f Al Kazeem—Kawartha
13 **LADY MANDER,** b f Albaasil (IRE)—Goldeva **Hollinshead & Pyle**
14 **MISS TRIXIE,** b f Bated Breath—Epiphany **Mrs D. A. Hodson**
15 **VELOCISTAR (IRE),** b f Starspangledbanner (AUS)—Mahsooba (USA) **Sleeve It Ltd**

### TWO-YEAR-OLDS
16 **EPICENTRE,** b f 21/03 Heeraat —Richter Scale (IRE)
17 **MALHAM TARN COVE,** gr ro c 18/03 Heeraat (IRE)—Spirit of Rosanna (Hellvelyn)
18 B f 25/04 Tamayuz—Music Pearl (IRE) (Oratorio (IRE)) (4286)

**Other Owners:** R. Bailey, Chapel Stud Ltd & Loughshore Racing Synd, Mr D. L. Chorlton, Mr A. C. Gray, Mrs S. C. Hawkins, Mr J Holcombe, Mrs L. A. Hollinshead, M. A. N. Johnson, Francesca Leyland, Longdon Stud, Maximum Racing, M. J. F. Pyle, Mr G. T. Rowley.

**Assistant Trainer:** Adam Hawkins.

---

## 284 MR JOHN HOLT, Peckleton
Postal: **Hall Farm, Church Road, Peckleton, Leicester, LE9 7RA**
Contacts: **PHONE 01455 821972 MOBILE 07850 321059**
EMAIL **hallfarmracing@btconnect.com** WEBSITE **www.hallfarmracing.co.uk**

1 **GLENTON,** 4, b g Casamento (IRE)—Sina (GER) **J. R. Holt**
2 **HERRING BAY,** 4, b f Heeraat (IRE)—Hikkaduwa **Mr M. S. Fonseka**
3 **LADY MONICA,** 5, b m Bated Breath—Sina (GER) **Mr M. Hollier**
4 **NUMBER THEORY,** 13, b g Halling (USA)—Numanthia (IRE) **Mr M. S. Fonseka**
5 **VICKY CRISTINA (IRE),** 6, b m Arcano (IRE)—And Again (USA) **Cleartherm Glass Sealed Units & J. Holt**

### TWO-YEAR-OLDS
6 **GLASSTREES,** gr f 01/02 Heeraat (IRE)—Goadby (Kodiac) **Cleartherm Glass Sealed Units Ltd**

**Other Owners:** Cleartherm Glass Sealed Units Ltd, J. R. Holt.

**Assistant Trainer:** Jessica Holt.

## 285    MR ANTHONY HONEYBALL, Beaminster

Postal: **Potwell Farm, Mosterton, Beaminster, Dorset, DT8 3HG**
Contacts: **PHONE 01308 867452 MOBILE 07815 898569**
EMAIL anthony@ajhoneyballracing.co.uk WEBSITE www.ajhoneyballracing.co.uk

1 **ACEY MILAN (IRE)**, 7, b g Milan—Strong Wishes (IRE) **Owners For Owners: Acey Milan**
2 **AVOIR DE SOINS (IRE)**, 7, ch g Flemensfirth (USA)—Garranlea Maree (IRE) **Richard & Shirl Smith**
3 **BELLE DE MANECH (FR)**, 5, gr m Vision d'Etat (FR)—Noor Forever (FR) **Mr M. R. Chapman**
4 **BLEUE AWAY (IRE)**, 7, b m Getaway (GER)—Majorite Bleue (FR) **Potwell Racing Syndicate I**
5 **BOB BACKUS (IRE)**, 6, b g Milan—Boro Bee (IRE) **Decimus Racing IV**
6 **CAPTAIN CLAUDE (IRE)**, 4, b g Soldier of Fortune (IRE)—Princess Supreme (IRE) **Decimus Racing V**
7 **COQUELICOT (FR)**, 5, b br m Soldier of Fortune (IRE)—Moscow Nights (FR) **Geegeez.co.uk PA**
8 **DEAR RALPHY (IRE)**, 5, b g Westerner—Letterwoman (IRE) **Mr J. M. Pike**
9 **DEJA VUE (IRE)**, 7, b m Fame And Glory—Westgrove Berry (IRE) **Axom LXXVI**
10 **DON LAMI (FR)**, 8, ch g Honolulu (FR)—Toutamie (FR) **Les Amis De Don**
11 **DREAMING BLUE**, 4, b g Showcasing—Got To Dream **R. W. Devlin**
12 **EMZARA (IRE)**, 5, b m Califet (FR)—Strike An Ark (IRE) **Hancock, Rowe & Wright**
13 **FANFARON DINO (FR)**, 6, gr g Doctor Dino (FR)—Kadjara (FR) **Mr J. P. McManus**
14 **FIRESTREAM**, 4, b g Yeats (IRE)—Swincombe Flame **Buckingham, Chapman, Langford & Ritzema**
15 **FORTUNA LIGNA (IRE)**, 4, br f Soldier of Fortune (IRE)—Quiet Thought (IRE) **Jon & Jacqueline Hughes**
16 **GABRIEL'S GETAWAY (IRE)**, 4, b g Getaway (GER)—Chosen Destiny (IRE) **Mr M. R. Chapman**
17 **GUSTAVIAN (IRE)**, 6, b g Mahler—Grange Oscar (IRE) **Decimus Racing I**
18 **HIDEAWAY VIC (IRE)**, 6, b g Stowaway—Cailin Vic Mo Cri (IRE) **Michael & Angela Bone**
19 **HOWLINGMADMURDOCK (IRE)**, 4, b g Soldier of Fortune (IRE)—Bell Storm (IRE) **The Soldiers of Fortune**
20 **JEPECK (IRE)**, 12, b g Westerner—Jenny's Jewel (IRE) **Mr J. M. Pike**
21 **KAYF SERA SERA**, 6, b m Kayf Tara—Fernello **Kingswood Stud Limited (Hants)**
22 **KHALINA STAR**, 4, b f Kayf Tara—Alina Rheinberg (GER) **Geegeez.co.uk PA**
23 **KID COMMANDO**, 7, b g Robin des Champs (FR)—Banjaxed Girl **Chapman, Hanger, Kingston & Langford**
24 **KILBEG KING**, 6, b g Doyen (IRE)—Prayuwin Drummer (IRE) **M.R.Chapman, E.Jones & H.Kingston**
25 **KILCONNY BRIDGE (IRE)**, 7, b m Stowaway—Wattle Bridge (IRE) **Potwell Racing Syndicate I**
26 **LE COEUR NET (FR)**, 9, ch g Network (GER)—Silverwood (FR) **Wessex Racing Club**
27 **LILITH (IRE)**, 6, b m Stowaway—Flirthing Around (IRE) **Decimus Racing VI**
28 **LILY THE PINK**, 7, b m Malinas (GER)—Carrigeen Queen (IRE) **Wessex Racing Club**
29 **MARCO ISLAND (IRE)**, 4, b g Mahler—Florida Belle (IRE) **Buckingham, Chapman, Langford & Ritzema**
30 **MARILYN MONROE (IRE)**, 8, b m Scorpion (IRE)—Go On Eileen (IRE) **Some Like It Hot**
31 **MIDNIGHT CALLISTO**, 6, br m Midnight Legend—Carrigeen Queen (IRE) **Ms G. S. Langford**
32 **MIDNIGHT TUNE**, 10, b m Midnight Legend—Harmonic Motion (IRE) **The Park Homes Syndicate**
33 **MILAN IN MAY (IRE)**, 6, gr g Milan—Nina Fontenail (FR) **Richard & Shirl Smith**
34 **MONT SEGUR (IRE)**, 6, ch g French Fifteen (FR)—Vie de Reine (FR) **Men Of Stone**
35 **MOONDANCER**, 5, b g Sea The Moon (GER)—Jalousie (FR) **Mr R. W. Huggins**
36 **MS PARFOIS (IRE)**, 10, ch m Mahler—Dolly Lewis **Kingswood Stud Limited (Hants)**
37 **NOW IS THE WINTER (IRE)**, 7, b g Fame And Glory—Supreme Melody (IRE) **Broderick, Reddin, Brown & Whittle**
38 **PRECIOUS**, 5, b m Midnight Legend—Carrigeen Queen (IRE) **Mr P. R. Cartwright**
39 **PURE VISION (IRE)**, 10, b g Milan—Distillery Lane (IRE) **Mr J. P. McManus**
40 **REGAL ENCORE (IRE)**, 13, b g King's Theatre (IRE)—Go On Eileen (IRE) **Mr J. P. McManus**
41 **RUBYS REWARD**, 5, b m Dr Massini (IRE)—Cresswell Ruby (IRE) **The Brambles**
42 **SAM BROWN**, 9, b g Black Sam Bellamy (IRE)—Cream Cracker **Mr T. C. Frost**
43 **SOJOURN (IRE)**, 8, b g Getaway (GER)—Toscar (IRE) **Jon & Jacqueline Hughes**
44 **SULLY D'OC AA (FR)**, 7, b g Konig Turf (GER)—Samarra d'Oc (FR) **Mr J. P. McManus**
45 **SWINCOMBE FLEAT**, 5, b m Yeats (IRE)—Swincombe Flame **Yeo Racing Partnership**
46 **UCANAVER**, 5, bl m Maxios—Purely By Chance **Ifuwonner Partnership**
47 **WAGNER (IRE)**, 6, b g Mahler—Astalanda (FR) **Potwell Racing Syndicate I**
48 **WINDANCE (IRE)**, 6, b g Shirocco (GER)—Maca Rince (IRE) **Decimus Racing III**
49 **WINDSWEPT GIRL (IRE)**, 6, ch m Getaway (GER)—Chicago Vic (IRE) **Geegeez.co.uk PA**
50 **WORLD OF DREAMS (IRE)**, 5, b g Kayf Tara—Rose of The World (IRE) **Atlantic Racing & R. W. Huggins**

## THREE-YEAR-OLDS

51 **MISTER ALLEGRO**, b g Bernardini (USA)—Joyful Hope **Mr S. C. Browning**

## MR ANTHONY HONEYBALL - continued

### TWO-YEAR-OLDS

52 **A WISH AWAY (IRE),** gr f 04/03 Mastercraftsman (IRE)—
First Love (IRE) (Galileo (IRE)) (25000) **The Wish Away Partnership**

**Other Owners:** Atlantic Racing Limited, Mrs A. P. Bone, Mr M. J. Bone, Mrs B. A. Broderick, Mr P. Brown, Mr M. R. Chapman, Mr N. Hancock, N. M. Hanger, Mr R. W. Huggins, Mr E. J. Hughes, Mrs J. Hughes, Mr E. Jones, Mr H. Kingston, Ms G. S. Langford, Mr S. D. Reddin, Mrs D. J. Ritzema, Mr M. W. Rowe, Mr R. S. Smith, Mrs S. A. Smith, Step By Step Supporting Independence Ltd, Mr J. S. Whittle, Mr B. J. C. Wright.

**Assistant Trainer:** Rachael Honeyball.

**NH Jockey:** Aidan Coleman, David Noonan. **Conditional Jockey:** Rex Dingle, Ben Godfrey.

---

**286** | **MR CHRIS HONOUR, Ashburton**
Postal: **Higher Whiddon Farm, Ashburton, Newton Abbot, Devon, TQ13 7EY**
Contacts: **PHONE 01364 652500**
EMAIL tojohonour@aol.com

1 **CHATO (FR),** 9, ch g Malinas (GER)—Queen Bruere (FR) **G. D. Thompson**
2 **GAELIC BELLE,** 4, b f Media Hype—Gaelic Ice **Miss E. M. Pearse**
3 **GAELIC THUNDER,** 6, b g Arvico (FR)—Gaelic Lime **Mrs J. Elliott**
4 **GRUMPY CHARLEY,** 6, gr g Shirocco (GER)—Whisky Rose (IRE) **G. D. Thompson**
5 **GRUMPY FREYA,** 6, ch m Malinas (GER)—Thedebottheyear **G. D. Thompson**
6 **HOT RYAN,** 8, b m Midnight Legend—Darn Hot **G. D. Thompson**
7 **MAYHEM MYA,** 4, b f Authorized (IRE)—Thedebottheyear **G. D. Thompson**
8 **OKHOTSK,** 5, gr m Dream Eater (IRE)—Darn Hot **Mr C. E. Honour**
9 **RAGTAG RASCAL (IRE),** 7, b g Tagula (IRE)—Trebles (IRE) **Mr C. E. Honour**
10 **TILE TAPPER,** 7, b g Malinas (GER)—Darn Hot **Cotswold Stone Supplies Ltd**
11 **TROED Y MELIN (IRE),** 9, b g Craigsteel—Kissangel (IRE) **No Illusions Partnership**
12 **TROED Y PARC,** 6, b g Lucarno (USA)—Theatre Belle **No Illusions Partnership**

---

**287** | **MISS LAURA HORSFALL, Towcester**
Postal: **Mobile Home ,Glebe Barn Stables, Blakesley Road, Maidford, Towcester, Northamptonshire, NN12 8HN**
EMAIL horsfalllaura@hotmail.co.uk

1 4, B g Mahler—Ashlings Princess (IRE)
2 **BAYLEY'S DREAM,** 12, b g Presenting—Swaythe (USA) **Mr B. Aprahamian**
3 **CESAR DU GOUET (FR),** 9, gr g Fragrant Mix (IRE)—
Querida de Ferbet (FR) **Jo Walton, Mick White & Laura Horsfall**
4 **HIT THE BOTTLE,** 6, ch m Malinas (GER)—Ruby Magern **Mick White & Steve Horsfall**
5 **HOT TO TROT,** 7, b m Brian Boru—Commanche Token (IRE) **Martin Redman & Maurice Thomas**
6 **JUST A WHIM,** 7, b m Gold Well—Redunderthebed (IRE) **Mr M. W. Redman**
7 **LOVEYOUTOTHEMOON,** 9, b m Bach (IRE)—Braceys Girl (IRE) **Martin Redman & Maurice Thomas**
8 4, Ch g Shirocco (GER)—Molly's Case (IRE)
9 **MULTISTORY,** 6, b g Multiplex—Cool Chron **The Expecting To Fly Racing Club**
10 **STAITHES (IRE),** 6, b g Watar (IRE)—Corlea (IRE) **Steven Astaire & Mark Astaire**
11 **STORM ARCADIO (IRE),** 5, b g Arcadio (GER)—Site Missy (IRE) **The Expecting To Fly Racing Club**
12 4, Ch g Well Chosen—Terrible Day (IRE)
13 **THATS THE ONE,** 5, b m Dr Massini (IRE)—Home By Midnight **Martin Redman & Maurice Thomas**

**Other Owners:** Mr M. Astaire, Mr S. Astaire, Miss L. Horsfall, Mr S. Horsfall, Mr M. W. Redman, Mr M. H. Thomas, Mrs J. Walton, Mr M. E. White.

## 288 MS GEORGIE HOWELL, Tenbury Wells
Postal: **Woodstock bower farm, Broadheath, Tenbury Wells, Worcestershire, WR15 8QN**
Contacts: **PHONE 07968 864433**
EMAIL **georgie@drill-service.co.uk**

1 **BETTERLATETHANNEVA (IRE)**, 10, b m Albano (IRE)—Acqua Pesante (IRE)  **Ms G. P. C. Howell**
2 **BLACK LIGHTNING (IRE)**, 8, br g Whitmore's Conn (USA)—Annie May (IRE)  **Ms G. P. C. Howell**
3 **CHAIN SMOKER**, 8, ch g Shantou (USA)—Handmerny Moneydown (IRE)
4 **POETIC PRESENCE (IRE)**, 11, b m Presenting—Johnston's Crest (IRE)  **Ms G. P. C. Howell**
5 **PUPPET WARRIOR**, 9, ch g Black Sam Bellamy (IRE)—Rakajack  **Ms G. P. C. Howell**
6 **SUB LIEUTENANT (IRE)**, 12, b g Brian Boru—Satellite Dancer (IRE)  **Ms G. P. C. Howell**
7 **TIS BUT A SCRATCH**, 5, br h Passing Glance—Shropshirelass

## 289 MRS DEBBIE HUGHES, Porth
Postal: **Tyr Heol Farm, Pantybrad, Tonyrefail, Rhondda, Mid Glamorgan, CF39 8HX**
EMAIL **dimots@btinternet.com**

1 **BORN TO FROLIC (IRE)**, 6, b g Born To Sea (IRE)—Desert Frolic (IRE)  **Mrs D. J. Hughes**
2 **DANCING LILLY**, 6, ch m Sir Percy—Bhima  **Mrs D. J. Hughes**
3 8, B m Mount Nelson—Focosa (ITY)  **Mrs D. J. Hughes**
4 **FREEZING (IRE)**, 4, b gr g Kingston Hill—Gimli's Treasure (IRE)  **Mrs D. J. Hughes**
5 **GIVEN (IRE)**, 4, b f Ivawood (IRE)—Annacurra (IRE)  **Mrs D. J. Hughes**
6 **IGNITE**, 10, ch g Compton Place—Time Clash  **Mrs D. J. Hughes**
7 **LESS OF THAT (IRE)**, 7, b m Canford Cliffs (IRE)—Night Glimmer (IRE)  **Mrs D. J. Hughes**
8 **LOVELY ACCLAMATION (IRE)**, 7, b m Acclamation—Titova  **Mrs D. J. Hughes**
9 **MAJOR ASSAULT**, 8, b g Kyllachy—Night Premiere (IRE)  **Mrs D. J. Hughes**
10 **NATTY DRESSER (IRE)**, 6, b g Dandy Man (IRE)—Parlour  **Mrs D. J. Hughes**
11 **PICC AN ANGEL**, 5, b m Piccolo—Bhima  **Mrs D. J. Hughes**
12 **STOP N START**, 9, ch m Piccolo—Dim Ots  **Mrs D. J. Hughes**
13 4, Ch g Indian Haven—Time Clash  **Mrs D. J. Hughes**
14 **WIRRAWAY (USA)**, 5, ch g Australia—Fly Past  **Mrs D. J. Hughes**

### THREE-YEAR-OLDS
15 Ch f Indian Haven—Jinks And Co  **Mrs D. J. Hughes**
16 B c Moohaajim (IRE)—Somerset Falls (UAE)  **Mrs D. J. Hughes**

### TWO-YEAR-OLDS
17 B c 11/05 Mayson—Elysee (IRE) (Fantastic Light (USA)) (3810)

## 290 MR RICHARD HUGHES, Upper Lambourn
Postal: **Weathercock House, Upper Lambourn, Hungerford, Berkshire, RG17 8QT**
Contacts: **PHONE 01488 71198 MOBILE 07768 894828**
EMAIL **office@richardhughesracing.co.uk WEBSITE www.richardhughesracing.co.uk**

1 **BLACKCASTLE STORM**, 4, bl g Showcasing—How High The Sky (IRE)  **Mrs J A Wakefield & Partners**
2 **BRENTFORD HOPE**, 4, b g Camelot—Miss Raven (IRE)  **Bernardine & Sean Mulryan**
3 **BRUNEL CHARM**, 4, b g Charm Spirit (IRE)—Manyara  **R Lane S Needham**
4 **CALLING THE WIND (IRE)**, 5, b g Authorized (IRE)—Al Jasrah (IRE)  **Mrs J. A. Wakefield**
5 **CHARLIE ARTHUR (IRE)**, 5, b g Slade Power (IRE)—Musical Bar (IRE)  **L Turland and A Smith**
6 **KARIBANA (IRE)**, 4, b g Hallowed Crown (AUS)—Queen Wasp (IRE)  **M Clarke, P Munnelly & D Waters**

## MR RICHARD HUGHES - continued

7 **KATH'S LUSTRE**, 6, b m Dick Turpin (IRE)—It's Dubai Dolly **Mr M. M. Cox**
8 **LIFE MATTERS (USA)**, 4, ch g Candy Ride (ARG)—Moon Catcher (USA) **Mr M Clarke & Mr R Rexton**
9 **MAORI KNIGHT (IRE)**, 4, b g Camelot—Chatham Islands (USA) **White Beech Farm**
10 **MISTER SNOWDON**, 4, gr g Lethal Force (IRE)—Welsh Cake **M. J. Caddy**
11 **PRINCE IMPERIAL (USA)**, 4, b g Frankel—Proportional **Highclere T'Bred Racing-Prince Imperial**
12 **PUNTING (IRE)**, 4, ch f Power—Lakatoi **M. H. Dixon**
13 **SUMMERONSEVENHILLS (USA)**, 4, b br g Summer Front (USA)—
Iboughtheranyway (USA) **Frank Deely & John McGarry**
14 **THE NOSEY PARKER (IRE)**, 4, b f Dream Ahead (USA)—Dorothy Parker (IRE) **Miss K. L. Leonard**
15 **TOP BREEZE (IRE)**, 5, b g Gale Force Ten—Shamarlane **Life's A Breeze**
16 **TWICE AS LIKELY**, 4, b f Tamayuz—Xaphania **Ms H. N. Pinniger**

### THREE-YEAR-OLDS

17 **APPELLATION (IRE)**, b f Kodiac—Stor Mo Chroi (IRE) **H Rosenblatt & D Thorpe**
18 **BASCULE (FR)**, ch g Kendargent (FR)—New River (IRE) **The New River Partnership**
19 **BEASTIE BOY (IRE)**, b g Dandy Man (IRE)—Gwyllion (USA) **P Cook & K Lawrence**
20 **BONNIE LAD**, ch c Havana Gold (IRE)—Bonnie Grey **BPC, Taylor & Young**
21 **CRIMSON SAND (IRE)**, b g Footstepsinthesand—Crimson Sunrise (IRE) **Mrs J. A. Wakefield**
22 **DON'T LOOK BACK**, gr g Oasis Dream—Ronaldsay **Clarke, Jeffries, Lawrence & Wakefield**
23 **ELEKTRONIC (IRE)**, b c Kodiac—Elektra Marino **Mrs J. A. Wakefield**
24 **GOT NO DOLLARS (IRE)**, b c Showcasing—Canada Water **The High Flyers**
25 **KATH'S TOYBOY**, gr g Gregorian (IRE)—It's Dubai Dolly **Mr M. M. Cox**
26 **LARGO BAY (USA)**, ch g Flintshire—No Panic (USA) **The Caledonians**
27 **LIGHTENING SHORE**, bl g Showcasing—Zora Seas (IRE) **The Heffer Syndicate & Mr P Merritt**
28 **LIKELY SUCCESSOR**, b f Equiano (FR)—Classic Vision **Ms H. N. Pinniger**
29 **MERLIN'S BEARD (IRE)**, b br c Dark Angel (IRE)—Welsh Cake **M. J. Caddy**
30 **MISS TIKI**, ch f Zoffany (IRE)—Teeky **The Lakota Partnership & Mrs Janie Blake**
31 **NAMASTE (IRE)**, b f Mastercraftsman (IRE)—Satopanth **Niarchos Family**
32 **NELSON GAY (IRE)**, b g Mehmas (IRE)—Rublevka Star (USA) **Mr R Gander & Partner**
33 B c Holy Roman Emperor (IRE)—Nur Jahan (IRE) **M. J. Caddy**
34 **ONE LAST DANCE (IRE)**, b f Camelot—Controversy **Mr B. Bailey**
35 **SCHWARTZ (IRE)**, b g Kodiac—Easy Times **Mr A. G. Smith**
36 **SUNSET IN PARIS (IRE)**, b g Camelot—Trail of Tears (IRE) **Bernardine & Sean Mulryan**
37 **TO THE BAR (IRE)**, ch c Tamayuz—Coachhouse Lady (USA) **Mr Jaber Abdullah**
38 **TOTEM**, b g Charm Spirit (IRE)—Frances Stuart (IRE) **Mr J. P. Henwood**
39 **TYNWALD**, b g Toronado (IRE)—Queen's Prize **Her Majesty The Queen**

### TWO-YEAR-OLDS

40 **APACHE GREY (IRE)**, gr c 04/03 El Kabeir (USA)—
Laurelita (IRE) (High Chaparral (IRE)) (47619) **K Lawrence, P Merritt & Mrs J Blake**
41 **AUSSIE BANKER**, b c 27/03 Muhaarar—Aristoteliccienne (IRE) (Acclamation) (38095) **Mr P. Cook**
42 **BETHERSDEN BOY (IRE)**, b c 15/03 Excelebration (IRE)—
Doctor's Note (Pursuit of Love) (32000) **Rj Rexton & Cd Dickens**
43 **BRILLIANT NEWS (IRE)**, b c 17/02 Camacho—Belle of The Blues (IRE) (Blues Traveller (IRE)) (25714) **The Queens**
44 **CAREWELL COVER (IRE)**, b c 14/02 Footstepsinthesand—
Golden Easter (USA) (Distorted Humor (USA)) (38095) **WKH (Hinksey Lane) Ltd**
45 **CAVALLUCCIO (IRE)**, br c 14/03 Caravaggio (USA)—
Gale Song (Invincible Spirit (IRE)) (61905) **Cognition Land & Water & M Clarke**
46 **CHIEF WHITE FACE**, ch c 03/03 Showcasing—
Martha Watson (IRE) (Dream Ahead (USA)) (45000) **Mr Jaber Abdullah**
47 B c 19/03 Acclamation—Clotilde (Dubawi (IRE)) (45000) **Cognition Land & Water & M Clarke**
48 B f 09/04 Profitable (IRE)—Coolnagree (IRE) (Dark Angel (IRE)) (32000)
49 **CRUSH AND RUN (IRE)**, b c 04/04 Zoffany (IRE)—Mooching Along (IRE) (Mujahid (USA)) (41905) **Thames Boys**
50 **DASH FOR IT (IRE)**, b c 17/03 Camacho—Jeewana (Compton Place) (25714) **Mrs Philip Snow & Partners**
51 B f 12/02 Pride of Dubai (AUS)—Gentle Breeze (Dubawi (IRE)) (23810) **Mr Jaber Abdullah**
52 B f 29/03 New Bay—High Haven (High Chaparral (IRE)) (13333) **Clarke, Devine, Munnelly A Regan**
53 Ch c 11/04 Australia—Honorine (IRE) (Mark of Esteem (IRE)) (22000) **Mr A. Al Mansoori**
54 B f 23/03 Highland Reel—Infatuation (Invincible Spirit (IRE)) (20000) **Clarke, Devine, Munnelly A Regan**
55 **LIGHT TRAVELLER (IRE)**, ch f 23/02 Siyouni (FR)—Shimmering Light (Dubawi (IRE)) **Her Majesty The Queen**

## MR RICHARD HUGHES - continued

56 B f 01/04 Profitable (IRE)—Ludynosa (USA) (Cadeaux Genereux) (40000)  **Mr Jaber Abdullah**
57 B f 03/04 Bungle Inthejungle—Majestic Desert (Fraam) (30476)  **Mr Jaber Abdullah**
58 B c 16/03 Australia—Maracuja (Medicean)  **M&O Construction & Civil Engineering Ltd**
59 B c 29/01 New Approach (IRE)—Mazuna (IRE) (Cape Cross (IRE))  **Mr A. Al Mansoori**
60 MYTHICAL STAR, b c 11/03 Starspangledbanner (AUS)—Timeless Gift (IRE) (Camacho) (16190)  **Mrs L. Bailey**
61 NAASHA (IRE), b f 11/02 Pride of Dubai (AUS)—Sugardrop (Cacique (IRE))  **K Dhunjibhoy & Z Dhunjibhoy**
62 B c 17/02 Havana Gold (IRE)—Never In (Elusive City (USA)) (52000)  **K. A. Dasmal**
63 B c 21/03 Australia—Nur Jahan (IRE) (Selkirk (USA)) (30000)  **M. J. Caddy**
64 ONE MORE DREAM, br c 21/03 Bated Breath—Gracefilly (Invincible Spirit (IRE)) (45000)  **Mr B. Bailey**
65 B f 24/01 Time Test—Punchy Lady (Invincible Spirit) (14000)  **Clarke, Devine, Munnelly A Regan**
66 B c 29/04 Galileo Gold—Quickstep Queen (Royal Applause) (24000)  **Sir David Seale**
67 ROSA MYSTICA (IRE), b f 27/03 Mehmas (IRE)—Champagne Aerial (IRE) (Night Shift (USA)) (21905)  **Gallaghers**
68 Ch c 27/04 Nathaniel (IRE)—Rosika (Sakhee (USA)) (8000)  **Mr J. W. Reed**
69 B c 29/01 Olympic Glory (IRE)—Velvet Revolver (IRE) (Mujahid (USA)) (55238)  **Mr Richard Hughes**
70 B f 22/04 Dark Angel (IRE)—West of Venus (USA) (Street Cry (IRE))  **Niarchos Family**

**Other Owners:** Mrs J. A. Blake, Mr S. Blight, B. Bull, Mr M. Clarke, Mr P Cook, Mrs E. Dadswell, Mr F. Deely, Mr R. J. Dellar, J. T. Devine, Mr K. Dhunjibhoy, Mr Z. K. Dhunjibhoy, Mr C. Dickens, Mr G. J. Doyle, Mr B. S. Galloway, R. A. Gander, Mr S. A. Geraghty, Mr J. Goddard, Mr R. Hannon, Mr H. R. Heffer, Mr R. P. Heffer, Mr R. Hosking, Mr Richard Hughes, Mr J. Jeffries, Mr R. Lane, Mr K. Lawrence, Mr E. Malone, Mr J. J. McGarry, Mr P.D. Merritt, Mrs B. Mulryan, Mr S. Mulryan, Mr P. A. Munnelly, Mr S. Needham, Ms H. N. Pinniger, Mr A. Regan, Mr R. J. Rexton, Ms F. E. Rogers, Mr H. Rosenblatt, Mr A. G. Smith, Mr R. C. Snedden, Spiers & Hartwell Ltd, Mr N. Taylor, The Heffer Syndicate, Ms D. Thomson, Mr D. A. Thorpe, Mr G. P. Triefus, L. R. Turland, Mrs J. A. Wakefield, Mr D. S. Waters, Mrs F. P. Young.

**Apprentice Jockey:** Tyler Heard, George Rooke.

---

**MRS SARAH HUMPHREY, West Wratting**
Postal: Yen Hall Farm, West Wratting, Cambridge, Cambridgeshire, CB21 5LP
Contacts: PHONE 01223 291445 MOBILE 07798 702484
EMAIL sarah@yenhallfarm.com WEBSITE www.sarahhumphrey.co.uk

1 BENNY FLIES HIGH (IRE), 5, br g Jet Away—Money Money Money  **Hook Lane Syndicate**
2 BLUE WHISPER, 6, ch g Bated Breath—Vivid Blue  **Mrs S. J. Humphrey**
3 BRECON HILL (IRE), 8, b g Arcano (IRE)—Bryanstown Girl (IRE)  **The Brecon Hill Partnership**
4 4, b f Pethers Moon—Call At Midnight  **Mrs S. J. Humphrey**
5 CITY ESCAPE (IRE), 4, b f Cityscape—Lady Gabrielle (IRE)  **The Friday Lunch Club**
6 DREAMBOAT DAVE (IRE), 5, b g Morpheus—Gatamalata (IRE)  **The Old Eatonians**
7 GLIMPSE OF GOLD, 10, b g Passing Glance—Tizzy Blue (IRE)  **Yen Hall Farm Racing**
8 GRAINEYHILL (IRE), 10, b g Craigsteel—Inca Hill (IRE)  **Yen Hall Farm Racing**
9 IRISH SOVEREIGN (IRE), 6, b g Getaway (GER)—Magdoodle (IRE)  **Mrs S. J. Humphrey**
10 KING CARLOS, 4, b g Casamento (IRE)—Little Annie  **Yen Hall Farm Racing**
11 MY DESIGN, 6, br m Scorpion (IRE)—Native Design (IRE)
12 NICKLE BACK (IRE), 5, b g Mustameet (USA)—Mill House Girl (IRE)  **The Friday Lunch Club**
13 OXNAM WARRIOR (IRE), 5, b g Califet (FR)—Kilmessan (IRE)  **Mrs S. J. Humphrey**
14 RUMBLE B (IRE), 7, b g Presenting—John's Eliza (IRE)  **The Pheasant Plotters**
15 STOWAWAY MAGIC (IRE), 10, b g Stowaway—Irish Mystics (IRE)
16 WHITTON LOCH (IRE), 5, b g Yeats (IRE)—Hazel Mist (IRE)  **Mrs J. Pitman**

## THREE-YEAR-OLDS

17 b f Clovis Du Berlais—Call At Midnight  **Mrs S. J. Humphrey**

## TWO-YEAR-OLDS

18 b f 13/03 Spill The Beans—Little Annie
19 ch f 05/03 Nayef (Usa)—Silver Lily  **Mr G Thomas, Mrs L Thomas, Mr J Thomas**

## MRS SARAH HUMPHREY - continued

**Other Owners:** Mr A. Eaton, Mrs S Greenlees, Mrs S. J. Humphrey, Mrs S Irwin, Mr D. F. Nott, Mrs E. Reid, Mrs C Stevens, Mr C. Sheen, The Friday Lunch Club.

**Assistant Trainer:** Mr A. R. Humphrey.

**NH Jockey:** Sean Bowen, Aidan Coleman, Nick Scholfield. **Conditional Jockey:** Alexander Thorne. **Apprentice Jockey:** William Humphrey.

---

## 292 | MR KEVIN HUNTER, Natland
Postal: **Larkrigg, Natland, Cumbria, LA9 7QS**
Contacts: PHONE **015395 60245**

1 DAVID JOHN, 10, b g Overbury (IRE)—Molly's Secret **J. K. Hunter**
2 RIP ROCKS PADDY OK (IRE), 6, b g Rip Van Winkle (IRE)—Marula (IRE) **J. K. Hunter**
3 THAT'S MY DUBAI (IRE), 8, b m Dubai Destination (USA)—Musical Accord (IRE) **J. K. Hunter**

---

## 293 | MISS LAURA HURLEY, Tiverton
Postal: **Ringstone Stables, Oakford, Tiverton, Devon, EX16 9EU**
Contacts: MOBILE **07999 693322**
EMAIL **lauramhurley@hotmail.com**

1 BROUGHTONS RHYTHM, 12, b g Araafa (IRE)—Broughton Singer (IRE) **Mrs R. E. Hurley**
2 CANDYMAN CAN (IRE), 11, b g Holy Roman Emperor (IRE)—Palwina (FR) **Mrs R. E. Hurley**
3 DARSI ROSE (IRE), 8, b g Darsi (FR)—Win A Rose (IRE) **Mrs R. E. Hurley**
4 LUCKY CIRCLE, 5, b m Yorgunnabelucky (USA)—Circle of Angels **Miss L. M. Hurley**
5 TIGER SAM (IRE), 11, ch g Beneficial—Colleen Donn **Miss L. M. Hurley**

**Other Owners:** Mrs J. A. Carpenter, Mr B. K. C. Young.

---

## 294 | MR ROGER INGRAM, Epsom
Postal: **Wendover Stables, Burgh Heath Road, Epsom, Surrey, KT17 4LX**
Contacts: PHONE **01372 749157, 01372 665980** MOBILE **07773 665980, 07715 993911** FAX **01372 748505**
EMAIL **roger.ingram.racing@virgin.net** WEBSITE **www.rogeringramhorseracing.com**

1 ARGENT BLEU, 6, b g Steele Tango (USA)—Silver Marizah (IRE)
2 CRISTAL PALLAS CAT (IRE), 6, b g Kodiac—Flower of Kent (USA)
3 DOUBLE LEGEND (IRE), 6, b g Finsceal Fior (IRE)—Damask Rose (IRE)
4 DUKES MEADOW, 10, b g Pastoral Pursuits—Figura
5 GIOVANNI TIEPOLO, 4, b g Lawman (FR)—Leopard Creek
6 LEMON SONG (FR), 4, b g Stormy River (FR)—Lemon Twist (IRE)
7 MAZEKINE, 4, b f Mukhadram—Dea Caelestis (FR)
8 MISS POLLYANNA (IRE), 5, ch m Helmet (AUS)—Ivy Batty (IRE)
9 NO SUCH LUCK (IRE), 4, b g Tamayuz—Laftah (IRE)
10 RAZIEL, 4, b f Heeraat (IRE)—Silver Marizah (IRE)

**Owners:** Mr P. J. Burton, Mr M. F. Cruse, Mrs C. E. Hallam, Mrs Cathy Hallam & Wendover Racing, Mrs S. Ingram, Mr J. Scott, Jeremy Scott & Wendover Racing, Miss C. Swift, The Stargazers.

**Assistant Trainer:** Sharon Ingram.

**Apprentice Jockey:** Rhiain Ingram.

## 295 MR ANDY IRVINE, East Grinstead

Postal: **Shovelstrode Racing Stables, Homestall Road, Ashurst Wood, East Grinstead, West Sussex, RH19 3PN**
Contacts: **PHONE 07970 839357**
**EMAIL andy01031976@yahoo.co.uk**

1 **BEAUFORT WEST (IRE)**, 7, b g Getaway (GER)—Blessingindisguise (IRE) **Taylor & O'Dwyer**
2 **BLARNEY BATELEUR (IRE)**, 8, b m Flemensfirth (USA)—Blarney Kestrel (IRE) **Miss S. Searle**
3 **BRANDY CROSS (IRE)**, 7, b g Le Fou (IRE)—Glenquin (IRE) **Surefire Racing**
4 **BROTHER BENNETT (FR)**, 11, gr g Martaline—La Gaminerie (FR) **The Lump Oclock the Secret Circle**
5 **BROWN BULLET (IRE)**, 6, b m Arcadio (GER)—Barrack Buster **Dan Shaw Simon Clare Andy Irvine**
6 **CAGLIOSTRO (FR)**, 9, gr g Lord du Sud (FR)—Belle de Liziere (FR) **The Secret Circle Racing Club**
7 **CLONDAW ROBIN (IRE)**, 8, ch g Robin des Champs (FR)—Old Town Queen (IRE) **The Plum Merchants**
8 **DEVIOUS DICKS DAME**, 6, b m Dick Turpin (IRE)—Bridal White **The Secret Circle Racing Club**
9 **DREAM DU GRAND VAL (FR)**, 8, b g Puit d'Or (IRE)—Apple Mille (FR) **Jokulhlaup Syndicate**
10 **DYLANSEOGHAN (IRE)**, 12, b g Pierre—Sabbatical (IRE) **The Lump O'Clock Syndicate**
11 **FINNEGAN'S GARDEN (IRE)**, 12, b g Definite Article—Tri Folene (FR) **Mr K. Corke**
12 **GLORIOUS BORU (IRE)**, 10, b g Brian Boru—Sea Off The Gales (IRE) **Eventmasters Racing**
13 **GUSTAV (IRE)**, 11, b g Mahler—Pakaradyssa (FR) **The Plum Merchants**
14 **HARRY HAZARD**, 7, b g Schiaparelli (GER)—Eveon (IRE) **Mr A. Lewers**
15 **HONEST OSCAR (IRE)**, 6, b m Oscar (IRE)—Honest Chance (FR) **Adrian Lewers the Lump Oclock Syndicate**
16 **IMPULSIVE LEADER (IRE)**, 8, b m Westerner—Impulsive Ita (IRE) **Mr K. Corke**
17 **KILINAKIN (IRE)**, 11, ch g Definite Article—Topanberry (IRE) **The Lump O'Clock Syndicate**
18 **KING OF THE SHARKS (IRE)**, 8, b g Flemensfirth (USA)—Kings Rose (IRE) **Go Faster Syndicate**
19 **MON PETIT CHERI**, 5, b m Nayef (USA)—Mon Petit Diamant **Exors of the Late Mr R. Devereux**
20 **MONTY'S AWARD (IRE)**, 9, b g Oscar (IRE)—Montys Miss (IRE) **Jokulhlaup Syndicate**
21 **MR JACK (IRE)**, 9, ch g Papal Bull—Miss Barbados (IRE) **Mr R. Dean**
22 **O'RAHILLY (IRE)**, 9, b g Aristotle (IRE)—Linoora (IRE) **The Lump Oclock the Secret Circle**
23 **OUR DOT'S BABY (IRE)**, 9, b m Helissio (FR)—Our Dot (IRE) **Mr D. Shaw**
24 **PETE'S CHOICE (IRE)**, 8, b br g Arcadio (GER)—Definite Design (IRE) **Jokulhlaup Syndicate**
25 **QUEEN AMONG KINGS (IRE)**, 7, b m Sans Frontieres (IRE)—Miss Legend (IRE) **Surefire Racing**
26 **RUACANA**, 12, b g Cape Cross (IRE)—Farrfesheena (USA) **Mr V. Lewis**
27 **SCRUTINISE**, 9, b g Intense Focus (USA)—Tetravella (IRE) **Mrs L. Bowtell**
28 4, B g Youmzain (IRE)—Waajida
29 **WATAR ALLSTAR (IRE)**, 7, ch g Watar (IRE)—All Star Lady (IRE) **Mr D. Shaw**

**Other Owners:** S. J. Clare, Exors of the Late Z. C. Davison, Mr A. J. Irvine, Mr A. Lewers, Mr D. Shaw, The Lump O'Clock Syndicate, The Secret Circle, Mr A. N. Waters.

## 296 MR DEAN IVORY, Radlett

Postal: **Harper Lodge Farm, Harper Lane, Radlett, Hertfordshire, WD7 7HU**
Contacts: **PHONE 01923 855337 MOBILE 07785 118658 FAX 01923 852470**
**EMAIL deanivoryracing@gmail.com WEBSITE www.deanivoryracing.co.uk**

1 **BADENSCOTH**, 7, b g Foxwedge (AUS)—Twice Upon A Time **P. J. Skinner**
2 **BRUYERE (FR)**, 5, b m Exceed And Excel (AUS)—Pale Mimosa (IRE) **Heather & Michael Yarrow**
3 **CHARMING KID**, 5, b g Charm Spirit (IRE)—Child Bride (USA) **The Cool Silk Partnership**
4 **CLASSIC CHARM**, 6, b m Rip Van Winkle (IRE)—Classic Lass **Mrs G. Thomas**
5 **DANCINGINTHEWOODS**, 4, b g Garswood—Pachanga **Solario Racing (Ashridge)**
6 **DOR'S DIAMOND**, 5, gr g Gregorian (IRE)—Primavera **Mrs D. A. Carter**
7 **DORS TOYBOY (IRE)**, 4, gr g Dark Angel (IRE)—Rathaath (USA) **Mrs D. A. Carter**
8 **FANTASTIC FLYER**, 6, br m Harbour Watch (IRE)—Lucky Flyer **Mr M. McGuinness**
9 **FIGHTING TEMERAIRE (IRE)**, 8, b g Invincible Spirit (IRE)—Hot Ticket (IRE) **Michael & Heather Yarrow**
10 **FLAMING SPEAR (IRE)**, 9, ch g Lope de Vega (IRE)—Elshamms **Mr A. G. Bloom**
11 **KERRERA**, 8, ch m Champs Elysees—Questa Nova **Mrs G. Thomas**
12 **LANCELOT DU LAC (ITY)**, 11, b g Shamardal (USA)—Dodie Mae (USA) **Michael & Heather Yarrow**

## MR DEAN IVORY - continued

13  **LAURENTIA (IRE)**, 5, b m Iffraaj—Brynica (FR)  **B.Edwards & M.Hayes**
14  **LIBRISA BREEZE**, 9, gr g Mount Nelson—Bruxcalina (FR)  **Mr A. G. Bloom**
15  **LOTHARIO**, 7, gr g Dark Angel (IRE)—Kisses For Me (IRE)  **Michael & Heather Yarrow**
16  **MIRAKUHL**, 4, b f Fast Company (IRE)—Four Miracles  **Radlett Racing & Richard Farleigh**
17  **NEZAR (IRE)**, 10, ch g Mastercraftsman (IRE)—Teddy Bears Picnic  **Mrs D. A. Carter**
18  **NICKY BABY (IRE)**, 7, gr g Dark Angel (IRE)—Moon Club (IRE)  **Mrs D. A. Carter**
19  **PLEDGE OF HONOUR**, 5, b g Shamardal (USA)—Lura (USA)  **Mr D. K. Ivory**
20  **SIR PRIZE**, 6, b g Sir Percy—Three Sugars (AUS)  **Mr M. J. Yarrow**
21  **SOARING SPIRITS (IRE)**, 11, ch g Tamayuz—Follow My Lead  **Mrs D. A. Carter**
22  **STAKE ACCLAIM (IRE)**, 9, b g Acclamation—Golden Legacy (IRE)  **Mr M. J. Yarrow**
23  **TROPICS (USA)**, 13, ch g Speightstown (USA)—Taj Aire (USA)  **Mr D. K. Ivory**

### THREE-YEAR-OLDS

24  **BROXI (IRE)**, b br g Kodi Bear (IRE)—Own Gift  **Heather Yarrow & Lesley Ivory**
25  **HOT CHESNUT**, ch f Camacho—Hot Ticket (IRE)  **Heather & Michael Yarrow**
26  **MAMUNIA**, b g Swiss Spirit—Shahrazad (IRE)  **Mr L. J. Doolan**
27  **MAZZORBO**, b g Cable Bay (IRE)—Pink Diamond  **Dr A. J. F. Gillespie**
28  **MOONLIT CLOUD**, b f Sea The Moon (GER)—Apple Blossom (IRE)  **Dr A. J. F. Gillespie**

### TWO-YEAR-OLDS

29  Ch c 13/04 Tamayuz—Pin Cushion (Pivotal) (22000)  **Solario Racing (Berkhamsted)**
30  **THOMAS EQUINAS**, ch c 03/03 Mayson—Hot Ticket (IRE) (Selkirk (USA))  **Michael & Heather Yarrow**
31  B f 07/04 Twilight Son—Winifred Jo (Bahamian Bounty)  **Solario Racing**

**Other Owners:** Mr D. K. Ivory, Mr M. J. Yarrow, Michael & Heather Yarrow.

**Assistant Trainer:** Chris Scally.

---

**297**  **MISS TINA JACKSON, Loftus**
Postal: **Tick Hill Farm, Liverton, Loftus, Saltburn, Cleveland, TS13 4TG**
Contacts: **PHONE 01287 644952 MOBILE 07774 106906**

1  **BLACK OPIUM**, 7, b m Black Sam Bellamy (IRE)—Fragrant Rose  **Mr H. L. Thompson**
2  **CUSTODIAN (IRE)**, 4, b c Muhaarar—Zuhoor Baynoona (IRE)  **Mr H. L. Thompson**
3  **GLACEON (IRE)**, 6, b m Zoffany (IRE)—Ihtiraam (IRE)  **Peter Jeffers & Howard Thompson**
4  **GRIMTHORPE**, 10, ch g Alflora (IRE)—Sally Scally  **Mr H. L. Thompson**
5  **HAVANA BAY**, 5, b g Havana Gold (IRE)—Bisou  **Mr H. L. Thompson**
6  **IVORS INVOLVEMENT (IRE)**, 9, b g Amadeus Wolf—Summer Spice (IRE)  **Mr H. L. Thompson**
7  **JAMIH**, 6, ch g Intello (GER)—Hannda (IRE)  **Peter Jeffers & Howard Thompson**
8  **JAMIL (IRE)**, 6, b g Dansili—Havant  **Peter Jeffers & Howard Thompson**
9  **JAN DE HEEM**, 11, ch g Dutch Art—Shasta  **H L Thompson & D Tucker**
10  **MADAM SCULLY**, 8, ch m Flying Legend (USA)—Sally Scally  **Mr H. L. Thompson**
11  **MR WIGGINS**, 9, ch g Alflora (IRE)—Winnie Wild  **Miss T. Jackson**
12  **POINT OF WOODS**, 8, b g Showcasing—Romantic Myth  **Mr H. L. Thompson**
13  **PURPLE HARRY**, 13, gr g Sir Harry Lewis (USA)—Ellfiedick  **Mr H. L. Thompson**
14  **ROSY RYAN**, 11, b m Tagula (IRE)—Khaydariya (IRE)  **Mr H. L. Thompson**
15  **SNITCH (IRE)**, 7, b g Witness Box (USA)—Kind Oscar (IRE)  **Mr H. L. Thompson**
16  **SORY**, 14, b g Sakhee (USA)—Rule Britannia  **Mr H. L. Thompson**
17  **THOMAS CRANMER (USA)**, 7, b g Hard Spun (USA)—House of Grace (USA)  **Peter Jeffers & Howard Thompson**
18  **WALLACE**, 8, gr m Fair Mix (IRE)—Winnie Wild  **Miss T. Jackson**
19  **WESTERN WOLF**, 5, b g Westerner—Winnie Wild  **Mr H. L. Thompson**
20  **YOUNOSO**, 10, b g Alflora (IRE)—Teeno Nell  **Mr H. L. Thompson**

## MISS TINA JACKSON - continued

### THREE-YEAR-OLDS

21 **ELISHEVA (IRE)**, ch f Camacho—Smoken Rosa (USA) **Peter Jeffers & Howard Thompson**
22 **ENAMAY**, b f Lethal Force (IRE)—Postulant **Peter Jeffers & Howard Thompson**

**Other Owners:** Mr P. Jeffers, Mr H. L. Thompson, Mr D. Tucker.

---

**298**

**MISS HANNAH JAMES, Malvern**
Postal: **The Merries Farm, Rye Street, Birtsmorton, Malvern, Worcestershire, WR13 6AS**

1 **BATCH ME**, 5, b m Native Ruler—Bach Me (IRE) **Miss H. L. James**
2 **EMMAS DILEMMA (IRE)**, 9, b m Gold Well—Emmas Island (IRE) **Miss H. L. James**
3 **JUNIOR MASSINI**, 6, b g Dr Massini—Bach Me (IRE) **Miss H. L. James**
4 **MEGASCOPE**, 4, b g Telescope (IRE)—Megan Mint **Miss H. L. James**
5 **MINNEIGH MOZZE (FR)**, 5, gr m Phoenix Reach (IRE)—Mickie **Miss H. L. James**

---

**299**

**MR LEE JAMES, Malton**
Postal: **Cheesecake Hill Stables, Norton, Malton, North Yorkshire, YO17 9PJ**
Contacts: **PHONE 01653 699466 MOBILE 07732 556322**

1 **ATTACK MINDED**, 20, ch g Timeless Times (USA)—French Ginger
2 **CRASHING WAVES**, 11, b m Dubai Destination (USA)—Palisandra (USA) **Mrs C. Lloyd James**
3 **GOLD VENTURE (IRE)**, 4, ch f Dandy Man (IRE)—Monroe **Mrs C. Lloyd James**
4 **ICONIC FIGURE (IRE)**, 8, b g Approve (IRE)—Tough Chic (IRE) **L. R. James**
5 **JACKMAN**, 7, gr g Aussie Rules (USA)—Fit To Burst **Mr Ian Johnson & Partner**
6 **MA PETIT LUMIER**, 11, b g Echo of Light—Alisdanza **L. R. James**

**Other Owners:** Mr I Johnson, Mrs C. Lloyd James.

**Assistant Trainer:** Carol James.

---

**300**

**MR IAIN JARDINE, Carrutherstown**
Postal: **Hetlandhill Farm, Carrutherstown, Dumfries, Dumfriesshire, DG1 4JX**
Contacts: **PHONE 01387 840347 MOBILE 07738 351232**
**WORK EMAIL office@iainjardineracing.com WEBSITE www.iainjardineracing.com**

1 **ANIMORE**, 8, b m Sulamani (IRE)—More Likely **Mrs A. F. Tullie**
2 **BLOWING DIXIE**, 5, b g Dubawi (IRE)—Time Control **Mr I. Jardine**
3 **CAMILE (IRE)**, 8, b m Captain Rio—Heroic Performer (IRE) **Mr I. Jardine**
4 **CLEARANCE**, 7, b g Authorized (IRE)—
   Four Miracles **Mr I. Jardine, Mr S. Brown, Kildonan Gold Racing 2, Brown, Jardine, Mr D. I. B. Livingstone, Mr C. A. Burness**
5 **COOL MIX**, 9, gr g Fair Mix (IRE)—Lucylou (IRE) **D&D Armstrong Limited**
6 **DINO BOY (FR)**, 8, b g Diamond Boy (FR)—Odeline (FR) **Mr & Mrs Raymond Anderson Green**
7 **ELITE ICON**, 7, b g Sixties Icon—Sailing Days **Iain Jardine Racing Club**
8 **EQUIDAE**, 6, ch h Equiano (IRE)—Dularame (IRE) **Mr I. Jardine, Jardine & Shannon, Mr N. Shannon**
9 **EXIT TO WHERE (FR)**, 7, b r Kapgarde (FR)—Rapsodie Sea (FR) **Mr & Mrs Raymond Anderson Green**
10 **FLOOD DEFENCE (IRE)**, 7, b m Harbour Watch (IRE)—Krynica (USA) **Let's Be Lucky Racing 20**

# MR IAIN JARDINE - continued

11 **FLOWERY (IRE)**, 9, b g Millenary—Dato Vic (IRE) **Mr I. Jardine**
12 **GLORY FIGHTER**, 5, b g Kyllachy—Isola Verde **Mr Kenneth MacPherson**
13 **GOLDEN SANDBANKS**, 4, b g Havana Gold (IRE)—Serrenia (IRE) **Mr I. Jardine**
14 5, B g Black Sam Bellamy (IRE)—I Got Rhythm **D&D Armstrong Limited**
15 **ISHEBAYORGREY (IRE)**, 9, gr g Clodovil (IRE)—Superjet (IRE) **Iain Jardine Racing Club**
16 **JUMP THE GUN (IRE)**, 4, b g Make Believe—Sound of Guns **Let's Be Lucky Racing 26**
17 **KINGS CREEK (IRE)**, 4, b g Elusive Quality (USA)—Nunavik (IRE) **K Jardine R Griffiths**
18 **LASTOFTHECOSMICS**, 6, b g Shirocco (GER)—Cosmic Case **The Cosmic Cases**
19 **LORD CONDI (IRE)**, 8, ch g Papal Bull—Wings To Soar (USA) **K Jardine R Griffiths**
20 **MERRICOURT (IRE)**, 5, gr g Mizzen Mast (USA)—Elite **Mr A. McLuckie**
21 5, B g Black Sam Bellamy (IRE)—Millie N Aire **M. R. Johnson**
22 **NAKEETA**, 10, b g Sixties Icon—Easy Red (IRE) **Alex & Janet Card**
23 **NEW DELHI EXPRESS (IRE)**, 5, ch g Leading Light (IRE)—
                          O What A Girl (IRE) **Mr I. Jardine, Mr S Brown & Mr I Jardine, Mr S. Brown**
24 **NUBOUGH (IRE)**, 5, b g Kodiac—Qawaasem (USA) **Mrs V. C. Macdonald**
25 **NYOUFSEA**, 6, gr g Fair Mix (IRE)—Just Smokie **D&D Armstrong Limited**
26 **O' THE PAIN (IRE)**, 4, b g Free Eagle (IRE)—Crimphill **Iain Jardine Racing Club**
27 **PEARL WARRIOR**, 5, ch g Dunaden (FR)—Pure Speculation **Owners Group 079**
28 **PURE SURF (IRE)**, 5, ch m Frammassone (IRE)—Eventide **Mr I. Jardine**
29 **REELY BONNIE**, 4, b f Showcasing—Dancing Moon (IRE) **Mr I. Jardine**
30 **RIVER ICON**, 9, b m Sixties Icon—River Alder **Mr I. Jardine, M & J. Jardine, Mr M. Friel**
31 **SHE'SASUPERMACK (IRE)**, 8, b m Arakan (USA)—
                    Castleknock (IRE) **Mrs C. Brown, Mrs C Brown & Mr Michael Wares, Mr M. P. Wares**
32 **SMART LASS (IRE)**, 6, b m Casamento (IRE)—Smart Ass (IRE) **Mr G. R. McGladery**
33 **SO SATISFIED**, 10, b g Aqlaam—Pirouetting **Mr I. Jardine, Wharton & Jardine, Mr R. E. Wharton**
34 **SOMETHING BREWING (FR)**, 7, gr g Clodovil (IRE)—Talwin (IRE) **Mrs C. Brown**
35 **STAR**, 5, ch g Black Sam Bellamy (IRE)—Ballinargh Girl (IRE) **M. R. Johnson**
36 **SWITZER (IRE)**, 4, b f Exceed And Excel (AUS)—
          Revealing **A.Stanton,M.Brennan,A.Brennan,M.Brennan, Ms M. Brennan, Dr A. Stanton, Ms A. Brennan, Ms M. Brennan**
37 **TARAMANDA**, 6, b m Kayf Tara—Millagros (IRE) **J. A. Cringan**
38 **THE DELRAY MUNKY**, 9, b m Overbury (IRE)—
                      Delray Beach (FR) **The Twelve Munkys, Mr B. Melrose, Mr R. J. Goodfellow**
39 **THE OGLE GOGLE MAN (IRE)**, 9, b g Yeats (IRE)—Miss Otis Regrets (IRE) **K Jardine R Griffiths, K Jardine R
          Griffiths S Greig, Mr K. Jardine, Mr R. M. Griffiths, Mr S. Greig**
40 **TITUS BOLT (IRE)**, 12, b g Titus Livius (FR)—Megan's Bay **I. G. M. Dalgleish**
41 **TOKARAMORE**, 9, b m Sulamani (IRE)—More Likely **Mrs A. F. Tullie**
42 **TRADITIONAL DANCER (IRE)**, 9, b g Danehill Dancer (IRE)—Cote Quest (USA) **I. G. M. Dalgleish**
43 **VOIX DU REVE (IRE)**, 9, br g Voix du Nord (FR)—
          Pommbelle (FR) **D&D Armstrong Limited, D & D Armstrong Ltd & Mr L Westwood, Mr L. J. Westwood**
44 **WEATHER FRONT (USA)**, 8, ch g Stormy Atlantic (USA)—Kiswahili **The Self Preservation Society, Mr Ken Eales
          & Self Preservation Society, K. R. Elliott, Mr T. J. Whiting, Mr K. F. Eales**
45 **ZABEEL STAR (IRE)**, 9, ch g Arcano (IRE)—Deep Winter **The Self Preservation Society**

## THREE-YEAR-OLDS

46 **ACONCAGUA MOUNTAIN (IRE)**, b g Requinto (IRE)—My Rules (IRE) **Mr I. Jardine**
47 **BULLS AYE (IRE)**, ch g Intello (GER)—Wo de Xin **Mr G. R. McGladery**
48 **FRENCH RED (IRE)**, ch g Camacho—
          Eclaircie (IRE) **Mr I. Jardine, Mr J Hay, Mr F Steele & Mr I Jardine, Mr F. T. Steele, Mr J. A. Hay**
49 **HAVANA PARTY**, ch g Havana Gold (IRE)—Ferayha (IRE) **Let's Be Lucky Racing 27**
50 **HAVEYOUMISSEDME**, b g Helmet (AUS)—Haydn's Lass **Mr I. Jardine, Mr S Brown & Mr I Jardine, Mr S. Brown**
51 **HAZALOU**, ch c Nathaniel (IRE)—Solar Magic **Mr I. C. Jones**
52 **INNSE GALL**, b g Toronado (IRE)—Reaf **C. H. McGhie**
53 **KATS BOB**, ch g Bobby's Kitten (USA)—
          Dreaming of Stella (IRE) **Colin Dorman & Tommy Dorman, Mr C. Dorman, Mr T. M. Dorman**
54 **KATTY D**, b g Bobby's Kitten (USA)—Rocknrollbaby (IRE) **Castle Construction (North East) Ltd**
55 **KRAKEN POWER (IRE)**, b g The Last Lion—
          Throne **Mr J. Fyffe, Mr James Fyffe & Mr Scott Fyffe, Mr S. Fyffe**
56 **LITTLE BY LITTLE**, ch f Sixties Icon—Steppe By Steppe **The Duchess of Sutherland**
57 **MACMERRY JIM**, b g The Last Lion—Life Is Golden (USA) **Mr J. Fyffe**

## MR IAIN JARDINE - continued

58 **MY SONNY (IRE)**, b f Kodi Bear (IRE)—Mudammera (IRE)  **Mr A. Dunford**
59 **PUSH FOR SIXTY**, bl g Sixties Icon—Push Me (IRE)  **Alex & Janet Card**
60 **RAVENSCRAIG CASTLE**, gr g Nathaniel (IRE)—In The Soup (USA)  **Castle Racing Scotland**
61 **SLEIGHT**, b g Showcasing—Magic (IRE)  **Bruce & Susan Jones, Mr B. Jones, Mrs S. Jones**
62 **THE BRAVEST (GER)**, ro g Jukebox Jury (IRE)—
                    Thunderstruck (GER)  **Mr I. Jardine, J P M O'Connor & I J Jardine, Mr J. P. M. O'Connor**
63 **THE GLOAMING (IRE)**, gr f Gutaifan (IRE)—On High  **The Strattonites**

## TWO-YEAR-OLDS

64 B c 23/04 Mukhadram—Another Day (Monsieur Bond (IRE)) (6000)  **Mr I. Jardine**
65 **CARNIVAL TIMES**, b f 10/03 Time Test—Gypsy Carnival (Trade Fair)  **The Duchess of Sutherland**
66 B c 19/03 Lawman (FR)—Dream Dancing (IRE) (Dream Ahead (USA)) (5904)  **Mr I. Jardine**
67 B c 23/04 The Last Lion (IRE)—Duchess Dora (IRE) (Tagula (IRE)) (20952)  **Mr J. Fyffe**
68 **GURKHALI GIRL (IRE)**, b f 25/03 The Gurkha (IRE)—
                    Ardbrae Lady (Overbury (IRE)) (50000)  **The Duchess of Sutherland**
69 **JOYOUS DAYS (IRE)**, b f 08/04 Dandy Man (IRE)—
                    Goodnight And Joy (IRE) (Rip Van Winkle (IRE)) (28000)  **The Duchess of Sutherland**
70 B f 11/04 Vadamos (FR)—Krynica (USA) (Danzig (USA))
71 B f 01/03 Havana Gold (IRE)—Littlemisssunshine (IRE) (Oasis Dream) (36190)  **Mr Kenneth MacPherson**
72 B f 15/02 Vadamos (FR)—Milldale (Bushranger (IRE)) (5000)  **The Duchess of Sutherland**
73 **MISS LILL**, b f 10/04 Golden Horn—Killachy Loose (Kyllachy) (60000)  **Mr I. C. Jones**
74 B f 21/01 Dragon Pulse (IRE)—Paradwys (IRE) (Exceed And Excel (AUS)) (36190)  **Mr Kenneth MacPherson**
75 Gr c 10/02 Mastercraftsman (IRE)—Parknasilla (IRE) (Dutch Art) (15000)  **Mrs J. M. MacPherson**
76 Br gr c 21/04 Markaz (IRE)—
                    Pretty Bonnie (Kyllachy) (10476)  **Mr I. Jardine, Mr S Brown & Mr I Jardine, Mr S. Brown**
77 **ST ANDREW'S CASTLE**, b c 25/03 Iffraaj—
                    Age of Chivalry (IRE) (Invincible Spirit (IRE)) (40000)  **Castle Racing Scotland**
78 **TORBAIN CASTLE**, b c 30/03 Iffraaj—Loaves And Fishes (Oasis Dream) (30000)  **Castle Racing Scotland**

**Head Man:** Robert Stevenson.

**Flat Jockey:** Jamie Gormley.  **NH Jockey:** Conor O'Farrell.  **Apprentice Jockey:** Shannon Watts.

---

## 301  MR WILLIAM JARVIS, Newmarket
Postal: **Phantom House Stables, Fordham Road, Newmarket, Suffolk, CB8 7AA**
Contacts: **HOME 01638 662677 PHONE 01638 669873 FAX 01638 667328**
EMAIL **mail@williamjarvis.com** WEBSITE **www.williamjarvis.com**

1 **ARIGATO**, 6, b g Poet's Voice—Xtrasensory  **Ms E. L. Banks**
2 **COLD SNAP (IRE)**, 8, b g Medicean—Shivering  **Mr W. Jarvis**
3 **INVENTUS**, 4, b g Brazen Beau (AUS)—Pearl Earing (IRE)  **The Raceology Partnership**
4 **LADY BOWTHORPE**, 5, b m Nathaniel—Maglietta Fina (IRE)  **Ms E. L. Banks**
5 **MICHAELS CHOICE**, 5, b g War Command (USA)—Todber  **The Music Makers 2**
6 **ONE NIGHT STAND**, 4, b g Swiss Spirit—Tipsy Girl  **David Batten & Partner**
7 **SERAPHINITE (IRE)**, 4, gr f Gutaifan (IRE)—Ellasha  **The Raceology Partnership**
8 **WANNABE BETSY (IRE)**, 4, b f Siyouni (FR)—Wannabe Special  **Ms E. L. Banks**
9 **WIMPOLE HALL**, 8, b g Canford Cliffs (IRE)—Sparkling Eyes  **Ms E. L. Banks**

## THREE-YEAR-OLDS

10 **ARQOOB (IRE)**, b g Estidhkaar (IRE)—Via Ballycroy (IRE)  **Little Staughton Farms Ltd**
11 **AUSTRIANA (IRE)**, b f Teofilo (IRE)—Flute Enchante (FR)  **Dr J. Walker**
12 **BERYL THE PERIL (IRE)**, ch f Dandy Man (IRE)—Lady of Rohan  **P. C. J. Dalby & R. D. Schuster**
13 **CONTEMPT**, b g Oasis Dream—Familliarity  **The Music Makers**
14 **COUSINS JOY (IRE)**, b f Markaz (IRE)—Our Joy (IRE)  **Ms E. L. Banks**
15 **DUKE OF VERONA (IRE)**, br gr c Belardo (IRE)—Somewhere (IRE)  **R. C. C. Villers**

## MR WILLIAM JARVIS - continued

16 **HUMAN ACTION**, b g Twilight Son—Modify  **Dr J. Walker**
17 **ILLUZZI (IRE)**, b f Kodiac—Diaminda (IRE)  **Ms E. L. Banks**
18 B g Brazen Beau (AUS)—Pearl Earing (IRE)  **The Raceology Partnership**
19 **PORFIN (IRE)**, b g Belardo (IRE)—Tropical Mist (IRE)  **Mr W. Jarvis**
20 **SCARLET BEAR (IRE)**, b f Kodi Bear (IRE)—Scarlet Plum  **Rathordan Partnership**

### TWO-YEAR-OLDS

21 **BRAZEN IDOL**, br c 31/01 Brazen Beau (AUS)—
     Babylon Lane (Lethal Force (IRE)) (17000)  **The Infinite Folly Partnership**
22 **BULLEIT**, ch c 10/03 Helmet (AUS)—Flora Medici (Sir Percy)  **The Raceology Partnership**
23 **GLEN ETIVE**, b c 21/03 Exceed And Excel (AUS)—Betty Loch (Pivotal) (36190)  **P. C. J. Dalby & R. D. Schuster**
24 B c 02/04 Acclamation—Katchy Lady (Kyllachy) (40000)  **The Phantom House Partnership**
25 B f 12/03 Camelot—Lucht Na Gaeilge (IRE) (Teofilo (IRE)) (60000)  **Ms E. L. Banks**
26 **MAYBURY**, b c 10/02 Adaay (IRE)—Azure Amour (IRE) (Azamour (IRE)) (32000)  **The Phantom House Partnership**
27 B f 19/02 Adaay (IRE)—Sing So Sweetly (Harbour Watch (IRE)) (21000)  **The Phantom House Partnership**
28 **SPY GAME (IRE)**, b br f 31/01 Awtaad (IRE)—
     Soul Mountain (IRE) (Rock of Gibraltar (IRE)) (18000)  **The Raceology Partnership**

**Other Owners:** Mr D. H. Batten, Mr P. P. Thorman.

**Assistant Trainer:** James Toller.

---

### MISS RUTH JEFFERSON, Malton
**302** Postal: **Newstead Stables, Beverley Road, Norton, Malton, North Yorkshire, YO17 9PJ**
Contacts: **PHONE 01653 697225 MOBILE 07976 568152**
WEBSITE www.ruthjefferson.co.uk

1 **CLONDAW CAITLIN (IRE)**, 6, b m Court Cave (IRE)—Kilmessan (IRE)  **Drew & Ailsa Russell**
2 **CYRUS KEEP (IRE)**, 8, b g Doyen (IRE)—Overbranch  **Ruth Jefferson Racing Club**
3 **EDMOND DANTES (FR)**, 5, b g Walk In The Park (IRE)—Divine Surprise (IRE)  **Drew & Ailsa Russell**
4 **FLINT HILL**, 5, ch g Excelebration (IRE)—Modify
5 **JAMPOT EDDIE**, 7, ch g Sulamani (IRE)—Thenford Lass (IRE)  **Mrs I C Straker & Steven Key**
6 **LEMON T**, 8, gr g Sulamani (IRE)—Altogether Now (IRE)  **Newstead Racing Partnership**
7 **MASTER ALAN**, 6, b g Norse Dancer (IRE)—Overbranch  **Mrs I C Straker & Steven Key**
8 **MAURITIAN BOLT (IRE)**, 6, ch g Le Fou (IRE)—Fleeting Arrow (IRE)  **Miss N. R. Jefferson**
9 **ROBYN PUD (IRE)**, 7, b m Kalanisi (IRE)—Quit The Noise (IRE)  **Derek Gennard & Gillian Gennard**
10 **SECRETE STREAM (IRE)**, 12, ch g Fruits of Love (USA)—Bonny River (IRE)  **Mr A. R. Dixon**
11 **SIR JIM (IRE)**, 6, b g Shirocco (GER)—Stick Together  **Derek Gennard & Gillian Gennard**
12 **TAYZAR**, 10, b g Kayf Tara—Matilda Too (IRE)  **C. D. Carr**
13 **TEMPLE MAN**, 9, b g Sulamani (IRE)—Altogether Now (IRE)  **Mrs I C Straker & Steven Key**
14 **WAITING PATIENTLY (IRE)**, 10, b g Flemensfirth (USA)—Rossavon (IRE)  **Mr R. Collins**

**Other Owners:** D. Gennard, Mrs G. Gennard, Miss N. R. Jefferson, Mr S. Key, Mrs A. Russell, A. J. R. Russell, Mrs R. A. Straker, Mr R. M. Wharton, Mr J. H. Wilson.

**303** **MR DAVID JEFFREYS, Stow-on-the-Wold**
Postal: **Mount Pleasant Farm, Oddington Road, Stow-on-the-Wold, Gloucestershire, GL54 1JJ**
Contacts: **PHONE 07917 714687**
EMAIL **djjeffreys15@hotmail.co.uk**

1  **AUGHNACURRA KING (IRE)**, 8, ch g Tajraasi (USA)—Cracking Kate (IRE)  **Mark E Smith & Jaykayjay Pals Ak**
2  **AYR OF ELEGANCE**, 9, b m Motivator—Gaelic Swan (IRE)  **Mrs A. Landale**
3  **BEN BRODY (IRE)**, 11, b g Beneficial—Thethirstyscholars (IRE)  **Mark E Smith & the Bb Pony Gang 5**
4  **BLOOD EAGLE (IRE)**, 5, br g Sea The Stars (IRE)—Directa Princess (GER)  **Mr M. E. Smith**
5  **BOOMTIME BANKER (IRE)**, 7, b m Kalanisi (IRE)—Tiger Tiffney (IRE)  **Ms K. J. Sweeting**
6  **CAVICIANA**, 8, b m Court Cave (IRE)—Viciana  **The Jukes Family**
7  **DUBAI OUTLAW (IRE)**, 8, b g Dubai Destination (USA)—Lady Outlaw (IRE)  **Mr M. E. Smith**
8  **ENEMENEMYNEMO (IRE)**, 6, b g Lakeshore Road (USA)—Portobello Sunrise (IRE)  **Mr M. E. Smith**
9  **EVA'S DIVA (IRE)**, 7, b m Getaway (GER)—Shouette (IRE)  **Over The Sticks**
10  **FIRST ONE D'ANA (FR)**, 6, b g Khalkevi (IRE)—Gamine d'Ici (FR)  **Mr M. E. Smith**
11  **FLIGHTY BRIDE**, 6, b m Bahri (USA)—Flighty Mist  **J. R. Jeffreys**
12  **GEROLAMO CARDANO**, 5, b g Motivator—Dark Quest  **Mr M. E. Smith**
13  **GETAMAN (IRE)**, 8, b g Getaway (GER)—Zingarella's Joy (IRE)  **Mrs A. Landale**
14  **GO HARD OR GO HOME (IRE)**, 8, b g Scorpion (IRE)—Site Eile (IRE)  **The Jeffreys Family**
15  **HIGHLAND LIGHT**, 5, b g Cameron Highland (IRE)—Lady In Chief  **Team CH Racing**
16  **KAYLEN'S MISCHIEF**, 8, ch g Doyen (IRE)—Pusey Street Girl  **Mr M. E. Smith**
17  **KILDIMO (IRE)**, 6, b br g Stowaway—Beananti (IRE)  **Mr M. E. Smith**
18  **LIVELY CITIZEN (IRE)**, 6, b g Frammassone (IRE)—Acinorev (IRE)  **Mark E Smith,Brake Horse Power Syndicate**
19  **MRS THATCHER (IRE)**, 6, b m Presenting—Tweedledrum  **Mr D. Jeffreys**
20  **NOTNOW SEAMUS**, 10, b g Notnowcato—Special Beat  **Mr G. Houghton**
21  **PERFECT PREDATOR**, 6, b g Passing Glance—Cosmea  **Mr G. Houghton**
22  **PETRASTAR**, 6, b g Passing Glance—Petrachick (USA)  **Mr M. E. Smith**
23  **PETRUCCI (IRE)**, 9, b g Azamour (IRE)—Spring Symphony (IRE)  **16.10 Fakenham**
24  **RAKHINE STATE (IRE)**, 8, b g Arakan (USA)—Oiselina (FR)  **Mr Stuart Stanley & Mr Adam Lucock**
25  **SIMPLY TRUE (IRE)**, 4, ch g Camacho—Faussement Simple (IRE)  **Mr M. E. Smith**
26  **THE GOLD BUG (IRE)**, 6, b g Shantou (USA)—Eva La Diva (IRE)  **Mrs M. Fleming**
27  **THIRTYFOURSTITCHES (IRE)**, 6, b g Fairly Ransom (USA)—Blue Berlais (IRE)  **Mr D. Jeffreys**
28  **TREE OF LIBERTY (IRE)**, 9, ch g Stowaway—The Wrens Nest (IRE)  **Mr M. E. Smith**

**Other Owners:** Mr A. T. Chatwin, Mrs M. A. Jukes, R. N. Jukes, Mr A. W. Lucock, Mr M. E. Smith, Mr S. Stanley, The BB Pony Gang 5, The Brake Horse Power Syndicate, The JayKayJay PALS AK Syndicate.

**304** **MR JOHN JENKINS, Royston**
Postal: **Kings Ride, Therfield Heath, Royston, Hertfordshire, SG8 9NN**
Contacts: **PHONE 01763 241141, 01763 246611 MOBILE 07802 750855 FAX 01763 248223**
EMAIL **john@johnjenkinsracing.co.uk WEBSITE www.johnjenkinsracing.co.uk**

1  **ACE TIME**, 7, b g Sinndar (IRE)—Desert Run (IRE)  **Mr B Dowling & Mr R Stevens**
2  **CHARLIE MY BOY (IRE)**, 4, b c Leading Light (IRE)—Theionlady (IRE)  **Mr A. J. Taylor**
3  **CHLOELLIE**, 6, b m Delegator—Caramelita  **Mrs Veronica Bullard & Mrs Wendy Jenkins**
4  **COMPANY MINX (IRE)**, 4, gr f Fast Company (IRE)—Ice Haven (IRE)  **Mrs C. Goddard**
5  **COOL ECHO**, 7, b m Mount Nelson—Ellcon (IRE)  **Mr M. Turner**
6  **DALKADAM (FR)**, 10, gr g Martaline—Cadoudame (FR)  **Mrs S. F. Hadida**
7  **DURATION (IRE)**, 6, b g Champs Elysees—Fringe  **Mr B Dowling & Mr R Stevens**
8  **GRANNY FRANKHAM**, 8, b m Authorized (IRE)—Faldal  **Mr R. Cooper**
9  **MAYKIR**, 5, b g Mayson—Kiruna  **Mrs C. Goddard**
10  , B f Cappella Sansevero—Mediterranean Sea (IRE)  **Ms Aurelija Juskaite**
11  **MOBHAM (IRE)**, 6, b g Teofilo (IRE)—Elegant Beauty  **Mr R. Stevens, Mrs C. Goddard**
12  **SAGA SPRINT (IRE)**, 8, b m Excellent Art—Queen of Malta (IRE)  **Ms Aurelija Juskaite**
13  **SHERELLA**, 5, b m Delegator—Mediterranean Sea (IRE)  **Mrs W. A. Jenkins**
14  **SIR RODNEYREDBLOOD**, 4, ch g Roderic O'Connor (IRE)—Red Blooded Woman (USA)  **Mrs C. Goddard**

## MR JOHN JENKINS - continued

15 **TILSWORTH LUKEY**, 8, b g Sixties Icon—Chara **Michael Ng & Phyllis Hutchins**
16 **TILSWORTH ROSE**, 7, b m Pastoral Pursuits—Pallas **Michael Ng**
17 **TILSWORTH TAIBO**, 4, ch f Coach House (IRE)—Cavallo da Corsa **Michael Ng**
18 **WALLY'S WISDOM**, 9, b g Dutch Art—Faldal **Mr R. Cooper**
19 **WHALEWEIGH STATION**, 10, b g Zamindar (USA)—Looby Loo
20 **WINALOTWITHALITTLE (IRE)**, 5, ch m Frozen Power (IRE)—Easy Going **Mr A. J. Taylor**
21 **ZAHIRAH**, 7, b m Mullionmileanhour (IRE)—Numanthia (IRE) **Crofters Racing Syndicate**
22 **ZAHRAANI**, 6, b g Mount Nelson—Mediterranean Sea (IRE) **The Zahraani Partnership**

### THREE-YEAR-OLDS

23 **AMAL (IRE)**, b f No Nay Never (USA)—Lundy Island **Mr Qiadar Khan**
24 **BE WITH THE BELL**, b g Equiano (FR)—Bella Beguine **Mr M. Turner**
25 **CARMELA SOPRANO**, gr f Hellvelyn—Caramelita **Golden Equinox Racing**
26 b c Cable Bay—Carvella Da Corsa **Michael Ng**
27 **COPPER KITTEN**, ch f Bobby's Kitten (USA)—Night Haven **Mrs C. Goddard**
28 b f Proconsul—Ellcon (IRE) **Mr M. Turner**
29 **JOE PROUD**, b c Sepoy (AUS)—Irrational **Mrs I. C. Hampson**
30 **MARTIN'S JUSIS**, b c Martinborough (JPN)—Rainbows For All **Mrs Ilona Leitendorfa-Lines**

### TWO-YEAR-OLDS

31 **BANG ON THE BELL**, b c 28/04 Heeraat (IRE)—Bella Beguine **Mr M. Turner**
32 **ELF RISING**, ch c 03/05 Hot Streak (IRE)—Rise (Polar Falcon (USA)) (8571) **Elf Rising Partnership**
33 B c 27/04 Heeraat (IRE)—Ellcon (IRE) **Mr M. Turner**
34 B f 16/03 Mount Nelson—Mediterranean Sea **Mr Qiadar Khan**
35 B c 25/01 Ardad—Pallas **Michael Ng**
36 **TEASYWEASY**, gr c 21/03 Outstrip—Dangerous Moonlite (IRE) (Acclamation) (2500)
**Mr N. Henderson, Mr J. Henderson**

**Other Owners:** Mrs V. Bullard, B. S. P. Dowling, Mrs Claire Goddard & Mr Robin Stevens, Mr M. D. Goldstein, Mrs I. C. Hampson, & Henderson, Mrs P. E. E. Hutchins, Mrs W. A. Jenkins, Michael Ng, Mr J. Sales, Mr R. Stevens, Mr A. J. Taylor.

---

**MRS LINDA JEWELL, Maidstone**
Postal: **Southfield Stables, South Lane, Sutton Valence, Maidstone, Kent, ME17 3AZ**
Contacts: **PHONE 01622 842788 MOBILE 07856 686657**
**EMAIL lindajewell@hotmail.com WEBSITE www.lindajewellracing.co.uk**

1 4, B g Casamento (IRE)—Atabaas Allure (FR)
2 **CHASING HIGHS (IRE)**, 8, b g September Storm (GER)—Rusada (IRE) **Valence Racing**
3 **CLONUSKER LADY (IRE)**, 6, b m Papal Bull—Goodthyne Miss (IRE) **Valence Racing Too**
4 **DEEWHY (IRE)**, 8, b g Papal Bull—Chanteuse de Rue (IRE) **Mr D. N. Yeadon**
5 5, B m Arakan (USA)—Goodthyne Miss (IRE) **H. J. Jarvis**
6 **HAB SAB (IRE)**, 9, b g Papal Bull—Tamburello (IRE) **Mrs P. Reynolds**
7 **MERYEMS WAY (IRE)**, 5, b m Tough As Nails (IRE)—Anne-Lise **Mr R. Churcher**
8 **MISS MALARKY (IRE)**, 8, b m Presenting—The Shan Gang (IRE) **Mr R. Churcher**
9 4, B g Red Jazz (USA)—Papal Spring (IRE) **Mr H J Jarvis & Mrs P Jarvis**
10 **PLEASURE GARDEN (USA)**, 4, b g Union Rags (USA)—Garden of Eden (USA) **Mr H J Jarvis & Mrs P Jarvis**
11 **ROYAL CONCORDE (IRE)**, 10, br g Kalanisi (IRE)—Talinas Rose (IRE) **Mr R. B. Morton**
12 4, Ch g Red Jazz (USA)—She's Humble (IRE) **Mrs L. C. Jewell**
13 **STEEL THE CHINA (IRE)**, 9, b g Craigsteel—Miss Colclough (IRE) **CS Partnership**
14 **SUNDAY SHOES (IRE)**, 5, b m Elzaam (AUS)—Pret A Porter (USA) **Mr T. Betteridge**
15 **TOOR GENERAL (IRE)**, 10, ch g Kaieteur (USA)—Alexander Euro **Mr R. Churcher**
16 **UALLRIGHTHARRY (IRE)**, 9, b g Craigsteel—Enchanted Valley (IRE) **Mrs S. M. Stanier**

## MRS LINDA JEWELL - continued

### THREE-YEAR-OLDS
17 B g Dansant—Goodthyne Miss (IRE)
18 **IMPACOBLE,** ch g Paco Boy (IRE)—Fashionable Gal (IRE)  **Mr J. C. Webb**
19 B f Blue Bresil (FR)—Sabreflight
20 B g Elzaam—Uncharted Waters

### TWO-YEAR-OLDS
21 Ch c 24/04 Life Force (IRE)—Indispensabelle (Passing Glance)
22 Ch c 18/02 Watar (IRE)—Jenna Pride (IRE) (Beneficial)
23 B c 23/04 Alhebayeb (IRE)—Maria Milena (Stravinsky (USA))

**Other Owners:** Mr C. M. Couldrey, Mr N. Couldrey, Mr M. G. Fitzjohn, Mrs S. M. Fitzjohn, Mrs A. P. Giggins, Mr B. J. Hensman, H. J. Jarvis, Mrs P. Jarvis, Mr K. Pinder, Mr J. J. Saxton.

**Assistant Trainer:** Karen Jewell.

**Conditional Jockey:** Oliver Brophy.

---

| | |
|---|---|
| **306** | **MR BRETT JOHNSON, Epsom**<br>Postal: **The Durdans Stables, Chalk Lane, Epsom, Surrey, KT18 7AX**<br>Contacts: **MOBILE 07768 697141**<br>EMAIL thedurdansstables@googlemail.com WEBSITE www.brjohnsonracing.co.uk |

1 **ANISOPTERA (IRE),** 4, ch f Casamento (IRE)—Dragonera  **Tann & Mr N Jarvis**
2 **BAY MAY,** 4, b f Helmet (AUS)—Ceilidh Band  **Daniels and Omni**
3 **DANGEROUS ENDS,** 7, b g Monsieur Bond (IRE)—Stolen Glance  **Mr C. Westley**
4 **HERON (USA),** 7, b g Quality Road (USA)—Dreamt  **O1 Racing Partnership**
5 **LITTLE FLOOZIE,** 4, b f Brazen Beau (AUS)—Sweet Wind Music  **Omni Colour Presentations Ltd**
6 **PRIME APPROACH (IRE),** 5, ch g Dawn Approach (IRE)—Remarkable Story  **Mr C. Westley**
7 **RAKEMATIZ,** 7, ch g Pivotal—Regal Velvet  **Mr C. Westley**
8 **RUN AFTER GENESIS (IRE),** 5, gr g Archipenko (USA)—She Is Great (IRE)  **Mr C. Westley**
9 **STOPNSEARCH,** 4, b g War Command (USA)—Secret Suspect  **Omni Colour Presentations Ltd**
10 **TREPIDATION,** 4, b g Bated Breath—True Pleasure (IRE)  **Tann & Mr N Jarvis**
11 **TRUE BELIEF (IRE),** 5, b g Excelebration (IRE)—It's True (IRE)  **Mr C. Westley**
12 **VIOLET'S LADS (IRE),** 7, b m Myboycharlie (IRE)—Cape Violet (IRE)  **The Savy Group**

### THREE-YEAR-OLDS
13 **BEAUTIFUL CROWN,** b g Helmet (AUS)—Bright Halo (IRE)  **Mr C. Westley**
14 **CASSANDRA ROSE (IRE),** b f Zoffany (IRE)—Havelovewilltravel (IRE)  **Only Fools Have Horses**
15 Ch f Dunaden (FR)—Jolie Chanson (FR)  **Mr C. Westley**

### TWO-YEAR-OLDS
16 Gr g 22/03 Markaz (IRE)—Impressive Victory (USA) (Street Cry (IRE)) (6800)  **Mr G. Tann**
17 **JOANIE'S GIRL,** b f 27/04 Pearl Secret—Jackline (Diktat) (3000)  **Only Fools Have Horses**

**Other Owners:** Mr M. Cumins, J. Daniels, Mr N. Hale, Mr S. Hills, Mr N. A. Jarvis, Omni Colour Presentations Ltd, Mr G. Peck, Mrs S. Rutherford, Mr G. Tann, Mr B. D. Townsend, Miss L. Wilde.

**Assistant Trainer:** Vanessa Johnson.

**307** **MR KENNY JOHNSON, Newcastle Upon Tyne**
Postal: **Grange Farm, Newburn, Newcastle Upon Tyne, Tyne and Wear, NE15 8QA**
Contacts: **PHONE 01388 721813, 0191 267 4464 MOBILE 07774 131121**
**EMAIL kennyjohnson68@hotmail.co.uk WEBSITE www.johnsonracing.co.uk**

1 **BOBBIE THE DAZZLER (IRE)**, 7, b m Lawman (FR)—Fashion Statement **Mr K. Johnson**
2 **CAIRNSHILL (IRE)**, 10, gr g Tikkanen (USA)—Ilikeyou (IRE) **Jewitt/carter Thompson**
3 **CONNERYS HILL (IRE)**, 8, b g Stowaway—Hillmar (IRE) **Johnson Racing /Paul O'Mara**
4 **CRYOGENICS (IRE)**, 7, b g Frozen Power (IRE)—New Blossom (IRE) **Johnson Racing /Paul O'Mara**
5 **GALUPPI**, 10, b g Galileo (IRE)—La Leuze (IRE) **Mr M. Kavanagh**
6 **KING GOLAN (IRE)**, 10, b g Golan (IRE)—Crimson Bow (GER) **Kenny Johnson & Mrs K Elliott**
7 5, B g Arcadio (GER)—Lady Kamando **Mr K. Johnson**
8 **ON WE GO (IRE)**, 8, b m Robin des Pres (FR)—Clan Music (IRE) **Kenny Johnson & Mrs K Elliott**
9 4, B g Intrinsic—Politelysed
10 **SWEET FLORA (IRE)**, 7, b m Arcadio (GER)—Country Flora **Mr Robert C. Whitelock/Mr Kenny Johnson**

**THREE-YEAR-OLDS**

11 Ch g Intrinsic—Politelysed

**Other Owners:** Mr I. M. Blacklock, Mr A. Carter, Carter Thompson Associates, Mrs K. Elliott, Mr R. W. Jewitt, Mr K. Johnson, Mr P. O'Mara, Mr S. Thompson, R. C. Whitelock.

**Conditional Jockey:** Callum Bewley, Tommy Dowson, Kane Yeoman.

**308** **MISS EVE JOHNSON HOUGHTON, Blewbury**
Postal: **Woodway, Blewbury, Didcot, Oxfordshire, OX11 9EZ**
Contacts: **HOME 01235 850500 PHONE 01235 850480 MOBILE 07721 622700 FAX 01235 851045**
**EMAIL Eve@JohnsonHoughton.com WEBSITE www.JohnsonHoughton.com**

1 **ACCIDENTAL AGENT**, 7, b g Delegator—Roodle **Mrs F. M. Johnson Houghton**
2 **ALEZAN**, 4, ch f Dawn Approach (IRE)—Sarinda **Mr M. Middleton-Heath**
3 **BUCKINGHAM (IRE)**, 5, gr g Clodovil (IRE)—Lizzy's Township (USA) **The Buckingham Partnership**
4 **CAPTAIN CLARET**, 4, b g Medicean—Shirazz **Sally Doyle & Partner**
5 **COSMIC POWER (IRE)**, 4, br g Power—Dhamma (USA) **McNamee Hewitt Harding Rice**
6 **GAMBON (GER)**, 5, b g Dutch Art—Guajara (GER) **Anthony Pye-Jeary & David Ian**
7 **GIN PALACE**, 5, b g Swiss Spirit—Regal Curtsy **Mrs Z. C. Campbell-Harris**
8 **GORING (GER)**, 9, b g Areion (GER)—Globuli (GER) **G. C. Stevens**
9 **HEDGING (IRE)**, 7, gr ro g Mastercraftsman (IRE)—Privet (IRE) **Eden Racing Club**
10 **HMS PRESIDENT (IRE)**, 4, b g Excelebration (IRE)—Dance Hall Girl (IRE) **HP Racing HMS President**
11 **HYANNA**, 6, b m Champs Elysees—Highly Spiced **Mr G. C. Vibert**
12 **KEPALA**, 4, gr f Mastercraftsman (IRE)—Kebaya **Aston House Stud**
13 **LADY ELYSIA**, 5, ch m Champs Elysees—Lost In Lucca **The Nigel Bennett Partnership**
14 **MADAME TANTZY**, 5, b m Champs Elysees—Roodle **Mrs F. M. Johnson Houghton**
15 **MISS MATTERHORN**, 4, b f Swiss Spirit—Support Fund (IRE) **The Ascot Colts & Fillies Club**
16 **MY STYLE (IRE)**, 5, gr g Holy Roman Emperor (IRE)—That's My Style **Hon Mrs J. M. The Corbett & Mr C. Wright**
17 **NOBLE MASQUERADE**, 4, b g Sir Percy—Moi Aussi (USA) **HP Racing Noble Masquerade**
18 **PUNCHBOWL FLYER (IRE)**, 4, b g Dream Ahead (USA)—All On Red (IRE) **The Punch Bunch**
19 **RIDGEWAY (FR)**, 4, gr g Outstrip—Bocca Bianca (GER) **Highclere Thoroughbred Racing-Ridgeway 1**
20 **SWORD BEACH (IRE)**, 4, ch g Ivawood (IRE)—Sleeping Princess (IRE) **Hp Racing Sword Beach & Ptnr**
21 **TIN HAT (IRE)**, 5, ch g Helmet (AUS)—Precautionary **Eden Racing IV**

**THREE-YEAR-OLDS**

22 **BARE GRILS (IRE)**, b c Kodi Bear (IRE)—By The Edge (IRE) **Mr W Clifford**
23 **BHUBEZI**, ch g Starspangledbanner (AUS)—Lulani (IRE) **Mr & Mrs James Blyth Currie**
24 **COLDSTREAM (IRE)**, b c Australia—Balandra **Aston House Stud**
25 **DANVILLE**, b g Muhaarar—Faustinatheyounger (IRE) **Viscount Astor**

## MISS EVE JOHNSON HOUGHTON - continued

26 **DARK ILLUSION,** b g Equiano (FR)—Magic Escapade (IRE)  **The Kimber Family**
27 **ENDURING,** b g Coulsty (IRE)—Yearbook  **Mr M. Middleton-Heath**
28 **ET TU BRUTE (IRE),** b g Holy Roman Emperor (IRE)—Xinji (IRE)  **G C Stevens & Partner**
29 **FAIRY CAKES,** b f Outstrip—Faery Song (IRE)  **Trinity Park Stud**
30 **FLAME OF FREEDOM (IRE),** b f Dragon Pulse—Catalan (IRE)  **Mr & Mrs Nicholas Johnston**
31 **GRANARY QUEEN (IRE),** ch f Dragon Pulse (IRE)—Multi Grain  **Mrs S Gray, Ian Gray & Mr J Whitworth**
32 **JUMBY (IRE),** b c New Bay—Sound of Guns  **Anthony Pye-Jeary & David Ian**
33 **MARSELAN (IRE),** b g Awtaad (IRE)—Monclaire (GER)  **Mick and Janice Mariscotti**
34 **MOUNT OLYMPUS,** b g Olympic Glory (IRE)—Ile Rouge  **HP Racing Mount Olympus**
35 **PERCY WILLIS,** b g Sir Percy—Peace Lily  **Mrs F. M. Johnson Houghton**
36 **PERCY'S LAD,** ch c Sir Percy—Victory Garden  **Jd Partnership**
37 **ROOFUL,** b f Charming Thought—Roodle  **Mrs F. M. Johnson Houghton**
38 **ROSE TIARA,** b f Helmet (AUS)—Crystal Rose (IRE)  **Mrs V. D. Neale**
39 **SANKALPA (IRE),** b f Zoffany (IRE)—Partita  **Aston House Stud**
40 **SCHILTHORN,** b g Swiss Spirit—Wall of Light  **The Mighty Mouse Partnership**
41 **SOLDIER LIONS (IRE),** b g Equiano (FR)—Stylos Ecossais  **Khk Racing & Partner**
42 **STIGWOOD (IRE),** b g Kodiac—Time Honoured  **Anthony Pye-Jeary & David Ian**
43 **STOCKHILL DREAM,** b f Mukhadram—Stockhill Diva  **Mrs M. Fairbairn & E. Gadsden**
44 B f Muhaarar—Sweet Nicole  **P. J. Gleeson**
45 **TATTOO,** b f Equiano (FR)—Belvoir Diva  **Mrs J. E. O'Halloran**
46 **TEMPLE LOCK,** ch g Pivotal—Graduation  **G. C. Stevens**
47 **THE PRINCES POET,** b c Brazen Beau (AUS)—Poesy  **HP Racing The Princes Poet**
48 **TIPSY LAIRD,** b g Gleneagles (IRE)—Lady Eclair (IRE)  **Mr & Mrs Nicholas Johnston**
49 **TORNADIC,** b g Toronado (IRE)—Fakhuur  **Mrs P. J. McCreery**
50 **UNCLE DICK,** b g Toronado (IRE)—Golden Waters  **Eden Racing Club**

## TWO-YEAR-OLDS

51 **ADAAYDREAMBELIEVER,** b f 22/03 Adaay (IRE)—Bertorizzia (FR) (Bertolini (USA))
52 **ARGIRL,** b f 09/04 Ardad (IRE)—Lassies Envoi (Makfi)  **The Johnson Grundy Partnership**
53 B c 28/01 Poet's Voice—Blynx (Equiano (FR)) (10000)  **Miss E. A. Johnson Houghton**
54 **CABINET OF CLOWNS (IRE),** gr ro c 05/03 Tamayuz—
⠀⠀⠀⠀⠀⠀⠀⠀⠀⠀⠀Silver Games (Verglas (IRE))  **Hon Mrs J. M. The Corbett & Mr C. Wright**
55 **CHIPOTLE,** b c 05/04 Havana Gold—Lightsome (Makfi) (10000)  **The Woodway 20**
56 **DAYEM (IRE),** b c 23/02 Acclamation—Slovak (IRE) (Iffraaj) (57143)  **KHK Racing Ltd**
57 **DREAMING,** b c 26/03 Territories (IRE)—Kerry's Dream (Tobougg (IRE)) (40000)  **Anthony Pye-Jeary & David Ian**
58 **DUE A RUM,** b g 01/04 Due Diligence (USA)—Rum Swizzle (Mawatheeq (USA))  **The Nigel Bennett Partnership**
59 Ch c 11/04 Helmet (AUS)—Finale (Holy Roman Emperor (IRE)) (12000)  **The Woodway 20**
60 **FLYING SECRET,** b c 18/01 Showcasing—
⠀⠀⠀⠀⠀⠀⠀⠀⠀⠀⠀Secret Sense (USA) (Shamardal (USA)) (75000)  **Jacobsconstructionholdings& Mr E Kelly**
61 Ch f 12/05 Cityscape—Golden Waters (Dubai Destination (USA))  **R. F. Johnson Houghton**
62 **GREEK PHILOSOPHER,** b c 29/01 Gutaifan (IRE)—Edessa (IRE) (Lawman (FR)) (8000)  **The Woodway 20**
63 **GREG THE GREAT,** bl c 19/03 Gregorian (IRE)—Fantasy Queen (Aqlaam)  **Mrs Z. C. Campbell-Harris**
64 **KING OF THE DANCE (IRE),** b c 09/02 Havana Gold (IRE)—
⠀⠀⠀⠀⠀⠀⠀⠀⠀⠀⠀Figurante (Excellent Art) (28571)  **HP Racing King Of The Dance**
65 B c 10/05 Aclaim (IRE)—King's Miracle (IRE) (King's Best) (11000)  **Miss E. A. Johnson Houghton**
66 B c 28/02 Time Test—Luang Prabang (Invincible Spirit (IRE)) (40000)  **Mick and Janice Mariscotti**
67 **ME NEXT,** ch f 30/04 Equiano (FR)—Next One (Cape Cross (IRE))  **Duchess Of Bedford**
68 **MISS METROPOLITAN,** ch f 18/04 Cityscape—Support Fund (IRE) (Intikhab (USA)) (9000)  **Miss E. A. Johnson Houghton**
69 Gr c 22/04 Mastercraftsman (IRE)—Notion of Beauty (USA) (Harlan's Holiday (USA))  **Eden Racing**
70 B f 29/04 Churchill (IRE)—Bezique (Cape Cross (IRE))  **Aston House Stud**
71 B c 30/04 Heeraat (IRE)—Courteous Crown (Helmet (AUS))  **Mr W Clifford**
72 B f 18/03 Havana Gold (IRE)—Lulani (IRE) (Royal Applause)  **Mr & Mrs James Blyth Currie**
73 b c 14/02 Kodiac—Partita (Montjeu (IRE))  **Aston House Stud**
74 B f 17/04 Muhaarar—Ronaldsay (Kirkwall)  **Mrs P. J. McCreery**
75 B f 25/03 Due Diligence (USA)—Peace Lily (Dansili)  **Mrs F. M. Johnson Houghton**
76 Gr c 19/04 Caravaggio (USA)—Premiere Danseuse (Gold Away (IRE)) (30000)  **Mr G. J. Owen**
77 B grf 11/05 Sixties Icon—Reprieval (FR) (Kendargent (FR))
78 **SHEER ROCKS,** ch c 09/02 Iffraaj—Paradise Cove (Harbour Watch (IRE)) (18000)  **Anthony Pye-Jeary & David Ian**
79 **SUZY'S SHOES,** ch f 13/04 Nathaniel (IRE)—Wittgenstein (IRE) (Shamardal (USA))  **Mr M. Middleton-Heath**

## MISS EVE JOHNSON HOUGHTON - continued

**Other Owners:** Mr J. Allison, Mr M. Bird, Mrs H. D. Blyth Currie, Mr J. M. Blyth Currie, Mr P. A. Buckley, Mr H. M. Butler, The Hon Mrs C. Corbett, Mrs S. J. Doyle, Mrs M. Fairbairn, Mr C. M. Fletcher, E. J. S. Gadsden, Mr I. J. B. Gray, Mrs S. Gray, Mr M. W. Gregory, HP Racing Sword Beach, Mrs P. A. Hall, Mr R. Harding, Mr L. N. Hewitt, Highclere Thoroughbred Racing - Ridgeway, Highclere Thoroughbred Racing Ltd, Jacobs Construction (Holdings) Limited, Miss E. A. Johnson Houghton, Mrs F. M. Johnson Houghton, R. F. Johnson Houghton, Mr N. Johnston, Mrs S. Johnston, Mr C. Jones, KHK Racing Ltd, Mr E. Kelly, Mr D. Lane, Mrs J. M. Mariscotti, Mr M. G. Mariscotti, Mr B. P. McNamee, Mrs J. A. McWilliam, Mrs A. J. Middis, Mr F. A. A. Nass, W. H. Ponsonby, Mr A. J. Pye-Jeary, Mrs E. R. Rice, G. C. Stevens, Mr D. L. Thomas, Mr R. Tincknell, Mrs R. L. Tincknell, Mr J. Whitworth, Mr C. N. Wright.

**Apprentice Jockey:** Georgia Dobie.

---

## 309 MR MARK JOHNSTON, Middleham

Postal: Kingsley Park, Middleham, Leyburn, North Yorkshire, DL8 4QZ
Contacts: **PHONE 01969 622237 FAX 01969 622484**
**EMAIL** info@johnston.racing **WEBSITE** www.johnston.racing

1 **ALPHA THETA**, 4, b f Archipenko (USA)—Alumna (USA) **Miss K. Rausing**
2 **ASDAA (IRE)**, 5, b g Dutch Art—Danseuse de Reve (IRE) **Owners Group 045**
3 **AVENTURIERE**, 4, b f Archipenko (USA)—Lady Jane Digby **Miss K. Rausing**
4 **DARK VISION (IRE)**, 5, b h Dream Ahead (USA)—Black Dahlia **Godolphin Management Company Ltd**
5 **DESERT SAFARI (IRE)**, 4, b g Slade Power (IRE)—Risen Sun **Sheikh Hamdan Bin Mohammed Al Maktoum**
6 **DONTASKMEAGAIN (USA)**, 4, ch c Karakontie (JPN)—Al Beedaa (USA) **Crone Stud Farms Ltd**
7 **DREAM WITH ME (IRE)**, 4, b c Frankel—Where (IRE) **Mr S. Suhail**
8 **DUTCH DECOY**, 4, ch g Dutch Art—The Terrier **Owners Group 052**
9 **ETON COLLEGE (IRE)**, 4, b g Invincible Spirit (IRE)—
Windsor County (USA) **Sheikh Hamdan Bin Mohammed Al Maktoum**
10 **FIRE FIGHTING (IRE)**, 10, b g Soldier of Fortune (IRE)—Savoie (FR) **A D Spence**
11 **FRED**, 4, ch g Frankel—Deirdre **The Burke Family**
12 **FREYJA (IRE)**, 4, ch f Gleneagles (IRE)—Crystal Valkyrie (IRE) **Mrs A G Kavanagh**
13 **HOCHFELD (IRE)**, 7, b g Cape Cross (IRE)—What A Charm (IRE) **Kingsley Park 23 - Ready To Run**
14 **JUSTIFIED**, 4, br g Authorized (IRE)—Caribbean Dancer (USA) **Mr H. C. Hart**
15 **KING'S ADVICE**, 7, ch h Frankel—Queen's Logic (IRE) **Mr S. J. A. Alharbi**
16 **LUCKY DEAL**, 6, ch g Mastercraftsman (IRE)—Barter **K. F. Leung**
17 **MAKYON (IRE)**, 4, b g Make Believe—Mise (IRE) **The Makyowners**
18 **MARIE'S DIAMOND (IRE)**, 5, b br h Footstepsinthesand—Sindiyma (IRE) **Middleham Park Racing LXXXVI**
19 **MERAAS**, 4, b c Oasis Dream—Rehn's Nest (IRE) **Mr S. M. Bel Obaida**
20 **MILDENBERGER**, 6, b h Teofilo (IRE)—Belle Josephine **Sheikh Hamdan Bin Mohammed Al Maktoum**
21 **MOUNTAIN BRAVE**, 5, b f Sepoy (AUS)—Plucky **East Layton Stud & James Lambert**
22 **MY GIRL MAGGIE**, 4, b f Camelot—African Plains **Mr & Mrs Paul & Clare Rooney**
23 **NAYEF ROAD (IRE)**, 5, ch h Galileo (IRE)—Rose Bonheur **M. Obaida**
24 **NOTATION (IRE)**, 4, b f Poet's Voice—Party Line **Kingsley Park 24 - Ready To Run**
25 **OVERWRITE (IRE)**, 4, ro g Zebedee—Negotiate **Sheikh Hamdan Bin Mohammed Al Maktoum**
26 **ROCHESTER HOUSE (IRE)**, 5, ch g Galileo (IRE)—Kalla **John Brown & Megan Dennis**
27 **ROSE OF KILDARE (IRE)**, 4, b f Make Believe—Cruck Realta **Qatar Racing Limited**
28 **SIR RON PRIESTLEY**, 5, ch h Australia—Reckoning (IRE) **P. Dean**
29 **SKY DEFENDER**, 5, b h Farhh—Al Mahmeyah **Mr H. R. Bin Ghedayer**
30 **STAR OF THE EAST (IRE)**, 7, b g Cape Cross (IRE)—Serenity Star **Kingsley Park 23 - Ready To Run**
31 **STREAK LIGHTNING (IRE)**, 4, ch g Night of Thunder (IRE)—Emreliya (IRE) **Kennet Valley Thoroughbreds XIII**
32 **SUBJECTIVIST (IRE)**, 4, b c Teofilo (IRE)—Reckoning (IRE) **Dr J. Walker**
33 **THAI TERRIER (USA)**, 5, b g Kitten's Joy (USA)—Perfect Agility (USA) **Mr C. R. Hirst**
34 **THE TRADER (IRE)**, 5, gr g Mastercraftsman (IRE)—Chinese White (IRE) **A. Saeed**
35 **THEMAXWECAN (IRE)**, 5, b g Maxios—Psychometry (FR) **Douglas Livingston**
36 **THUNDEROUS (IRE)**, 4, b c Night of Thunder (IRE)—Souviens Toi **Highclere T'Bred Racing - George Stubbs**
37 **TRUMPET MAN**, 4, b g Golden Horn—Concordia **Sheikh Hamdan Bin Mohammed Al Maktoum**

## MR MARK JOHNSTON - continued

38 **VICTORY STAR**, 4, ch g Night of Thunder (IRE)—Oud Metha  **Mr A. M. J. A. Al Harbi**
39 **WADACRE GIGOLO**, 4, ch g Makfi—Glenreef  **Wadacre Stud**
40 **WARNE'S ARMY**, 4, b f Fast Company (IRE)—Euro Empire (USA)  **DGA Racing Limited**
41 **WATERSMEET**, 10, gr g Dansili—Under The Rainbow  **Mr J. A. Barson**
42 **WEST END CHARMER (IRE)**, 5, b h Nathaniel (IRE)—Solar Midnight (USA)  **Mr M. McHale**
43 **ZABEEL CHAMPION**, 4, b c Poet's Voice—Stars In Your Eyes  **J. Alharbi**

## THREE-YEAR-OLDS

44 **AINE JORDAN (FR)**, b f Flintshire—Tabreed  **Wansdyke Farms Limited**
45 **ALBA ROSE**, b f Muhaarar—Reckoning (IRE)  **Dr J. Walker**
46 **ALETOILE**, ch f Sea The Stars (IRE)—Alamode  **Miss K. Rausing**
47 **ALFAYAATH (USA)**, b c Speightstown (USA)—Cat's Claw (USA)  **Hamdan bin Rashid Al Maktoum**
48 **ALHAAJEB (IRE)**, b c Exceed And Excel (AUS)—Landela  **Hamdan bin Rashid Al Maktoum**
49 **ALLEGRANZA**, b f Bobby's Kitten (USA)—Alboretta  **Miss K. Rausing**
50 **ALNAJEEB (IRE)**, ch g Sea The Stars (IRE)—Pretty Diamond (IRE)  **Hamdan bin Rashid Al Maktoum**
51 **ANDONNO**, b g Dansili—Lavender And Lace  **Rob Ferguson & Gary Pemberton**
52 **ANNANDALE (IRE)**, ch c Australia—Fountain of Honour (IRE)  **W. M. Johnstone**
53 **ARMY OF INDIA (IRE)**, gr ro c Sepoy (AUS)—Sudfah (USA)  **S. Ali**
54 **ART DEALER**, b g Showcasing—Siralen (USA)  **Sheikh Hamdan Bin Mohammed Al Maktoum**
55 **BAILEYS BREATHLESS**, ch f Pivotal—Baileys Jubilee  **G R Bailey Ltd (Baileys Horse Feeds)**
56 **BAILEYS DERBYDAY**, b c New Approach (IRE)—Posteritas (USA)  **G R Bailey Ltd (Baileys Horse Feeds)**
57 **BAILEYS WARRIOR**, b f The Gurkha (IRE)—Missisipi Star (IRE)  **G R Bailey Ltd (Baileys Horse Feeds)**
58 **BASILICATA (IRE)**, b f Iffraaj—Policoro (IRE)  **Sheikh Hamdan Bin Mohammed Al Maktoum**
59 **BELLE ROUGE**, b f Muhaarar—Clarietta  **Mr A D Spence & Mr M B Spence**
60 **BOWMAN (IRE)**, b g Lawman (FR)—Jo Bo Bo (IRE)  **KINGSLEY PARK 15**
61 **BRANDEGORIS**, b f Muhaarar—Highest  **Miss D Finkler, A Herd, Dr P Holloway 1**
62 **BRAVADO (FR)**, b c Showcasing—Ultradargent (FR)  **KINGSLEY PARK 18**
63 **CHASE THE DOLLAR**, b c Frankel—Cape Dollar  **Mr S. Suhail**
64 **CODEBOOK**, ch g New Approach (IRE)—Safe House (IRE)  **Sheikh Hamdan Bin Mohammed Al Maktoum**
65 **COUPE DE CHAMPAGNE (GER)**, ch f Gleneagles (IRE)—Capichera (GER)  **KINGSLEY PARK 17**
66 **CUBAN DANCER**, b g Toronado (IRE)—Mambo Halo (USA)  **KINGSLEY PARK 16**
67 **DANCING KING (IRE)**, b g Free Eagle (IRE)—Agnetha (USA)  **KINGSLEY PARK 16**
68 **DARK COMPANY (IRE)**, b c Fast Company (IRE)—Roseraie (IRE)  **Mr H. A. Lootah**
69 **DECODING (IRE)**, b f Dawn Approach (IRE)—Khazina (USA)  **Tactful Finance Limited & Partner**
70 **DEEP IMPRESSION (IRE)**, b f Footstepsintheasand—Parvenue (FR)  **KINGSLEY PARK 15**
71 **DREAM CAMELOT (IRE)**, b c Camelot—Opera Fan (FR)  **Mr A. Alharbi**
72 **DREAMS UNWIND**, b f Dansili—St Francis Wood (USA)  **Aynsford Holdings, LLC**
73 **DUBAI FOUNTAIN (IRE)**, b f Teofilo (IRE)—Nafura  **Sheikh Hamdan Bin Mohammed Al Maktoum**
74 **ELUSIVE ARTIST (IRE)**, ch g Zoffany (IRE)—Lady Pimpernel  **KINGSLEY PARK 15**
75 **EPIC PASS (IRE)**, b c Awtaad (IRE)—Kanes Pass (IRE)  **Teme Valley 2**
76 **EYE OF HEAVEN**, b c Exceed And Excel (AUS)—Risen Sun  **Sheikh Hamdan Bin Mohammed Al Maktoum**
77 **FAIRMAC**, br gr g Lethal Force (IRE)—Kenyan Cat  **Middleham Park Racing VI**
78 **FANDABIDOZI (IRE)**, ch g Mastercraftsman (IRE)—Cranky Spanky (IRE)  **KINGSLEY PARK 18**
79 **FOREST FALCON (IRE)**, b c Raven's Pass (USA)—Malmoosa (IRE)  **Sheikh Hamdan Bin Mohammed Al Maktoum**
80 **FRAGRANT STORM**, ch f Frankel—Rose Bonheur  **M. Obaida**
81 **GEAR UP (IRE)**, b c Teofilo (IRE)—Gearanai (USA)  **Teme Valley 2**
82 **GHOST RIDER (IRE)**, b c Dark Angel (IRE)—Priceless Jewel  **John & Jess Dance**
83 **GHUMAMA (IRE)**, ch f Dawn Approach (IRE)—Bishara (USA)  **Hamdan bin Rashid Al Maktoum**
84 **GLEN AGAIN (IRE)**, b c Gleneagles (IRE)—Four Eleven (CAN)  **Teme Valley 2**
85 **GOLDEN FLAME (IRE)**, b c Golden Horn—Flame of Gibraltar (IRE)  **Sheikh Hamdan Bin Mohammed Al Maktoum**
86 **HAPPY (IRE)**, b c Galileo (IRE)—Sent From Heaven (USA)  **Crone Stud Farms Ltd**
87 **HARLEM SOUL**, ch c Frankel—Giants Play (USA)  **Teme Valley 2**
88 **HEADINGLEY (IRE)**, b c Dawn Approach (IRE)—Gold Bubbles (USA)  **Gallop Racing**
89 **HOME AND DRY (IRE)**, ch c Sea The Stars (IRE)—Pale Mimosa (IRE)  **Barbara & Alick Richmond**
90 **IF YOU DARE**, b c Equiano (FR)—Love Action (IRE)  **Middleham Park Racing LXXIX**
91 **IMMACULATE**, b f Invincible Spirit (IRE)—Coquette Noire (IRE)  **Highclere Tbred Racing-Juliet Cursham**
92 **JULIE JOHNSTON**, b f Acclamation—Jeanie Johnston (IRE)  **Mr C. Chapman**
93 **KEHAILAAN (IRE)**, b c Gleneagles (IRE)—Defrost My Heart (IRE)  **Mr M. B. H. K. Al Attiya**
94 **KHEZAANA (IRE)**, b f Muhaarar—Memoria  **Hamdan bin Rashid Al Maktoum**

## MR MARK JOHNSTON - continued

95 **KING FRANKEL (IRE)**, b c Frankel—You'll Be Mine (USA) **M. Obaida**
96 **KING ZAIN (IRE)**, b c Kingman—Shreyas (IRE) **J. Alharbi**
97 **KINGS PRINCE**, b c Kingman—Dynaforce (USA) **Crone Stud Farms Ltd**
98 **KONDO ISAMI (IRE)**, ch c Galileo (IRE)—Zouzou (AUS) **Toshihiro Matsumoto & Partners**
99 **LADYWOOD (IRE)**, b f Dark Angel (IRE)—Beneventa **Mr J. A. Barson**
100 **LEOPARDO (USA)**, gr ro c Cairo Prince (USA)—Shovalla (USA) **Mr H. A. Lootah**
101 **LOVE IS GOLDEN (IRE)**, b c Golden Horn—Holy Moon (IRE) **Crone Stud Farms Ltd**
102 **LOVE OF ZOFFANY (IRE)**, ch c Zoffany (IRE)—Ithaca (USA) **Crone Stud Farms Ltd**
103 **MARCH LAW (IRE)**, b c Lawman (FR)—Dookus (IRE) **Susan & John Waterworth**
104 **MISS ROULETTE (IRE)**, b f Lope de Vega (IRE)—

            Sea of Heartbreak (IRE) **Nick Bradley Racing 11 & Ballylinch Stud**
105 **MR EXCELLENCY (IRE)**, b c Awtaad (IRE)—Katla (IRE) **Mr H. A. Lootah**
106 **NAAMOOS (FR)**, b c Wootton Bassett—Praise Dancing (IRE) **H.H. Shaikh Nasser Al Khalifa & Partner**
107 **NATURAL VALUE**, b c Exceed And Excel (AUS)—Kalsa (IRE) **Dr J. Walker**
108 **NEW DAY**, b f New Bay—This Is The Day **John O'Connor & Partner**
109 **NIGHT MOMENT (GER)**, b c Amaron—Noble Lady (GER) **KINGSLEY PARK 16**
110 **NOVELTY**, b f New Approach (IRE)—Welsh Angel **Kennet Valley Thoroughbreds V**
111 **OUTBACK BOY (IRE)**, ch g Australia—Permission Slip (IRE) **Teme Valley 2**
112 **OVERTHINK (IRE)**, b c Golden Horn—First Blush (IRE) **Sheikh Hamdan Bin Mohammed Al Maktoum**
113 **PARTY REBEL (IRE)**, ch f Excelebration (IRE)—Naomh Geileis (USA) **Mrs Christine E Budden & Partners**
114 **PERFECT TIMES**, b f Gleneagles (IRE)—Al Janadeirya **Times Of Wigan Ltd**
115 **PILLAR OF HOPE**, b c Awtaad (IRE)—Great Hope (IRE) **C. C. Buckley**
116 **PINA COLLADA**, b f Pearl Secret—Pilosa (IRE) **John & Jess Dance**
117 **PROSPECT**, b g Shalaa (IRE)—Souville **A D Spence**
118 **QAADER (IRE)**, b c Night of Thunder (IRE)—Redinha **Hamdan bin Rashid Al Maktoum**
119 **REAMS OF LOVE**, b c Frankel—Night of Light (IRE) **Crone Stud Farms Ltd**
120 **RED MIRAGE (IRE)**, ch c Showcasing—Duchess Dora (IRE) **Mr S. Suhail**
121 **RENBAWI (IRE)**, b c Dubawi (IRE)—Rehn's Nest (IRE) **Mr S. M. Bel Obaida**
122 **ROSEABAD (IRE)**, b f Awtaad (IRE)—Dayrose **Mr H. A. Lootah**
123 **RUN THIS WAY**, b f Cannock Chase (USA)—Prime Run **Mr S. Suhail**
124 **SAM BELLAMY**, ch g Iffraaj—Coral Mist **Kingsley Park 24 - Ready To Run**
125 **SANDS OF TIME**, b f Bobby's Kitten (USA)—Starlit Sands **Miss K. Rausing**
126 **SEA THE SHELLS**, b c Sea The Stars (IRE)—Seychelloise **Teme Valley 2**
127 **SHE GOT THE LOOK (IRE)**, b f Camelot—Jessie Jane (IRE) **M. W. Graff**
128 **SHEM (IRE)**, b g Kodiac—Noahs Ark (IRE) **Mr R. Walker**
129 **SIBAAQ (IRE)**, b g Dark Angel (IRE)—Maid To Dream **Hamdan bin Rashid Al Maktoum**
130 **SILVER SHADE (FR)**, gr g Kendargent (FR)—Lady's Secret (IRE) **KINGSLEY PARK 17**
131 **SILVESTRIS**, b g Bobby's Kitten (USA)—Heading North **KINGSLEY PARK 18**
132 **SIR JOHN BOWDLER (IRE)**, b c Exceed And Excel (AUS)—Gotta Have Her (USA) **P. Dean**
133 **SOAPY STEVENS**, b g Harzand (IRE)—Zubova **Mr J. M. Duggan & Mr S. Brown**
134 **STATE OF BLISS**, b c Gleneagles (IRE)—Crystal Valkyrie (IRE) **Barbara & Alick Richmond**
135 **SUKARNO**, ch c Sea The Stars (IRE)—Shama's Crown (IRE) **Mr H. A. Lootah**
136 **TADREEB (IRE)**, b c Oasis Dream—Wake Up Call **Hamdan bin Rashid Al Maktoum**
137 B g Muhaarar—Talampaya (USA) **Mr S. Suhail**
138 **TELLMEYOURSTORY (USA)**, ch f Karakontie (JPN)—Al Beedaa (USA) **Mr M. Doyle**
139 **THUNDER OF NIAGARA (IRE)**, b c Night of Thunder (IRE)—Cairncross (IRE) **Rabbah Racing**
140 **TOP OF THE POPS**, b c Kingman—Whirly Bird **A D Spence**
141 **TOUSSAROK**, b c Iffraaj—Frangipanni (IRE) **Titanium Racing Club**
142 **TRIBAL ART (IRE)**, b c Farhh—Chaquiras (USA) **Sheikh Hamdan Bin Mohammed Al Maktoum**
143 **TROPICAL CYCLONE (IRE)**, b f Shamardal (USA)—

            Spinning Cloud (USA) **Sheikh Hamdan Bin Mohammed Al Maktoum**
144 **VENTURA KINGDOM (FR)**, b g Dream Ahead (USA)—Fox Force Five (IRE) **Middleham Park Racing XV**
145 **VENTURA VISION (FR)**, b f No Nay Never (USA)—Great Trip (USA) **Middleham Park XVIII & Steven Rocco**
146 **WOOTTON CREEK**, b f Wootton Bassett—Tuileries **Sheikh Hamdan Bin Mohammed Al Maktoum**
147 **ZOOKEEPER (IRE)**, b c Dubawi (IRE)—Zara (BRZ) **Sheikh Hamdan Bin Mohammed Al Maktoum**

## TWO-YEAR-OLDS

148 **AGREEABILITY**, b f 02/05 Bobby's Kitten (USA)—Moi Aussi (USA) (Mt Livermore (USA)) **Miss K. Rausing**
149 B c 16/02 Kodiac—Albamara (Galileo (IRE)) (17143) **Mr P. F. M. D. Carmo**

## MR MARK JOHNSTON - continued

**150 ALLARMISTA,** b f 05/02 National Defense—Alta Moda (Sadler's Wells (USA))  **Miss K. Rausing**
**151** B f 27/01 El Kabeir (USA)—Amelia Dream (Kyllachy) (20000)  **Cliff Stud Limited**
**152** B c 11/05 Gleneagles (IRE)—An Saincheann (IRE) (Dylan Thomas (IRE)) (48000)  **P. Dean**
**153** B f 19/02 Fascinating Rock (IRE)—Anam Allta (IRE) (Invincible Spirit (IRE)) (14286)  **Kingsley Park 22**
**154** Ch c 26/02 Gleneagles (IRE)—Ange Bleu (USA) (Alleged (USA)) (15000)  **Nasir Askar**
**155** Ch c 05/04 Australia—Aoife Alainn (IRE) (Dr Fong (USA)) (22000)  **Kingsley Park 20**
**156 APPROACHABILITY,** ch c 28/01 New Approach (IRE)—
                                        Posterity (IRE) (Indian Ridge) (27000)  **Brian Yeardley & Partner**
**157** B c 24/03 War Command (USA)—
                    Assault On Rome (IRE) (Holy Roman Emperor (IRE))  **Mrs Christine E Budden & Partners**
**158 AUSTRIAN THEORY (IRE),** b c 16/02 Awtaad (IRE)—Cedar Sea (IRE) (Persian Bold) (30000)  **Dr J. Walker**
**159** B f 04/04 Iffraaj—Baileys Jubilee (Bahamian Bounty)  **G R Bailey Ltd (Baileys Horse Feeds)**
**160** B f 02/03 Golden Horn—Be Fabulous (GER) (Samum (GER))  **Sheikh Hamdan Bin Mohammed Al Maktoum**
**161** Ch c 03/04 Iffraaj—Bess of Hardwick (Dansili) (15000)  **Kingsley Park 22**
**162 BETTER HALF,** b f 02/05 Bobby's Kitten (USA)—Beta (Selkirk (USA))  **Miss K. Rausing**
**163 BIRDIE PUTT (IRE),** b f 24/05 Gleneagles (IRE)—
                                        Inch Perfect (USA) (Theatrical) (32000)  **N Browne, I Boyce & Partner**
**164 BOONDOGGLE,** b c 01/03 Bobby's Kitten (USA)—
                                        Fresh Strike (IRE) (Smart Strike (CAN)) (20000)  **Barbara & Alick Richmond**
**165 BOY ABOUT TOWN,** b c 28/01 Frankel—Miss Marjurie (IRE) (Marju (IRE)) (48000)  **Susan & John Waterworth**
**166** B c 18/04 Dubawi (IRE)—Cape Dollar (IRE) (Cape Cross (IRE))  **Mr S. Suhail**
**167 CAPITAL THEORY,** b c 22/03 Muhaarar—Montalcino (IRE) (Big Bad Bob (IRE)) (26000)  **Dr J. Walker**
**168** B f 12/03 Cotai Glory—Carry On Katie (USA) (Fasliyev (USA)) (9524)  **Kingsley Park 20**
**169 CASI CRUDO,** b c 06/02 Authorized (IRE)—Adalawa (IRE) (Barathea (IRE)) (24000)  **M. W. Graff**
**170** B c 24/03 Excelebration (IRE)—Cherry Creek (IRE) (Montjeu (IRE)) (57143)  **Middleham Park Racing XIV**
**171 CHUFFED TO BITS (IRE),** b c 05/05 Churchill (IRE)—
                                        Crystal Valkyrie (IRE) (Danehill (USA)) (22000)  **Barbara & Alick Richmond**
**172** Ch f 17/03 Teofilo (IRE)—Cite Veron (FR) (Tomorrows Cat (USA))  **AlMohamediya Racing**
**173 CLAIM THE STARS (IRE),** b c 02/03 Starspangledbanner (AUS)—
                                        Ponty Acclaim (IRE) (Acclamation) (30476)  **Teme Valley 2**
**174** B c 19/04 Muhaarar—Confidential Lady (Singspiel (IRE)) (15000)  **Kingsley Park 22**
**175** B c 27/03 Dubawi (IRE)—Danedream (GER) (Lomitas)  **Mr H. R. Bin Ghedayer**
**176** B c 12/03 Sea The Moon (GER)—Diablerette (Green Desert (USA)) (21000)  **The Kingsley Park 25 - The Originals**
**177 DR YOUMZAIN (IRE),** b c 12/03 Dark Angel (IRE)—Fine Blend (IRE) (Sakhee's Secret) (32000)  **J. Alharbi**
**178** B c 26/02 Australia—Dubka (Dubawi (IRE)) (16000)  **Kingsley Park 21**
**179** Gr f 21/02 Dark Angel (IRE)—Elas Diamond (Danehill Dancer (IRE)) (65000)  **Newsells Park Stud Limited**
**180** Gr c 20/02 Mastercraftsman (IRE)—
                    Elegant Peace (IRE) (Intense Focus (USA)) (45714)  **Kennet Valley Thoroughbreds XIII**
**181** B c 14/04 New Approach (IRE)—Enlace (Shamardal (USA))  **Sheikh Hamdan Bin Mohammed Al Maktoum**
**182** B f 25/04 Showcasing—Entree (Halling (USA)) (8571)  **Ali Abdulla Saeed**
**183 EXCLUSIVE TIMES,** b f 22/03 The Gurkha (IRE)—Al Janadeirya (Oasis Dream)  **Times Of Wigan Ltd**
**184 FIVE STARS,** b f 01/04 Sea The Stars (IRE)—Kissable (IRE) (Danehill Dancer (IRE)) (48000)  **M. W. Graff**
**185** B f 29/04 Fast Company (IRE)—Fork Handles (Doyen (IRE)) (6667)  **Kingsley Park 21**
**186** B c 28/04 Iffraaj—Galician (Redoute's Choice (AUS))  **Sheikh Hamdan Bin Mohammed Al Maktoum**
**187 GOLDEN DISC (IRE),** b c 05/03 Golden Horn—Mamonta (Fantastic Light (USA)) (40000)  **Crone Stud Farms Ltd**
**188 GOLDEN SANDS (IRE),** ch c 05/03 Footstepsinthesand—Varna (Efisio) (30476)  **HJW Partnership**
**189** B f 24/02 Postponed (IRE)—Heart's Content (IRE) (Daylami (IRE))  **Sheikh Hamdan Bin Mohammed Al Maktoum**
**190 I'M A GAMBLER (IRE),** b c 07/04 No Nay Never (USA)—
                    We Are Ninety (IRE) (Thewayyouare (USA)) (44762)  **John Brown & Megan Dennis**
**191** Ch c 09/03 Iffraaj—Lamentation (Singspiel (IRE)) (10000)  **Kingsley Park 20**
**192** B f 16/02 Golden Horn—Liberating (Iffraaj) (32381)  **Miss D Finkler, A Herd, Dr P Holloway 1**
**193 LIV LUCKY,** b f 14/04 Profitable (IRE)—
                                        Living Art (Trippi (USA)) (28571)  **Jane Newett and Dougie Livingston**
**194 LOVE DE VEGA (IRE),** ch c 09/02 Lope de Vega (IRE)—Ribble (FR) (Motivator) (92000)  **Crone Stud Farms Ltd**
**195** Ch f 31/01 Postponed (IRE)—Luminous (Champs Elysees) (28000)  **Sheikh Hamdan Bin Mohammed Al Maktoum**
**196 MACKENZIE ROSE (IRE),** b f 20/02 Dark Angel (IRE)—Kelsey Rose (Most Welcome) (59048)  **Mrs S. E. Rowett**
**197 MADAME AMBASSADOR,** ch f 05/02 Churchill (IRE)—Lady Jane Digby (Oasis Dream)  **Miss K. Rausing**
**198 MADAME BONBON (FR),** ch f 16/02 Iffraaj—Apres Midi (IRE) (Galileo (IRE))  **C. Bryce**
**199** B c 15/04 Muhaarar—Maid For Winning (USA) (Gone West (USA)) (110000)  **Hamdan bin Rashid Al Maktoum**
**200** B f 30/03 Aclaim (IRE)—Missisipi Star (IRE) (Mujahid (USA)) (62000)  **G R Bailey Ltd (Baileys Horse Feeds)**

# MR MARK JOHNSTON - continued

201 **MOON OF REALITY,** b c 26/03 Sea The Moon (GER)—Selenography (Selkirk (USA)) (40000) **Teme Valley 2**
202 Br f 25/03 Muhaarar—Muraaqaba (Dubawi (IRE)) **Hamdan bin Rashid Al Maktoum**
203 Br c 25/03 Intello (GER)—Murahana (IRE) (Invincible Spirit (IRE)) **Hamdan bin Rashid Al Maktoum**
204 Gr c 26/03 Dark Angel (IRE)—Muteela (Dansili) **Hamdan bin Rashid Al Maktoum**
205 Gr f 07/04 Iffraaj—Nahoodh (IRE) (Clodovil (IRE)) **Sheikh Hamdan Bin Mohammed Al Maktoum**
206 Ch f 27/03 Mehmas (IRE)—Najraan (Cadeaux Genereux) (42000) **Mr M. B. H. K. Al Attiya**
207 Ch c 02/05 Zoffany (IRE)—Naomh Geileis (USA) (Grand Slam (USA)) **Mrs Christine E Budden & Partners**
208 **NOONIE,** b f 25/02 Almanzor (FR)—Gallice (IRE) (Fuisse (FR)) **The Earl of R. L. Ronaldshay**
209 **NORDHALLA,** ch f 17/04 Divine Prophet (AUS)—Chellala (Elnadim (USA)) (30476) **Susan & John Waterworth**
210 Ch c 31/03 Galileo Gold—Open Verse (USA) (Black Minnaloushe (USA)) (18000) **J. Alharbi**
211 B c 17/04 Postponed (IRE)—Party Line (Montjeu (IRE)) **S. R. Counsell**
212 Ch c 27/01 Iffraaj—Perfect Light (IRE) (Galileo (IRE)) **Sheikh Hamdan Bin Mohammed Al Maktoum**
213 B f 21/04 Iffraaj—Pleasemetoo (IRE) (Vale of York (IRE)) **Sheikh Hamdan Bin Mohammed Al Maktoum**
214 **PONS AELIUS,** b c 28/04 Galileo (IRE)—Laugh Out Loud (Clodovil (IRE)) (95000) **Susan & John Waterworth**
215 Bc 20/02 Dark Angel (IRE)—Purr Along (Mount Nelson) (67000) **Qatar Racing Limited**
216 Ch f 29/03 Ulysses (IRE)—Reckoning (IRE) (Danehill Dancer (IRE)) (140000) **Mascalls Stud**
217 Ch c 14/04 Tamayuz—Rocana (Fastnet Rock (AUS)) **Hamdan bin Rashid Al Maktoum**
218 Bc 23/04 New Approach (IRE)—Rosewater (IRE) (Pivotal) **Sheikh Hamdan Bin Mohammed Al Maktoum**
219 **RUBY RUBY,** b f 13/03 Invincible Spirit (IRE)—Elas Ruby (Raven's Pass (USA)) (62000) **3 Batterhams and a Reay**
220 Gr c 19/01 Dark Angel (IRE)—Sea of Grace (IRE) (Born To Sea (IRE)) (67000) **Qatar Racing Limited**
221 B c 13/04 Wootton Bassett—
                               Shaloushka (IRE) (Dalakhani (IRE)) (62000) **Highclere T'Bred Racing - Woodland Walk**
222 Ch c 10/02 Night of Thunder (IRE)—Southern Belle (IRE) (Aqlaam) (155000) **Hamdan bin Rashid Al Maktoum**
223 **STONE AXE (IRE),** ro c 08/03 Zoffany (IRE)—
                               Roystonea (Polish Precedent (USA)) (34286) **Susan & John Waterworth**
224 Ch c 27/03 Farhh—Strictly Lambada (Red Ransom (USA)) **The Kingsley Park 25 - The Originals**
225 **SUPER STARS (IRE),** b c 04/05 Sea The Stars (IRE)—Valais Girl (Holy Roman Emperor (IRE)) (32381) **Mr M. Doyle**
226 Gr f 20/02 Showcasing—Sweet Alabama (Johannesburg (USA)) (104762) **Middleham Park Racing LIII**
227 **TIPPY TOES,** b f 28/02 Havana Gold—Mullein (Oasis Dream) (15000) **Barbara & Alick Richmond**
228 **TREBLE JOY (IRE),** b c 03/03 Kitten's Joy (USA)—Three Hearts (USA) (Hat Trick (JPN)) (50000) **Teme Valley 2**
229 **TROJAN HORSE (IRE),** ch c 04/05 Ulysses (IRE)—
                               Guardia (GER) (Monsun (GER)) (6000) **Atlantic Racing & R. W. Huggins**
230 **VALUE THEORY (IRE),** ch f 16/04 Gleneagles (IRE)—Venetian Beauty (USA) (Lear Fan (USA)) (50000) **Dr J. Walker**
231 Ch f 27/01 Ribchester (IRE)—Ventura Mist (Pastoral Pursuits) (48000) **J. Alharbi**
232 B c 20/03 Gleneagles (IRE)—Vive Les Rouges (Acclamation) (9524) **Kingsley Park 22**
233 B f 02/02 Nathaniel (IRE)—Yorkidding (Dalakhani (IRE)) **Mr P. R. York**
234 B c 28/04 Golden Horn—Zaeema (Zafonic (USA)) **Sheikh Hamdan Bin Mohammed Al Maktoum**

**Assistant Trainer:** Jock Bennett, Andrew Bottomley, Charlie Johnston, Deirdre Johnston, Hayley Kelly.

**Flat Jockey:** Ben Curtis, Joe Fanning, Franny Norton. **Apprentice Jockey:** Andrew Breslin, Jonny Peate, Oliver Stammers.

---

## 310 MR ALAN JONES, Timberscombe
Postal: **East Harwood Farm, Timberscombe, Minehead, Somerset, TA24 7UE**
Contacts: **MOBILE 07901 505064 FAX 01633 680232**
EMAIL heritageracing@btconnect.com WEBSITE www.alanjonesracing.co.uk

1 **COCARDIER (FR),** 4, b c My Risk (FR)—Tamaline (FR) **Mr A. E. Jones**
2 **DUHALLOW LAD (IRE),** 9, b g Papal Bull—Macca Luna (IRE) **Burnham Plastering & Drylining Ltd**
3 **I'M NOTAPARTYGIRL,** 8, b m Arvico (FR)—Lady Shirley Hunt **Mr A. E. Jones**
4 **JACK'S A LEGEND,** 6, b g Midnight Legend—Dancing Emily (IRE) **Burnham Plastering & Drylining Ltd**
5 **LADY AVERY (IRE),** 9, b m Westerner—Bobs Article (IRE) **Burnham Plastering & Drylining Ltd**
6 **LADY EXCALIBUR (IRE),** 4, b f Camelot—Market Forces **Burnham Plastering & Drylining Ltd**
7 **MISSMEBUTLETMEGO,** 11, b g With The Flow (USA)—Bay Bianca (IRE) **Mr A. E. Jones**
8 **POKARI (FR),** 9, ch g Bonbon Rose (FR)—Pokara (FR) **Mr A. E. Jones**
9 4, B c Bollin Eric—Rest And Be (IRE)

## MR ALAN JONES - continued

10 **STAND BY ME (FR)**, 11, b g Dream Well (FR)—In Love New (FR)  **Mr A. E. Jones**
11 **TIQUER (FR)**, 13, b g Equerry (USA)—Tirenna (FR)  **Burnham Plastering & Drylining Ltd**
12 4, B f Fame And Glory—Toile d'Auteuil (FR)
13 **VETONCALL (IRE)**, 9, b g Well Chosen—Miss Audacious (IRE)  **Burnham Plastering & Drylining Ltd**

### THREE-YEAR-OLDS

14 B g Clovis du Berlais (FR)—Dancing Emily (IRE)

**Assistant Trainer:** Miss A. Bartelink.

**NH Jockey:** Paddy Brennan, Richard Johnson, Tom O'Brien.

---

## 311 MR ADRIAN PAUL KEATLEY, MALTON
Postal: **36 The Gallops, Norton, Malton, North Yorkshire, YO17 9JU**
Contacts: **PHONE +353 87 354 5349**

1 **CHAMPAGNE TERRI (IRE)**, 5, b m Elzaam (AUS)—Cresta Rise  **Ontoawinner & B Keatley**
2 **COMPTON'S FINALE**, 5, b g Compton Place—Finalize  **Ontoawinner & B Keatley**
3 **DASH OF SPICE**, 7, br g Teofilo (IRE)—Dashiba  **Ontoawinner, Mr&Mrs Bainbridge**
4 **DRUMCONNOR LAD (IRE)**, 11, b g Winged Love (IRE)—
                               Drumconnor Lady (IRE)  **Mr David Keys & Mrs Breda Keatley**
5 **LISNAGOORNEEN (IRE)**, 6, b m Flemensfirth (USA)—Roses Dreams (IRE)  **Mr W. J. Fouhy**
6 **MO HENRY**, 9, b g Monsieur Bond (IRE)—Mo Mhuirnin (IRE)  **Ontoawinner and The Shevlins**
7 **SOCKS OFF (IRE)**, 4, br g Society Rock (IRE)—Deliziosa (IRE)  **Mrs J. Snailum**

### THREE-YEAR-OLDS

8 **DONNY MARLOW (IRE)**, b g Camacho—Mandella (ITY)  **Ontoawinner & B Keatley**
9 **MCGIVERN (IRE)**, b f Tamayuz—Dawaama (IRE)  **Ontoawinner & B Keatley**
10 **ONE PUNCH TERRI**, ch f Mukhadram—Engaging  **Ontoawinner & B Keatley**
11 **QUIET ASSASSIN (IRE)**, ch f Tamayuz—Dutch Rifle  **Ontoawinner & B Keatley**
12 **SADIE'S DAY (IRE)**, b f Fast Company (IRE)—Perfect Venture  **Ontoawinner 9**
13 **SHALAA ASKER (IRE)**, b c Shalaa (IRE)—Miracle Seeker  **Ontoawinner, Finneran**
14 **SPACE KID (IRE)**, ch g Tamayuz—Mymoonlightdancer (IRE)  **Mr A. Conneally**
15 **TENTH CENTURY**, b g Fountain of Youth (IRE)—Sukuma (IRE)  **Ontoawinner 8**
16 **THE QUIET REBEL (IRE)**, br g Moohaajim (IRE)—Rebel Aclaim (IRE)  **Ontoawinner & B Keatley**
17 **THERE'S NO DANGER (IRE)**, br c No Nay Never (USA)—Moment In The Sun  **Ontoawinner & B Keatley**
18 **TWICE ADAAY**, b f Adaay (IRE)—Amber Heights  **Ontoawinner & B Keatley**
19 **WOBWOBWOB (IRE)**, b g Prince of Lir (IRE)—Ishimagic  **Ontoawinner, Finneran**

### TWO-YEAR-OLDS

20 B f 07/04 El Kabeir (USA)—Apple Spirit (USA) (Lemon Drop Kid (USA)) (31429)  **Ontoawinner, Mr&Mrs Bainbridge**
21 B c 13/03 Ardad (IRE)—Cherrego (USA) (Borrego (USA)) (800)
22 B f 09/03 National Defense—City Vaults Girl (IRE) (Oratorio (IRE)) (4762)
23 B f 11/03 Kodiac—Dutch Destiny (Dutch Art) (20952)  **Ontoawinner, Mr&Mrs Bainbridge**
24 B f 03/03 Mehmas (IRE)—Miss Sally (IRE) (Danetime (IRE)) (25000)  **Ontoawinner & B Keatley**
25 B c 13/03 Due Diligence (USA)—Secret Romance (Sakhee's Secret) (4000)
26 **SHE'S THE DANGER (IRE)**, b f 23/03 Pride of Dubai (AUS)—
                               Moment In The Sun (Dubai Destination (USA))  **Ontoawinner & B Keatley**
27 B f 02/02 Adaay (IRE)—Sun Angel (IRE) (Sir Prancealot (IRE)) (5714)  **Ontoawinner & B Keatley**
28 B f 23/03 Fast Company (IRE)—Virtudes (IRE) (Invincible Spirit (IRE)) (4762)

**Other Owners:** Mr S. Bridge, Mrs B. Keatley, Mr D. Keys, Mr N. J. O'Brien.

## 312 MRS FIONA KEHOE, Leighton Buzzard
Postal: **The Croft Farm, Wing Road, Stewkley, Leighton Buzzard, Bedfordshire, LU7 0JB**
Contacts: **PHONE 07795 096908**
EMAIL f.kehoe@btinternet.com

1 ALLO ALLO, 5, b g Milan—Ravello Bay **M. Kehoe**
2 ALWAYS ABLE (IRE), 6, b m Stowaway—Twotrailerparkgirl (IRE) **M. Kehoe**
3 DINAH WASHINGTON (IRE), 5, ch m Australia—Gainful (USA) **M. Kehoe**

## 313 MR MARTIN KEIGHLEY, Moreton-In-Marsh
Postal: **Condicote Stables, Luckley, Longborough, Moreton-In-Marsh, Gloucestershire, GL56 0RD**
Contacts: **MOBILE 07767 472547**
EMAIL keighleyracing@btinternet.com WEBSITE www.martinkeighley.com

1 BACK ON THE LASH, 7, b g Malinas (GER)—Giovanna **M. Boothright**
2 BE THANKFUL, 6, ch m Helmet (AUS)—Be Joyful (IRE) **Martin Keighley Racing Club**
3 BEN BUIE (IRE), 7, br g Presenting—Change of Plan (IRE)
4 BIG NASTY, 8, b g Black Sam Bellamy (IRE)—Hello My Lovely **Peel Racing Syndicate**
5 BLACK PANTHER (IRE), 5, br g Nayef (USA)—Amjaad **Mr D. A. Maughan**
6 BREIZH ALKO (FR), 10, ch g Balko (FR)—Quisiera (FR) **Mr D. Parry**
7 CAPRICIA (IRE), 6, b m Mahler—Bobset Leader (IRE) **Martin Keighley Racing Partnership 5**
8 CITY NEVER SLEEPS (IRE), 9, b g Central Park (IRE)—Goodnightmrskelly (IRE) **Martin Keighley Racing Club**
9 4, B g Sageburg (IRE)—Constant Approach (IRE) **The Cotswold Lockdowners**
10 CUL DE POULE, 9, b g Multiplex—Madam Blaze **Mr & Mrs R. Allsop**
11 CUT AND RUN, 8, b m Getaway (GER)—Somethinaboutmolly (IRE) **Mrs Z. A. E. Tindall**
12 DARIYA (USA), 6, b m Include (USA)—Dubai (IRE) **Mr D. Parry**
13 DEBDEN BANK, 7, b g Cacique (IRE)—Rose Row **Martin Keighley Racing Partnership 6**
14 DREAMSUNDERMYFEET (IRE), 6, br g Yeats (IRE)—Change of Plan (IRE) **Owners for Owners Dreamers**
15 DUKE OF LUCKLEY (IRE), 4, b g Mahler—Emily's Princess (IRE) **Owners for Owners Duke Of Luckley**
16 ECLAT DES MOTTES (FR), 7, b g Poliglote—Sun des Mottes (FR) **Bishop, Bowkley, Parker, Dee and Davis**
17 ENFORCEMENT (IRE), 6, b g Lawman (FR)—Elodie **Martin Keighley Racing Club**
18 FOUND ON (IRE), 6, b m Mahler—Court Gamble (IRE) **Mr O. F. Ryan**
19 GOLD OF WIN POTIER (FR), 5, ch g Full of Gold (FR)—Princesse Tennis (FR) **Sharon & Grahame Lovett**
20 KAZONTHERAZZ, 5, b m Kayf Tara—Giovanna **The Meagher Family**
21 MISS ANTIPOVA, 9, b m Pasternak—Herballistic **Batsford Stud Racing Club**
22 MOZZARO (IRE), 6, b g Morozov (USA)—Baraza (IRE) **Owners for Owners Mozzaro**
23 MR MAFIA (IRE), 12, b g Zerpour (IRE)—Wizzy (IRE) **Mr Peter Boggis**
24 PINNACLE PEAK, 6, b g Passing Glance—Giovanna **M. Boothright**
25 REVE, 7, b g Nathaniel (IRE)—Rouge (FR) **Mr O. F. Ryan**
26 ROBSAM (IRE), 6, b g Mahler—Silver Set (IRE) **Mr M. Capp**
27 RUN A RIG, 6, ch m Black Sam Bellamy (IRE)—Somethinaboutmolly (IRE) **Mrs Z. A. E. Tindall**
28 SAMTARA, 7, b g Kayf Tara—Aunt Harriet **Mrs Y. E. Allsop, Mr R. Allsop**
29 SARASOTA STAR (IRE), 5, gr ro g Zebedee—Riviera Rose (IRE) **Mr E. J. Hughes, Mr T. Dal**
30 SOLSTICE STAR, 11, b g Kayf Tara—Clover Green (IRE) **Foxtrot Racing: Solstice Star**
31 TEN PAST MIDNIGHT, 5, b g Midnight Legend—Thornton Alice **Serendipity Syndicate 2006**
32 WITNESS PROTECTION (IRE), 8, b g Witness Box (USA)—Queen's Exit **Foxtrot Racing Witness Protection**

### THREE-YEAR-OLDS
33 BORDERLINE (IRE), b g Sans Frontieres (IRE)—Seana Ghael (IRE) **The Four Sages**
34 Br g Califet (FR)—Clondalee (IRE)
35 B g Sans Frontieres (IRE)—Killoughey Babe (IRE)

### TWO-YEAR-OLDS
36 B c 01/05 Black Sam Bellamy (IRE)—Karmest (Best of The Bests (IRE))
37 B c 30/03 Ocovango—Minoras Return (IRE) (Bob's Return (IRE))

## MR MARTIN KEIGHLEY - continued

**Racing Secretary:** Mrs Belinda Keighley, **Yard Sponsor:** Mr  Neil Lloyd FBC Manby Bowdler.

**NH Jockey:** James Best.

---

### 314  MR SHAUN KEIGHTLEY, Newmarket
Postal: Flat 1, Harraton Court Stables, Church Lane, Exning, Newmarket, Suffolk, CB8 7HF

1 **ALPINE MISTRAL (IRE)**, 4, b f Gale Force Ten—Snowtime (IRE)  **Empire State Racing Partnership**
2 **BERNARD SPIERPOINT**, 4, b g Harbour Watch (IRE)—Para Siempre  **Hever Stud Farm Ltd**
3 **CHELSEA SHOWCASE**, 4, b f Showcasing—Lunarian  **Mr S. L. Keightley**
4 **EL CONQUISTADOR (USA)**, 4, ch g Kitten's Joy (USA)—Bonita Donita (USA)  **Mrs C. C. Regalado-Gonzalez**
5 **FOX LEICESTER (IRE)**, 5, gr g Dark Angel (IRE)—Pop Art (IRE)  **D. S. Lovatt**
6 **IMAGE OF THE MOON**, 5, b m Mukhadram—Hamsat Elqamar  **Crowd Racing & R Christison**
7 **JOHN JOINER**, 9, b g Captain Gerrard (IRE)—Nigella  **Mr S. L. Keightley**
8 **LILKIAN**, 4, ch g Sepoy (AUS)—Janie Runaway (IRE)  **D. S. Lovatt**
9 **MASKED IDENTITY**, 6, b g Intello (GER)—Red Bloom  **D. S. Lovatt**
10 **MAYSON MOUNT**, 4, b g Mayson—Epernay  **Shelley Tucker & Shaun Keightley**
11 **SAHARAN SHIMMER**, 4, b g Oasis Dream—Come Touch The Sun (IRE)  **Mr C. A. Washbourn**
12 **SAN CARLOS**, 5, b h Havana Gold (IRE)—Ittasal  **Mrs C. C. Regalado-Gonzalez**
13 **SAN JUAN (IRE)**, 4, b g Tagula (IRE)—Bigasiwannabe (IRE)  **Mr S. L. Keightley**
14 **SECRATARIO (FR)**, 6, ch g Kendargent (FR)—Amoa (USA)  **D. S. Lovatt**
15 **SEPAHI**, 5, ch m Sepoy (AUS)—Katevan (IRE)  **Mrs Shelley Tucker Partnership**
16 **TAVRINA**, 5, b m New Approach (IRE)—Mizzava (IRE)  **Mrs C. C. Regalado-Gonzalez**
17 **TRIPLE DISTILLED**, 5, b g Tamayuz—So Refined (IRE)  **Derek Lovatt Colin Bacon**
18 **VOLUNTEER**, 8, b g Aqlaam—Blaenavon  **Crowd Racing Partnership**
19 **WILD FLOWER (IRE)**, 9, b m Approve (IRE)—Midsummernitedream (GER)  **Mrs Shelley Tucker Partnership**

### THREE-YEAR-OLDS
20 **ARCEUS (IRE)**, ch c Camacho—Foxtrot Pearl (IRE)  **Mr C. Bacon**
21 **CASSIOPEIA DREAM**, b f Coach House (IRE)—Nellie The Elegant  **Mr C. Bacon**
22 **EL MONTE**, b c Temple City (USA)—Eleusis  **Mrs D. M. Swinburn**
23 **MAX DILIGENCE**, b c Due Diligence (USA)—Noble Cause  **New Frontiers Ventures Limited**
24 **ORPHIUCHUS (IRE)**, b f Starspangledbanner (AUS)—Sho Girl (IRE)  **Mr C. Bacon**
25 B f Al Kazeem—Sign of Life  **Mrs D. M. Swinburn**
26 **SILKY SIXTY (IRE)**, ch f Dawn Approach (IRE)—Raw Silk (USA)  **Hever Stud Farm Ltd**
27 **SILVER NEMO (IRE)**, gr g Markaz (IRE)—Jealous Beauty (IRE)  **D. S. Lovatt**
28 **SOUND OF U A E (IRE)**, b g Champs Elysees—Sandbox Two (IRE)
29 **THOMAS DANIELL**, b g Equiano (FR)—Dark Skies (IRE)  **Mrs C. C. Regalado-Gonzalez**

### TWO-YEAR-OLDS
30 B c 28/03 Swiss Spirit—Faience (Holy Roman Emperor (IRE)) (9524)  **Hever Stud Farm Ltd**
31 Br f 21/03 Aclaim (IRE)—Nandiga (USA) (Bernardini (USA)) (800)  **Mr S. L. Keightley**

**Other Owners:** Mr C. Bacon, Mr R. Christison, Crowd Racing Partnership, Mr S. L. Keightley, D. S. Lovatt, Mr C. McKenna, Mr K. Tucker, Mrs S. M. Tucker.

## 315 MR CHRISTOPHER KELLETT, Lathom
Postal: 6 Canal Cottages, Ring O Bells Lane, Lathom, Ormskirk, Lancashire, L40 5TF
Contacts: PHONE 01704 643775 MOBILE 07966 097989
EMAIL CNKellett@outlook.com WEBSITE www.chriskellettracing.co.uk

1 BEGOODTOYOURSELF (IRE), 6, b g Getaway (GER)—Loreley (IRE) **Blythe Stables LLP**
2 BLISTERING BARNEY (IRE), 5, b g Sir Prancealot (IRE)—Eternal View (IRE) **Andy Bell & Fergus Lyons**
3 CHANCE FINALE (FR), 7, br g Blue Bresil (FR)—Ballade Nordique (FR) **Tracey Bell & Caroline Lyons**
4 CLONDAW STORM (IRE), 7, gr g September Storm (GER)—Oh So Smart (IRE) **Blythe Stables LLP**
5 DECONSO, 5, b g Dandy Man (IRE)—Tranquil Flight **Andy Bell & Fergus Lyons**
6 DORETTE (FR), 8, b m Kingsalsa (USA)—Ombrelle (FR) **Blythe Stables LLP**
7 KEEP WONDERING (IRE), 7, b g Scorpion (IRE)—Supreme Touch (IRE) **Andy Bell & Fergus Lyons**
8 KILFILUM CROSS (IRE), 10, gr g Beneficial—Singh Street (IRE) **Andy Bell & Fergus Lyons**
9 SHOWSHUTAI, 5, b g Showcasing—Sleeper **Andy Bell & Fergus Lyons**
10 SOLAR IMPULSE (FR), 11, b g Westerner—Moon Glow (FR) **Andy Bell & Fergus Lyons**
11 SOMTHINGPHENOMENAL, 4, b g Phenomena—Quite Something **Mrs J. S. Roscoe-Casey**
12 THE GRAND VISIR, 7, b g Frankel—Piping (IRE) **Andy Bell & Fergus Lyons**

Other Owners: Mr A. J. Bell, Mrs T. Bell, Blythe Stables LLP, Mrs C. Lyons, Mr F. Lyons, Fergus & Caroline Lyons.

## 316 MISS GAY KELLEWAY, Newmarket
Postal: Queen Alexandra Stables, 2 Chapel Street, Exning, Newmarket, Suffolk, CB8 7HA
Contacts: PHONE 01638 577778 MOBILE 07974 948768
EMAIL gaykellewayracing@hotmail.co.uk WEBSITE www.gaykellewayracing.com

1 ATAVIQUE, 4, b f Dubawi (IRE)—Avongrove **Ptr Ltd, A Lewis, J Moynihan, G Kelleway**
2 BOLT N BROWN, 5, b m Phoenix Reach (IRE)—Beat Seven **Logistics Terminal LLP**
3 CALM DOWN (FR), 4, b f Intello (GER)—Sydarra (IRE) **Chill Out Syndicate & Gay Kelleway**
4 CAPLA SPIRIT, 4, b g Cable Bay (IRE)—Warden Rose **Capla Developments & Partners**
5 CHOCOCO, 4, b f Phoenix Reach (IRE)—Chocolada **Winterbeck Manor Stud Ltd**
6 COSMELLI (ITY), 8, b g Mr Vegas (IRE)—Victorian Girl (GER) **M Walker, G Kelleway**
7 COUNTESS REACH, 4, b f Phoenix Reach (IRE)—Comtesse Noire (CAN) **Winterbeck Manor Stud & Partners**
8 GLOBAL HOPE (IRE), 6, b g Oasis Dream—Classic Remark (IRE) **M Walker, N Scandrett & Partners**
9 HABANERO STAR, 4, b f Mayson—Highly Spiced **Premier Thoroughbred Racing Ltd**
10 HUNTERS STEP, 5, b g Mukhadram—Step Softly **Mr J. Round**
11 INDURO DE FONTAINE (FR), 4, b g Manduro (GER)—Indian View (GER) **Shane Buy & Gay Kelleway**
12 LADY QUICKSTEP (IRE), 4, b f Sir Prancealot (IRE)—Quick Sketch (IRE) **Premier Thoroughbred R, the Glitter Ball**
13 MOVEONUP (IRE), 5, gr g Zebedee—Emma Dora (IRE) **B. C. Oakley**
14 MUKHA MAGIC, 5, b g Mukhadram—Sweet Lemon (IRE) **P Crook, J Moynihan, R Mortlock**
15 OLIVERS PURSUIT, 4, br g Pastoral Pursuits—Deep Blue Sea **G Kerr, N Scandrett, S Buy**
16 SCALE FORCE, 5, gr g Lethal Force (IRE)—Alectrona (FR) **A & Moynihan**
17 VASCO DA GAMA (FR), 4, b g Dansili—Some Spirit (IRE) **Capla Developments & G Kelleway**

### THREE-YEAR-OLDS
18 ASGOODASITGETS (IRE), b g Slade Power (IRE)—Tiger Spice **Strictly Fun Racing Club**
19 CAPLA KNIGHT (IRE), b c Sir Prancealot (IRE)—Rose Lilas **Capla Developments & G Kelleway**
20 CHOCO ICE, b c Phoenix Reach (IRE)—Chocolada **Winterbeck Manor Stud & Mr A Lewis**
21 CORDAROSA, b f Cable Bay (IRE)—Our Faye **Crook, Sawyer,Wigglesworth Kelleway**
22 GYPSY BOY (IRE), b g Showcasing—Moondust (IRE) **Mr J. D. A. Smith**
23 MONEY HONEY, b f Heeraat (IRE)—Lady O Malley (IRE) **R. Mortlock & G. Kelleway**
24 PRIDE OF QATAR (IRE), ch c Showcasing—Porthilly (FR) **Mr H. A. Almarri**
25 PRIDE OF UK, b c Starspangledbanner (AUS)—Zhanna (IRE) **Mr H. A. Almarri**
26 PROFESSOR GALANT, b f Coach House (IRE)—Calypso Music **Mr M. Wolkind**
27 SILVER BUBBLE, b gr f Mayson—Skyrider (IRE) **Fordham, Robinson, MacMahon & Kelleway**

## MISS GAY KELLEWAY - continued

### TWO-YEAR-OLDS

28 **GYPSY LADY**, ch f 27/03 Mayson—Reveille (Sakhee's Secret) (7000) **Mr J. D. A. Smith**
29 **SECRET BEAR**, ch c 10/05 Pearl Secret—Ceilidh Band (Celtic Swing) (7000) **B. C. Oakley**

**Other Owners:** Mr M. R. Brown, Mr S. Buy, Mr K. S. Chambers, Chill Out Syndicate, Mr J. B. Cohen, Miss P. F. Crook, Mrs K. M. Deveney, Mr S. J. Fordham, Miss G. M. Kelleway, Mr G. Kerr, Mr A. Lewis, Miss V. Macmahon, Mr R. Mortlock, Mr J. Moynihan, Mr R. A. Newbold, A. B. Parr, Premier Thoroughbred Racing Ltd, Mr W. A. Robinson, Mr J. Sawyer, Mr N. S. Scandrett, Mr M. J. Short, Mr P. Stubbins, The Glitter Ball Syndicate, Mr M. A. Walker, Mr R. Wigglesworth, Winterbeck Manor Stud Ltd, Mr M. Wolkind.

**Assistant Trainer:** Anne-Sophie Crombez, **Head Girl:** Liz Mullin.

---

**317** **MRS STEF KENIRY, Middleham**
Postal: **Barry Keniry Racing, Warwick Lodge, North Road, Middleham, North Yorkshire, DL8 4PB**

1 **BLOW BY BLOW (IRE)**, 10, ch g Robin des Champs (FR)—Shean Rose (IRE) **The Strattonites**
2 **DIONYSIS (FR)**, 8, ch g Lucarno (USA)—Oasice (FR) **Mr B. Lapham**
3 **FARADAY EFFECT (IRE)**, 8, b g Rip Van Winkle (IRE)—Faraday Light (IRE) **Mrs J. Snailum**
4 **HADEED**, 4, ch g Shamardal (USA)—Shurfah (IRE) **Mr B. Lapham & J Souster**
5 **HERMANUS (IRE)**, 9, ch m Golan (IRE)—Almost Trumps **Mrs S. J. Keniry**
6 **LA CACHEMIRA**, 5, b m Joshua Tree (IRE)—La Cabra (GER)
7 **LIVA (IRE)**, 6, ch g Champs Elysees—Resistance Heroine **Mr D. R. Gilbert**
8 **LOVE YOUR WORK (IRE)**, 5, ch g Helmet (AUS)—Little Italy (USA) **Flash Figs Racing**
9 **LUCARNIP**, 6, b g Lucarno (USA)—Millie N Aire **Mrs J. Snailum**
10 **MACS BLESSINGS (IRE)**, 5, b g Society Rock (IRE)—Lear's Crown (USA) **Mrs S. J. Keniry**
11 **MAMDOOD (IRE)**, 7, gr g Clodovil (IRE)—Fact **Mrs S. J. Keniry**
12 **OLD SALT (IRE)**, 9, b g Craigsteel—Andrea Gale (IRE) **Mrs J. Keys**
13 **RAJAPUR**, 8, gr ro g Dalakhani (IRE)—A Beautiful Mind (GER) **Mr B. Lapham**
14 **RED CARAVEL (IRE)**, 7, b g Henrythenavigator (USA)—Red Fantasy (IRE) **Mrs J. Snailum**
15 5, B m Kayf Tara—Shuil Gealach (IRE) **Mrs J. Snailum**
16 **SPIRIT OF SARWAN (IRE)**, 7, b g Elzaam (AUS)—Hidden Heart (USA) **Mrs S. J. Keniry**
17 **STRICT ORDER**, 4, b f War Command (USA)—Lady Chaparral **Mrs S. J. Keniry**
18 **WAR WHISPER (IRE)**, 8, b g Royal Applause—Featherweight (IRE) **The Marina Partnership**

### THREE-YEAR-OLDS

19 **SHAWSHANK**, b g Lethal Force (IRE)—Break Free **Flash Figs Racing**

**Other Owners:** Mr G. Hardy, Mr B. Lapham, Mr P. D. Simms, Miss S. M. Smith, Mr J. Souster.

---

**318** **MR NICK KENT, Brigg**
Postal: **Newstead House, Newstead Priory, Cadney Road, Brigg, Lincolnshire, DN20 9HP**
Contacts: **PHONE 01652 650628 MOBILE 07710 644428**
EMAIL nick@nickkent.co.uk WEBSITE www.nickkent.co.uk

1 **BALLYCALLAN FAME (IRE)**, 6, b m Fame And Glory—Sallie's Secret (IRE) **Mrs Wendy Wesley, Mr Nick Kent**
2 **BENE REGINA (IRE)**, 9, b m Beneficial—Lareine d'Anjou (FR) **BDS Pointers**
3 **CATLIN**, 6, b m Bollin Eric—Linen Line **Cynthia Commons, Nick Kent**
4 **DEXCITE (FR)**, 10, b m g Authorized (IRE)—Belle Alicia (FR) **Ms V. M. Cottingham**
5 **ERNE RIVER (IRE)**, 6, b g Califet (FR)—Lusty Beg (IRE) **Crossed Fingers Partnership**
6 **GILBERTINA**, 4, b f Universal (IRE)—Saaboog **Mrs M. E. Kent**

## MR NICK KENT - continued

7 **JUST TOTTIE**, 5, b m Fair Mix (IRE)—Just Smokie  **Mr J. N. Kent**
8 **KEEL OVER**, 10, b g Gamut (IRE)—Kayf Keel  **Miss L. M. Haywood**
9 4, B f Soldier of Fortune (IRE)—Kim Fontenail (FR)
10 4, B c Multiplex—Linen Line  **Mr J. N. Kent**
11 **MICK MAESTRO (FR)**, 8, b br g Air Chief Marshal (IRE)—Mick Maya (FR)  **Crossed Fingers Partnership**
12 **PICKNICK PARK**, 9, b g Sulamani (IRE)—Eva's Edge (IRE)  **Mr Andy Parkin, Nick Kent**
13 **REVEREND JACOBS**, 7, b g Nathaniel—Light Impact (IRE)  **Newstead Priory Racing Club**
14 **RUPERTS REFLECTION**, 6, ch g Midnight Legend—Twoy's Reflection  **Team Tom**
15 **SAYAR (IRE)**, 8, b g Azamour (IRE)—Seraya (FR)  **Nick Kent Racing Club II**
16 **WHO'S IN THE BOX (IRE)**, 7, b g Witness Box (USA)—See The Clouds  **Mr Andy Parkin, Nick Kent**

### THREE-YEAR-OLDS

17 B g Gentlewave (IRE)—Celtic Sixpence (IRE)
18 B f Gentlewave (IRE)—Saaboog

**Other Owners:** Mr R. A. Carter, Miss C. Commons, Mrs S. A. Daubney, Mr D. M. Evans, Mr J. M. Fawbert, Mr J. N. Kent, Mr A. R. P. Parkin, Mrs W. M. Wesley, Mr N. Williamson.

**Assistant Trainer:** Mrs Jane Kent.

**NH Jockey:** Adam Wedge.

---

**319** **MR TERRY KENT, Newmarket**
Postal: 16 Newmarket Road, Fordham, Ely, Cambridgeshire, CB7 5LL
Contacts: PHONE 07880 234291
EMAIL terry.kent966@btinternet.com

1 **BROADWAY LAD (USA)**, 4, b g The Factor (USA)—Northern Passion (CAN)  **Guaymas**
2 **GRAPHITE (FR)**, 7, gr g Shamardal (USA)—Fairly Grey (FR)  **Mr T. Kent**
3 **ROBERT FROST (USA)**, 4, ch g Munnings (USA)—Sorenstam (USA)  **Guaymas**
4 **SUPER DEN**, 4, b g Dutch Art—Loch Jipp (USA)  **Guaymas**
5 **TIE A YELLOWRIBBON**, 5, gr m Poet's Voice—Silver Games (IRE)  **Garrad Brothers Equine**

### THREE-YEAR-OLDS

6 **AMASOVA**, ch f Pivotal—Russian Heroine  **Garrad Brothers Equine**
7 **ATASER**, b c Sayif (IRE)—Psychic's Dream  **Guaymas**
8 B f Territories (IRE)—Crystal High  **Mr S. D. Bradley**
9 **DIFFIDENT SPIRIT**, b g Sayif (IRE)—Abbotsfield (IRE)  **Guaymas**
10 B f Nathaniel (IRE)—Haiti Dancer
11 **HEMMSA (IRE)**, b f Mehmas (IRE)—Hope And Faith (IRE)  **Elpis Syndicate**
12 Br c Awtaad (IRE)—Holda (IRE)  **Mr T. Kent**
13 **MR MARVLOS (IRE)**, b c Vadamos (FR)—Petite Boulangere (IRE)  **Mr S. Decani**
14 **ONE MORE SU**, b f Harzand (IRE)—Acampe  **Guaymas**
15 B f Pearl Secret—Yali (IRE)  **Mr T. Kent**

### TWO-YEAR-OLDS

16 B f 18/04 Cable Bay (IRE)—Beauty Within (Makfi) (6190)  **Mr T. Kent**
17 B c 08/02 Hot Streak (IRE)—Bybrook (Dubawi (IRE))  **Mr I. Butt**
18 B f 16/02 Havana Gold (IRE)—Calm Attitude (IRE) (Dutch Art)  **Mr T. Kent**
19 Ch f 25/04 Zoffany (IRE)—Crosstalk (IRE) (Cape Cross (IRE)) (15000)  **Mr I. Butt**
20 B c 01/04 Territories (IRE)—Indian Story (IRE) (Indian Ridge)
21 Ch c 27/03 Equiano (FR)—Laminka (Intikhab (USA))
22 B c 14/04 Stimulation (IRE)—Thicket (Wolfhound (USA)) (2500)  **Mr T. Kent**
23 B c 03/03 Adaay (IRE)—Ziefhd (Haafhd) (9000)  **Mr T. Kent**

## 320 MR LEONARD KERR, Irvine
Postal: **Annick Lodge, Irvine, Ayrshire, KA11 2AN**

1 MISTERMOONBOY (IRE), 7, ch g Mister Fotis (USA)—Sister Moon (IRE)  **Mr A Kerr Mr L Kerr**
2 SWORD OF FATE (IRE), 8, b g Beneficial—Beann Ard (IRE)  **Mr A Kerr Mr L Kerr**

**Other Owners:** Mr A. M. Kerr, Mr L. B. Kerr.

## 321 MR ALAN KING, Barbury Castle
Postal: **Barbury Castle Stables, Wroughton, Wiltshire, SN4 0QZ**
Contacts: **PHONE 01793 815009 MOBILE 07973 461233 FAX 01793 845080**
**EMAIL alan@alanking.biz WEBSITE www.alankingracing.co.uk**

1 ALARGEDRAM (IRE), 4, ch g Lope de Vega (IRE)—Myrica  **McNeill Family & Niall Farrell**
2 AZZERTI (FR), 9, b g Voix du Nord (FR)—Zalagarry (FR)  **McNeill Family and Prodec Networks Ltd**
3 BALLYWOOD (FR), 7, b g Ballingarry (IRE)—Miss Hollywood (FR)  **Highclere Thoroughbred Racing -Ballywood**
4 BERINGER, 6, b g Sea The Stars (IRE)—Edaraat (USA)  **L Field, B Cognet, N Farrell, J Spack**
5 BIG CHIEF BENNY (IRE), 10, ch g Beneficial—Be Airlie (IRE)  **Oitavos Partnership**
6 BLACKO (FR), 5, gr g Balko (FR)—Ascella (FR)  **Apple Tree Stud**
7 BOARD OF TRADE, 10, ch g Black Sam Bellamy (IRE)—Realms of Gold (USA)  **Ian Payne & Kim Franklin**
8 BURREN WALK, 6, ch m Lucarno (USA)—Persian Walk (FR)  **Mr D. J. Barry**
9 CANELO (IRE), 8, ch g Mahler—Nobody's Darling (IRE)  **Mr J. P. McManus**
10 CATBIRD SEAT (IRE), 4, b g Kingston Hill—Celestial Dream (IRE)  **D Gilbert, M Lawrence, A Bruce**
11 CHICAGO GUY, 5, ch h Cityscape—Hail Shower (IRE)  **Hunscote Stud Limited**
12 CHINESE WHISPERER (FR), 4, b g Poet's Voice—Shanghai Noon (FR)  **Barbury Lions 5**
13 CHOSEN PATH (IRE), 8, b g Well Chosen—Karsulu (IRE)  **McNeill Family and Prodec Networks Ltd**
14 COEUR DE LION, 8, b g Pour Moi (IRE)—Hora  **The Barbury Boys**
15 COLOURS OF MY LIFE (IRE), 6, b m Arcadio—Lough Roe Lady (IRE)  **Mr C. B. J. Dingwall**
16 COOL STONE, 5, b m Kayf Tara—Stoney Path  **Mrs Sue Welch & Alan King**
17 CRYSTAL MOON (IRE), 4, ch g Shirocco (GER)—Liscannor (IRE)  **Mrs J. A. Watts**
18 DAL HORRISGLE, 5, b g Nathaniel (IRE)—Dalvina  **St Albans Bloodstock Limited**
19 DANCE WITH FIRE, 5, ch g Norse Dancer (IRE)—Ruby Kew (IRE)  **Mrs S. C. Welch**
20 DANKING, 4, b g Dansili—Time Saved  **Niall Farrell & Ian Dodds-smith**
21 DEYRANN DE CARJAC (FR), 8, b g Balko (FR)—Queyrann (FR)  **Mr J. A. Law**
22 DIDONATO (IRE), 6, b m Milan—Dream Lass (IRE)  **Mr S. Smith**
23 DINGO DOLLAR (IRE), 9, ch g Golden Lariat (USA)—
Social Society (IRE)  **M Warren J Holmes R Kidner & J Wright**
24 DINO VELVET (FR), 8, b g Naaqoos—Matgil (FR)  **McNeill Family & Niall Farrell**
25 DUKE OF CONDICOTE, 4, b g No Nay Never (USA)—Duchess of Gazeley (IRE)  **Jamie Magee, A Bromley & A King**
26 EDWARDSTONE, 7, b g Kayf Tara—Nothingtoloose (IRE)  **Robert Abrey & Ian Thurtle**
27 ES PERFECTO (IRE), 6, ch g Shirocco (GER)—Shadow Dearg (IRE)  **Mrs E. A. Prowting**
28 ESCAPABILITY (IRE), 6, b g Excelebration (IRE)—Brief Escapade (IRE)  **S Love, H & C Barrett & D Gibbon**
29 EYES RIGHT, 6, b m Passing Glance—Call Me A Star  **Richardson, Metcalfe S Hardman**
30 4, B c Yeats (IRE)—Feathard Lady (IRE)
31 FIBONACCI, 7, ch g Galileo (IRE)—Tereschenko (USA)  **Mrs E. A. Prowting**
32 FIDUX (FR), 8, b g Fine Grain (JPN)—Folle Tempete (FR)  **AXOM LXVIII**
33 FINEST VIEW, 4, b f Passing Glance—Call Me A Legend  **Pitchall Stud Partnership**
34 FORGETTHESMALLTALK (IRE), 9, b g Flemensfirth (USA)—
Mylane du Charmil (FR)  **Tim Leadbeater & Barry Winfield**
35 FRATERNEL (FR), 6, b g Kap Rock (FR)—Valence (FR)  **Mr T. D. J. Syder**
36 GAVI DI GAVI (IRE), 6, b g Camacho—Blossom Deary (IRE)  **Alan King & Niall Farrell**
37 4, B g Fame And Glory—Glory Days (GER)  **Mr J. P. McManus**
38 GOOD MAN PAT (IRE), 8, b g Gold Well—Basically Supreme (IRE)  **Mr D. J. S. Sewell**
39 GREENROCK ABBEY (IRE), 5, ch g El Salvador (IRE)—Aos Dana (IRE)  **Million in Mind Partnership**
40 GRISBI DE BERCE (FR), 5, b g Tin Horse (IRE)—Volupia de Berce (FR)  **Charles Dingwall & Alan King**
41 GROSVENOR COURT, 5, b g Shirocco (GER)—Hurricane Milly (IRE)  **John J. Murray & Niall Farrell**

## MR ALAN KING - continued

42 **HARAMBE**, 8, br g Malinas (GER)—Crystal Princess (IRE) **Niall Farrell & Friends**
43 **HARROWBY**, 5, b g Gentlewave (IRE)—Cutielilou (FR) **The Harrowby Partnership**
44 **HASEEFAH**, 4, b f Teofilo (IRE)—Halaqa (IRE) **Michael Rembaum & Michael Tuckey**
45 **HAZARD COLLONGES (FR)**, 4, b g Coastal Path—Prouesse Collonges (FR) **Alan King**
46 **HEART OF A LION (IRE)**, 6, b g Yeats (IRE)—Lady Secret (FR) **Mr J. P. McManus**
47 **HER INDOORS (IRE)**, 4, b f Raven's Pass (USA)—Superfonic (FR) **McNeill Family & Niall Farrell**
48 **HOSTILE**, 7, ch g Malinas (GER)—Skew **Ian Wheeler & Alan King**
49 **HOTTER THAN HELL (FR)**, 7, ch m No Risk At All (FR)—Ombrelle (FR) **The Devil's Advocates**
50 **INCHICORE (IRE)**, 4, b f Galileo (IRE)—Luas Line (IRE) **Apple Tree Stud**
51 **ISOLATE (FR)**, 5, b g Maxios—Unaided **Noel Fehily Racing - Isolate**
52 **JABOTICABA (FR)**, 7, ch g Muhtathir—Janiceinwonderland (FR) **Owners Group 025**
53 **JAY BEE WHY (IRE)**, 6, b g Yeats (IRE)—Lady Bernie (IRE) **David J S Sewell & Tim Leadbeater**
54 **JERMINNIE GREEN (IRE)**, 7, b m Jeremy (USA)—Minnie Maguire (IRE) **Coupland, Farrell A King**
55 **JUST IN TIME**, 7, b g Exceleration (USA)—Flying Finish (FR) **HP Racing Just In Time**
56 **KARASTANI**, 5, gr m Dalakhani (IRE)—Karasta (IRE) **Mr M. J. Rembaum**
57 **KOZIER (GER)**, 7, ch g Muhtathir—Kasumi (GER) **Loose Cannon Racing**
58 6, Br g Great Pretender (IRE)—L'Aventure (FR) **Mr C. J. Harriman**
59 **LABEL DES OBEAUX (FR)**, 10, b g Saddler Maker (IRE)—La Bessiere (FR) **David Sewell & Terry Warner**
60 **LEXINGTON LAW (IRE)**, 8, b g Lawman (FR)—Tus Nua (IRE) **Alan King**
61 **LORD NEIDIN**, 4, br g Outstrip—Cosmea **Kingston Stud**
62 **LOVERBOY (FR)**, 10, b g Winged Love (IRE)—Tartan Belle **Mrs J. S. S. Page**
63 **LUNAR BOUNTY**, 4, b f Sea The Moon (GER)—The Pirate's Queen (IRE) **Apple Tree Stud**
64 **MADIBA PASSION (FR)**, 7, b g Al Namix (FR)—Birsheba (FR) **Alan King**
65 **MAHLERMADE (IRE)**, 8, ch g Mahler—Double Concerto (IRE) **The Lesser Lights**
66 **MAID ON THE MOON**, 4, b f Pether's Moon (IRE)—Handmaid **The Burling Family Ltd**
67 **MAJOR DUNDEE (IRE)**, 6, b g Scorpion (IRE)—Be My Granny **Mr T. J. Hemmings**
68 **MAROOCHI**, 4, b f Presenting—Makadamia **Hot To Trot Racing & Robert Waley-cohen**
69 **MASACCIO (IRE)**, 4, gr g Mastercraftsman (IRE)—Ange Bleu (USA) **McNeill Family & Niall Farrell**
70 4, Ch g Fuisse (FR)—Melodie Valtat (FR) **Mr & Mrs C. Harris**
71 **MESSIRE DES OBEAUX (FR)**, 9, b g Saddler Maker (IRE)—

Madame Lys (FR) **Mr Simon Munir & Mr Isaac Souede**
72 **METHUSALAR (IRE)**, 5, b g Sholokhov (IRE)—Pixie Dust (IRE) **Top Brass Partnership**
73 **MIDNIGHT GINGER**, 5, ch m Midnight Legend—Calamintha **Pitchall Stud Partnership**
74 **MIDNIGHT GLANCE**, 6, b g Passing Glance—Magical Legend **R. H. Kerswell**
75 **MIDNIGHTREFERENDUM**, 8, b m Midnight Legend—Forget The Ref (IRE) **Robert Abrey & Ian Thurtle**
76 **MIDNIGHTS LEGACY**, 4, b c Midnight Legend—Giving **Pitchall Stud Partnership**
77 **MIDNIGHTS' GIFT**, 5, gr m Midnight Legend—Giving **Pitchall Stud Partnership**
78 **MOONAMACAROONA**, 5, b m Flemensfirth (USA)—Forever Present (IRE) **Netherfield House Stud**
79 **MR PUMBLECHOOK**, 7, b g Midnight Legend—Definitely Pip (IRE) **Mr D. J. S. Sewell**
80 **NEBUCHADNEZZAR (FR)**, 6, b g Planteur (IRE)—Trexana **Top Brass 2**
81 **NINA THE TERRIER (IRE)**, 5, b m Milan—Shees A Dante (IRE) **Mr C. B. J. Dingwall**
82 **NOBBY**, 7, b g Authorized (IRE)—Magic Music (IRE) **R. Bailey**
83 **NOTACHANCE (IRE)**, 7, b g Mahler—Ballybrowney Hall (IRE) **David J S Sewell & Tim Leadbeater**
84 **ON TO VICTORY**, 7, b g Rock of Gibraltar (IRE)—Clouds of Magellan (USA) **HP Racing On To Victory**
85 **OUTONPATROL (IRE)**, 7, gr m Stowaway—Burnt Oil Babe (IRE) **McNeill Family & Niall Farrell**
86 **PEACE RIVER**, 5, b g Yeats (IRE)—Takotna (IRE) **Ian Payne & Kim Franklin**
87 **PECKINPAH (IRE)**, 5, ch g Excelebration (IRE)—Melodrama (IRE) **Coupland, Gemmell, Hues & Sullivan**
88 **PERFECT HARMONY (IRE)**, 9, b g Definite Article—Brandam Supreme (IRE) **Mrs E. A. Prowting**
89 **POTTERMAN**, 8, b g Sulamani (IRE)—Polly Potter **James and Jean Potter Ltd**
90 **PRESENTING PETE (IRE)**, 4, b g Presenting—Ciandarragh (IRE) **Mr & Mrs C. Harris**
91 **PUMPKIN'S PRIDE**, 5, b g Malinas (GER)—Peel Me A Grape **Mrs E. A. Prowting**
92 **RAINBOW DREAMER**, 8, b g Aqlaam—Zamhrear **The Maple Street Partnership**
93 **RAYMOND TUSK (IRE)**, 6, b h High Chaparral (IRE)—

Dancing Shoes (IRE) **Middleham Park Racing XXXI & K Sohi**
94 **REBEL ROYAL (IRE)**, 8, b g Getaway (IRE)—Molly Duffy (IRE) **Jerry Wright,Martin Walker & Tony Hughes**
95 **RIDEAU CANAL (IRE)**, 6, b g Robin des Champs (FR)—Miss Vinnie (IRE) **Farrell Field Sigler Lawson**
96 **ROSCOE TARA**, 6, b g Kayf Tara—Aunt Harriet **Mr & Mrs R. Allsop**
97 **ROYAL PRETENDER (FR)**, 7, b g Great Pretender (IRE)—Robinia Directa (GER) **Mrs C. Skan**
98 **SAN RUMOLDO**, 6, ch g Malinas (GER)—Ancora (IRE) **Mr J. P. McManus**
99 **SANTON (IRE)**, 6, b g Scorpion (IRE)—Nutmeg Tune (IRE) **Mr T. J. Hemmings**

## MR ALAN KING - continued

100 **SCARLET DRAGON**, 8, b g Sir Percy—Welsh Angel  **HP Racing Scarlet Dragon**
101 **SCEAU ROYAL (FR)**, 9, b g Doctor Dino (FR)—Sandside (FR)  **Mr Simon Munir & Mr Isaac Souede**
102 **SENIOR CITIZEN**, 8, b g Tobougg (IRE)—Mothers Help  **McNeill Family Ltd**
103 **SHESHOON SONNY (FR)**, 6, b g Youmzain (IRE)—Minnie's Mystery (FR)  **Mr N. Farrell**
104 **SMITH'S BAY**, 8, b g Midnight Legend—Takotna (IRE)  **Ian Payne & Kim Franklin**
105 **SON OF RED (IRE)**, 4, b g French Navy—Tarziyma (IRE)  **Ian Gosden & Richard House**
106 **SULA ISLAND**, 7, ch m Sulamani (IRE)—Cosmea  **Alan King**
107 **TALKISCHEAP (IRE)**, 9, b g Getaway (GER)—Carrigmoorna Oak (IRE)  **Mr C. B. J. Dingwall**
108 **TARTAN FLYER (FR)**, 5, b m Winged Love (IRE)—Tartan Belle  **Mrs J. S. S. Page**
109 **TERRAFIRMA LADY (IRE)**, 6, b m Court Cave (IRE)—Didn't You Know (FR)  **WKH (Hinksey Lane) Ltd**
110 **THANIELLE (FR)**, 4, b f Nathaniel (IRE)—Tingling (USA)  **Mrs E. C. Roberts**
111 **THE CINCINNATI KID (FR)**, 4, b c Charm Spirit (IRE)—Tocopilla (FR)  **Fanning, Griffith, Haddock**
112 **THE DEVILS DROP (IRE)**, 8, b g Court Cave (IRE)—Concernforkillen (IRE)  **Mr D. M. Mason**
113 **THE GLANCING QUEEN (IRE)**, 7, b m Jeremy (USA)—Glancing (IRE)  **Dingwall, Farrell, Hornsey & Murray**
114 **THE KICKING QUEEN (IRE)**, 5, b m Beat Hollow—Shivermetimber (IRE)  **Mr & Mrs C. Harris**
115 **THE OLYMPIAN (IRE)**, 5, ch g Olympic Glory (IRE)—Basira (FR)  **Mr J. P. McManus**
116 **THE TOURARD MAN (IRE)**, 15, b g Shantou (USA)—Small Iron  **Mr & Mrs F Bell,N Farrell, A Marsh**
117 **THE UNIT (IRE)**, 10, b g Gold Well—Sovana (FR)  **International Plywood (Importers) Ltd**
118 **TREMWEDGE**, 5, b g Foxwedge (AUS)—Tremelo Rouble (IRE)  **Ljp Racing**
119 **TRITONIC**, 4, ch g Sea The Moon (GER)—Selenography  **McNeill Family & Mr Ian Dale**
120 **TRUESHAN (FR)**, 5, b g Planteur (IRE)—Shao Line (FR)  **Barbury Lions 5**
121 **TRUST THE DREAMS**, 5, b g Farhh—River of Silence (IRE)  **Mrs P J Makin & J P Carrington**
122 **VALDEZ**, 14, ch g Doyen (IRE)—Skew  **Riverdee Stable**
123 **VALLERES (FR)**, 6, b g Coastal Path—Duchesse Pierji (FR)  **Mr Simon Munir & Mr Isaac Souede**
124 **WAR CHIEF**, 7, ch g Aqlaam—My Colleen (USA)  **Andrews Farrell King McNeill Sullivan**
125 **WHO DARES WINS (IRE)**, 9, b g Jeremy (USA)—Savignano  **HP Racing Who Dares Wins**
126 **WILLIAM H BONNEY**, 10, b g Midnight Legend—Calamintha  **Mr & Mrs R. Scott**
127 **WYNN HOUSE**, 6, ch m Presenting—Glorious Twelfth (IRE)  **Mr J. R. D. Anton**
128 **Y FYN DUW A FYDD**, 6, b m Nathaniel (IRE)—Dignify (IRE)  **R. Mathew**

### THREE-YEAR-OLDS
129 **DICKENS (IRE)**, b g Excelebration (IRE)—Open Book  **McNeill Family & Niall Farrell**
130 **DROMQUINNA**, ch f Mukhadram—Cosmea  **Kingston Stud**
131 **FOREVER WILLIAM**, ch g Sea The Moon (GER)—Archina (IRE)  **The Barbury Lions 6**
132 **GLIDE DOWN (USA)**, b g Point of Entry (USA)—On A Cloud (USA)  **James Wigan & Alan King**
133 **KALMA**, b f Mukhadram—Peters Spirit (IRE)  **Elysees Partnership**
134 **LETMELIVEMYLIFE**, b c Oasis Dream—Itiqad  **Qatar Racing & Ms L Judah**
135 **LUNAR SHADOW**, b f Sea The Moon (GER)—The Pirate's Queen (IRE)  **Apple Tree Stud**
136 **NO RECOLLECTION**, br c Dansili—Talawat  **M. Kerr-Dineen**
137 **OCEANLINE (IRE)**, b g Adaay—Ocean Bluff (IRE)  **Mainline Racing**
138 **OUT OF REASON**, ch g Outstrip—Perception (IRE)  **Nigel Bunter & David Anderson**
139 **PAINLESS POTTER (IRE)**, b g Camacho—Wider World (IRE)  **Mr R. Gilbert**
140 **QUINTESSA**, b f Iffraaj—Dolcetto (IRE)  **Field, Sigler A Murphy**
141 **RAFIKI (FR)**, b g The Last Lion (IRE)—Adalawa (IRE)  **Alan King & Niall Farrell**
142 **SONNING (IRE)**, gr g The Gurkha (IRE)—Moon Empress (FR)  **McNeill Family & Patrick&scott Bryceland**
143 **THE HOOD (IRE)**, b g Invincible Spirit (IRE)—Reclamation (IRE)  **Mr J. A. Law**
144 **TINCHOO**, b f Adaay (IRE)—Tinshu (IRE)  **Llewellyn,Runeckles**
145 **TWILIGHT TWIST**, b g Twilight Son—Fiftyshadesofpink (IRE)  **Magee Bickerton Monaghan Farrell & King**
146 **WHO CARES WINS (IRE)**, b f Hallowed Crown (AUS)—Savignano  **Windmill Racing III**
147 **WURLITZER**, b c Adaay (IRE)—Olympic Medal  **Owners Group 067**

### TWO-YEAR-OLDS
148 **ALHABOR**, b c 04/02 Intello (GER)—Eternally (Dutch Art) (95000)  **M. Kerr-Dineen**
149 B c 26/04 Churchill (IRE)—Mill Point (Champs Elysees)  **Mr D. J. Barry**
150 **TUDDENHAM GREEN**, b c c 17/03 Nathaniel (IRE)—
                Social Media (New Approach (IRE)) (24000)  **Munir, Souede, Levitt, Bromley & King**

**Other Owners:** Mr R. Abrey, Mr R. Allsop, Mrs Y. E. Allsop, Mrs D. J. Anderson, Mrs P. Andrews, Mr C. Barrett, Mrs H. A. Barrett, Mr F. D. Bell, Mrs H. L. Bell, Mr D. Bickerton, A. R. Bromley, Mr A. Bruce, Mr P. Bryceland, Mr S. Bryceland, Mr N. S. G. Bunter,

## MR ALAN KING - continued

Miss C. Burke, Mr J. P. Carrington, Mr B. R. Cognet, Mr A. P. Coupland, Mr W. I. C. Dale, Mr C. B. J. Dingwall, Mr I. Dodds-Smith, Mr O. Fanning, Mr N. Farrell, Mrs L. H. Field, Miss K. M. Franklin, Mr A. Gemmell, D. H. Gibbon, Mr D. R. Gilbert, Mr I. F. Gosden, Mr N. Griffith, Mrs H. M. Haddock, Mrs S. Hardman, Mrs C. A. Harris, Mr C. I. K. Harris, Mr D. F. Hill, J. Holmes, J. Hornsey, Mr R. S. Hoskins, Hot To Trot Jumping, Mr R. House, Mr D. Hues, Mr A. P. Hughes, Ms L. Judah, Mr R. A. Kidner, Alan King, Mr M. Lawrence, Mr M. S. Lawson, Mr E. T. D. Leadbeater, Exors of the Late W. P. Ledward, Mr R. M. Levitt, S. Love, Mr J. Magee, Mrs P. J. Makin, Mr A. R. W. Marsh, McNeill Family Ltd, Mrs S. Metcalfe, Mr J. Monaghan, S. E. Munir, H. A. Murphy, Mr J. J. Murray, Mr P. Nolan, Mr T. Nolan, Mr I. T. Payne, Prodec Networks Ltd, Qatar Racing Limited, Mr M. J. Rembaum, Mrs S. Richardson, Mr S. J. Rogers, Mr D. J. S. Sewell, Mr J. Sigler, Mr I. Souede, Mrs J. A. Spack, Mr R. T. Sullivan, Mr A. L. Tappin, Mr I. R. Thurtle, Mr J. Tuckey, Mr R. B. Waley-Cohen, Mr M. S. Walker, J. T. Warner, Mr M. K. Warren, Mrs S. C. Welch, Mr I. T. Wheeler, J. Wigan, Mrs L. J. Williams, B. Winfield, J. Wright.

**Assistant Trainer:** Dan Horsford, **Pupil Assistant:** Robin Smith, **Yard Sponsor:** HARE.

**NH Jockey:** Tom Bellamy, Tom Cannon. **Conditional Jockey:** Max Browne, Alexander Thorne. **Apprentice Jockey:** Georgia King.

---

**322** **MR NEIL KING, Marlborough**
Postal: Upper Herdswick Farm, Burderop, Wroughton, Swindon, Wiltshire, SN4 0QH
Contacts: PHONE 01793 845011 MOBILE 07880 702325 FAX 01793 845011
EMAIL neil@neil-king.co.uk WEBSITE www.neil-king.co.uk

1 AIDE MEMOIRE (IRE), 5, b m Rip Van Winkle (IRE)—Bessichka **The Ridgeway Racing For Fun Partnership**
2 ARRESSVEEPEE (FR), 5, bl g Way of Light (USA)—Treasure Rock (FR) **Mr A. L. Cohen**
3 BALAGAN, 6, b g Great Pretender (IRE)—Lovely Origny (FR) **Mr A. L. Cohen**
4 BALLYHAWKISH, 5, b g Kayf Tara—Massannie (IRE) **Ken Lawrence & Roy Mousley**
5 BIG MEADOW (IRE), 10, br g Marienbard (IRE)—Lakyle Lady (IRE) **The Ridgeway Racing For Fun Partnership**
6 BOULTING FOR GLORY (IRE), 6, b g Fame And Glory—Westgrove Berry (IRE) **Mr C. Boultbee-Brooks**
7 BRANDON CASTLE, 9, b g Dylan Thomas (IRE)—Chelsey Jayne (IRE) **Mr I. A. Low & Mr J. S. English**
8 CANYON CITY, 8, b g Authorized (IRE)—Colorado Dawn **A Whyte, J Bone, D Nott & B Smith**
9 CHENG GONG, 5, b g Archipenko (USA)—Kinetica **Three Kingdoms Racing**
10 CUBSWIN (IRE), 7, b m Zamindar (USA)—Moonlight Rhapsody (IRE) **Mr D Caldwell & Mr K Lawrence**
11 DANCING DORIS, 6, b m Malinas (GER)—Peggies Run **Mr P. M. H. Beadles**
12 DANEHILL KODIAC (IRE), 8, b g Kodiac—Meadow **Davies, Smith, Carr, Brown, Govier**
13 FFORBIDDEN LOVE, 7, b m Fastnet Rock (AUS)—Trinkala (USA) **Mr D. S. Lee**
14 FUNWAY MONARCH (IRE), 8, b g Imperial Monarch (IRE)—Mount Radhwa (IRE) **Mr R. N. Bothway**
15 GAME IN THE PARK (FR), 8, b g Walk In The Park (IRE)—Learning Game (USA) **N. King**
16 GATEWAY TO EUROPE, 7, b g Trans Island—Polly Doodle **A Whyte, K Loads & G Stevenson**
17 GIVE ME A CUDDLE (IRE), 5, b g Court Cave (IRE)—Social Society (IRE) **Mr A. L. Cohen**
18 I HOPE STAR (IRE), 5, b g Casamento (IRE)—Bint Nayef (IRE) **Sal's Pals**
19 IROLIN JACK, 6, b g Bollin Eric—Aoninch **Milsom Baker Racing & Royle**
20 KENYAN COWBOY (IRE), 5, b g Sholokhov (IRE)—Joleen (IRE) **Mrs C. Kendrick**
21 LIL ROCKERFELLER (USA), 10, ch g Hard Spun (USA)—Layounne (USA) **Davies Smith Govier & Brown**
22 MALINA JAMILA, 5, b m Malinas (GER)—Haveyoubeen (IRE) **Maundrell, Sawyer & Andrews**
23 MYPLACEATMIDNIGHT, 9, b g Midnight Legend—Zahra's Place **Mrs H. M. Buckle**
24 NACHTSTERN (GER), 4, ch g Lord of England (GER)—Navajo Queen (GER) **A Whyte & T Messom**
25 NEARLY PERFECT, 7, b g Malinas (GER)—The Lyme Volunteer (IRE) **Mr P. M. H. Beadles**
26 NORDANO (GER), 5, ch g Jukebox Jury (IRE)—Navajo Queen (GER) **A Whyte, T Messom & D Nott**
27 OH LAND ABLOOM (IRE), 11, b g King's Theatre (IRE)—Talinas Rose (IRE) **Milsom Baker Racing**
28 ONEMOREFORTHEROAD, 6, b g Yorgunnabelucky (USA)—Vinomore **Rupert Dubai Racing**
29 PERFECT MYTH, 7, b m Midnight Legend—Perfect Silence **R. J. Vines**
30 PRINCETON ROYALE (IRE), 12, br g Royal Anthem (USA)—Shelikesitstraight (IRE) **Peter Beadles, Roy Clarke**
31 REMEMBER THE MAN (IRE), 8, b g Dalakhani (IRE)—Perfect Hedge **Poynton Harrod Smith & Darlington**
32 ROGUE MALE, 7, b g Schiaparelli (GER)—Shikra **Mr N. J. Hussey**
33 SACKETT, 10, b g Midnight Legend—Gloriana **Woodward, Laurie & Smith**
34 SILENT STEPS (IRE), 10, b m Milan—Taking Silk (IRE) **The Silent Steps Partnership**

## MR NEIL KING - continued

35 **SLAINE,** 7, b m Brian Boru—Flowing On **Mrs A. E. Maundrell**
36 **SPORTING ACE (IRE),** 5, b g Shantou (USA)—Knockbounce View (IRE) **Ken Lawrence & Roy Mousley**
37 5, b m Shirocco (GER)—Storm In Front (IRE)
38 **THE KNOT IS TIED (IRE),** 6, b g Casamento (IRE)—Really Polish (USA) **Ken Lawrence & Roy Mousley**
39 **UNDOUBTEDLY,** 4, b f Authorized (IRE)—Lovely Origny (FR) **Mr A. L. Cohen**
40 **VENTURA MAGIC,** 6, b g Mount Nelson—Elle Desert (GER) **The Ridgeway Racing For Fun Partnership**
41 **VERY INTENSE (IRE),** 10, b g Intense Focus (USA)—Astralai (IRE) **Woodenco**
42 **WILLIE BUTLER (IRE),** 7, b g Yeats (IRE)—Belsalsa (FR) **Mr P. M. H. Beadles**

**Other Owners:** Mr T. P. Andrews, Mr S. R. Baker, Mr P. M. H. Beadles, Mr J. Bone, G. S. Brown, Mr D. R. Caldwell, A. Carr, Mr N. J. Catterwell, Mr R. Clarke, Mr P. J. Darlington, Mr J. Davies, Mr J. S. English, Mr P. Govier, Govier & Brown, Mrs D. J. Hagenbuch, Mr M. Harrod, N. King, Mr R. Laurie, Mr K. Lawrence, K. F. J. Loads, I. A. Low, Mrs A. E. Maundrell, Mr T. J. Messom, Mr G. Milsom, Milsom Baker Racing, Mr R. Mousley, Mr D. F. Nott, Mr B. Poynton, Mrs H. M. Royle, Mr A. F. Sawyer, Mr A. J. Smith, Mr D. P. Smith, Mr R. W. Smith, Mr G. E. Stevenson, Mr D. A. Sutton, Mr A. A. Whyte, Mr B. Woodward.

**Racing Secretary:** Oriana-Jane Baines.

**Flat Jockey:** Ben Curtis, Luke Morris. **NH Jockey:** Bryony Frost.

---

## 323 MR PHILIP KIRBY, Richmond
Postal: Green Oaks Farm, East Appleton, Richmond, North Yorkshire, DL10 7QE
Contacts: PHONE 01748 517337 MOBILE 07984 403558
EMAIL pkirbyracing@gmail.com WEBSITE www.philipkirbyracing.co.uk

1 **ABINGTON PARK,** 6, br g Passing Glance—Epicurean **Red Cap Racing**
2 **ADELPHI PRINCE,** 8, b g Schiaparelli (GER)—Cailin Na Ri (IRE) **Barry and Virginia Brown**
3 **ADELPHI SPRITE,** 5, b g Cityscape—Cailin Na Ri (IRE) **Barry and Virginia Brown**
4 **ALSVINDER,** 8, b h Footstepsinthesand—Notting Hill (BRZ) **Mr P. A. Kirby**
5 **ANOTHER THEATRE (IRE),** 8, b m Shantou (USA)—
Whats Another One (IRE) **The Vacuum Pouch Company Limited**
6 **ARMY'S DREAM (IRE),** 4, b g Dylan Thomas (IRE)—Cappa Or (IRE)
7 **ARTHUR MAC (IRE),** 8, ch g Getaway (GER)—Orchardstown Moss (IRE) **The Vacuum Pouch Company Limited**
8 **AUTONOMY,** 5, b g Dansili—Funsie (FR) **Mr P. A. Kirby**
9 **BARLEY BREEZE,** 4, gr g Kapgarde (FR)—Attente de Sivola (FR) **Tor Side Racing**
10 **BE THE DIFFERENCE (IRE),** 5, b g Califet (FR)—Rinroe Flyer (IRE) **The Vacuum Pouch Company Limited**
11 **BERTIE BLAKE (IRE),** 8, b g Beneficial—Diandrina **The Kirby Club Partnership**
12 **BIG EARS (IRE),** 5, b m Yeats (IRE)—Theleze (FR) **Mrs J. A. Darling**
13 **BLACK EBONY,** 7, br g Malinas (GER)—Our Ethel **The Mount Fawcus Partnership**
14 **BURROWS SEESIDE (IRE),** 4, b g Sidestep (AUS)—See Your Dream **Mrs C. Casterton & Mrs J. Morgan**
15 **BUSHYPARK (IRE),** 7, b g Le Fou (IRE)—Aztec Pearl **Mr P. A. Kirby**
16 **DAME DE RUBAN (FR),** 6, gr m Turgeon (USA)—Land of Soprani (FR) **ValueRacingClub.co.uk**
17 **DARES TO DREAM (IRE),** 7, br m Beneficial—Miss McGoldrick (IRE) **& Clark**
18 **DIAKOSAINT (FR),** 6, b g Saint des Saints (FR)—Diananisse (FR) **The Vacuum Pouch Company Limited**
19 **DIEU BENISSE (FR),** 8, b m Blue Bresil (FR)—Flowerfull (FR) **The Gathering & J Matthews**
20 **DUBH DES CHAMPS (IRE),** 9, br g Robin des Champs (FR)—Aneda Dubh (IRE) **The Des Champs Partnership**
21 **EN MEME TEMPS (FR),** 7, b g Saddler Maker (IRE)—Lady Reine (FR) **Hope Eden Racing Limited**
22 **EPSOM DES MOTTES (FR),** 7, b g Maresca Sorrento (FR)—Nellyssa Bleu (FR) **David Barlow & Lyn Rutherford**
23 **FILLE D'AVIGNON (IRE),** 6, br m Getaway (GER)—Site-Leader (IRE) **The Topspec II Partnership**
24 **FIRST GLORY (IRE),** 5, b m Fame And Glory—Ballyfourlass (IRE) **Mr A. Rogers**
25 **FIRST ILLUSION (IRE),** 5, b g Westerner—No Manners Molly (IRE) **The Vacuum Pouch Company Limited**
26 **GET REAL (IRE),** 7, br g Getaway (GER)—Viva Forever (FR) **The Vacuum Pouch Company Limited**
27 **GETAWAY MISSION (IRE),** 7, b g Getaway (GER)—Emeranna (IRE) **Andrew Dick & Steve Roberts**
28 **GLORY OF PARIS (IRE),** 7, b g Sir Prancealot (IRE)—Paris Glory (USA) **Mr A. Rogers**
29 **GOWANLAD,** 4, b c Mayson—Aahgowangowan (IRE) **Gowan Racing**
30 **HANGARD,** 9, b g Black Sam Bellamy (IRE)—Empress of Light **Mr D. C. Blake**

# MR PHILIP KIRBY - continued

31 **HIDDEN COMMANDER (IRE)**, 6, b g Shirocco (GER)—
Gift of Freedom (IRE) **The Vacuum Pouch Company Limited**
32 **ICE PYRAMID (IRE)**, 6, ch g New Approach (IRE)—Coolnagree (IRE) **Bill Fraser & Adrian Pritchard**
33 **ICONIC BELLE**, 7, ch m Sixties Icon—Five Bells (IRE) **Jowsey, Bainbridge, Cornforth & Everson**
34 **IDILICO (FR)**, 6, b g Lawman (FR)—Ydillique (IRE) **Mr A. D. Dick**
35 **IMAJORBLUSH**, 5, ch g Mukhadram—Winter Dress **Zoe Hassall & George Hassall**
36 **JURISTE (IRE)**, 7, b g Lawman (FR)—Green Lassy (FR) **Mrs J. Porter**
37 **KANGAROO VALLEY (USA)**, 5, b g Australia—Dundalk Dust (USA) **Dick, Townley & Allen**
38 **KERALA**, 5, b m Kayf Tara—Dourya **Mr P. A. Kirby**
39 **KINGS CAVE (IRE)**, 6, b g Court Cave (IRE)—Marble Article (IRE) **Mr A. Rogers**
40 **LADY CAMELOT (IRE)**, 6, b m Camelot—Queen Jock (USA) **The Ploughmen Syndicate**
41 **LADY'S PRESENT (IRE)**, 4, b f Presenting—Lady Chloe **The Team Kirby Partnership**
42 **LEOPOLDS ROCK (IRE)**, 5, ch g Rock of Gibraltar (IRE)—Trianon **Tor Side Racing**
43 **LITTLE BRUCE (IRE)**, 9, b g Yeats (IRE)—Lady Rolfe (IRE) **The Gps Partnership**
44 **LITTLE INDIA (FR)**, 5, ch m Manduro (GER)—Jolie Laide (IRE) **Hope Eden Racing Limited**
45 **LORD BUTTONS**, 5, b g Presenting—Lady Chapp (IRE) **Mrs J. Sivills**
46 **LORD TORRANAGA (FR)**, 6, b g Planteur (IRE)—Marie Cuddy (IRE) **Lord Torranaga Partnership**
47 **LOUIS' VAC POUCH (IRE)**, 9, b g Oscar (IRE)—Coming Home (FR) **The Vacuum Pouch Company Limited**
48 **LUCKY ICON (IRE)**, 7, b g Sixties Icon—Sauterelle (IRE) **Mrs J. Sivills**
49 **MADEEH**, 5, b h Oasis Dream—Ashaaqah (IRE) **Harbour Rose Partnership**
50 **MAGELLAN**, 7, b g Sea The Stars (IRE)—Hector's Girl **Mr P. A. Kirby**
51 **MAN OF VERVE (IRE)**, 7, b g Dandy Man (IRE)—She's Our Rock (IRE) **A Jowsey & R Bainbridge**
52 **MARTALINDY**, 4, b f Martaline—Helen Wood **The Vacuum Pouch Company Limited**
53 **MASTER NEWTON (IRE)**, 6, gr g Mastercraftsman (IRE)—French Friend (IRE) **Master Newton Partnership**
54 **MCGARRY (IRE)**, 7, b g Mahler—Little Pearl (IRE) **The Vacuum Pouch Company Limited**
55 **MICHAEL'S MOUNT**, 8, ch g Mount Nelson—Dumnoni **Andrew Dick & Mark Dennis**
56 **MIDNIGHT LEGACY (IRE)**, 7, b m Getaway (GER)—Lady of The Hall (IRE) **Hambleton Racing Ltd XXXIV**
57 **MILANVERA (IRE)**, 7, b m Milan—Sorivera **Mr A. Anderson**
58 **MISS MAHMITE (IRE)**, 6, b m Mahler—Davids Delight (IRE) **Mrs J. A. Thomas & Ms K. J. Austin**
59 **MISSCARLETT (IRE)**, 7, b m Red Rocks (IRE)—Coimbra (USA) **Mrs J. Porter**
60 **MOUNTAIN GLORY**, 4, b g Fame And Glory—Pickworth (IRE) **Mrs J. Sivills**
61 **MR CARBONATOR**, 6, b g Bated Breath—Diamond Lass (IRE) **Alan Fairhurst & David Fairhurst**
62 **MY STRONG MAN (IRE)**, 5, b g Authorized (IRE)—Lady Chloe **The Platinum Partnership**
63 **NIVEN (IRE)**, 8, b g Elusive Pimpernel (USA)—Ginger Lily (IRE) **John Birtles & Bill Allan**
64 **OAK VINTAGE (IRE)**, 11, b g Fruits of Love (USA)—Brandam Supreme (IRE) **Mrs J. Porter**
65 **PENNINE CROSS**, 6, b g Shirocco (GER)—Gaspara (FR) **The Well Oiled Partnership**
66 **RAIFF (IRE)**, 5, b g Shamardal (USA)—Estiqaama (USA) **Mr D. R. Platt**
67 **RAVENSCAR (IRE)**, 5, b m Helmet (AUS)—Cry Pearl (USA) **Mr J. A. Hall**
68 **RAYNA'S WORLD (IRE)**, 6, b m Poet's Voice—Salmon Rose (IRE) **Ace Bloodstock & Rayna Fitzgerald**
69 **RED FORCE ONE**, 6, ro g Lethal Force (IRE)—Dusty Red **The Yorkshire Puddings**
70 **ROBINCOLLETTE (IRE)**, 7, br m Robin des Champs (FR)—Western Cowgirl (IRE) **The Yorkshire Puddings**
71 **ROMEO BROWN**, 7, br g Yeats (IRE)—Santia **McGoldrick Racing 5 & Birrafun**
72 **SAKHEE'S CITY (IRE)**, 10, b g Sakhee (USA)—A Lulu Ofa Menifee (USA) **Mrs J. Sivills**
73 **SEXY BEAST**, 6, b g Teofilo (IRE)—Wadaat **The Good Looking Partnership**
74 **SHERIFF'S SISTER (IRE)**, 4, b br f Lawman (FR)—Teodelight (IRE)
75 **SHINE BABY SHINE**, 7, b m Aqlaam—Rosewood Belle (USA) **David Gray & P Kirby**
76 **SHOW PROMISE**, 7, b g Joor Algarhoud (IRE)—Show Potential (IRE) **The Philip Kirby Racing Partnership**
77 **SIR JIMMY ALLEN (FR)**, 4, gr g Spanish Moon (USA)—Uranus Le Dun (FR) **FDC Holdings Ltd**
78 **SON OF THE SOMME (IRE)**, 6, b g Yeats (IRE)—Present Venture (IRE) **Mr D. C. Blake**
79 **SOUTH TERRACE (IRE)**, 6, b g Fame And Glory—Supreme Sales (IRE) **The Vacuum Pouch Company Limited**
80 **SPLASHING**, 4, b f Equiano (FR)—Missouri **Mr P. A. Kirby**
81 **STARGAZER (IRE)**, 8, b g Canford Cliffs (IRE)—Star Ruby (IRE) **Zoe Hassall & George Hassall & P Kirby**
82 **STITCH UP (IRE)**, 5, b g Milan—Be My Granny **Mr D. Carter**
83 **SUNSET WEST (IRE)**, 6, b g Westerner—Sunshine Haven (IRE) **The Vacuum Pouch Company Limited**
84 **TEKIBLUE DE L'ORME (FR)**, 8, b g Blue Bresil (FR)—Tekila de l'Orme (FR) **Philippa Kirby & Elaine Fraser**
85 **THEFLICKERINGLIGHT (IRE)**, 7, b m Flemensfirth (USA)—Turtle Lamp (IRE) **The Yorkshire Puddings**
86 **TOP VILLE BEN (IRE)**, 9, b g Beneficial—Great Decision (IRE) **Harbour Rose Partnership**
87 **TOP VILLE BOBBY (IRE)**, 4, b g Yeats (IRE)—Great Decision (IRE) **Harbour Rose Partnership**
88 **TWO THIRTY YEAT (IRE)**, 6, b m Yeats (IRE)—Aneda Dubh (IRE) **Mr P. Bryan**
89 **WEMYSS POINT**, 9, b g Champs Elysees—Wemyss Bay **The Green Oaks Partnership**

## MR PHILIP KIRBY - continued

90 **WHOSHOTTHESHERIFF (IRE)**, 7, b g Dylan Thomas (IRE)—Dame Foraine (FR) **Hambleton Racing Ltd XXXIV**
91 **WINFOLA (FR)**, 7, gr m Motivator—Romance Bere (FR) **The Silver Linings Partnership**
92 **WYE AYE**, 6, b g Shirocco (GER)—A Media Luz (FR) **The Well Oiled Partnership**
93 **WYNYARD ICON**, 4, ch f Sixties Icon—Royalty (IRE) **Wynyard Racing**

### THREE-YEAR-OLDS

94 **BILLIAN (IRE)**, b c Mehmas (IRE)—Truly Magnificent (USA) **Bill Fraser & Adrian Pritchard**
95 **DARK ZEAS (IRE)**, b c Dark Angel (IRE)—Carallia (IRE) **AR Racing**
96 **FIRCOMBE HALL**, ch c Charming Thought—Marmot Bay (IRE) **RedHotGardogs**
97 **MAYWAY**, b f Mayson—Lighted Way **Knavesmire Partnership 2**
98 **MONT BLANC**, gr f Outstrip—Darling Grace **FDC Holdings Ltd**
99 **ROBERT JOHNSON**, ch c Helmet (AUS)—Sensationally **Mr M. V. Coglan**
100 **SMART BOYO**, b c War Command (USA)—Luluti (IRE) **smartwater utilities**

**Other Owners:** Ace Bloodstock Ltd, Mr W. Allan, Mr P. Allen, Ms K. J. Austin, Mr R. A. Bainbridge, Mr D. Barlow, The Birrafun Partnership, Mr J. Birtles, Mr K. Bourke, Mr A. Cartledge, Mrs C. J. Casterton, Mr A. G. Clark, Mrs S. M. Clark, Mr B. J. Connolly, Mr J. Cornforth, Mr B. Costello, Mr M. N. Dennis, Mr A. D. Dick, Mr B. H. Dolan, Mr B. R. Everson, Mr A. Fairhurst, Mr D. H. Fairhurst, Mrs R. Fitzgerald, Mr M. D. Foden, Mrs E. C. Fraser, W. R. Fraser, Mrs R. M. E. Gibbon, Mr D. W. Gray, Mrs G. L. Halder, Mr R. Hamilton, Mr G. A. Hassall, Mr N. A. D. Hassall, Mr Z. L. Hassall, Mrs L. J. Huddlestone, Mr A. Jowsey, Mr P. A. Kirby, Mrs P. R. Kirby, M. A. Leatham, Mrs E. M. Lloyd, Mr R. J. Longley, Mr J. Matthews, Mr J. McInerney, Mrs J. Morgan, Mr A. Pritchard, Ramscove Ltd, Mrs D. J. Ritzema, Mr S. Roberts, Mr W. G. Rolfe, L. M. Rutherford, Mr H. Stephenson, Mr M. C. P. Suddards, The Gathering, Mrs J. A. Thomas, Mr T. W. Townley, Mr L. Waugh, Mrs V. M. Waugh, Mr S. J. Wyatt.

**Assistant Trainer:** Simon Olley.

---

## 324 MR SYLVESTER KIRK, Upper Lambourn
Postal: **Cedar Lodge Stables, Upper Lambourn, Hungerford, Berkshire, RG17 8QT**
Contacts: **PHONE** 01488 73215 **MOBILE** 07768 855261
**EMAIL** info@sylvesterkirkracing.co.uk **WEBSITE** www.sylvesterkirkracing.co.uk

1 **BENNY AND THE JETS (IRE)**, 5, ch g Showcasing—Orange Pip **Deauville Daze Partnership**
2 **DEFTERA LAD (IRE)**, 9, b g Fast Company (IRE)—Speedbird (USA) **Mr Y. Mustafa**
3 **DISTURBING BEAUTY**, 5, b m Mazameer (IRE)—Deftera Fantutte (IRE) **Mr Y. Mustafa**
4 **FURTHER MEASURE (USA)**, 4, b c English Channel (USA)—Price Tag **Marchwood Aggregates**
5 **HTILOMINLO**, 5, b h Zoffany (IRE)—Haven's Wave (IRE) **Mr H. Balasuriya**
6 **KODIAK ATTACK (IRE)**, 5, b g Kodiac—Good Clodora (IRE) **Mrs J. A. Fowler**
7 **LAFONTAINE (FR)**, 4, b f Canford Cliffs (IRE)—Moma Lee **Homebred Racing**
8 **MOULMEIN**, 4, ch c Australia—Natty Bumppo (IRE) **Mr H. Balasuriya**
9 **PAINT IT BLACK**, 4, b g Iffraaj—Sister Ship **S. A. Kirk**
10 **RHINESTONE BLUE (IRE)**, 4, ch g Gleneagles (IRE)—Bora Blues **S. A. Kirk**
11 **SALOUEN (IRE)**, 7, b g Canford Cliffs (IRE)—Gali Gal (IRE) **Mr H. Balasuriya**
12 **WILFY**, 4, br g Kyllachy—Close To The Edge (IRE) **Marchwood Recycling Ltd**

### THREE-YEAR-OLDS

13 **ALICESTAR**, b f Charming Thought—Atheera (IRE) **Marchwood Recycling Ltd**
14 **ALL IN THE GAME (IRE)**, br f Dragon Pulse (IRE)—Density **Miss Alison Jones**
15 **BREAKFASTATIFFANYS**, b f Territories (IRE)—Alzanti (IRE) **Christopher Wright & Partner**
16 **DRURY LANE (IRE)**, b g Zoffany (IRE)—Soft Ice (IRE) **Martin White & Partner**
17 **EAUX DE VIE**, b f Swiss Spirit—Delagoa Bay (IRE) **Homebred Racing**
18 **FIVE RINGS**, ch g The Gurkha (IRE)—Olympic Runner **J. C. Smith**
19 **HE CAN DANCE (IRE)**, b g Es Que Love (IRE)—Balqaa (USA) **S. A. Kirk**
20 **LANIKA**, ch f Outstrip—Jaiyana **Mr R Clothier, Miss J Gray & Partner**
21 **RANIA (IRE)**, b f Estidhkaar (IRE)—Little Oz (IRE) **Mr R. Clothier & Miss J. Gray**
22 **SEATTLE ROCK**, b f Fastnet Rock (AUS)—Snoqualmie Girl (IRE) **J. C. Smith**
23 **SHADES OF RED (IRE)**, b f Acclamation—Marisol (IRE) **Miss Alison Jones & Partner**

## MR SYLVESTER KIRK - continued

24 **STUDY THE STARS**, b g Due Diligence (USA)—Celestial Bay **Homebred Racing**
25 **VINA BAY**, b g New Bay—Danvina (IRE) **N. Pickett**
26 **WHERE YOU AT**, b c Twilight Son—Peace Concluded **Fairway Racing**

### TWO-YEAR-OLDS

27 B c 11/02 Aclaim (IRE)—Calypso Choir (Bahamian Bounty) **J. C. Smith**
28 B c 14/03 Holy Roman Emperor (IRE)—Dirtybirdie (Diktat) (10476)
29 Ch f 19/01 The Gurkha (IRE)—Duchess of Marmite (IRE) (Duke of Marmalade (IRE))
30 B f 21/03 El Kabeir (USA)—Fantastic Spring (USA) (Fantastic Light (USA)) (19048) **Miss Alison Jones**
31 B f 28/03 No Nay Never (USA)—Inca Wood (UAE) (Timber Country (USA)) **Mrs J. A. Fowler**
32 B f 13/05 Profitable (IRE)—Logique (FR) (Whipper (USA)) (19048)
33 B c 14/02 Belardo (IRE)—Marmalade Cat (Duke of Marmalade (IRE)) (13000) **S. A. Kirk**
34 B f 26/03 Fast Company (IRE)—Melodique (FR) (Falco (USA)) (15000) **S. A. Kirk**
35 B f 12/03 Time Test—Opera Glass (Barathea (IRE)) **J. C. Smith**
36 Gr c 06/03 Caravaggio (USA)—Prize Diva (Motivator) **J. C. Smith**
37 Ch f 04/03 Norse Dancer (IRE)—Snow Squaw (Excelebration (IRE)) **J. C. Smith**
38 B c 09/04 Aclaim (IRE)—Wigan Lane (Kheleyf (USA)) (8000) **S. A. Kirk**

**Other Owners:** Mrs Catherine Cashman, Mr R. W. Clothier, Miss J. F. Gray, Miss Alison Jones, S. A. Kirk, Mr D. O'Loughlin, Mr M. White, Mr C. N. Wright.

**Assistant Trainer:** Fanny Kirk.

---

 **MR STUART KITTOW, Cullompton**
Postal: **Hayneifield Farm, Blackborough, Cullompton, Devon, EX15 2JD**
Contacts: **HOME 01823 680183 MOBILE 07714 218921 FAX 01823 680601**
**EMAIL stuartkittowracing@hotmail.com WEBSITE www.stuartkittowracing.com**

1 **BEYOND EQUAL**, 6, b g Kheleyf (USA)—Samasana (IRE) **Stuart Wood & Partner**
2 **CROWDED EXPRESS**, 4, b g Fast Company (IRE)—Dilys **Cushing, Boswell, Ingham & Kittow**
3 **DORA'S FIELD (IRE)**, 8, b m Rip Van Winkle (IRE)—Rydal Mount (IRE) **R. S. E. Gifford**
4 **FREDDY FANATAPAN**, 6, b g Nathaniel (IRE)—Pan Galactic (USA) **Dr G. S. Plastow**
5 **GHERKIN**, 4, b g Coach House (IRE)—Our Piccadilly (IRE) **Mrs G. R. Shire**
6 **GLOWETH**, 6, b m Pastoral Pursuits—Dancing Storm **M. E. Harris**
7 **HOME MADE WINE**, 4, ch f Casamento (IRE)—Arctic Royal (IRE) **Little Loxbrook Babes and Bays**
8 **IBERIO (GER)**, 4, b g Kamsin (GER)—Imogen (GER) **Mr T. J. Malone**
9 **MR CHILL**, 4, b g Gentlewave (IRE)—Arctic Magic (IRE) **Mrs G. R. Shire**
10 **NEWTON JACK**, 4, b g Fast Company (IRE)—Jackline **Newton Barn Racing**
11 **STARSKY (IRE)**, 7, b g Shantou (USA)—Lunar Star (IRE) **Mr T. J. Malone**
12 **THE DENHOLM BANDIT**, 7, b g Kayf Tara—Black Annie (IRE) **Alastair and Rachel Bell**
13 **THE LAST BUT ONE (IRE)**, 9, b g Kutub (IRE)—Last Hope (IRE) **Mr T. J. Malone**
14 **TIBBIE DUNBAR**, 5, b m Poet's Voice—Gold Approach **Mr J. R. Urquhart**
15 **VITESSE DU SON**, 4, b g Fast Company (IRE)—Sister Guru **D. R. Tucker**
16 **WINANDER**, 4, b g Ruler of The World (IRE)—Rydal Mount (IRE) **R. S. E. Gifford**
17 **WISHING GATE**, 4, b g Holy Roman Emperor (IRE)—Quiff **R. S. E. Gifford**
18 **YOUKAN (IRE)**, 6, b g Choisir (AUS)—Ellikan (IRE) **Mrs L. M. Francis**

### THREE-YEAR-OLDS

19 **ORIENTAL SPIRIT**, b g Swiss Spirit—Yat Ding Yau (FR) **The Oriental Spirit Partnership**
20 **POWER EM**, b g Power—Dilgura **The Power Em Partnership**
21 **SHARPENUPABIT**, b gr g Outstrip—Suzy Wong **Mrs P. J. Pengelly**

## MR STUART KITTOW - continued

### TWO-YEAR-OLDS
22 **BELLA'S PEARL**, b f 22/02 Pearl Secret—Plauseabella (Royal Applause) **Mrs G. R. Shire**
23 B g 18/02 Coach House (IRE)—Dancing Storm (Trans Island) **M. E. Harris**
24 B f 01/04 Lethal Force (IRE)—Dilgura (Ishiguru (USA))
25 **FAWN AT PLAY**, ch f 16/04 Recorder—Raymi Coya (CAN) (Van Nistelrooy (USA)) **R. S. E. Gifford**
26 **NOTRE MAISON**, b f 08/04 Coach House (IRE)—Our Piccadilly (IRE) (Piccolo) **Mrs G. R. Shire**

**Other Owners:** Mr A. R. Bell, Mrs R. Bell, John Boswell, Mr H. A. Cushing, Mr A. R. Ingham, W. S. Kittow, Mr S. C. Wood.

**Assistant Trainer:** Mrs Judy Kittow.

**Flat Jockey:** Rob Hornby. **NH Jockey:** David Noonan, Tom Scudamore.

---

**326**
### MR WILLIAM KNIGHT, Newmarket
Postal: **Rathmoy Stables, Hamilton Road, Newmarket, Suffolk, CB8 0GU**
Contacts: **PHONE 01638 664063 MOBILE 07770 720828**
**EMAIL** william@wknightracing.co.uk **WEBSITE** www.wknightracing.co.uk **TWITTER @**
**WKnightRacing**

1 **ALDRICH BAY (IRE)**, 4, b g Xtension (IRE)—Sail With The Wind **Mr Y. O. Wong**
2 **AUTHOR'S DREAM**, 8, gr g Authorized (IRE)—Spring Dream (IRE) **Mr & Mrs Conroy**
3 **COMMIT NO NUISANCE (IRE)**, 4, ch g Ivawood (IRE)—Free Lance (IRE) **G. C. Stevens**
4 **COODER**, 4, b g Mukhadram—Plover **Canisbay Bloodstock**
5 **EAGLE CREEK (IRE)**, 7, b g Raven's Pass (USA)—Blue Angel (IRE) **Mr J. F. Seabrook, Mr P. Seabrook**
6 **FRENCH MINSTREL (IRE)**, 4, b g Gutaifan (IRE)—C'Est Ma Souer (IRE) **W. J. Knight**
7 **GAUNTLET (IRE)**, 4, b g Galileo (IRE)—Danedrop (IRE) **J & P Seabrook & Tim Fisher**
8 **GOODWOOD REBEL (IRE)**, 4, b g Dandy Man (IRE)—
                                        Our Valkyrie (IRE) **Goodwood Racehorse Owners Group Limited**
9 **HENLEY PARK**, 4, b g Paco Boy (IRE)—Sunny Afternoon **Mrs S. A. Windus**
10 **KALIMOTXO**, 4, b f Equiano (IRE)—Royal Ivy **Canisbay Bloodstock**
11 **KELLY B**, 4, b f Equiano—Primavera **Mr R. Beadle**
12 **KING OF THE SOUTH (IRE)**, 4, b g Kingman—South Atlantic (USA) **Mr Saif Ali**
13 **PEARL BEACH**, 4, b f Footstepsinthesand—Western Pearl **Mr & Mrs N. Welby**
14 **SHIFTING GOLD (IRE)**, 5, b m Fast Company (IRE)—Elusive Gold (IRE) **Mrs Joanna Farrant & Partner**
15 **SIGNAL TWENTY NINE**, 4, gr g Gregorian (IRE)—Beacon Lady **Chasemore Farm & Mr J Dwyer**
16 **SIR BUSKER (IRE)**, 5, b g Sir Prancealot (IRE)—Street Kitty (IRE) **Kennet Valley Thoroughbreds Xi Racing**
17 **SONG AT TWILIGHT (IRE)**, 4, b f Zoffany (IRE)—Jasmine Blue (IRE) **Mr Saif Ali**
18 **SPANISH KISS**, 4, b g Lope de Vega (IRE)—Kissable (IRE) **Kennet Valley Thoroughbreds XIV**
19 **WITH PROMISE**, 4, b g Shamardal (USA)—Magical Crown (USA) **Mr A. Al Mansoori**

### THREE-YEAR-OLDS
20 **ANDELYSA**, b f Siyouni (FR)—Clotilde **Chasemore Farm LLP**
21 **AYLESFORD (IRE)**, b g Acclamation—Pearl Sea (IRE) **Gallagher Bloodstock Limited**
22 **BALLYSAX (IRE)**, gr f Dark Angel—Lismore (USA) **T. J. Rooney**
23 **BEAT THE STORM (IRE)**, b g Dragon Pulse (IRE)—Before The Storm **The Rumble Racing Club & Partner**
24 **BROADWAY DIVA (FR)**, b f Pivotal—Allumage **Mr Saif Ali**
25 **CAYMAN MOON**, b g Sea The Moon (GER)—Nota Bene (GER) **Middleham Park Racing CXII, I Black & P Leefe**
26 **DESERT GULF**, b g Kodiac—Sabaweeya **Mr Saif Ali**
27 **DUAL IDENTITY (IRE)**, b g Belardo (IRE)—Teide Lady **Kennet Valley Thoroughbreds IV**
28 **DUBAI TIGRESS**, b f The Last Lion—Al Cobra (IRE) **Mr Saif Ali**
29 **EXCEEDINGLY REGAL (IRE)**, b g Exceed And Excel (AUS)—Aquatinta (GER) **Mr A. Al Mansoori**
30 **GOODWOOD GLEN**, b g Territories (IRE)—Bonnie Brae **Goodwood Racehorse Owners Group Limited**
31 **HE'S A DREAM**, b g Oasis Dream—Deveron (USA) **Mr Saif Ali**
32 **LIGER KING (IRE)**, ch c The Last Lion—Fifth Wonder (USA) **Rathmoy Racing & Partner**
33 **MISS SUZIE B**, ch f Lethal Force (IRE)—Tempting **Mr R. Beadle**
34 **NEVEYAH (IRE)**, b f Mehmas (IRE)—Nina Bonita (IRE) **Mrs E. C. Roberts**
35 **PERCY'S PRIDE (IRE)**, b f Sir Percy—Cartoon **Mr Saif Ali**

## MR WILLIAM KNIGHT - continued

36 **PROGRESSIVE EZ (IRE),** b g Gutaifan (IRE)—Cuilaphuca (IRE) **Progressive Racing & Partner**
37 **QUIET THUNDER (IRE),** b f Night of Thunder (IRE)—Elevator Action (IRE) **Mr Sultan Ali**
38 **SUNDAYINMAY (GER),** b f Pastorius (GER)—Simply Noble (GER) **Mrs R. Baenziger-Gisi**
39 **VISIONS OF GLORY (IRE),** ch g The Last Lion (IRE)—Aunt Julia **Tom Earl & Apt Vi**
40 **YEAR OF THE DRAGON (IRE),** b c Dragon Pulse (IRE)—Poplar Close (IRE) **Mr J. Barnett**

### TWO-YEAR-OLDS

41 B f 31/03 Muhaarar—Al Fareej **Mr Saif Ali**
42 B c 25/04 Australia—Alf Guineas (IRE) (Sea The Stars (IRE)) (47000) **Kennet Valley Thoroughbreds X**
43 Ch c 03/02 Cotai Glory—Beat The Stars (IRE) (Verglas (IRE)) (35000) **Rathmoy Racing & G. Stevens**
44 **BONDI SPICE (IRE),** ch c 19/02 Australia—
                    La Spezia (IRE) (Danehill Dancer (IRE)) (32381) **One Day Rodney Partnership**
45 **CHECKANDCHALLENGE,** b br c 08/02 Fast Company (IRE)—Likeable (Dalakhani (IRE)) (35000) **Mr A. Hetherton**
46 Gr c 30/01 Caravaggio (USA)—Chiffonade (IRE) (Galileo (IRE)) **Mr Saif Ali**
47 B f 01/02 New Approach—Dance Awhile **Mr A. Al Mansoori**
48 B f 11/03 Golden Horn—Deveron (USA) (Cozzene (USA)) **Mr Saif Ali**
49 **FELLOWSHIP (IRE),** b c 06/03 Fulbright—Street Kitty (IRE) (Tiger Hill (IRE)) (15000) **Badger's Set**
50 B f 19/03 Brazen Beau—Keep The Secret **Mr & Mrs N. Welby**
51 B f 15/03 Dubawi (IRE)—Meeznah (USA) (Dynaformer (USA)) **Saif Ali & Saeed H. Altayer**
52 B f 20/02 Kingman—Oshiponga (Barathea (IRE)) (40000) **Mr Saif Ali**
53 Ch f 14/02 Lope De Vega—Parsnip **Chasemore Farm LLP**
54 **QUEL KAIMA (GER),** b f 13/04 Exceed And Excel (AUS)—
                    Queensberry (GER) (Tertullian (USA)) (40000) **Badger's Set II**
55 **SHARE THE PROFITS,** b f 27/04 Profitable—Muhadathat **Mr A. Al Mansoori**
56 B c 22/03 Night Of Thunder—Spinning Melody **Saif Ali & Saeed H. Altayer**
57 B c 18/02 Oasis Dream—Spirit Of Winning (Invincible Spirit (IRE)) **Mr Saif Ali**
58 B f 15/04 Adaay—Tempting **Mr R. Beadle**
59 **TIMESOFTHEESSENCE (IRE),** b c 22/04 Time Test—
                    Alys Love (New Approach (IRE)) (18000) **Mrs S Hartley & Mr A. Hetherton**
60 Ch f 17/03 Teofilo—Tunkwa **Mr A. Al Mansoori**

**Other Owners:** Angmering Park Thoroughbreds VI, A. W. Black, Mr I. Black, Mrs J. E. Black, Chasemore Farm LLP, Mr N. A. Coster, Mr M. Davidson, J. Dwyer, Mr T. E. Earl, Mr D. J. Erwin, Mrs J. D. Farrant, Mr T. J. Fisher, Mr D. T. Greathouse II, Mrs S. K. Hartley, Mr A. Hetherton, Mr R. S. Hoskins, Park I. & Leefe Leefe, Kennet Valley Thoroughbreds XI, R. F. Kilby, Mrs E. J. J. Knight, W. J. Knight, Mr P. Leefe, T. S. Palin, M. Prince, Progressive Racing, Rathmoy Racing, Rathmoy Racing II, Mr M. A. C. Rudd, & Seabrook, Mr J. F. Seabrook, Mr P. Seabrook, G. C. Stevens, Miss M. E. Stopher, Mr L. A. Stoten, The Rumble Racing Club, Mr M. J. Tracey.

**Assistant Trainer:** Kayleigh Flower.

---

| **327** | **MR HILAL KOBEISSI,** Newmarket |
|---|---|

Postal: **8 Tom Jennings Close, Newmarket, Suffolk, CB8 0DU**
Contacts: PHONE 07856 067990
EMAIL hilalkob@live.com

### THREE-YEAR-OLDS

1 **AL THUMAMA LORD (IRE),** b c Gleneagles (IRE)—Edwinstowe (IRE) **Mr A. A. A. Al Muslimani**
2 **FREE DEGREES (IRE),** ro f Free Eagle (IRE)—Celsius Degre (IRE) **Burns Farm Racing**
3 **KUKRI KLASS (IRE),** b f The Gurkha (IRE)—Blanche Dubawi (IRE) **Burns Farm Racing**
4 B g Olympic Glory (IRE)—La Seine (USA) **Al Jasra Racing**
5 **MADAD (IRE),** b c Footstepsinthesand—Deryshicca (IRE) **Mr K. H. Al Khalifa**

**Other Owners:** Mr W. R. Asquith, Mrs C. G. Scott.

## 328 DANIEL & CLAIRE KUBLER, Lambourn
Postal: **Sarsen Farm, Upper Lambourn, Hungerford, Berkshire, RG17 8RG**
Contacts: **PHONE 07984 287254**

1 **BAROSSA RED (IRE)**, 5, ch g Tamayuz—I Hearyou Knocking (IRE)  **Mr A. Kerr**
2 **CHITRA**, 5, b m Sea The Moon (GER)—Persian Star  **Mr & Mrs G. Middlebrook**
3 **DON'T TELL CLAIRE**, 4, ro f Gutaifan (IRE)—Avenbury  **Mr A. Stonehill**
4 **DREAM DESIGN**, 4, b f Invincible Spirit (IRE)—Distinctive  **Mr & Mrs G. Middlebrook**
5 **LADY DAUPHIN (IRE)**, 5, b m Bungle Inthejungle—Chateau Dauphin (USA)  **The Johnson's**
6 **OUTRAGE**, 9, ch g Exceed And Excel (AUS)—Ludynosa (USA)  **Capture the Moment Vi**
7 **REIMS**, 5, b m Invincible Spirit (IRE)—Riberac  **Mr & Mrs G. Middlebrook**
8 **RIVER SPRITE**, 4, b f Swiss Spirit—Camp Riverside (USA)  **Diskovery Partnership Vii**
9 **SECRET ACQUISITION**, 4, b f Sea The Moon (GER)—Maria Letizia  **Mr & Mrs G. Middlebrook**
10 **SENECA CHIEF**, 7, b g Invincible Spirit (IRE)—Albertine Rose  **Mr & Mrs G. Middlebrook**
11 **WITH REASON**, 4, ch f Frankel—Eminently  **Mr & Mrs G. Middlebrook**
12 **ZULU GIRL**, 4, b f Lethal Force (IRE)—Upskittled  **Trish and Colin Fletcher-Hall**

## THREE-YEAR-OLDS
13 **ABBEY HEIGHTS**, b c Dark Angel (IRE)—Ducissa  **Mr & Mrs G. Middlebrook**
14 **ALASKAN LADY (IRE)**, b br f Kodi Bear (IRE)—Always The Lady  **Diskovery VIII**
15 B f Charming Thought—Albertine Rose  **Mr & Mrs G. Middlebrook**
16 **BELLETTI**, b f Belardo (IRE)—Intrigue  **Mr & Mrs G. Middlebrook**
17 **BOWLAND PARK**, b c New Bay—Distinctive  **Mr & Mrs G. Middlebrook**
18 **EXCLUSIVELY YOURS**, b f Gleneagles (IRE)—Acquainted  **Mr & Mrs G. Middlebrook**
19 **HELM ROCK**, b g Pivotal—Nibbling (IRE)  **Capture the Moment VII**
20 B f Fast Company (IRE)—Jubilant Lady (USA)  **Mr & Mrs G. Middlebrook**
21 **L'ENCLUME**, ch f Gleneagles (IRE)—Mama Quilla (USA)  **Mr & Mrs G. Middlebrook**
22 B f Paco Boy (IRE)—La Donacella  **Ms V. O'Sullivan**
23 **LIBERTY WARRIOR (IRE)**, b c Muhaarar—Oui Say Oui (IRE)  **Capture the Moment VIII**
24 **LOOK AHEAD**, b f Fountain of Youth (USA)—Dance of Light (USA)  **Mr & Mrs G. Middlebrook**
25 **MUSTAVIM**, ch g Mustajeeb—Erebis
26 **NANTOSUELTA (IRE)**, b f Kodiac—Dearest Daisy  **Crowd, New Image Contracts & Partners**
27 **OCTAVE OF LIGHT**, b f Authorized (IRE)—Takarna (IRE)
28 B f Territories (IRE)—Penny Rose  **Mr & Mrs G. Middlebrook**
29 **SOGNATORE (IRE)**, b g Vadamos (FR)—Of Course Darling  **Capture the Moment & Crowd Racing**

## TWO-YEAR-OLDS
30 B c 24/04 Invincible Spirit (IRE)—Distinctive (Tobougg (IRE)) (33333)  **Mr & Mrs G. Middlebrook**
31 B gr f 06/03 Dark Angel (IRE)—Eminently (Exceed And Excel (AUS))  **Mr & Mrs G. Middlebrook**
32 B c 14/04 New Bay—Hall Hee (IRE) (Invincible Spirit (IRE)) (20952)  **D Blunt & G Middlebrook**
33 B f 02/04 Twilight Son—Heaven's Sake (Cape Cross (IRE)) (3500)
34 B c 04/04 Gleneagles (IRE)—Intrigue (Fastnet Rock (AUS)) (5000)  **Mr & Mrs G. Middlebrook**
35 B c 09/05 Gleneagles (IRE)—Jubilant Lady (USA) (Aptitude (USA)) (40000)  **Mr & Mrs G. Middlebrook**
36 Ch c 07/05 Australia—Mama Quilla (USA) (Smart Strike (CAN))  **Mr & Mrs G. Middlebrook**
37 **MARY MOUNT**, b f 13/03 Havana Gold (IRE)—
  Simmy's Temple (Royal Applause) (15000)  **Mr & Mrs G. Middlebrook**
38 B f 19/03 Havana Gold (IRE)—Melbourne Memories (Sleeping Indian) (11429)  **Mr & Mrs G. Middlebrook**
39 **OUTGATE**, br c 07/03 Outstrip—Penny Drops (Invincible Spirit (IRE))  **Mr & Mrs G. Middlebrook**
40 Ch c 15/05 Profitable (IRE)—Penny's Gift (Tobougg (IRE)) (18000)  **Mr & Mrs G. Middlebrook**
41 **PROMOTION**, b c 11/03 Fast Company (IRE)—
  Quiet Elegance (Fantastic Light (USA)) (7000)  **Mr & Mrs G. Middlebrook**
42 B f 25/02 Time Test—Rosaceous (Duke of Marmalade (IRE)) (9524)  **Mr & Mrs G. Middlebrook**
43 Ch c 26/03 Postponed (IRE)—Rue Cambon (IRE) (Exceed And Excel (AUS)) (45000)  **Oakmere Racing**
44 **SPOONFUL OF SUGAR**, b f 17/02 Exceed And Excel (AUS)—
  Sagres (Henrythenavigator (USA)) (32000)  **S R Hope & S W Barrow**

**Other Owners:** Mr S. W. Barrow, Mr A. G. Bell, Mr D. Blunt, David & Yvonne Blunt, Mrs Y. Blunt, Capture Syndicate I, Capture Syndicate II, Crowd Racing Partnership, Mrs F. Denniff, Diskovery Vii, Mr C. M. Fletcher, Mrs P. A. Hall, S. R. Hope, Mr G. Johnson, Mr G. Johnson, Mrs C. E. Kubler, Kubler Racing Ltd, Mr C. McKenna, Mr G. Middlebrook, Mr & Mrs G. Middlebrook, Mrs L. A. Middlebrook, Miss M. A. Thompson.

## 329 MR TOM LACEY, Woolhope

Postal: **Sapness Farm, Woolhope, Herefordshire, HR1 4RG**
Contacts: **MOBILE 07768 398604**
EMAIL tom@cottagefield.co.uk WEBSITE www.cottagefield.co.uk

1 **ADRIMEL (FR)**, 6, b br g Tirwanako (FR)—Irise De Gene (FR)  **Lady C. Bamford & Miss A. Bamford**
2 **ALGESIRAS**, 5, gr g Martaline—Message Personnel (FR)  **Mr T. F. Lacey**
3 **ARGONAUTA (IRE)**, 5, b g Getaway (GER)—Oscar Ladensa (IRE)  **Mr Jerry Hinds & Mr Ashley Head**
4 **BAILY GORSE (IRE)**, 7, b g Milan—Lillies Bordello (IRE)  **ValueRacingClub.co.uk**
5 **BENITO (FR)**, 4, b g Rail Link—Aspolina (IRE)  **Mrs C. Brooks**
6 **DORKING BOY**, 7, ch g Schiaparelli (GER)—Megasue  **Galloping On The South Downs Partnership**
7 **DORKING ROGUE**, 5, b g Dunaden (FR)—Megasue  **Galloping On The South Downs Partnership**
8 **DUBHEEN**, 7, b g Black Sam Bellamy (IRE)—Boleyn  **Mr T. F. Lacey**
9 **FAIR KATE**, 7, b m Fair Mix (IRE)—Silver Kate (IRE)  **Roberts, Churchward, Whittal-Williams**
10 **FLASHING GLANCE**, 8, b g Passing Glance—Don And Gerry (IRE)  **Barrett, Meredith, Panniers, Wilde**
11 **GINNY'S DESTINY (IRE)**, 5, b g Yeats—Dantes Term (IRE)  **Gordon & Su Hall**
12 **GLORY AND FORTUNE (IRE)**, 6, b g Fame And Glory—Night Heron (IRE)  **Mr J. Hinds**
13 **GLORY AND HONOUR (IRE)**, 5, b g Elusive Pimpernel (USA)—On Khee  **Mr Jerry Hinds & Mr Ashley Head**
14 **GOLD CLERMONT (FR)**, 5, b m Balko (FR)—Une Dame d'Or (FR)  **Doyoufollow Partnership**
15 **HAZZAAR (IRE)**, 7, b g Flemensfirth (USA)—Una Sorpresa (GER)  **Mr C. Boultbee-Brooks**
16 **HIGHSTAKESPLAYER (IRE)**, 5, b g Ocovango—Elivette (IRE)  **Mr Jerry Hinds & Mr Ashley Head**
17 **HUNTING PERCIVAL**, 6, b g Sir Percy—Motcombe (IRE)  **Lady N. F. Cobham**
18 **IMMORTAL FAME (IRE)**, 5, b g Fame And Glory—Calverleigh Court (IRE)  **Mr F. J. Allen**
19 **JOHNBB (IRE)**, 7, b g Stowaway—Flemins Evening (IRE)  **Mr C. Boultbee-Brooks**
20 **KATESON**, 8, gr g Black Sam Bellamy (IRE)—Silver Kate (IRE)  **DavidMRichardsandRobertsCWhittalWilliams**
21 **KIMBERLITE CANDY (IRE)**, 9, b g Flemensfirth (USA)—Mandys Native (IRE)  **Mr J. P. McManus**
22 **KING FERDINAND (IRE)**, 5, b g Milan—Nobody's Darling (IRE)  **Mr T. F. Lacey**
23 **L'INCORRIGIBLE (FR)**, 6, b g No Risk At All (FR)—Incorrigible (FR)  **Mr C. Boultbee-Brooks**
24 **LAGONDA**, 6, b m Great Pretender (IRE)—Lago d'Oro  **Mrs S. M. Newell**
25 **LAMANVER STORM**, 6, b g Geordieland—Lamanver Homerun  **Dr D. Christensen**
26 **LE GRAND FROMAGE**, 6, b g Kayf Tara—Megalex  **Galloping On The South Downs Partnership**
27 **LOSSIEMOUTH**, 6, b g Makfi—First Bloom (USA)  **Lady N. F. Cobham**
28 **MARTY TIME (FR)**, 5, gr g Martaline—Shahwarda (FR)  **Mr Jerry Hinds & Mr Ashley Head**
29 **MR MELDA (IRE)**, 6, b g Fame And Glory—Sister Imelda (IRE)  **Mr C. Boultbee-Brooks**
30 **NEVILLE'S CROSS (IRE)**, 6, b g Stowaway—Dancing Bird (IRE)  **Mr F Green & Mr J Chinn**
31 **NEW MOON (FR)**, 7, b g Kapgarde (FR)—Not Lost (FR)  **Mr L. R. Attrill**
32 **NOCTE VOLATUS**, 6, b g Midnight Legend—Aeronautica (IRE)  **Lady Cobham & Dauntsey Park**
33 **OUTLAW JESSE JAMES**, 6, b m Passing Glance—Don And Gerry (IRE)  **The Jesse James Posse**
34 **PIAFF BUBBLES (IRE)**, 5, b br g Fame And Glory—Liss Na Tintri (IRE)  **Mr Jerry Hinds & Mr Ashley Head**
35 **POLYDORA (IRE)**, 9, b g Milan—Mandysway (IRE)  **P. J. H. Wills & J. J. King**
36 **POUNDING POET (IRE)**, 5, b g Yeats—Pestal And Mortar (IRE)  **Mrs T. P. James**
37 **QUICK DRAW (IRE)**, 5, b g Getaway (GER)—Sept Verites (FR)  **Lady C. Bamford & Miss A. Bamford**
38 **RED NIKA (FR)**, 6, br g Denham Red (FR)—Nika Glitters (FR)  **Mr D. Kellett**
39 **ROGER RAREBIT**, 4, b g Black Sam Bellamy (IRE)—Rebekah Rabbit (IRE)  **Mr P. J. H. Wills**
40 **SAN AGUSTIN (IRE)**, 5, b g Ocovango—Presentingmissoats (IRE)  **P J King & Son**
41 **SCIPION (IRE)**, 5, b g Shantou (USA)—Morning Calm  **Mr T. F. Lacey**
42 **SEBASTOPOL (IRE)**, 7, b g Fame And Glory—Knockcroghery (IRE)  **Mr C. Boultbee-Brooks**
43 **SILENT MAN (IRE)**, 11, br g Morozov (USA)—Outdoor Heather (IRE)  **Ms H. Whittle**
44 **SINNDARELLA (FR)**, 5, b m Sinndar (IRE)—Ludwig Von (FR)  **Mr C. Boultbee-Brooks**
45 **STUNG FOR CASH (IRE)**, 8, b g Scorpion (IRE)—Cash A Lawn (IRE)  **ValueRacingClub.co.uk**
46 **STUNSAIL (FR)**, 5, b g Davidoff (GER)—Rio Athenas (FR)  **Mr T. F. Lacey**
47 **TEA CLIPPER (IRE)**, 8, b g Stowaway—A Plus Ma Puce (FR)  **Mr Jerry Hinds & Mr Ashley Head**
48 **TEESCOMPONENTSLASS (IRE)**, 6, ch m Presenting—Northern Native (IRE)  **ValueRacingClub.co.uk**
49 **THOMAS PATRICK (IRE)**, 8, b g Winged Love (IRE)—Huncheon Siss (IRE)  **Mr D. Kellett**
50 **UNOHU**, 6, b g Kayf Tara—Little Miss Flora  **P J King & Son**
51 **VADO FORTE (FR)**, 8, b g Walk In The Park (IRE)—Gloire (FR)  **Roberts, Churchward, Whittal-Williams**
52 **VELASCO (IRE)**, 5, b g Sholokhov (IRE)—Bilboa (FR)  **Mr D. Kellett**
53 **YOU NAME HIM**, 5, b g Proclamation (IRE)—Scarlett O'Tara  **HFT Forklifts Limited**

## MR TOM LACEY - continued

**Other Owners:** Miss A. C. Bamford, Lady Bamford, Mr P. L. Barrett, Mr W. J. Chinn, Lady N. F. Cobham, Mr N. D. Cox, Mr G. S. M. Day, F. M. Green, Mr G. A. Hall, Mrs S. L. Hall, Mr A. J. Head, Mr J. Hinds, Mr J. J. King, Mrs V. C. King, Mr G. J. Meredith, Mr N. J. Panniers, D. M. Richards, G. A. Roberts, Roberts, Churchward, Whittal-Williams, Miss V. C. Sturgis, Mr E. B. Whittal-Williams, Mr W. E. Wilde, Mr P. J. H. Wills.

**NH Jockey:** Richard Johnson. **Conditional Jockey:** Stan Sheppard. **Amateur Jockey:** Mr Tommie O'Brien.

---

**330** **MR CARLOS LAFFON-PARIAS, Chantilly**
Postal: **30, Avenue du General Leclerc, 60500 Chantilly, France**
WORK EMAIL ecuries.laffon.parias@wanadoo.fr

1 CONTORTIONISTE, 6, ch h Pivotal—Distortion **Wertheimer et Frere**
2 ECRIVAIN (FR), 4, ch c Lope de Vega (IRE)—Sapphire Pendant (IRE) **Wertheimer et Frere**
3 GALAWI (IRE), 4, b c Dubawi (IRE)—Galikova (FR) **Wertheimer et Frere**
4 HUETOR (FR), 4, ch g Archipenko (USA)—Briviesca **SARL Darpat France**
5 REVENTADOR (IRE), 4, b c Zoffany (IRE)—Frine (IRE) **Duc D'Alburquerque**
6 SEACHANGE (FR), 4, b f Siyouni (FR)—Ydillique (IRE) **Wertheimer et Frere**
7 SILASTAR, 4, b c Sea The Stars (IRE)—Silasol (IRE) **Wertheimer et Frere**
8 STANZO, 4, ch c Speightstown (USA)—Viva Rafaela (BRZ) **Wertheimer et Frere**
9 TWIST (FR), 4, ch c Pivotal—Distortion **Wertheimer et Frere**

## THREE-YEAR-OLDS

10 ABSURDE, b c Fastnet Rock—Incroyable **Wertheimer et Frere**
11 ANSILIA (IRE), b f Dansili—Incahoots **Wertheimer et Frere**
12 CAZALLA, ch f Archipenko—Aguafria **SARL Darpat France**
13 FRONTGATE (USA), b f War Front (USA)—Oceanique (USA) **Wertheimer et Frere**
14 GOLDISTYLE (IRE), ch f Dubawi (IRE)—Goldikova (IRE) **Wertheimer et Frere**
15 GRACE SHELBY, b f Shalaa—Naissance Royale **Al Shira'aa Farms SARL**
16 HYPOCONDRIAC (FR), b c Mastercraftsman (IRE)—Tristesse (USA) **Wertheimer et Frere**
17 IZNAJAR, b f Myboycharlie—Briviesca **SARL Darpat France**
18 KALAOS (IRE), gr c Helmet (AUS)—Pale Pearl (IRE) **Tolmi Racing**
19 KARKHOV (IRE), ch c Lope de Vega (IRE)—Akrivi (IRE) **Mr Alain Jathiere**
20 KOLKA, b f Shalaa (IRE)—Satiriste **Mr Alain Jathiere**
21 LEJENDARIO, b g Myboycharlie (IRE)—Tia Kia (IRE) **MR Mathieu Offenstadt**
22 RICLA, ch f Adlerflug—Highphar **SARL Darpat France**
23 RUMI, br f Frankel—Secrete (FR) **Al Shira'aa Farms SARL**
24 SEULOMONDE, b c Dubawi (IRE)—Solemia (IRE) **Wertheimer et Frere**
25 SILVESTRI, b f Siyouni—La Zubia **Al Shira'aa Farms SARL**
26 SOLANIA (IRE), b f Zoffany (IRE)—Solilea (IRE) **Wertheimer et Frere**
27 SOUPIR, b c Deep Impact (JPN)—Sasparella (FR) **Wertheimer et Frere**
28 TASMANIA (FR), ch br f Zoffany—Australienne **Wertheimer et Frere**
29 VANOUCHE, b c Invincible Spirit—Blarney Stone **Wertheimer et Frere**
30 WALLAROO (IRE), b c Australia—Dancequest (IRE) **Wertheimer et Frere**
31 WOOF (GER), b c Zoffany—Wanderina **Wertheimer et Frere**
32 ZILEO, b c Galileo (IRE)—Lady Zuzu (USA) **Wertheimer et Frere**

## TWO-YEAR-OLDS

33 CARTAOJAL (FR), b f 19/03 Exceed and Excel—Freedom Flashing
34 DESILUSION (USA), b f 02/02 English Chanel—Esneh
35 DUYFKEN, b c 22/02 Le Havre—Australienne
36 ELVIRIA (FR), b f 11/02 Pedro the Great—Osuna
37 FRIVOLE (FR), b f 25/05 Anodin—Houleuse
38 GAUCHER, b c 01/03 Frankel—Left Hand
39 GUADAIZA (FR), b f 23/02 Fast Company—Olanthia

## MR CARLOS LAFFON-PARIAS - continued

40 **HIT (IRE),** b c 10/04 Zoffany—Foreigh Tune **Wertheimer et Frere**
41 **HYPOTENUS,** b c 10/04 Lope de Vega—Mathematicienne
42 **IKATA (IRE),** b f 05/02 Zoffany—Petunia
43 **IMPITOYABLE (FR),** b c 20/06 Dark Angel—Impassable
44 **KISSING,** b c 10/05 Siyouni—Blarney Stone
45 **LEHMANN,** b c 01/03 Galileo—Goldikova
46 **LERMA (FR),** b f 09/04 Reliable Man—Briviesca
47 **PEDRA (IRE),** b f 01/02 Manduro—Atomique
48 **PLUMAGE (FR),** b f 04/05 Dubawi—Plumania
49 **QUECHUACH,** b f 05/02 Dark Angel—Incahoots
50 **REGALIS (FR),** b f 23/05 Dubawi—Baahama
51 **SITUVEUX (IRE),** b f 06/04 Siyouni—Only Green
52 **TING TING (FR),** b f 10/04 Frankel—Mydardhaan
53 **TUMBLER,** b c 02/03 Kingman—Distortion
54 **TWOFORTEA (USA),** b f 20/02 Temple City—Meteor Miracle
55 **VAGALAME (IRE),** b c 05/05 Lope de Vega—Solilea
56 **WAITING,** b c 23/04 Attendu—Belle de France

Other Owners: Haras d'Etreham, Tolmi Racing.

---

**331**
### MR NICK LAMPARD, Marlborough
Postal: **South Cottage, 2 The Crossroads, Clatford, Marlborough, Wiltshire, SN8 4EA**
Contacts: **PHONE 01672 861420**

1 **FOREST LORD,** 7, b g Native Ruler—La Belle Au Bois (IRE) **N. M. Lampard**
2 5, B g Gentlewave (IRE)—Goochypoochyprader **N. M. Lampard**
3 **LOGAN'S CHOICE,** 6, b g Redoute's Choice (AUS)—Bright Morning (USA) **The Ivy**
4 **MINMORE GREY (IRE),** 12, gr g Primary (USA)—Hopeful Memory (IRE) **N. M. Lampard**
5 **SADMA,** 12, gr g Street Cry (IRE)—Blue Dress (USA) **N. M. Lampard**
6 **WESSINGTON PARK,** 6, b m Bollin Eric—Sandend (IRE) **The Ivy**

---

**332**
### MR JUSTIN LANDY, Leyburn
Postal: **2 Beckwood, Spennithorne, Leyburn, North Yorkshire, DL8 5FB**
EMAIL jlandyracing@hotmail.com

1 **LIAR'S DICE (IRE),** 8, b g Milan—Dancing Baloo (IRE) **Miss C. Tinkler**
2 **MCCRACKENS GATE (IRE),** 10, br g Robin des Pres (FR)—Be My Libby (IRE) **Miss C. Tinkler**
3 **MELDRUM LAD (IRE),** 12, b g Fruits of Love (USA)—Meldrum Hall (IRE) **Mrs P. Southerington**
4 **MONTE ALBAN (IRE),** 8, ch g Soviet Star (USA)—Esee (IRE) **Mrs P. Southerington**
5 **MOONLIGHT BEAM (IRE),** 6, b g Kalanisi (IRE)—Assidua (IRE) **Mrs P. Southerington**
6 **SHETLAND BUS (GER),** 8, ch g Sholokhov (IRE)—Shali Tori (FR) **Mrs P. Southerington**
7 **SUNNYHILL LAD (IRE),** 6, ch g Casamento (IRE)—Tereed Elhawa **Mr J. P. G. Landy**
8 **TRAPPER PEAK (IRE),** 12, b g Westerner—Banningham Blaze **Mr J. P. G. Landy**

## 333 MISS EMMA LAVELLE, Marlborough

Postal: Bonita Racing Stables, Ogbourne Maizey, Marlborough, Wiltshire, SN8 1RY
Contacts: PHONE 01672 511544 MOBILE 07774 993998 FAX 01672 511544
EMAIL info@emmalavelle.com WEBSITE www.emmalavelle.com

1 **AURELIA OR (IRE)**, 6, b m Shantou (USA)—Aibrean (IRE) **Dr A. R. Sharkey**
2 **BOLD REASON (GER)**, 6, b g Invincible Spirit (IRE)—Bufera (IRE) **Mrs C. J. Djivanovic**
3 **BOREHAM BILL (IRE)**, 9, b g Tikkanen (USA)—Crimond (IRE) **Mrs S. P. Foran**
4 **BRICKLAGGER (IRE)**, 6, ch g Frozen Power (IRE)—Annaofcompton (IRE) **Mrs Linda Austin & Mr Dennis Coles**
5 **BUSTER THOMAS (IRE)**, 10, b g Westerner—Awesome Miracle (IRE) **Axom LXVII**
6 **CANTY BAY (IRE)**, 4, b g Shantou (USA)—Afairs (IRE) **Mr G. P. MacIntosh**
7 **CELTIC JOY (IRE)**, 8, b g Kayf Tara—No Time For Tears (IRE) **Hawksmoor Partnership**
8 **CLOSING CEREMONY (IRE)**, 12, b g Flemensfirth (USA)—Supreme Von Pres (IRE) **The High Altitude Partnership**
9 **DAGUENEAU (IRE)**, 6, b g Champs Elysees—Bright Enough **Mr A. Gemmell**
10 **DE RASHER COUNTER**, 9, b g Yeats (IRE)—Dedrunknmunky (IRE) **Makin' Bacon Partnership**
11 **DO YOU THINK**, 5, b m So You Think (NZ)—Leblon (USA) **Bonita Racing Club**
12 **DOC PENFRO**, 9, b g Dr Massini (IRE)—Prescelli (IRE) **Doc Redemption**
13 **DOLLNAMIX (FR)**, 10, b g Al Namix (FR)—Sleeping Doll (FR)
14 **EASTERLY**, 5, b m Shirocco (GER)—Easter Dancer **Easter Racing Club**
15 **ECLAIR SURF (FR)**, 7, b g Califet (FR)—Matasurf (FR) **Dominic Burke & Tim Syder**
16 **ENNISCOFFEY OSCAR (IRE)**, 9, b g Oscar (IRE)—Enniscoffey (IRE) **The Pick 'N' Mix Partnership**
17 **FEDELTA (IRE)**, 7, b g Flemensfirth (USA)—Old Moon (IRE) **Mr T. J. Hemmings**
18 **FLEMCARA (IRE)**, 9, b g Flemensfirth (USA)—Cara Mara (IRE) **Andy & The Frisky Fillies**
19 **FLYING NUN (IRE)**, 6, b m Robin des Champs (FR)—Mystic Masie (IRE) **N. Mustoe & A. Gemmell**
20 **GOLD LINK (FR)**, 5, b g Rail Link—Une de Montot (FR) **Owners Group 057**
21 **GREY FOX (IRE)**, 4, gr g Gutaifan (IRE)—Boucheron **Mrs Jennifer Simpson Racing**
22 **GUARD DUTY**, 4, b g Kapgarde (FR)—Ile de See (FR)
23 **GUNFLEET (IRE)**, 9, b g Oscar (IRE)—Lady Lincon (IRE) **Mrs P. J. Travis**
24 **HANG IN THERE (IRE)**, 7, b g Yeats (IRE)—Jaldemosa (FR) **Tim Syder & Andrew Gemmell**
25 **HAWK'S WELL (IRE)**, 7, b g Yeats (IRE)—Our Song **Mrs N. Turner & Mrs E. Fenton**
26 **HIGHLY PRIZED**, 8, b br g Manduro (GER)—Razzle (USA) **H.Pridham & D.Donoghue**
27 **HOI POLLOI (IRE)**, 6, b g Shantou (USA)—Backtothekingsnest (IRE) **N. Mustoe**
28 **HUNTING BROOK (IRE)**, 4, b g Presenting—Fleur d'Ainay (FR) **Bryan & Philippa Burrough**
29 **IRISH PROPHECY (IRE)**, 8, b g Azamour (IRE)—Prophets Honor (FR) **N. Mustoe**
30 **JEMIMA P (IRE)**, 7, b m Jeremy (USA)—Peig Alainn (IRE) **The Three A's Syndicate**
31 **JUBILYMPICS**, 9, b m Kapgarde (FR)—Pepite de Soleil (FR) **Hoe Racing**
32 **KILLER CLOWN (IRE)**, 7, b g Getaway (GER)—Our Soiree (IRE) **Mr T. D. J. Syder**
33 **KING'S THRESHOLD (IRE)**, 4, b g Yeats (IRE)—Pearl Buttons **Sailing to Byzantium**
34 **LET RIP (IRE)**, 7, b g Rip Van Winkle (IRE)—Al Ihsas (IRE) **P. G. Jacobs**
35 **LIGHT N STRIKE (IRE)**, 5, b g Leading Light—One Rose **Mr Niall Farrell, Mr Salvo Giannini**
36 **LISHEEN CASTLE (IRE)**, 6, b g Most Improved (IRE)—Mafaaza (USA) **Elite Racing Club**
37 **LUNA DORA**, 4, gr f Pether's Moon (IRE)—Ixora (IRE) **Greenlands Racing Syndicate**
38 **MANHATTAN BULLET (IRE)**, 6, br g Robin des Champs (FR)—Manhattan Babe (IRE) **Caloona Racing**
39 **MANOFTHEMOUNTAIN (IRE)**, 8, b g Mahler—Womanofthemountain (IRE) **P. G. Jacobs**
40 **MASTER MILLINER (IRE)**, 5, b g Helmet (AUS)—Aqualina (IRE) **Mrs Jennifer Simpson Racing**
41 **MINELLA BUSTER (IRE)**, 5, br g Beat Hollow—Itsallaracket (IRE)
42 **MISTY BLOOM (IRE)**, 8, b m Yeats (IRE)—Misty Mountain (IRE) **Bonita Racing Club**
43 **MUMBO JUMBO (IRE)**, 5, b g Califet (FR)—Touched By Angels (IRE) **N. Mustoe**
44 **NOLLYADOR (FR)**, 4, b g No Risk At All (FR)—Playa du Charmil (FR) **Highclere Thoroughbred Racing -Nollyador**
45 **OLD RASCALS (IRE)**, 8, b g Ask—Balleen Rose (IRE) **The Optimists**
46 **PAISLEY PARK (IRE)**, 9, b g Oscar (IRE)—Presenting Shares (IRE) **Mr A. Gemmell**
47 **PEMBERLEY (IRE)**, 8, b g Darsi (FR)—Eyebright (IRE) **Laurie Kimber & Partners**
48 **PITCH IT UP**, 5, b g Black Sam Bellamy (IRE)—Mtilly **Mrs S. Metcalfe**
49 **POTTERS VISION (IRE)**, 8, b m Getaway (GER)—Peripheral Vision (IRE) **James and Jean Potter Ltd**
50 **PRESENT DESTINY (IRE)**, 9, b g Dubai Destination (USA)—Anns Present (IRE) **& Reid**
51 **PRESENT DESTINY (IRE)**, 4, Ch g Helmet (AUS)—Quiquillo (USA) **Mr J. Wakefield**
52 **RAJARAN (FR)**, 4, gr g Martaline—Ravna (FR) **The High Altitude Partnership**
53 **RED ROOKIE**, 6, ch g Black Sam Bellamy (IRE)—Auction Belle **The Hawk Inn Syndicate 3**
54 **RUNSWICK BAY**, 6, b g Arvico (FR)—Chantal **The Hon J. R. Drummond**
55 **SAM BARTON**, 6, b g Black Sam Bellamy (IRE)—Bartons Bride (IRE) **Mr T. J. Hemmings**
56 **SAN GIOVANNI (IRE)**, 5, b g Milan—Down By The Sea (IRE)

## MISS EMMA LAVELLE - continued

57 **SANDINISTA (IRE)**, 6, ch g Vinnie Roe (IRE)—Bewildered (IRE)  **The Bonhamie Partnership**
58 **SHANG TANG (IRE)**, 7, b g Shantou (USA)—Ballyguider Bridge (IRE)  **T. Syder & N. Mustoe**
59 **SHIROCCAN ROLL**, 7, b g Shirocco (GER)—Folie Dancer  **J.R. Lavelle & Mrs L.N. Major**
60 **SHIROCCY ROAD**, 5, b m Shirocco (GER)—Folie Dancer  **J. R. Lavelle & Dr Mark Scott**
61 **SILENT ASSISTANT (IRE)**, 7, b g Sans Frontieres (IRE)—Monanig Lass (IRE)  **Lavelle, Awdry & Williams**
62 **STORM LORD (IRE)**, 5, br gr g Yeats (IRE)—Lady Sagamix (IRE)  **Kevin Lloyd & Nicky Turner**
63 **TABLE THIRTY FOUR**, 4, br g Blue Bresil (FR)—Whoops A Daisy  **D.Burke, T.Syder & Mrs D.L.Whateley**
64 **TARA NIECE**, 8, b m Kayf Tara—Pepite de Soleil (FR)  **Hoe Racing**
65 **TEDWIN HILLS**, 4, b c Getaway (GER)—Ashwell Lady  **N. Mustoe**
66 **THE DOMINO EFFECT (IRE)**, 7, b g Oscar (IRE)—Lively Lass (IRE)  **Mighty Acorn Stables**
67 **THE SWEENEY (IRE)**, 9, b g Oscar (IRE)—Banningham Blaze  **N. Mustoe**
68 **THUNDERSTRUCK (IRE)**, 7, b g Fame And Glory—Go Sandy Go (IRE)  **Mr T. D. J. Syder**
69 **TIERRA VERDE**, 10, b m Josr Algarhoud (IRE)—La Corujera  **Greenlands Racing Syndicate**
70 **VIVA VITTORIA**, 7, b m Stowaway—La Fisarmonica (IRE)  **Mr & Mrs A Millett**
71 **VOICE OF CALM**, 5, b m Poets Voice—Marliana (IRE)  **Mr T. D. J. Syder, Hungerford Park Partnership**
72 **WATER WAGTAIL**, 14, b g Kahyasi—Kentford Grebe  **D. I. Bare**
73 **WILD WILBUR (IRE)**, 5, ch g Presenting—Kon Tiky (IRE)  **Mr & Mrs W & Dr T Davies & Mrs T Grundy**
74 **WOULDUBEWELL (IRE)**, 7, b m Gold Well—Howrwedoin (IRE)  **Owners Group 063**
75 **YOUNG BUTLER (IRE)**, 5, b g Yeats (IRE)—Name For Fame (USA)  **Mr T. D. J. Syder**
76 **ZARAFSHAN (IRE)**, 5, b g Shamardal (USA)—Zarshana (IRE)  **Mr R. J. Lavelle**

### THREE-YEAR-OLDS

77 B g Kayf Tara—Folie Dancer  **J.R. Lavelle & Paul G. Jacobs**

**Other Owners:** Mrs L. L. Austin, Mr C. V. Awdry, Mr D. M. Bradshaw, Mr D. J. Burke, B. R. H. Burrough, Mrs P. J. Burrough, Mr D. L. Coles, Mrs S. C. Davies, Dr T. J. W. Davies, Mr W. P. L. Davies, Mr D. Donoghue, Mr J. B. Duffy, Mr S. W. Dunn, Mr A. Gemmell, Mrs T. A. Grundy, P.G. Jacobs, Mr R. S. Keck, Mr L. G. Kimber, Mr M. Kirkby, Miss I. G. Langton, Miss E. C. Lavelle, Mr J. R. Lavelle, Mr R. J. Lavelle, Mr K. A. Lloyd, Mrs L. N. Major, McCoy & O'Brien Syndicate, Mrs S. Metcalfe, Mr A. J. Millett, Mrs A. M. Millett, Mr J. H. Mills, Mrs M. A. Moore, N. Mustoe, Mr P. Nicholls, Mr B. G. Pomford, Ms H. A. Pridham, Mr M. G. Roberts, K. P. Ryan, Dr M. J. Scott, Mrs J. I. Simpson, Mr W. H. Simpson, Mr J. Smee, Mr T. D. J. Syder, Mrs N. C. Turner, Mr Scott Turner, Mrs V. A. Villers, Exors of the Late Mr P. R. Weston, Mrs D. L. Whateley, Mrs P. H. Williams, Mr I. P. Wixon, Mr B. J. Wren.

**Assistant Trainer:** Barry Fenton.

---

**334**  **MR TOBY LAWES, Beare Green**
Postal: Henfold House Cottage, Henfold Lane, Beare Green, Dorking, Surrey, RH5 4RW
EMAIL toby@tobylawesracing.com

1 **ALKOPOP (GER)**, 7, gr g Jukebox Jury (IRE)—Alkeste (GER)  **A. T. A. Wates**
2 **EYE OF AN EAGLE (FR)**, 8, b g Linda's Lad—Vie des Aigles (FR)  **A. T. A. Wates**
3 **GLENCOUM LASS (IRE)**, 7, b m Court Cave (IRE)—Clare Belle (IRE)  **The Beare With Us Partnership**
4 **GO FORRIT (IRE)**, 7, b g Jeremy (USA)—Ben Roseler (IRE)  **A. T. A. Wates**
5 **KANNAPOLIS (IRE)**, 6, b g Makfi—Alta Definizione (IRE)  **Henfold Harriers**
6 **KAP AUTEUIL (FR)**, 6, b g Kapgarde (FR)—Turboka (FR)  **A. T. A. Wates**
7 **NASHVILLE NIPPER (IRE)**, 7, b g Millenary—Benfrasea (IRE)  **The Beare With Us Partnership**
8 **NICKOBOY (FR)**, 6, b g Full of Gold (FR)—Dikanika (FR)  **A. T. A. Wates**
9 **OLD TIMES (IRE)**, 6, b m Doyen (IRE)—La Belle Bleu (IRE)  **Gait Expectations**
10 **POTTLEREAGHEXPRESS (IRE)**, 8, b m Beneficial—Needle Doll (IRE)  **The Beare With Us Partnership**
11 **QUEENS PRESENT (IRE)**, 10, ch m Presenting—Fairy Dawn (IRE)  **A. T. A. Wates**
12 **SAMEER (FR)**, 5, b g Nathaniel (IRE)—Sanabyra (FR)  **M. H. Watt**
13 **SOLDIER TO FOLLOW**, 6, b g Soldier Hollow—Nota Bene (GER)  **Mr A T A Wates & Mrs S Wates**
14 **SUBLIME HEIGHTS (IRE)**, 5, b g Arcadio (GER)—Corrag Lass (IRE)  **Mr A T A Wates & Mrs S Wates**
15 **VOYAGE DE RETOUR (IRE)**, 9, b g Craigsteel—Taipers (IRE)  **Mrs E. A. Bingley**
16 **ZACONY REBEL (IRE)**, 6, b g Getaway (GER)—Bay Rebel (IRE)  **Mr A T A Wates & Mrs S Wates**

**Other Owners:** Mr B. E. Alder, Mrs B. V. Evans, Mr A. Miller, Mrs S. Miller, A. T. A. Wates, Mrs S. M. Wates.

## 335 MR BARRY LEAVY, Stoke-on-Trent

Postal: Cash Heath Farm, Cash Heath, Forsbrook, Stoke on Trent, ST11 9DE
Contacts: PHONE 01782 398591 MOBILE 07540 806915
EMAIL lauraleavy@hotmail.co.uk WEBSITE www.leavyracing.co.uk

1 COME ON CHARLIE (FR), 9, b g Anzillero (GER)—End of Spring (FR) **May The Horse Be With You**
2 GENERATOR CITY (IRE), 8, b g Primary (USA)—Sabbatical (IRE) **Dove Valley Holdings Ltd**
3 GEORGIAN FIREBIRD, 11, b m Firebreak—Skovshoved (IRE) **Mrs E. A. Wilson**
4 HE'S A GOER (IRE), 7, b g Yeats (IRE)—Tessas Girl (IRE) **Here We Go Racing**
5 INFINITI (IRE), 8, b m Arcano (IRE)—Seraphina (IRE) **Mrs Susan Ashford and Partner**
6 JAXLIGHT, 9, b m Lucarno (USA)—Jaxelle (FR) **May The Horse Be With You**
7 POUCOR, 6, b g Pour Moi (IRE)—Corinium (IRE) **The Toffee Potters**
8 ZARAZENA, 6, b m Yeats (IRE)—Zarannda (IRE) **Dove Valley Holdings Ltd**

**Other Owners:** Mr B. Leavy, Mrs S. D. Williams-Ashford.

**Assistant Trainer:** Mrs L Leavy.

## 336 MISS KERRY LEE, Presteigne

Postal: Bell House, Byton, Presteigne, Powys, LD8 2HS
Contacts: PHONE 01544 267672 MOBILE 07968 242663
EMAIL kerry@kerrylee.co.uk WEBSITE www.kerrylee.co.uk

1 BALLYBEGG (IRE), 6, b g Mahler—Rebel Flyer (IRE) **Glass Half Full**
2 BRIGADIER BOB (IRE), 8, b g Excellent Art—Plausabelle **A & B Beard, C Davies S Harris M Hawkins**
3 DEMACHINE (IRE), 7, b g Flemensfirth (USA)—Dancingonthemoon (IRE) **West Coast Haulage Limited**
4 DESTINED TO SHINE (IRE), 9, b g Dubai Destination (USA)—Good Shine (IRE) **Campbell-mizen**
5 DO IT FOR THY SEN (IRE), 7, ch g Mountain High (IRE)—Ashlings Princess (IRE) **Campbell-Mizen & R L Baker**
6 EATON COLLINA (IRE), 6, b g Milan—Flowers On Sunday (IRE) **Mrs H. Watson**
7 EATON HILL (IRE), 9, b g Yeats (IRE)—Guilt Less (FR) **Mrs H. Watson**
8 FAY CE QUE VOUDRAS (IRE), 5, b m Getaway (GER)—Buck's Blue (FR) **W. Roseff**
9 FINANCIER, 8, ch g Dubawi (IRE)—Desired **W. Roseff**
10 HAPPY DIVA (IRE), 10, b m King's Theatre (IRE)—Megans Joy (IRE) **W. Roseff**
11 HELLFIRE PRINCESS, 4, ch f Dunaden (FR)—Ryde Back **W. Roseff**
12 HENRI LE BON (IRE), 6, b g Sea The Stars (IRE)—Speed Song **W. Roseff**
13 ICE COOL CHAMPS (IRE), 10, ch g Robin des Champs (FR)—Last of Many (IRE) **West Coast Haulage Limited**
14 KINGS MONARCH, 8, b g Schiaparelli (GER)—Monarch's View **Miss K. Lee**
15 LET'S GETAWAY (IRE), 6, b g Getaway (GER)—Roxtown **James & Jean Potter**
16 LICIA ST GOUSTAN (FR), 4, b f Great Pretender (IRE)—Saint Goustan (FR) **W. Roseff**
17 MAGIC DANCER, 9, b g Norse Dancer (IRE)—King's Siren (IRE) **The Magic Partnership**
18 NOT SURE (IRE), 5, b g Presenting—Pink Mist (IRE) **W. Roseff**
19 ORCHARD GROVE (IRE), 5, b g Valirann (IRE)—Little Vinnie (IRE) **Mr D. M. Morgan**
20 STORM CONTROL (IRE), 8, b g September Storm (GER)—Double Dream (IRE) **W. Roseff**
21 THE WELSH PADDIES (IRE), 9, b g Court Cave (IRE)—Masiana (IRE) **West Coast Haulage Limited**
22 TOP GAMBLE (IRE), 13, ch g Presenting—Zeferina (IRE) **Miss K. Lee**
23 TOWN PARKS (IRE), 10, b g Morozov (USA)—Outdoor Heather (IRE) **Mrs J. A. Beavan**

**Other Owners:** Mr R. L. Baker, A. C. Beard, B. M. Beard, Mr D. E. Campbell, Campbell-mizen, Mrs C. D. E. Davies, Mr G. T. Gilbert, Mr S. Harris, Mr M. R. Hawkins, Mr P. J. Mizen, Mr P. T. G. Phillips, W. Roseff.

**Assistant Trainer:** Richard Lee.

**NH Jockey:** Jamie Moore, Richard Patrick.

**337** **MRS SOPHIE LEECH, Westbury-on-Severn**
Postal: T/A Leech Racing Limited, Tudor Racing Stables, Elton Road, Elton, Newnham, Gloucestershire, GL14 1JN
Contacts: PHONE 01452 760691 MOBILE 07775 874630
EMAIL info@leechracing.co.uk WEBSITE www.leechracing.co.uk

1 ANTEROS (IRE), 13, b g Milan—Sovereign Star (IRE) **K. W. Bell**
2 APPLESANDPIERRES (IRE), 13, b g Pierre—Cluain Chaoin (IRE) **Exors of the Late C. J. Leech**
3 BONBON AU MIEL (FR), 10, b g Khalkevi (IRE)—Friandise II (FR) **Mr J. T. Finch**
4 BUONAROTTI BOY (IRE), 9, b g Galileo (IRE)—Funsie (FR) **Cheltenham Racing Club**
5 CHESTNUT PETE, 6, ch g Native Ruler—Rabbit **Mike Harris Racing Club**
6 CLONDAW CIAN (IRE), 11, br g Gold Well—Cocktail Bar (IRE) **G. D. Thompson**
7 DOUX PRETENDER (FR), 8, b g Great Pretender (IRE)—Lynnka (FR) **Mr J. T. Finch**
8 ENFANT ROI (FR), 7, b g Saint des Saints (FR)—Super Maman (FR) **Mr J. T. Finch**
9 EQUILIBRIUM (FR), 7, b m Balko (FR)—Tacoma Gaugain (FR) **Mr C. R. Leech**
10 FINNISTON FARM, 6, b g Helmet (AUS)—Logic **Mr J. T. Finch**
11 GARO DE JUILLEY (FR), 9, b g Ungaro (GER)—Lucy de Juilley (FR) **G. D. Thompson**
12 GENERAL BUX, 10, b g Lucarno (USA)—Cadoutene (FR) **The Scoobyless Partnership**
13 GRAPEVINE (IRE), 8, b g Lilbourne Lad (IRE)—High Vintage (IRE) **Mr J. T. Finch**
14 GUSTAVE AITCH (FR), 5, b g Maxios—Alyssandre (IRE) **Finch Moran Stone Smith Hooton Pearson-S**
15 HENRYVILLE, 13, b g Generous (IRE)—Aquavita **Mr J. T. Finch**
16 LIEUTENANT COLONEL, 12, b g Kayf Tara—Agnese **Mr C. R. Leech**
17 LYSANDER BELLE (IRE), 5, b m Exceed And Excel (AUS)—Switcher (IRE) **Mike Harris Racing Club**
18 MAN OF PLENTY, 12, ch g Manduro (GER)—Credit-A-Plenty **G. D. Thompson**
19 MILROW (IRE), 8, b g Tamayuz—Cannikin (IRE) **John Cocks & Roger Liddington**
20 NIBLAWI (IRE), 9, b g Vale of York (IRE)—Finnmark **Mr J. T. Finch**
21 OLD HARRY ROCKS (IRE), 9, b g Milan—Miss Baden (IRE) **G. D. Thompson**
22 PERCY (IRE), 7, gr g Kodiac—Bysshe **Cheltenhambuild Ltd**
23 PERFECT MAN (IRE), 10, b g Morozov (USA)—Garrisker (IRE) **Mr J. T. Finch**
24 TAMARILLO GROVE (IRE), 14, b g Cape Cross (IRE)—Tamarillo **Cheltenham Racing Club**
25 UTILITY (GER), 10, b g Yeats (IRE)—Ungarin (GER) **Mr J. T. Finch**
26 VANITEUX (FR), 12, br g Voix du Nord (FR)—Expoville (FR) **Mr C. R. Leech**
27 WE'VE GOT PAYET, 7, b g Authorized (IRE)—Missoula (IRE) **Mr Steve Ashley & Mr Gary Pettit**
28 WEST WIZARD (FR), 12, b br g King's Theatre (IRE)—Queen's Diamond (GER) **J. O'Brien**
29 YASIR (IRE), 13, b g Dynaformer (USA)—Khazayin (USA) **Mike Harris Racing Club**
30 ZERO TO HERO (IRE), 6, ch m Arakan (USA)—Blue Daze **Finch Moran Lamb Smith Boyd-Bowman**
31 ZUREKIN (IRE), 5, b g Martaline—Fleur d'Ainay (FR) **Mr J. T. Finch**

Other Owners: Mr S. A. Ashley, Mr J. J. Cocks, A. D. I. Harris, Mr M. E. Harris, Mr R. S. Liddington, Mr G. Pettit.

Assistant Trainer: Christian Leech.

**338** **MISS TRACEY LEESON, Towcester**
Postal: Glebe Stables, Blakesley Heath Farm, Maidford, Northants, NN12 8HN
Contacts: MOBILE 07761 537672
EMAIL traceyl31@hotmail.co.uk WEBSITE www.traceyleesonracing.co.uk

1 LOUPGAROU (FR), 9, gr g Martaline—Jasminette Doree (FR) **Miss T. A. Leeson**
2 MARY OF DE SORROWS (IRE), 6, br m Elusive Pimpernel (USA)—Ginger Lily (IRE) **Mr P. A. Long**
3 MOROVAL (IRE), 10, b g Morozov (USA)—Valerie Ellen (IRE) **The Blakesley Racing Club**
4 RINGMOYLAN (IRE), 9, b g Mahler—La Speziana (IRE) **Buzzing Again Partnership**
5 SLEVE DONARD (IRE), 7, b g Mountain High (IRE)—Ceart Go Leor (IRE) **The Blakesley Racing Club**
6 TOP DRAWER (IRE), 7, b g Doyen (IRE)—Merry Gladness (IRE) **The Peter Partnership**

## THREE-YEAR-OLDS

7 B g Fast Company (IRE)—Nouvelle Lune

## 339  MRS SHEILA LEWIS, Brecon
Postal: **Mill Service Station, Three Cocks, Brecon, Powys, LD3 0SL**
Contacts: **PHONE 01497 847081**
EMAIL sheilalewisracing1@gmail.com

1  COTTON END (IRE), 7, gr m Scorpion (IRE)—Scartara (FR)  **Mr G. Wilson**
2  FAMILY POT (FR), 6, gr g Monitor Closely (IRE)—Nikitries (FR)  **W. B. R. Davies**
3  FASHION'S MODEL (IRE), 5, gr m Flemensfirth (USA)—Fashion's Worth (IRE)  **W. B. R. Davies**
4  GRACEFUL ABBIE, 7, b m Black Sam Bellamy (IRE)—Banoo (IRE)  **Mr R. A. Jones**
5  INGEBORG ZILLING (IRE), 5, ch m Mahler—Lindy Lou  **Mr A. M. Lloyd**
6  KNIGHT COMMANDER, 8, br g Sir Percy—Jardin  **Foxhunters In Mind**
7  MITCHELL STREET, 4, br c Dunaden (FR)—Laurens Ruby (IRE)  **Hswho Partnership**
8  PEPPER POT BOY (IRE), 4, br g Laverock (IRE)—Jaya Bella (IRE)  **Hswho Partnership**
9  STRAW FAN JACK, 6, gr g Geordieland (FR)—Callerlilly  **Mr G. Wilson**
10  VOLCANO (FR), 7, gr g Martaline—Lyli Rose (FR)  **W. B. R. Davies**
11  WELL BRIEFED (IRE), 6, b m Mahler—The Irish Whip  **Mr A. M. Lloyd**

## 340  MR NICK LITTMODEN, Newmarket
Postal: **Inner Yard, Brickfield Stud, Cemetery Hill, Newmarket, Suffolk, CB8 7JH**
Contacts: **MOBILE 07770 964865**
EMAIL nicklittmoden@icloud.com

1  ARABESCATO, 4, gr g Outstrip—Cat Hunter  **D. Cohen**
2  BROUAINS (FR), 5, ch g Anodin (IRE)—Enzina  **Mr G. F. Chesneaux & Mr Nick Littmoden**
3  CAPTAIN SPEAKING (FR), 6, ch g Lina's Lad—Hillflower (FR)  **We Live In Norfolk Partnership**
4  FIGEAC (FR), 7, gr g Kendargent (FR)—Faviva (USA)  **Mr G. F. Chesneaux & Mr Nick Littmoden**
5  FLEUR IRLANDAISE (FR), 6, b m No Risk At All (FR)—Orlandaise (FR)  **G. Chesneaux N. Littmoden**
6  GREY D'ARS (FR), 5, gr g Rajsaman (FR)—Prisenflag (FR)  **R.Favarulo,G.Chesneaux,N.Littmoden**
7  IMPERIL (FR), 5, b g No Risk At All (FR)—Irevoltar Has (FR)  **Gerry Chesneaux ,Emma Littmoden**
8  NO DIGGITY (IRE), 5, b g Sir Prancealot (IRE)—Monarchy (IRE)  **Mr R. Favarulo**
9  NOVERRE DANCER (IRE), 5, b g Le Havre (IRE)—Irish Cliff (IRE)  **Mr G. F. Chesneaux & Mr Nick Littmoden**
10  ORIGINAL CHOICE (IRE), 7, ch g Dragon Pulse (IRE)—Belle Watling (IRE)  **N. P. Littmoden**
11  SACHAMAK (FR), 4, b g Makfi—Sachet (USA)  **G. Chesneaux N. Littmoden**
12  SHIELD OF HONOUR, 4, ch g Helmet (AUS)—Betty Brook (IRE)  **N. P. Littmoden**

### THREE-YEAR-OLDS
13  BODROY (IRE), b c Coulsty (IRE)—Youcouldntmakeitup (IRE)  **Newhorse**
14  LOYAL HAVANA, b c Havana Gold (IRE)—Honesty Pays  **Mr G. F. Chesneaux & Mr Nick Littmoden**
15  MISS BELLA BRAND, b f Poet's Voice—Miss Toldyaso (IRE)  **Mr R. A. G. Robinson**
16  B c Equiano (FR)—Miss Villefranche

Other Owners: G. F. Chesneaux, Mr R. Favarulo, Mrs E. Littmoden, N. P. Littmoden.

NH Jockey: Jack Quinlan. Amateur Jockey: Mr  Martin Dunne.

## 341 MR BERNARD LLEWELLYN, Bargoed

Postal: **Ffynonau Duon Farm, Pentwyn, Fochriw, Bargoed, Mid Glamorgan, CF81 9NP**
Contacts: **PHONE 01685 841259 MOBILE 07960 151083, 07971 233473 FAX 01685 843838**
EMAIL **bernard.llewellyn@btopenworld.com**

1 **ARTY CAMPBELL (IRE),** 11, b g Dylan Thomas (IRE)—Kincob (USA) **Mr Alex James & Mr B. J. Llewellyn**
2 **ASCOT DAY (FR),** 7, ch g Soave (GER)—Allez Hongkong (GER) **B. J. Llewellyn**
3 **CANAL ROCKS,** 5, br g Aussie Rules (USA)—In Secret **B. J. Llewellyn**
4 **CELTIC FORCE (IRE),** 5, gr g Gale Force Ten—Karlisse (IRE) **Mr G. S. Llewellyn**
5 **COGITAL,** 6, b g Invincible Spirit (IRE)—Galaxy Highflyer **PC Bloodstock**
6 **EARTHLY (USA),** 7, b g Spring At Last (USA)—Geographic (USA) **Mr D Maddocks & Partner**
7 **FLAMES OF YORK,** 4, b g Rock of Gibraltar (IRE)—Special Miss **B. J. Llewellyn**
8 **FLANAGANS FIELD (IRE),** 13, b g Araafa (IRE)—Zvezda (USA) **Mr M. Bilton**
9 **GALA DES LYS (FR),** 5, b g Maresca Sorrento (FR)—Royale Place (FR) **Mr D. A. Smerdon**
10 **KAISAN,** 8, b g Rip Van Winkle (IRE)—Orinoco (IRE) **Smerdon Tree Services Ltd**
11 **KING CHARLES (USA),** 4, b g Lemon Drop Kid (USA)—La Reine Lionne (USA) **B. J. Llewellyn**
12 **KOMMODITY KID (IRE),** 4, b g Kingston Hill—Sweetly Does It **Neil & Simon Racing Partners**
13 **PORT OR STARBOARD (IRE),** 4, b g Epaulette (AUS)—Galley **B. J. Llewellyn**
14 **SHADOW'S GIRL,** 9, gr m Fair Mix (IRE)—Special Beat **G. Mills**
15 **TRIPLE NICKLE (IRE),** 5, b m So You Think (NZ)—Secret Shine (IRE) **Mr Alex James & Mr B. J. Llewellyn**
16 **VALENTINE'S TURF (FR),** 6, b g Konig Turf (GER)—Polish Nana (FR) **Mr D. A. Smerdon**
17 **VOLTAIC,** 5, ch g Power—Seramindar **B. J. Llewellyn**
18 **ZAMBEZI FIX (FR),** 6, gr g Zambezi Sun—Lady Fix (FR) **Mr Gethyn Mills & Mr B. J. Llewellyn**
19 **ZAMBEZI MAGIC,** 4, b g Zoffany (IRE)—Millestan (IRE) **B. J. Llewellyn**

**Other Owners:** Mr N. J. Edwards, Mr A. James, Mr S. James, B. J. Llewellyn, Mr D. P. Maddocks, G. Mills, Mrs Beth Williams.

**Assistant Trainer:** J L Llewellyn.

**Flat Jockey:** Daniel Muscutt, David Probert. **Conditional Jockey:** Jordan Williams, Robert Williams. **Amateur Jockey:** Miss Jessica Llewellyn.

## 342 MR JOHN E. LONG, Brighton

Postal: **Southdown Stables, Bear Road, Brighton, East Sussex, BN2 6AB**
Contacts: **MOBILE 07815 186085, 07958 296945**
EMAIL **winalot@aol.com**

1 **CAPE GRECO (USA),** 6, b g Cape Blanco (IRE)—High Walden (USA) **R Blyth & S Colville**
2 **CATIVO RAGAZZO,** 6, b g Multiplex—Sea Isle **M. J. Gibbs**
3 **KINGMON'S BOY,** 6, b g Denounce—Ela d'Argent (IRE) **J. King**
4 **KNOCKOUT BLOW,** 6, b g Lethal Force (IRE)—Elidore **R Blyth & S Colville**
5 **LIBBRETTA,** 6, ch m Libranno—Dispol Katie **Mrs A. M. Sturges**
6 **MAGICINTHEMAKING (USA),** 7, br m Wildcat Heir (USA)—
Love in Bloom (USA) **Mr Martin J. Gibbs & Mr R. D. John**

**Other Owners:** Mr R. Blyth, S. E. Colville, M. J. Gibbs, R. D. John.

**Assistant Trainer:** Miss S Cassidy.

**Flat Jockey:** Hollie Doyle.

**343**  **MR CHARLIE LONGSDON, Chipping Norton**
Postal: Hull Farm Stables, Stratford Road, Chipping Norton, Oxfordshire, OX7 5QF
Contacts: WORK 01608 645556 MOBILE 07775 993263
EMAIL info@charlielongsdonracing.com WEBSITE www.charlielongsdonracing.com

1 ALMAZHAR GARDE (FR), 6, ch g Kapgarde (FR)—Loin de Moi (FR) **Kate & Andrew Brooks**
2 BALLYDINE (IRE), 11, ch g Stowaway—Bealaha Essie (IRE) **Mr D. A. Halsall**
3 BARTON ROSE, 12, b m Midnight Legend—Barton Flower **Ms G. E. Morgan**
4 4, B g Westerner—Beneficial Breeze (IRE)
5 BEYOND THE CLOUDS, 8, ch g Peintre Celebre (USA)—Evening **Mr R. J. Aplin**
6 BOLD PIMPERNEL (IRE), 6, br g Elusive Pimpernel (USA)—Mahee Island (IRE) **The Harlequins Racing**
7 CARDIGAN BAY (FR), 8, b m Turtle Bowl (IRE)—Nan's Catch (IRE) **Birch, Djivanovic & Doel**
8 CARLOW FARMER (IRE), 8, b g Stowaway—Supreme Fivestar (IRE) **Cracker Syndicate**
9 CASTLE ROBIN (IRE), 6, ch g Robin des Champs (FR)—Coco Opera (IRE) **Bradley Partnership**
10 CHAMPAGNE NOIR (IRE), 7, br g Stowaway—Prayuwin Drummer (IRE) **The Macechern Family & Robert Aplin**
11 DIGER DAUDAIE (FR), 8, b g Tiger Groom—Stone Again (FR) **Mrs R. S. Perkins**
12 DO WANNA KNOW (IRE), 7, b g Frammassone (IRE)—Mille Et Une Nuits (FR) **Girls Allowed**
13 ECLAIR ON LINE (IRE), 7, gr g Dream Well (FR)—Odeline (FR) **Eclair On Line Syndicate**
14 FREETHINKER, 5, b g Libertarian—Supreme Magical **The Free Thinkers**
15 GLENCASSLEY (IRE), 6, b g Yeats (IRE)—Reseda (GER) **Mr G. Leon**
16 GLIMPSE OF GALA, 5, b m Passing Glance—Apple Days **The Tweed Clad Fossils**
17 GUETAPAN COLLONGES (FR), 5, b g Saddler Maker (IRE)—Saturne Collonges (FR) **Mr J. P. McManus**
18 HAAS BOY (FR), 4, b g Diamond Boy (FR)—Naker Mome (FR)
19 HIGH YIELD, 4, b g Yeats (IRE)—Midsummer Magic **Her Majesty The Queen**
20 HOOT AT MIDNIGHT, 6, b m Midnight Legend—Kahooting **Mr & Mrs N. F. Maltby**
21 ILLEGAL MODEL (IRE), 7, b g Stowaway—She's So Beautiful (IRE) **Mr D. A. Halsall**
22 JAMACHO, 7, ch g Camacho—Obsessive Secret (IRE) **Stratford Racecourse & Robert Aplin**
23 JUST YOUR TYPE (IRE), 9, br g Morozov (USA)—Enistar (IRE) **Mr T. Hanlon**
24 LARGY NIGHTS (IRE), 7, b g Jeremy—Rowdy Nights (IRE) **Mrs J. A. Wakefield**
25 LISDOONVARNA LAD (IRE), 9, br g Westerner—Socialite Girl **Five Saints Racing**
26 LOCAL AFFAIR, 5, ch m Teofilo (IRE)—Local Spirit (USA) **Slater Stockwood Nicholson Partnership**
27 LOUSE TALK (IRE), 9, b g Mahler—Foxy-Lady (IRE) **Pauling,Perkins,Kerwood,King&Williams**
28 MANINSANE (IRE), 6, ch g Salutino (GER)—Don't Fall (IRE) **Barrels Of Courage**
29 MISS MOLINARI, 7, b m Malinas (GER)—Maiden Voyage **Mr N. Davies**
30 MOON KING (FR), 5, br g Sea The Moon (GER)—Maraba (FR) **Merriebelle Irish Farm Limited**
31 NIGHTFLY, 10, br m Midnight Legend—Whichway Girl **Mrs D. P. G. Flory**
32 NIGHTLINE, 11, b g Midnight Legend—Whichway Girl **Mrs D. P. G. Flory**
33 NO NO TANGO, 4, ch g Sixties Icon—Until Forever (IRE) **Don Sebastiao Partnership**
34 PARRAMOUNT, 5, b g Mount Nelson—Queen Soraya **Mr A. Fox-Pitt**
35 PETER'S PORTRAIT (IRE), 8, b g Portrait Gallery (IRE)—Fancyfacia (IRE) **Four Nags and a Horse**
36 PUNCTUATION, 4, b g Dansili—Key Point (IRE) **Mr G. Leon**
37 RAINMAKER (IRE), 5, b m Yeats (IRE)—Rubichamps **Mrs P. M. Scott**
38 RAVEN COURT (IRE), 7, b g Court Cave (IRE)—Lady Kate Ellen (IRE) **Slater Stockwood Nicholson Partnership**
39 RIVARROS (FR), 6, b g Agent Secret (IRE)—Rive Sarthe (FR) **100 Not Out**
40 SAINT DALINA (FR), 7, b m Saint des Saints (FR)—Dalina (FR) **Mr D. A. Halsall**
41 SCENE NOT HERD (IRE), 6, b g Aizavoski (IRE)—Jessaway (IRE) **Swanee River Partnership**
42 SHAH AN SHAH, 7, ch g Shirocco (GER)—Queen Soraya **Mr A. Fox-Pitt**
43 SNOW LEOPARDESS, 9, gr m Martaline—Queen Soraya **Mr A. Fox-Pitt**
44 STORM GODDESS (IRE), 7, br m Oscar (IRE)—Afasheen (IRE) **Don Sebastiao Partnership**
45 STORMY MILAN (IRE), 8, b g Milan—Socialite Girl **Stormy Milan Syndicate**
46 TEENAGE DIRTBAG (IRE), 5, b g Fame And Glory—Tavadden (IRE) **The Saddleworth Players**
47 THE MIGHTY ARC (IRE), 6, b g Arcadio (GER)—Funcheon Lady (IRE) **Leon & Thornton Families**
48 THE VOLLAN (IRE), 7, b g Scorpion (IRE)—Print It On Lips (IRE) **Mr M. S. Scott**
49 THE WISE TRAVELLER (IRE), 5, b g Getaway (GER)—Butterfly Betty (IRE)
50 THINQUE TANK, 5, b g So You Think (NZ)—Azharia **The Charlie Longsdon Racing Club**
51 TRAIN HILL (IRE), 5, b g Subtle Power—Aljapip (IRE) **Swanee River Partnership**
52 VIVAS (FR), 10, b br g Davidoff (GER)—Lavircas (FR) **Mr N. Davies**
53 WESTERN MILLER (IRE), 10, b g Westerner—Definite Miller (IRE) **The Pantechnicons IV**
54 WHAT ABOUT TIME (IRE), 7, br g Oscar (IRE)—Fennor Rose (IRE) **What About Time Syndicate**

## MR CHARLIE LONGSDON - continued

**Other Owners:** Mr R. J. Aplin, Mr N. M. Birch, Mr A. L. Brooks, Mrs K. L. Brooks, Mrs C. J. Djivanovic, Mrs R. J. Doel, Mr C. E. Longsdon, Gavin MacEchern, Mrs J. Maltby, Mr N. F. Maltby, The Stratford-On-Avon Racecourse Company, Ltd.

**Conditional Jockey:** Tom Buckley. **NH Jockey:** Paul O'Brien.

---

## 344 MR DAVID LOUGHNANE, Tern Hill
Postal: Helshaw Grange, Warrant Road, Tern Hill, Shropshire
Contacts: **MOBILE 07527 173197**
EMAIL info@daveloughnaneracing.com WEBSITE www.daveloughnaneracing.com

1 AMBER ISLAND (IRE), 4, b f Exceed And Excel (AUS)—Raphinae **Mr D. J. Lowe**
2 APEX KING (IRE), 7, b g Kodiac—Rainbowskia (FR) **Mr N. I. Willis**
3 BABY STEPS, 5, b g Paco Boy (IRE)—Stepping Out (IRE) **Mr D. J. Lowe**
4 CANDELISA (IRE), 8, br g Dream Ahead (USA)—Vasilia **Mr M. Godfrey**
5 CRITICAL THINKING (IRE), 7, b g Art Connoisseur (USA)—Cookie Cutter (IRE) **Mr J. Rocke**
6 CUPID'S BEAU, 4, b g Brazen Beau (AUS)—Oilinda **Mr D. J. Lowe**
7 DARANOVA (IRE), 7, b g Arctic Cosmos (USA)—Dara Supreme (IRE) **Mr C. F. Moore**
8 DARK PINE (IRE), 4, b g Dandy Man (IRE)—Suitably Discreet (USA) **Mr G. Dewhurst**
9 EASTERN GENERAL (IRE), 4, b g Brazen Beau (AUS)—Celestial Empire (USA) **Mr K. Sohi**
10 ELHAFEI (USA), 6, br g Speightstown (USA)—Albamara **Mr N. I. Willis**
11 FFION, 4, b f Sepoy (AUS)—Exceedingly **Mr A. Gray**
12 FIZZY FEET (IRE), 5, b m Footstepsinthesand—Champagne Mistress **Mr D. J. Lowe**
13 GHAITH, 6, b g Invincible Spirit (IRE)—Wild Mimosa (USA) **Miss S. L. Hoyland**
14 HELIX, 4, ch g Helmet (AUS)—Child Bride (USA) **Mr K. Sohi**
15 INEVITABLE OUTCOME (IRE), 4, b f Ivawood (IRE)—Foreplay (IRE) **Mr D. J. Lowe**
16 JOYFUL MISSION (USA), 5, b g Noble Mission—Hint of Joy (USA) **A&B Systems Ltd**
17 KASER (IRE), 6, b g Invincible Spirit (IRE)—Lethal Quality (USA) **Lowe, Lewis & Hoyland**
18 LAMMAS, 4, b g Heeraat (IRE)—Spate Rise **Mr P. Onslow**
19 LEODIS DREAM (IRE), 5, b g Dandy Man (IRE)—Paddy Again (IRE) **Mr K. Sohi**
20 LOLA SHOWGIRL (IRE), 4, gr f Night of Thunder (IRE)—Exempt **The Something Syndicate**
21 LOMU (IRE), 4, ch g Dandy Man (IRE)—Miss Me **Mr N. I. Willis**
22 MANJAAM (IRE), 8, ch g Tamayuz—Priory Rock (IRE) **Sohi & Sohi**
23 MONSARAZ, 4, b g Cityscape—Rattleyurjewellery **Mr P. Onslow**
24 MUST BE AN ANGEL (IRE), 4, gr f Dark Angel (IRE)—Lapis Blue (IRE) **Mr N. I. Willis**
25 PLYMOUTH ROCK (IRE), 4, b g Starspangledbanner (AUS)—
Welcome Spring (IRE) **Peter R Ball & Gentech Products Ltd**
26 PRAXEOLOGY (IRE), 4, b g Dark Angel (IRE)—Hartstown House (IRE) **Mr N. I. Willis**
27 RICHARD R H B (IRE), 4, b g Fulbright—Royal Interlude (IRE) **Peter R Ball & Gentech Products Ltd**
28 SARTAJ (USA), 5, b br g Giant's Causeway (USA)—Sarkiyla (FR) **Mr K. Sohi**
29 STAR OF WELLS (IRE), 4, b g Sea The Stars (IRE)—Seas of Wells (IRE) **Sohi & Hoyland**
30 STRINGYBARK CREEK, 7, b g Bushranger (IRE)—Money Note **Miss S. L. Hoyland**
31 TORONTO (IRE), 4, b g Galileo (IRE)—Mrs Marsh **Mr A. Owen**
32 TRANCHEE (IRE), 5, b g War Front (USA)—Terrific (IRE) **Mr K. Sohi**
33 UTOPIAN LAD (IRE), 4, b g Society Rock (IRE)—Perfect Pose (IRE) **Mr M. Batters**

## THREE-YEAR-OLDS

34 ACE OF HARTS, ch g Toronado (IRE)—Angeleno (IRE) **Mr R. K. Arrowsmith**
35 BE MY BEAU, b g Brazen Beau (AUS)—Sylvestris (IRE) **Mr K. Sohi**
36 CAROLINE DALE, b f Lethal Force (IRE)—Stepping Out (IRE) **Janet Lowe 1**
37 CASE OF THE EX (FR), b f Scissor Kick (AUS)—Winds Up (USA) **Mr K. Sohi**
38 CHICA BELLA (IRE), gr f Gutaifan (IRE)—Maracuja **A&b Air Systems Ltd & Partner**
39 CHORITZO, b f Lethal Force (IRE)—Choral Festival **Mr P. Onslow**
40 CITY STORM, ch g Cityscape—Spate Rise **Mr P. Onslow**
41 EL PATRON (IRE), b g Kodiac—Smart Bounty **Mr K. Sohi**
42 ENAITCHESS (IRE), b f Elzaam (AUS)—Cute **Mr K. Sohi**

## MR DAVID LOUGHNANE - continued

43 **FOOTSTEPSONTHEMOON (IRE)**, b f Footstepsinthesand—Rapid Eye (IRE) **Byerley Thoroughbreds Ltd**
44 **GOING BACK TO CALI**, b g Pride of Dubai (AUS)—Chelsey Jayne (IRE) **Mr K. Sohi**
45 **KIM WEXLER (IRE)**, b f Mehmas (IRE)—Foreplay (IRE) **Mr D. J. Lowe**
46 **LOLA REBEL (IRE)**, b f Dandy Man (IRE)—Copperbeech (IRE) **The Something Syndicate**
47 **PASSTHECOURVOISIER (IRE)**, b f Coulsty (IRE)—Miss Prim **Mr K. Sohi**
48 **REDHEADED STRANGER**, b f Muhaarar—Havergate **Lydonford Ltd**
49 **SHAQEEQA**, ch f Dawn Approach (IRE)—Tabassum (IRE) **Ms O. Arslanoglu**
50 **SHOWDANSE**, b f Showcasing—Alexander Ballet **Bearstone Stud Limited**
51 **SNAP OUT OF IT (IRE)**, b f Twilight Son—Excel Yourself (IRE) **Mr D. J. Lowe**
52 **TRUMBLE (IRE)**, b g Power—Picabo (IRE) **T. E. Ford**
53 **TWIGGYBARK CREEK**, ch g Twilight Son—Money Note **Miss S. L. Hoyland**

## TWO-YEAR-OLDS

54 B c 21/01 Fulbright—Dazzling Light (UAE) (Halling (USA))
55 **FORTUNA DUFFLECOAT**, ch c 15/03 National Defense—Almamia (Hernando (FR)) (6000) **Mr N. I. Willis**
56 B f 15/04 Coulsty (IRE)—Generous Heart (Sakhee's Secret) (18000) **Mr K. Sohi**
57 Gr c 20/04 Mastercraftsman (IRE)—
                            Impressionist Art (USA) (Giant's Causeway (USA)) (9523) **A&b Air Systems Ltd & Partner**
58 **LOLA AUGUSTUS (IRE)**, b c 21/01 Dabirsim (FR)—
                            Kazaroza (FR) (Redoute's Choice (AUS)) (9523) **The Something Syndicate**
59 **MITSY MOP**, b f 18/02 Coulsty (IRE)—Ringarooma (Erhaab (USA)) **Mr N. I. Willis**
60 **MOJOMAKER (IRE)**, b c 30/01 Mehmas (IRE)—Ajila (IRE) (Exceed And Excel (AUS)) (38095) **Mr D. J. Lowe**
61 Ch c 19/04 Brametot (IRE)—Money Note (Librettist (USA)) (5000) **Miss S. L. Hoyland**
62 **QUARTET**, ch f 01/05 Lethal Force (IRE)—Humouresque (Pivotal)
63 **RUBY JULES**, b f 28/01 The Gurkha (IRE)—Frances Stuart (IRE) (King's Best (USA)) (2500) **Mr R. A. Sankey**
64 Ch f 03/02 New Bay—Scatina (IRE) (Samum (GER)) (23810)
65 **SHARRON MACREADY (IRE)**, b f 17/04 Mehmas (IRE)—Foreplay (IRE) (Lujain (USA)) **Mr D. J. Lowe**
66 **SPACER (IRE)**, br gr c 18/04 Starspangledbanner (AUS)—First Party (Royal Applause) (33333) **Mr D. J. Lowe**
67 B c 28/04 Australia—Sweet Temptation (IRE) (Amadeus Wolf) (17142) **A&b Air Systems Ltd & Partner**
68 **WALKIN ON SONSHINE**, b c 15/03 Twilight Son—Stepping Out (IRE) (Tagula (IRE)) **Mr D. J. Lowe**
69 **WAR BRAVE (IRE)**, b c 02/04 Due Diligence (USA)—
                            Compass Rose (IRE) (Henrythenavigator (USA)) (10952) **Mr P. Clifton**
70 **WILLOW PILLOW**, gr f 28/01 Zoffany (IRE)—Divine Promesse (FR) (Verglas (IRE)) (8000) **Mr N. I. Willis**

**Other Owners:** A&B Air Systems Ltd, Mr P. Ball, Gentech Products Ltd, Miss S. L. Hoyland, Mr A. Lewis, Mr D. J. Lowe, Mrs J. Lowe, Mr J. Sohi, Mr K. Sohi.

---

## 345 MR MARK LOUGHNANE, Kidderminster
Postal: Rock Farm, Rock Cross, Rock, Kidderminster, Worcestershire, DY14 9SA
Contacts: **MOBILE** 07805 531021

1 **ANNIE MOORE (IRE)**, 5, b m Ocovango—Wattrey **Mrs C. M. Loughnane**
2 **AUNT HELEN (USA)**, 5, b m Verrazano (USA)—London Bid (USA) **Mrs C. M. Loughnane**
3 **BLUE MEDICI**, 7, b g Medicean—Bluebelle **Mr L. A. Bellman**
4 **BUY ME BACK**, 4, b f Lethal Force (IRE)—Delft **Mr B. M. Parish**
5 **CHOCOLATE BOX (IRE)**, 7, b g Zoffany (IRE)—Chocolate Mauk (USA) **Racing Facades Syndicate**
6 **COME ON MY SON**, 4, b g Mayson—Slinky McVelvet **Mr W Fisher, Mr R Gray & Partners**
7 **DAHEER (USA)**, 4, ch c Speightstown (USA)—Elraazy (USA) **The Likely Lads**
8 **DAYSAQ (IRE)**, 4, b g Invincible Spirit (IRE)—Fawaayed (IRE) **Mrs C. M. Loughnane**
9 **DREAM MAGIC (IRE)**, 7, b g Lord Shanakill (USA)—Pursuit of Passion **Ben Parish & Clare Loughnane**
10 **EL HOMBRE**, 7, ch g Camacho—Nigella **Over The Moon Racing**
11 **EMBER'S GLOW**, 7, ch g Sepoy (AUS)—Fading Light **T. D. Johnson**
12 **GREEN ETOILE**, 5, ch g Nathaniel (IRE)—Myriades d'Etoiles (IRE) **Against All Odds Racing**
13 **GYPSY DANCER (IRE)**, 4, b f Dandy Man (IRE)—Feet of Flame (USA) **Mr B. M. Parish**
14 **HOT SUMMER**, 4, b g Hot Streak (IRE)—Lahqa (IRE) **Mr K. Sohi**

## MR MARK LOUGHNANE - continued

15 **IMPERIAL COMMAND (IRE)**, 4, b g War Command (USA)—Acts Out Loud (USA) **M J Refrigeration Transport Ltd**
16 **INNER CIRCLE (IRE)**, 7, b g Choisir (AUS)—Eternity Ring **Mrs C. M. Loughnane**
17 **JACKSTAR (IRE)**, 5, gr g Dark Angel (IRE)—Starbright (IRE) **Mr L. A. Bellman**
18 **JEDDEYD (IRE)**, 4, b g Make Believe—Lady Shanghai (IRE) **Mr K. Sohi**
19 **JOYFILLY (IRE)**, 4, b f Kodiac—Table Bay (IRE) **Mr L. A. Bellman**
20 **LEO DAVINCI (USA)**, 5, b g Artie Schiller (USA)—Sweet Temper (USA) **Racing Facades Syndicate**
21 **LOOKING FOR CARL**, 6, b g Lope de Vega (IRE)—Dam Beautiful **Mr W Fisher, Mr R Gray & Partners**
22 **MANDARIN (GER)**, 7, ch g Lope de Vega (IRE)—Margarita (GER) **Sohi & Sohi**
23 **MOXY MARES**, 6, ch g Motivator—Privalova (IRE) **S. & A. Mares**
24 **MR DIB DAB (FR)**, 4, b g Dabirsim (FR)—Naan (IRE) **S. & A. Mares**
25 **NEVER SAID NOTHING (IRE)**, 4, b g Hallowed Crown (AUS)—Semiquaver (IRE) **Mrs A. J. Johnson**
26 **PRECISION STORM**, 4, gr g Dragon Pulse (IRE)—Way To The Stars **Precision Facades Ltd**
27 **QASBAZ (IRE)**, 4, b g Make Believe—Esuvia (IRE) **Mr L. A. Bellman**
28 **RED BRAVO (IRE)**, 5, b g Acclamation—Vision of Peace (IRE) **Out of Bounds Racing Club & Partner**
29 **RED GUNNER**, 7, b g Oasis Dream—Blue Maiden **2 Counties Racing**
30 **RICKSEN**, 4, b g Acclamation—Quantum (IRE) **Mr L. A. Bellman**
31 **ROCK BOY GREY (IRE)**, 6, gr g Dark Angel (IRE)—Encore View **The Likely Lads**
32 **ROCK OF PENSAX (IRE)**, 4, br g Society Rock (IRE)—China Pink **S. & A. Mares**
33 **ROGUE TIDE**, 4, b g Acclamation—Rocking The Boat (IRE) **The Likely Lads**
34 **ROLLER**, 8, b g Rail Link—Buffering **Over The Moon Racing**
35 **SMILEY BAGEL (IRE)**, 8, b g Kyllachy—Epistoliere (IRE) **Mr L. A. Bellman**
36 **SPRINGVALE LAD**, 4, b g Archipenko (USA)—Combustible (IRE) **Mr M. Millichamp**
37 **STARFIGHTER**, 5, b g Sea The Stars (IRE)—Starlit Sands **Mr L. A. Bellman**
38 **TAKEONEFORTHETEAM**, 6, b g Bahamian Bounty—Miss Bond (IRE) **S. & A. Mares**
39 **THE MET**, 5, b g Gregorian (IRE)—Kasalla (IRE) **Mr K. Sohi**
40 **TRIGGERED (IRE)**, 5, b g Dandy Man (IRE)—Triggers Broom (IRE) **L Bellman & S & A Mares**
41 **UNIVERSAL EFFECT**, 5, b m Universal (IRE)—Saaboog **S & A Mares & Precision Facades Ltd**
42 **WELL PREPARED**, 4, b g Due Diligence (USA)—Amazed **Mr L. A. Bellman**

### THREE-YEAR-OLDS

43 Br f Cityscape—Bailadeira
44 **FAYATHAAN (IRE)**, b c Mehmas (IRE)—Beauty of The Sea **Mr K. Sohi**
45 **GO OSCAR GO (IRE)**, b g Dragon Pulse (IRE)—Princess Aloof (IRE) **S. & A. Mares**
46 **MEANT TWO B (IRE)**, gr g Markaz (IRE)—Sayrah **Mr W. J. Fisher**
47 **RUBY RIBBONS**, ch f Stimulation (IRE)—Verus Delicia (IRE) **Mr R Brilley & Mrs A Townsend**
48 B g Fast Company (IRE)—Saffa Garden (IRE) **Mr L. A. Bellman**
49 B f Heeraat (IRE)—Shared Moment (IRE)
50 **SNOWBOMBER**, ro g Lethal Force (IRE)—Colourfilly **Mr L. A. Bellman**
51 **TILAAWAH**, b c Showcasing—Lady Estella (IRE) **Mr K. Sohi**
52 **TREENKEEL TIGER (IRE)**, b g Elzaam (AUS)—Fly By

### TWO-YEAR-OLDS

53 B g 14/04 Swiss Spirit—Annie Kenney (Showcasing) **Miss W. Smith**
54 B c 02/02 Showcasing—Bonfire Heart (Exceed And Excel (AUS)) (49524)
55 B f 27/02 Havana Gold (IRE)—Coillte Cailin (IRE) (Oratorio (IRE))
56 B f 11/04 Adaay (IRE)—Colourfilly (Compton Place) **Mr L. A. Bellman**
57 Ch c 05/03 Bobby's Kitten (USA)—Danlia (IRE) (Lando (GER))
58 B f 25/01 Bated Breath—Sighora (IRE) (Royal Applause)
59 B f 04/02 Stimulation (IRE)—Verus Delicia (IRE) (Chineur (FR)) **Mr R. M. Brilley**

**Other Owners:** Mr L. A. Bellman, Mr R. M. Brilley, Mr W. J. Fisher, Mr R. J. Gray, Mr M. E. Harris, Mrs C. M. Loughnane, Mrs A. Mares, Mr S. Mares, S. & A. Mares, Out Of Bounds Racing Club, Mr B. M. Parish, Precision Facades Ltd, Mr J. Sohi, Mr K. Sohi, The Likely Lads, Mrs A. E. Townsend.

**346**

## MR SHAUN LYCETT, Witney
Postal: **Fairspear Racing Stables, Fairspear Road, Leafield, Witney, Oxfordshire, OX29 9NT**
Contacts: **PHONE 01451 824143 MOBILE 07788 100894**
EMAIL trainer@bourtonhillracing.co.uk WEBSITE www.bourtonhillracing.co.uk

1 EXCELLENT PUCK (IRE), 11, b g Excellent Art—Puck's Castle **Bourton Racing**
2 MECHELEN STAR, 5, b g Malinas (GER)—Lily Lenor (IRE) **Dan Gilbert & Kristian Strangeway**
3 PARK PADDOCKS (IRE), 7, b g Sea The Stars (IRE)—Dream of The Hill (IRE) **Mr D. R. Gilbert**
4 RELATIVE EASE, 5, b m Sayif (IRE)—Shohrah (IRE) **L & M Atkins**
5 SCOTSBROOK NIGHT, 8, b m Midnight Legend—Won More Night **Mr P. E. T. Price**
6 SCOTSBROOK RHULA, 6, b m Native Ruler—Scots Brook Terror **Mr P. E. T. Price**
7 SIGLO SIX, 5, ch g Havana Gold (IRE)—Yensi **Mr D. R. Gilbert**
8 SPEECH ROOM (IRE), 4, b g Sea The Stars (IRE)—Dream of The Hill (IRE) **L & M Atkins**
9 THE KING'S STEED, 8, b g Equiano (FR)—King's Siren (IRE) **D Gilbert, J Lancaster, G Wills**
10 TORCELLO (IRE), 7, ch g Born To Sea (IRE)—Islandagore (IRE) **Mr D. R. Gilbert**
11 WEEKLY GOSSIP (IRE), 10, br g Kalanisi—Mary's Little Vic (IRE) **L & M Atkins**

Other Owners: Mr L. Atkins, Mrs M. Atkins, Mr D. R. Gilbert, Mr K. J. Strangeway.

**347**

## MISS JESSICA MACEY, Doncaster
Postal: **Mayflower Stables, Saracens Lane, Scrooby, Doncaster, South Yorkshire, DN10 6AS**
Contacts: **PHONE 07588 374797**
EMAIL macey.jess@gmail.com

1 BUMMBLE BERRY, 4, b g Tobougg (IRE)—Sarah Berry **Strawberry Fields Stud**
2 DARK SIDE PRINCE, 4, b g Equiano (FR)—Dark Side Princess **Mr M. M. Foulger**
3 PHOENIX STAR (IRE), 5, b g Alhebayeb (IRE)—Volcanic Lady (IRE) **Flying High Syndicate**
4 TRINITY GIRL, 4, b f Teofilo (IRE)—Micaela's Moon (USA) **G Robinson, Mr Fowler, S Dwyer**

### THREE-YEAR-OLDS

5 HELL OF A YEAR (FR), b g The Wow Signal (IRE)—Devout (IRE) **Not Now Partnership**
6 MISS FERNANDA (IRE), b f Prince of Lir (IRE)—Livadream (IRE) **Mr M. M. Foulger**

### TWO-YEAR-OLDS

7 B g 19/04 Equiano (FR)—Annie Salts (Zebedee) **Mrs S. Dwyer**
8 B f 13/03 Brazen Beau (AUS)—Chevise (IRE) (Holy Roman Emperor (IRE)) **Strawberry Fields Stud**
9 B c 14/02 Showcasing—Lamazonia (IRE) (Elusive City (USA)) (4000) **Mrs S. Dwyer**
10 B g 27/03 Fast Company (IRE)—Quick Thought (IRE) (Sir Percy) (5000) **Strawberry Fields Stud**

Other Owners: Mrs S. Dwyer, Mr I. J. Fowler, G. F. L. Robinson.

**348**

## MR JOHN MACKIE, Church Broughton
Postal: **The Bungalow, Barton Blount, Church Broughton, Derby**
Contacts: **PHONE 01283 585603, 01283 585604 MOBILE 07799 145283 FAX 01283 585603**
EMAIL jmackieracing@gmail.com

1 BALADIO (IRE), 5, ch m Iffraaj—Balamana (FR) **Derbyshire Racing III**
2 BARTON KNOLL, 9, b g Midnight Legend—Barton Flower **Mr S. W. Clarke**
3 BERTOG, 6, ch g Sepoy (AUS)—Lucky Token (IRE) **Sean Goodwin and Deborah Fern**
4 CUSTARD THE DRAGON, 8, b g Kyllachy—Autumn Pearl **Derbyshire Racing**
5 DUKE OF ALBA (IRE), 6, b g Lope de Vega (IRE)—Royal Alchemist **Allstars**

## MR JOHN MACKIE - continued

  **6 HEARTSTAR,** 4, b f Heeraat (IRE)—Available (IRE) **Derbyshire Racing IV**
  **7 HERMOCRATES (FR),** 5, b g Farhh—Little Shambles **M & W Yardley**
  **8 HURRICANE ALI (IRE),** 5, b g Alhebayeb (IRE)—Hurricane Irene (IRE) **Mr M. J. Fruhwald**
  **9 LUNAR JET,** 7, ch g Ask—Lightning Jet **County Charm Windows & Conservatories**
**10 MANY TALES,** 9, b g Multiplex—All Three Fables **Mrs E. M. Mackie**
**11 MISS BAMBY,** 6, b m Kayf Tara—Bamby (IRE) **Mrs S. P. Granger**
**12 MONTENAY,** 5, b m So You Think (NZ)—Jivry **Eventmasters Racing**
**13 MR TG (IRE),** 7, b g Flemensfirth (USA)—Bollin Jasmine **Mrs S. P. Granger**
**14 POLYPHONY (IRE),** 6, b m Power—Start The Music (IRE) **Eventmasters Racing & Mr Frank Murphy**
**15 RAINBOW JET (IRE),** 4, b f Dream Ahead (USA)—Star Jet (IRE) **Mrs E. M. Mackie**
**16 SHARPCLIFF,** 4, b g Farhh—Avonrose **Moorland Racing**
**17 TURANGA LEELA,** 7, ch m Paco Boy (IRE)—Sunday Bess (JPN) **Eventmasters Racing**

### THREE-YEAR-OLDS

**18 AVAILABLE ANGEL,** b f Heeraat (IRE)—Available (IRE) **Derbyshire Racing II**

**Other Owners:** Eventmasters Racing, Mr F. Murphy, Mrs D. Sheasby, Mr E. J. N. Sheasby, Mr M. Yardley, Mrs W. J. Yardley.

---

**349**
## MR PETER MADDISON, Skewsby
Postal: **5 West End Cottages, Skewsby, York, YO61 4SG**
Contacts: **PHONE 01347 888385**

  **1 KINGS OWN,** 7, b g Distant Peak (IRE)—Phoebe Nullis **P. Maddison**
  **2 THE SASKATOON,** 12, b g Desideratum—Skewsby Girl **P. Maddison**

**Conditional Jockey:** Jamie Hamilton.

---

**350**
## MR MICHAEL MADGWICK, Denmead
Postal: **Forest Farm, Forest Road, Denmead, Waterlooville, Hampshire, PO7 6UA**
Contacts: **PHONE 023 9225 8313 MOBILE 07835 964969**

  **1 DONO DI DIO,** 6, b m Nathaniel (IRE)—Sweet Cecily (IRE) **Mr O. Lodge**
  **2 ETHANDEXTER,** 6, ch g Alkaased (USA)—Miss Venice (IRE) **Sheepwash Syndicate**
  **3 FAMILY FORTUNES,** 7, ch g Paco Boy (IRE)—Barawin (IRE) **Los Leader**
  **4 FORESHORE,** 4, b g Footstepsinthesand—Skinny Love **Mr J. Lane**
  **5 HI THERE SILVER (IRE),** 7, gr g Clodovil (IRE)—Elaborate **Lane & Madgwick**
  **6 MAQUISARD (FR),** 9, ch g Creachadoir (IRE)—Gioiosa Marea (IRE) **M. K. George**
  **7 MARGIE'S CHOICE (GER),** 6, b m Redoute's Choice (AUS)—Margie's World (GER) **Mr G. Dixon**
  **8 MISS RECYCLED,** 6, b m Royal Applause—Steel Free (IRE) **Recycled Products Limited**
  **9 RESPLENDENT ROSE,** 4, b f Heeraat (IRE)—Attlongglast **Mrs L. N. Harmes**
**10 SING OUT LOUD (IRE),** 6, b g Vocalised (USA)—Tus Maith (IRE) **Lane & Madgwick**
**11 STORMBOMBER (CAN),** 5, ch g Stormy Atlantic (USA)—Swanky Bubbles (CAN) **Los Leader**
**12 VLANNON,** 6, b g Captain Gerrard (IRE)—Attlongglast **M Gannon, H Vlatas, M Willis, L N Harmes**
**13 WHAT'S MY LINE,** 4, b g Sixties Icon—Leading Star **M. J. Madgwick**
**14 WHERE'S TOM,** 6, b g Cape Cross (IRE)—Where's Susie **Recycled Products Limited**

**Other Owners:** Mr M. Gannon, Mrs L. N. Harmes, Mr J. Lane, M. J. Madgwick, Mr W. R. Oliver, Mr T. Smith, Mr H. Vlatas, Mr M. Willis.

**Assistant Trainer:** David Madgwick.

**Flat Jockey:** Adam Kirby. **NH Jockey:** Marc Goldstein. **Amateur Jockey:** Mr Lance Madgwick.

## 351 MRS HEATHER MAIN, Wantage

Postal: **Kingston Common Farm, Kingston Lisle, Wantage, Oxfordshire, OX12 9QT**
Contacts: **WORK 01367 820124 MOBILE 07920 558860**
**EMAIL** heather.main@hotmail.com **WEBSITE** www.heathermainracing.com

1 **AL KOUT**, 7, gr g Oasis Dream—Honorlina (FR) **Wetumpka Racing**
2 **CLOUD THUNDER**, 4, gr g Poet's Voice—Cloud Illusions (USA) **Coxwell Partnership**
3 **COLONEL WHITEHEAD (IRE)**, 4, b g Showcasing—Lady Brigid (IRE) **Mr. Andrew Tuck & Wetumpka Racing**
4 **GRATOT (FR)**, 6, br g Le Havre (IRE)—Absolute Lady (IRE) **Wetumpka Racing**
5 **ISLAND BRAVE (IRE)**, 7, b h Zebedee—Tip the Scale (USA) **D. M. Kerr**
6 **ISLAND STORM (IRE)**, 4, b g Anjaal—She's Neat (IRE) **Wetumpka Racing**
7 **LAPIDARY**, 5, b m Kodiac—Carved Emerald **Andrew Knott & Wetumpka Racing**
8 **MARSHAL DAN (IRE)**, 6, b g Lawman (FR)—Aunt Nicola **Coxwell Partnership**
9 **MOSTAWAA**, 5, ch g Poet's Voice—Mumtaza **The Haroldians**
10 **NIGELLA SATIVA**, 5, gr m Gentlewave (IRE)—Just Popsy **Wetumpka Racing**
11 **NUMITOR**, 7, gr g Schiaparelli (GER)—Just Popsy **Wetumpka Racing**
12 **POLAR CLOUD**, 5, gr g Mount Nelson—Cloud Illusions (USA) **Wetumpka Racing**
13 **SONG OF THE ISLES (IRE)**, 5, ch m Tagula (IRE)—Musicology (USA) **Wetumpka Racing**
14 **TINDRUM**, 4, ch g Mukhadram—Tinshu (IRE) **Llewelyn,Runeckles**

### THREE-YEAR-OLDS

15 **ACTAEA**, b f Adaay (IRE)—Aqaba **Mr J. P. Repard**
16 **DREAM NO MORE**, b c Dawn Approach (IRE)—Sweet Dream **Morera Partnership**
17 **ENGLISH SPIRIT**, ch g Swiss Spirit—Cloud Illusions (USA) **Wetumpka Racing**
18 **MISTER BLUEBIRD**, b gr g Outstrip—Childesplay **Dawn Aldham & Wetumpka Racing**
19 **SWISS TIME**, b f Swiss Spirit—Mestizo **Mondial Racing**

### TWO-YEAR-OLDS

20 B f 24/05 Outstrip—Byroness (Byron)
21 **DARK ISLAND STAR (IRE)**, b f 26/04 Caravaggio (USA)—
Saturn Girl (IRE) (Danehill Dancer (IRE)) (19048) **D. M. Kerr**
22 **DIAMOND GIRL**, b f 25/02 Profitable (IRE)—Lady Brigid (IRE) (Holy Roman Emperor (IRE)) (25000) **D. M. Kerr**
23 Ch c 12/01 Mastercraftsman (IRE)—Enjoy Life (IRE) (Acclamation) (19048) **Beccle, Moss and Wetumpka Racing**
24 B c 14/04 Churchill (IRE)—Esteemable (Nayef (USA)) (20952) **Llewelyn,Runeckles**
25 Ch c 01/03 Garswood—Front Page News (Assertive) (2000)
26 **ILEACH MATHAN (IRE)**, gr c 28/02 Kodi Bear (IRE)—
Juliette Fair (IRE) (Dark Angel (IRE)) (23810) **Coxwell Partnership**
27 **ISLAND BANDIT**, ch c 17/02 Zarak (FR)—Lady of The Court (IRE) (Camelot) **D. M. Kerr**
28 **LA BELLE VIE**, b f 23/01 Iffraaj—Belle Dauphine (Dalakhani (IRE)) (11000) **Andrew Knott & Wetumpka Racing**
29 B c 31/03 Farhh—Vizinga (FR) (Marju (IRE)) (8000)
30 B c 03/03 Night of Thunder (IRE)—Western Pearl (High Chaparral (IRE)) (28000) **D. M. Kerr**
31 **WIZARDING**, b c 24/03 Showcasing—Dutch S (Dutch Art) (9685) **Mondial Racing & Robert Haim**

**Other Owners:** Ms D. C. Aldham, Mr S. E. Beccle, Mr J. Bernstein, Miss C. A. Green, Mr R. Haim, Mr A. Knott, Sir J. A. Mactaggart, Mrs H. S. Main, J. P. M. Main, Mondial Racing, Mr M. J. Moss, Mr M. R. Telfer, Mr A. Tuck, Wetumpka Racing.

## 352 MRS JANE VICTORIA MAKIN, Monk Fryston

Postal: **Fryston Lodge Farm, Off A63, South Milford, Leeds, North Yorkshire, LS25 5JE**
Contacts: **PHONE 07836 763979**
**EMAIL** regmakin@gmail.com

1 4, B f Getaway (GER)—Rose's Emma (IRE) **Mr R. G. Makin**
2 **SCHIAPARANNIE**, 9, b m Schiaparelli (GER)—Annie's Answer (IRE) **Mr R. G. Makin**
3 **VICKY JANE**, 10, b m Kayf Tara—Annie's Answer (IRE) **Mr R. G. Makin**

**353** **MR PHILLIP MAKIN, Easingwold**
Postal: **Well Close Farm, York Road, Easingwold, York, North Yorkshire, YO61 3EN**
Contacts: PHONE **07968 045436**
EMAIL **philmakin.21@hotmail.co.uk**

1 COLONEL SLADE (IRE), 5, b g Dandy Man (IRE)—Sense of A Woman (USA) **P. J. Makin**
2 EXHALATION, 4, ch f Bated Breath—Pamushana (IRE) **P. R. C. Morrison**
3 FENNAAN (IRE), 6, br g Footstepsinthesand—Sanadaat **Mrs W. Burdett**
4 IMPRESSOR (IRE), 4, b c Footstepsinthesand—Little Empress (IRE) **P. J. Makin**
5 JACKSONIAN, 4, ch c Frankel—Kalima **Syps & Mrs Wendy Burdett**
6 JUNGLE INTHEBUNGLE (IRE), 5, ch g Bungle Inthejungle—Princess Banu **Mr John Hanbury & Partner**
7 LAHORE (USA), 7, br g Elusive Quality (USA)—Nayarra (USA) **Mrs W. Burdett**
8 MAGNIFICIA (IRE), 4, b f Sir Prancealot (IRE)—Star Bonita (IRE) **Mr J. Beard**
9 MUKHADRAM WAY, 4, b f Mukhadram—Mancunian Way **P. J. Makin**
10 POINT OF HONOUR (IRE), 6, b g Lope de Vega (IRE)—Shamayel **J. Binks**
11 PROFIT IN PEACE (IRE), 4, br g War Command (USA)—Attracted To You (IRE) **P. J. Makin**
12 STORM OVER (IRE), 7, b g Elnadim (USA)—Stormy View (USA) **Mrs W. Burdett**
13 THE BELL CONDUCTOR (IRE), 4, b g Dandy Man (IRE)—Saffian **Mrs W. Burdett**
14 THREE CARD TRICK, 5, ch g Piccolo—Card Games **Kingmaker Racedays & Phil Makin**
15 TOUGH CHARACTER, 4, b g Sepoy (AUS)—Navajo Rainbow **Mr G. Cahill**
16 TRUE MASON, 5, b g Mayson—Marysienka **Mr J. T. Hanbury**

**THREE-YEAR-OLDS**

17 AVIOR STAR (IRE), b g Requinto (IRE)—Oakley Star **Arcane Racing**
18 BEAU TINKER (IRE), b c Buratino (IRE)—Mecca's Missus (IRE) **Mrs S. Johnson**
19 BIG THANKS (IRE), b g Camacho—Thanks (IRE) **Syps & Mrs Wendy Burdett**
20 CAMMY (IRE), ch g Camacho—Swan Sea (USA) **SYPS (UK) Ltd**
21 CAPTAIN VALLO (IRE), ch c Mehmas (IRE)—Top Dollar **Mrs W. Burdett**
22 DEBATED, ch g Bated Breath—Lady Sledmere (IRE) **Ryedale Racing**
23 DESTACADO (IRE), b f Mehmas (IRE)—Esterlina (IRE) **Show Me The Money UK LTD**
24 EALAND (IRE), ch g Dutch Art—Impassioned **Syps & Mrs Wendy Burdett**
25 B g Dutch Art—Exceedingly
26 Ch g Eagle Top—Littlemiss
27 MAWGAN PORTH, ch g Showcasing—Macnamara **Mr P. S. Riley**
28 MR MCCALL, b g Farhh—Naayla (IRE) **Mrs W. Burdett**
29 MUKER (IRE), ch c Mehmas (IRE)—Naias (IRE) **SYPS (UK) Ltd**
30 PRINCE ALI, br g Twilight Son—Desert Liaison **Mrs W. Burdett**
31 SCOTA BESS, b f Bobby's Kitten (USA)—Gotcha Good (USA) **Mr J Toes & Mr J O'Loan**
32 TEMPESTUOUS (IRE), b f Harzand (IRE)—Stormy Blessing (USA) **Mr C. McHale**
33 TOMMY R (IRE), b g Holy Roman Emperor—Serafina's Flight **Mr P. S. Riley**
34 YORKSHIRE PIRLO (IRE), b c Mehmas (IRE)—Suffer Her (IRE) **C & Roofing**

**TWO-YEAR-OLDS**

35 B f 03/01 Kodiac—Abiquiu (IRE) (Roderic O'Connor (IRE)) (30476) **Mrs W. Burdett**
36 B c 12/04 Kodiac—Andry Brusselles (Hurricane Run (IRE)) (38095) **Syps & Mrs Wendy Burdett**
37 B f 24/01 Mehmas (IRE)—Bougainvilia (IRE) (Bahamian Bounty) (12381) **SYPS (UK) Ltd**
38 B f 09/03 Brazen Beau (AUS)—Broughtons Jewel (IRE) (Bahri (USA)) (9000) **Show Me The Money UK LTD**
39 Ch c 23/02 Cotai Glory—Classy Lassy (IRE) (Tagula (IRE)) (28571) **Mr J. T. Hanbury**
40 B c 19/03 Mondialiste (IRE)—Dansili Dutch (IRE) (Dutch Art) (15000)
41 B c 08/05 Mayson—Dutch Lady (Dutch Art) (5000)
42 B f 26/04 Vadamos (FR)—June (High Chaparral (IRE)) (8571)
43 B c 05/04 Zoffany (IRE)—Leniency (IRE) (Cape Cross (IRE))
44 B c 30/04 Kodiac—Lucrezia (Nathaniel (IRE)) (32000) **Mrs W. Burdett**
45 B f 04/04 Gleneagles (IRE)—Lydia's Place (Equiano (FR)) **Mrs W. Burdett**
46 Ch c 19/03 Galileo Gold—Masela (IRE) (Medicean) (4500)
47 B f 14/04 Awtaad (IRE)—Oasis Sunset (Oasis Dream) (22000) **Syps & Mrs Wendy Burdett**
48 B g 11/04 Mondialiste (IRE)—Ocean Princess (IRE) (Acclamation)
49 Ch c 09/04 Cotai Glory—Perfect Venture (Bahamian Bounty) (38095) **Syps & Mrs Wendy Burdett**
50 B c 20/02 Adaay (IRE)—Relaxez Vous (IRE) (Raven's Pass (USA)) (40000) **Syps & Mrs Wendy Burdett**
51 B f 14/03 Highland Reel (IRE)—Star of Spring (IRE) (Iffraaj) (20952)

## MR PHILLIP MAKIN - continued

52 B c 03/03 Camacho—Swish Dancer (IRE) (Whipper (USA)) (24762) **SYPS (UK) Ltd**
53 TINKERSTAR (IRE), b c 10/02 Fast Company (IRE)—Zebgrey (IRE) (Zebedee) (12000) **Mr W. Pooleman**

**Other Owners:** Mrs W. Burdett, Mr B. W. Fellows, Mr J. T. Hanbury, Mr I. Harle, Mr D. I. Jackson, Kingmaker Racedays Club, P. J. Makin, Mr John O'Loan, SYPS (UK) Ltd, Mr J. Toes, Mr K. Walton, Mr C. Wood.

---

**354**
**MRS ALYSON MALZARD, Jersey**
Postal: Les Etabl'yes, Grosnez Farm, St Ouen, JE3 2AD, Jersey
Contacts: MOBILE +44 7797 738128
EMAIL malzardracing@gmail.com

1 BAL AMIE (FR), 7, b g Ballingarry (IRE)—Amie Roli (FR) **Mr Tony Taylor**
2 BOWL IMPERIAL, 9, ch h Raven's Pass (USA)—Turtle Point (USA) **Mr Geoff Somers**
3 FOURNI (IRE), 12, ch m Rakti—Eckbeag (USA) **Miss Joan Lowery**
4 HARD TO HANDEL, 9, b g Stimulation (IRE)—Melody Maker **Mr Matt Watkinson, Baroque Partnership**
5 HONCHO (IRE), 9, gr g Dark Angel (IRE)—Disco Lights **Sheik A'Leg Racing**
6 ICE ROYAL (IRE), 8, b g Frozen Power (IRE)—Salford Princess (IRE) **Mr Tony Taylor**
7 ISLAND SONG (IRE), 7, b m Equiano (FR)—Fortuna Limit **Mr Geoff Somers**
8 MENDACIOUS HARPY (IRE), 10, b m Dark Angel (IRE)—Idesia (IRE) **Malzard Racing**
9 RELAXED BOY (FR), 8, b h Le Havre (IRE)—Joyce (GER) **Mr Geoff Somers**
10 SAFIRA MENINA, 9, b m Paco Boy (IRE)—Isla Azul (IRE) **Mr & Mrs Simon Harrison-White**
11 TIMETODOCK, 5, b g Harbour Watch (IRE)—Unwrapit (USA) **Mr Tony Taylor**
12 WINKLEVI (FR), 6, b g Maxios—Wild Star (IRE) **Mr Trevor Gallienne**

**NH Jockey:** Mattie Batchelor. **Amateur Jockey:** Miss Victoria Malzard, Mr Freddie Tett.

---

**355**
**MR CHARLIE MANN, Upper Lambourn**
Postal: **Neardown, Upper Lambourn, Hungerford, Berkshire, RG17 8QP**
Contacts: **PHONE 01488 71717, 01488 73118 MOBILE 07721 888333 FAX 01488 73223**
EMAIL charlie@charliemann.info WEBSITE www.charliemannracing.com

1 CAMOUFLAGED (IRE), 4, gr g Dark Angel (IRE)—Inner Secret (USA) **Mr J. D. Mayo**
2 CAPONE (GER), 6, br g Nathaniel (IRE)—Codera (GER) **Mr B. Kerr**
3 CHEAD SOLAS (IRE), 7, ch g Flemensfirth (USA)—Lunar Beauty (IRE) **The 25 Club**
4 COMMIT OR QUIT (IRE), 6, ch g Tobougg (IRE)—Gail Borden (IRE) **Mrs John Thorneloe**
5 DEFI DES CARRES (FR), 8, ch g Sumitas (GER)—Star des Carres (FR) **Thorneloe & Bannister**
6 GALIDERMES (FR), 4, b g Hunter's Light (IRE)—Angie Eria (FR) **The Steeple Chasers**
7 GIN COCO (FR), 5, b g Cokoriko (FR)—Qlementine (FR) **David's Partnership**
8 HOUSTON BERE (FR), 4, b g Hurricane Cat (USA)—Kunoichi (USA) **Mrs L. C. Taylor**
9 IVILNOBLE (IRE), 8, b g Alfred Nobel (IRE)—Almutamore (IRE) **Mrs L. C. Taylor**
10 JACK THUNDER (IRE), 7, b g Masterofthehorse (IRE)—Acqua Pesante (IRE) **Mr D. G. Christian**
11 LAURELDEAN CROSS (IRE), 5, b g Cape Cross (IRE)—Laureldean Spirit (IRE) **Mrs J. M. Mayo**
12 MISTERSISTER (FR), 4, gr g Wootton Bassett—Peace Mine (CAN) **S Frosell, R Frosell & Mrs D Stimson**
13 PRABENI, 6, ch g Teofilo (IRE)—Nyarhini **The 25 Club**
14 ROBADDAN (IRE), 7, ch g Flemensfirth (USA)—Tiarella (IRE) **Lady E. Mays-Smith**
15 SACRE COEUR (FR), 5, b m Montmartre (FR)—Singaporette (FR) **David's Partnership**
16 SID HOODIE (IRE), 7, b m Rip Van Winkle (IRE)—Universe **Mr D. G. Christian**
17 SONG OF THE SKY, 8, ch m Rip Van Winkle (IRE)—Holy Moly (USA) **The 25 Club**
18 STREAM OF STARS, 6, b g Sea The Stars (IRE)—Precious Gem (IRE) **Susie & Robert Frosell**
19 THE DUBAI WAY (IRE), 9, b g Dubai Destination (USA)—Britway Lady (IRE) **N.W.A. Bannister & M.J.R. Bannister**
20 THE LION DANCER (IRE), 9, b g Let The Lion Roar—Shesadoll (IRE) **The 25 Club**

## MR CHARLIE MANN - continued

21 **TOP UP THE FASHION (IRE)**, 7, b g Court Cave (IRE)—Aqua Breezer (IRE) **Mr Hunter & Mrs Taylor**
22 **WILL VICTORY (FR)**, 5, br m Willywell (FR)—Gesa Mixa (FR) **David's Partnership**
23 **WON'T TALK (IRE)**, 7, b g Scorpion (IRE)—Talk To The Missus (IRE) **The Steeple Chasers**

**Other Owners:** Mr M. J. R. Bannister, Mr N. W. A. Bannister, Mr R. N. Frosell, M. S. Hunter, Mr J. Lloyd-Townshend, Mr J. D. Mayo, Mrs D. L. Stimson, Mrs L. C. Taylor, Mrs John Thorneloe.

**Assistant Trainer:** Lilly Carson, **Head Lad:** Shaun Graham, **Racing Secretary:** Kate Mann.

---

## 356 MR GEORGE MARGARSON, Newmarket
Postal: **Graham Lodge, Birdcage Walk, Newmarket, Suffolk, CB8 0NE**
Contacts: **PHONE 01638 668043 MOBILE 07860 198303**
**EMAIL george@georgemargarson.co.uk WEBSITE www.georgemargarson.co.uk**

1 **BLAME CULTURE (USA)**, 6, b g Blame (USA)—Pearl In The Sand (IRE) **Mangiacapra, Hill, Hook Partnership**
2 **CARIBBEAN SPRING (IRE)**, 8, b g Dark Angel (IRE)—Bogini (IRE) **The Bean Club**
3 **LUNA WISH**, 4, b f Sea The Moon (GER)—Crystal Wish **Mr F. G. Butler**
4 **PROTECTED GUEST**, 6, b g Helmet (AUS)—Reem Star **John Guest Racing Ltd**
5 **ROPEY GUEST**, 4, b g Cable Bay (IRE)—Hadeeya **John Guest Racing Ltd**
6 **SPIRITED GUEST**, 5, b g Swiss Spirit—Choisette **John Guest Racing Ltd**

### THREE-YEAR-OLDS

7 **ALTISTE**, gr ro f Archipenko (USA)—Alsacienne **Miss K. Rausing**
8 **COMET WARRIOR**, ch g Sepoy (AUS)—Haley Bop (IRE) **Mr A. Al Mansoori**
9 **FARHH TO SHY**, b f Farhh—Coconut Shy **Mr F. G. Butler**
10 **FLIBBERTIGIBBET (IRE)**, ch f Prince of Lir (IRE)—Mairead Anne (USA) **Graham Lodge Partnership**
11 **MEDIA GUEST (FR)**, b br c Belardo (IRE)—Media Day (IRE) **John Guest Racing Ltd**
12 **SPIRITUOSO**, b f Charm Spirit (IRE)—Dusty Red **Mr J. M. Beever**

### TWO-YEAR-OLDS

13 B f 20/03 Golden Horn—Punita (USA) (Distorted Humor (USA)) **Mr A. Al Mansoori**

**Assistant Trainer:** Katie Margarson.

**Apprentice Jockey:** Miss Abbie Pierce. **Amateur Jockey:** Miss Rosie Margarson.

---

## 357 MR ANDREW MARTIN, Chipping Norton
Postal: **Yew Tree Barn, Hook Norton Road, Swerford, Chipping Norton, Oxfordshire, OX7 4BF**
Contacts: **MOBILE 07815 698359**

1 **CHARLIE'S GLANCE**, 5, b g Passing Glance—Call Me A Legend **A. J. Martin**
2 **MIDNIGHT MUSTANG**, 14, b g Midnight Legend—Mustang Molly **A. J. Martin**
3 **MIDNIGHT POPSTAR**, 7, b m Midnight Legend—It's Missy Imp **A. J. Martin**
4 **MIGHTY MUSTANG**, 11, b g Passing Glance—Mustang Molly **A. J. Martin**
5 **MILITARIAN**, 11, b g Kayf Tara—Mille Et Une (FR) **A. J. Martin**
6 **SCHIAPARELLI TEDDY**, 5, ch g Schiaparelli (GER)—Trifollet **A. J. Martin**
7 5, B m Beat All (USA)—Upton Legend **A. J. Martin**

## 358 MISS NICKY MARTIN, Minehead
Postal: Great Bradley, Withypool, Minehead, Somerset, TA24 7RS
Contacts: PHONE 01643 831175 MOBILE 07980 269510
EMAIL nickymartin3@hotmail.co.uk

1 BEAR GHYLLS (IRE), 6, br g Arcadio (GER)—Inch Princess (IRE) **Bradley Partnership**
2 CALL SIMON (IRE), 6, b g Fame And Glory—All My Judges **Bradley Partnership**
3 CAN YOU BELIEVE IT (IRE), 8, br g Oscar (IRE)—Cassilis (IRE) **Bradley Partnership**
4 COLONEL CUSTARD (IRE), 8, ch g Mahler—Criaire Princess (IRE) **Bradley Partnership**
5 CRAIC MAGIC (IRE), 6, b g Oscar (IRE)—Chantoue Royale (FR) **Bradley Partnership**
6 CUCUMBER GIN (IRE), 7, b m Oscar (IRE)—Redwood Lady (IRE) **Bradley Partnership**
7 FEVERTRE (IRE), 6, ch g Sans Frontieres (IRE)—Avoca Star (IRE) **Bradley Partnership**
8 JOG ON (IRE), 8, b g Definite Article—Azabu Juban (IRE) **Bradley Partnership**
9 LIGHT EM UP NIGEL (IRE), 5, b g Leading Light (IRE)—Hushed Up (IRE) **Bradley Partnership**
10 LUCKY SO AND SO (IRE), 4, b g Lucky Speed (IRE)—Limerick Rose (IRE) **Bradley Partnership**
11 MERRY MILAN (IRE), 9, b g Milan—Timerry (IRE) **Bradley Partnership**
12 MOLE TRAP, 10, b m Kayf Tara—Fairly High (IRE) **Bradley Partnership**
13 MY LAST OSCAR (IRE), 6, b g Oscar (IRE)—Power Again (GER) **Bradley Partnership**
14 PURE VODKA, 8, b m Westerner—Fairly High (IRE) **Bradley Partnership**
15 SONOFTHEKING (IRE), 13, b g King's Theatre (IRE)—Nikadora (FR) **Bradley Partnership**
16 STEADY AWAY (IRE), 7, b g Fame And Glory—Inch Pride (IRE) **Bradley Partnership**
17 SYKES (IRE), 12, b g Mountain High (IRE)—Our Trick (IRE) **Bradley Partnership**
18 THE TWO AMIGOS, 9, b g Midnight Legend—As Was **Bradley Partnership**
19 VODKA ALL THE WAY (IRE), 9, b g Oscar (IRE)—Fully Focused (IRE) **Bradley Partnership**
20 WRONG SHAPE BALL (IRE), 5, b g Mahler—Ask June (IRE) **Bradley Partnership**

## 359 MR CHRISTOPHER MASON, Caerwent
Postal: Whitehall Barn, Five Lanes, Caerwent, Newport, Monmouthshire, Np26 5pe
Contacts: PHONE 01291 422172 MOBILE 07970 202050 FAX 01633 666690
EMAIL cjmasonracing@yahoo.co.uk

1 AQUADABRA (IRE), 6, b m Born To Sea (IRE)—Amazing Win (IRE) **B. G. Hicks**
2 ATTY'S EDGE, 5, b g Coach House (IRE)—Belle's Edge **International Plywood (Importers) Ltd**
3 DEL'S EDGE, 5, b m Harbour Watch (IRE)—Elidore **C. J. Mason, Mr S Bishop & Mr C Mason, Mr S. Bishop**
4 DISEY'S EDGE, 5, b m Harbour Watch (IRE)—
   Edge of Light **Int Plywood (Importers) Ltd & C Mason, International Plywood (Importers) Ltd, C. J. Mason**
5 EDGE OF THE BAY, 4, b f Cable Bay (IRE)—
   Sharpened Edge **C. J. Mason, Mr S Bishop & Mr C Mason, Mr S. Bishop**
6 GILT EDGE, 5, b m Havana Gold (IRE)—Bright Edge **C. J. Mason, Mr S Bishop & Mr C Mason, Mr S. Bishop**
7 GLAMOROUS ANNA, 4, b f Cable Bay (IRE)—Go Glamorous (IRE) **Robert and Nina Bailey**
8 GLAMOROUS CRESCENT, 5, ch m Stimulation (IRE)—Go Glamorous (IRE) **Robert and Nina Bailey**
9 JUST GLAMOROUS (IRE), 8, b g Arcano (IRE)—Glamorous Air (IRE) **Robert and Nina Bailey**
10 OHNOTANOTHERONE, 4, b f Camacho—Saint Lucy **Mr K. B. Hodges**

### THREE-YEAR-OLDS
11 GLAMOROUS BREEZE, b f Cable Bay (IRE)—Go Glamorous (IRE) **Robert and Nina Bailey**
12 ON EDGE, b g Mayson—Edge of Light **Mr Christopher and Annabelle Mason Racing**

### TWO-YEAR-OLDS
13 B f 28/04 Aclaim (IRE)—Bright Edge (Danehill Dancer (IRE))

**Assistant Trainer:** Miss Evie Young.

## 360 MRS JENNIFER MASON, Cirencester
Postal: Manor Farm, Ablington, Bibury, Cirencester, Gloucestershire, GL7 5NY
Contacts: PHONE 01285 740445 MOBILE 07974 262438
EMAIL pwmason2002@yahoo.co.uk WEBSITE www.jennifermasonracing.com

1 AZURE FLY (IRE), 13, br g Blueprint (IRE)—Lady Delight (IRE) **Mrs P. M. Phillips**
2 BARLEY HILL (IRE), 8, ch g Stowaway—Saysi (IRE) **Mrs S. J. Ash**
3 BONANZA SAM, 8, ch g Black Sam Bellamy (IRE)—Double Hit **G. MacEchern family & Mr N Mills**
4 FRILLY FROCK (IRE), 7, b m Mahler—Killoughey Baby (IRE) **Mason Racing Club**
5 FULL TROTTLE (IRE), 12, ch g Vertical Speed (FR)—Keerou Lady (IRE) **Mr N. A. Thomas**
6 MADAM DELUXE, 6, b m Malinas (GER)—Easibrook Jane **Mason Racing Club**
7 NINTH WAVE (IRE), 7, b g September Storm (GER)—Royale Pearl **The Garland and Disney Families**
8 TEETON SURPRISE, 8, b g Black Sam Bellamy (IRE)—Teeton Priceless **Ms J. Tice**
9 WICK GREEN, 8, b g Sagamix (FR)—Jolly Dancer **Shy John Partnership**

**Other Owners:** Gavin MacEchern, Mr N. G. Mills.

**Assistant Trainer:** Mr Peter W. Mason.

**Amateur Jockey:** Mr Peter Mason.

## 361 MISS JANE MATHIAS, Llancarfan
Postal: Crosstown, Llancarfan, Vale of Glamorgan, CF62 3AD
Contacts: MOBILE 07779 382727

1 DEFINATELY VINNIE, 11, ch g Vinnie Roe (IRE)—Sohapara **Mrs S. E. Mathias**
2 SISTER SOPHIE, 5, b m Dr Massini (IRE)—Sohapara **Miss J. E. Mathias**

## 362 MR PHILIP MCBRIDE, Newmarket
Postal: Exeter House Stables, 33 Exeter Road, Newmarket, Suffolk, CB8 8LP
Contacts: PHONE 01638 667841 MOBILE 07929 265711

1 BLAUSEE (IRE), 4, b f Swiss Spirit—Fire Line **Maelor Racing**
2 CAMACHESS, 5, b m Camacho—Heeby Jeeby **The Narc Partnership**
3 CAPTAIN PUGWASH (IRE), 7, b g Sir Prancealot—Liscoa (IRE) **Three's A Crowd**
4 CHIARODILUNA, 4, b f Kyllachy—Falling Angel **Serafinoagodino,C.M.Budgett,P.J.Mcbride**
5 JUNGLE BOOGALOO (IRE), 4, b f Bungle Inthejungle—
Newton Bomb (IRE) **Mrs A L Lofts & Mrs Nicky Scott Knight**
6 MOLLY MAI, 5, b m Mayson—Handsome Molly **The Ten Fools & A Horse Partnership**
7 POKER MASTER (IRE), 4, b g Sepoy (AUS)—Three Cards **Mr Ian Pattle & P J Mcbride**
8 QUELLA COSA, 4, b f Fountain of Youth (IRE)—Bombalarina (IRE) **Mr Ian Pattle & P J Mcbride**
9 SHINING AITCH, 4, gr g Sepoy (AUS)—Light Shine **Mr Howard J. Cooke & Mr P. J. Mcbride**

### THREE-YEAR-OLDS
10 BARBARA ANN, b f Muhaarar—Pin Cushion **Pmracing (Uk) Ltd**
11 BROUGHTONS CHIEF, ch g Equiano (FR)—Broughtons Harmony **B. N. Fulton**
12 BROUGHTONS OYSTER, b f Due Diligence (USA)—Sunpearl **B. N. Fulton**
13 FIRST LANDING, b f Twilight Son—Caption **P. J. McBride**
14 PRISCILLA'S WISH, b f Adaay (IRE)—Ghedi (IRE) **Mr C Massie & Mr Pj McBride**
15 WILLYORWON'T HE, b c Helmet (AUS)—Miss Bunter **David & K Dixon**

**Other Owners:** Mr S. Agodino, Mr C. M. Budgett, Mr A. D. Bunce, Mr H. J. Cooke, N. L. Davies, Miss K. A. Dixon, Mr D. J. Fravigar, Mr D. L. Jackson, Mrs A. L. Lofts, Mr C. Massie, P. J. McBride, R. D. Musson, Mr W. J. Musson, Mr I. J. Pattle, Mrs N. M. Scott Knight, Mr P. S. Thompson, Mr R. Wilson.

**363** **MR DONALD McCAIN, Cholmondeley**
Postal: D McCain Racing Ltd, Bankhouse, Cholmondeley, Cheshire, SY14 8AL
Contacts: PHONE 01829 720351, 01829 720352 MOBILE 07903 066194
EMAIL info@donaldmccain.co.uk WEBSITE www.donaldmccain.co.uk

1 **AKENTRICK**, 5, b g Champs Elysees—Torcross **Mrs L. Middleton**
2 **ARAB MOON**, 7, b g Elnadim (USA)—Albeed **CP RACING**
3 **ARMATTIEKAN (IRE)**, 7, b g Arakan (USA)—Serpentine Mine (IRE) **Clwydian International**
4 **ARTISTIC STREAK**, 5, b m New Approach (IRE)—Artisti **Mrs C. A. Shaw**
5 **AWAY AT DAWN (IRE)**, 6, b g Getaway (GER)—Wings At Dawn (IRE) **Mr G. E. Fitzpatrick**
6 **BALLASALLA (IRE)**, 9, br g Presenting—Papoose (IRE) **David & Carol Shaw**
7 4, Br g Mahler—Ballinahow Ann (IRE) **Mrs Jayne Edwards**
8 **BANNIXTOWN GLORY (IRE)**, 7, b m Fame And Glory—Me Auld Segosha (IRE) **Miss C. McCracken**
9 **BAREBACK JACK (IRE)**, 5, b g Getaway (GER)—Dubh Go Leir (IRE) **T. G. Leslie**
10 **BARNABAS COLLINS (IRE)**, 6, b g Shantou (USA)—G Day Sile (IRE) **T. G. Leslie**
11 **BARRICHELLO**, 5, b g Gentlewave (IRE)—Tambourine Ridge (IRE) **Owners Group 066**
12 **BARRULE PARK**, 5, b g Kayf Tara—Rare Vintage (IRE) **Mr T. J. Hemmings**
13 **BEACH BREAK**, 7, b g Cacique (IRE)—Wemyss Bay **Mr G. E. Fitzpatrick**
14 **BIRD ON THE WIRE (FR)**, 6, ch g Martaline—Titi Jolie (FR) **T. G. Leslie**
15 **BLAKENEY POINT**, 8, b g Sir Percy—Cartoon **T W Johnson & G Maxwell**
16 **BLUEBERRY WINE (IRE)**, 5, b g Dylan Thomas (IRE)—Buttonhole Rose (IRE) **Birkdale Bloodstock**
17 **BOB'S BAR (IRE)**, 5, b g Darsi (FR)—Kilcoltrim Society (IRE) **Cheshire Bloodstock Racing**
18 **BROTHER PAT**, 6, b g Muhtathir—Comtesse du Sud (FR) **Birkdale Bloodstock**
19 **CALZA NERA (IRE)**, 4, b f Milan—Gazzas Dream (IRE) **Pbp Racing**
20 **CARRY ON**, 6, b g Footstepsinthesand—Evening **Richard & Holly Thomas**
21 **CENOTICE**, 7, b g Phoenix Reach (IRE)—Kenny's Dream
22 4, B g Blue Bresil (FR)—Cent Prime
23 4, B f Midnight Legend—Chocca Wocca **James & Jean Potter Ltd 1**
24 **CHTI BALKAN (FR)**, 9, br g Balko (FR)—Ina Scoop (FR) **Mr D. Carrington**
25 **CHUVELO (IRE)**, 6, b g Milan—Bargante (IRE) **T. G. Leslie**
26 **CONSTANCIO (IRE)**, 8, b g Authorized (IRE)—Senora Galilei (IRE) **Elite Racing Club**
27 **COURT JURADO (IRE)**, 7, b g Court Cave (IRE)—Glen Eile (IRE) **David & Carol Shaw**
28 **COUSIN OSCAR (IRE)**, 9, b g Oscar (IRE)—On The Jetty (IRE) **T. G. Leslie**
29 **CREATIVE CONTROL (IRE)**, 5, b g Battle of Marengo (IRE)—Intricate Dance (USA) **Clwydian Connections**
30 **DANGER MONEY**, 4, ch g Nayef (USA)—Generous Diana **Mr C. Taylor, Miss K. M. Wilding**
31 **DEAR SIRE (FR)**, 9, gr g Al Namix (FR)—Polismith (FR) **Green Day Racing**
32 **DONLADD (IRE)**, 7, b g Cloudings (IRE)—Kentford Serotina **Mr A Lake & Partners**
33 **DREAMS OF HOME (IRE)**, 5, b g Jet Away—Knocktartan (IRE) **Mr C. Taylor, Miss K. M. Wilding**
34 **ESME SHELBY (IRE)**, 6, b m Arctic Cosmos (USA)—Kyle Again (IRE) **Red Rum Racing 1**
35 **FALANGHINA**, 4, gr f Ocovango—Whisky Rose (IRE) **Mrs C. A. Shaw**
36 **FEDERICI**, 12, b g Overbury (IRE)—Vado Via **Mrs C Strang Steel & Partner**
37 **FIN AND GAME (IRE)**, 9, b g Oscar (IRE)—Miss Cilla (IRE) **T. G. Leslie**
38 **FINISK RIVER**, 8, gr g Red Rocks (IRE)—Scopa d'Assi (IRE) **L. Buckley**
39 **FIVEANDTWENTY**, 4, br f Farhh—Fen Guest **Middleham Park Racing XCVI**
40 **FRUIT N NUT (IRE)**, 5, b g Carlotamix (FR)—Perilously (USA) **L. Buckley**
41 **GAELIK COAST (FR)**, 7, br g Coastal Path—Gaelika (FR) **T. G. Leslie**
42 **GALLOPONGRAY (IRE)**, 6, gr m Shirocco (GER)—Caltra Princess (IRE) **Birkdale Bloodstock**
43 **GARRIX DE LA SEE (FR)**, 5, gr g Al Namix (FR)—Janita de La See (FR) **Miss C. McCracken**
44 **GENEVER DRAGON (IRE)**, 4, b g Dragon Pulse (IRE)—Glen Ginnie (IRE) **Middleham Park Racing C**
45 **GEROMINO (FR)**, 6, b g Masked Marvel—Romane Place (FR) **Mr G. E. Fitzpatrick**
46 **GET IN ROBIN (IRE)**, 6, ch m Robin des Champs (FR)—Get In There (IRE) **T. G. Leslie**
47 **GLEBE AALIN (IRE)**, 6, b br g Scorpion (IRE)—Glebe Dream (IRE) **Mr T. W. Fearn**
48 **GOOBINATOR (USA)**, 5, ch g Noble Mission—Lilac Lilly (USA) **T. G. Leslie**
49 **GRAIN D'OUDAIRIES (FR)**, 5, b g Kapgarde (FR)—Miss d'Estruval (FR) **Mr J. P. McManus**
50 **HANDY HOLLOW (IRE)**, 8, ch g Beat Hollow—Hesperia **Donald McCain Racing Club**
51 **HART OF STEEL (IRE)**, 6, gr g Ask—Boberelle (IRE) **Mr N. Hartley**
52 **HEARTBREAK KID (IRE)**, 6, b g Getaway (GER)—Bella's Bury **T. G. Leslie**
53 **HENRY'S JOY (IRE)**, 8, b g Craigsteel—Shocona (IRE) **Donald McCain Racing Club**
54 **HIDALGO DE L'ISLE (FR)**, 4, b g Coastal Path—Agence de L'Isle (FR) **T. G. Leslie**
55 **HILLS OF DUBAI (IRE)**, 12, ch g Dubai Destination (USA)—Mowazana (IRE) **Mrs S. K. McCain**

# MR DONALD McCAIN - continued

56 **HONNOLD**, 4, br g Sea The Moon (GER)—Aloha **Hale Racing Limited & Mr D. Mccain Jnr**
57 **INTHEBORISCAMP (IRE)**, 5, gr g Kalanisi (IRE)—Dabiyra (IRE) **Mr J. M. Glews**
58 **KENSINGTON ART**, 5, b g Dutch Art—Lady Luachmhar (IRE) **The Blue Nuns**
59 **KHAMSIN MOOR**, 6, b g Shirocco (GER)—Holme Rose **T. G. Leslie**
60 **LADY TREMAINE (IRE)**, 6, b m Kalanisi (IRE)—Lough Lein Leader (IRE) **Duncan, Dunnington, Nicholls & Shaw**
61 **A**, B f Walk In The Park (IRE)—Lakil Princess (IRE)
62 **LOUGH DERG JEWEL (IRE)**, 10, b g Oscar (IRE)—River Valley Lady (IRE) **Mrs A. E. Strang Steel**
63 **LUCK OF CLOVER**, 5, b m Phoenix Reach (IRE)—Diktalina **Red Rum Racing 2**
64 **MACKENBERG (GER)**, 6, b g Jukebox Jury (IRE)—Mountain Melody (GER) **T. G. Leslie**
65 **MAGHFOOR**, 7, b g Cape Cross (IRE)—Thaahira (USA) **Jo-co Partnership**
66 **MALPAS (IRE)**, 6, b g Milan—Skipping Along (IRE) **Mr N. Hartley**
67 **MASTER MALACHY (IRE)**, 5, b g Mastercraftsman (IRE)—Stroke of Six (IRE) **T. G. Leslie**
68 **MILANS EDGE (IRE)**, 6, b m Milan—The Keane Edge (IRE) **James and Jean Potter Ltd**
69 **MINELLA DRAMA (IRE)**, 6, b g Flemensfirth (USA)—Midsummer Drama (IRE) **Green Day Racing**
70 **MINELLA TRUMP (IRE)**, 7, b g Shantou (USA)—One Theatre (IRE) **T. G. Leslie**
71 **MORRAMAN (IRE)**, 8, b g Gold Well—Casa Queen (IRE) **Miss C. Lees-Jones**
72 **MOUNT MEWS (IRE)**, 10, b g Presenting—Kneeland Lass (IRE) **The Blue Nuns**
73 **MR GOLD (IRE)**, 4, b g Milan—Assistance **Sarah & Wayne Dale**
74 **MR MCGO (IRE)**, 10, b g Touch of Land (FR)—La Principal (IRE) **Mr J. M. Glews**
75 **NAVAJO PASS**, 5, b g Nathaniel (IRE)—Navajo Charm **T. G. Leslie**
76 **NAYATI (FR)**, 7, b g Spirit One (FR)—Smadouce (FR) **CP RACING**
77 **NEFYN POINT**, 5, gr g Overbury (IRE)—So Cloudy **Tim & Miranda Johnson**
78 **NELL'S BELLS (IRE)**, 5, b m Milan—Miss Cilla (IRE) **T. G. Leslie**
79 **O'HANRAHAN BRIDGE (IRE)**, 9, b g Gold Well—Greenacre Mandalay (IRE) **Mr M. Kelly**
80 **OBEY THE RULES (IRE)**, 6, br g Rule of Law (USA)—Mamie Buggles (IRE) **Mr J. M. Glews**
81 **OCTOBER STORM**, 8, br g Shirocco (GER)—Cyber Star **Donald McCain Racing Club**
82 **OFCOURSEIWILL (IRE)**, 9, b g Publisher (USA)—Camden Princess (IRE) **Mr N. Hartley**
83 **ONTHEFRONTFOOT (IRE)**, 7, b g Shantou (USA)—On The Backfoot (IRE) **Duncan, Dunnington, Nicholls & Shaw**
84 **OTTONIAN**, 7, ch g Dubawi (IRE)—Evil Empire (GER) **Nigel Dunnington & David Shaw**
85 **OUR RODNEY (IRE)**, 5, b g Canford Cliffs (IRE)—Sea Swell (USA) **Sarah & Wayne Dale 1**
86 **PINCH OF GINGER (IRE)**, 10, ch g Golden Lariat (USA)—Espiritu Santo (IRE) **Miss C. McCracken**
87 **POGUE (IRE)**, 8, gr g Stowaway—Night Palm (IRE) **Mr J. Turner**
88 **PRESENTANDCOUNTING (IRE)**, 7, b g Presenting—Count On Me (IRE) **Mr J. Turner**
89 **PRINCE KHURRAM**, 11, b g Nayef (USA)—Saree **T. G. Leslie**
90 **PULL GREEN (IRE)**, 6, b g Califet (FR)—Clogher Valley (IRE)
91 **RALF DES NOES (FR)**, 4, b g Balko (FR)—Summer Cider (IRE) **Tim & Miranda Johnson**
92 **RIVER WALK (IRE)**, 5, b g Scorpion (IRE)—Lucy Rouge (IRE) **Mr T. J. Hemmings**
93 **ROAD TO REWARD (IRE)**, 6, b g Gamut (IRE)—Lora Lady (IRE) **Birkdale Bloodstock**
94 **SAME CIRCUS (IRE)**, 10, b m Brian Boru—Curragh Orpen (IRE) **Penketh & Sankey Jech Racing Club 1**
95 **SEE THE SEA (IRE)**, 7, b m Born To Sea (IRE)—Shahmina (IRE) **The Shinton Family 1**
96 **SHABBA DADA DO (IRE)**, 7, b m Jeremy (USA)—Koral Bay (FR) **Beswick Brothers Bloodstock 1**
97 **SHALLOW RUN (IRE)**, 7, ch m Sholokhov (IRE)—Corrieann (IRE) **Mr E. Allen**
98 **SHANTALUZE (IRE)**, 9, b g Shantou (USA)—Nut Touluze (IRE) **Red Rum Racing**
99 **SNOUGAR (IRE)**, 8, b g Arakan (USA)—Thorbella **Tim & Miranda Johnson**
100 **SPIN THE COIN (IRE)**, 8, b g Witness Box (USA)—Kempinski (IRE) **Donald McCain Racing Club**
101 **STEINKRAUS (IRE)**, 6, b g Jeremy (USA)—Red Fern (IRE) **Mr M. Pryde**
102 **TAKINGITALLIN (IRE)**, 7, b m Fame And Glory—Gilt Benefit (IRE) **Mr G. E. Fitzpatrick**
103 **TAWSEEF (IRE)**, 13, b g Monsun (GER)—Sahool **D. R. McCain**
104 **TEASING GEORGIA (IRE)**, 5, b m New Approach (IRE)—Hallowed Park (IRE) **Mr J. Turner**
105 **THE CON MAN (IRE)**, 8, b g Oscar (IRE)—Phillis Hill **T. G. Leslie**
106 **THE HERDS GARDEN**, 12, b g Multiplex—Eternal Legacy (IRE) **Hale Racing Limited & Mr D. Mccain Jnr**
107 **THE SOME DANCE KID (IRE)**, 8, b g Shantou (USA)—River Rouge (IRE) **The Blue Nuns**
108 **TIME LEADER (IRE)**, 7, b g Scorpion (IRE)—Dancing Matilda (IRE) **Beswick Brothers Bloodstock**
109 **TOTALLY REJECTED (IRE)**, 6, b g Mustameet (USA)—Boro Katie (IRE) **Four Counties**
110 **TWO BLONDES (IRE)**, 5, ch g Dragon Pulse (IRE)—Itaya (IRE) **Mr J. Turner**
111 **VAL MOME (FR)**, 8, b g Turgeon (USA)—Valle Fleurie (FR) **Mr A. N. Brooke Rankin**
112 **WATCH AND LEARN**, 5, b m Havana Gold (IRE)—Charlecote **Mrs B. E. McCain**
113 **WAZOWSKI**, 12, b g Overbury (IRE)—Malay **D. R. McCain**
114 **WHITECHURCH (IRE)**, 7, b g Scorpion (IRE)—Flying Flame (IRE)
115 **WHITEOAK FLEUR**, 8, b m Black Sam Bellamy (IRE)—Harringay **Mr B. J. Richardson**

## MR DONALD McCAIN - continued

**116 WILLY NILLY (IRE)**, 4, b g Morpheus—Subtle Shimmer **J Fyffe & S Townshend**
**117 WINDING ROE (IRE)**, 7, ch g Vinnie Roe (IRE)—Brown Sheila (IRE) **Mr T. W. Fearn**
**118 WORD HAS IT (IRE)**, 7, b g Jeremy (USA)—Rathfeigh (IRE) **T. G. Leslie**

### THREE-YEAR-OLDS

**119** B f Milan—Assistance
**120 CORPORAL JONES (IRE)**, b c War Command (USA)—Bessie Lou (IRE) **Owners Group 071**
**121** B g Norse Dancer (IRE)—Grande Terre (IRE) **Mr & Mrs G Calder**
**122 GURKHA'S SURPRISE (IRE)**, ch g The Gurkha (IRE)—Miss Ellany (IRE) **Mr T. P. McMahon & Mr D. McMahon**
**123 MAYLAH (IRE)**, b g Mayson—Mahlah (IRE) **Birkdale Bloodstock**
**124 NACHO (IRE)**, b g Camacho—Equinette (IRE) **Beswick Brothers Bloodstock 1**
**125 RUSSCO (IRE)**, b g Coulsty (IRE)—Russian Spirit **Birkdale Bloodstock**
**126 SACRE PIERRE (FR)**, b c On Est Bien (IRE)—Goldance (FR) **D. R. McCain**
**127 ZERO HOUR**, ch f Monsieur Bond (IRE)—Eleventh Hour (IRE) **Mrs S. K. McCain**

### TWO-YEAR-OLDS

**128** Ch f 18/02 Champs Elysees—Clemency (Halling) **Mr David Lockwood**
**129** B f 22/02 Galileo Gold—Tooraweenah (Notnowcato) (4500)

**Other Owners:** Beswick Brothers Bloodstock, Beswick Brothers Bloodstock 1, Mrs S. J. Dale, Sarah & Wayne Dale, Mr W. R. Dale, Mr D. Duncan, Mr N. C. Dunnington, Mr J. Fyffe, Hale Racing Limited, Mr P. Haughey, James and Jean Potter Ltd, T. G. Leslie, D. R. McCain, Mr P. McCourt, Mr & Mrs G Calder, Mr C. Nicholls, Mr B. Ryan-Beswick, Mr W. Ryan-Beswick, Mrs C. A. Shaw, Mr D. M. Shaw, M. H. Shinton, Mr J. M. Smart, Mrs A. E. Strang Steel, Mr R. G. Thomas.

**Assistant Trainer:** Adrian Lane.

**NH Jockey:** Brian Hughes. **Conditional Jockey:** Theo Gillard, Peter Kavanagh, Abbie McCain.

---

**364**
### MR TIM McCARTHY, Godstone
Postal: **Nags Hall Farm, Oxted Road, Godstone, Surrey, RH9 8DB**
Contacts: **PHONE 01883 740379 MOBILE 07887 763062**
EMAIL tim@tdmccarthy.com

**1 MINDUROWNBUSINESS (IRE)**, 10, b g Cape Cross (IRE)—Whos Mindin Who (IRE) **Homecroft Wealth Racing**
**2 SOLDIER IN ACTION (FR)**, 8, ch g Soldier of Fortune (IRE)—Ripley (GER) **Surrey Racing Club**
**3 UNDERSTORY (USA)**, 14, b g Forestry (USA)—Sha Tha (USA) **Homecroft Wealth Racing & T D McCarthy**
**4 W G GRACE (IRE)**, 6, b g Exceed And Excel (AUS)—Ownwan (USA) **Homecroft Wealth Racing & T D McCarthy**
**5 WATER THIEF (USA)**, 9, b g Bellamy Road (USA)—Sometime (IRE) **Surrey Racing Club**
**6 WHITE TOWER (IRE)**, 7, b g Cape Cross (IRE)—Star Blossom (USA) **Surrey Racing Club**

**Other Owners:** Mr J. A. Collins, Homecroft Wealth Racing, T. D. McCarthy, Mr S. J. Piper.

**Assistant Trainer:** Mrs C.V. McCarthy.

## 365  MR PHIL MCENTEE, Newmarket
Postal: **Racefield Stables, Carriageway, Hamilton Road, Newmarket, Suffolk, CB8 7JQ**
Contacts: **PHONE 01638 662092 MOBILE 07802 663256**
**WORK EMAIL mcenteephil@yahoo.com**

1 **BERNIE'S BOY,** 8, b g Lilbourne Lad (IRE)—Stoney Cove (IRE) **T. D. Johnson**
2 **COMEATCHOO (IRE),** 4, b g Camacho—La Estatua **Mr S. Jakes**
3 **CONTINGENCY FEE,** 6, b g Helmet (AUS)—Hearsay **Mr M. B. Hall**
4 **GLOBAL MELODY,** 6, b g Hellvelyn—Dash of Lime **T. D. Johnson**
5 **IRISH MASTER (IRE),** 4, gr ro g Mastercraftsman (IRE)—Selva Real **Miss R. B. McEntee**
6 **LONDON (FR),** 8, b g Galileo (IRE)—Altana (USA) **T. D. Johnson**
7 **PEARL SPECTRE (USA),** 10, ch g Street Cry (IRE)—Dark Sky (USA) **Mr S. Jakes**
8 **RED BEACON (IRE),** 4, ch g Camacho—Beacon of Hope (IRE) **T. D. Johnson**
9 **ROCKESBURY,** 6, b g Foxwedge (AUS)—Nellie Ellis (IRE) **Mrs R. L. Baker**
10 **SPLIT DOWN SOUTH,** 5, gr g Dark Angel (IRE)—Brown Eyed Honey **T. D. Johnson**
11 4, B f Alhebayeb (IRE)—Stoney Cove (IRE) **Mr S. Jakes**

### THREE-YEAR-OLDS
12 **BLACK SPARROW,** bl f Swiss Spirit—Bronze Star **T. D. Johnson**
13 B f Golden Horn—Blue Beacon **Mrs R. L. McEntee**
14 **NORTONTHORPE BOY,** b g Swiss Spirit—Stoney Cove (IRE) **Miss M. Hancox**
15 **ROY J,** ch g Sepoy (AUS)—Jimmy's Girl (IRE) **Mr S. Jakes**
16 **YOUNG CHARLIE,** b g Fountain of Youth (IRE)—Margrets Gift **Mr S. Jakes**

### TWO-YEAR-OLDS
17 **DANGER CLOSE (IRE),** b g 16/03 War Command (USA)—Arosha (IRE) (Cape Cross (IRE)) (4762) **T. D. Johnson**
18 B f 04/04 Cotai Glory—Just A Runaway (Equiano (FR)) (1429) **T. D. Johnson**
19 Ch f 14/04 The Gurkha (IRE)—Weekend Lady (IRE) (Bahamian Bounty) (2857) **T. D. Johnson**

## 366  MR MURTY MCGRATH, Maidstone
Postal: **Galway Barn, Kiln Barn Road, East Malling, Kent, ME19 6BG**
Contacts: **PHONE 01732 840173 MOBILE 07818 098073**
**EMAIL mjmcgrath@hotmail.com**

1 **AUTHORISED SPEED (FR),** 4, b g Authorized (IRE)—Tangaspeed (FR) **Gallagher Bloodstock Limited**
2 4, B g Walk In The Park (IRE)—Maple Lady (IRE) **Gallagher Bloodstock Limited**
3 **SEI BELLA,** 7, b m Crosspeace (IRE)—Dizzy Whizz **M. McGrath**
4 **WHO WHAT WHEN,** 6, b m Champs Elysees—Freya Tricks **Gallaghers**

**Assistant Trainer:** Heidi McGrath.

## 367  MRS JEAN MCGREGOR, Milnathort
Postal: **Wester Tillyrie Steading, Milnathort, Kinross, KY13 0RW**
Contacts: **PHONE 01577 861792 MOBILE 07764 464299**
**EMAIL purebred68@hotmail.co.uk**

1 **BURLINGTON BERT (FR),** 10, b g Califet (FR)—Melhi Sun (FR) **The Good To Soft Firm**
2 **DIAMOND ROAD (IRE),** 7, b g Tikkanen (USA)—Silver Tassie (FR) **Off and Running**
3 **GIAMAS,** 8, b g Bollin Eric—Ginger Brandy **Mrs D. Thomson**
4 5, B m Bollin Eric—Ginger Brandy **Mrs D. Thomson**
5 **GO COMPLAIN,** 9, b m Mount Nelson—Trounce **Tillyrie Racing Club**

## MRS JEAN MCGREGOR - continued

6 JACKOFHEARTS, 13, b g Beat Hollow—Boutique **Mrs J. C. McGregor**
7 5, B m Dunaden (FR)—Light Dreams
8 OSCAR BLUE (IRE), 11, gr g Oscar (IRE)—Blossom Rose (IRE) **Tillyrie Racing Club**

**NH Jockey:** Henry Brooke, Sean Quinlan.

---

## 368 MR LUKE MCJANNET, Newmarket
Postal: **Heath View Stables, Hamilton Road, Newmarket, Suffolk, CB8 0NY**
Contacts: **PHONE 01638 664505**

1 ARLO'S SUNSHINE, 4, b g Cable Bay (IRE)—Touching (IRE) **Mr L. J. McJannet**
2 ARNOUL OF METZ, 6, b g Kyllachy—Appointee (IRE) **Mr D. M. Forrester**
3 BAD ATTITUDE, 4, b g Canford Cliffs (IRE)—Cry Freedom (IRE) **Harris S & Hardy Hardy**
4 BREATH OF SPRING (IRE), 5, br g Bated Breath—Welcome Spring (IRE) **Miss K. L. Eastwood**
5 DADDIES DIVA, 4, b f Coach House (IRE)—Pixey Punk **Mr I. Collier**
6 EMBOLDEN (IRE), 4, b g Kodiac—Sassy Gal (IRE) **Miss A. Haynes**
7 GOODBYE GRASS, 4, b g Helmet (AUS)—Daheeya **Hever Stud Farm Ltd**
8 MISS THOUGHTFUL, 4, gr f Gutaifan (IRE)—Lovely Thought **Hayley M , Leslie B, Luke M**
9 RADETSKY (USA), 4, b g Speightstown (USA)—Brooch (USA) **Mr S. A. Almutairi**
10 SMART CONNECTION (IRE), 4, b g Dutch Art—Endless Love (IRE) **Miss A. Haynes**
11 SONG OF POMPEIA, ch f Mukhadram—Pompeia **Hever Stud Farm Ltd**
12 STRIDING EDGE (IRE), 4, b g Canford Cliffs (IRE)—Assault On Rome (IRE) **Luke McJannet , Dean Forrester**
13 THAKI (IRE), 4, b g Lope de Vega (IRE)—Mickleberry (IRE) **Mr D. M. Forrester**
14 YUFTEN, 10, b g Invincible Spirit (IRE)—Majestic Sakeena (IRE) **Work Hard Play Hard Partnership**

### THREE-YEAR-OLDS
15 CUBAN POWER, ch c Havana Gold (IRE)—Sleep Dance **Miss A. Haynes**
16 B g Elzaam (AUS)—Ghostflower (IRE)
17 KOBENHAVN, ch c Charming Thought—Beat As One
18 MIGHTY POWER (IRE), gr c Markaz (IRE)—Tooley Woods (IRE) **Work Hard Play Hard Partnership**
19 QUEEN OF RIO (IRE), b f Prince of Lir (IRE)—Rio Yuma (ITY) **Mr I. Collier**
20 B c Fountain of Youth (IRE)—Rememberance Day **Mr L. J. McJannet**
21 B g Excelebration (IRE)—Sky Boat (IRE)
22 SPARK OF MAGIC, b br g Equiano (FR)—Kawaii **Four Winds Racing Partnership**
23 TAYLOR THE SAILOR, ch c New Approach (IRE)—Arwaah (IRE) **Mr I. Collier**

**Other Owners:** Mrs L. Buckley, Mr D. M. Forrester, Mr N. P. Hardy, Mr A. Harris, Miss A. Haynes, Mr L. J. McJannet, Miss H. McMurdo, Mr A. C. O Sullivan.

---

## 369 MR GRAEME MCPHERSON, Stow-On-The-Wold
Postal: **Martins Hill, Bledington Road, Stow-on-the-Wold, Gloucestershire, GL54 1JH**
Contacts: **PHONE 01451 830769 MOBILE 07815 887360**
**EMAIL info@mcphersonracing.co.uk WEBSITE www.mcphersonracing.co.uk**

1 AJAY'S WAYS (IRE), 7, b g Stowaway—Beechfield Queen (IRE) **BDRSyndicates**
2 ALEXANDER THE GREY, 10, gr g Fair Mix (IRE)—Cadourova (FR) **Mr Howard Burdett/Mr Graeme P. Mcpherson**
3 ALFOSKI (IRE), 6, b g Aizavoski (IRE)—Faraday Lady (IRE) **Foxtrot Racing: Cast In Grey**
4 AMI DESBOIS (FR), 11, b g Brave Well (FR)—Baroya (FR) **The Reserved Judgment Partnership**
5 ANDALEEP (IRE), 5, b g Siyouni (FR)—Oriental Magic (GER) **Finch Forbes and McPherson**
6 ANNUAL REVIEW (IRE), 6, b g Yeats (IRE)—Crafty Fancy (IRE) **H. W. Turcan**
7 ASK BEN (IRE), 8, b g Ask—Decheekymonkey (IRE) **Mrs E. A. Prowting**
8 ASK HENRY (IRE), 8, b g Ask—Miss Muppet (IRE) **Turf Club 2020 & Graeme McPherson**
9 4, B f Soldier of Fortune (IRE)—At The Pound Cross (IRE)

# MR GRAEME MCPHERSON - continued

10 **AVIEWTOSEA (IRE)**, 6, b g Where Or When (IRE)—Final Run (IRE) **Fry, Goulder & Mosvold**
11 **BABY BEN (IRE)**, 5, b g Ask—Decheekymonkey (IRE) **BDRSyndicates**
12 4, Ch g Malinas (GER)—Ballygambon Girl (IRE)
13 **BARRAKHOV (IRE)**, 5, b g Sholokhov (IRE)—Barrack Buster **DI Adams, Ja Adams & G McPherson**
14 **CALUM GILHOOLEY (IRE)**, 7, br g Kalanisi (IRE)—Honeyed (IRE) **BDRSyndicates**
15 **CAST IN GREY (IRE)**, 7, b gr m Fame And Glory—Derrinlanna (IRE) **Foxtrot Racing: Cast In Grey**
16 **DAWN TREADER (IRE)**, 5, b g Siyouni (FR)—Miss Elena **Mr J. T. Finch**
17 **DAYDREAM AULMES (FR)**, 8, b g Linda's Lad—My Wish Aulmes (FR) **Ms S Howell & Partner**
18 **DEHRADUN**, 5, b g Australia—Ridafa (IRE) **Mrs L.Day, Mr H.Burdett & Mr G.McPherson**
19 5, B g Fame And Glory—Derriana (IRE) **Mr G. P. McPherson**
20 **DOC EL (IRE)**, 4, ch g Fracas (IRE)—Magpie (USA) **BDRSyndicates**
21 **DUBLIN FOUR (IRE)**, 7, ch g Arakan (USA)—Eluna **DI Adams, Ja Adams & G McPherson**
22 **ELK BRIDGE (IRE)**, 7, b m Dansant—Just Jodie **Mrs E. A. Prowting**
23 **EXPLOITEUR (FR)**, 7, b br g Desir d'Un Soir (FR)—Sourya d'Airy (FR) **Shaw Racing Partnership 2**
24 **EYEOFTHESCORPION (IRE)**, 7, b g Scorpion (IRE)—Shuil Sharp (IRE) **First With Mortgages Limited**
25 **FIFTY PEACH WAY**, 9, b m Black Sam Bellamy (IRE)—Aphrodisia **Mr G. P. McPherson**
26 **FLANN**, 6, b g Brian Boru—Lady Karinga **Flann's Fans**
27 **FLEETING VISIT**, 8, b g Manduro (GER)—Short Affair **The FV Partnership**
28 **FOLLOW THE SWALLOW (IRE)**, 13, b g Dr Massini (IRE)—Old Chapel (IRE) **Mrs Mary M Gwillam & Partner**
29 **GETTHEPOT (IRE)**, 6, b g Getaway (GER)—Raheen Lady (IRE) **Shaw Racing & Graeme McPherson**
30 **HATTAAB**, 8, b g Intikhab (USA)—Sundus (USA) **You Can Be Sure**
31 **HELLO BUDDY (IRE)**, 7, ch g Salutino (GER)—Cotton Candy (IRE) **Mr J. Chamberlain**
32 **HIGH WELLS**, 7, b g High Chaparral (IRE)—Valencha **Mrs Jill Phillips & Graeme McPherson**
33 **HOMING STAR**, 6, b m Harbour Watch (IRE)—Nightunderthestars **The Cotswold Stars**
34 **JESSICA RABBIT**, 7, b m Mawatheeq (USA)—Intersky High (USA) **The Ladies Of Martins Hill**
35 4, Ch g Mahler—Jumpingjude (IRE)
36 4, B g Blue Bresil (FR)—Kentucky Sky
37 **LORD SCOUNDREL (IRE)**, 12, b g Presenting—Noble Choice **The Grand Cru Partnership**
38 **MARBLE SANDS (FR)**, 5, gr g Martaline—Sans Rien (FR) **DI Adams, Ja Adams & G McPherson**
39 **MISSTHECUDDLES (IRE)**, 7, b m Gold Well—Autumn Sky (IRE) **TyroneForSam**
40 **NEW ZEALANDER**, 4, b g Australia—Dalasyla (IRE) **The McPherson Racing Partnership**
41 **NORMAN STANLEY (IRE)**, 9, b g Flemensfirth (USA)—Ballerina Laura (IRE) **Foxtrot Racing: Cast In Grey**
42 **PASSING SHADOW**, 7, b g Passing Glance—Peel Me A Grape **Mrs E. A. Prowting**
43 **PHANTOMOFTHEOSCAR (IRE)**, 6, b g Oscar (IRE)—Notanotherone (IRE) **DI Adams, Ja Adams & G McPherson**
44 **PHIL HEALY (IRE)**, 5, b m Shirocco (GER)—Ariels Serenade (IRE) **Burnham Plastering & Drylining Ltd**
45 **PHILLAPA SUE (IRE)**, 6, b m Scorpion (IRE)—Shuil Sharp (IRE) **Adams, Burdett & McPherson**
46 **POP THE CHAMPAGNE (FR)**, 5, b m Spanish Moon (USA)—Six Pack (FR) **Mrs Jill Phillips & Graeme McPherson**
47 **PRELUDE TO GLORY (IRE)**, 5, b m Fame And Glory—Prelude **DI Adams, Ja Adams & G McPherson**
48 **RATFACEMCDOUGALL (IRE)**, 8, b g Robin des Champs (FR)—Milano Bay (IRE) **Mrs C. Kendrick**
49 **SAMMYLOU (IRE)**, 8, b g Beneficial—Carrigeen Diamond (IRE) **DI Adams, Ja Adams & G McPherson**
50 **SKIPTHECUDDLES (IRE)**, 10, b g Westerner—Autumn Sky (IRE) **TyroneForSam**
51 **TELSON BARLEY (IRE)**, 8, b g Scorpion (IRE)—El Monica (IRE) **Mrs L. Day**
52 **THE DISTANT LADY (IRE)**, 7, b m Fracas (IRE)—Misty Native (IRE) **4 Left Footers & A Blewnose**
53 **THUNDERSOCKSSUNDAE (IRE)**, 6, b g Yeats (IRE)—Roseabel (IRE) **4 Left Footers & A Blewnose**
54 **WILDE WATER (IRE)**, 7, b g Oscar (IRE)—Pay The Ferryman (IRE) **Mrs L. Day**
55 **ZULU DAWN (IRE)**, 7, b g Fame And Glory—Maslam (IRE) **The Grand Cru Partnership**

## THREE-YEAR-OLDS

56 **EAGLE'S REALM**, b g Free Eagle (IRE)—Regal Realm
57 Ch g Bated Breath—Valencha

**Other Owners:** Mr D. L. Adams, Mrs J. A. Adams, Mrs P. J. Buist, Mr H. Burdett, Mr A. N. Cheyne, Mr A. N. Clark, Mrs M. M. Gwillam, Ms S. A. Howell, Col A. J. E. Malcolm, Mr G. P. McPherson, Mr I. M. O'Doherty, Mrs J. D. Phillips, Shaw Racing Partnership 2, Ms D. J. Spencer, Ms C. L. Spencer-Herbert, Turf Club 2020, Mr P. Whitehead.

**Assistant Trainer:** Mick Finn, Jodie Mogford.

**NH Jockey:** Kielan Woods. **Conditional Jockey:** Tom Humphries. **Amateur Jockey:** Miss Lily Pinchin.

## 370 MR CHRISTOPHER MCSHARRY, Sheriff Hutton
Postal: **Dudley Hill Farm, Sheriff Hutton, York, North Yorkshire, YO60 6RU**
Contacts: **PHONE 01347 868156**
EMAIL **chris.mcsharry@dudleyhillfarm.co.uk**

1 **CEOLWULF**, 5, gr g Fame And Glory—Spieta (IRE) **Mr C. P. McSharry**
2 **LAID BACK SAM**, 5, b g Black Sam Bellamy (IRE)—Wet And Dry (IRE)
3 **TIGERPOMP**, 6, b m Fame And Glory—Saltbarrow **Mr C. P. McSharry**
4 **TIMETOTALK (IRE)**, 5, b g Milan—Zalda **Mr C. P. McSharry**
5 **VIN DE PAIL (FR)**, 5, b g Silver Frost (IRE)—Dame de Pail (FR) **Mr C. P. McSharry**
6 **VOSSI (IRE)**, 5, b g Fame And Glory—Seenya (IRE) **Mr C. P. McSharry**
7 **WELLFLEET WITCH**, 5, b m Black Sam Bellamy (IRE)—Indeed To Goodness (IRE) **Mr C. P. McSharry**
8 **WICKED WEST (IRE)**, 5, b g Westerner—Wilde Sapphire (IRE) **Mr C. P. McSharry**
9 **WOOLLOOMOOLOO (IRE)**, 6, b m Getaway (GER)—Rose's Emma (IRE) **Mr C. P. McSharry**

### TWO-YEAR-OLDS
10 B c 14/02 Belardo (IRE)—Lexington Sky (IRE) (Iffraaj) (17143)

## 371 MR MARTYN MEADE, Manton
Postal: **Manton Park, Marlborough, Wiltshire, SN8 4HB**
Contacts: **PHONE 01672 555000 MOBILE 07879 891811**
EMAIL **mmeade@martynmeaderacing.com WEBSITE www.martynmeaderacing.com**

1 **ADDITIONAL (IRE)**, 4, ch c Night of Thunder (IRE)—Aris (IRE)
2 **CONFIDING**, 5, b g Iffraaj—Entre Nous (IRE)
3 **CRACKLING (IRE)**, 5, b g Vale of York (IRE)—Almatlaie (USA)
4 **FOX VARDY (USA)**, 5, b g Frankel—Dance With Another (IRE)
5 **HOVER (IRE)**, 4, ch g Free Eagle (IRE)—Badr Al Badoor (IRE)
6 **INFRASTRUCTURE**, 6, ch g Raven's Pass (USA)—Foundation Filly
7 **RELATIVE (FR)**, 4, gr f Sea The Stars (IRE)—South Sister
8 **SYCAMORE (IRE)**, 4, b g Kingman—Scarborough Fair
9 **TECHNICIAN (IRE)**, 5, gr h Mastercraftsman (IRE)—Arosa (IRE)

### THREE-YEAR-OLDS
10 **BAKE (IRE)**, b g Toronado (IRE)—Rock Cake (IRE)
11 **CAMBRIDGESHIRE (IRE)**, b f Galileo (IRE)—Sahara Sky (IRE)
12 **EVERETT (IRE)**, b g Kendargent (FR)—Rajaratna (IRE)
13 **GLOUCESTERSHIRE (USA)**, b br c Flintshire—Ballade's Girl (USA)
14 **LEISUREWEAR (IRE)**, b f Kodiac—Pilates (IRE)
15 **LONE EAGLE (IRE)**, b c Galileo (IRE)—Modernstone
16 **METHOD (IRE)**, ch c Mehmas (IRE)—Darsan (IRE)
17 **NEVILE CHAMBERLAIN (IRE)**, b c Shalaa (IRE)—Black Rodded
18 **STATEMENT (IRE)**, b f Lawman (FR)—Fact Or Folklore (IRE)
19 **TECHNIQUE**, b gr f Mastercraftsman (IRE)—Lifting Me Higher (IRE)

### TWO-YEAR-OLDS
20 B f 30/04 Lawman (FR)—Adelasia (IRE) (Iffraaj) (45000)
21 B f 03/02 Aclaim (IRE)—Bazzana (Zebedee)
22 Ch c 04/03 Galileo Gold—Bukhoor (IRE) (Danehill (USA)) (32000)
23 B c 30/03 Excelebration (IRE)—Celsius Degre (IRE) (Verglas (IRE)) (22000)
24 B c 26/03 Mehmas (IRE)—Cornakill (USA) (Stormin Fever (USA)) (64762)
25 **CORSINI (IRE)**, ch f 26/02 Mastercraftsman (IRE)—Il Palazzo (USA) (Giant's Causeway (USA)) (140000)
26 B c 15/04 Profitable (IRE)—Crown (IRE) (Royal Applause) (61905)
27 Br g 05/04 Dabirsim (FR)—Dierama (IRE) (Dark Angel (IRE)) (14286)
28 Br f 15/03 Showcasing—Different (Bahamian Bounty) (35000)

## MR MARTYN MEADE - continued

**29** B c 18/02 Showcasing—Dream Dreamer (Dream Ahead (USA)) (50000)
**30** B gr f 03/03 Galileo (IRE)—Easton Angel (IRE) (Dark Angel (IRE))
**31** Ch c 17/04 Australia—Elbereth (Mount Nelson) (55000)
**32** B c 26/03 Prince of Lir (IRE)—Empress Theodora (Dansili) (38095)
**33** B c 04/03 Churchill (IRE)—Fairy Dancer (IRE) (Fastnet Rock (AUS)) (70000)
**34 GALLANTICUS (IRE),** ch c 16/03 Galileo Gold—Vexatious (IRE) (Shamardal (USA))
**35** B c 05/04 Awtaad (IRE)—Glorification (Champs Elysees) (30476)
**36** B f 28/04 Ribchester (IRE)—Guajira (FR) (Mtoto) (55238)
**37** B c 24/02 Dubawi (IRE)—Hoyam (Royal Applause) (60000)
**38** Ch c 25/02 New Bay—La Negra (IRE) (Dark Angel (IRE)) (20000)
**39** Ch f 28/01 Zoffany (IRE)—Look of Love (IRE) (New Approach (IRE)) (25000)
**40** B c 18/03 Acclamation—Miliika (Green Desert (USA)) (105000)
**41** B c 25/02 Nathaniel (IRE)—Nancy O (IRE) (Pivotal) (38095)
**42** B c 17/02 Almanzor (FR)—Nimbin (Champs Elysees) (75000)
**43** Br c 19/04 Lope de Vega (IRE)—Pale Mimosa (IRE) (Singspiel (IRE)) (71429)
**44** B c 19/02 Air Force Blue (USA)—Pellucid (Exceleration (IRE)) (105000)
**45** B c 14/02 Aclaim (IRE)—Quiet Protest (USA) (Kingmambo (USA))
**46** B c 11/03 Pivotal—Red Box (Exceed And Excel (AUS)) (65000)
**47** B f 21/03 Aclaim (IRE)—Rio's Cliffs (Canford Cliffs (IRE))
**48** B f 06/02 Aclaim (IRE)—Simballina (IRE) (Azamour (IRE))
**49** Ch f 27/03 Galileo Gold—Village Gossip (IRE) (Pivotal) (14286)
**50** B f 05/02 Kodiac—Vociferous Marina (IRE) (Vocalised (USA)) (37000)

**Owners:** Aquis Hong Kong Pty Ltd, Ballylinch Stud, Mr J. E. M. Barnes, Canning Downs, Caroline Cooper Racing, Chelsea Thoroughbreds Ltd, Mr D. A. Farrington, Highclere Thoroughbred Racing Ltd, King Power Racing Co Ltd, Mrs J. E. Mackay, Manton Park Racing, Mr C. J. Murfitt, Mrs J. E. Newett, Mr J. P. M. O'Connor, Mrs M. P. O'Rourke, Mr T. J. Ramsden, Raphie Bloodstock Trust, Sefton Syndicate, Mrs L. M. Shanahan, Team Valor LLC.

**Assistant Trainer:** Freddie Meade.

---

**372**

**MR NOEL MEADE, Navan**
Postal: **Tu Va Stables, Castletown KP, Navan, Co Meath, C15 F384, Ireland**
Contacts: **PHONE +353 46 905 4197 MOBILE +353 87 256 6039**
**EMAIL tuvastables@gmail.com WEBSITE www.noelmeade.com**

**1 ARGENTORATUM (IRE),** 6, b g Mustameet—Connemara Rose
**2 BARBARY MASTER,** 6, br g Presenting—Daisies Adventure
**3 BATTLE OF MIDWAY (IRE),** 7, b g Mahler—Womanofthemountain (IRE)
**4 BEACON EDGE (IRE),** 7, b g Doyen (IRE)—Laurel Gift (IRE)
**5 BEN THOMSON (IRE),** 5, b g Famous Name—Essaoira Jewel
**6 BILL DOOLIN,** 4, b g Australia—Star Waves (IRE)
**7 BOMBAY BLUE (IRE),** 7, b g Vocalised—Langfuhrina
**8 BRACE YOURSELF (IRE),** 8, ch g Mahler—Angelica Garnett
**9 CALICOJACK (IRE),** 9, b g Beneficial—Ballyoscar (IRE)
**10 CAPTAIN MC (IRE),** 6, b g Mahler—Deise Dreamer
**11 CASK MATE (IRE),** 8, b g Kalanisi (IRE)—Littleton Liberty
**12 CHARLIE BASSETT (IRE),** 4, b g Lawman (FR)—Xinji (IRE)
**13 CHARLIE SIRINGO,** 6, ch g Getaway (GER)—Drumderry (IRE)
**14 COOLBAWN LAD (IRE),** 6, b g Imperial Monarch (IRE)—Hollygrove Bonnie (IRE)
**15 CRASSUS (IRE),** 4, b c War Command—Buck Aspen
**16 CROSSGUNS (IRE),** 4, b g Epaulette (AUS)—Maoin Dor (IRE)
**17 CURIOUS BRIDE (IRE),** 4, b br f Exceleration—Padma
**18 DALY TIGER (FR),** 8, b g Tiger Groom—Reine Tresor (FR)
**19 DE NAME ESCAPES ME (IRE),** 11, ch g Vinnie Roe (IRE)—Heartlight (IRE)
**20 DEPLOYED (IRE),** 7, b g Mahler—Brook Style (IRE)

# MR NOEL MEADE - continued

21 **DINARD ROSE (IRE)**, 5, b m Champs Elysees—Rose of Petra (IRE)
22 **DIOL KER (FR)**, 7, b g Martalaine—Stiren Bleue (FR)
23 **DIS DONC (FR)**, 8, b g Kingsalsa (USA)—Skarina (FR)
24 **DREAM CONTI (FR)**, 8, br g Lauro (GER)—Posterite (FR)
25 **EUROBOT**, 7, ch g Malinas (GER)—L'Aventure (FR)
26 **FACE THE ODDS (IRE)**, 6, b g Presenting—Miss Otis Regrets
27 **FANNIE PORTER**, 4, b f Tagula (IRE)—Eucharist (IRE)
28 **FANTASIA ROQUE (FR)**, 6, b m Blue Bresil—Bible Gun
29 **FARCEUR DU LARGE (FR)**, 6, b g Turgeon (USA)—Antagua (FR)
30 **FAUGUERNON (FR)**, 7, b g Martalaine—I'm Right (USA)
31 **FIRST APPROACH (IRE)**, 8, b g Robin des Champs (FR)—Manhattan Babe (IRE)
32 **FLANKING MANEUVER (IRE)**, 6, b g Beat Hollow—Corskeagh Shadow
33 **FUTURE PROOF (IRE)**, 6, b g Dream Ahead (USA)—Moraga (IRE)
34 **GAIUS DE MARCIGNY (FR)**, 5, gr g Legolas—Quety De Marcigny
35 **GIPSI JOE (FR)**, 5, gr g Montmartre—Island Du Frene
36 **HARRY ALONZO (IRE)**, 5, ch g Montmartre—Patrola
37 **HEISENBERG (IRE)**, 5, b g Milan—Native Idea
38 **HELL OR HIGH WATER (IRE)**, 8, ch g Robin des Champs (FR)—Boragh Thyme (IRE)
39 **HELVIC DREAM**, 4, b c Power—Rachevie (IRE)
40 **HENRY BROWN (IRE)**, 6, b g Mahler—Blackeyedsue (IRE)
41 **HES A HARDY BLOKE (IRE)**, 6, b g Alzavoski—Talk Of Rain
42 **HIGHLAND CHARGE (IRE)**, 6, b g Fame And Glory—Full Of Birds
43 **HYMIE WEISS**, 5, ch g Ocovango—Had To Be Done
44 **IDAS BOY (IRE)**, 7, ch g Dubai Destination—Witness Express
45 **IFICUDIWUD (IRE)**, 8, b g Trans Island—Manucrin
46 **IN YOUR SHADOW (IRE)**, 7, gr g Stowaway—Classic Lin (FR)
47 **JEFF KIDDER (IRE)**, 4, b g Hallowed Crown (AUS)—Alpine
48 **JERANDME (IRE)**, 7, b g Azamour—Estrelle
49 **JESSE EVANS (IRE)**, 5, b g So You Think—American Princess
50 **JESSICA'S BOY (IRE)**, 7, b g Court Cave—Fanthom Cross Lady
51 **JOSHUA WEBB**, 6, b g Flemensfirth (USA)—Lady of Appeal (IRE)
52 **KILLER MODE (IRE)**, 6, b g Doyen—Cantou
53 **LAURA BULLION (IRE)**, 5, b m Canford Cliffs (IRE)—Vivachi (IRE)
54 **LAYFAYETTE (IRE)**, 4, b c French Navy—Scala Romana
55 **LIEUTENANT COMMAND (FR)**, 7, gr g Kendargent (FR)—Maternelle (FR)
56 **LIGNOU (FR)**, 6, b g Rajsaman (FR)—Lady Meydan (FR)
57 **LIVING'S BOY AN CO (FR)**, 6, b g Diamond Boy—Living Start
58 **LUKE SHORT**, 4, b g Sayif (IRE)—Acclamare (IRE)
59 **MAJOR DESTINATION (IRE)**, 10, b g Dubai Destination (USA)—Clara Allen (IRE)
60 **MELLY AND ME (IRE)**, 8, b g Kalanisi (IRE)—College Daisy (IRE)
61 **MINELLA FAIR (IRE)**, 10, b g Flemensfirth (USA)—Bell Walks Run (IRE)
62 **MOMUS (IRE)**, 8, b g Touch of Land (FR)—Accordion To Bob (IRE)
63 **MOYROSS**, 10, b g Kayf Tara—Dancing Dasi (IRE)
64 **NIGHT COMBAT (IRE)**, 6, b br g Presenting—Synthe Davis
65 **PART TIME FARMER (IRE)**, 5, b g Westerner—Sherin
66 **PAT'S PICK (IRE)**, 7, b g Shantou (USA)—Lady Lenson (IRE)
67 **PERRY OWENS (IRE)**, 4, b g Free Eagle (IRE)—Peace Signal (USA)
68 **PIENTA (USA)**, 6, b h Liaison (USA)—Belen (USA)
69 **PINKERTON**, 5, br g Ocovango—Mistress Pope
70 **POWERFUL TED (IRE)**, 6, b g Power—Haaf OK
71 **QUITE INCREDIBLE (IRE)**, 5, b g Shirocco—Daizinni
72 **RED GERRY (IRE)**, 5, b g Canford Cliffs (IRE)—Hollow Talk
73 **ROAD TO RESPECT (IRE)**, 10, ch g Gamut (USA)—Lora Lady (IRE)
74 **ROAD WARRIOR**, 7, gr g Fair Mix (IRE)—Mimi Equal
75 **ROSENCRANTZ (IRE)**, 7, b g Flemensfirth (USA)—Miss Brandywell (IRE)
76 **ROSGALME (IRE)**, 6, b g Mahler—Woodville Queen (IRE)
77 **SCHOOL BOY HOURS (IRE)**, 8, b g Presenting—Trinity Alley (IRE)
78 **SEEYOUINVINNYS (IRE)**, 7, b g Carlotamix (FR)—Deploy Or Die (IRE)
79 **SELLARBRIDGE (IRE)**, 6, b g Well Chosen—Dubai Petal (IRE)
80 **SHEISDIESEL**, 7, ch m Harbour Watch (IRE)—Rockme Cockney

## MR NOEL MEADE - continued

81 **SIXSHOOTER (IRE)**, 6, ch g Well Chosen—Lobinstown Girl (IRE)
82 **SNOW FALCON (IRE)**, 11, b g Presenting—Flocon de Neige (IRE)
83 **STEEL CABLE**, 6, b g Well Chosen—Apache Rose (IRE)
84 **THEDEVILSCOACHMAN (IRE)**, 5, br g Elusive Pimpernel—Hagawi
85 **TOUT EST PERMIS (FR)**, 8, gr g Linda's Lad—Kadalbleue (FR)
86 **TRAPPIST MONK (IRE)**, 8, b g Beneficial—Cush Jewel (IRE)
87 **VALDIEU (FR)**, 8, b g Diamond Boy (FR)—Vamuna (FR)
88 **YOUNG TED (IRE)**, 7, b g Fame And Glory—Last of Many (IRE)
89 **ZAMBEZIR (FR)**, 6, ch g Zambezi Sun—Lanciana (IRE)

### THREE-YEAR-OLDS

90 **APPROACH THE DAWN**, b f Dawn Approach—Thames Pageant
91 **BEN SIEGEL**, b c Tamayuz—Spring Crocus
92 **ELYSIUM**, b f Belardo—Sonning Rose
93 **EVERGREEN AND RED**, b g Requinto—Lukes Well
94 **FERMOYLE**, b g Fast Company—Mindy
95 **FUOCO**, b f Requinto—Buck Aspen
96 **GOING IN STYLE**, b g Dream Ahead—Loutka
97 **GREY ANGEL (IRE)**, ch gr f Lethal Force—Ski Slope
98 **HELVIC PRINCESS**, b f Marcel—Jersey Cream
99 **IN THE ATTIC**, gr c Markaz—Avaselle
100 **SCRUM HALF**, b g Dawn Approach—My Henrietta
101 **SHEISBYBRID (IRE)**, gr f Mastercraftsman—Empowermentofwomen
102 **THEBEAUJOLAISPOPE**, ch g Dragon Pulse—Keilogue
103 **TOSTO**, b f Alhebayeb—Glorious Melody
104 **VAZZY**, br g Tagula—Big Bad Lily
105 **WONDER SPIRIT**, b g Charm Spirit—Cloud Line
106 **XERES**, ch c Farhh—Impetious

**Assistant Trainer:** Damien McGillick, **Head Man:** Paul Cullen, **Travelling Head:** Emma Connolly, **Racing Secretary:** Katie Daley.

**NH Jockey:** Sean Flanagan, Jonathan Moore. **Conditional Jockey:** Eoin Walsh. **Amateur Jockey:** Finian Maguire.

---

**373** | ## MR NEIL MECHIE, Leyburn
Postal: **55 The Springs, Middleham, Leyburn, North Yorkshire, DL8 4RB**

1 **ARE YA WELLL (IRE)**, 5, ch g Beat Hollow—Given Moment (USA) **Mr F. O Toole**
2 **BEAUTIFUL MIX**, 9, b m Fair Mix (IRE)—Just Beautiful (FR) **The Kerr and Mechie Families**
3 6, Ch m Schiaparelli (GER)—Lucinda Lamb **N. Mechie**
4 **MONTICELLO (IRE)**, 7, b g Teofilo (IRE)—Towards (USA) **Mrs L. E. Mechie**
5 **WESTERN RAMBLER (IRE)**, 6, b g Westerner—From Above (IRE) **Mr F. O Toole**

**Other Owners:** Mrs L. E. Mechie, N. Mechie.

---

**374** | ## MR BRIAN MEEHAN, Manton
Postal: **Trainer did not wish details of their string to appear**

## 375 MR DAVID MENUISIER, Pulborough

Postal: Shinco Racing Limited, Coombelands Racing Stables, Coombelands Lane, Pulborough, West Sussex, RH20 1BP
Contacts: MOBILE 07876 674095
WORK EMAIL david@dmhorseracing.com WEBSITE www.dmhorseracing.com
TWITTER @DavidMenuisier

1 **ASIAAF,** 4, b f New Approach (IRE)—Baqqa (IRE) **Asiaaf Partners**
2 **ATALANTA'S BOY,** 6, b g Paco Boy (IRE)—Affirmatively **Mrs Monica Josefina Borton & Partner**
3 **BLUE CUP (FR),** 5, gr g Kendargent (FR)—Hunter Forward (AUS) **GerryRyan,MichaelWatt&BillySlater(AUS)**
4 **CHIAVE DI VOLTA,** 6, ch g Intello (GER)—Silca Chiave **Mr C. A. Washbourn**
5 **FLY FALCON (IRE),** 4, b g Free Eagle (IRE)—Regalline (IRE) **Fly Falcon Partners**
6 **FLYIN' SOLO,** 4, br c Roderic O'Connor (IRE)—Fille Good **Mrs H. Ringrose & Mrs D. Thompson**
7 **HISTORY WRITER (IRE),** 6, b g Canford Cliffs (IRE)—Abhasana (IRE) **Clive Washbourn & Partner**
8 **INTO FAITH (FR),** 4, b c Intello (GER)—Have Faith (IRE) **All for One Racing**
9 **LUIGI VAMPA (FR),** 4, b g Elvstroem (AUS)—Sunday Rose **Shinco Racing Limited**
10 **MIGRATION (IRE),** 5, b g Alhebayeb (IRE)—Caribbean Ace (IRE) **Gail Brown Racing (IX)**
11 **NUITS ST GEORGES (IRE),** 6, ch g Mount Nelson—Twelfth Night (IRE) **Boy George Partnership**
12 **RUSSIAN VIRTUE,** 4, b g Toronado (IRE)—Russian Rhapsody **The Cromhall Stud**
13 **SELSEY SIZZLER,** 4, b g Nathaniel (IRE)—Heho **I. J. Heseltine**
14 **SHOULDERING (IRE),** 4, b f Epaulette (AUS)—Abhasana (IRE) **Clive Washbourn & Robert Wasey**
15 **SOTO SIZZLER,** 6, b g Mastercraftsman (IRE)—Jalousie (IRE) **I. J. Heseltine**
16 **WINTER REPRISE (FR),** 4, b g Intello (GER)—Winter Fashion (FR) **Mr C. A. Washbourn**
17 **WONDERFUL TONIGHT (FR),** 4, b br f Le Havre (IRE)—Salvation **Mr C. N. Wright**

## THREE-YEAR-OLDS

18 **BELLOCCIO (FR),** ro c Belardo (IRE)—Three Cards **All for One Racing**
19 **BETTY CREAN L A (IRE),** b f Kingman—Ivory Gala (FR) **Mr J. L. Day**
20 **CHATEAU D'IF (FR),** b g Intello (GER)—Moonlight Cass (FR) **Shinco Racing Limited**
21 **DIAMOND CUTTER,** b g Harzand (IRE)—Djumama (IRE) **Australian Bloodstock & Mark Scott**
22 **FINDONO (FR),** b br g Wootton Bassett—Sapore di Roma (IRE) **Mr R. J. Scott**
23 **FOR LOVE OF LOUISE,** b f Nathaniel (IRE)—A Legacy of Love (IRE) **Mrs B. A. Karn-Smith**
24 **FOXTROT SIZZLER (GER),** b g Pride of Dubai (AUS)—Firedance (GER) **I. J. Heseltine**
25 **KELMSCOTT (IRE),** gr ro g Mastercraftsman (IRE)—Zaya (GER) **Gail Brown Racing (XII)**
26 **KING CREOLE,** ch c New Approach (IRE)—Fullaah (IRE) **Christopher Wright & Miss Emily Asprey**
27 **LAMORNA COVE,** b f Footstepsinthesand—Abbakova (IRE) **Gail Brown Racing (B)**
28 **LOVING KISS (IRE),** b f Le Havre (IRE)—Loving Things **Normandie Stud Ltd**
29 **MAGENTA (IRE),** b f Le Havre (IRE)—Roger Sez (IRE) **Chasemore Farm LLP**
30 **PIVOTAL TIME,** ch g Pivotal—Idealist **Heart of the South Racing 123**
31 **PRIVACY,** b f Swiss Spirit—Secret Insider (USA) **Gail Brown Racing (C)**
32 **REINE DU BAL,** b f Mukhadram—She's Gorgeous (IRE) **Johnstone Partnership**
33 **REWIRED,** ch g Power—Kekova **Mr T. G. Roddick**
34 **ROBERT HOOKE,** ch c French Fifteen (FR)—Wightgold **Mrs P. Ignarski**
35 **SHARSTED (GER),** b f Maxios—Shiramiyna (IRE) **Mrs A. K. Oldfield**
36 **STAY COUL (IRE),** b g Coulsty (IRE)—Daleside **Greens Racing**
37 **STEAMY,** b f Awtaad (IRE)—Bournemouth Belle **Mr Jeremy Gompertz & Mr Patrick Milmo**
38 **XAARIO (FR),** gr c Kendargent (FR)—Xaarina (FR) **Mr A. Almaddah**

## TWO-YEAR-OLDS

39 **APPEARING,** b c 18/03 Oasis Dream—
Abbakova (IRE) (Dandy Man (IRE)) (35000) **Mr Peter Mitchell, Mrs Susan Davis**
40 **BOBBY'S BLESSING,** bc 19/04 Bobby's Kitten—Affirmatively (Diktat) **Mrs Monica Josefina Borton & Partner**
41 B f 14/02 Golden Horn—Corpus Chorister (Soldier Of Fortune) **Mr C. A. Washbourn**
42 B f 12/02 Postponed (IRE)—Cradle of Life (IRE) (Notnowcato) **Chasemore Farm LLP**
43 B f 23/02 Almanzor—Dilbar (Galileo)
44 B c 21/02 Constitution (USA)—Elegant By Nature (IRE) (Footstepsinthesand) **Mr A. Almaddah**
45 **FALLEN FROM HEAVEN,** b f 05/03 Postponed—Fallen Star (Brief Truce) **Normandie Stud Ltd**
46 B c 08/03 Myboycharlie (IRE)—Fancy Green (FR) (Muhtathir) **Mr A. Almaddah**
47 **FLAMENCO FAN,** b f 18/02 Dark Angel—Annabelle's Charm (Indian Ridge) **Merry Fox Stud**
48 **FLORENT,** b c 18/02 Kingman—Fleurissimo (Dr Fong) **Normandie Stud Ltd**
49 B f 05/02 Iffraaj—Gallifrey (Sir Percy) **Chasemore Farm LLP**

## MR DAVID MENUISIER - continued

**50 GOLDSMITH (IRE),** b c 18/02 Shalaa (IRE)—Ingot of Gold (Dubawi (IRE)) (65000) **Gail Brown Racing (XIII)**
**51 GONNETOT (FR),** b c 09/05 Recorder—Gondole (Pivotal) (18563) **Gerard Augustin-normand & Partner**
**52** B c 20/03 Le Havre (IRE)—Gregoraci (FR) (Poet's Voice) (36320) **Ms E L Banks & Mr G Augustin-normand**
**53** B f 10/03 Kingman—Havre de Paix (FR) (Le Havre (IRE)) (170000) **Mr C. A. Washbourn, Mr Peter Fagan**
**54** B f 28/02 Johnny Barnes (IRE)—Kenzahope (FR) (Kendargent (FR)) **Bermuda Racing Ltd**
**55 LIONEL,** ch c 04/02 Lope de Vega—Gretchen (Galileo) **Normandie Stud Ltd**
**56** Gr c 10/03 Almanzor (FR)—Marie Rossa (Testa Rossa (AUS)) (60533) **Mr O. S. Harris**
**57** B c 27/02 Johnny Barnes (IRE)—Noble Manners (IRE) (Myboycharlie (IRE)) **Bermuda Racing Ltd**
**58** B c 22/02 Siyouni (FR)—Pacifique (IRE) (Montjeu (IRE)) (169492) **M. H. Watt**
**59 PINK CAVIAR,** b f 11/01 Starspangledbanner—Dalamar (Montjeu) **Mrs Anna Sundstrom**
**60** B f 13/04 Motivator—Radiation (Anabaa)
**61** B f 07/03 Due Diligence—Rocknrollbaby (Fastnet Rock) **Gallaghers**
**62** B f 23/03 Dariyan (FR)—Sanada (IRE) (Priolo (USA)) (24213) **About A Girl Racing**
**63** B c 16/03 Ardad—Sand Dancer (Footstepsinthesand) **Greens Racing**
**64 SECRET ARMY,** ch c 07/04 Territories (IRE)—
                            Secret Insider (USA) (Elusive Quality (USA)) (20000) **Gail Brown Racing (D)**
**65** Gr f 17/03 Kendargent—Sheringa (Oasis Dream) **Mr C. N. Wright**
**66** Ch c 22/02 Territories (IRE)—Show Aya (IRE) (Showcasing) **S. Al Ansari**
**67** B f 10/04 Sixties Icon—Sinndarina (IRE) (Sinndar (IRE)) **Mr C. N. Wright**
**68 SOAMES FORSYTE,** b c 26/01 Siyouni—Fleur Forsyte (Teofilo) **Normandie Stud Ltd**
**69** B c 23/03 Recorder—Starsic (FR) (Sageburg (IRE)) (10492) **Mr K Sohi & Partner**
**70** B f 20/02 Holy Roman Emperor—Vezina (Bering)
**71** B c 22/05 Muhaarar—White Dress (IRE) (Pivotal) (33000) **Mr Mike Francis**

**Other Owners:** Mr L. Arstall, Mr S. A. Ashley, Miss Emily Charlotte Asprey, Mr G. L. R. Augustin-Normand, Australian Bloodstock, Ms E. L. Banks, Mrs H. G. Clinch, A. J. J. Gompertz, Mrs R. G. Hillen, Mr H. A. Johnstone, Mr J. W. Johnstone, Mrs Zara Johnstone, Mr J. J. Lancaster, Mr J. Lovett, Mrs M. J. Martinez-Borton, Mrs D. J. Merson, Mr P. H. Milmo, D. R. Price, Mrs W. J. Price, Mr R. Rauscher, Mrs H. J. Ringrose, Mr Gerry Ryan, Mr M. L. L. Scott, Shinco Racing Limited, Mr W. N. Slater, Mr K. Sohi, Mrs D. Thompson, Mr R. G. Wasey, Mr C. A. Washbourn, M. H. Watt, Mr C. N. Wright, Mr R. J. Wright.

**Pupil Assistant:** Alexandre Vasseur, **Head Lad:** Kevin Bouillie, Philippe Mercier, **Travelling Head:** Christophe Aebi, **Secretary:** Anne Grzywacz.

---

**376** MISS REBECCA MENZIES, Sedgefield
Postal: Howe Hills Farm, Sedgefield, Stockton-On-Tees, Cleveland, TS21 2HG
Contacts: **MOBILE** 07843 169217
**WORK EMAIL** Rebecca@rebeccamenziesracing.co.uk **WEBSITE** www.rebeccamenziesracing.com
**TWITTER** @Rebeccaemenzies

**1 ALL HAIL CAESAR (IRE),** 7, b g Nathaniel (IRE)—Ragiam (ITY) **The Top Silk Syndicate**
**2 AMMA LORD (IRE),** 5, b g Arcadio (GER)—Emma Jane (IRE) **J. Wade**
**3 ARCANJA (IRE),** 7, gr g Arcadio (GER)—Nanja Monja (IRE) **J. Wade**
**4 AREYOUWITHUS (IRE),** 6, b g Watar (IRE)—Miss Sinnott (IRE) **J. Wade**
**5 ASK AROUND (IRE),** 5, b g Sageburg (IRE)—Ask My Granny (IRE) **J. Wade**
**6 BARNEY BULLET (IRE),** 6, b g Havana Gold (IRE)—Lalinde **Marwood Racing Limited**
**7 BUSY STREET,** 9, b g Champs Elysees—Allegro Viva (USA) **Mr J. A. Swinbank**
**8 BUZZKILLBOB (IRE),** 11, b g Gamut (IRE)—Mageney **Mile High Racing**
**9 CELTIC ARTISAN (IRE),** 10, ch g Dylan Thomas (IRE)—
                            Perfectly Clear (USA) **Rebecca Menzies Racing Partnerships**
**10 CHECK MY PULSE (IRE),** 5, b g Dragon Pulse (IRE)—Little Luxury (IRE) **Miss M. D. Myco**
**11 CLOUNCERNA (IRE),** 8, b g Presenting—Kinincha Girl (IRE) **Orsinaround**
**12 DARE THE BEAR (IRE),** 4, b g Milan—Dancing Baloo (IRE) **J. Wade**
**13** 4, B f Califet (FR)—Desert Moon (IRE) **Miss E. Hall**
**14 FERNHILL DANE (IRE),** 5, b g Dylan Thomas (IRE)—Tupia (FR) **John Johnson & John Wade**
**15 FEVER ROQUE (FR),** 6, gr g Diamond Boy (FR)—Belle Saga (FR) **Mr G. Seward**

## MISS REBECCA MENZIES - continued

16 **FIRSTEEN**, 5, b m Requinto (IRE)—Teide Mistress (USA) **Star Racing**
17 **GARDE FORESTIER (FR)**, 9, b g Forestier (FR)—Nette Rousse (FR) **J. Wade**
18 **GETAREASON (IRE)**, 8, ch g Getaway (GER)—Simple Reason (IRE) **Titanium Racing Club**
19 4, B c Ask—Gift Wrapped (IRE) **J. Wade**
20 **GREY FRONTIERES (IRE)**, 7, gr m Sans Frontieres (IRE)—Tally Em Up (IRE) **Lock Stock & Two Smoking Barratts**
21 **HALCYON DAYS**, 12, b g Generous (IRE)—Indian Empress **Centaur Racing Club**
22 **HUNTSMAN'S CALL (IRE)**, 4, b g Golden Horn—Fragrancy (USA) **Sapphire Print Solutions Ltd**
23 4, B f Yeats (IRE)—Innishmore (IRE) **Miss E. Hall**
24 **KOPA KILANA (IRE)**, 4, b g Milan—Kophinou (FR) **J. Wade**
25 5, Ch g Mr Medici (IRE)—Littlemiss
26 **MAGIC DARK**, 4, b f Heeraat (IRE)—Magic Echo **Mr D C Batey & Mr Foster Watson**
27 **MAJOR SNUGFIT**, 5, ch g Ruler of The World (IRE)—Bridle Belle **Mr A Greenwood & Mr S Windle**
28 **MONASH (IRE)**, 4, b g Lawman (FR)—True Crystal (IRE) **PMPro31 Ltd**
29 **NATIVE CHOICE (IRE)**, 5, ch g Well Chosen—Native Kin (IRE) **J. Wade**
30 **NORTONTHORPELEGEND (IRE)**, 11, b g Midnight Legend—Tanit **Miss M. D. Myco**
31 **ON THE RHINE (IRE)**, 4, b g War Command (USA)—Janna's Jewel (IRE) **Northern Network Partnership**
32 **ONWARD ROUTE (IRE)**, 7, b g Yeats (IRE)—Just Stunning (IRE) **J. Wade**
33 **PADDY ELLIOTT (IRE)**, 4, b g French Navy—Siphon Melody (USA) **J. Wade**
34 **PAIN AU CHOCOLAT (IRE)**, 10, b g Enrique—Clair Chene (FR) **Mike and Eileen Newbould**
35 **RAECIUS FELIX (IRE)**, 7, ch g Stowaway—Dances With Waves (IRE) **J. Wade**
36 **RAFFERTY'S RETURN**, 6, b g Schiaparelli (GER)—Duchess Theatre (IRE) **J. Wade**
37 **RETURN TICKET (IRE)**, 8, b g Getaway (GER)—Capelvenere (IRE) **J. Wade**
38 **RITSON (IRE)**, 6, b g Jeremy (USA)—Ellen's Choice (IRE) **Mr P R Walker & Mr R Walker**
39 **ROAD WARRIOR**, 7, gr g Fair Mix (IRE)—Mimi Equal **Mr N. Taylor**
40 4, B f Black Sam Bellamy (IRE)—Samrana (FR)
41 **SAO (FR)**, 7, b br g Great Pretender (IRE)—Miss Country (FR) **Gary Eves & Partner**
42 **SCHALKE**, 6, b g Malinas (GER)—Prospero's Belle (IRE) **Sapphire Print Solutions Ltd**
43 **SCORCHED BREATH**, 5, b g Bated Breath—Danvers **Mr J. Soiza**
44 **SCOTTISH ACCENT (IRE)**, 8, b g Golan (IRE)—Onthelongfinger (IRE) **Blacklock Simpson & Partner**
45 **SCOTTISH KING (IRE)**, 5, ch g Imperial Monarch (IRE)—Thanks Bobby (IRE) **Mr J. W. F. Veitch**
46 **SET IN STONE (IRE)**, 7, b m Famous Name—Storminateacup (IRE) **Weight, Howe & Oliver**
47 **SHE'S A DANCER (IRE)**, 6, b m Jeremy (USA)—Sugar Bullet (IRE) **J. Wade**
48 **SHINEDOWN (IRE)**, 6, b m Sholokhov (IRE)—Good Shine (IRE) **Centaur Racing & David Moore**
49 **SMOOTH DANCER**, 4, b f Saddler Maker (IRE)—The Cookie Jar (IRE) **BumpersToJumpers 1**
50 **SNOWY BURROWS (FR)**, 5, gr m Montmartre (FR)—Condoleezza (FR) **4Racing Owners Club**
51 **STRAIGHT ARM (IRE)**, 6, gr g Zebedee—Blackangelheart (IRE) **NP Racing Syndicate**
52 **SULAFAAT (IRE)**, 6, ch m Haatef (USA)—Elraabeya (CAN) **Mr J. A. Lister**
53 **TABOU BEACH BOY**, 5, b g Mukhadram—Illandrane (IRE) **J. Wade**
54 **THE MEKON**, 6, ch g Red Jazz (USA)—Date Mate (USA) **Marwood Racing Limited**
55 **THE REAPING RACE (IRE)**, 8, b g Flemensfirth (USA)—
Native Design (IRE) **Rebecca Menzies Racing Partnerships**
56 **TOI STOREY (IRE)**, 8, b g Winged Love (IRE)—Where's Herself (IRE) **Liz Dixon & Shelagh Fagen**
57 **TRAVEL LIGHTLY**, 6, b m Showcasing—Upton Seas **E. A. Brook**
58 **TWISTED DREAMS (USA)**, 4, b br g Twirling Candy (USA)—Sweet Promises (USA) **Titanium Racing Club**
59 **TWOSHOTSOFTEQUILA (IRE)**, 4, b g Snow Sky—Inouette (IRE) **Hetton Boys**
60 **UKNOWMYMEANING (IRE)**, 7, ch g Touch of Land (FR)—Lucy Lodge (IRE) **The Extra Time Partnership**
61 **VINTAGE POLLY (IRE)**, 4, br f Gutaifan (IRE)—Payphone **Club Racing Vintage Partnership**
62 **XPO UNIVERSEL (FR)**, 12, b g Poliglote—Xanadu Bliss (FR) **Club Racing Xpo Partnership**
63 **YOU SOME BOY (IRE)**, 5, b g Dylan Thomas (IRE)—You Some Massini (IRE) **J. Wade**

## THREE-YEAR-OLDS

64 **COLINTON**, b g Red Jazz (USA)—Magic Maisie **Star Racing**
65 B g Court Cave (IRE)—Dark Sari (IRE) **J. Wade**
66 **JAZZ REPUBLIC (IRE)**, b f Kodiac—Allegrissimo (IRE) **Titanium Racing Club**
67 **MIDNIGHT CHIEF (IRE)**, b g Conduit (IRE)—Presentingatdawn (IRE) **J. Wade**
68 B g Ask—Phecda (FR) **Mr D. Parry**
69 **RAINBOW APPLAUSE (IRE)**, b f Camacho—Dubai Sea (USA) **Rebecca Menzies Racing Partnerships**
70 **RATAAR**, b f Heeraat (IRE)—Ringtail (USA) **J. Wade**
71 **RED HEADED TIGER**, b g Coach House (IRE)—Spanish Gold **NP Racing Syndicate**

## MISS REBECCA MENZIES - continued

**72** B br g Charming Thought—Scented Garden **E. A. Brook**
**73 SEVEREEN,** b f Fulbright—Macqueen **Star Racing**
**74 SO SAVVY,** ch g Sepoy (AUS)—How Fortunate **J. Wade**

### TWO-YEAR-OLDS

**75** B c 03/04 Peace Envoy (FR)—Half Hangit Maggie (Sakhee (USA))
**76** Ch f 04/03 Cotai Glory—Magh Meall (Monsieur Bond (IRE))
**77** Gr c 08/03 Gutaifan (IRE)—One For June (IRE) (Arcano (IRE))
**78** B f 08/05 My Dream Boat (IRE)—Royal Blossom (IRE) (Royal Applause) (7619)
**79 STANLEY SNUGFIT,** b c 25/03 Adaay (IRE)—Magical Daze (Showcasing) (20952) **Mr A. G. Greenwood**

**Other Owners:** Mr N. Barratt - Atkin, D. C. Batey, Mr I. M. Blacklock, Centaur Racing Club, Mrs A. B. M. Cuddigan, Mrs E. M. Dixon, Mr G. Eves, Miss S. Fagen, Mrs S. H. Fawcett, Mr A. G. Greenwood, Mr P. J. Howe, Mr D. Hyman, Mr J. R. Johnson, Mr P. Lawrenson, Mrs J. O. E. Mangles, Miss R. E. A. Menzies, Mr D. Moore, Mrs E. E. Newbould, Mr J. M. Newbould, Mr R. G. Oliver, Mrs A. M. Rhind, Mr R. R. Riley, Mr I. Simpson, Major P. H. K. Steveney, Mr G. Stockley, Mr S. A. Taylor, Mr D. Towler, J. Wade, Mr P. R. Walker, Mr R. Walker, F. Watson, Mr A. C. Weight, Dr P. M. Weight, Mr S. A. Windle.

**Secretary:** Mrs Emma Ramsden, **Business & Racing Manager:** Philip Lawrenson, **Yard Sponsor:** Bluegrass Horse Feeds.

**Flat Jockey:** Cam Hardie, PJ McDonald, Megan Nicholls. **NH Jockey:** Nathan Moscrop, Conor O'Farrell. **Amateur Jockey:** Miss Leah Cooper.

---

## 377 MR PHIL MIDDLETON, Aylesbury
Postal: **Dorton Place, Dorton Park Farm, Dorton, Aylesbury, Buckinghamshire, HP18 9NR**
Contacts: **PHONE 01844 237503 MOBILE 07860 426607 FAX 01844 237503**

**1 EXITAS (IRE),** 13, b g Exit To Nowhere (USA)—Suntas (IRE) **P Middleton, M Lowther**
**2 GOLAN FORTUNE (IRE),** 9, b g Golan (IRE)—Ballyknock Alainn (IRE) **P Middleton, M Lowther**
**3 MAWLOOD (IRE),** 5, b g Dawn Approach (IRE)—Kalaatah (USA) **P Middleton, M Lowther**
**4 SKEAPING,** 8, b g Excellent Art—Gale Green **Mr P. W. Middleton**
**5 SOPAT (IRE),** 8, b m Gold Well—Silver Prayer (IRE) **Mr P. W. Middleton**

**Other Owners:** Mr M. Lowther, Mr P. W. Middleton.

---

## 378 MR PAUL MIDGLEY, Westow
Postal: **The View, Sandfield Farm, Westow, York, North Yorkshire, YO60 7LS**
Contacts: **PHONE 01653 658790 MOBILE 07976 965220 FAX 01653 658790**
**EMAIL** ptmidgley@aol.com **WEBSITE** www.ptmidgley.com

**1 BUNIANN (IRE),** 5, b g Tamayuz—Darajaat (USA) **Carl Chapman & Andrew Stephenson**
**2 DESERT PALMS,** 4, b g Oasis Dream—Be My Gal **Sandfield Racing, Carl Chapman & Northern Sealants**
**3 GOOD LUCK FOX (IRE),** 5, b g Society Rock (IRE)—Violet Ballerina (IRE) **Mrs S. Bradley**
**4 GORGEOUS GRACE,** 5, ch m Haafhd—Mornin' Gorgeous **Give Every Man His Due**
**5 HARROGATE (IRE),** 6, br g Society Rock (IRE)—Invincible Me (IRE)
**6 I AM A DREAMER,** 5, b g Dream Ahead (USA)—Alexander Ballet **Dab Hand Racing**
**7 INDIAN SOUNDS (IRE),** 5, b g Exceed And Excel (AUS)—Sarinda **Mr R. Bradley**
**8 JAMES WATT (IRE),** 5, b g Morpheus—Tomintoul Singer (IRE) **Mr C. Priestley & Mr M. Hammond**
**9 LATIN FIVE (IRE),** 4, b g Camacho—Penolva (IRE) **R Wardlaw & Partner**
**10 LONGROOM,** 9, b g Oasis Dream—Phantom Wind (USA) **The Slaters Arms & Marwood Racing**
**11 MID WINSTER,** 5, b m Burwaaz—Cayman Fox **John Blackburn & Alan Bell**
**12 MILITIA,** 6, b g Equiano (FR)—Sweet As Honey **A. Bell**

## MR PAUL MIDGLEY - continued

13 **MR ORANGE (IRE)**, 8, b g Paco Boy (IRE)—Shirley Blake (IRE) **Mr J Blackburn & Mr A Turton**
14 **MUTAFARRID (IRE)**, 6, gr g Dark Angel (IRE)—Margarita (IRE) **J. S. Morrison & Frank Brady**
15 **NIBRAS AGAIN**, 7, b g Kyllachy—Regina **Peedeetee Syndicate, Ta Stephenson & Twm**
16 **ORVAR (IRE)**, 8, b g Dandy Man (IRE)—Roskeen (IRE) **Taylor's Bloodstock Ltd**
17 **OSTILIO**, 6, ch h New Approach (IRE)—Reem Three **Taylor's Bloodstock Ltd**
18 **PAVERS PRIDE**, 7, ch g Bahamian Bounty—Pride of Kinloch **Mr G. J. Paver**
19 **REQUIEMS DREAM (IRE)**, 4, ch f Dream Ahead (USA)—Kerrys Requiem (IRE) **Mr R. Bradley**
20 **SALUTI (IRE)**, 7, b g Acclamation—Greek Easter (IRE) **R Bradley & M Hammond**
21 **SAMBUCCA SPIRIT**, 5, b g Charm Spirit (IRE)—Hokkaido **Carl Chapman & Partner**
22 **SON AND SANNIE (IRE)**, 5, b g Es Que Love (IRE)—Anamundi **Taylor's Bloodstock Ltd**
23 **TARBOOSH**, 8, b g Bahamian Bounty—Mullein **The Guys & Dolls & Sandfield Racing**
24 **THRILLA IN MANILA**, 5, b g Iffraaj—Tesary **Ian Massheder & Sandfield Racing**
25 **VAN GERWEN**, 8, ch g Bahamian Bounty—Disco Ball **Ryan Chapman & Partner**
26 **WASNTEXPECTINGTHAT**, 5, b g Foxwedge (AUS)—Carsulae (IRE) **Good Bad Ugly & Deaf**

### THREE-YEAR-OLDS

27 **BALLINTOY HARBOUR (IRE)**, b f Vadamos (FR)—Fingal Nights (IRE) **Mr H. Thornton**
28 **BURNING CASH (IRE)**, b g Strath Burn—Passified Lady (USA) **Mr C. Priestley & Mr M. Hammond**
29 **CARRIBEAN QUEEN**, b f Territories (IRE)—Bahamamia **Carl Chapman & Partner**
30 **DAPPER BOB (IRE)**, ch g Dandy Man (IRE)—Easy Lover **Mr R. Bradley**
31 **ELZAAL (IRE)**, b g Elzaam (AUS)—Alice Liddel (IRE) **The Blackburn Family**
32 **ENDERMAN**, b g Bated Breath—Wish You Luck **Mr C. Alton**
33 **INVINCIBLE DEAL (IRE)**, br g Ajaya—New Deal **Mr C. Priestley & Mr M. Hammond**
34 **J R CAVAGIN (IRE)**, b g Oasis Dream—International Love (IRE) **A Bell & M Hammond**

### TWO-YEAR-OLDS

35 B f 09/02 Kodiac—Ameliorate (IRE) (Galileo (IRE)) (16190) **Mr H. Thornton**
36 B f 16/03 Twilight Son—Border Minstral (IRE) (Sri Pekan (USA)) (4000) **Chapman, Hammond C Priestley**
37 **COTAI CREEK (IRE)**, ch c 28/02 Cotai Glory—Allegheny Creek (IRE) (Teofilo (IRE)) (6457) **Mrs S. Bradley**
38 **DARBY SABINI**, b c 25/04 Hot Streak (IRE)—
                         Holder's Hill (IRE) (Danehill Dancer (IRE)) (1000) **Ryan Chapman & Partner**
39 Br c 10/03 Mehmas (IRE)—Fonseca (IRE) (Red Clubs (IRE)) (24762)
40 B c 25/04 Alhebayeb (IRE)—Golden Anthem (USA) (Lion Cavern (USA)) (4036) **Marwood Racing Limited**
41 B f 27/03 Heeraat (IRE)—Jeany (IRE) (Kodiac)
42 B c 10/03 Elusive Pimpernel (USA)—Key To Love (IRE) (Key of Luck (USA)) **Mr F. Brady**
43 B c 09/04 Orientor—Killer Class (Kyllachy) **Mr F. Brady**
44 **MAKE A PROPHET (IRE)**, b g 21/02 Divine Prophet (AUS)—
                         Miss Mirabeau (Oasis Dream) (3809) **Sandfield Racing, Carl Chapman & Northern Sealants**
45 B f 22/04 Battle of Marengo (IRE)—Nufooth (IRE) (Elnadim (USA)) (1937)
46 B gr c 13/04 Aclaim (IRE)—Nutkin (Act One) (9524) **Mrs S. Bradley**
47 B c 02/04 Orientor—Ss Vega (Kheleyf (USA)) **Mr F. Brady**
48 **SUNSET OVER LOULE**, b c 29/03 Twilight Son—Pride of Kinloch (Dr Devious (IRE)) **Mr G. J. Paver**
49 Ch c 12/04 Dandy Man (IRE)—Texas Queen (Shamardal (USA)) (28571)
50 B f 11/04 Estidhkaar (IRE)—Tsaritsa (IRE) (Shirocco (GER)) (8571)
51 **VADAMIAH (IRE)**, b f 05/02 Vadamos (FR)—Ghanimah (Invincible Spirit (IRE)) (13333) **The Blackburn Family**
52 B g 27/04 Havana Gold (IRE)—Walk On Bye (IRE) (Danehill Dancer (IRE)) (28000)

**Other Owners:** A Bell & M Hammond, Mr Colin Alton & Mr P. T. Midgley, Mr M. R. Baker, Mr J. M. Barker, Mr P. Bateson, A. Bell, Mr A. Bell & Mr P.T. Midgley, Mr A. B. Blackburn, Mrs G. I. Blackburn, Mr J. N. Blackburn, Blackburn Family, Mr A. Bradley, Mr R. Bradley, Robert Bradley & P T Midgley, Sheila Bradley & P. T. Midgley, Mr F. Brady, Mr C. Chapman, Mr R. Chapman, Mr M. Grayson, Mr M. K. Hammond, Mr G. P. Henderson, Mr L. Horvath, J Blackburn M Grayson & Imperial Racing, D. Mann, Marwood Racing Limited, Mr I. R. Massheder, Mr P. T. Midgley, Mr T. W. Midgley, Mr J S Morrison, Northern sealants Ltd, Mr J. R. Owen, Mr G. J. Paver, D. Pearson, Peedeetee Syndicate, A. D. Pirie, Mr C. Priestley, Mr I. Robinson, Sandfield Racing, Slaters Arms Racing Club, T. A. Stephenson, Mr R. Sutcliffe, The Guys & Dolls Syndicate, Mr H. Thornton, Mr H. Thornton & Mr P. T. Midgley, Mr A. Turton, Mr A. D. Ward, Mr R. Wardlaw, Mr S. Wibberley.

**Assistant Trainer:** Mrs W. E. Midgley.

## 379  MR ROD MILLMAN, Cullompton

Postal: **The Paddocks, Dulford, Cullompton, Devon, EX15 2DX**
Contacts: **PHONE 01884 266620 MOBILE 07885 168447**
EMAIL rod.millman@ic24.net

1 **ABLE KANE**, 4, b g Due Diligence (USA)—Sugar Beet  **Mr T. H. Chadney**
2 **AIRSHOW**, 6, ch g Showcasing—Belle des Airs (IRE)  **Middleham Park Racing XXXIV**
3 **CRYSTAL CASQUE**, 6, ch m Helmet (AUS)—Crystal Moments  **The Dirham Partnership**
4 **HANDYTALK (IRE)**, 8, b g Lilbourne Lad (IRE)—Dancing With Stars (IRE)  **Cantay Racing**
5 **HAWRIDGE FLYER**, 7, b g Sir Percy—Strictly Lambada  **E. J. S. Gadsden**
6 **HAWRIDGE STORM (IRE)**, 5, b g Intello (GER)—Aneedah (IRE)  **E. J. S. Gadsden**
7 **MASTER GREY (IRE)**, 6, gr g Mastercraftsman (IRE)—Market Day  **The Links Partnership**
8 **MERCURIST**, 4, b g Muhaarar—Xceedingly Xcited (IRE)  **A. F. O'Callaghan**
9 **PRINCE OF HARTS**, 5, br g Dalakhani (IRE)—Reaf  **Mr T. W. Morley**
10 **SINGING THE BLUES (IRE)**, 6, b g Sir Prancealot (IRE)—Atishoo (IRE)  **Crown Connoisseurs**
11 **SIR PLATO (IRE)**, 7, b g Sir Prancealot (IRE)—Dessert Flower (IRE)  **M.J. Tidball & B.R. Millman**
12 **SIR RODERIC (IRE)**, 8, b g Roderic O'Connor (IRE)—Begin The Beguine (IRE)  **The Links Partnership**
13 **SWEET PURSUIT**, 7, b m Pastoral Pursuits—Sugar Beet  **Always Hopeful Partnership**

## THREE-YEAR-OLDS

14 **BAMA LAMA**, ch f Equiano (FR)—Kindia (IRE)  **Canisbay Bloodstock**
15 **COPPERKIN**, ch g Helmet (AUS)—Loulou (USA)  **Mr M J Watson & Deborah Collett**
16 **COSTA TEGUISE**, b f Twilight Son—Nicolasia (GER)  **Millman Racing Club**
17 **COUL KAT (IRE)**, b g Coulsty (IRE)—Katevan (IRE)  **The Coul Kat Partnership**
18 **CRAZY LUCK**, b f Twilight Son—Suerte Loca (IRE)  **Crown Connoisseurs**
19 **FOUR ADAAY (IRE)**, b f Adaay (IRE)—Sonko (IRE)  **The Four Adaay Syndicate**
20 **GAVIN**, b g Bated Breath—Under Milk Wood  **Mrs S. A. J. Kinsella**
21 **GREYCIOUS GIRL (IRE)**, gr f Markaz (IRE)—Cesca (IRE)  **Next Ones A Grey Partnership**
22 **HURRICANE HELEN**, br gr f Gutaifan (IRE)—Dame Helen  **JPM Racing I**
23 **LIGHTNING LOU (IRE)**, gr f Brazen Beau (AUS)—Lucky Token (IRE)  **Mr J. Millman**
24 **LITTLE BIT WELSH (IRE)**, b f Territories (IRE)—Milady  **D. J. Deer**
25 **MARIGOT BOY**, b c Hellvelyn—Glittering Prize (USA)  **Mr S G Lake**
26 **MOUNTAIN ASH (IRE)**, gr g Sir Prancealot (IRE)—El Morocco (USA)  **Always Hopeful Partnership 2**
27 **ONARAGGATIP**, b g Adaay (IRE)—Onlyyouknowme (IRE)  **Crown Connoisseurs**
28 **PRIDE OF HAWRIDGE (IRE)**, b g Vadamos (FR)—Face The Storm (IRE)  **E. J. S. Gadsden**
29 **SILENT FLAME**, b f Al Kazeem—Burnt Fingers (IRE)  **Miss G. J. Abbey**
30 **TEASE AND SEIZE (FR)**, b g Motivator—Serenada (FR)  **D. J. Deer**
31 **TIGHTEN UP**, b f Garswood—Royal Ivy  **Canisbay Bloodstock**
32 **TOPTIME**, b g Gregorian (IRE)—Dominance  **Deborah Collett & M. J. Watson**
33 **VITALLINE**, b c Due Diligence (USA)—Vitta's Touch (USA)  **Mainline Racing**

## TWO-YEAR-OLDS

34 **AMAZONIAN DREAM (IRE)**, b c 16/04 Bungle Inthejungle—
                                   Grandmas Dream (Kyllachy) (35000)  **Great Western Racing**
35 B f 25/04 Bungle Inthejungle—Anbella (FR) (Common Grounds)  **Great Western Racing**
36 **DEVON ENVOY**, b g 18/04 Peace Envoy (FR)—
                                   Favourite Girl (IRE) (Refuse To Bend (IRE))  **Horniwinks Racing Syndicate**
37 Ch f 28/02 Dream Ahead (USA)—Melrose Abbey (IRE) (Selkirk (USA)) (6000)
38 B f 12/02 Territories (IRE)—Plover (Oasis Dream) (9500)  **Canisbay Bloodstock**
39 **SOI DAO (IRE)**, b f 17/04 Twilight Son—
                                   Home Cummins (IRE) (Rip Van Winkle (IRE)) (11429)  **Daddies Girl Partnership**
40 B f 12/02 Adaay (IRE)—Sonko (IRE) (Red Clubs (IRE)) (6500)
41 **TWILIGHT TONE**, b br g 18/03 Twilight Son—Bikini (Trans Island) (10000)  **Crown Connoisseurs**
42 **TWISTALINE**, b f 31/01 Showcasing—Tongue Twista (Stimulation (IRE)) (21000)  **Mainline Racing**
43 **WHISPERING WINDS**, ch f 06/02 Buratino (IRE)—Guthanna Gaoithe (Poet's Voice) (2000)  **Book 3 Partnership & B.R. Millman**

Other Owners: Mr J. F. A. Berry, Book 3 Partnership, Mr S. J. Brown, Miss D. Collett, Mrs J. A. Daly, Mr R. W. Daly, Mr R. D. Gamlin, Mr M. Grant, Mr A. H. Hornby, R. F. Kilby, Mrs S. M. Langridge, B. R. Millman, Mr A. M. Nolan, Mr S. M. Perry, Ms Z. L. Pinchbeck, Mr C. H. Saunders, Miss M. E. Stopher, Mr M. J. Tidball, Mr T. Tompkins, Mr M. J. Watson, Mr R. C. Watts.

## MR ROD MILLMAN - continued

**Assistant Trainer:** Mr James Millman, Louise Millman, Pat Millman.

**Flat Jockey:** Oisin Murphy. **Apprentice Jockey:** Oliver Searle. **Amateur Jockey:** Mr Pat Millman.

---

**380** **MR NICK MITCHELL, Sherborne**
Postal: Sandhills Farm Racing, Sandhills Farm, Holwell, Sherborne, Dorset DT9 5LE
Contacts: **PHONE 01300 348049 MOBILE 07770 892085**
**EMAIL** nick.mitch@btinternet.com **WEBSITE** www.nickmitchellracing.com

1 ASKINVILLAR (IRE), 6, b g Jeremy (USA)—Cuddle In A Fog (IRE) **Sherborne Utilities Ltd**
2 BAIGNARD (FR), 7, gr g Al Namix (FR)—Virginia River (FR) **Sherborne Utilities Ltd**
3 COUP DE PINCEAU (FR), 9, b g Buck's Boum (FR)—Castagnette III (FR) **Sherborne Utilities Ltd**
4 DANNY PARK (IRE), 5, b g Ocovango—Kilbarry Flame (IRE) **Sherborne Utilities Ltd**
5 IRON MIKE, 5, gr g Gregorian (IRE)—Regal Velvet **Sherborne Utilities Ltd**
6 LET'S GET AT IT (IRE), 8, b g Mustameet (USA)—Last Hope (IRE) **Sherborne Utilities Ltd**
7 LIEUTENANT ROCCO (IRE), 6, ch g Shirocco (GER)—Five Star Present (IRE) **Sherborne Utilities Ltd**
8 LUCKY LARA (IRE), 6, ch m Mahler—Honour Own (IRE) **Sherborne Utilities Ltd**
9 MILANFORD (IRE), 7, b g Milan—Tabachines (FR) **Sherborne Utilities Ltd**
10 MONETE (GER), 4, gr f Jukebox Jury (IRE)—Mayumi (IRE) **Sherborne Utilities Ltd**
11 MYSTIC COURT (IRE), 8, b g Court Cave (IRE)—My Mystic Rose (IRE) **Sherborne Utilities Ltd**
12 PROMISING MILAN (IRE), 6, b g Milan—French Promise (IRE) **Sherborne Utilities Ltd**
13 SIEMPRE RAPIDO, 4, b g Outstrip—Cape Mystery **Sherborne Utilities Ltd**
14 TRUMP LADY (IRE), 6, b m Doyen (IRE)—Kris Krystal (IRE) **Sherborne Utilities Ltd**

---

**381** **MR RICHARD MITCHELL, Dorchester**
Postal: East Hill Stables, Piddletrenthide, Dorchester, Dorset, DT2 7QY
Contacts: **PHONE 01300 348739 MOBILE 07775 843136**
**EMAIL** easthillstables@tiscali.co.uk

1 COTTON CLUB (IRE), 10, b g Amadeus Wolf—Slow Jazz (USA) **Mr J. Boughey**
2 FILTHY LUCCA, 6, b g Lucarno (USA)—Aphrodisia **Ray & Sue Dodd Partnership**
3 MILBERRY (IRE), 10, b g Alflora (IRE)—Shuil Saoirse (IRE) **N. R. Mitchell**
4 POUR UNE RAISON (FR), 6, b br g Kapgarde (FR)—Got Aba (FR) **Mrs S. H. May**

**Other Owners:** Mr R. C. Dodd, Mrs S. P. Dodd.

**Assistant Trainer:** Mrs E. Mitchell.

## 382 MR RICHARD MITFORD-SLADE, Norton Fitzwarren
Postal: **Pontispool Farm, Allerford, Norton Fitzwarren, Taunton, Somerset, TA4 1BG**
Contacts: **PHONE 01823 461196 MOBILE 07899 994420 FAX 01823 461508**
EMAIL rms@pontispool.com

1 **APPLE MACK**, 8, b g Apple Tree (FR)—Allerford Annie (IRE) **Pontispool Racing Club**
2 **LAZY SUNDAY**, 7, b m Schiaparelli (GER)—Sari Rose (FR) **Pontispool Racing Club**
3 **MASTER TRADESMAN (IRE)**, 10, ch g Marienbard (IRE)—Tobeornotobe (IRE) **R Mitford-Slade & Lucy Johnson**
4 **NORMANDY SOLDIER**, 7, b g Apple Tree (FR)—Primitive Quest **Pontispool Racing Club**
5 **SAMUEL JACKSON**, 9, b g Alflora (IRE)—Primitive Quest **R Mitford-Slade & Lucy Johnson**
6 **START POINT**, 8, b m Getaway (GER)—Allerford Annie (IRE) **R Mitford-Slade & Lucy Johnson, James Burley**
7 5, Gr m Geordieland (FR)—Westbourne (IRE) **R Mitford-Slade & Lucy Johnson**

**Other Owners:** Mrs L. Fielding-Johnson, R. C. Mitford-Slade.

**Assistant Trainer:** Lucy Fielding-Johnson.

## 383 MR JAMES MOFFATT, Cartmel
Postal: **Pit Farm Racing Stables, Cartmel, Grange-Over-Sands, Cumbria, LA11 6PJ**
Contacts: **PHONE 015395 33808 MOBILE 07767 367282 FAX 015395 36236**
EMAIL jamesmoffatt@hotmail.co.uk WEBSITE www.jamesmoffatt.co.uk

1 **ALQAMAR**, 7, b g Dubawi (IRE)—Moonsail **Varlien Vyner-Brooks,Dave&Yvonne Simpson**
2 **ALTRUISM (IRE)**, 11, b g Authorized (IRE)—Bold Assumption **Mr V R Vyner-Brooks, Mr K Bowron**
3 **APTLY PUT (IRE)**, 9, b br g Yeats (IRE)—Versatile Approach (IRE) **The Vilprano Partnership**
4 **BURBANK (IRE)**, 9, b g Yeats (IRE)—Spring Swoon (FR) **Varlien Vyner-Brooks,Dave&Yvonne Simpson**
5 **DAGIAN (IRE)**, 6, ch g Dawn Approach (IRE)—Hen Night (IRE) **Bowes Lodge Stables**
6 **GOLDEN TOWN (IRE)**, 10, b g Invincible Spirit (IRE)—Princesse Dansante (FR) **STM Racing**
7 **GOOD LOOK CHARM (FR)**, 5, b m Cokoriko (FR)—Une d'Ex (FR) **Carl Hinchy & Mark Scott**
8 **IT'S A LILY**, 7, b m Sulamani (IRE)—It's A Discovery (IRE) **Glastonbury & Vyner-brooks Partnership**
9 **JELSKI (GER)**, 7, b g Kallisto (GER)—Just Zoud **The Running In Rail Partnership**
10 **LADY BOWES**, 7, b m Malinas (GER)—Blazing Bay (IRE) **Bowes Lodge Stables**
11 **MINELLA CHARMER (IRE)**, 10, b g King's Theatre (IRE)—
                                   Kim Hong (IRE) **Varlien Vyner-Brooks,Dave&Yvonne Simpson**
12 **NATIVE FIGHTER (IRE)**, 7, b g Lawman (FR)—Night of Magic (IRE) **Varlien Vyner-Brooks,Dave&Yvonne Simpson**
13 **NO HIDING PLACE (IRE)**, 8, b g Stowaway—Subtle Gem (IRE) **Racing in Furness**
14 **OAKMONT (FR)**, 8, ch g Turtle Bowl (IRE)—Onega Lake (IRE) **The Sheroot Partnership**
15 **ONE FINE MAN (IRE)**, 6, br g Jeremy (USA)—American Jennie (IRE) **Mr J. T. Hanbury**
16 **OUR SAM**, 5, b g Black Sam Bellamy (IRE)—Arisea (IRE) **Mr B. Walton**
17 **SAINT PATRIC**, 5, b g Universal (IRE)—Blazing Bay (IRE) **Bowes Lodge Stables**
18 **SHE GOT FAST (IRE)**, 6, b m Fastnet Rock (AUS)—Shegotloose (USA) **The Clock Tower Partnership**
19 **THE STEWARD (USA)**, 10, b g Street Cry (IRE)—Candlelight (USA) **Cartmel Six Pack**
20 **THINK AHEAD**, 10, b g Shamardal (USA)—Moonshadow **Mr V. R. Vyner-Brooks**
21 **TURTLE WARS (FR)**, 8, b g Turtle Bowl (IRE)—Forces Sweetheart **Dave & Yvonne Simpson & Mr Dennis Blyth**

**Other Owners:** Mr D. Blyth, Mr K. Bowron, Mrs A. J. Glastonbury, Mr K. J. Glastonbury, Kevin & Anne Glastonbury, Mr C. S. Hinchy, Mr M. S. Scott, Mr D. J. Simpson, Dave & Yvonne Simpson, Mrs Y. Simpson, Mr V. R. Vyner-Brooks, Mrs J. C. Wilson, Mr S. Wilson.

**Assistant Trainer:** Nadine Moffatt.

**NH Jockey:** Henry Brooke, Brian Hughes. **Conditional Jockey:** Charlotte Jones.

**384** **MR ISMAIL MOHAMMED, Newmarket**
Postal: **Grange House Stables, Hamilton Road, Newmarket, Suffolk, CB8 0TE**
Contacts: PHONE **01638 669074** MOBILE **07747 191606, 07766 570271**
EMAIL **justina.stone@dubairacingclub.com**

1 **CORAZONADA (IRE)**, 4, ch f Camacho—Giant Dancer (USA)  **Mr M. Al Suboosi**
2 **FANTASTIC BLUE**, 5, ch g Iffraaj—Blue Beacon  **N. Mourad**
3 **NIBRAS SHADOW (IRE)**, 4, gr f Dark Angel (IRE)—Althea Rose (IRE)  **S. H. Altayer**
4 **NIGHT TIME GIRL**, 4, ch f Night of Thunder (IRE)—Assabiyya (IRE)  **Mr A. Al Mansoori**
5 **STAR APPROACH (IRE)**, 4, ch c New Approach (IRE)—Starletina (IRE)  **S. Ali**
6 **VOLCANO BAY**, 4, b f Universal (IRE)—Ras Shaikh (USA)  **Mr A. Al Mansoori**

## THREE-YEAR-OLDS

7 **AADILA**, b f Due Diligence (USA)—Belatorio (IRE)  **Mr I. Mohammed**
8 **DEMBE**, b c Garswood—Disco Ball  **Mr A. Bintooq**
9 **ENCOUNTER ORDER (IRE)**, b c Siyouni (FR)—Miss Emma May (IRE)  **Mr A. Al Mansoori**
10 **FOUNTAIN OF DREAMS**, b f Fountain of Youth (IRE)—Symphonic Dancer (USA)  **S. H. Altayer**
11 **GOLDEN CLAIM**, b c Golden Horn—Counterclaim  **S. H. Altayer**
12 **GOOD REGAL**, ch f Universal (IRE)—Regal Sultana  **Mr A. Al Mansoori**
13 **JOY COAST (USA)**, ch c Kitten's Joy (USA)—Ivory Coast (USA)  **S. H. Altayer**
14 Ch f Night of Thunder (IRE)—Lily White Socks (IRE)  **Mr I. Mohammed**
15 **MAGICAL MILE (IRE)**, ch c Sepoy (AUS)—Magical Crown (USA)  **Mr A. Al Mansoori**
16 **NIBRAS GOLD (IRE)**, b c Golden Horn—Whipped (IRE)  **S. H. Altayer**
17 **NIBRAS SILK (IRE)**, ch c Mayson—Fine Silk (USA)  **S. H. Altayer**
18 **NIBRAS STORM**, b c Cable Bay (IRE)—Yensi  **S. H. Altayer**
19 **NIBRAS SUMMER**, b c Mayson—Divine Power  **S. H. Altayer**
20 B c Golden Horn—Tunkwa (FR)  **Mr A. Al Mansoori**
21 B c Universal (IRE)—Winner's Wish  **Mr A. Al Mansoori**

## TWO-YEAR-OLDS

22 B f 18/02 New Approach (IRE)—Bumptious (Acclamation)  **Mr I. Mohammed**
23 B f 21/02 Sea The Stars (IRE)—Chachamaidee (IRE) (Footstepsinthesand) (95000)  **S. H. Altayer**
24 Ch f 28/02 No Nay Never (USA)—Claudette (USA) (Speightstown) (19048)  **S. H. Altayer**
25 Gr f 05/03 Lethal Force (IRE)—Close To The Edge (IRE) (Iffraaj) (9000)  **S. H. Altayer**
26 B f 19/02 Ribchester (IRE)—Fading Light (King's Best) (USA)  **Mr A. Al Mansoori**
27 B f 24/03 Bobby's Kitten (USA)—Flashing Colour (GER) (Pivotal) (18095)  **S. H. Altayer**
28 Ch f 12/04 Dandy Man (IRE)—Illuminating Dream (IRE) (High Chaparral (IRE)) (20952)  **S. H. Altayer**
29 Ch c 05/04 Helmet (AUS)—Most Important (IRE) (Pivotal)  **S. Ali**
30 B c 26/01 Iffraaj—Panova (Invincible Spirit (IRE)) (18000)  **S. H. Altayer**
31 B c 21/02 Havana Gold (IRE)—Queen Zain (IRE) (Lawman (FR)) (14000)  **S. H. Altayer**
32 B c 16/05 Time Test—Red Blooded Woman (USA) (Red Ransom (USA)) (6667)  **S. H. Altayer**
33 B c 05/02 Muhaarar—Regal Hawk (Singspiel (IRE)) (20000)  **Mr I. Mohammed**
34 Gr f 14/01 Gleneagles (IRE)—Shirin of Persia (IRE) (Dylan Thomas (IRE)) (26667)  **Mr A. Al Mansoori**
35 B f 29/04 Mastercraftsman (IRE)—Silkwood (Singspiel (IRE)) (52000)  **S. H. Altayer**
36 F 08/04 Caravaggio (USA)—Tassina (GER) (Galileo (IRE)) (68000)  **S. H. Altayer**
37 Ch c 10/02 Mastercraftsman (IRE)—Totally Lost (IRE) (Rip Van Winkle (IRE)) (19048)  **Mr A. Al Mansoori**
38 B c 06/03 Sea The Stars (IRE)—White Moonstone (USA) (Dynaformer (USA))  **Mr A. Al Mansoori**

**Assistant Trainer:** Mike Marshall.

## 385  MRS LAURA MONGAN, Epsom
Postal: **Condover Stables, Langley Vale Road, Epsom, Surrey, KT18 6AP**
Contacts: **PHONE** 01372 271494 **MOBILE** 07788 122942 **FAX** 01372 271494
**EMAIL** ljmongan@hotmail.co.uk **WEBSITE** www.lauramongan.co.uk

1  **ASCRAEUS**, 4, b f Poet's Voice—Sciacca (IRE) **Mrs P. J. Sheen**
2  **BLACK MEDICK**, 5, gr m Dark Angel (IRE)—Penny's Gift **Mrs P. J. Sheen**
3  **BLAIRLOGIE**, 4, b g Roderic O'Connor (IRE)—Desert Morning (IRE) **Mrs L. J. Mongan**
4  **GOLDEN NECTAR**, 7, ch m Sakhee's Secret—Mildoura (FR) **Mrs P. J. Sheen**
5  **IMPART**, 7, b g Oasis Dream—Disclose **Charlie's Starrs & Laura Mongan**
6  **MILLIONS MEMORIES**, 5, b g Zoffany (IRE)—Millestan (IRE) **Mrs P. J. Sheen**
7  **MISS YEATS (IRE)**, 10, b m Yeats (IRE)—Mrs Wallensky (IRE) **Mrs P. J. Sheen**
8  **MY BOY JAMES (IRE)**, 9, br g Getaway (GER)—Parkality (IRE) **Mrs P. J. Sheen**
9  **NEW ARRIVAL (IRE)**, 4, gr f Gutaifan (IRE)—Doula (USA) **Mrs L. J. Mongan**
10  **PARADISE ON EARTH**, 4, b f Invincible Spirit (IRE)—Rainbow Springs **Mrs P. J. Sheen**
11  **PASS CARD (IRE)**, 5, b m Authorized (IRE)—Dinaria (IRE) **Mrs P. J. Sheen**
12  **PICKYOUROWN (IRE)**, 4, ch g Cityscape—Mildoura (FR) **Mrs P. J. Sheen**
13  **PLEDGE OF PEACE (IRE)**, 4, b g New Approach (IRE)—Hoodna (IRE) **Mrs P. J. Sheen**
14  **RAMATUELLE**, 5, ch m Champs Elysees—Florentia **Mrs L. J. Mongan**
15  **SEA TIDE**, 7, b m Champs Elysees—Change Course **Mrs P. J. Sheen**
16  **SWEET NATURE (IRE)**, 6, b m Canford Cliffs (IRE)—High Figurine (IRE) **Mrs L. J. Mongan**

### THREE-YEAR-OLDS
17  **ONE DAY**, b f Adaay (IRE)—Pelican Key (IRE) **Mrs P. J. Sheen**
18  **PATRIOCTIC (IRE)**, b c Vadamos (FR)—Height of Vanity (IRE) **Mrs P. J. Sheen**
19  **PATSY'S NUMBER ONE**, br g Avonbridge—Blaise For Me **Mrs L. J. Mongan**

**Other Owners:** Mr A. W. Bain, Mr S. W. Bain, Charlie's Starrs, Mrs L. J. Mongan.

**Assistant Trainer:** Ian Mongan.

**NH Jockey:** Tom Cannon.

## 386  MR GARY MOORE, Horsham
Postal: **Cisswood Racing Stables, Sandygate Lane, Lower Beeding, Horsham, West Sussex, RH13 6LR**
Contacts: **PHONE** 01403 891912
**EMAIL** info@garymooreracing.com

1  **A TOI PHIL (FR)**, 11, b g Day Flight—Lucidrile (FR) **Teme Valley 2**
2  **AGE OF WISDOM (IRE)**, 8, ch g Pivotal—Learned Friend (GER) **The 1901 Partnership**
3  **AGENT OF FORTUNE**, 6, ch m Kheleyf (USA)—Royal Bloom (IRE) **Foreign Legion**
4  **AIGUILLETTE**, 5, b g Epaulette (AUS)—Lucky Dice **Heart of the South Racing 108**
5  **ALBERT VAN ORNUM (FR)**, 4, b g Authorized (IRE)—Diena (FR) **Mr P. T. Mott**
6  **ANTONY (FR)**, 11, b g Walk In The Park (IRE)—Melanie du Chenet (FR) **The Winning Hand**
7  **AR MEST (FR)**, 8, bl g Diamond Boy (FR)—Shabada (FR) **G. L. Moore**
8  **AVORISK ET PERILS (FR)**, 6, b m No Risk At All (FR)—Pierre Azuree (FR) **Dedman Properties Limited**
9  **BALLYDOYLE**, 6, b g Masterstroke (USA)—Best Tune **Mr N. J. Roach & Mr G. L. Moore**
10  **BEALACH (IRE)**, 4, b g New Approach (IRE)—Samya **Foreign Legion**
11  **BEAT THE JUDGE (IRE)**, 6, b g Canford Cliffs (IRE)—Charmingly (USA) **Mr E. P. Babington**
12  **BENATAR (IRE)**, 9, b g Beneficial—Carrigeen Lily (IRE) **Mr A. J. Head**
13  **BENEVOLENTDICTATOR**, 7, ch g Schiaparelli (GER)—Kim Fontenail (FR) **The Knights Of Pleasure**
14  **BIG JIMBO**, 4, ch g Helmet (AUS)—Big Moza **Mr A Watson & Mr B Malyon**
15  **BLACK GERRY (IRE)**, 6, b g Westerner—Triptoshan (IRE) **Mrs M. Devine**
16  **BOTOX HAS (FR)**, 5, b g Dream Well (FR)—Bournie (FR) **Mr J. K. Stone**
17  **BRAMBLEDOWN**, 5, b g Canford Cliffs (IRE)—Pretty Flemingo (IRE) **E. A. Condon**
18  **BRIDLE LOANAN (IRE)**, 8, b g Getaway (GER)—Hanora O'Brien (IRE) **Mr A. J. Head**

## MR GARY MOORE - continued

19 **CALL OFF THE DOGS (IRE)**, 6, ch g Bienamado (USA)—
Lady Charmere (IRE) **Galloping On The South Downs Partnership**
20 **CAPRICORN PRINCE**, 5, ch g Garswood—Sakhee's Pearl **Mrs A. P. Wilkinson**
21 **CASA LOUPI**, 4, ch g Casamento (IRE)—Kameruka **Mrs V. Pritchard-Gordon**
22 **CHEQUE EN BLANC (FR)**, 9, b br g Bernebeau (FR)—Necossaise (FR) **Mrs E. A. Kiernan**
23 **DAREBIN (GER)**, 9, ch g It's Gino (GER)—Delightful Sofie (GER) **Chris Stedman & Mark Albon**
24 **DARKEST DAY (IRE)**, 6, b g Aizavoski (IRE)—Dempseys Luck (IRE) **GG Thoroughbreds XIII**
25 **DEEBAJ (IRE)**, 9, br g Authorized (IRE)—Athreyaa **G. L. Moore**
26 **DIABLE DE SIVOLA (FR)**, 8, b g Noroit (GER)—Grande Route (IRE) **Mr R. Forster**
27 **DISTINGO (IRE)**, 8, b g Smart Strike (CAN)—Distinctive Look (IRE) **Alan Jamieson Site Services Ltd**
28 **DONALD LLEWELLYN**, 4, b g Pivotal—Rose Law **Mr C. E. Stedman**
29 **DONNYTWOBUCKETS (IRE)**, 7, b g Jeremy (USA)—Manorville (IRE) **G. L. Moore**
30 **DORKING LAD**, 6, b g Sholokhov (IRE)—Brookville (IRE) **Galloping On The South Downs Partnership**
31 **EARLY DU LEMO (FR)**, 8, gr g Early March—Kiswa (FR) **Mr A. J. Head**
32 **EDITEUR DU GITE (FR)**, 7, b g Saddex—Malaga de St Sulpice (FR) **The Preston Family, Friends & T Jacobs**
33 **EL HAGEB ROSE (FR)**, 7, b g Coastal Path—Isle Rose (FR) **G. L. Moore**
34 **ELISEZMOI (FR)**, 7, gr g Lord du Sud (FR)—Diva de La Borie (FR) **The Knights Of Pleasure**
35 **EPISODE (FR)**, 7, ch m Kotky Bleu (FR)—Morvandelle (FR) **Mr P. Hunt**
36 **ERAGON DE CHANAY (FR)**, 7, b g Racinger (FR)—Rose Celebre (FR) **Five Star Racing Group**
37 **ESPRIT DE SOMOZA (FR)**, 7, b g Irish Wells (FR)—Topaze de Somoza (FR) **Mr R. Forster**
38 **FASCINATING LIPS (IRE)**, 4, b g Canford Cliffs (IRE)—Fantastic Lips (GER) **Mr H. Redknapp**
39 **FIFTY BALL (FR)**, 6, b g Cokoriko (FR)—Voix de Montot (FR) **Mr S. Packham**
40 **FILLES DE FLEUR**, 5, gr ro m Gregorian (IRE)—Big Moza **Mr A Watson & Mr B Malyon**
41 **FLAMINGER (FR)**, 6, gr g Racinger (FR)—Landalouse (FR) **Mrs E. H. Avery**
42 5, B g Kayf Tara—Fleur de Nikos (FR) **Mrs R. A. Arnold**
43 **FULL BACK (FR)**, 6, b g Sinndar (IRE)—Quatre Bleue (FR) **Mr A. J. Head**
44 **GENTLEMAN'S DREAM (FR)**, 9, b g Flemensfirth (USA)—Fair And Aisey (IRE) **Dedman Properties Limited**
45 **GLENO (IRE)**, 9, ch g Ask—Lwitikila **Crystal Racing Syndicate**
46 **GOLDEN BOY GREY (FR)**, 5, ch g Diamond Boy (FR)—Betwixt (IRE) **Mrs R. A. Arnold**
47 **GORHAM'S CAVE**, 7, b g Rock of Gibraltar (IRE)—Moiava (FR) **Mrs A. L. Lofts**
48 **GOSHEN (FR)**, 5, b g Authorized (IRE)—Hyde (FR) **Mr S. Packham**
49 **GUGUSS COLLONGES (FR)**, 5, b g Secret Singer (FR)—
Une Collonges (FR) **Mr David Gilmour & Mr James Dellaway**
50 **HERMINO AA (FR)**, 4, b g Sinndar (IRE)—Acqua Luna (FR) **Galloping On The South Downs Partnership**
51 **HIGH UP IN THE AIR (FR)**, 7, ch g Famous Name—You Got The Love **Mr P. T. Mott**
52 **HIT THE ROCKS (IRE)**, 6, br g Fast Company (IRE)—Skerries (IRE) **P Moorhead, H Moorhead, J Collins 1**
53 **HUDSON DE GRUGY (FR)**, 4, b g Falco (USA)—Queen de Grugy (FR) **Alan Jamieson Site Services Ltd**
54 **ICONIC MUDDLE**, 8, gr g Sixties Icon—Spatham Rose **Saloop**
55 **IL RE DI NESSUNO (FR)**, 6, b g Sinndar (IRE)—Lady Elgar (IRE) **Mr Ashley Head & Mr Garry Dreher**
56 **IMPHAL**, 7, b g Nathaniel (IRE)—Navajo Rainbow **G L Moore & Associates**
57 **IN REM (FR)**, 6, b g Kapgarde (FR)—Etoile des Iles (FR) **Mr R. Forster**
58 **ISAYALITTLEPRAYER**, 4, b f Nathaniel (IRE)—I Say (IRE) **Heart of the South Racing 117**
59 **ISLA'S DREAM (IRE)**, 7, b m Notnowcato—Daghashah **Benham & Hook**
60 **IT'S GOT LEGS (IRE)**, 8, b g Getaway (GER)—Lady Cadia (FR) **Galloping On The South Downs Partnership**
61 **JALWAN (USA)**, 4, b g Wicked Strong (USA)—City Run (USA) **Noel Fehily Racing Syndicates - Jalwan**
62 **JUMPING CATS**, 6, ch g Champs Elysees—Pivotal Drive (IRE) **Ashley Carr & Gary Moore**
63 **JUNKANOO**, 4, b g Epaulette (AUS)—Bahamian Music (IRE) **Jacobs Construction & Mr J Harley**
64 **KALAKAWA ENKI (FR)**, 7, b g Buck's Boum (FR)—Baba San Siro (FR) **Five Star Racing Group**
65 **KAPDAD (FR)**, 7, ch g Kapgarde (FR)—Reveries (FR) **G. L. Moore**
66 **KING COOL**, 10, b g King's Theatre (IRE)—Cool Spice **Mr P. T. Mott**
67 **KLOUD GATE (FR)**, 9, ch g Astronomer Royal (USA)—Talkata (IRE) **Hail Sargent Evans**
68 **KOST A COAT (FR)**, 6, b g Diamond Boy (FR)—Charming Princesse (FR) **Mrs R. A. Arnold**
69 **LADY MORPHEUS**, 5, b m Morpheus—Tatora **Mr P. B. Moorhead**
70 **LARRY**, 8, b g Midnight Legend—Gaspaisie (FR) **Galloping On The South Downs Partnership**
71 **LAVORANTE (FR)**, 5, br g Milan—Pinkeen Lady (IRE) **Mrs M. Devine**
72 **LIGHT OF AIR (FR)**, 8, b g Youmzain (IRE)—Height of Vanity (FR) **G. L. Moore**
73 **MAKE MY DAY (IRE)**, 5, b g Galileo (IRE)—Posset **Mr S. Packham**
74 **MICKEY BUCKMAN**, 8, b g Gleaming (IRE)—Mysaynoww **Mr & Mrs R Sage**
75 **MISTER TICKLE (IRE)**, 7, b g Morozov (USA)—Tatiana (IRE) **Sunville Rail Limited**
76 **MOTDEPAS (FR)**, 6, b g Davidoff (GER)—Singastar (FR) **Mr David Leon & James Devine**

## MR GARY MOORE - continued

77 **NASSALAM (FR)**, 4, ch g Dream Well (FR)—Ramina (GER) **Mr J. K. Stone**
78 **NATURAL HISTORY**, 6, b g Nathaniel (IRE)—Film Script **Hail Sargent Evans**
79 **NATURALLY HIGH (FR)**, 6, b g Camelot—Just Little (FR) **Hail Sargent Evans**
80 **NEEDHAMS GAP (IRE)**, 7, br g Flemensfirth (USA)—Blue Maxi (IRE) **G. L. Moore**
81 **NEFF (GER)**, 6, b g Pastorius (GER)—Nouvelle Fortune (IRE) **Past The Post Racing**
82 **NOT ANOTHER MUDDLE**, 10, b g Kayf Tara—Spatham Rose **Saloop**
83 **NOTE BLEU**, 4, b g Camelot—Silent Music (IRE) **Mr C. E. Stedman**
84 **OLD FRIEND (FR)**, 4, b g Fast Company (IRE)—Alpen Glen **Mr P. K. Siu**
85 **OZZIE MAN (IRE)**, 5, b g Ask—Parkdota (IRE) **Mr P. Hunt**
86 **PLATINUM PRINCE**, 4, gr g Harbour Watch (IRE)—Sakhee's Pearl **Mrs A. P. Wilkinson**
87 **PRINCE PERCY**, 4, b g Sir Percy—Crystal High **The Pride of Sussex Partnership**
88 4, B g Authorized (IRE)—Princess Roseburg (USA) **Mr S. Packham**
89 **QUIANA**, 6, b g Pour Moi (IRE)—Quisitor (IRE) **Shark Bay Racing & Mr G L Moore**
90 **QULOOB**, 7, b g New Approach (IRE)—Jadhwah **Heart of the South Racing 120**
91 **RAFIOT (USA)**, 5, b g Elusive Quality (USA)—Viva Rafaela (BRZ) **Mr B. Hepburn**
92 **RAY'S THE ONE**, 4, b g Mount Nelson—Tenpence **Mr C. Butler**
93 **RED MIX (FR)**, 8, b g Al Namix (FR)—Fidelety (FR) **Clare Salmon & Gary Moore**
94 **REINATOR (FR)**, 5, b g Motivator—Vie de Reine (FR) **Mr C. E. Stedman**
95 **RICHIDISH (FR)**, 6, b g Spanish Moon (USA)—Briere (FR) **Galloping On the South Downs & G L Moore**
96 **RIGHT HAND OF GOD**, 6, b g Norse Dancer (IRE)—Miss Sassi **Galloping On The South Downs Partnership**
97 **RIOHACHA (FR)**, 4, b g Sea The Moon (GER)—Beyond The Dream (USA) **Heart of the South Racing 125**
98 **ROBIN'S DREAM**, 5, b g Kayf Tara—Sudden Light (IRE) **Mr Jerry Hinds & Mr Ashley Head**
99 **ROCCO DU BERLAIS (IRE)**, 6, gr g Shirocco (GER)—Izzy du Berlais (IRE) **The Fourth Pillar Partnership**
100 **ROYAUME UNI (IRE)**, 4, b br g Galileo (IRE)—Night Lagoon (GER) **Mrs E. H. Avery**
101 **RUBY YEATS**, 10, b m Yeats (IRE)—Newbay Lady **Heart of the South Racing 122**
102 **SAGHIR (IRE)**, 4, ch g Nathaniel (IRE)—Sagawara **The Winning Hand**
103 **SAN PEDRO DE SENAM (FR)**, 8, br g Saint des Saints (FR)—Tetiaroa (FR) **Mrs Jane George & Mrs Helen Shelton**
104 **SCHELEM (FR)**, 4, b g Orpen (USA)—Sol Schwarz **Mr P. Hunt**
105 **SEABORN (IRE)**, 7, b g Born To Sea (IRE)—Next To The Top **Mr I. Beach**
106 **SHANTOU MASTER (IRE)**, 6, b g Shantou (USA)—Brown Bess (IRE) **Mr D. Channon**
107 **SOPRAN THOR (FR)**, 6, b g Authorized (IRE)—Sopran Slam (IRE) **Galloping On The South Downs Partnership**
108 **STORMINGIN (IRE)**, 8, gr g Clodovil (IRE)—Magadar (USA) **Mrs C. Reed**
109 4, B g Kayf Tara—Sudden Light (IRE) **Mr Jerry Hinds & Mr Ashley Head**
110 **SUSSEX RANGER (USA)**, 7, b g Hat Trick (JPN)—Purple (USA) **The The Tongdean Partnership**
111 **TAMARIS (IRE)**, 4, br g Dansili—Fleur de Cactus (IRE) **Team Tasker**
112 **TAZKA (FR)**, 6, b m Network (GER)—Tazminya **B. Noakes & Baroness S. Noakes**
113 **TENFOLD (IRE)**, 4, b g Born To Sea (IRE)—Dear Dream (IRE) **G. A. Jackman**
114 **THE FLYING SOFA (IRE)**, 8, b g Sholokhov (IRE)—La Julie (IRE) **Galloping On The South Downs Partnership**
115 **TOUCHTHESOUL (ITY)**, 6, b g Red Rocks (IRE)—Easy Hawk **The Soul Searchers**
116 **TRAFALGAR BOY**, 6, b h Mount Nelson—Aiaam Al Wafa (IRE) **Heart of the South Racing 114**
117 **TWENTY TWENTY (IRE)**, 6, b g Henrythenavigator (USA)—Distinctive Look (IRE) **Mark Albon & Gary Moore**
118 **VISION CLEAR (GER)**, 6, b g Soldier Hollow—Vive Madame (GER) **A. Head**
119 **VORASHANN (FR)**, 5, b g Sinndar (IRE)—Visorama (IRE) **T. Jacobs, J.E. Harley & Mr G.L. Moore**
120 **WAIKIKI WAVES (FR)**, 8, b g Alexandros—Lulabelle Spar (IRE) **Heart of the South Racing 119**
121 **WEST LAKE (FR)**, 11, b g Michel Georges—Darnaway (FR) **B. G. Homewood**
122 **WEST ON SUNSET (FR)**, 4, b f Westerner—Flute Bowl **Mr C. E. Stedman**
123 **ZAMPERINI (IRE)**, 9, ch g Fast Company (IRE)—Lucky Date (IRE) **Mr R. E. Tillett**
124 **ZHIGULI (IRE)**, 6, b g Flemensfirth (USA)—Grangeclare Flight (IRE) **Druzhba Racing Partnership**

### THREE-YEAR-OLDS

125 **CELESTIAL POINT (IRE)**, b f Pivotal—Hestia (FR) **Mr C. E. Stedman**
126 **CHAMPAGNE PIAFF (FR)**, b br g Le Havre (IRE)—Galaxe (FR) **Mr A. J. Head**
127 **DURDLE DOOR**, ch f Sepoy (AUS)—Dubai Media (CAN) **Mr C. E. Stedman**
128 **HE'S A LATCHICO (IRE)**, b g Fast Company (IRE)—Daliana **Danny & Gary Moore**
129 **JUMPING FOR JOY (FR)**, b f Authorized (IRE)—Soft Pleasure (USA) **Mr R. Forster**
130 **LANGAFEL (IRE)**, b g Fast Company (IRE)—Miracle Steps (CAN) **Mrs Arnold & Partner**
131 **NEMINOS (FR)**, ch g Showcasing—An Riocht (IRE) **The Lane Partnership**
132 **NIGHT EAGLE (IRE)**, b c Free Eagle (IRE)—Life At Night (IRE) **Mr S. Chambers**
133 **PURE BUBBLES (GER)**, b c Protectionist (GER)—Peace Society (USA) **Mr J. G. Jones**

## MR GARY MOORE - continued

**134** B g Kayf Tara—Sudden Wish (IRE) **G. L. Moore**
**135 THE WHIPMASTER (IRE)**, ch g Mastercraftsman (IRE)—Birdie Queen **The Golf Partnership**
**136 TORONADO GREY**, gr g Toronado (IRE)—Debutante Blues (USA) **Jacobs Construction (Holdings) Limited**

**Other Owners:** Mrs M. Abey, Mr M. L. Albon, Mrs R. A. Arnold, Mrs S. A. Ashley, Mrs E. H. Avery, Avery, Hodges, Moorhead & Collins, Mr H. Burch, A. Carr, Mr J. A. Collins, Mr J. A. Dellaway, J. T. Devine, Mr G. C. Dreher, Mr M. Duncan, Mr D. L. Evans, G L Moore Racing, Galloping On The South Downs Partnership, Mrs J. George, Mr D. S. Gilmour, Mr N. J. Grayston, Mr J. E. Hale, The Hon J. Hanham, J. E. Harley, Mr A. J. Head, Mr P. A. Herbert, Mr J. Hinds, Mr A. D. S. Hodges, Mr D. L. Ives, Jacobs Construction (Holdings) Limited, D. Leon, Mr D. Llambias, G. L. Moore, Mrs H. J. Moorhead, Mr J. Muir, C. B. Noakes, Baroness S. Noakes, Mr D. Oneill, P Moorhead, H Moorhead & J Collins, Mr N. J. Roach, Mr R. J. Sage, Mrs T. J. Sage, Mr N. J. Salkeld, Ms C. L. Salmon, Mr R. D. Sargent, Mrs H. J. Shelton, Mr C. E. Stedman, The Preston Family & Friends Ltd, Mr R. W. D. Trevelyan, Mr M. C. Waddingham, Miss C. A. Webb, Mr M. K. Webb.

**Assistant Trainer:** David Wilson, **Racing Secretary:** Maria Workman.

**Flat Jockey:** Hector Crouch, Ryan Moore. **NH Jockey:** Jamie Moore, Joshua Moore. **Conditional Jockey:** Niall Houlihan. **Apprentice Jockey:** Rhys Clutterbuck, Louis Garoghan, Anna Gibson. **Amateur Jockey:** Miss Katy Brooks, Mr George Gorman, Miss Hayley Moore, Miss Elysia Vaughan.

---

## 387 MR J. S. MOORE, Upper Lambourn
Postal: **Berkeley House Stables, Upper Lambourn, Hungerford, Berkshire, RG17 8QP**
Contacts: **PHONE 01488 73887 MOBILE 07860 811127, 07900 402856 FAX 01488 73997**
**EMAIL jsmoore.racing@btopenworld.com WEBSITE www.stanmooreracing.co.uk**

**1 BIRKIE QUEEN (IRE)**, 4, br f Gutaifan (IRE)—The Oldladysays No (IRE) **Mrs S Gray, Mr Ian Gray & Sara Moore**
**2 BROCKAGH CAILIN**, 6, b m Helmet (AUS)—Step Softly **Gridline Racing**
**3 FACT OR FABLE (IRE)**, 4, gr g Alhebayeb (IRE)—Unreal **Mrs Wendy Jarrett & J S Moore**
**4 GO WEST YOUNG LAD (IRE)**, 5, b g Es Que Love (IRE)—Winnifred **Mrs S. Kelly**
**5 MR SHADY (IRE)**, 4, gr g Elzaam (AUS)—Whitershadeofpale (IRE) **Enterprising Trio & Sara Moore**
**6 UTHER PENDRAGON (IRE)**, 6, b g Dragon Pulse (IRE)—Unreal **Mrs Wendy Jarrett & J S Moore**

### THREE-YEAR-OLDS
**7 BOMB SQUAD (IRE)**, gr g Lethal Force (IRE)—Dutch Destiny **Eventmasters Racing & J S Moore**
**8 EASY EQUATION (FR)**, b g Rajsaman (FR)—Simple Solution (USA) **Roy Humphrey & J S Moore**
**9 FRIENDLY PRINCESS (IRE)**, ch f Prince of Lir (IRE)—Tepeleni **Mrs Wendy Jarrett & J S Moore**
**10 HOT DAY**, b c Adaay (IRE)—Sunny York (IRE)
**11 OCTOBER UPSTATE (IRE)**, b f Estidhkaar (IRE)—She's A Minx (IRE) **J. S. Moore & Partner**
**12 PAPAS DREAM (IRE)**, b g Vadamos (FR)—Ms O'Malley (IRE) **Pc Bloodstock & J S Moore**
**13 PAPAS GIRL (IRE)**, b f Mehmas (IRE)—Sunny Harbor (IRE) **Pc Bloodstock & J S Moore**
**14** B f Helmet (AUS)—Penny Lane Forever
**15 SO TRUE (IRE)**, b c Acclamation—Precious Gem (IRE) **Mr Kieron Badger & J S Moore**
**16 SOMMER DAISY (FR)**, b f Sommerabend—Capannacce (IRE) **Mr D G Pryde & J S Moore**
**17 STILL THE SAME (IRE)**, b c Vadamos (FR)—Unfortunate **Mr Kieron Badger & J S Moore**
**18 THE GOOD TING**, ch f Dragon Pulse (IRE)—The Burnham Mare (IRE) **J. S. Moore**
**19 WHOLELOTAFUN (IRE)**, b c Sir Prancealot (IRE)—Gatamalata (IRE) **Mrs Wendy Jarrett & J S Moore**
**20 WOODVIEW (IRE)**, ch g Ajaya—Spacecraft (USA) **Miss Alison Jones**

### TWO-YEAR-OLDS
**21** B f 22/02 Kodiac—Altogether (IRE) (King's Best (USA)) (19048)
**22** B f 11/03 Aclaim (IRE)—Cape Good Hope (Cape Cross (IRE)) (1800)
**23** B c 08/03 Vadamos (FR)—Catamaran (Shamardal (USA))
**24** B f 11/04 Galileo Gold—Drifting Spirit (Clodovil (IRE))
**25** Ch c 25/03 Cotai Glory—Gaazaal (IRE) (Iffraaj) **J. S. Moore & Partner**
**26** B c 10/03 Estidhkaar (IRE)—Joy For Life (Pivotal) **J. S. Moore & Partner**
**27** B c 29/04 Aclaim (IRE)—Let's Dance (IRE) (Danehill Dancer (IRE)) (9524)

## MR J. S. MOORE - continued

**28** B g 22/01 Estidhkaar (IRE)—Lovely Dancer (IRE) (Yeats (IRE)) (3810) **Eventmasters Racing & J S Moore**
**29** B f 21/01 Markaz (IRE)—Mollymawk (IRE) (Teofilo (IRE))
**30** B f 12/03 Buratino (IRE)—Noble Nova (Fraam)
**31** Ch c 10/05 Dandy Man (IRE)—Noble View (USA) (Distant View (USA)) (7619)
**32** Ch f 25/02 Outstrip—Pose (IRE) (Acclamation)
**33** B c 22/04 Havana Gold (IRE)—Riot of Colour (Excellent Art) (2500)
**34** Ch c 29/04 The Gurkha (IRE)—Rohain (Singspiel (IRE)) (4762)
**35** B g 20/02 Fast Company (IRE)—Saffa Garden (IRE) (King's Best (USA)) **J. S. Moore & Partner**
**36** B c 28/04 Estidhkaar (IRE)—Shamiya (IRE) (Acclamation)
**37** Gr f 12/04 Mehmas (IRE)—Stone Roses (IRE) (Zebedee) (2500)
**38** B f 03/04 Gregorian (IRE)—Timeless Elegance (IRE) (Invincible Spirit (IRE))
**39** B c 24/04 Zoffany (IRE)—Whatelseaboutyou (IRE) (Canford Cliffs (IRE))

**Other Owners:** Mr K. P. Badger, Enterprising Trio, Eventmasters Racing, Mr I. J. B. Gray, Mrs S. Gray, Mr P. J. Grimes, Mr R. V. Humphrey, Mr A. James, Mrs W. J. Jarrett, Mr E. McGlinchey, Mr N. J. McGlinchey, J. S. Moore, Mrs S. J. Moore, PC Bloodstock, D. G. Pryde, Mrs D. Sheasby, Mr E. J. N. Sheasby, Mr L. Tofts.

**Assistant Trainer:** Mrs S. Moore, **Racing Secretary:** Miss Cathy Holding.

**Apprentice Jockey:** Miss Sophie Reed.

---

## 388 MISS LAURA MORGAN, Waltham On The Wolds
Postal: **Foxfield Stud, Goadby Road, Waltham On The Wolds, Melton Mowbray, Leicestershire, LE14 4AG**
Contacts: **PHONE 01664 464571 MOBILE 07817 616622**
EMAIL lauramorg@hotmail.co.uk

**1 AGAINST ALL ODDS (FR)**, 6, b m Saint des Saints (FR)—Cue To Cue **Mr & Mrs W. J. Williams**
**2 ALKANADA (IRE)**, 6, b g Alkaadhem—Ellie Forte **Mrs A. M. Williams**
**3 ANGEL'S ENVY**, 9, b m Yeats (IRE)—Caoba **A. Lyons**
**4** 5, B g Doyen (IRE)—Aphrodisias (FR) **Mr I. Guise**
**5 BEAUTIFUL BEN (IRE)**, 11, b g Beneficial—Almnadia (IRE) **A. Lyons**
**6 BIG PENNY (IRE)**, 9, b m Oscar (IRE)—Lady Marnay (IRE) **The Rann Family**
**7 BIOVERDIA (IRE)**, 6, b m Kalanisi (IRE)—Thats The Lot (IRE) **Pardy & Gray**
**8 BOLD ENDEAVOUR**, 5, b g Fame And Glory—Araucaria (IRE) **Mr A. Barney**
**9 BOLD LEADER**, 5, b g Dunaden (FR)—Queenoz (IRE) **Miss L. Morgan**
**10 CAKE DE L'ISLE (FR)**, 9, b g Fragrant Mix (IRE)—Taiga de L'Isle (FR) **Piece of Cake Partnership**
**11 CESAR COLLONGES (FR)**, 9, ch g Fragrant Mix (IRE)—Prouesse Collonges (FR) **The Stagger Inn**
**12 DJARKEVI (FR)**, 8, b g Khalkevi (IRE)—Onvavoir (FR) **Mrs E. Holmes**
**13 DREAM POINT (IRE)**, 6, b m Iffraaj—Dream Club **Mr T. H. A. Barton**
**14 FOR FITZ SAKE (IRE)**, 5, b g Califet (FR)—Hollygrove (IRE) **Mrs A. M. Williams**
**15 FOXISLE SUNNY JIM**, 4, b c Mayson—Seyasaat (IRE) **Mr E. Cumberland**
**16 GOLD FIELDS**, 7, b g Sakhee (USA)—Realms of Gold (USA) **Mrs M. J. Pepperdine**
**17 HAASAB (IRE)**, 8, b g Sakhee (USA)—Badweia (USA) **Roemex Ltd**
**18 HASANKEY (IRE)**, 5, gr g Mastercraftsman (IRE)—Haziyna (IRE) **The Hanky Panky Partnership**
**19 HERE WE HAVE IT (IRE)**, 6, b g Mahler—Islands Sister (IRE) **Hanbury & Fretwell**
**20 J'AI FROID (IRE)**, 8, b g Flemensfirth (USA)—Park Wave (IRE) **Mrs K. Bromley**
**21 LICKLIGHTER (IRE)**, 10, b g Brian Boru—Daranado (IRE) **Mr P. L. Read**
**22 MORE MUSIC (IRE)**, 7, b g Morozov (USA)—Back On Song (IRE) **Miss L. Morgan**
**23 MOTARAABET (IRE)**, 8, b g Dansili—Hawaafez **R. A. Jenkinson**
**24 OVERWORKDUNDERPAID (IRE)**, 8, b g Getaway (GER)—Another Whiparound (IRE) **Mr S. Townshend**
**25 SAINT MAC**, 6, b g Nathaniel (IRE)—Noahs Ark (IRE) **T. R. Pryke**
**26 SALT OF THE EARTH (IRE)**, 5, b g El Salvador (IRE)—Brambellina (IRE) **Mr A. Barney**
**27 SALUTE THE KING (IRE)**, 6, gr g Salutino (GER)—Ballymartintheatre (IRE) **J. W. Hardy**
**28 SKIPPING ON (IRE)**, 12, b g Westerner—Skipping Along (IRE) **Triumph In Mind**
**29 SOCIALIST AGENDA**, 5, ch g Sir Percy—Mercy Pecksniff **Mr James Fyffe & Mr Scott Fyffe**
**30 SUPREME YEATS (IRE)**, 5, b g Yeats (IRE)—Supreme Bailerina (IRE) **Mr A. Barney**

## MISS LAURA MORGAN - continued

31 **TAQWAA (IRE)**, 8, ch g Iffraaj—Hallowed Park (IRE) **Laura Morgan Racing Club**
32 **TARAS DAY**, 8, b m Kayf Tara—One of Those Days **Mrs H. M. Harvey**
33 **TARDREE (IRE)**, 7, ch g Mahler—Brownie Points (IRE) **Bennett & O'Brien**
34 **THOMAS TODD**, 11, b g Passing Glance—Miss Danbys **Burton, Copley & Todd**
35 4, B f Authorized (IRE)—Tricoteuse **Miss L. Morgan**
36 **UBETYA (IRE)**, 6, b g Le Fou (IRE)—Valentina Gaye (IRE) **Mr A. Barney**
37 **WHERES MAUD GONE (IRE)**, 5, b m Yeats (IRE)—Barchetta (IRE) **Mr A. Barney**
38 **ZAKHAROVA**, 7, ch m Beat Hollow—Tcherina (IRE) **Mr & Mrs W. J. Williams**

**Other Owners:** Mr S. J. Bennett, Mr J. S. Birch, Mr W. R. Bowler, Mr R. J. Burton, Mr M. Copley, J. C. Fretwell, Mr J. Fyffe, Mr S. Fyffe, Mr K. Gray, Mr I. Guise, Mr W. Hanbury, Mr L. J. Heaver, Miss L. Morgan, Mr M. P. Obrien, Mr I. K. Pardy, Mr G. P. D. Rann, Mrs L. E. Rann, Mr P. L. Read, Miss L. Todd, Mrs M. Williams, W. J. Williams.

**Assistant Trainer:** Tom Morgan.

**Amateur Jockey:** Miss A. Peck.

---

**389**
**MR MOUSE MORRIS, Fethard**
Postal: **Everardsgrange, Fethard, Co. Tipperary, Ireland**
Contacts: **PHONE +353 52 613 1474 MOBILE +353 86 854 3010 FAX +353 52 613 1654**
**EMAIL mouse@eircom.net**

1 **BARNEY STINSON (IRE)**, 5, b h Fame and Glory—Which Thistle
2 **BEYOND THE LAW (IRE)**, 9, b g Westerner—Thegoodwans Sister (IRE)
3 **CAESAR ROCK (IRE)**, 5, b g Mahler—Supreme Von Pres
4 **CLONDAW BERTIE (IRE)**, 6, b h Thewayyouare (USA)—Female (IRE)
5 **CONQUERALL (IRE)**, 4, b g Saddler Maker (IRE)—Melancholy Hill (IRE)
6 **FLYING COLUM (IRE)**, 6, b h Getaway—Curragheen
7 **FOXY JACKS (IRE)**, 7, b g Fame And Glory—Benefit Ball (IRE)
8 **FRENCH DYNAMITE (FR)**, 6, b r Kentucky Dynamite—Matnie
9 **FRIARY ROCK (FR)**, 6, b h Spanish Moon—Zenita Des Brosses
10 **GANDY MAN (IRE)**, 5, b h Arcadio—Topsham Belle
11 **GENTLEMANSGAME**, 5, b g Gentleware—Grainne Ni Maille
12 **GET MY DRIFT (FR)**, 5, b g Spanish Moon—Voila
13 **GRAND GOSIER (FR)**, 6, b h Khalkevi—Teresa Moriniere
14 **INDIANA JONES (IRE)**, 5, b h Blue Bresil—Matnie
15 **JOE BLOM (IRE)**, 4, b g Mahler—Gorgeousreach (IRE)
16 **LARGY FIX (IRE)**, 6, ch g Notnowcato—Fix It Lady
17 **LAST MAN STANDING (IRE)**, 8, ch g Flemensfirth (USA)—Tricky Present (IRE)
18 **LIMEKILN ROCK (IRE)**, 4, b g Doyen (IRE)—Distelle (IRE)
19 **LIMESTONE ROCK (IRE)**, 5, b g Leading Light—Accordion Royale
20 5, B br g Leading Light (IRE)—Liss Ui Riain (IRE)
21 4, B g Fame And Glory—Mrs Dempsey (IRE)
22 **NERO ROCK (IRE)**, 6, b h Shirocco—Gilt Benefit
23 **ROBIN SCHERBATSKY (IRE)**, 5, b m Milan—Benefit Ball (IRE)
24 **ROMAN ROCK (IRE)**, 7, b g Presenting—Native Idea (IRE)
25 **SAMS PROFILE (IRE)**, 7, b g Black Sam Bellamy (IRE)—Lucylou (IRE)
26 **THE LAST THROW (IRE)**, 5, b g Shirocco—Bridgequarter Girl
27 **THEBELLSOFSHANDON (IRE)**, 6, b h Fame and Glory—Western Cowgirl
28 **UNION ROCK (IRE)**, 5, b m Acadio—Janal
29 **WHATSNOTOKNOW (IRE)**, 6, b g Mahler—Whos To Know (IRE)

## 390 MR PATRICK MORRIS, Prescot
Postal: **Avenue House, George Hale Avenue, Knowsley Park, Prescot, Merseyside, L34 4AJ**
Contacts: **MOBILE 07545 425235**
EMAIL **Patrickmorris76@yahoo.com**

1 **ARABIST**, 5, b g Invincible Spirit (IRE)—Highest **Dr M. B. Q. S. Koukash**
2 **BELL HEATHER (IRE)**, 8, b m Iffraaj—Burren Rose (USA) **Dr M. B. Q. S. Koukash**
3 **GABRIAL (IRE)**, 12, b g Dark Angel (IRE)—Guajira (FR) **Dr M. B. Q. S. Koukash**
4 **GABRIAL THE SAINT (IRE)**, 6, b g Society Rock (IRE)—Green Briar **Dr M. B. Q. S. Koukash**
5 **GABRIAL THE TIGER (IRE)**, 9, b g Kodiac—Invincible **Dr M. B. Q. S. Koukash**
6 **GROWL**, 9, b g Oasis Dream—Desert Tigress (USA) **Dr M. B. Q. S. Koukash**
7 **HEART OF SOUL (IRE)**, 6, b g Makfi—Hadrian's Waltz (IRE) **Dr M. B. Q. S. Koukash**
8 **MANCINI**, 7, ch g Nathaniel (IRE)—Muscovado (USA) **Dr M. B. Q. S. Koukash**
9 **PENWORTHAM (IRE)**, 8, b g Dandy Man (IRE)—Portofino Bay (IRE) **Dr M. B. Q. S. Koukash**
10 **RESHOUN (FR)**, 7, b g Shamardal (USA)—Radiyya (IRE) **Dr M. B. Q. S. Koukash**
11 **RESTORER**, 9, gr g Mastercraftsman (IRE)—Moon Empress (FR) **Dr M. B. Q. S. Koukash**
12 **SALAM ZAYED**, 5, b g Exceed And Excel (AUS)—Long Face (USA) **Dr M. B. Q. S. Koukash**
13 **SCOTTISH BLADE (IRE)**, 5, b g Exceed And Excel (AUS)—Hecuba **Dr S. Lane**
14 **STREET LIFE**, 4, ch g Hot Streak (IRE)—Atheera (IRE) **Dr M. B. Q. S. Koukash**
15 **THE NEW MARWAN**, 4, b g Dark Angel (IRE)—Tiger Mist (IRE) **Dr M. B. Q. S. Koukash**
16 **ZAMJAR**, 7, b g Exceed And Excel (AUS)—Cloud's End **Dr M. B. Q. S. Koukash**

### THREE-YEAR-OLDS
17 **TOMMY AND ANDY (IRE)**, b c Mehmas (IRE)—Guajira (FR) **Dr M. B. Q. S. Koukash**

## 391 MR HUGHIE MORRISON, East Ilsley
Postal: **Summerdown, East Ilsley, Newbury, Berkshire, RG20 7LB**
Contacts: **PHONE 01635 281678 MOBILE 07836 687799 FAX 01635 281746**
EMAIL **hughie@hughiemorrison.co.uk** WEBSITE **www.hughiemorrison.co.uk**

1 **AFFAIR**, 7, b m Sakhee's Secret—Supatov (USA) **H. Morrison**
2 **COSMIC PRINCESS**, 4, b f Kingman—Galaxy Highflyer
3 **CURTIZ**, 4, b g Stimulation (IRE)—Supatov (USA) **Mrs J. Parkes**
4 **FINAL ENCORE**, 4, b g Dunaden (FR)—Act Three **One More Moment of Madness**
5 4, B f Kayf Tara—Flirtatious **Mrs M. D. W. Morrison**
6 5, B g Kayf Tara—Flirtatious **Mrs M. D. W. Morrison**
7 **KIPPS (IRE)**, 4, gr g War Command (USA)—Sixpenny Sweets (IRE) **Mr A. Kheir**
8 **MAXCEL**, 4, b g Excelebration (IRE)—Katess (IRE) **Mrs M. C. Sweeney**
9 **MISS FAIRFAX (IRE)**, 5, ch m Imperial Monarch (IRE)—Stein Castle (IRE) **The Hill Stud**
10 **MR POY**, 4, ch g Sepoy (AUS)—Quiz Mistress **The Fairy Story Partnership**
11 **NOT SO SLEEPY**, 9, ch g Beat Hollow—Papillon de Bronze (IRE) **Lady Blyth**
12 **OUR JESTER**, 5, b g Garswood—Cill Rialaig **Pangfield Racing V**
13 **QUICKTHORN**, 4, b g Nathaniel (IRE)—Daffydowndilly **Lady Blyth**
14 **RAVENS ARK**, 4, ch g Raven's Pass (USA)—Wonderful Desert **Beachview Corporation Ltd**
15 **REQUITED (IRE)**, 5, b g Requinto (IRE)—Joyfulness (USA) **H. Morrison**
16 **SCANNING**, 5, b g Pastoral Pursuits—Yonder **Mrs M. D. W. Morrison**
17 **STARCAT**, 4, ch g Lope de Vega (IRE)—Purr Along **Martin Hughes & Michael Kerr-Dineen**
18 **SULOCHANA (IRE)**, 4, br f Lope de Vega (IRE)—Yakshini (IRE) **Mr P. Brocklehurst**
19 **THIRD WIND**, 7, b br g Shirocco (GER)—Act Three **Mrs A. J. Hamilton-Fairley**
20 **URBAN ARTIST**, 6, ch m Cityscape—Cill Rialaig **Pangfield Racing V**
21 **WHITEHAVEN (FR)**, 4, bl g Le Havre (FR)—Passion Blanche **P. C. J. Dalby & R. D. Schuster**
22 **WITH RESPECT (IRE)**, 4, gr g Gutaifan (IRE)—More Respect (IRE) **Thurloe Thoroughbreds XLVIII**

## MR HUGHIE MORRISON - continued

### THREE-YEAR-OLDS

23 **AURORA STAR (FR)**, b g Harzand (IRE)—Maleficent  **Mr S. B. S. Ronaldson**
24 **BEARAWAY (IRE)**, b g Kodiac—Fair Sailing (IRE)
25 **CHARMING PARADISE**, b g Charming Thought—Amanjena  **M. E. Wates**
26 **EQUISENTIAL**, b f Equiano (FR)—
   Broadlands  **The Hon Miss M. A. Morrison, Miss D. Collett, Mr S. M. De Zoete, A. C. Pickford**
27 **FARHH SIGHTED**, br f Farhh—Respectfilly  **The Fairy Story Partnership**
28 **GWENHWYVAR (IRE)**, b f Camelot—Quiz Mistress  **The Fairy Story Partnership**
29 **HESPERIS**, b f Dubawi (IRE)—Rosinka (IRE)  **Mrs H Lascelles, Mr A Macdonald-buchanan**
30 **HONEY POT (IRE)**, b f Iffraaj—Jam Jar  **The End-R-Ways Partnership & Partners**
31 **HUDDLETON MAC (IRE)**, b c Awtaad (IRE)—Melodique (FR)  **Mr A McAlpine & Ms M Lund**
32 **KING OF CLUBS**, b c Intello (GER)—Queen Arabella  **Castle Down Racing**
33 **LADY PERCIVAL**, b f Sir Percy—Daffydowndilly  **Lady Blyth**
34 **LEGENDARY DAY**, b c Adaay (IRE)—Dubai Legend  **A. N. Solomons**
35 **MARSABIT (IRE)**, ch g Mehmas (IRE)—Masela (IRE)  **P. C. J. Dalby & R. D. Schuster**
36 **MRS FITZHERBERT (IRE)**, b f Kingman—Stupendous Miss (USA)  **Sonia M. Rogers & Anthony Rogers**
37 **PRIDE OF NEPAL**, b g The Gurkha (IRE)—
   Best Regards (IRE)  **The Hon Miss M. A. Morrison, Mr S. M. De Zoete, A. C. Pickford, Mr S. D. Malcolm, Mr R. A. Angliss**
38 **QUARANTINI**, ch f Showcasing—Valentine Glory  **The AAA Partnership**
39 **ROSEMARY AND THYME**, b f Camelot—Scarborough Fair  **Mr P. Brocklehurst**
40 **SCHEHERAZADE**, b f Adaay (IRE)—Pelagia (IRE)  **Wood Street Syndicate II**
41 **SPANGLER (IRE)**, gr c Starspangledbanner (AUS)—Sixpenny Sweets (IRE)  **Martin Hughes & Michael Kerr-Dineen**
42 **STAY WELL**, b c Iffraaj—Sweeping Up  **Ben & Sir Martyn Arbib**
43 **SURREY GOLD (IRE)**, b c Golden Horn—Shemiyla (FR)  **Surrey Racing (SG)**
44 **THUNDERCLAP (IRE)**, b g Night of Thunder (IRE)—
   Former Drama (USA)  **Mr R. A. Pilkington, Sir Thomas Pilkington**
45 **VINO VICTRIX**, b c Sir Percy—Valeria Victrix (IRE)  **Dr J. Wilson, Mr S. B. S. Ronaldson**

### TWO-YEAR-OLDS

46 **ALYTH**, b c 17/01 Muhaarar—Permission (Authorized)  **Mrs Julia Scott, Mr James Dean, Viscountess F Trenchard**
47 **BANNED**, b f 08/05 Ulysses—Clarietta (Sharmardal)  **Martin Hughes & Michael Kerr-Dineen**
48 **BUSHFIRE**, ch c 28/02 Australia—Aflame (Shamardal (USA))  (50000)  **Martin Hughes & Michael Kerr-Dineen**
49 **CANTATA**, b f 15/05 Oasis Dream—Summer's Eve (Singspiel)  **Wardley Bloodstock**
50 B f 17/02 Australia—Come Touch The Sun (Fusaichi Pegasus)  **Mr B Sangster, Mrs H Lascelles**
51 B f 19/03 Showcasing—Copy-Cat (Lion Cavern (USA))  (40000)  **Hottotrot Racing**
52 **HAYMAKER**, b c 13/03 Muhaarar—
   Squash (Pastoral Pursuits)  (42000)  **The Hon Miss M. A. Morrison, Mr C. M. Budgett, Miss D. Collett**
53 **JULIUS**, ch c 06/02 Ruler Of The World—Seraminder (Zamindar)  **The Fairy Story Partnership**
54 **LUCROSA (IRE)**, b f 08/04 Profitable (IRE)—Opportuna (Rock Hard Ten (USA))  (47000)  **Thurloe Thoroughbreds L**
55 B c 29/01 Sir Percy—Luisa Calderon (Nayef (USA))  (26000)  **Mr A. Kheir**
56 **PROMOTING**, b c 25/03 Showcasing—Aqualis (Sea The Stars)  **P. C. J. Dalby & R. D. Schuster**
57 **REELEMIN**, ch c 03/02 Highland Reel (IRE)—
   Rainbow's Arch (IRE) (Dubawi (IRE))  (18000)  **M. T. Bevan, Mrs M. T. Bevan**
58 **SHOCKWAVES**, gr c 29/03 Sea The Moon (GER)—
   Having A Blast (USA) (Exchange Rate (USA))  (80000)  **M. Kerr-Dineen, Mr M. B. Hughes, W. D. Eason**
59 **STAY ALERT**, b f 28/02 Fastnet Rock—Starfala (Galileo)
60 **SUGAR CANDIE**, b f 28/01 Highland Reel—
   Sweet Selection (Stimulation)  **Paul & Catriona Brocklehurst Bloodstock**
61 ch f 19/05 Cityscape—Jasmeno (Catcher In The Rye)  **Mnc Racing**
62 ch f 14/02 Pivotal—Last Tango In Paris (Aqlaam)  **MRC Racing, Helena Springfield Limited**
63 b c 22/05 KINGMAN—Peinture Abstraite (Holy Roman Emperor)  **Mr A. Kheir**
64 , b f 30/01 Bated Breath—Tropicana Bay (Oasis Dream)  **MRC Racing, Helena Springfield Limited**
65 **WAGGA WAGGA**, ch c 10/03 Australia—Quiz Mistress (Doyen)  **The Fairy Story Partnership**
66 Gr f 13/04 Ulysses (IRE)—White Wedding (IRE) (Green Desert (USA))  (28000)

## MR HUGHIE MORRISON - continued

**Other Owners:** Mr B. G. Arbib, M. Arbib, & M. Bevan, Collett, Morrison & Partners, Mrs A. M. Garfield, L. A. Garfield, Mr M. B. Hughes, M. Kerr-Dineen, Michael Kerr-Dineen & Martin Hughes, Mrs J. C. Lascelles, Ms M. B. Lund, M Kerr-Dineen, M Hughes & W Eason, Mr & Mrs A McAlpine & Partners, Mr A. R. Macdonald-Buchanan, Mr A. N. R. McAlpine, H. Morrison, Mr J. W. Parker, Pickford, Collett, Morrison & de Zoete, Pickfordmalcolmmorrisonanglissde Zoete, T. Pilkington & Mr R. A. Pilkington, Mr A. P. Rogers, Mrs S. Rogers, Scott, Dean & Trenchard, The End-R-Ways Partnership, Dr J Wilson & Mr S Ronaldson.

**Flat Jockey:** Charlie Bennett. **Amateur Jockey:** Mr Robert Pooles.

---

### 392 | MR MOHAMED MOUBARAK, Newmarket
Postal: 3C Sunnyside, Park Lane, Newmarket, Suffolk, CB8 8AX
EMAIL Moubarak.mohammed17@gmail.com

1 CHAMPAGNE ANGEL (IRE), 4, gr f Dark Angel (IRE)—On High **Mr M. Y. Moubarak**
2 KENTUCKY HARDBOOT (IRE), 4, ch g Starspangledbanner (AUS)—Fanditha (IRE) **D. P. Fremel**
3 LICIT (IRE), 4, b f Poet's Voice—Deserted **Mr M. Y. Moubarak**
4 RED NAOMI (IRE), 4, ch f Tamayuz—Dutch Rose (IRE) **Mr M. Y. Moubarak**
5 ROYAL DYNASTY, 5, b m Charm Spirit (IRE)—Millisecond **D. P. Fremel**
6 SALAM YA FAISAL (IRE), 4, b g Dark Angel (IRE)—Age of Chivalry (IRE) **Mr M. Y. Moubarak**
7 SPARKLING DIAMOND, 4, b f Cable Bay (IRE)—Read Federica **Mr M. Y. Moubarak**
8 TEXTING, 5, b m Charm Spirit (IRE)—Dreamily (IRE) **Mr M. Y. Moubarak**
9 VANDAD (IRE), 4, b g Dandy Man (IRE)—Ruby Girl (IRE) **Mr M. G. P. Sanaei**
10 WENTWORTH AMIGO (IRE), 4, gr g Gutaifan (IRE)—Burning Dawn (USA) **Davood Vakilgilani 1**

#### THREE-YEAR-OLDS
11 BABA REZA, ch g Garswood—Friendship Is Love **Mr D. Vakilgilani**
12 B f Acclamation—Chutney (IRE) **Mr M. Y. Moubarak**
13 DONYA (IRE), b f Dawn Approach (IRE)—Ibiza Dream **Mr D. Vakilgilani**
14 MIND THAT JET (IRE), b g Kodiac—Rate **Mr D. Vakilgilani**
15 SIR TAWEEL (IRE), b g Sir Prancealot (IRE)—Qualia (IRE) **Kevin O'Donnell & David Fremel**
16 SOLID GOLD, ch c Helmet (AUS)—Self Centred **Mr D. Vakilgilani**

#### TWO-YEAR-OLDS
17 PAHLEVAN, b c 04/03 Muhaarar—Always Remembered (IRE) (Galileo (IRE)) (15000) **Mr M. Y. Moubarak**

**Other Owners:** D. P. Fremel, Mr K. O'Donnell, Mr M. G. P. Sanaei, Mr D. Vakilgilani.

---

### 393 | MR WILLIAM MUIR, Lambourn
Postal: Linkslade, Wantage Road, Lambourn, Hungerford, Berkshire, RG17 8UG
Contacts: HOME 01488 73748 PHONE 01488 73098 MOBILE 07831 457074 FAX 01488 73490
EMAIL william@williammuir.com WEBSITE www.williammuir.com

1 DATA PROTECTION, 6, b g Foxwedge (AUS)—Midnight Sky **Muir Racing Partnership - Santa Anita**
2 EPIC ENDEAVOUR (IRE), 4, b g Epaulette (AUS)—Doubt (IRE) **Clarke, Edginton, Niven**
3 FAR FROM A RUBY, 4, b f Farhh—Pretty Miss **Mr C. L. A. Edginton & Mr W. R. Muir**
4 FINAL OPTION, 4, bl f Lethal Force (IRE)—If So **Foursome Thoroughbreds**
5 GENERAL ZOFF, 6, b g Zoffany (IRE)—Aunt Julia **Purple & Lilac Racing X**
6 HAMMY END (IRE), 5, b g Mount Nelson—Northern Affair (IRE) **Mr J. M. O'Mulloy**
7 JUST HUBERT (IRE), 5, b g Dunaden (FR)—La Tulipe (FR) **Foursome Thoroughbreds**
8 NEWYORKSTATEOFMIND, 4, b g Brazen Beau (AUS)
                                    Albany Rose (IRE) **Purple & Lilac Racing-Spotted Dog P'ship**
9 PYLEDRIVER, 4, b c Harbour Watch (IRE)—La Pyle (FR) **La Pyle Partnership**
10 RETROSPECT (IRE), 4, b g Frankel—Looking Back (IRE) **Muir Racing Partnership - Saint Cloud**

## MR WILLIAM MUIR - continued

### THREE-YEAR-OLDS

**11 ANJELLA,** b f Anjaal—Lookslikeanangel  **Mr F Hope & Mr G Hope**
**12 COUNTRY PYLE,** b f New Approach (IRE)—La Pyle (FR)  **La Pyle Partnership**
**13 FAST MOON (IRE),** b g Fastnet Rock (AUS)—Mzyoon (IRE)  **Muir Racing Partnership - Saint Cloud**
**14 GOSNAY GOLD (FR),** b g Goken (FR)—Vesly (FR)  **C. L. A. Edginton**
**15** Gr f Dark Angel (IRE)—Just Devine (IRE)  **Carmel Stud**
**16 MITROSONFIRE,** gr g Lethal Force (IRE)—Blaugrana (IRE)  **Mr J. M. O'Mulloy**
**17 PERFECT MATCH (IRE),** b f Dubawi (IRE)—Purr Along  **Mr C. L. A. Edginton & Mr W. R. Muir**
**18 REINFORCER,** ch g Lethal Force (IRE)—Heavenly Dawn  **Foursome Thoroughbreds**
**19 SHUV H'PENNY KING,** b g Twilight Son—Cardrona  **Mr M. P. Graham**
**20 SUNSET MEMORY,** ch f Shamardal (USA)—Final Stage  **Foursome Thoroughbreds**

### TWO-YEAR-OLDS

**21** B c 26/04 Dark Angel (IRE)—Ballymore Celebre (IRE) (Peintre Celebre (USA))  **Carmel Stud**
**22** B br c 05/03 Dabirsim (FR)—
                    Faustinatheyounger (IRE) (Antonius Pius (USA)) (11000)  **Muir Racing Partnership - Leicester**
**23 GALIAC,** b c 17/04 Kodiac—Gallipot (Galileo (IRE)) (30000)  **Perspicacious Punters Racing Club**
**24 KING'S COURSE (IRE),** b br c 09/02 Gleneagles (IRE)—
                    Desert Run (IRE) (Desert Prince (IRE)) (50000)  **C. L. A. Edginton**
**25** B c 18/03 Mehmas (IRE)—Loveisreckless (IRE) (Mount Nelson)  **Mr J. M. O'Mulloy**
**26 MAKING MUSIC (IRE),** b f 26/04 Mastercraftsman (IRE)—Rapacity Alexander (IRE) (Dandy Man (IRE)) (75000)
                    **Foursome Thoroughbreds**
**27 MIMI'S ODYSSEY,** ch f 12/04 Ulysses—Sara Lucille (Dansili) (30000)  **Foursome Thoroughbreds**
**28** B br g 04/04 Lawman (FR)—Moonlight Silver (Makfi)  **Foursome Thoroughbreds**
**29 RED VINEYARD (IRE),** ch c 21/03 Slade Power (IRE)—
                    Artisia (IRE) (Peintre Celebre (USA))  **Foursome Thoroughbreds**
**30** Ch c 22/03 National Defense—Salty Sugar (Oasis Dream) (22000)  **Muir Racing Partnership - Flemington**
**31 STOCKPYLE,** b c 16/04 Oasis Dream—La Pyle (FR) (Le Havre (IRE)) (120000)  **La Pyle Partnership**
**32** B f 30/03 Zoffany (IRE)—Sweet Coconut (Bahamian Bounty) (34000)  **K. A. Dasmal**
**33** B c 23/02 Acclamation—Sweet Secret (Singspiel (IRE))  **Carmel Stud**
**34** B c 10/02 Kodiac—Termagant (IRE) (Powerscourt)  **Carmel Stud**
**35** B f 05/02 Slade Power (IRE)—Three D Alexander (IRE) (Aqlaam) (10000)  **Purple & Lilac Racing**
**36** Ch c 21/03 Havana Gold (IRE)—Varnish (Choisir (AUS))  **Carmel Stud**

**Other Owners:** Mr N. Clark, Mr D. G. Clarke, C. L. A. Edginton, Mr M. P. Graham, Mr R. Haim, F. P. Hope, Mr Gary Hope, Mr K. Jeffery, Mr C. Moore, W. R. Muir, Mr A. J. Niven, Mr J. M. O'Mulloy, Mr D. L. Quaintance, Mr P. D. Quaintance.

**Flat Jockey:** Martin Dwyer.

---

**394**  **MR CLIVE MULHALL, Scarcroft**
Postal: **Scarcroft Hall Farm, Thorner Lane, Scarcroft, Leeds, Yorkshire, LS14 3AQ**
Contacts: **HOME** 0113 289 3095 **MOBILE** 07979 527675
**EMAIL** clive@scarcrofthallracing.co.uk **WEBSITE** www.clivemulhallracing.co.uk

**1 ANEEDH,** 11, b g Lucky Story (USA)—Seed Al Maha (USA)  **Mrs C. M. Mulhall**
**2 BIGBADBOY (IRE),** 8, b g Big Bad Bob (IRE)—Elegantly (IRE)  **Ms Y Featherstone & Mrs M Mulhall**
**3 LORD SERENDIPITY (IRE),** 9, gr g Lord Shanakill (USA)—Elitista (FR)
**4 SHE IS WHAT SHE IS,** 6, b m Desideratum—Alimure

**Other Owners:** Ms Y. P. Featherstone, Mrs C. M. Mulhall.

**Assistant Trainer:** Mrs Martina Mulhall.

**Apprentice Jockey:** Sean Kirrane. **Amateur Jockey:** Miss Charlotte Mulhall.

**395** **MR NEIL MULHOLLAND, Limpley Stoke**
Postal: **Conkwell Grange Stables, Conkwell, Limpley Stoke, Bath, Avon, BA2 7FD**
Contacts: **MOBILE 07739 258607**
EMAIL neil@neilmulhollandracing.com WEBSITE www.neilmulhollandracing.com

1 **AGENT SAONOIS (FR)**, 5, gr g Saonois (FR)—Agosta (FR) **Walters Plant Hire Ltd**
2 **ANGELA'S HOPE**, 6, b m Kayf Tara—Follow My Leader (IRE) **The Affordable Partnership**
3 **ANN'S EMERALD REEL (FR)**, 5, ch m Sholokhov (IRE)—Ruby Reel (IRE) **The Affordable Partnership**
4 **ANY NEWS (IRE)**, 6, ch g Stowaway—Kisskiss Bang Bang (IRE) **Mrs J. N. Cartwright**
5 **ASHLEY HOLLOW**, 7, b m Beat Hollow—Hazel Bank Lass (IRE) **Mrs A. C. Crofts**
6 **BALLYMILAN**, 6, b m Milan—Ballyhoo (IRE) **Heart Racing HR2**
7 **BLUMEN GLORY (IRE)**, 5, b g Fame And Glory—Blume (IRE) **Colony Stable Llc**
8 4, B f Recharge (IRE)—Bonne Anniversaire **Neil Mulholland Racing Ltd**
9 **CANADA KID**, 9, ch g Apple Tree (FR)—Island of Memories (IRE) **P. C. Tory**
10 **CAROLINES CHARM (IRE)**, 7, b g Masterofthehorse (IRE)—Truckers Princess (IRE) **The Affordable Partnership**
11 **CESAR ET ROSALIE (FR)**, 9, ch g Network (GER)—Regle de L'Art (FR) **Mrs J. M. Abbott**
12 **CHINWAG**, 6, b g Trans Island—Clohamon Gossip (IRE) **The Boot Inn Partnership**
13 **CHIRICO VALLIS (FR)**, 9, b g Poliglote—Quora Vallis (FR) **Mr J. P. McManus**
14 4, B f Walk In The Park (IRE)—Clear Riposte (IRE) **Mrs P. L. Bridel**
15 **CONKWELL LEGEND**, 7, b g Midnight Legend—Gallimaufry **Mrs H. R. Cross & Mrs S. A. Keys**
16 **CONKWELL ROSIE**, 5, b m Sulamani (IRE)—Maori Legend **Mrs H. R. Cross**
17 **CREMANT (IRE)**, 7, b g Getaway (GER)—Opera Season (IRE) **Mr P. M. Simmonds**
18 **DANDOLO DU GITE (FR)**, 8, b g Khalkevi (IRE)—Lavande d'Eproniere (FR) **Equi ex Incertis Partners**
19 **DARKSIDEOFTARNSIDE (IRE)**, 7, b g Intense Focus (USA)—Beautiful Dancer (IRE) **D. R. Fear**
20 **DEAD RIGHT**, 9, b g Altfora (IRE)—April Queen **Mr J. P. McManus**
21 **DEPUTY JONES (IRE)**, 8, b m Milan—Hudson Hope (IRE) **Drayton Park Racing**
22 **DOING FINE (IRE)**, 13, b g Presenting—Howaya Pet (IRE) **Neil Mulholland Racing Club**
23 **DREAM MACHINE (IRE)**, 7, ch g Dream Ahead (USA)—Last Cry (FR) **D. M. Bell**
24 **DYNAMIC KATE (IRE)**, 5, b m Yeats (IRE)—Alverstone **BG Racing Partnership**
25 **EAGLE'S FIRST**, 4, b f Free Eagle (IRE)—Al Kahina **Stephen & Gloria Seymour**
26 **ENDLESS PROMISE (IRE)**, 5, b m Leading Light (IRE)—Eternal Promise **The Affordable Partnership**
27 **EXELERATOR EXPRESS (FR)**, 7, b g Poliglote—Reine de Lestrade (FR) **Walters Plant Hire & Potter Group**
28 4, B br f Sir Percy—Fairy Slipper **Dajam Ltd**
29 **FERN OWL**, 6, ch g Nayef (USA)—Snow Goose **Mr J. Hobbs**
30 **FINGERONTHESWITCH (IRE)**, 11, b g Beneficial—Houseoftherisinsun (IRE) **Cahill, Atwell & Crofts**
31 **FIRST QUEST (USA)**, 7, b g First Defence (USA)—Dixie Quest (USA) **The Affordable (2) Partnership**
32 **FRAU GEORGIA (IRE)**, 7, b m Germany (USA)—Sumability (IRE) **Mr J. Henderson**
33 **FULL OF SURPRISES (FR)**, 6, b m No Risk At All (FR)—Fontaine Riant (FR) **Mr J. P. McManus**
34 **GOLDEN EMBLEM (IRE)**, 7, ch m Presenting—Merry Excuse (IRE) **Diamond Racing Ltd**
35 **GOLDENEYE VEE**, 6, b m Bollin Eric—Hazel Bank Lass (IRE) **Mrs A. C. Crofts**
36 **GREEN OR BLACK (IRE)**, 9, gr m Zebedee—Boucheron **The Chosen Few**
37 **HARBOUR FORCE (FR)**, 7, b g Harbour Watch (IRE)—Dam Beautiful **Mr D. B. Harris**
38 **HEAVEY**, 7, b g Trans Island—Clohamon Gossip (IRE) **Qdos Racing**
39 **HEREIA (IRE)**, 5, b g Olympic Glory (IRE)—Rolled Gold (USA) **Mr O. S. Harris**
40 **HIDDEN DEPTHS (IRE)**, 9, b g Dark Angel (IRE)—Liber Nauticus (IRE) **Mr A. J. Russell**
41 **HOBB'S DELIGHT**, 5, b g Milan—Hobb's Dream (IRE) **Mr J. Hobbs**
42 **HYGROVE PERCY**, 8, ch g Sir Percy—Hygrove Welshlady (IRE) **G. P. and Miss S. J. Hayes**
43 **INDIAN BRAVE (IRE)**, 10, b g Definite Article—Fridays Folly (IRE) **J. J. Maguire**
44 **IRISH ODYSSEY (IRE)**, 8, gr g Yeats (IRE)—Ma Furie (FR) **Mr A. G. Bloom**
45 **JAUNTY SORIA**, 8, ch m Malinas (GER)—Jaunty Spirit **Miss J. A. Goddard**
46 **JEWELINTHENAME (IRE)**, 6, b g Califet (FR)—Essaoira Jewel (IRE) **Mr T. J. Abbott**
47 **JOE WARBRICK**, 6, b g Universal (IRE)—Maori Legend **Mrs H. R. Cross**
48 **JUST HENNY**, 7, b m Midnight Legend—Exchanging Glances **Abbott & Bunch**
49 **KAHINA RULES**, 6, b m Aussie Rules (USA)—Al Kahina **Stephen & Gloria Seymour**
50 **KALONDRA (IRE)**, 10, b g Spadoun (FR)—Mystic Vic (IRE) **Mr J. Henderson**
51 **KANSAS CITY CHIEF (IRE)**, 12, b g Westerner—Badawi Street **Jersey Racing Friends**
52 **LA CAVSA NOSTRA (IRE)**, 9, b g Flemensfirth (USA)—Pharenna (IRE) **Neil Mulholland Racing Ltd**
53 5, B g Trans Island—La Vie Est Belle **Mr N. P. Mulholland**
54 **LIBBDAN (IRE)**, 7, b m Oscar (IRE)—Benefique (IRE) **Mr Peter Gray & Jackie Abbott**
55 **LORD ACCORD (IRE)**, 6, b g Yeats (IRE)—Cush Jewel (IRE) **Lynne & Angus Maclennan**

## MR NEIL MULHOLLAND - continued

56 **LOUGH RYN (IRE)**, 9, br g Court Cave (IRE)—Media View (IRE) **Level Par Racing**
57 **LYRICAL BALLAD (IRE)**, 5, gr m Dark Angel (IRE)—Iffraaj Pink (IRE) **Dajam Ltd**
58 **MAGICAL THOMAS**, 9, ch g Dylan Thomas (IRE)—Magical Cliche (USA) **G. P. and Miss S. J. Hayes**
59 **MALIBOO (IRE)**, 8, b m Mahler—Aboo Lala (IRE) **Premier Care Management**
60 **MALINAS ISLAND**, 6, ch g Malinas (GER)—Island of Memories (IRE) **P. C. Tory**
61 **MAN OF THE SEA (IRE)**, 5, ch g Born To Sea (IRE)—Hurricane Lily (IRE) **Dajam Ltd**
62 **MASQUERADE BLING (IRE)**, 7, b m Approve (IRE)—Mataji (IRE) **Neil Mulholland Racing Ltd**
63 **MASTER BURBIDGE**, 10, b g Pasternak—Silver Sequel **Dajam Ltd**
64 **MILKWOOD (IRE)**, 7, b g Dylan Thomas (IRE)—Tropical Lake (IRE) **Ms J. Bridel**
65 **MILREU HAS (FR)**, 6, b g Kapgarde (FR)—Miss Benedicte (FR) **Mr J. P. McManus**
66 **MIND YOUR BACK (IRE)**, 8, b g Getaway (GER)—Local Hall (IRE)
67 **MISS JEANNE MOON (IRE)**, 7, b m Getaway (GER)—Moon Approach (IRE) **Mrs H. R. Cross & Mrs S. A. Keys**
68 **MISS MOLLY MAE (IRE)**, 9, b m Getaway (GER)—Miss Mary Mac (IRE) **H A Marks Ltd**
69 **MISTER SWEETS (IRE)**, 6, b g Scorpion (IRE)—Fast Finisher (IRE) **Neil Mulholland Racing Ltd**
70 **MOLLIANA**, 6, b m Olden Times—The Screamer (IRE) **Dajam Ltd**
71 **MOLLY CAREW**, 9, b m Midnight Legend—Moyliscar **Mrs S. A. Keys**
72 **MONGOL EMPEROR (IRE)**, 6, b g Imperial Monarch (IRE)—Hurricane Bella (IRE) **Equi ex Incertis Partners**
73 **MONT SAINT VINCENT (IRE)**, 5, gr g Montmartre (FR)—Chamanka (FR) **Walters Plant Hire Ltd**
74 **NEACHELLS BRIDGE (IRE)**, 9, ch g Getaway (GER)—Strawberry Lane (IRE) **Mr M. C. Creed**
75 **NO HIDDEN CHARGES (IRE)**, 8, b g Scorpion (IRE)—Soniadoir (IRE) **Stephen & Gloria Seymour**
76 **NO WORRIES**, 7, b g Passing Glance—Silver Sequel **Dajam Ltd**
77 **NOVIS ADVENTUS (IRE)**, 9, b g New Approach (IRE)—Tiffed (USA) **The General Asphalte Company Ltd**
78 **NUM NUM**, 4, b f Finjaan—Valjarv (IRE) **Dajam Ltd**
79 **PELTWELL (IRE)**, 8, b m Milan—Fast Finisher (IRE) **Mrs P. L. Bridel**
80 **PENNY POET (IRE)**, 8, b m Intikhab (USA)—Mneme (FR) **The Boot Inn Partnership**
81 **PERCY POPS**, 7, ch g Getaway (GER)—Popsie Hall **Birchenhough, Dewilde, Dod**
82 **PRETTYLITTLETHING (IRE)**, 11, b m Tajraasi (USA)—Cloncunny Girl (IRE) **Neil Mulholland Racing Ltd**
83 **PRINCESS T**, 6, gr m Aussie Rules (USA)—Fairy Slipper **Harte Investments Ltd & Dajam Ltd**
84 **PUTTING GREEN**, 9, ch g Selkirk (USA)—Ryella (USA) **Neil Mulholland Racing Ltd**
85 **RAGAMUFFIN (IRE)**, 6, b g Arcadio (GER)—Mill Race Annie (IRE) **Mrs J. N. Cartwright**
86 **RENEGADE ARROW (FR)**, 5, ch g Motivator—Cinders' Prize **The General Asphalte Company Ltd**
87 **ROCK ON RITA (IRE)**, 5, b m Shirocco (GER)—Gilt Free (IRE) **Mr J. P. McManus**
88 **ROOKIE TRAINER (IRE)**, 7, b g Gold Well—Crazy Falcon (IRE) **Noel Fehily Racing Syndicates-Rookie Tra**
89 **RUNASIMI RIVER**, 8, ch m Generous (IRE)—Zaffaranni (IRE) **Mrs G. A. Davies**
90 **SAINTE DOCTOR (FR)**, 5, gr m Doctor Dino (FR)—Pakoonah **Mr J. P. McManus**
91 **SAMBELLA**, 6, ch m Black Sam Bellamy (IRE)—Chant de L'Aube (IRE) **Mr I. P. Dale-Staples**
92 **SANDYMOUNT ROSE (IRE)**, 7, b m Yeats (IRE)—Ma Furie (FR) **Proudley & Whymark Partnership**
93 **SCARDURA (IRE)**, 7, b g Stowaway—Sosua (IRE) **Mrs J. N. Cartwright**
94 **SEA EWE**, 4, b f Proclamation (IRE)—Dispol Katie **J. J. Maguire**
95 **SHANTOU VILLAGE (IRE)**, 11, b g Shantou (USA)—Village Queen (IRE) **Mrs J. Gerard-Pearse**
96 **SIMPLY SIN (IRE)**, 6, b g Footstepsinthesand—Miss Sally (IRE) **Neil Mulholland Racing Ltd**
97 **SKY CENTRAL**, 5, ch g Sun Central (IRE)—Top Level (IRE)
98 **SOLWARA ONE (IRE)**, 7, b g Gold Well—Turquoise Green (IRE) **Mrs J. Gerard-Pearse**
99 **SOME MIGHT SAY (IRE)**, 6, b m Dylan Thomas (IRE)—Hidden Ability (IRE) **Mr P. W. Scott**
100 **SOUPY SOUPS (IRE)**, 10, ch g Stowaway—Near Dunleer (IRE) **Equi ex Incertis Partners**
101 **SPIDER'S BITE (IRE)**, 9, b g Scorpion (IRE)—Model Girl **The Risk Takers Partnership**
102 **SUPER DUPER SAM**, 5, ch g Black Sam Bellamy (IRE)—With Grace **D. V. Stevens**
103 **TANGO BOY (IRE)**, 8, ch g Flemensfirth (USA)—Hello Kitty (IRE) **Mr A. G. Bloom**
104 **TEST RIDE (IRE)**, 7, b g Rip Van Winkle (IRE)—Easter Fairy (USA) **The Affordable (3) Partnership**
105 **THE TWISLER**, 9, b g Motivator—Panna **Mrs V. J. Hodsoll**
106 **THE WEASEL (IRE)**, 7, ch g Vinnie Roe (IRE)—Countess of Milan (IRE) **Neil Mulholland Racing Club**
107 **THE WICKET CHICKEN (IRE)**, 9, b m Milan—Soniadoir (IRE)
108 **THE YOUNG MASTER**, 12, b g Echo of Light—Fine Frenzy (IRE) **Mike Burbidge & The Old Masters**
109 **TRANSLINK**, 6, b g Rail Link—Ocean Transit (IRE) **Mr B. F. Mulholland**
110 **VANCOUVER**, 9, ch g Generous (IRE)—All Told (IRE) **J. J. Maguire**
111 **VIKING RUBY**, 8, ch m Sulamani (IRE)—Viking Torch **Ms S. M. Exell**
112 **VIS A VIS**, 7, b g Dansili—Pretty Face **Ashley Carr, Eismark & Packham**

## MR NEIL MULHOLLAND - continued

### THREE-YEAR-OLDS

113 B f Hot Streak (IRE)—Belle Dormant (IRE)  **Neil Mulholland Racing Ltd**
114 **EMANATE,** b g Coach House (IRE)—Emerald Girl (IRE)  **Mr J. Heaney**
115 **NINA'S FIELD,** ch f Cannock Chase (USA)—Art Critic (USA)  **Dajam Ltd**
116 B f Equiano (FR)—Royal Obsession (IRE)  **Neil Mulholland Racing Ltd**

**Other Owners:** Mrs J. M. Abbott, Mr T. J. Abbott, Mrs L. Atwell, Mrs K. Birchenhough, Sir M. F. Broughton, Mr S. W. Broughton, Mrs P. M. Bunch, Mr M. S. Burbidge, Mr P. A. Cafferty, Mr M. G. Cahill, A. Carr, Mrs A. C. Crofts, Mrs H. R. Cross, Dajam Ltd, Mrs S. De Wilde, Mrs P. I. Dod, Mr E. Eismark, Mr P. Gray, Mr S. Harbour, Harte Investments Limited, Mr G. P. Hayes, Miss S. J. Hayes, Mrs S. A. Keys, Mr A. Maclennan, Mrs L. Maclennan, Mr S. Packham, Mr P. J. Proudley, Mrs G. P. Seymour, Mr S. G. Seymour, Sundorne Products (Llanidloes) Ltd, Mr D. Tiernan, Mr J. N. Trueman, Mrs R. A. Turner, Mr R. F. Turner, Mr R. B. Waley-Cohen, Walters Plant Hire Ltd, Mr J. K. Whymark.

**Assistant Trainer:** Andrew Doyle.

**NH Jockey:** James Best, Robbie Dunne, Tom Scudamore, Sam Twiston-Davies. **Conditional Jockey:** Philip Donovan, Harry Reed. **Amateur Jockey:** Millie Wonnacott.

---

## 396   MR LAWRENCE MULLANEY, Malton
Postal: Raikes Farm, Great Habton, Malton, North Yorkshire, YO17 6RX
Contacts: **PHONE** 01653 668595 **MOBILE** 07899 902565
**EMAIL** nicolamullaney@yahoo.co.uk

1 **BOBBA TEE,** 9, b g Rail Link—Trompette (USA)  **David Furman & John Sugarman**
2 **GORGEOUS GENERAL,** 6, ch g Captain Gerrard (IRE)—Gorgeous Goblin (IRE)  **& Humphries**
3 **JACK IS BACK,** 4, b g Due Diligence (USA)—Rosa Luxemburg  **L. A. Mullaney**
4 **KYLLACHY WARRIOR (IRE),** 5, gr g Kyllachy—Silver Act (IRE)  **L. A. Mullaney**
5 **SNAZZY JAZZY (IRE),** 6, b h Red Jazz (USA)—Bulrushes  **Ian Buckley**

### THREE-YEAR-OLDS

6 **DUSK ART,** b g Twilight Son—Renaissant  **Ian Buckley James Lomas**
7 **MARVE,** ch g Twilight Son—Miss Marvellous (USA)  **The Usual Suspects**
8 B g Swiss Spirit—Silver Act (IRE)  **Exors of the Late Mr G. Turnbull**

### TWO-YEAR-OLDS

9 **CAPTAINHUGHJAMPTON,** ch c 01/04 Mondialiste (IRE)—Sibaya (Exceed And Excel (AUS))  **Ian Buckley**
10 B c 20/04 Heeraat (IRE)—Evocative (Dalakhani (IRE)) (1905)
11 B c 14/04 Mondialiste (IRE)—File And Paint (IRE) (Chevalier (IRE))
12 B c 24/02 Mondialiste (IRE)—Shuttlecock (Dubawi (IRE)) (18000)  **Ian Buckley**

**Other Owners:** Ian Buckley, M. J. Dyas, Mr D. E. Furman, Mrs L. Humphries, Mr S. Humphries, Mr J. Lomas, L. A. Mullaney, Mr J. B. Sugarman.

## 397 MR MICHAEL MULLINEAUX, Tarporley
Postal: **Southley Farm, Alpraham, Tarporley, Cheshire, CW6 9JD**
Contacts: **PHONE 01829 261440 MOBILE 07753 650263 FAX 01829 261440**
EMAIL southlearacing@btinternet.com WEBSITE www.southleyfarm.co.uk

1 **ANTON DOLIN (IRE),** 13, ch g Danehill Dancer (IRE)—Ski For Gold **S. A. Pritchard**
2 **BAHUTA ACHA,** 6, b g Captain Gerrard (IRE)—Rosein **M. Mullineaux**
3 **BOB'S GIRL,** 6, b m Big Bad Bob (IRE)—Linda (FR) **S. A. Pritchard**
4 **DAVID'S BEAUTY (IRE),** 8, b m Kodiac—Thaisy (USA) **Mr G. B. Hignett**
5 **DODGY BOB,** 8, b g Royal Applause—Rustam **M. Mullineaux**
6 **GEORGE EDWARD (IRE),** 7, b g Jeremy (USA)—Ancone (FR) **Mrs A. J. Swadling**
7 **INMEMORYOFMILLY (IRE),** 4, b f Fruits of Love (USA)—Lake Wakatipu **P. Clacher**
8 **JEANE DE BELLVILLE,** 5, ch m Black Sam Bellamy (IRE)—Majeeda (IRE) **Mr K. Jones**
9 **LUCKYANGEL,** 4, gr f Yorgunnabelucky (USA)—Ya Halla (IRE) **Mrs A. Turner**
10 **NO FRONTIER (IRE),** 7, ch m Sans Frontieres (IRE)—County Gate (IRE) **Mr L. Tomlinson**
11 **OVERCHURCH,** 10, b m Overbury (IRE)—Namoi **Mr R. A. Royle**
12 **PEACHEY CARNEHAN,** 7, ch g Foxwedge (AUS)—Zubova **Mr K. Jones**
13 **POOR DUKE (IRE),** 11, b g Bachelor Duke (USA)—Graze On Too (IRE) **M. Mullineaux**
14 **PRINCE OF ROME (IRE),** 5, gr g Lethal Force (IRE)—Garraun (IRE) **Mrs A. Turner**
15 **RED ALLURE,** 6, ch m Mayson—Lark In The Park (IRE) **Mia Racing**
16 **RED BRAE RAINY MAY,** 5, b g Lucarno (USA)—Breezy B's **Mrs C. S. Wilson**
17 **ROCK WARBLER (IRE),** 8, ch g Raven's Pass (USA)—Rare Tern (IRE) **Mr R. A. Royle**
18 **SCREECHING DRAGON (IRE),** 4, b g Tagula (IRE)—
Array of Stars (IRE) **County Charm Windows & Conservatories**
19 **SECRET IDENTITY,** 4, b f Equiano (FR)—Onlyyouknowme (USA) **S. A. Pritchard**
20 **SECRETINTHEPARK,** 11, ch g Sakhee's Secret—Lark In The Park (IRE) **Mia Racing**
21 **SHESADABBER,** 5, b m Heeraat (IRE)—Saorocain (IRE) **Mrs A. Turner**
22 **SOMEWHERE SECRET,** 7, ch g Sakhee's Secret—Lark In The Park (IRE) **Mia Racing**
23 9, Ch m Sulamani—Sunny Parkes **M. Mullineaux**
24 **TSARMINA (IRE),** 5, b m Ruler of The World (IRE)—Caelis **Miss B. Rose**
25 **WE'VE GOT THE LOVE (IRE),** 5, b m Charm Spirit—Olympic Medal **Mr K. Jones**

### THREE-YEAR-OLDS

26 **GIZZA JOB,** b f Equiano (FR)—Masque Rose **Mr P. Gregory**
27 **PACOPASH,** b f Paco Boy (IRE)—Passionada **Mia Racing**
28 **SWISS SANCERRE,** b f Swiss Spirit—Adele Blanc Sec (FR) **Mr G. B. Hignett**

**Other Owners:** A. Tickle, Mrs I. M. Tickle, M. A. Tickle.

**Assistant Trainer:** Susan Mullineaux, Stuart Ross.

**Amateur Jockey:** Miss M. J. L. Mullineaux.

## 398 MR SEAMUS MULLINS, Amesbury
Postal: **Wilsford Stables, Wilsford-Cum-Lake, Amesbury, Salisbury, Wiltshire, SP4 7BL**
Contacts: **PHONE 01980 626344 MOBILE 07702 559634**
EMAIL info@jwmullins.co.uk WEBSITE www.seamusmullins.co.uk

1 5, B g Shirocco (GER)—Agoura (IRE) **High Oaks Racing**
2 **ARDBRUCE (IRE),** 8, b g Scorpion (IRE)—An Bothar Ard (IRE) **Mr Clive Dunning, Mr F G Matthews & S Pitt**
3 **BARROWMOUNT (IRE),** 5, b g Mountain High (IRE)—Nans Mare (IRE) **J. W. Mullins**
4 **EN COEUR (FR),** 7, b g Kap Rock (FR)—Fairyleap (FR) **Woodford Valley Racing**
5 **FERNY KNAP,** 6, b m Arcadio (GER)—Heather Glen (IRE) **J. H. Young**
6 **GRANITIC (IRE),** 8, b g Court Cave (IRE)—Like A Miller (IRE) **J. W. Mullins**
7 **HEWN FROM GRANITE,** 6, b g Yeats (IRE)—Luccombe Chine **The Hopeful Partnership**

## MR SEAMUS MULLINS - continued

8 **I SEE YOU WELL (FR)**, 8, b g Air Chief Marshal (IRE)—
Bonne Mere (FR) **Philippa Downing, Clive Dunning & S Pitt**
9 **INSPIREUS (IRE)**, 8, b g Scorpion (IRE)—Miniconjou (IRE) **Geoff Barnett & Brian Edgeley**
10 **JARLATH**, 10, b g Norse Dancer (IRE)—Blue Lullaby (IRE) **Mr D D Sutherland & Mr Charles Wilson**
11 **JULLY LES BUXY**, 11, b m Black Sam Bellamy (IRE)—Jadidh **Mr M. S. Rose**
12 **KENTFORD DRAKE**, 5, b g Norse Dancer (IRE)—Kentford Dabchick **D. I. Bare**
13 **KENTFORD HEIRESS**, 11, b m Midnight Legend—Kentford Duchess **D. I. Bare**
14 **KENTFORD MALLARD**, 8, b m Sulamani (IRE)—Kentford Grebe **D. I. Bare**
15 **LAKESIDE LAD**, 8, b g Alkaased (USA)—Kimmeridge Bay **Simon & Christine Prout**
16 **MAHLER'S PROMISE (IRE)**, 6, b g Mahler—Loadsapromise (IRE) **The One More Sleep Racing Syndicate**
17 **5**, B g Dylan Thomas (IRE)—Miss Platinum (IRE) **Andrew Cocks & Tara Johnson**
18 **MOGESTIC (IRE)**, 12, gr g Morozov (USA)—Crosschild (IRE) **Mrs J. C. Scorgie**
19 **MORFEE (IRE)**, 5, b g Dylan Thomas (IRE)—Ma Baker (IRE) **Mrs A. Leftley**
20 **MORODER (IRE)**, 7, b g Morozov (USA)—Another Tonto (IRE) **Mrs A. Leftley**
21 **MRS BAILEY (IRE)**, 6, b m Westerner—Put On Hold (IRE) **S Mullins Racing Club**
22 **4**, Gr f Kingston Hill—Music On D Waters (IRE) **J. H. Young**
23 **NELSON'S TOUCH**, 8, gr g Mount Nelson—Lady Friend **Mrs P. de W. Johnson**
24 **PLANTAGENET**, 9, b g Midnight Legend—Marsh Court **Mrs P. de W. Johnson**
25 **PLAYA BLANCA (IRE)**, 6, b g Zoffany (IRE)—Aiming Upwards **The Rumble Racing Club**
26 **POSTMAN (FR)**, 8, ch g American Post—Pepperjuice (GER) **Dr & Mrs John Millar**
27 **ROKO GEORGE (IRE)**, 5, b g Shirocco (GER)—Needed The Run (IRE) **The St Georges Hill Racing Syndicate**
28 **ROMANOR**, 7, b g Holy Roman Emperor (IRE)—Salinia (IRE) **Mrs R. A. Jowett**
29 **SAKHEE'S CONQUEST**, 6, br g Sakhee's Secret—Another Conquest **Mr F G Matthews & Mr S Mullins**
30 **SHELDON (IRE)**, 5, ch g Shantou (USA)—Feabhra (IRE) **Andrew Cocks & Tara Johnson**
31 **SILVER NICKEL**, 7, gr g Gold Well—Cooper's Rose (IRE) **Mrs D. H. Potter**
32 **SUMTIME**, 6, b m Doyen (IRE)—Seemarye **J. W. Mullins**
33 **THE PINK'N**, 5, gr g Dunaden (FR)—Lady Friend **Mrs P. de W. Johnson**
34 **THE RAVEN'S RETURN**, 8, b g Scorpion (IRE)—Mimis Bonnet (FR) **The Rumble Racing Club**
35 **THINK FOR A MINIT**, 5, b g Sixties Icon—Time To Think **Mrs V. F. Hewett**
36 **TOMMIE BEAU (IRE)**, 6, b g Brian Boru—Bajan Girl (FR) **Simon & Christine Prout**
37 **WILDERNESS**, 6, b m Cityscape—Moonlight Applause **Mrs R Jowett, C R Dunning & Up the Glens**

### THREE-YEAR-OLDS

38 Br g Mount Nelson—Lady Friend **J. W. Mullins**
39 **MONTJUIC FORCE (IRE)**, b c La Force (IRE)—Busy Bimbo (IRE) **J. W. Mullins**
40 **THISTLETON (IRE),** b g Battle of Marengo (IRE)—Nebraska Lady (IRE) **J. W. Mullins**

**Other Owners:** Mr G. Barnett, Miss P. M. Downing, Mr C. R. Dunning, B. R. Edgeley, Mr D. J. Erwin, Miss S. Gorman, Mrs R. A. Jowett, F. G. Matthews, Mrs J. D. Millar, Dr J. W. Millar, J. W. Mullins, C. I. C. Munro, Ms S. Pitt, Mrs C. A. Prout, Mr S. P. Prout, Mr A. Randle, D. Sutherland, The Up The Glens Partnership, Miss R. Toppin, Mr C. Wilson.

**Assistant Trainer:** Paul Attwater.

**NH Jockey:** Kevin Jones, Jeremiah McGrath, Daniel Sansom.

**399** **MR WILLIAM P. MULLINS, Carlow**
Postal: Closutton, Bagenalstown, Co. Carlow, Ireland
Contacts: PHONE +353 59 972 1786 MOBILE +353 87 256 4940 FAX +353 59 972 2709
EMAIL wpmullins@eircom.net WEBSITE www.wpmullins.com

1 **ACAPELLA BOURGEOIS (FR)**, 11, ch g Network (GER)—Jasmine (FR) **Slaneyville Syndicate**
2 **AIONE (FR)**, 8, b g Coastal Path—La Horquela (IRE) **Mrs S Ricci**
3 **AL BOUM PHOTO (FR)**, 9, b g Buck's Boum (FR)—Al Gane (FR) **Mrs J Donnelly**
4 **ALLAHO (FR)**, 7, b g No Risk At All (FR)—Idaho Falls (FR) **Cheveley Park Stud**
5 **ANDALUSA (FR)**, 6, gr m Martaline—Cadix (FR) **Lansdowne Partnership**
6 **ANNAMIX (FR)**, 8, gr g Martaline—Tashtiyana (IRE) **Mrs S Ricci**

## MR WILLIAM P. MULLINS - continued

 7 **ANTEY (GER)**, 8, b g Lord of England (GER)—Achinora  **Mrs S. Ricci**
 8 **APPRECIATE IT (IRE)**, 7, b g Jeremy (USA)—Sainte Baronne (FR)  **Miss M A Masterson**
 9 **ARAMON (GER)**, 8, b g Monsun (GER)—Aramina (GER)  **Aramon Syndicate**
10 **ARCTIC WARRIOR (GER)**, 5, b g Pastorius (GER)—Adelma (GER)  **J. P. McManus**
11 **ASLUKWOODHAVIT**, 5, b g Yorgunnabelucky (USA)—She's The Lady  **Roger Brookhouse**
12 **ASTERION FORLONGE (FR)**, 7, gr g Coastal Path—Belle du Brizais (FR)  **Mrs J Donnelly**
13 **AUTHORIZED ART (FR)**, 6, b g Authorized (IRE)—Rock Art (IRE)  **Nicholas Peacock**
14 **BACARDYS (FR)**, 10, b br g Coastal Path—Oasice (FR)  **Shanakiel Racing Syndicate**
15 **BACHASSON (FR)**, 10, gr g Voix du Nord (FR)—Belledonne (FR)  **Edward O'Connell**
16 **BAPAUME (FR)**, 8, b g Turtle Bowl (IRE)—Brouhaha (FR)  **Mrs S. Ricci**
17 **BELLE METAL (IRE)**, 4, b f Soldier of Fortune (IRE)—Elphis Supreme (IRE)  **Leinster Partnership**
18 **BELLOW MOME (FR)**, 10, b g Honolulu (IRE)—Oll Mighty Fellow (IRE)  **Mrs Audrey Turley**
19 **BENIE DES DIEUX (FR)**, 10, b m Great Pretender (IRE)—Cana (FR)  **Mrs S. Ricci**
20 **BERET ROUGE (IRE)**, 6, b m Big Bad Bob (IRE)—Pink Hat (IRE)  **Mrs J M Mullins**
21 **BERKSHIRE ROYAL**, 6, b g Sir Percy—Forest Express (AUS)  **Mrs J M Mullins**
22 **BILLAWAY (IRE)**, 9, b g Well Chosen—Taipans Girl (IRE)  **J Turner**
23 **BLACKBOW (IRE)**, 8, b g Stowaway—Rinnce Moll (IRE)  **Roaringwater Syndicate**
24 **BLAZER (FR)**, 10, ch g Network (GER)—Juppelongue (FR)  **J. P. McManus**
25 **BLEU BERRY (IRE)**, 10, b g Special Kaldoun (IRE)—Somosierra (FR)  **Luke McMahon**
26 **BLUE LORD (FR)**, 6, b g Blue Bresil (FR)—Lorette (FR)  **Simon Munir & Isaac Souede**
27 **BLUE SARI (FR)**, 6, b g Saddex—Blue Aster (FR)  **John P. McManus**
28 **BOHEMIAN BIRCH (IRE)**, 6, b m Mahler—Over It  **N G King**
29 **BON RETOUR (IRE)**, 6, b m Fame And Glory—Rosy de Cyborg (FR)  **Jim Ennis**
30 **BRAHMA BULL (IRE)**, 10, ch g Presenting—Oligarch Society (IRE)  **Mrs S. Ricci**
31 **BRANDY LOVE (IRE)**, 5, b m Jet Away—Bambootcha (IRE)  **C M Grech**
32 **BREAKEN (FR)**, 7, b g Sunday Break (JPN)—Kendoretta (FR)  **Mrs J. Donnelly**
33 **BRONAGH'S BELLE (IRE)**, 6, b m High Chaparral (IRE)—South Atlantic (USA)  **Sean Sweeney**
34 **BROOKLYNN GLORY (IRE)**, 6, b m Fame And Glory—Clamit Brook (IRE)  **Swords Bloodstock**
35 **BUCK'S BILLIONAIRE (FR)**, 8, ch g Kapgarde (FR)—Buck's (FR)  **Mrs J M Mullins**
36 **BUILDMEUPBUTTERCUP**, 7, ch m Sixties Icon—Eastern Paramour (IRE)  **J. Turner**
37 **BURNING VICTORY (IRE)**, 5, b m Nathaniel (IRE)—M'Oubliez Pas (USA)  **Mrs Audrey Turley**
38 **BURROWS SAINT (FR)**, 8, b g Saint des Saints (FR)—La Bombonera (FR)  **Mrs S. Ricci**
39 **CABARET QUEEN**, 9, b m King's Theatre (IRE)—La Dame Brune (FR)  **Syndicates.Racing**
40 **CAPODANNO (FR)**, 5, ch g Manduro (GER)—Day Gets Up (FR)  **J. P. McManus**
41 **CAPTAIN KANGAROO (IRE)**, 6, ch h Mastercraftsman (IRE)—
　　　　　　　　　　　　　We Can Say It Now (AUS)  **Kanga Racing & Brett Graham Syndicate**
42 **CAREFULLY SELECTED (IRE)**, 9, b g Well Chosen—Knockamullen Girl (IRE)  **Miss M. A. Masterson**
43 **CASH BACK (FR)**, 9, b g Linda's Lad—Holding (FR)  **Watch This Space Syndicate**
44 **CASTLEBAWN WEST (IRE)**, 8, b g Westerner—Cooksgrove Lady (IRE)  **Mrs Rose Boyd Partnership**
45 **CAVALLINO (FR)**, 6, ch g Presenting—Roque de Cyborg (FR)  **Malcolm C. Denmark**
46 **CHACUN POUR SOI (FR)**, 9, b g Policy Maker (IRE)—Kruscyna (FR)  **Mrs S Ricci**
47 **CIEL DE NEIGE (FR)**, 6, b g Authorized (IRE)—In Caso di Neve (FR)  **John P. McManus**
48 **CILAOS EMERY (FR)**, 9, b g Califet (FR)—Queissa (FR)  **Luke McMahon**
49 **CLASS CONTI (FR)**, 9, b g Poliglote—Gazelle Lulu (FR)  **Simon Munir & Isaac Souede**
50 **COLREEVY (IRE)**, 8, b m Flemensfirth (USA)—Poetics Girl (IRE)  **Mrs N. Flynn**
51 **CONCERTISTA (FR)**, 7, ch m Nathaniel (IRE)—Zagrig  **Simon Munir & Isaac Souede Partnership**
52 **CONTINGENCY**, 8, b m Champs Elysees—Cyclone Connie  **Bowes Lodge Stables Partnership**
53 **COOL JET (IRE)**, 5, b g Jet Away—Cool Trix (IRE)  **Douglas Taylor**
54 **CRACK MOME (FR)**, 9, ch g Spanish Moon (USA)—Peche Mome (FR)  **Mrs J M Mullins**
55 **DANDY MAG (FR)**, 8, br g Special Kaldoun (IRE)—Naiade Mag (FR)  **G Mercer/D Mercer/Mrs Caren Walsh**
56 **DARK VOYAGER (IRE)**, 4, b g Raven's Pass (USA)—Je T'Adore (IRE)  **Mrs J Donnelly**
57 **DATA BREACH (IRE)**, 4, b g Pether's Moon (IRE)—Bochafina (FR)  **McNeill Family**
58 **DEAL D'ESTRUVAL (FR)**, 8, b g Balko (FR)—Option d'Estruval (FR)  **Mrs S. Ricci**
59 **DEPLOY THE GETAWAY (IRE)**, 6, b g Getaway (GER)—Gaelic River (IRE)  **Cheveley Park Stud**
60 **DIAMOND HILL (IRE)**, 8, b m Beat Hollow—Sixhills (FR)  **Mrs A F Mee Partnership**
61 **DON'T TELL ALLEN (IRE)**, 6, b g Presenting—Liss Alainn (IRE)  **John Joseph Flynn**
62 **DOUVAN (FR)**, 11, b g Walk In The Park (IRE)—Star Face (FR)  **Mrs S. Ricci**
63 **DOWNTOWN GETAWAY (IRE)**, 8, b g Getaway (GER)—Shang A Lang (IRE)  **J Turner**
64 **DRAGON D'ESTRUVAL (FR)**, 8, b g Enrique—Rose d'Estruval (FR)  **Simon Munir & Isaac Souede**
65 **DYSART DIAMOND (IRE)**, 6, ch m Shirocco (GER)—Dysart Dancer (IRE)  **Eleanor Manning**

## MR WILLIAM P. MULLINS - continued

66 **EASY GAME (FR)**, 7, b g Barastraight—Rule of The Game (FR) **Nicholas Peacock**
67 **ECHOES IN RAIN (FR)**, 5, b m Authorized (IRE)—Amarantine (FR) **Barnane Stud**
68 **EDEN FLIGHT (FR)**, 7, b g Great Pretender (IRE)—Traviata (FR) **Mrs S Ricci**
69 **EGALITY MANS (FR)**, 7, bl g Network (GER)—Quissisia Mans (FR) **Mrs J Donnelly**
70 **EL BARRA (FR)**, 7, br g Racinger (FR)—Oasaka (FR) **Mrs S Ricci**
71 **ELFILE (FR)**, 7, b m Saint des Saints (FR)—Rapide (FR) **Kenneth Alexander**
72 **ELIMAY (FR)**, 7, gr m Montmartre (FR)—Hyde (FR) **John P. McManus**
73 **ELITE CHARBONIERE (FR)**, 7, gr g Gris de Gris (IRE)—Star Folle Prail (FR) **Mrs S Ricci**
74 **ELIXIR D'AINAY (FR)**, 7, ch g Muhtathir—Perle du Bocage (FR) **John P. McManus**
75 **EN BETON (FR)**, 7, br g Network (GER)—Nee A Saint Voir (FR) **Cheveley Park Stud**
76 **ENERGUMENE (FR)**, 7, b g Denham Red (FR)—Olinight (FR) **Anthony Bloom**
77 **ET DITE (FR)**, 7, b m Limnos (JPN)—Truffe (FR) **Hammer & Trowel Syndicate**
78 **EUROTIEP (FR)**, 7, b g Lauro (GER)—Naltiepy (FR) **Down The Hatch Syndicate**
79 **FAIS TON CHEMIN (FR)**, 6, b g Coastal Path—Tiree d'Affaire (FR) **M L Bloodstock**
80 **FAN DE BLUES (FR)**, 6, b g Poliglote—Tire En Touche (FR) **Simon Munir & Isaac Souede**
81 **FAUGHEEN (IRE)**, 13, b g Germany (USA)—Miss Pickering (IRE) **Mrs S. Ricci**
82 **FERNY HOLLOW (IRE)**, 6, b br g Westerner—Mirazur (IRE) **Cheveley Park Stud**
83 **FIGHTER ALLEN (FR)**, 6, b g Vision d'Etat (FR)—Reaction (FR) **Chris Jones**
84 **FILS SPIRITUEL (FR)**, 6, b g Presenting—Toque Rouge (FR) **Mrs J Donnelly**
85 **FINEST EVERMORE (IRE)**, 5, b m Yeats (IRE)—St Helans Bay (IRE) **J. Turner**
86 **FIVE O'CLOCK (FR)**, 6, b g Cokoriko (FR)—Rodika (FR) **Mrs S Ricci**
87 **FLY SMART (FR)**, 6, b g Day Flight—Abacab (FR) **Mrs S Ricci**
88 **FOVEROS (FR)**, 6, b g Authorized (IRE)—Fanurio's Angel (FR) **Luke McMahon**
89 **FRANCIN (FR)**, 8, b g Air Chief Marshal (IRE)—Fulgence (FR) **Mrs S. Ricci**
90 **FRANCO DE PORT (FR)**, 6, b h Coastal Path—Ruth (FR) **Bruton Street IV Partnership**
91 **FRENCH ASEEL (FR)**, 4, ch g French Fifteen (FR)—Aseelah (FR) **Mrs J. Donnelly**
92 **FRERE TUCK (FR)**, 6, br g Secret Singer (FR)—Tete Et Corde (FR) **Cathal Hughes**
93 **GAILLARD DU MESNIL (FR)**, 5, gr g Saint des Saints (FR)—Athena du Mesnil (FR) **Mrs J. Donnelly**
94 **GALOPIN DES CHAMPS (FR)**, 5, bl g Timos (GER)—Manon des Champs (FR) **Mrs Audrey Turley**
95 **GANAPATHI (FR)**, 5, b g Samum (GER)—Une Dame d'Avril (FR) **Mrs J. Donnelly**
96 **GARS EN NOIR (FR)**, 5, b g Masked Marvel—Touche Noire (FR) **Mrs J. Donnelly**
97 **GAULOISE (FR)**, 5, ch m Samum (GER)—Sans Histoire (FR) **Kenneth Alexander**
98 **GELEE BLANCHE (FR)**, 5, b m Samum (GER)—Voix du Coeur (FR) **Tiger Tail Again Syndicate**
99 **GENERAL COUNSEL (IRE)**, 8, b g Shantou (USA)—Josephine Cullen (IRE) **Clipper Logistics Group Limited**
100 **GETABIRD (IRE)**, 9, b g Getaway (GER)—Fern Bird (IRE) **Mrs S. Ricci**
101 **GETAWAY GORGEOUS (IRE)**, 7, b m Getaway (GER)—Impudent (IRE) **Whitegrass Getaway Syndicate**
102 **GJOUMI (FR)**, 5, ch m Maresca Sorrento (FR)—Onvavoir (FR) **S McManus**
103 **GLENS OF ANTRIM (IRE)**, 6, b m Flemensfirth (USA)—Cottage Theatre (IRE) **J. P. McManus**
104 **GOLDEN SPREAD**, 8, b g Duke of Marmalade (IRE)—Purely By Chance **Probus Racing & Ken Sharp Syndicate**
105 **GORKI D'AIRY (FR)**, 5, b g Legolas (JPN)—Norsa d'Airy (FR) **Mrs J. M. Mullins**
106 **GRAND BORNAND (FR)**, 5, gr g Montmartre (FR)—Ubriska (FR) **Mrs S Ricci**
107 **GRANGEE (FR)**, 5, br m Great Pretender (IRE)—Quelle Mome (FR) **Syndicates.Racing**
108 **GREAT WHITE SHARK (FR)**, 7, gr m Le Havre (IRE)—Trip To Fame (FR) **Malcolm C. Denmark**
109 **HA D'OR (FR)**, 4, b g Nidor (FR)—Rosewort (FR) **Mrs S Ricci**
110 **HARA KIRI (FR)**, 4, b g Diamond Boy (FR)—Beauty du Bidou (FR) **Leinster Partnership**
111 **HARRIE (FR)**, 9, ch g Le Havre (IRE)—Honorable Love **Harrie/Brett Graham/Ken Sharp Syndicate**
112 **HAUT EN COULEURS (FR)**, 4, b g Saint des Saints (FR)—Sanouva (FR) **Mrs J. Donnelly**
113 **HI HO PHOENIX (FR)**, 5, gr g Phoenix Reach (IRE)—Silverlined **Mrs A.M & RJD Varmen**
114 **HOOK UP (FR)**, 5, b m No Risk At All (FR)—Mission Accomplie (FR) **Mrs S Ricci**
115 **HOPEFULLY (IRE)**, 6, b m Beat Hollow—Strina (IRE) **Joseph E Keeling**
116 **HYBERY (FR)**, 7, b g Centennial (IRE)—Zalagarry (FR) **Hybery Racing Syndicate**
117 **JAMES DU BERLAIS (FR)**, 5, ch g Muhtathir—King's Daughter (FR) **Simon Munir & Isaac Souede**
118 **JANIDIL (FR)**, 7, b g Indian Daffodil (IRE)—Janidouce (FR) **John P. McManus**
119 **JAZZAWAY (IRE)**, 6, b m Shantou (USA)—Backaway (IRE) **Whitegrass Racing Syndicate**
120 **JON SNOW (FR)**, 6, br g Le Havre (IRE)—Saroushka (FR) **Mrs S Ricci**
121 **JUNGLE BOOGIE (IRE)**, 7, b g Gold Well—A Better Excuse (IRE) **Malcolm C. Denmark**
122 **KARL DER GROSSE (GER)**, 7, gr g Jukebox Jury (IRE)—Karsawina (GER) **Mrs S Ricci**
123 **KEMBOY (FR)**, 9, b g Voix du Nord (FR)—Vitora (FR) **Kemboy/Brett Graham/Ken Sharp Syndicate**
124 **KILCRUIT (IRE)**, 6, b g Stowaway—Not Broke Yet (IRE) **Miss M A Masterson**
125 **KLASSICAL DREAM (FR)**, 7, b g Dream Well—Klassical Way (FR) **Mrs Joanne Coleman**

## MR WILLIAM P. MULLINS - continued

126 **KLASSY KAY (IRE)**, 7, ch m Presenting—On The Horizon (IRE) **Syndi 101 Partnership**
127 **KOSHARI (FR)**, 9, br g Walk In The Park (IRE)—Honor May (FR) **Mrs S. Ricci**
128 **LADY BREFFNI (IRE)**, 7, br m Yeats (IRE)—Time To Shine **Mr Mark Dobbin**
129 **LEGAL SPIN (IRE)**, 6, b g Lawman (FR)—Spinning Well (IRE) **Ballylinch Stud**
130 **LIVELOVELAUGH (IRE)**, 11, b g Beneficial—Another Evening (IRE) **Mrs S. Ricci**
131 **LORD ROYAL (FR)**, 6, gr g Lord du Sud (FR)—Tinoroyale **Paul Connell & Alan McGonnell**
132 **LOW SUN**, 8, b g Champs Elysees—Winter Solstice **Mrs S. Ricci**
133 **M C MULDOON (IRE)**, 6, gr g Mastercraftsman (IRE)—Alizaya (IRE) **Mrs J M Mullins**
134 **MANITOPARK AA (FR)**, 5, b m Walk In The Park (IRE)—Manitoba (FR) **Simon Munir & Isaac Souede**
135 **MARAJMAN (FR)**, 7, gr g Rajsaman (FR)—Mascarpone (FR) **Roaringwater Syndicate**
136 **MAZE RUNNER (IRE)**, 6, b g Authorized (IRE)—Alice Rose (IRE) **Mrs J. M. Mullins**
137 **MELON**, 9, ch g Medicean—Night Teeny **Mrs J. Donnelly**
138 **MICRO MANAGE (IRE)**, 5, ch h Rip Van Winkle (IRE)—Lillebonne (FR) **Merriebelle Irish Farm Limited**
139 **MIN (FR)**, 10, b g Walk In The Park (IRE)—Phemyka (FR) **Mrs S. Ricci**
140 **MISTER BLUE SKY (IRE)**, 7, gr g Royal Applause—Mujdeya **Shanakiel Racing Syndicate**
141 **MONKFISH (IRE)**, 7, ch g Stowaway—Martovic (IRE) **Mrs S Ricci**
142 **MR ADJUDICATOR (IRE)**, 7, b g Camacho—Attlongglast **David Bobbett**
143 **MR COLDSTONE (IRE)**, 5, b g Tamayuz—Dance Lively (USA) **David Bobbett**
144 **MT LEINSTER (IRE)**, 7, ch g Beat Hollow—Sixhills (FR) **Roaringwater Syndicate**
145 **MY SISTER SARAH (IRE)**, 7, ch m Martaline—Reste Ren Or (IRE) **Barnane Stud**
146 **N'GOLO (IRE)**, 6, gr g Galileo (IRE)—Dame Again (AUS) **Mrs S Ricci**
147 **NESSUN DORMA (IRE)**, 8, b g Canford Cliffs (IRE)—Idle Chatter (IRE) **N. D. Kennelly Partnership**
148 **ONTHEROPES (IRE)**, 7, b g Presenting—Dushion (IRE) **Cheveley Park Stud**
149 **ORION D'AUBRELLE (FR)**, 8, b g Saint des Saints (FR)—Erbalunga (FR) **Multi Nationals Syndicate**
150 **PONT AVAL (FR)**, 8, b m Soldier of Fortune (IRE)—Panzella (FR) **N G King**
151 **PONT AVEN (FR)**, 8, b g Doyen (IRE)—Behlaya (IRE) **Roderick Ryan Partnership**
152 **POWER OF PAUSE (IRE)**, 6, ch g Doyen (IRE)—Shady Pines (IRE) **Miss M A Masterson**
153 **PRINCESS VEGA (IRE)**, 6, b m Beat Hollow—Quevega (FR) **Hammer & Trowel Syndicate**
154 **PURPLE MOUNTAIN (IRE)**, 6, b m Beat Hollow—Bluemountainbeach (IRE) **Mrs A. F. Mee**
155 **RAMILLIES (IRE)**, 6, gr g Shantou (USA)—Mrs Wallensky (IRE) **Mrs J Donnelly**
156 **REBELLITO (FR)**, 7, gr g Montmartre (FR)—Saga d'Or (FR) **Mrs S Ricci**
157 **ROBIN DE CARLOW**, 8, br m Robin des Champs (FR)—

                           La Reine de Riogh (IRE) **Catchherifyoucan & Brett Graham Syndicate**
158 **ROBIN DES FORET (IRE)**, 11, br g Robin des Pres (FR)—Omyn Supreme (IRE) **Byerley Racing Syndicate**
159 **ROBINNIA (IRE)**, 6, b m Robin des Champs (FR)—Dreams And Songs **Closutton Racing Club**
160 **ROYAL ILLUSION (IRE)**, 9, b m King's Theatre (IRE)—Spirit Run (IRE) **Ballylinch Stud**
161 **ROYAL RENDEZVOUS (IRE)**, 9, b g King's Theatre (IRE)—Novacella (FR) **Dr S P Fitzgerald**
162 **RUAILLE BUAILLE (IRE)**, 6, b m Salutino (GER)—Cyclone Lorraine (FR) **Ri Ra Racing Syndicate**
163 **RUNRIZED (FR)**, 6, b g Authorized (IRE)—Courseulles (FR) **Clipper Logistics Group Limited**
164 **SAINT ROI (FR)**, 6, b g Coastal Path—Sainte Vigne (FR) **John P. McManus**
165 **SAINT SAM (FR)**, 4, b g Saint des Saints (FR)—Ladeka (FR) **Edward J Ware**
166 **SALDIER (FR)**, 7, b g Soldier Hollow—Salve Evita **Mrs S Ricci**
167 **SALSARETTA (FR)**, 8, b m Kingsalsa (USA)—Kendoretta (FR) **Mrs S. Ricci**
168 **SAPPHIRE LADY (IRE)**, 9, b m Beneficial—Cloghoge Lady (IRE) **Anthony P. Butler**
169 **SATURNAS (FR)**, 10, b g Davidoff (GER)—Sayuri (GER) **Nicholas Peacock**
170 **SAYO**, 7, gr g Dalakhani (IRE)—Tiyi (FR) **Miss M A Masterson**
171 **SCARPETA (FR)**, 8, b g Soldier of Fortune (IRE)—Sanada (IRE) **Thurloe Thoroughbreds Ireland Limited**
172 **SHADOW RIDER (FR)**, 7, ch g Martaline—Samansonnienne (FR) **J. P. McManus**
173 **SHANNING (FR)**, 8, b m Spanish Moon (USA)—Idaho Falls (FR) **Lady In Waiting & Brett Graham Syndicate**
174 **SHARJAH (FR)**, 8, b g Doctor Dino (FR)—Saaryeh **Mrs S. Ricci**
175 **SHEWEARSITWELL (IRE)**, 6, b m Shirocco (GER)—Ware It Vic (IRE) **Closutton Racing Club**
176 **STATE MAN (FR)**, 4, ch g Doctor Dino (FR)—Arret Station (FR) **Mrs J. Donnelly**
177 **STATTLER (IRE)**, 6, br g Stowaway—Our Honey (IRE) **R. A. Bartlett**
178 **STONES AND ROSES (IRE)**, 7, b g Shantou (USA)—Compelled (IRE) **P. Reilly & C. Reilly**
179 **STRATUM**, 8, b g Dansili—Lunar Phase (IRE) **Anthony Bloom**
180 **TAKE TEA (IRE)**, 6, b m Flemensfirth (USA)—Saine d'Esprit (FR)
181 **TAX FOR MAX (GER)**, 4, b c Maxios—Tomato Finish (GER) **Simon Munir & Isaac Souede**
182 **THALITLEOZIBATLER (AUS)**, 7, b g Onemorenomore (AUS)—My Keepsake (NZ) **Old Mates Syndicate**
183 **THE BIG GETAWAY (IRE)**, 7, b g Getaway (IRE)—Saddlers Dawn (IRE) **Mrs J Donnelly**
184 **THE NICE GUY (IRE)**, 6, b g Fame And Glory—Kilbarry Beauty (IRE) **Malcolm C. Denmark**

## MR WILLIAM P. MULLINS - continued

185 **THE WEST AWAITS (IRE)**, 6, b m Flemensfirth (USA)—Lonesome Dove (IRE) **Mrs John Magnier**
186 **TIGER TAP TAP (GER)**, 6, ch g Jukebox Jury (IRE)—Tomato Finish (GER) **Mrs S Ricci**
187 **TORNADO FLYER (IRE)**, 8, b g Flemensfirth (USA)—Mucho Macabi (IRE) **TFP Partnership**
188 **TRUE SELF (IRE)**, 8, b m Oscar (IRE)—Good Thought (IRE) **Three Mile House Partnership, OTI Racing**
189 **UNEXCEPTED (FR)**, 7, br g Anzillero (GER)—Eaton Lass (IRE) **John P. McManus**
190 **URADEL (GER)**, 10, b g Kallisto (GER)—Unavita (GER) **Luke McMahon**
191 **VALLEY BREEZE (FR)**, 7, b g Sunday Break (JPN)—Valdemossa (FR) **Luke McMahon**
192 **VIS TA LOI (FR)**, 7, ch g Smadoun (FR)—Dicte Ta Loi (FR) **Creighton Family**
193 **WHATDEAWANT (IRE)**, 5, b g Aizavoski (IRE)—Hidden Reserve (IRE) **Sean & Bernadine Mulryan**
194 **WHISKEY SOUR (IRE)**, 8, b h Jeremy (USA)—Swizzle Stick (IRE) **Luke McMahon**
195 **YOUMDOR (FR)**, 4, b g Youmzain (IRE)—Decize (FR) **McNeill Family**
196 **YUKON LIL**, 7, b m Flemensfirth (USA)—Dare To Doubt **Mrs John Magnier**
197 **ZENON (IRE)**, 7, b g Galileo (IRE)—Jacqueline (IND) **Dreaming Cups Syndicate**

---

**400** **MISS AMY MURPHY, Newmarket**
Postal: Southgate Stables, Hamilton Road, Newmarket, Suffolk, CB8 0WY
Contacts: PHONE 01638 484907 MOBILE 07711 992500
EMAIL info@amymurphyracing.com WEBSITE www.amymurphyracing.com

1 **ALBORKAN (FR)**, 4, b g Joshua Tree (IRE)—Plaine Monceau (FR) **Alan & Sally Coney, Mr J. Hambro**
2 **ANGEL'S WHISPER (IRE)**, 6, gr m Dark Angel (IRE)—Tasheyaat **Box Clever Display & Shepherd Global**
3 **BAILEYS EXCELERATE (IRE)**, 6, gr g Excelebration (IRE)—Cruel Sea (USA) **G R Bailey Ltd (Baileys Horse Feeds)**
4 **BEAUVALLON BAY (IRE)**, 5, b g Kalanisi (IRE)—Stability Treaty (IRE) **Mr C. Boultbee-Brooks**
5 **BILLY'S ANGEL (IRE)**, 9, ch g Vertical Speed (FR)—Lady Rockabilly (IRE) **D. L. de Souza**
6 **BREATH OF JOY**, 4, b f Kodiac—Island Dreams (USA) **Mr I. Alsagar**
7 **CALIDUS MIRABILIS**, 4, b g Hot Streak (IRE)—Rose Ransom (IRE) **Miss A. L. Murphy**
8 **CAROLE'S TEMPLER**, 6, ch g Shirocco (GER)—Carole's Legacy **Mr P. Murphy**
9 **CAROLE'S TZARINA (FR)**, 5, b m Sholokhov (IRE)—Carole's Destiny **Mr P. Murphy**
10 **EASTER ERIC**, 7, b g Martaline—Easter Comet **Mr & Mrs S. C. Willes**
11 **ESPRIT DE BAILEYS (FR)**, 9, b g Le Havre (IRE)—Lit (IRE) **G R Bailey Ltd (Baileys Horse Feeds)**
12 4, B g Kalanisi (IRE)—Fairy On The Moor (IRE) **Mr P. Murphy**
13 **FUSEAU (FR)**, 6, b g Barastraight—Monepopee (FR) **Michael Rembaum & Michael Tuckey**
14 **HAWTHORN COTTAGE (IRE)**, 8, b m Gold Well—Miss Kilkeel (IRE) **Melbourne 10 Racing**
15 **HUNTER'S DAWN**, 4, ch f Hunter's Light (IRE)—Corniche (FR) **Mr P. Murphy**
16 **JAMESSAINTPATRICK (IRE)**, 8, br g Stowaway—Cadia's Lady (IRE) **Melbourne 10 Racing**
17 **KALASHNIKOV (IRE)**, 8, br g Kalanisi (IRE)—Fairy Lane (IRE) **Mr P. Murphy**
18 **LILYPAD (IRE)**, 6, b m New Approach (IRE)—Vow **Amy Murphy Racing Club**
19 **LOGAN ROCKS (IRE)**, 6, b g Yeats (IRE)—Countess Comet (IRE) **The Rann Family**
20 **MARLBOROUGH SOUNDS**, 6, b g Camelot—Wind Surf (USA) **Vitality Cbd Partners & Mr Julian Taylor**
21 **MERCIAN KNIGHT (IRE)**, 7, b g Saint des Saints (FR)—Carole's Legacy **Mr P. Murphy**
22 **MERCIAN PRINCE (IRE)**, 10, b g Midnight Legend—Bongo Fury (FR) **Mr P. Murphy**
23 **NAPPING**, 8, b m Sleeping Indian—Vax Rapide **Eclipse Sports Racing Club**
24 **NIRODHA (IRE)**, 4, ch f Camacho—Ekagra **Daniel MacAuliffe & Anoj Don**
25 **REALLY SUPER**, 7, b m Cacique (IRE)—Sensationally **White Diamond Racing Partnership 1**
26 **ROARING FURY (IRE)**, 7, br m Sholokhov (IRE)—Bongo Fury (FR) **Charles Auld & Partner**
27 **SAMILLE (IRE)**, 4, b f Kodiac—Monicalew **Mick Jaselsky & Partner**
28 **SOLDIER ON PARADE**, 4, b g Dunaden (FR)—Litewska (IRE) **Hostages To Fortune**
29 5, B m Martaline—Strawberry (IRE) **Mr P. Murphy**
30 **THE ACCOUNTANT**, 6, ch g Dylan Thomas (IRE)—Glorybe (GER) **The Rann Family**
31 **THEGREATESTSHOWMAN**, 5, ch g Equiano (FR)—Conversational (IRE)
32 **TONYX**, 5, b m Nathaniel (IRE)—Kadoma **Mrs L. E. Rann, Mr G. P. D. Rann**
33 **TOPKAPI STAR**, 4, b f Golden Horn—Burlesque Star (IRE) **Mr C. Johnston**
34 **TROUSER THE CASH (IRE)**, 4, b f Starspangledbanner (AUS)—Bint Malyana (IRE) **A & P Braithwaite**

## MISS AMY MURPHY - continued

### THREE-YEAR-OLDS

35 **BABY BOO**, b f Iffraaj—Babycakes (IRE) **Mr J. Acheson**
36 **BURN THE CAKES**, ch f Strath Burn—Candycakes (IRE) **Mr J. Acheson**
37 **DISAPPEARANCE (IRE)**, b f Invincible Spirit (IRE)—Steal The Show (NZ) **Mr Gerry Ryan**
38 **EHRMANN (IRE)**, b g Dragon Pulse (IRE)—Desiderada (IRE) **D. L. de Souza**
39 **JENNIVERE**, ch f Strath Burn—Guinnevre (IRE) **Mr J. Acheson**
40 **LOVE BAILEYS**, ch f Garswood—Ring of Love **G R Bailey Ltd (Baileys Horse Feeds)**
41 **NIGHTFIORI (IRE)**, ch g Night of Thunder (IRE)—Millefiori (IRE) **Miss A. L. Murphy**
42 **SABRE JET (IRE)**, b g Zoffany (IRE)—Star Jet (IRE) **Ladas**
43 **URBAN WAR (IRE)**, b g Mehmas (IRE)—Urban Beauty (IRE) **Constellation Syndicate & Partner**

### TWO-YEAR-OLDS

44 B c 22/03 Footstepsinthesand—Amethystos (IRE) (Danehill Dancer (IRE)) (55000) **Ben CM Wong**
45 B br c 11/03 Holy Roman Emperor (IRE)—
Baileys Mirage (FR) (Desert Style (IRE)) **G R Bailey Ltd (Baileys Horse Feeds)**
46 B f 17/04 Bated Breath—Chicita Banana (Danehill Dancer (IRE)) (14286) **For Sale**
47 B c 16/03 Aclaim (IRE)—Illegally Blonde (IRE) (Lawman (FR)) **Mrs Claire Barratt**
48 B f 28/02 Requinto (IRE)—Lunette (IRE) (Teofilo (IRE)) (4036)
49 Ch g 26/02 Tamayuz—Peace Summit (Cape Cross (IRE)) (8000)
50 Ch f 19/04 Profitable (IRE)—Ring For Baileys (Kyllachy) **G R Bailey Ltd (Baileys Horse Feeds)**
51 B c 26/03 Twilight Son—Ring of Love (Magic Ring (IRE)) (15238) **Mr Paul Venner**
52 B f 23/02 Twilight Son—Sally (FR) (Whipper (USA)) (15238)
53 B f 05/03 Camacho—Winged Harriet (IRE) (Hawk Wing (USA)) (11000)

**Other Owners:** Amy Murphy Racing Club, Mr W. R. Asquith, Mr C. C. Auld, Box Clever Display, Mr A. W. Braithwaite, Mrs P. J. Braithwaite, Mrs M. P. Burling, Mr P. A. Burling, Mr T. Castle, Mr A. R. Coney, Jamie & & Coney, Mrs S. Coney, Constellation Syndicate, Mr C. E. Dale, Mr M. S. J. Dyer, Mr D. R. Flatt, Miss A. Haynes, Mr R. S. Hoskins, Mr M. Jaselsky, Mrs V. A. Knight, Mr C. Mullin, Mrs M. T. Mullin, Miss A. L. Murphy, Mr P. Murphy, Mr N. Nathwani, P. A. Oppenheimer, Miss N. K. Rajani, Mr G. P. D. Rann, Mrs L. E. Rann, Mr M. J. Rembaum, Mr J. P. Ryan, Mrs C. G. Scott, Shepherd Global Ltd, Mr A. J. Taylor, The Rann Family, M. J. Tuckey, Vitality Partnership, White Diamond Racing Partnership, Mrs M. Willes, Mr S. C. Willes.

---

**401** **MR MIKE MURPHY, Westoning**
Postal: **Broadlands, Manor Park Stud, Westoning, Bedfordshire, MK45 5LA**
Contacts: **PHONE 01525 717305 MOBILE 07770 496103 FAX 01525 717305**
EMAIL mmurphy@globalnet.co.uk WEBSITE www.mikemurphyracing.com

1 **ARIA ROSE**, 6, b g Cityscape—Leelu **P. Banfield**
2 **DUSTY DAMSEL**, 5, ch m Toronado (IRE)—Dusty Answer **The Calm Partnership**
3 **GARTH ROCKETT**, 7, b g Delegator—Leelu **P. Banfield**
4 **KYLLA LOOKS**, 4, br f Kyllachy—Love Your Looks **The Calm Partnership**
5 **LE REVEUR (IRE)**, 4, b g Dream Ahead (USA)—Don't Be **Sarabex**
6 **MULZIM**, 7, b g Exceed And Excel (AUS)—Samaah (IRE) **Victoria Taylor & Family**
7 **OWHATANIGHT**, 4, gr g Night of Thunder (IRE)—White Wedding (IRE) **Ms A. D. Tibbett**
8 **SPACESUIT**, 4, b g Sea The Moon (GER)—Casaca
9 **STRAWBS**, 5, b m Garswood—Final Rhapsody **Mr D. C. Mead**
10 **VELVET VISION**, 6, b m Nathaniel (IRE)—Battery Power **Sarabex**
11 **VELVET VISTA**, 5, b m Sea The Moon (GER)—Battery Power **Sarabex**
12 **YOUNG JOHN (IRE)**, 8, b g Acclamation—Carpet Lady (IRE) **Murphy, Cooper & East**

### THREE-YEAR-OLDS

13 **BREEZYANDBRIGHT (IRE)**, b g Epaulette (AUS)—Tranquil Sky **Mr M. Murphy, Moir & Murphy, Mr S. Moir**
14 B f Territories (IRE)—Clarentine
15 **HEED MY ADVICE**, b f Paco Boy (IRE)—Secret Advice
16 **HERECOMESARCHIE (FR)**, b g Hunter's Light (IRE)—Our Time Will Come (IRE) **Mr R. J. Moore**
17 **MERLIN'S MISSION (IRE)**, b c Awtaad (IRE)—Witnessed **The Magicians**

## MR MIKE MURPHY - continued

### TWO-YEAR-OLDS

18 Ch c 23/03 Helmet (AUS)—Bestfootforward (Motivator)
19 Ch c 12/05 Dandy Man (IRE)—Charmgoer (USA) (Nureyev (USA)) (28000)
20 Ch f 01/05 No Nay Never (USA)—Impressible (Oasis Dream) (17000)
21 **LA EQUINATA**, b f 27/03 Equiano (FR)—La Fortunata (Lucky Story (USA)) (6000)
22 **PERSUADE**, b f 10/05 Postponed (IRE)—Souter's Sister (IRE) (Desert Style (IRE)) (3000) **Miss S. J. Ballinger**
23 **VELVET VULCAN**, b c 06/03 Nathaniel (IRE)—Battery Power (Royal Applause) **Sarabex**

**Other Owners:** Mr Jim Patton.

**Assistant Trainer:** Michael Keady.

---

**402** **MR OLLY MURPHY, Wilmcote**
Postal: **Warren Chase Stables, Wilmcote, Stratford-Upon-Avon, Warwickshire, CV37 9XG**
Contacts: **PHONE 01789 613347**
EMAIL office@ollymurphyracing.com WEBSITE www.ollymurphyracing.com

1 AFRICAN DANCE (IRE), 6, br g Shirocco (GER)—
    Dani California **Noel & Valerie Moran, Mr N. Moran, Mrs V. Moran**
2 ALLAVINA (IRE), 6, b m Getaway (GER)—One Cool Kate (IRE) **Mr C. Boultbee-Brooks**
3 ALPHA CARINAE (IRE), 6, ch m Robin des Champs (FR)—Annas Present (IRE) **Mr T. D. J. Syder**
4 ARMAND DE BRIGNAC (IRE), 5, b g Fame And Glory—Bolly (IRE) **Mrs D. L. Whateley**
5 AUDITORIA, 4, b f Gleneagles (IRE)—Authora (IRE) **Nick Brown Racing**
6 BARRICANE, 6, b g Kayf Tara—Alina Rheinberg (GER) **Mrs D. L. Whateley**
7 BEYOND EVERYTHING (FR), 5, gr g Cima de Triomphe (IRE)—Dear Valentine (FR) **Mr C. J. Haughey**
8 BLAZER'S MILL (IRE), 7, b g Westerner—Creation (IRE) **Mrs J. A. Wakefield**
9 BREWIN'UPASTORM (IRE), 8, b g Milan—Daraheen Diamond (IRE) **Ms B. J. Abt**
10 BRIGHT EYED EAGLE (IRE), 4, ch g Gleneagles (IRE)—Euphrasia (IRE) **Mrs J. A. Wakefield**
11 BUBBLES OF GOLD (IRE), 8, b g Gold Well—Bubble Bann (IRE) **Noel & Valerie Moran, Mr N. Moran**
12 CALIPSO COLLONGES (FR), 9, b g Crossharbour—Ivresse Collonges (FR) **The Black Horse Hotel Bridgnorth**
13 CAPTAIN BIGGLES (IRE), 6, gr g Milan—Timon's Present **Mrs D. L. Whateley**
14 CELTIC TARA, 7, b m Kayf Tara—Valdas Queen (GER) **A. P. Racing**
15 CHAMPAGNESUPEROVER (IRE), 6, b g Jeremy (USA)—
    Meldrum Hall **Mr S. Bryceland, McNeill Family & Patrick&scott Bryceland**
16 CHOSEN PORT (IRE), 5, b m Well Chosen—Despute (IRE) **Noel & Valerie Moran**
17 CHURCHILL FLYER (IRE), 4, b g Policy Maker (IRE)—Chill The Beans (IRE) **Millennium Racing Club**
18 COLLOONEY (IRE), 7, b g Yeats (IRE)—Amber Trix (IRE) **Mr J. P. McManus**
19 COPPERLESS, 6, b g Kayf Tara—Presenting Copper (IRE) **Aiden Murphy & Alan Peterson, Mr A. E. Peterson**
20 COREY'S COURAGE, 5, b m Dunaden (FR)—Valdas Queen (GER) **A. P. Racing**
21 CORINTO (IRE), 8, b g Flemensfirth (USA)—Fashion Target (IRE) **Mrs D. L. Whateley**
22 CRAIGMOR (IRE), 9, b g Craigsteel—Twilight Princess (IRE) **Mr Peter. P. Elliott & Partners**
23 DEAUVILLE DANCER (IRE), 10, b g Tamayuz—Mathool (IRE) **Mr G.Brandrick & Partner**
24 DEL DUQUE (IRE), 6, b g Fame And Glory—Chirouble (IRE) **Deva Racing Del Duque**
25 DENS DELIGHT (FR), 6, gr g Tin Horse (IRE)—Mille Flora (IRE) **Kate & Andrew Brooks**
26 DOCTOR KEN (FR), 5, b g Doctor Dino (FR)—Kendoretta (FR) **Mrs D. L. Whateley**
27 DUBAI GUEST (IRE), 6, b g Dubai Destination (USA)—Formidable Guest **Oceana Racing**
28 DUCA DE THAIX (FR), 8, b g Voix du Nord (FR)—Nouca de Thaix (FR) **Tyrrells Racing Club**
29 DUKE OF ROCKINGHAM, 5, b g Kayf Tara—Our Jess (IRE) **Mrs D. L. Whateley**
30 DUNDRUM WOOD (IRE), 7, b g Flemensfirth (USA)—Ruby Isabel (IRE) **Sky's The Limit**
31 EAGLEHILL (FR), 7, gr g Blue Bresil (FR)—Ratina de Vaige (FR) **Mr J. P. McManus**
32 ENDLESSLY (IRE), 6, b g Nathaniel (IRE)—What's Up Pussycat (IRE) **Mr R. Treacy**
33 ENEMY COAST AHEAD, 7, b g Malinas (GER)—Penang Princess **McNeill Family Ltd**
34 ESKENDASH (USA), 8, ch g Eskendereya (USA)—Daffaash (USA) **Boyle Racing**
35 EWOOD PARK (IRE), 6, b g Shirocco (GER)—Windfola (FR) **McNeill Family Ltd**
36 FABRIQUE EN FRANCE (FR), 6, b g Yeats (IRE)—Knar Mardy **Noel & Valerie Moran**
37 FEARLESS (IRE), 6, b g Arakan (USA)—La Spezia (IRE) **Tim Syder & Dominic Burke**
38 FIESOLE, 9, b g Montjeu (IRE)—Forgotten Dreams (IRE) **Deva Racing Fiesole**

# MR OLLY MURPHY - continued

39 **FINAWN BAWN (IRE)**, 8, b g Robin des Champs (FR)—Kayanti (IRE) **Ready Steady Go**
40 **FIRST CLASS RETURN (IRE)**, 8, b g Let The Lion Roar—Chitty Bang Bang (IRE) **Mr O. J. Murphy**
41 **FITZROY (IRE)**, 7, b g Fame And Glory—Forces of Destiny (IRE) **Tim Syder & Aiden Murphy**
42 **FIVETOTWELVE**, 7, b m Midnight Legend—To The Left (IRE) **Alan Marsh & Partner**
43 **FLETCH (FR)**, 6, b g Kayf Tara—Oeuvre Vive (FR) **Ms B. J. Abt**
44 **FOLLOW THAT**, 7, b m Malinas (GER)—Leading On **B. Hawkins**
45 **FOXINTHEBOX (IRE)**, 5, b g Presenting—Forces of Destiny (IRE) **A. Butler**
46 **FRANKLY MR SHANKLY (GER)**, 4, b g Maxios—Four Roses (IRE) **Patrick & Scott Bryceland**
47 **FRESH NEW DAWN (IRE)**, 9, ch g Flemensfirth (USA)—Star Shuil (IRE) **Not For Friends Partnership**
48 **FRIARY LAND**, 7, b g Schiaparelli (GER)—Brochrua (IRE) **Premier Thoroughbred Racing Ltd**
49 **GENERAL CUSTARD**, 8, b g Shirocco (GER)—Diamant Noir **Syder, Whateley, Murphy, Burke**
50 **GENERAL PROBUS**, 7, b br g Geordieland (FR)—Drop The Hammer **E G M Beard & R A Scott**
51 **GEOMATRICIAN (FR)**, 5, gr g Mastercraftsman (IRE)—Madonna Dell'orto **Ray Treacy & Shaun Staplehurst**
52 **GETAWAY LUV (IRE)**, 6, b g Getaway (GER)—Ut Love (FR) **Mr C. Boultbee-Brooks**
53 **GINISTRELLI (IRE)**, 5, b g Frankel—Guaranda **Mrs J. A. Wakefield**
54 **GO DANTE**, 5, b g Kayf Tara—Whoops A Daisy **Ms B. J. Abt**
55 **GRACES ORDER (IRE)**, 6, b m Mahler—Janebailey **Peaky Blinders**
56 **GRANDADS COTTAGE (IRE)**, 6, ch g Shantou (USA)—Sarah's Cottage (IRE) **Mr J. Hales**
57 **GREY SPIRIT (IRE)**, 6, gr g Dark Angel (IRE)—Buttonhole **A J Wall & Briton International**
58 **GUNSIGHT RIDGE**, 6, b g Midnight Legend—Grandma Griffiths **Mrs D. L. Whateley**
59 **HAURAKI GULF**, 6, b g Kayf Tara—Leading On **Mrs D. L. Whateley**
60 **HERE COMES JOHNY (IRE)**, 6, b g Yeats—Strike An Ark (IRE) **Foxtrot Racing: Here Comes Johny**
61 **HERE COMES MCCOY (IRE)**, 6, br g Dylan Thomas (IRE)—Is It Here (IRE) **Mr C. J. Haughey**
62 **HERE COMES TRUBLE (IRE)**, 6, b g Flemensfirth (USA)—Old Moon (IRE) **Ms B. J. Abt**
63 **HIGHATE HILL (IRE)**, 7, b g Presenting—Lisrenny Lady **Patrick & Scott Bryceland**
64 **HOGAN (IRE)**, 5, b g Fame And Glory—Don't Be Upset (IRE) **Farrell Field Cognet Sigler**
65 **HOOROO (IRE)**, 4, b g Hallowed Crown (AUS)—Hflah (IRE) **Ladies In Racing**
66 **HUNTERS CALL (IRE)**, 11, b g Medaaly—Accordiontogelica (IRE) **Holloway,Clarke,Black**
67 **I K BRUNEL**, 7, b g Midnight Legend—Somethinaboutmolly (IRE) **McNeill Family and Prodec Networks Ltd**
68 **ISLAND NATION (IRE)**, 4, ch g Ruler of The World (IRE)—Rethink **ROOFNET LIMITED**
69 **IT'S O KAY**, 8, b m Shirocco (GER)—Presenting Copper (IRE) **Aiden Murphy & Alan Peterson**
70 **ITALIAN SPIRIT (IRE)**, 5, b g Fame And Glory—Coco Milan (IRE) **Mrs J. A. Wakefield**
71 **ITCHY FEET (IRE)**, 7, b g Cima de Triomphe (IRE)—Maeva Candas (FR) **Kate & Andrew Brooks**
72 **JAN WELLENS**, 4, ch g Dutch Art—Upstanding **Deva Racing Jan Wellens**
73 **JETAWAY JOEY (IRE)**, 6, b g Getaway—Present Your Own (IRE) **Ms B. J. Abt**
74 **JONES WELL (IRE)**, 8, b g Gold Well—Mrs Jones (FR) **H. A. Murphy**
75 **KAPROYALE**, 6, gr g Kapgarde (FR)—As You Leave (FR) **Tommy Elphick & Mary Shalvey**
76 **KRAZY PAVING**, 9, b g Kyllachy—Critical Path (IRE) **All The Kings Horses & Mr Aiden Murphy**
77 **LINELEE KING (FR)**, 6, gr g Martaline—Queen Lee (FR) **Mrs D. L. Whateley**
78 **LORD OF KERAK**, 6, b g Martaline—Mille Et Une (FR) **Mrs D. L. Whateley**
79 **LUCKELLO**, 5, b m Yorgunnabelucky (USA)—Timarello (IRE) **Skylark Racing**
80 **MACKELDUFF**, 5, gr g Martaline—Evitta (FR) **Tommy Elphick & Mary Shalvey**
81 **MADE FOR YOU**, 6, b g Cape Cross (IRE)—Edallora (IRE) **H. A. Murphy**
82 **MAKTHECAT (FR)**, 5, b g Makfi—Troiecat (FR) **geegeez.co.uk OM**
83 **MARKOV (IRE)**, 11, b g Morozov (USA)—Willoughby Sue (IRE) **Mr A. R. W. Marsh**
84 **MASADA KNIGHT (IRE)**, 5, b g Fame And Glory—Rematch (IRE) **Mrs D. L. Whateley**
85 **MASTER TEMPLAR (IRE)**, 6, br g Robin des Champs (FR)—Which Thistle (IRE) **Mrs D. L. Whateley**
86 **MEXICAN BOY (IRE)**, 5, gr g Kayf Tara—J'Y Viens (FR) **The Four Timers**
87 **MIGHTY MEG**, 7, b m Malinas (GER)—Harry's Bride **The Mighty Men**
88 **MISS GOLD DEN (IRE)**, 6, ch m Shantou (USA)—Miss Denman (IRE) **James and Jean Potter Ltd**
89 **MOORE MARGAUX (IRE)**, 6, b g Flemensfirth (USA)—Omas Glen (IRE) **Graeme Moore, Kate & Andrew Brooks**
90 **MORE THAN A PRINCE**, 4, b g Oasis Dream—La Petite Reine **Mrs J. A. Wakefield**
91 **MR KATANGA (IRE)**, 7, b g Flemensfirth (USA)—Pomme Tiepy (FR) **Graeme Moore, Kate & Andrew Brooks**
92 **NICKOLSON (FR)**, 7, b g No Risk At All (FR)—Incorrigible (FR) **Mr T. D. J. Syder**
93 **NO RISK DES FLOS (FR)**, 6, gr g No Risk At All (FR)—Marie Royale (FR) **Mrs D. L. Whateley**
94 **NOTRE PARI (IRE)**, 7, br g Jeremy (USA)—Glynn Approach (IRE) **Mr J. P. McManus**
95 **OVERTHETOP (IRE)**, 7, b g Flemensfirth (USA)—Dawn Bid (IRE) **What the Elle**
96 **PEACHEY (IRE)**, 7, b g Robin des Champs (FR)—Zita Hall (IRE) **Mrs D. L. Whateley**
97 **PLENTY IN THE TANK (IRE)**, 6, b g Champs Elysees—Lunathea (IRE) **Mrs D. L. Whateley**
98 **PORT OF MARS (IRE)**, 7, b g Westerner—Sarahall (IRE) **Noel & Valerie Moran**

# MR OLLY MURPHY - continued

  99 **PRESENCE OF MIND (IRE)**, 6, b g Presenting—Alleygrove Lass (IRE) **Noel & Valerie Moran**
100 **PROPOSING**, 5, b m Dunaden (FR)—Hilden **All The Kings Horses**
101 **RESTANDBETHANKFUL**, 5, br g Califet (FR)—Persian Forest **McNeill Family & Patrick&scott Bryceland**
102 **RIO QUINTO (FR)**, 8, b g Loup Breton (IRE)—Seal of Cause (IRE) **Mrs D. L. Whateley**
103 **RIPPER ROO (FR)**, 6, gr g Smadoun (FR)—Sninfia (IRE) **Deva Racing Ripper Roo,Shalvey&Partners**
104 **ROCK ON TOMMY**, 6, gr g Fair Mix (IRE)—Little Carmela **Premier Thoroughbred Racing Ltd**
105 **ROCK THE HOUSE (IRE)**, 6, b g Scorpion (IRE)—Holiday Time (IRE) **FGD Limited**
106 **SALLEY GARDENS (IRE)**, 5, b g Yeats (IRE)—Glenlogan (IRE) **Touchwood Racing**
107 **SEEMINGLY SO (IRE)**, 8, br g Dubai Destination (USA)—Jane Hall (IRE) **Emily Boultbee Brooks Racing**
108 **SMACKWATER JACK (IRE)**, 7, b g Flemensfirth (USA)—Malachy's Attic (IRE) **Par Four**
109 **SMART GETAWAY (IRE)**, 9, b m Getaway (GER)—Legendsofthefall (IRE) **Jacques Law P'ship & M Lyons**
110 **SPIRIT OF WATERLOO**, 7, b g Malinas (GER)—Warm Front **Salmon Racing**
111 **SPRINGVALE**, 6, b m Haafhd—Summervale (IRE) **A. Butler**
112 **ST GALLEN (IRE)**, 8, b g Majestic Missile (IRE)—Fly With Me (IRE) **Tommy Elphick & Mary Shalvey**
113 **ST LAWRENCE GAP (IRE)**, 9, ch g Tagula (IRE)—Kannon **Stephen R Hodgkinson & Partner**
114 **STORM OF LIGHT (IRE)**, 5, b g Fame And Glory—Blazing Moon (IRE) **Mrs D. L. Whateley**
115 **STRONG GLANCE**, 8, bl g Passing Glance—Strong Westerner (IRE) **Welfordgolf syndicate**
116 **SURE TOUCH**, 5, b g Yeats (IRE)—Liberthine (FR) **Mr R. B. Waley-Cohen**
117 **TAMANGO (IRE)**, 5, ch m Shirocco (GER)—Liss Na Siog (IRE) **Heart Racing Hr3 & Mrs J A Thomas**
118 **TAMAR BRIDGE (IRE)**, 6, b g Jeremy (USA)—Mise En Place **McNeill Family and Prodec Networks Ltd**
119 **THE BUTCHER SAID (IRE)**, 8, b g Robin des Champs (FR)—Georgina Valleya (IRE) **McNeill Family Ltd**
120 **THE WOLF (FR)**, 7, ch g Kapgarde (FR)—Ges (FR) **McNeill Family and Prodec Networks Ltd**
121 **THE WORLDS END (IRE)**, 10, b g Stowaway—Bright Sprite (IRE) **McNeill Family Ltd**
122 **THOMAS DARBY (IRE)**, 8, b g Beneficial—Silaoce (FR) **Mrs D. L. Whateley**
123 **THUNDER ROCK (IRE)**, 5, b g Shirocco (GER)—La Belle Sauvage **McNeill Family & Mr Ian Dale**
124 **TIGERBYTHETAIL (IRE)**, 5, b g Yeats (IRE)—Talktothetail (IRE) **Ms B. J. Abt**
125 **TINNAHALLA (IRE)**, 4, b g Starspangledbanner (AUS)—Bright Bank (IRE) **Mrs J. A. Wakefield**
126 **VALENTINO DANCER**, 6, ch g Mastercraftsman—Bertie's Best **Richard Hames & Alex Govorusa**
127 **VINNIE'S GETAWAY (IRE)**, 7, b g Getaway (GER)—Trixskin (IRE) **B McDonald, B Mellon & P McBride**
128 **VOCALISER (IRE)**, 9, b g Vocalised (USA)—Bring Back Matron (IRE) **The Songsters**
129 **WALKONTHEWILDSIDE (FR)**, 5, b g Walk In The Park (FR)—
                                                   My Lady Link (FR) **Mrs Diana L. Whateley & Mr Aiden Murphy**
130 **WASHINGTON**, 5, br g Westerner—Present Leader **Mr T. D. J. Syder**
131 **WHAT WILL BE (IRE)**, 5, b g Thewayyouare (USA)—Gali Gal (IRE) **The Dream Big Syndicate**
132 **WHATYA ON ABOUT**, 6, b g Schiaparelli (GER)—Grace Dieu **Ready Steady Go**
133 **WIRELESS OPERATOR (IRE)**, 6, b g Presenting—Princess Gaia (IRE) **McNeill Family and Prodec Networks Ltd**
134 **WOLFSPEAR (IRE)**, 5, b g Fame And Glory—Espresso Lady (IRE) **Mrs D. L. Whateley**
135 **WORLD TRIP**, 6, b m Universal (IRE)—Maiden Voyage **Touchwood Racing**
136 **ZEE MAN (FR)**, 7, b g Soldier of Fortune (IRE)—Sky High Flyer **geegeez.co.uk OM**

**Other Owners:** All The Kings Horses, Miss R Bailey, Mr E. G. M. Beard, Mr S. T. Black, Boultbee Brooks Ltd, Miss E. Boultbee-Brooks, Mr P. J. J. Boyle, Mr S. Boyle, Mr G. J. E. Brandrick, Briton International, Mr A. L. Brooks, Mrs K. L. Brooks, Mr P. Bryceland, Mr S. Bryceland, Mr D. J. Burke, Mrs V. F. Burke, Mr A. Carr, Miss E. J. Clarke, Mr B. R. Cognet, Mr W. I. C. Dale, Deva Racing Ripper Roo, Mr P. P. Elliott, Mr T. Elphick, Mr N. Farrell, Mrs L. H. Field, B. H. Goldswain, Exors of the Late Mrs J. B. H. Goldswain, Mr A. Govorusa, Mr J. R. Hales, Miss L. J. Hales, Mr R. D. A. Hames, Heart Racing HR3, Mr P. Henchoz, Mr S. R. Hodgkinson, Mr J. R. Holloway, Mrs A. C. Houldsworth, Mr D. Jacques, Jacques Law Partnership, Mr M. J. D. Lambert, Mr M. J. E. Lyons, Mr A. R. W. Marsh, Mr J. A. J. Martin, Mr L. Martin, Mr P. McBride, B. T. McDonald, McNeill Family Ltd, Mr B. H. Mellon, Mr G. Moore, Mr N. Moran, Mrs V. Moran, Mr M. Muldoon, Mrs A. L. M. Murphy, H. A. Murphy, Mr O. J. Murphy, Non League Racing, Mr A. E. Peterson, Mrs S. Powell, Prodec Networks Ltd, Mrs J. Rees, Mr B. Reynolds, Mr D. B. Salmon, Mrs Lynn Salmon, Mr M. W. Salmon, Mr R. A. Scott, Ms M. Shalvey, Mr J. Sigler, Mr G. N. Spurway, Mr S. Staplehurst, Mr T. D. J. Syder, Mrs J. A. Thomas, Mr R. Tongue, Mr R. Treacy, A. J. Wall, Mrs D. L. Whateley, Mrs M. G. Whittaker.

**Assistant Trainer:** Gerard Tumelty.

**NH Jockey:** Aidan Coleman, David England, Richard Johnson. **Conditional Jockey:** Fergus Gregory, Callum McKinnes, Lewis Stones. **Amateur Jockey:** Mr James King, Mr Luke Scott.

**403**

### MR PAT MURPHY, Hungerford
Postal: **Glebe House, School Lane, East Garston, Hungerford, Berkshire, RG17 7HR**
Contacts: PHONE **01488 648473**
EMAIL **patgmurphy13@gmail.com**

1 **GALTEE MOUNTAIN (IRE)**, 6, br g Mountain High (IRE)—Kings Queen (IRE) **P. G. Murphy**
2 **NESSFIELD BLUE**, 7, b g Kayf Tara—Bella Medici **Murphy & Chantler**

**Other Owners:** Mrs B. I. Chantler, P. G. Murphy.

**404**

### MR BARRY MURTAGH, Carlisle
Postal: **Hurst Farm, Ivegill, Carlisle, Cumbria, CA4 0NL**
Contacts: PHONE **017684 84649** MOBILE **07714 026741** FAX **017684 84744**
EMAIL **suemurtagh7@gmail.com**

1 **AINMISFEARR (IRE)**, 6, b m Famous Name—Virevolle (FR) **Mrs S. A. Murtagh**
2 **BORDER VICTOR**, 9, b g Beat All (USA)—Sambara (IRE) **Mrs A. Stamper**
3 **CAPTAIN COURAGEOUS (IRE)**, 8, b g Canford Cliffs (IRE)—Annacloy Pearl (IRE) **Mrs S. A. Murtagh**
4 **CURTANA**, 4, b f Saddler's Rock (IRE)—Lady Blade (IRE) **Mrs A. Stamper**
5 **ELIXER (IRE)**, 8, b g Oscar (IRE)—Sunny Native (IRE) **Hurst Farm Racing**
6 **ELUSIVE RED (IRE)**, 7, b g Elusive Pimpernel (USA)—Spin In The Wind (IRE) **Mrs S. A. Murtagh**
7 **GEYSER**, 5, b g Gale Force Ten—Popocatepetl (FR) **Mrs A. Stamper**
8 **LOVE AT DAWN (IRE)**, 8, br m Winged Love (IRE)—Presentingatdawn (IRE) **Mrs S. A. Murtagh**
9 **NAKADAM (FR)**, 11, b g Nickname (FR)—Cadoudame (FR) **Mrs S. A. Murtagh**
10 **SAMTU (IRE)**, 10, b g Teofilo (IRE)—Samdaniya **A. R. White**
11 **SUE ELLEN (IRE)**, 6, b m Califet (FR)—Pretty Valira (IRE) **Mrs S. A. Murtagh**
12 **WEAREWEREWEARE (IRE)**, 5, b g Enrique—Staraba (FR) **Famous Five Racing**

**Assistant Trainer:** S A Murtagh.

**Conditional Jockey:** Lorcan Murtagh. **Apprentice Jockey:** Connor Murtagh.

**405**

### DR JEREMY NAYLOR, Shrewton
Postal: **The Cleeve Stables, Elston, Shrewton, Salisbury, Wiltshire, SP3 4HL**
Contacts: PHONE **01980 620804** MOBILE **07771 740126**
EMAIL **info@jeremynaylor.com** WEBSITE **www.jeremynaylor.com**

1 **COCO LIVE (FR)**, 9, b g Secret Singer (FR)—Iona Will (FR) **Mr S. J. Rawlins**
2 **CROUCHING HARRY (IRE)**, 12, b g Tiger Hill (IRE)—Catwalk Dreamer (IRE) **Mrs S. P. Elphick**
3 **FEARSOME FRED**, 12, b g Emperor Fountain—Ryewater Dream **Mrs S. P. Elphick**
4 **FLEUR DU POMMIER**, 8, br m Apple Tree (FR)—Jersey Countess (IRE) **Mr S. J. Rawlins**
5 **SEERAJ**, 6, b h Fastnet Rock (AUS)—Star On High (USA) **Dr J. R. J. Naylor**

**406** **MRS HELEN NELMES, Dorchester**
Postal: **Warmwell Stables, 2 Church Cottages, Warmwell, Dorchester, Dorset, DT2 8HQ**
Contacts: **PHONE 01305 852254 MOBILE 07977 510318**
EMAIL warmwellstud@tiscali.co.uk WEBSITE www.warmwellstables.co.uk

1 **ARC OF BUBBLES (IRE)**, 6, br g Arcadio (GER)—Bubble Bann (IRE) **Mr M. J. Hoskins**
2 **ITSABOUTIME (IRE)**, 11, gr g Whitmore's Conn (USA)—Blazing Love (IRE) **K. A. Nelmes**
3 **KALMBEFORETHESTORM**, 13, ch g Storming Home—Miss Honeypenny (IRE) **Warmwellcome Partnership**
4 **KEEPYOURHEADUP**, 10, b g Sir Percy—Sweet Lemon (IRE) **Mr K. Tyre**
5 **LAOCH BEAG (IRE)**, 10, gr g King's Theatre (IRE)—Innocentines (FR) **KA Nelmes & LJ Burden**
6 **MENAPIAN (IRE)**, 10, b br g Touch of Land (FR)—Mannequin (IRE) **T M W Partnership**
7 **MERCHANT IN MILAN (IRE)**, 9, b g Milan—Azaban (IRE) **Mr L. J. Burden**
8 **NATIVEGETAWAY (IRE)**, 8, b g Getaway (GER)—Clonsingle Native (IRE) **Mr M. J. Hoskins**
9 **OVER THE RIVER (IRE)**, 5, b m Avonbridge—First Among Equals **Mr J. R. Dyer**
10 **SERVEONTIME (IRE)**, 10, b g Echo of Light—Little Lovely (IRE) **K. A. Nelmes**

Other Owners: Mr L. J. Burden, K. A. Nelmes.

Assistant Trainer: K Nelmes.

Conditional Jockey: Conor Ring.

**407** **MR TONY NEWCOMBE, Barnstaple**
Postal: **Lower Delworthy, Yarnscombe, Barnstaple, Devon, EX31 3LT**
Contacts: **PHONE 01271 858554 MOBILE 07785 297210**
EMAIL huntshawequineforest@talktalk.net

1 **AMAZON PRINCESS**, 4, b f War Command (USA)—Last Lahar **Joli Racing**
2 **BUG BOY (IRE)**, 5, b g Big Bad Bob (IRE)—Velvetina (IRE) **Dr S. P. Hargreaves**
3 **JOYFUL SONG (IRE)**, 4, b f Teofilo (IRE)—Good Friend (IRE) **Joli Racing**
4 **KNOW NO LIMITS (IRE)**, 4, b f Outstrip—Singing Field (IRE) **A. G. Newcombe**
5 **LIGHTNING ATTACK**, 5, b g Lethal Force (IRE)—Afrodita (IRE) **Mr G. Darling**
6 **LIIMARI**, 8, b m Authorized (IRE)—Snow Polina (USA) **A. G. Newcombe**
7 **LIPPY LADY (IRE)**, 5, b m Bungle Inthejungle—Sayrah **A. G. Newcombe**
8 **PRINCELY**, 6, b h Compton Place—Royal Award **Mr G. Darling**
9 **ROSE WHISPER (IRE)**, 4, gr f Dark Angel (IRE)—Warshah (IRE) **A. G. Newcombe**
10 **SOVEREIGN STATE**, 6, b g Compton Place—One Night In May (IRE) **R. Eagle**
11 **WAR OF SUCCESSION (IRE)**, 7, b g Casamento (IRE)—Rohlindi **Dr S. P. Hargreaves**

**THREE-YEAR-OLDS**

12 **JOLI'S LEGACY (IRE)**, b f Elzaam (AUS)—Joli Elegant (IRE) **Joli Racing**

**TWO-YEAR-OLDS**

13 **TARKA COUNTRY**, gr c 12/01 Outstrip—Turaathy (IRE) (Lilbourne Lad (IRE)) **A. G. Newcombe**

Assistant Trainer: John Lovejoy.

**408**

**DR RICHARD NEWLAND, Claines**
Postal: **Linacres Farm, Egg Lane, Claines, Worcester, WR3 7SB**
Contacts: **PHONE 07956 196535**
EMAIL richard.newland1@btopenworld.com

1 **AARON LAD (IRE)**, 10, b g Daylami (IRE)—Borntobepampered **Off The Clock Partners & Dr RDP Newland**
2 **AL ROC (FR)**, 10, br g Great Pretender (IRE)—Al Cov (FR) **Comedy Club Partnership**
3 **ARBOR VITAE (IRE)**, 7, b m Arcadio (GER)—Drinadaly (IRE) **Foxtrot Racing: Arbor Vitae**
4 **ASTROMACHIA**, 6, b g Sea The Stars (IRE)—Fontley **John Connolly & Odile Griffith**
5 **BAASEM (USA)**, 6, ch g New Approach (IRE)—Ausus (USA) **Mr C. E. Stedman**
6 **BALI BODY (IRE)**, 6, b g Doyen (IRE)—Burnt Oil Babe (IRE) **Foxtrot Racing Bali Body**
7 **BBOLD (IRE)**, 7, b g Aizavoski (IRE)—Molly Be **BAA Management Ltd**
8 **BEAU BAY (FR)**, 10, b g Bernebeau (FR)—Slew Bay (FR) **Mr Peter Green & Dr Rdp Newland**
9 **BENNY'S BRIDGE (IRE)**, 8, b g Beneficial—Wattle Bridge (IRE) **Biddestone Racing I**
10 **BENSON**, 6, b g Beat Hollow—Karla June **Pump & Plant Services Ltd**
11 **BIG G**, 6, b g Cityscape—Crazy (GER) **BAA Management Ltd**
12 **BILLY BRONCO**, 10, ch g Central Park (IRE)—Nan **The Choirboys & Partner**
13 **BLUE RIBBON**, 6, b g Sayif (IRE)—Mar Blue (FR)
14 **BOLTISSIME (FR)**, 6, b g Dawn Approach (IRE)—Be Yourself (FR) **M Albon & M P Tudor**
15 **C'EST LE BONHEUR (FR)**, 9, b g Laverton—Joie de La Vie (FR) **J A Provan & Partner**
16 **CAID DU LIN (FR)**, 9, gr g Della Francesca (USA)—Asia du Lin (FR) **Foxtrot Racing**
17 **CAPTAIN TOM CAT (IRE)**, 6, b g Dylan Thomas (IRE)—Miss Molly Malone (IRE) **Deva Racing Captain Tom Cat**
18 **CATAMARAN DU SEUIL (FR)**, 9, b g Network (GER)—Fleur du Tennis (FR) **Mr M. P. Tudor**
19 **CHEF DE TROUPE (IRE)**, 8, b g Air Chief Marshal (IRE)—Tazminya **Mr C. E. Stedman**
20 **CLASSIC ESCAPE (IRE)**, 8, b g Golan (IRE)—Seana Ghael (IRE) **Hold My Beer Syndicate**
21 **CLEVER AS A FOX (IRE)**, 8, b g Gold Well—Inouette (IRE) **The Leicester Lads**
22 **DANCING IN THE SKY (IRE)**, 8, b g Court Cave (IRE)—Agasaya (IRE) **Foxtrot Racing: Dancing In The Sky**
23 **DASHING PERK**, 10, b g Kayf Tara—Dashing Executive (IRE) **Mr P. Jenkins**
24 **DOUBLEUBEE (IRE)**, 7, b g Yeats (IRE)—Eastertide (IRE) **Lady Dulverton**
25 **DUBAI ANGEL (IRE)**, 10, b g Dubai Destination (USA)—Just Another Penny (IRE) **Mrs D. W. Davenport**
26 **EMMA LAMB**, 7, b m Passing Glance—Lucinda Lamb **Doom Bar Beach Club**
27 **ENQ ARD (FR)**, 7, b g Kapgarde (FR)—Usachaga (FR) **Off The Clock Partners & Dr RDP Newland**
28 **FANTASTIC MS FOX**, 5, b m Foxwedge (AUS)—Cracking Lass (IRE) **Mr T. A. Lee**
29 **FIRST SOLDIER (FR)**, 5, ch g Soldier of Fortune (IRE)—First Choice (FR) **Mr C. E. Stedman**
30 **FLEUR DU SEUIL (FR)**, 6, b m Youmzain (IRE)—Tulipe du Seuil (FR) **Mr M. P. Tudor**
31 **FOILLAN (IRE)**, 6, b g Le Fou (IRE)—Castlevennon (IRE) **Hold My Beer Syndicate**
32 **FORECAST**, 9, ch g Observatory (USA)—New Orchid (USA) **The The Tenovus Partnership**
33 **FOREIGN SECRETARY**, 6, ch g Galileo (IRE)—Finsceal Beo (IRE) **Mr R. M. Evans**
34 **GALATA BRIDGE**, 4, b c Golden Horn—Infallible **The Imperium Syndicate**
35 **GALSWORTHY**, 4, b c Dansili—Gallipot
36 **GAME SOCKS (IRE)**, 5, ch g Leading Light (IRE)—Late Night Deed **Chris Stedman & Mark Albon**
37 **GARBANZO (IRE)**, 7, gr g Mastercraftsman (IRE)—Noble Fantasy (GER) **Mr C. E. Stedman**
38 **GOSPELUS (FR)**, 5, b g Rail Link—Precieuze (FR) **The Choirboys**
39 **GRIMM STAR (FR)**, 5, b g Cokoriko (FR)—Beauty Blue (FR) **Deva Racing Grimm Star**
40 **HIGGS (IRE)**, 8, b g Scorpion (IRE)—Captain Supreme (IRE) **Pump & Plant Services Ltd**
41 **I'M SO BUSY**, 6, gr g Carlotamix (FR)—Ballcrina Girl (IRE) **Foxtrot Racing I'm So Busy**
42 **INDIGO LAKE**, 4, b g Frankel—Responsible **The Imperium Syndicate**
43 **KATPOLI (FR)**, 6, b g Poliglote—Katkogarie **Mr C. E. Stedman**
44 **LE PATRIOTE (FR)**, 9, b g Poliglote—Sentosa (FR) **Canard Vert Racing Club**
45 **LITTLE RORY MAC (IRE)**, 7, b g Yeats (IRE)—Solar Quest (IRE) **Foxtrot Racing: Little Rory Mac**
46 **LORD SCHNAPPS (FR)**, 8, b g Apsis—Nithaelle (FR)
47 **MAKKA PAKKA (IRE)**, 8, b g Duke of Marmalade (IRE)—Betray **Ardroe Developments Ltd**
48 **MARINE ONE**, 7, b g Frankel—Marine Bleue (FR) **Deva Racing Kingston**
49 **MARY KANE**, 7, b g Oscar (IRE)—Mission Hills **Mark Albon & Partner**
50 **MASON JAR (FR)**, 7, ch g No Risk At All (FR)—Queen's Theatre (FR) **Foxtrot Racing Mason Jar**
51 **MCGROARTY (IRE)**, 10, b g Brian Boru—Uffizi (IRE) **Chris Stedman & Mark Albon**
52 **MINELLA ENCORE (IRE)**, 9, b g King's Theatre (IRE)—Stashedaway (IRE) **Foxtrot Racing Minella Encore**
53 **MISTER CHIANG**, 5, b g Archipenko (USA)—Robe Chinoise **Foxtrot Racing: Mister Chiang**
54 **MR MULDOON (IRE)**, 8, ch g Rajj (IRE)—Miss Muldoon (IRE) **Foxtrot Racing Mr Muldoon**
55 **NORDICAN BLEUE (FR)**, 6, b m Anabaa Blue—Nordican Queen (FR) **Canard Vert Racing Club**

## DR RICHARD NEWLAND - continued

56 **OLYMPIC CONQUEROR (IRE)**, 5, b g Olympic Glory (IRE)—Queen's Conquer **Mr T. A. Lee**
57 **ON THE WILD SIDE (IRE)**, 8, b g Robin des Champs (FR)—Clear Riposte (IRE) **M Albon & M P Tudor**
58 **OPERATIC EXPORT (IRE)**, 5, b m Vocalised (USA)—Teofolina (IRE) **J A Provan & Partner**
59 **ORCHESTRAL RAIN (IRE)**, 4, b g Born To Sea (IRE)—Musical Rain (IRE) **Mark Albon & Chris Stedman**
60 **OTTAVIO**, 4, b c Nathaniel (IRE)—Our Queen of Kings
61 **PHOENIX DAWN**, 7, b g Phoenix Reach (IRE)—Comtesse Noire (CAN) **Dr R. D. P. Newland**
62 **PURPLE KING (IRE)**, 7, ch g Lope de Vega (IRE)—Dixie Dance (IRE) **Foxtrot Racing Purple King**
63 **REBEL LEADER (IRE)**, 7, b g Milan—Chicharito's Gem (IRE) **The Rebel Leaders**
64 **RIKOBOY (FR)**, 5, b g Enrique—Dikanika (FR) **Mr D. J. Smith**
65 **ROMAN ROCK (IRE)**, 7, b g Presenting—Native Idea (IRE) **Three Pears Racing**
66 **ROSE SEA HAS (FR)**, 6, gr g Kapgarde (FR)—Vaibuscar Has (FR) **The Berrow Hill Partnership**
67 **ROSTELLO (FR)**, 6, ch g Fuisse (FR)—Rose d'Ete (FR) **Dr R. D. P. Newland**
68 **SAGE ADVICE (IRE)**, 4, b g Make Believe—Purple Sage (IRE) **The Imperium Syndicate**
69 **SAQUON (IRE)**, 5, b g Arcadio (GER)—Seana Ghael (IRE) **Foxtrot Racing Saquon**
70 **SEINESATIONAL**, 6, b g Champs Elysees—Kibara **Mr C. E. Stedman**
71 **SOMETHINBOUTANGELA (IRE)**, 8, b m Milan—Cush Ramani (IRE) **Spur of the Moment & Partner**
72 **STATE VISION (IRE)**, 7, b g Vision d'Etat (FR)—Dona Rez (FR) **Mr D. A. Halsall**
73 **STORM RISING (IRE)**, 8, b g Canford Cliffs (IRE)—Before The Storm **M Albon & M P Tudor**
74 **SUDDEN DESTINATION (IRE)**, 9, ch g Dubai Destination (USA)—
                                    Sudden Approach (IRE) **Foxtrot Nh Racing Syndicate**
75 **SUMMER MOON**, 5, ch g Sea The Moon (GER)—Songerie **The Imperium Syndicate**
76 **SWEETTOWATCH (IRE)**, 7, b m Fracas (IRE)—Molly's Mate (IRE) **Mr M. P. Tudor**
77 **TANGO ECHO CHARLIE (IRE)**, 7, b g Stowaway—Wrong In Okanagan (IRE) **Briton International & Partner**
78 **TASTE THE FEAR (IRE)**, 6, b g Mores Wells—No Complaints But (IRE) **In It For Fun Partnership & Dr R Newland**
79 **THE DARLEY LAMA (IRE)**, 7, b g Carlotamix (FR)—Last Sunrise (IRE) **Foxtrot Racing the Darley Lama**
80 **THEO (IRE)**, 11, b g Westerner—Jemima Jay (IRE) **Dr R. D. P. Newland**
81 **VULCAN (IRE)**, 4, b g Free Eagle (IRE)—Quixotic **The Imperium Syndicate**
82 **WHATSDASTORY (IRE)**, 8, b m Beneficial—Supreme Contender (IRE) **Plan B**
83 **WHOSHOTWHO (IRE)**, 10, br g Beneficial—Inishbeg House (IRE) **Foxtrot Racing Whoshotwho & Partner**
84 **WIGGLESWORTH (IRE)**, 6, b g Doyen (IRE)—Arctic Aunt (IRE) **Rioja Raiders 04**
85 **YCCS PORTOCERVO (FR)**, 6, gr g Martaline—Griva (FR) **Mrs M C Litton&mrs F D McInnes Skinner**

**Other Owners:** Mr D. Abraham, Mrs J. Abraham, Mr M. L. Albon, Mr M. P. Ansell, Mr L. A. Bolingbroke, Briton International, Mr N. A. Clark, J. P. Connolly, Mr A. S. P. Drake, Mr A. C. Elliott, Mr J. M. Q. Evans, Mr P. M. Evans, Foxtrot Racing Management Ltd, Foxtrot Racing Purple King, **Foxtrot Racing:** Whoshotwho, Mr J. M. Gibbs, B. H. Goldswain, Exors of the Late Mr J. B. H. Goldswain, Mr P. C. W. Green, Ms O. L. Griffith, Mr R. Gudge, In It For Fun, Mrs P. J. Litton, Mr R. Marks, Mrs F. D. McInnes Skinner, Dr R. D. P. Newland, C. G. Nicholl, Off The Clock Partners, Mr J. A. Provan, Mr A. J. Ramsden, Spur of the Moment, Mr C. E. Stedman, The Choirboys, Mr M. P. Tudor.

**Assistant Trainer:** Rod Trow.

**Amateur Jockey:** Mr T Weston.

---

 **409**

## MISS ANNA NEWTON-SMITH, Jevington
Postal: **Bull Pen Cottage, Jevington, Polegate, East Sussex, BN26 5QB**
Contacts: **PHONE 01323 488354 MOBILE 07970 914124**
**EMAIL annanewtonsmith@gmail.com WEBSITE www.annanewtonsmith.co.uk**

1 **BURGESS DREAM (IRE)**, 12, b g Spadoun (FR)—Ennel Lady (IRE) **The Beano Partnership**
2 **DASHING SPIRIT (IRE)**, 4, b g Sir Prancealot (IRE)—Gwyllion (USA) **The Hamptons Racing Partnership**
3 5, B g Battle of Marengo (IRE)—Great Wave (IRE)
4 **MAID OF CAMELOT (IRE)**, 6, b m Camelot—Dea Mhein (IRE) **The Alice Partnership**
5 **MIS CASEY (IRE)**, 5, b m Sageburg (IRE)—The Real Casey (IRE) **The Hamptons Racing Partnership**

## MISS ANNA NEWTON-SMITH - continued

**Other Owners:** Mr I. S. Berger, Mr M. J. Dolan, Mr S. K. Dolan, Mr N. Lambert.

**Assistant Trainer:** Nicola Worley.

**NH Jockey:** Paddy Brennan, Charlie Deutsch, Jeremiah McGrath, David Noonan. **Conditional Jockey:** Rex Dingle.

---

## 410 MR ADRIAN NICHOLLS, Sessay
Postal: **The Ranch, Sessay, Thirsk, North Yorkshire, YO7 3ND**
Contacts: **PHONE 01845 597428**

1 **ABATE**, 5, br g Bated Breath—Red Kyte  **The Never Say No Racing Club**
2 **PENELOPE QUEEN**, 4, b f Dream Ahead (USA)—Belvoir Diva  **Dr H. Amouzad Khalili**
3 **SFUMATO**, 7, br g Bated Breath—Modern Look  **J. A. Rattigan**
4 **STRAWMAN (IRE)**, 4, b g Starspangledbanner (AUS)—Youve Got A Friend (IRE)  **The Strawman Partnership**
5 **THE BIG HOUSE (IRE)**, 5, b g Coach House (IRE)—Tekhania (IRE)  **Mr D. Stone**

### THREE-YEAR-OLDS

6 **BEAR ME IN MIND (IRE)**, ch f Ruler of The World (IRE)—Alaskan Breeze (IRE)  **Mr A. Nicholls**
7 **DAEMON'S HEIR**, b g Twilight Son—Grand Depart  **Mr D. Stone**
8 **FIVE AND DIME**, ch g Mustajeeb—Porthgain  **Ackworth Racing & Mr D. R. Wellicome**
9 **MAMBA WAMBA (IRE)**, b f Mehmas (IRE)—Mistress of Rome  **Mr D. Stone**

### TWO-YEAR-OLDS

10 **BRAZEN BEST**, b c 28/04 Brazen Beau (AUS)—All On Red (IRE) (Red Clubs (IRE)) (15000)  **Mr A. Nicholls**
11 **FANTASTICAL**, b f 25/02 Ulysses (IRE)—
 Futureland (Echo of Light) (6667)  **Saxtead Livestock Ltd & Gordon Bulloch**
12 B c 22/04 Elzaam (AUS)—Instant Memories (IRE) (Ad Valorem (USA)) (12381)  **Mr D. Stone**
13 B f 02/03 New Approach (IRE)—Jawaayiz (Kodiac) (6000)  **Mr A. Nicholls**
14 B f 10/03 Lethal Force (IRE)—Lady Tabitha (IRE) (Tamayuz)
15 **POETIKEL PIECE**, b f 14/03 Mayson—Nardin (Royal Applause) (19000)  **Mr A. Nicholls**
16 Gr f 23/01 Lethal Force (IRE)—Really Lovely (IRE) (Galileo (IRE)) (10000)
17 B f 17/02 Elzaam (AUS)—Secret Liaison (IRE) (Dandy Man (IRE)) (7143)  **Mr D. Stone**
18 B f 29/03 Pride of Dubai (AUS)—Short Affair (Singspiel (IRE)) (18000)  **Mr D. Stone**

**Other Owners:** Ackworth Racing, Mr C. Bennett, Mr G. Bulloch, Mr L. Cleland, Mr L. Goldthorpe, Mr M. G. Hancock, Mr A. Nicholls, Saxtead Livestock Ltd, Mr K. Till, Mr D. R. Wellicome.

---

## 411 MR PAUL NICHOLLS, Ditcheat
Postal: **Manor Farm Stables, Ditcheat, Shepton Mallet, Somerset, BA4 6RD**
Contacts: **PHONE 01749 860656 MOBILE 07977 270706**
**EMAIL info@paulnichollsracing.com WEBSITE www.paulnichollsracing.com**

1 **ACCOMPLICE (FR)**, 7, gr g Network (GER)—Miss Vitoria (FR)  **Mrs K. A. Stuart**
2 **ADRIEN DU PONT (FR)**, 9, b g Califet (FR)—Santariyka (FR)  **Mrs Johnny De La Hey**
3 **ALCALA (FR)**, 11, gr g Turgeon (USA)—Pail Mel (FR)  **Owners Group 016**
4 **AMENON (FR)**, 6, b g Saint des Saints (FR)—La Couetrie (FR)  **Mr & Mrs J. D. Cotton**
5 **AMOUR DE NUIT (IRE)**, 9, b g Azamour (IRE)—Umthoulah (IRE)  **Mr Andrew Williams**
6 **AS DE MEE (FR)**, 11, br br g Kapgarde—Koeur de Mee (FR)  **The Stewart Family & Judi Dench**
7 **ASHUTOR (FR)**, 7, gr g Redoute's Choice (AUS)—Ashalanda (FR)  **The Stewart Family**
8 **ASK FOR GLORY (IRE)**, 7, b g Fame And Glory (IRE)—Ask Helen (IRE)  **Mr Colm Donlon & Mr & Mrs P. K. Barber**
9 **ATHOLL STREET (IRE)**, 6, b g Jeremy (USA)—Allthewhile (IRE)  **Mr T. J. Hemmings**

# MR PAUL NICHOLLS - continued

10 **BARBADOS BUCK'S (IRE)**, 6, b g Getaway (GER)—Buck's Blue (FR) **The Stewart Family**
11 **BATHSHEBA BAY (IRE)**, 6, br g Footstepsinthesand—Valamareha (IRE) **Mr M. F. Geoghegan**
12 **BLACK CORTON (FR)**, 10, br g Laverock (GER)—Pour Le Meilleur (FR) **The Brooks Family & J. Kyle**
13 **BLACKJACK KENTUCKY (IRE)**, 8, b g Oscar (IRE)—My Name's Not Bin (IRE) **Owners Group 026**
14 **BOB AND CO (FR)**, 10, b g Dom Alco (FR)—Outre Mer (FR) **David Maxwell Racing Limited**
15 **BRAVEMANSGAME (FR)**, 6, b g Brave Mansonnien (FR)—Genifique (FR) **John Dance & Bryan Drew**
16 **BRELAN D'AS (FR)**, 10, b g Crillon (FR)—Las de La Croix (FR) **Mr J. P. McManus**
17 **BREWERS PROJECT (IRE)**, 7, b g Aizavoski (IRE)—Shaylee Wilde (IRE) **The Hon Mrs C. A. Townshend**
18 **BROKEN HALO**, 6, b g Kayf Tara—Miss Invincible **Giraffa Racing - BH**
19 4, B g Kingston Hill—Buena Notte (IRE) **M. C. Denmark**
20 **CALVA D'AUGE (FR)**, 6, b g Air Chief Marshal (IRE)—Hill Ou Elle (FR) **Owners Group 040**
21 **CAP DU MATHAN (FR)**, 6, b g Kapgarde (FR)—Nounjya du Mathan (FR) **The Stewart Family**
22 **CAPELAND (FR)**, 9, b g Poliglote—Neiland (FR) **Mrs K. A. Stuart**
23 **CAPTAIN DESTINY**, 4, b g Kapgarde (FR)—New Destiny (FR) **Diana Whateley & Dominic Burke**
24 **CARRY ON THE MAGIC (FR)**, 7, b br g Jeremy (USA)—Bisoguet (IRE) **Highclere Thoroughbred Racing - Magic**
25 **CAT TIGER (FR)**, 7, b g Diamond Boy (FR)—Miss Canon (FR) **David Maxwell Racing Limited**
26 **CELESTIAL FORCE (IRE)**, 6, b g Sea The Stars (IRE)—Aquarelle Bleue **John and Jess Dance**
27 **CHAVEZ (IRE)**, 5, b g Yeats (IRE)—Rock The Baby (IRE) **M. C. Denmark**
28 **CHEZ HANS (GER)**, 5, b g Mamool (IRE)—Chandos Rose (IRE) **Owners Group 038**
29 **CHRISTOPHER WOOD (IRE)**, 6, b g Fast Company (IRE)—Surf The Web (IRE) **Mrs S. A. J. Kinsella**
30 **CILL ANNA (IRE)**, 6, b m Imperial Monarch (IRE)—Technohead (IRE) **The Stewart Family**
31 **CLAN DES OBEAUX (FR)**, 9, b g Kapgarde (FR)—
                                       Nausicaa des Obeaux (FR) **Mr&Mrs P.K.Barber,G.Mason,Sir A Ferguson**
32 **CONFIRMATION BIAS (IRE)**, 6, b g Presenting—Bonnie Parker (IRE) **Mr Colm Donlon**
33 **COPAIN DE CLASSE (FR)**, 9, b g Enrique—Toque Rouge (FR) **The Stewart Family**
34 4, Ch g Flemensfirth (USA)—Cottage Theatre (IRE) **McNeill Family Ltd**
35 **CUT THE MUSTARD (FR)**, 9, br m Al Namix (FR)—Tadorna (FR) **Sullivan Bloodstock Limited**
36 **CYRNAME (FR)**, 9, b g Nickname (FR)—Narquille (FR) **Mrs Johnny De La Hey**
37 **DANCINGONTHEEDGE (FR)**, 4, b f Kapgarde (FR)—Solarize (FR) **Old Gold Racing 4**
38 **DANNY KIRWAN (IRE)**, 8, b g Scorpion (IRE)—Sainte Baronne (FR) **Mrs Johnny De La Hey**
39 **DANNY WHIZZBANG (IRE)**, 8, b g Getaway (GER)—Lakil Princess (IRE) **Mrs A. Tincknell**
40 4, Br c Sageburg (IRE)—Davids Delight (IRE) **M. C. Denmark**
41 5, B g Nathaniel (IRE)—Deana (FR) **Sullivan Bloodstock Limited**
42 **DENILIQUIN (IRE)**, 6, gr g Mastercraftsman (IRE)—Bernie's Moon (USA) **McNeill Family Ltd**
43 **DIEGO DU CHARMIL (FR)**, 9, b g Rallingarry (IRE)—Daramour (FR) **Mrs Johnny De La Hey**
44 **DIESE DES BIEFFES (FR)**, 8, gr g Martaline—Chanel du Berlais (FR) **Sullivan Bloodstock Limited**
45 **DOIN'WHATSHELIKES (IRE)**, 6, b m Presenting—Karkiyla (IRE) **The Brooks Family & J. Kyle**
46 **DOLOS (FR)**, 8, b g Kapgarde (FR)—Redowa (FR) **Mrs Johnny De La Hey**
47 **DON ALVARO**, 5, b g Muhtathir—New Destiny (FR) **Diana Whateley & Dominic Burke**
48 **DR SANDERSON (IRE)**, 7, b g Jeremy (USA)—Guydus (IRE) **Mr J. P. McManus**
49 **DUC DE BOURBON (FR)**, 5, b g Buck's Boum (FR)—Astre Eria (FR) **Mr J. P. McManus**
50 **DUC DES GENIEVRES (FR)**, 8, gr g Buck's Boum (FR)—Lobelie (FR) **Sullivan Bloodstock Limited**
51 **EASYRUN DE VASSY (FR)**, 7, b g Muhtathir—Royale The Best (FR) **Mr P. J. Vogt, P. F. Nicholls**
52 **ECCO**, 6, b g Maxios—Enjoy The Life **Mr Colm Donlon**
53 **EGLANTINE DU SEUIL (FR)**, 7, b m Saddler Maker (IRE)—Rixia du Seuil (FR) **Sullivan Bloodstock Limited**
54 **ENRILO (FR)**, 7, b g Buck's Boum (FR)—Rock Treasure (FR) **Martin Broughton & Friends 4**
55 **ERITAGE (FR)**, 7, b g Martaline—Sauves La Reine (FR) **Mrs A. Tincknell**
56 **ETOILE REBELLE (FR)**, 6, gr g Walk In The Park (IRE)—Line Mexia (FR) **Sullivan Bloodstock Limited**
57 **FABULOUS SAGA (FR)**, 9, b g Saint des Saints (FR)—Fabalina (FR) **Sullivan Bloodstock Limited**
58 **FAMOSO (IRE)**, 5, b g Fame And Glory—Mucho Macabi (IRE) **Mr P K Barber & Mr P J Vogt**
59 **FAST BUCK (FR)**, 7, gr g Kendargent (FR)—Juvenil Delinquent (USA) **Sullivan Bloodstock Limited**
60 **FAVORITO BUCK'S (FR)**, 9, b g Buck's Boum (FR)—Sangrilla (FR) **Mrs Johnny De La Hey**
61 **FIDELIO VALLIS (FR)**, 6, b g Saint des Saints (FR)—Quora Vallis (FR) **Mr J. Hales**
62 **FLASH COLLONGES (FR)**, 6, b g Saddler Maker (IRE)—Prouesse Collonges (FR) **The Gi Gi Syndicate**
63 **FLEMENSTIDE (IRE)**, 6, b g Flemensfirth (USA)—Keep Face (FR) **Mr P K Barber & Mr P J Vogt**
64 **FLIC OU VOYOU (FR)**, 7, b g Kapgarde (FR)—Hillflower (FR) **Mr Colm Donlon**
65 **FORCE TEN (FR)**, 6, b g Al Namix (FR)—Quick Siren Mae (FR) **Owners Group 029**
66 **FRIEND OR FOE (FR)**, 6, b g Walk In The Park (IRE)—Mandchou (FR) **Gordon & Su Hall**
67 **FRODON (FR)**, 9, b g Nickname (FR)—Miss Country (FR) **Mr P. J. Vogt**
68 **FROSTY LADY (FR)**, 4, gr f Silver Frost (IRE)—Beautiful Gem (FR) **Mr & Mrs J. D. Cotton**

## MR PAUL NICHOLLS - continued

69 **GALA DE CORTON (FR)**, 5, b g Secret Singer (FR)—Pour Le Meilleur (FR)  **Gordon & Su Hall**
70 **GELINO BELLO (FR)**, 5, b g Saint des Saints (FR)—Parade (FR)  **Mr & Mrs J. D. Cotton**
71 **GET THE APPEAL (IRE)**, 7, b m Getaway (GER)—Lady Appeal (IRE)  **Middleham Park Racing IX**
72 **GETAWAY TRUMP (IRE)**, 8, b g Getaway (GER)—Acinorev (IRE)  **Owners Group 023**
73 **GIVE ME A COPPER (IRE)**, 11, ch g Presenting—
　　　　　　　　　　　　　Copper Supreme (IRE)  **Done, Ferguson, Mason, Nicholls & Wood**
74 **GLAJOU (FR)**, 5, br g Network (GER)—Toscane (FR)  **Middleham Park Racing XLVIII & Peter Lamb**
75 **GOLD BULLION (FR)**, 5, b g Fame And Glory—Tornade d'Ainay (FR)  **M. C. Denmark**
76 **GOOD BALL (FR)**, 4, b g Doctor Dino—Set Et Match (IRE)  **Sir A Ferguson G Mason J Hales & L Hales**
77 **GRAND SANCY (FR)**, 7, b g Diamond Boy (FR)—La Courtille (FR)  **Martin Broughton Racing Partners**
78 **GREANETEEN (FR)**, 7, b g Great Pretender (IRE)—Manson Teene (FR)  **Mr C. M. Giles**
79 **GREAT GABLE (IRE)**, 5, b g Fame And Glory—Mistress Mole (FR)  **Owners Group 050**
80 **GROOVY KIND (FR)**, 5, b m Masked Marvel—Toscane de Laroque (FR)  **Owners Group 056**
81 **HACKER DES PLACES (FR)**, 4, b g Great Pretender (IRE)—Plaisance (FR)  **Owners Group 068**
82 **HARD FROST (FR)**, 4, b g Silver Frost (IRE)—Lottie Belle (FR)  **Mr & Mrs J. D. Cotton**
83 **HASHTAG BOUM (FR)**, 4, b f Al Namix (FR)—Engagee (FR)  **Mr Colm Donlon**
84 **HELL RED (FR)**, 4, gr g Martaline—Queen Margot (FR)  **Sir Martin Broughton & Friends 6**
85 **HENRI THE SECOND (FR)**, 4, b g Saddler Maker (IRE)—Rock Treasure (FR)  **Martin Broughton & Friends 7**
86 **HIGHLAND HUNTER (IRE)**, 8, gr g Subtle Power (IRE)—Loughine Sparkle (IRE)  **T. Barr**
87 **HITMAN (FR)**, 5, b g Falco (USA)—Tercah Girl (FR)  **Mason, Hogarth, Ferguson & Done**
88 **HOLETOWN HERO (FR)**, 4, br g Buck's Boum (FR)—Voix du Coeur (FR)  **Mr M. F. Geoghegan**
89 **HOUX GRIS (FR)**, 4, gr g Gris de Gris (IRE)—Qarera (FR)  **M.Booth, R.Evans & Sullivan Bloodstock**
90 **HUELGOAT (FR)**, 4, b g Voiladenuo (FR)—Cavadee (FR)  **Owners Group 080**
91 **HUGOS NEW HORSE (FR)**, 4, b g Coastal Path—Pour Le Meilleur (FR)  **The Stewart Family**
92 **HUGOS OTHER HORSE**, 7, b g Gold Well—Wicked Crack (IRE)  **The Stewart Family**
93 **IDIDNTFORGET**, 4, b f Blue Bresil (FR)—Clever Mode (FR)  **Coles, Smith, McManus & Broughton**
94 **JEREMY PASS (IRE)**, 4, b g Jeremy (USA)—Toulon Pass (IRE)  **John and Jess Dance**
95 **KANDOO KID (FR)**, 5, gr g Kapgarde (FR)—Scarlett du Mesnil (FR)  **Mr M. F. Geoghegan**
96 **KAPCORSE (FR)**, 8, br g Kapgarde (FR)—Angesse (FR)  **Mr J. P. McManus**
97 **KAYF TAOI**, 5, b g Kayf Tara—Patsie Magern  **Mr Colm Donlon**
98 **KILMINGTON ROSE (IRE)**, 6, ch m Presenting—Robyn's Rose (IRE)  **Mr Charles Pelham & Mr Henry Pelham**
99 **KNAPPERS HILL (IRE)**, 5, b g Valirann (FR)—Brogella (IRE)  **Mr P K Barber & Mr P J Vogt**
100 **LE CHIFFRE D'OR (FR)**, 5, gr g No Risk At All (FR)—Miss Vitoria (FR)  **Gordon & Su Hall**
101 **LIGHT IN THE SKY (FR)**, 5, b g Anodin (IRE)—Arsila (IRE)  **Light In the Sky Syndicate & Partners**
102 **LIME AVENUE (IRE)**, 4, b f Walk In The Park (IRE)—
　　　　　　　　　　　　　Carrigeen Kohleria (IRE)  **Highclere Thoroughbred Racing - WITP**
103 **LOUGH DERG SPIRIT (IRE)**, 9, b g Westerner—Sno-Cat Lady (IRE)  **The Stewart Family**
104 **LUCKY ONE (FR)**, 6, br g Authorized (IRE)—Lady Anouchka (IRE)  **Sullivan Bloodstock & Hughes Crowley**
105 **LYONS (IRE)**, 5, ch g Australia—Light Quest (USA)  **Martin Broughton & Friends 2**
106 **MAGIC SAINT (FR)**, 7, bl g Saint des Saints (FR)—Magic Poline (FR)  **Mr & Mrs J. D. Cotton**
107 **MALAYA (FR)**, 7, b m Martaline—Clarte d'Or (FR)  **Mrs Johnny De La Hey**
108 **MANORBANK (IRE)**, 6, b g Arcadio (GER)—Kind Word (IRE)  **Owners Group 065**
109 5, B g Blue Bresil (FR)—Maralypha (FR)  **The Stewart Family**
110 **MASTER TOMMYTUCKER**, 10, b g Kayf Tara—No Need For Alarm  **A. G. Fear**
111 **MCFABULOUS (IRE)**, 7, b g Milan—Rossavon (IRE)  **Giraffa Racing**
112 **MICK PASTOR (FR)**, 5, b g Meshaheer (USA)—Mick Oceane (FR)  **Mr J. P. McManus**
113 **MIRANDA (IRE)**, 6, b m Camelot—Great Artist (FR)  **Owners Group 034**
114 **MODUS**, 11, ch g Motivator—Alessandra  **Mr J. P. McManus**
115 **MON FRERE (FR)**, 5, b g Pour Moi (IRE)—Sistine  **Elite Racing Club**
116 **MONDORA (FR)**, 4, gr f Montmartre (FR)—Clarte d'Or (FR)  **Mrs Johnny De La Hey**
117 **MONMIRAL (FR)**, 4, b g Saint des Saints (FR)—Achere (FR)  **Sir A Ferguson G Mason J Hales & L Hales**
118 **MONT DES AVALOIRS (FR)**, 8, b g Blue Bresil (FR)—Abu Dhabi (FR)  **Mrs Johnny De La Hey**
119 **MONTYS MEDOC (FR)**, 5, b g Westerner—Kilbarry Medoc (IRE)  **Insurance Friends**
120 **MR GLASS (IRE)**, 5, b g Sholokhov (FR)—Maryota (FR)  **John and Jess Dance**
121 **MY WAY (FR)**, 7, ch g Martaline—Royale Majesty (FR)  **Mr C. M. Giles**
122 **NEXT DESTINATION (IRE)**, 9, b g Dubai Destination (USA)—Liss Alainn (IRE)  **M. C. Denmark**
123 **OFFYOUPOP (IRE)**, 5, b g Getaway (GER)—Crossbar Lady (FR)  **Mr S. White**
124 **ONETHREEFIVENOTOUT (IRE)**, 5, b g Milan—Back To Loughadera (IRE)  **The Stewart Family**
125 **OSCARS MOONSHINE (IRE)**, 6, b g Oscar (IRE)—Scrapper Jack (IRE)  **Mrs E. Lane**
126 **PASO DOBLE (IRE)**, 4, br g Dawn Approach (IRE)—Baila Me (GER)  **Mr G. F. Brooks**

# MR PAUL NICHOLLS - continued

127 5, B g Lope de Vega (IRE)—Pearly Avenue **M. C. Denmark**
128 **PETROSSIAN (IRE)**, 5, br g Sageburg (IRE)—Innisfree Dawn (IRE) **M. C. Denmark**
129 **PIC D'ORHY (FR)**, 6, b g Turgeon (USA)—Rose Candy (FR) **Mrs Johnny De La Hey**
130 **POLITOLOGUE (FR)**, 10, gr g Poliglote—Scarlet Row (FR) **Mr J. Hales**
131 **POZO EMERY (FR)**, 6, b g Le Havre (IRE)—Chic Et Zen (FR) **The Stewart Family**
132 **PRESENT MAN (IRE)**, 11, b g Presenting—Glen's Gale (IRE) **Mr & Mrs Mark Woodhouse**
133 **PRINCE NINO (FR)**, 4, ch g It's Gino (GER)—Down On My Knees (FR) **The Brooks Family & J. Kyle**
134 4, B c Fame And Glory—Princess Mairead (IRE) **M. C. Denmark**
135 **QUEL DESTIN (FR)**, 8, b g Muhtathir—High Destiny (FR) **Martin Broughton & Friends**
136 **RAINYDAY WOMAN**, 6, b m Kayf Tara—Wistow **Mr S. White**
137 **REAL STEEL (FR)**, 8, b g Loup Breton (IRE)—Kalimina (FR) **Mrs Kathy Stuart&sullivan Bloodstock Ltd**
138 **RED RISK (FR)**, 6, b g No Risk At All (FR)—Rolie de Vindecy (FR) **Middleham Park Racing Xliv & A&j Ryan**
139 **RHYTHM IS A DANCER**, 8, b g Norse Dancer (IRE)—Fascinatin Rhythm **W. A. Harrison-Allan**
140 **ROCHESTON (FR)**, 6, b g Kapgarde (FR)—Ravna (FR) **Sullivan Bloodstock Limited**
141 **ROCKADENN (FR)**, 5, b g High Rock (IRE)—Nijadenn (FR) **Million in Mind Partnership**
142 **ROQUE IT (IRE)**, 7, b g Presenting—Roque de Cyborg (IRE) **Gordon & Su Hall**
143 **SAINT DE REVE (FR)**, 7, b g Saint des Saints (FR)—Ty Mat (FR) **Mrs Johnny De La Hey**
144 **SAINT SONNET (FR)**, 6, b g Saint des Saints (FR)—Leprechaun Lady (FR) **Mr Colm Donlon**
145 **SAMARRIVE (FR)**, 4, b g Coastal Path—Sambirane (FR) **Mrs Johnny De La Hey**
146 **SAMETEGAL (FR)**, 12, b g Saint des Saints (FR)—Loya Lescribaa (FR) **Mr & Mrs J. D. Cotton**
147 **SAN BENEDETO (FR)**, 10, ch g Layman (USA)—Cinco Baidy (FR) **Mr P. J. Vogt**
148 **SANDALWOOD (FR)**, 4, ch g Martaline—Balli Flight (FR) **Owners Group 072**
149 **SCARAMANGA (IRE)**, 6, b g Mastercraftsman (IRE)—Herboriste **M. C. Denmark**
150 **SECRET INVESTOR**, 9, b g Kayf Tara—Silver Charmer **Hills of Ledbury Ltd**
151 **SECRET POTION (GER)**, 5, b g Dabirsim (FR)—Sola Gratia (IRE) **Mr Andrew Williams**
152 **SEELOTMOREBUSINESS (IRE)**, 6, b g Sholokhov (IRE)—Land of Pride (IRE) **The Stewart Family**
153 **SENDING LOVE (IRE)**, 8, b g Scorpion (IRE)—Dato Vic (IRE) **Sullivan Bloodstock Limited**
154 **SETTLE DOWN (FR)**, 6, b g Motivator—Zarafsha (IRE) **The Rosecroft Partnership**
155 **SHEARER (IRE)**, 5, b g Flemensfirth (USA)—The Crown Jewel (IRE) **McNeill Family Ltd**
156 **SHOLOKJACK (IRE)**, 5, b g Sholokhov (IRE)—Another Pet (IRE) **Sullivan Bloodstock Limited**
157 **SILENT REVOLUTION (IRE)**, 5, b g Sholokhov (IRE)—Watson River (IRE) **Mr Colm Donlon**
158 **SILVER FOREVER (IRE)**, 7, gr m Jeremy (USA)—Silver Prayer (IRE) **Mr Colm Donlon**
159 **SIR PSYCHO (IRE)**, 5, b g Zoffany (IRE)—Open Book **Martin Broughton & Friends 3**
160 **SIROCO JO (FR)**, 4, ch g Hurricane Cat (USA)—Diana Vertica (FR) **Mr P. J. Vogt**
161 **SISTER SAINT (FR)**, 4, gr f Martaline—Minirose (FR) **Mrs Johnny De La Hey**
162 **SKATMAN (IRE)**, 6, br g Mustameet (USA)—Maid For Action (IRE) **Mr C. M. Giles**
163 **SOLDIER OF LOVE**, 8, b g Yeats (IRE)—Monsignorita (IRE) **M. C. Denmark**
164 **SOLO (FR)**, 5, b g Kapgarde (FR)—Flameche (FR) **Mrs Johnny De La Hey**
165 **SONNY CROCKETT (IRE)**, 6, b g Robin des Champs (FR)—Onewayortheother (IRE) **M. C. Denmark**
166 **SOUTHFIELD HARVEST**, 7, b g Kayf Tara—Chamoss Royale (FR) **Mrs Angela Yeoman & Mr Paul K. Barber**
167 **SOUTHFIELD STONE**, 8, gr g Fair Mix (IRE)—Laureldean Belle (IRE) **Mrs Angela Hart & Mrs Angela Yeoman**
168 **STAGE STAR (IRE)**, 5, b g Fame And Glory—Sparky May **Owners Group 044**
169 **STANLEY STANLEY**, 4, b f Camelot—Seaham Hall **Mrs S. A. J. Kinsella**
170 **STORM ARISING (IRE)**, 7, b g Yeats (IRE)—Ceol Rua (IRE) **Barry Fulton & Mrs Angela Hart**
171 **STRATAGEM (FR)**, 5, gr g Sunday Break (JPN)—Our Ziga (FR) **David Maxwell Racing Limited**
172 **SWITCH HITTER (IRE)**, 6, b g Scorpion (IRE)—Country Time (IRE) **Hills of Ledbury Ltd**
173 4, B g Fame And Glory—Tabachines (FR) **Hills of Ledbury Ltd**
174 **TAKE YOUR TIME (IRE)**, 6, b g Dubai Destination (USA)—Don't Be Bleu (IRE) **Owners Group 060**
175 **TAMAROC DU MATHAN (FR)**, 6, b g Poliglote—Thisbee du Mathan (FR) **Mrs Johnny De La Hey**
176 **TAMGHO BORGET (FR)**, 5, gr g Martaline—Ges (FR) **Booth, Evans, Murray&sullivan Bloodstock**
177 **TANGO TARA**, 5, b g Kayf Tara—Bling Noir (FR) **Middleham Park XXXIX & Peter Lamb**
178 **THREEUNDERTHRUFIVE (IRE)**, 6, b g Shantou (USA)—Didinas (FR) **McNeill Family Ltd**
179 **THYME WHITE (FR)**, 5, b g Anodin (IRE)—Jane (GER) **The Stewart Family**
180 **TIME TO TINKER (IRE)**, 6, br g Stowaway—Zuzka (IRE) **Mrs A. Tincknell**
181 **TOMORROW MYSTERY**, 7, b m Nathaniel (IRE)—Retake **Mr J. P. McManus**
182 **TOPOFTHEGAME (IRE)**, 9, ch g Flemensfirth (USA)—Derry Vale (IRE) **Mr Chris Giles & Mr&mrs P K Barber**
183 **TREVELYN'S CORN (IRE)**, 8, b g Oscar (IRE)—Present Venture (IRE) **Mr C. M. Giles**
184 **TRUCKERS LODGE (IRE)**, 9, b g Westerner—Galeacord (IRE) **Gordon & Su Hall**
185 **TULIN**, 4, b g Gleneagles (IRE)—Talawat **Elite Racing 001**
186 **URBAN SOLDIER (IRE)**, 4, b br g Soldier of Fortune (IRE)—She's No Pet (IRE) **Middleham Park CXI**

## MR PAUL NICHOLLS - continued

187 **VIROFLAY (FR)**, 4, b g Air Chief Marshal (IRE)—Red Vixen (IRE)  **The Stewart Family**
188 **WESTHILL (IRE)**, 6, b g Westerner—Brogarais (IRE)  **Hills of Ledbury Ltd**
189 **WHISKEY LULLABY (IRE)**, 6, b m Stowaway—Joie de Cotte (FR)  **Highclere Thoroughbred Racing - Whiskey**
190 **WILD MAX (GER)**, 6, b g Maxios—Wildfahrte (GER)  **Owners Group 036**
191 **WISE GLORY (IRE)**, 4, b g Muhaarar—Bint Almukhtar (IRE)  **Foxhills Racing Limited**
192 **WORTHY FARM (IRE)**, 8, b g Beneficial—Muckle Flugga (IRE)  **YOLO**
193 **YALA ENKI (FR)**, 11, b br g Nickname (FR)—Cadiane (FR)  **Hills of Ledbury Ltd**
194 **YOUNG BUCK (IRE)**, 7, b g Yeats (IRE)—Pepsi Starlet (IRE)  **The Stewart Family**
195 **ZORAN**, 4, b g Invincible Spirit (IRE)—Filia Regina  **Owners Group 077**
196 **ZYON**, 7, gr g Martaline—Temptation (FR)  **Mrs Johnny De La Hey**

### THREE-YEAR-OLDS
197 **ISAAC DES OBEAUX (FR)**, b g Kapgarde (FR)—
                                        Varda des Obeaux (FR)  **G Mason,Sir A Ferguson,Mr&Mrs P K Barber**

**Other Owners:** Mr S. R. Aston, Mrs M. G. Barber, P. K. Barber, Mr J. Barnard, Mr M. Booth, Mr N. Brand, Mr G. F. Brooks, Lady J. M. Broughton, Sir M. F. Broughton, Mr S. W. Broughton, Mr A. P. Brown, Mr D. J. Burke, Mr D. J. Coles, Mr J. E. Dance, Dame J. O. Dench, Mr J. Diver, Mr P. E. Done, Mr Colm Donlon, Mr B. J. C. Drew, Miss R. Evans, Sir A. Ferguson, B. N. Fulton, Mr C. M. Giles, Mrs D. M. Gregory, Mr J. R. Hales, Miss L. J. Hales, Mr R. Hales, Mr G. A. Hall, Mrs S. L. Hall, Mr M. P. Hammond, Mrs A. R. Hart, P. H. Hogarth, Mr M. J. Holman, Mr N. Hughes, Mr P. Jackson, Mrs N. Jones, Mr J. Kyle, Light in The Sky Syndicate, Mr P. D. Maddocks, Mr T. J. Malone, G. A. Mason, Mr B. J. McManus, Middleham Park XXXIX, Mr K. Monk, Mrs M. E. Moody, Mr G. Murray, P. F. Nicholls, Mr C. T. Pelham, Mr H. T. Pelham, Mr S. P. Price, Mr J. W. Randall, Miss Claire Simmonds, Mr B. D. Smith, Mr D. D. Stevenson, Mr A. Stewart, Mrs J. A. Stewart, Mrs K. A. Stuart, Sullivan Bloodstock Limited, The Stewart Family, Mr R. C. Tydings, Mr P. J. Vogt, Mrs D. L. Whateley, Mr R. J. Wood, M. J. M. Woodhouse, Mrs T. A. Woodhouse, Mrs A. B. Yeoman.

**Assistant Trainer:** Charlie Davies, Harry Derham, Natalie Parker.

**Flat Jockey:** Megan Nicholls. **NH Jockey:** Sean Bowen, Harry Cobden, Bryony Frost, Sam Twiston-Davies. **Conditional Jockey:** Bryan Carver, Angus Cheleda, Lorcan Williams. **Amateur Jockey:** Mr Will Biddick, Miss Natalie Parker.

---

## 412  MR ADAM DAVID NICOL, Seahouses
Postal: **Springwood, South Lane, North Sunderland, Seahouses, Northumberland, NE68 7UL**
Contacts: **PHONE 01665 720320**
**EMAIL adamnicol89@hotmail.co.uk**

1 **ECONOMIC EDITOR (IRE)**, 5, b g Jet Away—How Provincial (IRE)  **UP4B**
2 **VELKERA (IRE)**, 7, br m Sholokhov (IRE)—April Gale (IRE)  **The Seahouses Syndicate**
3 **WISE EAGLE (IRE)**, 4, ch g Free Eagle (IRE)—Best Be Careful (IRE)  **The Seahouses Syndicate**

---

## 413  MR PETER NIVEN, Malton
Postal: **Clovafield, Barton-Le-Street, Malton, North Yorkshire, YO17 6PN**
Contacts: **PHONE 01653 628176 MOBILE 07860 260999 FAX 01653 627295**
**EMAIL pruniven@btinternet.com WEBSITE www.peterniven.co.uk**

1 **AMBER**, 5, ch m Dunaden (FR)—Secret Virtue  **Keep The Faith Partnership**
2 **BRIAN BORANHA (IRE)**, 10, b g Brian Boru—Tapneiram (IRE)  **Mrs K. J. Young**
3 **EARLY MORNING DEW (FR)**, 5, ch g Muhtathir—Rosee Matinale (FR)  **Mr A. M. Kitching**
4 **HURSTWOOD**, 4, br gr g Dark Angel (IRE)—Haigh Hall  **Mr David John Lumley**
5 **MALYSTIC**, 7, b g Malinas (GER)—Mystic Glen  **Clova Syndicate & Mrs J A Niven**
6 **MINUTE WALTZ**, 4, b f Sixties Icon—Mystic Glen  **K & J Niven**

## MR PETER NIVEN - continued

  7 **MISTY MANI**, 6, b m Sulamani (IRE)—Mystic Glen   **Mrs K Young & Mrs J A Niven**
  8 4, Bl f Turgeon (USA)—Nicknack (FR)
  9 **ROCK ON SWEETIE**, 4, b f Nayef (USA)—Rock Candy (IRE)   **Hedley, Little, Sharkey & Tomkins**
 10 **SIMPLY MANI**, 9, ch g Sulamani (IRE)—Simply Mystic   **Mrs J A Niven & Angus Racing Club**
 11 **STORM FORCE ONE**, 5, b m Schiaparelli (GER)—Force In The Wings (IRE)   **Hedley, Little, Sharkey & Tomkins**
 12 **WICKLOW WARRIOR**, 6, b g Sleeping Indian—Vale of Clara (IRE)   **Mr P. D. Niven**

### THREE-YEAR-OLDS

 13 **BARNONE**, b g Nayef (USA)—Barwah (USA)   **Keep The Faith Partnership**
 14 **SUGAR BABY**, b g Monsieur Bond (IRE)—Sugar Town   **Angus Racing Club & Mr P. D. Niven**

**Other Owners:** Angus Racing Club, Clova Syndicate, Mr B. W. Ewart, Mr C. R. Hedley, Mr K. J. Little, Mrs J. A. Niven, Mr M. W. G. Niven, Mr P. D. Niven, Mrs K. M. Richardson, Mr W. K. D. Sharkey, Mrs G. M. Swinglehurst, J. M. Swinglehurst, Ms L. P. Tomkins, Mrs K. J. Young.

---

**414**   **MR JOHN NORTON, Barnsley**
Postal: **Globe Farm, High Hoyland, Barnsley, South Yorkshire, S75 4BE**
Contacts: **HOME 01226 387633 MOBILE 07970 212707**
**HOME EMAIL johnrnorton@hotmail.com FACEBOOK JRNorton**

 1 **AL MIKDAM (USA)**, 5, ch g City Zip (USA)—Brattothecore (CAN)   **Jaffa Racing Syndicate**
 2 **BLACK MARKET (IRE)**, 7, b g Yeats (IRE)—Aneda Dubh (IRE)   **Fellowship Of The Rose Partnership 2**
 3 **MAGIC SHIP (IRE)**, 6, b g Kodiac—Baltic Belle (IRE)   **J. R. Norton Ltd**
 4 **MUFTAKKER**, 7, gr g Tamayuz—Qertaas (IRE)   **Colin Holder Racing**
 5 **NAASIK**, 8, b g Poet's Voice—Shemriyna (IRE)   **Fellowship Of The Rose Partnership 2**
 6 **SPY FI**, 7, b m Dick Turpin (IRE)—Sindarbella   **J. R. Norton Ltd**
 7 **WILLIAMWILBERFORCE**, 4, b g Dream Ahead (USA)—Isabella Bird   **A. Tattersall & Mrs Diane Widdowson**

**Other Owners:** Fellowship Of The Rose Partnership, Mr C. Holder, J. R. Norton Ltd, Mr P. R. Woodcock-Jones.

---

**415**   **MR A. P. O'BRIEN, Ballydoyle**
Postal: **Ballydoyle Stables, Cashel, Co. Tipperary, Ireland**
Contacts: **PHONE +353 62 62615**
**EMAIL racingoffice@ballydoyle.com**

 1 **AMHRAN NA BHFIANN (IRE)**, 4, b c Galileo (IRE)—Alluring Park (IRE)
 2 **ARMORY (IRE)**, 4, b c Galileo (IRE)—After (IRE)
 3 **BROOME (IRE)**, 5, b h Australia—Sweepstake (IRE)
 4 **INNISFREE (IRE)**, 4, b c Galileo (IRE)—Palace (IRE)
 5 **JAPAN**, 5, b h Galileo (IRE)—Shastye (IRE)
 6 **LANCASTER HOUSE (IRE)**, 5, b h Galileo (IRE)—Quiet Oasis (IRE)
 7 **LOPE Y FERNANDEZ (IRE)**, 4, b c Lope de Vega (IRE)—Black Dahlia
 8 **LOVE (IRE)**, 4, ch f Galileo (IRE)—Pikaboo
 9 **MOGUL**, 4, b c Galileo (IRE)—Shastye (IRE)
 10 **ORDER OF AUSTRALIA (IRE)**, 4, b c Australia—Senta's Dream
 11 **PASSION (IRE)**, 4, b f Galileo (IRE)—Dialafara (FR)
 12 **SANTIAGO (IRE)**, 4, b c Authorized (IRE)—Wadyhatta
 13 **SERPENTINE (IRE)**, 4, ch c Galileo (IRE)—Remember When (IRE)
 14 **TIGER MOTH (IRE)**, 4, b c Galileo (IRE)—Lesson In Humility (IRE)

## MR A. P. O'BRIEN - continued

### THREE-YEAR-OLDS

15 **ADMIRAL NELSON**, b c Kingman—Shamandar (FR)
16 **APOLLO THIRTEEN (IRE)**, b br c No Nay Never (USA)—Nasty Storm (USA)
17 **ARTURO TOSCANINI (IRE)**, b c Galileo (IRE)—Snow Queen (IRE)
18 **AWHILE (IRE)**, br f War Front (USA)—Wonder of Wonders (USA)
19 **BATON ROUGE (IRE)**, b c Galileo (IRE)—Absolutelyfabulous (IRE)
20 **BATTLEGROUND (USA)**, b c War Front (USA)—Found (IRE)
21 **BLUE PLANET**, b c Kingman—One Last Dance (AUS)
22 **BOLSHOI BALLET (IRE)**, b c Galileo (IRE)—Alta Anna (FR)
23 **BRAZIL (IRE)**, b c Galileo (IRE)—Dialafara (FR)
24 **CALL ME SWEETHEART (IRE)**, b f Australia—Potion
25 **CARLISLE BAY (IRE)**, b c Galileo (IRE)—Toogoodtobetrue (IRE)
26 **CARLO LANDOLFI (IRE)**, b c Galileo (IRE)—Along The Beach (USA)
27 **CARTOUCHE (IRE)**, b f Galileo (IRE)—Awesome Maria (USA)
28 **CATCH (IRE)**, b f Galileo (IRE)—Even Song (IRE)
29 **CHAIN MAIL (IRE)**, b c American Pharoah (USA)—Wading (IRE)
30 **CHIEF LITTLE HAWK (USA)**, ch c Air Force Blue (USA)—Marylebone (USA)
31 **CHIFFON (IRE)**, b f Galileo (IRE)—Acapulco (USA)
32 **CLEVELAND (IRE)**, b c Camelot—Venus de Milo (IRE)
33 **COUNTY WICKLOW (USA)**, b c War Front (USA)—Coolmore (IRE)
34 **DIVINELY (IRE)**, b f Galileo (IRE)—Red Evie (IRE)
35 **DRUMMER GIRL (IRE)**, ch f Galileo (IRE)—Quiet Oasis (IRE)
36 **DUKE OF MANTUA (IRE)**, b c No Nay Never (USA)—Pietra Dura
37 **EAVES (IRE)**, b f Galileo (IRE)—Where (IRE)
38 **ELIZABETHAN (USA)**, b f War Front (USA)—Misty For Me (IRE)
39 **EMPRESS JOSEPHINE (IRE)**, b f Galileo (IRE)—Lillie Langtry (IRE)
40 **ESPANIA (IRE)**, b f Galileo (IRE)—Green Room (USA)
41 **ETERNAL FLAME (IRE)**, gr c Galileo (IRE)—Laddies Poker Two (IRE)
42 **EXUMA (IRE)**, b c Galileo (IRE)—Glass Slipper (IRE)
43 **FATHER'S DAY (IRE)**, b c Galileo (IRE)—Fire Lily (IRE)
44 **FINEST (IRE)**, b f The Gurkha (IRE)—Pearl Grey
45 **FLORA (IRE)**, ch f Galileo (IRE)—Moonstone
46 **FOREST OF DREAMS (IRE)**, ch c No Nay Never (USA)—Winning Sequence (FR)
47 **FRIENDLY (IRE)**, ch f Galileo (IRE)—Massarra
48 **FRILL (IRE)**, ch f Galileo (IRE)—Penchant
49 **GIORGIO VASARI (IRE)**, b c Air Force Blue (USA)—Dream The Blues (IRE)
50 **GLINTING (IRE)**, b br f Galileo (IRE)—One Moment In Time (IRE)
51 **HANDEL (USA)**, b c Pioneerof The Nile (USA)—Party Starter (USA)
52 **HARVARD (IRE)**, ch c Galileo (IRE)—Life Happened (USA)
53 **HECTOR DE MARIS (IRE)**, b c Camelot—Frequential
54 **HIGH DEFINITION (IRE)**, b c Galileo (IRE)—Palace (IRE)
55 **HIGH HEELS (IRE)**, b f Galileo (IRE)—Charlotte Bronte
56 **HMS SEAHORSE (IRE)**, ch c Galileo (IRE)—After (IRE)
57 **HOROSCOPE (IRE)**, b c No Nay Never (USA)—Inca Wood (UAE)
58 **INTERPRETATION (IRE)**, b c Galileo (IRE)—Daldiyna (FR)
59 **IOWA (IRE)**, b c Galileo (IRE)—Bridal Dance (IRE)
60 **IRISH CHIEF (USA)**, b c War Front (USA)—Wedding Vow (IRE)
61 **JEROBOAM (USA)**, b c War Front (USA)—Outstanding (IRE)
62 **JOAN OF ARC (IRE)**, b f Galileo (IRE)—You'resothrilling (USA)
63 **KEY TO THE KINGDOM (IRE)**, b c Galileo (IRE)—Miarixa (FR)
64 **KHARTOUM (USA)**, b c Pioneerof The Nile (USA)—Up (IRE)
65 **KING OF THE CASTLE (IRE)**, ch c Galileo (IRE)—Remember When (IRE)
66 **KYPRIOS (IRE)**, ch c Galileo (IRE)—Polished Gem (IRE)
67 **LA JOCONDE (IRE)**, b f Frankel—Wadyhatta
68 **LIPIZZANER (USA)**, b br c Uncle Mo (USA)—Irish Lights (AUS)
69 **LORD OF THE MANOR (IRE)**, b c Galileo (IRE)—Wave (IRE)
70 **LOUGH DERG (IRE)**, gr c Galileo (IRE)—Easton Angel (IRE)
71 **LOYAL (IRE)**, b f Galileo (IRE)—Chartreuse (IRE)
72 **MADONNA (IRE)**, b f Galileo (IRE)—Sumora (IRE)

## MR A. P. O'BRIEN - continued

73 **MALAWI (IRE)**, ch c Galileo (IRE)—Weekend Strike (USA)
74 **MARTINIQUE**, b f Le Havre (IRE)—Phiz (GER)
75 **MATCHLESS (IRE)**, b c Galileo (IRE)—Bye Bye Birdie (IRE)
76 **MERCHANTS QUAY (FR)**, ch c No Nay Never (USA)—Painting (IRE)
77 **METAPHORICAL (IRE)**, b c No Nay Never (USA)—High Savannah (IRE)
78 **MILITARY STYLE (USA)**, b c War Front (USA)—Together Forever (IRE)
79 **MODUS OPERANDI (IRE)**, b c Frankel—Auld Alliance (IRE)
80 **MONDAY (USA)**, b br f Fastnet Rock (AUS)—Ballydoyle (IRE)
81 **MONTEGO BAY (IRE)**, b f No Nay Never (USA)—Lesson In Life
82 **MORE BEAUTIFUL (USA)**, b f War Front (USA)—Maybe (IRE)
83 **MOTHER EARTH (IRE)**, b f Zoffany (IRE)—Many Colours
84 **NATIONAL BALLET (JPN)**, b c Deep Impact (JPN)—Fluff (IRE)
85 **ONTARIO (IRE)**, b c Galileo (IRE)—Timbuktu (IRE)
86 **PREAMBLE (IRE)**, b c No Nay Never (USA)—Falling Rain (IRE)
87 **QUEEN'S SPEECH (USA)**, ch f American Pharoah (USA)—Paradise Playgirl (USA)
88 **ROMAN EMPIRE (IRE)**, b c Galileo (IRE)—Shermeen (IRE)
89 **ROSES ARE RED (IRE)**, b f Galileo (IRE)—Keenes Royale
90 **SAN MARTINO (IRE)**, ch c The Gurkha (IRE)—Euphrasia (IRE)
91 **SANDHURST (IRE)**, b c Galileo (IRE)—How's She Cuttin' (IRE)
92 **SANTA BARBARA (IRE)**, b f Camelot—Senta's Dream
93 **SHINING BRIGHT (IRE)**, ch f Galileo (IRE)—Lady Lara (IRE)
94 **SIMPLY INCREDIBLE (IRE)**, b f Galileo (IRE)—Race For The Stars (USA)
95 **SIR LAMORAK (IRE)**, b c Camelot—Simply A Star (IRE)
96 **SIR LUCAN (IRE)**, b c Camelot—Sparrow (IRE)
97 **SIR WILLIAM BRUCE (IRE)**, b c Galileo (IRE)—Chanting (USA)
98 **SNOWFALL (JPN)**, b f Deep Impact (JPN)—Best In The World (IRE)
99 **SONG OF PEACE (USA)**, b c Uncle Mo (USA)—Mythical Bride (USA)
100 **ST MARK'S BASILICA (FR)**, b c Siyouni (FR)—Cabaret (IRE)
101 **SURELY (IRE)**, b f Galileo (IRE)—Again (IRE)
102 **SWEET MOLLY MALONE (USA)**, b f American Pharoah (USA)—Cherry Hinton
103 **SWISS ACE**, b c Kingman—Swiss Lake (USA)
104 **THE MEDITERRANEAN (IRE)**, ch c Galileo (IRE)—Flashy Wings
105 **THE PIANO PLAYER (IRE)**, b c No Nay Never (USA)—Chasing Ice (IRE)
106 **TIGNANELLO (IRE)**, b c Galileo (IRE)—Discreet Marq (USA)
107 **VAN GOGH (USA)**, b c American Pharoah (USA)—Imagine (IRE)
108 **WEMBLEY (IRE)**, b c Galileo (IRE)—Inca Princess (IRE)
109 **WILLOW (IRE)**, b f American Pharoah (USA)—Peeping Fawn (USA)
110 **WOODLAND GARDEN (IRE)**, b f Galileo (IRE)—Chintz (IRE)
111 **WORDSWORTH (IRE)**, ch c Galileo (IRE)—Chelsea Rose (IRE)
112 **YARRAWONGA (IRE)**, ch c Australia—Gems

## TWO-YEAR-OLDS

113 B f 23/04 Galileo (IRE)—Acapulco (USA) (Scat Daddy (USA))
114 Ch f 01/02 Dubawi (IRE)—Alice Springs (IRE) (Galileo (IRE))
115 B c 04/05 Galileo (IRE)—Alive Alive Oh (Duke of Marmalade (IRE))
116 B c 05/05 Galileo (IRE)—Atlantic Jewel (AUS) (Fastnet Rock (AUS))
117 B c 24/03 Camelot—Attire (IRE) (Danehill Dancer (IRE)) (150000)
118 B br c 07/03 War Front (USA)—Ballydoyle (IRE) (Galileo (IRE))
119 B c 27/04 Galileo (IRE)—Beauty Is Truth (IRE) (Pivotal)
120 B f 11/01 Galileo (IRE)—Believe'n'succeed (AUS) (Exceed And Excel (AUS))
121 B c 03/03 No Nay Never (USA)—Best of My Love (IRE) (Canford Cliffs (IRE))
122 B c 08/03 Galileo (IRE)—Bonanza Creek (IRE) (Anabaa (USA))
123 B f 23/01 War Front (USA)—Butterflies (IRE) (Galileo (IRE))
124 Br c 16/04 Caravaggio (USA)—Cape Joy (IRE) (Cape Cross (IRE)) (110000)
125 Br gr f 27/01 Caravaggio (USA)—Chenchikova (IRE) (Sadler's Wells (USA))
126 B f 29/03 American Pharoah (USA)—Cherry Hinton (Green Desert (USA))
127 Br c 04/04 Camelot—Crazy Volume (IRE) (Machiavellian (USA))
128 Ch c 22/02 Australia—Defrost My Heart (IRE) (Fastnet Rock (AUS)) (135000)
129 Gr f 21/04 Galileo (IRE)—Dialafara (FR) (Anabaa (USA)) (850000)

## MR A. P. O'BRIEN - continued

**130** B c 14/03 Galileo (IRE)—Diamond Fields (IRE) (Fastnet Rock (AUS))
**131** Gr c 04/05 Lope de Vega (IRE)—Diamond Sky (IRE) (Montjeu (IRE)) (171429)
**132** B f 20/04 Galileo (IRE)—Discreet Marq (USA) (Discreet Cat (USA))
**133** B c 19/02 Churchill (IRE)—Empowering (IRE) (Encosta de Lago (AUS))
**134** B br c 21/01 No Nay Never (USA)—Enharmonic (USA) (E Dubai (USA)) (214822)
**135** B f 09/04 Zoffany (IRE)—Entreat (Pivotal) (580000)
**136** B c 29/03 No Nay Never (USA)—Gems (Haafhd)
**137** Gr c 11/04 Caravaggio (USA)—Gorband (USA) (Woodman (USA)) (180000)
**138** B c 23/04 Churchill (IRE)—Hairy Rocket (Pivotal)
**139** Ch c 20/01 Galileo (IRE)—Halfway To Heaven (IRE) (Pivotal)
**140** B c 31/05 Camelot (IRE)—Holy Moon (IRE) (Hernando (FR))
**141** B f 21/03 American Pharoah (USA)—Imagine (IRE) (Sadler's Wells (USA))
**142** B f 11/03 Caravaggio (USA)—Immortal Verse (IRE) (Pivotal)
**143** B f 12/03 Galileo (IRE)—Inca Princess (IRE) (Holy Roman Emperor (IRE))
**144** B c 25/01 Caravaggio (USA)—Instant Sparkle (IRE) (Danehill (USA)) (150000)
**145** B c 27/03 Caravaggio (USA)—Jigsaw (IRE) (Galileo (IRE))
**146** B c 03/02 Kodiac—Khaimah (Nayef (USA)) (350000)
**147** B c 10/05 Galileo (IRE)—Kheleyf's Silver (IRE) (Kheleyf (USA))
**148** B c 23/04 Dubawi (IRE)—Kissed (IRE) (Galileo (IRE))
**149** B c 21/03 War Front (USA)—Lady Eli (USA) (Divine Park (USA))
**150** B c 16/04 Galileo (IRE)—Lady Lara (IRE) (Excellent Art)
**151** B f 04/01 Galileo (IRE)—Legatissimo (IRE) (Danehill Dancer (IRE))
**152** B f 03/06 Galileo (IRE)—Lillie Langtry (IRE) (Danehill Dancer (IRE))
**153** B c 22/02 No Nay Never (USA)—Madam Baroque (Royal Applause) (240000)
**154** B c 02/05 Churchill (IRE)—Madame Hoi (IRE) (Hawk Wing (USA))
**155** B f 29/04 Quality Road (USA)—Marvellous (IRE) (Galileo (IRE)) (1074114)
**156** B c 05/05 Churchill (IRE)—Milanova (AUS) (Danehill (USA))
**157** Br c 10/02 No Nay Never (USA)—Moment Juste (Pivotal) (350000)
**158** Br gr f 10/03 Caravaggio (USA)—Muravka (IRE) (High Chaparral (IRE))
**159** B c 04/02 Churchill (IRE)—Muwakaba (IRE) (Elusive Quality (USA))
**160** B c 16/03 Galileo (IRE)—Mystical Lady (IRE) (Halling (USA))
**161** Gr f 21/03 Caravaggio (USA)—On Ice (IRE) (Galileo (IRE))
**162** B c 16/04 Churchill (IRE)—Pivotalia (IRE) (Pivotal) (209524)
**163** B c 21/01 Deep Impact (JPN)—Promise To Be True (IRE) (Galileo (IRE))
**164** B c 13/05 Galileo (IRE)—Prudenzia (IRE) (Dansili) (1614205)
**165** B f 11/02 Frankel—Queen Cleopatra (IRE) (Kingmambo (USA))
**166** B c 27/01 Caravaggio (USA)—Rain Goddess (IRE) (Galileo (IRE))
**167** B c 12/02 Invincible Spirit (IRE)—Rajeem (Diktat) (600000)
**168** B c 14/02 Churchill (IRE)—Regency Girl (IRE) (Pivotal) (150000)
**169** B c 19/04 Caravaggio (USA)—Ruby Quest (IRE) (Fastnet Rock (AUS))
**170** B c 18/03 No Nay Never (USA)—Saucy Spirit (Invincible Spirit (IRE)) (123810)
**171** B f 23/02 Dubawi (IRE)—Seventh Heaven (IRE) (Galileo (IRE))
**172** B f 23/01 Galileo (IRE)—Shastye (IRE) (Danehill (USA)) (3400000)
**173** B f 27/01 Mastercraftsman (IRE)—Simkana (IRE) (Kalanisi (IRE)) (325000)
**174** B c 09/05 Galileo (IRE)—Snow Queen (IRE) (Danehill Dancer (IRE))
**175** B c 27/02 Caravaggio (USA)—Sparrow (IRE) (Oasis Dream)
**176** B c 15/03 Showcasing—Spicy (IRE) (Footstepsinthesand) (190476)
**177** Ch c 17/04 Galileo (IRE)—Stellar Wind (USA) (Curlin (USA))
**178** Ch c 05/02 No Nay Never (USA)—Strut (Danehill Dancer (IRE)) (650000)
**179 SUN KING (IRE),** b c 18/02 Galileo (IRE)—Song of My Heart (IRE) (Footstepsinthesand)
**180** B c 01/03 Australia—Sweepstake (IRE) (Acclamation) (575000)
**181** B f 30/04 Galileo (IRE)—Switch (USA) (Quiet American (USA))
**182** B f 17/02 Churchill (IRE)—Tanaghum (Darshaan)
**183** B c 27/04 American Pharoah (USA)—Tapestry (IRE) (Galileo (IRE))
**184** B c 22/04 Churchill (IRE)—Tarbela (IRE) (Grand Lodge (USA))
**185** B f 22/05 Galileo (IRE)—Tepin (USA) (Bernstein (USA))
**186** B c 16/02 Galileo (IRE)—Vanzara (FR) (Redoute's Choice (AUS))
**187** B c 04/01 American Pharoah (USA)—Virginia Waters (USA) (Kingmambo (USA))
**188** Br gr f 04/03 Dark Angel (IRE)—Wading (IRE) (Montjeu (IRE))
**189** B c 20/02 Camelot (IRE)—War Goddess (IRE) (Champs Elysees)

## MR A. P. O'BRIEN - continued

**190** B c 18/03 Churchill (IRE)—Where's Sue (IRE) (Dark Angel (IRE)) (320000)
**191** B f 14/01 Deep Impact (JPN)—Winter (IRE) (Galileo (IRE))
**192** Ch f 27/04 Galileo (IRE)—You'resothrilling (USA) (Storm Cat (USA))

---

**416**
## MR DANIEL O'BRIEN, Tonbridge
Postal: **Knowles Bank, Capel, Tonbridge, Kent, TN11 0PU**
Contacts: **PHONE 01892 824072**

**1 BOSTIN (IRE),** 13, ch g Busy Flight—Bustingoutallover (USA) **D. C. O'Brien**
**2 CABERNET D'ALENE (FR),** 9, b g Day Flight—Haifa du Noyer (FR) **D. C. O'Brien**
**3 GOLD MERLION (IRE),** 8, b m Alhaarth (IRE)—Sea of Time (USA) **D. C. O'Brien**
**4 MOJAMBO (IRE),** 6, ch m Zoffany (IRE)—Mojita (IRE) **D. C. O'Brien**

**Assistant Trainer:** Christopher O'Bryan.

**NH Jockey:** Mattie Batchelor, Sam Twiston-Davies.

---

**417**
## MR DONNACHA O'BRIEN, Cashel
Postal: **Bawnmore Racing Stables, Ballyroe, Cashel, Tipperary, Ireland**
EMAIL donnachaobrien50@gmail.com

**1 EMPEROR OF THE SUN (IRE),** 4, ch c Galileo (IRE)—Zouzou (AUS)
**2 LUGNAQUILLA (IRE),** 4, b f Galileo (IRE)—Wave (IRE)
**3 OH SO TRUE (USA),** 4, b f American Pharoah (USA)—Shawara (IRE)

### THREE-YEAR-OLDS
**4 ABSOLUTELY (IRE),** b f Uncle Mo (USA)—Bracelet (IRE)
**5 APRIL SHOWERS (IRE),** b f Galileo (IRE)—Butterfly Cove (USA)
**6 EASILY (IRE),** ch f Galileo (IRE)—Beyond Brilliance (IRE)
**7 EMPORIO (IRE),** ch c Zoffany (IRE)—Eirnin (IRE)
**8 FERNANDO VICHI (IRE),** ch c Australia—Pernica
**9 GREAT SUGAR LOAF (IRE),** b c Galileo (IRE)—Mrs Marsh
**10 HAZEL (IRE),** b f No Nay Never (USA)—Asteya (IRE)
**11 IGRAINE (IRE),** b f Camelot—Sea Picture (IRE)
**12 MOON DAISY (IRE),** b f Australia—Holy Alliance (IRE)
**13 NICEST (IRE),** b f American Pharoah (USA)—Chicquita (IRE)
**14 OH SO FINE (IRE),** b f Galileo (IRE)—Nell Gwyn (IRE)
**15 ON TIPTOES (IRE),** ch f Galileo (IRE)—Nechita (AUS)
**16 ONES ARE WILD (IRE),** ch c Bated Breath—Bouvardia
**17 SHALE (IRE),** b f Galileo (IRE)—Homecoming Queen (IRE)
**18 SHINSENGUMI (IRE),** b c Galileo (IRE)—Native Force (IRE)
**19 SNOWY OWL (IRE),** ch c Galileo (IRE)—Californiadreaming (IRE)
**20 SOUTHERN CAPE (IRE),** b br c Galileo (IRE)—Tiggy Wiggy (IRE)
**21 TORINO (IRE),** b c Fastnet Rock (AUS)—Sacrosanct (IRE)
**22 ZOZIMUS (IRE),** b c Footstepsinthesand—Comment

### TWO-YEAR-OLDS
**23** Ch f 09/03 Galileo (IRE)—After (IRE) (Danehill Dancer (IRE))
**24** Br gr f 17/03 Caravaggio (USA)—Airwave (Air Express (IRE))
**25** Br f 21/02 Caravaggio (USA)—All For Glory (USA) (Giant's Causeway (USA))
**26** B c 21/01 No Nay Never (USA)—All To Do With It (IRE) (Canford Cliffs (IRE)) (90000)
**27** B f 24/04 Caravaggio (USA)—Aqua de Vida (IRE) (Fastnet Rock (AUS))
**28** B f 10/05 Galileo (IRE)—Butterfly Cove (USA) (Storm Cat (USA))

## MR DONNACHA O'BRIEN - continued

29  Br c 24/02 Caravaggio (USA)—Chicago Girl (IRE) (Azamour (IRE)) (120000)
30  B f 03/04 War Front (USA)—Coin Broker (IRE) (Montjeu (IRE))
31  Gr c 27/04 Caravaggio (USA)—Daidoo (IRE) (Shamardal (USA))
32  B c 31/03 Gleneagles (IRE)—Daneleta (IRE) (Danehill (USA)) (123810)
33  Gr c 25/02 Caravaggio (USA)—Eccentricity (USA) (Kingmambo (USA))
34  Ch c 03/05 No Nay Never (USA)—Flashy Wings (Zafonic (USA)) (140000)
35  Br c 22/03 No Nay Never (USA)—Instinctively (IRE) (Cape Cross (IRE))
36  B f 03/05 Galileo (IRE)—La Traviata (USA) (Johannesburg (USA))
37  B c 26/04 Iffraaj—Larceny (IRE) (Cape Cross (IRE))
38  B c 05/05 Australia—Love Excelling (FR) (Polish Precedent (USA)) (65000)
39  B f 09/04 Galileo (IRE)—Missvinski (USA) (Stravinsky (USA))
40  B f 18/04 War Front (USA)—Misty For Me (IRE) (Galileo (IRE))
41  B f 11/01 Almanzor (FR)—Mujabaha (Redoute's Choice (AUS)) (45000)
42  B f 30/03 Galileo (IRE)—Music Box (IRE) (Invincible Spirit (IRE))
43  Gr c 11/05 Caravaggio (USA)—Neutral (Beat Hollow)
44  B c 06/04 Territories (IRE)—Never Change (IRE) (New Approach (IRE)) (65000)
45  B c 01/05 Zoffany (IRE)—On A Pedestal (IRE) (Montjeu (IRE))
46  B c 01/04 Caravaggio (USA)—Peeping Fawn (USA) (Danehill (USA))
47  **PIZ BADILE (IRE)**, b br c 03/02 Ulysses (IRE)—That Which Is Not (USA) (Elusive Quality (USA))
48  B f 13/02 Caravaggio (USA)—Queen Titi (IRE) (Sadler's Wells (USA))
49  B c 23/03 Caravaggio (USA)—Remember Alexander (Teofilo (IRE)) (110000)
50  B c 20/03 Churchill (IRE)—Rien Ne Vas Plus (IRE) (Oasis Dream) (210000)
51  Bl c 11/02 Caravaggio (USA)—Riskit Fora Biskit (IRE) (Kodiac) (100000)
52  B c 06/03 Galileo (IRE)—Sky Lantern (IRE) (Red Clubs (IRE))
53  Gr c 26/02 Caravaggio (USA)—Social Honour (IRE) (Entrepreneur)
54  B c 06/03 Galileo (IRE)—Sun Shower (IRE) (Indian Ridge)
55  B br c 13/03 No Nay Never (USA)—Sweetasever (IRE) (Power)
56  B f 28/03 Caravaggio (USA)—Traou Mad (IRE) (Baratheo (IRE))
57  B f 05/05 Dark Angel (IRE)—Venus de Milo (IRE) (Duke of Marmalade (IRE)) (100000)
58  B f 19/04 Galileo (IRE)—Wave (IRE) (Dansili)

---

## 418  MR FERGAL O'BRIEN, Cheltenham
Postal: **Upper Yard, Grange Hill Farm, Naunton, Cheltenham, Gloucestershire, GL54 3AY**
Contacts: **PHONE 01451 850538 MOBILE 07771 702829**
EMAIL admin@fergalobrienracing.com

1  **AGENT VALDEZ**, 8, b m Arvico (FR)—Soleil Sauvage  **The FOB Racing Partnership 6**
2  **ALAPHILIPPE (IRE)**, 7, b g Morozov (USA)—Oscar Bird (IRE)  **Mr N. Brereton**
3  **ALEXANDER JAMES (IRE)**, 5, b g Camelot—Plying (USA)  **Craig & Laura Buckingham**
4  **ALL CLENCHED UP**, 5, b m Fame And Glory—Laetitia (IRE)  **Mr F. M. O'Brien**
5  **APRES LE DELUGE (FR)**, 7, gr g Stormy River—Ms Cordelia (USA)  **R. C. Tooth**
6  **ART APPROVAL (FR)**, 5, b g Authorized (IRE)—Rock Art (IRE)  **Mr R. J. G. Lowe**
7  **AS HIGH SAY (IRE)**, 6, b m Mountain High (IRE)—Broken Gale (IRE)  **Mr F. M. O'Brien**
8  **ASK A HONEY BEE (IRE)**, 7, b g Ask—Pure Honey (IRE)  **Lewis, Lawson and Hope**
9  **ASK DILLON (IRE)**, 8, b g Ask—Mum's Miracle (IRE)  **4 The Fun Partnership**
10  **ASK THE LADY (IRE)**, 6, b m Ask—Romy's Birthday (IRE)  **Mr J. C. Collett**
11  **ASTON SMOKEY JOE (IRE)**, 4, ch g Zebedee—Smokey Ryder  **P G Lowe & Friends**
12  **AVOID DE MASTER (IRE)**, 7, b g Getaway (GER)—Tanit  **Mrs J. Rees**
13  **AYE AYE CHARLIE**, 9, b g Midnight Legend—Trial Trip  **All Four One**
14  **BALGEMMOIS (FR)**, 8, ch g Balko (FR)—Venise Doree (FR)  **Marlborough Racing-(Balgemmois)**
15  **BALLYHOME (IRE)**, 10, b g Westerner—Nostra (FR)  **A & K Ecofilm Ltd**
16  **BATHIVA (FR)**, 7, b g Spanish Moon (USA)—Thithia (FR)  **Mrs J. Rees**
17  **BECKY THE BOO**, 5, b m Schiaparelli (GER)—Sunnyland  **The FOB Racing Partnership 10**
18  **BENNIE BOY**, 5, b g Cameron Highland (IRE)—Dollythedreamer  **Team CH Racing**
19  **BEYOND THE PALE (IRE)**, 6, b g Shirocco (GER)—Miss Mary Mac (IRE)  **The FOB Racing Partnership 7**
20  **BILLAMS LEGACY**, 6, b m Black Sam Bellamy (IRE)—Liqueur Rose  **The Cod and Chips Twice Racing Syndicate**
21  **BILLY THE SQUID (IRE)**, 4, b g Requinto (IRE)—Edrea (FR)  **Blue StaRR Racing FOB**

# MR FERGAL O'BRIEN - continued

22 **BLUE LUNA**, 5, b m Lucarno (USA)—Mighty Merlin  **Mrs J. A. Watts**
23 **BLUE MONDAY (IRE)**, 8, b g Beneficial—Bradbury Baby (IRE)  **The FOB Racing Partnership 5**
24 **BLUE SANS (IRE)**, 6, b m Sans Frontieres (IRE)—California Blue (FR)  **The FOB Racing Partnership 12**
25 **BRIEF AMBITION**, 7, b g Yeats (IRE)—Kentucky Sky  **C Coley, D Porter, H Redknapp, P Smith**
26 **BUTTE MONTANA (IRE)**, 6, b g Presenting—My Cool Lady (IRE)  **Mr T. Crowe**
27 **CAGE OF FEAR (IRE)**, 7, b g Milan—Baile An Droichid (IRE)  **Five Go Racing**
28 **CALL ME TARA**, 4, b f Kayf Tara—Call Me Emma (IRE)  **Upthorpe Racing**
29 **CALL ME VIC (IRE)**, 14, b g Old Vic—Call Me Dara (IRE)  **Mrs R. J. Tufnell**
30 **CAPTAIN CATTISTOCK**, 8, b g Black Sam Bellamy (IRE)—Pearl Buttons  **Mrs R. J. Tufnell**
31 **CAPTAIN CLIPPO (IRE)**, 6, ch g Golden Lariat (USA)—Rose of Taipan (IRE)
32 **CARROLLS MILAN (IRE)**, 8, b m Milan—Native Crystal (IRE)  **The Gud Times Partnership**
33 **CASTEL GANDOLFO (IRE)**, 4, gr g Dark Angel (IRE)—Capulet Monteque (USA)  **Mr N. Brereton**
34 **CHAMPAGNE WELL (IRE)**, 8, b g Gold Well—Perkanod (IRE)  **The Bolly Champagne Crew**
35 **CITY DERBY (IRE)**, 5, ch g Ask—Reine d'Or (IRE)  **Richard D A Hames & Walter O'Connor**
36 **CLEMENTO (IRE)**, 7, b g Canford Cliffs (IRE)—Street Style (IRE)  **J.N. & D. Balfe**
37 **COILLTE EILE (IRE)**, 8, b m Stowaway—Aughwilliam Lady (IRE)  **Mr P K & Mrs A J Adams**
38 **COOL DESTINATION (IRE)**, 8, ch g Dubai Destination (USA)—

Coolafancy (IRE)  **Nautilus, Mennell, Logan and Partner**
39 **COOLANLY (IRE)**, 9, b g Flemensfirth (USA)—La Fisarmonica (IRE)  **Five Go Racing**
40 **COURTANDBOULD (IRE)**, 7, b g Court Cave (IRE)—Seaneen Mac Ri (IRE)  **Craig & Laura Buckingham**
41 **CROSSGALESFAMEGAME (IRE)**, 7, b m Mahler—Fame Forever (IRE)  **Walid Marzouk & Richard Rowland**
42 **CROSSRAIL**, 6, b m Rail Link—Get Me Home (IRE)  **M. C. Denmark**
43 **DE NAME EVADES ME (IRE)**, 9, b g Vinnie Roe (IRE)—Sound of The Crowd (IRE)  **Brown Campbell James Foylan**
44 **DIAMOND FORT (IRE)**, 9, ch g Gamut (IRE)—Ellie Forte  **D. J. Shorey**
45 **DIV INE TARA**, 6, b m Kayf Tara—Mid Div And Creep  **Mrs K Exall & Mr G Molen**
46 **DOLCITA (FR)**, 6, b m Saint des Saints (FR)—Orcantara (FR)  **Sullivan Bloodstock Limited**
47 **DOLLY MCQUEEN**, 5, b m Canford Cliffs (IRE)—Caterina de Medici (FR)  **Don't Tell The Missus Partnership**
48 **DON'T STOP NOW**, 4, b g Champs Elysees—Trapeze  **Mr F. M. O'Brien**
49 **DONT HESITATE (FR)**, 8, b m Diamond Boy (FR)—Quibble (FR)  **Sullivan Bloodstock Limited**
50 **DOYEN DANCER (IRE)**, 7, b g Doyen (IRE)—Grangeclare Dancer (IRE)  **Mr R. Treacy**
51 **DREAMING OF GLORY (IRE)**, 5, b m Fame And Glory—Dream Function (IRE)  **C. B. Brookes**
52 **ELHAM VALLEY (FR)**, 4, gr g Tin Horse (IRE)—Dame du Floc (IRE)  **Caveat Emptor Partnership**
53 **FASHION NOVA (IRE)**, 6, gr m Flemensfirth (USA)—Fashion's Worth (IRE)  **A & K Ecofilm Ltd**
54 **FEEL THE PINCH**, 7, b g Librettist (USA)—Liqueur Rose  **Mr B Jones & Son**
55 **FINAL NUDGE (IRE)**, 12, b g Kayf Tara—Another Shot (IRE)  **Mrs J. Rees**
56 **FORTHEGREATERGOOD (IRE)**, 7, b m Yeats (IRE)—Feast Or Famine (IRE)  **Mrs J. A. Watts**
57 **GINO TRAIL (IRE)**, 14, br g Perugino (USA)—Borough Trail (IRE)  **Mrs J. Smith**
58 **GLOBAL FAME (IRE)**, 7, b g Fame And Glory—

Kinard True (IRE)  **Chris Coley, Exors of the late Lord Vestey & ROA Arkle**
59 **GOLDEN TAIPAN (IRE)**, 7, b g Golden Lariat (USA)—Rose of Taipan (IRE)  **Double Barrels Of Courage**
60 **GOOD AND HARDY (IRE)**, 8, b g Westerner—Kilganey Maid (IRE)  **The Groovy Gang**
61 **GOODBYE DANCER (FR)**, 10, b g Dragon Dancer—Maribia Bella (FR)  **The Yes No Wait Sorries & Mr Chris Coley**
62 **GORTROE JOE (IRE)**, 9, b g Beneficial—Rowlands Star (IRE)  **J. T. Warner**
63 **GREAT HEART'JAC (FR)**, 6, br g Blue Bresil (FR)—Aqua Fontana (FR)  **Mr L. D. Craze**
64 **HEAVENLY PROMISE (IRE)**, 10, ch m Presenting—Ambrosia's Promise (IRE)  **Mr D. Brace**
65 **HORSE POWER (FR)**, 4, b g Coastal Path—Valle d'Ossau (FR)  **Actionclad 2001 Ltd**
66 **HULLNBACK**, 4, b c Schiaparelli (GER)—Freydis (IRE)  **We're Having A Mare (WHAM)**
67 **HUNNY MOON**, 7, ch m Flemensfirth (USA)—No More Money  **C. B. Brookes**
68 **HUNTSMANS JOG (IRE)**, 7, b g Milan—Faucon  **The Box 8 Partnership**
69 **HURRICANE HARVEY**, 7, b g Doyen (IRE)—Camp Fire (IRE)  **Walid Marzouk & Richard Rowland**
70 **IMPERIAL ALCAZAR (IRE)**, 7, b g Vinnie Roe (IRE)—Maddy's Supreme (IRE)  **Imperial Racing Partnership 2016**
71 **IMPERIAL ELYSIAN (IRE)**, 7, br g Kalanisi (IRE)—Diva Antonia (IRE)  **Imperial Racing Partnership**
72 **IMPERIAL STORM (IRE)**, 5, ch g Shantou (USA)—Vindonissa (IRE)  **Imperial Racing Partnership 2016**
73 **JARVEYS PLATE (IRE)**, 8, b g Getaway (GER)—She's Got To Go (IRE)  **The Yes No Wait Sorries & Mr Chris Coley**
74 **KALELULA**, 4, br f Kalanisi (IRE)—Akdara (IRE)  **Craig & Laura Buckingham**
75 **KARL PHILIPPE (IRE)**, 6, ch g Kentucky Dynamite (USA)—Kaer Gwell (FR)  **C Coley, D Porter, H Redknapp, P Smith**
76 **LADY JANE P (IRE)**, 5, b m Walk In The Park (IRE)—Rosee des Bieffes (FR)  **Ms L. Pienaar**
77 **LADY VALERIE**, 9, b m Darnay—Lackofcash  **Mr M. N. Jenkins**
78 **LANDEN CALLING (IRE)**, 5, gr g Watar (IRE)—Gill Hall Lady  **The B Lucky Partnership**
79 **LIES ABOUT MILAN (IRE)**, 10, b g Milan—The Millers Tale (IRE)  **D. J. Shorey**

## MR FERGAL O'BRIEN - continued

80 LILY OF LEYSBOURNE, 8, b m Shirocco (GER)—Alegralil **C. B. Brookes**
81 LONG STAY, 6, b g Nathaniel (IRE)—Mainstay **Mr R. Treacy**
82 LORD P, 4, b g Brazen Beau (AUS)—Netta (IRE) **P G Lowe & Friends**
83 LOUGH HAR (IRE), 7, b g Doyen (IRE)—Time To Act **Mr H. M. Posner**
84 LUNAR SOVEREIGN (IRE), 5, b g Dubawi (IRE)—Surprise Moment (IRE) **Craig & Laura Buckingham**
85 LUNGARNO PALACE (USA), 10, b g Henrythenavigator (USA)—Good Time Sally (USA) **Caveat Emptor Partnership**
86 LUTINEBELLA, 5, b m Kayf Tara—West River (GER) **Blue StaRR Racing FOB**
87 MANOTHEPEOPLE (IRE), 6, b g Mahler—Midnight Insanity (IRE) **The FOB Racing Partnership 2**
88 MERRY BERRY, 5, b m Malinas (GER)—Mayberry **Keeping The Dream Alive**
89 MILANESE ROSE (IRE), 5, gr m Milan—Ma Furie (FR) **Mr J. K. Whymark**
90 MINELLA TARA (IRE), 6, b g Kayf Tara—Jolie Landaise (FR) **Graham & Alison Jelley**
91 MOOT COURT (IRE), 6, b g Court Cave (IRE)—Leney Dancer (IRE) **Ravenswell Renegades**
92 NAIZAGAI, 4, b g Dark Angel (IRE)—Nazym (IRE) **Mrs C. Kendrick**
93 NO NO JULIET (IRE), 8, b m Scorpion (IRE)—Full Imperatrice (FR) **Don Sebastiao Partnership**
94 NO NO MAESTRO (IRE), 6, b g Mahler—Maisey Down **Don Sebastiao Partnership**
95 NOTHIN TO ASK (IRE), 6, b g Ask—Nothin To Say (IRE) **The FOB Racing Partnership 11**
96 OCEAN COVE (IRE), 9, ch g Ask—Sand Eel (IRE) **The FOB Racing Partnership**
97 ONAGATHERINGSTORM (IRE), 6, b g Imperial Monarch (IRE)—Springfield Mary (IRE) **Craig & Laura Buckingham**
98 ORDERED LIVES (IRE), 6, b m Shirocco (GER)—Count On Me (IRE) **Mr M. G. St Quinton**
99 OSCAR ROSE (IRE), 9, b m Oscar (IRE)—Ben Roseler (IRE) **Mrsk.Exall/Thegeneralasphaltecompanyltd**
100 OSKI (IRE), 9, b g Oscar (IRE)—Mossville (FR) **Mrs C. Kendrick**
101 OUR COLOSSUS (IRE), 6, b g Yeats (IRE)—Itsalark (IRE) **Ray Treacy & Shaun Staplehurst**
102 PAINT THE DREAM, 7, b g Brian Boru—Vineuil (FR) **Mr D. Brace**
103 PAXMAN (IRE), 7, b g Jeremy (USA)—Dreamy Lagoon (IRE) **Mr & Mrs William Rucker**
104 PEKING ROSE, 6, br g Passing Glance—Miniature Rose **The Coln Valley Partnership**
105 PELLADY, 7, b m Le Fou (IRE)—Suetsu (IRE) **Mrs S. Tucker**
106 PERFECT CANDIDATE (IRE), 14, b g Winged Love (IRE)—Dansana (IRE) **ISL Recruitment**
107 PETITE POWER (IRE), 12, b g Subtle Power (IRE)—Little Serena **P J King & Son**
108 POLISH, 6, b g Teofilo (IRE)—Polygon (USA) **Caveat Emptor Partnership**
109 PRIDE OF LECALE, 10, b g Multiplex—Rock Gossip (IRE) **Noel Fehily Racing Syndicate 01**
110 PROJECT MARS (IRE), 9, b g Presenting—Molly Massini (IRE) **The FOB Racing Partnership 9**
111 PROPER TICKET (IRE), 8, b m Gold Well—Strand Lady (IRE) **The FOB Racing Partnership 8**
112 QUICK GRABIM (IRE), 9, b g Oscar (IRE)—Top Her Up (IRE) **Mrs G. S. Worcester**
113 REBEL ROXY (IRE), 5, ch m Sholokhov (IRE)—Sorivera **Mr I. Slatter**
114 RIGHT DESTINATION (IRE), 7, b g Dubai Destination (USA)—Sainte Careigne (FR) **The FOB Racing Partnership 11**
115 ROBYNDZONE (IRE), 7, b g Frammassone (IRE)—Rebecca Susan **East India Racing**
116 ROYAL PRACTITIONER, 8, b m Dr Massini (IRE)—Valdas Queen (GER) **A. P. Racing**
117 SAINTBURY LADY, 7, b m Kayf Tara—Miss Flower Girl **Mr D. W. Pocock**
118 SAN SEB (GER), 6, br g Mamool (IRE)—Sunshine Story (IRE) **Riverbank Racehorse Association**
119 SCARLETT CLIPPER (IRE), 4, b f Milan—Crimson Flower (IRE) **Blue StaRR Racing FOB**
120 SHE'LL BITE (IRE), 6, ch m Shirocco (GER)—Accordingtoeileen (IRE) **Mr F. M. O'Brien**
121 SHE'S A NOVELTY (IRE), 6, b m Approve (IRE)—Novel Fun (IRE) **Sally's Angels**
122 SILVER HALLMARK, 7, br gr g Shirocco (GER)—Gaye Sophie **Mr & Mrs William Rucker**
123 SLEEPYSAURUS (GER), 6, br g Authorized (IRE)—Saloon Rum (GER) **Superior Enterprises LTD**
124 STERNRUBIN (GER), 10, b g Authorized (IRE)—Sworn Mum (IRE) **J. T. Warner**
125 STONER'S CHOICE, 6, br g Great Pretender (IRE)—High Benefit (IRE) **Mrs C. Kendrick**
126 TASHUNKA (IRE), 8, b m Flemensfirth (USA)—Las Palmlas (IRE) **The FOB Racing Partnership 3**
127 TED DA TITAN, 5, b g Kayf Tara—Aeronautica (IRE) **Mrs C. Kendrick**
128 TED'S FRIEND (IRE), 5, b g Dylan Thomas (IRE)—Water Rock **Mr F. M. O'Brien**
129 TEMPLEPARK, 8, b g Phoenix Reach—Kenny's Dream **Mrs C. Kendrick**
130 TEQANY (IRE), 7, gr g Dark Angel (IRE)—Capulet Monteque (IRE) **Mrs J. A. Watts**
131 TEQUILA BLAZE, 7, b m Sakhee (USA)—Miss Sassi **The Tequila Tipplers**
132 THE BEES KNEES (IRE), 6, b g Oscar (IRE)—Dolphins View (IRE) **Mrs C. Kendrick**
133 THE TURTLE SAID, 4, b g Manduro (GER)—Goslar **F&M Bloodstock Limited**
134 THEGALLANTWAY (IRE), 8, b g Stowaway—Imogens Fancy (IRE) **Caveat Emptor Partnership**
135 TIMBERMAN (IRE), 6, b g Califet (IRE)—Millrock Lady (IRE) **Mr J. Turner**
136 TIME TO MOVE ON (IRE), 8, ch g Flemensfirth (USA)—Kapricia Speed (FR) **4 The Fun Partnership**
137 TIMETOCHILL (IRE), 8, br m Scorpion (IRE)—Kilcoleman Lady (IRE) **Mr N. D. Wellington**
138 TOTTERDOWN, 10, b g Pasternak—Yeldham Lady **Fairford Goes Racing**
139 TRAILBOSS (IRE), 6, b g High Chaparral (IRE)—Seeking Solace **Noel Fehily Racing Syndicate - Trailboss**

## MR FERGAL O'BRIEN - continued

140 **TRIOPAS (IRE)**, 9, b g Stowaway—Aine Dubh (IRE) **P J King & Son**
141 **ULTIMATE FAME (IRE)**, 5, b m Fame And Glory—Ultimate Echo (IRE) **Foxtrot Racing Syndicate 1**
142 **ULTIMATE GETAWAY (IRE)**, 7, b g Getaway (GER)—Ultimate Echo (IRE) **Foxtrot Racing: Ultimate Getaway**
143 **UNE DE LA SENIERE (FR)**, 6, ch m Noroit (GER)—Smabelle (FR) **Millennium Racing Club**
144 **VICTORIAS PEAK (IRE)**, 6, b m Fame And Glory—Rosin de Beau (IRE) **Superior Enterprises LTD**
145 **VOLKOVKA (FR)**, 4, b f Camelot—Drole de Dame (IRE) **The Tyringham Partnership**
146 **YAUTHYM (GER)**, 5, b m Authorized (IRE)—Ymlaen (IRE) **The Oakley Partnership**

### THREE-YEAR-OLDS
147 **BURRISTO (IRE)**, ch c Buratino (IRE)—Gin Twist **P G Lowe & Friends**

**Other Owners:** Mr D. E. Balfe, Mr R. H. Beevor, Mr J. N. Blackburn, Sir M. F. Broughton, Mr C. Buckingham, Mrs L. K. Buckingham, Mr D. J. Burke, C. S. J. Coley, Mr M. Costello, Mrs K. G. Exall, Mrs A. J. Gardiner, Mrs P. K. Gardiner, Mr R. D. A. Hames, Mrs A. D. Jelley, G. S. Jelley, Mr B. M. Jones, Mrs N. Jones, Mrs S. H. Jones, Mr W. Jones, Mrs C. M. Keys, G. F. Keys, Mr J. J. King, Mrs V. C. King, Mr J. B. Lawson, Mr W. Marzouk, Mr G. Molen, Mr W. O'Connor, Mr C. H. Plumb, Dr R. N. Rowland, Mr S. Staplehurst, Mr N. J. Statham, The General Asphalte Company Ltd, The Yes No Wait Sorries, Mr M. A. W. Thompson, Mr R. Treacy, Mr M. K. Warren, Mrs R. B. Weaver, Mr R. Williams, T. C. Wilson.

**Assistant Trainer:** Sally Randell.

**NH Jockey:** Connor Brace, Paddy Brennan.

---

**419** **MR JOSEPH O'BRIEN, Pilltown**
Postal: **Carriganog Racing, Owning Hill, Pilltown, Kilkenny, Ireland**
Contacts: PHONE +353 51 643 796
EMAIL mark@carriganogracing.com

1 **ANYTHING WILL DO (IRE)**, 6, b g Westerner—Aylesbury Park (IRE)
2 **ASSEMBLE**, 7, b g Getaway (GER)—Annaghbrack (IRE)
3 **BANBRIDGE (IRE)**, 5, ch g Doyen (IRE)—Old Carton Lass (IRE)
4 **BARON SAMEDI**, 4, b g Harbour Watch (IRE)—Dame Shirley
5 **BATTLE OF ACTIUM (IRE)**, 6, b g Fame And Glory—Flying Flame (IRE)
6 **BOLLEVILLE (FR)**, 5, b m Camelot—Brasileira
7 **BRIGHT IDEA (IRE)**, 4, b g Zoffany (IRE)—Cushion
8 **BUSSELTON (FR)**, 4, b g Mastercraftsman (IRE)—Blessed Luck (IRE)
9 **CASTRA VETERA (IRE)**, 6, bl m Jeremy (USA)—Mystic Cherry (IRE)
10 **CHOUNGAYA (FR)**, 8, b g Walk In The Park (IRE)—Autorite (FR)
11 **DANCE JUPITER (IRE)**, 5, br g Kingsbarns (IRE)—Mascara
12 **DANCING APPROACH**, 4, b f Camelot—Dream Approach (IRE)
13 **DARASSO (FR)**, 8, br g Konig Turf (GER)—Nassora (FR)
14 **DHABYAH**, 4, ch f Australia—Sola Gratia (IRE)
15 **DRUID'S ALTAR (IRE)**, 4, b g Mastercraftsman (IRE)—Shell Garland (USA)
16 **DUC D'ALLIER (FR)**, 8, b g Lauro—Peur Bleue (FR)
17 **EMBITTERED (IRE)**, 7, b g Fame And Glory—Kilbarry Classic (IRE)
18 **ENTOUCAS (FR)**, 7, b g Network (GER)—Mousse des Bois (FR)
19 **ERIC BLOODAXE (IRE)**, 6, bl g Saint des Saints (FR)—Diorissima (GER)
20 **FAKIR (FR)**, 6, b g Day Flight—Lazary (FR)
21 **FAKIR D'OUDAIRIES (FR)**, 6, b g Kapgarde (FR)—Niagaria du Bois (FR)
22 **FAME AND ACCLAIM (IRE)**, 4, b g Acclamation—Applause (IRE)
23 **FILS D'OUDAIRIES (FR)**, 6, b g Saint des Saints (FR)—Pythie d'Oudairies (FR)
24 **FIRE ATTACK (IRE)**, 6, b g Westerner—Seesea (IRE)
25 **FRONT VIEW (FR)**, 6, gr g Konig Turf (GER)—Tumavue (FR)
26 **FUN LIGHT (FR)**, 6, b g Saddler Maker (IRE)—Or Light (FR)
27 **GLOBAL EQUITY (IRE)**, 6, b m Shirocco (GER)—Geek Chic (IRE)
28 **GRACCHUS DE BALME (FR)**, 5, b g Manbolix (FR)—Olympe de Coudray (FR)
29 **GRANDMASTER FLASH (IRE)**, 5, ch g Australia—Kittens
30 **HIGH SPARROW (IRE)**, 8, ch g Shantou (USA)—Belladventure (IRE)

## MR JOSEPH O'BRIEN - continued

31 **HOME BY THE LEE (IRE)**, 6, b g Fame And Glory—Going For Home (IRE)
32 **JACK DILLINGER (IRE)**, 10, b g Westerner—Peppardstown (IRE)
33 **KESKONRISK (FR)**, 6, b g No Risk At All (FR)—La Courtille (FR)
34 **LADY DAHLIA (IRE)**, 4, ch f Australia—Attire (IRE)
35 **LUNAR DISPLAY (IRE)**, 5, ch m Getaway (GER)—Lunar Beauty (IRE)
36 **MASTER OF REALITY (IRE)**, 6, b g Frankel—L'Ancresse (IRE)
37 **MENAGERIE (IRE)**, 4, b f Fastnet Rock (AUS)—Cocoon (IRE)
38 **MERROIR (IRE)**, 4, b f Born To Sea (IRE)—Mozetta (IRE)
39 **MIGHTY BLUE (FR)**, 5, b m Authorized (IRE)—Millionaia (IRE)
40 **MORTAL (IRE)**, 9, b g King's Theatre (IRE)—Pomme Tiepy (FR)
41 **MUSIC TO MY EARS (IRE)**, 4, ch f Australia—Back On Top (IRE)
42 **NEVER FORGOTTEN (IRE)**, 4, b f Galileo (IRE)—Ishvana (IRE)
43 **NUMERIAN (IRE)**, 5, b g Holy Roman Emperor (IRE)—Delicate Charm (IRE)
44 **PALM BEACH (IRE)**, 4, b c Galileo (IRE)—Alta Anna (FR)
45 **PATRICK SARSFIELD (FR)**, 5, b g Australia—Ultra Appeal (IRE)
46 **PONDUS**, 5, b g Sea The Moon (GER)—Diablerette
47 **RAISE YOU (IRE)**, 5, ch h Lope de Vega (IRE)—Hikari (IRE)
48 **SCARLET AND DOVE (IRE)**, 7, b m Jeremy (USA)—Dark Mimosa (IRE)
49 **SEMPO (IRE)**, 7, b g Oscar (IRE)—Miss Cozzene (IRE)
50 **SLIGE DALA (IRE)**, 6, ch g Sholokhov (IRE)—Lady's Gesture (IRE)
51 **SMOKING GUN (IRE)**, 8, b g Gold Well—The Wounded Cook (IRE)
52 **SPEAK EASY**, 8, b g Beneficial—For Bill (IRE)
53 **SPEAK IN COLOURS (IRE)**, 6, gr h Excelebration (IRE)—Maglietta Fina (IRE)
54 **SUMMER SANDS**, 4, b g Coach House (IRE)—Koharu
55 **THE MOYGLASS FLYER (IRE)**, 7, b g Galileo (IRE)—Luas Line (IRE)
56 **THUNDERING NIGHTS (IRE)**, 4, b f Night of Thunder (IRE)—Cape Castle (IRE)
57 **TRAISHA (IRE)**, 5, b m Invincible Spirit (IRE)—Dress Rehearsal (IRE)
58 **TRIPLICATE (IRE)**, 8, b g Galileo (IRE)—Devoted To You (IRE)
59 **TWILIGHT PAYMENT (IRE)**, 8, b g Teofilo (IRE)—Dream On Buddy (IRE)
60 **UHTRED (IRE)**, 6, b g Fame And Glory—Ingred Hans (IRE)
61 **US AND THEM (IRE)**, 8, b g Stowaway—Manorville (IRE)
62 **VICTORY ROAD (IRE)**, 4, b g Frankel—Dietrich (USA)

## THREE-YEAR-OLDS

63 **BALDOMERO (IRE)**, b c Shalaa (IRE)—Besotted (IRE)
64 **BAMBOO BAY (IRE)**, b c Camelot—Anna Karenina (USA)
65 **BELMONT AVENUE (IRE)**, ch c Zoffany (IRE)—Single (FR)
66 **BENAUD (IRE)**, br g Australia—Kawaha (IRE)
67 **BOYNE RIVER**, b f Kingman—Adonesque (IRE)
68 **CAMDEBOO (IRE)**, b f Muhaarar—Carioca (IRE)
69 **CHAMPION GREEN (IRE)**, b g The Gurkha (IRE)—Back On Top (IRE)
70 **COLLINS STREET (IRE)**, b c Camelot—Uliana (USA)
71 **CORSA (USA)**, ch f Kitten's Joy (USA)—Alta Love (USA)
72 **DEVIL'S OUTLAW (USA)**, b br c War Front (USA)—Devil By Design (USA)
73 **DUNMAIN POWER (IRE)**, gr g Protectionist (GER)—Cru Paradis (FR)
74 **EARLY WARNING (CAN)**, ch br c Air Force Blue (USA)—Orchard Beach (CAN)
75 **EGYPTIAN ROCK (IRE)**, b c Fastnet Rock (AUS)—Incitatus Girl (IRE)
76 **EMPHATIC ANSWER (IRE)**, b f No Nay Never (USA)—Ask Me Nicely (IRE)
77 **EQUUS DEUS (IRE)**, b c Galileo (IRE)—Mystical Lady (IRE)
78 **FEDERAL (IRE)**, b c Zoffany (IRE)—Zee Zee Gee
79 **GAHERIS (GER)**, b c Camelot—Guavia (GER)
80 **GRID**, b c Siyouni (FR)—Toi Et Moi (IRE)
81 **HALA JOUD (IRE)**, gr f Belardo (IRE)—Sifter (USA)
82 **HAPPYWIFEHAPPYLIFE (IRE)**, b f Camelot—Dusty In Memphis (USA)
83 **HOBSONS BAY (IRE)**, b c Camelot—Emirates Joy (IRE)
84 **HYPE (IRE)**, b c Siyouni (FR)—Eavesdrop (IRE)
85 **IRWIN (IRE)**, ch c Australia—Sugar House (USA)
86 **ISLE OF SARK (USA)**, b c Kitten's Joy (USA)—Endless Fancy (USA)
87 **JO MARCH (IRE)**, b f Zoffany (IRE)—Bird's Eye View

## MR JOSEPH O'BRIEN - continued

**88 KADUPUL (FR),** b f Dark Angel (IRE)—Cup Cake (IRE)
**89 KIRKLAND LADY (IRE),** b f Camelot—Itqaan (USA)
**90 LIFFEY RIVER (FR),** b c Lope de Vega (IRE)—Black Dahlia
**91 LOVELY ESTEEM,** b f Siyouni (FR)—Persona Grata
**92 MAGNANIMOUS (IRE),** b c Mehmas (IRE)—Lillebonne (FR)
**93 MARIESQUE (IRE),** b f Lawman (FR)—Mireille (IRE)
**94 MAX MAYHEM,** b c New Bay—Maybe Grace (IRE)
**95 MESSIDOR (IRE),** b f Vadamos (FR)—Pyrenean Queen (IRE)
**96 NEPTUNE ROCK (IRE),** b f Muhaarar—Silent Thoughts (IRE)
**97 POINT NEPEAN (IRE),** b c Camelot—Sea Goddess (IRE)
**98 PORT PHILIP (IRE),** b c Camelot—Aymara
**99 PRAIRIE DANCER (IRE),** b g Territories (IRE)—Polka Dot (IRE)
**100 PRETTY GORGEOUS (FR),** b f Lawman (FR)—Lady Gorgeous
**101 QUEENSHIP (IRE),** b f Excelebration (IRE)—Height of Elegance (IRE)
**102 RATIB,** ch c Frankel—Posset
**103 REKERO (IRE),** b c Fastnet Rock (AUS)—Pride (FR)
**104 RIVER EDEN (IRE),** b f Invincible Spirit (IRE)—Lady Heidi
**105 ROCK CHANT (USA),** b c Flintshire—High Chant (USA)
**106 ROLLET (IRE),** b c Kingman—Foreign Legionary (IRE)
**107 ROYAL BLEND,** b f Zoffany (IRE)—Timely
**108 RULING (GER),** b c Camelot—Rosenreihe (GER)
**109 RUSSIAN RIVER (IRE),** b f Dandy Man (IRE)—Kazatzka
**110 SANTA FLORENTINA,** b f Oasis Dream—Entree
**111 SENSE OF STYLE (IRE),** b f Zoffany (IRE)—Attire (IRE)
**112 SHEER CHANCE (IRE),** b f Fulbright—Sheer Bliss (IRE)
**113 SNAPRAETEREA (IRE),** b c Buratino (IRE)—Snap Alam (IRE)
**114 SO FASCINATING (IRE),** b f Fascinating Rock (IRE)—So Secret (IRE)
**115 SOUTHERN LIGHTS (IRE),** b c Sea The Stars (IRE)—Ownwan (USA)
**116 SPINNING MOON (IRE),** ch f The Gurkha (IRE)—Shake The Moon (GER)
**117 STARTEDWITHAKISS (IRE),** b f Fastnet Rock (AUS)—Shaleela (IRE)
**118 STATE OF REST (IRE),** b c Starspangledbanner (AUS)—Repose (USA)
**119 STOUR,** b c Frankel—Moment In Time (IRE)
**120 TAR HEEL (IRE),** b g Zoffany (IRE)—Nidhaal (IRE)
**121 THINKING OF YOU (USA),** b f American Pharoah (USA)—Fabulous (IRE)
**122 THUNDER MOON (IRE),** b c Zoffany (IRE)—Small Sacrifice (IRE)
**123 TIME TO BURN (IRE),** b f Bobby's Kitten (USA)—Wholesome (USA)
**124 TOSHIZOU (IRE),** b c Galileo (IRE)—Remember You (IRE)
**125 TRUCE (USA),** b f Declaration of War (USA)—My Way (USA)
**126 UBUNTU (IRE),** b f Fastnet Rock (AUS)—On A Pedestal (IRE)
**127 ULSTER BLACKWATER (IRE),** b f Camelot—Silver Rain (FR)
**128 VAFORTINO (IRE),** b c New Bay—Arbaah (USA)
**129 VISUALISATION (IRE),** b br c No Nay Never (USA)—Roselita (IRE)
**130 WENSUM RIVER,** b c Free Eagle (IRE)—Nans Joy (IRE)
**131 WITHAM RIVER (IRE),** ch c Galileo (IRE)—Withorwithoutyou (IRE)

## TWO-YEAR-OLDS

**132** B c 27/04 Churchill (IRE)—Annabelle Ja (FR) (Singspiel (IRE)) (8878)
**133** B c 03/04 Camelot—Another Storm (USA) (Gone West (USA)) (175000)
**134** B f 16/04 Fastnet Rock (AUS)—Anzhelika (IRE) (Galileo (IRE))
**135** B c 20/01 Australia—Apticanti (USA) (Aptitude (USA)) (95238)
**136** B f 13/03 No Nay Never (USA)—Beach of Falesa (IRE) (Dylan Thomas (IRE))
**137** B c 14/04 Galileo (IRE)—Beauty Bright (IRE) (Danehill (USA))
**138** Ch f 14/03 Dubawi (IRE)—Bracelet (IRE) (Montjeu (IRE))
**139** Ch c 23/04 Gleneagles (IRE)—Celeste de La Mer (IRE) (Zoffany (IRE)) (55238)
**140 COMET LINE (IRE),** b f 04/04 No Nay Never (USA)—Honourably (IRE) (Galileo (IRE)) (475000)
**141 DARK NOTE,** ch c 10/05 Night of Thunder (IRE)—Rosa Grace (Lomitas) (70000)
**142** B f 16/03 Galileo (IRE)—Dawn Wall (AUS) (Fastnet Rock (AUS))
**143** B f 27/01 The Gurkha (IRE)—Early Addition (IRE) (Makfi)
**144** B c 16/03 Garswood—Fantasy In Blue (Galileo (IRE)) (22857)

## MR JOSEPH O'BRIEN - continued

**145 FEARLESS FUTURES,** ch c 24/04 Churchill (IRE)—Maureen (IRE) (Holy Roman Emperor (IRE))
**146** B f 27/04 Pivotal—Final Dynasty (Komaite (USA)) (61905)
**147 FLASH BULB (IRE),** b f 20/04 Camelot—Ethel (Exceed And Excel (AUS)) (123810)
**148** B f 16/04 Siyouni (FR)—Fork Lightning (USA) (Storm Cat (USA)) (238095)
**149 HADMAN (IRF),** ch c 16/02 Starspangledbanner (AUS)—Anneli (IRE) (Galileo (IRE)) (52381)
**150** B c 10/04 Zoffany (IRE)—Hold Me Now (USA) (Bernstein (USA)) (45714)
**151** B c 05/02 Wootton Bassett—Holy Cat (IRE) (Kitten's Joy (USA)) (140000)
**152** B c 27/04 Camelot—Homepage (Dansili) (125000)
**153** B c 26/02 Churchill (IRE)—Imalwayshotforyou (USA) (Discreetly Mine (USA)) (130000)
**154 IN ECSTASY (IRE),** gr c 29/03 Caravaggio (USA)—Longing (IRE) (Galileo (IRE)) (205000)
**155** Ch c 05/02 Australia—Into The Lane (IRE) (Excelebration (IRE)) (52380)
**156** Ch f 14/03 Footstepsinthesand—Lisfannon (Bahamian Bounty) (41905)
**157** B f 17/04 Australia—Lonely Rock (Fastnet Rock (AUS)) (30000)
**158** Br gr f 03/02 Dark Angel (IRE)—Loreto (IRE) (Holy Roman Emperor (IRE)) (115000)
**159** B c 20/03 Zoffany (IRE)—Loved (IRE) (Galileo (IRE)) (76190)
**160** B c 01/02 National Defense—Mademoiselle Marie (FR) (Evasive)
**161** Gr f 02/04 Caravaggio (USA)—Me and Miss Jones (USA) (Smarty Jones (USA)) (130000)
**162** B f 28/02 Fastnet Rock (AUS)—Mont Etoile (IRE) (Montjeu (IRE))
**163 NATIONAL GALLERY (IRE),** gr c 01/04 Caravaggio (USA)—Dora de Green (IRE) (Green Tune (USA)) (190000)
**164** B f 14/04 Galileo (IRE)—Nechita (AUS) (Fastnet Rock (AUS)) (133333)
**165** B c 25/01 Zoffany (IRE)—Never Busy (USA) (Gone West (USA)) (41905)
**166 NUSRET,** b c 02/02 Golden Horn—Serres (IRE) (Daylami (IRE)) (50040)
**167 OBLIVIATE (IRE),** gr f 28/02 Estidhkaar (IRE)—Spinamix (Spinning World (USA))
**168** B c 23/03 Lope de Vega (IRE)—Oh Sedulous (IRE) (Lawman (FR)) (32381)
**169** B c 18/03 Zoffany (IRE)—Onyali (IRE) (Rip Van Winkle (IRE)) (55000)
**170** B c 28/02 Dubawi (IRE)—Perihelion (IRE) (Galileo (IRE)) (150000)
**171** B c 06/02 Camelot—Pioneer Bride (USA) (Gone West (USA)) (200000)
**172** B c 12/03 Protectionist (GER)—Pioneer Girl (Anabaa (USA))
**173 PRETTY BLUE (IRE),** b c 02/04 Camelot—Fast And Pretty (IRE) (Zamindar (USA)) (76675)
**174** B f 17/01 Fastnet Rock (AUS)—Pure Art (Dutch Art) (59048)
**175** B f 04/02 Zoffany (IRE)—Renaissance Rio (IRE) (Captain Rio)
**176** Gr f 17/02 Dark Angel (IRE)—Ring The Bell (IRE) (Galileo (IRE)) (140000)
**177 RIVER OF HEYDAY (IRE),** ch f 14/05 No Nay Never (USA)—Three Mysteries (IRE) (Linamix (FR))
**178** B c 16/02 Galileo (IRE)—Rock Orchid (IRE) (Fastnet Rock (AUS)) (240000)
**179 ROSSO CORSA (USA),** ch f 22/04 Kitten's Joy (USA)—Joya Real (USA) (Eddington (USA)) (572861)
**180 SCARLETT DUBOIS (IRE),** b f 12/02 Fastnet Rock (AUS)—Terrific (IRE) (Galileo (IRE))
**181 SCHIELE (IRE),** gr c 22/04 Dark Angel (IRE)—The Hermitage (IRE) (Kheleyf (USA)) (338095)
**182 SEISAI (IRE),** b f 16/03 Gleneagles (IRE)—Lillebonne (FR) (Danehill Dancer (IRE)) (74286)
**183** B c 30/05 Buratino (IRE)—Snap Alam (IRE) (Alamshar (IRE)) (24213)
**184** B f 18/04 Holy Roman Emperor (IRE)—Speciality (FR) (Lawman (FR))
**185** Ch gr f 29/03 New Bay—Spectacle (Dalakhani (IRE))
**186** Ch c 14/03 National Defense—Spiaggia (IRE) (Makfi)
**187 ST ADELAIDE (IRE),** b f 26/03 Holy Roman Emperor (IRE)—Gentle Spirit (IRE) (Sea The Stars (IRE))
**188** B f 28/03 National Defense—Summer Blues (IRE) (Summer Bird (USA))
**189** B c 06/02 Galileo (IRE)—Terror (IRE) (Kodiac) (300000)
**190 TRANQUIL LADY (IRE),** ch f 30/04 Australia—Repose (USA) (Quiet American (USA)) (152381)
**191** Ch c 09/04 No Nay Never (USA)—Twinkling Ice (USA) (Elusive Quality (USA)) (11428)
**192** B br f 09/05 American Pharoah (USA)—Two Oceans (USA) (Cape Town (USA))
**193 UXMAL (IRE),** b c 23/04 Galileo (IRE)—Only Mine (IRE) (Pour Moi (IRE))
**194** B c 11/03 Protectionist (GER)—Vagabonde (IRE) (Acclamation)
**195 VEGA MAGNIFICO (IRE),** ch c 15/05 Lope de Vega (IRE)—Hit The Sky (IRE) (Cozzene (USA)) (260000)
**196** Gr c 01/04 Caravaggio (USA)—Vitello (IRE) (Raven's Pass (USA)) (71428)
**197 VOLAROSSA (IRE),** b f 03/03 Footstepsinthesand—Time Passes (IRE) (Dalakhani (IRE)) (28571)
**198 WISH FOR ME (IRE),** b f 10/03 Mehmas (IRE)—Big Boned (IRE) (Street Sense (USA)) (314286)
**199** B f 15/04 Gutaifan (IRE)—Wojha (IRE) (Pivotal) (185000)
**200** B f 05/04 No Nay Never (USA)—Xaphania (Sakhee (USA)) (52381)
**201** B c 22/04 Zoffany (IRE)—Za'hara (IRE) (Raven's Pass (USA)) (43810)
**202 ZOFFANY PORTRAIT (IRE),** ch c 26/04 Zoffany (IRE)—Bunood (IRE) (Sadler's Wells (USA)) (57143)

**420** | **MR JEDD O'KEEFFE, Leyburn**
Postal: **Highbeck Lodge, Brecongill, Coverham, Leyburn, North Yorkshire, DL8 4TJ**
Contacts: **PHONE 01969 640330 MOBILE 07710 476705**
**EMAIL jedd@jeddokeefferacing.co.uk WEBSITE www.jeddokeefferacing.co.uk**

1 **AIR RAID**, 6, b g Raven's Pass (USA)—Siren Sound **Caron & Paul Chapman**
2 **BRASINGAMANBELLAMY**, 4, b g Black Sam Bellamy (IRE)—Brasingaman Hivlive **Mr R. J. Morgan**
3 **BURROW SEVEN**, 4, gr g Kayf Tara—Gaye Sophie **Racing4Business Ltd**
4 4, Ch g Mahler—Credo Star (IRE) **Caron & Paul Chapman**
5 **DEVIL'S ANGEL**, 5, gr g Dark Angel (IRE)—Rocking The Boat (IRE) **Titanium Racing Club**
6 **DREAM TOGETHER (IRE)**, 4, ch g Dream Ahead (USA)—Shamsalmaidan (IRE) **The Fatalists**
7 **ECHO (IRE)**, 6, b g Zoffany (IRE)—Aweebounce (IRE) **Miss S.E. Hall & Mr C. Platts**
8 **FAIRFIELD FERRATA**, 5, b m Kayf Tara—Via Ferrata (FR) **Mrs J. A. Darling**
9 **HIGH MOOR FLYER**, 4, b f Pour Moi (IRE)—A Media Luz (FR) **Mrs J. A. Darling**
10 **JEDHI**, 6, b m Big Bad Bob (IRE)—Capriolla **Quantum**
11 **MIAH GRACE**, 6, b m Malinas (GER)—Silver Gypsy (IRE) **Caron & Paul Chapman**
12 4, Ch g Sulamani (IRE)—Milan Athlete (IRE) **Manor House Racing**
13 **MIRACLE EAGLE (IRE)**, 4, b f Free Eagle (IRE)—Tartessian (IRE) **Yorkshire Owners Racing Club 2**
14 **MISS LAMB**, 5, b m Passing Glance—Lucinda Lamb **Miss S. E. Hall**
15 **MR SCRUMPY**, 7, b g Passing Glance—Apple Days **Mr H. M. Posner**
16 **RARE GROOVE (IRE)**, 6, ch h Lope de Vega (IRE)—Ascot Lady (IRE) **Mr J. E. Dance, Mrs J. Dance**
17 **RATTLE OWL**, 5, b g Kayf Tara—Rattlin **Racing4Business Ltd**
18 **SAISONS D'OR (IRE)**, 6, ro g Havana Gold (IRE)—Deux Saisons **The Fatalists**
19 **SALSADA (IRE)**, 4, ch f Mukhadram—Mokaraba **Mr & Mrs G. Turnbull**
20 **SAM SPINNER**, 9, gr g Black Sam Bellamy (IRE)—Dawn Spinner **Caron & Paul Chapman**
21 **SEVEN FOR A POUND (USA)**, 5, b g Scat Daddy (USA)—Gimlet Witha Twist (USA) **Mr Eric Broadwith**
22 **ST JUST**, 4, b g Golden Horn—Alfajer **Quantum**
23 **STRAIT OF HORMUZ (IRE)**, 4, b g Sir Percy—Sliabh Luachra (IRE) **Quantum**
24 **SWEET DIME**, 5, b br m Toronado (IRE)—Rainbow's Edge **Miss M.A. Thompson & Miss S.E. Hall**
25 4, B f Martaline—Urticaire (FR) **Caron & Paul Chapman**

## THREE-YEAR-OLDS

26 **ABUNDANT MOON (IRE)**, b f Galileo (IRE)—Replete **Mr J. E. Dance, Mrs J. Dance**
27 **CALL CLWYD (IRE)**, b f Flintshire—Spinamiss (IRE) **The City & Provincial Partnership**
28 **CLANSMAN**, b c Nathaniel (IRE)—Pearl Dance (USA) **Mr J. E. Dance, Mrs J. Dance**
29 **COLTON**, gr g Lethal Force—Lady Poppy **Mr T. S. Ingham & Mrs Liz Ingham**
30 **ITALIAN BREEZE**, ch c Bated Breath—Novellara **Highbeck Racing 2**
31 **JIANZI (IRE)**, b f Acclamation—Shuttlecock **Mr & Mrs G. Turnbull**
32 **LIBERTY BLAZE (IRE)**, b f Starspangledbanner (AUS)—Afrodita (IRE) **Hope Eden Racing**
33 Ch g Proconsul—Lucinda Lamb **Miss S.E. Hall & Mr C. Platts**
34 **MIDNIGHT POPPY (IRE)**, b f Kodi Bear (IRE)—Top Row **Ingham Racing Syndicate**
35 **OUT THE HAT (AUS)**, b g Helmet (AUS)—Random **Highbeck Racing 4**
36 **RAINBOW'S GIFT**, b g Nathaniel (IRE)—Riot of Colour **Highbeck Racing 1**
37 **RAQISA**, b f Mukhadram—Hazy Dancer **Highbeck Racing 3**

## TWO-YEAR-OLDS

38 Ch c 06/02 Anjaal—Champion Place (Compton Place) **Yorkshire Owners Racing Club 1**
39 B c 01/05 Highland Reel (IRE)—Destalink (Rail Link) (16000) **Highbeck Racing 5**
40 B f 16/03 Showcasing—Dream of Joy (IRE) (Dream Ahead (USA)) (27000) **Racing4Business Ltd**
41 B c 24/01 Poet's Voice—Future Energy (Frankel) (21000) **Mr B. McAllister & Mr A. Walker**
42 **HILTS (IRE)**, b c 26/03 New Bay—Creme Anglaise (Motivator) (45000) **Ellipsis**
43 B c 10/04 Mondialiste (IRE)—La Arcadia (FR) (Lope de Vega (IRE)) **Mr & Mrs G. Turnbull**
44 Ch c 21/02 Mondialiste (IRE)—Moghrama (Nayef (Motivator Watch (IRE)) (60000) **Mr & Mrs G. Turnbull**
45 B c 07/03 Invincible Spirit (IRE)—More Mischief (Azamour (IRE)) **Caron & Paul Chapman**
46 **NIKHI**, ch f 25/02 Nathaniel (IRE)—Elysion Fields (GER) (Champs Elysees) (16000) **Ellipsis**
47 B f 27/02 Mondialiste (IRE)—Only Together (IRE) (Montjeu (IRE)) **Mr & Mrs G. Turnbull**
48 Ch c 29/03 Churchill (IRE)—Organza (Pour Moi (IRE)) **Caron & Paul Chapman**
49 B f 15/02 Profitable (IRE)—Passcode (Camacho) (20952) **The City & Provincial Partnership**

## MR JEDD O'KEEFFE - continued

**Other Owners:** Mr D. G. Colledge, Mr K. Everitt, Miss S. E. Hall, Highbeck Racing, Highbeck Racing 2, Highbeck Racing 4, Kildaragh Stud, Normandie Stud Ltd, Mr M. D. Parker, Stoneleigh Racing, W A Tunstall & Son.

**Assistant Trainer:** Tim Hogg, Leanne Kershaw.

**Apprentice Jockey:** Owen Payton.

---

## 421 MR DAVID O'MEARA, Upper Helmsley
Postal: Willow Farm, Upper Helmsley, York, Yorkshire, YO41 1JX
Contacts: PHONE 01759 372427 MOBILE 07747 825418
EMAIL info@davidomeara.co.uk WEBSITE www.davidomeara.co.uk

1 AGINCOURT (IRE), 6, b m Declaration of War (USA)—El Diamante (FR) **Sir Robert Ogden**
2 AL QAASIM (IRE), 4, ch g Free Eagle (IRE)—Nebraas **Lee Bond & Partner 2**
3 ALLIGATOR ALLEY, 4, b g Kingman—Overturned **Akela Construction Ltd**
4 AVEBURY (IRE), 4, b f Dark Angel (IRE)—Wiltshire Life (IRE) **Cheveley Park Stud Limited**
5 AZANO, 5, b g Oasis Dream—Azanara (IRE) **M J Taylor & L A Taylor**
6 COLD STARE (IRE), 6, b g Intense Focus (USA)—Ziria (IRE) **Middleham Park Racing XC**
7 CUSTOM CUT (IRE), 12, b g Notnowcato—Polished Gem (IRE) **Frank Gillespie & Pat Breslin**
8 DANCING RAVE, 5, b m Coach House (IRE)—Right Rave (IRE) **David Lumley & Partner**
9 DANIEL DERONDA, 4, b g Siyouni (FR)—Madonna Dell'orto **Mr F. Gillespie**
10 DAZZLING DES (IRE), 4, b g Brazen Beau (AUS)—Secret Liaison (IRE) **Mr E. M. Sutherland**
11 DICK DATCHERY (IRE), 4, b g Make Believe—Bayja (IRE) **Mr F. Gillespie**
12 EAGLE COURT (IRE), 4, b g Free Eagle (IRE)—Classic Remark (IRE) **Brook Farm Bloodstock**
13 EAGLES BY DAY (IRE), 5, b br h Sea The Stars (IRE)—Missunited (IRE) **Clipper Group Holdings Ltd**
14 EL GHAZWANI (IRE), 6, b h Cape Cross (IRE)—Almansoora (USA) **Mr H. R. Bin Ghedayer**
15 ESCOBAR (IRE), 7, b g Famous Name—Saying Grace (IRE) **Withernsea Thoroughbred Limited**
16 FIGHTING IRISH (IRE), 4, b h Camelot—Quixotic **Daniel MacAuliffe & Anoj Don**
17 FIRMAMENT, 9, b g Cape Cross (IRE)—Heaven Sent **Gallop Racing**
18 FLAMMARION (GER), 5, b g Sea The Moon (GER)—Favorite (GER) **Dixon Bloodstock**
19 GOLDEN HIND, 4, b f Golden Horn—Messias da Silva (USA) **Sir Robert Ogden**
20 GULLIVER, 7, b g Sayif (IRE)—Sweet Coincidence **Withernsea Thoroughbred Limited**
21 HARD SOLUTION, 5, ch g Showcasing—Copy-Cat **Mr D. B. O'Meara**
22 HORTZADAR, 6, b g Sepoy (AUS)—Clouds of Magellan (USA) **Akela Construction Ltd**
23 INGLEBY HOLLOW, 9, ch g Beat Hollow—Mistress Twister **Dave Scott & The Fallen Angels**
24 JOHN JASPER (USA), 4, gr ro c Stormy Atlantic (USA)—Pooh Corner (USA) **Mr F. Gillespie**
25 KING OF TONGA (IRE), 5, gr g Dark Angel (USA)—Bronze Queen (IRE) **Middleham Park Racing LXV**
26 KLOPP OF THE KOP (IRE), 4, ch g Excelebration (IRE)—Avomcic (IRE) **Alderson Burke Francis**
27 LORD GLITTERS (FR), 8, gr ro g Whipper (USA)—Lady Glitters (FR) **Mr & Mrs G. Turnbull**
28 MAHARG'S PRINCESS (IRE), 4, ch f Night of Thunder (IRE)—Giveupyeraulsins (IRE) **Mr Stuart Graham & Partner**
29 MAKAWEE (IRE), 6, b m Farhh—Storming Sioux **Mr & Mrs G. Turnbull**
30 MISCHIEF STAR, 4, b g Due Diligence (USA)—Red Mischief (IRE) **Three Men & A Trainer**
31 MUSAHABA, 4, b g Muhaarar—Handassa **Mr E. M. Sutherland**
32 MUSCIKA, 7, b g Kyllachy—Miss Villefranche **Gallop Racing**
33 MYTHICAL MADNESS, 10, b g Dubawi (IRE)—Miss Delila (USA) **Mr C. G. J. Chua**
34 ONE FOR NAVIGATION (IRE), 4, b g Born To Sea (IRE)—Valmari (IRE) **Dympna O'Meara & Partner**
35 ORBAAN, 6, b g Invincible Spirit (IRE)—Contradict **JCG Chua & CK Ong**
36 PENITENT, 15, b g Kyllachy—Pious **Middleham Park Racing XVII**
37 POWER OF TIME (IRE), 4, b g Galileo (IRE)—Terror (IRE) **Dynast Racing**
38 QUEEN'S COURSE (IRE), 4, b f Gleneagles (IRE)—Dingle View (IRE) **Clipper Group Holdings Ltd**
39 SAGAUTEUR (FR), 5, b g Literato (FR)—Saga d'Ouilly (FR) **Diamond Racing & Rasio Cymru Racing 1**
40 SAVE THE SPIRIT (IRE), 4, b g Invincible Spirit (IRE)—Savanne (IRE) **Mr R. Treacy**
41 SEAS OF ELZAAM (IRE), 4, b g Elzaam (AUS)—Ocean Sands **Mr L. Bond**
42 SEGARELLI (IRE), 5, ch g Sea The Stars (IRE)—Samba Brazil (GER) **Mpr, Northern Monkeys & Woodhurst**
43 SHELIR (IRE), 5, b gr g Dark Angel (IRE)—Shelina (IRE) **Akela Construction Ltd**
44 SO BELOVED, 11, b g Dansili—Valencia **Thoroughbred British Racing & Partner**

## MR DAVID O'MEARA - continued

45 **SOUL SEEKER (IRE)**, 4, b g Oasis Dream—Mad About You (IRE) **Rasio Cymru Racing 1**
46 **SPIORAD (IRE)**, 6, b g Invincible Spirit (IRE)—Gift From Heaven (IRE) **Hambleton Racing Ltd XXXVII**
47 **STAR SHIELD**, 6, ch g Helmet (AUS)—Perfect Star **Middleham Park Racing XXIX**
48 **STONIFIC (IRE)**, 8, b g Sea The Stars (IRE)—Sapphire Pendant (IRE) **Rasio Cymru 1 & Hurn Racing Club**
49 **SUDONA**, 6, b m Zoffany (IRE)—Vickers Vimy **D. Hulse S. Saunders & Lady Cobham**
50 **SUMMERGHAND (IRE)**, 7, b g Lope de Vega (IRE)—Kate The Great **Mr H. R. Bin Ghedayer**
51 **TOUTATIS (USA)**, 4, b g Karakontie (JPN)—Afleet Lass (USA) **Always Smiling**
52 **TUKHOOM (IRE)**, 8, b g Acclamation—Carioca (IRE) **Slipstream Racing**
53 **UNKNOWN PLEASURES (IRE)**, 4, b f Zoffany (IRE)—Three Mysteries (IRE) **Niarchos Family**
54 **WAARIF (IRE)**, 8, b g Arcano (IRE)—Indian Belle (IRE) **Middleham Park Racing XLIX**
55 **WATCHABLE**, 11, ch g Pivotal—Irresistible **Mr P Bamford & the Roses Partnership**
56 **YOUNG FIRE (FR)**, 6, b g Fuisse (FR)—Young Majesty (USA) **Mr E. M. Sutherland**
57 **YUKON (IRE)**, 4, br g Lope de Vega (IRE)—Alegra **Mr D. B. O'Meara**

### THREE-YEAR-OLDS

58 Ch f American Pharoah (USA)—Adeste Fideles (USA) **Mr & Mrs G. Turnbull**
59 **BRAZEN BELLE**, b f Brazen Beau (AUS)—Pepper Lane **Mr K. Nicholson**
60 **CHARGING THUNDER**, b g War Command (USA)—Storming Sioux **Mr & Mrs G. Turnbull**
61 **COMETH THE MAN (IRE)**, b g Dandy Man (IRE)—Be My Queen (IRE) **Dixon Bloodstock Ltd & Partner**
62 **COSMOS RAJ**, b g Iffraaj—Cosmos Pink **Mr D. B. O'Meara**
63 **COUNTRY CARNIVAL (IRE)**, b f Mayson—Rural Celebration **Hambleton Racing Ltd 2c & Partner**
64 **DOCTOR PARNASSUS (IRE)**, b g Make Believe—We'll Go Walking (IRE) **Gallop Racing & Partner 3**
65 **DON'T TELL DJ (IRE)**, gr g Gutaifan (IRE)—Maybe Now Baby (IRE) **David Lumley & Nick Crummack**
66 **DR T J ECKLEBURG (IRE)**, b g Lawman (FR)—Imtidaad (USA) **Mrs M. C. Hancock**
67 **FORD MADOX BROWN (IRE)**, gr g Oasis Dream—Bruxcalina (FR) **Mr A. G. D. Hogarth**
68 **FROG AND TOAD (IRE)**, b g Mehmas (IRE)—Fast Pick (IRE) **Mr D. B. O'Meara**
69 **GENERAL SAGO (IRE)**, b g Fascinating Rock (IRE)—Why Now **Mr F. Gillespie**
70 **GOLDEN MELODY (IRE)**, ch f Belardo (IRE)—Chanter **Willow Racing Partnership**
71 **HIGHLY DANCER (IRE)**, ch f Helmet (AUS)—Caldy Dancer (IRE) **Mr M. Rashid**
72 **HOPE OF LIFE (IRE)**, b f Kodiac—Bobby Jane **Willow Racing Partnership**
73 **IMPERIAL EIGHT (IRE)**, b f Lawman (FR)—Avomcic (IRE) **Gallop Racing & Partner 2**
74 B c Helmet (AUS)—Jillanar (IRE) **Mr S. R. Bin Ghadayer**
75 **KING'S COMMANDER (FR)**, b g Authorized (IRE)—Millionaia (IRE) **Mrs S. Holtby**
76 **KUZNETSOVA**, b f Shalaa (IRE)—Vesnina **Cheveley Park Stud Limited**
77 **MALTBY RAIDER (FR)**, b g Fast Company (IRE)—Maundays Bay (IRE) **Mr A. G. D. Hogarth**
78 **MORTY**, b g Kingman—Ultrasonic (USA) **Morty Knew Best**
79 **MY BEST FRIEND (IRE)**, b gr g Gutaifan (IRE)—School Holidays (USA) **Ontoawinner 9 & Partner 3**
80 **NIGHT TERRORS (IRE)**, b g Zoffany (IRE)—Dream of Tara (IRE) **G. Murray**
81 **NOMADIC EMPIRE (IRE)**, b c Kodiac—Beatify (IRE) **AlMohamediya Racing**
82 **NOORBAN**, b f Sepoy (AUS)—Hoyamy **Mr S. R. Bin Ghadayer**
83 **NORMAN KINDU**, b g Lawman (FR)—Kindu **Mr D. B. O'Meara**
84 **ODD SOCKS HAVANA**, b g Havana Gold (IRE)—Hamloola **Mr P. Renoso**
85 **PATONTHEBACK (IRE)**, b g Kodi Bear (IRE)—Miss Brief (IRE) **Mr R & Mrs J E Huin**
86 **RHOSCOLYN**, b g Territories (IRE)—Zeyran (IRE) **The Horse Watchers**
87 **STAY SMART**, b c Brazen Beau (AUS)—Absolutely Right (IRE) **Mr H. R. Bin Ghedayer**
88 **SWING LOW**, ch g Mayson—Velvet Band **Gallop Racing & Lee Bond**
89 **TAMASKA**, ch g Starspangledbanner (AUS)—Premiere Danseuse **Jcg Chua & Akela Construction Ltd**
90 **TENDENTIOUS**, b g Intello (GER)—Capacious **Quantum Leap Racing XIII & Partner**
91 **THESETHINGSHAPPEN**, b g Siyouni (FR)—National Day (IRE) **Ray Treacy & Jason Reed**
92 **THRONE POWER (IRE)**, b g Slade Power (IRE)—Khaleesi Wind (IRE) **Mr H. R. Bin Ghedayer**
93 **TURANDOT (IRE)**, b f Frankel—Messias da Silva (USA) **Sir Robert Ogden**
94 **TWILIGHT SPINNER**, b f Twilight Son—Spinatrix **Hambleton Racing Ltd XXXIX & Partner**
95 **VALLEY OF FLOWERS (IRE)**, b f Slade Power (IRE)—Miss Cape (IRE) **Mr D. B. O'Meara**
96 **WATER IRIS**, b f Pivotal—Sea The Bloom **Cheveley Park Stud Limited**
97 B f Marcel (IRE)—What's Up Pussycat (IRE)
98 **WHITE AIME**, b g Brazen Beau (AUS)—Jadeamie **Highbank Stud**
99 **YADDLE (IRE)**, b f Buratino (IRE)—Firecrown (IRE) **Dundalk Racing Club**
100 **ZENZERO (IRE)**, ch g Twilight Son—Evangelical **John Blackburn & Nick Tritton**

## MR DAVID O'MEARA - continued

### TWO-YEAR-OLDS

**101 AILISH T,** b f 14/03 Bated Breath—Meddling (Halling (USA)) **Mr R. Treacy**

**102** B c 02/05 Invincible Spirit (IRE)—Al Mahmeyah (Teofilo (IRE)) **Mr H. R. Bin Ghedayer**

**103** B f 18/03 Muhaarar—All About Time (Azamour (IRE)) (20000) **Hambleton Racing Ltd XXII**

**104** B f 02/04 Mayson—Almond Branches (Dutch Art) **Hambleton Racing Ltd 2c & Partner**

**105** B c 16/02 Awtaad (IRE)—Always A Dream (Oasis Dream) (80000) **Brook Farm Bloodstock**

**106** Gr c 17/05 Dark Angel (IRE)—Anahita (FR) (Turtle Bowl (IRE)) **Mr S. R. Bin Ghadayer**

**107 ANIMATO,** ch c 23/03 Ulysses (IRE)—Blithe (Pivotal) **Cheveley Park Stud Limited**

**108** Gr f 18/03 Gutaifan (IRE)—Ardessie (Bahamian Bounty) (5500)

**109** B c 08/02 Kodiac—Beatify (IRE) (Big Bad Bob) (68571) **AlMohamediya Racing**

**110** B f 17/02 Profitable (IRE)—Blanche Neige (Halling (USA)) (45000) **Daniel MacAuliffe & Anoj Don**

**111** B c 29/04 Profitable (IRE)—Caldy Dancer (IRE) (Soviet Star (USA)) **Mr M. Rashid**

**112** B c 28/02 Highland Reel (IRE)—Candy Ride (IRE) (Pivotal) (21905)

**113** B f 16/04 Belardo (IRE)—Chanter (Lomitas) (20000) **From the Front Racing & Partners**

**114** B f 09/04 Mondialiste (IRE)—Dame Hester (IRE) (Diktat) **Mr & Mrs G. Turnbull**

**115** Ch c 01/04 Exceed And Excel (AUS)—Dear Dancer (IRE) (Teofilo (IRE)) **Mr M. Rashid**

**116 DEBIT CARD,** b f 02/04 Adaay (IRE)—Starbotton (Kyllachy) (4762) **Mr C. Napthine**

**117** B c 24/04 New Approach (IRE)—Gimasha (Cadeaux Genereux) (15000) **Mr Ray Treacy & Partner**

**118** B f 19/02 Ribchester (IRE)—Greek Goddess (IRE) (Galileo (IRE)) (60000) **Quantum Leap Racing VII**

**119** B c 20/02 The Last Lion (IRE)—Hope Against Hope (IRE) (Dark Angel (IRE)) (2857) **Ontoawinner 9 & Partner 3**

**120 HOT WOOD,** ch c 10/04 Hot Streak (IRE)—Moonwood (Three Valleys (USA)) **Gallop Racing**

**121 HOTTER IN TIME,** ch f 15/01 Hot Streak (IRE)—Sciarra (Monsieur Bond (IRE)) (9000) **Mr J. Matthews**

**122 ICONICDAAY,** b f 19/01 Adaay (IRE)—Bond Bombshell (Monsieur Bond (IRE)) (1429) **Trendy Ladies**

**123 IUR CINN TRA (IRE),** ch c 29/01 Starspangledbanner (AUS)—
          Appreciating (New Approach (IRE)) (28571) **Mr & Mrs Grant**

**124** B c 26/01 Ribchester (IRE)—Khaleesi Wind (IRE) (Exceed And Excel (AUS)) **Mr H. R. Bin Ghedayer**

**125** B f 18/04 Mondialiste (IRE)—Kocollada (IRE) (Kodiac) **Mr & Mrs G. Turnbull**

**126** Br f 28/02 Twilight Son—La Rosiere (USA) (Mr Greeley (USA)) **Empire State Racing Partnership**

**127 LACONIC,** b c 18/02 Oasis Dream—
          Brevity (USA) (Street Cry (IRE)) (30476) **Middleham Park Racing Cii & Partner 3**

**128** Ch c 12/05 Postponed (IRE)—Lawless Secret (Lawman (FR)) **Mr C. Napthine**

**129** B f 24/04 Profitable (IRE)—Maramba (USA) (Hussonet (USA)) (38095) **Mr S. R. Bin Ghadayer**

**130 MONCHIQUE,** b g 02/03 Mondialiste (IRE)—Lozah (Lawman (FR)) (7143) **Trendy Ladies**

**131** B c 04/04 Twilight Son—Nickels And Dimes (IRE) (Teofilo (IRE)) (22857)

**132** B c 08/02 Brazen Beau (AUS)—Pepper Lane (Exceed And Excel (AUS)) **Mr K. Nicholson**

**133** Gr c 05/02 Dark Angel (IRE)—Priceless Jewel (Selkirk) (55000) **Withernsea Thoroughbred Limited**

**134** B c 15/03 Charming Thought—Royal Confidence (Royal Applause) (7000) **Mr P. Hancock**

**135** B g 21/03 Mondialiste (IRE)—Royal Crown (IRE) (Kodiac)

**136 RUBY RED,** b f 28/03 Mayson—Red Bloom (Selkirk) (USA) **Cheveley Park Stud Limited**

**137 SCALDED,** ch c 09/02 Hot Streak (IRE)—Beldale Memory (IRE) (Camacho) (19048) **The Horse Watchers & Partner**

**138** B c 11/04 Acclamation—
          Shanooan (USA) (English Channel (USA)) (28571) **Highclere T'bred Racing-monkey Puzzle I**

**139** Ch f 10/03 Pastoral Pursuits—Sheoak (Medicean)

**140** B c 16/03 Belardo (IRE)—Snowtime (IRE) (Galileo (IRE)) **Empire State Racing Partnership**

**141** B c 16/02 Myboycharlie (IRE)—Summarily (IRE) (Shamardal (USA)) (30670)

**142 SYNONYMOUS,** ch f 25/01 Garswood—Unified (Oasis Dream) **Cheveley Park Stud Limited**

**143 TIME QUEST,** b c 28/02 Time Test—Rainbow's Edge (Rainbow Quest (USA)) (32000) **Ray Treacy & Richard Hames**

**144** Ch f 19/04 Bated Breath—Viola d'Amour (IRE) (Teofilo (IRE)) (20000) **York Thoroughbred Racing-viola d'Amour 1**

**145 WHISKY SPRINTER (IRE),** b c 13/03 Fast Company (IRE)—
          Cheherazad (IRE) (Elusive City (USA)) (11429) **Dynast Racing**

**146** B f 28/03 Kodiac—Yukon Girl (IRE) (Manduro (GER)) (26667) **Gallop Racing**

**Other Owners:** Akela Construction Ltd, P. S. Alderson, Mr P. I. Baker, P. Bamford, Mr J. M. Binns, Mr J. N. Blackburn, Mr K. Blessing, Mr P. Blessing, Mr L. Bond, Mr P. Breslin, Mr S. Bridge, Mr P. A. Burgess, Mr D. J. Burke, Mr C. G. J. Chua, Lady N. F. Cobham, Mr J. Cox, Mr J. W. Cox, Diamond Racing Ltd, Mr C. Dixon, Mr M. Dixon, Dixon Bloodstock, Mr D. P. Duffy, Mr M. Dunn, Mr A. W. Ellis, Ms J. C. Finucane, Mr M. R. Francis, Mr S. Franks, From The Front Racing, Mr P. J. Gallagher, Gallop Racing, Mr A. N. Gargan, Mr F. Gillespie, Mr S. M. Graham, Mr C. Grant, Mrs E. Grant, Hambleton Racing Ltd, Hambleton Racing Ltd - Two Chances, Hambleton Racing Ltd XXXIX, Mr R. D. A. Hames, Highclere T'bred Racing - Monkey Puzzle, Highclere Thoroughbred Racing Ltd, Mr R. Hoiles, Mrs J. E. Huin, Mr R. Huin, The Hon Mrs D. Hulse, Hurn Racing Club, Mrs I. M. Jessop,

## MR DAVID O'MEARA - continued

Mr J. J. Jones, Mr J. Kelly, Mr David John Lumley, Middleham Park Racing CII, Middleham Park Racing V, N D Crummack Ltd, Northern Monkeys, Mr N. J. O'Brien, Mr E. M. O'Connor, Mr J. P M. O'Connor, Ms D. O'Meara, Mr D. B. O'Meara, Ontoawinner 9, T. S. Palin, Mr J. D. Pierce, M. Prince, Quantum Leap Racing VIII, Rasio Cymru Racing 1, Mr J. Reed, Rod In Pickle Partnership, Mrs S. Saunders, Mr D. Scott, Mr S. Stephens, Mr L. A. Taylor, Mr M. J. Taylor, Mr M. J. Taylor, The Fallen Angels, The Horse Watchers, The Roses Partnership, Thoroughbred British Racing, Mr R. Treacy, Mr N. H. Tritton, Mr S. R. H. Turner, Miss A. M. Walker, Mr R. Walker, Mr B. R. Warn, Willow Racing Partnership, Woodhurst Construction Ltd, York Thoroughbred Racing - Viola d'Amour.

**Assistant Trainer:** Jason Kelly.

**Flat Jockey:** Daniel Tudhope.

---

**422** **MRS DANIELLE O'NEILL, North Fawley**
Postal: **The Old Granary, North Fawley, Wantage, Oxfordshire, OX12 9NJ**
Contacts: **PHONE 01488 639350 MOBILE 07931 193790**
EMAIL danni@fawleyhousestud.com

1 **BARDD (IRE)**, 9, b g Dylan Thomas (IRE)—Zarawa (IRE) **Fawley House Stud**
2 **COMMANDER MILLER**, 7, b g Shirocco (GER)—Milliegait **Fawley House Stud**
3 **DEER HUNTER (IRE)**, 5, b g Fame And Glory—Subtle Gem (IRE) **Fawley House Stud**
4 **GOAHEADWITHTHEPLAN (IRE)**, 6, b g Stowaway—Backandillo (IRE) **Fawley House Stud**
5 **TALES OF THE TWEED (IRE)**, 9, b g Robin des Champs (FR)—Dancer Privado (IRE) **Fawley House Stud**

**Other Owners:** Mrs S. D. McGrath, Mr R. H. Mcgrath.

**Assistant Trainer:** Stephen O'Neill.

---

**423** **MR JOHN O'NEILL, Bicester**
Postal: **Hall Farm, Stratton Audley, Nr Bicester, Oxfordshire, OX27 9BT**
Contacts: **PHONE 01869 277202 MOBILE 07785 394128**
EMAIL jgoneill4@gmail.com

1 **BITE MY TONGUE (IRE)**, 8, b g Vale of York (IRE)—Near Relation **Mr J. W. Stevenson**
2 **CAPPARATTIN**, 6, b g Universal (IRE)—Little Miss Prim **J. G. O'Neill**
3 **ONURBIKE**, 13, b g Exit To Nowhere (USA)—Lay It Off (IRE) **J. G. O'Neill**
4 **PHOENIX SONG**, 8, b g Phoenix Reach (IRE)—Temple Heather **J. G. O'Neill**
5 **SLEPTWITHMEBOOTSON**, 6, b m Universal (IRE)—Temple Heather **Ms L. M. Keane**
6 **W S GILBERT**, 7, b g Librettist (USA)—Little Miss Prim **Ms L. M. Keane**

**424** **MR JONJO O'NEILL, Cheltenham**
Postal: **Jackdaws Castle, Temple Guiting, Cheltenham, Gloucestershire, GL54 5XU**
Contacts: **PHONE 01386 584209**
**EMAIL racingoffice@jonjooneillracing.com WEBSITE www.jonjooneillracing.com**

1 **A DISTANT PLACE (IRE),** 6, b g Sunday Break (JPN)—South Africa (FR) **The Four Bosses**
2 **ADICCI (IRE),** 6, b g Shirocco (GER)—Lughnasa (IRE) **Mrs S. McAuley**
3 **AN TAILLIUR (FR),** 5, gr g Authorized (IRE)—Dirama (FR) **Mr P. Hickey**
4 **ANNIE MC (IRE),** 7, b m Mahler—Classic Mari (IRE) **Coral Champions Club**
5 **ANYWAYYOULOOKATIT (IRE),** 8, b g Presenting—Whyalla (IRE) **Mr J. P. McManus**
6 **APACHE CREEK (IRE),** 6, ch g Shantou (USA)—Galshan (IRE) **Team Tuff**
7 **ARRIVEDERCI (FR),** 6, gr g Martaline—Etoile d'Ainay (FR) **Martin Broughton & Friends 1**
8 **AS YOU LIKE (IRE),** 10, b br g Beneficial—Rubys Shadow (IRE) **Mr J. P. McManus**
9 **ASHFIELD PADDY (IRE),** 7, b g Publisher (USA)—Thats Grace (IRE) **The Hon Mrs E. J. Wills**
10 **AT FIRST GLANCE (IRE),** 6, b m Stowaway—Mazza's Magic (IRE) **Mr A. Bound**
11 **BEAN IN TROUBLE,** 7, gr g Sulamani (IRE)—Bouncing Bean **Fanning, Griffith, Haddock**
12 **BERTIE'S BANDANA (IRE),** 4, b g Notnowcato—Alright Kitty (IRE) **DYDB Marketing Limited**
13 **BIOWAVEGO (IRE),** 4, b g Presenting—Clara Bel La (IRE) **P14 Medical Ltd & Dydb Marketing Ltd.**
14 **BLUE SHARK (IRE),** 4, b g Shirocco (GER)—Meara Trasna (IRE) **The Ocean Partnership**
15 **CARYS' COMMODITY,** 6, b g Fame And Glory—Native Sunrise (IRE) **Mrs F. H. Hay**
16 **CAWTHORNE LAD,** 5, ch g Coach House (IRE)—Upton Seas **Woodbridge Construction Partnership**
17 **CLONDAW PROMISE (IRE),** 7, b g Gold Well—Present Promise (IRE) **Highfields Farm Partnership**
18 **CLOTH CAP (IRE),** 9, b g Beneficial—Cloth Fair (IRE) **Mr T. J. Hemmings**
19 **COBOLOBO (FR),** 9, br g Maresca Sorrento (FR)—Nanou des Brosses (FR) **Anne, Harriet & Lucinda Bond**
20 **COEUR SEREIN (IRE),** 7, b g Fame And Glory—Balvenie (IRE) **Mr A. T. S. Ralph**
21 **COPPER COVE (IRE),** 4, b g Jet Away—Cherry Island (IRE) **The Hon Mrs E. J. Wills**
22 **DELILAH (IRE),** 4, b br f Flemensfirth (USA)—Garranlea Maree (IRE) **Mr M. J. Tedham**
23 **DESTIN D'AJONC (FR),** 8, b g Martaline—Fleur d'Ajonc (FR) **Mr J. P. McManus**
24 **DJANGO DJANGO (IRE),** 8, gr g Voix du Nord (FR)—Lady Jannina **Martin Broughton & Friends 5**
25 **DREAM BERRY (FR),** 10, gr g Dream Well (FR)—Kalberry (FR) **Mr J. P. McManus**
26 **DREWSCOURT (IRE),** 6, b g Mahler—Supreme Adventure (IRE) **Mrs Jonjo O'Neill**
27 **DYNAMO BOY (IRE),** 6, b g Jeremy (USA)—Mary's Little Vic (IRE) **C Boultbee Brooks**
28 **EDINBURGH CASTLE (IRE),** 5, b g Sea The Stars (IRE)—Evensong (GER) **Mrs F. H. Hay**
29 **EY UP ROCKY,** 8, b g Dylan Thomas (IRE)—Polo **Martyn & Elaine Booth**
30 **FAME AND CONCRETE (IRE),** 5, b g Fame And-Glory—Masiana (IRE) **Mr P. Hickey**
31 **FAST GETAWAY (IRE),** 5, b g Getaway (GER)—Maddy's Supreme (IRE) **Martin Broughton Racing Partners 2**
32 **FILE ILLICO (FR),** 6, b g Cokoriko (FR)—Noryane (FR) **The Hon Mrs E. J. Wills**
33 **FLAMES OF PASSION (IRE),** 5, b m Flemensfirth (USA)—Night of Passion (IRE) **Deva Racing Champagne Wilde**
34 **FLIGHT DECK (IRE),** 7, b g Getaway—Rate of Knots (IRE) **Mr J. P. McManus**
35 **FOLKS ON THE HILL,** 6, b g Black Sam Bellamy (IRE)—Any Pearl **Mr R. J. Stanton-Gleaves**
36 **FRASCATO BELLO (FR),** 6, ch g No Risk At All (FR)—Tchi Tchi Bang Bang (FR) **Mr P. Hickey**
37 5, Ch g Haafhd—Freedom Song
38 **FRISCO BAY (IRE),** 6, b g Yeats (IRE)—Heath Heaven **Bassaire Cleanrooms Ltd.**
39 **GARRY CLERMONT (FR),** 6, b g Maresca Sorrento (FR)—Kalidria Beauchene (FR) **Mrs C. M. Walsh**
40 **GENERATION GAP (IRE),** 7, b g Olden Times—Kerso (FR) **The Hon Mrs E. J. Wills**
41 **GULLIVER COLLONGES (FR),** 5, b g Tiger Groom—Roxane Collonges (FR) **Mr J. P. McManus**
42 **HANG TOUGH,** 7, b g Geordieland—Allerford Lily **Tough Troop Partnership**
43 4, B f Norse Dancer (IRE)—Hazel Bank Lass (IRE) **Angela Crofts & Martin Tedham**
44 **HENRY GONDOFF (IRE),** 8, b g Great Pretender (IRE)—Mi Money **The Sting Partnership**
45 **HEY JOE (IRE),** 6, b g Oscar—Jordrell (IRE) **J. C. & S. R. Hitchins**
46 **HIS DREAM (IRE),** 8, b g Yeats (IRE)—Rosa Muscosa (USA) **Jonjo O'Neill Racing Club**
47 **HUNGRY HILL (IRE),** 4, b g Fame And Glory—Echo Queen (IRE) **Mr M. J. Tedham**
48 **KILBROOK (IRE),** 6, b g Watar (IRE)—Daly Lady (IRE) **Mr D.J. Burke & Delancey**
49 **KNIGHT DESTROYER (IRE),** 7, b g Dark Angel (IRE)—Do The Deal (IRE) **Mrs D. Carr**
50 **LA DOMANIALE (FR),** 5, b m No Risk At All (FR)—La Pinede (FR) **Mr J. P. McManus**
51 **LITHIC (IRE),** 10, b g Westerner—Acoola (IRE) **The Stone Composers**
52 **LOCK'S CORNER (IRE),** 7, b g Gold Well—Last Century (IRE) **Mr J. P. McManus**
53 **MANINTHESHADOWS (IRE),** 6, ch g Well Chosen—Grannys Kitchen (IRE) **Mr A. Riley**
54 **MARCH IS ON (IRE),** 8, b g Gold Well—Shannon Tiara (IRE) **Steve Killalea & Richard & Maralyn Seed**

# MR JONJO O'NEILL - continued

55 **MAYPOLE CLASS (IRE)**, 7, b g Gold Well—
Maypole Queen (IRE) **Delancey Real Estate Asset Management Limited**
56 **MERCUTIO ROCK (FR)**, 5, b g Maresca Sorrento (FR)—Mondovi (FR) **Mr Michael O'Flynn & Delancey**
57 **MONBEG GENIUS (IRE)**, 5, b g Shantou (USA)—Ella Watson (IRE) **Barrowman Racing Limited**
58 **MORNING SPIRIT (IRE)**, 6, b g Milan—Morning Legend (IRE) **Mr P. Hickey**
59 **MR BIGGS**, 4, b g Telescope (IRE)—Linagram **P14 Medical Ltd T/A Platform 14**
60 **ON THE BANDWAGON (IRE)**, 6, b g Oscar (IRE)—Deep Supreme (IRE) **Mr A. F. Nolan**
61 **OPINE (IRE)**, 4, b g Authorized (IRE)—Tocqueville (FR) **Secular Stagnation**
62 **ORRISDALE (IRE)**, 7, b g Oscar (IRE)—Back To Loughadera (IRE) **Miss K. J. Holland**
63 **PAGERO (FR)**, 6, b g Nathaniel (IRE)—Pagera (FR) **Mr J. P. McManus**
64 **PALMERS HILL (IRE)**, 8, b g Gold Well—Tosca Shine (IRE) **Mr J. P. McManus**
65 **PAPA TANGO CHARLY (FR)**, 6, ch g No Risk At All (FR)—Chere Elenn (FR) **Mr M. J. Tedham**
66 **PENS MAN (IRE)**, 6, ch g Sholokhov (IRE)—Dudeen (IRE) **Girls on Lockdown**
67 **PERFECT CITY (IRE)**, 6, b g Elusive City (USA)—Tall Perfection (USA) **The Perfect Partnership**
68 **PHIL THE THRILL (FR)**, 5, gr g Dabirsim (FR)—Parirou (GER) **Miss B. Connop**
69 **PIGGY WINKLE (IRE)**, 7, b g Fame And Glory—Ar Muin Na Muice (IRE) **Mrs Gay Smith**
70 **POP ROCKSTAR (IRE)**, 9, b br g Flemensfirth (USA)—Special Ballot (IRE) **Mrs L. Day**
71 **POP THE CORK**, 5, b g Harbour Watch (IRE)—Gospel Music **Martyn & Elaine Booth**
72 **POWERFUL HERO (AUS)**, 4, br g Better Than Ready (AUS)—Glennie West (AUS) **Creative Earth Productions**
73 **PRESENT CHIEF (IRE)**, 7, b g Presenting—Daizinni **Mr P. Hickey**
74 **PRESSURE SENSITIVE (IRE)**, 5, b g Shirocco (GER)—Bellavic (IRE) **Mr D. W. N. Walker**
75 **PRINCE ESCALUS (IRE)**, 6, b g Jeremy (USA)—So You Said (IRE) **The As You Like It Syndicate**
76 **PRIORY WOOD (IRE)**, 6, b g Shirocco (GER)—Passlands (IRE) **J. Priday**
77 **PUNCHES CROSS (IRE)**, 8, b g Stowaway—The Marching Lady (IRE) **Mr J. P. McManus**
78 **QUARENTA (FR)**, 9, b br g Voix du Nord (FR)—Negresse de Cuta (FR) **Martin, Jocelyn & Steve Broughton**
79 **QUARTZ DU RHEU (FR)**, 6, b g Konig Turf (GER)—Lady Akara (FR) **Mr J. P. McManus**
80 **RABSKI (IRE)**, 5, b g Beat Hollow—Scarlet Feather (IRE) **Mrs S. McAuley**
81 **RACING SNAKE**, 6, b g Mount Nelson—Queen Soraya **C Boultbee Brooks**
82 **READY AND ABLE (IRE)**, 8, b g Flemensfirth (USA)—Gypsy Mo Chara (IRE) **J. C. & S. R. Hitchins**
83 **RED MAPLE (IRE)**, 5, b g Sholokhov (IRE)—Champagne Ruby (IRE) **Mr T. Cole**
84 **SERMANDO (FR)**, 7, ch g Fuisse (FR)—Josephjuliusjodie (IRE) **Mrs Jonjo O'Neill**
85 **SHANTOU'S MELODY (IRE)**, 5, b g Shantou (USA)—Glens Melody (IRE) **Perfect Strangers Partnership**
86 **SKY PIRATE**, 8, b g Midnight Legend—Dancingwithbubbles (IRE) **Mr M. J. Tedham**
87 **SKYLANNA BREEZE (IRE)**, 6, b g Primary (USA)—Waist Deep (IRE) **The Three Cabelleros**
88 **SOARING GLORY (IRE)**, 6, b g Fame And Glory—Hapeney (IRE) **Mr P. Hickey**
89 **SPANISH JUMP (FR)**, 5, b g Brave Mansonnien (FR)—Spanish Delight **Kate & Andrew Brooks**
90 **STEADY THE SHIP (IRE)**, 5, ch g Ocovango—Vinnie's Princess (IRE) **Pitch Racing**
91 **STOP THE WORLD (IRE)**, 8, b g Oscar (IRE)—Coolsilver (IRE) **McNeill Family Ltd**
92 **TEDHAM**, 7, b g Shirocco (GER)—Alegralil **Mr M. J. Tedham**
93 **TEGEREK (FR)**, 7, b g Mount Nelson—Takaniya (IRE) **Local Parking Security Limited**
94 **THATS THE TRUTH (IRE)**, 7, b m Darsi (FR)—Lucy Walters (IRE) **Bond Brewin Chapman**
95 **THE COMPOSEUR (IRE)**, 6, b g Mahler—Oscar's Reprieve (IRE) **London Design Group Limited**
96 **THE MANUSCRIPT (IRE)**, 8, b g Mahler—Limavady (IRE) **The Valentine Partnership**
97 **THEME TUNE (IRE)**, 6, b g Fame And Glory—Supreme Melody (IRE) **Mr T. J. Hemmings**
98 **TIDAL WATCH (IRE)**, 7, b g Harbour Watch (IRE)—Najmati **Mr D. Carr**
99 **TIME TO GET UP (IRE)**, 8, ch g Presenting—Gales Return (IRE) **Mr J. P. McManus**
100 **TRANSPENNINE STAR**, 8, ch g Mount Nelson—Brave Mave **Transpennine Partnership**
101 **UPTOWN LADY (IRE)**, 6, b m Milan—Lady Zephyr (IRE) **Recycling Pallet Services**
102 **WALK IN MY SHOES (IRE)**, 5, b m Milan—Bonnies Island (IRE) **Creative Earth Productions**
103 **WASDELL DUNDALK (FR)**, 6, ch g Spirit One (FR)—Linda Queen (FR) **Mr M. J. Tedham**
104 **WHEN YOU'RE READY (IRE)**, 7, gr g Malinas (GER)—Royale Wheeler (IRE) **Jonjo O'Neill Racing Club**
105 **WRITE IT DOWN (IRE)**, 7, b g Getaway (GER)—Kylebeg Krystle (IRE) **Mr J. P. McManus**
106 **YOUNG WOLF (IRE)**, 8, b g Vinnie Roe (IRE)—Missy O'Brien (IRE) **Mrs Gay Smith**
107 **YULONG MAGICREEF (IRE)**, 4, b g Fastnet Rock (AUS)—Lindikhaya (IRE) **The Magic Circle Partnership**

## THREE-YEAR-OLDS

108 **SOLDIEROFTHESTORM (IRE)**, ch c Soldier of Fortune (IRE)—Fiddlededee (IRE) **Mr Tom Bond**

## MR JONJO O'NEILL - continued

**Other Owners:** Mr J. Barnard, Mr N. J. Bate, Mrs A. F. Bond, Miss H. Bond, Miss L. Bond, Mrs E. Booth, Mr M. Booth, Mr N. Brand, Mr L. H. Brewin, Mr A. Brookes, Mr A. L. Brooks, Mrs K. L. Brooks, Lady J. M. Broughton, Sir M. F. Broughton, Mr S. W. Broughton, Mr A. P Brown, Mr D. J. Burke, Mr E. Chapman, Mr D. J. Coles, Mrs A. C. Crofts, DYDB Marketing Limited, Delancey Real Estate Asset Management Limited, Mr O. Fanning, Mr N. Griffith, Mrs H. M. Haddock, Mrs S. Hall-Tinker, Mr M. P. Hammond, J. C. Hitchins, S. R. Hitchins, Mr T. Jackson, Mrs N Jones, Mr D. Kehoe, Mr S. J. Killalea, London Design Group Limited, Mr M. O'Flynn, P14 Medical Ltd T/A Platform 14, Ms S. Payne, Mr C. J. Pearce, Mr S. P. Perryman, Mrs M. L. Seed, Mr R. Seed, Mr B. D. Smith, Mr M. J. Tedham, The Commercial Flooring Company, Mrs L. Vaines, Mrs R. B. Weaver, White Horse Telecom Ltd., Mr N. H. H. Wilks.

**NH Jockey:** Alain Cawley, Adrian Heskin, Will Kennedy, Richie McLernon, Jonjo O'Neill Jr, Nick Scholfield, Gavin Sheehan.
**Conditional Jockey:** Philip Armson, Kevin Brogan, William Marshall. **Amateur Jockey:** AJ O'Neill.

---

## 425 MR JOHN O'SHEA, Newnham-on-Severn
Postal: **The Stables, Bell House, Lumbars Lane, Newnham, Gloucestershire, GL14 1LH**
Contacts: PHONE **01452 760835** MOBILE **07917 124717** FAX **01452 760233**
WEBSITE www.johnoshearacing.co.uk

1 **BOLLY BULLET (IRE)**, 4, b g Helmet (AUS)—Champagne Aerial (IRE) **The Cross Racing Club**
2 **CLOG NA FOLA (IRE)**, 4, b f Sir Prancealot (IRE)—Tranquil Ways (IRE) **Mr N. G. H. Ayliffe**
3 **COUGAR KID (IRE)**, 10, b g Yeats (IRE)—Western Skylark (IRE) **The Cross Racing Club**
4 **FLIP MODE**, 4, b g Lethal Force (IRE)—Canukeepasecret **Mr S. P. Price**
5 **FORTUNE TRAVELLER**, 4, b f Soldier of Fortune (IRE)—When In Roam (IRE) **Mr J. R. Salter**
6 **GENERAL BROOK (IRE)**, 11, b g Westerner—Danse Grecque (IRE) **K. W. Bell**
7 **GET UP THEM STEPS**, 7, b g Excelebration (IRE)—Flag Day **K. W. Bell**
8 **JIMMY BELL**, 10, b g Tiger Hill (IRE)—Armada Grove **K. W. Bell**
9 **JUST THE MAN (FR)**, 5, gr g Rajsaman (FR)—Yachtclubgenoa (IRE) **K. W. Bell**
10 **KNIGHT CRUSADER**, 9, b g Sir Percy—Lac Marmot (FR) **S. P. Bloodstock**
11 **MAJOR VALENTINE**, 9, b g Major Cadeaux—Under My Spell **Mr P. Smith**
12 **RICHIE VALENTINE**, 7, b g Native Ruler—Karmest **Mr N. G. H. Ayliffe**
13 **SCARLET RUBY**, 4, b f Al Kazeem—Monisha (FR) **The Cross Racing Club**
14 **SHOW ME THE BUBBLY**, 5, b m Showcasing—Folly Bridge **The Cross Racing Club**
15 **SOME NIGHTMARE (IRE)**, 4, b g Dream Ahead (USA)—Isolde's Return **The Cross Racing Club**
16 **SONIC GOLD**, 5, b g Schiaparelli (GER)—Sonic Weld **K. W. Bell**
17 **SWISSAL (IRE)**, 6, b g Swiss Spirit—Al Gharrafa **The Cross Racing Club**
18 **THE BELFRY BOY**, 6, ch g Black Sam Bellamy (IRE)—Lac Marmot (FR) **K. W. Bell**
19 4, Ch g Anjaal—Turban Bay (IRE) **Mr P. Smith**

### THREE-YEAR-OLDS

20 **JESSIE PYE**, b f Heeraat (IRE)—Under My Spell **Mr J. R. Salter**
21 **MONSIEUR FANTAISIE (IRE)**, b g Make Believe—Rachel Tiffany (USA) **The Cross Racing Club**

**Flat Jockey:** Robert Havlin, Luke Morris.

---

## 426 MR GEOFFREY OLDROYD, Pocklington
Postal: **Yapham Grange, Pocklington, York, Yorkshire, YO42 1PB**
Contacts: PHONE **01653 668279**
EMAIL oldroydgeoff@gmail.com

1 **CAPTAIN VAN DYKE**, 4, b g Slade Power (IRE)—Forever's Girl **Bond Thoroughbred Ltd**
2 **EDDIEBET**, 7, ch g Monsieur Bond (IRE)—Champagne Katie **Bond Thoroughbred Ltd**
3 **RISE HALL**, 6, b g Frankel—Forever Bond **Bond Thoroughbred Ltd**
4 **SEA STORM**, 5, ch m Monsieur Bond (IRE)—Chez Cherie **Casino Royale Racing Syndicate**

## MR GEOFFREY OLDROYD - continued

### THREE-YEAR-OLDS

5 Ch g Monsieur Bond (IRE)—Champagne Katie **Bond Thoroughbred Ltd**
6 **FOREVER'S LADY,** b f Toronado (IRE)—Forever's Girl **Bond Thoroughbred Ltd**
7 **HIGHEST WAVE,** b f Muhaarar—Tibesti **Bond Thoroughbred Ltd**
8 **NEVER SAY NEVER (IRE),** b f No Nay Never (USA)—Tahara (IRE) **Bond Thoroughbred Ltd**

### TWO-YEAR-OLDS

9 B f 16/03 Monsieur Bond (IRE)—Bond Artist (IRE) (Excellent Art) **Bond Thoroughbred Ltd**
10 Ch g 01/04 Monsieur Bond (IRE)—Champagne Katie (Medicean) **Bond Thoroughbred Ltd**
11 **DOCTOR KHAN JUNIOR,** b c 25/02 Muhaarar—Ladies Are Forever (Monsieur Bond (IRE)) **Bond Thoroughbred Ltd**
12 B f 08/04 Muhaarar—Forever's Girl (Monsieur Bond (IRE)) **Bond Thoroughbred Ltd**

---

**427** **MR HENRY OLIVER, Abberley**
Postal: **Stable End, Worsley Racing Stables, Bank Lane, Abberley, Worcester, Worcestershire, WR6 6BQ**
Contacts: **PHONE 01299 890143 MOBILE 07701 068759**
EMAIL henryoliverracing@hotmail.co.uk WEBSITE www.henryoliverracing.co.uk

1 **ADMIRALS BAY (GER),** 5, b g Mount Nelson—Astragal
2 **AGAMEMMON (IRE),** 9, b g Getaway (GER)—Oscar Road (IRE)
3 **AVANTGARDIST (USA),** 7, ch g Campanologist (USA)—Avocette (GER)
4 **BADNESS BACKFIRES (IRE),** 7, b g Sans Frontieres (IRE)—Style Majic (USA)
5 **BEHRESS,** 4, b f Kalanisi (IRE)—Behra (IRE)
6 **CHEROKEE BILL,** 10, b g Robin des Champs (FR)—Daizinni
7 **CORRI LINDO (FR),** 11, br g Corri Piano (FR)—Daresta (FR)
8 **COURT GLORY (IRE),** 8, b m Court Cave (IRE)—Ad Gloria (IRE)
9 **DETATCHED (IRE),** 9, b g Beneficial—Witneses Daughter (IRE)
10 **DIAMOND BRIG,** 9, b g Black Sam Bellamy (IRE)—Lady Brig
11 **DR OAKLEY (IRE),** 7, ch g Le Fou (IRE)—Two Choices (IRE)
12 **DUROUYN,** 7, b g Yeats (IRE)—Douryna
13 **GENEROUS DAY (IRE),** 9, b g Daylami (IRE)—Our Pride
14 **HARD TO FORGET (IRE),** 8, b g Gold Well—Raheen Na Hoon (IRE)
15 **HIJRAN (IRE),** 8, ch m Mastercraftsman (IRE)—Sunny Slope
16 **K'CHOU DU PECOS AA (FR),** 7, b g Walk In The Park (IRE)—Rose Chou (FR)
17 **KILCHREEST MOON (IRE),** 10, ch g Moon Ballad (IRE)—Kilchreest Queen (IRE)
18 **KILLARO BOY (IRE),** 12, ch g Mr Dinos (IRE)—Auburn Roilelet (IRE)
19 **LILL SMITH (IRE),** 8, b m Gold Well—Vivachi (IRE)
20 4, Ch c Schiaparelli (GER)—Massannie (IRE)
21 **MRSGREY (IRE),** 7, gr m Court Cave (IRE)—Caroline Fontenail (IRE)
22 **OUTISAID (IRE),** 6, gr g Carlotamix (FR)—Bounty's Sister
23 **OZZY THOMAS (IRE),** 11, b g Gold Well—Bramble Leader (IRE)
24 4, B f Schiaparelli (GER)—Persian Gaye (IRE)
25 **SINGLEFARMPAYMENT,** 11, b g Milan—Crevamoy (IRE)
26 **THE BIG BITE (IRE),** 8, b g Scorpion (IRE)—Thanks Noel (IRE)
27 **WESTERN CLIMATE (IRE),** 12, b g Westerner—Jo Peeks (IRE)

**Owners:** Andyfreight Holdings Limited, Best Foot Forward, Best Foot Forward Two, Catch Twenty Two, Catchtwentytwo,Andyfreight Holdingsltd, Crowd Racing Partnership, Mr I. M. Gray, Mr N. Griffith, Mr N T Griffith & H M Haddock, Mrs H. M. Haddock, B. Hawkins, Mr M. S. Hitchcroft, Ms S. A. Howell, Racing, - Lindo, Mr D. M. J. Lloyd, Martingrayracing2, Mr C. Mastoras, Mr C. McKenna, Mrs C. Oliver, Mr H. J. Oliver, Roy & Louise Swinburne, Talking Pictures TV Limited, The H & H Partnership, R. G. Whitehead, martingrayracing.

**NH Jockey:** James Davies, Jeremiah McGrath.

**428**

## MR JAMIE OSBORNE, Upper Lambourn
Postal: **The Old Malthouse, Upper Lambourn, Hungerford, Berkshire, RG17 8RG**
Contacts: **PHONE 01488 73139 MOBILE 07860 533422**
EMAIL **info@jamieosborne.com** WEBSITE **www.jamieosborne.com**

1 **BRAINS (IRE)**, 5, b g Dandy Man (IRE)—Pure Jazz (IRE) **The Judges & Partner**
2 **CLIFFS OF CAPRI**, 7, b g Canford Cliffs (IRE)—Shannon Spree **Melbourne 10 Racing**
3 **GOOD EARTH (IRE)**, 4, b g Acclamation—Madhatten (IRE) **Mrs J A Wakefield & Partner**
4 **HASHTAGMETOO (USA)**, 4, b f Declaration of War (USA)—Caribbean Princess (USA) **The Other Club**
5 **LIAM'S LEGEND (USA)**, 4, gr ro c Liam's Map (USA)—Indian Legend (USA) **Mr Khalid bin Mishref**
6 **MEKONG**, 6, b g Frankel—Ship's Biscuit **Mr Khalid bin Mishref**
7 **MISS SLIGO (IRE)**, 4, b f New Approach (IRE)—Illandrane (IRE) **The Q Party**
8 **MR ALCHEMY**, 4, gr g Leroidesanimaux (BRZ)—Albaraka **The Q Party**
9 **MR BEAU BLUE**, 4, br g Brazen Beau (AUS)—Precious Secret (IRE) **The Other Club**
10 **MYKONOS ST JOHN**, 4, b g Swiss Spirit—Royal Pardon **Mrs J A Wakefield & Partner**
11 **NICKS NOT WONDER**, 4, b c Siyouni (FR)—Singuliere (IRE) **Mr J. A. Osborne**
12 **PEAKED TOO SOON**, 4, b g Iffraaj—Libys Dream (IRE) **The Joy of Six**
13 **RAISING SAND**, 9, b g Oasis Dream—Balalaika **Nick Bradley Racing 22 & Partner**
14 **SUNSHINE FUN (USA)**, 4, b f Bernardini (USA)—Claire Soleil (USA) **Phoenix Thoroughbred Limited**

## THREE-YEAR-OLDS
15 **ALVARINO**, b c Bobby's Kitten (USA)—Alinstante **Miss K. Rausing**
16 **ARID STEEL (IRE)**, b gr f Exceed And Excel (AUS)—First Party **Mr A. Al Kamda**
17 B c Estidhkaar (IRE)—Attracted To You (IRE)
18 **BIG LITTLE LIE (FR)**, b f Dark Angel (IRE)—Felcine (IRE) **Dargle Equine (uk) Ltd & Partner**
19 **CREMA INGLESA (IRE)**, b f Lope de Vega (IRE)—Creme Anglaise **Hunscote Stud Ltd & John O'Connor**
20 **DRAG RACE (IRE)**, ch f Zoffany (IRE)—Aja (IRE)
21 B c Noble Mission—Dreamt **Mr Khalid bin Mishref**
22 **DUKE'S TRAVELS (IRE)**, b g Elzaam (AUS)—Cozzene's Pride (USA) **Mr R J Tufft & Partner**
23 **EYES (IRE)**, b f Dandy Man (IRE)—Ebony Street (USA) **The Judges & Partner**
24 **FAITHHOPEANDGLORY**, b f Coach House (IRE)—Queen Hermione (IRE) **Dr D. Chapman-Jones**
25 B c Gutaifan (IRE)—Fanciful Dancer
26 **FIGHTING KHABIB (IRE)**, b c Zoffany (IRE)—Aurora Spring (IRE) **Phoenix Thoroughbred Limited & Partner**
27 **FIGHTING POET (IRE)**, b c The Gurkha (IRE)—Inkling (USA) **Phoenix Thoroughbred Limited & Partner**
28 **HASHTAG BE KIND (IRE)**, b f Camelot—Civility Cat (USA) **The Other Club**
29 **HOT SCOOP**, b g Hot Streak (IRE)—News Desk **The 10 For 10 Partnership**
30 **JERRIAIS**, br g Geordieland (FR)—La Verte Rue (USA) **Mr A. Taylor**
31 **JERSEY GIFT (IRE)**, b c Nathaniel (IRE)—Pharadelle (IRE) **Mr Mr A. Taylor & Partner**
32 B f Iffraaj—Majenta (IRE) **Mrs L. M. Shanahan**
33 **MYLIE (IRE)**, b f Gutaifan (IRE)—Burning Dawn (USA) **Jacobs Construction (holdings) Ltd & Ptn**
34 **NO DAY NEVER (IRE)**, b g No Nay Never (USA)—Starlight Princess (IRE) **Mrs J A Wakefield & Partner**
35 **NORTHERN (IRE)**, b c Camelot—Myrica **V7 Recruitment**
36 **NURSE FLORENCE (IRE)**, gr f Gutaifan (IRE)—Ellasha **The 10 For 10 Partnership**
37 **OLIVIA MARY (IRE)**, b gr f Dark Angel (IRE)—Lapis Blue (IRE) **Mr J. A. Osborne**
38 **RESTRICTED AREA (IRE)**, b g Lethal Force (IRE)—
                                              L'lle Aux Loups (IRE) **Mr M S Cresswell, Mr J Vermaak & Partner**
39 **ROCKSTAR BLONDE**, b f Fascinating Rock (IRE)—Illegally Blonde (IRE) **Mr & Mrs I. Barratt**
40 Ch f Zoffany (IRE)—Seatone (USA) **Mrs L. M. Shanahan**
41 **TACORA (IRE)**, b c Gutaifan (IRE)—Pindrop **The 10 For 10 Partnership**
42 **THE CHAIN (IRE)**, b f Coulsty (IRE)—Lucky Leigh **R. J. Tufft**
43 **VELOCITY (IRE)**, b f Vadamos (FR)—Naqrah (IRE) **R. J. Tufft**
44 **VIN ROUGE (IRE)**, ch g Zoffany (IRE)—Adventure Seeker (FR) **Mr Michael Buckley & Partner**
45 **VIVID IMAGINATION (IRE)**, b f Make Believe—Shifting (IRE) **The 10 For 10 Partnership**
46 **YANIFER**, b g Dandy Man (IRE)—Fondie (IRE) **Hugo Hunt Racing**
47 **YUHIBU (IRE)**, b c Gutaifan (IRE)—Love In The Desert **Phoenix Thoroughbred Limited & Partner**
48 **ZOFFALAY (IRE)**, b c Zoffany (IRE)—Layalee (IRE) **Phoenix Thoroughbred Limited & Partner**
49 **ZOOLANDER (IRE)**, b c Zoffany (IRE)—Shahralasal (IRE) **R. J. Tufft**

# MR JAMIE OSBORNE - continued

## TWO-YEAR-OLDS

**50** B c 13/04 Churchill (IRE)—Beyond Desire (Invincible Spirit (IRE)) (59048) **Rothstein & Held Racing Limited & Ptn**
**51** B c 17/02 Kodi Bear (IRE)—Classic Legend (Galileo (IRE)) (19048) **Rothstein & Held Racing Limited & Ptn**
**52** B c 18/03 Bungle Inthejungle—Convidada (IRE) (Trans Island) (33333) **Rothstein & Held Racing Limited & Ptn**
**53** B f 08/04 Bated Breath—Enigmatique (Arcano (IRE)) (14286) **The 10 For 10 Partnership**
**54** Ch f 07/04 Australia—French Flirt (Peintre Celebre (USA)) (35000)
**55** Gr c 13/02 Mastercraftsman (IRE)—Gelenschik (IRE) (Dalakhani (IRE)) (42857)
**56** B f 14/02 Caravaggio (USA)—Greatest Place (IRE) (Shamardal (USA)) (28571)
**57** B c 26/02 Bated Breath—Israfel (Dark Angel (IRE)) (23000) **The 10 For 10 Partnership**
**58** B c 28/02 Mondialiste (IRE)—Just Jealous (IRE) (Lope de Vega (IRE)) (47619)
**59** Ch f 05/02 Churchill (IRE)—Kaabari (USA) (Seeking The Gold (USA)) (28571) **The 10 For 10 Partnership**
**60** B f 17/02 Showcasing—Lady Lockwood (Harbour Watch (IRE)) (65000) **The 10 For 10 Partnership**
**61** B c 03/05 Lawman (FR)—Luminata (IRE) (Indian Ridge) (14000)
**62** B c 26/02 Le Havre (IRE)—Mt of Beatitudes (IRE) (Fastnet Rock (AUS)) (37000)
**63** B f 09/03 Kodiac—Natural Blues (New Approach (IRE)) (20000)
**64** B c 12/02 Dabirsim (FR)—New Providence (Bahamian Bounty) (14000) **The 10 For 10 Partnership**
**65** **NOTIONS (IRE),** ch c 19/03 Lope de Vega (IRE)—
　　　　　　　　　　　　　　　Golden Shadow (IRE) (Selkirk (USA)) (76190) **Maxwell Morris & Partner**
**66** B f 14/04 Kodiac—Parasail (New Approach (IRE)) (12000) **The 10 For 10 Partnership**
**67** B f 14/02 Zoffany (IRE)—Rhiannon (IRE) (High Chaparral (IRE)) (23810)
**68** B c 16/04 Lope de Vega (IRE)—
　　　　　　　　　　　　　　Royal Empress (IRE) (Holy Roman Emperor (IRE)) (71429) **Rothstein & Held Racing Limited & Ptn**
**69** B c 21/02 Muhaarar—Silent Thoughts (IRE) (Galileo (IRE)) (38095) **The 10 For 10 Partnership**
**70** B c 27/02 Holy Roman Emperor (IRE)—So You Dream (IRE) (So You Think (NZ)) (11000) **The 10 For 10 Partnership**
**71** Gr c 06/02 Dark Angel (IRE)—Swiss Kiss (Dansili) (30000) **The 10 For 10 Partnership**
**72** B c 27/03 Dark Angel (IRE)—Thawrah (IRE) (Green Desert (USA)) (40000)
**73** B f 15/02 No Nay Never (USA)—Time Ahead (Spectrum (IRE)) (28571) **The 10 For 10 Partnership**

**Assistant Trainer:** Jimmy McCarthy.

**Flat Jockey:** Nicola Currie. **Apprentice Jockey:** Saffie Osborne. **Amateur Jockey:** Miss Alexandra Bell, Mr Alex Ferguson.

---

**429**
## MISS EMMA OWEN, Nether Winchendon
Postal: **Muskhill Farm, Nether Winchendon, Aylesbury, Buckinghamshire, HP18 0EB**
Contacts: **PHONE** 01844 290282 **MOBILE** 07718 984799
**EMAIL** emma.l.owen@hotmail.com

**1** **ANNAJEMIMA,** 7, b m Firebreak—Leaping Flame (USA) **Miss E. L. Owen**
**2** **AUSTIN FRIARS,** 9, b g New Approach (IRE)—My Luigia (IRE) **Miss E. L. Owen**
**3** **BAHAMIAN HEIGHTS,** 10, b g Bahamian Bounty—Tahirah **Miss E. L. Owen**
**4** **DIVINE MESSENGER,** 7, b g Firebreak—Resentful Angel **Miss E. L. Owen**
**5** **DUTIFUL SON (IRE),** 11, b g Invincible Spirit (IRE)—Grecian Dancer **Miss E. L. Owen**
**6** **FIREGUARD,** 8, b g Firebreak—Leaping Flame (USA) **Miss E. L. Owen**
**7** **HIGHER COURT (USA),** 13, b g Shamardal (USA)—Nawaiet (USA) **Miss E. L. Owen**
**8** **HIGHPLAINS DRIFTER (IRE),** 10, b g High Chaparral (IRE)—Qhazeenah **Miss E. L. Owen**
**9** **JOSHLEE (IRE),** 7, b c Dark Angel (IRE)—Kay Es Jay (FR) **Miss E. L. Owen**
**10** **LEGAL MIND,** 8, ch h Firebreak—La Sorrela (IRE) **Miss E. L. Owen**
**11** **MILLDEAN BILLY (IRE),** 5, b g Dandy Man (IRE)—Strawberriesncream (IRE) **Miss E. L. Owen**
**12** **MILLDEAN PANTHER,** 5, b g Mayson—Silver Halo **Miss E. L. Owen**
**13** **MUSICAL COMEDY,** 10, b g Royal Applause—Spinning Top **Miss E. L. Owen**
**14** **PEDDERY,** 5, b g Pastoral Pursuits—Resentful Angel **Miss E. L. Owen**
**15** **RED HANRAHAN (IRE),** 10, b g Yeats (IRE)—Monty's Sister (IRE) **Miss E. L. Owen**
**16** **REIGNITE,** 6, b g Firebreak—Resentful Angel **Miss E. L. Owen**
**17** **SEA THE WAVES,** 8, b g Canford Cliffs (IRE)—April (IRE) **Mr L. F. Daly**
**18** **THE ARISTOCAT (IRE),** 6, b m Kitten's Joy (USA)—Letters (FR) **Miss E. L. Owen**
**19** **VERETA (IRE),** 5, b m Dick Turpin (IRE)—Vera Lou (IRE) **Mr L. F. Daly**

## 430 MR PATRICK OWENS, Newmarket
Postal: **Authorized Yard, St Gatien Stables, Vicarage Road, Newmarket, Suffolk, CB8 8HP**
Contacts: **PHONE 07796 036878**
EMAIL powens@patrickowens.co.uk

1 **MISS VELVETEEN (IRE)**, 4, b f Free Eagle (IRE)—Velvet Star (IRE)  **Mr Patrick Owens**

### THREE-YEAR-OLDS
2 **ADAALADY**, b f Adaay (IRE)—Marmalady (IRE)  **Mrs H. A. Buxton**
3 **ADAAY TO REMEMBER**, b f Adaay (IRE)—Cross My Heart  **GB Horseracing**
4 **DIVINE BALANCE (USA)**, b br f Union Rags (USA)—Divine Presence (USA)
5 **LADY ALLEGRO**, ch f Australia—Lysanda (GER)  **Mrs H. A. Buxton**
6 **PRONTISSIMO**, b g Toronado (IRE)—Eastern Glow  **K. A. Dasmal**

### TWO-YEAR-OLDS
7 B c 27/03 Bated Breath—Kerrys Requiem (IRE) (King's Best (USA)) (10476)  **Mr Patrick Owens**
8 B c 30/04 Ardad (IRE)—News Desk (Cape Cross (IRE)) (22000)  **K. A. Dasmal**

## 431 MR HUGO PALMER, Newmarket
Postal: **Kremlin Cottage Stables, Snailwell Road, Newmarket, Suffolk, CB8 7DP**
Contacts: **PHONE 01638 669880 MOBILE 07824 887886 FAX 01638 666383**
EMAIL info@hugopalmer.com WEBSITE www.hugopalmer.com

1 **ACQUITTED (IRE)**, 4, b br g Night of Thunder (IRE)—Blameless (IRE)  **John Livock & Nat Lacy**
2 **BATTERED**, 7, b g Foxwedge (AUS)—Swan Wings  **Mr H Palmer**
3 **CARAVAN OF HOPE (IRE)**, 5, b g Nathaniel (IRE)—Caravan of Dreams (IRE)  **Dr A. Ridha**
4 **COMBINE (IRE)**, 4, b f Zoffany (IRE)—Unity (IRE)  **Lady Manton & Partners 1**
5 **CONVERTIBLE (IRE)**, 4, b g Helmet (AUS)—Empress Ella (IRE)  **Mr L. L. Lee**
6 **DOUBLING DICE**, 4, br g Teofilo (IRE)—Garanciere (FR)  **Mr V. I. Araci**
7 **EASTERN SHERIFF**, 4, b g Lawman (FR)—Abunai  **Sheikh I. S. Al Khalifa**
8 **GOLDEN PASS**, 4, b f Golden Horn—Lovely Pass (IRE)  **Dr A. Ridha**
9 **IMRAHOR**, 4, b g Kingman—She's Mine (IRE)  **Mr V. I. Araci**
10 **MARGARET DUMONT (IRE)**, 4, b f Camelot—Sapphire Waters (IRE)  **Lady Manton & Partner**
11 **POWER OF STATES (IRE)**, 5, b g Lope de Vega (IRE)—Allegation (FR)  **Dr A. Ridha**
12 **RED OCTOBER (IRE)**, 5, ch g Dawn Approach (IRE)—Mamonta  **Mrs Clodagh McStay & Partner**
13 **SHEILA (IRE)**, 4, ch f Australia—Donnelly's Hollow (IRE)  **Ed Tynan & Ms S Khaw**
14 **SILENT PERFORMANCE (IRE)**, 4, b f Zoffany (IRE)—Silent Thoughts (IRE)  **Dr A. Ridha**
15 **STRAWBERRY ROCK (IRE)**, 4, b g Rock of Gibraltar (IRE)—Strawberry Vodka  **FOMO (Rock) Syndicate**
16 **SYSTEMIC**, 4, b g Toronado (IRE)—Saskia's Dream  **P Moorhead, H Moorhead & J Collins**
17 **UTILE**, 4, ch f Frankel—Straight Thinking (USA)  **Exors of the late Mr K. Abdullah**

### THREE-YEAR-OLDS
18 **ADDOSH**, b f The Gurkha (IRE)—Wild Storm  **Mr V. I. Araci**
19 **ADRASTUS**, b c Dubawi (IRE)—Filia Regina  **The Earl Of Derby**
20 **AHLAWI**, ch c Shamardal (USA)—Lovely Pass (IRE)  **Dr A. Ridha**
21 **BARRET (IRE)**, b g Kodiac—Some Site (IRE)  **Mr L. L. Lee**
22 **BRUNNERA**, b f Dubawi (IRE)—Romantica  **Exors of the late Mr K. Abdullah**
23 **CHOCOYA**, ch f Sepoy (AUS)—Silver Games (IRE)  **Mr C. N. Wright**
24 **COLONIAL LOVE**, b f Australia—Fondly (IRE)  **MPH O'Connor & Reinsurance Partners**
25 **COUNTESSA (FR)**, b br f Camelot—Elitiste (IRE)  **Sheikh I. S. Al Khalifa**
26 **DANCING TO WIN**, b g Iffraaj—Smart Step  **The Hls Partnership**
27 **DANTORA**, b c Dansili—Rostova (USA)  **Exors of the late Mr K. Abdullah**
28 **ECHO BEACH**, b g Adaay (IRE)—Last Echo (IRE)  **Kremlin Cottage IX**
29 **ECOSSE**, b f Acclamation—Dumfriesshire  **Exors of the late Mr K. Abdullah**
30 **GLESGA GAL (IRE)**, ch f Lope de Vega (IRE)—Crystany (IRE)  **Next Wave Racing / E Tynan / E Babington**

## MR HUGO PALMER - continued

31 **GOOD SOUL**, gr f Mukhadram—Royal Dalakhani (IRE) **Kremlin Cottage IX**
32 **IRISH LEGEND (IRE)**, b c Sea The Stars (IRE)—Stealth Missile (IRE) **Mr K. K. B. Ho**
33 **KIZOMBA**, b f Kodiac—Zulema **Exors of the late Mr K. Abdullah**
34 **KOMORE**, b f Australia—Chigun **Exors of the late Mr K. Abdullah**
35 **LIBERATED LADY (IRE)**, b br f Iffraaj—Isobel Archer **Old Road Securities & Partners**
36 **LONDON PALLADIUM**, b g Showcasing—Dam Beautiful **Livock, Lacy, Seabrook & Tarbuck**
37 **LOVELY BREEZE (IRE)**, b f Sepoy (AUS)—Power of Light (IRE) **Dr A. Ridha**
38 **MILITARY MISSION (IRE)**, gr g Mastercraftsman (IRE)—Atlantic Isle (GER) **Military Syndicate & Mrs Clodagh McStay**
39 **MISS FASTNET**, b f Fastnet Rock (AUS)—Heaven's Angel (IRE) **Mr H. Dalmook Al Maktoum**
40 **NEPTUNE'S WONDER (IRE)**, b f Kodiac—Prance (IRE) **Dr A. Ridha**
41 **NEW FORCE**, ch c New Approach (IRE)—Honky Tonk Sally **Sheikh I. S. Al Khalifa**
42 **NOMAN (IRE)**, b c Shalaa (IRE)—Mathool (IRE) **Al Shaqab Racing UK Limited**
43 **OCEAN ROAD (IRE)**, b f Australia—Love And Laughter (IRE) **Qatar Racing Ltd**
44 B f Olympic Glory (IRE)—Ornelia Ruee (FR) **Ed Tynan & Partner**
45 **OZ LEGEND (IRE)**, b c Australia—Ultra Appeal (IRE) **Mr K. K. B. Ho**
46 **PINK GOLD (IRE)**, b g Havana Gold (IRE)—Lara Amelia (IRE) **Mr L. L. Lee**
47 **QUENELLE D'OR**, b f Golden Horn—Quenelle **Lady Derby & Lady Ritblat**
48 **SET POINT (IRE)**, b c Sea The Stars (IRE)—Hot Sauce (IRE) **John Livock & Nat Lacy**
49 **SPIRIT OF IFFRAAJ**, b c Iffraaj—Catchline (USA) **Dr A. Ridha**
50 **SURPRISE PICTURE (IRE)**, b g Kodiac—Lovely Surprise (IRE) **Dr A. Ridha**
51 **THE ROSSTAFARIAN (IRE)**, ch c Starspangledbanner (AUS)—Via Lattea (IRE) **Middleham Park Racing LXXXVII**

## TWO-YEAR-OLDS

52 Ch c 20/02 Galileo Gold—Al Jawza (Nathaniel (IRE)) (23810) **Highclere T'Bred Racing, C Fahy & Partner**
53 **ASEAN LEGEND (IRE)**, b c 05/03 Australia—Queenscliff (IRE) (Danehill Dancer (IRE)) (74286) **Mr K. K. B. Ho**
54 Ch c 15/03 Starspangledbanner (AUS)—Barnet (Manduro (GER)) (65000) **Mr L. L. Lee**
55 B c 04/05 Slade Power (IRE)—Beautiful Filly (Oasis Dream) **Dr A. Ridha**
56 B f 22/04 Night of Thunder (IRE)—Best Side (IRE) (King's Best (USA)) **Mr V. I. Araci**
57 B f 09/02 Bated Breath—Chigun (Oasis Dream) **Mr V. I. Araci**
58 B f 01/04 Time Test—Comic (IRE) (Be My Chief (USA)) (50000) **Duchess Of Roxburghe**
59 Ch f 15/04 Hot Streak (IRE)—Cross Pattee (IRE) (Oasis Dream) (25000) **Qatar Racing Ltd & Partner**
60 Ch f 08/02 Bungle Inthejungle—Elegante Bere (FR) (Peer Gynt (JPN)) **Mr C. N. Wright**
61 Ch f 07/05 Highland Reel (IRE)—Flawless Beauty (Excellent Art) **Mrs V. Palmer**
62 B f 25/03 Dark Angel (IRE)—Freedom Pass (USA) (Gulch (USA)) (40952) **Tony O'Connor & Reinsurance Partners**
63 B c 18/04 Gleneagles (IRE)—House Point (Pivotal) **Mr V. I. Araci**
64 B c 28/01 Frankel—Hyper Dream (IRE) (Oasis Dream) **Mr V. I. Araci**
65 Ch c 19/04 Dubawi (IRE)—Lovely Pass (IRE) (Raven's Pass (USA)) **Dr A. Ridha**
66 Ch f 24/04 Ribchester (IRE)—Lovely Surprise (IRE) (Shamardal (USA)) **Dr A. Ridha**
67 B c 03/03 Dark Angel (IRE)—Minnaloushe (IRE) (Lawman (FR)) (60000)
68 B f 19/02 Zoffany (IRE)—MI Angel (Native Khan (FR)) **Mr V. I. Araci**
69 **NEPTUNE LEGEND (IRE)**, b c 28/02 Invincible Spirit (IRE)—Kate The Great (Xaar) (333333) **Mr K. K. B. Ho**
70 **NOVA LEGEND (IRE)**, b c 09/05 Galileo (IRE)—Ghurra (USA) (War Chant (USA)) (550000) **Mr K. K. B. Ho**
71 **NOVEL LEGEND (IRE)**, b c 08/03 Nathaniel (IRE)—Majestic Dubawi (Dubawi (IRE)) (95238) **Mr K. K. B. Ho**
72 B c 06/04 Dark Angel (IRE)—Pandora's Box (IRE) (Galileo (IRE)) **Middleham Park Racing XCII**
73 **PLANET LEGEND (IRE)**, ch c 12/02 Galileo (IRE)—Zut Alors (IRE) (Pivotal) (169492) **Mr K. K. B. Ho**
74 **SKY LEGEND (IRE)**, ch c 18/03 Galileo (IRE)—Spectre (FR) (Siyouni (FR)) (450000) **Mr K. K. B. Ho**
75 Ch c 25/01 Galileo Gold—Soft Power (IRE) (Balmont (USA)) (75000) **Al Shaqab Racing UK Limited**
76 B f 21/02 Le Havre (IRE)—Spinning Queen (Spinning World (USA)) (65000) **Mr E Babington**
77 **STAR LEGEND (IRE)**, b c 13/04 Galileo (IRE)—Thai Haku (IRE) (Oasis Dream) (450000) **Mr K. K. B. Ho**
78 **STATE LEGEND (IRE)**, b c 03/05 Churchill (IRE)—Zibeline (IRE) (Cape Cross (IRE)) (48426) **Mr K. K. B. Ho**
79 B f 13/02 Havana Gold (IRE)—Stroll Patrol (Mount Nelson) **Qatar Racing Ltd**
80 Ch c 28/03 Cotai Glory—Vulnicura (IRE) (Frozen Power (IRE)) (26667) **Mr L. L. Lee**

**432** **MR JOSEPH PARR, Newmarket**
Postal: **5 Greenfields, Newmarket, Suffolk, CB8 8DR**
Contacts: PHONE **07876 262169**
EMAIL **josephparr@hotmail.com**

1 **CONSCIOUS,** 4, b g Oasis Dream—Deliberate **Trevor & Ruth Milner**
2 **ENIGMATIC (IRE),** 7, b g Elnadim (USA)—Meanwhile (IRE) **Trevor & Ruth Milner**
3 **ESSPEEGEE,** 8, b g Paco Boy (IRE)—Goldrenched (IRE) **The Skills People Group Ltd**
4 **FAIRY RING,** 4, b f Casamento (IRE)—Fairy Steps **Ms S. J. Humber**
5 **LADY ISABEL (IRE),** 4, b f Hallowed Crown (AUS)—Meanwhile (IRE) **Trevor & Ruth Milner**
6 **SIR HAMILTON (IRE),** 6, b g Canford Cliffs (IRE)—Cawett (IRE) **Away Days Racing Club**
7 **THREE DRAGONS,** 4, ch g Sakhee (USA)—Three Heart's **Ms S. J. Humber**
8 **TRANSITION,** 4, b g Oasis Dream—Nancy O (IRE) **Mr O. S. Harris**

### THREE-YEAR-OLDS

9 **CRESTWOOD,** b g Garswood—Cresta Gold **Team Lodge Racing**
10 **G'DAAY,** b g Adaay (IRE)—Gilt Linked **Trevor & Ruth Milner**
11 B c Garswood—Granny McPhee **A J McNamee & L C McNamee**
12 **HELLO ME (IRE),** b f Mehmas (IRE)—Safe Place (USA) **CS Family Ltd**
13 **ONLY DEBRIS (IRE),** b c Exceed And Excel (AUS)—Shapoura (FR) **CS Family Ltd**
14 **OWEN LITTLE,** b g Sakhee (USA)—Three Heart's **Ms S. J. Humber**
15 **PRINCE OF BEL LIR (IRE),** b g Prince of Lir (IRE)—Harvest Joy (IRE) **The Skills People Group Ltd**
16 **ROMAN DYNASTY (IRE),** b c Mehmas (IRE)—Empress Ella (IRE) **Trevor & Ruth Milner**
17 **STRANGER THINGS,** ch f Mukhadram—Fairy Steps **Ms S. J. Humber**

**Other Owners:** A. J. McNamee, Mr L. McNamee, Mrs R. L. Milner, Mr T. Milner.

**433** **MR MARK PATTINSON, Epsom**
Postal: **Flat 3, White House Stables, Tattenham Corner Road, Epsom, Surrey, KT18 5PP**
Contacts: MOBILE **07961 835401**

1 **MYKINDOFSUNSHINE (IRE),** 5, gr g Zebedee—Silk Fan (IRE) **M I Pattinson Racing**
2 **OUR OYSTERCATCHER,** 7, br g Pastoral Pursuits—The Dark Eider **Mrs F A Veasey & G. B. Partnership**
3 **PERFECT SYMPHONY (IRE),** 7, b g Dandy Man (IRE)—Fields of Joy (GER) **Lynne Stanbrook & Julian Power**

### THREE-YEAR-OLDS

4 **BELLA COLOROSSA,** b f Toronado (IRE)—Shesells Seashells **Smarden Thoroughbreds**
5 **HAVERGATE ISLAND,** b g Coach House (IRE)—Jethou Island **Mrs F A Veasey & G. B. Partnership**
6 **RAINBOW SIGN,** b g Adaay (IRE)—Pax Aeterna (USA) **M. G. H. Heald**

**Other Owners:** Mr S. D. Bradley, Mrs H. J. Fitzsimons, Mr A. M. H. Heald, M. G. H. Heald, Mr J. Power, Mrs L. C. Stanbrook, Mrs F. A. Veasey.

**434** **MR BEN PAULING, Bourton-on-the-Water**
Postal: **Bourton Hill Farm, Bourton Hill, Bourton-On-The-Water, Cheltenham, Gloucestershire, GL54 2LF**
Contacts: **PHONE 01451 821252 MOBILE 07825 232888**
**EMAIL ben@benpaulingracing.com WEBSITE www.benpaulingracing.com**

1 **ANGE ENDORMI (IRE)**, 5, ch g Leading Light (IRE)—Maxford Lady (IRE) **Mrs G. Morgan**
2 **ANIGHTINLAMBOURN (IRE)**, 7, b m Gold Well—Madgehil (IRE) **The Megsons**
3 **APPLE ROCK (IRE)**, 7, b g Royal Anthem (USA)—Wayward Cove **Presumption in Favour Partnership**
4 **ARTEMISION**, 5, b g Gentlewave (IRE)—Miss Fahrenheit (IRE) **T K Racing Ltd**
5 **BANGERS AND CASH (IRE)**, 5, b g Fame And Glory—Cash Customer (IRE) **OAP II**
6 **BAXTER BASICS (IRE)**, 5, br g Getaway (GER)—Limekiln Lass (IRE) **Ardley, Bickmore & Pauling**
7 **BIG DIFFERENCE (IRE)**, 8, b g Presenting—Roque de Cyborg (IRE) **Mr M. Waters**
8 **BOBBY BOW (IRE)**, 7, b g Frammassone (IRE)—Bramble Cottage (IRE) **Mrs G. Morgan**
9 **BOWTOGREATNESS (IRE)**, 5, br g Westerner—Miss Baden (IRE) **Harry Redknapp & Sophie Pauling**
10 , B f Schiaparelli (GER)—Burgundy Betty (IRE) **Mrs B. M. Henley**
11 **CHESS PLAYER (IRE)**, 6, ch g No Risk At All (FR)—Merci Jandrer (FR) **Mrs Rachel Brodie & Mr John Brodie**
12 **CONCEAL (IRE)**, 6, ch g Stowaway—Babyshan (IRE) **Highclere Thoroughbred Racing - Stowaway**
13 **CURIO BAY (IRE)**, 5, b g Milan—Anna Magdalena (IRE) **Mrs Rachel Brodie & Mr John Brodie**
14 **DE BARLEY BASKET (IRE)**, 8, b g Alkaadhem—Lady Willmurt (IRE) **Mrs S N J Embiricos & Ms A Embiricos**
15 **DEL LA MAR ROCKET (IRE)**, 5, b g Fame And Glory—Pipe Lady (IRE) **Les de La Haye & Martin Mundy**
16 **DELAHAYE GOLD (IRE)**, 5, b g Ocovango—The Millers Tale (IRE) **Mr L. De la Haye**
17 **DELIRE D'ESTRUVAL (FR)**, 8, b g Youmzain (IRE)—Question d'Estruval (FR) **Mr Simon Munir & Mr Isaac Souede**
18 **DOCK ROAD (IRE)**, 5, ch g Shirocco (GER)—Representing (IRE) **Mr J. P. McManus**
19 , 4, Br g Califet (FR)—Dontcallerthat (IRE)
20 **EARL BIFFY BIFFEN (FR)**, 7, bl g Day Flight—Similaresisoldofa (FR) **The Megsons**
21 **EAU TOP (FR)**, 7, b g Barastraight—Monepopee (FR) **Mr O. Troup**
22 **ENCHANCIA (IRE)**, 7, b g Milan—Dancingwithbubbles (IRE) **Mrs S. Pauling**
23 **FAWSLEY SPIRIT (IRE)**, 8, b g Stowaway—Apple Trix (IRE) **Mrs Rachel Brodie & Mr Clive Bush**
24 **FINE CASTING (IRE)**, 5, b g Shantou (USA)—Fine Fortune (IRE) **Mrs S. P. Davis**
25 **FOLLY HILL**, 5, b m Mount Nelson—Burton Ash **Mr S. Lee & Mr E. Lee**
26 **GENTLEMAN VALLEY (FR)**, 5, b g Kapgarde (FR)—Richona (FR) **The Megsons**
27 **GERBOISE BORGET (FR)**, 6, b m Martaline—Ges (FR) **Mr J. P. McManus**
28 **GET PREPARED**, 6, b g Black Sam Bellamy (IRE)—Star Ar Aghaidh (IRE) **The Aldaniti Partnership**
29 **GLOBAL CITIZEN (IRE)**, 9, b g Alkaadhem—Lady Willmurt (IRE) **The Megsons**
30 **GLORIOUS OSCAR (IRE)**, 4, b g Fame And Glory—Flowers On Sunday (IRE) **Mr & Mrs J Tuttiett**
31 **GRANNY'S SECRET (IRE)**, 7, b m Stowaway—Ask My Granny (IRE) **The Jp Girls**
32 **GUARDINO (FR)**, 5, br g Authorized (IRE)—Monicker **Merriebelle Irish Farm Limited**
33 **HARDY BOY (FR)**, 4, gr g Diamond Boy (FR)—Alize du Berlais (FR)
34 **HARPER'S BROOK (FR)**, 5, b g Ask—Un Jour D Ete (FR) **Mrs S. Pauling**
35 **HAWK WIND (IRE)**, 6, b g Dubai Destination (USA)—
The Legislator (IRE) **The E Nicolson, V Embiricos & A Embiricos**
36 **HONOR GREY (IRE)**, 6, b g Flemensfirth (USA)—Rose Island **Mr & Mrs J Tuttiett**
37 **I'M SPELLBOUND (IRE)**, 5, ch g Doyen (IRE)—Magic Park (IRE) **Mr Simon Munir & Mr Isaac Souede**
38 **IMPERIAL KNIGHT (IRE)**, 5, b g Mahler—And Whatever Else (IRE) **Middleham Park Racing LXXXIX**
39 , 4, B g Getaway (GER)—Jennys Joy (IRE)
40 **KALINITE (IRE)**, 9, b br g Kalanisi (IRE)—Gerarda (IRE) **Mr P. R. Corbett**
41 **KENNACK BAY (FR)**, 6, br g Balko (FR)—Nuance Tartare (FR) **The Kennack Bay Partnership**
42 **KILDISART (IRE)**, 9, b g Dubai Destination (USA)—Princess Mairead (IRE) **Mr Simon Munir & Mr Isaac Souede**
43 **LADY CHUFFNELL (IRE)**, 7, b m Jeremy (USA)—Taraval (IRE) **The Megsons**
44 **LANDACRE BRIDGE**, 5, b g Kayf Tara—Wee Dinns (IRE) **Mrs S. Pauling**
45 **LE BREUIL (FR)**, 9, ch g Anzillero (GER)—Slew Dancer **Mrs E. A. Palmer**
46 **LE GRAND LION (FR)**, 5, gr g Turgeon (USA)—Grande Cavale (FR) **The Lion Tamers**
47 **LEADING KNIGHT (IRE)**, 5, b g Leading Light (IRE)—Miss McGoldrick (IRE) **Mr M. Jones**
48 **LIFEISAHIGHWAY (IRE)**, 7, b g Court Cave (IRE)—Miss Top (IRE) **The Rascal Flatts Partnership**
49 **LINENHALL (IRE)**, 9, ch g Stowaway—Option (IRE) **Mrs E. L. Kendall**
50 **MALINELLO**, 6, b g Malinas (GER)—Wyldello **Mr M. Jones**
51 , 4, B g Kayf Tara—Mariah's Way
52 , 4, B g Court Cave (IRE)—Marys Article (IRE)
53 **MILITARY TACTIC (IRE)**, 5, b g Iffraaj—Lunar Spirit **Mrs L. Osborne**
54 **MINELLA AWAY (IRE)**, 6, b g Stowaway—Grangeclare Gold (IRE) **Mrs G. Morgan**

## MR BEN PAULING - continued

55 **MISTER WATSON**, 7, b g Mawatheeq (USA)—Island Odyssey **Pump & Plant Services Ltd**
56 **MUCHO MAS (IRE)**, 5, b g Fame And Glory—Ceart Go Leor (IRE) **Mrs J. A. Wakefield**
57 **NADAITAK**, 7, b g Teofilo (IRE)—Tanfidh **The Megsons**
58 **NESTOR PARK (FR)**, 8, b g Walk In The Park (IRE)—Cila (FR) **Mrs S. P. Davis**
59 **NORTHERN BOUND (IRE)**, 7, b g Fruits of Love (USA)—Noble Choice **Mrs E. L. Kendall**
60 **NOT AT PRESENT (IRE)**, 6, br g Presenting—Anna Magdalena (IRE) **Mrs Rachel Brodie & Mr John Brodie**
61 **OISTRAKH LE NOIR (FR)**, 7, b g Kentucky Dynamite (USA)—
Linares Noire (FR) **Mr Simon Munir & Mr Isaac Souede**
62 **ON SPRINGS (IRE)**, 6, b g Mahler—Wild Fuchsia (IRE) **Sophie Pauling & Les de La Haye**
63 **ONE TOUCH (IRE)**, 7, b g Court Cave (IRE)—Star Bui (IRE) **Mr M. Jones**
64 **OPTIMISE PRIME (IRE)**, 5, b g Shantou—Wilde Ruby (IRE) **Mrs Rachel Brodie & Mr John Brodie**
65 **PENCREEK (FR)**, 8, ch g Konig Shuffle (GER)—Couture Fleurs (FR) **Mrs G. S. Worcester**
66 **PERFECT PIRATE**, 9, b g Black Sam Bellamy (IRE)—Supreme Gem (IRE) **Mrs S. Pauling**
67 4, B g Fame And Glory—Quinnsboro Native (IRE)
68 **QUINTA DO MAR (IRE)**, 6, b g Califet (FR)—Cara Mara (IRE) **The Bourtoneers**
69 **RAF TAVEL (FR)**, 5, b g Al Namix (FR)—Blue Road (FR) **Mr Simon Munir & Mr Isaac Souede**
70 **RAVEN'S TOWER (USA)**, 11, b g Raven's Pass (USA)—Tizdubai (USA) **Mrs S. Pauling**
71 **RINTULLA (IRE)**, 7, ch g Tobougg (IRE)—The Millers Tale (IRE) **The Three Legs Partnership**
72 4, B g Court Cave (IRE)—Running Wild (IRE)
73 **SEASIDE GIRL (IRE)**, 7, b m Mahler—Jade River (FR) **Quevega Consulting LLP**
74 **SEBASTIAN BEACH (IRE)**, 10, b g Yeats (IRE)—Night Club **The Megsons**
75 **SEVERANCE**, 5, b g Nathaniel (IRE)—Decorative (IRE) **The Megsons**
76 **SHAKEM UP'ARRY (IRE)**, 7, b g Flemensfirth (USA)—Nun Better (IRE) **Mr H. Redknapp**
77 **SHANROE TIC TEC (IRE)**, 9, b g Flemensfirth (USA)—Bonny Hall (IRE) **Easy Going Racing**
78 **SLIPWAY (IRE)**, 6, b g Stowaway—Little Sioux (IRE) **Mrs S. N. J. Embiricos**
79 **SOUTH MOUNTAIN (IRE)**, 5, b g Westerner—Maryiver (IRE) **Bruton Street UK - III**
80 **SPECIAL BUDDY (IRE)**, 7, b g Robin des Pres (FR)—Annees d'Or (IRE) **Fortnum Racing**
81 **STOKES (IRE)**, 6, b g Califet (FR)—Iktitafs Sister (IRE) **Mrs S. Pauling**
82 **TEL'ART (FR)**, 7, gr g Montmartre (FR)—Textuelle (FR) **Mr & Mrs J Tuttiett**
83 **THE CAPTAINS INN (IRE)**, 7, b g Flemensfirth (USA)—Killeen (IRE) **The Megsons**
84 **THE COB (IRE)**, 7, b g Let The Lion Roar—Millenium Love (IRE) **The Ben Pauling Racing Club**
85 **THE MACON LUGNATIC (IRE)**, 5, b g Shirocco (GER)—Didbrook **Genesis Racing Partnership II**
86 **UISCE UR (IRE)**, 9, b m City Honours (USA)—Luna Fairy (IRE) **Launde Park Farm Partnership**
87 **UNAI (IRE)**, 6, b g Court Cave (IRE)—The Millers Tale (IRE) **Mr Simon Munir & Mr Isaac Souede**
88 **UNIT SIXTYFOUR (IRE)**, 6, b g Sholokhov (IRE)—Dixie Chick (IRE) **Owners Group 062**
89 **WHATSUPWITHYOU (IRE)**, 7, b g Shantou (USA)—Whats Up Britta (IRE) **Co-Foundations Ltd**
90 **YOUR DARLING (IRE)**, 6, b g Shirocco (GER)—Carries Darling **Exors of the late Lord Vestey & Lady Vestey**

**Other Owners:** Mr M. P. Ardley, Mr A. R. Bickmore, Mr J. W. Brodie, Mrs R. A. Brodie, Mr C. Bush, Mr J. Byrne, Mr Charles E. Noell Esq, Mr M. Collie, Mr L. De la Haye, Ms A. E. Embiricos, Mrs S. N. J. Embiricos, Mrs J. D. Farrant, Mr C. Fenwick, Mr T. R. Gittins, Glassex Holdings Ltd, Mr M. D. Hankin, J H & N J Foxon Ltd, Mr S. L. Leach, Mr E. Lee, Mrs S. M. Lee, Mr M. Mundy, S. E. Munir, Mr E. D. Nicolson, Mr B. P. Pauling, Mrs S. Pauling, Mr H. Redknapp, Mr B. Ryan-Beswick, Mr I. Souede, Mrs A. J. Tuttiett, Mr J. E. Tuttiett, Lady Vestey, Exors of the late Lord Vestey, Mrs C. A. Waters, Mrs N. J. White.

**Assistant Trainer:** Thomas David.

**NH Jockey:** David Bass, Nico De Boinville, Daryl Jacob. **Amateur Jockey:** Mr A. Rid.

## 435 MR SIMON PEARCE, Newmarket
Postal: **1 Whitegates, Newmarket, Suffolk, CB8 8DS**
Contacts: **PHONE 01638 664669**
EMAIL spearceracing@hotmail.co.uk

1 **BARTHOLOMEW J (IRE)**, 7, ch g Fast Company (IRE)—Mana (IRE) **Nigel Hanger, Eric Jones & Partners**
2 **CLARION LADY**, 5, b m Epaulette (AUS)—Tanwir **Clarion Racing**
3 **DYAGILEV**, 6, ch g Kheleyf (USA)—Dancernetothemoon **Killarney Glen & Lydia Pearce**
4 **EBONY GIRL**, 4, br f Brazen Beau (AUS)—Ziraun **Deerfield Syndicate**
5 **FRANKIE JAZ**, 4, b g Royal Applause—Pretty Kool **Killarney Glen & Lydia Pearce**
6 **FULL INTENTION**, 7, b g Showcasing—My Delirium **Killarney Glen & Lydia Pearce**
7 **INFLAMED**, 4, ch g New Approach (IRE)—Indignant **Howard Duff Racing**
8 **MIGHTY MIND**, 4, b c Poet's Voice—Cool Catena **Mr A. Dal Pos**
9 **NOBLE PEACE**, 8, b g Kyllachy—Peace Concluded **Killarney Glen**
10 **SEXY SECRET**, 10, b g Sakhee's Secret—Orange Walk (IRE) **Mrs L. S. Pearce**
11 **VICTORY ROSE**, 5, b m Bated Breath—Albany Rose (IRE) **Deerfield Syndicate**

### THREE-YEAR-OLDS
12 **HANOVERIAN KING (GER)**, b c Showcasing—Hasay **The Showstoppers**
13 **RED EVELYN**, ch f Garswood—Skara Brae **Deerfield Syndicate**
14 **STAGE LIGHTS (IRE)**, b br f Showcasing—Trempjane **The Talent Spotters**
15 **STORM CATCHER**, b c Vadamos (FR)—Next Life **Nigel Hanger & Eric Jones**

### TWO-YEAR-OLDS
16 Gr f 26/03 El Kabeir (USA)—High Drama (IRE) (High Chaparral (IRE)) (6000) **Simon Pearce**
17 Gr f 27/02 El Kabeir (USA)—Nouveau Foret (Myboycharlie (IRE)) (4500) **Simon Pearce**
18 **STUBBLE FIELD**, b f 20/03 Adaay (IRE)—Lady Estella (IRE) (Equiano (FR)) (9000) **Howard Duff Racing**

**Other Owners:** S. Andrews, Mr H. Crothers, N. M. Hanger, J. Harrison, Mr E. Jones, Killarney Glen, Mrs L. Matthews, Mr D. Meah, Nigel Hanger & Eric Jones, Mrs L. S. Pearce, Simon Pearce, Mr G. Troeller.

## 436 MR OLLIE PEARS, Malton
Postal: **The Old Farmhouse, Beverley Road, Norton, Malton, North Yorkshire, YO17 9PJ**
Contacts: **PHONE 01653 690746 MOBILE 07760 197103**
EMAIL info@olliepearsracing.co.uk WEBSITE www.olliepearsracing.co.uk

1 **BILLYOAKES (IRE)**, 9, b g Kodiac—Reality Check (IRE) **Keith West & Ollie Pears**
2 **CHRISTMAS NIGHT**, 6, ch g Compton Place—Night Haven **Ownaracehorse Ltd & Mr Ollie Pears**
3 **HARRY LOVE (IRE)**, 4, b g Lawman (FR)—Gimmick (IRE) **Ownaracehorse Ltd & Mr Ollie Pears**
4 **KIPLIN**, 6, b g Desideratum—Another Paris **Mr J. D. Spensley & Mrs M. A. Spensley**
5 **KROY**, 7, b g Sleeping Indian—Valley of The Moon (IRE) **Mrs S. A. Elsey**
6 **MOSAKHAR**, 5, b g Dawn Approach (IRE)—Min Banat Alreeh (IRE) **Mrs S. D. Pearson**
7 **ROARING RORY**, 8, ch g Sakhee's Secret—Barbieri (IRE) **Ownaracehorse Ltd & Mr Ollie Pears**
8 **SUSIE JAVEA**, 4, b f Coach House (IRE)—Charlevoix (IRE) **Mr A. Caygill**

### THREE-YEAR-OLDS
9 **BLISSFUL SONG (IRE)**, b f Mehmas (IRE)—Kummel Excess (IRE) **Mr N. Brereton**
10 **CROWN PRINCESS (IRE)**, b f Mehmas (IRE)—Al Hanyora **Ownaracehorse Ltd, M Reay & O Pears**
11 **DANDINI (IRE)**, ch g Dandy Man (IRE)—Moving Waves (IRE) **Mr J O'Connor & Ollie Pears**
12 **FLISS FLOSS**, gr f Lethal Force (IRE)—Raggle Taggle (IRE) **Mr A. Caygill**
13 **HORACE GREASLEY (IRE)**, gr g Markaz (IRE)—Whisper Dance (USA) **A Caygill & Huggymac Racing**
14 **KRYSTAL MAZE (IRE)**, b f Kodiac—Escapism (IRE) **T. Elsey**
15 **LUCY RULES (IRE)**, b f Vadamos (FR)—Kodafine (IRE) **Mr A. Caygill**
16 **MUTAKAAMIL (IRE)**, b g Markaz (IRE)—Min Banat Alreeh (IRE) **Mrs S. D. Pearson**
17 **NORTHERN CRACKER**, ch g Monsieur Bond (IRE)—Bond Casino **Mr R. S. Marshall**

## MR OLLIE PEARS - continued

18 **READY FREDDIE GO (IRE)**, b g Swiss Spirit—Barbieri (IRE) **Ownaracehorse Ltd, Keates & West**

## TWO-YEAR-OLDS

19 B g 06/03 Gutaifan (IRE)—Afnoon (USA) (Street Cry (IRE)) (4500) **Nic Brereton & Ollie Pears**
20 **DO IT TODAY**, b f 12/02 Adaay (IRE)—Hindsight (Sayif (IRE)) (2000) **O. J. Pears**
21 Ch f 25/04 Garswood—Dubai Walk (ITY) (Vita Rosa (JPN))
22 B f 04/04 Cotai Glory—Equijade (Equiano (FR)) (3810) **Nic Brereton & Ollie Pears**
23 B f 29/01 Galileo Gold—Fainleog (IRE) (Rock of Gibraltar (IRE)) (7619) **T. Elsey**
24 B g 22/01 Cappella Sansevero—Flip Flop (IRE) (Footstepsinthesand) (7000) **Nic Brereton & Ollie Pears**
25 B f 02/04 The Last Lion (IRE)—Glen Molly (IRE) (Danetime (IRE)) (4500) **Nic Brereton & Ollie Pears**
26 **GOLDEN GAL (IRE)**, br f 08/04 Galileo Gold—
　　　　　　　Dubai Princess (IRE) (Dubai Destination (USA)) (3000) **Ownaracehorse Ltd & Mr Ollie Pears**
27 **ICE SHADOW (IRE)**, b g 23/02 Buratino (IRE)—Chicane (Motivator) (17000) **G. Morrill**
28 Gr c 17/04 Outstrip—Mi Rubina (IRE) (Rock of Gibraltar (IRE)) **O. J. Pears**
29 **QWICKEN (IRE)**, gr f 24/03 Gutaifan (IRE)—
　　　　　　　Miss Wicklow (IRE) (New Approach (IRE)) (2000) **Ownaracehorse Ltd & Mr Ollie Pears**
30 **SKY KNIGHT (IRE)**, ch g 27/04 Free Eagle (IRE)—
　　　　　　　Sassy (FR) (Sinndar (IRE)) (3810) **Ownaracehorse Ltd & Mr Ollie Pears**

**Other Owners:** Mr N. Brereton, Mr A. Caygill, Mr A. Huggins, HuggyMac Racing, Mr D. Keates, Mr J. Mcalpine, Mr J. P. M. O'Connor, Ownaracehorse Ltd, O. J. Pears, Mr M. A. Reay, Mr J. D. Spensley, Mrs M. A. Spensley, K. C. West.

**Assistant Trainer:** Vicky Pears.

**NH Jockey:** Brian Hughes.

---

**437**
**MISS LINDA PERRATT, East Kilbride**
Postal: **North Allerton Farm, East Kilbride, Glasgow, Lanarkshire, G75 8RR**
Contacts: **PHONE 01355 303425 MOBILE 07931 306147**
EMAIL linda.perratt@btinternet.com

1 **CHINESE SPIRIT (IRE)**, 7, gr g Clodovil (IRE)—In The Ribbons **Mr Sandy Jarvie & Miss L. Perratt**
2 **GRANDADS BEST GIRL**, 4, b f Intrinsic—Mitchelland **Miss L. A. Perratt**
3 **HARD NUT (IRE)**, 4, b g Gutaifan (IRE)—With A Twist **Mr W. F. Perratt**
4 **INDIARO**, 5, b g Sleeping Indian—Cafe Express (IRE) **The Hon Miss H. Galbraith**
5 **KEEP COMING (IRE)**, 5, b g Leading Light (IRE)—Pretty Present (IRE) **M & L Perratt**
6 **LAOISE (USA)**, 5, b m Noble Mission—Lilbourne Eliza (IRE) **Linda Perratt Racing Club**
7 **LET RIGHT BE DONE**, 9, gr g Lawman (FR)—Cheerfully **Miss L. A. Perratt**
8 **LUCKY VIOLET (IRE)**, 9, b m Dandy Man (IRE)—Rashida **The Hon Miss H. Galbraith**
9 **POPPING CORKS (IRE)**, 5, b m Camacho—Shamardyh (IRE) **Mr B. A. Jordan**
10 **RETIREMENT BECKONS**, 6, b g Epaulette (AUS)—Mystical Ayr (IRE) **Mr W. F. Perratt**
11 **SALTMARKET**, 6, b g Multiplex—Kiera Marie (IRE) **M. Sawers**
12 **WAHWEI SPIRIT (IRE)**, 6, b g Mustameet (USA)—La Belle de Serk (IRE) **Mr Peter Tsim & Miss Linda Perratt**

## THREE-YEAR-OLDS

13 **NOAH'S CAFE**, b f Bated Breath—Cafe Express (IRE) **Miss L. A. Perratt**

## TWO-YEAR-OLDS

14 B g 14/04 Cable Bay (IRE)—Cafe Express (IRE) (Bertolini (USA))

**Other Owners:** Mr A. Jarvie, Miss L. A. Perratt, M. Sawers, P. Tsim.

**Flat Jockey:** Tom Eaves, P. J. McDonald. **Apprentice Jockey:** Leanne Ferguson.

**438** **MRS AMANDA PERRETT, Pulborough**
Postal: **Coombelands Racing Stables, Pulborough, West Sussex, RH20 1BP**
Contacts: **PHONE 01798 873011 MOBILE 07803 088713**
EMAIL aperrett@coombelands-stables.com WEBSITE www.amandaperrett.com

1 AHORSECALLEDWANDA, 4, b f Music Master—Lady Mascot (IRE) **Mason Brown Partnership**
2 ART FOR ART'S SAKE (IRE), 4, ch g Dutch Art—Anayid **Mr R. J. B. Cheadle**
3 COUNT OTTO (IRE), 6, b g Sir Prancealot (IRE)—Dessert Flower (IRE) **Count Otto Partnership**
4 FRONTISPIECE, 7, b g Shamardal (USA)—Free Verse **The Frontispiece Partnership**
5 LAVENDER'S BLUE (IRE), 5, b m Sea The Stars (IRE)—Beatrice Aurore (IRE) **B. Andersson**
6 MAZZURI (IRE), 6, ch m Raven's Pass (USA)—Essexford (IRE) **Mrs S. M. Conway**
7 OPEN WIDE (USA), 7, b br g Invincible Spirit (IRE)—Nunavik (IRE) **George Materna & John McInerney**
8 PERCY'S PRINCE, 5, b g Sir Percy—Attainable **Mrs A. M. Lewis**
9 PLATITUDE, 8, b g Dansili—Modesta (IRE) **Mrs S. M. Conway**
10 SAAHEQ, 7, b g Invincible Spirit (IRE)—Brevity (USA) **Coombelands Racing Syndicate**
11 SAUCY ENCORE, 4, b f Showcasing—Saucy Minx (IRE) **Mrs S. H. Cotton, Mrs S. M. Conway**
12 SUNS UP GUNS UP, 4, ch g Lope de Vega (IRE)—Strictly Silca **G. C. Stevens**
13 TINTO, 5, b g Compton Place—Amirah (IRE) **D M James & Steve Jenkins**
14 YOU'RE HIRED, 8, b g Dalakhani (IRE)—Heaven Sent **G. D. P. Materna**

**THREE-YEAR-OLDS**

15 AUTHORA DREAM, b f Oasis Dream—Authora (IRE) **Authora Dream Partnership**
16 EAGLE ONE, b g Gleneagles (IRE)—Gloryette **John Connolly & A D Spence**
17 MIRRIE DANCERS (IRE), b g Harzand (IRE)—Beatrice Aurore (IRE) **B. Andersson**
18 NELLIE MOON, b br f Sea The Moon (GER)—Queen's Dream **Star Pointe Ltd**
19 REBEL TERRITORY, b g Territories (IRE)—Saucy Minx (IRE) **Mrs S. H. Cotton, Mrs S. M. Conway**
20 SAYIFYOUWILL, b f Sayif (IRE)—Amirah (IRE) **Richard Cheadle & Partners**
21 SIR JOSEPH SWAN, b g Paco Boy—Candle **Mrs B. A. Karn-Smith**

**TWO-YEAR-OLDS**

22 BORNTOBEALEADER (IRE), ch c 30/04 Churchill (IRE)—
Shake The Moon (GER) (Loup Solitaire (USA)) (40000) **The Borntobealeader Partnership**
23 LATER DARLING, b c 05/03 Postponed (IRE)—
Saucy Minx (IRE) (Dylan Thomas (IRE)) **Mrs S. H. Cotton, Mrs S. M. Conway**
24 MISS DOWN UNDER (IRE), ch f 20/05 Australia—
Pocket of Stars (IRE) (Sea The Stars (IRE)) (6000) **D. James, S. Jenkins & Partners**

**Other Owners:** Mr S. Brown, J. P. Connolly, F & P Conway, Mr D. M. James, Mr S. J. Jenkins, Mr A. Mason, G. D. P. Materna, Dr J. P. McInerney, Mrs A. J. Perrett, Mr Alan Spence, Star Pointe Ltd.

**Assistant Trainer:** Mark Perrett.

**439** **MR PAT PHELAN, Epsom**
Postal: **Ermyn Lodge, Shepherds Walk, Epsom, Surrey, KT18 6DF**
Contacts: **PHONE 01372 229014 MOBILE 07917 762781 FAX 01372 229001**
EMAIL pat.phelan@ermynlodge.com WEBSITE www.ermynlodge.com

1 CRIMSON KISS (IRE), 5, ch m Sepoy (AUS)—Crimson Year (USA) **Mr P. J. Wheatley**
2 DARK WHITE, 4, gr g Lethal Force (IRE)—Dark Skies (IRE) **Epsom Downers**
3 DEFINITE DILEMMA (IRE), 8, b g Definite Article—Pandalute (IRE) **I. W. Harfitt**
4 DEVIZES (IRE), 5, b g Dubawi (IRE)—Dalasyla (IRE) **Celtic Contractors Limited**
5 EPSOM FAITHFULL, 4, b f Coach House (IRE)—La Fortunata **Epsom Racegoers No.2**
6 ERMYN'S EMERALD, 9, b br g Alflora (IRE)—Emerald Project (IRE) **Ermyn Lodge Stud Limited**
7 HACKBRIDGE, 6, br g Archipenko (USA)—Famcred **Southdown Holdings Ltd**
8 HERRE DITTERY, 4, b br g Cable Bay (IRE)—Young Dottie **Mr A. Smith**
9 LEGEND OF FRANCE, 8, ch m Flying Legend (USA)—Bonne Anniversaire **Ermyn Lodge Stud Limited**

## MR PAT PHELAN - continued

10 **MAYTHEORSEBEWITHU (IRE)**, 6, b m Shirocco (GER)—Amoya (GER)  **Mr A. Smith**
11 **MAZALTO (IRE)**, 8, b m Teofilo (IRE)—Mazaaya (USA)  **Maginn Smith**
12 **PRINCESSE ANIMALE**, 4, b f Leroidesanimaux (BRZ)—Isabella Beeton  **Mr A. Smith**
13 **REECELTIC**, 6, b g Champs Elysees—Sense of Pride  **Celtic Contractors Limited**
14 **SINGER IN THE SAND (IRE)**, 6, b m Footstepsinthesand—Village Singer (USA)  **I. W. Harfitt**
15 **WITCHES GLEN (IRE)**, 9, b m Helissio (FR)—Native Cheer (IRE)  **Ermyn Lodge Stud Limited**

### THREE-YEAR-OLDS

16 **DOTTIES DREAM**, b br f Swiss Spirit—Auntie Dot Com  **Mr A. Smith**
17 **ERMYNS PERCY**, b g Sir Percy—My Amalie (IRE)  **Ermyn Lodge Stud Limited**
18 **ICONIC MOVER**, ch g Sixties Icon—Run For Ede's  **Mr A. Smith**
19 **STAR OF EPSOM**, b f Sir Percy—Isabella Beeton  **Epsom Racegoers No.3**

**Other Owners:** Mrs J. K. Lukas, Mr G. Maginn, Exors D. J. Prosser, Mr A. Smith, Mr T. D. J. Syder.

**Flat Jockey:** J. F. Egan, Shane Kelly, Kieran O'Neill.  **NH Jockey:** James Best, Josh Moore.  **Conditional Jockey:** Sean Houlihan.  **Apprentice Jockey:** Paddy Bradley, Sophie Ralston.

---

## 440  MR KEVIN PHILIPPART DE FOY, Newmarket
Postal: **Machell Place Stables, Old Station Road, Newmarket, Suffolk, CB8 8DW**
Contacts: **PHONE 07551 498273**
**EMAIL kevin@kpfracing.com**

1 **ALMOST YOU (FR)**, 6, b m Youmzain (IRE)—Almohades (FR)  **Mrs B. C. D. Jacques**
2 **CONSTRAINT**, 5, b m Sinndar (IRE)—Inhibition  **Mr H. K. Ma**
3 **EPHEMERAL (IRE)**, 5, b m Footstepsinthesand—Mycenae  **Dr C. M. H. Wills**
4 **GOLDEN CYGNET**, 4, b f Cable Bay (IRE)—Dark Swan (IRE)
5 **GREEK KODIAC (IRE)**, 5, b g Kodiac—Greek Easter (IRE)  **The Zodiacs**
6 **HEPTATHLETE (IRE)**, 6, gr m Mount Nelson—Jessica Ennis (USA)  **Mrs B. C. D. Jacques**
7 **HINT OF STARS (IRE)**, 4, ch g Sea The Stars (IRE)—Rosenreihe (IRE)  **Midlands Racing Club**
8 **LADY IRONSIDE (IRE)**, 4, gr f Lawman (FR)—Expedience (USA)  **Ballylinch Stud**
9 **LIKE SUGAR**, 4, ch f Showcasing—Ivory Gala (FR)  **Run Away Racing Candarel Syndicate**
10 **MINSTER (IRE)**, 4, ch g Mastercraftsman (IRE)—Mycenae  **Dr C. M. H. Wills**
11 **POET'S EYE**, 4, b br f Poet's Voice—Monasada  **JCK Partnership**
12 **SHUTHOOR (IRE)**, 4, b f Kodiac—Mulkeyya (IRE)
13 **SPINNING DREAMS (IRE)**, 4, b f Dream Ahead (USA)—Spinning Well (IRE)  **Ballylinch Stud**

### THREE-YEAR-OLDS

14 **SEALED OFFER**, b f Lethal Force (IRE)—Royal Seal  **Silver, Steed, Eccles-Williams**
15 **STREET KID (IRE)**, ch g Street Boss (USA)—Brushed Gold (USA)  **Run Away Racing Syndicate**

### TWO-YEAR-OLDS

16 **ADORABLE YOU (IRE)**, b f 09/03 Zarak (FR)—Embraceable You (New Approach (IRE))  **Normandie Stud Ltd**
17 B f 12/04 Moohaajim (IRE)—Azzurra du Caprio (IRE) (Captain Rio)
18 B c 20/04 Gutaifan (IRE)—Baileys Pursuit (Pastoral Pursuits) (11429)
19 B f 27/03 Decorated Knight—Grain de Beaute (IRE) (Lawman (FR)) (19047)
20 B f 19/04 Fascinating Rock (IRE)—Legal Lyric (IRE) (Lawman (FR)) (14286)  **Mr John O'Connor**
21 **NICHOLAS GEORGE**, ch c 01/04 Reliable Man—Carisolo (Dubai Millennium)  **Normandie Stud Ltd**
22 **SEISMIC**, ch g 25/01 Poet's Voice—Symbol (Nathaniel (IRE))  **Dr C. M. H. Wills**
23 B c 06/05 The Gurkha (IRE)—Shagra (IRE) (Pivotal) (14285)  **Run Away Racing Syndicate**
24 Ch c 03/05 New Bay—Soliza (IRE) (Intikhab (USA)) (30000)  **Run Away Racing Syndicate**
25 B c 04/02 Aclaim (IRE)—Velvet Charm (Excelebration (IRE))  **Pantile Stud**
26 B c 21/01 Vadamos (FR)—Zakyah (Exceed And Excel (AUS)) (23000)

**441** **MR ALAN PHILLIPS, Callow End**
Postal: **Jennet Tree Farm, Kents Green, Callow End, Worcestershire, WR2 4UA**
Contacts: **PHONE 01905 831774 MOBILE 07870 112235**
EMAIL **alan@alanphillipsracing.com** WEBSITE **www.alanphillipsracing.com**

1 BIGBILLRIGLEY (IRE), 7, b g Jammal—Carrig Bluebell (IRE) **K & M Payne**
2 BOHER LAD (IRE), 14, b g Gold Well—Shindeesharnick (IRE) **Miss R. L. Edwards**
3 DANSANT EXPRESS (IRE), 6, b g Dansant—Was My Valentine **Mr A. J. Phillips**
4 ELFRIDE, 5, ch m Black Sam Bellamy (IRE)—Just Missie **Mr D. G. Redfern**
5 GABRIEL OATS, 12, ch g Grape Tree Road—Winnow **Miss R. L. Edwards**
6 5, Ch m Gentlewave (IRE)—Our Ethel
7 ROYAL BORN (IRE), 5, b g Born To Sea (IRE)—Albarouche **Mr N. A. Marks**
8 SIR EGBERT, 8, b g Kayf Tara—Little Miss Flora **Mr A. J. Phillips**
9 TARRONA, 12, b g Kayf Tara—Lisrona (IRE) **Mr D. G. Redfern**
10 THE MODEL COUNTY (IRE), 11, b m Robin des Champs (FR)—Ware It Vic (IRE) **Mr D. G. Redfern**

Other Owners: Mr K. Brookes, Mr M. Payne.

**442** **MR RICHARD PHILLIPS, Moreton-in-Marsh**
Postal: **Adlestrop Stables, Adlestrop, Moreton-in-Marsh, Gloucestershire, GL56 0YN**
Contacts: **WORK 01608 658710 MOBILE 07774 832715**
EMAIL **info@richardphillipsracing.com** WEBSITE **www.richardphillipsracing.com**

1 AVION, 6, ch g Arvico (FR)—Tiger Line **Mrs S. C. Welch**
2 BEAUTIFUL PEOPLE (FR), 10, b br m Early March—Night Fever (FR) **Beautiful People**
3 BIG FIDDLE, 8, b m Kayf Tara—Fiddling Again **Mrs E. C. Roberts**
4 BLUE HOUR BAY (IRE), 5, b m Leading Light (IRE)—Kapricia Speed (FR) **Newport, Cutbill, Betts, Todd & Ward**
5 4, B g Sageburg (IRE)—Brown Arrow (IRE)
6 4, B g Pether's Moon (IRE)—Fleetstone
7 FLYING DRAGON (FR), 5, b g War Command (USA)—Histoire de Jouer (FR)
8 GREAT STAR (IRE), 4, gr g Dylan Thomas (IRE)—Pandorama Lady (IRE) **Mrs J. A. Watts**
9 IRON HORSE, 10, b g Kayf Tara—What A Vintage (IRE) **The Someday's Here Racing Partnership**
10 J GAYE (IRE), 5, b m Canford Cliffs (IRE)—Ice Pie **S. F. Benton**
11 KEEP IT BRIEF, 4, b c Muhaarar—Brevity (USA) **Mr E. J. Ware**
12 LADY OF AUTHORITY, 6, b m Kheleyf (USA)—Miss Authority **The Listeners**
13 LESSER (IRE), 7, b g Stowaway—Aine Dubh (IRE) **The C Level Partnership**
14 MASTER VINTAGE, 13, b g Kayf Tara—What A Vintage (IRE) **The Adlestrop Club**
15 MATTIE ROSS, 5, b m Champs Elysees—Ommadawn (IRE) **The Zara Syndicate**
16 METHODTOTHEMAGIC (IRE), 6, b m Sans Frontieres (IRE)—
Cindy's Fancy (IRE) **Dalziel Family, T White, J Inverdale**
17 MIGHTY ELSA, 8, b m Schiaparelli (GER)—Tiger Moss **Mr S. Smith**
18 MINELLA WHISPER, 10, b g Kayf Tara—Celtic Native (IRE) **Mrs E. A. Prowting**
19 MRS BARNES (IRE), 8, b m Ask—Jills Oscar (IRE) **Mr & Mrs R. Scott**
20 MUTHABIR (IRE), 11, b g Nayef (USA)—Northern Melody (IRE) **The Adlestrop Club**
21 OCHO GRANDE (IRE), 4, b g Tamayuz—Soul Custody (CAN) **Race Against Prostate Cancer**
22 ORGANDI (FR), 9, br m Early March—Creme Pralinee (FR) **Beautiful People**
23 POP MISTRESS, 5, ch m Sixties Icon—Mayolynn (USA) **Goodwood Owners Drinks Session**
24 PRESENT FROM DUBAI (IRE), 8, b g Dubai Destination (USA)—Inch Promise (IRE) **Hopeful Travellers**
25 ROBIN DES SMOKE (IRE), 6, b m Robin des Pres (FR)—Thanks For Smoking (IRE) **Mrs E. A. Prowting**
26 ROSSBEIGH STRAND (IRE), 6, b g Mahler—Could Do **Nut Club Partnership**
27 RUN ROSIE RUN, 5, b m Native Ruler—No Compromise **Better Than Working**
28 SHADOW WALKER (IRE), 7, b g Stowaway—Ilikeyou (IRE) **Mr C. Pocock**
29 TULANE (IRE), 6, br g Arcano (IRE)—Jeunesse Doree (IRE)

**MR RICHARD PHILLIPS - continued**

**TWO-YEAR-OLDS**

 30 Ch f 06/05 Prince of Lir (IRE)—Shadow Mountain (Selkirk (USA))

**Yard Sponsor:** Tori Global.

---

**443**
**MISS ELLA PICKARD, Umberleigh**
Postal: **Langridge Farm, Atherington, Umberleigh, Devon, EX37 9HP**
Contacts: **PHONE 07921 088893**
**EMAIL ellapickard@outlook.com**

 1 **ALL HOPE NO SCOPE,** 4, b g Telescope (IRE)—Brians Dream (IRE)  **Mr M. P. P. Brend**
 2 4, B f Telescope (IRE)—Azione  **Mr M. P. P. Brend**
 3 **CASTKITELLO (IRE),** 5, b m Milan—Correctandpresent (IRE)  **Sue & Clive Cole & Ann & Tony Gale**
 4 **DEEP INFERNO (IRE),** 5, b br g Flemensfirth (USA)—Waist Deep (IRE)  **Mr M. Tucker**
 5 **FLUTISTE (FR),** 6, b g Secret Singer (FR)—Nanny (FR)  **Mr M. G. Tucker**
 6 **GETALEAD (IRE),** 5, b g Getaway (GER)—Site-Leader (IRE)  **Miss R. Pickard**
 7 **GETAROUND (IRE),** 6, gr g Getaway (GER)—Playing Around  **Mr G. J. Wilson**
 8 **JOHNNY BOY,** 4, b br g Great Pretender (IRE)—First Wonder (FR)  **Mr M. G. Tucker**
 9 **LIGHTNING GOLD,** 6, ch m Black Sam Bellamy (IRE)—Santera (IRE)  **Mr P. W. Gillbard**
 10 **LUCKYJOHNHOBBS (IRE),** 5, b g Milan—Hazlewood (IRE)  **Mr G. J. Wilson**
 11 4, Ch g Getaway (GER)—Robins Turn (IRE)  **Mr G. J. Wilson**
 12 **ROD'S DREAM,** 8, ch g Midnight Legend—Norton Sapphire  **Mr R. Harding**
 13 **STANS THE MAN (IRE),** 4, b g Milan—Strong Roe (IRE)  **Having the craic**
 14 **WHATABOUTWALT (IRE),** 5, ch g Salutino (GER)—Cyclone Lorraine (IRE)  **In it to Win it Syndicate**

**Other Owners:** Mr C. Cole, Mrs S. S. Cole, Mrs A. G. Gale, Mr A. P. Gale.

---

**444**
**MR DAVID PIPE, Wellington**
Postal: **Pond House, Nicholashayne, Wellington, Somerset, TA21 9QY**
Contacts: **PHONE 01884 840715 FAX 01884 841343**
**EMAIL david@davidpipe.com WEBSITE www.davidpipe.com**

 1 **A PERFECT GIFT (IRE),** 7, br m Presenting—Keyras Choice (IRE)
 2 **ADAGIO (GER),** 4, b g Wiener Walzer (GER)—Aspidistra (GER)  **Bryan Drew and Friends / Prof. C.Tisdall**
 3 **AIRTON,** 8, b g Champs Elysees—Fly In Style  **David Pipe Racing Club**
 4 **ASTIGAR (FR),** 5, gr g No Risk At All (FR)—Sissi de Teille (FR)  **The Angove Family**
 5 **BALDUR'S GATE (IRE),** 6, b g Stowaway—Like A Miller (IRE)  **The Angove Family**
 6 **BALLYWILLIAM (IRE),** 11, b g Mahler—Henrietta Howard (IRE)  **The Hon Mrs D. Hulse**
 7 **BARRIER PEAKS (FR),** 5, b g Blue Bresil (FR)—La Balzane (FR)  **The Angove Family**
 8 **BELGUARDO (FR),** 4, b g Kapgarde (FR)—Bella Giaconda (GER)  **Decimus Racing VII**
 9 **BRINKLEY (FR),** 6, gr g Martaline—Royale Majesty (FR)  **Brocade Racing**
 10 **BUMPY JOHNSON (IRE),** 5, ch g Imperial Monarch (IRE)—Country Flora  **Brocade Racing**
 11 **BUSTER EDWARDS (IRE),** 8, b g Kalanisi (IRE)—Hot Oscar (IRE)  **The Willpower Partnership**
 12 **COLLINGWOOD COURT (IRE),** 7, gr g Court Cave (IRE)—West Hill Rose (IRE)  **City AM**
 13 **CROSSING LINES (IRE),** 7, b g Jeremy—Coco Opera (IRE)  **Middleham Park Racing CXVII**
 14 **DELFACE (FR),** 8, b g Della Francesca (USA)—Septieme Face (USA)  **Pipe's Prospectors**
 15 **DELL' ARCA (IRE),** 12, b g Sholokhov (IRE)—Daisy Belle (GER)  **Prof C. Tisdall**
 16 **DO YA FEEL LUCKY (IRE),** 7, b m Aizavoski (IRE)—Carthanoora (IRE)  **Somerset Racing**
 17 **DOYEN LA LUTTE (IRE),** 5, b m Doyen (IRE)—Castletown Girl  **The Contractors**
 18 **DUC DE BEAUCHENE (FR),** 8, b g Saddler Maker (IRE)—Quatia d'Angron (FR)  **Mr J. P. McManus**
 19 **DUSKY HERCULES (IRE),** 7, b g Shantou (USA)—Annalecky (IRE)  **David Pipe Racing Club**
 20 **EAMON AN CNOIC (IRE),** 10, b g Westerner—Nutmeg Tune (IRE)  **The Angove Family**

## MR DAVID PIPE - continued

21 **EDEN DU HOUX (FR)**, 7, b g Irish Wells (FR)—Maralypha (FR) **Prof C. Tisdall**
22 **ELAN DE BALME (FR)**, 7, b g Cachet Noir (USA)—Jebarde Rederie (FR) **Prof C. Tisdall**
23 **EXTRA MAG (FR)**, 7, b g Kapgarde (FR)—Qrystale Mag (FR) **The Angove Family**
24 **FIRST LORD DE CUET (FR)**, 7, gr g Lord du Sud (FR)—Alyce (FR) **Potter, Pipe and Pete**
25 **FORT SUMMER (IRE)**, 6, b g Kalanisi (IRE)—Glen Ellie (IRE) **Two Hopes**
26 **GABRIELLE DU SEUIL (FR)**, 5, b m Cokoriko (FR)—Marie du Seuil (FR) **N. Shutts**
27 **GERICAULT ROQUE (FR)**, 5, b g Montmartre (FR)—Nijinska Delaroque (FR) **Prof C. Tisdall & Mr B. Drew**
28 **GRANGECLARE GLORY (IRE)**, 6, b g Fame And Glory—Annies Joy (IRE) **Prof C. Tisdall**
29 **GREAT TEMPO (FR)**, 8, b g Great Pretender (IRE)—Prima Note (FR) **David Pipe Racing Club**
30 **HEURE DE GLOIRE (FR)**, 4, b f Kapgarde (FR)—Lounoas (FR)
31 **HIGHLANDER MADRIK (FR)**, 4, ch g Masterstroke (USA)—Crazy Madrik (FR) **The Arthur White Partnership**
32 **HOME FARM HOUSE (IRE)**, 6, bl m Winged Love (IRE)—Recession Lass (IRE) **H. M. W. Clifford**
33 **HUGO 'N TAZ**, 10, b g Kayf Tara—Ryde To Arms **ValueRacingClub.co.uk**
34 **INDUNO (IRE)**, 7, b g Flemensfirth (USA)—Vast Consumption (IRE) **R. A. Bartlett**
35 **IRON HEART**, 4, b c Muhaarar—Kiyoshi **Decimus Racing VIII**
36 **ISRAEL CHAMP (IRE)**, 6, b g Milan—La Dariska (FR) **John White & Anne Underhill**
37 **KEPAGGE (IRE)**, 7, b g Getaway (IRE)—Miracle Lady **Mrs S. J. Ling**
38 **KING'S SOCKS (FR)**, 9, b g King's Best (USA)—Alexandrina (GER) **Mr B. J. C. Drew**
39 **KINGSFORT HILL**, 6, b g Multiplex—Pugnacious Lady **Ms D. O Connor**
40 **LADY RESET**, 5, ch m Yorgunnabelucky (USA)—Reset City **Mrs L. Webb**
41 **LADYKILLER (GER)**, 5, ch g Kamsin (GER)—Lady Jacamira (GER) **Prof C. Tisdall & Mr B. Drew**
42 **LEGAL HISTORY (IRE)**, 6, b g Lawman (FR)—Nina Celebre (IRE) **Middleham Park Racing XXXII & Partner 2**
43 **LEONCAVALLO (IRE)**, 9, br g Cape Cross (IRE)—Nafura **ValueRacingClub.co.uk**
44 **LITTLE RED LION (IRE)**, 7, b g Sans Frontieres (IRE)—Rever Up (IRE) **David Pipe Racing Club**
45 **MAGGIES MOGUL (IRE)**, 5, b m Valirann (FR)—Grangeclare Gold (IRE) **The Angove Family**
46 **MAIN FACT (USA)**, 8, b g Blame (USA)—Reflections **Munrowd's Partnership**
47 **MAJOR ROBINSON (IRE)**, 5, b g Kalanisi (IRE)—Annalore (IRE) **Mr W Frewen, Mrs R White & Drm**
48 **MAKE ME A BELIEVER (IRE)**, 6, br g Presenting—Kiltiernan Robin (IRE) **Prof. C. Tisdall & Jane Gerard-Pearse**
49 **MARTINHAL (IRE)**, 6, b g Westerner—Gweedara (IRE) **Mrs L. Maclennan**
50 **MEEP MEEP MAG (IRE)**, 7, b m Getaway (IRE)—Deadly Pursuit (IRE) **Mr M. Lambert & Mrs R. White**
51 **MISS M (IRE)**, 7, b m Mastercraftsman (IRE)—Tintern **Sporting Pay Ltd**
52 **MR CLARKSON (IRE)**, 9, b g Jeremy (USA)—Wynsleydale (USA) **Pipe's Prospectors**
53 **NABVUTIKA (IRE)**, 5, b m Poet's Voice—Elope (GER) **D. E. Pipe**
54 **NEON MOON (IRE)**, 5, b g No Risk At All (FR)—Hidden Horizons (IRE) **Brocade Racing**
55 **NEW AGE DAWNING (IRE)**, 7, ch g Stowaway—Captain Supreme (IRE) **Brocade Racing**
56 **NIGHT EDITION (FR)**, 5, b g Authorized (IRE)—Night Serenade (IRE) **Mr Mr Stuart & Simon Mercer & John Gent**
57 **NOBEL JOSHUA (AUT)**, 5, b g Joshua Tree (IRE)—Namat (IRE) **Avalon Surfacing & Construction Co Ltd**
58 **NORDIC COMBINED (IRE)**, 7, b g Haafhd—Chilly Filly (IRE) **Chris & David Stam**
59 **OFF MY ROCCO (IRE)**, 5, b g Shirocco (GER)—Croise Naofa (IRE) **Mrs J. Gerard-Pearse**
60 **ORCHARD THIEVES (IRE)**, 9, b g Ask—Ballycleary (IRE) **Brocade Racing**
61 **PANIC ATTACK (IRE)**, 5, b m Canford Cliffs (IRE)—Toto Corde Meo (IRE) **Mr B. J. C. Drew**
62 **PARICOLOR (FR)**, 5, b g Orpen (USA)—Kadiana (IRE) **Mrs J P E Cunningham & Mr G M Cunningham**
63 **PERCY STREET**, 8, br g Sir Percy—Star of Gibraltar **Chris & David Stam**
64 **POKER PLAY (FR)**, 8, ch g Martaline—Becquarette (FR) **The Angove Family**
65 **QUEENS CAVE (FR)**, 8, b m Court Cave (IRE)—Shuilan (IRE) **Mr K. Alexander**
66 **RAMSES DE TEILLEE (FR)**, 9, gr g Martaline—Princesse d'Orton (FR) **John White & Anne Underhill**
67 **RANCO (IRE)**, 4, b c Makfi—Guerande (IRE) **Mr M. J. D. Lambert**
68 **RATHLIN ROSE (IRE)**, 13, b g Bonbon Rose (FR)—A Plus Ma Puce (FR) **Somerset Racing**
69 **RED LION LAD (IRE)**, 5, b g Flemensfirth (USA)—Hotline (FR) **C & Star**
70 **REMASTERED**, 8, ch g Network (GER)—Cathodine Cayras (FR) **Brocade Racing**
71 **SANS LOGIQUE**, 4, b g Toronado (IRE)—Miss Fifty (IRE) **W. F. Frewen**
72 **SETME STRAIGHTMATE**, 5, ch g Malinas (GER)—Karamel **Prof C Tisdall & The Angove Family**
73 **SEXY LOT (GER)**, 5, b m Camelot—Saldennahe (GER) **Mr P. W. Garnsworthy**
74 **SHOOT TO FAME (IRE)**, 7, b m Fame And Glory—Native Wood (IRE) **The Blue Ball Syndicate**
75 **SIRUH DU LAC (FR)**, 8, b g Turgeon (USA)—Margerie (FR) **John White & Anne Underhill**
76 **STORY OF FRIENDS (FR)**, 7, b g Kingsalsa (USA)—Royale Malinelle (FR) **Brocade Racing**
77 **THEDABBER (IRE)**, 6, b br m Aizavoski (IRE)—Quay Moment (IRE) **Mr A. Whitty**
78 **THINKING (IRE)**, 6, b g So You Think (NZ)—Laetoli (ITY) **N. Shutts**
79 **THIRST FOR FAME (IRE)**, 4, b g Fame And Glory—Mill Meadow (IRE) **ValueRacingClub.co.uk**
80 **TO FLY FREE**, 4, b f Soldier Hollow—Telling Stories (FR) **David Pipe Racing Club**

## MR DAVID PIPE - continued

81 UMBRIGADO (IRE), 7, br g Stowaway—Dame O'Neill (IRE) **John White & Anne Underhill**
82 VIEUX LION ROUGE (FR), 12, ch g Sabiango (GER)—Indecise (FR) **Prof Caroline Tisdall & Mr John Gent**
83 WHAT A MOMENT (IRE), 11, b g Milan—Cuiloge Lady (IRE) **Bryan Drew & Steve Roper**

**Other Owners:** Mrs A. E. M. Broom, Mr G. R. Broom, Mr G. M. Cunningham, Mrs J. P. E. Cunningham, Mr B. J. C. Drew, W. F. Frewen, J. A. Gent, Mrs J. Gerard-Pearse, Mr P. J. Green, The Hon Mrs D. Hulse, Ms H. Ibrahim, James & Jean Potter, Mr M. J. D. Lambert, Mrs S. M. Mercer, Mr S. S. Mercer, Middleham Park Racing XXXII, Mr M. A. Munrowd, Miss S. B. Munrowd, Odfloors Ltd, T. S. Palin, M. C. Pipe, Mr J. E. Potter, Mrs M. J. Potter, M. Prince, Mr S. R. Roper, Dr C. Stam, Mr D. B. Stam, Prof C. Tisdall, Mrs A. Underhill, Mr A. J. White, Mrs R. E. White.

**Assistant Trainer:** Mr M. C. Pipe C.B.E.

**NH Jockey:** Kieron Edgar, David Noonan, Tom Scudamore. **Conditional Jockey:** Fergus Gillard. **Amateur Jockey:** Martin McIntyre, Sean O'Connor.

---

### 445 CHARLES & ADAM POGSON, Farnsfield
Postal: **Allamoor Farm, Mansfield Road, Farnsfield, Nottinghamshire, NG22 8HZ**
Contacts: **PHONE 07977 016155**
EMAIL adampogson@hotmail.co.uk

1 BARACALU (FR), 10, gr g Califet (FR)—Myragentry (FR) **C. T. Pogson**
2 BRIDEY'S LETTUCE (IRE), 9, b g Iffraaj—Its On The Air (IRE) **C. T. Pogson**
3 GEORGE MALLORY, 5, b g Kingman—Rose Et Noire (IRE) **Pete & Pauline Wordingham & Partner**
4 GETAWAY NORTH, 8, b g Getaway (GER)—Kings Equity (IRE) **C. T. Pogson**
5 MOIDORE, 12, b g Galileo (IRE)—Flash of Gold (IRE) **C. T. Pogson**
6 OVERTOUGEORGE, 7, b g Overbury (IRE)—Captivating Tyna (IRE) **C. T. Pogson**
7 SHADY OAKS (IRE), 8, b g Getaway (GER)—Naked Poser (IRE) **C. T. Pogson**
8 SIANNES STAR (IRE), 8, b g Arakan (USA)—Musical Madam (IRE) **Stephanie Kaye and M.T Hughes**
9 WEST TO CROSSGALES (IRE), 10, b g Westerner—Mooreshill Bay (IRE) **Pete & Pauline Wordingham & Partner**

**Other Owners:** Mrs S. K. Bunch, M. T. Hughes, Pete & Pauline Wordingham, C. T. Pogson, Mrs P. A. Wordingham, P. L. Wordingham.

---

### 446 MR JONATHAN PORTMAN, Upper Lambourn
Postal: **Whitcoombe House Stables, Upper Lambourn, Hungerford, Berkshire, RG17 8RA**
Contacts: **PHONE 01488 73894 MOBILE 07798 824513**
EMAIL jonathan@jonathanportmanracing.com WEBSITE www.jonathanportmanracing.com

1 BROAD APPEAL, 7, ch g Medicean—Shy Appeal (IRE) **J. G. B. Portman**
2 CHARLES LE BRUN, 4, b g Equiano (FR)—Miss Work of Art **Portlee Bloodstock**
3 6, B g Malinas (GER)—Desert Secrets (IRE) **Whitcoombe Park Racing**
4 DEVILS ROC, 5, gr m Lethal Force (IRE)—Ring For Baileys **Roc Steady Partnership**
5 MY LAW, 5, b m Mayson—Lawyers Choice **Mr H. E. Wigan**
6 ORIN SWIFT (IRE), 7, b g Dragon Pulse (IRE)—Hollow Green (IRE) **Mr L. A. Bellman**
7 QUICK BREATH, 6, b g Bated Breath—Shy Appeal (IRE) **Portlee Bloodstock**
8 RUSSIAN RUMOUR (IRE), 4, b f Make Believe—Russian Rave **Fillies First**
9 SWEET REWARD (IRE), 4, b g Acclamation—Dangle (IRE) **Old Stoic Racing Club & Partner**
10 SWISS CHEER (FR), 5, b g Swiss Spirit—Happy Clapper **Whitcoombe Park Racing**
11 THE BLUE BOWER (IRE), 4, b f Morpheus—Blue Holly (IRE) **Mr A. I. F. Sim**
12 TOYBOX, 5, ch m Paco Boy (IRE)—Play Street **J. G. B. Portman**
13 VILLANELLE, 4, b f Muhaarar—Station House (IRE) **Mascalls Stud**

# MR JONATHAN PORTMAN - continued

## THREE-YEAR-OLDS

14 Ch f Equiano (FR)—Agony And Ecstasy
15 **BELAFONTE,** b g Twilight Son—Scarlet Royal **Mr L. A. Bellman**
16 **BROADHAVEN,** b f Cable Bay (IRE)—Shy Appeal (IRE) **Berkeley Racing**
17 **BYE DAY,** b f Adaay (IRE)—Saffron Fox **Fillies First**
18 **CUBAN FOX,** b g Havana Gold (IRE)—Lolamotion **Whitcoombe Park Racing**
19 **FULL APPROVAL (IRE),** b f Mehmas (IRE)—Drifting Spirit (IRE) **Mr L. A. Bellman**
20 **GUNNER BAY,** b g Sepoy (AUS)—Thiqa (IRE) **Whitcoombe Park Racing**
21 **HEADORA,** b g Charming Thought—Keladora (USA) **Mr & Mrs J Laws & Partners**
22 **HELLAVAPACE,** gr b f Hellvelyn—Hasten (USA) **Fillies First**
23 **HELLYN,** gr f Hellvelyn—Bellotta **Fillies First**
24 **HESTERCOMBE,** b f Hellvelyn—Heartsease **Mrs R Pease**
25 **MAJOR FORCE,** gr g Lethal Force (IRE)—Vesper **Whitcoombe Park Racing**
26 **MARK OF RESPECT (IRE),** b g Markaz (IRE)—Music Pearl (IRE) **Berkeley Dollar Powell**
27 **MIA MIA,** b f Charm Spirit (IRE)—Curly Come Home **M Sinclair & Partner**
28 **MOONLET (BHR),** b f Multiplex—El Toreador (USA) **Sheikh A. B. I. Al Khalifa**
29 **NEW HEIGHTS,** b f Intello (GER)—How High The Sky (IRE) **Simon Skinner & Partner**
30 **PEPPERCORN,** gr g Lethal Force (IRE)—Tavy **Mrs Anita Wigan**
31 **PROUD AND FREE,** ch f Iffraaj—Station House (IRE) **Mascalls Stud**
32 **SHEILA O'SHEA,** b f Pearl Secret—Jessie's Spirit (IRE) **Farraday Equine**
33 **SHOOT FOR THE MOON,** b f Hellvelyn—Arctic Moon (USA)
34 **STRIKE,** gr g Lethal Force (IRE)—Midnight Fling **Mr S. Emmet & Miss R. Emmet**
35 **SWALLOWDALE,** b f Mukhadram—Windermere Island **C.R. Lambourne, M. Forbes, D. Losse**
36 **VIVE LA DANSE,** ch g French Navy—Alice's Dancer (IRE)
37 **WARM PRAISE,** ch g Hot Streak (IRE)—Accede **J. G. B. Portman**
38 **WAY OF LIFE,** b g Havana Gold (IRE)—Upskittled **Whitcoombe Park Racing**

## TWO-YEAR-OLDS

39 **ARDITA,** b f 15/04 Ardad (IRE)—Royal Circles (Royal Applause) (1429) **Berkeley Dollar Powell**
40 **BABY BAY,** ch f 30/01 New Bay—Albertine Rose (Namid) (5000) **Jaliza Partnership**
41 **BELISA DE VEGA (IRE),** b f 17/03 Fascinating Rock (IRE)—
                                    Royal Razalma (IRE) (Lope de Vega (IRE)) (20952) **One More Moment of Madness**
42 **FRITH,** gr g 29/01 Hellvelyn—Rebecca de Winter (Kyllachy) **Mark & Connie Burton**
43 **ICKYTOO,** b f 03/04 Heeraat (IRE)—
                        Icky Woo (Mark of Esteem (IRE)) (22000) **Cr Lambourn, M Forbes, D Losse & Partner**
44 **INFINITE APPEAL,** b f 21/04 Equiano (FR)—Shy Appeal (IRE) (Barathea (IRE)) **Wood Street Syndicate**
45 B f 19/04 Pearl Secret—Lightable (Shamardal (USA)) **Chapel Stud & Partners**
46 **MILD REFLECTION,** b f 20/02 Aclaim (IRE)—Drift And Dream (Exceed And Excel (AUS)) (13000) **Berkeley Racing**
47 **NEVER NO TROUBLE,** b f 08/02 Time Test—Kitba (New Approach (IRE)) (6000) **Mr A. N. Brooke Rankin**
48 **OCEAN POTION,** b c 16/04 Havana Gold (IRE)—Sunburnt (Haafhd) **Absolute Solvents Ltd**
49 **ROMANTIC MEMORIES,** b f 20/04 Time Test—Midnight Fling (Groom Dancer (USA)) **S A and Miss R Emmet**
50 **SIENNA BONNIE (IRE),** b f 23/01 Kodi Bear (IRE)—
                                    Cucuma (FR) (Invincible Spirit (IRE)) (4000) **Mrs Suzanne Williams & Partner**
51 **SILVERDALE,** gr f 23/04 Hellvelyn—Silvala Dance (Kyllachy) (1200)
52 **TIDDLYWINX (IRE),** b f 01/04 Fascinating Rock (IRE)—
                                    Deviate (IRE) (Acclamation) (4286) **Old Stoic Racing Club & Partner**
53 Br c 14/03 Vadamos (FR)—Way To The Stars (Dansili) (15238)

**Other Owners:** Mr E Ankarcrona, Mr M Bartram, Mr I Bath, Mr B Booker, Mr D Brocklehurst, J. W. M. Brownlee, Mr F Camis, Mr G Clark, Mr G. Davies, Mr A Edwards, Mr P Edwards, M. I. Forbes, Mr A Franklin, Mrs R Franklin, B. M. W. Hearn, Mrs J Hobson, Mr H. Kimbell, C.R. Lambourne, M. Forbes, D. Losse, Mrs L. J. Losse, Mr R Lycett Green, Mr S Mcphee, Mrs C Mordaunt, Mr Mustapha Phee, Mr R Pritchard, Mr H Symmonds, Mrs A Tearne, Mr G Thomas, Mr P Wales, Mr R White.

**Amateur Jockey:** Mr J. Harding.

## 447 MR RYAN POTTER, Sellack
Postal: **The Coach House, Sellack, Ross-on-Wye, Herefordshire, HR9 6LS**
EMAIL rdpotter88@googlemail.com

1 **BRAVE JAQ (FR)**, 10, ch g Network (GER)—Galaxie (FR) **Mr F. J. Butler**
2 **BRUSHED UP**, 8, b m Doyen (IRE)—Definite Artist (IRE) **R. F. Bailey**
3 **D'EDGE OF GLORY (IRE)**, 5, b m Fame And Glory—D'Gigi **Mr R. D. Potter**
4 **DON BERSY (FR)**, 8, b g Califet (FR)—Tropulka God (FR) **Mr R. D. Potter**
5 **EATON MILLER (IRE)**, 9, b g Milan—Four Fields (IRE) **Mr R. D. Potter**
6 **FAMILY MAN (IRE)**, 8, b g Gold Well—Greenacre Mandalay (IRE) **Miss E. H. Yardley**
7 **FIRST DU CHARMIL (FR)**, 9, ch g Ballingarry (IRE)—Famous Member (FR) **Mr R. D. Potter**
8 **FOXCUB (IRE)**, 13, b g Bahri (USA)—Foxglove **Miss E. H. Yardley**
9 **FULL SHIFT (FR)**, 12, b g Ballingarry (IRE)—Dansia (GER) **Mrs P. S. Yardley**
10 **GUATEMALA LE DUN (FR)**, 5, gr g Poliglote—Uranus Le Dun (FR) **Mrs L. P. Vaughan**
11 **HIGH GROUNDS (IRE)**, 8, b g High Chaparral (IRE)—Civility Cat (USA) **Mr R. D. Potter**
12 **LIGHT FLICKER (IRE)**, 9, b g Royal Anthem (USA)—Five Cents More (IRE) **S & V Peets**
13 **LITTLE WINDMILL (IRE)**, 11, ch g Mahler—Ennismore Queen (IRE) **Mr R. D. Potter**
14 **LLANCILLO LORD (IRE)**, 11, b g Beneficial—Llancillo Lady (IRE) **Mr R. D. Potter**
15 **MR JIM**, 12, b g Fraam—Coddington Susie **Miss H. S. Chapman**
16 **NORUKI (IRE)**, 11, b g Flemensfirth (USA)—Classic Material **Mr A. G. Gardner**
17 **R BREN (IRE)**, 8, b m Curtain Time (IRE)—Bramblehill Dream **W. R. Gaskins**
18 **SISSINGHURST (IRE)**, 11, b g Kalanisi (IRE)—Sissinghurst Storm **Mr R. D. Potter**
19 4, B f Court Cave (IRE)—Supreme Cove
20 **TB BROKE HER (IRE)**, 11, br m Indian River (FR)—Catch Ball **W. R. Gaskins**
21 **WUDYASTOPASKING (IRE)**, 5, ch g Ask—Ardnataggle (IRE) **Miss E. H. Yardley**

**Other Owners:** Ms V. Peets, Mr S. A. B. Steel.

## 448 MRS CAMILLA POULTON, Lewes
Postal: **White Cottage, Stud Farm, Telscombe Village, Lewes, BN7 3HZ**
Contacts: **PHONE 01273 300127**
EMAIL camilla.poulton67@outlook.com

1 **ACED IT (IRE)**, 5, b g Lope de Vega (IRE)—Farranjordan **Crowd Racing & R Christison**
2 **INTO DEBT**, 5, b g Paco Boy (IRE)—Katherine Parr **Sweetheart Racing**
3 **MICKEY DRIPPIN (IRE)**, 4, b g Mustajeeb—Ghaidaa (IRE) **Crowd Racing Partnership**
4 **MILITRY DECORATION (IRE)**, 6, b g Epaulette (AUS)—Funcheon Vale (IRE) **Crowd Racing & R Christison**
5 **MILLIE MALOO (IRE)**, 4, b f Mustameet (USA)—Deploythetank (IRE) **Mr T. R. Richardson**
6 **MINELLA RISING (IRE)**, 9, b g King's Theatre (IRE)—Heltornic (IRE) **Sweetheart Racing**
7 **MOROMAC (IRE)**, 7, b g Morozov (USA)—May Bay Lady **Mrs C. D. Poulton**
8 **NOBLE GLANCE**, 8, b m Schiaparelli (GER)—Ragdollianna **D. M. Newland**
9 **NORMAN THE RED**, 11, ch g Tobougg (IRE)—Linden Lime **Mrs C. D. Poulton**
10 **SASHCORD**, 5, b m Pour Moi (IRE)—Ms Cordelia (USA) **Mr J. N. Allen**
11 **TERRI RULES (IRE)**, 6, b m Camacho—Hawaiian Storm **Kestonracingclub**
12 **THAT'S A SHAME (IRE)**, 6, b g Arcadio (GER)—World of Ballet (IRE) **Mr L. Stevens**
13 **THE DETAINEE**, 8, b g Aqlaam—Jakarta Jade (IRE) **Crowd Racing & R Christison**

### THREE-YEAR-OLDS

14 **D'AMBONNAY (IRE)**, b g Hallowed Crown (AUS)—Encore du Cristal (USA) **P. S. Wardle**
15 **GOKOTTA (IRE)**, b f Pride of Dubai (AUS)—Sivensen (IRE) **Mrs L. G. Talbot**
16 **LADY ARIELLA**, b f Dawn Approach (IRE)—Perfectly Spirited **Crowd Racing Partnership**

### TWO-YEAR-OLDS

17 B f 07/02 Bobby's Kitten (USA)—Righteous Renee (USA) (Dixie Union (USA)) **Mrs C. D. Poulton**
18 B f 07/05 Telescope (IRE)—Strawberry Spirit (IRE) (Saint des Saints (FR)) **Mrs C. D. Poulton**

**Other Owners:** Mr R. Christison, Crowd Racing Partnership, Mr C. McKenna, Mrs C. D. Poulton, Mr L. Stevens.

## 449 SIR MARK PRESCOTT BT, Newmarket

Postal: Heath House, Moulton Road, Newmarket, Suffolk, CB8 8DU
Contacts: PHONE 01638 662117 FAX 01638 666572
EMAIL sirmark@heathhousestables.com WEBSITE www.heathhousestables.com
TWITTER @HeathHouseNkt

1 ALPHABETICAL, 4, gr c Archipenko (USA)—Albanova **Tim Bunting - Osborne House III**
2 ALPINISTA, 4, gr f Frankel—Alwilda **Miss K. Rausing**
3 ANIMAL INSTINCT, 4, ch c Leroidesanimaux (BRZ)—Alea Iacta **G. Moore - Osborne House**
4 BODYLINE (IRE), 4, b g Australia—Eurirs (FR) **Tim Bunting and Charlie Walker**
5 CARIBENO, 4, ch g Archipenko (USA)—Cubanita **Charles C Walker - Osborne House IV**
6 CEDAR CAGE, 4, b g Golden Horn—Faslen (USA) **Paddy Barrett**
7 GENESIUS (IRE), 4, ch g Teofilo (IRE)—Craic Agus Spraoi (IRE) **Owners Group 076**
8 LONGSIDER (IRE), 4, b g Ruler of The World (IRE)—Lady Dettoria (FR) **Middleham Park Racing LXXVII**
9 SUNSET BREEZE, 4, b g Pivotal—Sunrise Star **Baxter, Gregson, Jenkins & Warman**

## THREE-YEAR-OLDS

10 ALAGAPPA, b f Archipenko (USA)—Alma Mater **Miss K. Rausing**
11 ALAMBRISTA, ch f Bobby's Kitten (USA)—Almiranta **Miss K. Rausing**
12 ALERTA ROJA, gr f Golden Horn—Albaraka **Miss K. Rausing**
13 CAPTAIN BONNY, b f Charm Spirit (IRE)—Sea Pride (IRE) **Bluehills Racing Limited**
14 CARPENTIER (FR), b g Intello (GER)—Ellary (FR) **Middleham Park Racing XLV**
15 CHILL OUT (IRE), b f Dark Angel (IRE)—Al Jasrah (IRE) **Mt. Brilliant Farm & Ranch, LLC**
16 DUKE OF PRUSSIA, b g Oasis Dream—Marika **Mrs Baxter, W Charnley, C Jenkins, P Lee**
17 FASHION, b f Lope de Vega (IRE)—All The Rage **Denford Stud**
18 B g Sakhee (USA)—Florie **Strawberry Fields Stud**
19 HEAT AND DUST, b g Oasis Dream—Here To Eternity (USA) **Miss K. Rausing**
20 JACK BEAN, b g Golden Horn—Faslen (USA) **Paddy Barrett**
21 JEBEL DUKHAN (IRE), b c Exceed And Excel (AUS)—Alchemilla **H.H. SH Nasser Bin Hamad Al Khalifa**
22 LINDWALL (IRE), ch g Australia—Cochabamba (USA) **J. Fishpool - Osborne House**
23 MEISTERZINGER (IRE), br g Mastercraftsman (IRE)—Zingeeyah **Budd,Greenwood,Gregson,Troubridge,Mailer**
24 MIDFIELD, b f Le Havre (IRE)—Between Us **Cheveley Park Stud**
25 MISS PALOMA, b f Sea The Moon (GER)—Miss Cap Estel **John Pearce Racing Ltd**
26 PISELLI MOLLI (IRE), ch f Dragon Pulse (IRE)—Dancing Duchess (IRE) **Paddy Barrett**
27 POLAR ICE, b g Dansili—Queen of Ice **Charles C Walker - Osborne House**
28 PURRZEALOT, b f Bobby's Kitten (USA)—Blue Zealot (IRE) **J. M. Castle, J. Fill**
29 ROYAL PLEASURE (IRE), b c Kingman—Merry Jaunt (USA) **Tim Bunting - Osborne House**
30 SECRET BOX, b g Le Havre (IRE)—Red Box **Cheveley Park Stud**
31 SISU, b f Lawman (FR)—Salonmare (GER) **Lady Fairhaven & Erik Penser**
32 SUMMER'S KNIGHT, b g Camelot—Summer's Eve **P. J. McSwiney-Osborne House**
33 THE TIDE TURNS, ch g Sea The Moon (GER)—Red Roxanne **Sir Mark Prescott**
34 VANISHING GRACE (FR), b f Dark Angel (IRE)—Fleeting Dream (IRE) **Denford Stud**
35 YAGAN (IRE), b g Australia—Navajo Moon (IRE) **Middleham Park Racing L**

## TWO-YEAR-OLDS

36 ABBADO, ch c 30/03 Almanzor (FR)—Allegretto (IRE) (Galileo (IRE)) (60000) **Cheveley Park Stud**
37 ALDABRA, b f 26/02 Bobby's Kitten (USA)—Altitude (Green Desert (USA)) **Miss K. Rausing**
38 ALLONS DANSER, gr f 29/01 Bobby's Kitten (USA)—Alba Stella (Nashwan (USA)) **Miss K. Rausing**
39 ALPENBLUME, gr f 25/02 Kendargent (FR)—Alwilda (Hernando (FR)) **Miss K. Rausing**
40 ANATOMIC, gr c 10/04 Ulysses (IRE)—Diagnostic (Dutch Art) **Cheveley Park Stud**
41 ARCADIAN FRIEND, b c 06/02 Lope de Vega (IRE)—Best Friend (IRE) (Galileo (IRE)) **John Pearce Racing Ltd**
42 ARCLIGHT, b f 07/02 Champs Elysees—Florentia (Medicean) (14000) **Neil Greig & Sir Mark Prescott**
43 AT THE DOUBLE (FR), br g 22/04 Almanzor (FR)—
                              Express American (FR) (American Post) (85000) **Charlie Walker - Osborne House II**
44 BUTTRESS, b f 02/02 Ulysses (IRE)—Vaulted (Kyllachy) **Cheveley Park Stud**
45 CANDYTUFT, b f 06/02 Sea The Moon (GER)—Macleya (GER) (Winged Love (IRE)) **Cheveley Park Stud**
46 CAPPOQUIN (IRE), b f 13/03 Muhaarar—Tecla (IRE) (Whipper (USA)) (28571) **Sonia Rogers, Anthony Rogers**
47 CAPTAIN HOWSE (IRE), b g 03/04 Australia—Merritt Island (Exceed And Excel (AUS)) **Mr & Mrs John Kelsey-Fry**
48 B f 22/01 Muhaarar—Chanterelle (FR) (Trempolino (USA)) (161421) **KHK Racing Ltd**
49 DENNING, ch c 04/03 Recorder—Undress (IRE) (Dalakhani (IRE)) **J. B. Haggas**

# SIR MARK PRESCOTT BT - continued

50 **EAGLE'S WAY,** ch c 18/03 Gleneagles (IRE)—Martlet (Dansili) (95000) **Tim Bunting - Osborne House II**
51 **FLYAWAYDREAM,** b c 05/04 Farhh—
                          Mockinbird (IRE) (Makfi) (40000) **The GD Partnership, Mrs Caroline Gregson**
52 **GLENISTER (IRE),** b c 15/03 Gleneagles (IRE)—Sistine (Dubai Destination (USA)) **Elite Racing Club**
53 **GOLDEN SHOT,** b c 20/02 Golden Horn—Quenelle (Nayef (USA)) (30000) **W E Sturt - Osborne House**
54 **GORDONS AURA (IRE),** b c 13/03 Golden Horn—
                          Sequined (USA) (Street Cry (IRE)) (47619) **John Brown & Megan Dennis**
55 **MAHAGONI,** b c 23/03 Muhaarar—Festoso (IRE) (Diesis) (32000) **Heath House Optimists**
56 **MEZZANOTTE (IRE),** b f 26/04 Decorated Knight—Middle Persia (Dalakhani (IRE)) (41905) **Lady C. J. O'Reilly**
57 **NOBLE MARK (IRE),** ch g 06/02 Animal Kingdom (USA)—
                          Above The Mark (USA) (Street Cry (IRE)) (35238) **Jones, Julian, Lee & Royle**
58 **NORTH LINCOLN (IRE),** b c 14/02 Acclamation—
                          Molly Dolly (IRE) (Exceed And Excel (AUS)) (40000) **Mr Timothy J. Rooney**
59 **OMNISCIENT,** b c 09/04 Mukhadram—Miss Dashwood (Dylan Thomas (IRE)) (52000) **Ne'er Do Wells VII**
60 Ch f 10/02 Almanzor (FR)—
                          Penny Lane (GER) (Lord of England (GER)) (201776) **H.H. Shaikh Nasser Al Khalifa & Partner**
61 **PRETENDING (IRE),** gr f 21/04 Make Believe—Gala (Galileo (IRE)) **Denford Stud**
62 **QUELLA SPERANZA,** ch f 04/03 Zoffany—Quite A Thing (Dutch Art) **Lady Fairhaven**
63 Ch f 09/02 Bated Breath—Rahaala (IRE) (Indian Ridge) (33333) **H.H. Shaikh Nasser Al Khalifa & Partner**
64 **RUSHFORD,** b c 10/04 Danon Ballade (JPN)—Cushat Law (IRE) (Montjeu (IRE)) **M & M Franklin**
65 **SEA KING,** br c 02/02 Sea The Stars (IRE)—
                          Pamona (IRE) (Duke of Marmalade (IRE)) (87000) **Charlie Walker - Osborne House III**
66 **SPECTATRICE,** b f 22/04 Fast Company (IRE)—Songerie (Hernando (FR)) **Miss K. Rausing**
67 **THEMOONSABALLOON,** b f 15/02 Sea The Moon (GER)—
                          Shembara (FR) (Dylan Thomas (IRE)) (28000) **Denford Stud**
68 **VICTORY CLAP,** b f 02/03 Ulysses (IRE)—Hooray (Invincible Spirit (IRE)) **Cheveley Park Stud**

**Other Owners:** N Attenborough, P Bamford, E. A. Baxter, Mrs J. Budd CBE, B. D. Burnet, D Casterton, M Dabner, Dr & Mrs J. Royle, R. P. Fry, Mrs O. Hoare, M. Julian, P. A. Lee OBE, I Mailer, Mr & Mrs C. Jones, Mr & Mrs H. Glyn-Davies, Mr & Mrs R. Greenwood, F. A. A. Nass, Mrs E. Penser, M. A. C. Rudd, Sir Tom & Lady Troubridge, M. J. Tracey, Mrs S. L. Warman, E. J. Williams.

**Assistant Trainer:** William Butler, **Pupil Assistant:** Thomas Humphries.

**Flat Jockey:** Luke Morris, Ryan Tate.

---

**450** **MISS KATY PRICE, Llanigon**
Postal: **Willow Croft, Llanigon, Hay-On-Wye, Herefordshire, HR3 5PN**
Contacts: **PHONE 07976 820819**
EMAIL **katyprice2005@aol.com** WEBSITE **www.facebook.com/katypriceracing**

1 **ALBERTO'S DREAM,** 12, b g Fantastic Spain (USA)—Molly's Folly **Wallys Dream Syndicate**
2 4, Ch g Black Sam Bellamy (IRE)—Blurred Lines (IRE)
3 **BUCKSKIN (IRE),** 6, b g Kalanisi (IRE)—Our Soiree (IRE) **McLeish & Elliott**
4 **CLONDAW RIGGER (IRE),** 9, b g Stowaway—Daytona Lily (IRE) **Katy Price Racing Club**
5 **DONT PUSH IT PALL (IRE),** 8, br g Kalanisi (IRE)—Honeybrook (IRE) **Alastair & Pippa McLeish**
6 **ECLAIR DES SABLONS (FR),** 7, b g Noriot (GER)—Jolie Fabi (FR) **Mr N. Elliott**
7 **GALLOW FORD (IRE),** 6, b g Westerner—Magical Theatre (IRE) **Mr N. Elliott**
8 **ITSAMANSLIFE (IRE),** 8, b g Mahler—Medieval Banquet (IRE) **McLeish & Elliott**
9 **JAYCOLS STAR (IRE),** 6, ch g Medicean—A Lulu Ofa Menifee (USA) **Out Of Bounds Racing Club**
10 **JENNYS DAY (IRE),** 10, b g Daylami (IRE)—Jennys Oscar (IRE) **Mr N. Elliott**
11 **JILLIONAIRE (IRE),** 5, b m Jet Away—Our Dot (IRE) **Alastair & Pippa McLeish**
12 4, B g Arcadio (GER)—Karinswift **Mike Harris Racing Club**
13 **KEEPSCALLING (IRE),** 7, b m Kalanisi (IRE)—Lady Daisy (IRE) **Out of Bounds & Katy Price**
14 **LUCCA LADY (IRE),** 10, b m Milan—Trail Storm (IRE) **Making Hay**
15 **MINELLACELEBRATION (IRE),** 11, b g King's Theatre (IRE)—Knocktartan (IRE) **Mr N. Elliott**
16 **OUT FOR JUSTICE (IRE),** 8, b g Beneficial—Dustys Delight (IRE) **Alastair & Pippa McLeish**

## MISS KATY PRICE - continued

17 **RATHNURE RANGER (IRE)**, 7, ch g Beneficial—Euro Magic (IRE) **Katy Price Racing Club**
18 **ROSEISAROSEISAROSE (IRE)**, 7, gr m Jeremy (USA)—Roses And Wine (IRE) **Alastair & Pippa McLeish**
19 **SHUDISTAYORSHUDIGO (IRE)**, 6, b m Shirocco (GER)—Clash Artist (IRE) **Katy Price Racing Club**
20 **STEPHANIE SUNSHINE (IRE)**, 8, b m Dubai Destination (USA)—Shyanne (IRE) **Mike Harris Racing Club**

**Other Owners:** Mr N. Elliott, A. D. I. Harris, Mr M. E. Harris, Katy Price Racing Club, Mr A. D. McLeish, Mrs P. J. McLeish, Out Of Bounds Racing Club, Miss K. J. Price.

---

**451** **MR RICHARD PRICE, Hereford**
Postal: **Criftage Farm, Ullingswick, Hereford, Herefordshire, HR1 3JG**
Contacts: **PHONE 01432 820263 MOBILE 07929 200598**

1 **BELLEVARDE (IRE)**, 7, b m Kodiac—Pearl Mountain (IRE) **B. Veasey**
2 **CLARA'S LILY**, 5, gr m Dream Eater (IRE)—Its Clara **Mr S. E. Priest**
3 **EASTERN LADY (IND)**, 8, ch m Dancing Forever (USA)—Oriental Lady (IRE) **K. Reece**
4 **FLIGHT TO NOWHERE**, 9, ch m Aeroplane—River Beauty **Mrs V. J. Morse**
5 **GRANDSTAND (IRE)**, 5, b g Kodiac—Lady Shanghai (IRE) **B. Veasey**
6 **HELLOFAGAME**, 6, b g Hellvelyn—Gracie's Games **Mr D. Prosser & Mr K. Warrington**
7 **INITIATIVE (IRE)**, 6, b g Excelebration (IRE)—Viking Fair **Mrs V. J. Morse**
8 **LILI WEN FACH (IRE)**, 4, gr f Gregorian (IRE)—Zuzinia (IRE) **My Left Foot Racing Syndicate**
9 **MAD BARRY**, 6, ch g Norse Dancer (IRE)—River Beauty **Mrs V. J. Morse**
10 **OCEAN REACH**, 5, b m Phoenix Reach (IRE)—Ocean Transit (IRE) **Mr G E Amey & Mr D M Boddy**
11 **RHUBARB**, 4, b f Nayef (USA)—Cockney Fire **Ocean's Five**

**Other Owners:** Mr G. E. Amey, Mr D. Boddy, D. J. Prosser, K. A. Warrington.

**Assistant Trainer:** Jane Price.

---

**452** **MR PETER PRITCHARD, Shipston-on-Stour**
Postal: **Upper Farm Lodge, Upper Farm, Whatcote, Shipston-On-Stour, Warwickshire, CV36 5EF**
Contacts: **MOBILE 07376 500499**
**EMAIL pennypritch55@hotmail.co.uk**

1 4, B f Passing Glance—Astral Affair (IRE)
2 **EARCOMESALI**, 8, b m Passing Glance—Earcomesannie (IRE) **Mrs Alison Pritchard &mr R W Stowe**
3 **EARCOMESTHEDREAM (IRE)**, 18, b g Marignan (USA)—Play It By Ear (IRE)
4 **FRANZ KLAMMER**, 9, b g Midnight Legend—Ski **Mr M. J. Miller**

### THREE-YEAR-OLDS

5 B f Passing Glance—Tilinisi (IRE)

### TWO-YEAR-OLDS

6 B c 05/06 Passing Glance—Astral Affair (IRE) (Norwich)
7 Br f 27/05 Passing Glance—Earcomesannie (IRE) (Anshan)
8 B c 08/05 Passing Glance—Tilinisi (IRE) (Kalanisi (IRE))

**Other Owners:** Mrs A. D. Pritchard, Mr R. W. Stowe.

**Assistant Trainer:** Mrs E. Gardner.

**NH Jockey:** Tom Bellamy. **Conditional Jockey:** Charlie Hammond. **Amateur Jockey:** Claire Hardwick, Jordan Nailor.

## 453 MR DENIS QUINN, Newmarket
Postal: **Stockbridge Stables, 192 High Street, Newmarket, Suffolk, CB8 9AP**
Contacts: **MOBILE 07435 340008**

1 **BO TAIFAN (IRE)**, 4, gr g Gutaifan (IRE)—Scarlet Rosefinch **Mr A. F. Keane**
2 **CASABLANCA KID (IRE)**, 4, b g Worthadd (IRE)—Coill Cri (IRE) **Exors of the Late Mr J. T. Mangan**
3 **DAN'S CROSS (IRE)**, 5, b g Dansant—Capparoe Cross (IRE) **Mr D. P. Quinn**
4 **FLYING FAIRY (IRE)**, 4, b f Sir Prancealot (IRE)—Abby Cadabby (IRE) **Mr D. P. Quinn**
5 **NAVAJO EAGLE**, 4, b g Gleneagles (IRE)—Don't Forget Faith (USA) **Exors of the Late Mr J. T. Mangan**
6 **RED ALL STAR (IRE)**, 11, b g Haatef (USA)—Star of Russia (IRE) **Mr A. F. Keane**
7 **ROCKY SEA (IRE)**, 5, b h Born To Sea (IRE)—Ice Rock (IRE) **Miss C. McKernan**
8 **STAR OF ST LOUIS (FR)**, 4, b g Style Vendome (FR)—Momix **Exors of the Late Mr J. T. Mangan**
9 **STRICTLY ART (IRE)**, 8, b g Excellent Art—Sadinga (IRE) **Mr D. P. Quinn**
10 **THE BANNER MAN (IRE)**, 7, b g Cape Cross (IRE)—Bunood (IRE) **Mr D. P. Quinn**

### THREE-YEAR-OLDS
11 **ALJOMAANA (IRE)**, ch f Belardo (IRE)—Dheyaa (IRE) **Mr A. F. Keane**
12 **CLIFFCAKE (IRE)**, b c Canford Cliffs (IRE)—Cake (IRE) **Mr A. F. Keane**
13 **SEE THE CELEBRITY**, b c Fountain of Youth (IRE)—So Discreet **Mr H. U. Khan**
14 **THE MEHMAS TOUCH (IRE)**, ch f Mehmas (IRE)—Good Speech (IRE) **Mr D. P. Quinn**

## 454 MR JOHN QUINN, Malton
Postal: **Bellwood Cottage Stables, Settrington, Malton, North Yorkshire, YO17 8NR**
Contacts: **PHONE 01944 768370 MOBILE 07899 873304**
**EMAIL info@johnquinnracing.co.uk WEBSITE www.johnquinnracing.co.uk**

1 **AL KHERB**, 6, b g Al Kazeem—Perfect Spirit (IRE) **Blackburn, Balfe & Partner**
2 **AL SUIL EILE (FR)**, 5, gr g Alhebayeb (IRE)—Visual Element (USA) **JJ Quinn Racing Ltd**
3 **BUSINESS (FR)**, 4, b g Siyouni (FR)—Mambo Mistress (USA) **The Hibernia Partnership**
4 **CAPTAIN JAMESON (IRE)**, 6, b g Camacho—Cross Section (USA) **The JAM Partnership**
5 **COASTAL MIST (IRE)**, 4, gr g Gutaifan (IRE)—She's A Character **Hart Inn 1 & Partner**
6 **EL ASTRONAUTE (IRE)**, 8, ch g Approve (IRE)—Drumcliffe Dancer (IRE) **Mr Ross Harmon Racing**
7 **FIRE EATER (FR)**, 4, b g Motivator—Wendy House (USA) **Trainers House Enterprises Ltd**
8 **FIRST IMPRESSION (IRE)**, 4, b g Make Believe—Charmgoer (USA) **Blackburn, Fox, Mcwilliams & Pendelbury**
9 **FRANKENSTELLA (IRE)**, 4, b f Frankel—L'Ancresse (IRE) **Phoenix Thoroughbred Limited**
10 **GEONICE (FR)**, 5, gr g Samum (GER)—Terenice (FR) **The Desperados 3**
11 **INDIAN PURSUIT (IRE)**, 8, b g Compton Place—Church Melody **JJ Quinn Racing Ltd**
12 **KEEP BUSY (IRE)**, 4, b f Night of Thunder (IRE)—Look Busy (IRE) **Mrs D. A. Tabor**
13 **LIBERTY BEACH**, 4, b f Cable Bay (IRE)—Flirtinaskirt **Mr P. A. Wilkins**
14 **LOOK MY WAY**, 7, b g Pour Moi (IRE)—Casual Glance **Drew & Ailsa Russell**
15 **LORD RIDDIFORD (IRE)**, 6, gr g Zebedee—Beacon of Hope (IRE) **The JAM Partnership**
16 **MAGNA MORALIA (IRE)**, 4, gr g Gregorian (IRE)—Trentini (IRE) **The Desperados**
17 **MELODY KING (IRE)**, 4, b g Kodiac—Mekong Melody (IRE) **JJ Quinn Racing Ltd**
18 **MR WAGYU (IRE)**, 6, ch g Choisir (AUS)—Lake Louise (IRE) **The New Century Partnership**
19 **PARK LANE DANCER (IRE)**, 4, br g Elzaam (AUS)—Greatest Dancer (IRE) **Simon Mulvany & Partner**
20 **REBEL REDEMPTION**, 4, gr g Lethal Force (IRE)—Tempting **The JAM Partnership**
21 **SAFE VOYAGE (IRE)**, 8, b g Fast Company (IRE)—Shishangaan (IRE) **Mr R. Harmon**
22 4, B f Telescope—Santia **Rebels Without A Claus**
23 **SEA ART (IRE)**, 5, b g Born To Sea (IRE)—Kekova **JJ Quinn Racing Ltd**
24 **TIME VOYAGE (IRE)**, 4, b f Raven's Pass (USA)—
                                Katherine Lee (IRE) **Honeycomb Stud Mr JO'Rourke & Mr G Fagan**
25 **WELL EDUCATED (IRE)**, 5, ch g Getaway (GER)—Collegeofknowledge **The Desperados 2**
26 **WELL PLANTED (FR)**, 4, b g Planteur (IRE)—Next Dream (FR) **Drew & Ailsa Russell**
27 **YUKON MISSION (IRE)**, 4, b f Kodiac—Refuse To Give Up (IRE) **Phoenix Thoroughbred Limited**

## MR JOHN QUINN - continued

### THREE-YEAR-OLDS

28 **ALBEN FORCE,** ch g Tamayuz—My Love Thomas (IRE) **J. K. Shannon**
29 **AUTUMN AURORA (IRE),** ch f Buratino (IRE)—Southern House (IRE) **Racing Connexions 11**
30 **DENY KNOWLEDGE (IRE),** b f Pride of Dubai (AUS)—

The Paris Shrug **Honeycomb Stud Mr JO'Rourke & Mr G Fagan**
31 **DOUBLE SALMON (IRE),** b f Adaay (IRE)—Paella (IRE) **Alchemy Bloodstock**
32 **EL HAMRA (IRE),** b f Gleneagles (IRE)—Elbasana (IRE) **Phoenix Ladies Syndicate Limited**
33 **EMIRATI DIRHAM (IRE),** b g Mehmas (IRE)—Golden Legacy (IRE) **Mrs Thompson Mrs Allen Adams & Cranston**
34 **EMPIRESTATEOFMIND (IRE),** b g Starspangledbanner (AUS)—Adore **Mr S. A. T. Quinn**
35 **FOOTSTEPSTOTHEHART (IRE),** ch g Camacho—Beach Candy (IRE) **Mr I. P. Homer**
36 **HAVEN LADY (IRE),** b f Belardo (IRE)—Fork Handles **Red Cow Racing**
37 **HOPE PROBE (IRE),** b gr g Gutaifan (IRE)—Beacon of Hope (IRE) **Mr A. Mohamdi**
38 **LIBBY AMI (IRE),** b f The Gurkha (IRE)—Moore's Melody (IRE) **S & R Racing Partnership**
39 **MISS NAY NEVER (IRE),** b f No Nay Never (USA)—Desert Sky (IRE) **The Wild Rovers**
40 **POSSIBLE AMBITION,** b c Territories (IRE)—Kotsi (IRE) **Mr A. Reed**
41 **SUGARPIEHONEYBUNCH (IRE),** b f Fast Company (IRE)—Jeewana **Mr C. R. Hirst**
42 **TITAN ROCK,** b g Belardo (IRE)—Frabjous **Mr Ross Harmon & Partner**
43 **TOMMYTWOHOOTS,** b c Bated Breath—Lady Lube Rye (IRE) **D. & S. L. Tanker Transport Limited**
44 **VIRGINIA PLANE,** b f Mehmas (IRE)—Flirtinaskirt **Mr P. A. Wilkins**
45 B g The Wow Signal (IRE)—Winter Robin **JJ Quinn Racing Ltd**

### TWO-YEAR-OLDS

46 Ch c 10/02 The Last Lion (IRE)—Acts Out Loud (USA) (Mr Greeley (USA)) (2857) **JJ Quinn Racing Ltd**
47 **AUTUMN ANGEL (IRE),** b f 27/03 Dark Angel (IRE)—Elshabakiya (IRE) (Diktat) (20952) **Racing Connexions 14**
48 **AUTUMN SYMPHONY (IRE),** ch f 26/01 Profitable (IRE)—

Comeraincomeshine (IRE) (Night Shift (USA)) (17143) **Racing Connexions 12**
49 Gr f 20/04 El Kabeir (USA)—Beacon of Hope (IRE) (Barathea (IRE)) (38095)
50 Br c 25/04 No Nay Never (USA)—

Caribbean Princess (USA) (Henrythenavigator (USA)) (50000) **Mr Ross Harmon & Partner**
51 B c 30/03 Ardad (IRE)—Cherubic (Dark Angel (IRE)) (16190) **JJ Quinn Racing Ltd**
52 B c 05/05 Belardo (IRE)—Grain of Truth (Gulch (USA)) (6667) **Mr R. L. Houlton**
53 B c 31/01 Fast Company (IRE)—Jazzy Belle (Caradak (IRE)) (14286) **The New Century Partnership**
54 Ch c 08/04 Profitable (IRE)—Ma Nikitia (IRE) (Camacho) (9048) **The Ayrshire Tradesmen**
55 B f 05/04 Acclamation—Our Joy (IRE) (Kodiac) (17000) **Mr D. W. Armstrong**
56 B c 19/03 Brazen Beau (AUS)—Pamushana (IRE) (Teofilo (IRE)) **P. R. C. Morrison**
57 Ch c 09/04 Twilight Son—Rapid Recruit (IRE) (Fast Company (IRE)) (13000) **The Racing Emporium**
58 B f 25/01 Havana Gold (IRE)—Secret Hint (Oasis Dream) (13500) **JJ Quinn Racing Ltd**
59 B c 06/05 Sea The Moon (GER)—Veiled Beauty (USA) (Royal Academy (USA)) (62000) **Mr Ross Harmon & Partner**

**Other Owners:** Mr R. Blades, Mr A. I. Derry, Mr J. I. Derry, Mr S. Furniss, Mr R. Harmon, JJ Quinn Racing Ltd, N. E. F. Luck, Mr R. Maddocks, Mr S. Mulvany, Mrs S. Quinn, Mr S. A. T. Quinn, Mr M. Rapley, Mrs A. Russell, A. J. R. Russell, M. A. Scaife.

**Assistant Trainer:** Sean Quinn.

**Flat Jockey:** Jason Hart. **Amateur Jockey:** Mr Kaine Wood.

---

### 455 MR MICK QUINN, Newmarket
Postal: 50 Edinburgh Road, Newmarket, Suffolk, CB8 0QF
Contacts: PHONE 01638 660017 MOBILE 07973 260054 FAX 01638 660017
EMAIL mickquinn2562@gmail.com

1 **GREAT HALL,** 11, b g Halling (USA)—L'Affaire Monique **Mr M. Quinn**
2 **INVINCIBLE LARNE (IRE),** 5, b g Invincible Spirit (IRE)—Caphene **Mr K. F. C. Bruce**
3 **KELINDA DICE,** 4, b f Hot Streak (IRE)—Dora's Sister (IRE) **Mr M. Quinn**
4 **PINK SHEETS (IRE),** 7, b m Gold Well—Soft Skin (IRE) **Mr K. F. C. Bruce**

## MR MICK QUINN - continued

5 **PRINCESS SIYOUNI (IRE)**, 4, b f Siyouni (FR)—Librettista (AUS)  **Mr K. F. C. Bruce**
6 **PURPLE POWER**, 4, b br f Slade Power (IRE)—Peace Summit  **Mr K. F. C. Bruce**
7 **RECALL THE SHOW**, 4, ch g Showcasing—Rappel  **Mr K. F. C. Bruce**
8 **THE SUNDAY CLUB**, 4, b g Heeraat (IRE)—Anfield  **Mr M. Quinn**

### THREE-YEAR-OLDS

9 **BRAZEN BRUCE**, b f Brazen Beau (AUS)—Dora's Sister (IRE)  **Mr K. F. C. Bruce**
10 **INVER PARK**, b c Pivotal—Red Baton  **Mr K. F. C. Bruce**
11 B f Havana Gold (IRE)—Raiysina  **Tim and Miranda Johnson**
12 **WOO WOO**, b f Heeraat (IRE)—Icky Woo  **Mr K. F. C. Bruce**

**Assistant Trainer:** Miss Karen Davies.

---

**456** **MR ALASTAIR RALPH, Bridgnorth**
Postal: **Bynd Farm, Bynd Lane, Billingsley, Bridgnorth, Shropshire, WV16 6PQ**
Contacts: **WORK** 01746 860807 **PHONE** 07912 184217
**WORK EMAIL** info@alastairralphracing.co.uk **WEBSITE** www.alastairralphracing.co.uk

1 **AMANOFHISWORD (IRE)**, 6, gr g Mahler—Castle Lake (IRE)  **The Hawkins Partnership**
2 **BILLINGSLEY (IRE)**, 9, b g Milenary—Retain That Magic (IRE)  **Walters Plant Hire & Potter Group**
3 **BUTLER'S BRIEF (IRE)**, 6, b g Yeats (IRE)—She's On The Case (IRE)  **You Can Be Sure**
4 **CADDYHILL (IRE)**, 6, b g Arcadio (GER)—Ring Hill  **B. Hawkins**
5 **CHAMPAGNE MIST (IRE)**, 9, b g Stowaway—Valentines Misty (IRE)  **Only Fools Own Horses**
6 **CHANCEUX (IRE)**, 5, b g Mahler—Granny Mc Cann (IRE)  **Rskm Bloodstock**
7 **CORAL (FR)**, 6, gr g Martaline—Clipsy (FR)  **Against All Odds Racing**
8 **CUT THE CORNER (IRE)**, 13, br g Vinnie Roe (IRE)—Snipe Victory (IRE)  **Mr M. A. Fothergill**
9 **DAMUT I'M OUT (IRE)**, 11, b g Gamut (IRE)—Five Cents More (IRE)  **Costello/ralph Racing Partnership**
10 **DRENAGH (IRE)**, 6, b g Kalanisi (IRE)—Diva Antonia (IRE)  **B. Hawkins**
11 **ENCOUNTER A GIANT (IRE)**, 9, b g Kalanisi (IRE)—Sumability (IRE)  **The Hawkins Partnership**
12 **EVENSTEVENS (IRE)**, 6, b g Getaway (GER)—Native Diva (IRE)  **Not The Turf Club**
13 **GALURIN (FR)**, 5, b g Sunday Break (JPN)—Rirta (FR)  **Million in Mind Partnership**
14 **GENTLE RIVER**, 5, b g Gentlewave (IRE)—Absalom's Girl  **Mr A. Ralph**
15 **GETAWAY TOTHEROCK (IRE)**, 8, b g Getaway (GER)—Theft  **James, Archer, Ralph & Gentech**
16 **GIOVANNI ROYALE**, 5, ch g Schiaparelli (GER)—Benefique Royale  **Len,Jon,Davies,Downes,Sumner,White,Booth**
17 **GLANCE FROM CLOVER**, 6, b g Passing Glance—Allforclover (IRE)  **Miss S. Troughton**
18 **GROOVEUR (FR)**, 5, b g Ballingarry (IRE)—Kelle Home (FR)  **Prm Bloodstock**
19 **IN OUR DREAMS (IRE)**, 5, b g Cloudings (IRE)—No Moore Bills  **Spiers & Hartwell, Ralph & Black**
20 **INN THE BULL (GER)**, 8, ch g Lope de Vega (IRE)—Ile Rousse  **Loose Cannon Racing**
21 **IONTACH CHEVAL**, 5, b g Dunaden (FR)—Dancing Emily (IRE)  **Rskm Bloodstock**
22 **JACK SHARP (IRE)**, 6, b br g Scorpion (IRE)—That's Amazing (IRE)  **Walters Plant Hire & Potter Group**
23 **KABRIT (IRE)**, 6, ch g Mastercraftsman (IRE)—Twinkling Ice (USA)  **Alastair Ralph Racing**
24 **KNICKERBOCKERGLORY (IRE)**, 5, b g Fame And Glory—The Brass Lady (IRE)  **Prm Bloodstock**
25 **LADY SALLY (IRE)**, 7, b m Scorpion (IRE)—Broken Gale (IRE)  **Mr D. M. J. Lloyd**
26 **LLANTARA**, 10, b m Kayf Tara—Lady Llancillo (IRE)  **That's Racing**
27 **LOST IN MONTMARTRE (FR)**, 5, gr m Montmartre (FR)—Lost Maiby (FR)  **Mr Gary White & Mr Gary Wood**
28 **LUNAR LANDER (IRE)**, 5, b g Shirocco (GER)—Bean Ki Moon (IRE)  **Prm Bloodstock**
29 **MEMPHIS BLEEK**, 5, ch g Olympic Glory—Party (IRE)  **Only Fools Own Horses 01**
30 **METHOD MADNESS (IRE)**, 6, b g Sans Frontieres (IRE)—Inishbeg House (IRE)  **Mr M. A. Fothergill**
31 **MICK MONA (FR)**, 7, ro m Blue Bresil (FR)—Mick Toscane (FR)  **The Burling Family Ltd**
32 **MIDNIGHT HENRY**, 5, b g Midnight Legend—Silver Kate (IRE)  **D. M. Richards**
33 **OSPREY CALL (IRE)**, 6, b g Winged Love (IRE)—Courting Whitney (IRE)  **Gentech, Franklin, Archer & James**
34 **OUR ROCKSTAR (IRE)**, 7, b m Gold Well—Hazel Mist (IRE)  **Strutting Cockerels Syndicate**
35 **QUEEN'S SOLDIER (GER)**, 5, b g Soldier Hollow—Queen Mum (GER)  **The Hawkins Partnership**
36 **RISK D'ARGENT (FR)**, 5, gr g My Risk (FR)—Villebruyere (FR)  **Prm Bloodstock**
37 **SEYMOUR SOX**, 7, b g Multiplex—Seymour Chance  **Mrs C J Black & Mrs Sue Briscoe**
38 **TAP TAP BOOM**, 7, ro g Foxwedge (AUS)—Exclusive Approval (USA)  **Gentech,James,Franklin,Bickmore&ralph**
39 **TEMPURAN**, 12, b g Unbridled's Song (USA)—Tenderly (IRE)  **Rrrs Partnership**

## MR ALASTAIR RALPH - continued

40 **TENNERROW (IRE)**, 9, b m Stowaway—Silent Supreme (IRE) **Mr A. R. Bickmore**
41 **THE GREY FALCO (FR)**, 6, gr g Falco (USA)—Take A Chance (FR) **The Roaming Roosters**
42 **TOM O'ROUGHLEY (IRE)**, 6, b g Yeats (IRE)—Thegoodwans Sister (IRE) **Mr A. Ralph**
43 **WHEESHT (IRE)**, 7, br m Scorpion (IRE)—Retain That Magic (IRE) **James and Jean Potter Ltd**
44 **WHITE TURF (IRE)**, 6, gr g Clodovil (IRE)—Holda (IRE) **Only Fools Own Horses**
45 **YOUR BAND**, 6, b g Helmet (AUS)—Kampai **Only Fools & Cockerels**

**Other Owners:** Mrs C. A. Archer, Mr A. R. Bickmore, Mrs C. J. Black, Mrs S. Briscoe, Mrs M. P Costello, Mr N. Franklin, Gentech Products Ltd, B. Hawkins, Mr I. James, Mrs K. L. Maxwell, Mr B. Morgan, Only Fools Own Horses, Mr A. Ralph, Mrs D. J. Ralph, Mr R. D. Ralph, Mr R. J. Simpson, Spiers & Hartwell Ltd, Strutting Cockerels Syndicate, Sundorne Products (Llanidloes) Ltd, Walters Plant Hire Ltd, Mr G. White, Mr J. Wilks, Mr G. D. Wood.

**Head Lad:** Callum Griffiths, **Secretary:** Bundle Pickard, **Yard Sponsor:** Planned Office Interiors Ltd.

**NH Jockey:** Lee Edwards. **Conditional Jockey:** Tabitha Worsley. **Amateur Jockey:** Mr Alex Edwards, Mr Adam O'Shea.

---

## 457 MR TIM REED, Hexham
Postal: **Moss Kennels, Haydon Bridge, Hexham, Northumberland, NE47 6NL**
Contacts: PHONE **01434 344016** MOBILE **07703 270408**
EMAIL timreedracing@gmail.com

1 **ALF 'N' DOR (IRE)**, 10, ch g Flemensfirth (USA)—Greenflag Princess (IRE) **Mr W. T. Reed**
2 **LEVEROCK LASS (IRE)**, 8, b m Olden Times—Hazelhall Princess (IRE) **Beswick Bloodstock & Mr W T Reed**
3 **RUINOUS (IRE)**, 6, b br g Aizavoski (IRE)—Will She Smile (IRE) **Mothers & Daughters**

**Other Owners:** Beswick Brothers Bloodstock, Mr J. K. Huddleston, Mr W. T. Reed, Mr B. Ryan-Beswick, Mr W. Ryan-Beswick.

**Assistant Trainer:** Mrs E. J. Reed.

**Conditional Jockey:** Harry Reed.

---

## 458 MR DAVID REES, Haverfordwest
Postal: **Knock Moor, Clarbeston Road, Haverfordwest, Pembrokeshire, SA63 4SL**
Contacts: PHONE **01437 731308** MOBILE **07775 662463** FAX **01437 731308**
EMAIL accounts@davidreesfencing.co.uk

1 **AIKEN DRUM**, 5, b g Fight Club (GER)—Moll Flanders
2 **BENI LIGHT (FR)**, 10, b g Crossharbour—Or Light (FR) **Another Day Out**
3 **BUCK BRAVO (IRE)**, 9, b g Mahler—Damoiselle **D. A. Rees**
4 **DREAM BOLT (IRE)**, 13, ch g Urban Ocean (FR)—Riviera Dream (IRE) **Mr D A Rees & Mr N Adams**
5 **DUNBAR (FR)**, 8, gr g Lord du Sud (FR)—Jiletta (FR) **D. A. Rees**
6 **FLYING GARRY (FR)**, 6, gr g Ballingarry (IRE)—Quezac du Boulay (FR) **Harp Racing**
7 **GONE PLATINUM (IRE)**, 12, b g Mountain High (IRE)—Miss Platinum (IRE) **D. A. Rees**
8 **HITDROADJACK (IRE)**, 8, ch g Wareed (IRE)—Mo Cuisle (IRE) **Mr M. Price**
9 **KARANNELLE (IRE)**, 6, b m Nathaniel (IRE)—Dance Lively (USA) **D. A. Rees**
10 **KIERA ROYALE (IRE)**, 10, ch m Beneficial—Llancillo Lady (IRE) **D. A. Rees**
11 **KINGSTON KING (IRE)**, 7, b g Morozov (USA)—Gra Mo Chroi **D. A. Rees**
12 **MISTY MAI (IRE)**, 11, b m Westerner—Arcanum (IRE) **D. A. Rees**
13 **ROBIN OF SHERWOOD (IRE)**, 8, b br g Robin des Pres (FR)—Galleta **West Is Best**
14 **STEEL NATIVE (IRE)**, 10, b g Craigsteel—Princess Gloria (IRE) **D & J Rees**

**Other Owners:** Mr N. W. Adams, Miss A. Freeman, Mrs J. Mathias, D. A. Rees, Mr J. E. Rees, Mr R. Williams.

## 459 MRS HELEN REES, Dorchester

Postal: **Distant Hills, Chalmington, Dorchester, Dorset, DT2 0HB**
Contacts: **PHONE 07715 558289**
EMAIL **helen-rees@live.co.uk**

1 BEYOND SUPREMACY (IRE), 9, b g Beneficial—Slaney Athlete (IRE)  **Mrs H. E. Rees**
2 SERJEANT PAINTER, 6, b g Royal Applause—Szabo's Art  **Mrs H. E. Rees**

## 460 MRS LYDIA RICHARDS, Chichester

Postal: **Lynch Farm, Hares Lane, Funtington, Chichester, West Sussex, PO18 9LW**
Contacts: **PHONE 01243 574882 MOBILE 07803 199061**
EMAIL **lydia.richards@sky.com**

1 CERTAINLY RED, 7, ch g Midnight Legend—Venetian Lass  **The Venetian Lad Partnership**
2 CITY TOUR, 5, b g Dutch Art—Privacy Order  **Mrs E. F. J. Seal**
3 4, Ch g Paco Boy (IRE)—Demoiselle Bond  **The Demoiselle Bond Partnership**
4 GO YOGI (IRE), 5, b g Kodiac—Security Interest (USA)  **Mrs L. Richards**
5 GOOD NEWS, 9, b g Midnight Legend—Venetian Lass  **The Good News Partnership**
6 HILL HOLLOW (IRE), 5, ch g Helmet (AUS)—Bint Doyen  **Mrs L. Richards**
7 MURHIB (IRE), 9, b g Sea The Stars (IRE)—Mood Swings (IRE)  **The Murhib Partnership**
8 SMITH (IRE), 5, ch g Dawn Approach (IRE)—Alazeya (IRE)  **Mrs L. Richards**
9 5, B m Alkaased (USA)—Venetian Lass  **Mrs L. Richards**

### THREE-YEAR-OLDS

10 B f Toronado (IRE)—Demoiselle Bond

## 461 MR NICKY RICHARDS, Greystoke

Postal: **Rectory Farm, Greystoke, Penrith, Cumbria, CA11 0UJ**
Contacts: **HOME 017684 83160 PHONE 017684 83392 MOBILE 07771 906609 FAX 017684 83933**
EMAIL **office@nickyrichardsracing.com** WEBSITE **www.nickyrichardsracing.com**

1 AMBEROSE, 8, ch m Sulamani (IRE)—Miss Nellie (IRE)  **Langdale Bloodstock**
2 BIG BAD BEAR (IRE), 7, br g Jeremy (USA)—Our Polly (IRE)  **Tor Side Racing**
3 BLAKERIGG (IRE), 10, b g Presenting—Azalea (IRE)  **David & Nicky Robinson**
4 BULLION BOSS (IRE), 5, b g War Command (USA)—
Gold Bubbles (USA)  **Multiple Sclerosis Borders Racing Club 1**
5 CAIUS MARCIUS (IRE), 10, b g King's Theatre (IRE)—
Ain't Misbehavin (IRE)  **Mr C P Norbury & Tarzan Bloodstock**
6 CASTLE RUSHEN (IRE), 6, b g Fame And Glory—Rosie Suspect (IRE)  **Mr T. J. Hemmings**
7 CATHAL'S STAR, 8, ch g Malinas (GER)—Hand Inn Glove  **Charlie Doocey / Cathal Doocey**
8 CHAPEL STILE (IRE), 9, b g Scorpion (IRE)—Peggy Cullen (IRE)  **Langdale Bloodstock**
9 CHIDSWELL (IRE), 12, b g Gold Well—Manacured (IRE)  **Dark Horse Racing Ltd**
10 COURT DREAMING (IRE), 8, b g Court Cave—Louis's Teffia (IRE)  **Mr James Westoll**
11 DUKE OF NAVAN (IRE), 13, b br g Presenting—Greenfieldflyer (IRE)  **David & Nicky Robinson**
12 EVERYDAY CHAMPAGNE (IRE), 5, gr g Doyen (IRE)—Magie de Toulouse (FR)  **Katie & Brian Castle**
13 FLY BY MILAN (IRE), 6, b g Milan—So Proper (IRE)  **Langdale Bloodstock**
14 GLENDUFF (IRE), 7, b g Gold Well—Last of The Bunch  **Mr T. J. Hemmings**
15 GLINGER FLAME (IRE), 9, ro g Daylami (IRE)—Titian Flame (IRE)  **Mr James Westoll**
16 GLITTERING LOVE (IRE), 9, b g Winged Love (IRE)—Glittering Image (IRE)  **The Fife Boys + 1**
17 GLORIOUS SPIRIT (IRE), 5, b m Fame And Glory—Mrs Dempsey (IRE)  **The Spirit Partnership**

## MR NICKY RICHARDS - continued

18 **GUITAR PETE (IRE)**, 11, gr g Dark Angel (IRE)—Innishmore (IRE) **Mrs E. E. R. Sloan**
19 **HEADSCARF LIL (IRE)**, 7, b m Getaway (GER)—Bleu Money (IRE) **Tarzan Bloodstock & Mr Oliver Brownlee**
20 **HOME FIRE**, 5, b g Frankel—Hot Snap **Langdale Bloodstock**
21 **KAJAKI (IRE)**, 8, gr g Mastercraftsman (IRE)—No Quest (IRE) **Mr F. Gillespie**
22 **KITTY HALL (IRE)**, 7, b m Fame And Glory—Set In Her Ways (IRE) **Langdale Bloodstock**
23 **LANTY SLEA (IRE)**, 6, b g Beat Hollow—Catleen (IRE) **Langdale Bloodstock**
24 **LEGAL BEAGLE (IRE)**, 6, b g Rule of Law (USA)—
                                  Knockamullen Girl (IRE) **Mrs I. C. Sellars & Major & Mrs P. Arkwright**
25 **LESS OF THE LIP (IRE)**, 4, b f Califet (FR)—The Tabster (IRE) **Mrs E. E. R. Sloan**
26 **LOOKING WELL (IRE)**, 12, b g Gold Well—Different Level (IRE) **D. Wesley-Yates**
27 **MAROWN (IRE)**, 7, b g Milan—Rosie Suspect (IRE) **Mr T. J. Hemmings**
28 **MAYO STAR (IRE)**, 9, b g Stowaway—Western Whisper (IRE) **Charlie Doocey / Cathal Doocey**
29 **MILLIE OF MAYO**, 6, b m Overbury (IRE)—Gertrude Webb **Mr & Mrs E Norris & Partners**
30 **MURVAGH BEACH (IRE)**, 6, ch g Doyen (IRE)—Magic Park (IRE) **David & Nicky Robinson**
31 **MY OLD GOLD (IRE)**, 11, b m Gold Well—Tenbo (IRE) **Tor Side Racing**
32 **NELLS SON**, 6, b g Trans Island—Miss Nellie (IRE) **Langdale Bloodstock**
33 **NO REGRETS (IRE)**, 7, b g Presenting—E Mac (IRE) **Jim Ennis & Tony Killoran**
34 **PADDOCK COTTAGE (IRE)**, 5, b g Pour Moi (IRE)—Blend **D. Wesley-Yates**
35 **PARISENCORE (FR)**, 5, b g Walk In The Park (IRE)—
                                  Folk Dancing (FR) **Mrs I. C. Sellars & Major & Mrs P. Arkwright**
36 **PETITE GANACHE (IRE)**, 9, ch g Presenting—Ain't Misbehavin (IRE) **Golden Dragon Racing**
37 **REIVERS LAD**, 10, b g Alflora (IRE)—Reivers Moon **Mr J. M. Stenhouse**
38 **RELEASE THE KRAKEN (IRE)**, 5, b g Shantou (USA)—Guydus (IRE) **Mr J. Fyffe**
39 **RIBBLE VALLEY (IRE)**, 8, b g Westerner—Miss Greinton (GER) **D. Wesley-Yates**
40 **SAUCE OF LIFE (IRE)**, 6, b g Califet (FR)—Salsaparilla (FR) **Mrs I. C. Sellars & Major & Mrs P. Arkwright**
41 **SERIOUS EGO (GER)**, 8, b g Sholokhov (IRE)—Sunshine Story (IRE) **Kenny & Laura Haughey**
42 **SKIDDAW VALLEYS**, 9, ch g Three Valleys (USA)—Skiddaw Wolf **J. R. Wills**
43 **SOFT RISK (FR)**, 5, b g My Risk (FR)—Douce Ambiance (FR) **Mr James Westoll**
44 **TAKING FLIGHT (IRE)**, 7, b g Stowaway—Cailin Vic Mo Cri (IRE) **Mr F. Bird**
45 **TAKINGRISKS (IRE)**, 12, b g Golden Tornado (IRE)—Downtown Rosie (IRE) **Mr F. Bird**
46 **TFOU (FR)**, 5, b g Authorized (IRE)—Fire Moon Julie (FR) **Tarzan Bloodstock**
47 **TIDAL POINT (IRE)**, 5, br g Sea The Moon (GER)—Centred (IRE) **Sleeve It Ltd**
48 **UNCLE ALASTAIR**, 9, b g Midnight Legend—Cyd Charisse **Eddie Melville & Partners**
49 **UNIVERSAL FOLLY**, 6, b g Universal (IRE)—Madam Jolie (IRE) **Tor Side Racing**
50 **WETLANDS (IRE)**, 6, b g Westerner—Un Jour D Ete (FR) **Mr T. J. Hemmings**

**Other Owners:** Major P. W. F. Arkwright, Mrs Sandra G. E. Arkwright, Mr O. Brownlee, Mr A. Cartledge, Mr B. C. Castle, Mrs C. Castle, Mr C. Doocey, Mr C. P. Doocey, Mr Jimmy Dudgeon, Mrs R. L. Elliot, J. T. Ennis, Mr N. T. Gallagher, Mr R Hale, Mr K. Haughey, Mrs L. Haughey, Miss R. K. Hill, R. Kent, Mr T. A. Killoran, Mrs E. M. Lloyd, E. Q. Melville, Multiple Sclerosis Borders Racing Club, C. P. Norbury, Mr E. C. Norris, Miss J. R. Richards, Mr N. G. Richards, Mr D. Robinson, Mrs N. G. Robinson, Mrs N. P. Sellars, Mr A. C. R. Stubbs, Mr A Sutcliffe, Tarzan Bloodstock.

**Assistant Trainer:** Miss Joey Richards, Mr Harry Haynes, **Secretary:** Antonia Reid.

**NH Jockey:** Ryan Day, Brian Hughes. **Conditional Jockey:** Danny McMenamin. **Amateur Jockey:** Miss Josie Elliot, Mr Lyall Hodgins.

**462** **MR JOHN DAVID RICHES, Pilling**
Postal: **Moss Side Farm, Off Lancaster Road, Scronkey, Pilling, Lancashire, PR3 6SR**
Contacts: PHONE **01253 799190**
EMAIL **jrracing@btinternet.com**

1 **ANGEL EYES,** 6, b m Piccolo—Miacarla **J R Racing**
2 **MR GAMBINO,** 4, b g Music Master—Snow Dancer (IRE) **J R Racing**
3 **PICKS PINTA,** 10, b g Piccolo—Past 'n' Present **J R Racing**
4 **RAIN CAP,** 4, b g Fountain of Youth (IRE)—Rough Courte (IRE) **J R Racing**
5 **STORM MASTER,** 4, b g Music Master—Miacarla **J R Racing**
6 **TRULOVE,** 8, b m Piccolo—Snow Dancer (IRE) **J R Racing**

**THREE-YEAR-OLDS**

7 **ASTAPOR,** b g Sixties Icon—Good Morning Lady **J R Racing**

**Other Owners:** J. D. Riches, Mrs L. Wohlers.

**463** **MR MARK RIMELL, Witney**
Postal: **Fairspear Equestrian Centre, Fairspear Road, Leafield, Witney, Oxfordshire, OX29 9NT**
Contacts: PHONE **01993 878551 MOBILE 07778 648303, 07973 627054**
EMAIL **rimell@rimellracing.com** WEBSITE **www.rimellracing.com**

1 **ENDLESS ADVENTURE,** 6, b g And Beyond (IRE)—Gulshue **Mrs C. Mackness**
2 **HALLWOOD (FR),** 4, gr g Martaline—Ball of Wood (FR) **Roel Hill Farm limited**
3 **I'M A STARMAN,** 8, ch g Schiaparelli (GER)—Strathtay **M. G. Rimell**
4 **KYLLACHY DRAGON (IRE),** 6, b g Dragon Pulse (IRE)—Lafayette (GER) **M. G. Rimell**
5 **RAINBOW MIRAGE,** 4, ch f Garswood—Oasis Mirage **Miss S. M. Howes**

**Assistant Trainer:** Anne Rimell.

**464** **MR DAVE ROBERTS, Kenley**
Postal: **Leasowes Farm, Kenley, Shrewsbury, Shropshire, SY5 6NY**
Contacts: PHONE **07854 550606**

1 **ADMAN SAM (IRE),** 10, b g Black Sam Bellamy (IRE)—Koral Bay (FR) **Mr P. A. Downing**
2 **CALIFORNIA SOUL (IRE),** 10, b g Yeats (IRE)—Pointing North (USA) **D. B. Roberts**
3 5, B m Norse Dancer (IRE)—Cat Six (USA) **D. B. Roberts**
4 **CURRENT,** 4, ch f Equiano (FR)—Updated (FR) **D. B. Roberts**
5 **G'DAY AUSSIE,** 8, b g Aussie Rules (USA)—Moi Aussi (USA) **Mr D. Bradbury**
6 **PLUMETTE,** 5, b m Compton Place—Belatorio (IRE) **Mr J. Rocke**
7 **RACING SPIRIT,** 9, ch g Sir Percy—Suertuda **D. B. Roberts**
8 **RAVEN'S RAFT (IRE),** 6, gr m Raven's Pass (USA)—Sea Drift (FR) **D. B. Roberts**

**THREE-YEAR-OLDS**

9 Ch g Cannock Chase (USA)—Cat Six (USA) **D. B. Roberts**
10 B g Bathyrhon (GER)—Russian Memories (FR) **Mr P. A. Downing**

**465** **MR MIKE ROBERTS, Hailsham**
Postal: **Summertree Farm, Bodle Street Green, Hailsham, East Sussex, BN27 4QT**
Contacts: **PHONE 01435 830231 MOBILE 07774 208040**
EMAIL mike@summertree-racing.com

1 **AASLEAGH FAWN (IRE),** 6, b m Kalanisi (IRE)—Aasleagh Lady (IRE) **M. J. Roberts**
2 **ANDAPA (FR),** 7, br m Kapgarde (FR)—Daniety (FR) **M. J. Roberts**
3 **CONCHITA (GER),** 6, b m Zoffany (IRE)—Cross Check (IRE) **M. J. Roberts**
4 **DREAM BAIE (FR),** 8, b g Crillon (FR)—Montaraza (FR) **M. J. Roberts**
5 **KING MURO,** 11, b g Halling (USA)—Ushindi (IRE) **M. J. Roberts**
6 **KIRUNA PEAK (IRE),** 7, ch m Arcano (IRE)—Kirunavaara (IRE) **M. J. Roberts**
7 **PERFECT MOMENT (IRE),** 8, b m Milan—Faucon **M. J. Roberts**
8 **VIA VOLUPTA,** 11, b m Kayf Tara—Via Ferrata (FR) **M. J. Roberts**

Assistant Trainer: Marie Martin.

**466** **MISS SARAH ROBINSON, Bridgwater**
Postal: **Newnham Farm, Shurton, Stogursey, Bridgwater, Somerset, TA5 1QG**
Contacts: **PHONE 01278 732357 MOBILE 07866 435197, 07518 785291 FAX 01278 732357**
EMAIL info@sarahrobinsonracing.co.uk WEBSITE www.sarahrobinsonracing.co.uk

1 **CONTROL ME (IRE),** 7, b m Yeats (IRE)—Cullian **Neil & Simon Racing Partners**
2 **DONT CALL ME DORIS,** 11, b m Franklins Gardens—Grove Dancer **Mr M. L. J. Fooks**
3 **MARTHA'S DREAM,** 7, ch m Captain Gerrard (IRE)—Rose Bounty **Mr B. Robinson**
4 **MILLIE'S FLYING,** 8, b m Franklins Gardens—Grove Dancer **Mr M. L. J. Fooks**
5 **NECK OR NOTHING (GER),** 12, b g Intikhab (USA)—Nova (GER) **Mr R. J. Bailey**
6 **RITA O'HARA,** 6, b m Bollin Eric—Ritas Ruby **Neil & Simon Racing Partners**
7 **TIME IS TIME (IRE),** 12, ch g Golan (IRE)—Minnie Ray (IRE) **Mr A. Woodley-Milburn**

Other Owners: Mr N. J. Edwards, Mr S. James.

Assistant Trainer: Mr B. Robinson, Mr R. J. Bailey.

**467** **MR ADAM ROBSON, Hawick**
Postal: **1 Spittal On Rule, Hawick, Roxburghshire, TD9 8TA**
EMAIL spittalonrule@gmail.com

1 **ARKYN (FR),** 6, ch g Champs Elysees—Fever Fever (USA) **A. Robson**
2 **CLATTERING FORD (IRE),** 6, b g Shirocco (GER)—Hollygrove Gabbana (IRE) **Mr P. D. Robson**
3 **CROW TREE (IRE),** 5, b m Califet (FR)—Lillando (IRE) **Mr P. D. Robson**
4 **ECHO EXPRESS (IRE),** 9, b g Echo of Light—If Dubai (USA) **A. Robson**
5 **JUST DON'T KNOW (IRE),** 8, b g Kalanisi (IRE)—Desperado Queen (IRE) **Mr P. D. Robson**
6 **TEDDY TEE (IRE),** 12, b g Mountain High (IRE)—Knocksouna Lady (IRE) **Mr P. D. Robson**
7 **WHATSGOINGON (FR),** 5, b g Ballingarry (IRE)—Califea (FR) **Mr P. D. Robson**

**468**
## MISS PAULINE ROBSON, Capheaton
Postal: Kidlaw Farm, Capheaton, Newcastle Upon Tyne, NE19 2AW
Contacts: **PHONE 01830 530241 MOBILE 07814 708725, 07721 887489**
**EMAIL pauline@prracing.co.uk**

1 **BALLYDONAGH BOY (IRE)**, 7, b g Le Fou (IRE)—Hindi (FR) **It's a Bargain Syndicate**
2 **CASTLETOWN (FR)**, 9, gr g Poliglote—Message Personnel (FR) **Mr & Mrs Raymond Anderson Green**
3 **COOKING FAT**, 10, ch g Tobougg (IRE)—Ostfanni (IRE) **Mr J. R. Callow**
4 **GEORDIES DREAM**, 6, gr g Geordieland (FR)—Dream Leader (IRE) **J. Wade**
5 **MARTILA (FR)**, 9, b m Martaline—Paola Pierji (FR) **Mr & Mrs Raymond Anderson Green**
6 **NORTHERN FALCON**, 6, b g Kayf Tara—Special Trinket (IRE) **Mr I. Kurdi**
7 **SPECIAL PREP (IRE)**, 9, b g Brian Boru—Schindler's Dame (IRE) **Mr E. A. Elliott**
8 **UPSILON BLEU (FR)**, 13, b g Panoramic—Glycine Bleue (FR) **Mr & Mrs Raymond Anderson Green**

**Other Owners:** D&D Armstrong Limited, Mr L. J. Westwood.

**Assistant Trainer:** David Parker.

**NH Jockey:** Brian Hughes, Craig Nichol.

**469**
## MR RUSSELL ROSS, Consett
Postal: Rock Cottage Farm, 79 Iveston Lane, Consett, County Durham, DH8 7TB

1 **EMORY**, 11, ch g Midnight Legend—Punjabi Rose **R. A. Ross**
2 **FRIARY GOLD (IRE)**, 9, b g Mountain High (IRE)—Platinium Ambition (IRE) **R. A. Ross**
3 **YORGUNNABEAMUNKY**, 5, b m Yorgunnabelucky (USA)—Delray Beach (FR) **R. A. Ross**

**470**
## MR BRIAN ROTHWELL, Malton
Postal: Old Post Office, Oswaldkirk, York, North Yorkshire, YO62 5XT
Contacts: **PHONE 01439 788859 MOBILE 07969 968241**
**EMAIL brian.rothwell1@googlemail.com**

1 **AETHON**, 4, b f Multiplex—Bonnie Burnett (IRE) **Mr A. J. Sparks**
2 **ALLERTHORPE**, 4, b g Casamento (IRE)—Shirocco Passion **S. P. Hudson**
3 **BRIGHT DAWN (IRE)**, 4, b g Helmet (AUS)—Skywards Miles (IRE) **B. S. Rothwell**
4 **GLORYELLA**, 5, b m Yorgunnabelucky (USA)—Ceiriog Valley **The Jelly Boys**
5 5, B m Heeraat (IRE)—Lady Azamour (IRE) **B. S. Rothwell**
6 **OUTOFTHEGLOOM**, 4, b f Heeraat (IRE)—Srimenanti **Mr S. P. Hudson & Mr Brian Rothwell**
7 **YASMIN FROM YORK**, 5, b m Sixties Icon—Bonnie Burnett (IRE) **Mrs G. Sparks**
8 4, B c Pour Moi (IRE)—Yawail **Mr S. P. Hudson & Mr Brian Rothwell**

### THREE-YEAR-OLDS

9 B c Ruler of The World (IRE)—Artistic Dawn (IRE) **B. S. Rothwell**
10 B g Mustajeeb—Byton **S. P. Hudson**
11 B f Power—Skywards Miles (IRE) **Mr S. P. Hudson & Mr Brian Rothwell**
12 Gr g Gregorian (IRE)—Symphony Star (IRE) **The Jelly Boys & Brian Rothwell**
13 Ch g Mustajeeb—Yawail **B. S. Rothwell**

### TWO-YEAR-OLDS

14 Gr c 29/05 Gregorian (IRE)—Bertha Burnett (IRE) (Verglas (IRE)) **Mrs G. Sparks**
15 B g 25/04 Proconsul—Bonnie Burnett (IRE) (Hawk Wing (USA)) **Mrs G. Sparks**
16 B f 08/04 Time Test—Yawail (Medicean) **B. S. Rothwell**

**Other Owners:** Mr N. J. Brannan, S. P. Hudson, Mr A. R. Morgan, B. S. Rothwell.

## MR RICHARD ROWE, Pulborough

Postal: **Ashleigh House Stables, Sullington Lane, Storrington, Pulborough, West Sussex, RH20 4AE**
Contacts: PHONE **01903 742871** MOBILE **07831 345636**
EMAIL **richard@richardroweracing.com** WEBSITE **www.richardroweracing.co.uk/horses** FACEBOOK **RichardRoweRacehorseTrainer** TWITTER **@rowe_racing**

1　**AZTEC DREAMS (IRE)**, 8, b g Oasis Dream—Agathe Rare (IRE)　**Captain Adrian Pratt & Lord Clinton**
2　**BANNIXTOWN BOY (IRE)**, 7, b g Oscar (IRE)—Lucky Loch (IRE)　**Any Port In a Storm**
3　**BATTLE ANTHEM (IRE)**, 10, b g Royal Anthem (USA)—Chika Boom (IRE)　**The Battle Anthem Partnership**
4　**CELMA DES BOIS (FR)**, 9, b g Ballingarry (IRE)—Palafixe (FR)　**Encore Partnership V**
5　**COLONEL KEATING (IRE)**, 9, b g Yeats (IRE)—Jabroot (IRE)　**Capt Adrian Pratt & Friends**
6　**DARK FLAME (IRE)**, 12, b g Gold Well—Glorys Flame (IRE)　**The Encore Partnership III**
7　**DELGANY MONARCH (IRE)**, 6, ch g Imperial Monarch (IRE)—Naughty Marietta (IRE)　**Encore Partnership V11**
8　**EL PACO**, 5, b g Paco Boy (IRE)—Miss Marauder　**R. Rowe**
9　**FLASHDANZA**, 6, ch g Sepoy (AUS)—Photo Flash (IRE)　**B. H. Page**
10　**IDIDITFORYOOOO (IRE)**, 7, b g Fast Company (IRE)—Ann's Annie (IRE)　**Richard Rowe Racing Partnership**
11　**MISTER MURCHAN (IRE)**, 8, b g Westerner—So Supreme (IRE)　**The Battle Anthem Partnership**
12　**REMEMBER ME WELL (IRE)**, 8, b m Doyen (IRE)—Creidim (IRE)　**Pink Birds**
13　**SOARLIKEANEAGLE (IRE)**, 9, b g Scorpion (IRE)—Wayward Cove　**Richard Rowe Racing Partnership**
14　**TATTLETALE (FR)**, 7, b g Linda's Lad—Barbarasse (FR)　**Richard Rowe Racing Partnership**
15　**TRUCKERS TIME (IRE)**, 9, b g Curtain Time (IRE)—Truckers Lady (IRE)　**Mr J. L. J. Butcher**
16　**TZAR DE L'ELFE (FR)**, 11, b g Satri (IRE)—Rue Tournefort (FR)　**Lord Clinton & Captain Adrian Pratt**
17　**UP THE STRAIGHT (IRE)**, 7, b g Arcadio (GER)—Kings Artist (IRE)　**The Forever Partnership**
18　**VITAL SIGN (IRE)**, 8, b g Let The Lion Roar—Grace N' Favour (IRE)　**Winterfields Farm Ltd**

**Other Owners:** Mr R. W. Baker, Mr D. M. Bradshaw, Mrs H. C. G. Butcher, Mrs J. Case, Lord Clinton, Mr C. S. Coombe-Tennant, Mrs S. K. Coombe-Tennant, Dr C. Cowell, Mrs J. E. Debenham, K. L. Hunter, Capt A. Pratt, Mrs J. D. M. Sadler, Scott Parnell Limited, T. W. Wellard, Mr P. D. West, Mr P. R. Wilby, Winterfields Farm Ltd.

---

## MISS MANDY ROWLAND, Lower Blidworth

Postal: **Kirkfields, Calverton Road, Lower Blidworth, Nottingham, Nottinghamshire, NG21 0NW**
Contacts: PHONE **01623 794831** MOBILE **07768 224666**
EMAIL **kirkfieldsriding@hotmail.co.uk**

1　**BOOBOROWIE (IRE)**, 8, b br g Big Bad Bob (IRE)—Rejuvenation (IRE)　**Miss M. E. Rowland**
2　**CHINA EXCELS**, 14, b g Exceed And Excel (AUS)—China Beauty　**Miss M. E. Rowland**
3　**GO ANNIE GO**, 5, b m Es Que Love (IRE)—Make It Snappy　**Miss M. E. Rowland**
4　**JAZZ LEGEND (USA)**, 8, b g Scat Daddy (USA)—Champion Ride (USA)　**Miss M. E. Rowland**
5　**LET'S BE HAPPY (IRE)**, 7, gr m Mastercraftsman (IRE)—Corrozal (GER)　**Miss M. E. Rowland**
6　**MABAADY**, 7, b g Bated Breath—Fifty (IRE)　**Miss M. E. Rowland**
7　**MISS NORA ABU (IRE)**, 7, b m Gold Well—Miss Toulon (IRE)　**Miss M. E. Rowland**

**Assistant Trainer:** Sarah Thomas.

**Flat Jockey:** Rob Hornby, Adam Kirby, Jimmy Quinn. **Apprentice Jockey:** William Cox.

**473** **MS LUCINDA RUSSELL, Kinross**
Postal: **Arlary House Stables, Milnathort, Kinross, Tayside, KY13 9SJ**
Contacts: PHONE **01577 865512** MOBILE **07970 645261** FAX **01577 861171**
EMAIL **lucindarussellracing@outlook.com** WEBSITE **www.lucindarussell.com**

1 A LADIES MILAN (IRE), 7, b g Milan—Rag's Lady (IRE) **Dig In Racing**
2 AHOY SENOR (IRE), 6, b g Dylan Thomas (IRE)—Dara Supreme (IRE) **Mrs C Wymer & Mr Pjs Russell**
3 AIN'T MY FAULT (IRE), 8, b g Beneficial—Coolnasneachta (IRE) **Foresight Racing**
4 4, Ch f Notnowcato—Another Burden **Mrs H. Kelly**
5 AURORA THUNDER, 7, b m Malinas (GER)—Ninna Nanna (FR) **Allson Sparkle Ltd**
6 BALLYARE, 4, b g Hot Streak (IRE)—Saddlers Bend (IRE) **The Bristol Boys**
7 BAYFRIARS BOBBY (IRE), 5, b g Dylan Thomas (IRE)—Zarata (IRE) **Moyles, & Pjs Russell**
8 BEHINDTHELINES (IRE), 9, b g Milan—Sunset Leader (IRE) **London Scots for Doddie**
9 4, B f Milan—Belle Rebelle (IRE) **Mr S. Townshend**
10 BIALCO (FR), 10, gr g Dom Alco (FR)—Lacanale (FR) **The Vikings**
11 BIG RIVER (IRE), 11, b g Milan—Call Kate (IRE) **Two Black Labs**
12 BLOORIEDOTCOM (IRE), 6, b g Holy Roman Emperor (IRE)—Peaceful Kingdom (USA) **Mutual Friends**
13 BOLLINGERANDKRUG, 6, b g Getaway (GER)—Out Performer (IRE) **Ms D. Thomson**
14 BOOK OF INVASIONS (IRE), 6, ch g Declaration of War (USA)—Cedar Sea (IRE) **Mr G. R. McGladery**
15 BOY'S ON TOUR (IRE), 9, b g Beneficial—Galant Tour (IRE) **Foresight Racing**
16 BRODICK, 4, b f Teofilo (IRE)—Bedecked (IRE) **London Scots for Doddie**
17 BUDDHA SCHEME (IRE), 7, b g Milan—Benefit Scheme (IRE) **Mr G. R. McGladery**
18 CABOY (FR), 9, b g Nidor (FR)—Cadouya Girl (FR) **Goodtimes**
19 CALLE MALVA (IRE), 6, b m Getaway (GER)—Waydale Hill **Mrs C Wymer & Mr Pjs Russell**
20 CELTIC FLAMES (IRE), 11, gr g Celtic Swing—Don't Forget Shoka (IRE) **Mr W. T. Scott**
21 CHANCEITON (IRE), 10, b g Vinnie Roe (IRE)—Lissnabrucka (IRE) **Mr P. J. S. Russell**
22 CHARMIX (FR), 11, br g Laveron—Open Up (FR) **King For A Day & Mr Pjs Russell**
23 COCKLE BAY (IRE), 9, b g Milan—Theredandthegreen (IRE) **The Kestrel Partnership**
24 CORACH RAMBLER (IRE), 7, b g Jeremy (USA)—Heart N Hope (IRE) **The Ramblers**
25 DESTINY IS ALL (IRE), 7, b g Prince Flori (GER)—Hearts Delight (IRE) **Mr J. R. Adam**
26 DIAMOND STATE (FR), 5, b g Vision d'Etat (FR)—
                                   Wonderful Diamond (GER) **Mr Gerry McGladery & Mr PJS Russell**
27 DOMANDLOUIS (IRE), 4, b g Getaway (GER)—Drive On Kate (IRE) **Ms D. Thomson**
28 DR HOOVES (IRE), 8, b g Yeats (IRE)—Sejour (IRE) **Mr G. R. McGladery**
29 EEYORE (FR), 7, b m Bernebeau (FR)—Nosika d'Airy (FR) **Mr & Mrs Raymond Anderson Green**
30 EFFET SPECIAL (FR), 7, b g Network (GER)—Tisane (FR) **Brahms & Liszt**
31 ELMONO (FR), 10, ch g Epalo (GER)—Monareva (FR) **Gerry And The Pacemakers**
32 EMIRAT DE CATANA (FR), 7, b g Linda's Lad—Kolada (FR) **Kelso Lowflyers & Mr PJS Russell**
33 EMISSAIRE (FR), 7, b g Kap Rock (FR)—Jacee (FR) **A Nicol & L S Russell**
34 FAIRE PART SIVOLA (FR), 6, b g Noroit (GER)—Lettre d'Estruval (FR) **K Alexander/ R Watts**
35 FLUTTER DOWN (FR), 6, b g Rob Roy (USA)—Florifere (FR) **Peter & Suzy Brown & Tony Evans**
36 FORTUNE STAR (DEN), 5, ch g Center Divider (USA)—Elaine (DEN) **Mr P. J. S. Russell**
37 FUDGEMAN (IRE), 5, b g Sholokhov (IRE)—Odeeka (IRE) **Mr P. J. S. Russell**
38 FYFIN PATSY (IRE), 7, b m September Storm (GER)—Poshly Presented (IRE) **Fyfin Four**
39 GEMOLOGIST (IRE), 6, b m Sir Percy—Tiffany Diamond (IRE) **Musselburgh Lunch Club**
40 GRAND MORNING, 9, b g Midnight Legend—Valentines Lady (IRE) **Mr J. P. McManus**
41 HAUL US IN (IRE), 9, br m Kalanisi (IRE)—Shuilan (IRE) **Mr & Mrs J. Morrison-Bell**
42 HAUTE ESTIME (FR), 4, b f Walk In The Park (IRE)—Terre Haute (FR) **Mr P. J. S. Russell**
43 HECTOR MASTER (FR), 4, b g Masterstroke (USA)—Queen Maresca (FR) **Mrs S Russell & A M Russell**
44 ITS A MIDNIGHT, 4, ch f Midnight Legend—Just For Pleasure (IRE) **The Midnight Chasers**
45 IZZY'S CHAMPION (IRE), 7, b g Gold Well—Native Crystal (IRE) **Mr & Mrs T. P. Winnell**
46 LE FRANK (IRE), 9, b g King's Theatre (IRE)—Dream Lass (IRE) **Smith, Fitzpatrick & Shiner**
47 LIFE MADE SIMPLE, 4, b g Sulamani (IRE)—Swift Getaway (IRE) **The Crick Girls**
48 LUCKY FLIGHT (FR), 7, b g Linda's Lad—Lili Flight (FR) **The Vikings**
49 MAJESTIC STORM, 5, b g Shantou (USA)—Oh So Beautiful (IRE) **G. S. Brown**
50 MANNOCHMORE, 6, b g Dylan Thomas (IRE)—Loch Dhu (IRE) **Distillery Racing Club**
51 METHODTOTHEMADNESS (IRE), 7, b m Gold Well—Odeeka (IRE) **Mrs S Russell & A M Russell**
52 MIGHTY THUNDER, 8, b g Malinas (GER)—Cool Island (IRE) **Allson Sparkle Ltd**
53 MINT GOLD (IRE), 7, b g Gold Well—Lady Flyer (IRE) **Mrs S Russell & A M Russell**
54 MISFITS (IRE), 10, b g Beneficial—Park Rose (IRE) **County Set Four & Keith Hunter**
55 NETYWELL (FR), 4, b g Willywell—Netova (FR) **Mr P. J. S. Russell**

## MS LUCINDA RUSSELL - continued

56 **ONE FOR ARTHUR (IRE)**, 12, b g Milan—Nonnetia (FR)  **Two Golf Widows**
57 **OPERATION OVERLORD (IRE)**, 6, b g Jeremy (USA)—Alfreeze  **Mr J. P. McManus**
58 **ORDER OF THISTLE (IRE)**, 6, b g High Chaparral (IRE)—Law of The Jungle (IRE)  **Mr P. J. S. Russell**
59 **ORIONINVERNESS (IRE)**, 10, b g Brian Boru—Woodville Leader (IRE)  **Tay Valley Chasers Racing Club**
60 **OTELLO MOOR (IRE)**, 6, b g Milan—Founding Daughter (IRE)  **Mrs R. A. Stobart**
61 **PETITE RHAPSODY (IRE)**, 6, b g Shirocco (GER)—Peggy Cullen (IRE)  **Mr P. J. S. Russell**
62 **POSH ROIS (IRE)**, 5, ch m Leading Light (IRE)—Top Her Up (IRE)  **Mrs H. Kelly**
63 **PRINCE DUNDEE (IRE)**, 8, b g Stowaway—Miss Dundee (IRE)  **Jw McNeill & County Set Three**
64 **RAPID RAIDER (IRE)**, 7, ch g Golden Lariat (USA)—Golden Court (IRE)  **Mrs S Russell & A M Russell**
65 **READYSTEADYBEAU (FR)**, 5, ch g Kapgarde (FR)—La Ville Aux Dames (FR)  **Joanne & Peter Russell**
66 **RED MISSILE (IRE)**, 4, b g Battle of Marengo (IRE)—Plym  **Mr Michael & Lady Jane Kaplan**
67 **REDWING LASS (FR)**, 4, bl f Maxios—La Zubia  **Mrs S Russell & A M Russell**
68 **RISING MARIENBARD (IRE)**, 9, b g Marienbard (IRE)—Dromkeen Wood  **Mr P. J. S. Russell**
69 **RIVABODIVA (IRE)**, 11, ch m Flemensfirth (USA)—Sheebadiva (IRE)  **Mrs S Russell & A M Russell**
70 **ROYAL RESERVE**, 8, b g Duke of Marmalade (IRE)—Lady Hawkfield (IRE)  **London Scots for Doddie**
71 **RYALEX (IRE)**, 10, b g Arcadio (GER)—Lady Ramona (IRE)  **County Set Five & Keith Hunter**
72 **SAINT LEO (FR)**, 8, b g Maresca Sorrento (FR)—Sainte Lea (FR)  **Mr & Mrs Raymond Anderson Green**
73 **SHANROE STREET (IRE)**, 11, b g Mustameet (USA)—Zaffran Lady (IRE)  **Kelso Lowflyers & Mr PJS Russell**
74 **SHE'S A STEAL (IRE)**, 4, b f Flemensfirth (USA)—Thanks Awfully (IRE)  **Mr & Mrs J. Morrison-Bell**
75 **SIGNIFIANT (FR)**, 7, bl g Saint des Saints (FR)—Signature (FR)  **Bolton, Moyles, Frame, Smart**
76 **SLAINTE MHOR (IRE)**, 7, b g Milan—Founding Daughter (IRE)  **Mr P. J. S. Russell**
77 **SONGOFTHELARK (IRE)**, 5, ch g Flemensfirth (USA)—Norabelle (FR)  **Mr G. R. McGladery**
78 **SOUTHERN GIRL (IRE)**, 7, ch m Getaway (GER)—She's Got To Go (IRE)  **Mr K. Alexander**
79 **SPARK OF MADNESS (FR)**, 5, b g Walk In The Park (IRE)—Prosopopee (FR)  **Mrs S Russell & A M Russell**
80 **SPEAK OF THE DEVIL (IRE)**, 8, ch g Mahler—A Fine Romance (IRE)  **The County Set & Mr P Russell & Friends**
81 **SUTTON MANOR (IRE)**, 10, b g Gold Well—Nighty Bless (IRE)  **County Set Five & the Red Shoes**
82 **THE COMPELLER (IRE)**, 9, b g Lawman (FR)—Mark Too (IRE)  **W M D Racing**
83 **THE ROAD HOME (IRE)**, 9, b g Oscar (IRE)—In Fact (IRE)  **Mr P. J. S. Russell**
84 4, B f Getaway (GER)—The Toft  **Mr P. J. S. Russell**
85 **THEGLASGOWWARRIOR**, 7, b g Sir Percy—Sweet Cando (IRE)  **Mrs L. B. K. Bone**
86 **THUNDER IN MILAN (IRE)**, 5, b g Milan—Baby Briggs (IRE)  **Allson Sparkle Ltd**
87 **VENGEUR DE GUYE (FR)**, 12, b g Dom Alco (FR)—Mascotte de Guye (FR)  **Brahms & Liszt**
88 **VINO'S CHOICE (IRE)**, 9, b g Kalanisi (IRE)—Ard's Pet (IRE)  **Two Black Labs**
89 **VOIX D'EAU (FR)**, 11, b g Voix du Nord (FR)—Eau de Chesne (FR)  **Mr G. R. McGladery**
90 **WELL ABOVE PAR (IRE)**, 9, b g Gold Well—Glynn Glory (IRE)  **The Eagle Partnership**
91 **WEST END LADY (IRE)**, 6, b m Westerner—Nightofthe Oscars (IRE)  **Mr P. J. S. Russell**
92 **WITHOUT CONVICTION (IRE)**, 6, b m Aizavoski (IRE)—With Conviction (IRE)  **Mrs C Wymer & Mr PJS Russell**
93 **YOUR PLACE (IRE)**, 5, b m Scorpion (IRE)—Sheebadiva (IRE)  **Mr P. J. S. Russell**

### THREE-YEAR-OLDS

94 **AONE ALLY**, b g Mayson—Infatuate  **Mrs H. Kelly**
95 **BIX BEIDERBECKE (FR)**, b gr g Mawatheeq (USA)—Like It Is (FR)  **Mrs S Russell & A M Russell**
96 **OUR MARTY (FR)**, b g Martinborough (JPN)—Dercia (FR)  **Mrs S Russell & A M Russell**
97 **TOROSAY (GER)**, b f Getaway (GER)—The Toft  **Mr P. J. S. Russell**

### TWO-YEAR-OLDS

98 Ch c 01/05 Free Eagle (IRE)—Infatuate (Dalakhani (IRE)) (6667)  **Mrs H. Kelly**

**Other Owners:** Mr J. A. Aitkenhead, Mr K. Alexander, Mr W. M. Allan, Mrs J. Bilsland, Mr G. Bolton, Bolton, Moyles, Frame, Mr G. R. Brown, Mr P.R. Brown, Mrs S. Brown, Mrs Suzy Brown & Mr Peter R Brown, A. Cadger, County Set Four, Mr N. A. Crofts, Mr A. B. Cuthill, Mr C. Dempster, Mr E. W. Dempster, Mr R. Doak, Mrs J. E. Dodd, Mr A. Evans, Mr M. J. Fitzpatrick, Mr A. T. Galloway, Gilbert McClung (Kelso) Ltd, G. Godsman, Mrs I. M. Grant, Mr J. Grant, E. D. Haggart, Mr I. Harle, K. L. Hunter, Mr D. R. James, Mrs P. James, Kelso Members Lowflyers Club, Mrs M Kennedy, Mr A. Kerr, King For A Day Club, Mrs C. J. Lamb, Mr R. M. Landale, Mrs Y. M. V. Learmonth, Ms A. M. MacInnes, Ms F. E. MacInnes, Ms S. C. Mackay, Mr G. R. McGladery, Exors of the Late J. W. McNeill, Mr M. G. Mellor, Mr J. Morrison-Bell, Mrs A. K. Morrison-Bell, Mr Peter J Russell & Friends, Mr A. G. Nicol, Mr A. M. Russell, Mr L. S. Russell, Ms L. V. Russell, Mr P. J. S. Russell, Mrs S. C. Russell, Mr A. Shiner, A. W. Sinclair, Miss M. M. Smith, Mr S. Smith, Ms P. Spours, Mrs R. A. Stobart, The County Set, The County Set (Five), The County Set Three, the Red Shoes, Mr R. D. Thompson, Ms D. Thomson, Mr N. J. Turnbull, Mr G. T. Wallace, Mr R. C. Watts, Mrs M. Winnell, Mr T. P. Winnell, Mrs C. E. Wymer.

## MS LUCINDA RUSSELL - continued

**Assistant Trainer:** Jaimie Duff, Peter Scudamore, Jamie Turnbull.

**NH Jockey:** Derek Fox, Stephen Mulqueen. **Conditional Jockey:** Blair Campbell, Patrick Wadge. **Amateur Jockey:** Miss Ailsa McClung, Mr Cameron Wadge.

---

**474** **MR JOHN RYAN, Newmarket**
Postal: **Cadland Stables, Moulton Road, Newmarket, Suffolk, CB8 8DU**
Contacts: PHONE **01638 664172** MOBILE **07739 801235**
EMAIL john.ryan@jryanracing.com WEBSITE www.jryanracing.com TWITTER @JohnRyanRacing

1 **BATTLE OF MARATHON (USA)**, 9, b g War Front (USA)—Sayedah (IRE)  **Emma Ryan & Partner**
2 **CATCH MY BREATH**, 5, gr g Bated Breath—Likeable  **The Out of Puff Partnership**
3 **GODDESS OF FIRE**, 4, b f Toronado (IRE)—Burnt Fingers (IRE)  **Mr M. M. Foulger**
4 **HIROSHIMA**, 5, b g Nathaniel (IRE)—Lisiere (IRE)  **Russell, Thompson, DAS Racing, Ryan**
5 **HOMEGROWNALLIGATOR**, 4, b g Poet's Voice—Samar Qand  **Mr J. B. Ryan**
6 **JACK RYAN (IRE)**, 4, b g Harbour Watch (IRE)—Anything (IRE)  **Mr Gerry McGladery & Partner**
7 **MARLY (FR)**, 4, b f Siyouni (FR)—Means of Assent (USA)  **Mr Graham Smith Bernal & Mr Jon Thompson**
8 **MERHOOB (IRE)**, 9, b g Cape Cross (IRE)—Lady Slippers (IRE)  **Mr G. R. McGladery**
9 **PISTOLETTO (USA)**, 4, b g War Front (USA)—Lerici (USA)  **McGladery G, J A Thompson & S Russell**

## THREE-YEAR-OLDS
10 **ARTHUR'S ANGEL (IRE)**, gr g Dark Angel (IRE)—Jellicle Ball (IRE)  **Mr G. F. Smith-Bernal**
11 B f Sea The Stars (IRE)—Dalandra
12 **DARK AGENT (IRE)**, gr g Dark Angel (IRE)—Lethal Lena (IRE)  **Mr Gerry McGladery & Mr Jon A Thompson**
13 B f Awtaad (IRE)—Flirty Thirty (IRE)  **Mr J. B. Ryan**
14 B g Kingman—Mary Boleyn (IRE)  **Mr G. R. McGladery**
15 **OCEAN WILDE**, b g Fountain of Youth (IRE)—New Falcon (IRE)  **The Little John Partnership**
16 **POCKETEER (IRE)**, b f Adaay (IRE)—Dry Your Eyes (IRE)  **Mr G. F. Smith-Bernal**

## TWO-YEAR-OLDS
17 B c 20/03 Ribchester (IRE)—Despatch (Nayef (USA))
18 **FLURRY HEART**, ch f 01/02 Sea The Moon (GER)—
Twilight Sparkle (IRE) (Rock of Gibraltar (IRE))  **Mr G. R. McGladery**
19 Ch f 04/04 Havana Gold (IRE)—Mercy Me (Mawatheeq (USA))
20 B c 16/05 Night of Thunder (IRE)—Pencarrow (Green Desert (USA)) (6000)
21 Gr c 10/04 Ardad (IRE)—Reaching Ahead (USA) (Mizzen Mast (USA)) (12000)
22 **REEL OF FORTUNE (IRE)**, b f 17/02 Highland Reel (IRE)—
Romantic Stroll (IRE) (Oratorio (IRE)) (5000)  **Das Racing & Mr J Ryan**

**Other Owners:** BB Thoroughbreds, DAS Racing Limited, Mr C. W. Little, Mr G. R. McGladery, Mr B. Meadwell, Mr S. D. Russell, Mrs E. Ryan, Mr J. B. Ryan, Mr G. S. Samra, Mr G. F. Smith-Bernal, Mr J. A. Thompson.

**Apprentice Jockey:** Darragh Keenan. **Amateur Jockey:** Miss Tia Phillips.

**475** **MR KEVIN RYAN, Hambleton**
Postal: Hambleton Lodge, Hambleton, Thirsk, North Yorkshire, YO7 2HA
Contacts: PHONE 01845 597010, 01845 597622 MOBILE 01845 597622 FAX 01845 597622
EMAIL office@kevinryanracing.com WEBSITE www.kevinryanracing.com

1 ARROW OF GOLD (IRE), 4, ch g Galileo (IRE)—Fleche d'Or  Sheikh Mohammed Obaid Al Maktoum
2 BIELSA (IRE), 6, b g Invincible Spirit (IRE)—Bourbon Ball (USA)  King Power Racing Co Ltd
3 BLACK CASPIAN (IRE), 4, b g Dark Angel (IRE)—Catch The Sea (IRE)  Sheikh Mohammed Obaid Al Maktoum
4 BRANDO, 9, ch g Pivotal—Argent du Bois (USA)  Mrs A. Bailey
5 DUBAI QUALITY (IRE), 4, ch f Dubawi (IRE)—Local Time  Mrs R G Hillen & Partner
6 EMARAATY ANA, 5, b g Shamardal (USA)—Spirit of Dubai (IRE)  Sheikh Mohammed Obaid Al Maktoum
7 GLASS SLIPPERS, 5, b m Dream Ahead (USA)—Night Gypsy  Bearstone Stud Limited
8 HEY JONESY (IRE), 6, b g Excelebration (IRE)—Fikrah  Pallister Racing
9 HUBOOR (IRE), 4, b f More Than Ready (USA)—Glorification  Mrs R G Hillen & Partner
10 JUAN ELCANO, 4, ch g Frankel—Whatami  Sheikh Mohammed Obaid Al Maktoum
11 JUSTANOTHERBOTTLE (IRE), 7, ch g Intense Focus (USA)—Duchess K (IRE)  Mr Steve Ryan & Mr M J Tedham
12 LAST EMPIRE, 5, b m Pivotal—Final Dynasty  Clipper Logistics
13 MAGICAL MOMENT (IRE), 5, b f Dubawi (IRE)—Maka (FR)  Magical Moment Partners
14 MAGICAL SPIRIT (IRE), 5, ch g Zebedee—La Dame de Fer (IRE)  Hambleton Racing Ltd XXXII
15 MAJOR JUMBO, 7, gr g Zebedee—Gone Sailing  Mr T A Rahman
16 MIDNITE BRIDE, 4, br f Kodiac—Silkenveil (IRE)  Mr T A Rahman
17 NA BLIANTA BEO (IRE), 4, b f Invincible Spirit (IRE)—Finsceal Beo (IRE)  M A Ryan & Micheal D Ryan
18 QUEEN JO JO, 5, gr m Gregorian (IRE)—River Song (USA)  Mr Roger Peel & Clipper Logistics
19 QUEEN'S ORDER, 4, b f Delegator—Kirunavaara (IRE)  Clipper Logistics
20 QUEEN'S SARGENT (FR), 6, gr g Kendargent (FR)—Queen's Conquer  Mr Dave Stone
21 RATHBONE, 4, b g Foxwedge (AUS)—Frequent  Mrs A. Bailey
22 REPARTEE (IRE), 4, br c Invincible Spirit (IRE)—Pleasantry  Sheikh Mohammed Obaid Al Maktoum
23 SECRET VENTURE, 5, b g Kyllachy—Resort  Hambleton Racing Ltd XLVI & Partner
24 SOARING STAR (IRE), 4, b g Starspangledbanner (AUS)—Peig (IRE)  Hambleton Racing Ltd XXV
25 SPIRITOFTHENORTH (FR), 4, br g Bated Breath—Danlepordamsterdam (IRE)  Middleham Park Racing XLVI
26 STARS IN THE NIGHT (IRE), 4, b f Starspangledbanner (AUS)—On The Dark Side (IRE)  Hambleton Racing Ltd XVI
27 THE GREAT HEIR (FR), 5, b g Pedro The Great (USA)—Lady McKell (IRE)  Mr Dave Stone
28 THRONE HALL, 4, b g Kingman—Appearance  Sheikh Mohammed Obaid Al Maktoum
29 TREBLE TREBLE (IRE), 4, b g Brazen Beau (AUS)—Sugar Blossom (IRE)  Mr B T McDonald
30 VENTURA RASCAL, 4, b g Fountain of Youth—Choisette  Middleham Park Racing CVII
31 WILD HOPE, 5, b g Kingman—Wild Mimosa (IRE)  Hambleton Racing Ltd XLIV
32 WILL SOMMERS, 4, b g Teofilo (IRE)—Dubai Queen (USA)  Sheikh Mohammed Obaid Al Maktoum

**THREE-YEAR-OLDS**

33 AIR TIME, b c Oasis Dream—Al Fareej (IRE)  Hambleton Racing Ltd XVIII & Partner
34 AUNT AGATHA, b f Oasis Dream—La Napoule  Guy Reed Racing
35 BABY ALYA (IRE), ch f Rio de La Plata (USA)—Queen's Logic (IRE)  Mr Jaber Abdullah
36 BANNOW, b g Invincible Spirit (IRE)—Angel Vision (IRE)  Sheikh Mohammed Obaid Al Maktoum
37 BEECHWOOD DONNA, b f Hot Streak (IRE)—Sabrewing (IRE)  Ontoawinner & Partner 1
38 BELLISSIME (IRE), b f No Nay Never (USA)—Dancing On Air (IRE)  Mrs R G Hillen & Partner
39 BEN MACDUI (IRE), b g Kodiac—Candiland (IRE)  K&J Bloodstock Ltd
40 BERGERAC (IRE), b g Kodi Bear (IRE)—Fancy Vivid (IRE)  Mrs A. Bailey
41 BROOMY LAW, b g Gleneagles (IRE)—Hooray  Sheikh Mohammed Obaid Al Maktoum
42 CAIRN ISLAND (IRE), b g Kodiac—Landmark (USA)  Sheikh Mohammed Obaid Al Maktoum
43 CAPTAIN COOPER (IRE), b g Muhaarar—Miss Delila (USA)  Highbank Stud 1
44 COPPER QUEEN (IRE), ch f Tamayuz—Coppull Moor  The Racing Emporium
45 COTTAM LANE, b g Twilight Son—Alsium (IRE)  Steve Ryan & the Racing Emporium
46 COUGAR ANNIE, b f Toronado (IRE)—La Pomme d'Amour  Guy Reed Racing
47 DAJRAAN, b c Frankel—Mossfun (AUS)  Emirates Park PTY Ltd
48 DARVEL (IRE), b g Dark Angel (IRE)—Anthem Alexander (IRE)  Sheikh Mohammed Obaid Al Maktoum
49 DEPP (IRE), b c Acclamation—Sweet Coconut  Mrs A. Bailey
50 DEXTER BELLE (IRE), b f Ajaya—Thousandfold (USA)  Clipper Logistics
51 DIGITAL (IRE), b g Kodi Bear (IRE)—Notte Illuminata (IRE)  Highclere T'bred Racing - Kodi Bear 1
52 EGO TRIP (IRE), b f No Nay Never (USA)—Pure Vanity  Ego Partners
53 ELLAND ROAD BOY (IRE), b c Dandy Man (IRE)—Red Ivy (IRE)  Mr Roger Peel & Clipper Logistics

## MR KEVIN RYAN - continued

54 **FIGHTER PILOT (IRE)**, b c Kodiac—Jira  **Clipper Logistics**
55 B g Fastnet Rock (AUS)—Follow A Star (IRE)  **Highbank Stud**
56 **FOLLOW YOUR HEART (IRE)**, b c Estidhkaar (IRE)—Al Gharrafa  **Mr T A Rahman**
57 **GRIGORA (IRE)**, b g Zoffany (IRE)—Sindirana (IRE)  **Hambleton Racing Ltd XXVII**
58 **HALA HALA HALA (IRE)**, b f Exceed And Excel (AUS)—Hala Hala (IRE)  **Sultan Ali**
59 **HANIYA**, b f Toronado (IRE)—Have Fun (AUS)  **Emirates Park PTY Ltd**
60 **HELLO ZABEEL (IRE)**, b c Frankel—Lady of The Desert (USA)  **Mr Jaber Abdullah**
61 **LIFE ON THE ROCKS (IRE)**, b c Fascinating Rock (IRE)—Spirited Girl (IRE)  **Clara Stud & Partner**
62 **MANASSAS**, b c Dubawi (IRE)—Without You Babe (USA)  **Sheikh Mohammed Obaid Al Maktoum**
63 **MAXIOS SHOW (IRE)**, b c Maxios—Monaco Show (FR)  **Mr Jaber Abdullah**
64 **POET'S KING**, b g Paco Boy (IRE)—Danega  **Mr Jaber Abdullah**
65 **PRINCE OF PEARLS**, b g Kingman—Martha Watson (IRE)  **Sheikh Mohammed Obaid Al Maktoum**
66 **ROMAN ENCOUNTER**, b f Holy Roman Emperor (IRE)—Meeting In Paris (IRE)  **Hambleton Racing Ltd XVIII**
67 **SEACLUSION**, b f Fountain of Youth (IRE)—On The Brink  **Bearstone Stud Limited**
68 **SEVEN BROTHERS (IRE)**, b g Slade Power (IRE)—Ihtifal  **Mr Steve Ryan**
69 **SHAAHER**, b c Galileo (IRE)—Shahad (AUS)  **Emirates Park PTY Ltd**
70 **SIGNORA PRINCESS**, b f Harbour Watch (IRE)—Signora Queen (FR)  **Mr Jaber Abdullah**
71 **SOUND REASON**, ch g Hot Streak (IRE)—Brown Eyed Honey  **Hambleton Racing Ltd XXIX**
72 **SPEED OF LIFE (IRE)**, b f Helmet (AUS)—Voltairine  **Clara Stud**
73 **STAR SHAKEERA**, ch f Mayson—Najim Al Thraya (FR)  **Mr Ahmed Jaber**
74 **TAHONTA (IRE)**, b g Red Jazz (USA)—Jedward (IRE)  **My Vein Clinic Syndicate 1**
75 **TEN IN A ROW (IRE)**, b c Shalaa (IRE)—African Skies  **Mr B T McDonald & Partners**
76 **TINOCHIO (IRE)**, ch g Buratino (IRE)—Endless Peace (IRE)  **Hambleton Racing Ltd XXXVIII**
77 **TINY DANSER**, gr f Markaz (IRE)—Aunt Nicola  **Bearstone Stud Limited**
78 **TROMSO (FR)**, ch g Twilight Son—Soar  **Sheikh Mohammed Obaid Al Maktoum**
79 **TWO COP BOP**, b g Dutch Art—Rocking The Boat (IRE)  **Allan Kerr & Partner**
80 **UNCLE JUMBO**, gr g Territories (IRE)—Gone Sailing  **Mr T A Rahman**
81 **VINCENT VEGA (IRE)**, b g Lope de Vega (IRE)—Quixada (GER)  **Mrs Jane Dwyer**
82 **VISION OF VICTORY (IRE)**, br f Camelot—Runway Dancer  **Sultan Ali**

## TWO-YEAR-OLDS

83 B c 28/02 Night of Thunder (IRE)—Al Nassa (USA) (Bernardini (USA)) (80000)  **Mrs A. Bailey**
84 **ALEEZDANCER (IRE)**, b c 03/04 Fast Company (IRE)—
                                Clifton Dancer (Fraam) (11905)  **Jack Berry & John Matthews**
85 B f 14/02 Invincible Spirit (IRE)—Ashadihan (Kyllachy)  **Mr T A Rahman**
86 Ch c 18/03 Cotai Glory—Atlas Silk (Dansili) (20952)
87 **BAIKAL**, b c 31/01 No Nay Never (USA)—
                    Foreign Assignment (IRE) (Mastercraftsman (IRE)) (325000)  **Sheikh Mohammed Obaid Al Maktoum**
88 Ch c 10/02 Galileo Gold—Big Violett (IRE) (Haatef (USA)) (25714)  **Mr Roger Peel**
89 **BOONIE (IRE)**, b c 06/02 Brazen Beau (AUS)—
                    Dice Game (Shamardal (USA))  **Seymour Bloodstock & Mark Balnaves**
90 B f 08/04 Ardad (IRE)—Brown Eyed Honey (Elusive City (USA))  **Hambleton Racing Ltd XLVII**
91 Ch f 23/02 Pride of Dubai (AUS)—Camargue (Invincible Spirit (IRE))  **Emirates Park PTY Ltd**
92 B br f 22/02 Profitable (IRE)—Cline (Pivotal) (8571)  **Mr B. A. Cloney**
93 B g 01/03 Kodi Bear (IRE)—Coachhouse Lady (USA) (Rahy (USA)) (25714)  **Hambleton Racing Ltd XVI**
94 B c 05/03 Starspangledbanner (AUS)—Dark Seductress (IRE) (Dark Angel (IRE)) (42000)
95 B f 15/03 Mehmas (IRE)—Duchess of Foxland (IRE) (Medecis) (25714)
96 **EMIRATES EMPRESS**, b f 18/03 Dark Angel (IRE)—Emirates Queen  **Sheikh Mohammed Obaid Al Maktoum**
97 B f 08/02 Adaay (IRE)—Flighty Clarets (IRE) (Bahamian Bounty) (19048)  **Mr Jaber Abdullah**
98 **FRANZ**, b c 25/04 Almanzor (FR)—Gemstone (IRE) (Galileo (IRE)) (100000)  **Haras d'Etreham & Cambridge Stud**
99 **OFFREEZE**, b c 09/04 Goken (FR)—Damdam Freeze (FR) (Indian Rocket) (22000)  **Mr Guy Pariente**
100 Gr c 04/04 Brazen Beau (AUS)—Gone Sailing (Mizzen Mast (USA)) (20952)  **Mr T A Rahman**
101 **GREEN TEAM (FR)**, b c 05/02 Wootton Bassett—On The Line (FR) (Green Tune (USA)) (52381)  **Ahmad Al Shaikh**
102 Ch f 31/03 Mehmas (IRE)—Height of Vanity (IRE) (Erhaab (USA)) (40000)  **Mr Jaber Abdullah**
103 B f 06/02 Dubawi (IRE)—How (IRE) (Galileo (IRE))  **Mr Craig Bernick**
104 B c 15/04 Mehmas (IRE)—Jolly Juicester (IRE) (Jeremy (USA)) (20000)
105 B f 08/03 Havana Gold (IRE)—Keladora (USA) (Crafty Prospector (USA)) (22000)
106 **KING OF YORK (IRE)**, b c 08/02 Kingman—
                    Archangel Gabriel (USA) (Arch (USA)) (350000)  **Sheikh Mohammed Obaid Al Maktoum**

## MR KEVIN RYAN - continued

**107** B f 11/03 Oasis Dream—La Napoule **Guy Reed Racing**
**108** B f 03/04 Farhh—Luzia (Cape Cross (IRE)) **Sheikh Mohammed Obaid Al Maktoum**
**109** B c 09/03 No Nay Never (USA)—Madam Valentine (Primo Valentino (IRE)) (68571) **Mr Steve Ryan**
**110** **MELAYU KINGDOM (IRE)**, ch c 02/03 Mehmas (IRE)—Lauren's Girl (IRE) (Bushranger (IRE))
**111** **MERLIN'S LADY (IRE)**, b f 04/02 Camelot—
                                          Mora Bai (IRE) (Indian Ridge) (320000) **Sheikh Mohammed Obaid Al Maktoum**
**112** B f 17/03 Frankel—Mossfun (AUS) (Mossman (AUS)) **Emirates Park PTY Ltd**
**113** B f 03/04 Kodiac—Necklace (AUS) (Eavesdropper (USA)) **Emirates Park PTY Ltd**
**114** **OLIVER'S ARMY (FR)**, b c 18/03 Pedro The Great (USA)——
                                          Douria (USA) (Giant's Causeway (USA)) (25020) **Mr Dave Stone**
**115** B f 13/02 Kodi Bear (IRE)—Omanome (IRE) (Acclamation) **Riverside Racing Syndicate**
**116** Gr c 26/02 Caravaggio (USA)—Pretty Darling (IRE) (Le Havre (IRE)) (80952) **Mr T A Rahman**
**117** **QUEEN'S HEIR (IRE)**, b f 03/04 Footstepsinthesand—Lady Morel (IRE) (Arcano (IRE)) (23810) **Mr Dave Stone**
**118** **RAVENSWING (IRE)**, b c 01/03 Dark Angel (IRE)—
                                          Future Generation (IRE) (Hurricane Run (IRE)) (180000) **Sheikh Mohammed Obaid Al Maktoum**
**119** Ch c 27/02 Kitten's Joy (USA)—Red Lodge (USA) (Midshipman (USA)) **Emirates Park PTY Ltd**
**120** **ROCKPRINCESS (IRE)**, b f 24/02 Belardo (IRE)—Princess Rock (Fastnet Rock (AUS)) (14000) **Bearstone Stud Limited**
**121** **ROMANOVICH (IRE)**, gr c 27/03 Dark Angel (IRE)—
                                          My Favourite Thing (Oasis Dream) **Sheikh Mohammed Obaid Al Maktoum**
**122** **SMULLEN (IRE)**, ch c 26/03 Camacho—Day By Day (Kyllachy) (38095) **Mrs J Ryan**
**123** **SUN MAGIC (IRE)**, b f 18/03 Invincible Spirit (IRE)—
                                          Amplifier (Dubawi) (IRE)) **Sheikh Mohammed Obaid Al Maktoum**
**124** **THUNDERING**, b c 18/04 Night of Thunder (IRE)—Cosmea (Compton Place) (180000) **Mr Steve Ryan**
**125** **TRIPLE TIME (IRE)**, b c 19/03 Frankel—
                                          Reem Three (Mark of Esteem) (IRE)) **Sheikh Mohammed Obaid Al Maktoum**
**126** **TUDOR QUEEN (IRE)**, b f 07/03 Starspangledbanner (AUS)—
                                          Queen Elsa (IRE) (Frozen Power (IRE)) (28571) **Highclere T'Bred Racing - Cedar Tree 1**
**127** B c 02/03 Shalaa (IRE)—Ultradargent (FR) (Kendargent (FR)) (28571) **Hambleton Racing Ltd XLVII**
**128** B c 25/02 Profitable (IRE)—Viking Fair (Zamindar (USA)) (52381) **Mr T A Rahman**
**129** B c f 05/05 Aclaim (IRE)—Virginia Hall (Medicean) (24762) **Mr Jaber Abdullah**
**130** B c 05/02 Iffraaj—Yellowhammer (Raven's Pass (USA)) (190000) **Mr Steve Ryan**

**Other Owners:** J. Berry, Mr S. Bridge, Clara Stud, Clipper Logistics, Mr N. De Chambure, Mrs A. M. Doyle, Mr H. P. Easterby, P. Easterby, Hambleton Racing Ltd, Hambleton Racing Ltd XLVI, Hambleton Racing Ltd XVIII, Highbank Stud, Highclere Thoroughbred Racing Ltd, Highclere Thoroughbred Racing-Kodi Bear, Mrs R. G. Hillen, B. E. Holland, K&J Bloodstock Ltd, Mr A. Kerr, Mr B. J. Lindsay, Mrs T. Marnane, Mr J. Matthews, Mr B T McDonald, My Vein Clinic Syndicate, Mr N. J. O'Brien, Ontoawinner, Ontoawinner 8, Mrs A. H. Pallister, Mrs J. E. Pallister, Mr J. G. Pallister, Mr Roger Peel, A. J. Picton, Mrs J Ryan, Mr M. A. Ryan, Mr M. D. Ryan, Mr Steve Ryan, Mrs L. M. Shanahan, Mr M. J. Tedham, The Racing Emporium, Mr S. R. H. Turner, Mrs I. M. Wainwright, Mr M. A. Wainwright.

**Assistant Trainer:** Adam Ryan.

**Flat Jockey:** Tom Eaves, Shane Gray, Kevin Stott. **Apprentice Jockey:** Oisin McSweeney.

---

**476** **MR AYTACH SADIK, Kidderminster**
Postal: **Wolverley Court Coach House, Wolverley, Kidderminster, Worcestershire, DY10 3RP**
Contacts: **PHONE 01562 852362 MOBILE 07803 040344**

**1** **FULL GLASS (FR)**, 8, b g Diamond Green (FR)—Full Tune (FR) **A. M. Sadik**
**2** **SUSSEX ROAD (IRE)**, 11, b g Mahler—Rose Island **A. M. Sadik**
**3** **THECORNISHBARRON (IRE)**, 9, b g Bushranger (IRE)—Tripudium (IRE) **A. M. Sadik**
**4** **YOUNG TURK (FR)**, 10, b g Poliglote—Jasminette Doree (FR) **A. M. Sadik**

**477** **MR MALCOLM SAUNDERS, Wells**
Postal: **Blue Mountain Farm, Wells Hill Bottom, Haydon, Wells, Somerset, BA5 3EZ**
Contacts: PHONE **01749 841011** MOBILE **07771 601035**
EMAIL **malcolm@malcolmsaunders.co.uk** WEBSITE **www.malcolmsaunders.co.uk**

1 AMBERINE, 7, b m Equiano (FR)—Crimson Fern (IRE) **M. S. Saunders**
2 BLUEBELL TIME (IRE), 5, br m Coach House (IRE)—Matterofact (IRE) **Mrs Ginny Nicholas & Mr M. S. Saunders**
3 CORONATION COTTAGE, 7, b m Pastoral Pursuits—Avrilo **Pat Hancock & Eric Jones**
4 DIAMOND COTTAGE, 4, ch f Cappella Sansevero—Avrilo **Pat Hancock & Eric Jones**
5 LADY FLORENCE (IRE), 4, b f Zebedee—Lady Caprice **Paul Nicholas / M S Saunders**
6 PASTFACT, 7, br g Pastoral Pursuits—Matterofact (IRE) **Premier Conservatory Roofs**
7 REDREDROBIN, 4, b f Helmet (AUS)—Cape Rosie **Paul Nicholas / M S Saunders**
8 SECRETFACT, 8, br g Sakhee's Secret—Matterofact (IRE) **Premier Conservatory Roofs**

### THREE-YEAR-OLDS

9 JOY CHOI (IRE), b f Territories (IRE)—Vintage Molly **M. S. Saunders**

**Other Owners:** D. J. Collier, Mr P. K. Hancock, Mr E. W. Jones, Mr P. S. G. Nicholas, Mrs V. L. Nicholas, M. S. Saunders.

---

**478** **MRS DIANNE SAYER, Penrith**
Postal: **Town End Farm, Hackthorpe, Penrith, Cumbria, CA10 2HX**
Contacts: PHONE **01931 712245** MOBILE **07980 295316**

1 BEENO (IRE), 12, b g Exit To Nowhere (USA)—Kay Theatre (IRE) **Mrs Margaret Coppola & Mr Arthur Slack**
2 CALLIOPE, 8, b m Poet's Voice—Costa Brava (IRE) **Mr E. G. Tunstall**
3 DETECTIVE, 5, b g Kingman—Promising Lead **A. Slack**
4 FRIGHTENED RABBIT (USA), 9, b g Hard Spun (USA)—Champagne Ending (USA) **Mr R. A. Harrison**
5 HOT GOSSIP (IRE), 7, b m Fast Company (IRE)—On The Make (IRE) **Mr Dennis J. Coppola & Mrs Dianne Sayer**
6 IOLANI (GER), 9, b g Sholokhov (IRE)—Imogen (GER) **SJD Racing & Dianne Sayer**
7 JACKHAMMER (IRE), 7, b g Thewayyouare (USA)—Ask Annie (IRE) **Mrs H. D. Sayer**
8 JEU DE MOTS (FR), 8, b g Saint des Saints (FR)—Nanouska (GER) **Mrs Margaret Coppola & Mr Arthur Slack**
9 LEGALIZED, 7, br m Authorized (IRE)—Laurena (GER) **Boom Racing**
10 MILLIE THE MINX, 7, b m Medicean—Popocatepetl (FR) **A. R. White**
11 REDARNA, 7, ch g Aqlaam—Curtains **Graham Lund & Dianne Sayer**
12 SAMS ROSEABELLE, 5, b m Black Sam Bellamy (IRE)—Cashback Rose (IRE) **Mrs M. R. Lewis**
13 SUMMER LIGHTENING, 7, gr m Fair Mix (IRE)—Kristineau **Messrs A & R Lyle**
14 THE NAVIGATOR, 6, gr g Mastercraftsman (IRE)—Blessing (USA) **Mr G. H. Bell**
15 TICO TIMES (IRE), 8, br g Arcadio (GER)—Roomier (IRE) **Mrs D. E. Slack**
16 TONTO'S SPIRIT, 9, b g Authorized (IRE)—Desert Royalty (IRE) **A. Slack**

### THREE-YEAR-OLDS

17 B g Shirocco (GER)—Cool Baranca (GER)

**Other Owners:** Mr D. J. Coppola, Mrs M. Coppola, Mr G. Lund, Mrs A. Lyle, Mr J. R. Lyle, R. Lyle, Mr S. Nicholson, S J D Racing, Mrs H. D. Sayer, A. Slack.

**Assistant Trainer:** Miss Joanna Sayer.

**Amateur Jockey:** Miss Liz Butterworth, Miss Emma Sayer.

## 479 DR JON SCARGILL, Newmarket
Postal: **Red House Stables, Hamilton Road, Newmarket, Suffolk, CB8 0TE**
Contacts: **PHONE 01638 667767 MOBILE 07785 350705**
**EMAIL jdscargill@gmail.com WEBSITE www.jonscargill.co.uk**

1 DISARMING (IRE), 4, b f War Command (USA)—Gloved Hand **Dr Edna Robson & Partner**
2 GLEAM ON FLORENCE, 5, b m Arabian Gleam—Delightful Martha
3 LOVE POEMS (IRE), 4, b f Camelot—Dansable (IRE) **Theme Tune Partnership**
4 MY PERFECT COUSIN, 7, b g Showcasing—Torver **Mrs S. M. Scargill**

### THREE-YEAR-OLDS
5 FRUITCAKE, b f Mukhadram—Winter Dress **Mr P. J. Darlington**
6 MISTER SWIFT, ch g Eagle Top—Speedy Senorita (IRE) **J P T Partnership**
7 OVERQUALIFIED, b f Nayef (USA)—Qualification (IRE) **Mrs S. M. Scargill**
8 PLACATED, b f Archipenko—Cosseted
9 B f Slade Power (IRE)—Publilia **Dr Edna Robson & Partner**
10 VERTICAL, ch f Al Kazeem—Greenery (IRE) **Dr Edna Robson & Partner**

Other Owners: Dr E. M. Robson, Mrs S. M. Scargill.

## 480 MR DERRICK SCOTT, Minehead
Postal: **East Lynch, Minehead, Somerset, TA24 8SS**
Contacts: **PHONE 01643 702430 FAX 01643 702430**

1 ACTONETAKETWO, 11, b m Act One—Temple Dancer **Mrs R. Scott**
2 ROYBUOY, 14, b g Royal Applause—Wavy Up (IRE) **Mrs R. Scott**

NH Jockey: James Best.

## 481 MR GEORGE SCOTT, Newmarket
Postal: **Eve Lodge Stables, Hamilton Road, Hamilton Road, Newmarket, Suffolk, CB8 0NY**
Contacts: **WORK 07833 461294**
**EMAIL george@georgescottracing.com WEBSITE www.georgescottracing.com**

1 AU CLAIR DE LUNE (IRE), 4, br f Sea The Stars (IRE)—Missunited (IRE)
2 CRANTOCK BAY, 5, b g Havana Gold (IRE)—Orton Park (IRE) **Mr K. J. Breen**
3 JACK THE TRUTH (IRE), 7, ch g Dandy Man (IRE)—Friendly Heart (CAN) **Mr J. Stephenson**
4 KOOLA BUALA (IRE), 4, ch f Raven's Pass (USA)—Naizah (IRE) **The Black Dragon**
5 MISS MULLIGAN (IRE), 4, b f Gleneagles (IRE)—Banimpire (IRE) **Mr C. O. P. Hanbury**
6 RELOADED (IRE), 5, b g Excelebration (IRE)—Wooded Glade **Mr K. J. Breen**
7 ROBERT WALPOLE, 4, b g Golden Horn—Whazzat **W. J. and T. C. O. Gredley**
8 SARVAN, 4, gr g Lope de Vega (IRE)—Tequila Sunrise **Mr K Breen & Mr C Wright**
9 SHOOT TO KILL (IRE), 4, b g Dandy Man (IRE)—Nancy Astor **Bartram,Kilburn & Ware**
10 STRAWBERRY JACK, 5, b g Foxwedge (AUS)—Strawberry Leaf **Mr J. Stephenson**
11 STRONG POWER (IRE), 4, b g Kodiac—Soft Power (IRE) **K Breen,J Stephenson,M Lilley Et.,Al**
12 YANKEE STADIUM (IRE), 4, b g Galileo (IRE)—Switch (USA) **The Home Run Partnership**

### THREE-YEAR-OLDS
13 ACCRINGTON STANLEY, ch g Outstrip—Round Midnight **The Black Dragon**
14 CABLE NEWS, b f Cable Bay (IRE)—Wemyss Bay **W. J. and T. C. O. Gredley**
15 CHARLIE FELLOWES (IRE), b g Swiss Spirit—Filatelia (IRE) **Offthebridle Podcast**

# MR GEORGE SCOTT - continued

16 **FINAL RENDEZVOUS**, b f Brazen Beau (AUS)—Moonlight Mystery **H.H. Shaikh Nasser Al Khalifa & Partner**
17 **GEORGE PEABODY (IRE)**, b g Holy Roman Emperor (IRE)—Swordhalf **W. J. and T. C. O. Gredley**
18 **GREAT VIBES**, b f Showcasing—Whazzat **W. J. and T. C. O. Gredley**
19 **IBN ARABI (IRE)**, b g No Nay Never (USA)—Lovelocks (IRE) **Mr E. A. Al Afoo**
20 **LATIFFA**, b f Kingman—Lady Nouf **Mr I. Alsagar**
21 **LIVIA THE EMPRESS (IRE)**, b f Holy Roman Emperor (IRE)—Chastushka (IRE) **KHK Racing Ltd**
22 **MELLYS FLYER**, b g Dandy Man (IRE)—Azhar **Investasurge Consulting Ltd**
23 **PERFECT COUNTRY (IRE)**, gr f Australia—Scarlet Empire (IRE) **Dr Bridget Drew & Mr R. A. Farmiloe**
24 **PRINCESS ELEKTRA (USA)**, ch f Noble Mission—Gigahertz (USA) **Hunscote Stud Limited**
25 **PRYDWEN (IRE)**, b g Camelot—Honey Hunter (IRE) **Blue StaRR Racing**
26 **PUNTA ARENAS (USA)**, b g Quality Road (USA)—Absolute Crackers (IRE) **Flaxman Stables Ireland Ltd**
27 **RED CARPET QUEEN**, b f Hot Streak (IRE)—Dark Reckoning **Ms L. Zissman**
28 **REVERENTIAL (IRE)**, b f Lope de Vega (IRE)—Fifth Commandment (IRE) **Ms Emma Banks & Mr John O'Connor**
29 **RWANDA MIST**, b g Maxios—Nyanza (GER) **Hunscote Stud Limited**
30 **SAVEATREE**, ch g Iffraaj—Angelic Air **The Black Dragon**
31 **SIMULATION THEORY (IRE)**, ch g Starspangledbanner (AUS)—Barawin (IRE) **Ms E. L. Banks**
32 **SMASH HIT**, ch g Territories (IRE)—Sell Out **Dr B Drew & Eve Lodge Racing, Dr S. B. Drew**
33 **TEQUILA TEQUILA**, gr f Iffraaj—Tequila Sunrise **The Grey Racehorse**
34 **TOO FRIENDLY**, b c Camelot—Chatline (IRE) **W. J. and T. C. O. Gredley**
35 **TRIBUNA UFFIZI (IRE)**, b g Zoffany—Bunood (IRE) **Mr E. W. B. Williams**
36 **WAIKIKI SOL**, b g Brazen Beau (AUS)—Wiki Tiki **Mr M. Bartram**

## TWO-YEAR-OLDS

37 B c 28/04 Dabirsim (FR)—Akhmatova (Cape Cross (IRE)) (20000) **Offthebridle Podcast II**
38 **CHANSON D'AMOUR**, gr f 11/03 Dark Angel (IRE)—
    Coral Mist (Bahamian Bounty) (27000) **Hon Mrs J. M. The Corbett & Mr C. Wright**
39 B f 05/02 No Nay Never (USA)—Clip Art (Acclamation) (20952) **Mr F. A. A. Nass**
40 **EXCEEDINGLY SONIC**, ch f 04/04 Exceed And Excel (AUS)—Modify (New Approach (IRE)) (70000) **Mr M. Chan**
41 **EXCITING NEWS**, b f 11/04 Night of Thunder (IRE)—Nashama (IRE) (Pivotal) **W. J. and T. C. O. Gredley**
42 Ch c 10/03 Ulysses (IRE)—Foundation Filly (Lando (GER)) (30000) **Mr M. J. Lilley**
43 B c 22/03 Ulysses (IRE)—Heho (Dansili) (19047) **Ms E Banks, Mr A Cooper & Mr M Lilley**
44 **HIGHLIGHTER (IRE)**, b c 19/02 Australia—Cosmic Fire (FR) (Dalakhani (IRE)) **Niarchos Family**
45 **LOVE NEVER ENDING**, b f 05/03 Siyouni (FR)—Encore L'Amour (Azamour (IRE)) (50000) **Mr E. W. B. Williams**
46 Ch f 02/03 Ribchester (IRE)—Mikandy (IRE) (Arcano (IRE)) (40000) **Mr F. A. A. Nass**
47 B c 30/04 Fast Company (IRE)—Pudding (IRE) (Bushranger (IRE)) **Mr C. Woodhouse**
48 B c 12/04 Kodiac—Question (USA) (Coronado's Quest (USA)) (38095) **Mr F. A. A. Nass**
49 **RUBBELDIEKATZ**, b f 18/02 Helmet (AUS)—For Henry (IRE) (Galileo (IRE)) **Mr R. A. H. Evans**
50 **TIME LAPSE (IRE)**, b f 21/05 Dark Angel (IRE)—Synchronic (Dansili) **Niarchos Family**
51 B f 29/03 Exceed And Excel (AUS)—Whazzat (Daylami (IRE)) **W. J. and T. C. O. Gredley**

**Other Owners:** H.H. Sheikh Nasser Al Khalifa, Ms E. L. Banks, Mr M. Bartram, Mr A. R. Boyd-Rochfort, Mr K. J. Breen, Mr A. K. Cooper, The Hon Mrs C. Corbett, Dr Bridget Drew & Partners, N. R. R. Drew, Miss P.B. Drew, Dr S. B. Drew, Eve Lodge Racing, Mr R. A. Farmiloe, D. Kilburn, Mr M. J. Lilley, Mr E Williams & Partner, Mr F. A. A. Nass, Mr J. P.M. O'Connor, Mr G. O. Scott, Mrs J. A. Scott, Mr J. Stephenson, The Grey Racehorse 1, Mr E. J. Ware, Mr E. W. B. Williams, Mr C. N. Wright.

---

**482**
## MR JEREMY SCOTT, Dulverton
Postal: **Higher Holworthy Farm, Brompton Regis, Dulverton, Somerset, TA22 9NY**
Contacts: **PHONE** 01398 371414 **MOBILE** 07709 279483
**EMAIL** holworthyfarm@yahoo.com

1 **BALLYBOUGH NORA (IRE)**, 8, b m Oscar (IRE)—Perspex Queen (IRE) **Pillhead House Partners**
2 **BANG ON (IRE)**, 8, ch g Fracas (IRE)—Carramanagh Lady (IRE) **Cash For Honours**
3 **BELLEVARDE EXPRESS (IRE)**, 6, b br m Shirocco (GER)—Senora Snoopy (IRE) **Kit James & Matt James**
4 **BLAZING SADDLES**, 6, b g High Chaparral (IRE)—Desert Sage **Mr J. P. Carrington**
5 **CHAMPAGNE COURT (IRE)**, 8, b g Court Cave (IRE)—Lady Taipan (IRE) **Mr I F Gosden & Mr Dj Coles**

# MR JEREMY SCOTT - continued

6 **CLONDAW DANCER (IRE)**, 7, b g Big Bad Bob (IRE)—Berocco (IRE) **Friends From Insurance**
7 **DASHEL DRASHER**, 8, b g Passing Glance—So Long **Mrs B Tully & Mr R Lock**
8 **DE YOUNG WARRIOR**, 8, b g Schiaparelli (GER)—Nobratinetta (FR) **Mrs H. L. Stoneman**
9 **DEMON FOU (FR)**, 8, b g Le Fou (IRE)—Nevka (FR) **Friends From Insurance**
10 **DRASH ON RUBY**, 5, b m Passing Glance—So Long **Mrs B Tully & Mr R Lock**
11 **ELLENS WAY**, 9, b m Black Sam Bellamy (IRE)—Function Dreamer **Bet The Farm Partners**
12 **ESPALION (FR)**, 7, b g Khalkevi (IRE)—Somosierra (FR) **Mr J. H. Frost**
13 **FANTASIA STORM (IRE)**, 6, gr m Mahler—Fantasia Filly (FR) **Govier & Brown**
14 **GARRANE (IRE)**, 9, b g Tikkanen (USA)—Ballooley (IRE) **Friends From Insurance**
15 **HEY BUD**, 8, b g Fair Mix (IRE)—Azione **Mr M. P. P. Brend**
16 **KERB LINE (IRE)**, 8, b g Arcadio (GER)—Native Craft (IRE) **Langley's**
17 **KILCARA (IRE)**, 8, b m Court Cave (IRE)—Easter Day (IRE) **London Erratics Racing Club**
18 **KISSESFORKATIE (IRE)**, 7, b m Jeremy (USA)—Now Were Broke (IRE) **Derek Coles & Ian Gosden**
19 **KURAKA**, 7, b g Cacique (IRE)—Puzzling **Susan Frost & Caren Walsh**
20 **LADY KK (IRE)**, 6, br m Shirocco (GER)—Lissard Lady (IRE) **Friends From Insurance**
21 **LITTLE ELSE**, 5, b m Midnight Legend—Real Treasure **The Real Partnership**
22 **MALACHYS GIRL (IRE)**, 8, b m Darsi (FR)—Borleagh Princess (IRE) **Mrs S. J. Lanz**
23 **NATIVE ROBIN (IRE)**, 11, br g Robin des Pres (FR)—Homebird (IRE) **The Punchestown Syndicate**
24 **ORCHARDSTOWN CROSS (IRE)**, 10, b g Westerner—Shang A Lang (IRE) **Mr J. H. Frost**
25 **PELORIC**, 6, ch g Intello (GER)—New Orchid (USA) **Wot No Coz**
26 **SIENNA ROYALE (IRE)**, 7, b m Sholokhov (IRE)—Dartmeet (IRE) **Air Cdre Hallam & Mrs Martin Hallam**
27 **SIZABLE SAM**, 6, ch g Black Sam Bellamy (IRE)—Halo Flora **The Hopefuls & Kelvin-hughes**
28 **STORMY FLIGHT (IRE)**, 7, gr g Cloudings (IRE)—Help Yourself (IRE) **Mr Ian Murray & Mr Dave Smith**
29 **TACTICAL MANOEUVRE (IRE)**, 10, b g Marienbard (IRE)—Pride O'Fleet (IRE) **The Tacticians**
30 **THAT OLE CHESTNUT (IRE)**, 6, ch g Fracas (IRE)—Minnie Turbo (IRE) **The Exmoor High Hopes**
31 **THE EAGLEHASLANDED (IRE)**, 11, b g Milan—Vallee Doree (FR) **Coles, Smith, McManus & Broughton**
32 **THE PLIMSOLL LINE (IRE)**, 5, b g Dylan Thomas (IRE)—Patsy Choice (IRE) **Dave Smith & Mike Wright**
33 **THE WORTHY BRAT (IRE)**, 4, b g Worthadd (IRE)—Khibraat **Wayne Clifford & Ian Gosden**
34 **TIKKINTHEBOX (IRE)**, 9, b g Tikkanen (USA)—Surfing France (FR) **On A Mission**
35 **TUSCAN PEARL**, 6, b m Medicean—Western Pearl **Mr & Mrs N. Welby**
36 **URTHEONETHATIWANT (IRE)**, 8, ch g Shantou (USA)—Roberta Supreme (IRE) **THE BARMY MEN 4**
37 **WAVERING DOWN (IRE)**, 6, b g Jeremy (USA)—Gortbofearna (IRE) **Mr J. H. Frost**

**Other Owners:** Mr S. W. Broughton, H. M. W. Clifford, Mr D. J. Coles, Mr V. P. Finn, Mrs S. A. Frost, Mrs G. D. Giles, Mr G. R. Giles, Mr I. F. Gosden, Mr P. Govier, Mr P. F. Govier, Mrs M. Hallam, Air Commodore M. R. Hallam, Mr S. Hill, Mr C. J. James, Mr M. J. James, Mrs E. A. Kelvin-Hughes, Mr & Mrs R. G. Kelvin-Hughes, R. G. Kelvin-Hughes, Mr R. J. Lock, Mr B. J. McManus, I. R. Murray, Mrs C. C. Scott, Mr J. R. M. Scott, Mr B. D. Smith, David H. Smith, Mr M. J. Swallow, The Hopefuls, Mrs B. J. Tully, Mrs C. J. Walsh, Mr R. M. E. Wright.

**Assistant Trainer:** Camilla Scott, **Head Girl:** Laura Scott, **Yard Sponsor:** Chris Hendy Brendon Powerwashers.

**NH Jockey:** Rex Dingle, Matt Griffiths, Nick Scholfield.

---

**483** **MISS KATIE SCOTT, Galashiels**
Postal: Stables Cottage, Millhaugh, Lindean, Galashiels, Scottish Borders
Contacts: **MOBILE 07826 344577**

1 5, B m Passing Glance—Addiction
2 **AL QAHWA (IRE)**, 8, b g Fast Company (IRE)—Cappuccino (IRE) **Elite Partners**
3 **CRYSTAL LAD (FR)**, 9, ch g Kapgarde (FR)—Qrystale Mag (FR) **James & Katie Scott**
4 **EPSON ROQUE (FR)**, 7, b g Irish Wells (FR)—Corthalina (FR) **Miss K. Scott**
5 **FLAMING GLORY (IRE)**, 7, b g Gold Well—Pearlsforthegirls **The Wee Guys**
6 **GETAWAY GERRY**, 7, b g Getaway (GER)—Loch Dhu (IRE) **Mark Hay, Andrew Machray, Murray Scott**
7 **GREY TIKKANA**, 6, gr m Tikkanen (USA)—Think Green **Mr R. M. Boyd**
8 **GWEEDORE**, 4, b g Epaulette (AUS)—Ares Choix **Lamont Racing**
9 **MONCHIQUE'S LASS**, 6, b m Fame And Glory—Twilight Eclipse (IRE) **Louise Kelly & Murray Scott**

## MISS KATIE SCOTT - continued

10 **NELLIE FRENCH (IRE)**, 4, b f Dragon Pulse (IRE)—Texas Ruby (USA)  **Mrs S. Scott**
11 **ROCKLEY POINT**, 8, b g Canford Cliffs (IRE)—Statua (IRE)  **The Vintage Flyers**
12 **SLADE STORM (IRE)**, 8, b g September Storm (GER)—Katie Kelly (IRE)  **Miss K. Scott**
13 **TADASANA**, 5, b m Battle of Marengo (IRE)—Letters (FR)  **Miss K. Scott**
14 **THAT'S YOUR LOTTIE**, 6, b m Imperial Monarch (IRE)—Caoba  **The Jackson Partnership**

### THREE-YEAR-OLDS

15 **ELLADORA**, b f Equiano (FR)—Somersault  **Stevens Taylor Clark Raeburn Scott**
16 **MR LUIGI**, b g Bobby's Kitten (USA)—Tottie  **Lamont Racing**
17 **ONNA BUGEISHA (IRE)**, b f Zoffany (IRE)—Dingle View (IRE)  **Lamont Racing**
18 **SCOTTISH WIND (FR)**, b g Territories (IRE)—Isalou (FR)  **Lamont Racing**
19 **SPARTAKOS**, b g Rajsaman (FR)—Medicean Bliss (IRE)  **Making Headway Racing**
20 **WEE DRACULA (IRE)**, br g Awtaad (IRE)—North Mare (GER)  **Lamont Racing**

### TWO-YEAR-OLDS

21 B f 04/02 Cotai Glory—M'Selle (IRE) (Elnadim (USA))  **Making Headway Racing**

**Other Owners:** Mr M. W. Hay, Mrs L. M. Kelly, Mr A. Machray, Mr J. Scott, Miss K. Scott, Mr W. M. Scott.

---

| **484** | **MR MICHAEL SCUDAMORE, Bromsash** |
|---|---|

Postal: Ecclesall Court, Bromsash, Nr. Ross-on-Wye, Herefordshire, HR9 7PP
Contacts: PHONE 01989 750844 MOBILE 07901 853520
EMAIL michael.scu@btconnect.com WEBSITE www.michaelscudamoreracing.co.uk

1 **AJAX TAVERN**, 4, b g Canford Cliffs (IRE)—Gimme Some Lovin (IRE)
2 **ALFIDA**, 6, gr m Sulamani (IRE)—Dissolve
3 **ASK HIMSELF (IRE)**, 7, ch g Ask—Wintry Day (IRE)
4 **CALDWELL**, 4, b c Dansili—Milford Sound
5 **CALTEX (FR)**, 9, bl g Network (GER)—Oomposita (IRE)
6 **CATFISH ROW**, 5, ch g Shamardal (USA)—Folk Opera (IRE)
7 **CHEZ HANS (IRE)**, 7, b g Aizavoski (IRE)—Hidden Reserve (IRE)
8 **COPPER COIN**, 8, ch g Sulamani (IRE)—Silken Pearls
9 **COURT MASTER (IRE)**, 8, b g Court Cave (IRE)—Lusos Wonder (IRE)
10 **CZECH HER OUT (IRE)**, 7, b m Fame And Glory—Molly Hussey (IRE)
11 **DINSDALE**, 8, b g Cape Cross (IRE)—Emmy Award (IRE)
12 **DO YOUR JOB (IRE)**, 7, b g Fame And Glory—Full of Birds (FR)
13 **ELUSIVE POLLY**, 4, b f Kalanisi (IRE)—Parlez Vous
14 **ENVOL DE LA COUR (FR)**, 7, b g Maresca Sorrento (FR)—Reveuse de La Cour (FR)
15 **FANCY SHAPES (IRE)**, 7, ch m Golden Lariat (USA)—Panglao Island (IRE)
16 **FIRST FURLOUGH**, 4, b g Phenomena—Madam Molly
17 **HORIZON BLEU (FR)**, 4, b g Spanish Moon (USA)—Lili Bleue (FR)
18 **ISAAC WONDER (IRE)**, 6, b g Born To Sea (IRE)—Najaaba (USA)
19 **KARLIE**, 6, b m Schiaparelli (GER)—Deianira (IRE)
20 **KINGSWELL THEATRE**, 12, b g King's Theatre (IRE)—Cresswell Native (IRE)
21 **LET ME ENTERTAIN U**, 5, gr g Saint des Saints (FR)—My Belle (FR)
22 5, B m Kalanisi (IRE)—Mini Adventure (IRE)
23 **MONBEG AQUADUDE (IRE)**, 10, b g Flemensfirth (USA)—Mite Dash (IRE)
24 **MR CHUA (IRE)**, 5, b g Cape Cross (IRE)—Shama's Song (IRE)
25 **NADA TO PRADA**, 6, b m Kayf Tara—Ambrosia's Promise (IRE)
26 **NORTHERN BEAU (IRE)**, 8, b m Canford Cliffs (IRE)—View (IRE)
27 **PLENTY OF BUTTY (IRE)**, 8, b g Germany (USA)—Jump For Joy (IRE)
28 **PRINCESS OF MERCIA**, 4, b f Blue Bresil (FR)—Very Special One (IRE)
29 **ROBBIE DAZZLER**, 4, ch g Leading Light (IRE)—Mrs Roberts
30 **ROBIN DES THEATRE (IRE)**, 6, b br m Robin des Champs (FR)—Shannon Theatre (IRE)
31 **ROLLERCOSTER (IRE)**, 9, b m Helissio (FR)—Full Deck (IRE)

# MR MICHAEL SCUDAMORE - continued

32 **ROSIE AND MILLIE (IRE)**, 8, ch m Flemensfirth (USA)—Madgehil (IRE)
33 **SASHENKA (GER)**, 5, b m Maxios—Sarabia (GER)
34 **SATURN 'N SILK**, 6, b m Universal (IRE)—Manaphy (FR)
35 **SHATTERED GLASS (IRE)**, 7, b g Sholokhov (IRE)—Anns Present (IRE)
36 **SMITHS CROSS (IRE)**, 9, b g Westerner—Blue Supreme (IRE)
37 **SOME CHAOS (IRE)**, 10, b g Brian Boru—Iruna Iris (IRE)
38 **SPARKLING RIVER (IRE)**, 11, gr m Indian River (FR)—Full Deck (IRE)
39 **SUMELIA**, 6, ch m Sulamani (IRE)—Aimela (FR)
40 **THE CRAZED MOON (IRE)**, 9, b m Yeats (IRE)—Rose Gallery (IRE)
41 **THE DAWN MAN (IRE)**, 10, b g Milan—Calling Classy (IRE)
42 **THOR DE CERISY (FR)**, 7, b g Enrique—Midalisy (FR)
43 **UPTON ROAD (IRE)**, 7, b g Jeremy (USA)—Reynard's Glen (IRE)
44 **WIZARDS BRIDGE**, 12, b g Alflora (IRE)—Island Hopper
45 **YORGONNAHEARMEROAR (IRE)**, 10, b g Scorpion (IRE)—Etoile Margot (FR)

## THREE-YEAR-OLDS

46 **BLAZER TWO**, b c Cable Bay (IRE)—Tamara Moon (IRE)
47 **CENTS IN THE CITY**, b g Cityscape—Six Cents (IRE)
48 B g Gregorian (IRE)—Forever Loved
49 **LET IT SHINE**, bl g Pether's Moon (IRE)—My Belle (FR)
50 **ROLFE REMBRANDT**, ch g Dutch Art—Rebecca Rolfe

**Owners:** Mr M. R. Blandford, Mr C. Breeze, BumpersToJumpers 1, Mr C. G. J. Chua, & N Dower, Mrs A. C. Dower, Mr N. Dower, Mr M. P Dunphy, Mrs B. V. Evans, Mrs J. Frieze, Mr & Mrs M. Frieze, Mr M. A. Frieze, Frieze Racing & Charles M Graham, Gabby Gajova and Friends, Mr C. M. Graham, Mr R. R. Green, Having A Mare, Hunscote Stud Limited, Hunscote Stud Ltd & Michael Scudamore, Mr A. Maclennan, Mrs L. Maclennan, Lynne & Angus Maclennan, Mr A. Mason, Mason Scudamore Racing, Mr Mark Savidge Mr Richard Green, Mr J. J. Murray, Mr John J Murray & Mrs Lynne MacLennan, N. Pickett, Mr N. A. Price, G. A. Roberts, Mr S. Robson, Mr M. G. Savidge, Savidge, Roberts, Whittal-williams, A & Scudamore, Mr M. Scudamore, Mark & Michael Scudamore, Mr P.E. Truscott, Mr P. E. Truscott & Mr M. Scudamore, Mr E. B. Whittal-Williams.

**Racing Secretary:** Marilyn Scudamore.

**NH Jockey:** Richard Patrick, Ben Poste, Brendan Powell, Tom Scudamore.

---

**485** | **MR DEREK SHAW, Sproxton**
Postal: **The Sidings, Saltby Road, Sproxton, Melton Mowbray, Leicestershire, LE14 4RA**
Contacts: **PHONE** 01476 860578 **MOBILE** 07721 039645 **FAX** 01476 860578
**EMAIL** mail@derekshawracing.com **WEBSITE** www.derekshawracing.com

1 **AMAZING AMAYA**, 6, b m New Approach (IRE)—Faslen (USA) **P. E. Barrett**
2 **DAAFY (USA)**, 4, b g The Factor (USA)—Ishraak (USA) **Mr D. Shaw**
3 **DUBAI ELEGANCE**, 7, ch m Sepoy (AUS)—Some Sunny Day **Million Dreams Racing 1**
4 **DUE A DIAMOND**, 4, b f Due Diligence (USA)—Shaws Diamond (USA) **Mrs L. J. Shaw**
5 **DYNAMO WALT (IRE)**, 10, b g Acclamation—Cambara **Shawthing Racing Partnership (d Shaw)**
6 **FARHHSICAL**, 4, b g Farhh—Nabat Sultan **Mrs L. J. Shaw**
7 **FINAL LEGACY**, 5, b m Coach House (IRE)—Tartatartufata **Mrs L. J. Shaw**
8 **GO ON MY COCKER**, 5, b g Acclamation—Missisipi Star (IRE) **Mr N. P. Franklin**
9 **GRENADIER GUARD (IRE)**, 5, ch g Australia—Another Storm (USA) **Mr J. R. Saville**
10 **HAMMER GUN (USA)**, 8, b g Smart Strike (CAN)—Caraboss **Mr A. Flint**
11 **IT'S A SIN**, 4, b g Sea The Stars (IRE)—Tahlia Ree (IRE) **P. E. Barrett**
12 **ITS ALL CLOVER NOW (IRE)**, 6, b g Most Improved (IRE)—All In Clover (IRE) **Mr D. Shaw**
13 **JAZZ MUSIC**, 4, b f Muhaarar—Propel (IRE) **Mrs L. J. Shaw**
14 **JUMIRA BRIDGE**, 7, b g Invincible Spirit (IRE)—Zykina **333racing**
15 **LITTLEMISSATTITUDE**, 4, b f Due Diligence (USA)—Lady Elalmadol (IRE) **Million Dreams Racing 1**
16 **PRINCE ABU (IRE)**, 4, gr g Dark Angel (IRE)—Saoirse Abu (USA) **Million Dreams Racing**

## MR DEREK SHAW - continued

17 **SAMPHIRE COAST**, 8, b g Fastnet Rock (AUS)—Faslen (USA) **P. E. Barrett**
18 **SIX STRINGS**, 7, b g Requinto (IRE)—Island Music (IRE) **S & R Racing Partnership**
19 **THE KYLLACHY TOUCH**, 4, gr g Kyllachy—The Manx Touch (IRE) **Mrs L. J. Shaw**
20 **TINA TEASPOON**, 7, b m Kheleyf (USA)—Button Moon (IRE) **P. E. Barrett**
21 **ULYSSES (GER)**, 7, b g Sinndar (IRE)—Ungarin (GER) **Million Dreams Racing**
22 **WALTZING HOME**, 4, b f Coach House (IRE)—Dancing Duo **Ownaracehorse & Lyndsey Shaw**
23 **YOU'RE COOL**, 9, b g Exceed And Excel (AUS)—Ja One (IRE) **Mr D. Bichan**

### THREE-YEAR-OLDS

24 Br f Hellvelyn—Midnite Motivation
25 B f Coach House (IRE)—Saktoon (USA) **Mrs L. J. Shaw**
26 **THE TRON**, gr g Outstrip—Ming Meng (IRE) **P. E. Barrett**

### TWO-YEAR-OLDS

27 B f 20/02 Brazen Beau (AUS)—Ming Meng (IRE) (Intikhab (USA)) (10000) **P. E. Barrett**
28 B f 12/02 Brazen Beau (AUS)—Spree (IRE) (Dansili) (6500) **P. E. Barrett**

**Other Owners:** Mr S. Furniss, Mr R. Maddocks, Million Dreams Racing, Ownaracehorse Ltd, Mr I. D. Sellens, Mr D. Shaw, Mrs L. J. Shaw, Shawthing Racing Partnership.

**Yard Sponsor:** Grosvenor Contracts Leasing Ltd.

---

**486**
### MRS FIONA SHAW, Dorchester
Postal: **Skippet Cottage, Bradford Peverell, Dorchester, Dorset, DT2 9SE**
Contacts: **PHONE 01305 889350 MOBILE 07970 370444**
EMAIL fiona.shaw05@gmail.com

1 **HIGHDAWN (IRE)**, 8, b m Alflora (IRE)—Wychnor Dawn (IRE) **John & Heather Snook**
2 **HOLLYWOOD KEN (IRE)**, 8, b g Arcano (IRE)—Third Dimension (FR) **Miss A. E. Fletcher**
3 **HYMN AND A PRAYER**, 8, br g Eastern Anthem (IRE)—Kryssa **Mrs F. M. Shaw**
4 6, Br m Bollin Eric—Kiwi Katie **John & Heather Snook**
5 **KIWI MYTH**, 9, b m Midnight Legend—Kiwi Katie **John & Heather Snook**
6 **MANGETOUT**, 5, b m Schiaparelli (GER)—Petite Pois **Mrs F. M. Shaw**
7 **SHOW ON THE ROAD**, 10, b g Flemensfirth (USA)—Roses of Picardy (IRE) **Mrs F. M. Shaw**

**Other Owners:** Mrs H. A. Snook, J. W. Snook.

---

**487**
### MR MATT SHEPPARD, Ledbury
Postal: **Home Farm Cottage, Eastnor, Ledbury, Herefordshire, HR8 1RD**
Contacts: **MOBILE 07770 625061 FAX 01531 634846**
EMAIL matthew.sheppard@cmail.co.uk

1 **ALL GOOD THINGS (IRE)**, 9, b g Dahjee (USA)—Material Lady (IRE) **Mrs N. Sheppard**
2 **BROKEN QUEST (IRE)**, 9, b g Ask—Broken Thought (IRE) **Wright Morgan Ltd**
3 **CYCLOP (IRE)**, 10, b g King's Theatre (IRE)—Tasmani (FR) **DD Racing & Professor L Hardwick**
4 **FUNKY SENSATION**, 7, b g Black Sam Bellamy (IRE)—Sambara (IRE) **Mr G. Saville**
5 **GETAFRIEND (IRE)**, 5, b g Getaway (GER)—Minnie Maguire (IRE) **Lost In The Summer Wine**
6 **HARDY ARTICOS (IRE)**, 6, b g Arctic Cosmos (USA)—Hardy Lamb (IRE) **DD Racing 3**
7 **INNISFREE LAD (IRE)**, 9, b g Yeats (IRE)—Tasmani (FR) **Lorna Hardwick & Bob Allum**
8 **JUST SO COOL (IRE)**, 10, gr g Acambaro (GER)—Lauras Dote (IRE) **Legacy Racing & D Dennis**
9 **JUST TOBY (IRE)**, 5, b g Tobougg (IRE)—Whistling Gypse (IRE) **Professor L. P. Hardwick**

## MR MATT SHEPPARD - continued

10 **KESTREL VALLEY**, 7, b m Dr Massini (IRE)—Lady Karinga **Mrs J. M. Johnson**
11 **MERRY MISTRESS (IRE)**, 5, br m Getaway (GER)—Merry Missed (IRE) **Mr G. Saville**
12 **ONE FER MAMMA (IRE)**, 5, b g Dylan Thomas (IRE)—Miss Martel (IRE) **Mrs N. Sheppard**
13 **ORGANISED SOLUTION (FR)**, 7, b g Azamour (IRE)—Phille Phuong (USA) **Mr & Mrs Ben Herbert & Family**
14 **RISK AND ROLL (FR)**, 7, b g No Risk At All (FR)—Rolie de Vindecy (FR) **Mr & Mrs Ben Herbert & Family**
15 **ROCK ON AUSSIE (IRE)**, 10, b g Aussie Rules (USA)—Sue N Win (IRE) **Veronica Silber & Marcus Jordan**
16 **THE BAY BIRCH (IRE)**, 10, b m Beneficial—Tournant Vic (IRE) **Mr A. J. Scrivin**

**Assistant Trainer:** David Dennis.

**NH Jockey:** Stan Sheppard.

---

**488** **MR OLIVER SHERWOOD, Upper Lambourn**
Postal: Rhonehurst House, Upper Lambourn, Hungerford, Berkshire, RG17 8RG
Contacts: **PHONE** 01488 71411 **MOBILE** 07979 591867 **FAX** 01488 72786
**EMAIL** oliver.sherwood@virgin.net **WEBSITE** www.oliversherwood.co.uk

1 **A TIME TO SHINE (IRE)**, 6, b br g Malinas (GER)—Royal Bride **Tim Syder & Dominic Burke**
2 **BAYAANAAT**, 5, ch g Dawn Approach (IRE)—Khothry (IRE) **Jeremy Dougall & Will Watt**
3 **BEMBRIDGE (IRE)**, 5, b g Westerner—Brotenstown (IRE) **Mr J. Palmer-Brown**
4 **BOOK OF GOLD (IRE)**, 9, b g Flemensfirth (USA)—Ballerina Queen (IRE) **Mr A Lousada & Mr A Kaplan**
5 **BRAVE BAIRN (FR)**, 5, b m Brave Mansonnien (FR)—Miss Laveron (FR) **Kate & Andrew Brooks**
6 **BRINGTHEHOUSEDOWN (IRE)**, 7, b g Royal Applause—Raskutani **Mrs S. Steele**
7 **BRUMMIE BOYS (IRE)**, 6, b g Flemensfirth (USA)—Bobs Article (IRE) **Mr Andrew Cohen & Mr Alan Kaplan**
8 **CERVARO MIX (FR)**, 7, gr g Al Namix (FR)—Semiramiss (FR) **Kate & Andrew Brooks**
9 **CILAOS GLACE (FR)**, 8, br g Voix du Nord (FR)—Miss Glacee (FR) **Heart of the South Racing 118**
10 **COSSACK DANCER**, 5, br g Sholokhov (IRE)—Lecon Benefique (IRE) **Valda Burke & Bryan Burrough**
11 **DEVONSHIRE ROCCO (IRE)**, 5, b g Shirocco (GER)—Duplicate Daughter (IRE) **Mrs S. A. White**
12 **DOMINATEUR (FR)**, 8, b g Desir d'Un Soir—Sourya d'Airy (FR) **Kate & Andrew Brooks**
13 **FELIX D'AUTRY (FR)**, 7, b g Khalkevi (IRE)—Hassaya (FR) **Lady Thompson & Julia Lukas**
14 **FEODORA**, 4, b m Kayf Tara—La Harde (FR) **Mr R. Chugg**
15 **FRANCOLIN (FR)**, 6, b g Cokoriko (FR)—Crow Spinney **Mrs N. A. Hanbury**
16 **GRANDEUR D'AME (FR)**, 5, b g Desir d'Un Soir (FR)—Sourya d'Airy (FR) **Kate & Andrew Brooks**
17 **IMPERIAL HOPE (IRE)**, 5, b g Imperial Monarch (IRE)—Ebony Hope (IRE) **Michael Fiddy & Richard Fleming**
18 **JERSEY BEAN (IRE)**, 8, b g Court Cave (IRE)—Jennifers Diary (IRE) **Mr A. Taylor**
19 **JERSEY LADY (IRE)**, 5, ch m Martaline—La Bombonera (FR) **Mr A. Taylor**
20 **JERSEY WONDER (IRE)**, 5, ch g Zoffany (IRE)—Magena (USA) **Mr A. Taylor**
21 **KAPHUMOR (FR)**, 5, b g Kapgarde (FR)—Money Humor (IRE) **Million in Mind Partnership**
22 **LADY IN HIDING (IRE)**, 7, br m Stowaway—Crackin' Liss (IRE) **Mr A. F. Lousada**
23 **LAURIE COME ON (IRE)**, 7, b g Robin des Champs (FR)—Seekayclaire (IRE) **Mr P. Mellett**
24 **LE BOULEVARDIER**, 5, b g Champs Elysees—Daffydowndilly **Lady Blyth**
25 **LITTLE AWKWARD (IRE)**, 5, gr g Montmartre (FR)—Seven Even (IRE) **Michael Fiddy & Richard Fleming**
26 **MACLAINE**, 4, ch g Masked Marvel—Aisance (FR) **Mr T. D. J. Syder**
27 **MANNING ESTATE (IRE)**, 7, b g Stowaway—Specifiedrisk (IRE) **Mr & Mrs Norman**
28 **METHODY (IRE)**, 4, ch g Getaway (GER)—This Is Bollyduff (IRE) **Dr P. Kelly**
29 4, B g Telescope—Mi Money **Mr O. M. C. Sherwood**
30 **MILLY'S DAUGHTER**, 4, b f Geordieland (FR)—Mischievous Milly (IRE) **Mr A. R. Stewart**
31 **MINELLA ROYALE (IRE)**, 8, b g Shirocco (GER)—Lisa du Chenet (FR) **Mr O. M. C. Sherwood**
32 **MONKEY PUZZLE**, 9, ch g Sulamani (IRE)—Hunca Munca (IRE) **Melbourne 10 Racing**
33 **NORLEY (IRE)**, 6, b g Yeats (IRE)—No Moore Bills **Mr T. J. Hemmings**
34 **OCEAN DRIFTER (IRE)**, 6, b g Aizavoski (IRE)—Driftaway (IRE) **Mr T. D. J. Syder**
35 **PASEO**, 5, b g Champs Elysees—Posteritas (USA) **The Daughters of Minella Partnership**
36 **PEBBLY NEW MOON (IRE)**, 6, b g Mahler—Pharney Fox (IRE) **Mr J. Beswick**
37 **PEUR DE RIEN (FR)**, 8, b g Kapgarde (FR)—Tango Princess (FR) **Mr O. M. C. Sherwood**
38 **PONTRESINA (FR)**, 8, b g Milan—Gilt Benefit (IRE) **Winterfields Farm Ltd, M Burton & H Cox**
39 **RAINBOW STORM (FR)**, 5, b g On Est Bien (IRE)—Rainbow Oceane (FR) **Mr P. Mellett**

## MR OLIVER SHERWOOD - continued

40 **REPUBLICAN,** 6, b g Kayf Tara—Noun de La Thinte (FR)  **Mr E. J. Ware**
41 **SEASTON SPIRIT,** 8, b g Kayf Tara—Aphrodisias (FR)  **Mr M. Fiddy**
42 **SEVARANO (IRE),** 8, b g Shantou (USA)—Eva La Diva (IRE)  **Mr T. D. J. Syder**
43 **SQUAW VALLEE,** 7, b m Phenomena—Attishoe  **Mrs A. M. Wood**
44 **STORM KATIE,** 5, ch m Kapgarde (FR)—Stone Flash (FR)  **Dominic Burke & Kate & Andrew Brooks**
45 **THE FRESH PRINCE (IRE),** 11, b g Robin des Pres (FR)—Hayley Cometh (IRE)  **Rhonehurst Raiders**
46 **VINNIE THE HODDIE (IRE),** 7, b g Vinnie Roe (IRE)—Blackwater Babe (IRE)  **Five Guys & A Striker Syndicate**
47 **VOLTURNUS,** 7, b g Azamour (IRE)—Daffydowndilly  **The Hon A. A. Blyth**
48 **WALK IN THE WILD (FR),** 5, b g Walk In The Park (IRE)—Sublimissime (FR)  **Heart of the South Racing 121**
49 **WEST COAST FLYER,** 8, b g Cape Cross (IRE)—La Felicita  **A. Saeed**
50 **WESTSTREET (IRE),** 11, b g Westerner—Klipperstreet (IRE)  **Weststreet Partnership**
51 **WHAT A GLANCE,** 6, b g Passing Glance—Audley  **Mrs E. A. Taylor**
52 **WHAT'S OCCURRING (IRE),** 8, b g Rail Link—Lovely Origny (FR)  **Mr Andrew Cohen & Mr Alan Kaplan**

**Other Owners:** Mr C. Austin, Mr A. L. Brooks, Mrs K. L. Brooks, Mr D. J. Burke, Mrs V. F. Burke, B. R. H. Burrough, Mr M. A. Burton, Mr A. L. Cohen, Mr H. W. Cox, Mr J. M. Dougall, Mr M. Fiddy, Mr R. Fleming, Alan Kaplan, Mr A. F. Lousada, Mrs J. K. Lukas, Mr R. R. Norman, Mrs S. D. Norman, Mr M. E. O'Hara, Mr O. M. C. Sherwood, Mr T. D. J. Syder, Lady Thompson, Mr W. S. Watt, Winterfields Farm Ltd.

**Assistant Trainer:** Andy Llewellyn, **Head Lad:** Stefan Namesansky, **Secretary:** Emma Chugg.

---

**489**

### MISS LYNN SIDDALL, Tadcaster
Postal: **Stonebridge Farm, Colton, Tadcaster, North Yorkshire, LS24 8EP**
Contacts: **PHONE 01904 744291 MOBILE 07778 216694, 07778 216692 FAX 01904 744291**

1 **ALLSFINEANDANDY (IRE),** 5, b g Dandy Man (IRE)—Swish Dancer (IRE)  **Mr G. Kennington**
2 **ASTROPHYSICS,** 9, ch g Paco Boy (IRE)—Jodrell Bank (IRE)  **Lynn Siddall Racing II**
3 **BEVSBOY (IRE),** 7, b g Elzaam (AUS)—Eurolink Sundance  **Mr A. Longden**
4 **FIRST OF NEVER (IRE),** 15, b g Systematic—Never Promise (FR)  **Lynn Siddall Racing II**
5 **IN VINO VERITAS (IRE),** 10, b g Art Connoisseur (IRE)—Robin  **Mr J. A. Kay**
6 **KYLLACHY CASTLE,** 5, ch g Kyllachy—Amicable Terms  **Mr G. Kennington**
7 **MR CONUNDRUM,** 8, b g Paco Boy (IRE)—Folly Drove  **Lynn Siddall Racing II**
8 **PADDY'S ROCK (IRE),** 10, b g Whipper (USA)—Hedera (USA)  **Mr J. A. Kay**
9 **SERVO (IRE),** 7, b g Power—Parade Scene (USA)  **Mr J. A. Kay**
10 **STAR OF VALOUR (IRE),** 6, b g Invincible Spirit (IRE)—Birthstone  **Mr J. A. Kay**
11 **YORKSHIREMAN (IRE),** 11, b g Red Clubs (IRE)—Ossiana (IRE)  **Jan Slater & Partners**

**Other Owners:** Miss L. C. Siddall, Miss J. M. Slater.

**Assistant Trainer:** Stephen Hackney.

---

**490**

### MR OLIVER SIGNY, Lambourn
Postal: **The Croft Stables, Upper Lambourn, Hungerford, Berkshire, RG17 8QH**
EMAIL **oliver@oliversignyracing.com**

1 **ANNUAL FLAVOUR (IRE),** 6, ch m Gamut (IRE)—Sprightly Gal (IRE)
2 **BE THE BEST (USA),** 5, b g Declaration of War (USA)—Memories For Us (USA)  **Adam Signy and Ben Spiers**
3 **CHEF BOGO (FR),** 4, b g Balko (FR)—Ascella (FR)  **Dunkley, Gumienny, Mackenzie & Signy**
4 **COME DANCING (IRE),** 4, b g Fame And Glory—Minnie Ray (IRE)  **Come Dancing Partnership**
5 **COURTLY LOVE,** 8, b m Kayf Tara—Tessanoora  **Mrs S. McLean**
6 **DAVE AND BERNIE (IRE),** 6, b g Papal Bull—Iseult (IRE)  **Oliver Signy Racing Club**

## MR OLIVER SIGNY - continued

7 **DREAM DE DREAM (IRE)**, 9, ch m Flemensfirth (USA)—Rudy Renata (IRE) **The LSRFC SALVPS**
8 **ETAT MAJOR AULMES (FR)**, 7, b g Della Francesca (USA)—River Gold Aulmes (FR) **Mr & Mrs A. Signy**
9 **FIGHT FOR LOVE (FR)**, 8, b g Fuisse (FR)—Love Affair (FR)
10 **FRENCH PARADOXE (FR)**, 6, b g Day Flight—Sculture (FR) **Mick Fitzgerald Racing Club**
11 **LIKE THE SOUND (FR)**, 10, b g Soldier of Fortune (IRE)—Zalida (IRE) **STG Racing Partnership**
12 **MAD ABOUT SALLY (IRE)**, 6, b br m Califet (FR)—Lou's Coole Girl (IRE) **The LSRFC SALVPS**
13 **NO WORD OF A LIE**, 5, b g Milan—Agnese **Dunkley, Gumienny, Mackenzie & Signy**
14 **SAMBEZI (FR)**, 5, b g Rajsaman (FR)—Tunis (FR) **Mrs S. McLean**
15 **SOMETHING ROSIE (IRE)**, 7, b m Gold Well—Pakaradyssa (FR) **Mrs F. Kempe**
16 **TWITTERING (IRE)**, 4, b g Kodiac—Swallow Falls (IRE) **Oliver Signy Racing Club**

Other Owners: Mrs F. Kempe, Oliver Signy Racing Club, Mr A. Signy, Mrs C. B. Signy, Mr O. Signy, Mr B. P. J. Spiers.

**Head Lad:** Albert Ennis, **Racing Secretary:** Mrs Katherine Signy.

---

**491**  **MR DAVID SIMCOCK, Newmarket**
Postal: **The Office, Trillium Place, Birdcage Walk, Newmarket, Suffolk, CB8 0NE**
Contacts: **PHONE 01638 662968 MOBILE 07808 954109, 07702 851561 FAX 01638 663888**
**EMAIL david@davidsimcock.co.uk WEBSITE www.davidsimcock.co.uk**

1 **BLESS HIM (IRE)**, 7, b g Sea The Stars (IRE)—Happy Land (IRE)
2 **BURNISTON ROCKS**, 4, ch g Monsieur Bond (IRE)—Miss Fridaythorpe
3 **CLOSING SHOW**, 4, br f Intello (GER)—Kamarinskaya (USA)
4 **DEAL A DOLLAR**, 5, b g Frankel—Cape Dollar (IRE)
5 **DESERT ENCOUNTER (IRE)**, 9, b g Halling (USA)—La Chicana (IRE)
6 **DESERT FRIEND (IRE)**, 5, ch g Universal (IRE)—Assabiyya (IRE)
7 **EL SALVAJE**, 4, b g Dutch Art—Crying Lightening (IRE)
8 **FOLK DANCE**, 4, b f Golden Horn—Folk Opera (IRE)
9 **GREEN PLANET (IRE)**, 4, b g Australia—Maleha (IRE)
10 **INDIGO TIMES (IRE)**, 4, gr g Alhebayeb (IRE)—Easy Times
11 **ISPAHAN**, 4, ch g Lope de Vega (IRE)—Elle Galante (GER)
12 **MAGNETISED**, 4, b g Shamardal (USA)—Princess Nada
13 **MORLAIX**, 4, b g Mayson—Estemaala (USA)
14 **NONIOS (IRE)**, 9, b g Oasis Dream—Young and Daring (USA)
15 **OMNIVEGA (FR)**, 5, b g Siyouni (FR)—Vermentina (IRE)
16 **ORIENTAL MYSTIQUE**, 4, b f Kingman—Madame Chiang
17 **PAX BRITANNICA (IRE)**, 4, b f Zoffany (IRE)—Athreyaa
18 **RAAKIB ALHAWA (IRE)**, 5, b g Kingman—Starlet (IRE)
19 **REPERTOIRE**, 5, b g Bated Breath—Binche (USA)
20 **RODRIGO DIAZ**, 4, b g Golden Horn—Kitty Wells
21 **SMART CHAMPION**, 6, b g Teofilo (IRE)—Soryah (IRE)
22 **SOLAR SCREEN (IRE)**, 4, gr g Golden Horn—Screen Star (IRE)
23 **STARCZEWSKI (USA)**, 5, b g Magician (IRE)—Lucifer's Stone (USA)
24 **THOMAS LANFIERE (FR)**, 4, b g No Nay Never (USA)—Lexi The Princess (IRE)
25 **TIGER CRUSADE (FR)**, 4, b c No Nay Never (USA)—Folle Allure (FR)
26 **TOORA LOORA**, 4, ch f Nathaniel (IRE)—Victoria Regina (IRE)
27 **UNIVERSAL ORDER**, 5, ch g Universal (IRE)—My Order

### THREE-YEAR-OLDS

28 **AD INFINITUM**, b f Golden Horn—Madame Hoi (IRE)
29 **APPROACH THE LAND**, b c New Approach (IRE)—Royale Danehill (IRE)
30 **BILL PEYTO (IRE)**, b g Acclamation—Ardeola (GER)
31 **CARROTHERS (USA)**, b br c Mshawish (USA)—Queenofperfection (USA)
32 **CHEROKEE DANCE (USA)**, b br f Honor Code (USA)—Keowee Clai (USA)
33 **CLOVIS POINT (FR)**, b c Fastnet Rock (AUS)—Khaleesy (IRE)

## MR DAVID SIMCOCK - continued

34 **DEEP SIGH (FR),** b f Muhaarar—Sospira
35 **DIRHAM EMIRATI (IRE),** b g Vadamos (FR)—Allez Y (IRE)
36 **DUBAI EMPEROR (IRE),** b g Gleneagles (IRE)—Nateeja (IRE)
37 **EAST COAST ROAD (IRE),** ch c Iffraaj—Pacifica Highway (USA)
38 **FORGOTTEN REALM,** br g Oasis Dream—Tymora (USA)
39 **FRANTOIO,** b g Lope de Vega (IRE)—Alpine Spirit (IRE)
40 **GIFT OF STARS (IRE),** b br f Sea The Stars (IRE)—Twilight Sky
41 **HACKNESS HARRY,** b g Swiss Spirit—Miss Fridaythorpe
42 **HARVEST TIME (IRE),** b f Shalaa (IRE)—Muhadathat
43 **HEART OF THE SUN,** b f Fastnet Rock (AUS)—Heartless
44 **HEATH RISE,** b g Gleneagles (IRE)—Cubanita
45 **JUDGMENT CALL,** br c Pivotal—Madonna Dell'orto
46 B g Sepoy (AUS)—Kahalah Fantasy
47 **KANARI SENSE (USA),** b g Street Sense (USA)—Fortheloveofnell (IRE)
48 **LAST MISSION (FR),** br c Invincible Spirit (IRE)—Magic Mission
49 **LOWER STREET,** b f Kingman—Upper Street (IRE)
50 **LUCKINESS (FR),** gr c Mehmas (IRE)—Ventura Ice (IRE)
51 **MEXICAN SONG (IRE),** b f Vadamos (FR)—La Chicana (IRE)
52 B br c Temple City (USA)—Mien (IRE)
53 **MINDSPIN,** b g Shalaa (IRE)—Inner Sea (USA)
54 **MINT JULEP,** b f Helmet (AUS)—Ya Latif (IRE)
55 **ONESMOOTHOPERATOR (USA),** br c Dialed In (USA)—Sueno d'Oro (USA)
56 **ORIENTAL ART,** b c Archipenko (USA)—Robe Chinoise
57 **QR PASSION (USA),** b c Quality Road (USA)—Hailey d'Oro (USA)
58 **RANI OF JHANSI,** b f Invincible Spirit (IRE)—Madame Chiang
59 **RONAN ACCUSER,** b g Sepoy (AUS)—Boadicee
60 **SHENU (USA),** b c American Pharoah (USA)—Gitchee Goomie (USA)
61 **SHINING SUCCESS (IRE),** b f Awtaad (IRE)—Pivotal's Princess (IRE)
62 **STREET VIEW (IRE),** b c Awtaad (IRE)—Street Style (IRE)
63 **TERRIFY (IRE),** b f Galileo (IRE)—Terror (IRE)
64 **UNDERCOVER AGENT (IRE),** b c Kodiac—Multicolour Wave (IRE)
65 B f Dialed In (USA)—Unique Ride (USA)
66 **VICTORIA LINE (IRE),** b g Kingman—Islington (IRE)
67 **WOKE MEDIA (USA),** ch f Orb—Distorsionada (USA)

## TWO-YEAR-OLDS

68 B f 27/02 Twilight Son—Aiming (Highest Honor (FR)) (52000)
69 **AIMING HIGH,** ch f 13/03 Lope de Vega (IRE)—High Hopes (Zamindar (USA))
70 B br c 30/04 No Nay Never (USA)—Alabama Ashley (USA) (Tale of The Cat (USA)) (40000)
71 **BOUNCE THIS WAY,** b c 23/01 Showcasing—Bounce (Bahamian Bounty) (60000)
72 B c 07/02 Mastercraftsman (IRE)—Casila (IRE) (High Chaparral (IRE)) (130000)
73 **CHING SHIH (IRE),** b f 24/03 Lope de Vega (IRE)—Madame Chiang (Archipenko (USA))
74 **CHOLA EMPIRE,** b c 18/03 Territories (IRE)—Veena (FR) (Elusive City (USA))
75 **CROMARTY (FR),** b br f 13/02 Lope de Vega (IRE)—Carnachy (IRE) (Mastercraftsman (IRE))
76 **DALBY FOREST,** ch c 10/02 Equiano (FR)—Primrose Valley (Pastoral Pursuits)
77 **FLOWER MOON,** b f 17/03 Nathaniel (IRE)—Roanne (USA) (Lemon Drop Kid (USA))
78 Ch c 24/04 Siyouni (FR)—Folk Opera (IRE) (Singspiel (IRE)) (110000)
79 B c 15/03 El Kabeir (USA)—Impasse (Dansili) (40000)
80 Gr c 24/03 Lethal Force (IRE)—Kensington Gardens (Oasis Dream) (17000)
81 **KINGSTON JOY (IRE),** b f 04/04 Kingston Hill—Archetypal (IRE) (Cape Cross (IRE)) (27000)
82 B f 02/04 Lope de Vega (IRE)—Lady Darshaan (IRE) (High Chaparral (IRE)) (190000)
83 B c 14/01 Sea The Stars (IRE)—Legitimus (IRE) (Lawman (FR)) (97000)
84 **LITTLE RAVEN (IRE),** b c 26/03 Iffraaj—Azameera (IRE) (Azamour (IRE))
85 B br c 22/04 Ardad (IRE)—North East Bay (USA) (Prospect Bay (CAN)) (34000)
86 B f 10/05 Wootton Bassett—Reyamour (Azamour (IRE)) (65000)
87 B c 22/02 Tamayuz—Sakarya (IRE) (Duke of Marmalade (IRE)) (25000)
88 Gr c 09/02 Mastercraftsman (IRE)—Sworn Sold (GER) (Soldier Hollow) (26000)
89 B f 11/04 Intello (GER)—Tahirah (Green Desert (USA))
90 **THREE DIAMONDS (IRE),** b c 06/04 Night of Thunder (IRE)—L'Eglise (Le Havre (IRE)) (28000)

## MR DAVID SIMCOCK - continued

**91** B f 19/04 Lope de Vega (IRE)—Xaarienne (Xaar) (67000)
**92** Br f 29/01 Equiano (FR)—Zawiyah (Invincible Spirit (IRE)) (7000)
**93** B c 07/02 Ulysses (IRE)—Zoella (USA) (Invincible Spirit (IRE)) (70000)

**Owners:** Al Asayl Bloodstock Ltd, Sheikh J. D. Al Maktoum, Mr A. Al Mansoori, A. Al Shaikh, S. Ali, Mrs J. M. Annable, Australian Bloodstock, Mr W. Baker, Mr P. Booth, Mr R. G. W. Brown, Mr S. E. Chappell, Mr C. L. Chen, Chola Dynasty, J. M. Cook, K. A. Dasmal, Khalifa Dasmal & Bryan Payne, Mr D. P. Duffy, Mr E. Elhrari, Mr M. Eves, P. J. Gleeson, Mrs F. H. Hay, Mr S. M. A. Hillen, Mr A. Howells, Mrs A. Jackson, John Cook & Partner, Mr Jos & Mrs Jane Rodosthenous, Ms L. Judah, Khalifa Dasmal & Partners, J. A. Knight, Mr A. Menahi, Millingbrook Racing, Millingbrook Racing & Partners, Mr S Hillen & Ms L Judah, Mr C. J. Murfitt, Never Say Die & Star Bloodstock, Never Say Die Partnership, A. F. O'Callaghan, Mr R. O'Callaghan, Mr E. M. O'Connor, A. J. Perkins, Philip Booth & Peter Gleeson, A. M. Pickering, Qatar Racing Limited, Quantum Leap Racing XI, Miss K. Rausing, Mrs C. B. Rogers, A. Saeed, Sahara Thoroughbreds, Dr A. Sivananthan, Mrs K. Sivananthan, St Albans Bloodstock Limited, Star Bloodstock Racing, Mrs K. Stewart, Sun Bloodstock Sarl & Partners, Talentschmiede Racing, Tick Tock Partnership, Tony Perkins & Partners, Twenty Stars Partnership, Major M. G. Wyatt.

**Assistant Trainer:** Sam Goldsmith.

**Flat Jockey:** Jamie Spencer.

---

### MR DAN SKELTON, Alcester
Postal: **Lodge Hill, Shelfield Green, Shelfield, Alcester, Warwickshire, B49 6JR**
Contacts: **PHONE 01789 336339**
EMAIL office@danskeltonracing.com WEBSITE www.danskeltonracing.com

1 **ACCORDINGTOGINO (IRE)**, 8, ch g Perugino (USA)—Accordintomags (IRE) **Mrs Gill Duckworth & Mrs Pat Dry**
2 **ACROSS THE LINE (IRE)**, 6, b g Fame And Glory—La Protagonista (IRE) **Craig & Laura Buckingham**
3 **AGGY WITH IT (IRE)**, 7, b m Presenting—Agathe du Berlais (FR) **Andy & Sharon Measham**
4 **AHEADFULLOFDREAMS (IRE)**, 8, b g Sandmason—Aphra Benn (IRE) **Mr I. Lawrence**
5 **ALL SHOOK UP (IRE)**, 5, b g Fame And Glory—Kadalville (FR) **Mrs S. Magnier**
6 **ALLMANKIND**, 5, b g Sea The Moon (GER)—Wemyss Bay **W. J. and T. C. O. Gredley**
7 **ALNADAM (FR)**, 8, b g Poliglote—Rosadame (FR) **Mr B. J. C. Drew**
8 **AMBASSADOR (IRE)**, 4, b g Invincible Spirit (IRE)—Natural Bloom (IRE) **M Boothright R Lloyd**
9 **AMOOLA GOLD (GER)**, 8, b g Mamool (IRE)—Aughamore Beauty (IRE) **Mr & Mrs Gordon Pink**
10 **ANTUNES**, 7, b g Nathaniel (IRE)—Aigrette Garzette (IRE) **Mr M. Adams**
11 **ARONIUS (GER)**, 6, b g Pastorius (GER)—Aronia (IRE) **Mr M. Adams**
12 **ASHTOWN LAD (IRE)**, 7, b g Flemensfirth (USA)—Blossom Trix (IRE) **Mr & Mrs D. Yates**
13 **AUTHORIZED PURSUIT**, 4, gr f Authorized—Zariziyna (IRE) **Stonegrave Thoroughbreds**
14 **AZZURI**, 9, b g Azamour (IRE)—Folly Lodge **The Blind Squirrels**
15 **BENNY'S OSCAR (IRE)**, 6, b br g Oscar (IRE)—Benefit Ball (IRE) **Craig & Laura Buckingham**
16 **BENNYS KING (IRE)**, 10, b g Beneficial—Hellofafaithful (IRE) **Mezzone Family**
17 **BETTY GETAWAY**, 4, b f Getaway (GER)—At The Top (FR) **Judy Craymer & Nick Skelton**
18 **BLAKLION**, 12, b g Kayf Tara—Franciscaine (FR) **Mr & Mrs D. Yates**
19 **BORN SURVIVOR (IRE)**, 10, b g King's Theatre (IRE)—Bob's Flame (IRE) **Mrs G. Widdowson & Mrs R. Kelvin-Hughes**
20 **BREAKWATER BUOY (IRE)**, 5, br g Milan—Mega Mum (IRE) **Simon & Lisa Hobson**
21 **CABOT CLIFFS (IRE)**, 4, ch g Gleneagles (IRE)—Hallouella **Craig & Laura Buckingham**
22 **CADZAND (IRE)**, 6, b g Stowaway—Queens Mark (IRE) **Chelsea Thoroughbreds - Cadzand**
23 **CALICO (GER)**, 5, b g Soldier Hollow—Casanga (IRE) **Mr J. J. Reilly**
24 **CAPTAIN CHAOS (IRE)**, 10, ch g Golan—Times Have Changed (IRE) **Mike and Eileen Newbould**
25 **CARLOS FELIX (IRE)**, 4, ch g Lope de Vega (IRE)—Quad's Melody (IRE) **Mr & Mrs D. Yates**
26 **CH'TIBELLO (FR)**, 10, b g Sageburg (IRE)—Neicha (FR) **The Can't Say No Partnership**
27 4, B g Blue Bresil (FR)—Chasse En Mer (FR) **Mrs S. Carsberg**
28 **CHECKINFORSQUIRELS (IRE)**, 5, ch m Flemensfirth (USA)—Nivalf **Foxtrot Nh Racing Syndicate**
29 **COLDEN'S DREAM (IRE)**, 4, b g Ocovango—Now Were Broke (IRE) **Mr I F Gosden & Mr Dj Coles**
30 **COUSU MAIN (FR)**, 5, b g Buck's Boum (FR)—Just Pegasus (USA) **Kings Head Duffield Racing Partnership**
31 **CRAYLANDS**, 4, b f Golden Horn—Madame Defarge (USA) **W. J. and T. C. O. Gredley**
32 **CROOKS PEAK**, 8, b g Arcadio (GER)—Ballcrina Girl (IRE) **Simon & Lisa Hobson - Crooks Peak**

## MR DAN SKELTON - continued

33 DAZZLING GLORY (IRE), 6, b m Califet (FR)—Market Niche (IRE)
34 DEFINING BATTLE (IRE), 5, gr g Lope de Vega (IRE)—Royal Fortune (IRE)  **Mr & Mrs D. Yates**
35 DESTRIER (FR), 8, b g Voix du Nord (FR)—Razia (FR)  **Three Celts**
36 DIOMEDE DES MOTTES (FR), 8, ch g Kapgarde (FR)—Nellyssa Bleu (FR)  **Belbroughton Racing Club**
37 DOG OF WAR (FR), 7, b g Soldier of Fortune (IRE)—Zainzana (FR)  **Mr C. A. Donlon**
38 DON HOLLOW (GER), 4, b g Soldier Hollow—Donna Philippa (GER)  **Mr D. N. Skelton**
39 4, B f Walk In The Park (IRE)—Down By The Sea (IRE)  **Mrs John Magnier & Mrs Paul Shanahan**
40 DOYOUKNOWWHATIMEAN, 4, b g Martaline—Knar Mardy  **R. M. Kirkland**
41 ECLAIR D'AINAY (FR), 7, b br g Network (GER)—Etoile d'Ainay (FR)  **Mr J. Hales**
42 ELEVENERIFE (FR), 4, br g Full of Gold (FR)—Go Tic (FR)
43 ELLE EST BELLE, 5, b m Fame And Glory—Katalina  **Mrs S. Lawrence**
44 EMBOLE (FR), 7, b g Buck's Boum (FR)—Urielle Collonges (FR)  **Rio Gold Racing Club**
45 EMILY'S STAR, 4, b f Kayf Tara—Lisa du Chenet (FR)
46 EMMAS JOY (IRE), 8, bm Gold Well—Fame Jane (IRE)  **Julian Howl & Ian Tyrrell**
47 ENCORE CHAMPS (IRE), 7, b g Robin des Champs (FR)—Dani California  **Mr B. J. C. Drew**
48 ETALON (IRE), 4, br g Sholokhov (IRE)—So You Said (IRE)  **Mrs S. Lawrence**
49 EYREN (IRE), 6, b m Rip Van Winkle (IRE)—Ella Ransom (GER)  **Mrs Gill Duckworth & Mrs Pat Dry**
50 FAIR MOUNTAIN (GER), 9, b g Tiger Hill (IRE)—Fair Breeze (GER)  **Mr M. Adams**
51 FAIVOIR (FR), 6, b g Coastal Path—Qape Noir (FR)  **Mrs S. Lawrence**
52 FALCON SUN (FR), 7, b g Falco (USA)—Pray For Sun (FR)  **Mezzone Family**
53 FINISTERE (FR), 6, b g Coastal Path—Dundalk (FR)  **Mike and Eileen Newbould**
54 FIRAK (FR), 6, b g Fuisse (FR)—Nosika d'Airy (FR)  **Charles & Rachel Wilson**
55 FLASH THE STEEL (IRE), 9, b br g Craigsteel—Anna's Melody (IRE)  **Mr J. J. Reilly**
56 FLEGMATIK (FR), 6, ch g Fuisse (FR)—Crack d'Emble (FR)  **N. W. Lake**
57 FRANKEUR (FR), 6, b g Khalkevi (IRE)—Razia (FR)  **Mr D. Hanafin**
58 FRISSON COLLONGES (FR), 6, b g Coastal Path—Roxane Collonges (FR)  **Mr C. M. Giles**
59 GADJET D'AINAY (FR), 5, gr g Montmartre (FR)—Ne M'Oubliez Pas (FR)  **3 Sons**
60 GET A TONIC (IRE), 5, b m Getaway (GER)—Atomic Winner (IRE)
61 GET SKY HIGH (IRE), 6, ch m Getaway (GER)—Tell Me Emma (IRE)  **Mr & Mrs Gordon Pink**
62 GETARIVER (IRE), 8, br m Getaway (GER)—Watson River (IRE)  **Mr & Mrs Gordon Pink**
63 GETAWAY MAG (IRE), 7, b m Getaway (GER)—Aggies Girl (IRE)  **Mrs J. A. Watts**
64 GLOBAL FAMENGLORY (IRE), 5, b m Fame And Glory—Noble Pearl (GER)  **Mrs S. Carsberg**
65 GLOBAL HARMONY (IRE), 6, b m Flemensfirth (USA)—Violin Davis (FR)  **Mrs S. Carsberg**
66 GO STEADY, 9, b g Indian Danehill (IRE)—Pyleigh Lady  **Popham, Rogers**
67 GREATEST STAR (IRE), 5, gr g Lord du Sud (FR)—Sacree Mome (FR)  **Mrs J. A. Watts**
68 GREGOR (FR), 5, gr g Montmartre (FR)—Agathe du Berlais (FR)  **Coles, Langley D Skelton**
69 GYLO (IRE), 5, b g Tamayuz—She's A Character  **Owners Group 054**
70 HARDKORE (FR), 4, b g Cokoriko (FR)—Kario de Sormain (FR)  **Mr C. A. Donlon**
71 HATCHER (IRE), 8, b g Doyen (IRE)—African Keys (IRE)  **P. H. Betts**
72 HERCULE POINT (IRE), 4, ch g Network (GER)—Dam Royale (FR)  **Mr D. N. Skelton**
73 HORIZON D'AINAY (FR), 4, ch g Network (GER)—Sirene d'Ainay (FR)  **Simon & Lisa Hobson**
74 INTERCONNECTED, 7, br g Network (GER)—R de Rien Sivola (FR)  **Mr & Mrs D. Yates**
75 JAY JAY REILLY (IRE), 5, b g Fame And Glory—Garden City (IRE)  **Mr J. J. Reilly**
76 JERSEY (IRE), 5, br g Presenting—Synthe Davis (FR)  **Elouise Renouard M Boothright**
77 JET PLANE (IRE), 5, b g Jet Away—Court Gamble (IRE)  **Norman Lake & Susan Catchpole**
78 JOHN LOCKE, 4, ch g Mastercraftsman (IRE)—Sacred Shield  **Sullivan Bloodstock Ltd & Chris Giles**
79 KAYF HERNANDO, 5, b g Kayf Tara—Thrice Nice
80 KING D'ARGENT (FR), 6, ch g Kendargent (FR)—Ephigenie (IRE)  **Andrew Dick & John Stevenson**
81 KOBRA (GER), 4, ch f Farhh—Kheshvar (IRE)  **Chelsea Thoroughbreds & Partners**
82 KRACKA NUT, 4, b g Blue Bresil (FR)—More Like That (IRE)  **Stonegrave Thoroughbreds**
83 4, B f Montmartre (FR)—La Bombonera (FR)  **Mrs S. J. Faulks**
84 LAC DE CONSTANCE (FR), 5, gr g Martaline—Kendova (FR)  **Mr A. L. Cohen**
85 LAKOTA WARRIOR (IRE), 5, br g Valirann (FR)—Talkin Madam (IRE)  **A G J & Diver**
86 LANGER DAN (IRE), 5, b g Ocovango—What A Fashion (IRE)  **Mr C. A. Donlon**
87 LET'S GET REAL (FR), 5, b m Born To Sea (IRE)—Next To The Top  **Mr M. Fennessy**
88 LEYLAK (IRE), 4, b g Born To Sea (IRE)—Lidaya (USA)  **Notalotterry**
89 LOUGHAN (IRE), 6, b g Yeats (IRE)—Quiet Thought (IRE)  **Craig & Laura Buckingham**
90 MABELA, 7, b m Oscar (IRE)—Histoire de Moeurs (FR)  **S Smith & S Campion**
91 MARADA, 6, ch m Martaline—Kerada (FR)  **Mrs J. S. Chugg**
92 MARRACUDJA (FR), 10, b g Martaline—Memorial (FR)  **Foxtrot Racing Marracudja**

# MR DAN SKELTON - continued

93 **MESSAGE TO MARTHA**, 6, b m Milan—Message Personnel (FR) **R. K. Aston**
94 **MIDNIGHT AURORA**, 8, ch m Midnight Legend—Bekkaria (FR) **Rio Gold Racing Club**
95 **MIDNIGHT RIVER**, 6, ch g Midnight Legend—Well Connected **Mr Frank McAleavy & Mr Ian McAleavy**
96 **MOLLY OLLYS WISHES**, 7, b m Black Sam Bellamy (IRE)—September Moon **West Mercia Fork Trucks Ltd**
97 **MONSIEUR D'ARQUE (IRE)**, 7, b g Muhtathir—Nervous Breakdown (FR) **Mr I. Lawrence**
98 **MY DROGO**, 6, b g Milan—My Petra **Mr & Mrs R. G. Kelvin-Hughes**
99 **NIGHT IN MANHATTAN**, 5, b g Kayf Tara—One Gulp **Share My Dream**
100 **NO GETAWAY (IRE)**, 8, ch g Getaway (GER)—Nonnetia (FR) **Dick, Keenan, Sawer, Stevenson**
101 **NOT THAT FUISSE (FR)**, 8, b g Fuisse (FR)—Edelmira (FR) **Mr C. A. Donlon**
102 **NUBE NEGRA (SPA)**, 7, br g Dink (FR)—Manly Dream (FR) **Mr T. Spraggett**
103 **NURSE SUSAN (FR)**, 4, ch f Doctor Dino (FR)—Hembra (FR) **Mr C. A. Donlon**
104 **OFF THE HOOK (IRE)**, 9, b m Getaway (GER)—Call Her Again (IRE) **Mrs I. Hodge**
105 **OLDGRANGEWOOD**, 10, b g Central Park (IRE)—Top of The Class (IRE) **Chris Giles & Sandra Giles**
106 **PARKIN FINE**, 4, b f Blue Bresil (FR)—Pumped Up Kicks (IRE) **Stuart & Shelly Parkin**
107 **PERCY'S WORD**, 7, b g Sir Percy—Laverre (IRE) **Mezzone Family**
108 **PLAYFUL SAINT (FR)**, 6, b g Saint des Saints (FR)—Playact (IRE) **Mr & Mrs J. D. Cotton**
109 **PROSCHEMA (IRE)**, 6, ch g Declaration of War (USA)—Notable **Empire State Racing Partnership**
110 **PROTEKTORAT (FR)**, 6, b g Saint des Saints (FR)—Protektion (FR) **Sir A Ferguson G Mason J Hales & L Hales**
111 **QUID PRO QUO (IRE)**, 5, ch g Beat Hollow—Thieving Gypsy (IRE) **Mr J. P. McManus**
112 **QUIET FLOW**, 6, b g Sholokhov (IRE)—Sardagna (FR) **Mr C. A. Donlon**
113 **REAL STONE**, 6, b g Arvico (FR)—Stoney Path **Mrs S. C. Welch**
114 **REILLY (IRE)**, 5, b g Milan—Flowers On Sunday (IRE) **Mr J. J. Reilly**
115 **RIGGS (IRE)**, 6, b g Mahler—Cousin Kizzy (IRE) **Noel Fehily Racing Syndicates - Riggs**
116 **RIVER LEGEND (IRE)**, 5, ch g Ocovango—China Reel (IRE) **R. M. Kirkland**
117 **ROBIN GOLD (IRE)**, 8, b m Gold Well—One Song (IRE) **Rio Gold Racing Club**
118 **ROCK LEGEND (IRE)**, 4, b g Maxios—Moraine **Owners Group 073**
119 **ROCKSTAR RONNIE (IRE)**, 6, b g Stowaway—Dimona (IRE) **Highclere Thoroughbred Racing - Rockstar**
120 **ROKSANA (IRE)**, 9, b m Dubai Destination (USA)—Talktothetail (IRE) **Mrs S. J. Faulks**
121 **ROMAIN DE SENAM (FR)**, 9, b g Saint des Saints (FR)—Salvatrixe (FR) **Mr C. M. Giles**
122 **SAIL AWAY (FR)**, 5, gr g Martaline—Baraka du Berlais (FR) **Mr & Mrs J. D. Cotton**
123 **SEVEN NO TRUMPS (IRE)**, 6, b g Milan—Ballyknock Present (IRE) **Mr Frank McAleavy & Mr Ian McAleavy**
124 **SHAKE A LEG (IRE)**, 4, b g Exceleration (IRE)—Sos Brillante (CHI) **Kings Head Duffield Racing Partnership**
125 **SHAN BLUE (IRE)**, 7, b g Shantou (USA)—Lady Roberta (IRE) **Mr C. A. Donlon**
126 **SHANNON BRIDGE (IRE)**, 8, ch g Flemensfirth (USA)—Bridgequarter Lady (IRE) **M. Boothright**
127 **SHE'S GINA (GER)**, 8, b m It's Gino (GER)—Song of Night (GER) **Four Candles Partnership**
128 **SHENTRI (FR)**, 4, b g Sri Putra—Shentala (FR) **Mr J. Lane**
129 **SIGNAL POINT (IRE)**, 5, br m Fame And Glory—Derravaragh Native (IRE) **Nick Skelton & Enda Carroll**
130 **SIMPLY LOVELEH**, 8, b m Beneficial—Pippedatthepost **Mr J. J. Reilly**
131 **SOFIA'S ROCK (FR)**, 7, b g Rock of Gibraltar (IRE)—Princess Sofia (UAE) **Mezzone Family 1**
132 **SOFTKORE (FR)**, 5, b g Cokoriko (FR)—Nakille (FR) **Mr C. A. Donlon**
133 **SOUL EMOTION (FR)**, 8, b g Martaline—Second Emotion (FR) **Mr & Mrs J. D. Cotton**
134 **SOYOUTHINKSOAGAIN (IRE)**, 6, b g So You Think (NZ)—Al Saqiya (USA) **Mr I. Lawrence**
135 **SPIRITOFTHEGAMES (IRE)**, 9, b g Darsi (FR)—Lucy Walters (IRE) **N. W. Lake**
136 **STEPNEY CAUSEWAY**, 4, b g New Approach (IRE)—Wake Up Call **W. J. and T. C. O. Gredley**
137 **SUPREMELY LUCKY (IRE)**, 9, b g Milan—Lucky Supreme (IRE) **Mr M. Olden**
138 **TERRIERMAN (IRE)**, 7, br g Getaway (GER)—Dibella (IRE) **Mr & Mrs Price & Mr Keith Loads**
139 4, B g Presenting—The Folkes Choice
140 **THE HOAX**, 6, br g Great Pretender (IRE)—Lily Potter **James and Jean Potter Ltd**
141 **THE KING OF RYHOPE**, 5, ch g Malinas (GER)—Eleven Fifty Nine **Sullivan Bloodstock Ltd & Chris Giles**
142 **THE MULCAIR (IRE)**, 7, b g Flemensfirth (USA)—Black Lassie (IRE) **Mr D. W. Fox**
143 **THIRD TIME LUCKI (IRE)**, 6, br g Arcadio (GER)—Definite Valley (IRE) **Mike and Eileen Newbould**
144 **TOMMY RAPPER (IRE)**, 10, b g Milan—Supreme Evening (IRE) **Judy Craymer & Nick Skelton**
145 **UNEXPECTED PARTY (FR)**, 6, gr g Martaline—Reform Act (USA) **The Unexpected Party Syndicate**
146 **VERY FIRST TIME**, 9, b g Champs Elysees—Like A Virgin (IRE) **The Can't Say No Partnership**
147 **VIGILANCE (IRE)**, 4, b g Flemensfirth (USA)—Erins Stage (IRE) **Simon & Lisa Hobson**
148 **VISION DU PUY (FR)**, 6, b m Vision d'Etat (FR)—Fontaine Guerard (FR) **Mr J. P. McManus**
149 **VIVA LAVILLA (IRE)**, 5, br g Getaway (GER)—Viva Forever (FR) **Mr & Mrs D. Yates**
150 **WAR CALL (FR)**, 5, gr g Martaline—Bourbonnaise (FR) **Dick and Mandy Higgins**
151 **WEST TO THE BRIDGE (IRE)**, 8, b g Flemensfirth (USA)—Godlylady (IRE) **Mr P. J. Tierney**
152 **WHISPERING GYPSY (IRE)**, 6, ch m Beat Hollow—Thieving Gypsy (IRE) **Foxtrot Nh Racing Syndicate**

## MR DAN SKELTON - continued

153 **WHITE WALKER**, 6, gr g Dream Eater (IRE)—Soleil Sauvage **Winter Gold Racing**
154 **WILD ROMANCE (IRE)**, 6, br m Kalanisi (IRE)—Aboo Lala (IRE) **Masomo**
155 **WILDE ABOUT OSCAR (IRE)**, 6, b g Oscar (IRE)—Baie Barbara (IRE) **Mike and Eileen Newbould**
156 **WINTER OF YORK**, 5, b g Kayf Tara—Shady Anne **Mike and Eileen Newbould**

### THREE-YEAR-OLDS

157 **KNOTTY ASH (IRE)**, b c Most Improved (IRE)—Pushkar **Owners Group 070**

**Other Owners:** Mr D. Abraham, Mr D. Balchin, M. Boothright, Mr C. Buckingham, Mrs L. K. Buckingham, Ms J. S. Campion, Mr E. Carroll, Mrs S. Carsberg, Chelsea Thoroughbreds Ltd, Mr D. J. Coles, Miss J. Craymer, Mr A. D. Dick, Mr J. Diver, Mrs P. Dry, Mrs G. Duckworth, Mrs L. Fellows, Sir A. Ferguson, Foxtrot Racing Management Ltd, Mrs A. E. Giles, Mr C. M. Giles, Mr J. B. Gilruth, Mr I. F. Gosden, Mr J. R. Hales, Miss L. J. Hales, Mrs A. J. Higgins, Mr R. S. Higgins, Ms L. C. Hobson, Mr S. E. Hobson, Simon & Lisa Hobson, Mr J. Howl, Johnston Racing Ltd, Mr K. D. Jones, R. G. Kelvin-Hughes, N. W. Lake, Mr D. E. Langley, Mr R. B. Lloyd, K. F. J. Loads, Mr K. MacLennan, Mrs E. Magnier, Mr J. P. Magnier, Mrs S. Magnier, G. A. Mason, Mr F. McAleavy, Mr I. McAleavy, Mr A. R. Measham, Mrs S. M. Measham, Mr G. G. Mezzone, Mr L. M. Mezzone, Mrs S. M. Mezzone, Mrs E. E. Newbould, Mr J. M. Newbould, Mr H. J. O'Reilly, Mrs S. Parkin, Mr S. J. Parkin, Mr G. K. G. Pink, Mrs K. M. Pink, P. F. Popham, Mrs J. Price, Mr N. Price, Miss E. d. V. Renouard, Mr M. P. Rogers, Mrs L. M. Shanahan, Mr D. N. Skelton, Mr N. Skelton, Mrs S. Smith, Anthony Speelman, Mr M. Speelman, Mr J. M. Stevenson, Sullivan Bloodstock Limited, Mr E. D. Tynan, Mr I. Tyrrell, C. M. Wilson, Mrs R. E. Wilson, Mrs A. V. Yates, Mr D. Yates.

**Assistant Trainer:** Tom Messenger. **Head Lad:** Tolley Dean, Nick Pearce.

**NH Jockey:** Bridget Andrews, Harry Skelton. **Amateur Jockey:** Mr Murray Dodd, Mr Tristan Durrell.

---

**493** **MRS PAM SLY, Peterborough**
Postal: **Singlecote, Thorney, Peterborough, Cambridgeshire, PE6 0PB**
Contacts: **PHONE 01733 270212 MOBILE 07850 511267**
**EMAIL pamslyracing@btconnect.com**

1 **ACERTAIN CIRCUS**, 11, ch g Definite Article—Circus Rose **Mrs P. M. Sly**
2 **ALL MY LOVE (IRE)**, 9, b m Lord Shanakill (USA)—Afilla **D. L. Bayliss**
3 **BELLICA**, 4, b f War Command (USA)—Asteroidea **Michael H. Sly & Mrs Pam Sly**
4 **DARK SPEC**, 6, b h Dark Angel (IRE)—Speciosa (IRE) **M. H. Sly, Dr T. Davies & Mrs P. Sly**
5 **DAZZLING DAN (IRE)**, 5, b g Dandy Man (IRE)—Scrumptious **Thorney Racing Partners**
6 **EILEENDOVER**, 4, b f Canford Cliffs (IRE)—Specialty (IRE) **Michael H. Sly & Mrs Pam Sly**
7 **ELEANOR DUMONT**, 4, b f Westerner—Circus Rose **Mrs P. M. Sly**
8 **FRANSHAM**, 7, b g Sulamani (IRE)—Circus Rose **G. Libson,D. Bayliss,T. Davies & P. Sly**
9 **GAYTON**, 7, ch m Haafhd—Wistow **Mrs P. M. Sly**
10 **GENTLE ROSE**, 5, b m Gentlewave (IRE)—Iconic Rose **The Stablemates**
11 **GROUSEMAN**, 4, b g Kyllachy—Speciosa (IRE) **M. H. Sly, Dr T. Davies & Mrs P. Sly**
12 **HAAFAPIECE**, 8, ch g Haafhd—Bonnet's Pieces **Mrs I. A. Coles**
13 **JOHN CLARE (IRE)**, 5, b g Poet's Voice—Specialty (IRE) **Michael H. Sly & Mrs Pam Sly**
14 **KEEPUP KEVIN**, 7, b g Haafhd—Black Salix (USA) **Mrs P. M. Sly**
15 **LIAM'S LASS (IRE)**, 5, b m Dandy Man (IRE)—Rupa (IRE) **Mrs P. M. Sly**
16 **MIXEDWAVE (IRE)**, 4, b g Gentlewave (IRE)—Chicklemix **Mrs P. M. Sly**
17 **PYRRHA LAGOON**, 4, ch g Universal (IRE)—Kaloni (IRE) **Mrs P. M. Sly**
18 **RED DIAMOND (IRE)**, 5, b g Elusive Pimpernel (USA)—Truly Precious (IRE) **Mrs R. L. Banks**
19 **SILKSTONE (IRE)**, 5, b g Alhebayeb (IRE)—Fine Silk (USA) **Pam's People**
20 **TAKEIT EASY**, 6, b g Malinas (GER)—Circus Rose **Pam's People**
21 **WELLAND**, 8, ch g Beat Hollow—Circus Rose **Mrs P. M. Sly**
22 **WILLIAM CODY**, 4, b g Westerner—Wistow **Mrs P. M. Sly**
23 **XCITATIONS**, 6, b g Universal (IRE)—Bonnet's Pieces **G. Libson,D. Bayliss,T. Davies & P. Sly**

### THREE-YEAR-OLDS

24 **DUBH ROSE**, b g Black Sam Bellamy (IRE)—Iconic Rose **The Stablemates**
25 **SPECIAL MAYSON**, b g Mayson—Specialty (IRE) **Michael H. Sly & Mrs Pam Sly**

## MRS PAM SLY - continued

**Other Owners:** D. L. Bayliss, Dr T. J. W. Davies, Mr S. R. T. Jones, Mr G. A. Libson, M. H. S. Sly, Mrs P. M. Sly.

**Assistant Trainer:** Chris Scudder.

**NH Jockey:** Kielan Woods. **Amateur Jockey:** Miss Gina Andrews.

---

**494**    **MR DAVID SMAGA, Lamorlaye**
Postal: **17 Voie de la Grange des Pres, 60260 Lamorlaye, France**
Contacts: **PHONE +33 3 44 21 50 05 MOBILE +33 6 07 83 72 87 FAX +33 3 44 21 53 56**
**EMAIL david-smaga@wanadoo.fr**

1. **DOMAGNANO (IRE)**, 6, b g Planteur—Daloisi
2. **EL MANIFICO (FR)**, 6, b h High Chaparral (IRE)—Envoutement (FR) **Mr A. Louis-Dreyfus**
3. **FIVE ICE CUBES (FR)**, 6, ch h Rip Van Winkle (IRE)—Victoria College (FR) **Mr A. M. Haddad**
4. **FOFO (FR)**, 5, ch h Kendargent (FR)—Envoutement (FR) **A. Louis-Dreyfus, D. Smaga**
5. **FRAOULA**, 4, ch f Le Havre (IRE)—Mezzo Mezzo (FR)
6. **HAVENVOUS (FR)**, 4, ch g Le Havre (IRE)—Envoutement (FR) **A. Louis-Dreyfus, D. Smaga**
7. **JEITOSO BAYER (BRZ)**, 9, b h Peintre Celebre (USA)—Kyanite (BRZ) **Benjamin Steinbruch**
8. **KIWI GREEN SUITE (BRZ)**, 8, b h T H Approval (USA)—Hypnose (BRZ) **Benjamin Steinbruch**
9. **MAKTAVA (FR)**, 6, b h Makfi—Poltava (FR)
10. **MILLFIELD (FR)**, 8, b h Whipper (USA)—Victoria College (FR) **Mr A. M. Haddad**
11. **NAMASSE (BRZ)**, 5, gr m T. H. Approval—Yiddish Mama
12. **NAO DA MAIS (BRZ)**, 5, b h T. H. Approval—Espetacular
13. **NUBLE (URU)**, 5, gr m Hero Of The Night—Brilliant Speed
14. **PIKES PEAK (FR)**, 5, b m Sepoy (AUS)—Pietra Santa (FR) **Aleyrion Bloodstock Ltd, David Smaga**
15. **PRIMUS INCITATUS (IRE)**, 10, ch h Mastercraftsman (IRE)—Chaibia (IRE) **Mr A. M. Haddad**
16. **SAPHIRSIDE (IRE)**, 12, b g Elusive City (USA)—Silirisia (FR) **Mr G. Augustin-Normand**
17. **SITUMELEDEMANDAIS (FR)**, 4, b g Oasis Dream—Scalambra
18. **STAR LAD (FR)**, 4, b c Planteur (IRE)—La Fee de Breizh (FR) **Mr A. Louis-Dreyfus**
19. **VILARO (FR)**, 8, b h Whipper (USA)—Envoutement (FR) **Mr A. Louis-Dreyfus**

### THREE-YEAR-OLDS

20. **AMERICAN GENTLEMAN (FR)**, b g Shalaa—Aquamerica
21. **BARC (FR)**, b c Anodin—Bomba Nova
22. **EXCITING (FR)**, b c Exosphere—Pietra Santa
23. **GOUVIEUX (FR)**, b c Le Havre (IRE)—Envoutement
24. **INCARVILLE (FR)**, gr f Wootton Bassett—Ilhabela
25. **INTELLECTUELLE (FR)**, ch f Intello—Mezzo Mezzo (FR)
26. **LARCHAMP (FR)**, b g Wootton Bassett—Larme
27. **LESSAY (FR)**, b c Kendargent—Lumiere du soir
28. **MATE SISTER (FR)**, b f Siyouni—Tierra Luna
29. **MISEREY (FR)**, b f Rajsaman—Mysterious Champ
30. **NEMBO KID (FR)**, b c Siyouni—Victoria College
31. **PINGO (FR)**, b f Anodin—Sula's Charm
32. **PRELUNA (FR)**, b f Iffraaj—Porza
33. **TRANSFORMER (FR)**, b c Scissor Kick—Northern Ocean

Trainer did not supply details of their two-year-olds.

**Other Owners:** Ecurie Haras du Cadran, Mr A. M. Haddad.

**495**

**MR BRYAN SMART, Hambleton**
Postal: Hambleton House, Sutton Bank, Thirsk, North Yorkshire, YO7 2HA
Contacts: PHONE 01845 597481 MOBILE 07748 634797 FAX 01845 597480
EMAIL office@bryansmart.plus.com WEBSITE www.bryansmart-racing.com

1 ANTAGONIZE, 5, b g Epaulette (AUS)—Hakuraa (IRE) **Crossfields Racing**
2 ASTROZONE, 4, ch f Fast Company (IRE)—Rhal (IRE) **Crossfields Racing**
3 DEBAWTRY (IRE), 6, b m Camacho—Muluk (IRE) **Akebar Park Leisure Ltd**
4 DUE A WIN, 4, b g Due Diligence (USA)—Malelane (IRE) **D. Blake,C. Dinsdale,S.McCay & M.Beadle**
5 FENDALE, 9, b g Exceed And Excel (AUS)—Adorn **Mr S. Chappell & Partner**
6 KENTUCKYCONNECTION (USA), 8, b g Include (USA)—Youcanringmybell (USA) **Woodcock Electrical Limited**
7 KISKADEE, 4, b f Mukhadram—Generously Gifted **Mr P. Darling & Mrs A. Smith**
8 MYTHMAKER, 9, b g Major Cadeaux—Mythicism **Crossfields Racing**
9 NORTHERNPOWERHOUSE, 5, b g Harbour Watch (IRE)—Mortitia **Mr Michael Moses & Mr Terry Moses**
10 PALAZZO, 5, b g Morpheus—Sweet Power **Mr B. Smart**
11 RED PIKE (IRE), 10, ch g Kheleyf (USA)—Fancy Feathers (IRE) **Mr T.Eyre & Mr P.Watson**
12 REDZONE, 4, b g Sepoy (AUS)—Mythicism **Crossfields Racing**
13 SIYAHAMBA (IRE), 7, ch g Helmet (AUS)—Kalabunga (IRE) **Mr B. Smart**
14 SWISS CONNECTION, 5, b g Swiss Spirit—Sofonisba **Woodcock Electrical Limited**
15 WRENTHORPE, 6, b g Hellvelyn—Milly-M **Dan Maltby Bloodstock Limited & Mr B. Smart**

## THREE-YEAR-OLDS

16 BLACKBERRY, b f Brazen Beau (AUS)—She's A Worldie (IRE) **Mr S. Chappell & Partner**
17 BLAZING SON, ch g Mayson—Emblaze **The Smart Emblaze Partnership**
18 EQUATE, b c Equiano (FR)—Spontaneity (IRE) **Crossfields Racing**
19 HAGAR (IRE), b f Epaulette (AUS)—Sharqawiyah **Mr B. Smart**
20 HEART THROB, b f Brazen Beau (AUS)—Generously Gifted **Mr M. Barber Racing**
21 PENOMBRE, b g Twilight Son—Hayba **The Unscrupulous Judges**
22 PORTH DIANA (IRE), b f Cable Bay (IRE)—Musicora **Ceffyl Racing**
23 PRUDHOE, b f Heeraat (IRE)—Hakuraa (IRE) **Dan Maltby Bloodstock Limited**
24 REGIMENTO, b g Casamento (IRE)—Last Dance **Mrs Freda Moody & Mr Bryan Smart**
25 SIR TITUS (IRE), ch c Dandy Man (IRE)—Moss Top (IRE) **Mr Michael Moses & Mr Terry Moses**
26 UNLEASH, gr g Showcasing—Two In The Pink (IRE) **Michael & Terry Moses & Partner**
27 ZOOM STAR, b f Mayson—Chinaconnection (IRE) **Woodcock Electrical Limited**

## TWO-YEAR-OLDS

28 BOND CHAIRMAN, br c 02/03 Kodiac—Wunders Dream (IRE) (Averti (IRE)) (120000) **Bond Thoroughbred Limited**
29 BOND POWER, b c 05/02 War Command (USA)—Rhal (IRE) (Rahy (USA)) (25000) **Bond Thoroughbred Limited**
30 DOOMSDAY, b c 04/02 Lethal Force (IRE)—Ayasha (Indesatchel (IRE)) **Crossfields Racing**
31 DRAWDOWN, b f 27/03 Profitable (IRE)—Choisette (Choisir (AUS)) (23000) **Crossfields Racing**
32 B f 25/01 Fountain of Youth (IRE)—Finalize (Firebreak) **Middleham Park Racing LXXX & Partners**
33 FIREBOMB, b c 03/04 Swiss Spirit—Emblaze (Showcasing) **Crossfields Racing**
34 B c 06/05 Mehmas (IRE)—Gatamalata (IRE) (Spartacus (IRE)) (19048)
35 HIGHLAND QUEEN (IRE), b f 16/04 Acclamation—
Medicean Queen (IRE) (Medicean) (26667) **Moody, Thompson & Powell**
36 INSTINCTION, b f 12/02 Brazen Beau (AUS)—
Spontaneity (IRE) (Holy Roman Emperor (IRE)) (16000) **Crossfields Racing**
37 LADY OF YAPHAM (IRE), ch f 14/04 Twilight Son—
Danehill Destiny (Danehill Dancer (IRE)) (18095) **Bond Thoroughbred Limited**
38 B br f 25/03 Showcasing—Luna Moon (Equiano (FR)) (16000) **Rj Cornelius, G Godfrey & Partner**
39 POLITICISM, b f 27/02 Churchill (IRE)—Mythicism (Oasis Dream) (40000) **Crossfields Racing**
40 PRINCESS KARINE, b f 11/03 Aclaim (IRE)—Hakuraa (IRE) (Elnadim (USA)) (9524) **Mr N. Derbyshire & Partner**
41 PROJECT DANTE, ch c 26/02 Showcasing—
Thatsallimssaying (IRE) (Dandy Man (IRE)) (115000) **Bond Thoroughbred Limited**
42 B r f 18/03 Brazen Beau (AUS)—Romp (Pivotal) (17000) **Mr Michael Moses & Mr Terry Moses**
43 B f 29/03 Twilight Son—She's A Worldie (IRE) (Kodiac) **Mr S. Chappell & Partner**
44 B c 05/04 Hellvelyn—Vanity (IRE) (Thatching) (17143) **The Smart Set**
45 WHEAL KITTY, b f 24/03 Charming Thought—Katabatik Katie (Sir Percy) (4000) **Mrs P. A. Clark**
46 WHITEANDBLUE, b f 24/03 Fountain of Youth (IRE)—Whiteandgold (Major Cadeaux) **Crossfields Racing**

## MR BRYAN SMART - continued

**Other Owners:** M. Barber, Mr M. J. Beadle, Mr D. S. Blake, Mr M. G. Bullock, Mrs T. Bullock, Mr S. E. Chappell, R. J. Cornelius, Crossfields Racing, Mr P. A. Darling, Mr N. V. Derbyshire, Mr J. C. Dinsdale, Mr A D Eyre, Mr G. Godfrey, Mrs A. C. Hudson, Mr S. McCay, Middleham Park Racing LXXX, Mrs F. B. Moody, Mr M. Moses, Mr T. J. Moses, R. A. Page, T. S. Palin, D. F. Powell, M. Prince, Mr B. Smart, Mrs A. N. Smith, Mr S. Thompson, Mr P. J. Watson, Woodcock Electrical Ltd.

**Assistant Trainer:** Kevin Edmunds, Victoria Smart, **Pupil Assistant:** Beth Smart.

**Flat Jockey:** Graham Lee. **Apprentice Jockey:** Jade Goodwin.

---

### 496 MR JULIAN SMITH, Tirley
Postal: **Tirley Court, Tirley, Gloucester**
Contacts: **PHONE 01452 780461 MOBILE 07748 901175 FAX 01452 780461**
**EMAIL nicola.smith9156@o2.co.uk**

1 **CARO DES FLOS (FR)**, 9, b g Tiger Groom—Royale Marie (FR) **Mrs J.A. Benson & Miss S.N. Benson**
2 **DIAMOND ROSE**, 9, b m Sagamix (FR)—Swiss Rose **Grand Jury Partnership**
3 **FINE BY HER**, 5, b m Shirocco (GER)—High Benefit (IRE) **Mrs J.A. Benson & Miss S.N. Benson**
4 **IONA DAYS (IRE)**, 16, br g Epistolaire (IRE)—Miss Best (FR) **Mrs J.A. Benson & Miss S.N. Benson**
5 **MIDNIGHT SENSATION**, 9, gr m Proclamation (IRE)—Midnight Ocean **Exors of the Late Mr D. E. S. Smith**
6 **PENNIES AND POUNDS**, 14, b m Sir Harry Lewis (USA)—Sense of Value **Exors of the Late Mr D. E. S. Smith**
7 4, B f Black Sam Bellamy (IRE)—Shayana **Grand Jury Partnership**
8 **THE RORY STORY (IRE)**, 10, b g Flemensfirth (USA)—Phardester (IRE) **Exors of the Late Mr D. E. S. Smith**

**Other Owners:** Mrs J. A. Benson, Miss S. N. Benson.

**Assistant Trainer:** Mrs Nicky Smith.

**NH Jockey:** Mark Grant, Sam Twiston-Davies. **Amateur Jockey:** Mr J. M. Ridley.

---

### 497 MR MARTIN SMITH, Newmarket
Postal: **Stable Cottage, Calder Park, Hamilton Road, Newmarket, Suffolk, CB8 0NY**
Contacts: **MOBILE 07712 493589**
**WEBSITE www.martinsmithracing.com**

1 **ALEATORIC (IRE)**, 5, b g Dylan Thomas (IRE)—Castalian Spring (IRE) **Mr M. P. B. Smith**
2 **BREAK THE RULES**, 5, br m Aussie Rules (USA)—Fairy Slipper **Mr Robert P Clarke & Partners**
3 **FRIENDS DON'T ASK**, 6, b g Champs Elysees—Kintyre **Mr Robert P Clarke & Partners**
4 **IN THE RED (IRE)**, 8, b g Elusive Pimpernel (USA)—Roses From Ridey (IRE) **Sunville Rail Limited**
5 **LADY PENDRAGON**, 4, b f Camelot—Arthur's Girl **Sunville Rail Limited**
6 **OFTHESEA**, 5, ch m Gentlewave (IRE)—Miss Duffy **Andrea & Smith Racing**

### THREE-YEAR-OLDS

7 **MORANI KALI**, ch g Charming Thought—Crystal Moments **Mr M. P. B. Smith**
8 **RISKY BUSINESS (IRE)**, ch g Mastercraftsman (IRE)—Duljanah (IRE) **Power Distribution Support Ltd**
9 **ZEN DANCER**, b c Equiano (FR)—Inagh River **Lord R. Kemshell**

### TWO-YEAR-OLDS

10 B c 29/03 Helmet (AUS)—Beyond Fashion (Motivator) (1500)
11 B f 25/01 Excelebration (IRE)—Castalian Spring (IRE) (Oasis Dream) **The Affluence Partnership**
12 B c 29/04 Aclaim (IRE)—Inagh River (Fasliyev (USA)) (23810)

**Other Owners:** Mr R. P. Clarke, Miss A. R. Hurley, Mrs R. T. Rennie, Mr M. P. B. Smith.

**Apprentice Jockey:** Jacob Clark.

## 498 MISS PAULA SMITH, Malton
Postal: **Woodyard Barn, Ruffin Lane, Eddlethorpe, Malton, North Yorkshire, YO17 9QU**
Contacts: **PHONE 07760 247207**
EMAIL Paulamsmith4@gmail.com

1 **BRAWNY,** 5, b g Dark Angel (IRE)—Natty Bumppo (IRE)  **Miss M. Chaston**
2 **DALLAS COWBOY (IRE),** 11, b g Beneficial—Watson River (IRE)  **Miss P. M. Smith**
3 **HALLOWED GROUND (IRE),** 6, b g Mahler—Castlehaven (IRE)  **Miss P. M. Smith**
4 **MELROSE JACK,** 4, ch g Shirocco (GER)—Daisies Adventure (IRE)  **Miss M. Chaston**
5 **MINSTREL SONG,** 8, br g Dark Angel (IRE)—Sing Acapella (IRE)  **Miss P. M. Smith**
6 **MOLLY WHUPPIE,** 8, br m Beat Hollow—Daisies Adventure (IRE)  **Miss P. M. Smith**
7 **PETRULER,** 4, b f Native Ruler—Petrarchick (USA)
8 **SPORTING PRESS (IRE),** 8, b g Flemensfirth (USA)—Rudy Renata (IRE)  **Miss P. M. Smith**

## 499 MR R. MIKE SMITH, Galston
Postal: **West Loudoun Farm, Galston, Ayrshire, KA4 8PB**
Contacts: **PHONE 01563 822062 MOBILE 07711 692122**
EMAIL mike@mikesmithracing.co.uk WEBSITE www.mikesmithracing.co.uk

1 **AKAMANTO (IRE),** 7, b g Cape Cross (IRE)—Allofus (IRE)  **Reid Ross Smith**
2 **ASTUTE BOY (IRE),** 7, b g Arcano (IRE)—Spa  **Mr R. M. Smith**
3 **COLE NOIR,** 4, b g Sepoy (AUS)—Just Like A Woman  **Whyte, Hamilton & the Covenanters**
4 **COOPERS BOY (IRE),** 5, b g Arcadio (GER)—Detonante (FR)  **Serena & Michael Smith**
5 **DON'T NEED TO KNOW (IRE),** 7, b g Flemensfirth (USA)—Phardester (IRE)  **Mr D. Orr**
6 **EAST HARLEM (IRE),** 5, b g Leading Light (IRE)—Jill's Girl (IRE)  **Spittal & Smith**
7 **FAODAIL,** 5, b m Gregorian (IRE)—Vallani (IRE)  **Dal Riata - A Barclay**
8 **FARRAN DANCER (IRE),** 8, b g Winged Love (IRE)—Fairylodge Scarlet (IRE)  **Mr R. Cooper**
9 **FLYING MOON (GER),** 5, b g Sea The Moon (GER)—Finity (USA)  **West Loudoun Racing Club**
10 **FOUR KINGDOMS (IRE),** 7, b g Lord Shanakill (USA)—Four Poorer (IRE)  **The Covenanters**
11 **FOURTH OF JULY (IRE),** 6, b g Salutino (GER)—Akasha (IRE)  **Quigley & Smith**
12 **GLASSES UP (USA),** 6, ch g English Channel (USA)—Hurricane Hallie (USA)  **The Jolly Beggars**
13 **GO BOB GO (IRE),** 4, b g Big Bad Bob (IRE)—Fire Up  **Riverside Racing**
14 **GRANITE CITY DOC,** 8, b g Arabian Gleam—Hansomis (IRE)  **Corsby Racing**
15 **HOPEFULL,** 11, br bl m Overbury (IRE)—Maryscross (IRE)  **Mr R. M. Smith**
16 4, B g Aiken—I'll Have It (IRE)
17 **LAS TUNAS (FR),** 9, b br g Country Reel (USA)—Grey Winner (FR)  **Spittal Family**
18 **LIVELIFETOTHEMAX (IRE),** 4, ch g Leading Light (IRE)—Maxford Lass  **Miss P A Carnaby & Mr P Carnaby**
19 **MELANAMIX (IRE),** 6, gr m Carlotamix (FR)—Melanjo (IRE)  **Six In the Mix**
20 **PICKING PEACHES (IRE),** 6, b m Shantou (USA)—Detonante (FR)  **Spittal & Smith**
21 **ROYAL COUNTESS,** 5, b m Coach House (IRE)—Dont Tell Nan  **Mr S. W. Dick**
22 **ROYAL REGENT,** 9, b g Urgent Request (IRE)—Royal Citadel (IRE)  **Mr S. W. Dick**
23 **THE ELECTRICIAN (IRE),** 5, ch g Leading Light (IRE)—Spring Flower (IRE)  **Quigley Smith & Spittal**
24 **THE JAD FACTOR (IRE),** 5, b g Arcadio (GER)—Sumability (IRE)  **Mr J. A. Dickson**
25 **TRONGATE (IRE),** 9, b g Dansant—Val Eile (IRE)  **Irving ,Russell & Smith**
26 **WEST DRIVE (IRE),** 8, ch g Sea The Stars (IRE)—Fair Sailing (IRE)  **P. Tsim**

### THREE-YEAR-OLDS
27 **AUTUMN FLAME,** b f Ruler of The World (IRE)—Pesse (IRE)  **Racing Connexions 10**
28 **IRIS DANCER,** b f Kodiac—Rainbow's Arch (IRE)  **Auld Pals**
29 B f Epaulette (AUS)—Midnight Bahia (IRE)
30 **WRECKED IT RALPH,** b g Orientor—Rafta (IRE)  **Toytown**

### TWO-YEAR-OLDS
31 Br c 01/03 Orientor—Rafta (IRE) (Atraf)
32 **SPORTY BILLY,** ch g 10/04 Hot Streak (IRE)—Dolly Daydreamer (Equiano (FR)) (800)  **Mr A. D. Green**

## MR R. MIKE SMITH - continued

**Other Owners:** Mr A. Barclay, Mr A. J. Bogle, Mr G. W. B. Bryson, Mr P. Carnaby, Miss P. A. Carnaby, Mr T. Clannachan, Mr R. Cooper, Mrs S. E. Cooper, Dal Riata, Mr R. Gibson, Mr A. D. Green, Mr S. D. Hamilton, Mr K. Irving, Mr F. Milligan, Mr R. Quigley, Mr G. Reid, Mr I. Robertson, Mr A. C. Rodger, Mr A. M. Ross, Mr M. J. Russell, Mr R. M. Smith, Mr A. H. Spittal, Miss B. Spittal, Mr I. Stewart, Mr H. S. Watson, Mr A. G. Whyte.

---

**500**

### MR RALPH J. SMITH, Wiltshire
Postal: **Trainer did not wish details of their string to appear**

---

**501**

### MRS SUE SMITH, Bingley
Postal: **Craiglands Farm, High Eldwick, Bingley, West Yorkshire, BD16 3BE**
WORK EMAIL office@craiglandsracing.co.uk WEBSITE www.suesmithracing.co.uk

1  **ABSOLUTELY DYLAN (IRE)**, 8, b g Scorpion (IRE)—Cash Customer (IRE) **Mrs S. J. Smith**
2  **AIRE VALLEY LAD**, 7, b g Schiaparelli (GER)—Bonnie Rock (IRE) **Mrs S. J. Smith**
3  **AMERDALE**, 6, b g Schiaparelli (GER)—Bonnie Rock (IRE) **Mrs S. J. Smith**
4  4, Br g Sageburg (IRE)—Applause For Amy (IRE) **Mrs S. J. Smith**
5  **ASHOVER HILLS (IRE)**, 5, b g Yeats (IRE)—Bobnval (IRE) **Mr D. Sutherland**
6  **BLASTER YEATS**, 6, b g Yeats (IRE)—Jayjay Joules **McGoldrick Racing & Mr Gareth Plimley**
7  **BURROWS DIAMOND (FR)**, 6, b m Diamond Boy (FR)—La Vie de Boitron (FR) **Mrs C. Casterton & Mrs J. Morgan**
8  **BURROWS HALL (FR)**, 4, b g Hunter's Light (IRE)—La Vie de Boitron (FR) **Mrs J. Morgan**
9  **CAPTAIN MOIRETTE (FR)**, 9, gr g Kap Rock (FR)—Rahana Moirette (FR) **Mrs A. Clarke**
10  **CERENDIPITY (IRE)**, 4, b g Sageburg (IRE)—Check The Forecast (IRE) **Mrs A. Clarke**
11  **CRACKING FIND (IRE)**, 10, b g Robin des Pres (FR)—Crack The Kicker (IRE) **Mrs A. Ellis**
12  **CUBAN SUN**, 5, b m Havana Gold (IRE)—Sunseek **Dr T. Fielding**
13  **DARSI'S DARLING (IRE)**, 5, b m Darsi (FR)—The Farmers Sister (IRE) **Mrs S. J. Smith**
14  **DUNOVER**, 5, b g Dunaden (FR)—I'm Delilah **Mrs S. J. Smith**
15  **FLAMBOYANT JOYAUX (FR)**, 6, b g Crossharbour—Merka (FR) **Formulated Polymer Products Ltd**
16  **FRIMEUR DE LANCRAY (FR)**, 6, b g Saddler Maker (IRE)—Jecyfly (FR) **Mrs A. Ellis**
17  **GETAWAY BAY (IRE)**, 9, b g Getaway (GER)—Wayward Star (IRE) **Mrs S. J. Smith**
18  **GOLDEN ROBIN (IRE)**, 7, br m Robin des Champs (FR)—Countess Eileen (IRE) **Mr G. J. Plimley**
19  **HEY BOY**, 6, b g Paco Boy (IRE)—Colourways (IRE) **Mrs S. J. Smith**
20  **I JUST KNOW (IRE)**, 11, b g Robin des Pres (FR)—Desperado Queen (IRE) **Mr C. M. Scholey**
21  **INFORMATEUR (FR)**, 8, b g Maresca Sorrento (FR)—Isarella (GER) **Mrs J M Gray & Mr G R Orchard**
22  **ISKABEG LANE (IRE)**, 10, b g Westerner—Nosey Oscar (IRE) **Mrs S. J. Smith**
23  **JAYAAAH (IRE)**, 6, b g Yeats (IRE)—Nolans Legacy (IRE) **Mrs A. Ellis**
24  **JOKE DANCER**, 8, ch g Authorized (IRE)—Missy Dancer **Mrs A. Clarke**
25  **JUST GEORGIE**, 11, b g Kayf Tara—Just Kate **Mrs S. J. Smith**
26  **JUST JESS (IRE)**, 5, b m Yeats (IRE)—She's On The Case (IRE) **A. D. Hollinrake**
27  **KAUTO D'AMOUR (FR)**, 6, b g Anabaa Blue—Kauto Luisa (FR) **Mrs S. J. Smith**
28  4, Ch g Getaway (GER)—Lady McBride (IRE) **Mrs S. J. Smith**
29  **LE DRAPEAU (FR)**, 9, ch g Satri (FR)—La Bandera **A. D. Hollinrake**
30  **LOUGH DERG FARMER (IRE)**, 9, b g Presenting—Maryiver (IRE) **Mrs S. J. Smith**
31  **LOUGH LEGEND (IRE)**, 7, b g Watar (IRE)—Gibboghstown (IRE) **Broadway Racing Club 15**
32  **MANCINELLIE**, 6, ch g Schiaparelli (GER)—Shankhouse Wells (IRE) **Mrs S. J. Smith**
33  **MIDNIGHT HUNTER**, 5, b g Midnight Legend—Autumn Spirit **Mrs S. J. Smith**
34  **MIDNIGHT MYTH**, 5, b m Midnight Legend—Very Special One (IRE) **Mrs S. J. Smith**
35  **MIDNIGHT SHADOW**, 8, b g Midnight Legend—Holy Smoke **Mrs A. Clarke**
36  **MONARCA (IRE)**, 5, b g Kayf Tara—Nurse Ratched (IRE) **Mrs S. J. Smith**
37  **MYBURG (IRE)**, 5, br g Sageburg (IRE)—Prairie Call (IRE) **Mrs S. J. Smith**
38  **NEVER UP (GER)**, 10, b g Danehill Dancer—Never Green (IRE) **Mrs S. J. Smith**
39  **NORTH PARADE (IRE)**, 6, br g Dylan Thomas (IRE)—Retain That Magic (IRE) **Mrs S. J. Smith**

## MRS SUE SMITH - continued

40 **OSCAR WILDE (IRE)**, 7, b g Oscar (IRE)—Deep Supreme (IRE) **Formulated Polymer Products Ltd**
41 **PARELLIROC**, 5, b g Schiaparelli (GER)—Roc Mirage **Mrs S. J. Smith**
42 4, B g Dylan Thomas (IRE)—Patsy Choice (IRE) **Mrs S. J. Smith**
43 **RAVENHILL ROAD (IRE)**, 10, ch g Exit To Nowhere (USA)—Zaffarella (IRE) **Phil & Julie Martin**
44 **SCORCHIN**, 7, b g Multiplex—Lemon Queen (IRE) **Teme Valley 3**
45 **SEVEN ARCHES**, 6, b g Yeats (IRE)—Santia **Mrs S. J. Smith**
46 **SHARP RESPONSE (IRE)**, 10, b g Oscar (IRE)—Lambourne Lace (IRE) **Formulated Polymer Products Ltd**
47 **SILVA ECLIPSE**, 8, gr g Multiplex—Linen Line **The Acre Bottom Syndicate**
48 **SMALL PRESENT (IRE)**, 6, b g Presenting—Serpentaria **Mrs A. Clarke**
49 **THE PADDY PIE (IRE)**, 8, b g Beneficial—Salsita (FR) **J. Wade**
50 **THELONGWAYAROUND (IRE)**, 8, b g Fruits of Love (USA)—Brass Neck (IRE) **Mrs J. Morgan**
51 **TRESHNISH (FR)**, 8, ch g Gold Away (IRE)—Didn't I Tell You (IRE) **D G Pryde & D Van Der Hoeven**
52 **TUMBLING DICE**, 6, b g Lucarno (USA)—Arctic Ring **Mr D. Sutherland**
53 **VALENCE D'AUMONT (FR)**, 7, b g Sinndar (IRE)—Ice Ti (ITY) **Mrs J. Morgan**
54 **VERY PATIENT (IRE)**, 7, b g Mahler—Venusorserena (IRE) **J. Wade**
55 **VINTAGE CLOUDS (IRE)**, 11, gr g Cloudings (IRE)—Rare Vintage (IRE) **Mr T. J. Hemmings**
56 **WAITING FOREVER (IRE)**, 7, b g Witness Box (USA)—You Some Massini (IRE) **J. Wade**
57 **WHAT'S THE SCOOP (IRE)**, 11, ch g Presenting—Dame d'Harvard (USA) **Mrs S. J. Smith**
58 **WOLF RUN (IRE)**, 6, b br g Presenting—Our Pride **Mr G. R. Orchard & Mrs J. M. Gray**

**Other Owners:** Mrs C. J. Casterton, Mr M. J. S. Cockburn, Mrs J. M. Gray, Mr R. J. Longley, Mrs J. A. Martin, Mr P. J. Martin, McGoldrick Racing, Mrs J. Morgan, G. R. Orchard, Mr A. M. Phillips, Mr G. J. Plimley, D. G. Pryde, Mrs S. J. Smith, Mr D. P. van der Hoeven.

**Assistant Trainer:** Joel Parkinson, **Head Lad:** Reece Jarosiewicz, **Racing Secretary:** Rachel Swinden.

**NH Jockey:** Ryan Mania. **Conditional Jockey:** Sam Coltherd, Alexander Fielding, Thomas Willmott.

---

**502**

## MISS SUZY SMITH, Angmering
Postal: **Lower Coombe Stables, Angmering Park, Angmering, Littlehampton, West Sussex, BN16 4EX**
Contacts: **MOBILE 07970 550828**
EMAIL suzy@suzysmithracing.co.uk WEBSITE www.suzysmithracing.co.uk
FACEBOOK @suzysmithracing

1 4, B f Telescope (IRE)—Aimigayle
2 **ANIMAL (IRE)**, 5, b g Arcadio (GER)—Fantine (IRE) **James Rimmer & Chris Ames**
3 **CLONDAW BISTO (IRE)**, 10, b g September Storm (GER)—Solo Venture (IRE) **Miss S. Smith**
4 **COUNTERACT**, 6, b g Dr Massini (IRE)—Aimigayle **Ms S. A. S. Palmer**
5 **DEBESTYMAN (IRE)**, 8, b g Mahler—Deise All Star (IRE) **The Plumpton Party**
6 **GETAWAY SUZY (IRE)**, 8, b m Getaway (GER)—Ashanti Dancer (IRE) **Miss S. Smith**
7 **INVICTA LAKE (IRE)**, 14, b g Dr Massini (IRE)—Classic Material **The Invicta Partnership**
8 **LIGHTNING BUG (IRE)**, 4, b f Starspangledbanner (AUS)—Redinha **The Bright Lights**
9 **LITTLE BOY BORU (IRE)**, 13, b g Brian Boru—How Is Things (IRE) **J Logan, D Harrison, T Loftus & S Smith**
10 **MARBLE PALACE**, 4, b f Sholokhov (IRE)—Easibrook Jane **The Palace Syndicate**
11 4, B g Shirocco (GER)—Material World
12 **OSCARSMAN (IRE)**, 7, b g Oscar (IRE)—Ashwell Lady (IRE) **D Harrison J Logan J Rimmer & S Smith**
13 **PEDLINGHAM**, 5, b g Dunaden (FR)—Aunt Harriet **Mr & Mrs R. Allsop**
14 **ROSY WORLD**, 8, b m Shirocco (GER)—Material World **Mrs K. Allisat & Exors of the Late Mrs H. Ames**
15 **STRIKE THE FLINT**, 7, b m Shirocco (GER)—Material World **For & Smith**
16 **VUE CAVALIERE (FR)**, 7, b m Spirit One (FR)—Grande Cavale (FR) **Mr G. Jones, Mr C. Ames & Mr D. Harrison**

## TWO-YEAR-OLDS

17 B g 11/05 Court Cave (IRE)—Aimigayle (Midnight Legend)
18 B f 29/05 September Storm (GER)—Material World (Karinga Bay) **Miss S. Smith**
19 **SILVER HILL FLYER (IRE)**, b f 20/05 Court Cave (IRE)—
Jennifer Eccles (Midnight Legend) **Mrs K. Allisat & Exors of the Late Mrs H. Ames**

## MISS SUZY SMITH - continued

**Other Owners:** Mrs K. H. Allisat, Mr R. Allsop, Mrs Y. E. Allsop, Mr C. B. Ames, Mr D. J. Harrison, Mr G. R. Jones, Mr T. H. Loftus, J. A. A. S. Logan, Mr J. Rimmer, Mrs C. A. Smith, Miss S. Smith, Table For Six, Mrs H. M. T. Woods.

**Assistant Trainer:** Mr S E Gordon-Watson.

**Flat Jockey:** Jane Elliott, Luke Morris, Jason Watson. **NH Jockey:** Micheal Nolan, Tom O'Brien, Gavin Sheehan.

---

### 503 MR JAMIE SNOWDEN, Lambourn

Postal: Folly House, Upper Lambourn Road, Lambourn, Hungerford, Berkshire, RG17 8QG
Contacts: PHONE 01488 72800 MOBILE 07779 497563
EMAIL info@jamiesnowdenracing.co.uk WEBSITE www.jamiesnowdenracing.co.uk
TWITTER @jamiesnowden INSTAGRAM jamie_snowden

1 ALRIGHTJACK (IRE), 7, b g Stowaway—Brogella (IRE) **The GD Partnership**
2 ANYTHINGFORLOVE, 6, b m Black Sam Bellamy (IRE)—La Perrotine (FR) **Foxtrot Racing: Anythingforlove**
3 ARBENNIG (IRE), 5, b br g Yeats (IRE)—Ultra Light (FR) **Awr Consultancy, Stacey, Kirk & Fields**
4 BEHOLDEN, 5, b g Cacique (IRE)—Pure Joy **Foxtrot Racing Beholden**
5 BETWEEN THE WATERS (IRE), 10, ch g Indian River (FR)—Catch Ball **The Folly Partnership**
6 BUCKO'S BOY, 6, b g Midnight Legend—Buxom (IRE) **A. J. & Mrs J. Ward**
7 BUCKSOME, 5, b g Phoenix Reach (IRE)—Buxom (IRE) **The Galloping Grannies - Bucksome**
8 4, B f Walk In The Park (IRE)—Calomeria **A Walk In The Park Partnership**
9 CHAPMANSHYPE (IRE), 7, b g Aizavoski (IRE)—Call Her Something (IRE) **The GD Partnership**
10 CHARLIE GEORGE (IRE), 5, b g Presenting—Lareine d'Anjou (FR) **Sir Chippendale Keswick**
11 CLEMANTINI, 4, ch f Dylan Thomas—Full of Fruit (FR) **ValueRacingClub.co.uk**
12 COLLEGE OAK, 6, ch g Norse Dancer—Katmai (FR) **Radleian Society, L Lovell & P Stacey**
13 COOLE WELL (IRE), 8, b g Gold Well—Bobs Lass (IRE) **Mrs C. Kendrick**
14 DATSALRIGHTGINO (GER), 5, b g It's Gino (GER)—Delightful Sofie (GER) **The GD Partnership**
15 DIDDLY DO, 5, ch m Presenting—Lakaam **Mr E. J. M. Spurrier**
16 DONNIE AZOFF (IRE), 5, ch g Dylan Thomas (IRE)—Bonny River (IRE) **The Footie Partnership**
17 EARLY MORNING RAIN (FR), 7, gr m Martaline—Rosewater (GER) **Mrs J A Thomas & Heart Racing**
18 EXOD'ELA (FR), 7, b g Saddler Maker (IRE)—Queen'ela (FR) **Duckworth Jordan Wright Cw Dellar Doel**
19 FACT OF THE MATTER (IRE), 11, b g Brian Boru—Womanofthemountain (IRE) **The Sandylini Racing Partnership**
20 FLORAL BOUQUET, 8, bl m Fair Mix (IRE)—Florarossa **The Picnic Party**
21 FORTUNATE FRED (FR), 6, b g Cokoriko (FR)—Rosalie Malta (FR) **Kate & Andrew Brooks, Mr A. L. Brooks**
22 GA LAW (FR), 5, b g Sinndar (FR)—Law (FR) **The Footie Partnership**
23 GUINNESS AFFAIR (FR), 5, b g Fuisse (FR)—Ashkiyra (FR) **Kate & Andrew Brooks**
24 HOGAN'S HEIGHT (IRE), 10, b g Indian River (FR)—Electre du Berlais (FR) **Foxtrot Racing: Hogan's Height**
25 HOWDILYOUDO (IRE), 6, b m Presenting—Little Dil (IRE) **Chasing Gold Limited**
26 HUDSON YARD (IRE), 7, b m Yeats (IRE)—That's Moyne (IRE) **Mr A. Devaney**
27 KALAHARI QUEEN, 8, br m Kalanisi (IRE)—Queen's Leader **The Cherry Pickers**
28 KILTEALY BRIGGS (IRE), 7, b g Fame And Glory—Baby Briggs (IRE) **McNeill Family Ltd**
29 LEADING EWE ON (IRE), 5, b m Leading Light (IRE)—April Thistle (IRE) **Sheep As A Lamb Syndicate**
30 LEGENDS RYDE, 6, ch m Midnight Legend—Ryde Back **AWTP Racing Partnership**
31 MIDNIGHT CENTURION, 5, b g Midnight Legend—Centoria (IRE) **The Wife Loves It Partnership**
32 MONBEG THEATRE (IRE), 12, b g King's Theatre (IRE)—Amberina (IRE) **Heather Pinniger & Lynda Lovell**
33 MUSTANG ALPHA (IRE), 6, b g Stowaway—Tupia (FR) **Mrs C. Kendrick**
34 NO ANXIETY (IRE), 5, ch g Presenting—Joanne One (IRE) **Chips Keswick, Simon Munir, Isaac Souede**
35 OTTOMAN STYLE, 5, b g Kayf Tara—Oligarch Society (IRE) **Buckett Flach Woodward Moran Sperling**
36 OVERRATED PASSTIME (IRE), 5, b g Arctic Cosmos (USA)—Jodi (IRE) **McCoy & O'Brien Syndicate**
37 PISGAH PIKE (IRE), 6, br g Famous Name—Music On D Waters (IRE) **ValueRacingClub.co.uk**
38 QUIET PENNY, 7, b m Sholokhov (IRE)—Pennys Pride (IRE) **ValueRacingClub.co.uk**
39 REDBRIDGE GOLD (IRE), 8, b m Gold Well—Marikala (IRE) **O'Connor, Coomes, Scholefield, Allen**
40 REPRESENTING BOB (IRE), 5, ch g Presenting—Some Bob Back (IRE) **Beccle, Sperling, Allen & Hague**
41 ROSE OHARA, 5, b m Kayf Tara—Cinderella Rose **Jones Broughtons Wilson Weaver**
42 SANDAROC, 5, b m Shirocco (GER)—Shali San (FR) **The Sandaroc Syndicate**
43 SAZERAK (IRE), 5, br m Sinndar (IRE)—Toile d'Auteuil (FR) **Mrs J. A. Thomas**
44 SERENISA, 5, gr m Kayf Tara—Sisella (IRE) **DASH Racing**

## MR JAMIE SNOWDEN - continued

45 **SKANDIBURG (FR)**, 7, b g Sageburg (IRE)—Skandia (FR) **Kate & Andrew Brooks**
46 **SOME DAY SOON (IRE)**, 8, b g Robin des Champs (FR)—
Creative Approach (IRE) **Ogilvy, Shaw, Morley&the Racegoers Club**
47 **SOVEREIGN DUKE (GER)**, 6, b g Jukebox Jury (IRE)—Shadow Queen (GER) **One Too Many Partners**
48 **STAREVITCH (FR)**, 5, b g Sinndar (IRE)—Folie Star Gate (FR) **Sir Chippendale Keswick**
49 **STONEY MOUNTAIN (IRE)**, 8, ch g Mountain High (IRE)—Cherry Pie (FR) **Mrs A. Gillies**
50 **TALLOW FOR COAL (IRE)**, 5, b g Arctic Cosmos (USA)—South Queen Lady (IRE) **Apache Star Racing**
51 **THE LONGEST DAY (IRE)**, 5, b g Milan—Court Leader (IRE) **McNeill Family Ltd**
52 **THEBANNERKINGREBEL (IRE)**, 8, b g Arakan (USA)—One Love (IRE) **League Of Nations**
53 **THISTLE DO NICELY (IRE)**, 7, b g Arcadio (GER)—April Thistle (IRE) **Appletree Stud, M Gumienny & A Signy**
54 **THOMAS MACDONAGH**, 8, b g Black Sam Bellamy (IRE)—
Taqreem (IRE) **Sperling, Coomes, Davies, Hague, Collins**
55 **THREE WAYS**, 10, b g Flemensfirth (USA)—Serenique **We Accidentally Bought Another Horse**
56 **TIMOSHENKO**, 6, ch g Archipenko (USA)—Nezhenka **Mr P Mendoza & Mr Stephen Williams**
57 **TINSMITH**, 6, gr ro g Mastercraftsman (IRE)—Catopuma (USA) **ValueRacingClub.co.uk**
58 **TOP OF THE BAY (IRE)**, 4, b g Doyen (IRE)—Bay Dove **The Poised To Pounce Partnership**
59 **TRACTOR FRED (IRE)**, 7, b g Curtain Time (IRE)—Bonny Blackdoe (IRE) **Mrs K. A. Buckett**
60 **UP FOR PAROL (IRE)**, 5, b g Flemensfirth (USA)—Clarification (IRE) **Sir Chippendale Keswick**
61 **VALAMIX (IRE)**, 4, b g Valirann (FR)—Julimark (IRE) **The Poised To Pounce Partnership**
62 4, Br f Getaway (GER)—Viva Forever (FR)

**Other Owners:** AWR Consultancy Ltd, Miss B. Allen, Apple Tree Stud, Ms K. J. Austin, Miss R Bailey, Mr S. E. Beccle, Mr A. L. Brooks, Mrs K. L. Brooks, Sir M. F. Broughton, Mr S. W. Broughton, Mr S. Coomes, Cw Dellar Doel, Miss C. E. Davies, Mr G. Davison, Mrs R. Duckworth, Duckworth, Jordan, Wright, Miss C. E. Davies, Mr G. Davison, Mrs R. Duckworth, Duckworth, Jordan, Wright, Mrs M. Hill, Mrs N. Jones, Sir Chippendale Keswick, Mr J. C. Kirk, Mrs L. R. Lovell, Exors of the Late Mrs I. M. J. Matthews, R. T. S. Matthews, Mr P.V. Mendoza, Ms P. S. Mohabir, Mr A. M. Morley, S. E. Munir, Mr J. D. O'Connor, Dr M. M. Ogilvy, Mr A. M. Palk, Mr W. Palk, Ms H. N. Pinniger, Racegoers Club Owners Group, Mr A. Rice, Mr N. R. Robinson, Mr A. Scholefield, W. G. C. Shaw, Mr A. Signy, Mr J. E. Snowden, Mr I. Souede, Mrs J. Sperling, Mr P.A. Stacey, Stacey, Kirk & Fields, The Galloping Grannies, The Radleian Society Racing Syndicate, Mrs J. A. Thomas, Mr M. J. Wainwright, Mr A. J. Ward, Mrs J. Ward, Mrs R. B. Weaver, Mr D. P. Wiggin, Mr S. Williams, T. C. Wilson.

**Assistant Trainer:** Freddie Mitchell, **Head Girl:** Kate Robinson.

**NH Jockey:** Gavin Sheehan, Sam Twiston-Davies. **Conditional Jockey:** Page Fuller.

---

**504**  **MR MIKE SOWERSBY, York**
Postal: **Southwold Farm, Goodmanham Wold, Market Weighton, York, East Yorkshire, YO43 3NA**
Contacts: **PHONE 01430 810534 MOBILE 07855 551056**

1 **EFFRETAIS (FR)**, 7, b g Blue Bresil (FR)—Teriniere (FR) **M. E. Sowersby**
2 **HIDDEN GLEN (IRE)**, 8, ch g Stowaway—Gleanntan (IRE) **M. E. Sowersby**
3 **KIWAYU**, 12, b g Medicean—Kibara **Mounted Gamess Assoc Syndicate**
4 **LIQUIDISER**, 5, b g Monsieur Bond (IRE)—Kaloni (IRE) **M. E. Sowersby**
5 **NO CEILING (IRE)**, 11, b g Turtle Island (IRE)—Pyrexie (FR) **Mrs Janet Cooper & Mr M. E. Sowersby**
6 **PENNY HILL (IRE)**, 7, b m Frammassone (IRE)—Mystical Megan (IRE) **Miss E. C. Forman**
7 **RANN OF KUTCH (IRE)**, 6, b m Dylan Thomas (IRE)—Scartara (IRE) **Miss E. C. Forman**
8 **RIP VAN GO**, 7, b g Rip Van Winkle (IRE)—Thousandkissesdeep (IRE) **M. E. Sowersby**
9 **SIMPLY LUCKY (IRE)**, 12, b g Flemensfirth (USA)—Derrygowna Court (IRE) **The Southwold Set**
10 **SMASHING LASS (IRE)**, 5, ch m Sir Prancealot (IRE)—Gilded Truffle (IRE) **J. Payne**
11 **STRATEGIC (IRE)**, 6, b g Kodiac—Run To Jane (IRE) **R. D. Seldon**
12 **SWEETEST SMILE (IRE)**, 6, b m Champs Elysees—Scorn (USA)

**Other Owners:** Mrs J. H. Cooper, M. E. Sowersby.

**Assistant Trainer:** Mary Sowersby.

**Flat Jockey:** Tom Eaves, James Sullivan. **NH Jockey:** Brian Hughes. **Amateur Jockey:** Mr Russell Lindsay.

**505** **MR JOHN SPEARING, Kinnersley**
Postal: **Kinnersley Racing Limited, Kinnersley Racing Stables, Kinnersley, Severn Stoke, Worcestershire, WR8 9JR**
Contacts: **PHONE 01905 371054 MOBILE 07801 552922 FAX 01905 371054**
**EMAIL jlspearing@aol.com**

1 A SURE WELCOME, 7, b g Pastoral Pursuits—Croeso Bach **Kinnersley Partnership 3**
2 A TOUCH OF SASS (IRE), 11, b m Mahler—Lwitikila **Miss C. J. Ive**
3 CAPTAIN SEDGWICK (IRE), 7, b m Approve (IRE)—Alinda (IRE) **Oakridge Racing**
4 COOL STRUTTER (IRE), 9, b g Kodiac—Cassava (IRE) **Kinnersley Partnership**
5 HY EALES (IRE), 4, b f Passing Glance—Miss Conduct **Graham Eales & Kate Ive**
6 IT'S HOW WE ROLL (IRE), 7, b g Fastnet Rock (AUS)—Clodora (IRE) **Kinnersley Partnership**
7 LADY GWHINNYVERE (IRE), 7, b m Sir Prancealot (IRE)—Johar Jamal **Mr J. L. Spearing**
8 LOST HISTORY (IRE), 8, b g Strategic Prince—Prelude **Mr J. J. Reilly**
9 MIDNIGHT AIR, 6, b m Midnight Legend—Starlight Air **Mrs W. M. Badger**
10 PILLAR OF STEEL, 6, b m Shirocco (GER)—Miss Conduct **Miss C. J. Ive**
11 SHUTTHEGATE (IRE), 7, b g Milan—Miss Conduct **Miss C. J. Ive**
12 STYLISH DANCER, 7, b m Nathaniel (IRE)—Hazy Dancer **Mr J. J. Reilly**
13 SWEEPING ROCK (IRE), 11, b g Rock of Gibraltar (IRE)—Sweeping Story (USA) **Kinnersley Partnership II**

**THREE-YEAR-OLDS**

14 KINZ (IRE), b f Footstepsinthesand—Talitha Kum (IRE) **Mr H. James**
15 Ch f Prince of Lir (IRE)—Malory Towers
16 B c Califet (FR)—Miss Conduct **Miss C. J. Ive**

**Other Owners:** G. M. Eales, Miss C. J. Ive.

**Assistant Trainer:** Miss C. Ive.

**506** **MR RICHARD SPENCER, Newmarket**
Postal: **Sefton Lodge, 8 Bury Road, Newmarket, Suffolk, CB8 7BT**
Contacts: **PHONE 01638 675780 MOBILE 07720 064053**
**WORK EMAIL richard.spencer@rebel-racing.co.uk**

1 ALL OF THE LIGHTS (IRE), 4, b g Elzaam (AUS)—Abandon (USA) **Mr A. Cunningham**
2 BERNARDO O'REILLY, 7, b g Intikhab (USA)—Baldovina **Rebel Racing (2)**
3 BORN TO DESTROY, 4, b g Camacho—Sahafh (USA) **William&Camilla Haines &Phil Cunningham**
4 CHAMPAGNE SUPANOVA (IRE), 4, b g Camacho—Flawless Pink **Mr P. M. Cunningham**
5 CIGARETTESNALCOHOL (IRE), 5, ch g Ocovango—Moylisha Red (IRE) **Rebel Jumping II**
6 DUTUGAMUNU (IRE), 4, ch g Ivawood (IRE)—Bunditten (IRE) **Balasuriya,CookCunningham,Gowing,Spencer**
7 GERTCHA (IRE), 4, b c Slade Power (IRE)—Elouges (IRE) **Team DCL**
8 HANDSOME SAMSON, 6, b g Nathaniel (IRE)—Factice (USA) **Rebel Racing**
9 JOANIE STUBBS, 4, b f Garswood—Cherry Malotte **Mr P. M. Cunningham**
10 KEYSER SOZE (IRE), 7, ch g Arcano (IRE)—Causeway Queen (IRE) **Rebel Racing (2)**
11 LOUIS TREIZE (IRE), 5, b g Slade Power (IRE)—Black Rodded **Rebel Racing Premier**
12 4, B g Shantou (USA)—Maggies Oscar (IRE) **Mr P. M. Cunningham**
13 NIGHTBOAT TO CAIRO (IRE), 4, br g Soldier of Fortune (IRE)—Bobbina (IRE) **Mr P. M. Cunningham**
14 ODYSSEY GIRL (IRE), 4, gr f Gutaifan (IRE)—Playa du Charmil (FR) **Mr E. Cunningham**
15 ONE STEP BEYOND (IRE), 4, b g Exceed And Excel (AUS)—Yours Truly (IRE) **Rebel Racing Premier II**
16 OUTLANDER (IRE), 13, b g Stowaway—Western Whisper (IRE) **Gowing's Eleven**
17 PEEJAYBEE (FR), 5, ch g Ballingarry (IRE)—Playa du Charmil (FR) **Mr M.R Gowing**
18 PHILAMUNDO (IRE), 6, b g Sir Prancealot (IRE)—Rublevka Star (USA) **Mr P. M. Cunningham**
19 REVICH (IRE), 5, b g Requinto (IRE)—Kathleen Rafferty (IRE) **Middleham Park LXVII & Phil Cunningham**
20 ROLL WITH IT (IRE), 5, b g Sholokhov (IRE)—Que Pasa (IRE) **Rebel Jumping II**
21 SEFTON WARRIOR, 4, b g Frankel—Maid To Master (IRE) **Rebel Racing Premier II**
22 SIR JACK YEATS (IRE), 10, b g Yeats (IRE)—Quadrennial (IRE) **Gowing's Eleven**
23 SKONTONOVSKI (IRE), 4, b g Harbour Watch (IRE)—An Ghalanta (IRE) **Rebel Racing Premier II**
24 STAY CLASSY (IRE), 5, ch m Camacho—Hollow Green (IRE) **Balasuriya,CookCunningham,Gowing,Spencer**

## MR RICHARD SPENCER - continued

25 **THE CITY'S PHANTOM,** 4, b g Free Eagle (IRE)—Meet Marhaba (IRE)  **Edward Babington & Phil Cunningham**
26 **THISTIMENEXTYEAR,** 7, gr g New Approach (IRE)—Scarlet Empire (IRE)  **Rebel Racing (2)**
27 **TOO SHY SHY (IRE),** 4, gr f Kodiac—Satwa Ruby (FR)  **Mr P. M. Cunningham**
28 **TWISTEDFIRESTARTER (IRE),** 5, b g Sageburg (IRE)—Mercy Mission  **Rebel Jumping II**
29 **TYSON FURY,** 4, ch c Iffraaj—Za Za Zoom (IRE)  **Balasuriya,CookCunningham,Gowing,Spencer**
30 **WONDERWALL (IRE),** 5, b g Yeats (IRE)—Rock Me Gently  **Rebel Jumping II**

## THREE-YEAR-OLDS

31 **BIG NARSTIE (FR),** b br c Cable Bay (IRE)—Granadilla  **Rebel Racing Premier III**
32 **CHIM CHIMNEY,** b g Cockney Rebel (IRE)—Wonderful Life (IRE)  **Mr P. M. Cunningham**
33 **DANDY MAESTRO,** ch g Dandy Man (IRE)—Maids Causeway (IRE)  **Mr J. Power**
34 **DANNI CALIFORNIA (IRE),** gr f The Gurkha (IRE)—Satwa Ruby (FR)  **Mr P. M. Cunningham**
35 **HAROLD SHAND (IRE),** b c Acclamation—Shy Audience (IRE)  **Rebel Racing Premier III**
36 **INSOMNIA,** b c Due Diligence (USA)—River Song (USA)  **Rebel Racing Premier III**
37 **IVAN DRAGO,** br g Equiano (FR)—Tesary  **Rebel Racing Premier III**
38 **NO ESCAPE,** b f Cityscape—Elegant Annie  **Mr Phil Cunningham & Mr Richard Spencer**
39 **OCEAN EYES (IRE),** b f Mehmas (IRE)—Rise Up Lotus (IRE)  **Mr P. M. Cunningham**
40 **PROFESSIONAL WIDOW (IRE),** gr f Markaz (IRE)—Petite Cherie  **Mrs E. Cunningham**
41 **PUMP IT UP,** ch f Charming Thought—Cherry Malotte  **Mr P. M. Cunningham**
42 **SKATERBOI,** b g Cockney Rebel (IRE)—Encantar  **Miss L. Cunningham**
43 **THEFASTNTHECURIOUS,** ch f Fast Company (IRE)—Dame Plume (IRE)  **Mr P. M. Cunningham**
44 **WINGS OF A DOVE (IRE),** gr f Dark Angel (IRE)—Silk Bow  **Mr P. M. Cunningham**
45 **WISPERING ANGEL (IRE),** b f Awtaad (IRE)—Intapeace (IRE)  **Miss M. L. Evans**

## TWO-YEAR-OLDS

46 **FUEGO,** b c 08/02 Cityscape—La Pantera (Captain Rio)  **Mr A. Cunningham**
47 **INTOXICATED,** b f 10/03 Fountain of Youth (IRE)—River Song (USA) (Siphon (BRZ)) (40000)  **Mr P. M. Cunningham**
48 **LITTLE PRAYER,** b f 27/03 Mehmas (IRE)—Nasimi (Shamardal (USA)) (26000)  **Mr P. M. Cunningham**
49 **MR BIG STUFF,** b c 09/02 Iffraaj—Groovejet (Cockney Rebel (IRE))  **Mr P. M. Cunningham**
50 **RED FEZ,** b c 29/04 Lethal Force (IRE)—Red Turban (Kyllachy) (8000)  **Mr Jonny Allison & Mr Phil Cunningham**
51 **SUPERSTAR DJ,** b c 16/03 Time Test—Excello (Exceed And Excel (AUS)) (40000)  **Mr P. M. Cunningham**
52 B f 22/02 Lethal Force (IRE)—Survived (Kyllachy) (23000)  **Mr P. M. Cunningham**
53 **THE MAD MONK (IRE),** gr c 16/02 Gregorian (IRE)—
                                       Broadway Musical (IRE) (Exceed And Excel (AUS)) (55238)  **Rebel Racing Premier IV**
54 **TOO FUNKY,** b f 09/02 Mayson—Instructress (Diktat)  **Mr P. M. Cunningham**
55 **UNFINISHEDSYMPATHY (IRE),** b br f 06/02 El Kabeir (USA)—
                                       Bella Ophelia (IRE) (Baltic King) (11905)  **Mrs E. Cunningham**
56 B c 26/03 Kodi Bear (IRE)—Usem (Bahamian Bounty) (104762)  **Rebel Racing Premier IV**
57 B c 15/02 Kodi Bear (IRE)—Vastitas (IRE) (Green Desert (USA)) (66667)  **Rebel Racing Premier IV**

**Other Owners:** Mr J. Allison, Mr E. P. Babington, Mr P. M. Cunningham, Mrs C. Haines, Mr W. R. Haines, Middleham Park Racing LXVII, T. S. Palin, M. Prince, Mr R. G. R. Spencer.

**Assistant Trainer:** Mr Joe Akehurst, **Pupil Assistant:** Mr Jack Jones, **Travelling Head:** Miss Tegan Kerr.

**Apprentice Jockey:** Mr Angus Villiers.

---

**507**   **MR SEB SPENCER, Malton**
Postal: **79 Harvest Drive, Malton, North Yorkshire, YO17 7BF**
Contacts: **MOBILE 07790 060050**
EMAIL sebspencerracing@gmail.com

1 **BANDSMAN RICE,** 4, b g Haafhd—Allashka (FR)  **E.A. Moorey & E.G. Moorey**
2 **BIG MUDDY,** 4, b g Monsieur Bond (IRE)—Nine Red  **N. Bycroft**
3 **COOLAGH MAGIC,** 5, b g Sepoy (AUS)—Miliika  **N. Bycroft**
4 **COTTAM,** 4, b g Harbour Watch (IRE)—Gadfly  **The Racing Emporium**
5 **DESERT DREAM,** 7, b g Oasis Dream—Rosika  **The Racing Emporium**

# MR SEB SPENCER - continued

6 **DON'T BE SURPRISED**, 6, ch g Monsieur Bond (IRE)—Julie's Gift **Dukes Group**
7 **DONNCHA (IRE)**, 10, br g Captain Marvelous (IRE)—Seasonal Style (IRE) **Mr D. Bannon**
8 **INTERNATIONALTIGER**, 4, b c Garswood—Elusive Sue (USA) **P. D. Smith Holdings Ltd**
9 **JET SET GO**, 6, ch m Equiano (FR)—Golden Valley **D Bainbridge & N Bycroft**
10 **MUST DREAM**, 4, ch g Mustajeeb—Golden Valley **Enjoy Racing**
11 **QUICK GETAWAY (IRE)**, 9, b g Getaway (GER)—Ragtime Lucy (IRE) **Mr P. J. Howard**
12 **RIVERBANK DRAMA**, 7, b m Overbury (IRE)—Granny Shona (IRE) **N. Bycroft**
13 5, B m Mr Medici (IRE)—Secret Oasis

**Other Owners:** Mr D. R. Bainbridge, N. Bycroft, Mr E. A. Moorey, Mr E. G. Moorey.

---

**508** ## MR HENRY SPILLER, Newmarket
Postal: **Henry Spiller Racing, Sackville House Stables, Sackville Street, Newmarket, Suffolk, CB8 8DX**
Contacts: **MOBILE 07786 263997**
**WORK EMAIL** henry@henryspiller.com **EMAIL** office@henryspiller.com **WEBSITE** www.henryspiller.com

1 **AMMAYYA**, 4, b f Sepoy (AUS)—Appointee (IRE) **Mr R. P. A. Spiller**
2 **CRACK REGIMENT (FR)**, 4, b g Siyouni (FR)—Coiffure **Mr R. P. A. Spiller**
3 **GLINT OF AN EYE (IRE)**, 4, b f Australia—Call This Cat (IRE) **Mr K. Clarke & Partner**
4 **HUNTERS STEP**, 5, b g Mukhadram—Step Softly
5 **IRISH TIMES**, 6, b g Swiss Spirit—Amouage Royale (IRE) **Dark Horse Partnership**
6 **LAST TO BID (FR)**, 5, ch h Makfi—Last Song **Mr R. P. A. Spiller**
7 **LEGENDE D'ART (IRE)**, 4, b g Kingman—Legende Bleue **Dethrone Racing**
8 **PARKNACILLA (IRE)**, 5, br m Mukhadram—Patuca **Charles & Fiona Spiller**
9 **PASSING NOD**, 4, b g Zoffany (IRE)—Superstar Leo (IRE) **Dethrone Racing**
10 **ROCHFORD (IRE)**, 4, b g Ivawood (IRE)—Lady Berta **Birdie Racing Club**
11 **SEA WILLOW**, 4, ch f Dream Ahead (USA)—Showbird **Birdie Racing Club**
12 **THE THIRD MAN**, 10, gr g Dalakhani (IRE)—Spinning Queen **Mrs D. Spiller**

## THREE-YEAR-OLDS

13 **AMY C**, b f Charming Thought—Alzahra **Franconson Partners**
14 **BESTING (FR)**, b f Evasive—Biloka (FR)
15 **CATCHTHESNITCH (FR)**, b c Captain Chop (FR)—Bolga Bere (FR)
16 **COMPLEXO**, b c Twilight Son—Embroidery (IRE) **Mr P. Moyles**
17 B g Captain Gerrard (IRE)—Country Madam (IRE)
18 B f Ivawood (IRE)—Hazel Blue (IRE)
19 **LUTHER CEE (FR)**, b c War Command (USA)—Last Cast (FR)
20 **NED (FR)**, gr g Kendargent (FR)—Nova Zarga (IRE) **Franconson Partners**
21 **PUFFIN ISLAND (IRE)**, b f Awtaad (IRE)—Patuca **Charles & Fiona Spiller**
22 **SAVISE L'AMOUR (FR)**, b g Evasive—Salpare **Franconson Partners**
23 **SECRET GIRL**, b f Myboycharlie (IRE)—Sertolina (USA)
24 **TREENA (FR)**, b f Goken (FR)—Tout Une Histoire (FR)
25 **TRIPLE PEEL (FR)**, b f Le Havre (IRE)—Scalambra **Mr R. P. A. Spiller**

## TWO-YEAR-OLDS

26 B f 12/02 Intello (GER)—Appointee (IRE) (Exceed And Excel (AUS)) **Mr R. P. A. Spiller**
27 B f 28/03 Iffraaj—Figment (Acclamation) (9524) **Dethrone Racing**
28 B c 23/02 Markaz (IRE)—Piacere (IRE) (New Approach (IRE)) (5500) **Dark Horse Partnership**
29 **VICTORIA GROVE**, b f 06/03 Siyouni (FR)—Baltic Best (IRE) (King's Best (USA)) (70000) **Mr R. P. A. Spiller**

**Other Owners:** Mr K. Clarke, Mr H. Simcock, Mr C. R. G. Spiller, Mrs F. J. D. Spiller.

## 509 MR FOZZY STACK, Cashel
Postal: Thomastown Castle Stud, Golden, Cashel, Co. Tipperary, Ireland
Contacts: PHONE +353 62 54129
EMAIL contact@stackracing.ie WEBSITE www.stackracing.ie

1 BACK TO BRUSSELS, 4, ch f Starspangledbanner (AUS)—Big Boned (USA)
2 BAMBARI (IRE), 8, b g Arcano (IRE)—Blue Dahlia (IRE)
3 KEW PALACE, 4, b f Kingman—Shama
4 STALINGRAD, 4, b c War Front (USA)—I Am Beautiful (IRE)
5 STAR OF CASHEL, 4, b c No Nay Never (USA)—Queen of Lyons (USA)
6 TOO SOON TO PANIC, 4, b f Gleneagles (IRE)—Scream Blue Murder (IRE)
7 TOOREEN ANGEL, 4, b f Battle of Marengo (IRE)—Annmary Girl

## THREE-YEAR-OLDS

8 AHANDFULOFSUMMERS, b f Galileo (IRE)—Scream Blue Murder (IRE)
9 ALOHA STAR, b f Starspangledbanner (AUS)—Zain Art (IRE)
10 B f Mastercraftsman (IRE)—Blessing (USA)
11 BLUE CABOCHAN, b f Holy Roman Emperor (IRE)—Holly Blue
12 CAN'THELPFALLIN, b f Starspangledbanner (AUS)—Acid
13 CHAZZESMEE (IRE), b c Excebelration—Elope
14 CHEVAL BLANC, b gr c Dark Angel (IRE)—La Collina (IRE)
15 COCOBANANA, ch f Starspangledbanner (AUS)—Brazilian Samba (IRE)
16 CORMAC, b g Holy Roman Emperor (IRE)—Divisme (USA)
17 DOLCE NOTTE, ch f The Gurkha (IRE)—Await (IRE)
18 FLYING ROCK, b f Air Force Blue (USA)—Cry Me A River (IRE)
19 HAIR OF GOLD, b f Fastnet Rock (AUS)—Khione
20 IVY ROCK, b f Zoffany (IRE)—Loved (IRE)
21 KHLASS, b f No Nay Never (USA)—Subtle Charm
22 LINDA BARRETT (IRE), b gr f Dark Angel (IRE)—Plagiarism (USA)
23 MELAINE PIM, b f Pride of Dubai (AUS)—Rohain (IRE)
24 MOVING FOR GOLD (IRE), b g Acclamation—Church Melody
25 MYBOYCHARLES, b c Air Force Blue (USA)—Sense of Class (USA)
26 NOTORIOUSLY RISKY, b f Starspangledbanner (AUS)—Precariously Good
27 PITA PINTA (IRE), b f Sir Percy—Bantam (IRE)
28 SANOSUKE, b c Galileo (IRE)—Fix (NZ)
29 SHINAPACHI, b c Galileo (IRE)—Sea Siren (AUS)
30 SLOANE PETERSON (IRE), b f Kodiac—Capriole
31 STORM LEGEND (IRE), b c Night of Thunder—Kymera
32 WAIT A LITTLE, b f The Last Lion (IRE)—Blue Dahlia (IRE)

## TWO-YEAR-OLDS

33 B c 23/04 Starspangledbanner (AUS)—Awohaam
34 B f 10/03 Starspangledbanner (AUS)—Come Softly
35 Ch f 28/04 Profitable—Crossanza
36 B f 16/03 New Bay—Dumfriesshire
37 B f 25/03 Lope de Vega—Elle Woods
38 B c 11/03 Holy Roman Emperor (IRE)—Emirate Jewel
39 Ch f 21/05 Ulysses—Fountain of Peace
40 B f 29/04 Kodiac—Full Mandate
41 B f 14/04 Ribchester—Ghostflower
42 B c 13/04 Starspangledbanner (AUS)—Hollow Talk
43 B f 20/02 Frankel—Love is Blindless
44 B f 26/05 No Nay Never (USA)—Mala Mala
45 MANNIX (IRE), ch c 02/03 Australia—Many Hearts
46 Ch f 10/05 Starspangledbanner (AUS)—Medican Star (IRE)
47 B f 01/03 Starspangledbanner (AUS)—Meetyouatthemoon
48 OTTEY, b f 19/01 Starspangledbanner (AUS)—North Wedge
49 B f 28/04 Camelot—Polish Belle
50 B f 30/03 No Nay Never (USA)—Pure Greed
51 RULER LEGEND (IRE), b c 05/03 Camelot—Avenue Dargent

# MR FOZZY STACK - continued

52 B c 20/04 Caravaggio—Scream Blue Murder (IRE)
53 Ch f 31/01 Highland Reel—Sirici
54 B f 08/02 Starspangledbanner (AUS)—The Last Sister
55 B f 11/02 Starspangledbanner (AUS)—Time will Tell

**Owners:** Mr Rick Barnes, Mr Michael Begley, Craig Bernick, Peter Chiu, Iman Hartono, Mr T. Hyde Jnr, Mr D. Keoghan, Mrs J. Magnier, Mr Casey McLiney, Mr B. Parker, Mr P. Piller, Mrs Jane Rowlinson, Mary Slack, Mr Michael Tabor, Genevieve Britton, Richard Brodie, Francis Brooke, Flaxman Stables, Forthepeopleracing, Pension Fund IV Syndicate, Toshihiro Matsumoto, R O'Callaghan, D Pearson, Phoenix Thoroughbred Ltd, B Sangster, Cayton Park Stud, Pension Fund V Syndicate.

**Flat Jockey:** Mark Enright, Chris Hayes, Conor Maxwell, Andrew Slattery. **Apprentice Jockey:** Michael Beresford, Olivia Shanahan.

---

## 510 MR EUGENE STANFORD, Newmarket
Postal: **2 Rous Memorial Cottages, Old Station Road, Newmarket, Suffolk, CB8 8DP**
Contacts: **PHONE 01638 665507 MOBILE 07761 223096**
**EMAIL e.stanford077@btinternet.com WEBSITE www.eugenestanfordracing.com**

1 **AMNA,** 7, b m Sayif (IRE)—Island Dreams (USA) **Mr E. V. Stanford**
2 **BELLA BLUR,** 9, ch m Showcasing—Ellablue **Miss C. R. Williams**
3 **Q CEE,** 8, b g Denounce—Gibraltar Lass (USA) **Mr M. W. Goodridge**
4 **TINKERBIRD,** 5, br h Gregorian (IRE)—Swan Queen **Mr E. V. Stanford**

### THREE-YEAR-OLDS

5 **ALEHANDRO,** b g Toronado (IRE)—Rosacara **Mr P. J. Ransley**
6 B f Acclamation—Nymfia (IRE) **Mr P. J. Ransley**

### TWO-YEAR-OLDS

7 B f 14/03 Ardad (IRE)—Mea Parvitas (IRE) (Oasis Dream) (1500) **Mr E. V. Stanford**

---

## 511 MR DANIEL STEELE, Henfield
Postal: **Blacklands House, Wheatsheaf Road, Wineham, Henfield, West Sussex, BN5 9BE**
Contacts: **PHONE 07809 405036**
**EMAIL danielsteele14@hotmail.co.uk**

1 8, B g Golan (IRE)—Broadfield Cruiser (IRE)
2 **CHIVERS (IRE),** 10, b g Duke of Marmalade (IRE)—Thara (USA) **Mr D. R. Steele**
3 **CLONGOWES (IRE),** 7, b g New Approach (IRE)—Punctilious **Sam Tingey & Charlie Tingey**
4 **COBRA EYE,** 4, b g Kodiac—Annie The Doc **Mr L. Zarghani**
5 **DELL ORO (FR),** 8, b g Walk In The Park (IRE)—Kallistea (FR) **D Steele S Tingey C Tingey**
6 **ELEVATED (IRE),** 4, b g Siyouni (FR)—Kahira (IRE) **Sam Tingey & Charlie Tingey**
7 **GOLD SOUK (IRE),** 4, b g Casamento (IRE)—Dubai Sunrise (USA) **Sam Tingey & Charlie Tingey**
8 **INFITAAH,** 4, b f Intello (GER)—Hawraa **Sam Tingey & Charlie Tingey**
9 **MADNESS LIGHT (FR),** 12, b g Satri (FR)—Majestic Lady (FR) **Mr C. G. Russell**
10 **RACING COUNTRY (IRE),** 6, b g Dubawi (IRE)—Movin' Out (AUS) **Sam Tingey & Charlie Tingey**
11 4, B f Blue Bresil (FR)—Rosygo (IRE)
12 **SPANISH PERSUADER (FR),** 4, b g Motivator—Alava (IRE) **Vectis Racing**

### THREE-YEAR-OLDS

13 B g Linda's Lad—Dainty Diva (IRE) **Vectis Racing**
14 B f Arvico (FR)—Mad Moll (IRE)

**Other Owners:** Mr D. R. Steele, Mr C. Tingey, Mr S. Tingey.

## 512 MRS JACKIE STEPHEN, Inverurie
Postal: **Conglass Farmhouse, Inverurie, Aberdeenshire, AB51 5DN**
Contacts: **PHONE 01467 621267 MOBILE 07980 785924 FAX 01467 620511**
**EMAIL** jackiestephen123@hotmail.com **WEBSITE** www.jackiestephenracing.com

1 **ANY JOB WILL DO (IRE)**, 5, ch g Shirocco (GER)—Funcheon Lady (IRE) **Mrs J. S. Stephen**
2 **DROGON (IRE)**, 5, b g Zoffany (IRE)—Flames To Dust (GER) **APCC Limited**
3 **DUNNOTTAR CASTLE**, 5, b g Kalanisi (IRE)—Sister Shannon (IRE) **Mr P. G. Stephen**
4 **KILFINAN BAY (IRE)**, 6, b g Mahler—Midnight Special (IRE) **Mrs J. S. Stephen**
5 **LADYVIE (FR)**, 14, b m Vic Toto (FR)—Ladykish (FR) **Mrs J. S. Stephen**
6 **LOCK DOWN LUKE**, 5, b g Lucarno (USA)—La Grande Villez (FR) **P. & Mark Fleming**
7 **LOVELY SCHTUFF (IRE)**, 9, b g Court Cave (IRE)—The Long Bill (IRE) **High Country Racing**
8 **SCULLYS FORGE (IRE)**, 7, ch g Doyen (IRE)—Queen of Questions (IRE) **Mrs J. S. Stephen**
9 **SPUTNIK (IRE)**, 6, b g Recital (FR)—Itíallendintears (IRE) **Neracehorses, Hamilton,, Stephen&whyte**
10 **THE GREAT GEORGIE**, 6, b g Multiplex—For More (FR) **Mr P. G. Stephen**
11 **WHOA BLACK BETTY (IRE)**, 6, br m Jeremy (USA)—Strong Lady (IRE) **Jackie Stephen Racing Club**
12 **WOLFCATCHER (IRE)**, 9, b g King's Best (USA)—Miss Particular (IRE) **Northern Lights Racing**

**Other Owners:** Mr D. L. Dunbar, Mr M. R. D. Fleming, Mr S. D. Hamilton, North East Racehorses, Mrs J. S. Stephen, Mr P. G. Stephen, Mr A. G. Whyte.

**Assistant Trainer:** Patrick Stephen.

## 513 MRS KATIE STEPHENS, Shaldon
Postal: **Sikymsa Meadow, Short Lane, Shaldon, Devon, TQ14 0HE**
**EMAIL** sikymsaracing@gmail.com

1 **ELLAS EREN**, 5, b m Norse Dancer (IRE)—Legion of Merit **Mrs K. J. Stephens**
2 **ROYAL PLAZA**, 10, b g King's Theatre (IRE)—Friendly Craic (IRE) **Friends Have Fun Racing**
3 **TEMPLIER (IRE)**, 8, b g Mastercraftsman (IRE)—Tigertail (FR) **Catherine Payne & Melvyn Langdell**

**Other Owners:** Mr M. J. Langdell, Mrs C. Payne, Mrs K. J. Stephens.

## 514 MR ROBERT STEPHENS, Caldicot
Postal: **The Knoll, St. Brides Netherwent, Caldicot, Gwent, NP26 3AT**
Contacts: **MOBILE 07717 477177**
**EMAIL** robertdavidstephens@btinternet.com **WEBSITE** www.robertstephensracing.com

1 **BELTOR**, 10, b g Authorized (IRE)—Carahill (AUS) **A. J. Mossop**
2 **BROPHIES DOLL**, 9, ch m Gamut (IRE)—Crossbar Lady (IRE) **Mr T. J. Moynihan**
3 **BUMBLE BAY**, 11, b g Trade Fair—Amica **A Mossop & H Scale**
4 **COMEONTHEBULL (IRE)**, 9, ch g Papal Bull—Maratanas Gift (IRE) **M Duthie & T Moynihan**
5 **ECHO DU LARGE (FR)**, 7, b g Blue Bresil (FR)—Gardagua (FR) **Castle Farm Racing**
6 **ESPRESSO FREDDO (IRE)**, 7, b g Fast Company (IRE)—Spring Bouquet (IRE) **Threes Company**
7 **FAIR GO MATE (FR)**, 5, b g Australia—Main Spring **Mr R. D. Stephens**
8 **FATEH (IRE)**, 8, b g Big Bad Bob (IRE)—Passarelle (USA) **The Shinton Family**
9 **FIRST DESTINATION**, 9, b m Rail Link—Hollow Quaill (IRE) **A. J. Mossop**
10 **GOLDEN GLORY (IRE)**, 7, b m Fame And Glory—Howyakeepan (IRE) **Castle Farm Racing Golden Syndicate**
11 **GOLDEN GROVE (IRE)**, 6, b g Stowaway—Follyfoot (IRE) **Castle Farm Racing Golden Syndicate**
12 **HAVANA DAWN**, 4, gr f Havana Gold (IRE)—Rock Ace (IRE) **Mr R. D. Stephens**
13 **HEDGEINATOR (IRE)**, 11, ch g Beneficial—Annalecky (IRE) **Threes Company**
14 **INTERNATIONALANGEL (IRE)**, 4, gr f Dark Angel (IRE)—Wrong Answer **Mr R. D. Stephens**

## MR ROBERT STEPHENS - continued

15 **MERE ANARCHY (IRE)**, 10, b g Yeats (IRE)—Maracana (IRE) **Les Oxley & R Stephens**
16 **MILE HOUSE (IRE)**, 13, b g Close Conflict (USA)—Clogheen Lass (IRE) **Castle Farm Racing**
17 **MUSKETEER**, 9, ch g Schiaparelli (GER)—Suave Shot **Mr R. D. Stephens**
18 **NEW CLARE**, 6, gr m Arcadio (GER)—Pippedatthepost **Colmix Contracting and Groundworks Ltd**
19 **OUR SHAKILA**, 4, b f War Command (USA)—Sterling Sound (USA) **Mr H. Sultan Saeed**
20 **PASSIN' THRU**, 5, b m Nathaniel (IRE)—Go Between **M Duthie & T Moynihan**
21 **PUSH THE TEMPO (IRE)**, 8, b g Gold Well—Fairpark (IRE) **Castle Farm Racing**
22 **QUINNSBOROTEMPTRES (IRE)**, 9, ch m Gamut (IRE)—Quinnsboro Native (IRE) **Mr R. D. Stephens**
23 **SECONDO (FR)**, 11, b g Sakhee's Secret—Royal Jade **Robert Stephens Racing Club**
24 **SEMPIONE PARK (IRE)**, 6, b g Milan—Cashalass (IRE) **Castle Farm Racing**
25 **SON OF OZ**, 4, ch g Australia—Ambria (GER) **Threes Company**
26 **SWEET FAB'S**, 7, b g Dr Massini (IRE)—Whimberry (IRE) **Mr P. Williams**
27 **TIFFANY ROSE**, 5, ch m Black Sam Bellamy (IRE)—Maria Antonia (IRE) **Threes Company**
28 **TUDORS TREASURE**, 10, b g Dr Massini (IRE)—Rude Health **Four Seasons Partnership**
29 **TURPIN GOLD**, 5, b g Dick Turpin (IRE)—Tamara **The Shinton Family**

### THREE-YEAR-OLDS

30 **GHAYAHIB (IRE)**, ch f Twilight Son—Rosamaria (IRE) **Mr A. A. A. Bin Ghalita Almheiri**
31 **HIGHLAND DANDY (IRE)**, br g Dandy Man (IRE)—Star Bonita (IRE) **Mr R. D. Stephens**
32 **JUMIERAH CHALLENGE**, b c Mayson—Green Silk (IRE) **Mr A. A. A. Bin Ghalita Almheiri**
33 Br gr g Gutaifan (IRE)—Last Bid **Mr R. D. Stephens**
34 **MELAKAZ (IRE)**, br g Markaz (IRE)—Melatonina (IRE) **Mr T. J. Moynihan**

### TWO-YEAR-OLDS

35 B c 27/03 Elzaam (AUS)—Elusive Legend (USA) (Elusive Quality (USA)) (8000) **Mr H. Sultan Saeed**

**Other Owners:** Mr I. J. K. Croker, Mr M. Duthie, A. J. Mossop, Mr T. J. Moynihan, Mr L. T. Oxley, Mr W. B. H. Scale, D. T. Shorthouse, Mr K. Slade, Mr R. D. Stephens.

**Assistant Trainer:** Rosie Stephens.

**NH Jockey:** Micheal Nolan, Tom O'Brien, Ciaran Gethings. **Amateur Jockey:** Mr Craig Dowson, Mr Morgan Winstone.

---

**515**

## MR JOHN STIMPSON, Newcastle-under-Lyme
Postal: **Trainers Lodge, Park Road, Butterton, Newcastle-under-Lyme, Staffordshire, ST5 4DZ**
Contacts: **PHONE 01782 636020**
**EMAIL** john@redskyuk.com

1 **APACHITO**, 4, b g Fountain of Youth (IRE)—Apache Glory (USA) **Mr J. Stimpson**
2 **HURRICANE DYLAN (IRE)**, 10, b g Brian Boru—Definetly Sarah (IRE) **Mr J. Stimpson**
3 **MY BROTHER MIKE (IRE)**, 7, b g Bated Breath—Coming Back **Mr J. Stimpson**
4 **MY TOWN CHICAGO (USA)**, 6, b g Medaglia d'Oro (USA)—Say You Will (IRE) **Mr J. Stimpson**
5 **PERUVIAN SUMMER (IRE)**, 5, ch g Lope de Vega (IRE)—Need You Now (IRE) **Mr J. Stimpson**
6 **POPPOP (FR)**, 5, b g Great Pretender (IRE)—Bloody Sunday (FR) **Mr J. Stimpson**
7 **THE GREY BANDIT**, 4, bl g Gregorian (IRE)—Reel Cool **Mr J. Stimpson**

## 516 MR WILLIAM STONE, West Wickham
Postal: **The Meadow, Streetly End, West Wickham, Cambridge, Cambridgeshire, CB21 4RP**
Contacts: **MOBILE 07788 971094**
**EMAIL williamstone1@hotmail.co.uk**

1 **AQUASCOPIC**, 4, b f Telescope (IRE)—Satin Waters **Ron Spore & P D West**
2 **DASHING ROGER**, 4, b g Fast Company (IRE)—Croeso Cusan **R. C. Spore**
3 **FOLLIA**, 4, b f Toronado (IRE)—Filona (IRE) **Ron Spore & Dr C Scott**
4 **JEANETTE MAY**, 5, b m Dick Turpin (IRE)—Clock Opera (IRE) **Mr Shane Fairweather & Dr C Scott**
5 **LALANIA**, 6, br m Kheleyf (USA)—George's Gift **Dr C. M. Scott**
6 **LITTLE BROWN TROUT**, 4, b g Casamento (IRE)—Clock Opera (IRE) **Dr C. M. Scott**
7 **MISTRESS NELLIE**, 6, ch m Mount Nelson—Watchoverme **Mrs Denis Haynes & Dr Caroline Scott**
8 **SEA TROUT**, 4, ch g Equiano (FR)—Smile For Me (IRE) **Dr C. M. Scott**
9 **THE JEAN GENIE**, 7, b br m Lawman (FR)—Miracle Seeker **Dr C. M. Scott**

### THREE-YEAR-OLDS
10 **DASHING DICK (IRE)**, b g Cable Bay (IRE)—Raggiante (IRE) **Ron Spore & Dr C Scott**
11 **LITTLE SUNFLOWER**, ch f Pearl Secret—Dance In The Sun **Dr C. M. Scott**

### TWO-YEAR-OLDS
12 B c 12/04 Adaay (IRE)—Hot Secret (Sakhee's Secret) (6000) **Ron Spore & Sheryl Meldram**
13 B c 29/04 Slade Power (IRE)—Irrational (Kyllachy) (6500) **Ron Spore & Dr C Scott**
14 B c 04/03 Showcasing—Khaki (IRE) (Key of Luck (USA)) (10000) **Ron Spore & Sheryl Meldram**
15 B c 27/01 Olympic Glory (IRE)—Libre A Vous (FR) (Redoute's Choice (AUS)) (10000) **Ron Spore & Dr C Scott**
16 **ROMANTIC TIME**, b f 17/03 Time Test—Percy's Romance (Sir Percy) **Mrs E. A. P. Haynes**
17 B c 22/04 Gregorian (IRE)—Satin Waters (Halling (USA)) **Ron Spore & P D West**

**Other Owners:** Mr S. A. Fairweather, Mrs E. A. P. Haynes, Miss S. C. A. Meldram, Dr C. M. Scott, R. C. Spore, Mr P. D. West.

## 517 MR WILF STOREY, Consett
Postal: **Grange Farm & Stud, Muggleswick, Consett, County Durham, DH8 9DW**
Contacts: **PHONE 01207 255259 MOBILE 07860 510441**
**EMAIL wlstorey@metronet.co.uk WEBSITE www.wilfstorey.com**

1 **ALESSANDRO ALLORI (IRE)**, 6, ch g Dawn Approach (IRE)—Truly Mine (IRE) **Mr W. L. Storey**
2 **BETTY GRABLE (IRE)**, 7, b m Delegator—Danella (IRE) **Flash Figs Racing**
3 **CARD HIGH (IRE)**, 11, b g Red Clubs (IRE)—Think (FR) **Gremlin Racing**
4 **MAISIE MOO**, 5, b m Swiss Spirit—Al Hawa (USA) **Mr W. L. Storey**
5 **NEARLY THERE**, 8, b g Virtual—Nicoise (IRE) **Geegeez.co.uk 1**
6 **PERFECT SOLDIER (IRE)**, 7, b g Kodiac—Independent Girl (IRE) **Gremlin Racing**
7 **RAIL DANCER**, 9, b g Rail Link—Mara Dancer **Mr W. L. Storey**
8 **TARNHELM**, 6, b m Helmet (AUS)—Anosti **H. S. Hutchinson & W. Storey**

### THREE-YEAR-OLDS
9 Ch f Poet's Voice—Mofeyda (IRE) **Mr W. L. Storey**
10 **MYTHICAL WATERS**, b f Fountain of Youth (IRE)—Distant Waters **Mr W. L. Storey**

**Other Owners:** Mr M. Bisogno, H. S. Hutchinson, Mr W. L. Storey, the durhamcompany ray hawthorne.

**Assistant Trainer:** Miss S. Storey.

**Amateur Jockey:** Miss S. M. Doolan.

**518** **SIR MICHAEL STOUTE**, Newmarket
Postal: Freemason Lodge, Bury Road, Newmarket, Suffolk, CB8 7BY
Contacts: **PHONE 01638 663801 FAX 01638 667276**

1 **A LA VOILE**, 4, b f Invincible Spirit (IRE)—All At Sea
2 **ALIGNAK**, 5, gr h Sea The Moon (GER)—Albanova
3 **ALMAREEKH (USA)**, 4, b br f War Front (USA)—Orate (USA)
4 **ASTRO KING (IRE)**, 4, b c Kingman—Astroglia (USA)
5 **BOSS POWER (IRE)**, 4, b g Frankel—La Vinchina (GER)
6 **CHAI YO POWER**, 4, b g Le Havre (IRE)—Stella Bellissima (IRE)
7 **CHAIRMAN POWER**, 4, b g Galileo (IRE)—Best Terms
8 **CROSSING THE BAR (IRE)**, 4, b g Poet's Voice—Ship's Biscuit
9 **DOLLAR BID**, 4, b c Frankel—Cape Dollar (IRE)
10 **DREAM OF DREAMS (IRE)**, 7, ch g Dream Ahead (USA)—Vasilia
11 **HASTY SAILOR (IRE)**, 4, b g Fastnet Rock (AUS)—Galileano (IRE)
12 **HIGHEST GROUND (IRE)**, 4, b c Frankel—Celestial Lagoon (JPN)
13 **HYDROS**, 4, b c Frankel—Trojan Queen (USA)
14 **KATARA (FR)**, 4, b f Deep Impact (JPN)—Asyad (IRE)
15 **LAAFY (USA)**, 5, b g Noble Mission—Miner's Secret (USA)
16 **LAW OF ONE (IRE)**, 4, ch c Galileo (IRE)—Strawberry Fledge (USA)
17 **LIGHTS ON**, 4, ch f Siyouni (FR)—In The Light
18 **MARS LANDING (IRE)**, 4, b g Dark Angel (IRE)—Psychometry (FR)
19 **MY FRANKEL**, 4, b c Frankel—My Special J's (USA)
20 **QUEEN POWER (IRE)**, 5, ch m Shamardal (USA)—Princess Serena (USA)
21 **RANSOM**, 4, b g Kingman—Arizona Jewel
22 **RAOOF**, 4, gr g Dark Angel (IRE)—Swiss Diva
23 **REGAL REALITY**, 6, b g Intello (GER)—Regal Realm
24 **SANGARIUS**, 5, b h Kingman—Trojan Queen (USA)
25 **SATONO JAPAN (JPN)**, 4, b c Deep Impact (JPN)—Dubawi Heights
26 **SHAMAROON (IRE)**, 4, ch c Shamardal (USA)—Prime Run
27 **SOFFIKA (IRE)**, 4, b f Zoffany (IRE)—Rosika
28 **SOLID STONE (IRE)**, 5, br g Shamardal (USA)—Landmark (USA)
29 **THIBAAN (USA)**, 4, b c War Front (USA)—Lahudood

## THREE-YEAR-OLDS

30 **AERION POWER (IRE)**, b c Kingman—Applauded (IRE)
31 **ALMAAN (USA)**, ch c Speightstown (USA)—Rosalind (USA)
32 **ATACAMA DESERT (IRE)**, ch c Galileo (IRE)—Ikat (IRE)
33 **BAWAADY**, ch f Dubawi (IRE)—Rifqah (USA)
34 **BAY BRIDGE**, b c New Bay—Hayyona
35 **BEATING ALL (USA)**, b c American Pharoah (USA)—Ann of The Dance (USA)
36 **BLOW THAT HORN**, b c Golden Horn—Samira Gold (FR)
37 **CLEOPATRA'S GIFT (USA)**, b br f American Pharoah (USA)—Grosse Pointe Anne (USA)
38 **CRYSTAL STARLET**, b f Frankel—Crystal Zvezda
39 **DEGREE**, b f Dubawi (IRE)—Echelon
40 **DELIGHTSNSURPRISES (USA)**, b c Street Sense (USA)—Snapdragon (USA)
41 **DIAMONDS ARE KING (USA)**, b c Air Force Blue (USA)—High Finance (IRE)
42 **DIVINE HERALD**, b f Frankel—Heaven Sent
43 Ch c Exceed And Excel (AUS)—Duquesa (IRE)
44 **DUTY OF CARE**, b c Kingman—Exemplify
45 **EASTERN DELIGHT (IRE)**, b f Camacho—Glamorous Air (IRE)
46 **EVALUATION**, b g Dubawi (IRE)—Estimate (IRE)
47 Ch c Gleneagles (IRE)—Fastnet Mist (IRE)
48 **FETNA (FR)**, b f Shalaa (IRE)—Iltemas (USA)
49 **GEOMETRIST**, b f Kingman—Hypoteneuse (IRE)
50 **HALIC**, b c Golden Horn—Pavlosk (USA)
51 **INIGO JONES**, b c New Approach (IRE)—Spacious
52 **JUST FINE**, b g Sea The Stars (IRE)—Bint Almatar (USA)
53 **KING ALHBAB (IRE)**, b c Kingman—Toquette (IRE)
54 **KING CAPELLA**, b c Kingman—Crystal Capella

## SIR MICHAEL STOUTE - continued

55 **MARDOOF (IRE),** b g Awtaad (IRE)—Yanabeeaa (USA)
56 **MASHHOOR,** b c Kingman—Sunsemperchi
57 **MASNOON,** gr c Shalaa (IRE)—Vayasa (FR)
58 **MAXIMAL,** b c Galileo (IRE)—Joyeuse
59 **MAYTAL,** ch f Sea The Stars (IRE)—Midsummer
60 **MOONLIT NIGHT (IRE),** b f Sea The Stars (IRE)—Donau (IRE)
61 **MOSAAHEB,** ch c Lope de Vega (IRE)—Spirit of Xian (IRE)
62 **MY SWALLOW,** b c Shalaa (IRE)—Green Swallow (FR)
63 **NEVER SAY WHEN (IRE),** b c No Nay Never (USA)—Lady Soldier (IRE)
64 **NOON STAR (USA),** b f Galileo (IRE)—Midday
65 **PORTFOLIO (JPN),** b f Deep Impact (JPN)—Diploma
66 **POSSIBLE MAN,** b c Le Havre (IRE)—Baldovina
67 **POTAPOVA,** b f Invincible Spirit (IRE)—Safina
68 **QAASID (IRE),** b c Awtaad (IRE)—Nisriyna (IRE)
69 **QUEEN'S FAIR,** b f Dansili—Queen's Best
70 **RED HOT MAMA,** b f Kingman—Hi Calypso (IRE)
71 **SABOUSI (IRE),** ch c New Approach (IRE)—Glenmayne (IRE)
72 **SAILED AWAY (GER),** b c Sea The Moon (GER)—Sail (IRE)
73 **SAMOOT (IRE),** ch f Dubawi (IRE)—Muthabara (IRE)
74 **SATONO CHEVALIER (IRE),** b c Invincible Spirit (IRE)—Albisola (IRE)
75 **STAR SEEKING (IRE),** ch f Gleneagles (IRE)—Saturn Girl (IRE)
76 **SUNRISE VALLEY (USA),** b f Karakontie (JPN)—Story (USA)
77 **SWOON (FR),** b f Frankel—Marine Bleue (IRE)
78 **TAWAAREQ (IRE),** b g Shamardal (USA)—Sundus (USA)
79 **THALER,** b c Dubawi (IRE)—Timepiece
80 **THUNDER SUN (FR),** b c Siyouni (FR)—Bal de La Rose (IRE)
81 **TIGER BEETLE,** b c Camelot—Beach Frolic
82 **TRAILA,** ch g Australia—Waila
83 **TUCSON CLOUD (IRE),** b f Fastnet Rock (AUS)—Transhumance (IRE)
84 **VILLE DE GRACE,** b f Le Havre (IRE)—Archangel Gabriel (USA)
85 **WAHRAAN (FR),** ch c Le Havre (IRE)—Al Jassasiyah (IRE)
86 **ZIKANY,** b c Zoffany (IRE)—Rosika
87 **ZOFFANY'S GIRL (FR),** b f Zoffany (IRE)—Geisha Girl (IRE)

## TWO-YEAR-OLDS

88 **AEONIAN (IRE),** b c 10/02 Ulysses (IRE)—Ama (USA) (Storm Cat (USA))
89 **ALTJERINGA,** b f 12/01 Iffraaj—Altesse (Hernando (FR))
90 **ASSESSMENT,** b c 04/04 Kingman—Clinical (Motivator)
91 B c 09/01 Zelzal (FR)—Asyad (IRE) (New Approach (IRE))
92 **BOLD AND LOYAL,** b c 02/02 Frankel—Birdwood (Oasis Dream) (100000)
93 B f 12/03 Siyouni (FR)—Carnoustie (FR) (Acclamation)
94 **CHICHEN ITZA,** b f 28/02 Fastnet Rock (AUS)—Phaenomena (IRE) (Galileo (IRE))
95 B c 17/04 Make Believe—Cruck Realta (Sixties Icon) (175000)
96 **CRYSTAL CAPRICE (IRE),** b f 17/03 Frankel—Crystal Zvezda (Dubawi (IRE))
97 **CRYSTAL DELIGHT,** ch c 25/03 New Approach (IRE)—Crystal Capella (Cape Cross (IRE))
98 **CRYSTAL ESTRELLA,** b f 09/02 Iffraaj—Crystal Etoile (Dansili)
99 B c 02/03 Nathaniel (IRE)—Desert Berry (Green Desert (USA)) (280000)
100 Ch c 12/02 Australia—Dubian To (IRE) (Sea The Stars (IRE))
101 B c 26/03 Toronado (IRE)—Ella Ransom (GER) (Ransom O'War (USA)) (25827)
102 B c 03/02 Ulysses (IRE)—End of An Era (IRE) (Azamour (IRE)) (72000)
103 **EVERY BLUE MOON (IRE),** ch f 25/02 Lope de Vega (IRE)—Celestial Lagoon (JPN) (Sunday Silence (USA))
104 **FINE CHINA,** b f 24/01 Mastercraftsman (IRE)—Chinoiseries (Archipenko (USA))
105 **HAVAILA,** ch c 18/03 Le Havre (IRE)—Waila (Notnowcato)
106 B c 01/02 Shalaa (IRE)—Iltemas (USA) (Galileo (IRE))
107 **INFINITIVE,** b f 15/03 Ulysses (IRE)—Integral (Dalakhani (IRE))
108 B c 07/03 Muhaarar—Jadanna (IRE) (Mujadil (USA)) (80000)
109 **KIRILENKO,** b f 08/03 Ulysses (IRE)—Marenko (Exceed And Excel (AUS))
110 **KITEFLYER,** b c 21/01 Iffraaj—Star Value (IRE) (Danehill Dancer (IRE))
111 B c 25/03 Shalaa (IRE)—Lady Gorgeous (Compton Place) (250000)

## SIR MICHAEL STOUTE - continued

112 B c 20/04 Cotai Glory—Lady Lucia (IRE) (Royal Applause) (110000)
113 B c 05/04 Lope de Vega (IRE)—Laganore (Fastnet Rock (AUS)) (430000)
114 B c 17/04 War Front (USA)—Lahudood (Singspiel (IRE))
115 **LOVE YOU GRANDPA (IRE),** b f 09/04 Frankel—Baldovina (Tale of The Cat (USA))
116 Ch c 10/04 Ulysses (IRE)—Lysanda (GER) (Lando (GER))
117 B c 18/04 Churchill (IRE)—Melodious (Cape Cross (IRE))
118 B c 04/05 Almanzor (FR)—Moojeh (IRE) (King's Best (USA))  (76675)
119 **NEW DIMENSION,** b c 01/04 Ulysses (IRE)—Azhar (Exceed And Excel (AUS)) (120000)
120 **PARAMETER,** b f 25/02 Le Havre (IRE)—Criteria (IRE) (Galileo (IRE))
121 **PROFESSION,** ch c 22/03 Ulysses (IRE)—Echelon (Danehill (USA)) (75000)
122 B f 09/02 Awtaad (IRE)—Qareenah (USA) (Arch (USA))
123 B c 26/04 Kodiac—Querulous (USA) (Raven's Pass (USA)) (90000)
124 **RED RAMBLER,** ch c 05/04 Iffraaj—Blushing Rose (Dalakhani (IRE))
125 Ch c 14/05 Dubawi (IRE)—Rifqah (Elusive Quality (USA))
126 **ROCK SIREN,** b f 09/03 Ulysses (IRE)—Rock Choir (Pivotal)
127 **SCHNEEMANN,** b c 22/02 Sea The Moon (GER)—Snow Ballerina (Sadler's Wells (USA)) (480000)
128 B c 22/04 Kingman—Secret Keeper (New Approach (IRE)) (260000)
129 **SEE (USA),** br f 12/04 War Front (USA)—Faufiler (IRE) (Galileo (IRE))
130 B f 02/05 Australia—Split Trois (FR) (Dubawi (IRE))
131 **TABLES TURNED,** ch c 04/02 Ulysses (IRE)—Mesa Fresca (USA) (Sky Mesa (USA))
132 **TERRA MITICA (IRE),** ch f 02/02 Ulysses (IRE)—Mississippi Delta (USA) (Giant's Causeway (USA))
133 B c 04/04 Kitten's Joy (USA)—Uniformly Yours (CAN) (Grand Slam (USA))
134 **WISTFUL,** b f 19/03 Sea The Stars (IRE)—Ardent (Pivotal)

**Owners:** Her Majesty The Queen, Exors of the late Mr K. Abdullah, Hamdan bin Rashid Al Maktoum, Al Shaqab Racing UK Limited, Mr S. M. Bel Obaida, Cheveley Park Stud Limited, Mr P. E. Done, Flaxman Stables Ireland Ltd, Mrs E. A. P. Haynes, Mr C. M. Humber, Hunscote Stud Limited, Hunscote Stud Ltd & Mr Chris Humber, King Power Racing Co Ltd, Lady C. Laidlaw, Mr R. Ng, Niarchos Family, M. Obaida, Orchard Bloodstock Ltd, Qatar Racing Limited, Miss K. Rausing, Satomi Horse Company Ltd, Mr S. Suhail, M. Tabor, J. Wigan, Sir Evelyn de Rothschild.

---

## 519 MRS ALI STRONGE, Eastbury
Postal: **Castle Piece Racing Stables, Eastbury, Hungerford, Berkshire, RG17 7JR**
Contacts: **PHONE** 01488 72818 **MOBILE** 07779 285205 **FAX** 01488 670378
**EMAIL** office@castlepiecestables.com **WEBSITE** www.castlepiecestables.com

1 **AL VERDE,** 4, ch g Al Kazeem—Greenery (IRE) **Larkhills & Shaw Racing 2**
2 **AMANTO (GER),** 11, b g Medicean—Amore (GER) **Shaw Racing Partnership 2**
3 **ARDMAYLE (IRE),** 9, ch g Whitmore's Conn (USA)—Welsh Connection (IRE) **The Wishful Thinkers**
4 **BAASHIQ (IRE),** 7, b g New Approach (IRE)—Fatanah (IRE) **P. Kelly**
5 **CHEZ CASTEL MAIL (FR),** 9, ch g My Risk (FR)—Queenly Mail (FR) **The One and Only Partnership**
6 **DREWMAIN LEGEND,** 9, b m Midnight Legend—Ryders Hill **Hot To Trot Jumping & Mrs Jane Andrews**
7 **EAIRSIDH (IRE),** 6, b g Arcadio (GER)—Inch Rose (IRE) **& A Hyde**
8 **ESTRELA STAR (IRE),** 5, ch g Casamento (IRE)—Reem Star **Kevin & Ali Stronge**
9 **GETABUCK (IRE),** 8, ch g Getaway (IRE)—Buck's Blue (FR) **Shawracing Partnership 2 & Miss. A. Hyde**
10 **GLORY TIME,** 5, b g Olympic Glory (IRE)—Tunkwa (FR) **Mrs A. J. Stronge**
11 **GOTTARDO (IRE),** 6, b g Choisir (AUS)—Chantarella (IRE) **Mrs C. L. Smith**
12 **GRANDSCAPE,** 6, b g Lemon Drop Kid (USA)—Unnatural (USA) **Mrs C. L. Smith**
13 **HANNALITE,** 4, ch f Nathaniel (IRE)—Bravia **Mr L. A. Bellman**
14 **HEPBURN,** 8, b m Sixties Icon—Mighty Splash **ROA Racing Partnership V**
15 **HERESMYNUMBER (IRE),** 11, b g Kalanisi (IRE)—Broken Rein (IRE) **Kings Of The Castle**
16 **JALINGO (IRE),** 10, b g Cape Cross (IRE)—Just Special **Paul Whitehead & Clare Spencer-Herbert**
17 **LAKE SAND (IRE),** 4, b g Footstepsinthesand—Lake Louise (IRE) **Mr L. A. Bellman**
18 **RENARDEAU,** 5, b g Foxwedge (AUS)—La Cucina (IRE) **Mr L. A. Bellman**
19 **ROSEARELLI,** 6, ch m Schiaparelli (GER)—Vin Rose **Miss A. B. Hyde**
20 **SCORPION HAZE (IRE),** 8, b g Scorpion (IRE)—Sea Maiden **Shaw Racing Partnership 2**
21 **SIR CANFORD (IRE),** 5, b g Canford Cliffs (IRE)—Alexander Divine **The Select Racing Club Limited**

## MRS ALI STRONGE - continued

22 **SKY STORM**, 4, ch f Night of Thunder (IRE)—Dinvar Diva
23 **STORM MELODY**, 8, b g Royal Applause—Plume **Shaw Racing Partnership 2**
24 **YORKTOWN (IRE)**, 4, b g Free Eagle (IRE)—Bryanstown (IRE)
25 **ZAYRIYAN (IRE)**, 6, ch g Shamardal (USA)—Zariyna (IRE) **Friends Of Castle Piece**

### THREE-YEAR-OLDS

26 **ACQUISITOR**, b g Due Diligence (USA)—Nellie Ellis (IRE) **Mr Tim Dykes & Hope Eden Racing Ltd**
27 **HELLUVABOY (IRE)**, ch g Helmet (AUS)—Catbells (IRE) **Laurence Bellman & Keith Trowbridge**
28 **KENSINGTON GREY (FR)**, gr g Kendargent (FR)—Clara Luna (FR) **Mr L. A. Bellman**
29 **NAVAJO BEAUTY**, b f Helmet (AUS)—Navajo Rainbow **G Bishop & A Kirkland**
30 **RAFFLES REBEL**, ch g Al Kazeem—Go Between **Hope Eden Racing Ltd & Mrs Ali Stronge**

### TWO-YEAR-OLDS

31 B c 06/04 Nathaniel (IRE)—Joshua's Princess (Danehill (USA)) (16000) **Spencer-Herbert,Herbert,Simmons&Kidger**
32 Ch c 01/05 Sir Percy—Lady Stardust (Spinning World (USA)) (11000) **Mrs A. J. Stronge**

**Other Owners:** Mrs J. Andrews, Mr L. A. Bellman, Mr G. S. Bishop, Mr T. J. Dykes, K. R. Elliott, Mrs S. Evans, Hope Eden Racing Limited, Mr R. S. Hoskins, Hot To Trot Jumping, Miss A. B. Hyde, Dr A. I. Kirkland, Larkhills Racing Partnership, Shaw Racing Partnership 2, Ms A. M. Simmons, Ms C. L. Spencer-Herbert, Mrs A. J. Stronge, The Select Racing Club Limited, K. P. Trowbridge, Dr P. G. Walker, Mr P. Whitehead.

**Assistant Trainer:** Sam Stronge.

---

**520**

### MRS LINDA STUBBS, Malton
Postal: **Beverley House Stables, Beverley Road, Malton, North Yorkshire, YO17 9PJ**
Contacts: **HOME 01653 698731 MOBILE 07801 167707**
**EMAIL l.stubbs@btconnect.com**

1 **CAREY STREET (IRE)**, 5, b g Bungle Inthejungle—Undulant Way **Mr P. G. Shorrock, P.G.Shorrock & L.Stubbs**
2 **CASIET**, 5, b g Iffraaj—Caskelena (IRE) **Mr M. Steel**
3 **FIRST RESPONSE**, 6, b g First Defence (USA)—
Promising Lead **Mr P. G. Shorrock, D.M.Smith, P.G.Shorrock & L.Stubbs, Mr D. M. Smith**
4 **IVA REFLECTION**, 4, b g Ivawood (IRE)—Mirror Image
5 **OAKENSHIELD (IRE)**, 4, b g Invincible Spirit (IRE)—War Effort (USA) **Mr J. L. White**
6 **OLD NEWS**, 4, b g Dutch Art—Queen's Charter **Mr P. G. Shorrock**

---

**521**

### MR ROB SUMMERS, Solihull
Postal: **Summerhill Cottage, Danzey Green, Tanworth-in-Arden, Solihull**
Contacts: **PHONE 01564 742667 MOBILE 07775 898327**

1 **ATLANTIC STORM (IRE)**, 9, b g September Storm (GER)—Double Dream (IRE) **Mr A. R. Price**
2 **GIVE OVER**, 7, b m Overbury (IRE)—Delray Beach (FR) **Mr A. D. Sansome**
3 **HIGHLAND BOBBY**, 6, b g Big Bad Bob (IRE)—Eolith **Mrs G. M. Summers**
4 **SECRET BERI**, 7, ch m Schiaparelli (GER)—Secret Whisper **Mrs G. M. Summers**
5 **SECRET MOSS**, 6, ch m Schiaparelli (GER)—Secret Whisper **Mrs G. M. Summers**
6 **SOME BUCKLE (IRE)**, 12, b g Milan—Miss Moppit (IRE) **Mr S. W. Dunn**
7 **ST MERRYN (IRE)**, 10, b g Oscar (IRE)—Kigali (IRE) **Mrs G. M. Summers**

**Assistant Trainer:** Mrs G. M. Summers.

## 522 MR TOM SYMONDS, Hentland

Postal: **Dason Court Cottage, Hentland, Ross-On-Wye, Herefordshire, HR9 6LW**
Contacts: **PHONE 01989 730869 MOBILE 07823 324649**
EMAIL **dasoncourt@gmail.com** WEBSITE **www.thomassymonds.co.uk**

1 AUBIS PARK (FR), 6, b m Walk In The Park (IRE)—Aubisquinette (FR) **Prof L. P. Hardwick**
2 BAY OF INTRIGUE, 6, b g Sulamani (IRE)—Kahlua Cove **Mr Oscar Singh & Miss Priya Purewal**
3 BLUEBELL POLKA (IRE), 4, b f Flemensfirth (USA)—Lady Petit (IRE) **Clan McNeil**
4 BOBO MAC (IRE), 10, gr g Whitmore's Conn (USA)—Blazing Love (IRE) **C & M Baker, K Ibberson, H Pearman**
5 COBRA COMMANDER (IRE), 7, b g Beneficial—Run For Help (IRE) **Dean, Willetts & Vernon**
6 EVERYTHING NOW (IRE), 7, b g Gold Well—Givehertime (IRE) **Mr T. R. Symonds**
7 FAZAYTE (FR), 6, b g Spider Flight (FR)—Vakina (FR) **Mrs C. M. Antcliff**
8 FIL D'ARIANE (FR), 6, b g Gris de Gris (IRE)—Vibraye (FR) **Sir Peter & Lady Gibbings**
9 FLAMING HOT (IRE), 6, b m Fame And Glory—I Never Knew That (IRE)
10 FLEURSALS, 5, b m Poet's Voice—Entitlement **Simon Davies & Tom Symonds**
11 HEMERA DU BERLAIS (FR), 5, b m Great Pretender—Wendy du Berlais (FR) **Mr S. Davies**
12 HIDOR DE BERSY (FR), 4, ch g Nidor (FR)—Tropulka God (FR) **Sir Peter & Lady Gibbings**
13 HOLLYWOODIEN (FR), 10, gr g Martaline—Incorrigible (FR) **Sir Peter & Lady Gibbings**
14 HYSTERY BERE (FR), 4, b g Planteur (IRE)—Thalie Hurley (FR) **Mr S. Davies**
15 IMPERIAL HURLEY (FR), 4, gr g Planteur (IRE)—Thalie Hurley (FR) **Mr S. Davies**
16 INDY FIVE (IRE), 11, b g Vertical Speed (FR)—Beesplease (IRE) **The Dobbin Club**
17 KAKI DE LA PREE (FR), 14, b g Kapgarde (FR)—Kica (FR) **Mr T. R. Symonds**
18 LEGENDARY RHYTHM, 5, b m Midnight Legend—Hot Rhythm **David Clark & Partner**
19 LEXI'S CHOICE (IRE), 5, b m Presenting—Gilt Ridden (IRE) **Palmer-Brown, Mason & Murphy**
20 LLANDINABO LAD, 6, ch g Malinas (GER)—Hot Rhythm **Celia & Michael Baker**
21 LOUD AS LIONS (IRE), 8, b g Flemensfirth (USA)—Misspublican (IRE) **C & M Baker, K Ibberson, H Pearman**
22 LUGG RIVER, 7, b m Kayf Tara—Supreme Gem (IRE) **Frank Green & Mike Roberts**
23 MARTA DES MOTTES (FR), 4, b f Montmartre (FR)—Oktavia des Mottes (FR) **Mr S. Davies**
24 METEORITE, 7, b g Bollin Eric—Running Hotter **Matthew Engel & David Clark**
25 MIGHTY LEADER (IRE), 13, b g Milan—Madam Leader (IRE) **Mr Oscar Singh & Miss Priya Purewal**
26 MORIKO DE VASSY (FR), 4, b g Cokoriko (FR)—Mona Vassy (FR) **Amis de Vassy**
27 MR WASHINGTON, 8, b g Vinnie Roe (IRE)—Anna Bird (IRE) **Mrs J. Hitchings**
28 OUT BY SIX (FR), 7, b g Scalo—Sixty Six (IRE) **Mr Oscar Singh & Miss Priya Purewal**
29 PRESENTEDWITHWINGS (IRE), 7, br g Presenting—Rosa Rugosa (IRE) **Mr S. Davies**
30 5, B g Camelot—Princess Caetani (IRE) **Mr T. A. Killoran**
31 PRINCESS PRIYA (IRE), 4, b f Flemensfirth (USA)—Rosa Rugosa (IRE) **Mr Oscar Singh & Miss Priya Purewal**
32 RHIAN DE SIVOLA, 5, b m Kayf Tara—R de Rien Sivola (FR) **Mr S. Davies**
33 ROYAL CLARET, 9, b m Yeats—Kerada (FR) **The Nigel Jones & Roy Ovel Syndicate**
34 RUNNING D'OR (IRE), 5, b m Archange d'Or (IRE)—Running Running (FR) **Mr S. Davies**
35 SAINT DE VASSY (FR), 8, br g Saint des Saints (FR)—Mona Vassy (FR) **Jakeman,Booth,Lanchbury,Mason,Hewlett**
36 SONG FOR SOMEONE (GER), 6, ch g Medicean—Sweni Hill (IRE) **Sir Peter & Lady Gibbings**
37 TABLE MOUNTAIN, 4, b f Phoenix Reach (IRE)—Cape Victoria **Mr S. Davies**
38 VEILED SECRET (IRE), 7, b g Teofilo (IRE)—Seven Veils (IRE) **Clan McNeil**

**Other Owners:** Mr R. Allum, Mrs C. A. M. Baker, Mr M. J. Baker, Mr D. J. Clark, Mr S. Davies, Mr T. Dean, Mr D. R. Dennis, Mr D. W. Doolittle, Mr M. L. Engel, Miss T. A. Fulcher, Sir Peter Gibbings, The Hon Lady Gibbings, F. M. Green, Prof L. P. Hardwick, M. Hingley, Mr A. R. Hitchings, Mr S. K. J. Ibberson, Mr N. A. Jones, Mr J. G. G. Mason, Mr J. McNeil, Mr P. J. McNeil, Mr R. M. Ovel, Mr J. Palmer-Brown, Mr H. J. Pearman, Mrs Y. Prichard, Miss P. Purewal, Exors of the Late Mr M. B. Roberts, Mr A. Singh, Mr T. R. Symonds, Miss J. Upton-Murphy, Miss S. J. Vernon, Mr P. J. Willetts.

**523** **MR JAMES TATE, Newmarket**
Postal: **Jamesfield Place, Hamilton Road, Newmarket, Suffolk, CB8 7JQ**
Contacts: **PHONE 01638 669861 MOBILE 07703 601283 FAX 01638 676634**
**EMAIL james@jamestateracing.com WEBSITE www.jamestateracing.com**

1 **AIM FOR THE STARS**, 4, b f Muhaarar—Bright Approach (IRE) **S. Manana**
2 **BIG IMPRESSION**, 4, b c Dubawi (IRE)—Nashmiah (IRE) **S. Manana**
3 **GARDEN PARADISE (IRE)**, 4, b f Night of Thunder (IRE)—Coral Garden **S. Manana**
4 **MELODIC CHARM (IRE)**, 4, ch f Exceed And Excel (AUS)—Folk Melody (IRE) **S. Manana**
5 **SHIMMERING DAWN (IRE)**, 5, b m Morpheus—Subtle Shimmer **Sheikh J. D. Al Maktoum**
6 **SKY COMMANDER (USA)**, 4, b c War Command (USA)—Queen of Skies (IRE) **S. Manana**
7 **TOP RANK**, 5, gr h Dark Angel (IRE)—Countess Ferrama **S. Manana**
8 **WALHAAN (IRE)**, 5, gr g Dark Angel (IRE)—Back In The Frame **Allwins Stables**
9 **WISE WORDS**, 5, b m Sepoy (AUS)—Akhmatova **Sheikh R. D. Al Maktoum**

## THREE-YEAR-OLDS

10 **ABOVE THE STORM**, b f Frankel—Cloud Castle **S. Manana**
11 **AIR OF APPROVAL (IRE)**, gr f Mastercraftsman (IRE)—Rhiannon (IRE) **S. Manana**
12 B f Camacho—Boucheron **S. Manana**
13 **DESERT HISTORY**, b c New Approach (IRE)—Al Baidaa **S. Ali**
14 **EARTH GIANT (IRE)**, b c Zoffany (IRE)—Snowgal (IRE) **S. Manana**
15 **ELECTRIC BLUE**, ch f Gleneagles (IRE)—Blue Geranium (IRE) **S. Manana**
16 **ENCHANTED NIGHT**, ch f Night of Thunder (IRE)—Khaseeb **S. Manana**
17 **FINAL VOYAGE (IRE)**, b c Camacho—Shamayel **S. Manana**
18 **FIRST VERSE (IRE)**, b f Dandy Man (IRE)—Bronte Sister (IRE) **S. Manana**
19 **FORECAST THUNDER (IRE)**, ch f Night of Thunder (IRE)—Orange Pip **S. Manana**
20 **GLOBAL RESPONSE (IRE)**, b c Territories (IRE)—Terentia **Sheikh J. D. Al Maktoum**
21 **GLOBAL VISION (IRE)**, gr gr c Markaz (IRE)—Vision of Peace (IRE) **S. Manana**
22 **HEADLINER (IRE)**, b f The Last Lion (IRE)—Countess Ferrama **S. Manana**
23 **HIT THE HEIGHTS (IRE)**, b c Iffraaj—I'm Yours **S. Manana**
24 **ILLUSTRATOR**, ch c Bobby's Kitten (USA)—Amelia May **S. Manana**
25 **INSIGHTFUL**, ch f Sepoy (AUS)—Queen's Novel **S. Manana**
26 **INTO THE UNKNOWN (IRE)**, b br f Sea The Stars (IRE)—Galactic Heroine **S. Manana**
27 **JOIN FORCES (IRE)**, gr ro f Lethal Force (IRE)—Enrol **S. Manana**
28 **JOURNEY TO SEA (IRE)**, b c Sea The Stars (IRE)—Sea My Angel (FR) **S. Manana**
29 **LA SENSAZIONE (IRE)**, b f Kodiac—Fair Nashwan **Sheikh J. D. Al Maktoum**
30 Gr f Dark Angel (IRE)—Lady Duxyana **Sheikh J. D. Al Maktoum**
31 **LIVE STREAM (IRE)**, b f Awtaad (IRE)—Fluvial (IRE) **Sheikh R. D. Al Maktoum**
32 **MISS CALACATTA (IRE)**, ch f Frankel—Dulcet (IRE) **Mr H. Dalmook Al Maktoum**
33 **NEW DYNASTY (IRE)**, b c Dawn Approach (IRE)—Brown Diamond (IRE) **S. Manana**
34 **NEW SEASON (IRE)**, b c New Approach (IRE)—Fashionable Spirit (IRE) **S. Manana**
35 **OCEAN WAVE**, ch f Le Havre (IRE)—Gold Sands (IRE) **S. Manana**
36 **ONE OVER PAR**, b c Gleneagles (IRE)—Cherrington (IRE) **Sheikh J. D. Al Maktoum**
37 **PRIORITISE (IRE)**, b f Camelot—Penny Post (IRE) **S. Manana**
38 **PUBLICIST**, b f Dark Angel (IRE)—Diary (IRE) **S. Manana**
39 **RAIN GAUGE (IRE)**, b c Zoffany (IRE)—Rain Flower (IRE) **S. Manana**
40 **RAISE THE ROOF (IRE)**, b f Free Eagle (IRE)—Starletina (IRE) **S. Manana**
41 **RISK OF THUNDER (IRE)**, ch f Night of Thunder (IRE)—Lady Vyrnwy (IRE) **S. Manana**
42 **RIVER CHORUS (IRE)**, b f Mehmas (IRE)—Scarlet Pimpernel **S. Manana**
43 **SENSE OF ROMANCE (IRE)**, ch f Dutch Art—Infatuation **Sheikh J. D. Al Maktoum**
44 **SHOW YOURSELF**, b f Acclamation—Dare To Dream **S. Manana**
45 **STATE OF PLAY (IRE)**, b c Dark Angel (IRE)—Ambiguous **Sheikh R. D. Al Maktoum**
46 **TWILIGHT SECRET**, b c Twilight Son—Crinkle (IRE) **S. Manana**
47 **VICTORY HEIGHTS (IRE)**, b c Siyouni (FR)—Zibeling (IRE) **S. Manana**
48 **VILLEURBANNE**, b c Iffraaj—Ninas Rainbow **Mr H. Dalmook Al Maktoum**
49 **WORLDS APART (IRE)**, b f New Bay—Oriental Magic (GER) **S. Manana**

# MR JAMES TATE - continued

## TWO-YEAR-OLDS

**50** B c 05/05 Postponed (IRE)—Al Baidaa (Exceed And Excel (AUS)) **S. Ali**
**51** B c 27/04 Kodiac—Alice Liddel (IRE) (Dark Angel (IRE)) (24762) **Mr H. Dalmook Al Maktoum**
**52** B f 26/02 New Bay—Bellwether (Three Valleys (USA)) (42000) **Sheikh J. D. Al Maktoum**
**53** B f 02/04 Invincible Spirit (IRE)—Blhadawa (IRE) (Iffraaj) **Sheikh J. D. Al Maktoum**
**54** B f 10/03 Shamardal (USA)—Bright Approach (IRE) (New Approach (IRE)) **S. Manana**
**55** B c 16/02 Dark Angel (IRE)—Ceaseless (IRE) (Iffraaj) **Sheikh R. D. Al Maktoum**
**56 DIVINE RAPTURE,** gr f 27/02 Dark Angel (IRE)—Titivation (Montjeu (IRE)) (75000) **S. Manana**
**57** B f 16/04 Invincible Spirit (IRE)—Dulcet (IRE) (Halling (USA)) **Mr H. Dalmook Al Maktoum**
**58** Ch f 08/04 Sea The Stars (IRE)—El Manati (IRE) (Iffraaj) **Sheikh R. D. Al Maktoum**
**59** Ch c 13/02 El Kabeir (USA)—Encore View (Oasis Dream) (13000) **S. Manana**
**60** B f 20/02 Mehmas (IRE)—Flat White (IRE) (Elusive Quality (USA)) (140000) **Sheikh J. D. Al Maktoum**
**61** B f 17/01 Decorated Knight—Gadwa (Oasis Dream) **S. Manana**
**62** B f 04/02 Shamardal (USA)—Galactic Heroine (Galileo (IRE)) **S. Manana**
**63 GIFT HORSE,** b f 15/04 Havana Gold (IRE)—
Cool Question (Polar Falcon (USA)) (13000) **James Tate Racing Limited**
**64 HIDDEN SANDS,** ch f 20/02 Dubawi (IRE)—Demurely (IRE) (Galileo (IRE)) **S. Manana**
**65** B c 21/02 Frankel—Impala (Oasis Dream) **S. Manana**
**66** Gr c 20/02 El Kabeir (USA)—Inourthoughts (IRE) (Desert Style (IRE)) (27000) **S. Manana**
**67** B f 17/04 Shamardal (USA)—Jira (Medicean) **S. Manana**
**68** B c 23/02 Kingman—Lamar (IRE) (Cape Cross (IRE)) **S. Ali**
**69** Gr ro f 14/01 Dark Angel (IRE)—Miss Albane (FR) (Choisir (AUS)) (62857) **Sheikh J. D. Al Maktoum**
**70** Ch c 05/04 Night of Thunder (IRE)—Moonstone Rock (Rock of Gibraltar (IRE)) (46000) **Sheikh J. D. Al Maktoum**
**71** B f 11/03 Postponed (IRE)—Mount Elbrus (Barathea (IRE)) **S. Ali**
**72 MOVING IMAGE,** b f 25/01 Aclaim (IRE)—
Killermont Street (IRE) (Dream Ahead (USA)) (22000) **J Shack, G Barnard & James Mj Moore**
**73** B f 25/03 Frankel—Nashmiah (IRE) (Elusive City (USA)) (50000) **S. Manana**
**74** B f 03/02 Poet's Voice—Navajo Chant (Cape Cross (IRE)) **S. Ali**
**75 OCEAN RULER,** b c 15/03 Shamardal (USA)—Saltanat (IRE) (Duke of Marmalade (IRE)) **S. Manana**
**76** Ch c 06/03 Night of Thunder (IRE)—Overtones (New Approach (IRE)) (42000) **S. Manana**
**77** B f 14/02 Territories (IRE)—Pivotal's Princess (IRE) (Pivotal) (28000) **S. Manana**
**78** B f 07/04 Elzaam (AUS)—Pleasure Place (IRE) (Compton Place) (5714) **Sheikh J. D. Al Maktoum**
**79** B f 11/03 Farhh—Red Tulip (Kheleyf (USA)) (57000) **Mr H. Dalmook Al Maktoum**
**80** Gr c 31/01 Gutaifan (IRE)—Reflect Alexander (Kodiac) (20000) **S. Manana**
**81** B f 23/02 Dark Angel (IRE)—Roseraie (IRE) (Lawman (FR)) (105000) **S. Ali**
**82 SAHARA DESERT (IRE),** b f 12/02 Dubawi (IRE)—Asanta Sana (IRE) (Galileo (IRE)) **S. Manana**
**83** B f 12/03 Shamardal (USA)—Samdaniya (Machiavellian (USA)) **S. Manana**
**84** B f 13/02 Dandy Man (IRE)—Shirley (IRE) (Arcano (IRE)) (42000) **Mr H. Dalmook Al Maktoum**
**85 SPECIAL FORCES,** b c 24/02 Holy Roman Emperor (IRE)—Affectionately (Galileo (USA)) **S. Manana**
**86 STYLISH ICON (IRE),** b f 02/02 Starspangledbanner (AUS)—
Refreshed (IRE) (Rip Van Winkle (IRE)) (32000) **S. Manana**
**87** B f 29/04 Pivotal—Taaqah (USA) (Arch (USA)) **Sheikh J. D. Al Maktoum**
**88** B f 30/04 Profitable (IRE)—Todelight (IRE) (Teofilo (IRE)) (68000) **S. Manana**
**89** B f 06/05 Equiano (FR)—Three Ducks (Diktat) (10000) **S. Manana**
**90** B c 18/04 Australia—Twilight Sky (Authorized (IRE)) **S. Manana**
**91** B f 04/02 Kingman—Uleavemebreathless (Tiger Hill (USA)) (85000) **Sheikh J. D. Al Maktoum**
**92 VISION OF HOPE,** b f 09/02 Mastercraftsman (IRE)—Utopian Dream (High Chaparral (IRE)) (30000) **S. Manana**
**93** B br f 26/02 Churchill (IRE)—Wadaa (USA) (Dynaformer (USA)) **S. Manana**
**94** B c 13/03 Invincible Spirit (IRE)—You're Back (USA) (Street Cry (IRE)) **S. Manana**

**Assistant Trainer:** Mrs Lucinda Tate.

## 524 MR TOM TATE, Tadcaster
Postal: **Castle Farm, Hazelwood, Tadcaster, North Yorkshire, LS24 9NJ**
Contacts: PHONE **01937 836036** MOBILE **07970 122818**
EMAIL **tomptate@zen.co.uk** WEBSITE **www.tomtate.co.uk**

1 AWAKE MY SOUL (IRE), 12, ch g Teofilo (IRE)—Field of Hope (IRE) **T T Racing**
2 BAYRAAT, 5, b g Heeraat (IRE)—Baymist **T T Racing**
3 DESTROYER, 8, b g Royal Applause—Good Girl (IRE) **T T Racing**
4 EQUIANO SPRINGS, 7, b g Equiano (FR)—Spring Clean (FR) **T T Racing**
5 FAIR ALIBI, 5, b g Paco Boy (IRE)—Alybgood (CAN) **T T Racing**
6 FIRST DANCE (IRE), 7, b m Cape Cross (IRE)—Happy Wedding (IRE) **T T Racing**
7 GROUPIE, 7, b m Requinto (IRE)—Amour Fou (IRE) **T T Racing**
8 RIVER GLADES, 6, b g Cape Cross (IRE)—Everglades **T T Racing**
9 THUNDER GAP, 4, b g Night of Thunder (IRE)—Regal Hawk **T T Racing**
10 YOUNG TIGER, 8, b g Captain Gerrard (IRE)—Blades Princess **T T Racing**

### THREE-YEAR-OLDS
11 FREEWHEELIN, b g Poet's Voice—Certral **T T Racing**
12 B g Twilight Son—Riccoche (IRE) **T T Racing**

### TWO-YEAR-OLDS
13 B c 19/02 Bated Breath—Calima Breeze (Oasis Dream) (9524)

**Assistant Trainer:** Hazel Tate.

**Flat Jockey:** Tom Eaves, James Sullivan

## 525 MR COLIN TEAGUE, Wingate
Postal: **Bridgefield Farm, Trimdon Lane, Station Town, Wingate, County Durham, TS28 5NE**
Contacts: PHONE **01429 837087** MOBILE **07967 330929**
EMAIL **colin.teague@btopenworld.com**

1 INGLEBY MOLLY (IRE), 6, ch m Choisir (AUS)—Mistress Twister **Mr N. Old**
2 KOROPICK (IRE), 7, b g Kodiac—Kathoe (IRE) **Mr A. Rice**
3 TAAMER, 4, ch f Tamayuz—Abhajat (IRE) **Mr A. Rice**
4 THORNABY NASH, 10, br g Kheleyf (USA)—Mistress Twister **Collins Chauffeur Driven Executive Cars**
5 THORNABY PRINCESS, 10, b m Camacho—Ingleby Princess **Collins Chauffeur Driven Executive Cars**

## 526 MR ROGER TEAL, Hungerford
Postal: **Windsor House Stables, Crowle Road, Lambourn, Hungerford, Berkshire, RG17 8NR**
Contacts: PHONE **01488 491623** MOBILE **07710 325521**
EMAIL **info@rogertealracing.com** WEBSITE **www.rogertealracing.co.uk**

1 AGINCOURT REEF (IRE), 12, b g Gold Well—Hillside Native (IRE) **Mrs S. M. Teal**
2 ARANS CHOICE (IRE), 8, b m Scorpion (IRE)—Miss Greylands **The Rat Racers**
3 BEAR ATTRACTION, 4, b f Due Diligence (USA)—Shesha Bear **Joe Bear Racing**
4 BEAR FORCE ONE, 5, b g Swiss Spirit—Shesha Bear **Joe Bear Racing**
5 BRUTE FORCE, 5, ch g Paco Boy (IRE)—Free Falling **A.C. Entertainment Technologies Limited**
6 CINZENTO (IRE), 5, gr g Lawman (FR)—Silver Samba **Mr & Mrs G. Bhatti**
7 COCKSPUR BALLA, 4, br g Passing Glance—Flora Joy **Mrs D. F. Turner**
8 FITWOOD STAR, 5, b g Archipenko (USA)—Sasheen **Calne Engineering Ltd**

## MR ROGER TEAL - continued

9 **GERT LUSH (IRE)**, 4, b f Bated Breath—Agent Allison  **Mrs Muriel Forward & Dr G C Forward**
10 **GOLD RIBBON**, 4, b f Golden Horn—Chan Tong (BRZ)  **Mr M. J. Goggin**
11 **GREY GALLEON (USA)**, 7, gr g Mizzen Mast (USA)—Floresta (USA)  **BA Racing**
12 **KAMAXOS (FR)**, 4, b g Maxios—Kamellata (FR)  **Mr A. J. Edwards**
13 **KENZAI WARRIOR (USA)**, 4, b br c Karakontie (JPN)—Lemon Sakhee (CAN)  **Rae & Carol Borras**
14 **LUCKY LOUIE**, 8, ch g Dutch Art—Ardessie  **Great Shefford Racing**
15 **MARION'S BOY (IRE)**, 4, ch g Mastercraftsman (IRE)—Freddie's Girl (USA)  **Mrs A. Cowley**
16 **MOONLIGHTING**, 4, gr f Hot Streak (IRE)—Blue Moon  **Rockingham Reins Limited**
17 **OCEAN WIND**, 5, b h Teofilo (IRE)—Chan Tong (BRZ)  **Rockingham Reins Limited**
18 **OXTED**, 5, b g Mayson—Charlotte Rosina  **S Piper,T.Hirschfeld,D.Fish & J.Collins**
19 **PETITE JACK**, 8, ch g Champs Elysees—Pilcomayo (IRE)  **Mr W. Burn**
20 **ROCKING REG (IRE)**, 4, gr g Gutaifan (IRE)—Princess of Troy (IRE)  **Mr T. J. Smith**
21 **ROCKINGHAM JILL**, 4, b f Cable Bay—Bubbly Ballerina  **Rockingham Reins Limited**
22 **SPIRIT OF MAY**, 5, ch g Coach House (IRE)—Bengers Lass (USA)  **Mrs C. A. Borras**
23 **SWISS PRIDE (IRE)**, 5, b g Swiss Spirit—Encore Encore (FR)  **Idle B's & Sue Teal**

## THREE-YEAR-OLDS

24 **ALCAZAN**, b f Al Kazeem—Glorious Dreams (USA)  **John O'Donnell & Noel Kelly**
25 **BLAZEON FIVE**, b f Indian Haven—Precision Five  **Calne Engineering Ltd**
26 **CHIPSTEAD**, b c Mayson—Charlotte Rosina  **Homecroft, Crampsie & Sullivan**
27 **DANCING MASTER (IRE)**, br gr c Mastercraftsman (IRE)—Poisson d'Or  **Fishdance Ltd**
28 **DARK ESTEEM (IRE)**, b g Estidhkaar (IRE)—Poker Hospital  **Windsor House Racing**
29 **FOLLOWTHEFOOTSTEPS (IRE)**, b f Footstepsinthesand—Gush (USA)  **Rockingham Reins Limited**
30 **GURKHA GIRL (IRE)**, b f The Gurkha (IRE)—Freddie's Girl (USA)  **Mrs A. Cowley**
31 **GUSSY MAC (IRE)**, b g Dark Angel (IRE)—Masaya  **Mr A. Whelan**
32 **HUGOSTHERE**, b g Cannock Chase (USA)—Ellablue  **HOG Racing**
33 **KALASH PRINCESS**, b f Proconsul—Magical Daze  **GB Horseracing**
34 **KINGHENRYTHENINTH**, b g Heeraat (IRE)—Annaluna (IRE)  **Buckingham,Butler, Chapman & Langford**
35 **KNOWWHENTORUN**, b c Mayson—Josefa Goya  **Mr A. Whelan**
36 **MICKS DREAM**, b c Adaay (IRE)—Malelane (IRE)  **M. F. Waghorn**
37 **MUSTANG KODI (IRE)**, b g Kodi Bear (IRE)—Modello (IRE)  **Rockingham Reins Limited**
38 **REBEL SPIRIT**, b f Swiss Spirit—Rosie Rebel  **Mr C. R. Basson**
39 **SHARLA**, b f Outstrip—Shersha (IRE)  **Mrs M. Parker**
40 **TAUREAN EMERALD (IRE)**, ch f Showcasing—Casual  **C. B. Goodyear**
41 **WHENTHEDEALINSDONE**, b c Dark Angel (IRE)—Maureen (IRE)  **Mr A. Whelan**
42 **WUDASHUDACUDA**, b c Awtaad (IRE)—Chicita Banana  **Mr M. J. Goggin**
43 **YOULLOVEMEWHENIWIN (IRE)**, b c Cable Bay (IRE)—Ventura Falcon (IRE)  **Mr M. J. Goggin**

## TWO-YEAR-OLDS

44 **DANCING REEL (IRE)**, b c 21/02 Highland Reel (IRE)—Poisson d'Or (Cape Cross (IRE))  **Fishdance Ltd**
45 Ch c 26/02 Hot Streak (IRE)—Deep Dream (Dream Ahead (USA)) (14000)
46 **DICKTATE**, b c 15/02 Lawman (FR)—Gakku (Pivotal) (9000)  **Mrs S. M. Teal**
47 Bl c 22/03 Slade Power (IRE)—Jumeirah Palm Star (Invincible Spirit (IRE))  **Mr A. Whelan**
48 **NEVER IN FOURTH**, ch c 17/03 Coach House (IRE)—
   Bengers Lass (USA) (Orientate (USA)) (5500)  **Mrs Muriel Forward & Dr G C Forward**

**Other Owners:** Mrs C. J. Bhatti, Mr G. Bhatti, Mrs C. A. Borras, Mr R. D. Borras, Mr W. M. Brackstone, Mr R. Butler, A. J. Chambers, Mr M. R. Chapman, Mr J. A. Collins, Mr D. Crampsie, Fishdance Ltd, Dr G. C. Forward, Mrs M. E. Forward, Homecroft Wealth Racing, Mrs H. I. Jinks, Mr W. E. N. Kelly, B. Kitcherside, Mr R. B. Kolien, Ms G. S. Langford, Mr J. O'Donnell, Mr S. J. Piper, Mr M. A. Ransom, Mr S. M. Ransom, Step By Step Supporting Independence Ltd, Mr J. A. Sullivan, Mr R. A. Teal, Mrs S. M. Teal, The Idle B'S, Mr S. J. Whitear.

**Assistant Trainer:** Harry Teal.

**527** **MR SAM THOMAS, Cardiff**
Postal: **Crossways, St Mellons Road, Lisvane, Cardiff, South Glamorgan, CF14 0SH**
Contacts: **PHONE 07929 101751**
EMAIL samthomast@outlook.com, emma@samthomasracing.com
WEBSITE www.samthomasracing.com

1  **AMAZING TANGO (GER)**, 4, b g Tai Chi (GER)—Amazing Model (GER) **Walters Plant Hire Ltd**
2  **BEFORE MIDNIGHT**, 8, ch g Midnight Legend—Lady Samantha **Walters Plant Hire & Potter Group**
3  **COAL STOCK (IRE)**, 6, ch g Red Jazz (USA)—Scar Tissue **Walters Plant Hire Ltd Egan Waste Ltd**
4  **DOBRYN (FR)**, 5, b g No Risk At All (FR)—Brava (FR) **Walters Plant Hire Ltd**
5  4, B g Fame And Glory—Gales Present (IRE) **Walters Plant Hire Ltd**
6  **GALILEO SILVER (IRE)**, 6, gr g Galileo (IRE)—Famous (IRE) **Walters Plant Hire & Potter Group**
7  **GLENTROOL**, 8, b g Passing Glance—Killala Bay (IRE) **Mr S. C. Appelbee**
8  **GOOD RISK AT ALL (FR)**, 5, ch g No Risk At All (FR)—Sissi Land (FR) **Walters Plant Hire Ltd**
9  4, B g Shantou (USA)—Grapevine Sally (IRE) **Walters Plant Hire Ltd**
10  **GREAT SNOW (FR)**, 4, b br f Great Pretender (IRE)—Snow Berry (FR) **Walters Plant Hire Ltd**
11  **GREY DIAMOND (FR)**, 7, b g Gris de Gris (IRE)—Diamond of Diana (FR) **Walters Plant Hire Ltd**
12  **HELIOS DE GRUGY (FR)**, 4, b g No Risk At All (FR)—Diane de Grugy (FR) **Walters Plant Hire Ltd**
13  4, B g Pether's Moon (IRE)—Henri Bella **Walters Plant Hire Ltd**
14  **HURRICANE DEAL (FR)**, 4, gr g Hurricane Cat (USA)—Diluvienne (FR) **Walters Plant Hire Ltd**
15  **IVY'S SHADOW (IRE)**, 6, b m Jammaal—Red Chili (FR) **Mr W. D. Morris**
16  **IWILLDOIT**, 8, b g Flying Legend (IRE)—Lyricist's Dream **Diamond Racing Ltd**
17  **JABULANI (FR)**, 8, gr g Martaline—Incorrigible (FR) **Walters Plant Hire Ltd**
18  **JAZZ KING (FR)**, 5, gr g Kapgarde (FR)—Jaragua (FR) **Walters Plant Hire Ltd**
19  **JET FANTASTIQUE (IRE)**, 5, b m Jet Away—C'Est Fantastique (IRE) **Diamond Racing Ltd**
20  **JUBILEE EXPRESS (FR)**, 4, b g No Risk At All (FR)—Bella Lawena (FR) **Walters Plant Hire Ltd**
21  **KALA NOIRE (IRE)**, 7, b g Kalanisi (IRE)—Lady Taipan (IRE) **Mr & Mrs Capper, Mr Trolan & Mr Stovin**
22  **LA REINE POUTINE (FR)**, 6, b m Kapgarde (FR)—Miss Poutine (FR) **Walters Plant Hire & Potter Group**
23  **MARIO DE PAIL (FR)**, 6, gr g Blue Bresil (FR)—Sauveterre (FR) **Walters Plant Hire & Potter Group**
24  **NEXT ONE PLEASE (FR)**, 4, gr g Cima de Triomphe (IRE)—Next More (GER) **Walters Plant Hire Ltd**
25  **NO RISK NO FUN (FR)**, 4, b g No Risk At All (FR)—Incorrigible (FR) **Walters Plant Hire Ltd**
26  **NOT A ROLE MODEL (IRE)**, 9, b g Helissio (FR)—Mille Et Une Nuits (FR) **St Mamadasado**
27  **PADDYS MOTORBIKE (IRE)**, 9, ch g Fast Company (IRE)—
                                      Saffa Garden (IRE) **Walters Plant Hire Ltd Egan Waste Ltd**
28  **PIPES OF PEACE (IRE)**, 7, b g Galileo (IRE)—Coachella **Egan Waste Services Ltd**
29  **POWERSTOWN PARK (IRE)**, 8, b g Craigsteel—Smiths Lady (IRE) **The Ipsden Invincibles**
30  **PRINCE DES FICHAUX (FR)**, 4, b c No Risk At All (FR)—Princesse Kap (FR) **Walters Plant Hire Ltd**
31  **ROYAL MAGIC (IRE)**, 9, b g Whitmore's Conn (USA)—Room To Room Magic (IRE) **Luke Harvey Racing Club**
32  **SHOMEN UCHI (FR)**, 4, b g Great Pretender (IRE)—Vavea (FR) **Walters Plant Hire Ltd**
33  **SKYTASTIC (FR)**, 5, b g Way of Light (USA)—Verzasca (IRE) **Walters Plant Hire Ltd**
34  **SLIP ROAD (IRE)**, 6, gr g Shantou (USA)—Agladora (FR) **Walters Plant Hire Ltd**
35  **SPONTHUS (FR)**, 6, b g Alianthus (GER)—Pavane du Kalon (FR) **Walters Plant Hire Ltd**
36  **SWEDISHHORSEMAFIA (IRE)**, 6, b g Shantou (USA)—Carrigmoorna Style (IRE) **Mr S. J. Thomas**
37  4, B g Blue Bresil (FR)—Tara Potter **Walters Plant Hire Ltd**
38  **WILLIAM HENRY (IRE)**, 11, b g King's Theatre (IRE)—Cincuenta (IRE) **Walters Plant Hire Ltd**
39  **WORD TO THE WISE (FR)**, 5, gr m Montmartre (FR)—Rosewater (GER) **Walters Plant Hire Ltd**

**THREE-YEAR-OLDS**

40  B f Norse Dancer (IRE)—Another Kate (IRE) **Mr S. J. Thomas**
41  **ED KEEPER (FR)**, b c Hunter's Light (IRE)—Charbelle (FR) **Walters Plant Hire Ltd**
42  B f Universal (IRE)—Haidees Reflection
43  **INOUI MACHIN (FR)**, b g Honolulu (IRE)—Firmini (FR) **Walters Plant Hire Ltd**
44  **INTEL DES BRUYERES (FR)**, b g Spanish Moon (USA)—Innsbruck (FR) **Walters Plant Hire Ltd**
45  **KATATE DORI (FR)**, b g Bathyrhon (GER)—Vavea (FR) **Walters Plant Hire Ltd**
46  **LUMP SUM (FR)**, b c Authorized (IRE)—Fleur Enchantee (FR) **Walters Plant Hire Ltd**
47  **PALACIO (FR)**, b g Khalkevi (IRE)—Belle Yepa (FR) **Walters Plant Hire Ltd**
48  **REMEMBER ALLY (FR)**, b c Sinndar (IRE)—Blue Lullaby (IRE) **Walters Plant Hire Ltd**
49  **STEEL ALLY (FR)**, b g Doctor Dino (FR)—Poprock du Berlais (FR) **Walters Plant Hire Ltd**
50  **TZARMIX (FR)**, ch g Gemix (FR)—Tzarine de La Mone (FR) **Walters Plant Hire Ltd**
51  **VINCENZO (FR)**, b g Doctor Dino (FR)—Sweet Nano (FR) **Walters Plant Hire Ltd**
52  **WE DONE IT (FR)**, ro c Montmartre (FR)—Glicine (GER) **Walters Plant Hire Ltd**

## MR SAM THOMAS - continued

**Other Owners:** Mrs P. L. Capper, Egan Waste Services Ltd, Mr A. P. G. Holmes, Mr T. L. Llewellyn, Mrs J. C. Noel, Mr W. D. Stovin, Sundorne Products (Llanidloes) Ltd, Mr S. J. Thomas, Mr J. Trolan, Walters Plant Hire Ltd.

**NH Jockey:** James Davies, Charlie Deutsch. **Conditional Jockey:** Harry Beswick, Richard Patrick.

---

### 528 MRS JOANNE THOMASON-MURPHY, Chelmsford
Postal: **Oakview, Leighams Road, Bicknacre, Chelmsford, Essex, CM3 4HF**

1 **AFRICAN SUN (IRE)**, 4, b g Teofilo (IRE)—Castle Cross (IRE)  **Mrs J. Thomason-Murphy**
2 **CANDY LOU**, 7, b m Schiaparelli (GER)—Candello  **Mrs J. Thomason-Murphy**
3 **DANDY TIMES (IRE)**, 8, b g Central Park (IRE)—Distinctly Flo Jo (IRE)  **Mrs J. Thomason-Murphy**
4 **EASTER DAY (FR)**, 13, b g Malinas (GER)—Sainte Lea (FR)  **Mrs J. Thomason-Murphy**
5 **LORD HOWARD (IRE)**, 5, b g Havana Gold (IRE)—Lady Gabrielle (IRE)  **Mrs J. Thomason-Murphy**

---

### 529 MR DAVID THOMPSON, Darlington
Postal: **South View Racing, Ashley Cottage, South View, Bolam, Darlington, County Durham, DL2 2UP**
Contacts: **PHONE 01388 832658, 01388 835806 MOBILE 07795 161657 FAX 01325 835806**
**EMAIL dwthompson61@hotmail.co.uk WEBSITE www.dwthompson.co.uk**

1 **BAWAADER (IRE)**, 6, gr g Dark Angel (IRE)—Aspen Falls (IRE)  **Mr N. Park**
2 **CHARLOTTES WAY (IRE)**, 6, b m Arctic Cosmos (USA)—Sharifa (GER)  **Mr F. B. Hawkins**
3 **COMBER MILL (FR)**, 9, ch g Le Fou (IRE)—Kalistina (FR)  **Mr T. J. A. Thompson**
4 **COUP DE GOLD (IRE)**, 5, br g Maxios—Astroglia (USA)  **Mr N. Park**
5 **DIRCHILL (IRE)**, 7, b g Power—Bawaakeer (USA)  **Mr S. Murray**
6 **GLAN Y GORS (IRE)**, 9, b br g High Chaparral (IRE)—Trading Places  **Mr B. Lapham & J Souster**
7 **HOTELMIKEPAPA**, 7, b m High Chaparral (IRE)—Alexander Celebre (IRE)
8 **IRISH MINISTER (USA)**, 6, b g Americain (USA)—Spanked (USA)  **Mrs D. D. Jefferson**
9 **JEREJAK**, 4, b g Nathaniel (IRE)—Penang Power  **J. A. Moore**
10 **KHULU**, 5, ch g Burwaaz—Ingenti  **D. A. J. Bartlett**
11 **LOSTNFOUND**, 8, b m Midnight Legend—La Cerisaie  **Mr S. Murray**
12 **LUKOUTOLDMAKEZEBAK**, 8, b g Arabian Gleam—Angelofthenorth  **NE1 Racing Club**
13 **MARTIN'S BRIG (IRE)**, 4, b g Equiano (FR)—Weeza (IRE)  **J. A. Moore**
14 **MAZZA ROCKS (IRE)**, 6, b m Red Rocks (IRE)—Sun City  **Mr B. Lapham**
15 **MOVIN'ON UP (IRE)**, 6, b m Milan—Kalygarde (FR)  **J. A. Moore**
16 **MR SUNDOWNER (USA)**, 9, b br g Scat Daddy (USA)—Bold Answer (USA)  **Mr R. Glendinning**
17 **PIVELLO**, 6, ch g Intello (GER)—Pivotting  **Mrs K. L. Matthews**
18 **POCO CONTANTE**, 4, b f Fast Company (IRE)—Littlemoor Lass  **NE1 Racing Club**
19 **PRIZE WINNER (IRE)**, 6, ch g Teofilo (IRE)—Beta  **Mr J. Souster**
20 **SEABOROUGH (IRE)**, 6, b g Born To Sea (IRE)—Nobilissima (IRE)  **Mr J. Souster & Mr A. Livingston**
21 **SHAIYZAR (IRE)**, 12, b g Azamour (IRE)—Shaiyzima (IRE)  **J. A. Moore**
22 **SOMEONE EXCITING**, 8, b m Notnowcato—Quite Something  **Mr J. Souster**
23 **SPLASH OF VERVE (IRE)**, 9, b g Fast Company (IRE)—Ellistown Lady (IRE)  **B & Anna Kenny**
24 **TRINITY STAR (IRE)**, 10, gr g Kheleyf (USA)—Zamyla (IRE)  **Trinity Racing**
25 **VALGOR DU RONCERAY (FR)**, 12, gr g Al Namix (FR)—Malta de Ronceray (FR)  **Mick Martin Keith Boddy & Son**

**Other Owners:** Mr K. Boddy, Mr J. Cockcroft, Mr R. Cockcroft, Mr S. Cockcroft, Mr W. Cockcroft, Mrs A. Kenny, Mr B. Lapham, Mr A. J. Livingston, Mr M. Martin, Mr J. Souster.

**Assistant Trainer:** J. A. Moore.

**Flat Jockey:** Tony Hamilton.

**530** **MR RONALD THOMPSON, Doncaster**
Postal: **No 2 Bungalow, Haggswood Racing Stable, Stainforth, Doncaster, South Yorkshire, DN7 5PS**
Contacts: **PHONE 01302 845904 MOBILE 07713 251141 FAX 01302 845904**
**EMAIL ronracing@gmail.com**

1 **BILLYFAIRPLAY (IRE)**, 7, b g Dark Angel (IRE)—Nurture (IRE)  **Mr M. Marsh**
2 **CHEAP JACK**, 5, b g Coach House (IRE)—Ice Mayden  **Ronald Thompson**
3 **ENCRYPTION (IRE)**, 6, b g High Chaparral (IRE)—Challow Hills (USA)  **Ronald Thompson**
4 **ICE AGE (IRE)**, 8, b g Frozen Power (IRE)—Incendio  **Mr M. Marsh**
5 **LADY VALLETTA (IRE)**, 4, ch f Ivawood (IRE)—Cesca (IRE)  **Mr A Bell & Mr R Thompson**
6 **MAAWARD (IRE)**, 6, b g Kodiac—Caterina di Cesi  **Mr M. Marsh**
7 **MR STRUTTER (IRE)**, 7, ch g Sir Prancealot (IRE)—Khajool (IRE)  **Mrs A. Harrison**
8 **THECHILDREN'STRUST (IRE)**, 6, br g Society Rock (IRE)—Estemaala (IRE)  **Shaun Taylor & Ron Thompson**
9 **VAMPISH**, 6, b m Sir Percy—Falling Angel  **Shaun Taylor & Michael Marsh**

### THREE-YEAR-OLDS
10 **ELIZABETH'S DREAM (IRE)**, b f Pride of Dubai (AUS)—Princess Nala (IRE)  **B. Bruce & R. Thompson**
11 **FURNITURE FACTORS (IRE)**, b g Pride of Dubai (AUS)—I Hearyou Knocking (IRE)  **B. Bruce & R. Thompson**

### TWO-YEAR-OLDS
12 B c 10/03 Koropick (IRE)—Melodize (Iceman) (1429)  **Mr M. Marsh**

**Other Owners:** A. Bell, Mr B. Bruce, Mr M. Marsh, Mr S. Taylor, Ronald Thompson.

---

**531** **MR VICTOR THOMPSON, Alnwick**
Postal: **Link House Farm, Newton By The Sea, Embleton, Alnwick, Northumberland, NE66 3ED**
Contacts: **PHONE 01665 576272 MOBILE 07739 626248**

1 **CHALLOW (IRE)**, 7, b g Acclamation—Starlight Smile (USA)  **V. Thompson**
2 **DEAUVILLE SOCIETY (IRE)**, 6, b m Society Rock (IRE)—Dorothy Dene  **V. Thompson**
3 **GLORY**, 5, b g Olympic Glory (IRE)—Updated (FR)  **V. Thompson**
4 **HERE IN THE DARK**, 6, b g Harbour Watch (IRE)—Behest  **V. Thompson**
5 **MUROOR**, 8, ch g Nayef (USA)—Raaya (USA)  **V. Thompson**
6 **PC DIXON**, 8, ch g Sixties Icon—Lakaam  **V. Thompson**
7 **RAPID FRITZ (IRE)**, 12, ch g Kutub (IRE)—Another Pet (IRE)  **V. Thompson**
8 **SCORPO (IRE)**, 10, b g Scorpion (IRE)—Maltesse (IRE)  **V. Thompson**

**Assistant Trainer:** M Thompson.

---

**532** **MR SANDY THOMSON, Greenlaw**
Postal: **Lambden, Greenlaw, Duns, Berwickshire, TD10 6UN**
Contacts: **PHONE 01361 810211 MOBILE 07876 142787**
**EMAIL sandy@lambdenfarm.co.uk WEBSITE www.sandythomsonracing.co.uk**

1 **ALFSBOY (IRE)**, 6, b g Shirocco (GER)—Full of Spirit (IRE)  **Carl Hinchy & Mark Scott**
2 **ALOOMOMO (FR)**, 11, b g Tirwanako (FR)—Kayola (FR)  **The Large G & T Partnership**
3 **BAD RABBIT (IRE)**, 4, b g Iffraaj—Bint Nayef (IRE)  **Mike and Eileen Newbould**
4 **BASS ROCK (FR)**, 5, b g Martaline—Horta (FR)  **Mr & Mrs Raymond Anderson Green**
5 **BELLSHILL (IRE)**, 11, b g King's Theatre (IRE)—Fairy Native (IRE)  **D & D Armstrong Ltd & Mr L Westwood**
6 **BROTHERLY COMPANY (IRE)**, 9, b g Fast Company (IRE)—Good Lady (IRE)  **The Reign It In Partnership**
7 **BUCKLED**, 11, b g Midnight Legend—Mulberry Wine  **Mrs M. Coppola**
8 **CAPARD KING (IRE)**, 12, b g Beneficial—Capard Lady (IRE)  **E Chapman, J Beaumont, Q Thomson**
9 **CAVENTARA**, 9, b g Kayf Tara—L'Aventure (FR)  **Mr C. J. Harriman**
10 **CEDAR HILL (IRE)**, 7, br g Frammassone (IRE)—Dayamen  **Mr & Mrs S Townshend**

# MR SANDY THOMSON - continued

**11** 5, Ch g Schiaparelli (GER)—Classic Fantasy **Mrs A. E. Lee**
**12 COOLKILL (IRE)**, 7, b g Arcadio (GER)—Elisabetta (IRE) **Mr A. M. Thomson**
**13 CURRAMORE (IRE)**, 7, br g Arcadio (GER)—Beale Native (IRE) **Mrs F. E. Bocker**
**14 DELUXE RANGE (IRE)**, 6, b g Westerner—Kildea Cailin (IRE) **Watson & Lawrence**
**15 DIMPLE (FR)**, 10, gr g Montmartre (FR)—Dynella (FR) **D&D Armstrong Limited**
**16 DONNA'S DOUBLE**, 5, b g Fair Mix (IRE)—Elegant Accord (IRE) **D&D Armstrong Limited**
**17 DOYEN BREED (IRE)**, 6, ch g Doyen (IRE)—Sweet Empire (IRE) **The Explorers**
**18 DUC DE GRISSAY (FR)**, 8, b g Denham Red (FR)—Rhea de Grissay (FR) **Quona Thomson & Ken McGarrity**
**19 ELF DE RE (FR)**, 7, ch g Anabaa Blue—Ninon de Re (FR) **Mr J. K. McGarrity**
**20 EMPIRE STEEL (IRE)**, 7, gr g Aizavoski (IRE)—Talk of Rain (FR) **Mr A. J. Wight**
**21 FAIR MINX**, 7, gr m Fair Mix (IRE)—Blazing Diva (IRE) **Mr J. K. McGarrity**
**22 FANTASTIC ROCK (FR)**, 6, ch g Konig Turf (GER)—Rock Treasure (FR) **Mr W. D. Macdonald**
**23 FLOGGING MOLLY (IRE)**, 5, b m Sholokhov (IRE)—Good Shine (IRE) **Mr & Mrs S Townshend**
**24 FLOWER OF SCOTLAND (FR)**, 6, gr m Lord du Sud (FR)—Theme Song (FR) **Mr & Mrs Raymond Anderson Green**
**25** 4, B f Martaline—Gaspaisielle
**26 GERONIMO**, 10, ch g Kadastrof (FR)—Triggers Ginger **Mr J. K. McGarrity**
**27 GET OUT THE GATE (IRE)**, 8, b g Mahler—Chartani (IRE) **Mr J. Fyffe**
**28 GOAST DANCER (FR)**, 5, b g Network (GER)—Verka de Thaix (FR) **Carl Hinchy & Mark Scott**
**29 HASTRUBAL (FR)**, 11, b g Discover d'Auteuil (FR)—Miss Montrose **Varlien Vyner-Brooks & Midnight Racing**
**30 JUST JERRY (IRE)**, 8, b g Wareed (IRE)—Made For Sharing (IRE) **Midnight Racing Club**
**31 KING'S WHARF (IRE)**, 12, gr g Clodovil (IRE)—Global Tour (USA) **Ken McGarrity & the Western Chasers**
**32 LARGY PERK (IRE)**, 7, b g Scorpion (IRE)—Ellens Perk (IRE) **Mrs Q. R. Thomson**
**33 LITTLE MO (IRE)**, 9, b m Stowaway—What A Princess (IRE) **Mr A. M. Thomson**
**34 MCGOWAN'S PASS**, 10, b g Central Park (IRE)—Function Dreamer **Mrs A. E. Lee**
**35 MIDNIGHT FIDDLER**, 5, ch g Midnight Legend—Overlady **Mr W. F. Jeffrey**
**36 MILVALE (IRE)**, 7, b g Ask—House-of-Hearts (IRE) **Trading Products Limited**
**37 MYMILAN (IRE)**, 8, b g Milan—Jill's Girl (IRE) **Tweed Valley Racing Club**
**38 OFF THE BEAT**, 7, ch g Black Sam Bellamy (IRE)—Off By Heart **Mrs Q. R. Thomson**
**39 OVERCOURT**, 7, b g Court Cave (IRE)—Overlady **Mr W. F. Jeffrey**
**40** 4, B br g Malinas (GER)—Poulnasherry Dove (IRE)
**41** 6, B m Getaway (GER)—Present Leader **Mrs Q. R. Thomson**
**42 ROMAN'S EMPRESS (IRE)**, 4, b f Holy Roman Emperor (IRE)—Dabtiyra (IRE) **Stonegrave Thoroughbreds**
**43 SALVINO (IRE)**, 5, b g Leading Light (IRE)—Sagabolley (IRE) **Mr A. J. Wight**
**44 SARYSHAGANN (FR)**, 8, gr g Iffraaj—Serasana **Mr J. K. McGarrity**
**45 SEEMORELIGHTS (IRE)**, 9, b g Echo of Light—Star Lodge **Watson & Lawrence**
**46 SEEYOUATMIDNIGHT (IRE)**, 13, b g Midnight Legend—Morsky Baloo **Mrs Q. R. Thomson**
**47 SIRWILLIAMWALLACE (IRE)**, 8, b g Getaway (GER)—Mrs Milan (IRE) **Mr J. K. McGarrity**
**48 SOPHIE FATALE**, 9, b m Robin des Champs (FR)—Buffy **Crowd Racing & Midnight Racing**
**49 SPACE SAFARI (FR)**, 8, b g Kapgarde (FR)—Prodiga (FR) **Mrs F. E. Bocker**
**50 STONEY ROVER (IRE)**, 8, b g Scorpion (IRE)—Consultation (IRE) **Mr K. J. Telfer**
**51 STORM NELSON (IRE)**, 8, b g Gold Well—Dabiyra (IRE) **Mrs F. E. Bocker**
**52 THE FERRY MASTER (IRE)**, 8, b g Elusive Pimpernel (USA)—Dinghy (IRE) **The Potassium Partnership**
**53 YORKHILL (IRE)**, 11, ch g Presenting—Lightning Breeze (IRE) **D & D Armstrong Ltd & Mr L Westwood**
**54 ZAMARKHAN (FR)**, 8, b g Great Journey (JPN)—Zannkiya **Racing, Christison, F Bocker**

## THREE-YEAR-OLDS

**55** B f Fountain of Youth (IRE)—Goya Girl (IRE) **Mrs Q. R. Thomson**
**56** B f Nathaniel (IRE)—Helter Helter (USA) **Mrs Q. R. Thomson**

**Other Owners:** J. J. Beaumont, Mrs F. E. Bocker, Mr N. Boyle, Mr E. Chapman, Mr R. Christison, Crowd Racing Partnership, D&D Armstrong Limited, Mr C. S. Hinchy, Mr S. A. Hollings, Mr J. K. McGarrity, Mr D. W. McIntyre, Mr C. McKenna, Midnight Racing Club, Mrs E. E. Newbould, Mr J. M. Newbould, Mr M. J. Roche, Mr M. S. Scott, The Western Chasers, Mr P. Thompson, Mr A. M. Thomson, Mrs Q. R. Thomson, Mr S. Townshend, Mrs S. Townshend, J. Townson, Mr V. R. Vyner-Brooks, Mr L. J. Westwood.

**Assistant Trainer:** Mrs A. M. Thomson.

**NH Jockey:** Rachael McDonald.

## 533 MR NIGEL TINKLER, Malton

Postal: Woodland Stables, Langton, Malton, North Yorkshire, YO17 9QR
Contacts: HOME 01653 658245 MOBILE 07836 384225 FAX 01653 658542
WORK EMAIL nigel@nigeltinkler.com EMAIL sam@nigeltinkler.com

1  ABSTEMIOUS, 4, b g Mukhadram—So Refined (IRE)  **Mr J. R. Saville**
2  ARCHIE PERKINS (IRE), 6, b g Arcano (IRE)—Sidney Girl  **Mr J Raybould & Mr S Perkins**
3  ATHOLLBLAIR BOY (IRE), 8, ch g Frozen Power (IRE)—Ellxell (IRE)  **The Geezaaah Partnership**
4  CITRON MAJOR, 6, ch g Major Cadeaux—Citron  **Ms S. V. Hattersley**
5  CMON CMON (IRE), 4, b g Slade Power (IRE)—Ramamara (IRE)  **Dearing Plastics Ltd & Mark Ollier**
6  FIRMDECISIONS (IRE), 11, b g Captain Rio—Luna Crescente (IRE)  **Mr A. Chapman**
7  GINGER JAM, 6, ch g Major Cadeaux—Day By Day  **Mr N. Tinkler**
8  HELLO GIRL, 6, ch m Bated Breath—Elysee (IRE)  **Mr A. Chapman**
9  JUPITER ROAD, 5, b g Charm Spirit (IRE)—Thankful  **G Maidment Racing**
10  KAESO, 7, b g Exceleberation (IRE)—Bahia Breeze  **Mr M. Webb**
11  KILBAHA LADY (IRE), 7, b m Elnadim (USA)—Sidney Girl  **The Dapper Partnership**
12  NOT ON YOUR NELLIE (IRE), 4, b f Zebedee—Piccadilly Filly (IRE)  **Exors of the Late J. D. Gordon**
13  PRINCESS POWER (IRE), 5, b m Slade Power (IRE)—Flurry of Hands (IRE)  **Mr T. A. Killoran**
14  ROUNDHAY PARK, 6, ch g Mayson—Brave Mave  **Leeds Plywood & Doors Ltd**
15  SHEEPSCAR LAD (IRE), 7, b g Arcano (IRE)—Piccadilly Filly (IRE)  **Leeds Plywood & Doors Ltd**
16  SINGE ANGLAIS (IRE), 4, ch g Footstepsinthesand—Callanish  **Geoff Maidment & John Raybould**
17  STAR PRIZE (IRE), 4, b f Power—In My Dreams (IRE)  **Mr G. B. Davidson**
18  STEALING SILK (IRE), 4, b f Canford Cliffs (IRE)—The Silver Kebaya (FR)
19  TELE COED, 4, b f Telescope (IRE)—Discoed  **Ms S. V. Hattersley**
20  TENAX (IRE), 5, b g Slade Power (IRE)—Stravina (GER)  **Mr James Marshall & Mr Chris Marshall**
21  VIOLETTE SZABO (IRE), 4, b f Exceleberation (IRE)—Forthefirstime  **Crawford Society 1**

### THREE-YEAR-OLDS

22  ACKLAM EXPRESS (IRE), b g Mehmas (IRE)—York Express  **MPS Racing & M B Spence**
23  AS IF BY CHANCE, b g Fountain of Youth (IRE)—Citron  **Ms Sara Hattersley & Miss Tracey Mann**
24  BELVEDERE BLAST (IRE), ch g Buratino (IRE)—Zelie Martin (IRE)  **Swanland Partnership**
25  CAMERILY JOE, b g Helmet (AUS)—Final Dynasty  **W Burton & D Fielding**
26  COBWEB CORNER (IRE), ch g Buratino (IRE)—Diminish (IRE)  **Three Plus One**
27  COLEY'S KOKO, b f Kodiac—Acclimatisation (IRE)  **Mr J. R. Saville**
28  DORA'S COED, b f Cannock Chase (USA)—Discoed  **Ms S. V. Hattersley**
29  FULL OF SASS, b f Fulbright—Tides  **Last of the Summer Whine Partnership**
30  GOLDEN CLUSTER, b g Havana Gold (IRE)—Florett (IRE)  **David Balfe Racing**
31  HIGH SECURITY, b g Acclamation—Excelette (IRE)  **Reliance Racing Partnership**
32  IMPERIUM BLUE, gr c Lethal Force (IRE)—Exist  **Mr & Mrs I. H. Bendelow**
33  ISLA KAI (IRE), b g Awtaad (IRE)—Sidney Girl  **Martin Webb Racing**
34  IT JUST TAKES TIME (IRE), br g Power—War Bride (GER)  **Ms S. V. Hattersley**
35  MAYBE ONE DAY (FR), b g Acclamation—Baileys Parisienne (FR)  **Mrs J. M. Dwyer**
36  MITCHAM FAIR, b f Monsieur Bond (IRE)—Next Stop  **Mr S. E. Hussey**
37  MOLLYS BROTHER, b g Mayson—Bacall  **Mr P. Burdett**
38  NIGHT ON EARTH (IRE), b c Kodiac—Eternal View (IRE)  **Mr N. Tinkler**
39  SHE'S A DEVA, b f Fountain of Youth (IRE)—Rosein  **D M Caslin & Partner**
40  STRANGERONTHESHORE, b f Cable Bay—Stolen Glance  **R. S. Cockerill (Farms) Ltd**
41  TRUTH IN JEST, ch g Mayson—Where's Broughton  **The Dapper Partnership**
42  UBETTABELIEVEIT (IRE), b c Kodiac—Ladylishandra (IRE)  **Martin Webb Racing**

### TWO-YEAR-OLDS

43  ACKLAM GOLD (IRE), ch g 17/04 Galileo Gold—Tides (Bahamian Bounty) (45714)  **Maxwell Morrison Racing**
44  ANOTHER BERTIE (IRE), b c 18/04 Acclamation—Temerity (IRE) (Zoffany (IRE)) (48000)  **Mr J. R. Saville**
45  B f 03/04 Kodiac—Causeway Charm (USA) (Giant's Causeway (USA)) (28571)  **Mr N. Tinkler**
46  B c 18/04 Dandy Man (IRE)—Coconut Kisses (Bahamian Bounty) (24762)  **Mr N. Tinkler**
47  Ch c 15/04 Hot Streak (IRE)—Commencing (IRE) (Compton Place)  **Mr Y. T. Szeto**
48  COZICAN (IRE), b c 16/04 Kodiac—Shared Humor (USA) (Distorted Humor (USA)) (38095)  **Martin Webb Racing**
49  DOUGIES DREAM (IRE), b c 11/05 Fast Company (IRE)—
                                   Sidney Girl (Azamour (IRE)) (45000)  **Martin Webb Racing**
50  B c 18/03 Cable Bay (IRE)—Ego (Green Desert (USA)) (11429)

## MR NIGEL TINKLER - continued

**51** Gr c 05/03 Lethal Force (IRE)—Grace Hull (Piccolo) **Mr R. Hull**
**52** ITSGOODTOBEUS (IRE), b g 28/02 Mastercraftsman (IRE)—
Mill Guineas (USA) (Salse (USA)) (9523) **The Flying Raconteurs**
**53** Ch c 25/04 Cityscape—Just Emma (Bertolini (USA))
**54** Ch c 17/03 Dream Ahead (USA)—Kashtan (Sakhee's Secret) (952) **D. G. Pryde**
**55** B f 14/03 Kodiac—Kiss From A Rose (Compton Place) (35000)
**56** B f 09/04 Galileo Gold—Ladylishandra (IRE) (Mujadil (IRE)) (61905)
**57** LUCKY LUCKY LUCKY (IRE), b g 27/04 Footstepsinthesand—Lovers Peace (IRE) (Oratorio (IRE)) (39048) **G Maidment Racing**
**58** B f 17/03 Showcasing—Majestic Song (Royal Applause) (1000) **Mr G. B. Davidson**
**59** B c 23/03 Belardo (IRE)—No Nightmare (USA) (Lion Heart (USA)) (4000)
**60** NOD AND A WINK, b f 04/03 Monsieur Bond (IRE)—
Stolen Glance (Mujahid (USA)) (3810) **R. S. Cockerill (Farms) Ltd**
**61** PRODIGIOUS BLUE (IRE), b c 20/02 Brazen Beau—Hellofahaste (Hellvelyn) (37143) **Mr & Mrs I. H. Bendelow**
**62** B f 06/05 Ribchester—Spirit of Dubai (IRE) (Cape Cross (IRE)) (140000)
**63** B f 17/03 Awtaad (IRE)—Tingleo (Galileo (IRE))
**64** B f 12/04 Iffraaj—Tropical Paradise (IRE) (Verglas (IRE)) (35000)
**65** URSINE (IRE), b f 17/01 Kodi Bear (IRE)—Titova (Halling (USA)) (5000)
**66** B f 04/04 Garswood—Where's Broughton (Cadeaux Genereux) (7500)

**Other Owners:** Amity Finance Ltd, Mr D. E. Balfe, Mr P. Burdett, W. F. Burton, Ms D. M. Caslin, Mr G. Darling, Dearing Plastics Ltd, F. Drabble, Mr D. A. Fielding, Ms S. V. Hattersley, MPS Racing Ltd, Mr G. R. Maidment, Mr C. R. Marshall, J. R. Marshall, Mrs T. L. McGowan, Mr L. Murray, Mr M. A. Ollier, Mrs J. J. Parvin, Mr A. M. Pear, Mr S. Perkins, J. Raybould, Mr A. A. Smith, Mr M. B. Spence, The Crawford Society, Mr N. Tinkler, Mr M. Webb.

---

**534** | **MR COLIN TIZZARD, Sherborne**
Postal: **Venn Farm, Milborne Port, Sherborne, Dorset, DT9 5RA**
Contacts: **PHONE 01963 250598 MOBILE 07976 778656 FAX 01963 250598**
**EMAIL info@colintizzard.co.uk WEBSITE www.colintizzard.co.uk**

**1** AINCHEA (IRE), 8, b g Flemensfirth (USA)—Lady Petit (IRE) **Ann & Alan Potts Limited**
**2** AKI BOMAYE (IRE), 6, gr g Stowaway—Line Grey (FR) **Mrs M. Middleton**
**3** AMARILLO SKY (IRE), 5, b g Westerner—Bag of Tricks (IRE) **J P Romans & Taylor, O'Dwyer**
**4** AMBION HILL (IRE), 6, b br g Getaway (GER)—Vertality (IRE) **Mr O. C. R. Wynne & Mrs S. J. Wynne**
**5** AUTONOMOUS CLOUD (IRE), 5, b g Flemensfirth (USA)—
August Hill (IRE) **Mr Terry Warner & the McNeill Family**
**6** BATTLE OF IDEAS (IRE), 8, ch g Fracas (IRE)—Haven't A Notion **Coral Champions Club**
**7** BIRDMAN BOB (IRE), 4, ch g Flemensfirth (USA)—Brijomi Queen (IRE) **Taylor & O'Dwyer**
**8** BOLD CONDUCT (IRE), 7, b g Stowaway—Vics Miller (IRE) **J P Romans & Terry Warner**
**9** BORN IN BORRIS (IRE), 7, b m Arcadio (GER)—Honour Own (IRE) **Mr R. M. Harvey-Bailey**
**10** BOURBALI (FR), 4, b g Sinndar (IRE)—Saintheze (FR) **Pope, Legg, Green T Swaffield**
**11** BUCKHORN GEORGE, 6, gr g Geordieland (FR)—Waimea Bay **The Buckhorn Racing Team**
**12** BUCKHORN ROCCO, 5, ch g Saddler's Rock (IRE)—Waimea Bay **The Buckhorn Racing Team**
**13** BUTTERWICK BROOK (IRE), 6, b g Getaway (GER)—Sheriussa (IRE) **The Butterwick Syndicate**
**14** CARRICK ROADS (IRE), 7, ch g Robin des Champs (FR)—Jay Lo (IRE) **Brocade Racing**
**15** CATCH THE CUBAN, 5, b g Havana Gold (IRE)—Reyamour **C. L. Tizzard**
**16** CHAMPAGNE MESDAMES (FR), 4, b g Diamond Boy (FR)—Olerone (FR) **The Wychwood Partnership**
**17** CHARLIE MAGRI, 5, b g Midnight Legend—Psychosis **Reed Truan & Spershott**
**18** CHRISTMAS IN APRIL (FR), 9, b g Crillon (FR)—Similaresisoldofa (FR) **Swallowfield Racing**
**19** COASTAL DRIFT, 7, b g Black Sam Bellamy (IRE)—Absalom's Girl **Brocade Racing**
**20** 4, B g Milan—Consider Her Lucky (GER)
**21** COPPERHEAD, 7, ch g Sulamani (IRE)—How's Business **Mrs G. C. Pritchard**
**22** COULD TALKABOUTIT (IRE), 4, b g Kayf Tara—Glen Countess (IRE) **Mr J. P. Romans**
**23** DARLAC (FR), 8, b br g Lucarno (USA)—Pail Mel (FR) **Mrs G. C. Pritchard**
**24** DUC KAUTO (FR), 8, b g Ballingarry (FR)—Kauto Lorette (FR) **Ann & Alan Potts Limited**

## MR NIGEL TINKLER - continued

25 **DYLAN'S DOUBLE (IRE)**, 4, b g Getaway (GER)—Summer Again (IRE) **Brocade Racing**
26 **EARL OF WISDOM**, 6, ch g Flemensfirth (USA)—Golden Sunbird (IRE) **The Wychwood Partnership**
27 **EARLY DAYS (IRE)**, 7, b m Stowaway—Inchiquin Cailin (IRE) **Gale Force Seven**
28 **EARTH BUSINESS (IRE)**, 5, b g Westerner—Shellys Creek (IRE) **Mrs C. E. Penny**
29 **ELDORADO ALLEN (FR)**, 7, gr g Khalkevi (IRE)—Hesmeralda (FR) **J P Romans & Terry Warner**
30 **ELEGANT ESCAPE (IRE)**, 9, b g Dubai Destination (USA)—Graineuaile (IRE) **Mr J. P. Romans**
31 **ELIXIR DE NUTZ (FR)**, 7, gr g Al Namix (FR)—Nutz (FR) **J. T. Warner**
32 **FAUSTINOVICK**, 7, b g Black Sam Bellamy (IRE)—Cormorant Cove **Taylor & O'Dwyer**
33 **FIDDLERONTHEROOF (IRE)**, 7, b g Stowaway—Inquisitive Look **Taylor, Burley & O'Dwyer**
34 **FLOY JOY (IRE)**, 5, b g Arcadio (GER)—The Scorpion Queen (IRE) **Nigel Hanger & Eric Jones**
35 **FLY TO MARS**, 7, b g Schiaparelli (GER)—Patsie Magern **Brocade Racing**
36 **FOX NORTON (FR)**, 11, b g Lando (GER)—Natt Musik (FR) **Ann & Alan Potts Limited**
37 **FULGURIX (FR)**, 6, b g Maresca Sorrento (FR)—Union de Sevres (FR) **Mr Simon Munir & Mr Isaac Souede**
38 **FURKASH (FR)**, 6, b g Al Namix (FR)—Meralda (FR) **Swallowfield Racing**
39 **GETAWAY FRED (IRE)**, 7, b g Getaway (GER)—Cloch Anna (IRE) **Victor & Celia Goaman**
40 **GETMEGOLD (IRE)**, 6, ch g Getaway (GER)—Sunset Gold (IRE) **Anne Broom & Wendy Carter**
41 **GOLDEN SUNRISE (IRE)**, 8, ch g Stowaway—Fairy Dawn (IRE) **Brocade Racing**
42 **GUY DE GUYE (FR)**, 5, b g Tiger Groom—Kasibelle de Guye (FR) **Mr J. P. McManus**
43 **HELFORD RIVER**, 7, b g Presenting—Lovely Origny (FR) **Brocade Racing**
44 **HIGHEST SUN (FR)**, 7, b g Sunday Break (JPN)—Highest Price (FR) **Mr A. J. Head**
45 **HONEST EXCHANGE (IRE)**, 7, b g Gold Well—Final Instalment (IRE) **Victor & Celia Goaman & Jenny Perry**
46 **INVESTMENT MANAGER**, 5, b g Nathaniel (IRE)—Two Days In Paris (FR) **Brocade Racing**
47 **KALARIKA (IRE)**, 8, br m Kalanisi (IRE)—Katariya (IRE) **Gale Force Three**
48 **KATAHDIN (IRE)**, 8, b g Kayf Tara—Keyaza (IRE) **Nigel Hanger & Eric Jones**
49 **KAUTO THE KING (FR)**, 7, b g Ballingarry (IRE)—Kauto Luisa (FR) **Jenny Perry & Celia Goaman**
50 **KILBRICKEN STORM (IRE)**, 10, b g Oscar (IRE)—Kilbricken Leader (IRE) **A Selway & P Wavish**
51 **KILLER KANE (IRE)**, 6, b g Oscar (IRE)—Native Idea (IRE) **J P Romans & Taylor, O'Dwyer**
52 **KINGS WALK (IRE)**, 10, b g King's Theatre (IRE)—Shuil Sionnach (IRE) **Mrs J. R. Bishop**
53 **L'AIR DU VENT (FR)**, 7, b g Coastal Path—Bleu Perle (FR) **Brocade Racing**
54 **LAMANVER PIPPIN**, 8, b g Apple Tree (FR)—Lamanver Homerun **Dr D. Christensen**
55 **LANSPARK (IRE)**, 6, b g Milan—Sparky May **Ruxley Holdings Ltd**
56 **LILLINGTON (IRE)**, 9, br g Westerner—Kind Word (IRE) **The Colin Tizzard Racing Club**
57 **LITTLE VERN (IRE)**, 7, b g Oscar (IRE)—Silver Valley (IRE) **Nightingale Syndicate**
58 **LOSTINTRANSLATION (IRE)**, 9, b g Flemensfirth (USA)—Falika (FR) **Taylor & O'Dwyer**
59 **MISTER MALARKY**, 8, ch g Malinas (GER)—Priscilla **Wendy & Malcolm Hezel**
60 **MOCACREME HAS (FR)**, 6, b g Saint des Saints (FR)—Monika (FR) **Mr J. P. McManus**
61 **MOLINEAUX (IRE)**, 10, b g King's Theatre (IRE)—Steel Grey Lady (IRE) **John & Heather Snook**
62 **MOVING DAY (IRE)**, 6, b g Getaway (GER)—Little Demand (IRE) **The Reserve Tankers**
63 **MUFFINS FOR TEA**, 11, ch g With The Flow (USA)—Countess Point **Mr D. S. Purdie**
64 **MY LADY GREY**, 7, gr m Presenting—Wassailing Queen **Mr J. Reed**
65 **NAME IN LIGHTS (IRE)**, 5, b g Fame And Glory—Chevalier Jet (IRE) **Mrs M. Middleton**
66 **NATIVE RIVER (IRE)**, 11, ch g Indian River (FR)—Native Mo (IRE) **Brocade Racing**
67 **NELSONS ROCK**, 6, b g Mount Nelson—Neardown Beauty (IRE) **Middleham Park Racing LXXXVIII**
68 **NEW TO THIS TOWN (IRE)**, 10, b g Milan—Jade River (FR) **Ann & Alan Potts Limited**
69 **NO HUBS NO HOOBS (IRE)**, 5, b g Flemensfirth (USA)—Miss Brandywell (IRE) **Taylor & O'Dwyer**
70 **NUMBERS MAN (IRE)**, 5, b g Arctic Cosmos (USA)—Duchessofthehall (IRE) **The Reserve Tankers**
71 **OFALLTHEGINJOINTS (IRE)**, 7, b g Stowaway—Dinos Luso (IRE) **The Reserve Tankers**
72 **OFTEN OVERLOOKED (IRE)**, 5, b br g Elusive Pimpernel (USA)—Alpinia (IRE) **Coral Champions Club**
73 **OSCAR ELITE (IRE)**, 6, b g Oscar (IRE)—Lady Elite (IRE) **Mrs M. Middleton**
74 **PADLEYOUROWNCANOE**, 7, b g Nayef (USA)—Pooka's Daughter (IRE) **K.A.C. Bloodstock Limited**
75 5, B gr m Geordieland (FR)—Pems Gift
76 **PINGSHOU (IRE)**, 11, b g Definite Article—Quest of Passion (FR) **Ann & Alan Potts Limited**
77 **PREMIUMACCESS (IRE)**, 6, b g Milan—De Loose Mongoose (IRE) **Taylor & O'Dwyer**
78 **PRINCESS MIDNIGHT**, 7, ch m Midnight Legend—Setter's Princess **The Gardens Entertainments Ltd**
79 **QUEEN OF THE WIND**, 8, b m Shirocco (GER)—Kaydee Queen (IRE) **Chasing Gold Limited**
80 **RAREST DIAMOND (IRE)**, 7, b m Milan—Lace Parasol (IRE) **The Colin Tizzard Racing Club**
81 **RECTORY OAK (IRE)**, 6, b g Oscar (IRE)—Betty Roe (IRE) **Mrs G. C. Pritchard**
82 **RESERVE TANK (IRE)**, 7, b g Jeremy (USA)—Lady Bellamy (IRE) **The Reserve Tankers**
83 **ROAD SENAM (FR)**, 5, b g Saint des Saints (FR)—Madison Road (IRE) **Mr Simon Munir & Mr Isaac Souede**
84 **ROCKPOINT**, 8, b g Shirocco (GER)—Tinagoodnight (FR) **John & Heather Snook**

# MR COLIN TIZZARD - continued

85 **ROSE OF ARCADIA (IRE)**, 6, b m Arcadio (GER)—Rosie Lea (IRE) **Cheveley Park Stud Limited**
86 **ROYAL CROWN (FR)**, 6, ch g Creachadoir (IRE)—Royal Army (GER) **The Wychwood Partnership**
87 **ROYAL VACATION (IRE)**, 11, b g King's Theatre (IRE)—Summer Break (IRE) **Mrs J. R. Bishop**
88 **RUSSIAN EXILE**, 7, b g Pasternak—Psychosis **Reed, Abrahams & Spershott**
89 **SEYMOUR PROMISE (IRE)**, 5, b g Flemensfirth (USA)—Loadsapromise (IRE) **Mrs M. Middleton**
90 **SHANAHAN'S TURN (IRE)**, 13, b g Indian Danehill (IRE)—Chanson Indienne (FR) **Ann & Alan Potts Limited**
91 **SHERBORNE (IRE)**, 5, b g Getaway (GER)—Luck of The Deise (IRE) **Sharp, Nicholas & Kennington**
92 **SHIROCCO'S DREAM (IRE)**, 6, b m Shirocco (GER)—Dream Function (IRE) **J P Romans & Taylor, O'Dwyer**
93 **SHOAL BAY (IRE)**, 8, b g Gold Well—Ring Hill **Mrs C. Skan**
94 **SHYBAIRNSGETNOWT (IRE)**, 5, gr g Cloudings (IRE)—Quarry Endeavour (IRE) **Susan & John Waterworth**
95 **SIXTY DOLLARS MORE (FR)**, 5, b g Buck's Boum (FR)—Sacree City (FR) **Wendy & Malcolm Hezel**
96 **SIZING AT MIDNIGHT (IRE)**, 9, br g Midnight Legend—Issaquah (IRE) **Ann & Alan Potts Limited**
97 **SIZING CODELCO (IRE)**, 12, b g Flemensfirth (USA)—La Zingarella (IRE) **Ann & Alan Potts Limited**
98 **SIZING CUSIMANO**, 8, b g Midnight Legend—Combe Florey **Ann & Alan Potts Limited**
99 **SIZING GRANITE (IRE)**, 13, br g Milan—Hazel's Tisrara (IRE) **Ann & Alan Potts Limited**
100 **SIZING PLATINUM (IRE)**, 13, b g Definite Article—Quest of Passion (FR) **Ann & Alan Potts Limited**
101 **SIZING TARA**, 8, b g Kayf Tara—As Was **Ann & Alan Potts Limited**
102 **SKERRIES HARBOUR (IRE)**, 5, b g Sholokhov (IRE)—The Malteasiereyes (IRE) **Mr W. P. Drew**
103 **SLATE HOUSE (IRE)**, 9, b g Presenting—Bay Pearl (FR) **Eric Jones, Geoff Nicholas, John Romans**
104 **SO SAID I**, 5, gr m Malinas (GER)—Wassailing Queen **And So Say All Of Us Partnership**
105 **STORM HOME (IRE)**, 9, b g King's Theatre (IRE)—Miss Mayberry (IRE) **Mr J. P. Romans**
106 **STRIKING A POSE (IRE)**, 5, b g Getaway (GER)—Clonsingle Native (IRE) **& Gosden, Sharp G Kennington**
107 **TECHNOLOGY (IRE)**, 4, b g Yeats (IRE)—Little Fashionista (IRE) **McNeill Family Ltd**
108 **THATSENTERTAINMENT (IRE)**, 5, b g Leading Light (IRE)—Dyrick Daybreak (IRE) **Susan & John Waterworth**
109 **THE BIG BREAKAWAY (IRE)**, 6, ch g Getaway (GER)—
 Princess Mairead (IRE) **Eric Jones, Geoff Nicholas, John Romans**
110 **THE CHANGING MAN (IRE)**, 4, b g Walk In The Park (IRE)—Bitofapuzzle **Susan & John Waterworth**
111 **THE STRAP MAN**, 7, b g Schiaparelli (GER)—Lady Racquet (IRE) **M, V & JM Messenger & Buob-Aldorf**
112 **THE WIDDOW MAKER**, 7, ch g Arvico (FR)—Countess Point **Mr D. S. Purdie**
113 **THEATRE GUIDE (IRE)**, 14, b g King's Theatre (IRE)—Erintante (IRE) **Mrs J. R. Bishop**
114 **THIS TOWN**, 8, b m Kayf Tara—Ardstown **John & Heather Snook**
115 **THISTLECRACK**, 13, b g Kayf Tara—Ardstown **John & Heather Snook**
116 **TRIPLE TRADE**, 5, b g Norse Dancer (IRE)—Doubly Guest **SJS Racing**
117 **VISION DES FLOS (FR)**, 8, b g Balko (FR)—Marie Royale (FR) **Ann & Alan Potts Limited**
118 **WAR LORD (GER)**, 6, gr g Jukebox Jury (IRE)—Westalin (GER) **The Wychwood Partnership**
119 **WEST APPROACH**, 11, b g Westerner—Ardstown **John & Heather Snook**
120 **WEST ORCHARD (IRE)**, 4, b g Westerner—Shellys Creek (IRE) **Orchard Racing**
121 **WESTERN BARON (IRE)**, 4, b g Westerner—Aylesbury Park (IRE) **The Alyasan Partnership**
122 **WHITE MOON (IRE)**, 9, gr g Sholokhov (IRE)—Westalin (GER) **Brocade Racing**
123 **WHO SHOT JR (IRE)**, 7, b g Scorpion (IRE)—Ariesanne (IRE) **Wednesday Night Syndicate**
124 **WHYDAH GALLY**, 5, b g Black Sam Bellamy (IRE)—Reverse Swing **Sam's Crew**

## THREE-YEAR-OLDS

125 **COLDEN'S PASSION (IRE)**, ch c Twilight Son—Coco Rouge (IRE) **Ian & Claire Gosden, J Coles M Sharp**

Other Owners: Ms J. Abrahams, Mr G. S. Bennet, Mr J. G. Bennet, Mrs A. E. M. Broom, Mr G. R. Broom, Mr J. P. R. Buob-Aldorf, Mrs V. K. Buob-Aldorf, Mr N. Burley, Mrs W. Carter, Mr D. J. Coles, Mrs C. J. Goaman, Mr V. Goaman, Mrs E. C. Gosden, Mr I. F. Gosden, Mr M. Green, Mr M. W. Hezel, Mrs W. M. Hezel, M. M. Hooker, Mr E. Jones, Mr R. Jones, Mr G. Kennington, Mr G. J. Le Prevost, Miss B. E. Legg, Mr D. A. Makins, Mr D. A. Mayes, Mr D. R. Mayes, Mrs S. A. Mayes, McNeill Family Ltd, Mrs M. Messenger, S. E. Munir, Mr G. Nicholas, Mr R. O'Dwyer, Mrs J. M. Perry, Mrs W. M. Pope, Miss J. E. Reed, Mr J. P. Romans, Mr D. J. Rushbrook, A. G. Selway, Mr M. L. Sharp, Mrs H. A. Snook, J. W. Snook, Mr I. Souede, Mr D. G. Spershott, Mr T. J. Swaffield, Mr L. Tappin, Mr P. A. Taylor, Mr M. R. Truan, J. T. Warner, Mr J. A. Waterworth, Mrs S. Waterworth, Mr P. T. J. Wavish, O. C. R. Wynne, Mrs S. J. Wynne.

**Assistant Trainer:** Joe Tizzard, Chris Wald, **Racing Secretary:** Amanda Hibbs, **Secretary:** Deborah White, **Yard Sponsor:** Coral.

**NH Jockey:** Harry Cobden, Jonjo O'Neill jr, Robbie Power, Tom Scudamore. **Conditional Jockey:** Harry Kimber.

## 535 SIR MARK TODD, Swindon
Postal: **Badgerstown, Foxhill, Swindon, Wiltshire, SN4 0DR**
Contacts: **PHONE 01793 791228**
**EMAIL mtoddracing@gmail.com**

1 DUTCH HARBOR, 4, b g Kodiac—Complexion **Dutch Harbor Partnership**
2 ENCHANTEE (IRE), 4, b f Gale Force Ten—Love Valentine (IRE) **Enchantee**
3 KYLLINGA (IRE), 4, ch f Kyllachy—Katevan (IRE) **The Katchy Partnership**
4 MY FOOTSTEPS, 6, b g Footstepsinthesand—Luminous Gold **Mrs B. M. Cuthbert**
5 PETIT BAY, 5, b m Dick Turpin (IRE)—Sky High Diver (IRE) **Mr B. Allan**
6 SOYOUNIQUE (IRE), 4, ch g Siyouni (FR)—Adventure Seeker (FR) **MTV Syndicate**

### THREE-YEAR-OLDS
7 L'OPERATEUR, b c Siyouni (FR)—Nessun Dorma (GER) **B & J Lindsay Cambridge Stud**
8 LIBERATED LAD, b c Muhaarar—Puzzler (IRE) **Lord A. Lloyd Webber**
9 MARSDEN CROSS (IRE), b f Camelot—First of Many **Sir P. J. Vela**
10 MERCIAN HYMN, b g Siyouni (FR)—Astronomy Domine
11 RADIANT LIGHT, b c Fastnet Rock (AUS)—Gertrude Gray (IRE) **Lady Bamford**
12 ROSE FANDANGO, ch f Exceed And Excel (AUS)—Mumtaza **Rose Fandango Partnership**
13 SEIXAS (IRE), ch f Footstepsinthesand—Miss Brazil (IRE) **The Seixas Partnership**
14 TASMAN BAY (FR), b c Le Havre (IRE)—Purely Priceless (IRE) **Sir P. J. Vela**
15 WOW WILLIAM (FR), b g The Wow Signal (IRE)—Naive (IRE) **Wow William Partnership**

### TWO-YEAR-OLDS
16 PROPHET'S DREAM, gr c 24/03 Outstrip—Fool's Dream (Showcasing) (12000) **Mrs B. M. Cuthbert**

**Other Owners:** Mr C. Bernick, Bloomsbury Stud, Mrs A. Christie, Mr H. D. J. De Burgh, Dame L. P Goddard, Mr T. Henderson, Mr B. J. Lindsay, Mrs J. E. A. Lindsay, Mr S. O'Donnell, O.T.I. Racing, Mrs D. A. Sidebottom, Lady C. Todd, Sir M. J. Todd, Sir P. J. Vela.

## 536 MR MARTIN TODHUNTER, Penrith
Postal: **The Park, Orton, Penrith, Cumbria, CA10 3SD**
Contacts: **PHONE 015396 24314 MOBILE 07976 440082 FAX 015396 24314**
**WEBSITE www.martintodhunter.co.uk**

1 AFRICAN GLORY (IRE), 7, b m Fame And Glory—African Miss (IRE) **Coniston Old Men Syndicate**
2 ARCTIC FOX, 5, ch m Mastercraftsman (IRE)—Aurora Borealis (IRE) **Colin & Kay Wilding**
3 ASKING FOR ANSWERS (IRE), 8, ch g Ask—Equation (IRE) **Mrs Mrs Matthews & Mrs G Hazeldean**
4 BOUNCING BOBBY (IRE), 4, b g Raven's Pass (USA)—Silicon Star (FR) **J. W. Hazeldean**
5 COOL COUNTRY (IRE), 6, b g Dylan Thomas (IRE)—Mae's Choice (IRE) **Exors of the Late J. D. Gordon**
6 FIRST REVOLUTION (IRE), 7, b g Jeremy (USA)—Shaigino (IRE) **Colin & Kay Wilding**
7 JOIE DE VIVRE (IRE), 6, gr m Mastercraftsman (IRE)—Fragonard **Leeds Plywood & Doors Ltd**
8 KITTY'S COVE, 6, b m High Chaparral (IRE)—Juniper Girl (IRE)
9 MOLINARI (IRE), 4, gr c Mastercraftsman (IRE)—Moon Empress (FR) **Mr & Mrs Ian Hall**
10 PLAN OF ESCAPE (IRE), 8, ch g Presenting—Pilgara (IRE) **Mr Bill Hazeldean & Mr & Mrs Ian Hall**
11 SIMPLE RULES (IRE), 5, b g Aizavoski (IRE)—Dawn Native (IRE) **Exors of the Late J. D. Gordon**
12 SOPHIE OLIVIA (IRE), 9, gr m Ask—Gill's Honey (IRE) **Mr A. Bell**
13 SOUTHEAST ROSE (IRE), 8, b m Beat Hollow—Sunny South East (IRE) **The Surf & Turf Partnership**
14 TEME SPIRIT (IRE), 7, b m Sans Frontieres (IRE)—Newtown Dancer (IRE)

**Other Owners:** Mr P. G. Airey, Mr & Mrs Ian Hall, Mrs G. M. Hazeldean, J. W. Hazeldean, Mrs S. J. Matthews, Mr C. Taylor, Miss K. M. Wilding.

## 537 MR MARCUS TREGONING, Whitsbury

Postal: Whitsbury Manor Racing Stables, Whitsbury, Fordingbridge, Hampshire, SP6 3QQ
Contacts: **PHONE** 01725 518889 **MOBILE** 07767 888100
**EMAIL** info@marcustregoningracing.co.uk **WEBSITE** www.marcustregoningracing.co.uk

1 **ATALANTA BREEZE**, 5, b m Champs Elysees—Craighall **Miss S. M. Sharp**
2 **BARON SLICK (IRE)**, 5, b g Raven's Pass (USA)—Namely (IRE) **Mr M. P. Tregoning**
3 **DARTINGTON (IRE)**, 4, b g Siyouni (FR)—Secret Pursuit (IRE) **Mr G. C. B. Brook**
4 **GHALYOON**, 6, b g Invincible Spirit (IRE)—Swiss Lake (USA) **Hamdan bin Rashid Al Maktoum**
5 **MARGUB**, 6, ch g Bated Breath—Bahamian Babe **Hamdan bin Rashid Al Maktoum**
6 **MISS BLONDELL**, 8, ch m Compton Place—Where's Broughton **Miss S. M. Sharp**
7 **MODMIN (IRE)**, 4, b g Tamayuz—Arsheef (USA) **Hamdan bin Rashid Al Maktoum**
8 **POWER OF DARKNESS**, 5, b g Power—Summers Lease **R. C. C. Villers**
9 **SADLERS BEACH (IRE)**, 5, b m Pour Moi (IRE)—Dusty Boots (IRE) **Mr R. E. Kingston**
10 **SILENT PARTNER**, 4, b g Fast Company (IRE)—Peace Lily **Park Walk Racing - 2019**
11 **SMUGGLER**, 4, b g Sir Percy—Patronella (IRE) **Park Walk Racing - 2019**
12 **STRATHSPEY STRETTO (IRE)**, 6, ch m Kyllachy—

Rhythm And Rhyme (IRE) **Miss S Sharp & Mr M. P. N. Tregoning**
13 **TRELINNEY (IRE)**, 5, b m Dandy Man (IRE)—Silvertine (IRE) **Mr M. P. Tregoning**

### THREE-YEAR-OLDS

14 **ALCACHOCA**, gr f Bobby's Kitten (USA)—Albacocca **Miss K. Rausing**
15 **ALDEENAARY (IRE)**, b c Awtaad (IRE)—Lucky Clio (IRE) **Hamdan bin Rashid Al Maktoum**
16 **ALGHEED (IRE)**, b f Dark Angel (IRE)—Rathaath (IRE) **Hamdan bin Rashid Al Maktoum**
17 **ALKUMAIT**, b c Showcasing—Suelita **Hamdan bin Rashid Al Maktoum**
18 **ALMOSHAHAR (IRE)**, br g Invincible Spirit (IRE)—Rihaam (IRE) **Hamdan bin Rashid Al Maktoum**
19 **ARTEMIS SKY**, ch f Hunter's Light (IRE)—Starlit Sky **The Artemis Partnership.**
20 **ENSYAABY (IRE)**, b g Dark Angel (IRE)—Staceymac (IRE) **Hamdan bin Rashid Al Maktoum**
21 **HAIZOOM**, ch f Sea The Stars (IRE)—Sortita (GER) **Hamdan bin Rashid Al Maktoum**
22 **HALCYON SPIRIT**, b g Charm Spirit (IRE)—Stybba **Halcyon Thoroughbreds - MT2**
23 **LA FORZA**, b g Shalaa (IRE)—Seven Magicians (USA)
24 **MEADRAM**, b g Mukhadram—Mea Parvitas (IRE) **Mrs C. J. Wates**
25 **MOTARAJJA (IRE)**, b c Frankel—Rumoush (USA) **Hamdan bin Rashid Al Maktoum**
26 **MUTASALLEM (IRE)**, ch c Showcasing—Bright Glow **Hamdan bin Rashid Al Maktoum**
27 **ORIGINATOR (IRE)**, ch c New Approach (IRE)—Gimasha **R. C. C. Villers**
28 **PEROTTO**, ch g New Bay—Tschierschen (IRE) **Halcyon Thoroughbreds**
29 **QASAAD**, b c Adaay (IRE)—Flemish School **Hamdan bin Rashid Al Maktoum**
30 **RAQRAAQ (USA)**, b g War Front (USA)—Firdaws (USA) **Hamdan bin Rashid Al Maktoum**
31 **TAQSEEMAAT**, b f Nayef (USA)—Mooakada (IRE) **Hamdan bin Rashid Al Maktoum**
32 **TASFEEQ**, b c Oasis Dream—Blinking **Hamdan bin Rashid Al Maktoum**
33 **TISTAAHAL**, b g Showcasing—Blue Bayou **Hamdan bin Rashid Al Maktoum**
34 **VALPARAISO**, b c Sir Percy—Entre Nous (IRE) **Halcyon Thoroughbreds**
35 **WAAJEEHA**, b f Kingman—Hawaafez **Hamdan bin Rashid Al Maktoum**
36 **ZUHAIR**, ch g Showcasing—Rowan Brae **Hamdan bin Rashid Al Maktoum**

### TWO-YEAR-OLDS

37 **A LA FRANCAISE**, ch f 08/03 Postponed (IRE)—Alamode (Sir Percy) (50000) **Miss K. Rausing**
38 B c 30/01 Invincible Spirit (IRE)—Arabian Comet (IRE) (Dubawi (IRE)) **Hamdan bin Rashid Al Maktoum**
39 B f 05/03 Markaz (IRE)—Arsheef (USA) (Hard Spun (USA)) **Hamdan bin Rashid Al Maktoum**
40 B c 10/03 Markaz (IRE)—Baqqa (IRE) (Shamardal (USA)) **Hamdan bin Rashid Al Maktoum**
41 **DEIRA STATION (IRE)**, b c 17/02 Churchill (IRE)—Queen of India (IRE) (Fastnet Rock (AUS)) (23810) **A. Al Shaikh**
42 B c 24/04 Showcasing—Life of Pi (Sea The Stars (IRE)) (150000) **Hamdan bin Rashid Al Maktoum**
43 B c 18/02 Dark Angel (IRE)—Maqaasid (Green Desert (USA)) **Hamdan bin Rashid Al Maktoum**
44 **OLIVETTI**, b c 04/04 Showcasing—Tschierschen (Acclamation) (28571) **Halcyon Thoroughbreds**
45 Ch f 22/04 Showcasing—Qawaasem (IRE) (Shamardal (USA)) **Hamdan bin Rashid Al Maktoum**
46 B f 09/04 Outstrip—Quail Landing (Mark of Esteem (IRE)) (3000) **Mr M. P. Tregoning**
47 Gr c 20/01 Markaz (IRE)—Rathaath (IRE) (Oasis Dream) **Hamdan bin Rashid Al Maktoum**
48 Gr c 27/02 Dark Angel (IRE)—Rihaam (IRE) (Dansili) **Hamdan bin Rashid Al Maktoum**
49 B c 12/01 Bated Breath—Sparkle (Oasis Dream) (50000) **Hamdan bin Rashid Al Maktoum**
50 B c 14/04 Sea The Stars (IRE)—Umniyah (IRE) (Shamardal (USA)) (625000) **Hamdan bin Rashid Al Maktoum**

## MR MARCUS TREGONING - continued

**Other Owners:** Miss S. M. Sharp, Mr J. A. Tabet, Lady Tennant, Mr M. P. Tregoning.

**Assistant Trainer:** Angie Kennedy.

**Flat Jockey:** Martin Dwyer. **Amateur Jockey:** Mr George Tregoning.

---

### 538   MR GRANT TUER, Northallerton
Postal: **Home Farm, Great Smeaton, Northallerton, North Yorkshire, DL6 2EP**
Contacts: **PHONE 01609 881094 MOBILE 07879 698869 FAX 01609 881094**
EMAIL grant_tuer@btinternet.com

1  **ANGELS FACES (IRE)**, 4, b f Gutaifan (IRE)—Worthington (IRE)  **Miss M. A. Thompson**
2  **ARABIC CULTURE (USA)**, 7, b g Lonhro (AUS)—Kydd Gloves (USA)  **Mr G. F. Tuer**
3  **ATHABASCA (IRE)**, 4, b f Nathaniel (IRE)—Sibaya  **Mr & Mrs G. Turnbull**
4  **CUSTARD**, 5, ch g Monsieur Bond (IRE)—Ailsa Craig (IRE)  **Mr G. F. Tuer**
5  **EMARATY HERO**, 4, b g Lope de Vega (IRE)—Valtina (IRE)  **NG Racing**
6  **ETIKAAL**, 7, ch g Sepoy (AUS)—Hezmah  **Moment Of Madness**
7  **FORUS**, 4, b g Mukhadram—Anbella (FR)  **NG Racing**
8  **FYRECRACKER (IRE)**, 10, ch g Kheleyf (USA)—Spirit of Hope (IRE)  **Allerton Racing**
9  **GUNNERSIDE (IRE)**, 4, gr g Gutaifan (IRE)—Suite (IRE)  **Mr G. F. Tuer**
10 **GUVENOR'S CHOICE (IRE)**, 6, gr g Intikhab (USA)—Exempt  **Royale Racing Syndicate**
11 **HART STOPPER**, 7, b g Compton Place—Angel Song  **Mr G. F. Tuer**
12 **ILE DE BREHAT**, 4, b f Harbour Watch (IRE)—Rise  **D. R. Tucker**
13 **ILLUSIONIST (GER)**, 4, b g Hot Streak (IRE)—Irishstone (IRE)  **Miss M. A. Thompson**
14 **INDIAN VICEROY**, 5, b g Kodiac—Broadlands  **Miss M. A. Thompson**
15 **KAAFY (IRE)**, 5, b g Alhebayeb (IRE)—Serene Dream  **Miss M. Thompson & Moment of Madness**
16 **LEZARDRIEUX**, 4, b g Due Diligence (USA)—M'Selle (IRE)  **Allerton Racing & G Tuer**
17 **LION TOWER (IRE)**, 4, b g Exceed And Excel (AUS)—Memorial (AUS)  **Hornby Hornets**
18 **MYWAYISTHEONLYWAY (IRE)**, 8, b g Tamayuz—Soul Custody (CAN)  **Moment Of Madness**
19 **OUT OF BREATH**, 4, b g Bated Breath—Parisi  **Allerton Racing & G Tuer**
20 **REAL TERMS**, 4, b f Champs Elysees—Easy Terms  **Mr G. F. Tuer**
21 **RESTLESS ENDEAVOUR (IRE)**, 4, b f Dandy Man (IRE)—Belgique (IRE)  **Mr S. Laffan**
22 **SEVENTEEN O FOUR (IRE)**, 4, ro g Gutaifan (IRE)—Bali Breeze (IRE)  **Mr E. J. Ware**
23 **SWINGING EDDIE**, 5, b g Swiss Spirit—Bling Bling (IRE)  **NG Racing**
24 **TERMONATOR**, 5, ch g Monsieur Bond (IRE)—Easy Terms  **Mr G. F. Tuer**

### THREE-YEAR-OLDS

25 **BUFORD**, b g Lawman (FR)—Sibaya  **Mr & Mrs G. Turnbull**
26 **CATHAYENSIS (IRE)**, b f Twilight Son—Chaenomeles (USA)  **Moment of Madness 2**
27 **DREAMCASING**, br c Showcasing—Nandiga (USA)  **David Macleod & Grant Tuer**
28 B f French Navy—Glyndebourne (USA)  **Mrs J. Keys**
29 **MAISON DE YORK (IRE)**, b g War Command (USA)—Malayan Mist (IRE)  **York Forty Four Ltd & Grant Tuer**
30 **MOKAMAN**, b g Dandy Man (IRE)—Percolator  **Moment of Madness 2**
31 B f Hot Streak (IRE)—Nassaakh  **Fillies for fun**
32 Ch g Hot Streak (IRE)—Pigeon Pie  **Mr G. F. Tuer**
33 **ROYAL JAZZ**, b f Awtaad (IRE)—Royal Blush  **Fillies for fun**
34 **SUNSET GLOW (IRE)**, b g Pride of Dubai (AUS)—Golden Shine  **Moment Of Madness**
35 **UNASHAMED**, b g Brazen Beau (AUS)—Glace (IRE)  **Mr G. F. Tuer**

### TWO-YEAR-OLDS

36 B c 15/04 Holy Roman Emperor (IRE)—Inca Trail (USA) (Royal Academy (USA)) (40000)  **Miss M. A. Thompson**
37 Ch f 10/04 Showcasing—Khaseeb (Dutch Art) (40000)  **Mr D. Stone**
38 B f 28/02 Bated Breath—Rosehill Artist (IRE) (Excellent Art) (20952)  **Mr G. F. Tuer**

**Other Owners:** Allerton Racing, Mr J. Black, Mr A. G. Leggott, Mr D. A. Macleod, Moment Of Madness, Miss M. A. Thompson, Mrs V. Thompson, Mr G. F. Tuer, York Forty Four Ltd.

**539** **MR JOSEPH TUITE, Lambourn**
Postal: **Felstead Stables, Folly Road, Lambourn, Hungerford, Berkshire, RG17 8QE**
Contacts: **MOBILE 07769 977351**
EMAIL joe.tuite@tuiteracing.com WEBSITE www.tuiteracing.co.uk

1 **ALCHEMYSTIQUE (IRE)**, 4, b f Authorized (IRE)—Nice To Know (FR) **Mr P. Hancock**
2 **ATTRACTED**, 4, b g New Approach (IRE)—Interesting (IRE) **Attracted Partners**
3 **BLACK KALANISI (IRE)**, 8, b g Kalanisi (IRE)—Blackthorne Winter (IRE) **The Harefield Racing Club**
4 **BYTHEBAY**, 4, br g Cable Bay (IRE)—Kristollini **Red Hot Partnership**
5 **CONKERING HERO (IRE)**, 7, ch g Arakan (USA)—Brioney (IRE) **Mr J. M. Tuite**
6 **FORTUNE AND GLORY (USA)**, 8, b g War Front (USA)—Spain (USA) **Mr R. J. Gurr**
7 **KIMIFIVE (IRE)**, 6, ch g Born To Sea (IRE)—Appletreemagic (IRE) **Mr R. J. Gurr**
8 **KING'S CASTLE (IRE)**, 4, b g Camelot—Kikonga **Kings Partners**
9 **LOTTIE MARIE**, 4, ch f Intello (GER)—Heavenly Dawn **High Rollers**
10 **NORMA**, 5, ch m New Approach (IRE)—Deirdre **Mrs R. G. Hillen**
11 **REDGRAVE (IRE)**, 7, b g Lope de Vega (IRE)—Olympic Medal **Crab Apple Racing Limited**
12 **SOPHOSC (IRE)**, 5, ch g Society Rock (IRE)—Ichiuma (USA) **The Harefield Racing Club**
13 **SURREY PRIDE (IRE)**, 4, b c Lope de Vega (IRE)—La Conquerante **Surrey Racing (SP)**
14 **TIGERTEN**, 4, b g Born To Sea (IRE)—Morning Bride (IRE) **Mr R. J. Gurr**
15 **WHO TOLD JO JO (IRE)**, 7, b g Bushranger (IRE)—Shenkara (IRE) **Felstead Court Flyers**

**THREE-YEAR-OLDS**

16 **BAYAMON BELLE (IRE)**, b f Camacho—Ho Hey **David Klein & Lech Racing**
17 **DREAM DATE DIVA**, b f Sir Percy—Monaco Dream (IRE) **Folly Syndicate**
18 B f Mastercraftsman (IRE)—Dynalosca (USA)
19 **GENTLEMAN JOE**, b c Authorized (IRE)—Bella Lulu **Mr P. Hancock**
20 **HOT DIVA**, ch f Hot Streak (IRE)—Flashy Queen (IRE) **Penny/Adrian Burton, Bob/Angela Lampard**
21 **NATURAL INSTINCT (IRE)**, b f Dandy Man (IRE)—Play Bouzouki **New Normals**
22 **SHADOW ANGEL (IRE)**, b f Dark Angel (IRE)—Villanueva (IRE) **Klein, Pascoe, Lech Racing Ltd**
23 B f War Front (USA)—Tell Me Now (IRE)
24 **VIA SISTINA (IRE)**, b f Fastnet Rock (AUS)—Nigh (IRE) **Mrs R. G. Hillen**
25 **WON LOVE (IRE)**, b g Frankel—Blhadawa (IRE) **Mr J. M. Tuite**
26 **ZEALOT**, b g Pivotal—Devotion (IRE) **Mr J. M. Tuite**

**TWO-YEAR-OLDS**

27 **CHARLIFAN (IRE)**, b c 28/04 Gutaifan (IRE)—Appletreemagic (IRE) (Indian Danehill (IRE)) **Mr R. J. Gurr**
28 **DAYSLEEPER**, b f 26/02 Twilight Son—Early Start (Arcano (IRE)) (26000) **GB Horseracing**
29 **EVERLOVING (IRE)**, b gr f 17/03 Acclamation—Chiringuita (USA) (Hard Spun (USA)) (45714) **GB Horseracing**
30 **FAST DANSEUSE (IRE)**, b f 20/02 Fast Company (IRE)—
                                       Zalanga (IRE) (Azamour (IRE)) (16000) **Alan & Christine Bright**
31 **HEERS HARRY**, b c 25/03 Heeraat (IRE)—Air Stricker (FR) (Acclamation) (3000) **Mrs C. L. Dee**
32 B c 14/04 Coach House (IRE)—Poudretteite (Royal Applause) (3810)
33 B f 08/04 Equiano (FR)—Royal Obsession (Val Royal (FR))
34 **THE ALCHEMIST (FR)**, ch c 01/01 Havana Gold (IRE)—Zahrat Narjis (Exceed And Excel (AUS)) (20178)

**Other Owners:** Mr A. D. Bright, Mrs C. Bright, Lady J. Brookeborough, M. I. Forbes, Mrs C. S. Gregson, Mrs R. G. Hillen, Mrs
O. Hoare, B. E. Holland, Mr D. A. Klein, Lech Racing Ltd, L. Lillingston, G. J. Pascoe, Mr J. M. Tuite.

---

**540** **MR BILL TURNER, Sherborne**
Postal: **Sigwells Farm, Sigwells, Corton Denham, Sherborne, Dorset, DT9 4LN**
Contacts: **PHONE 01963 220523 MOBILE 07932 100173 FAX 01963 220046**
EMAIL billturnerracing@gmail.com

1 **BORN AT MIDNIGHT**, 6, b g Midnight Legend—Wavet **Mr B. J. Goldsmith**
2 **CASSIS DE REINE**, 7, ch m Quatre Saisons—Reine de Violette **Mrs P. A. Turner**
3 **DARK STORM**, 5, b g Geordieland (FR)—Flaviola **C.P.S. Syndicate**
4 **HOLDENHURST**, 6, gr g Hellvelyn—Michelle Shift **Ansells Of Watford**

## MR BILL TURNER - continued

5 **KATHERINE PLACE**, 6, b m Showcasing—Folly Drove  **Ansells Of Watford**
6 **LETSBE AVENUE (IRE)**, 6, b g Lawman (FR)—Aguilas Perla (IRE)  **Mr C. J. Sprake**
7 **LITTLE BOY BLUE**, 6, gr g Hellvelyn—Dusty Dazzler (IRE)  **Mrs P. A. Turner**
8 **LUCKY PURCHASE**, 8, ch m Apple Tree (FR)—Gracious Pearl  **C. J. White**
9 **MARETTIMO (IRE)**, 7, b g Harbour Watch—Renowned (IRE)  **Mrs P. A. Turner**
10 **MIDNIGHT CALAMITY**, 7, ch m Malinas (GER)—Miss Calamity  **The Floral Farmers**
11 **MIDNIGHT WAVE**, 5, b g Midnight Legend—Wavet  **Mrs C. M. Goldsmith**
12 **QUEENS ROAD (IRE)**, 4, b f Make Believe—Okba (USA)  **Mrs B. C. Ansell**
13 **STREAK OF LIGHT**, 4, ch g Hot Streak (IRE)—Lomapamar  **Mrs S. J. Hearn**
14 **YOUVEBROKENMYDREAM**, 6, b m Geordieland (FR)—Mollycarrs Gambul  **Mrs J A Carr-Evans & Ms Susan Evans**

## THREE-YEAR-OLDS

15 Ch g Garswood—Halfwaytoparadise  **Mascalls Stud**
16 **HILLBILLY**, b g Coach House—Dusty Dazzler (IRE)  **Mrs P. A. Turner**
17 Gr g Hellvelyn—Hound Music  **Mrs P. A. Turner**
18 B g Epaulette (AUS)—Jessie K  **Mrs P. A. Turner**
19 **LITTLE RED ROOSTER (IRE)**, ch g Dawn Approach (IRE)—Sou Anguillarina (IRE)  **Mr J. Pyatt**
20 **PACO LOCO**, b g Heeraat (IRE)—Pack of Dreams (IRE)  **Mr & Mrs RJ Manning**

## TWO-YEAR-OLDS

21 **MAJOR GATSBY (IRE)**, gr c 13/04 The Grey Gatsby (IRE)—
Monteamiata (IRE) (Dream Ahead (USA)) (26000)  **Mr & Mrs RJ Manning**
22 B f 05/02 Bobby's Kitten (USA)—Signorina Roseina (Captain Gerrard (IRE)) (3048)  **Mrs P. A. Turner**

**Other Owners:** Mr B. C. Ansell, Mrs B. C. Ansell, Mrs J. A. Carr-Evans, Ms S. L. Evans, B. M. W. Hearn, Mrs S. J. Hearn, R. J. Manning, Mrs S. M. Manning.

**Assistant Trainer:** Kathy While.

---

## 541 MRS KAREN TUTTY, Northallerton
Postal: Trenholme House Farm, Osmotherley, Northallerton, North Yorkshire, DL6 3QA
Contacts: PHONE 01609 883624 MOBILE 07967 837406 FAX 01609 883624
EMAIL karentutty@btinternet.com WEBSITE www.karentuttyracing.co.uk

1 **ELIXSOFT (IRE)**, 6, b m Elzaam (AUS)—Grandegrandegrande (IRE)  **Thoroughbred Homes Ltd**
2 **ELUSIVE HEIGHTS (IRE)**, 8, br g Elusive Pimpernel (USA)—Berg Bahn (IRE)  **Thoroughbred Homes Ltd**
3 **GLOBAL EXCEED**, 6, b g Exceed And Excel (AUS)—Blue Maiden  **Kingmaker Racedays & Thoroughbred Homes**
4 **IDEAL CANDY (IRE)**, 6, b m Canford Cliffs (IRE)—Forever More (IRE)  **Mr D. A. Robinson**
5 **LITTLE JO**, 7, b g Major Cadeaux—Discoed  **Thoroughbred Homes Ltd**
6 **LITTLE MISS MOO**, 4, ch f Iktibas—Orchestrion  **Mrs H. Moorhouse**
7 **LYDIATE LADY**, 9, b m Piccolo—Hireath  **Kingmaker Racedays & Thoroughbred Homes**
8 **MUQARRED (USA)**, 9, b br g Speightstown (USA)—Bawaara (FR)  **Mr David Vernon & Thoroughbred Homes Ltd**
9 **SANDS CHORUS**, 9, b g Footstepsinthesand—Wood Chorus  **Thoroughbred Homes Ltd**
10 **TANGLED (IRE)**, 6, b g Society Rock (IRE)—Open Verse (USA)  **Grange Park Racing XIX**
11 **TWIN APPEAL (IRE)**, 10, b g Oratorio (IRE)—Velvet Appeal (IRE)  **Mrs Mary Winetroube & Thoroughbred Homes**
12 **WAR OF CLANS (IRE)**, 4, b g Ivawood (IRE)—Precautionary  **Thoroughbred Homes Ltd**
13 **YOLO AGAIN (IRE)**, 5, b m Toronado (IRE)—Suite (IRE)  **Thoroughbred Homes Ltd**

## TWO-YEAR-OLDS

14 Ro c 30/04 Kodiac—Loving (Mayson) (7619)
15 B f 20/04 Galileo Gold—Windy Lane (Dubai Destination (USA)) (6667)

**Other Owners:** Mr I. Harle, Thoroughbred Homes Ltd, Mr D. Vernon, Mrs M. T. Winetroube.

**Flat Jockey:** Gemma Tutty.

## 542 MR NIGEL TWISTON-DAVIES, Cheltenham

Postal: **T/a Grange Hill Farm Limited, Grange Hill Farm, Naunton, Cheltenham, Gloucestershire, GL54 3AY**
Contacts: PHONE **01451 850278** MOBILE **07836 664440**
EMAIL **nigel@nigeltwistondavies.co.uk** WEBSITE **www.nigeltwistondavies.co.uk**

1 **AL DANCER (FR),** 8, gr g Al Namix (FR)—Steel Dancer (FR)
2 **ANOTHER FRONTIER (IRE),** 10, b g Darsi (FR)—Scent With Love (IRE)
3 **ARTHUR'S GIFT (IRE),** 10, b g Presenting—Uncertain Affair (IRE)
4 **BALLYANDY,** 10, b g Kayf Tara—Megalex
5 **BALLYBOUGH MARY (IRE),** 5, b m Shirocco (GER)—In Sync (IRE)
6 **BALLYHILL (FR),** 10, b br g Al Namix (FR)—Laly Light (FR)
7 **BALLYMILLSY,** 5, b g Lucarno (IRE)—Brackenmoss (IRE)
8 **BALLYMOY (IRE),** 8, b g Flemensfirth (USA)—John's Eliza (IRE)
9 **BALLYOPTIC (IRE),** 11, b g Old Vic—Lambourne Lace (IRE)
10 **BEAUPORT (IRE),** 5, b g Califet (FR)—Byerley Beauty (IRE)
11 **BIT ON THE SIDE (IRE),** 6, b m Presenting—Tara Rose
12 **BLENDED STEALTH,** 4, b g Walk In The Park (IRE)—Wyldello
13 **BRISTOL DE MAI (FR),** 10, gr g Saddler Maker (IRE)—La Bole Night (FR)
14 **CAFE PUSHKIN (FR),** 5, b g Montmartre (FR)—Chausey (FR)
15 **CALETT MAD (FR),** 9, b br g Axxos (GER)—Omelia (FR)
16 **CHAMPAGNE LILLY,** 8, gr m Malinas (GER)—Champagne Lil
17 **CHANCE A TUNE (IRE),** 6, b g My Risk (FR)—Lyric Melody (FR)
18 **CHECKITOUT (IRE),** 7, b g Salutino (GER)—Akasha (IRE)
19 **COGRY,** 12, b g King's Theatre (IRE)—Wyldello
20 **COUNT MERIBEL,** 9, ch g Three Valleys (USA)—Bakhtawar (IRE)
21 **CRIEVEHILL (IRE),** 9, b g Arcadio (GER)—Ma Douce (IRE)
22 **DINGHY YOUNG (IRE),** 5, br g Sholokhov (IRE)—I'm A Character
23 **DON'T SHOUT (IRE),** 7, b g Oscar (IRE)—Asta Belle (FR)
24 **DONT GO GENTLE (IRE),** 5, b g Dylan Thomas (IRE)—Caedlih Davis (FR)
25 **EARLOFTHECOTSWOLDS (FR),** 7, bl g Axxos (GER)—Sissi Land (FR)
26 **ELMDALE (FR),** 7, gr g Martaline—Victoire Jaguine (FR)
27 **EMPHATIC QUALM (IRE),** 6, b g Califet (FR)—Supreme Touch (IRE)
28 **EQUUS MILLAR (IRE),** 8, b g Masterofthehorse (IRE)—Lets Get Busy (IRE)
29 **FANTASTIKAS (FR),** 6, b g Davidoff (GER)—Negresse de Cuta (FR)
30 **FANTOMAS (FR),** 5, b g Sinndar (IRE)—Trudente (FR)
31 **FELICISSIMUS (IRE),** 6, b g Most Improved (IRE)—Cattiva Generosa
32 **FLYING ANGEL (IRE),** 10, gr g Arcadio (GER)—Gypsy Kelly (IRE)
33 **FONTANA ELLISSI (FR),** 5, b g Sinndar (IRE)—Leni Riefenstahl (IRE)
34 **GEORGE OF NAUNTON (IRE),** 6, br g Arakan (USA)—Rosee des Bieffes (FR)
35 **GINGER DU VAL (FR),** 5, b m Rail Link—Ahkel Vie (FR)
36 **GOA LIL (FR),** 5, br g Samum (GER)—Unekaina (FR)
37 **GOLD LEADER,** 7, b m Gold Well—Present Leader
38 **GOOD BOY BOBBY (IRE),** 8, b g Flemensfirth (USA)—Princess Gaia (IRE)
39 **GOWEL ROAD (IRE),** 5, b br g Flemensfirth (USA)—Hollygrove Samba (IRE)
40 **GUARD YOUR DREAMS,** 5, b g Fame And Glory—Native Sunrise (IRE)
41 **GUY (FR),** 6, ch g Getaway (GER)—Sept Verites (FR)
42 **HIGHLAND PARC (IRE),** 5, ch g Leading Light (IRE)—Back To My Place (IRE)
43 **HILL SIXTEEN,** 8, b g Court Cave (IRE)—Chasers Chic
44 **I LIKE TO MOVE IT,** 4, b g Trans Island—Nobratinetta (FR)
45 **IMPERIAL ACOLYTE,** 7, b g Kalanisi (IRE)—Isabello (IRE)
46 **IMPERIAL NEMESIS (IRE),** 8, b g Stowaway—Liss Alainn (IRE)
47 **JUST NO RISK (FR),** 5, ch g No Risk At All (FR)—Just Divine (FR)
48 **KAPGARRY (FR),** 8, b g Ballingarry (IRE)—Kaprissima (FR)
49 **KILPIN (FR),** 6, b g Milan—Come And Fight (IRE)
50 **KINGOFTHECOTSWOLDS (IRE),** 7, b g Arcadio (GER)—Damoiselle
51 **KINGSPLACE (IRE),** 9, b g Ask—Winsome Breeze (IRE)
52 **KOTKIWORK (FR),** 5, b g Network (GER)—Kotkieglote (FR)
53 **LEROY BROWN,** 6, b g Pasternak—Grenfell (IRE)
54 **LET IT LOOSE (IRE),** 5, br g Robin des Champs (FR)—Manhattan Babe (IRE)
55 **LUCKOFTHEDRAW (FR),** 8, gr g Martaline—La Perspective (FR)
56 **MACFIN (IRE),** 5, br g Dylan Thomas (IRE)—Justfour (IRE)

## MR NIGEL TWISTON-DAVIES - continued

57 **MILANSTORM (IRE)**, 8, b g Milan—Deise Rose (IRE)
58 **MONARCHOFTHEGRANGE (IRE)**, 6, ch g Imperial Monarch (IRE)—Saipan Storm (IRE)
59 **MOSSY FEN (IRE)**, 6, b g Milan—Inch Native (IRE)
60 **MUCKAMORE (IRE)**, 7, b g Sholokhov (IRE)—Gales Return (IRE)
61 **NOBLE SAVAGE (IRE)**, 6, b g Arcadio (GER)—Callerdiscallerdat (IRE)
62 **NYE BEVAN (IRE)**, 6, b g Arcadio (GER)—Emma Jane (IRE)
63 **ONCHAN (IRE)**, 6, b g Oscar (IRE)—Satellite Dancer (IRE)
64 **ONE FORTY SEVEN (IRE)**, 9, b g Beneficial—Still Bubbly (IRE)
65 **ONE TRUE KING (IRE)**, 6, ch g Getaway (GER)—Final Leave (IRE)
66 **OUR POWER (IRE)**, 6, b g Power—Scripture (IRE)
67 **POPPA POUTINE (IRE)**, 5, b g Sholokhov (IRE)—Sherchanceit (IRE)
68 **REDFORD ROAD**, 7, b g Trans Island—Maryscross (IRE)
69 **RIDERS ONTHE STORM (IRE)**, 8, br g Scorpion (IRE)—Endless Moments (IRE)
70 **RIZZARDO**, 9, gr g Tikkanen (USA)—Last Storage (USA)
71 **ROBINSHILL (IRE)**, 10, ch g Robin des Champs (FR)—I Remember It Well (IRE)
72 **ROCCO (IRE)**, 8, b g Shantou (USA)—Navaro (IRE)
73 **ROCKINGHAM SOUTH**, 5, b g Kayf Tara—Safari Run (IRE)
74 **SEASON IN THE SUN**, 4, b g Blue Bresil (FR)—Kentford Dabchick
75 **SIR VALENTINE (GER)**, 8, b g Cacique (GER)—Singuna (GER)
76 **STOLEN SILVER (FR)**, 6, gr g Lord du Sud (FR)—Change Partner (FR)
77 **SUMMIT LIKE HERBIE**, 9, ch g Sulamani (IRE)—Colline de Fleurs
78 **SUPAKALANISTIC (IRE)**, 8, b g Kalanisi (IRE)—Keys Hope (IRE)
79 **SUPER SIX**, 4, b gr g Montmartre (FR)—Hiho Silver Lining
80 **TEMPLEHILLS (IRE)**, 10, b br g Kalanisi (IRE)—Sissinghurst Storm (IRE)
81 **THE HOLLOW GINGE (IRE)**, 8, b g Oscar (IRE)—Some Gem (IRE)
82 **THE MICK PRESTON (IRE)**, 5, gr g Shirocco (GER)—Izzy du Berlais (IRE)
83 **THE NEWEST ONE (IRE)**, 6, b g Oscar (IRE)—Thuringe (FR)
84 **TIP TOP CAT (IRE)**, 6, b g Milan—Pilgara (IRE)
85 **TOOK THE LOT**, 7, b g Black Sam Bellamy (IRE)—Riverbank Rainbow
86 **TOP OF THE BILL (IRE)**, 5, b g Fame And Glory—Glory Days (GER)
87 **TOPOFTHECOTSWOLDS (IRE)**, 7, b g Arcadio (GER)—Bambootcha (IRE)
88 **TORN AND FRAYED (FR)**, 7, b g Califet (FR)—Chic Et Zen (FR)
89 **TOWNSHEND (GER)**, 10, b g Lord of England (GER)—Trikolore (GER)
90 **TWO TAFFS (IRE)**, 11, b g Flemensfirth (USA)—Richs Mermaid (IRE)
91 **UNDERSUPERVISION (IRE)**, 5, ch g Doyen (IRE)—Dances With Waves (IRE)
92 **VIENNA COURT (IRE)**, 6, br m Mahler—Gales Present (IRE)
93 **WICKED WILLY (IRE)**, 10, br g Arcadio (GER)—How Provincial (IRE)
94 **YAAZAAIN**, 5, b g Iffraaj—Tamazirte (IRE)
95 **ZAMBELLA (FR)**, 6, b m Zambezi Sun—Visby (FR)

## THREE-YEAR-OLDS

96 **BULLET TOOTH TONY (IRE)**, b g Starspangledbanner (AUS)—Mary's Daughter

**Owners:** Arthur's Gift Partnership, Mr M. L. Berryman, Bryan & Philippa Burrough, B. R. H. Burrough, Mrs P. J. Burrough, Mrs J. Carter, Mr & Mrs P Carter, Mr P. A. Carter, Mrs J. S. Chugg, Mr R. D. Chugg, Alan & Sally Coney, Miss S. A. Dawson, Egan Waste Services Ltd, Friends Of Herbie, Plant & Coast Haulage, Mr T. J. Hemmings, Highclere T'Bred Racing- Crievehill, Mr C. S. Hinchy, Carl Hinchy & Mark Scott, Mrs M. J. Hughes, Imperial Racing Partnership 2016, James & Jean Potter, James and Jean Potter Ltd, Mrs A. D. Jelley, G. S. Jelley, Graham & Alison Jelley, Jump For Fun Racing, Mr D. M. Mason, G. A. Mason, Ged Mason & Jim McGoff, Ms J. E. McGivern, Mr J. M. McGoff, Million in Mind Partnership, F. J. Mills, Mrs J. M. Mills, Mrs M. Mills, W. R. Mills, Mills & Mason Partnership, Mrs M Mills & Mrs J Mills, S. E. Munir, Mr Simon Munir & Mr Isaac Souede, Mr J. Neild, Noel Fehily Racing Syndicate- Muckamore, Options O Syndicate, Mr P Preston, Mr M. A. Reay, Mr R. J. Rexton, S Such & CG Paletta, Mr M. S. Scott, & Shepperd, Mrs A. Shepperd, Mr J. Shepperd, Mr I. Souede, Spiers & Hartwell Ltd, Sundorne Products (Llanidloes) Ltd, Teme Valley 2, The Champagne Party, The Ginge Army, The Preston Family Racing, The True Acre Partnership, The Wasting Assets, Mr N. A. Twiston-Davies, Twiston-Davies Equine, Twiston-Davies, Mason, Greer & Kiely, Verdansk Racing, The Hon A. G. Vestey, The Hon W. G. Vestey, The Hons W. G. & A. G. Vestey, C. C. Walker, Walters Plant Hire & Potter Group, Walters Plant Hire Ltd, Walters Plant,Spiers&hartwell,Egan Waste, J. Wenman, Jimmy & Susie Wenman, Mrs S. Wenman, West Coast Haulage Limited.

**NH Jockey:** Jamie Bargary, Tom Bellamy, Sam Twiston-Davies. **Conditional Jockey:** Jordan Nailor.

**543** **MR JAMES UNETT, Wolverhampton**
Postal: **1 Dunstall Mews, Gorsebrook Road, Wolverhampton, West Midlands, WV6 0PE**
Contacts: **PHONE 01691 610001 MOBILE 07887 534753 FAX 01691 610001**
**EMAIL jamesunett1327@yahoo.co.uk WEBSITE www.jamesunettracing.com**

1  CITTA D'ORO, 6, b g Cityscape—Corsa All Oro (USA) **P. S. Burke**
2  EBQAA (IRE), 7, b m Cape Cross (IRE)—Estedaama (IRE) **J. W. Unett**
3  POPE GREGORY, 4, gr g Gregorian (IRE)—La Gifted **J. W. Unett**
4  SCAPALLORO, 4, b f Cityscape—Corsa All Oro (USA) **P. S. Burke**
5  TOM TULLIVER, 4, b g Hot Streak (IRE)—Belle Isle **Mr F. Gillespie**

## THREE-YEAR-OLDS
6  SENORITA EVA ROSE (IRE), b f Clodovil (IRE)—Spark Up **M. Watkinson & Partner**

Other Owners: J. W. Unett, Mr M. Watkinson.

Assistant Trainer: Miss C. H. Jones.

**544** **MR MARK USHER, Lambourn**
Postal: **Rowdown House Stables, Upper Lambourn, Hungerford, Berkshire, RG17 8QP**
Contacts: **PHONE 01488 73630, 01488 72598 MOBILE 07831 873531**
**EMAIL markusher.racing@btconnect.com WEBSITE www.markusherracing.co.uk**

1  ARLECCHINO'S ARC (IRE), 6, ch g Arcano (IRE)—Sir Cecil's Girl (IRE)
2  BAGATELLE, 4, ch f Kendargent (FR)—Blushing Beauty
3  BAYSTON HILL, 7, br g Big Bad Bob (IRE)—Jessica Ennis (USA)
4  BIRD FOR LIFE, 7, b m Delegator—Birdolini
5  BIRD TO LOVE, 7, b m Delegator—Bird Over
6  BORN TO PLEASE, 7, b m Stimulation (IRE)—Heart Felt
7  DREAMBOAT ANNIE, 6, b m Piccolo—Bold Rose
8  DYLAN'S SEA SONG, 7, b m Dylan Thomas (IRE)—Mary Sea (FR)
9  EVAPORUST (IRE), 4, b g Gale Force Ten—Bigalo's Laura B (IRE)
10  MISU PETE, 9, b g Misu Bond (IRE)—Smart Ass (IRE)
11  ON THE RIGHT TRACK, 4, gr g Mukhadram—Jessica Ennis (USA)
12  THORNDALE, 6, b m Multiplex—Oscar's Lady (IRE)
13  TIMEFORASPIN, 7, b g Librettist (USA)—Timeforagin
14  TIN FANDANGO, 6, b g Steele Tango (USA)—Littlemoor Lass
15  WAQAAS, 7, b g Showcasing—Red Mischief (IRE)
16  WILLINGLY, 4, ch f Hot Streak (IRE)—Paradise Place

## THREE-YEAR-OLDS
17  BLUE GALAXY, gr g Telescope (IRE)—Indigo
18  LIBERTY BAY, b f Iffraaj—Light Fantastic
19  PERTHSHIRE (IRE), b g Gleneagles (IRE)—Destalink
20  SKIBBEREEN, b g Harbour Watch (IRE)—Fruit Pastille
21  SPIRIT OF ROWDOWN, b g Charm Spirit (IRE)—Columella
22  THE BAY WARRIOR (IRE), b g The Gurkha (IRE)—Fraulein

## TWO-YEAR-OLDS
23  ADAAYINOURLIFE, b c 17/04 Adaay (IRE)—Sans Reward (IRE) (Barathea (IRE)) (40000)
24  ARLECCHINO'S GIFT, b c 04/02 Shalaa (IRE)—Represent (IRE) (Exceed And Excel (AUS)) (28000)
25  PICOTA, b c 07/02 Havana Gold (IRE)—Break Time (Dansili) (20000)

## MR MARK USHER - continued

**Owners:** Mr P. Brett, Champagne And Shambles, Mrs T. J. Channing-Williams, Mr A. Cova, Andy & Lizzie Cova, Mrs E. Cova, Mr D. P. Duffy, GAF Racing, Gaf Racing & Partner, Goodracing Partnership, Miss S. R. Haynes, High Five Racing, High Five Racing and Partners, Mr P. Hobbs, Mr M. A. Humphreys, Miss J. Hynes, Jacintha Hynes & Lee Thompson, Mr N. P. McEntyre, Mr R. C. Penney & Partner, PDuffyD.SemmensVWilliamsRHarperMLoveday, Mr R. C. Penney, Ms D. M. Ray, Mr B. C. Rogan, Rowdown Racing Partnership, Mr D. M. Semmens, Mr K. Senior, The Mark Usher Racing Club, The Unraceables, Mr L. Thompson, Mr M. D. I. Usher, Ushers Court.

**Assistant Trainer:** Michael Usher.

---

## 545 MR ROGER VARIAN, Newmarket
Postal: **Carlburg Stables, 49 Bury Road, Newmarket, Suffolk, CB8 7BY**
Contacts: **PHONE 01638 661702 FAX 01638 667018**
**EMAIL office@varianstable.com WEBSITE www.varianstable.com**

1 **AFFWONN (IRE)**, 4, b c Free Eagle (IRE)—Shauna's Princess (IRE) **Sheikh Ahmed Al Maktoum**
2 **ANGEL POWER**, 4, gr f Lope de Vega (IRE)—Burning Rules (IRE) **King Power Racing Co Ltd**
3 **APPARATE**, 5, b h Dubawi (IRE)—Appearance **Sheikh Mohammed Obaid Al Maktoum**
4 **ASCENSION**, 4, gr g Dark Angel (IRE)—Making Eyes (IRE)
5 **AUSTRALIS (IRE)**, 5, b g Australia—Quiet Down (USA) **Biddestone Racing XX**
6 **BELIEVE IN LOVE (IRE)**, 4, b f Make Believe—Topka (FR) **Mr K. Maeda**
7 **CABALETTA**, 4, gr f Mastercraftsman (IRE)—Allegretto (IRE) **Cheveley Park Stud Limited**
8 **CAPE BYRON**, 7, ch g Shamardal (USA)—Reem Three **Sheikh Mohammed Obaid Al Maktoum**
9 **DUBLIN PHARAOH (USA)**, 4, ch g American Pharoah (USA)—Wile Cat (USA) **Mr D. Brennan**
10 **FATHER OF JAZZ**, 4, b c Kingman—Bark (IRE) **W. J. and T. C. O. Gredley**
11 **FOORAAT (IRE)**, 4, b f Dubawi (IRE)—Nahrain **Sheikh Ahmed Al Maktoum**
12 **FUJAIRA PRINCE (IRE)**, 7, gr ro g Pivotal—Zam Zoom (IRE) **Sheikh Mohammed Obaid Al Maktoum**
13 **GOLD MAZE**, 4, b c Golden Horn—Astonishing (IRE) **Teme Valley 2**
14 **JUMAIRA BAY (FR)**, 4, b g Siyouni (FR)—Desert Sunrise **A & R Al Kamda**
15 **KHALOOSY (IRE)**, 4, gr g Dubawi (IRE)—Elshaadin **Hamdan bin Rashid Al Maktoum**
16 **KHUZAAM (USA)**, 5, ch g Kitten's Joy (USA)—Afraah (USA) **Hamdan bin Rashid Al Maktoum**
17 **LORD CAMPARI (IRE)**, 4, b c Kingman—Blanche Dubawi (IRE) **Sheikh Mohammed Obaid Al Maktoum**
18 **LYDFORD**, 4, b c Fastnet Rock (AUS)—Miss Brown To You (IRE) **W. J. and T. C. O. Gredley**
19 **MOLATHAM**, 4, ch c Night of Thunder (IRE)—Cantal **Hamdan bin Rashid Al Maktoum**
20 **MONTATHER (IRE)**, 4, ch g Dubawi (IRE)—Lanansaak (IRE) **Hamdan bin Rashid Al Maktoum**
21 **MORROOJ (IRE)**, 4, b f Invincible Spirit (IRE)—Alwarqa (USA) **Sheikh Ahmed Al Maktoum**
22 **MUSICALITY**, 4, b g Kyllachy—Allegro Viva (USA) **Biddestone Racing XIII**
23 **PIERRE LAPIN (IRE)**, 4, b g Cappella Sansevero—Beatrix Potter (IRE) **Sheikh Mohammed Obaid Al Maktoum**
24 **POSTILEO (IRE)**, 4, b c Galileo (IRE)—Posterity (IRE) **Sheikh Mohammed Obaid Al Maktoum**
25 **PREMIER POWER**, 4, ch c Siyouni (FR)—Pelerin (IRE) **King Power Racing Co Ltd**
26 **PRINCE EIJI**, 5, ch g Dubawi (IRE)—Izzi Top **Sheikh Mohammed Obaid Al Maktoum**
27 **QUEEN DAENERYS (IRE)**, 4, b f Frankel—Song to Remember (IRE) **H.H. Sheikh Nasser Al Khalifa**
28 **ROSEMAN (IRE)**, 5, b h Kingman—Go Lovely Rose (IRE) **Sheikh Mohammed Obaid Al Maktoum**
29 **SAN DONATO (IRE)**, 5, b h Lope de Vega (IRE)—Boston Rocker (IRE) **Sheikh Mohammed Obaid Al Maktoum**
30 **SEPTEMBER POWER (IRE)**, 4, b f Mastercraftsman (IRE)—Lisanor **King Power Racing Co Ltd**
31 **SEVEN POCKETS (IRE)**, 4, b c Frankel—Vodka (JPN) **Mrs H. Varian**
32 **SHANDOZ**, 4, b c Golden Horn—Shabyt **N. Bizakov**
33 **SPANISH CITY**, 8, ch g Exceed And Excel (AUS)—Annabelle's Charm (IRE) **Merry Fox Stud Limited**
34 **STYLISTIQUE**, 4, b f Dansili—Sleek **Miss Y. M. G. Jacquis**
35 **TAMMOOZ**, 5, b g Lawman (FR)—La Concorde (IRE) **Sheikh Ahmed Al Maktoum**
36 **TINKER TOY**, 4, b c War Front (USA)—Cursory Glance (USA) **Merry Fox Stud Limited**
37 **TROLL PENINSULA (IRE)**, 4, b g Karakontie (JPN)—Perfect Step (USA) **Flaxman Stables Ireland Ltd**
38 **VALYRIAN STEEL (IRE)**, 4, b c Frankel—Sabratah **H.H. Sheikh Nasser Al Khalifa**
39 **WALIYAK (FR)**, 4, br f Le Havre (IRE)—Vadariya **Mr F. A. A. Nass**
40 **ZEEBAND (IRE)**, 4, b g Sea The Stars (IRE)—Zeeba (IRE) **Sheikh Mohammed Obaid Al Maktoum**

# MR ROGER VARIAN - continued

## THREE-YEAR-OLDS

41 **ALBANMAN (IRE)**, b g Lawman (FR)—Albanka (USA) **N. Bizakov**
42 **ALEXI BOY**, b c Kingman—Putyball (USA) **Amo Racing Limited**
43 **ALFAADHEL (IRE)**, ch c Night of Thunder (IRE)—Divisimo **Hamdan bin Rashid Al Maktoum**
44 **ALHEZABR (IRE)**, b g Raven's Pass (USA)—Petit Calva (FR) **A & R Al Kamda**
45 **AQUAMAN (IRE)**, b c Kodiac—Aqualis **Sheikh Mohammed Obaid Al Maktoum**
46 **AQWAAM**, gr g Sea The Stars (IRE)—Aghaany **Hamdan bin Rashid Al Maktoum**
47 **ARION FOX**, b f Kingman—Rive Gauche **King Power Racing Co Ltd**
48 **ASJAD**, b g Iffraaj—Riskit Fora Biskit (IRE) **Hamdan bin Rashid Al Maktoum**
49 **ATHERS (IRE)**, ch g Dubawi (IRE)—Kelly Nicole (IRE) **Sheikh Mohammed Obaid Al Maktoum**
50 **BARADAR (IRE)**, b br c Muhaarar—Go Lovely Rose (IRE) **Amo Racing Limited**
51 **BASHOSH**, ch c Dubawi (IRE)—Ferdoos **Sheikh Ahmed Al Maktoum**
52 **BATRAAN (IRE)**, ch c Camacho—Testimony **Sheikh Ahmed Al Maktoum**
53 **BEAU JARDINE (IRE)**, b c Make Believe—Akira (IRE) **Opulence Thoroughbreds**
54 **BILHAYL (IRE)**, ch c Shamardal (USA)—Soraaya (IRE) **Sheikh Ahmed Al Maktoum**
55 **BOOMSHALAA**, b c Shalaa (IRE)—Summer Collection (IRE) **Sheikh Mohammed Obaid Al Maktoum**
56 **CHEEKY AZ**, b c Teofilo (IRE)—Azma (USA) **Promenade Bloodstock Limited**
57 **DARK LION (IRE)**, b g Dark Angel (IRE)—Graciously **H.H. Shaikh Nasser Al Khalifa & Partner**
58 **DIAVOLO (IRE)**, b c Dubawi (IRE)—Sultanina **Normandie Stud Ltd**
59 **DINOO (IRE)**, b c Starspangledbanner (AUS)—Sultanina **Mr D. Vakilgilani**
60 **DUBAWI SANDS**, ch c Dubawi (IRE)—Galicuix **Sheikh Mohammed Obaid Al Maktoum**
61 **DUSKY LORD**, b c Twilight Son—Petit Trianon **The Dusky Lord Partnership**
62 **EL DRAMA (IRE)**, ch c Lope de Vega (IRE)—Victoire Finale **Sheikh Mohammed Obaid Al Maktoum**
63 **ELEGANT QUEEN**, b f Bated Breath—Princess Pearl (IRE) **Z. A. Galadari**
64 **ENSEMBLE (IRE)**, b f Nayef (USA)—Alqubbah (IRE) **Clipper Group Holdings Ltd**
65 **ERTIKAAZ (IRE)**, b g Cable Bay (IRE)—Ballet Move **Hamdan bin Rashid Al Maktoum**
66 **ESHAADA**, b f Muhaarar—Muhawalah (IRE) **Hamdan bin Rashid Al Maktoum**
67 **EXPECT TO SUCCEED (IRE)**, b g Exceed And Excel (AUS)—Gwael (USA) **Teme Valley 2**
68 **EXUDING**, b f Showcasing—Exceptionelle **D. J. Deer**
69 **FAMILLE ROSE (FR)**, b f Shalaa (IRE)—Sarlisa (FR) **Varian Racing II**
70 **FANTASTIC FOX**, ch c Frankel—Vasilia **King Power Racing Co Ltd**
71 **FIFTYSHADESOFRED (FR)**, b c Siyouni (FR)—Candinie (USA) **H.H. Shaikh Nasser Al Khalifa & Partner**
72 **GEORGE BANCROFT**, ch g Australia—Extensive **W. J. and T. C. O. Gredley**
73 **GOOD MEMORIES (IRE)**, ch f Sea The Stars (IRE)—Khor Sheed **Sheikh Mohammed Obaid Al Maktoum**
74 **GREAT KING (FR)**, b c Shamardal (USA)—Darysina (USA) **Amo Racing Limited**
75 **GREATGADIAN (GER)**, b c Siyouni (FR)—Goathemala (GER) **King Power Racing Co Ltd**
76 **HAMOUDI**, b c Dark Angel (IRE)—A Huge Dream (IRE) **Sheikh Mohammed Obaid Al Maktoum**
77 **HEY MR**, b c Territories (IRE)—Filona (IRE) **Amo Racing Limited**
78 **IMPERIAL YELLOW (IRE)**, b c New Bay—Soteria (IRE) **Varian Racing III**
79 **INVINCIBLE SWAGGER (IRE)**, b c Invincible Spirit (IRE)—Los Ojitos (USA) **Mr M. Khalid Abdul Rahim**
80 **JAMMRAH**, ch f Sea The Stars (IRE)—Nahrain **Sheikh Ahmed Al Maktoum**
81 **JARAMILLO**, b c Oasis Dream—Guajara (GER) **Teme Valley 2 & Partner**
82 **JET ENGINE (IRE)**, b br g No Nay Never (USA)—Double Fantasy (GER) **Sheikh Mohammed Obaid Al Maktoum**
83 **KINDRED SPIRIT (IRE)**, b f Invincible Spirit (IRE)—Pontenuovo (FR) **Merry Fox Stud Limited**
84 **KING FRANCIS (IRE)**, b c Le Havre (IRE)—Princess Nada **Sheikh Mohammed Obaid Al Maktoum**
85 **KING TRITON (IRE)**, b c Invincible Spirit (IRE)—Nada **Sheikh Mohammed Obaid Al Maktoum**
86 **KRATOS**, ch c Equiano (FR)—Miss Rimex **Varian Racing V**
87 **LA TIHATY (IRE)**, b c New Bay—Sister Dam's (IRE) **H.H. Shaikh Nasser Al Khalifa & Partner**
88 **LADY HAYES**, br f Kodiac—Andry Brusselles **Mr G. B. Bolton**
89 Ch c Shamardal (USA)—Lady Liberty (IRE) **H.H. Shaikh Nasser Al Khalifa & Partner**
90 **LANEQASH**, b c Cable Bay (IRE)—Bonhomie **Hamdan bin Rashid Al Maktoum**
91 **LANKARAN**, gr c Kendargent (FR)—Lashyn (USA) **N. Bizakov**
92 **LEGEND OF DUBAI**, b c Dubawi (IRE)—Speedy Boarding **Sheikh Mohammed Obaid Al Maktoum**
93 **LEGION OF HONOUR**, b c Wootton Bassett—Miss Vendome (IRE) **Teme Valley 2**
94 **LINE OF DEPARTURE (IRE)**, b c Mehmas (IRE)—Entreat **H.H. Shaikh Nasser Al Khalifa & Partner**
95 **MALHOOB (USA)**, ch c Kitten's Joy (USA)—Street Interest (USA) **Hamdan bin Rashid Al Maktoum**
96 **MASHKOORAH (IRE)**, b f Zoffany (IRE)—Week End **Mr M. Almarzooqi**
97 **MILITARY MAN**, ch g Gleneagles (IRE)—Blue Butterfly **Mr P. D. Smith**
98 **MOBADRA**, b f Oasis Dream—Longing To Dance **Sheikh Ahmed Al Maktoum**

## MR ROGER VARIAN - continued

  99 **MORAAHEQ (USA),** b c Speightstown (USA)—Takrees (USA) **Hamdan bin Rashid Al Maktoum**
100 **MOSHAAWER,** gr c Frankel—Hadaatha (IRE) **Hamdan bin Rashid Al Maktoum**
101 **MOVIN TIME,** b c Fastnet Rock (AUS)—Time On **Sheikh Mohammed Obaid Al Maktoum**
102 **MS GANDHI (IRE),** b f Kingman—Dress Rehearsal (IRE) **Mr H. A. Lootah**
103 **MULBERRY SILK,** ch f Al Kazeem—Poplin **D. J. Deer**
104 **MUSHIRIF (IRE),** b c Belardo (IRE)—Albemarle **Mr M. Almarzooqi**
105 **MUTABAADAL,** b g Mukhadram—Markabah (IRE) **Hamdan bin Rashid Al Maktoum**
106 **MUTAHAMISA (IRE),** ch f Mehmas (IRE)—Il Palazzo (USA) **Mr M. Almarzooqi**
107 **MYSTICAL AIR,** b f Kingman—Dark Promise **Lordship Stud**
108 **NAGANO,** b g Fastnet Rock (AUS)—Nazym (IRE) **N. Bizakov**
109 **NAZUNA (IRE),** b f Kodiac—Night Fever (IRE) **Mrs H. Varian**
110 **NINE TALES (IRE),** b c Kingman—Sotka **King Power Racing Co Ltd**
111 **NIZAAKA (FR),** b f New Bay—Dusky Queen (IRE) **Mr M. Al-Qatami & Mr K. M. Al-Mudhaf**
112 **ON MY WAY,** b f Oasis Dream—Zamoura **D. J. Deer**
113 **PAPACITO (IRE),** br c Estidhkaar (IRE)—Out of Time (IRE) **Sheikh Mohammed Obaid Al Maktoum**
114 **PAQUITA (FR),** b f Raven's Pass (USA)—Muwalaah (USA) **Mrs H. Varian**
115 **POSITANO,** b f War Front (USA)—Perihelion (IRE) **George Bolton & W S Farish**
116 **PRAIANO (GER),** b c Dubawi (IRE)—Praia (GER) **Sheikh Mohammed Obaid Al Maktoum**
117 **PUY MARY,** ch f Intello (GER)—Cantal **Cheveley Park Stud Limited**
118 **QUICK APPROACH,** ch f New Approach (IRE)—Gee Kel (USA) **Sheikh J. D. Al Maktoum**
119 **RAADOBARG (IRE),** b c Night of Thunder (IRE)—Queen Bodicea (IRE) **Amo Racing Limited**
120 **REACT,** b g Dark Angel (IRE)—Facade (IRE) **A D Spence & John Connolly**
121 **ROLLING DEEP,** b br f Kingman—Ellbeedee (IRE) **Mr I. Alsagar**
122 **ROYAL CHAMPION (IRE),** b c Shamardal (USA)—Emirates Queen **Sheikh Mohammed Obaid Al Maktoum**
123 **RUMAYTHAH (IRE),** b f Kodiac—Compostela **H.H. Shaikh Nasser Al Khalifa & Partner**
124 **SAINT LAWRENCE (IRE),** b c Al Kazeem—Affluent **D. J. Deer**
125 **SAMMARR,** b f Golden Horn—Ta Ammol **Sheikh Ahmed Al Maktoum**
126 **SAVE A FOREST (IRE),** b f Kingman—Bark (IRE) **W. J. and T. C. O. Gredley**
127 **SHABANDOZ,** b c Wootton Bassett—Shabyt **N. Bizakov**
128 **SHE DO,** b f Siyouni (FR)—Minnaloushe (IRE) **W. J. and T. C. O. Gredley**
129 **STRAWBERRI,** ch f Gleneagles (IRE)—Altesse Imperiale (IRE) **D. J. Deer**
130 **TEONA (IRE),** b f Sea The Stars (IRE)—Ambivalent (IRE) **A. Saeed**
131 **THIRD REALM,** b c Sea The Stars (IRE)—Reem Three **Sheikh Mohammed Obaid Al Maktoum**
132 **THREE PLATOON,** b c Kingman—Brevity (USA) **H.H. Sheikh Nasser Al Khalifa**
133 **THUNDER POWER (IRE),** ch c Night of Thunder (IRE)—Paris To Peking (ITY) **Mr M. Saeed**
134 **TIMELESS SOUL (GER),** ch f Night of Thunder (IRE)—Tatienne (IRE) **Mr M. Almarzooqi**
135 **TITLE (IRE),** b c Camelot—Danehill's Dream (IRE) **Highclere Tbred Racing-Charles Church**
136 **TONY MONTANA,** gr c Frankel—Tropical Paradise (IRE) **Amo Racing Limited**
137 **TOTALLY HIP HOP,** b f Pivotal—Hippy Hippy Shake **Helena Springfield Ltd**
138 **TYRRHENIAN SEA (IRE),** gr c Dark Angel (IRE)—Nocturne (GER) **Flaxman Stables Ireland Ltd**
139 **UNDER THE TWILIGHT,** b f Twilight Son—Rococoa (IRE) **Elaine Chivers Racing**
140 **WALDLOWE,** b c Le Havre (IRE)—Waldnah (IRE) **Newsells Park Stud Limited**
141 B f Lope de Vega (IRE)—Wonderfully (IRE) **Ballylinch Stud**
142 **ZAAJEL,** gr f Awtaad (IRE)—Elshaadin **Hamdan bin Rashid Al Maktoum**
143 **ZAAJIRAH (IRE),** b f Shamardal (USA)—Lanansaak (IRE) **Hamdan bin Rashid Al Maktoum**
144 **ZABEEL QUEEN (IRE),** b f Frankel—Dubai Queen (USA) **Sheikh Mohammed Obaid Al Maktoum**
145 **ZEYAADAH (IRE),** ch f Tamayuz—Masaafat **Hamdan bin Rashid Al Maktoum**
146 **ZOOMA,** b f Exceed And Excel (AUS)—Monzza **Helena Springfield Ltd**

## TWO-YEAR-OLDS

147 **AKHU NAJLA,** b c 20/04 Kingman—Galicuix (Galileo (IRE)) (2700000) **KHK Racing Ltd**
148 B f 22/03 Lope de Vega (IRE)—Ambassadrice (Oasis Dream) (92000) **Opulence Thoroughbreds**
149 B f 22/04 Fast Company (IRE)—Annee Lumiere (IRE) (Giant's Causeway (USA)) (38095)
150 B c 16/02 Frankel—Aris (IRE) (Danroad (AUS)) (360000) **Sheikh Mohammed Obaid Al Maktoum**
151 B f 10/04 Zoffany (IRE)—Athreyaa (Singspiel (IRE)) (60000) **Mr F. A. Al Harthi**
152 **AUSTRALIAN HARBOUR,** b c 08/03 Australia—Cashla Bay (Fastnet Rock (AUS)) (40000) **Z. A. Galadari**
153 B c 12/04 No Nay Never (USA)—Azenzar (Danehill Dancer (IRE)) (85000) **Mr I. Alsagar**
154 B c 01/03 Acclamation—Balayage (IRE) (Invincible Spirit (IRE)) (90476) **Promenade Bloodstock Limited**
155 B f 19/02 Lope de Vega (IRE)—Blending (Medicean) (85714) **Toudo LLC**

## MR ROGER VARIAN - continued

**156 BOLD RIBB,** b c 15/04 Ribchester (IRE)—Bold Bidder (Indesatchel (IRE)) (78095)  **Teme Valley 2**
**157 BROADSPEAR,** b c 29/03 Le Havre (IRE)—
Flower of Life (IRE) (Galileo (IRE)) (105000)  **Highclere T'Bred Racing - Broadspear**
**158 CLAIM THE CROWN (IRE),** b c 01/03 Acclamation—Crown Light (Zamindar (USA)) (109524)  **Teme Valley 2**
**159** B f 07/04 New Approach (IRE)—Craighall (Dubawi (IRE)) (80000)  **Hamdan bin Rashid Al Maktoum**
**160 CROACHILL (IRE),** b f 16/02 Churchill (IRE)—Cronsa (GER) (Martino Alonso (IRE)) (96852)  **Mr M. Saeed**
**161 DEFERRED,** ch c 11/03 Postponed (IRE)—Platinum Pearl (Shamardal (USA))  **Z. A. Galadari**
**162 DEVOTED POET,** b c 31/03 Iffraaj—Devotion (IRE) (Dylan Thomas (IRE)) (65000)  **Teme Valley 2 & Partner**
**163** Ch f 17/04 Australia—Elektra Street (Exceed And Excel (AUS)) (66667)  **Opulence Thoroughbreds**
**164 EYDON (IRE),** b c 26/03 Olden Times—Moon Mountain (Frankel)  **Prince A. A. Faisal**
**165** B c 09/02 Holy Roman Emperor (IRE)—Fire Heroine (USA) (Pivotal) (235000)  **King Power Racing Co Ltd**
**166** B c 12/03 Holy Roman Emperor (IRE)—Fiuise (IRE) (Montjeu (IRE)) (50000)  **Opulence Thoroughbreds**
**167 FLAG OF TRUTH (FR),** b c 19/01 Starspangledbanner (AUS)—
Dalakania (IRE) (Dalakhani (IRE)) (161905)  **Teme Valley 2**
**168** B c 09/03 Dark Angel (IRE)—Golden Rosie (IRE) (Exceed And Excel (AUS)) (260000)  **King Power Racing Co Ltd**
**169** B c 23/03 Galileo (IRE)—Homecoming Queen (IRE) (Holy Roman Emperor (IRE))
**170 INDEMNIFY,** gr c 18/02 Lope de Vega (IRE)—Karisma (IRE) (Lawman (FR))  **Miss Y. M. G. Jacques**
**171 IRISH FLAME,** b c 06/02 Dark Angel (IRE)—Dream of Tara (IRE) (Invincible Spirit (IRE)) (95238)  **Teme Valley 2**
**172 KIND GESTURE,** ch f 14/02 Decorated Knight—Dawn of Hope (IRE) (Mastercraftsman (IRE))  **Prince A. A. Faisal**
**173 KINGMAX (IRE),** b c 13/03 Kingman—Baino Hope (FR) (Jeremy (USA)) (114286)  **Amo Racing Limited**
**174 KODIAC BLUE,** b c 30/01 Kodiac—Grande Bleue (IRE) (Oasis Dream) (66667)  **Brightwalton Bloodstock Two**
**175** B c 04/04 Ribchester (IRE)—Malaspina (IRE) (Whipper (USA)) (70000)  **Amo Racing Limited**
**176** B c 20/03 Showcasing—Mathool (IRE) (Alhaarth (IRE)) (150000)  **Sheikh Mohammed Obaid Al Maktoum**
**177 MEDRARA,** b c 24/02 Lope de Vega (IRE)—Moderah (Makfi) (100000)  **Z. A. Galadari**
**178** B f 22/02 Kingman—Miss Katie Mae (IRE) (Dark Angel (IRE))
**179** B f 22/02 Shamardal (USA)—Nada (Teofilo (IRE))  **Sheikh Mohammed Obaid Al Maktoum**
**180** B c 09/03 Postponed (IRE)—Nargys (IRE) (Lawman (FR))  **Sheikh Mohammed Obaid Al Maktoum**
**181 NEGLIGENT,** b f 21/03 Kodiac—Orpha (New Approach (IRE))  **Prince A. A. Faisal**
**182** Ch c 01/03 Almanzor (FR)—Nehalennia (USA) (Giant's Causeway (USA)) (210000)  **King Power Racing Co Ltd**
**183** Gr f 26/02 Dark Angel (IRE)—Night Fever (IRE) (Galileo (IRE)) (142857)
**184** Br f 16/03 Oasis Dream—Princess de Lune (IRE) (Shamardal (USA)) (428571)  **Hamdan bin Rashid Al Maktoum**
**185** B c 09/02 Starspangledbanner (AUS)—Princess Desire (IRE) (Danehill (USA)) (200000)
**186** Ch c 30/01 American Pharoah (USA)—Sea of Snow (USA) (Distorted Humor (USA)) (258273)  **KHK Racing Ltd**
**187** B f 26/03 Divine Prophet (AUS)—Simsimah (IRE) (Poet's Voice)  **Mrs S. Yoshimura**
**188 SOLAR ORBITER (IRE),** b c 10/03 Showcasing—
Heliosphere (USA) (Medaglia d'Oro (USA))  **Flaxman Stables Ireland Ltd**
**189** Ch f 12/04 Dubawi (IRE)—Starlet's Sister (IRE) (Galileo (IRE)) (2017756)
**190** B c 04/05 Sea The Stars (IRE)—Suba (USA) (Seeking The Gold (USA))  **Sheikh Mohammed Obaid Al Maktoum**
**191** B c 29/03 Kodiac—Swiss Diva (Pivotal) (100000)  **Lordship Stud**
**192 TOOPHAN (IRE),** ch c 08/04 New Approach (IRE)—
Maoineach (USA) (Congaree (USA)) (180952)  **Amo Racing Limited**
**193** B c 01/02 Bated Breath—Tremelo Pointe (IRE) (Trempolino (USA)) (290000)  **Sheikh Ahmed Al Maktoum**
**194** Ch c 05/04 Cotai Glory—Triggers Broom (IRE) (Arcano (IRE)) (180000)  **King Power Racing Co Ltd**
**195** B c 13/03 Galileo (USA)—Weekend Strike (USA) (Smart Strike (CAN))
**196** B c 26/01 Muhaarar—Wowcha (IRE) (Zoffany (IRE)) (62000)  **Mr M. Khalid Abdul Rahim**
**197** B c 01/05 Profitable (IRE)—Wrood (USA) (Invasor (ARG)) (47619)

**Other Owners:** Mr A. Al Kamda, Mr R. Al Kamda, H.H. Sheikh Nasser Al Khalifa, K. M. Al-Mudhaf, Mohammed Jasem Al-Qatami, Mrs J. A. Allen, Ballylinch Stud, Mr J. Barnett, R. Barnett, Mr G. B. Bolton, Brightwalton Bloodstock Limited, Miss C. I. Chivers, Ms E. C. Chivers, Ms L. D. Chivers, Mr M. J. S. Cockburn, J. P. Connolly, Mr W. S. Farish, Mrs E. A. Harris, T. F. Harris, Mr G. Moss, Mr F. A. A. Nass, Mr Alan Spence, Teme Valley 2, Mrs H. Varian.

**Assistant Trainer:** John O'Donoghue, **Racing Secretary:** Jim Hiner.

**Flat Jockey:** Andrea Atzeni, David Egan, Jack Mitchell, Eoin Walsh.

**546**   **MR TIM VAUGHAN, Cowbridge**
Postal: Pant Wilkin Stables, Aberthin, Cowbridge, CF71 7GX
Contacts: **PHONE** 01446 771626 **MOBILE** 07841 800081
**EMAIL** tim@timvaughanracing.com **WEBSITE** www.timvaughanracing.com

1 **ADHERENCE**, 8, b g Sir Percy—Straight Laced **The Bill & Ben Partnership**
2 **AERONISI (IRE)**, 5, b g Kalanisi (IRE)—Carrigeen Lonicera (IRE) **Aircraft Tool Hire Ltd**
3 **AKKAPENKO (FR)**, 7, b g Archipenko (USA)—Akka **The Bill & Ben Partnership**
4 **ALASKAN BOY (FR)**, 6, b g Muhtathir—Laskaline (FR) **T. E. Vaughan**
5 **BARNTOWN (IRE)**, 7, b g Jeremy (USA)—Anna's Melody (IRE) **The Pant Wilkin Partnership**
6 **BASSARABAD (FR)**, 10, b g Astarabad (USA)—Grivette (FR) **Pearn's Pharmacies Ltd**
7 **BEBRAVEFORGLORY (IRE)**, 5, b g Fame And Glory—Brave Betsy (IRE) **Aircraft Tool Hire Ltd**
8 **BELLS OF BARNACK (IRE)**, 8, b g Jeremy (USA)—Gimli's Treasure (IRE)
9 **BELLS OF PETERBORO (IRE)**, 6, gr g Carlotamix (FR)—Power of Future (GER) **Mr S. Grys & Mr M. O'Boyle**
10 **BLUNDER BUSS (IRE)**, 8, b g Court Cave (IRE)—Shantou Rose (IRE) **Kings Head Duffield Racing Partnership**
11 **BOBMAHLEY (IRE)**, 6, b g Mahler—Supreme Von Pres (IRE) **Mrs B. N. Ead**
12 **BRIAC (FR)**, 10, b g Kapgarde (FR)—Jarwin Do (FR) **Mr O. S. Harris**
13 **BRIGADE OF GUARDS (IRE)**, 7, b g Presenting—Lasado (IRE) **Lycett Racing Ltd**
14 **CAFFE MACCHIATO (IRE)**, 6, b g Fast Company (IRE)—Cappuccino (IRE) **Michael Owen Racing Club**
15 **CALARULES (IRE)**, 8, gr g Aussie Rules (USA)—Ailincala (IRE) **Oceans Racing**
16 **CAP ST VINCENT (FR)**, 8, b g Muhtathir—Criquetot (FR) **Mr B Jones & Son**
17 **CAPE ROBIN (IRE)**, 7, ch g Robin des Champs (FR)—Our Pride **Optimumracing.Co.Uk & Mr Andrew P. Bell**
18 **CAROLINE'S QUEST (IRE)**, 6, b m Beat Hollow—Tramp Stamp (IRE) **Lycett Racing Ltd**
19 **CHIMES OF DYLAN (IRE)**, 8, b g Court Cave (IRE)—What A Princess (IRE) **Oceans Racing**
20 **CHOZEN (IRE)**, 9, b g Well Chosen—Kneeland Lass (IRE) **Pearn's Pharmacies Ltd**
21 **CLEMENCIA (IRE)**, 5, b g Pour Moi (IRE)—Cleofila (IRE) **Mr D. W. Fox**
22 **CONCRETE KING (IRE)**, 7, b g Morozov (USA)—Mags Millar (IRE) **Mr O. S. Harris**
23 **CONNARD (IRE)**, 8, b g Shantou (USA)—Sparkling Sword **Pimlico Racing Partnerships I**
24 **DADSINTROUBLE (IRE)**, 11, b g Presenting—Gemini Lucy (IRE) **Mr J. P. M. Bowtell**
25 **DALAMOI (IRE)**, 4, b g Pour Moi (IRE)—Dalamine (FR) **Mrs B. N. Ead**
26 **DANBORU (IRE)**, 10, b g Brian Boru—Dandouce **Chepstow & Ffos Las Racing Club**
27 **DESIGNER DESTINY (IRE)**, 7, b m Jeremy (USA)—Gaye Steel (IRE) **T. E. Vaughan**
28 **ELECTRON BLEU (FR)**, 7, b g Saddex—Odyssee du Cellier (FR) **Mr B Jones & Son**
29 **EVA'S OSKAR (IRE)**, 7, gr g Shirocco (GER)—Sardagna (FR) **Mrs Sally & Richard Prince**
30 **FORT DENISON (IRE)**, 7, b g Galileo (IRE)—Honour Bright (IRE) **Mr L. DI Franco**
31 **FREEDELIVERY (IRE)**, 7, b g Sholokhov (IRE)—Gaye Melody (IRE) **Lycett Racing Ltd**
32 **GYLLEN (USA)**, 6, b g Medaglia d'Oro (USA)—Miss Halory (USA) **Mr D. Williams**
33 **HAWA BLADI (IRE)**, 5, ch g Sea The Stars (IRE)—Gentle On My Mind (IRE) **Pimlico Racing Partnerships I**
34 **ISLE OF ARON**, 5, gr g Kayf Tara—Maggie Aron **Oceans Racing**
35 **JEAN GENIE (FR)**, 5, gr g Turgeon (USA)—Lady Koko **Oceans Racing**
36 **JEFFERSON DAVIS (IRE)**, 8, b g Duke of Marmalade (IRE)—Samorra (IRE) **Syson & Vaughan**
37 **JEMBUG DRUMMER (IRE)**, 7, b g Jeremy (USA)—Drumbug (IRE) **Paul & Louise Bowtell**
38 **JOSEPH HOBSON (IRE)**, 6, b g Dubawi (IRE)—Profound Beauty (IRE) **The Wheatsheafs**
39 **JUDEX LEFOU (IRE)**, 6, b g Le Fou (IRE)—Knockalaghan Maid (IRE) **S. Clarke & and the Late Mr M. S. Clarke**
40 **KONIGSBERG**, 5, b g Dansili—Modesta (IRE) **Mr D. R. Passant**
41 **LANDSMAN (IRE)**, 8, b g Canford Cliffs (IRE)—Mowaadah (IRE) **Graham & Lynne Handley**
42 **LAUGHARNE**, 10, b g Authorized (IRE)—Corsican Sunset (USA) **Oceans Racing**
43 **LE MILOS**, 6, b g Shirocco (GER)—Banjaxed Girl **Bovian Racing**
44 **LEN BRENNAN (IRE)**, 8, b g Westerner—Letthedancebegin (IRE) **The Oxymorons**
45 **LET THE HEIRS WALK (IRE)**, 7, b g Vocalised (USA)—Heir Today (IRE) **Mr O. S. Harris**
46 **LOCO COCO (IRE)**, 6, br g Califet (FR)—Clondalee (IRE) **Mrs Sally & Richard Prince**
47 **LOOKSNOWTLIKEBRIAN (IRE)**, 10, b g Brian Boru—Sheebadiva (IRE) **SC Botham & RG Botham**
48 **MADERA MIST (IRE)**, 7, ch m Stowaway—Odonimee (IRE) **Paul & Louise Bowtell**
49 **MANUCCI (IRE)**, 5, b g Nathaniel (IRE)—American Spirit (IRE) **Mr O. S. Harris**
50 **MASTERDREAM (FR)**, 4, b g Sea The Stars (IRE)—Santa Christiana (FR) **Mr O. S. Harris**
51 **MICKYH (IRE)**, 5, b g Sageburg (IRE)—Anna's Melody (IRE) **Mr M. J. Hemmings**
52 **NOAHTHIRTYTWORED (IRE)**, 5, b g Court Cave (IRE)—Royale Video (FR) **Mr O. S. Harris**
53 **NORWEGIAN WOODS (IRE)**, 8, b g Arcadio (GER)—Water Ore (IRE) **David & Susan Luke & the Lucky Strats**
54 **NUMERO UNO**, 5, b g Dubawi (IRE)—Casual Look (USA) **Recommended Freight Ltd & Trade Trux**
55 **ORIENTAL CROSS (IRE)**, 8, b m Cape Cross (IRE)—Orion Girl (GER) **Mr J Durston & Mr N Harris**

# MR TIM VAUGHAN - continued

56 **OSCA LOCA (IRE)**, 8, b m Oscar (IRE)—Lohort Castle (IRE) **Paul & Louise Bowtell**
57 **PLENEY**, 7, b g Martaline—Knock Down (IRE) **Pearn's Pharmacies Ltd**
58 **POINT OF PRINCIPLE (IRE)**, 8, b g Rip Van Winkle (IRE)—L'Ancresse (IRE) **Oceans Racing**
59 **ROBINS FIELD (IRE)**, 6, b g Robin des Champs (FR)—Sweet Poli (IRE) **R. M. Kirkland**
60 **SAD EYED DYLAN (IRE)**, 8, br g Multiplex—Congressional (IRE) **S. Clarke & and the Late Mr M. S. Clarke**
61 **SILVER IN DISGUISE**, 7, gr g Sulamani (IRE)—Silver Spinner **Mr J Durston & Mr N Harris**
62 **SPECTATOR**, 10, br g Passing Glance—Averami **Pearn's Pharmacies Ltd**
63 **STICKY SITUATION (IRE)**, 10, ch g Hurricane Run (IRE)—Lightning Queen (USA) **Mr B Jones & Son**
64 **TAKE EM OUT (IRE)**, 9, b g Amadeus Wolf—Toorah Laura La (USA) **The Bill & Ben Partnership**
65 **THELIGNY (FR)**, 10, gr g Martaline—Romilly (FR) **Pearn's Pharmacies Ltd**
66 **THREE COLOURS RED (IRE)**, 9, b g Camacho—Colour's Red (IRE) **The Red Partnership**
67 **TIGHT CALL (IRE)**, 7, ch g Mahler—Victory Anthem (IRE) **ER Newnham & JD Shinton**
68 **TIMELY GIFT (IRE)**, 8, b g Presenting—Give It Time **Carl, JJ, Chris, Mike, John & Hugh**
69 **TIPPINGITUPTONANCY (IRE)**, 7, ch m Stowaway—Dyrick Daybreak (IRE) **Mr J. P. M. Bowtell**
70 **TRIANGLE ROCK (IRE)**, 8, b g Stowaway—Lucy Cooper (IRE) **Mr S. Grys & Mr M. O'Boyle**
71 **TRIXSTER (IRE)**, 8, b g Beneficial—Our Trick (IRE) **The Pant Wilkin Partnership**
72 **TWASN'T THE PLAN (IRE)**, 8, b g Presenting—Gentle Alice (IRE) **Mr B Jones & Son**
73 **VOCAL DUKE (IRE)**, 5, b g Vocalised (USA)—Heir Today (IRE)
74 **WAX AND WANE**, 6, br g Maxios—Moonavvara (IRE) **ER Newnham & JD Shinton**

**Other Owners:** Mr N. Barnett, Mr A. Bell, Mr R. G. Botham, S. C. Botham, Mr J. P. M. Bowtell, Mrs L. Bowtell, Exors of the Late Mr M. S. Clarke, Mr S. A. Clarke, Mr C. Davies, Mr J. Durston, Mr S. Grys, Mr S. Grys & Mr M. O'Boyle, Mr G. Handley, Mrs L. P. Handley, Mr N. Harris, Mr B. Jagger, Mr D. M. Jenkins, Mr B. M. Jones, Mr W. Jones, Mr T. E. Kerfoot, A. D. Lowrie, Mrs D. J. Lowrie, Mr D. A. Luke, David & Susan Luke, Mrs S. Luke, Mr E. R. Newnham, Mr M. O'Boyle, R. J. Prince, Mrs S. Prince, Recommended Freight Ltd, A. Robinson, Mr J. D. Shinton, Mr M. A. Stratford, Mr P. A. Syson, The Lucky Strats, The Select Racing Club Limited, Tradetrux Ltd, T. E. Vaughan, Mr N. D. Whitham, optimumracing.co.uk.

**Flat Jockey:** David Probert. **NH Jockey:** Alan Johns, Richard Johnson. **Conditional Jockey:** Charlie Price.

---

# MR CHRISTIAN VON DER RECKE, Weilerswist

Postal: **Rennstall Recke GmbH, Hovener Hof 1, D-53919, Weilerswist, Germany**
Contacts: **PHONE** +49 2254 845314 **FAX** +49 2254 845315
**EMAIL** recke@t-online.de **WEBSITE** www.rennstall-recke.de

1 **CASTLETROY (IRE)**, 4, b g Famous Name—Gilah (IRE) **Rennstall Recke GmbH**
2 **CHRISTOPH COLUMBUS (GER)**, 14, b g Noroit (GER)—Crying Love (GER) **Susanne Blau**
3 **FAIR HURRICANE (GER)**, 6, b g Hurricane Run (IRE)—Fair Vision (GER) **Stall Margarethe**
4 **GALWAY GIRL (GER)**, 4, b f Thewayyouare (USA)—Giralda (IRE) **Marquardt von Hodenberg**
5 **GLORY DAB (FR)**, 4, b g Zambezi Sun (GB)—Aziali (FR) **Eugen-Andreas Wahler**
6 **HEAD LAD (FR)**, 8, b br g Linda's Lad—Orabelle (FR) **Rennstall Recke GmbH**
7 **HURRICANE HERO (FR)**, 5, b g George Vancouver (USA)—Memoire (FR) **Bernd Robert Gossens**
8 **LADY JANE WILDE (IRE)**, 4, ch f Dragon Pulse (IRE)—Lastdanceforme (IRE) **BMK Racing**
9 **MAYNE (IRE)**, 5, b g Dansili—Pink Damsel (IRE) **Rennstall Recke GmbH**
10 **MELODINO (GER)**, 6, b g Dabirsim (FR)—Melody Fair (IRE) **Stall Chevalex**
11 **MONCEAU**, 5, b h Dansili—Palmette **Stall Wollin**
12 **NIPPON (IRE)**, 4, b g Dylan Thomas (IRE)—Neele (IRE) **Stall Michigan**
13 **NOTRE RULER (GER)**, 4, b g Ruler of The World (IRE)—Nordtanzerin (GER) **Red & White Racing**
14 **ORIHIME (IRE)**, 4, br f Canford Cliffs (IRE)—Rub A Dub Dub **Ulrike Alck und Heiner**
15 **PERISTERA (IRE)**, 4, ch f New Approach (IRE)—Prem Ramya (GER) **Gestut Romerhof**
16 **PETUNIE (FR)**, 4, b f Slickly (FR)—Pepples Shuffle (FR) **Stall Konigshorst**
17 **PRETTY SOLDIER (GER)**, 4, b g Soldier Hollow—Pretty Smart (GER) **Stall Tommy**
18 **REDEMPTORIST (GER)**, 6, b g Frozen Power (IRE)—Fly With Me (IRE) **Rennstall Recke GmbH**
19 **SHADOW STAR (GER)**, 4, ch c Amaron—Shadow Queen (GER) **Rennstall Recke GmbH**
20 **SHERIN (GER)**, 4, b f Adlerflug (GER)—Shahil (GER) **Gestut Haus Hahn**
21 **SIR CHANCELOT (IRE)**, 4, b g Sir Prancealot (IRE)—Hypocrisy **Stephanie Sofsky**

## MR CHRISTIAN VON DER RECKE - continued

22 **SUCCESSOR (IRE)**, 8, b g Galileo (IRE)—Dame Again (AUS) **Stall Wollin**
23 **SUNCHYME (GER)**, 4, b g Makfi—Saldentigerin (GER) **Gestut Bona**
24 **THE RIGHT CHOICE (IRE)**, 6, ch g Choisir (AUS)—Expedience (USA) **M-B-A Racing**
25 **VEXED**, 5, b g Charm Spirit (IRE)—Kite Mark **Eugen-Andreas Wahler**
26 **WELAN (GER)**, 7, b g Mamool (IRE)—Weissagung (FR) **M. Trommershausen**

### THREE-YEAR-OLDS

27 **AIDENSFIELD (GER)**, b c Guiliani (IRE)—A Night Like This **Dieter Brand**
28 **AIKIDO (GER)**, b c Nutan (IRE)—Athenry (GER) **Stall Nizza**
29 **INTERSTELLA (GER)**, b f Nutan (IRE)—Invisible Flash **Stall Nizza**
30 **LARRY LOBSTER (GER)**, ch g Lord of England (GER)—Lutindi (GER) **M-B-A Racing**
31 **LIONHEART (GER)**, b c Nutan (IRE)—Larmina (FR) **Stall Nizza**
32 **MODULATION**, b f Helmet (AUS)—Maybe Tomorrow **Mr Wilhelm Bischoff**
33 **NEWA (IRE)**, ch f Australia—Night of Magic (IRE) **Stall Nizza**
34 **NOWATLAST (GER)**, ch g Amaron—Nocturna (GER) **Gestut Am Schlossgarten**
35 **SEVEN O SEVEN (IRE)**, br g Excelebration (IRE)—Sanadaat **Stall Sternental**
36 **SMUDO (IRE)**, b g Canford Cliffs (IRE)—Sacre Fleur (IRE) **Stall Sternental**
37 **STAR IS BORN NIKA (FR)**, b f Evasive—Stars Alight (IRE) **The Persuaders**
38 **VIOLET RUN (IRE)**, b f Heeraat (IRE)—Violet Ballerina (IRE) **M-B-A Racing**

### TWO-YEAR-OLDS

39 **ARCHER (GER)**, b c 02/03 Nutan (IRE)—Amora (IRE) (High Chaparral (IRE)) **Stall Nizza**
40 **BAMBITA (IRE)**, ch f 06/04 De Treville—Bambara (High Chaparral (IRE)) **Cabkhat s.r.o.**
41 **DOROTHY (FR)**, b f 20/02 De Treville—Time Pressure (Montjeu (IRE)) **Cabkhat s.r.o.**
42 **EARLY EIGHTIES (GER)**, ch f 05/03 Recorder—Evie (FR) (King's Best (USA)) **Enno Albert**
43 **JORDAN (GER)**, ch c 28/03 Guiliani (IRE)—Juvena (GER) (Platini (GER)) **Stall Nizza**
44 **KARLITO (FR)**, b c 29/03 De Treville—Knightsbridge (BRZ) (Yagli (USA)) **Cabkhat s.r.o.**
45 **KAZAR (FR)**, b c 14/02 De Treville—Kyzim (GER) (High Chaparral (IRE)) **Cabkhat s.r.o.**
46 **LARIO (GER)**, b c 01/03 Nutan (IRE)—Larmina (FR) (Thewayyouare (USA)) **Stall Nizza**
47 **NADIM (IRE)**, b c 29/03 Highland Reel (IRE)—Nymphea (FR) (Dylan Thomas (IRE)) **Stall Nizza**
48 **SILIA (GER)**, b f 16/02 Amarillo (GER)—Saving Grace (GER) (Manduro (GER)) **Stall Nizza**
49 **SIR FILIP (GER)**, ch c 10/03 Ito (GER)—South Carolina (GER) (Kallisto (GER)) **Christin Barsig**
50 **TIRANA (GER)**, b f 28/02 Nutan (IRE)—Turmalina (GER) (Doyen (IRE)) **Stall Nizza**

---

## 548 MRS LUCY WADHAM, Newmarket
Postal: **The Trainer's House, Moulton Paddocks, Newmarket, Suffolk, CB8 7PJ**
Contacts: **PHONE 01638 662411 MOBILE 07980 545776**
**EMAIL lucy@wadhamracing.com WEBSITE www.lucywadhamracing.co.uk**

1 **ABOUND**, 4, b f Sir Percy—Atwix **The Considered Speculators**
2 **ADMIRAL BARRATRY (FR)**, 8, b g Soldier of Fortune (IRE)—Haskilclara (FR) **Forster, Pepper & Summers**
3 **BOMBYX**, 6, ch g Sir Percy—Bombazine (IRE) **The FOPS**
4 **CODE NAME LISE (IRE)**, 5, b m Fame And Glory—Firth of Five (IRE) **Ms E. L. Banks**
5 **CONNIE WILDE (IRE)**, 6, b m Oscar (IRE)—Mandys Native (IRE) **The Sanguiners**
6 **DANCE TO PARIS**, 6, b m Champs Elysees—Riabouchinska **The Calculated Speculators**
7 4, B f Pether's Moon (IRE)—Drop of Spirit (IRE) **Suiter Developments Limited**
8 **EAST END GIRL**, 4, b f Youmzain (IRE)—Bermondsey Girl **Mr & Mrs A E Pakenham & J J W Wadham**
9 **EASTER GOLD (FR)**, 7, b m Kapgarde—Une Dame d'Or (FR) **Mr J. Summers**
10 **ECLAIR DE GUYE (FR)**, 7, gr g Lord du Sud (FR)—
Jouvence de Guye (FR) **E R Wakelin, R W Hayward & J J W Wadham**
11 **FLAT WHITE (FR)**, 4, ch f Olympic Glory (IRE)—Bolivia (GER) **Mr & Mrs A. E. Pakenham**
12 **GAME ON FOR GLORY (IRE)**, 5, b m Fame And Glory—Jeunopse (IRE) **Mr J. Summers**
13 5, B m Shirocco (GER)—Gentle Alice (IRE) **Ms E. L. Banks**
14 **GIGABIT**, 4, b g Dunaden (FR)—Fashionable Gal (IRE) **Dr & Mrs Clive Layton**

## MRS LUCY WADHAM - continued

15 **HURRICANE BAY,** 5, b g Malinas (GER)—Another Storm **Mrs V. Wales**
16 **ICONIC SKY,** 8, gr m Sixties Icon—Kentucky Sky **The Sky Partnership**
17 **LITTLE LIGHT (FR),** 7, b m Walk In The Park (IRE)—Luna Rossa (IRE) **Suiter Developments Limited**
18 **MARTELLO SKY,** 5, gr m Martaline—Kentucky Sky **The Sky Partnership**
19 **MISS HERITAGE (IRE),** 7, b m Pour Moi (IRE)—Haretha (IRE) **The Miss Heritage Partnership**
20 4, B f Mount Nelson—Mistral Reine **M. A. Kemp, Mrs S. Dennis, Mr D. G. J. Reilly**
21 **MOVIE LEGEND,** 11, b g Midnight Legend—Cyd Charisse **Dale Hing & Nicole Langstaff**
22 **NORTHERN PRINCESS,** 7, b m Authorized (IRE)—Julatten (IRE) **Mr J. D. Abell**
23 **OASIS PRINCE,** 5, br g Oasis Dream—Demisemiquaver **Mr J. D. Abell**
24 **PEARLY ISLAND,** 5, b g Trans Island—Shinrock Pearl (IRE) **Mr S. C. McIntyre**
25 **POTTERS HEDGER,** 9, b g Midnight Legend—Loose Morals (IRE) **Mrs J. May**
26 **POTTERS LEGEND,** 11, b g Midnight Legend—Loose Morals (IRE) **Mrs J. May**
27 **REGARDING RUTH (IRE),** 7, b m Flemensfirth (USA)—
                                    May's June (IRE) **Suiter Developments Ltd & JJW Wadham**
28 **REVASSER (IRE),** 4, b g Ask—Open Cry (IRE) **P. H. Betts**
29 **SAMOURAI ONE (FR),** 4, gr g Montmartre (FR)—Northern Ocean (FR) **Suiter Developments Limited**
30 **SHANROE SANTOS (IRE),** 12, b g Definite Article—Jane Hall (IRE) **Mr J. Summers**
31 **SHANTUNG (IRE),** 8, ch m Shantou (USA)—Sarah's Cottage (IRE) **Mrs G J Redman & Sons of Peter Philipps**
32 **SOMEKINDOFSTAR (IRE),** 8, ch g Getaway (GER)—Katty Barry (IRE) **Mrs J. May**
33 **SORBET,** 6, b m Passing Glance—Fireburst **Mrs P. J. Toye**
34 **THE QUIET DON (IRE),** 6, b g Sholokhov—Ailincala (IRE) **Mr J. Summers**
35 **THE WHITE MOUSE (IRE),** 7, br m Stowaway—Maxwells Demon (IRE) **Ms E. L. Banks**
36 **TINY TANTRUM (IRE),** 5, b g Fame And Glory—Sara's Smile **Mr N. C. Kappler**
37 **TRINCOMALEE (IRE),** 8, b g Malinas (GER)—Royal Tango **Hot to Trot Jumping&Mrs E Gordon Lennox**
38 **WILL STING (IRE),** 6, br g Scorpion (IRE)—Undecided Hall (IRE) **The Cyclones**

### THREE-YEAR-OLDS

39 **DOUBLETHETROUBLE,** ch c Pearl Secret—Kirunavaara (IRE) **Mr R. W. Hayward**
40 **GRAYSTONE (IRE),** gr ro g Dark Angel (IRE)—Crown of Diamonds (USA) **Mr J. Summers**
41 **SIENNA BREEZE (IRE),** b f Camacho—Viking Rose (IRE) **Mr B. J. Painter**

### TWO-YEAR-OLDS

42 B f 25/02 Awtaad (IRE)—Famusa (Medicean) **Mr & Mrs A. E. Pakenham**
43 B f 04/02 Dabirsim (FR)—Pernickety (Sir Percy) **Mr & Mrs A. E. Pakenham**
44 B f 28/02 Bated Breath—Temple of Thebes (IRE) (Bahri (USA)) **Mr & Mrs A. E. Pakenham**

**Other Owners:** Mrs S. Dennis, Mr R. Forster, Mrs E. C. Gordon Lennox, D. J. Hing, Mr R. S. Hoskins, Hot To Trot Jumping, M. A. Kemp, Miss N. J. Langstaff, Mr C. A. Layton, Mrs H. M. Layton, Mistral Sam Partnership, Mr A. E. Pakenham, Mr & Mrs A. E. Pakenham, Mrs V. H. Pakenham, M. L. Pepper, Mr C. E. L. Philipps, Mr G. P. A. Philipps, Mr J. A. H. Philipps, Mrs G. J. Redman, Mr D. G. J. Reilly, Suiter Developments Limited, Mr J. Summers, J. J. W. Wadham.

**NH Jockey:** Bryony Frost. **Conditional Jockey:** Corey McGivern.

---

**549** **MISS TRACY WAGGOTT, Spennymoor**
Postal: Awakening Stables, Merrington Road, Spennymoor, County Durham, DL16 7HD
Contacts: PHONE 01388 819012 MOBILE 07979 434498
EMAIL tracywaggott@hotmail.com

1 **BILLY WEDGE,** 6, b g Arabian Gleam—Misu Billy **Mr D. Tate**
2 **CURFEWED (IRE),** 5, br g Most Improved (IRE)—Evening Sunset (GER) **Tracy Waggott & Sally Booth**
3 **FLASH POINT (IRE),** 5, ch g Iffraaj—Permission Slip (IRE) **Elsa Crankshaw Gordon Allan**
4 **GHATHANFAR (IRE),** 5, br g Invincible Spirit (IRE)—Cuis Ghaire (IRE) **Mr W. J. Laws**
5 **GOOD NIGHT MR TOM (IRE),** 4, b g Tagula (IRE)—Babylonian **Miss T. Waggott**
6 **GREY MIST,** 7, gr g Mastercraftsman (IRE)—Kekova **Miss S. A. Booth**
7 **HAJEY,** 4, ch g Raven's Pass (USA)—Almashooqa (USA) **Tracy Waggott & Sally Booth**

## MISS TRACY WAGGOTT - continued

    8 **HENLEY**, 9, b g Royal Applause—Making Waves (IRE)  **Miss T. Waggott**
    9 **INTRINSIC BOND**, 4, b g Intrinsic—Misu Billy  **Mr D. Tate**
   10 **KIND REVIEW**, 5, b g Kodiac—Melodique (FR)  **Elsa Crankshaw Gordon Allan**
   11 **PROCEEDING**, 6, b g Acclamation—Map of Heaven  **Mr D. Tate**
   12 **SPIRIT OF SAHARA (IRE)**, 4, b g Invincible Spirit (IRE)—Sahara Sky (IRE)  **Mr Jon Rider & Mr Charles Bellwood**
   13 **VERTICE (IRE)**, 4, ch f Toronado (IRE)—Asima (IRE)  **Miss T. Waggott**

### THREE-YEAR-OLDS

   14 **SHOWTIME EARNIE**, b g Intrinsic—She's So Pretty (IRE)  **Mr D. Tate**
   15 **SHOWTIME ELLE**, b f Intrinsic—Nice One  **Mr D. Tate**
   16 **VINDOBALA (IRE)**, b f Pride of Dubai (AUS)—Sphere of Grace (FR)  **Mr W. J. Laws**

### TWO-YEAR-OLDS

   17 B f 14/05 Hot Streak (IRE)—Broughtons Mystery (Sakhee's Secret) (952)  **Elsa Crankshaw Gordon Allan**
   18 B g 10/02 War Command (USA)—Wajaha (IRE) (Haafhd) (3632)  **Miss T. Waggott**

**Other Owners:** Mr G. Allan, Mr S. C. Bellwood, Miss S. A. Booth, Miss E. Crankshaw, Mr J. P. Rider, Miss T. Waggott.

---

## 550  MR JOHN WAINWRIGHT, Malton
Postal: **Granary House, Beverley Road, Norton, Malton, North Yorkshire, YO17 9PJ**
Contacts: **PHONE 01653 692993 MOBILE 07798 778070**
**EMAIL jswainwright@googlemail.com**

    1 **BOBBY SHAFT**, 5, b g Garswood—She Mystifies  **Wayne Bavill & John Wainwright**
    2 **BUZZ LIGHTYERE**, 8, b g Royal Applause—Lady Gloria  **Caballo Racing**
    3 **CLAYTON HALL (IRE)**, 8, b g Lilbourne Lad (IRE)—Hawk Dance (IRE)  **I. J. Barran**
    4 **DANDY'S ANGEL (IRE)**, 4, b f Dandy Man (IRE)—Party Pipit (IRE)  **Anthony Ross & Amy Abbott**
    5 **EZANAK (IRE)**, 8, b g Sea The Stars (IRE)—Ebaza (IRE)  **Gareth Davis & John Wainwright**
    6 **FARAMMAN**, 4, b g Fastnet Rock (AUS)—Nessina (USA)  **Dukes Group**
    7 **INTERNATIONAL LION**, 4, ch g Kyllachy—Redskin Dancer (IRE)  **Mr W Bavill & Mr D. Bavill**
    8 **JUST HEATHER (IRE)**, 7, gr m Zebedee—Miss Sundance (IRE)  **Mr T. G. Davies**
    9 **MESMERIC (GER)**, 4, b g Casamento (IRE)—Mambo Rhythm  **I. J. Barran**
   10 **MUATADEL**, 8, b g Exceed And Excel (AUS)—Rose Blossom  **Caballo Racing**
   11 **POWER POINT**, 4, br g Cable Bay (IRE)—Frabjous  **Mr W Bavill & Mr D. Bavill**
   12 **SWEET EMBRACE (IRE)**, 4, b f Kodiac—Zarkalia (IRE)  **Caballo Racing**
   13 **THE SADDLE ROCK (IRE)**, 4, b f Bated Breath—Dream Role  **D. R. & E. E. Brown**

### THREE-YEAR-OLDS

   14 B f Epaulette (AUS)—Selina Kyle  **Mr W Bavill & Mr D. Bavill**

**Other Owners:** Mrs A. E. Abbott, Mr W. C. Bavill, D. R. Brown, Mrs E. E. Brown, Mr T. G. Davies, Mr A. J. Ross, J. S. Wainwright.

**Assistant Trainer:** Mrs Fiona Wainwright.

**Flat Jockey:** Tom Eaves.

## 551 MR ROBERT WALEY-COHEN, Banbury
Postal: **Upton Viva, Banbury, Oxfordshire, OX15 6HT**
Contacts: **PHONE 01295 670538**

1 **FACILE BIEN (IRE)**, 10, b g Beneficial—Up A Dee (IRE) **Mr R. B. Waley-Cohen**
2 **IMPULSIVE STAR (IRE)**, 11, b g Busy Flight—Impulsive Ita (IRE) **Mr R. B. Waley-Cohen**
3 **KABUKI**, 5, b m Kayf Tara—Violet Express (FR) **Mr R. B. Waley-Cohen**
4 **MAITREE EXPRESS**, 7, br g Malinas (GER)—Shatabdi (IRE) **Mr R. B. Waley-Cohen**
5 **WYKHAM**, 7, b g Shirocco (GER)—Liberthine (FR) **Mr R. B. Waley-Cohen**

## 552 MR MARK WALFORD, Sheriff Hutton
Postal: **Cornborough Manor, Cornborough Road, Sheriff Hutton, York, North Yorkshire, YO60 6QN**

1 4, B g Westerner—Annimation (IRE)
2 **AOIFE'S JOY (IRE)**, 4, b f Elzaam (AUS)—Spavento (IRE) **Mr K. Brown**
3 **BIT OF A QUIRKE**, 8, ch g Monsieur Bond (IRE)—Silk (IRE) **Mr A. Quirke & Mrs G. B. Walford**
4 **BRAVANTINA**, 6, b m Trans Island—Falbrina (IRE) **Nunstainton Racing Club & Partner**
5 4, B g Getaway (GER)—Bright Cloud (IRE) **Mrs M. Cooper**
6 **BUSTER VALENTINE (IRE)**, 8, b g Ask—Femme du Noir (IRE) **The Mount Fawcus Partnership**
7 **CARLOVIAN**, 8, b g Acclamation—Mimisel **Pony & Racing**
8 **CASH TO ASH (IRE)**, 8, b g Westerner—Knocklayde Rose (IRE) **Amigos, Morrell, Johnson, Evans & Cowan**
9 **CLASSIC LADY (IRE)**, 6, ch m Flemensfirth (USA)—Another Gaye (IRE) **Allott & Wordingham**
10 **CLIFFTOP HEAVEN**, 4, b g Canford Cliffs (IRE)—Heaven's Sake **Ursa Major Racing, S Morrell & A Parrish**
11 **CORNBOROUGH**, 10, ch g Sir Percy—Emirates First (IRE) **Cornborough Racing Club**
12 **DORSET BLUE (IRE)**, 4, b g Canford Cliffs (IRE)—Spinning Lucy (IRE) **Vision Bloodstock & Partner**
13 **EVENT OF SIVOLA (FR)**, 7, ch g Noroit (GER)—Surprise de Sivola (FR) **Cw Racing Club & Ursa Major Racing**
14 **FLOATING ROCK (GER)**, 6, b g It's Gino (GER)—Fly Osoria (GER) **L & P Molony**
15 **FOAD**, 4, b g Kodiac—Slatey Hen (IRE) **Go Alfresco Racing Partners**
16 **GIOVANNI CHANGE (FR)**, 6, gr g French Fifteen (FR)—Ask For Rain **Readers & Wiggy, the 8 Amigos & J Burns**
17 **JANEYMAC (IRE)**, 7, b m Milan—Haraqaan **Ursa Major Racing & Partner**
18 **JANTE LAW**, 5, gr g Gentlewave (IRE)—Ixora (IRE) **Cambridge People & Mr P Drury**
19 **JOELJALU**, 4, b g Multiplex—O Fourlunda **Mickley Stud, Mrs J Johnson, Mrs Walford**
20 **KODIMOOR (IRE)**, 8, b g Kodiac—Victoria Lodge (IRE) **Ursa Major Racing & Partner**
21 **LETS GO LUCKY**, 4, ch f Yorgunnabelucky (USA)—Reset City **Ursa Major Racing & Partner**
22 **LOW PROFILE**, 6, ch g Galileo (IRE)—Dynaforce (USA) **Ms M Austerfield & the 8 Amigos**
23 **MAGICAL MAX**, 4, gr g Coach House (IRE)—Vellena **Mrs E Holmes, Mr M Johnson & Mrs Walford**
24 **MASTERS APPRENTICE (IRE)**, 6, ch g Mastercraftsman (IRE)—Maghzaa (IRE) **Vision Bloodstock & Partner**
25 **MEGA YEATS (IRE)**, 7, br m Yeats (IRE)—Mega Mum (IRE) **The Mount Fawcus Partnership**
26 **MISS AMELIA**, 8, b m Midnight Legend—Miss Pross **Cambridge People & Mr John Craggs**
27 **MIZEN MASTER (IRE)**, 8, b g Captain Rio—Nilassiba **URSA Major Racing**
28 **ORKAN**, 7, b g Shirocco (GER)—Zefooha (FR) **Mr C J I & Mr J A Scarrow**
29 **PARA QUEEN (IRE)**, 5, b m Slade Power (IRE)—Dancer's Leap **URSA Major Racing**
30 **PARIS PROTOCOL**, 8, b g Champs Elysees—Island Vista **Mrs G. B. Walford**
31 **QUEST FOR LIFE**, 9, b g Dapper—Lewesdon Duchess **Miss E. L. Todd**
32 **RISAALAAT (IRE)**, 5, b m Mukhadram—Naadrah **Let's Get Racing & Partners**
33 **ROCKMANN (FR)**, 6, b g Kap Rock (FR)—All Berry (FR) **Mr C. N. Herman**
34 **SUPER LUNAR (IRE)**, 12, b g Super Celebre (FR)—Kapricia Speed (FR) **Mrs C. Milburn**
35 **TOUR DE PUB (IRE)**, 7, ch g Aizavoski (IRE)—Gallant Express (IRE) **J Scarrow, J Cowan & S Evans**
36 **WILLIAM OF ORANGE**, 10, b g Duke of Marmalade (IRE)—Critical Acclaim **Mr I. P. Drury**
37 **ZUMURUD (IRE)**, 6, gr g Zebedee—Thaisy (USA) **Ms M. Austerfield**

### THREE-YEAR-OLDS

38 **AMAZING ANNA**, ch f Coach House (IRE)—Talqaa **J A Scarrow, The 8 Amigos & Mr Burns**
39 **CANDESCENCE**, ch f Power—Bright Flash **Ursa Major Racing, Lady Legard, John Craggs**
40 **DEFINITELY ALRIGHT**, b g Cannock Chase (USA)—Hawsies Dream **Let's Get Racing & Partners**

## MR MARK WALFORD - continued

41 **MEHRAKI STAR (IRE)**, b g Mehmas (IRE)—Aqlette **Ursa Major Racing & Partner**
42 **MY NAME'S NIPPER**, b g Due Diligence (USA)—New Road Side **Mrs E Holmes, the 8 Amigos & Mr M Graham**

### TWO-YEAR-OLDS

43 B c 31/03 Slade Power (IRE)—City Dazzler (IRE) (Elusive City (USA)) (5714) **Mrs G. B. Walford**
44 B c 10/02 War Command (USA)—Kiringa (Kyllachy) (4500) **Mrs G. B. Walford**
45 B f 07/04 Estidhkaar (IRE)—Lashkaal (Teofilo (IRE)) (1429) **Mrs G. B. Walford**
46 **ODAAT**, b f 30/03 Equiano (FR)—
Oilinda (Nayef (USA)) (3000) **Clayton Civil Engineering & Environmental Services Ltd**
47 **TESTING TIMES**, b f 19/02 Time Test—Quadri (Polish Precedent (USA)) (9000) **Mrs G. B. Walford**

**Other Owners:** Mr J. Allott, Ms M. Austerfield, Mr N. J. Blencowe, Mr L. A. Bolingbroke, Mr J. R. Burns, Mr D. Burrell, CW Racing Club, Cambridge People, Cambridge Racing Limited, Mr D. L. Chorlton, Mr P. A. P. Clays, Mr James E. Cowan, Mr J. Craggs, Mr C. T. Dawson, D. J. Dickson, Mr I. P. Drury, Mr P. A. Emerson, Mr S. N. Evans, Mr G. S. Felston, Mr D. I. Firth, Mr M. C. R. Graham, C. J. Grindal, Mrs E. Holmes, Mrs J. Johnson, Mr M. Johnson, R. Kent, Lady Legard, Mr M. Lenton, Let's Get Racing Ltd, Maximum Racing, Mrs S. V. Milner, Mr P. Molony, Mrs S. E. Morrell, Nunstainton Racing Club, A. R. Parrish, Mr D. Percival, Mr A. K. Quirke, Mr J. N. Readman, Mr J. A. Scarrow, Spoon Consulting Ltd, Mr C. Talbot, The 8 Amigos, URSA Major Racing, Vision Bloodstock, Mrs G. B. Walford, Mr P. L. Welsby, Mr T. J. Wigglesworth, Mr G. Wilson, P. L. Wordingham.

---

## 553 MR ROBERT WALFORD, Blandford
Postal: **Heart of Oak Stables, Okeford Fitzpane, Blandford, Dorset, DT11 0LW**
Contacts: **MOBILE 07815 116209**
EMAIL robertwalford1@gmail.com

1 **AMELIA'S DANCE (IRE)**, 6, ch m Flemensfirth (USA)—Madame McGoldrick (IRE) **Major-Gen R. Keightley**
2 **BLISTERING BOB**, 6, b g Big Bad Bob (IRE)—Kristalette (IRE) **Bex Design & Print Ltd**
3 **CASTCARRIE (IRE)**, 6, b m Yeats (IRE)—Turtle Lady (IRE) **Sue & Clive Cole & Ann & Tony Gale**
4 **CHLOE'S COURT (IRE)**, 8, br m Court Cave (IRE)—Howaya Pet (IRE) **Cole, Gale, Levy & Mortimer**
5 **CUCKLINGTON**, 10, b g Kayf Tara—Ardrma **Mrs C. M. Hinks**
6 **DUSKY LARK**, 11, b g Nayef (USA)—Snow Goose **Mrs Sara Biggins & Mrs Celia Djivanovic**
7 **EDE'IFFS ELTON**, 7, b g Geordieland (FR)—Ede'iff **Mr A. Lees**
8 **ELIOS D'OR (FR)**, 7, b g Puit d'Or (IRE)—Naker Mome (FR) **Mrs C Djivanovic & Mr M Rose**
9 **ENRY IGGINS**, 7, b g Schiaparelli (GER)—Eliza Doalott (IRE) **The Pygmalion Syndicate**
10 **FIRENZO (FR)**, 6, b g Network (GER)—Toscane (GER) **Mrs S. De Wilde**
11 **FLAGRANT DELITIEP (FR)**, 6, gr g Fragrant Mix (IRE)—Naltiepy (FR) **Mrs C. M. Hinks**
12 **FOXBORO (GER)**, 6, b g Maxios—Fair Breeze (GER) **Lewis Nettley Racing**
13 **FRESNO EMERY (FR)**, 6, b g Vision d'Etat (FR)—Urfie Star (FR) **Mr E Eames, Mr A Ham & Mr R Trevor**
14 **HOT SMOKED**, 8, br m Eastern Anthem (IRE)—Waheeba **Starting Gate Racing**
15 **MANVERS HOUSE**, 8, b g Schiaparelli (GER)—Freydis (IRE) **K S B, Mr M Doughty & Mrs Sarah Tizzard**
16 **ONE FOR DUNSTAN (IRE)**, 6, b g Sholokhov (IRE)—Park Rose (IRE) **Gale Force Six**
17 **SHUTUPSHIRLEY**, 4, b g Saddler's Rock (IRE)—Ede'iff **Chris Pugsley & Nigel Skinner**
18 **TIP TOP MOUNTAIN (IRE)**, 6, b g Mountain High (IRE)—The Central Lady (IRE) **Mr R. J. Brown**
19 **VAZIANI (FR)**, 7, b g Sinndar (IRE)—Visinova (FR) **Chris Pugsley & Acorn Builders Dorset**
20 **WILLIAM PHILO**, 4, ch g Black Sam Bellamy (IRE)—Jambles **Tony & Susan Brimble**

**Other Owners:** Acorn Builders Dorset LTD, Mrs S. J. Biggins, Mr A. F. G. Brimble, Mrs S. L. Brimble, Mr C. Cole, Mrs S. S. Cole, Mrs C. J. Djivanovic, Mr M. Doughty, Mr E. R. D. Eames, Mrs A. G. Gale, Mr A. P. Gale, Mr A. G. Ham, Mr D. T. Hoyland, Mr J. S. Hoyland, K S B Bloodstock, Mr A. R. Levy, Mr A. Lewis, Mrs J. D. Millar, Dr J. W. Millar, Exors of the Late Mr B. Mortimer, Mr B. J. Nettley, C. C. Pugsley, Mr J. P. Romans, Mr M. C. Rose, N. Skinner, Mrs S. L. Tizzard, Mr R. Trevor.

**NH Jockey:** James Best.

## 554 MR ED WALKER, Upper Lambourn
Postal: Kingsdown Stables, Upper Lambourn, Hungerford, Berkshire, RG17 8QX
Contacts: PHONE 01488 674148 MOBILE 07787 534145
EMAIL ed@edwalkerracing.com WEBSITE www.edwalkerracing.com

1 ALMODOVAR (IRE), 9, b g Sea The Stars (IRE)—Melodramatic (IRE) B. E. Nielsen
2 AMNIARIX (USA), 4, ch f Speightstown (USA)—Bold Lass (IRE) B. E. Nielsen
3 ASSIMILATION (IRE), 5, b g Xtension (IRE)—Park Glen (IRE) Mr B Greenwood,Mrs J Cestar & Mr C Dale
4 CAME FROM THE DARK (IRE), 5, gr g Dark Angel (IRE)—Silver Shoon (IRE) Mr P. K. Siu
5 CAP FRANCAIS, 5, b g Frankel—Miss Cap Ferrat John Pearce Racing Limited
6 CAPRIOLETTE (IRE), 6, b m Most Improved (IRE)—Greta d'Argent (IRE) Mr & Mrs Andrew Blaxland
7 CARADOC (IRE), 6, b g Camelot—Applause (IRE) Mr P. K. Siu
8 CONSTANCE (IRE), 4, b f Camelot—Emirates Joy (USA) Mr D. Ward
9 CRITIQUE (IRE), 4, b g Cacique (IRE)—Noble Fantasy (GER) Mr P. Afia
10 DARK SPECTRE (IRE), 4, b g Declaration of War (USA)—Easton Arch (USA) Mr C. U. F. Ma
11 DESERT DOCTOR (IRE), 6, ch g Society Rock (IRE)—Dorn Hill Mrs F. H. Hay
12 DREAMLOPER (IRE), 4, b f Lope de Vega (IRE)—Livia's Dream (IRE) Mr J. S. M. Fill
13 DREAMWEAVER (IRE), 5, b g Mastercraftsman (IRE)—Livia's Dream (IRE) Mr J. S. M. Fill
14 DUCKETT'S GROVE (USA), 5, b g Point of Entry (USA)—Xylonia (USA) Mr P. K. Siu
15 FIRST CHARGE (IRE), 4, b g Dansili—Melodramatic (IRE) Mr L. A. Bellman
16 FIRST STREET, 4, b g Golden Horn—Ladys First Lady Bamford
17 GREAT AMBASSADOR, 4, ch g Exceed And Excel (AUS)—Snoqualmie Girl (IRE) Ebury Racing 6
18 ICONIC KNIGHT (IRE), 6, b g Sir Prancealot (IRE)—Teutonic (IRE) John Moorhouse & Partner
19 JACK D'OR, 5, b g Raven's Pass (USA)—Inchberry Ebury Racing 2
20 JONAH JONES (IRE), 5, b g No Nay Never (USA)—Conniption (IRE) Mr D. Ward
21 MATTHEW FLINDERS, 4, b g Siyouni (FR)—Cascata (IRE) Mr S. A. Stuckey
22 MOLLS MEMORY, 6, ch m Helmet (AUS)—Bright Moll Mr A. R. F. Buxton
23 MOUNT MOGAN, 4, b g Helmet (AUS)—Super Midge Mr P. Chau
24 MOUNTAIN PEAK, 6, b g Swiss Spirit—Nolas Lolly (IRE) Ebury Racing
25 NOBLE QUEEN, 5, gr m Noble Mission—Dinvar Diva Brightwalton Bloodstock Limited
26 PAXOS (IRE), 4, gr g Outstrip—Ella Fitz Mr R Pegum & Partner
27 PRODUCTION, 5, b g Oasis Dream—Pure Excellence The Royal Ascot Racing Club
28 SIBERIAN NIGHT (IRE), 4, b g Siyouni (FR)—Sweet Dream Dubai Thoroughbred Racing
29 SILENT WITNESS (IRE), 5, b m First Defence (USA)—Stealth Bolt (USA) Windmill Racing Ii
30 STARMAN, 4, b c Dutch Art—Northern Star (IRE) Mr D. Ward
31 STORMY ANTARCTIC, 8, b g Stormy Atlantic (USA)—Bea Remembered Mr P. K. Siu
32 TOP FOX, 5, b g Frankel—Lady Linda (USA) King Power Racing Co Ltd
33 TRUE SCARLET (IRE), 4, b f Make Believe—Lady Pimpernel Mr P. K. Siu

## THREE-YEAR-OLDS
34 ABSOLUTELY DIVINE (IRE), b f Golden Horn—All's Forgotten (USA) Lady Bamford
35 ALABAMA BOY (IRE), b c Awtaad (IRE)—Gabardine Mr L. A. Bellman
36 BELOVED (IRE), b f Frankel—Love And Bubbles (USA) Mr D. Ward
37 BEOWULF (IRE), b g Camelot—Hug And A Kiss (USA) Mr M. J. Cottis
38 CANOODLED (IRE), b f Mehmas (IRE)—Fondled Mr L. A. Bellman
39 CHICA BOOM (IRE), ch c Tamayuz—Chicane Mr A Nicholls & Mr J Moorhouse
40 CLOSING BELL, b f Siyouni (FR)—Wiener Valkyrie Car Colston Hall Stud
41 COTAI BEAR (IRE), b g Kodi Bear (IRE)—Solace (USA) Kangyu International Racing (HK) Limited
42 CROCUS (IRE), b f New Bay—Bluebell (IRE) Mindy Hammond & Partners
43 DREAM A LITTLE, b f Oasis Dream—Got To Dream Hot To Trot Racing 1 & Fittocks Stud
44 FOREVER GLORIOUS, b g Archipenko (USA)—Aksaya Kangyu International Racing (HK) Limited
45 GIRL FROM IPANEMA (IRE), ch f Fast Company (IRE)—Siphon Melody (USA) Mr D. Ward
46 GLENARTNEY, b f Le Havre (IRE)—Willoughby (IRE) The Hon N. P. V. J. Rothschild
47 LODESTAR, b f Kingman—Northern Star (IRE) Mr D. Ward
48 LOWNDES SQUARE (IRE), b c Zoffany (IRE)—Catch The Moon (IRE) Mrs F. H. Hay
49 MARIE ANTOINETTE, b f Kingman—Contredanse (IRE) Mr S. A. Stuckey
50 MISS SCALETTA, b f Sea The Stars (IRE)—Miss Cap Ferrat John Pearce Racing Limited
51 MY MIRAGE (IRE), b f Iffraaj—Interception (USA) B. E. Nielsen
52 NASTASIYA, ch f Archipenko (USA)—Nezhenka Miss K. Rausing
53 NAVEGAON GATE, b c Frankel—Cascata (IRE) Mr S. A. Stuckey

## MR ED WALKER - continued

54 **NELL THE THIEF,** b br f Zoffany (IRE)—Betty The Thief (IRE)  **Mr D. Ward**
55 **PARACHUTE,** ch c Sea The Stars (IRE)—Fly  **Highclere Racing, T Vestey & P Silver**
56 **PEERLESS (IRE),** b g Kodiac—Etesian Flow  **Ebury Racing 3**
57 **PEINTRE D'ETOILES (FR),** b f Sea The Stars (IRE)—Persian Sky  **Mr D. Ward**
58 **PETALITE,** b f Kingman—Gemstone (IRE)  **Highclere Thoroughbred Racing - Petalite**
59 **POPMASTER (IRE),** gr c Gutaifan (IRE)—Best New Show (IRE)  **Mr L. A. Bellman**
60 **PRIMO BACIO (IRE),** b f Awtaad (IRE)—Suvenna (IRE)  **Mr D. Ward**
61 **QUEEN OF THORNS,** b f Acclamation—Cradle of Life (IRE)  **Chasemore Farm LLP**
62 **RANDOM HARVEST (IRE),** b f War Front (USA)—Star Approval (IRE)  **Lady Bamford**
63 **RAY DAY,** b f Adaay (IRE)—Rahyah  **Mrs G. Walker**
64 **REINA DEL MAR (IRE),** b f Awtaad (IRE)—Star Approval (IRE)  **Mr D. Ward**
65 **SCHABANG (GER),** b f Pastorius (GER)—Staying Alive (GER)  **Quantum Leap Racing Xii & Partner**
66 **SEMPER AUGUSTUS,** ch g Dutch Art—Pink Flames (IRE)  **Kennet Valley Thoroughbreds VI**
67 **SIBLING,** ch f New Approach (IRE)—Prowess (IRE)  **Mr J L Rowsell & Mr M H Dixon**
68 **SKY BRIGHT,** ch f Dawn Approach (IRE)—Angara  **The Hon N. P. V. J. Rothschild**
69 **SONG LYRIC (IRE),** b f Zoffany (IRE)—Pink Damsel (IRE)  **Mrs F. H. Hay**
70 **ST GEORGE'S BAY,** b c Cable Bay (IRE)—Basque Beauty  **Lady Coventry & Partners**
71 **SUNSET BAY,** b f Cable Bay (IRE)—Light of Love  **Brightwalton Bloodstock Limited**
72 **TEMPLE BRUER,** b g Showcasing—Kendal Mint  **Mrs Julia Scott & Partner**
73 **TENAYA CANYON,** b f Due Diligence (USA)—Clouds Rest  **Racegoers Club Owners Group**

## TWO-YEAR-OLDS

74 **AMERICAN STAR (IRE),** b c 12/01 Starspangledbanner (AUS)—
                Signora Valentina (IRE) (Henrythenavigator (USA)) (170000)  **Mr D. Ward**
75 Ch c 28/04 Bungle Inthejungle—Ayr Missile (Cadeaux Genereux) (95238)  **Mr P. K. Siu**
76 Br c 19/03 Slade Power (IRE)—Black Mascara (IRE) (Authorized (IRE)) (50000)  **Mr P. K. Siu**
77 **BOBBY THE THIEF,** br c 22/02 Camelot—Betty The Thief (IRE) (Teofilo (IRE))  **Mr D. Ward**
78 B c 05/04 Dark Angel (IRE)—Choose Me (IRE) (Choisir (AUS)) (100000)  **Mr P. K. Siu**
79 Ch c 10/03 Cotai Glory—Clef (Dutch Art) (38095)  **Mr C. U. F. Ma**
80 **GLAM UP,** b f 19/03 Showcasing—Complexion (Hurricane Run (IRE))  **Brightwalton Bloodstock Limited**
81 **GLORY GALORE,** b c 02/03 Postponed (IRE)—Classic Code (IRE) (Galileo (IRE)) (38000)  **A. Al Shaikh**
82 B c 18/02 Dark Angel (IRE)—Hay Chewed (IRE) (Camacho) (130000)  **Mr P. K. Siu**
83 **KAWIDA,** b f 10/03 Sir Percy—Kandahari (Archipenko (USA))  **Miss K. Rausing**
84 **KINDNESS,** b f 14/02 No Nay Never (USA)—Nancy Hart (Sepoy (AUS))  **Mr D. Ward**
85 **KING ALFRED (IRE),** b c 01/04 The Gurkha (IRE)—Vestavia (IRE) (Alhaarth (IRE)) (72000)  **Mr M. J. Cottis**
86 **LETUSGOTHENYOUANDI,** ch f 27/04 Frankel—Cascata (Montjeu (IRE))  **Mr S. A. Stuckey**
87 **MOSTLY SUNNY (IRE),** ch c 27/01 Zarak (FR)—Belle Above All (New Approach (IRE)) (30670)  **A. Al Shaikh**
88 **PIFFLE (IRE),** b f 24/03 Camacho—Siphon Melody (USA) (Siphon (BRZ)) (10000)  **Mrs G. Walker**
89 **QUAYBIRD (IRE),** ch f 18/03 New Bay—Pocket Watch (Pivotal) (15238)  **Mr S. A. Stuckey**
90 Ch f 04/02 New Approach (IRE)—Silent Music (IRE) (Peintre Celebre (USA))  **Mr C. E. Stedman**
91 **TIDAL STORM,** b c 06/03 Sea The Moon (GER)—Kinetica (Stormy Atlantic (USA)) (42000)  **Mrs G. Austen-Smith**
92 B f 03/03 Acclamation—Vesnina (Sea The Stars (IRE))  **Brightwalton Bloodstock Limited**

**Other Owners:** Mr P. Afia, Mr A. N. C. Bengough, A. Blaxland, Mrs T. J. Blaxland, Mr J. J. Brummitt, Mrs J. Cestar, Colin Dale & Partner, Mr L. Cowan, Mr C. E. Dale, M. H. Dixon, Fittocks Stud, Mrs J. M. Forman Hardy, N. J. Forman Hardy, B. J. R. Greenwood, Highclere Thoroughbred Racing - Fly, Mrs A. L. Hammond, Mrs E. A. Harris, T. F. Harris, Highclere Thoroughbred Racing Ltd, Mrs E. M. Hobson, Exors of the Late J. Hobson, Mr R. Homburg, Mr R. S. Hoskins, Hot To Trot Racing 1, Mr D. M. James, Mrs Fiona Marner, Lady E. Mays-Smith, Mr J. H. Moorhouse, Mr J. A. M. Nicholls, Mr E. M. O'Connor, Mr R. A. Pegum, D. F. Powell, Mr R. Pritchard, Quantum Leap Racing XII, J. L. Rowsell, Mrs J. M. M. Scott, Mr P. G. S. Silver, Mr S. Straker, Mr I. R. Twigden, T. R. G. Vestey, Mr E. C. D. Walker.

## 555 MR CHRIS WALL, Newmarket
Postal: **Induna Stables, Fordham Road, Newmarket, Suffolk, CB8 7AQ**
Contacts: HOME 01638 668896 MOBILE 07764 940255 FAX 01638 667279
EMAIL christianwall@btconnect.com WEBSITE www.chriswallracing.co.uk

1 **BLACK LOTUS**, 6, b m Declaration of War (USA)—Ravensburg **Mr S. Fustok**
2 **BUCEPHALUS (GER)**, 4, b g Soldier Hollow—Batya (IRE) **Wayman & Thomas**
3 **CAPLA HUNTRESS**, 5, gr m Sir Percy—Great White Hope (IRE) **Strawberry Fields Stud**
4 **CHEESE AND WINE**, 4, b f Nathaniel (IRE)—Meet Me Halfway **Mr D. M. Thurlby**
5 **DELILAH PARK**, 7, b m Delegator—Sarah Park (IRE) **Mr & Mrs Mr & Mrs DE & J Cash and Mr P Turner**
6 **DOUBLE OR BUBBLE (IRE)**, 4, b f Exceed And Excel (AUS)—Mango Lady **Mr S. Fustok**
7 **FLYING STANDARD (IRE)**, 4, ch g Starspangledbanner (AUS)—Snow Scene (IRE) **Hintlesham Racing Ltd**
8 **FRONT OF LINE**, 4, b f Cable Bay (IRE)—Pivotal Drive (IRE) **Mr D. M. Thurlby**
9 **GLEN ESK**, 4, b g Kyllachy—Ski Slope **P. J. W. Botham, Mr M. Tilbrook, Mr D. A. Hutchinson**
10 **GOLDIE HAWK**, 4, b f Golden Horn—Always Remembered (IRE) **Mr S. Fustok**
11 **HAN SOLO BERGER (IRE)**, 6, b g Lord Shanakill (USA)—Dreamaway (IRE) **Mrs B. J. Berresford**
12 **HI HO SILVER**, 7, gr g Camacho—Silver Spell **Mrs C. A. Wall**
13 **MOLLY SHAW**, 4, b f Helmet (AUS)—Paradise Isle **Mr D. M. Thurlby**
14 **OH IT'S SAUCEPOT**, 7, b m Sir Percy—Oh So Saucy **The Eight of Diamonds**
15 **TURNTABLE**, 5, b g Pivotal—Masarah (IRE) **Induna Racing**

## THREE-YEAR-OLDS

16 **B B PARK**, b f Brazen Beau (AUS)—Sarah Park (IRE) **Mr & Mrs Mr & Mrs DE & J Cash and Mr P Turner**
17 **BAGUE D'OR (IRE)**, ch g Belardo (IRE)—Ravensburg **Mr S. Fustok**
18 **CASTANA DIA (IRE)**, ch f Dandy Man (IRE)—Day By Day **B. R. Westley**
19 **DIVINE COMEDY (IRE)**, b f Le Havre (IRE)—Epic Emirates **The Equema Partnership**
20 **DRIFTING SANDS**, b f Pride of Dubai (AUS)—Drift And Dream **Lady Juliet Tadgell**
21 **KINGMANIA (IRE)**, b f Kingman—Greek Goddess (IRE) **Mr S. Fustok**
22 **MANGO BOY**, gr g New Bay—Mango Lady **Mr S. Fustok**
23 **MINI RIVO (IRE)**, b f Nathaniel (IRE)—Toujours L'Amour **Mr S. Fustok**
24 **MODERN BEAUTY (IRE)**, b br g Helmet (AUS)—Ludi Lu (FR) **Mr S. Fustok**
25 **MUSTAZEED (IRE)**, br g Territories (IRE)—Mejala (IRE) **Newmarket Racing Club HQ**
26 **OH ITS OH SO SMART**, b g Mukhadram—Oh So Saucy **The Eight of Diamonds**
27 **POET'S PARK**, b f Poet's Voice—Sparkle Park **Mr & Mrs Mr & Mrs DE & J Cash and Mr P Turner**
28 **POSH GIRL**, gr f Outstrip—Sauvage (FR) **Mr S. Fustok**
29 **SWEET EXPECTATION**, b f Charming Thought—
Hope Island (IRE) **Sweet Expectation Partners, Mrs C. A. Wall, P. J. W. Botham**

## TWO-YEAR-OLDS

30 B c 16/01 Poet's Park—Be Free (Selkirk) **Hintlesham Racing Ltd**
31 **CHIPS AND RICE**, b f 28/02 Golden Horn—Semaral (IRE) (High Chaparral (IRE)) (25000) **Mr D. M. Thurlby**
32 **GLOBE PLAYER**, b c 24/01 Nathaniel (IRE)—La Dorotea (IRE) (Lope de Vega (IRE)) **Mr S. Fustok**
33 B c 23/02 Postponed (IRE)—Hector's Girl (Hector Protector (USA)) **Pierpont Scott & Genesis Green Stud**
34 **OH SO AUDACIOUS**, b f 05/03 Mukhadram—Oh So Saucy (Imperial Ballet (IRE)) **The Eight of Diamonds**
35 B f 06/04 Muhaarar—Oriental Step (Tamayuz) (14000) **Hughes & Scott, C. J. A. Hughes, Mr K. D. Scott**
36 **ROSE CAMIRA**, b f 13/04 Camelot—Silent Act (USA) (Theatrical) (36000) **Ms R. Grubmuller**
37 **SAVROLA (IRE)**, b c 14/03 Churchill (IRE)—Toujours L'Amour (Authorized (IRE)) (52000) **Mr S. Fustok**
38 **SPIT SPOT**, ch f 02/04 Sir Percy—Taweyla (IRE) (Teofilo (IRE)) **Mr D. M. Thurlby**
39 **TOTAL JOY (IRE)**, b c 05/03 Ribchester (IRE)—Ludi Lu (FR) (New Approach (IRE)) **Mr S. Fustok**

**Other Owners:** Botham & Partners, D. E. Cash, Mrs J. Cash, P.J. Turner.

**Assistant Trainer:** Arthur Berry.

**Apprentice Jockey:** Pam Du Crocq, Seb Woods.

## 556 MR TREVOR WALL, Ludlow
Postal: **Gorsty Farm Flat, Whitcliffe, Ludlow, Shropshire, SY8 2HD**
Contacts: PHONE **01588 660219** MOBILE **07972 732080**
EMAIL **trevorwall56@outlook.com**

1 **DOWNTON FOX**, 13, b g Oscar (IRE)—Leinthall Fox **Miss J. C. L. Needham**
2 **HOT MADRAS (IRE)**, 13, b m Milan—Hot Fudge (IRE)
3 **LONGVILLE LILLY**, 6, b m Mawatheeq (USA)—Curtains **A. H. Bennett**
4 **MAY MIST**, 9, b m Nayef (USA)—Midnight Mist (IRE) **A. H. Bennett**
5 **MY FOXY LADY**, 9, br m Sagamix (FR)—Marlbrook Fox **Miss J. C. L. Needham**
6 **PAT'S LIGHT**, 5, b m Black Sam Bellamy (IRE)—Kansas City (FR) **C. G. Johnson**
7 **RIGHT ROYALS DAY**, 12, b m Beneficial—Just For A Laugh **Miss J. C. L. Needham**

### THREE-YEAR-OLDS

8 B g Telescope (IRE)—Fairy Alisha

**Assistant Trainer:** Mrs J. A. Wall.

## 557 MR CHARLIE WALLIS, Ardleigh
Postal: **Benson Stud, Harts Lane, Ardleigh, Colchester, Essex, CO7 7QE**
Contacts: PHONE **01206 230779** MOBILE **07725 059355**
EMAIL **cwallis86@hotmail.com**

1 **ACES (IRE)**, 9, b g Dark Angel (IRE)—Cute Ass (IRE) **Mrs H. Wallis**
2 **AGUEROOO (IRE)**, 8, b g Monsieur Bond (IRE)—Vision of Peace (IRE) **P. E. Axon**
3 **ALFIE'S ANGEL (IRE)**, 7, b g Dark Angel (IRE)—Penolva (IRE) **E. A. Hayward**
4 **ARZAAK (IRE)**, 7, br g Casamento (IRE)—Dixieland Kiss (USA) **Mr M. M. Foulger**
5 **BADGER BERRY**, 5, b g Epaulette (AUS)—Snow Shoes **Strawberry Fields Stud**
6 **BINT DANDY (IRE)**, 10, b m Dandy Man (IRE)—Ceol Loch Aoidh (IRE) **Mr M. M. Foulger**
7 **BORN TO SIRE (IRE)**, 4, b g Born To Sea (IRE)—Sea of Wonders (IRE) **P. E. Axon**
8 **ENGLISHMAN**, 11, b g Royal Applause—Tesary **E. A. Hayward**
9 **HIBERNIAN WARRIOR (USA)**, 4, b br g War Front (USA)—Quarter Moon (IRE) **P. E. Axon**
10 **INDIAN AFFAIR**, 11, br g Sleeping Indian—Rare Fling (USA) **Mrs H. Wallis**
11 **KING ROBERT**, 8, b g Royal Applause—Generously Gifted **J A Challen & H Wallis**
12 **KYLLUKEY**, 8, b g Kyllachy—Money Note **Mrs H. Wallis**
13 **MURAAQEB**, 7, b g Nathaniel (IRE)—Tesary **E. A. Hayward**
14 **POTTERS QUESTION**, 5, ch g Cardinal—Scipmylo **Mrs J. May**
15 **PRECIOUS PLUM**, 7, b m Equiano (FR)—Miss Polly Plum **Mrs J. V. Hughes**
16 **SIR HECTOR (IRE)**, 6, ch g Sir Prancealot (IRE)—Awwal Malika (USA) **J.Titley & Jane Challen**
17 **SMOKEY**, 4, gr f Outstrip—Lady Tabitha (IRE) **P. E. Axon**
18 **TARSEEKH**, 8, b g Kyllachy—Constitute (USA) **P. E. Axon**
19 **THE NIGHT WATCH**, 5, b g Dutch Art—Scarlet Runner **E. A. Hayward**

### THREE-YEAR-OLDS

20 B g Cardinal—Craughwell Suas (IRE) **Mrs J. May**
21 **POTTERS FREDDIE**, b g Cardinal—Scipmylo **Mrs J. May**
22 **RED SPARROW**, ch f Intrinsic—Kodi da Capo (IRE) **J. J. May**
23 **YOU DIDN'T DID YOU**, ch f Twilight Son—Castaway Queen (IRE) **Mr D. A. Clark**

### TWO-YEAR-OLDS

24 **HEMSBY PINE (IRE)**, b g 31/03 Bated Breath—Pearl Diva (IRE) (Acclamation) (1000) **Pine Developments Limited**
25 B f 13/02 Bated Breath—Lady Glinka (Galileo)

**Other Owners:** Miss J. A. Challen, J. E. Titley, Mrs H. Wallis.

**Assistant Trainer:** Hayley Wallis.

## 558 MRS JANE WALTON, Otterburn
Postal: **Dunns Houses Stables, Otterburn, Newcastle upon Tyne, Northumberland, NE19 1LB**
Contacts: **PHONE 01830 520677 MOBILE 07808 592701 FAX 01830 520677**
**EMAIL dunnshouses@hotmail.com WEBSITE www.janewaltonhorseracing.co.uk**

1 **EVEQUE (FR),** 7, ch g Kotky Bleu (FR)—Gloria IV (FR) **Mrs J. M. Walton**
2 **PARELLI POWER,** 5, ch m Schiaparelli (GER)—Shankhouse Wells (IRE) **Jane Walton & George Charlton Partner**
3 **REAL ARMANI,** 9, ch g Sulamani (IRE)—Reel Charmer **Jane Walton & George Charlton Partner**
4 **REVERSE THE CHARGE (IRE),** 14, b g Bishop of Cashel—Academy Jane (IRE) **Mrs J. M. Walton**
5 **UPTOWN HARRY (IRE),** 7, b br g Morozov (USA)—Tudor Glyn (IRE) **Fresh Start Partnership**
6 **WESTEND THEATRE (IRE),** 12, b g Darsi (FR)—Ballyvelig Lady (IRE) **Mrs J. M. Walton**

**Other Owners:** Mr G. A. G. Charlton, Mrs M. R. Ridley, Miss J. Rutherford, Mrs J. M. Walton.

## 559 MR JIMMY WALTON, Morpeth
Postal: **Flotterton Hall, Thropton, Morpeth, Northumberland, NE65 7LF**
Contacts: **PHONE 01669 640253 MOBILE 07831 894120**

1 **CENTRAL FLAME,** 13, ch g Central Park (IRE)—More Flair
2 **CROW STONE,** 7, b g Sulamani (IRE)—Merry Tina
3 **CUDGEL,** 8, b g Sulamani (IRE)—Posh Stick
4 **FRANKIES FIRE,** 8, b m Flying Legend (USA)—Watch The Wind
5 **MATTHEW MAN,** 10, b g Bollin Eric—Garden Feature
6 **ROLL OF THUNDER,** 12, b g Antonius Pius (USA)—Ischia
7 **STILL A SPARK,** 6, gr m Proclamation (IRE)—Merry Tina
8 **SUPER SUNDIAL,** 6, gr m Proclamation (IRE)—Garden Feature

**Owners:** F. A. Walton, Messrs F. T. Walton, J. B. Walton.

## 560 MRS SHEENA WALTON, Hexham
Postal: **Linacres, Wark, Hexham, Northumberland, NE48 3DP**
Contacts: **PHONE 01434 230656 MOBILE 07752 755184**
**EMAIL linacres@btconnect.com**

1 **SAILING AWAY (IRE),** 8, ch m Stowaway—Drama Chick **R. H. & S. C. Walton**

**Other Owners:** R. H. Walton, Mrs S. Walton.

**Assistant Trainer:** Mr R. H. Walton.

**Amateur Jockey:** Miss C. Walton.

## 562    MR TOM WARD, Upper Lambourn
Postal: **Whitehouse Stables, Upper Lambourn, Hungerford, Berkshire, RG17 8QP**
WORK EMAIL tom@tomwardracing.com

1 **BEAUTY STONE (IRE)**, 4, b f Australia—Za'hara (IRE)
2 **CAPOTE'S DREAM (IRE)**, 4, br g Dream Ahead (USA)—Capote West (USA)
3 **CULTURE (FR)**, 5, b g Dream Ahead (USA)—Talon Bleu (FR)
4 **MOURIYANI (USA)**, 5, b g City Zip (USA)—Mouraniya (IRE)
5 **TINTORETTO (IRE)**, 6, b g Lilbourne Lad (IRE)—Fanacanta (IRE)
6 **VALENTINE BLUES (IRE)**, 4, gr f Clodovil (IRE)—Grecian Artisan (IRE)
7 **VINTAGE RASCAL (FR)**, 4, b g Nathaniel (IRE)—Irish Vintage (FR)
8 **ZHUI FENG (IRE)**, 8, b g Invincible Spirit (IRE)—Es Que

### THREE-YEAR-OLDS
9 **AFTA PARTY (IRE)**, gr g Mastercraftsman (IRE)—Wood Fairy
10 **ALPHONSE KARR (IRE)**, b g Dandy Man (IRE)—Plus Ca Change (IRE)
11 **AMBARELLA (IRE)**, b f Fast Company (IRE)—Bright New Day (IRE)
12 **AUSSIE RASCAL (IRE)**, ch c Australia—Refusetolisten (IRE)
13 B c Sir Percy—Cadixia
14 **DEVIL'S CUB**, b c Hellvelyn—Noor Al Haya (IRE)
15 **DIAMOND BAY**, ch g New Bay—Amarillo Starlight (IRE)
16 **FARASI LANE (IRE)**, b g Belardo (IRE)—No Such Zone
17 **FILLE D'OR (IRE)**, b f Dandy Man (IRE)—Frabrika (IRE)
18 **LITTE MISS RASCAL**, b f Zoffany (IRE)—Hibiscus (IRE)
19 **LUISA CASATI (IRE)**, b f Vadamos (FR)—La Marchesa (IRE)
20 **MISHAL STAR (IRE)**, ch f Mehmas (IRE)—Ruzma (IRE)
21 **MOONSHINER (IRE)**, ch f Mehmas (IRE)—Obsara
22 **RAGING RASCAL (IRE)**, b c Coulsty—Limousine
23 **RED FLYER (IRE)**, ch g Free Eagle (IRE)—Hip
24 **ROMAN MIST (IRE)**, gr f Holy Roman Emperor (IRE)—Drifting Mist
25 **STAR OF DEAUVILLE (IRE)**, b f Dandy Man (IRE)—Happy Land (IRE)
26 **THE WATERMAN**, b g Charm Spirit (IRE)—Amira

### TWO-YEAR-OLDS
27 **BRAVE LILY (IRE)**, ch f 20/04 Camacho—Song of Sixpence (IRE) (Among Men (USA)) (5500)
28 B c 04/02 Gutaifan (IRE)—Light of Love (Dylan Thomas (IRE)) (14285)

**Head Lad:** Anthony James, **Travelling Head:** Joe Kirby, **Business & Racing Manager:** Alex Lowe, **Yard Sponsor:** The Pheasant Inn, Hungerford.

**Apprentice Jockey:** Laura Coughlan.

## 563    MR ARCHIE WATSON, Upper Lambourn
Postal: **Saxon Gate, Upper Lambourn, Hungerford, Berkshire, RG17 8QH**
Contacts: **PHONE 01488 491247**
EMAIL office@archiewatsonracing.com WEBSITE www.archiewatsonracing.com

1 **ABOVE (FR)**, 4, b c Anjaal—Broken Applause (IRE)
2 **AL HAAMY (IRE)**, 4, b g Shamardal (USA)—Sharedah (IRE)
3 **BAZAROV (IRE)**, 8, br g Stowaway—Booley Bay (IRE)
4 **BURMESE WALTZ**, 5, b m Showcasing—Heho
5 **CORINTHIA KNIGHT (IRE)**, 6, ch g Society Rock (IRE)—Victoria Lodge (IRE)
6 **GLEN SHIEL**, 7, ch g Pivotal—Gonfilia (GER)
7 **GOING PLACES**, 5, ch g Frankel—Khor Sheed
8 **GREAT ESTEEM (IRE)**, 5, b g Dubawi (IRE)—Woven Lace
9 **HARRISON POINT (FR)**, 4, ch g Speightstown (USA)—Summer Surprice (FR)

# MR ARCHIE WATSON - continued

10 **HIGHLAND DRESS**, 5, b g Shamardal (USA)—Crinoline (USA)
11 **JAARIYAH (USA)**, 4, b br f Shamardal (USA)—Jiwen (CAN)
12 **LETMESTOPYOUTHERE (IRE)**, 7, ro g Sir Prancealot (IRE)—Romanylei (IRE)
13 **LUNA MAGIC**, 7, br m Mayson—Dayia (IRE)
14 **MENIN GATE (IRE)**, 5, gr g Farhh—Telegraphy (USA)
15 **MIQUELON**, 4, b g Kingman—Canada Water
16 **ONE TO GO**, 5, gr g Champs Elysees—Tina's Spirit (IRE)
17 **ONLY THE BRAVE (USA)**, 5, b br m Exchange Rate (USA)—Contact (USA)
18 **OUTBOX**, 6, b g Frankel—Emirates Queen
19 **PARENT'S PRAYER (IRE)**, 4, b f Kingman—Pure Excellence
20 **PERCY PROSECCO**, 6, b g Sir Percy—Grapes Hill
21 **PORTUGUESEPRINCESS (IRE)**, 4, b f Camacho—Royal Visit (IRE)
22 **STAG HORN**, 4, b g Golden Horn—Starfala
23 **STONE SOLDIER**, 4, ch g Mayson—La Adelita (IRE)
24 **VARIYANN (FR)**, 5, b g Shamardal (USA)—Vazira (FR)

## THREE-YEAR-OLDS

25 **ACTION HERO (IRE)**, b c Dandy Man (IRE)—Saga Celebre (FR)
26 **AMERICAN ANTHEM (IRE)**, ch f Starspangledbanner (AUS)—Cloudy Girl (IRE)
27 **AMOR DE MI VIDA (FR)**, b f Dabirsim (FR)—Troiecat (FR)
28 **ARCTIC EMPEROR**, b c Territories (IRE)—Selkirk Sky
29 **BADLANDS (IRE)**, b c Territories (IRE)—Quiritis
30 **COLONEL FAULKNER (IRE)**, b c Wootton Bassett—Kortoba (USA)
31 **DID SHE THOUGH (IRE)**, ch f Prince of Lir (IRE)—Batuta
32 **DRACOSTELLA (IRE)**, b f Dragon Pulse (IRE)—Starbright (IRE)
33 **DRAGON SYMBOL**, gr c Cable Bay (IRE)—Arcamist
34 **EXCEL POWER (IRE)**, b c Slade Power (IRE)—Rhythm Excel
35 **IGOTATEXT (IRE)**, b g Ajaya—Tifawt
36 **IMPERIAL SANDS (IRE)**, b c Footstepsinthesand—Hadrienne
37 **INVINCIBLE GIFT**, b c Kodiac—Yarrow (IRE)
38 **JUST FOR YUSE (IRE)**, br g Dandy Man (IRE)—Mollie's Girl (IRE)
39 **KIND THOUGHTS (IRE)**, b f Charming Thought—Badminton
40 **LADY LEONIE (IRE)**, b f The Last Lion (IRE)—Hallowed Park (IRE)
41 **LAOS (FR)**, b c Territories (IRE)—Amarinda (GER)
42 **MEHMENTO (IRE)**, b c Mehmas (IRE)—Invincible Me (IRE)
43 **MIGHTY GURKHA (IRE)**, b c Sepoy (AUS)—Royal Debt
44 **MYSTERY SHOW (IRE)**, b f Showcasing—Mystery Bet (IRE)
45 **ROSIE POWERS (FR)**, b f Siyouni (FR)—Rosey de Megeve
46 **RUNWAY QUEEN**, ch f Kitten's Joy (USA)—Puzzled Look
47 **SECRET HANDSHEIKH**, b g Mayson—Descriptive (IRE)
48 **SHERBET LEMON (USA)**, gr ro f Lemon Drop Kid (USA)—Famous (IRE)
49 **SOUTHERN VOYAGE (FR)**, b c Wootton Bassett—Blue Blue Sea
50 **STRIKE ME A POSE**, b g Adaay (IRE)—Mookhlesa
51 **SUPER OVER (IRE)**, ch c Pearl Secret—First Rains
52 **SURPRISE EXHIBIT**, b g Showcasing—Astonishing (IRE)
53 **THREAD COUNT**, b f Adaay (IRE)—Wigan Lane
54 **TIO MIO (IRE)**, b c Teofilo (IRE)—Celeste de La Mer (IRE)
55 **ZUMAATY (IRE)**, b c Tamayuz—Blackangelheart (IRE)

Trainer did not supply details of their two-year-olds.

**Assistant Trainer:** Stephanie Joannides.

**Flat Jockey:** Hollie Doyle, Adam McNamara. **Amateur Jockey:** Miss Brodie Hampson.

## 564 MR FRED WATSON, Sedgefield
Postal: Beacon Hill, Sedgefield, Stockton-On-Tees, Cleveland, TS21 3HN
Contacts: PHONE 01740 620582 MOBILE 07773 321472
EMAIL fredwatson@talktalk.net

1 DESTINATION AIM, 14, b g Dubai Destination (USA)—Tessa Reef (IRE) **F. Watson**
2 GLEAMING ARCH, 7, b g Arabian Gleam—Mrs Quince **F. Watson**
3 GLEAMING MAIZE, 5, b m Arabian Gleam—Mrs Quince **F. Watson**
4 JOYFUL STAR, 11, b g Teofilo (IRE)—Extreme Beauty (USA) **F. Watson**
5 NEWSPEAK (IRE), 9, b g New Approach (IRE)—Horatia (IRE) **F. Watson**
6 ROYAL LEGEND, 7, ch g New Approach (IRE)—Villarrica (USA) **F. Watson**
7 STAR CITIZEN, 9, b g New Approach (IRE)—Faslen (USA) **F. Watson**
8 THE MONSIEUR MAN, 4, b g Monsieur Bond (IRE)—Mad Jazz **F. Watson**

## 565 MRS SHARON WATT, Richmond
Postal: Rosey Hill Farm, Scorton Road, Brompton on Swale, Richmond, North Yorkshire, DL10 7EQ
Contacts: PHONE 01748 812064 MOBILE 07970 826046 FAX 01748 812064
EMAIL wattfences@aol.com

1 ARCTIC VODKA, 9, gr g Black Sam Bellamy (IRE)—Auntie Kathleen **Rosey Hill Partnership**
2 CHAMPAGNE RULES, 10, gr g Aussie Rules (USA)—Garabelle (IRE) **Rosey Hill Partnership**
3 TOO MANY CHIEFS (IRE), 10, br g Indian River (FR)—Wahiba Hall (IRE) **Major E. J. Watt**

## 566 MR SIMON WAUGH, Morpeth
Postal: A G Waugh & Sons Limited, Molesden House, Molesden, Morpeth, Northumberland, NE61 3QF
Contacts: MOBILE 07860 561445
EMAIL swaugh@dircon.co.uk

1 BORIC, 13, b g Grape Tree Road—Petrea **Mrs S. A. York**
2 DARK AND DANGEROUS (IRE), 13, b g Cacique (IRE)—Gilah (IRE) **Yacht London Racing Ltd**
3 FAIRENOUGHWHYNOT, 7, b g Fair Mix (IRE)—Ashnaya (FR) **Mr J. M. B. Cookson**
4 HELLFIRE KODE, 4, b g Helmet (AUS)—Secret Kode (IRE) **Yacht London Racing Ltd**
5 IMPERIAL FOCUS (IRE), 8, b g Intense Focus (USA)—Mrs Cee (IRE) **Yacht London Racing Ltd**
6 INFINITE SUN, 10, b g And Beyond (IRE)—Kingussie Flower **Mrs V. J. R. Ramm**
7 KIDMAN (IRE), 5, b g Arcadio (GER)—Kilganey Maid (IRE) **Mr J. D. Thompson**
8 LITTLE ORANGE, 7, ch g Trans Island—Falbrina (IRE) **Mrs S. A. York**
9 LOUGHERMORE (IRE), 7, b g Milan—Seductive Dance **Miss A. Waugh**
10 MAYBE MURPHY, 6, b g Kayf Tara—Mays Delight (IRE) **A. R. G. Waugh**
11 PASSNOTALEGEND, 8, b g Flying Legend (USA)—Passmenot **Northumberland Racing Club**
12 ROYAL FLUSH, 10, b g Multiplex—Mystical Feelings (BEL) **S. G. Waugh**
13 SHANTOU STREET (IRE), 7, b m Shantou (USA)—Par Street (IRE) **S. G. Waugh**
14 SKYE CHIEF, 9, b g Sulamani (IRE)—Isle of Skye **Mrs S. A. Sutton**
15 SON OF SUZIE, 13, gr g Midnight Legend—Suzie Cream Cheese (IRE) **Miss A. Waugh**
16 THE SILVER PRINCE (IRE), 7, gr g Vinnie Roe (IRE)—Gallery Gale (IRE) **Mrs R. C. Calder**

### THREE-YEAR-OLDS
17 SEGEDUNUM, b g Cannock Chase (USA)—Arabian Sunset (IRE) **Yacht London Racing Ltd**
18 YOUNG ALEXANDER, b c Cannock Chase (USA)—Secret Kode (IRE) **Yacht London Racing Ltd**

**567**
**MR MARK WEATHERER, Leyburn**
Postal: **The Flat, Bolton Hall Racing Stables, Wensley, Leyburn, North Yorkshire, DL8 4UF**
Contacts: **PHONE 01969 625735**
EMAIL markweatherer@btinternet.com

1 DEE DAY LANDING, 4, b c Intrinsic—Heidenheim (IRE) **M. Weatherer**
2 MUZETTA'S WALTZ (IRE), 7, ch m Tobougg (IRE)—Brer Rabbit **M. Weatherer**
3 RED STAR DANCER (IRE), 7, b g Tamayuz—Red Planet
4 SIR TAAJ, 5, b h Sintarajan (IRE)—Brer Rabbit **M. Weatherer**
5 UNIQUE COMPANY (IRE), 6, ch g Fast Company (IRE)—Unique Blanche **M. Weatherer**

## THREE-YEAR-OLDS

6 MAGDALANA, b f Intrinsic—Parisien Tea Dance **M. Weatherer**
7 SPIRITTAPPERGOODE, b g Eagle Top—Dutch Girl

**568**
**MR PAUL WEBBER, Banbury**
Postal: **Cropredy Lawn, Cropredy, Banbury, Oxfordshire, OX17 1DR**
Contacts: **PHONE 01295 750226 MOBILE 07836 232465**
EMAIL paul@paulwebberracing.com WEBSITE www.paulwebberracing.com

1 AGENT ZIGZAG (IRE), 7, ch g Shamardal (USA)—Farranjordan **Mr P. Bowden**
2 BOUGHTBEFORELUNCH (IRE), 8, b g Dubai Destination (USA)—Anie (IRE) **The Let's Do Lunch Partnership**
3 BRAQUEUR D'OR (FR), 10, b g Epalo (GER)—Hot d'Or (FR) **Mr E. J. N. Seyfried**
4 CECI WELLS, 4, b f Orientor—Theatrical Dancer **Mrs & Exors of The Late Mr P. C. Smith**
5 CLOUDY HILLS (IRE), 5, b g Cloudings (IRE)—Phillis Hill **Miss S. Pilkington**
6 EURKASH (FR), 7, b g Irish Wells (FR)—Meralda (FR) **P. R. Webber**
7 EYED, 4, b g Kayf Tara—One Gulp **Mr Martin Hughes**
8 FIRST ROMANCE, 6, b m Shirocco (GER)—Alasi **Swanbridge Bloodstock Limited**
9 FORGET YOU NOT (FR), 6, ch g Smadoun (FR)—Baby Sitter (FR) **The Unforgettables**
10 GLORIANO (IRE), 4, b g Authorized (IRE)—Gloriana (FR) **Mr Martin Hughes**
11 GO AS YOU PLEASE (IRE), 8, b g Jeremy (USA)—Aweebounce (IRE) **Mr J. P. McManus**
12 GUMBO FLYER (FR), 5, b g Rail Link—Sariette de L'Isle (FR) **The Train Wreck Partnership**
13 HARRY THE NORSEMAN, 5, ch g Norse Dancer (IRE)—Titled Lady **Mr Julian Nettlefold**
14 HE'S A KNOWALL (IRE), 6, b br g Oscar (IRE)—Miss Knowall (IRE) **Old Gold Racing 5**
15 HELLO SUNSHINE (FR), 5, ch m Kapgarde (FR)—Louvisy (FR) **Nigel Jones & Paul Bowden**
16 4, B g Kayf Tara—Hot Rhythm **Mrs Paul Shanahan**
17 HOUSE ISLAND (IRE), 7, ch g Casamento (IRE)—Fuaigh Mor (IRE) **Economic Security 1**
18 IN THE DETAIL (IRE), 6, b g Milan—Customary Chorus (IRE) **Mr Martin Hughes**
19 INDEFATIGABLE (IRE), 8, b m Schiaparelli (GER)—Spin The Wheel (IRE) **Mr Philip Rocher**
20 IVAHUNCH, 4, b g Ivawood (IRE)—Galante (FR) **Strictly Legal**
21 JAYCEEBEE, 5, b m Gentlewave (IRE)—Alasi **Swanbridge Bloodstock Limited**
22 JEFFREY HARRIS, 6, b g Orientor—Theatrical Dancer **Mrs & Exors of The Late Mr P. C. Smith**
23 LADY DE VEGA, 4, b f Lope de Vega (IRE)—Red Boots (IRE) **Old Gold Racing 3**
24 LEADING MAN (IRE), 4, gr g Leading Light (IRE)—Nina Fontenail (FR) **Mr Philip Rocher**
25 LITIGATE (IRE), 6, b g Shantaram—Spin The Wheel (IRE) **Mr Philip Rocher**
26 LUNAR FLIGHT, 4, br f Pether's Moon (IRE)—Vanilla Delight (IRE) **Miss S. Pilkington**
27 MAXI JAZZ (FR), 6, gr g Enrique—Andria (FR) **Mr B. Bailey**
28 MISS BLAH BLAH, 5, b m Gentlewave (IRE)—Manaphy (FR) **Triple Crown Partnership**
29 MORDRED (IRE), 5, b g Camelot—Endure (IRE) **Mr Martin Hughes**
30 NAVY GIRL (IRE), 6, b m Westerner—Qeasy **Mr Philip Rocher**
31 PAWPAW, 4, b g Showcasing—Papaya (IRE) **Nigel Jones & Paul Bowden**
32 SPECIAL ACCEPTANCE, 8, b g Malinas (GER)—Doubly Guest **The Syndicators 2**
33 STARJAC (FR), 7, gr g Linda's Lad—Star's Mixa (FR) **The Starjac Partnership**
34 THE CITY COBBLER, 6, b m Mount Nelson—Galante (FR) **Sir W. J. A. Timpson**
35 TIKA MOON (IRE), 4, b g Casamento (IRE)—Trikala (IRE) **Mr Doug Mossop & Partners**

## MR PAUL WEBBER - continued

36 **VERNIER**, 4, ch g Nathaniel (IRE)—Tolerance (USA)  **Mr Martin Hughes**
37 **WAY PAST MIDNIGHT**, 6, ch m Midnight Legend—Royale Performance  **Swanbridge Bloodstock Limited**
38 **WINGED AFFAIR (IRE)**, 6, b g Winged Love (IRE)—Kiss Jolie (FR)  **Mr Philip Rocher**

### THREE-YEAR-OLDS

39 **ESTEEM (IRE)**, ch g Zoffany (IRE)—Sleeveless (USA)  **Vitality Partnership**

### TWO-YEAR-OLDS

40 B c 04/02 Nathaniel (IRE)—Sparring Queen (USA) (War Front (USA)) (25000)  **P. R. Webber**
41 Br c 20/03 Nayef (USA)—Tindomiel (Bertolini (USA)) (6000)  **D. Taylor**

---

**569**

**MR ADAM WEST, Epsom**
Postal: **Flat 2, Lorretta Lodge, Tilley Lane, Headley, Epsom, Surrey, KT18 6EP**
Contacts: **MOBILE 07939 030046**
EMAIL westtraining@outlook.com

1 **ADVANCE TO GO**, 7, b m Flemensfirth (USA)—Plumton Dawn (IRE)  **Mrs A. Cantillon**
2 **ALNASHERAT**, 5, b g Kingman—Split Trois (FR)  **Mr P. Naughton**
3 **BAMBINO LOLA**, 6, b m Helmet (AUS)—Lifetime Romance (IRE)  **Flawless Racing Limited**
4 **BRAVO FAISAL (IRE)**, 4, b g Kodiac—Israar  **Mrs J. M. West**
5 **BROUGHTONS FLARE (IRE)**, 5, ch g Rip Van Winkle (IRE)—Purple Glow (IRE)  **Mrs J. M. West**
6 **CAP'N (IRE)**, 10, b g Gamut (IRE)—Dawn Princess (IRE)  **Ishtar**
7 **CAPALA (IRE)**, 5, b g Swiss Spirit—Jezebel  **Mr R. C. P. Deacon**
8 **CESIFIRE (IRE)**, 4, b f War Command (USA)—Caterina di Cesi  **The Maverick Syndicate**
9 **COULDN'T COULD SHE**, 6, b m Sixties Icon—Emperatriz  **Ross Deacon & Partners**
10 **FAADIYAH (IRE)**, 4, ch f New Approach (IRE)—Ghasabah  **Mr S. K. McPhee**
11 **FAVOURED DESTINY (USA)**, 4, b f Noble Mission—Faraway Flower (USA)  **Mr S. K. McPhee**
12 **FINAL CHOICE**, 8, b g Makfi—Anasazi (IRE)  **Mr A. J. Morton**
13 **HEPTONSTALL**, 5, b m Thewayyouare (USA)—Dubaianswer  **All Seasons Racing**
14 **ILLEGITIMATE GAINS**, 5, b m Zebedee—Jillolini  **Mr S. W. Lang**
15 **KILGANER QUEEN (IRE)**, 11, b m Trans Island—La Prima Diva (IRE)  **Ishtar**
16 **KING RAJ**, 4, b c Footstepsinthesand—Cape Rocker  **Mr R. S. Matharu**
17 **LITTLE TIPSY**, 4, b f Harbour Watch—B Berry Brandy (USA)  **Mr A. J. Morton**
18 **LIVE IN THE MOMENT (IRE)**, 4, ch g Zebedee—Approaching Autumn  **Steve & Jolene de'Lemos**
19 **MEWS HOUSE**, 4, ch g Coach House (IRE)—Beauty Pageant (IRE)  **Flash Figs Racing**
20 **NOAFENCE (IRE)**, 4, gr f Outstrip—Strasbourg Place  **Farm fencing limited**
21 **PRINCESS MAYSON (IRE)**, 4, b f Mayson—Queen Athena (IRE)  **A Cantillon, J West & Ownaracehorse**
22 **REGULAR INCOME (IRE)**, 6, b g Fast Company (IRE)—Max Almabrouka (USA)  **Ian & Amanda Maybrey & Partners**
23 **SOCRU (IRE)**, 5, b g Kodiac—Hemaris (USA)  **AR Racing**
24 **SURRAJAH (IRE)**, 4, b g Camelot—Sharaarah (IRE)  **Mr R. S. Matharu**
25 **TATTENHAMS**, 5, b m Epaulette (AUS)—Tattling  **Mr Peter Hagger & Mrs Roseanne Hagger**
26 **THESPINNINGWHEEL (IRE)**, 6, b g Arakan (USA)—Dancing Jest (IRE)  **Padraic O'Neill & Janice West**
27 **THIBAULT**, 8, b g Kayf Tara—Seemarye  **Farm Fencing & West Racing**
28 **TUNED FOR POWER (IRE)**, 4, br g Slade Power (IRE)—An Chulainn (IRE)  **Mrs J. M. West**
29 **UNDERLAY**, 4, b g Harbour Watch—Kodiac Island  **Mr S. Wingrove**
30 **VIVID LUMINOSITY (FR)**, 4, ch f Hunter's Light (IRE)—Belle Lumiere  **All Seasons Racing**

### THREE-YEAR-OLDS

31 **ARTISAN BLEU (IRE)**, b f Mastercraftsman (IRE)—Washington Blue  **Cavendish Bloodstock Racing**
32 **BLACKTHIRTYONE**, gr g Gregorian (IRE)—Morena Park  **Ross Deacon, Tom Cusden & Janice West**
33 **CHUBBA**, b c Toronado (IRE)—Chetwynd (IRE)  **Tom Cusden, Darren Amass & Ross Deacon**
34 **DAPHNE MAY**, b f Mayson—Cambridge Duchess  **Ownaracehorse & Partners Iii**

## MR ADAM WEST - continued

35 **FALINE,** b f Hellvelyn—Lifetime Romance (IRE) **Ross Deacon, Tom Cusden & Janice West**
36 **GLEN ROSA,** b g Heeraat (IRE)—Aunt Minnie **Ownaracehorse & Partners V**
37 **JAFFATHEGAFFA,** ch g Havana Gold (IRE)—Actionplatinum (IRE) **Lee Broughton, Janice West & Tom Cusden**
38 **LAVISH OVATIONS,** b g Hellvelyn—Sing Me Sing Me **Mr C. D. J. O'Dowd**
39 **MOUNTRATH,** b f Helmet (AUS)—Malladore (IRE) **Mr D. Phelan**
40 **MY BOY FRANKIE,** b g Fountain of Youth (USA)—Lady Moscou (IRE) **Mr C. D. J. O'Dowd**
41 **ON THE NOSE,** b f Brazen Beau (AUS)—Little Annie **Shine & Pay**
42 B f Heeraat (IRE)—Sophie'jo **Mr F. Hutchinson**
43 **TELEFINA,** b f Telescope (IRE)—Haatefina **Silver Lining Racing**
44 **TREVOLLI,** b g Outstrip—Petit A Petit (IRE) **AR Racing**

## TWO-YEAR-OLDS

45 Gr g 24/04 Hellvelyn—Actionplatinum (IRE) (Act One) **Mr T. J. Cusden**
46 B f 11/03 Ardad (IRE)—Azita (Tiger Hill (IRE)) (1429) **O'Dowd, Slater, Gray J West**
47 **BYHOOKORBYCROOK,** b c 31/03 Garswood—
                        Broadlands (Kheleyf (USA)) (6000) **Ownaracehorse By Hook Or By Crook**
48 **COULDN'T COULD HE,** b c 21/03 Alhebayeb (IRE)—
                        Emperatriz (Holy Roman Emperor (IRE)) (4762) **Mr R. C. P. Deacon**
49 Ro f 04/04 Outstrip—Dame Plume (IRE) (Amadeus Wolf) (800) **Mr T. J. Cusden**
50 B g 19/02 Heeraat (IRE)—Elzebieta (IRE) (Monsun (GER)) (6500)
51 Ch f 11/04 Twilight Son—Fire Line (Firebreak) (1000) **Mrs J. M. West**
52 **GILBERT,** b c 26/04 Cityscape—Merry Diva (Bahamian Bounty) (5000) **Ownaracehorse & Partners Ii**
53 Ch f 28/04 Dawn Approach (IRE)—How Fortunate (Haafhd) (2000) **Amass, Cusden & Allen**
54 B f 19/04 Heeraat (IRE)—Kenyan Cat (One Cool Cat (USA)) (10476) **Mr D. R. Botterill**
55 Gr c 24/03 Outstrip—Lady Benedicte (IRE) (Shamardal (USA)) (3000) **Sills, Colegate, Amass & West**
56 **LAND OF EAGLES,** ch c 19/04 Havana Gold (IRE)—Disposition (Selkirk (USA)) (11000) **Tom Cusden & Partner**
57 **LIVE IN THE DREAM (IRE),** ch c 02/05 Prince of Lir (IRE)—
                        Approaching Autumn (New Approach (IRE)) (22857) **Steve & Jolene de'Lemos**
58 Ch f 17/04 Sea The Moon (GER)—Mouriyana (IRE) (Akarad (FR)) **Mrs A. Cantillon**
59 B c 16/04 Heeraat (IRE)—Peace Lilly (USA) (Distorted Humor (USA)) (762)
60 B f 27/03 Dragon Pulse (IRE)—Quite Smart (IRE) (Arcano (IRE)) **Mrs A. Cantillon**
61 B f 02/02 Belardo (IRE)—Silkenveil (IRE) (Indian Ridge)
62 Ch c 30/04 Spill The Beans (AUS)—Synaesthesia (IRE) (High Chaparral (IRE))
63 B c 05/04 Kodiac—Tides Reach (IRE) (Mastercraftsman (IRE)) **Lee Broughton & Padraic O'Neill**
64 B f 22/04 The Gurkha (IRE)—Tureyth (USA) (Street Cry (IRE)) (24000) **Mr S. K. McPhee**
65 B f 09/04 Estidhkaar (IRE)—Veladiya (IRE) (Zamindar (USA)) **Padraic O'Neill & Janice West**
66 **VOLENTI (IRE),** b c 11/02 Estidhkaar (IRE)—Izba (IRE) (Mastercraftsman (IRE)) (5000) **West Racing Partnership**

**Other Owners:** Mr P. Allen, Mr D. Amass, Mr D. R. Botterill, Mr E. Boumans, Mr L. Broughton, Mrs A. Cantillon, Mrs L. R. Colegate, Mr T. J. Cusden, Mr S. De'Lemos-Pratt, Mr R. C. P. Deacon, Farm fencing limited, Mr J. Gray, Mr P. Hagger, Mrs R. Hagger, D. Hassan, Mrs A. J. Maybrey, Mr I. N. Maybrey, Mr C. D. J. O'Dowd, Mr P. O'Neill, Ownaracehorse Ltd, Mr B Pay, SSLS LTD, Mr P. Sills, Mr T. G. Slater, The Slater Family, Mr J. Webb, Mrs J. M. West, West Racing Partnership, Wing It West, Mrs J. de'Lemos.

---

**570** | **MISS SHEENA WEST,** Lewes
Postal: **5 Balmer Farm Cottages, Brighton Road, Lewes, East Sussex, BN7 3JN**
Contacts: MOBILE **07748 181804** FAX **01273 622189**
EMAIL **sheenawest11@aol.com** FACEBOOK **@sheenawestracing**

1 **AIR HAIR LAIR (IRE),** 5, ch g Zebedee—Blond Beauty (USA) **I Poysden,R Heal,B Beesley,D Harper-Jones**
2 **ANYONEWHOHADAHEART,** 4, b f Sixties Icon—Bridie Ffrench **Miss S. West**
3 **BARD OF BRITTANY,** 7, b g Sayif (IRE)—Lily Le Braz **Mr M. Moriarty**
4 **CHERRY COLA,** 5, ch m Sixties Icon—Rose Cheval (USA) **Mr A. J. Head**
5 **CRAZY LOVE,** 4, b f Sixties Icon—Follow The Faith **Miss S. West**
6 **CRYSTAL TIARA,** 5, gr m Gregorian (IRE)—Petaluma **Mark Albon & Sheena West**
7 **DECORA (IRE),** 4, ch f Conduit (IRE)—Grevillea (IRE) **Miss S. West**

## MISS SHEENA WEST - continued

8  **DING DING**, 10, ch m Winker Watson—Five Bells (IRE)  **Mr I. E. Poysden**
9  **EVIE MAY**, 5, b m Excelebration (IRE)—Visanilla (FR)  **Miss M. M. Poulton**
10  **HARMONISE**, 7, b m Sakhee's Secret—Composing (IRE)  **Mr I. E. Poysden**
11  **JUSTANOTHER MUDDLE**, 12, gr g Kayf Tara—Spatham Rose  Saloop
12  **KENNY GEORGE**, 6, b g Mawatheeq (USA)—One For Philip  **Miss M. M. Poulton**
13  **LIMELIGHTER**, 5, b g Harbour Watch (IRE)—Steal The Curtain  **Mr Ricki Vaughan & Partner, Mr R. Vaughan**
14  **LYRICA'S LION (IRE)**, 7, b g Dragon Pulse (IRE)—Shishangaan (IRE)  **Mr R. Vaughan**
15  4, B g Captain Gerrard (IRE)—Natalie Jay
16  **NOW I'M A BELIEVER**, 4, b f Gregorian (IRE)—Alpha Spirit  **Mr A. J. Head**
17  **RALLY DRIVER**, 4, b g Gregorian (IRE)—Exentricity
18  4, Ch f Sixties Icon—Russian Empress (IRE)
19  **SAO JORGE**, 5, b g Dunaden (FR)—Bach To Front (IRE)
20  **SIXTIES SECRET**, 6, b m Sixties Icon—Jollyhockeysticks  **Mr M. Moriarty**
21  **THE TOPP NOTES**, 5, b g Sixties Icon—Hi Note  Onwoodsandupwoods
22  **ZOLTAN VARGA**, 7, b g Sayif (IRE)—Mar Blue (FR)  **Mr Ashley Head & Mr Garry Dreher**

## THREE-YEAR-OLDS

23  B f Sixties Icon—Hi Note

**Other Owners:** Mr M. L. Albon, Mr B. R. D. Beesley, M. R. Channon, Mr G. C. Dreher, Mr D. T. Harper-Jones, Mr A. J. Head, Mr R. J. Heal, Mr I. E. Poysden, Mr R. Vaughan, Miss S. West.

**Assistant Trainer:** Megan Poulton.

**NH Jockey:** Marc Goldstein.

---

**571**  **MR SIMON WEST, Middleham**
Postal: **14A St Alkeldas Road, Middleham, Leyburn, North Yorkshire, DL8 4PW**
Contacts: **MOBILE 07855 924529**
EMAIL simonwest21@hotmail.co.uk WEBSITE www.mkmracing.co.uk

1  **AMOOD (IRE)**, 10, ch g Elnadim (USA)—Amanah (USA)  **Mr S. G. West**
2  **BANDOL (IRE)**, 13, b g Zagreb (USA)—Formal Affair  **Mr P. Hothersall**
3  **CRANK EM UP (IRE)**, 10, b g Royal Anthem (USA)—Carrawaystick (IRE)  **Mr P. Hothersall**
4  **DORA DE JANEIRO (FR)**, 8, b m Ballingarry (IRE)—Katana (GER)  **Mr P. Hothersall**
5  **ELLA NUTRARGILE (FR)**, 7, gr m Kapgarde (FR)—Odile de Neulliac (FR)  **Mrs B. Hothersall**
6  **ERUDIT (FR)**, 7, b g Maresca Sorrento (FR)—Miss d'Anjou (FR)  **Mr P. Hothersall**
7  **FABULEUX DU CLOS (FR)**, 6, b g Blue Bresil (FR)—Osmazome (FR)  **Mr P. Hothersall**
8  **GHOSTEEM FLECHOIS (FR)**, 5, gr g Smadoun (FR)—Lesteem (FR)  **Exors of the Late J. D. Gordon**
9  **IT'S JUST TOMMY (IRE)**, 8, b g Tikkanen (USA)—Dusty Road (IRE)  **Mr S. G. West**
10  **JESSE JUDE (IRE)**, 8, ch g Doyen (IRE)—La Belle Bleu (IRE)  **Exors of the Late J. D. Gordon**
11  **JIMINY CRICKET (IRE)**, 10, ch g Golden Lariat (USA)—Lady Smurfette (IRE)  **Exors of the Late J. D. Gordon**
12  **KODI KOH (IRE)**, 6, b m Kodiac—Laywaan (USA)  **Wild West Racing**
13  **MAXIMISER (IRE)**, 13, gr g Helissio (FR)—Clydeside (IRE)  **Exors of the Late J. D. Gordon**
14  **MIKE MCCANN (IRE)**, 13, b g Helissio (FR)—Inzamaam (IRE)  **Wild West Racing**
15  **NELLIE DEEN (IRE)**, 8, b m Dream Ahead (USA)—Dorothy Dene  **Mr S. G. West**
16  **NEWS FOR PASCAL (IRE)**, 13, b g Kutub (IRE)—Direction  **Mr P. Hothersall**
17  **SHORT HEAD (GER)**, 6, b m Fastnet Rock (AUS)—Slight Advantage (IRE)  **Wild West Racing**
18  **SO YOU THOUGHT (USA)**, 7, b g So You Think (NZ)—Lady of Akita (USA)  **Exors of the Late J. D. Gordon**
19  **TOUCH KICK (IRE)**, 10, b g Presenting—Bay Pearl (FR)  **Hothersall & West**
20  **WESTY'S SUPER MARE (IRE)**, 6, ch m Golden Lariat (USA)—Lady Smurfette (IRE)  **Mr S. G. West**

## THREE-YEAR-OLDS

21  Ch f Garswood—Abonos (IRE)  **Mr S. G. West**
22  **LITTLE CHANCE**, b f Milk It Mick—Slim Chance (IRE)  **Mrs B. Hothersall**

**Other Owners:** Mrs B. Hothersall, Mr P. Hothersall, Mr S. G. West.

**572** **MR DAVID WESTON, West Overton**
Postal: c/o Flintstone Stud, West Overton, Marlborough, Wiltshire, SN8 4ER
Contacts: MOBILE 07966 641001
EMAIL flintstone007@icloud.com

1 ADMIRAL'S SUNSET, 8, b m Mount Nelson—Early Evening **Miss E. Tanner**
2 MAGICAL ORLA, 5, b m Flemensfirth (USA)—Fabrika **Miss E. Tanner**
3 SOLSTALLA, 9, b m Halling (USA)—Solstice **Miss E. Tanner**
4 THE LION QUEEN, 6, b m Helmet (AUS)—Bisaat (USA) **Miss E. Tanner**

**573** **MR TOM WESTON, Hindlip**
Postal: Offerton Farm, Offerton Lane, Hindlip, Worcester, Worcestershire, WR3 8SX
Contacts: MOBILE 07752 313698

1 COOPERS SQUARE (IRE), 10, b g Mahler—Jessaway (IRE) **Mr T. H. Weston**
2 CROCODILE DUNDEE (IRE), 11, b g Westerner—Outback Ivy (IRE) **Mr T. H. Weston**
3 HOLLOW STYLE (IRE), 5, b g Beat Hollow—Carrigmoorna Style (IRE) **Mr T. H. Weston**
4 IRON PORT (IRE), 5, b g Morozov (USA)—Portobello Lady (IRE) **Mr D. M. J. Lloyd**
5 LEVER DU SOLEIL (FR), 6, b g Le Havre (IRE)—Morning Dust (IRE) **Sunrise Partnership**
6 NOTNOWNOTNEVER (IRE), 5, br g Notnowcato—Truffle Fairy (IRE) **Mr T. H. Weston**
7 THE LATE LEGEND, 8, ch g Midnight Legend—Vin Rose **Mr G. J. Fisher**

**574** **MR ALISTAIR WHILLANS, Hawick**
Postal: Hilltop House, Newmill on Slitrig, Hawick, Roxburghshire, TD9 9UQ
Contacts: PHONE 01450 376642 MOBILE 07771 550555 FAX 01450 376082
EMAIL acwracing@hotmail.com

1 AJMAN PRINCE (IRE), 8, b g Manduro (GER)—Jumaireyah **Mr J. D. Wright & Mrs S. Wright**
2 AMAZING ALBA, 5, ch m Helmet (AUS)—Silcasue **John & Liz Elliot**
3 ANNIE BROWN, 6, b m And Beyond (IRE)—Nevsky Bridge **Mr J. R. L. Wilson**
4 BABY BLUESKY, 7, gr m Shirocco (GER)—Lady Bluesky **Mrs L. M. Whillans**
5 BATTLE OF WILLS (IRE), 5, b g Lawman (FR)—Maidin Maith (IRE) **The Battle of Wills Partnership**
6 BELLA BLUESKY, 5, br m Dylan Thomas (IRE)—Lady Bluesky **A. C. Whillans**
7 BELLA GLENEAGLES (IRE), 4, b br f Gleneagles (IRE)—Miss Lacey (IRE) **Mr L. W. Cook**
8 BILLY BATHGATE, 5, ch g New Approach (IRE)—Bustling **Mrs E. B. Ferguson**
9 5, B g Yeats (IRE)—Blue Nymph
10 BRACKENMOSS RORY, 9, b g Overbury (IRE)—Thorterdykes Lass (IRE) **John & Liz Elliot**
11 CORKED (IRE), 8, b m Mastercraftsman (IRE)—Dama'a (IRE) **Shmelt For Gold**
12 CORRIEBEN REIVER, 7, ch g Malinas (GER)—Wild Child Lucy **John & Liz Elliot**
13 COURT BALOO (IRE), 10, b g Court Cave—Tremplin (IRE) **A. C. Whillans**
14 CRACKING DESTINY (IRE), 8, b g Dubai Destination (USA)—Cracking Gale (IRE) **Mr A. G. Williams**
15 DANCING DOUG (IRE), 8, br g Kalanisi (IRE)—Drumcay Polly (IRE) **On the Road Again 2**
16 DONNACHIES GIRL (IRE), 8, b m Manduro (GER)—Russian Society **Mrs K. Spark**
17 EMPTY QUARTER, 6, b g Pivotal—Desert Skies (IRE) **Mr W. J. Muir**
18 FOLKS LIKE US (IRE), 6, b g Sans Frontieres (IRE)—Nia (IRE) **Mr W. J. Muir**
19 FORRESTERS PARK (IRE), 7, b g Scorpion (IRE)—Creanna Lady (IRE) **A. C. Whillans**
20 GHAYYAR (IRE), 7, b g Power—Al Ihtithar (IRE) **Mr R. Greggan**
21 GRUMPY BOOTS (IRE), 7, b g Stowaway—Reina Reed (IRE) **Mr A. S. Crawford**
22 GUN CASE, 9, b g Showcasing—Bassinet (USA) **A. C. Whillans**
23 HOUSTON TEXAS (IRE), 7, b g Dylan Thomas (IRE)—Royal Robin (IRE) **Mr A. S. Crawford**

## MR ALISTAIR WHILLANS - continued

24 HUNGRY HELEN HIPPO, 4, ch f Footstepsinthesand—Vicky Valentine  Mr F. Lowe
25 JORDAN ELECTRICS, 5, b g Dandy Man (IRE)—Ruby Slippers  Mr Brian Jordan,B.Jordan &stephen Jordan
26 JORDAN'S CHRIS (IRE), 5, ch m Society Rock (IRE)—
                                        Crimson Sunrise (IRE)  Mr Brian Jordan,B Jordan,Nicola McConnell
27 K C BAILEY, 5, b m Norse Dancer (IRE)—Wild Child Lucy  John & Liz Elliot
28 KAIZER, 6, ch g Nathaniel (IRE)—Perse  Mrs E. B. Ferguson
29 KALAHARRY (IRE), 9, b g Kalanisi (IRE)—Full Imperatrice (FR)  A. C. Whillans
30 KILCONQUHAR, 4, b g Hallowed Crown (AUS)—Passing Stranger (IRE)  Mr N. Dalgarno
31 LADY GRIGIO (IRE), 6, gr m Casamento (IRE)—Park Approach (IRE)  Big Teeree Racing
32 LEOSTAR, 7, ch g Nathaniel (IRE)—Gaditana  Mrs E. B. Ferguson
33 LIZZIE LOCH, 5, br m Maxios—Quenched  Mrs E. B. Ferguson
34 LYFORD (IRE), 6, ch g Intense Focus (USA)—Nurture (IRE)  A. C. Whillans
35 MISTER MANDURO (FR), 7, ch g Manduro (GER)—Semenova (FR)  A. C. Whillans
36 NEW RHYTHM, 6, b m Monsieur Bond (IRE)—Social Rhythm  A. C. Whillans
37 PITEMPTON POWER (IRE), 6, b g Yeats (IRE)—Western Euro (IRE)  Mr J. Fyffe
38 PUT THE LAW ON YOU (IRE), 6, b g Declaration of War (USA)—Spirit of Tara (IRE)  Mr J D Wright & Mrs S Wright
39 RALPHY BOY TWO (IRE), 4, b g Gutaifan (IRE)—St Athan  Mr F. Lowe
40 ROOM AT THE TOP (IRE), 6, b g New Approach (IRE)—Baila Me (GER)  Mrs E. B. Ferguson
41 ROYAL SHAHEEN (IRE), 8, b g Myboycharlie (IRE)—Viola Royale (IRE)  A. C. Whillans
42 SAMSTOWN, 14, b g Kingsalsa (USA)—Red Peony  Mrs E. B. Ferguson
43 SIENNA DREAM, 6, b m Swiss Spirit—Angry Bark (USA)  A. C. Whillans
44 THE BRORA POBBLES, 6, b m Helmet (AUS)—Snow Blossom  Mrs L. M. Whillans
45 WEST END WOODY (IRE), 6, b g Court Cave (IRE)—Poncho Murray (IRE)  Mrs K. Spark
46 WIND OF HOPE (IRE), 12, b g September Storm (GER)—Ciara's Run (IRE)  A. J. Brown
47 WISE COCO, 8, b m Shirocco (GER)—Sensible  Mclafferty & Pacheco
48 ZEALOUS (IRE), 8, br g Intense Focus (USA)—Velvet Kiss (IRE)  Mr W J E Scott & Mrs M A Scott

## THREE-YEAR-OLDS

49 DESERT QUEST (IRE), b g Footstepsinthesand—Waha (IRE)  Whillans, Orr, Spark, Wright
50 LADY ARTELA (IRE), br f Kodiac—Lyric of Fife (IRE)  Mrs K. Spark
51 MISS BOBCAT (IRE), b f Bobby's Kitten (USA)—Irrevocable (IRE)  A. C. Whillans

Other Owners: Mr D. Brooks, Mr F. A. D. Currie, Mrs E. J. Elliot, Mr J. J. Elliot, Mr D. N. French, Mr S. W. Hogg, Mr B. Jordan, Mr B. A. Jordan, Mr S. Jordan, Mrs N. McConnell, Mr M. McLafferty, Mr W. Orr, Mrs M. A. Scott, W. J. E. Scott, Mr C. Spark, A. C. Whillans, Mr J. J. Wilkinson, J. D. Wright, Mrs S. L. Wright.

---

**575**  **MR DONALD WHILLANS, Hawick**
Postal: **Dodlands Steading, Hawick, Roxburghshire, TD9 8LG**
Contacts: MOBILE **07565 609007**
EMAIL garrywhillans@gmail.com WEBSITE www.donaldwhillansracing.com

1 BABY TICKER, 12, ch m Endoli (USA)—Baby Gee  D. W. Whillans
2 5, B g Frammassone (IRE)—Ball Park (IRE)
3 5, B g Libertarian—Be Donn (IRE)  The Buyers Club
4 BIG BAD DREAM (IRE), 9, b g Mountain High (IRE)—Stay At Home (IRE)  The Brave Lads Partnership
5 BONNY HOUXTY, 8, b m Native Ruler—Izons Croft  Mr W. M. Aitchison
6 DALI MAIL (FR), 8, gr g Satri (IRE)—Queenly Mail (FR)  Mrs N. Mackin
7 4, B c Passing Glance—Ellistrin Belle  Ellistrin Partnership
8 ENEMY AT THE GATE (IRE), 5, b g Fame And Glory—Biondo (IRE)  D. W. Whillans
9 ETERNALLY YOURS, 8, b m Sulamani (IRE)—Well Disguised (IRE)  D. W. Whillans
10 HONDA FIFTY (IRE), 7, b g Arakan (USA)—Shuil Le Vic (IRE)  D. W. Whillans
11 KEYBOARD GANGSTER (IRE), 10, b g Gamut (IRE)—Vic O'Tully (IRE)  The Buyers Club
12 LADY VILLANELLE (IRE), 6, b m Shantou (USA)—Definite Deploy (IRE)  Td9 Racing
13 MAID OF HOUXTY, 6, b m Native Ruler—Izons Croft  Mr W. M. Aitchison
14 OUR ELSIE, 6, b m Yeats (IRE)—Well Disguised (IRE)  Mr S. B. Chamberlain

## MR DONALD WHILLANS - continued

15 **REQUINTO'S ROSE (IRE)**, 4, b f Requinto (IRE)—Castalian Spring (IRE) **D. W. Whillans**
16 5, B m Califet (FR)—Rose Vic (IRE) **D. W. Whillans**
17 **SEE MY BABY JIVE**, 5, ch m Coach House (IRE)—Lady Fiona **Mrs H. M. Whillans**
18 **SHOESHINE BOY (IRE)**, 5, b br g Valirann (FR)—Godlylady (IRE) **Mousetrap Racing**
19 5, B h Jet Away—Southway Queen **Robert Bewley**
20 **STAINSBY GIRL**, 7, ch m Shirocco (GER)—Charmaine Wood **Mr A. J. M. Duncan**
21 **STOLEN MONEY (IRE)**, 6, b g Prince Flori (GER)—Dark Daisy (IRE) **The Buyers Club**
22 **UNDECIDED (IRE)**, 5, b g Sageburg (IRE)—Your Place Or Mine (IRE) **The Buyers Club**
23 5, Ch g Midnight Legend—Well Disguised (IRE) **Mr A. J. M. Duncan**

**Other Owners:** Mr G. Aitken, D. W. Whillans, Mrs H. M. Whillans, Mr M. Young.

**Assistant Trainer:** Mr Callum Whillans.

---

**576** **MR RICHARD WHITAKER, Scarcroft**
Postal: Hellwood Racing Stables, Hellwood Lane, Scarcroft, Leeds, West Yorkshire, LS14 3BP
Contacts: PHONE 0113 289 2265 MOBILE 07831 870454
EMAIL rmwhitaker@btconnect.com WEBSITE www.richardwhitaker.org

1 **BILLY ROBERTS (IRE)**, 8, b g Multiplex—Mi Amor (IRE) **Mr R. M. Whitaker**
2 **CINDY LOOPER**, 4, gr f Coach House (IRE)—Velvet Band **Mr A. Melville**
3 **DAWN BREAKING**, 6, b g Firebreak—Jubilee Dawn **D Gration, G Sutcliffe, N Farman, Jeaton**
4 **GMASHA**, 4, ch f Intrinsic—She's So Pretty (IRE) **Mr R. M. Whitaker**
5 **HAWK IN THE SKY**, 5, ch g Coach House (IRE)—Cocabana **Mr M. Hawkins**
6 **JILL ROSE**, 5, ch m Coach House (IRE)—Wotatomboy **J.W.'s Wotafun Club**
7 **PENNY POT LANE**, 8, b m Misu Bond (IRE)—Velvet Band **Mr A. Melville**
8 **ROUND THE ISLAND**, 8, b g Royal Applause—Luanshya **Nice Day Out Partnership**
9 **SILK MILL BLUE**, 7, b g Piccolo—Marysienka **Mr R. M. Whitaker**
10 **STARBO (IRE)**, 4, ch g Starspangledbanner (AUS)—Jamesbo's Girl **White Rose Racing**
11 **STONEY LANE**, 6, b g Mayson—Spin A Wish **Country Lane Partnership**
12 **THRILLER'S MOON**, 4, ch g Mayson—Rio's Rosanna (IRE) **Mr James Marshall & Mr Chris Marshall**

## THREE-YEAR-OLDS

13 **COUNTRY CHARM**, b f Charming Thought—Alushta **Mrs Y Mee & Mrs E Whitaker**
14 **HAWK IN THE WIND**, br g Outstrip—Tumblewind **Mr M. Hawkins**
15 B g Slade Power (IRE)—Hot Wired **Mr R. M. Whitaker, Mr Kenneth Walters**
16 **LIBERTY BREEZE**, b f Equiano (FR)—Avon Breeze **Grange Park RacingXVII**

## TWO-YEAR-OLDS

17 B c 16/01 Spill The Beans (AUS)—Love Island (Acclamation) **Mr R. M. Whitaker**
18 Ch f 05/04 Spill The Beans (AUS)—Mey Blossom (Captain Rio) **Mr R. M. Whitaker**
19 Bl g 23/04 Lethal Force (IRE)—Rio's Rosanna (IRE) (Captain Rio) **Mr James Marshall & Mr Chris Marshall**
20 B f 10/02 Spill The Beans (AUS)—Tumblewind (Captain Rio) **Mr R. M. Whitaker**
21 B g 10/02 Spill The Beans (AUS)—Velvet Band (Verglas (IRE)) (9524) **Mr R. M. Whitaker**
22 B f 27/03 Outstrip—Wotatomboy (Captain Rio) **Mr R. M. Whitaker**

**Other Owners:** Mr N. Farman, Mr D. Gration, Jeaton Ltd, Mr C. R. Marshall, J. R. Marshall, Mrs Y. E. Mee, Mr G. Sutcliffe, Mrs R. M. Whitaker.

**Assistant Trainer:** Simon R Whitaker.

## 577   MR HARRY WHITTINGTON, Sparsholt
Postal: **Harry Whittington Racing Ltd, Hill Barn, Sparsholt, Wantage, Oxfordshire, OX12 9XB**
Contacts: **PHONE 01235 751869 MOBILE 07734 388357**
**EMAIL info@harrywhittington.co.uk WEBSITE www.harrywhittington.co.uk**

1 **ANEMOI (FR)**, 7, b g Manduro (GER)—Recambe (IRE) **Kate & Andrew Brooks**
2 **ARTISTIC LANGUAGE**, 5, b g Archipenko (USA)—Kiswahili **ValueRacingClub.co.uk**
3 **BIGMARTRE (FR)**, 10, b g Montmartre (FR)—Oh La Miss (FR) **Mr P J Dixon & Mr C Nash**
4 **BLACK ABBEY (FR)**, 5, bl g Hannouma (FR)—Alta Stima (IRE) **Black Abbey Partnership**
5 **BOOLEY BEACH (IRE)**, 5, b m Valirann (FR)—Booley Bay (IRE) **Wacky Racers Limited**
6 **BRAVE KINGDOM (FR)**, 5, b g Brave Mansonnien (FR)—
New Foundation (IRE) **Graeme Moore, Kate & Andrew Brooks**
7 **BREAKING WAVES (IRE)**, 7, b g Yeats (IRE)—Accola (IRE) **Colin Peake & Julie Slater**
8 **CALIDAD (IRE)**, 5, b g Califet (FR)—La Feuillarde (FR) **Harry Whittington & Partners II**
9 **CALVARIO (FR)**, 6, gr g Falco (USA)—Ashkiyra (FR) **Kate & Andrew Brooks**
10 **CAPTAIN TOMMY (IRE)**, 7, b g Court Cave (IRE)—Freemantle Doctor (IRE) **Mr R. J. Gurr**
11 **CATELINE (IRE)**, 6, b m Martaline—Kitara (GER) **The Atkin Family**
12 **CAUGHT INTHE SLIPS**, 7, b m Black Sam Bellamy (IRE)—
Greenlough (IRE) **The HWR Salty Crisp Fan Club Syndicate**
13 **DARGIANNINI (IRE)**, 6, b g Fame And Glory—You Take Care (IRE) **Dominic Burke & Kate & Andrew Brooks**
14 **DOCPICKEDME (IRE)**, 5, ch g Getaway (GER)—Hard Luck (IRE) **Jockey Club Ownership (SW 2020) Limited**
15 **EMERGING FORCE (IRE)**, 11, b g Milan—Danette (GER)
16 **FITZ IN (IRE)**, 5, b g Getaway (GER)—Tastytimes (IRE)
17 **FLASH DE CLERVAL (FR)**, 6, b g Maresca Sorrento (FR)—Nonita de Clerval (FR) **ValueRacingClub.co.uk**
18 **FRANIGANE (FR)**, 6, ch g Coastal Path—Nobless d'Aron (FR) **Edgedale & Robinson**
19 **GIVE US A SWIG**, 6, b g Trans Island—Touch of Ivory (FR) **Kate & Andrew Brooks**
20 **HENRIETTA BELL (IRE)**, 8, b m Shantou (USA)—Close To Shore (IRE) **The Racing Demon Partnership**
21 **JUNIPER**, 7, b m Malinas (GER)—Prescelli (IRE) **Gin n It**
22 **LANTIERN (IRE)**, 7, ch g Salutino (GER)—Luas Luso (IRE)
23 **MANY DOVES**, 4, b g Multiplex—Clover Dove **G. R. Prest**
24 **NEVERBEEN TO PARIS (IRE)**, 6, b g Champs Elysees—Island Paradise (IRE) **Mr P. M. Claydon**
25 **NUMBERONESON (IRE)**, 4, b g Camelot—Never Busy (USA) **Wacky Racers Limited**
26 **POLDARK CROSS (IRE)**, 6, b g Shantou (USA)—Diaconate (IRE) **The Racing Demons**
27 **QUALISMART (FR)**, 5, b g Martaline—Qualita (GER) **Kate & Andrew Brooks**
28 **RAFFLES GITANE (FR)**, 4, b f Kapgarde (FR)—Gitane du Berlais (FR) **Mr Simon Munir & Mr Isaac Souede**
29 **ROUGE VIF (FR)**, 7, b g Sageburg (IRE)—Rouge Amour (FR) **Kate & Andrew Brooks**
30 **RULING DE ROOST (IRE)**, 5, b g Rule of Law (USA)—Silent Memory (IRE)
31 **SAINT CALVADOS (FR)**, 8, b g Saint des Saints (FR)—Lamorrese (FR) **Kate & Andrew Brooks**
32 **SCARDINO (FR)**, 5, ch g Doctor Dino (FR)—Scarlock (FR) **Harry Whittington & Partners II**
33 **SEA THE CLOUDS (IRE)**, 4, b g Born To Sea (IRE)—Leo's Spirit (IRE) **ValueRacingClub.co.uk**
34 **SEDDON (IRE)**, 8, b g Stowaway—Andreas Benefit (IRE) **McNeill Family Ltd**
35 **SEE THE EAGLE FLY (IRE)**, 4, ch f Free Eagle (IRE)—Glassatura (IRE) **Sullivan Racing**
36 **SERGEANT O'LEARY (IRE)**, 5, b g Milan—Fuel Queen (IRE) **Incitatus**
37 **SHAMBRA (IRE)**, 7, b m Clodovil (IRE)—Shambodia (IRE) **Pali Pali Syndicate**
38 **SHANTOU VOW (IRE)**, 6, b g Shantou (USA)—Holy Vow (IRE)
39 **SHE'SONEOFOUROWN (IRE)**, 5, br m Sageburg (IRE)—Seavelvet (IRE) **Graeme Moore, Kate & Andrew Brooks**
40 **SHEILA NASH (IRE)**, 6, b m Flemensfirth (USA)—Hollygrove Rumba (IRE) **Mr C. T. Nash**
41 **SHORE SHANTY (IRE)**, 4, b m Shantou (USA)—Close To Shore (IRE)
42 **SIMPLY STRAWBERRY**, 4, b g Kayf Tara—The Strawberry One **The Kykie Allsopp Partnership**
43 **SIMPLY THE BETTS (IRE)**, 8, b g Arcadio (GER)—Crimson Flower (IRE) **Kate & Andrew Brooks**
44 **SIR SHOLOKHOV (IRE)**, 6, b g Sholokhov (IRE)—Menepresents (IRE) **Mr Simon Munir & Mr Isaac Souede**
45 **SIROBBIE (IRE)**, 7, br g Arakan (USA)—Presentbreeze (IRE) **Mr R. J. Gurr**
46 **SO EASY WAY (IRE)**, 5, br g Sageburg (IRE)—No Easy Way (IRE) **Kate & Andrew Brooks**
47 **TORIGNI (FR)**, 5, b g Palace Episode (USA)—Princesse Stesa (FR) **Mr Simon Munir & Mr Isaac Souede**
48 **WARRANTY (FR)**, 4, b g Authorized (IRE)—Ballymena Lassie **The Guaranteed Success Syndicate**
49 **WATERLEFE GETAWAY (IRE)**, 5, b m Getaway (GER)—Lucky Start (IRE)
50 **YOUNG BULL (IRE)**, 7, b g Dubai Destination (USA)—Jane Hall (IRE) **Nash & Webb**

## MR HARRY WHITTINGTON - continued

**Other Owners:** Mr A. L. Brooks, Mrs K. L. Brooks, Mr D. J. Burke, Mr G. Clemett, Mr P. J. Dixon, Mr J. W. Edgedale, Mrs L. N. Major, Mr G. Moore, S. E. Munir, Mr C. T. Nash, Mr C. Peake, Mr P. J. Robinson, Mrs J. E. Slater, Mr I. Souede, M. J. Vandenberghe, Exors of the late Mr H. J. M. Webb.

**Assistant Trainer:** Joe Quintin.

**NH Jockey:** Harry Bannister.

---

### 578   MR MICHAEL WIGHAM, Newmarket
Postal: **Hamilton Stables, Hamilton Road, Newmarket, Suffolk, CB8 7JQ**
Contacts: **PHONE 01638 668806 MOBILE 07831 456426**
**EMAIL michaelwigham@hotmail.co.uk WEBSITE www.michaelwighamracing.co.uk**

1 ASBAAGH (IRE), 4, b f Siyouni (FR)—Brynica (FR) **Mr T. Akman**
2 BARTAT, 4, b f Heeraat (IRE)—Pacches (IRE) **The December Lunch**
3 CAP D'ANTIBES (IRE), 4, b g Society Rock (IRE)—Miss Verdoyante **Mr P. Trainor**
4 DEPUTISE, 5, b g Kodiac—Dolly Colman (IRE) **Mr Glenn Simons & Id Heerowa**
5 EGRECIO, 5, b g Intello (GER)—Aspiring Diva (USA) **M. Wigham**
6 FEMININE FELICITY, 4, b f Dawn Approach (IRE)—Emirates Holidays (USA) **Glenn Simons & Michael Wigham**
7 GLOVES LYNCH, 5, b g Mukhadram—Suelita **Id & Burns**
8 MOSTAQQER (IRE), 4, b g Brazen Beau (AUS)—Rose Kazan (IRE) **D & Stevens**
9 MUJID (IRE), 6, b g Frankel—Bethrah (IRE) **Glenn Simons & Jerry Stevens**
10 MURAT ASSET, 4, b g Mount Nelson—Elis Eliz (IRE) **Mr T. Akman**
11 MY TARGET (IRE), 10, b g Cape Cross (IRE)—Chercheuse (USA) **G Linder,M Wigham,J Williams,A Dearden**
12 OMRAN, 7, ch g Choisir (AUS)—Ruff Shod (USA) **Clan Burns Tugay Akman D Hassan**
13 POOL FUND (IRE), 4, b f Tagula (IRE)—Perfect Pursuit **M. Wigham**
14 ROSE GREY (USA), 4, gr ro f The Factor (USA)—Smitten (USA) **The Gin & Tonic Partnership**
15 SANAADH, 8, ch g Exceed And Excel (AUS)—Queen's Logic (IRE) **M. Wigham, G.D.J. Linder, S Hassiakos**
16 SHAMAROUSKI (IRE), 5, b g Bungle Inthejungle—Masela (IRE) **M. Wigham**
17 VERNE CASTLE, 8, ch g Sakhee's Secret—Lochangel **M. Wigham**

### THREE-YEAR-OLDS
18 HYDE PARK BARRACKS (USA), b g Air Force Blue (USA)—Secret Charm (IRE) **M. Wigham**

### TWO-YEAR-OLDS
19 STORM ASSET, b c 08/04 Postponed (IRE)—Clear Water (IRE) (Hard Spun (USA)) (25714) **Mr T. Akman**

**Other Owners:** Mr T. Akman, Mr C. T. Appleton, Mr E. Baker, Mr P. Burns, Clan Burns, J. Cullinan, Mr A. Dearden, Mr P. J. Edwards, D. Hassan, S. Hassiakos, Ms I. D. Heerowa, Mr P. Jackson, G. D. J. Linder, Mr J. Searchfield, Mr G. Simons, Mr J. Stevens, M. Wigham, Mr J. B. Williams.

**Assistant Trainer:** Sharon Kenyon.

---

### 579   MR MARTIN WILESMITH, Dymock
Postal: **Bellamys Farm, Dymock, Gloucestershire, GL18 2DX**
Contacts: **PHONE 01531 890410, 01684 561238 MOBILE 07970 411638 FAX 01684 893488**
**EMAIL martin.wilesmith@linkbusinesscentre.co.uk**

1 BELLAMYS BELLE, 11, b m Black Sam Bellamy (IRE)—Mrs White (IRE) **M. S. Wilesmith**
2 BELLAMYS BOY, 7, b g Black Sam Bellamy (IRE)—Mrs White (IRE) **M. S. Wilesmith**
3 FAIR ALICE, 12, gr m Fair Mix (IRE)—Mrs White (IRE) **M. S. Wilesmith**
4 MIDNIGHT FRENSI, 12, b g Midnight Legend—Flame O'Frensi **M. S. Wilesmith**

**Assistant Trainer:** Ms E. C. Wilesmith

## 580 MR CHRISTIAN WILLIAMS, Bridgend
Postal: The Hollies, Heol Yr Ysgol, Coity, Bridgend, Mid Glamorgan, CF35 6BL
Contacts: MOBILE 07702 896759

1 ANNIE DAY (IRE), 6, br m Arcadio (GER)—Aunt Annie (IRE) **BDRSyndicates**
2 BARDEN BELLA (IRE), 5, b m Mahler—Princess Bella (IRE) **All Stars Sports Racing**
3 BIG CHIP AND PIN, 9, b g Generous (IRE)—Supreme Cove **Smerdon Tree Services Ltd**
4 CAP DU NORD (FR), 8, br g Voix du Nord (FR)—Qualite Controlee (FR) **The Can't Say No Partnership**
5 DEFUTURE IS BRIGHT (IRE), 7, b g Westerner—Dustys Delight (IRE) **The Can't Say No Partnership**
6 DUNEOMENO (FR), 5, gr g No Risk At All (FR)—Dulcamira (FR) **Mr C. R. P. Williams**
7 FIVE STAR GETAWAY (IRE), 7, b g Getaway (GER)—Hapeney (IRE) **Carl Hinchy & Mark Scott**
8 GOD KNOWS WHY (IRE), 6, b g Oscar (IRE)—Ballys Baby (IRE) **Ms S. Howell & Partner 1**
9 GOLDENCARD (IRE), 8, b g Golden Lariat (USA)—Flemensfirth Lady (IRE) **Deva Racing Value**
10 GROOM D'OUDAIRIES (FR), 5, b g Policy Maker (IRE)—Sonate d'Oudairies (FR) **Ms S. A. Howell**
11 ICE PIGEON (IRE), 6, br m Mastercraftsman (IRE)—Elusive Legend (USA) **Smerdon Tree Services Ltd**
12 JOEY STEEL (IRE), 8, b g Craigsteel—Tower Project (IRE) **Christian Williams Racing Club**
13 JONY MAX (IRE), 8, b g Mahler—Supreme Sunday (IRE) **Stquintonmauleintplyw'dvordermans-daniel**
14 JOSIE ABBING (IRE), 7, b m Fame And Glory—Bella Venezia (IRE) **BDRSyndicates**
15 JUST FOR TARA, 8, b m Malinas (GER)—Just For Jean (IRE) **Mr C. R. P. Williams**
16 JUST IN A MUDDLE (IRE), 6, b g Finsceal Fior (IRE)—Just Josie **Saloop**
17 KITTY'S LIGHT, 5, b g Nathaniel (IRE)—Daraiyna (FR) **R J Bedford & Partners**
18 KUIPER BELT (USA), 7, b g Elusive Quality (USA)—Youre So Sweet (USA) **Christian Williams Racing Club**
19 LIMITED RESERVE (IRE), 9, b g Court Cave (IRE)—Lady Blackie (IRE) **All Stars Sports Racing**
20 MAGNIFICENT BEN (IRE), 6, b g Sans Frontieres (IRE)—Lakeshore Lodge (IRE) **Mr O. S. Harris**
21 MAID ON MENDIP, 7, b m Schiaparelli (GER)—Sericina (FR)
22 MOVETHECHAINS (IRE), 7, b g Robin des Champs (FR)—Clash Artist (IRE) **Mr O. S. Harris**
23 NEWLANDS CROSS (IRE), 9, b g Stowaway—Honey Mustard (IRE) **Holloway,Clarke,Black**
24 PADDYS RUNNER, 9, gr g Sir Percy—Frosty Welcome (USA) **Paddys Runner Partnership**
25 POTTERS CORNER (IRE), 11, b g Indian Danehill (IRE)—
                              Woodford Beauty (IRE) **All Stars Sports Racing & J Davies**
26 POWERFUL POSITION (IRE), 6, b g Mahler—Molly Con (IRE) **J & Stars Racing**
27 PRIMAL FOCUS (IRE), 7, b g Intense Focus (USA)—
                              Churn Dat Butter (USA) **John & Paul Stanaway & Nicola Reed**
28 REALTA DAWN (IRE), 9, b m Craigsteel—Silver Grouse (IRE) **Christian Williams Racing Club**
29 ROOTLESS TREE (IRE), 6, b g Jeremy (USA)—Miss Compliance (IRE) **Mr C. S. Hinchy**
30 ROSERIVER HAS (FR), 8, gr g Astarabad (USA)—Vaibuscar Has (FR) **BDRSyndicates**
31 STRICTLYADANCER (IRE), 7, b g Yeats (IRE)—Feale Dancer (IRE) **Encore Racing**
32 UNO MAS, 7, b g Morozov (USA)—Broomhill Lady **Christian Williams Racing Club**
33 WIN MY WINGS (IRE), 8, b m Gold Well—Telstar (IRE) **Ms S. A. Howell**

**Other Owners:** All Stars Sports Racing, Mr R. J. Bedford, Mr S. T. Black, Mr A. L. Brooks, Mrs K. L. Brooks, Miss E. J. Clarke, Mr J. J. V. Davies, Mr C. S. Hinchy, Mr J. R. Holloway, Ms S. A. Howell, International Plywood (Importers) Ltd, Mr A. James, Mr G. C. Maule, Mr M. S. Scott, Mr J. D. Simpson-Daniel, Mr M. G. St Quinton, Ms C. J. Vorderman, Mr C. R. P. Williams.

**Assistant Trainer:** Nicky Williams.

## 581 MR EVAN WILLIAMS, Llancarfan
Postal: Fingerpost Farm, Llancarfan, Nr Barry, Vale of Glamorgan, CF62 3AE
Contacts: PHONE 01446 754069 MOBILE 07950 381227 FAX 01446 754069
EMAIL cath@evanwilliams.co.uk WEBSITE www.evanwilliamsracing.co.uk

1 ANNSAM, 6, b g Black Sam Bellamy (IRE)—Bathwick Annie **H. M. W. Clifford**
2 ARCADE ATTRACTION (IRE), 7, b g Arcadio (GER)—Tobetall **Border Pointers & Feilim O'Muiri**
3 ARCTIC SNOW, 5, b g Frankel—Winter Solstice **R. E. R. Williams**
4 ARIZONA GLORY, 5, gr g Universal (IRE)—Phoenix City (USA) **H. M. W. Clifford**
5 ASTRA VIA, 6, b m Multiplex—Wou Oodd **Mrs J. Davies**
6 BALKARDY (FR), 4, ch g Balko (FR)—Kalimnos (FR) **Balkardy Breezers**

## MR EVAN WILLIAMS - continued

7 **BALLINSKER (IRE)**, 6, b g Court Cave (IRE)—Brownie Points (IRE) **Gg Thoroughbreds Xii & Partner**
8 **BALLYBREEN (IRE)**, 8, b g Gold Well—Miss Colclough (IRE) **R. E. R. Williams**
9 **BALZAC**, 4, b g Lope de Vega (IRE)—Miss You Too **Opulence Thoroughbreds**
10 **BLUEBERG (IRE)**, 5, br g Sageburg (IRE)—Swell Sister (IRE) **Chris Trigg & Rer Williams**
11 **BOLD PLAN (IRE)**, 7, b g Jeremy (USA)—Kings Orchid (IRE) **Mr & Mrs William Rucker**
12 **BRANDY COVE (IRE)**, 4, b g Getaway (GER)—Gently Go (IRE) **Mr D. M. Williams**
13 **BROOKSWAY FAIR (IRE)**, 5, b g Mahler—Brook Style (IRE) **Opulence Thoroughbreds Nh & Partner**
14 **CAN YOU CALL**, 6, b g Passing Glance—Call Me A Legend **Mr & Mrs William Rucker**
15 **CARPOOL (IRE)**, 7, b m Mahler—Buslane (IRE) **Hush Hush Partnership**
16 **CASWELL BAY**, 6, b g Fame And Glory—Lauderdale (GER) **Mr David M. Williams**
17 **CHAMPAGNE RHYTHM (IRE)**, 6, b g Oscar (IRE)—Before (IRE) **Mrs Janet Davies**
18 **CLYNE**, 11, b g Hernando (FR)—Lauderdale (GER) **Mr D. M. Williams**
19 **COCONUT SPLASH (IRE)**, 6, ch g Stowaway—Presenting Chaos (IRE) **Mr & Mrs William Rucker**
20 **COOLE CODY (IRE)**, 10, b g Dubai Destination (USA)—Run For Cover (IRE) **H. M. W. Clifford**
21 **COURT ROYALE (IRE)**, 8, b g Court Cave (IRE)—Windsor Dancer (IRE) **Mrs Janet Davies**
22 **CRACKLE LYN ROSIE**, 7, b m Kayf Tara—Native Sunrise (IRE) **R. E. R. Williams**
23 **DANS LE VENT (FR)**, 8, b g Skins Game—Boreade (FR) **R J Gambarini Racing**
24 **DIAMON DES FLOS (FR)**, 5, b g Balko—Marie Royale (FR) **Mr & Mrs William Rucker**
25 **ESPRIT DU LARGE (FR)**, 7, b g No Risk At All (FR)—Tuffslolyloly (FR) **Mr & Mrs William Rucker**
26 **FADO DES BROSSES (FR)**, 6, b g Balko (FR)—Nanou des Brosses (FR) **Mr & Mrs William Rucker**
27 **FALETHAO D'ANA (FR)**, 6, b g Khalkevi (IRE)—Histoire des Ifs (FR) **T Harris & O Chandler**
28 **GIGA WHITE (IRE)**, 5, gr g Dark Angel (IRE)—Lightwood Lady (IRE) **Tony Cromwell & Partner**
29 **GILWEN GRAYSON**, 6, b g Multiplex—Gilwen Glory (IRE) **Keith & Sue Lowry**
30 **GILWEN REACHER**, 5, b g Phoenix Reach (IRE)—Gilwen Glory (IRE) **Keith & Sue Lowry**
31 **GO LONG (IRE)**, 11, b g Hurricane Run (IRE)—Monumental Gesture **Mr & Mrs William Rucker**
32 **GOLDEN WHISKY (IRE)**, 8, ch g Flemensfirth (USA)—Derry Vale (IRE) **Mr & Mrs William Rucker**
33 **GRANIA O'MALLEY (IRE)**, 8, ch m Beat Hollow—Oh Susannah (FR) **Ms Sue Howell I**
34 **GUNS FOR HIRE (IRE)**, 6, b g Scorpion (IRE)—Royal Robin (IRE) **Mr W. P. Bates**
35 **HOLDBACKTHERIVER (IRE)**, 9, b g Presenting—Fairy Lane (IRE) **W J Evans Racing**
36 **HOLLY JAMES**, 7, b g Black Sam Bellamy (IRE)—Miss Chinchilla **Walters Plant, Spiers & Hartwell, Pt Eng**
37 **IMPERIAL FLEM (IRE)**, 6, b g Flemensfirth (USA)—Glamorous Leader (IRE) **Mr & Mrs William Rucker**
38 **JOHN CONSTABLE (IRE)**, 10, b g Montjeu (IRE)—Dance Parade (USA) **W J Evans Racing**
39 **KHANISARI (IRE)**, 7, gr g Dark Angel (IRE)—Kadayna (IRE) **Pos Partnership 2**
40 **KING'S ODYSSEY (IRE)**, 12, b g King's Theatre (IRE)—Ma Furie (FR) **Mr & Mrs William Rucker**
41 **LOCKDOWN LEADER (IRE)**, 5, b g Leading Light (IRE)—Holy Vow (IRE) **Mr & Mrs William Rucker**
42 **LUSITANIEN (FR)**, 5, b g Muhtathir—Easter Rose (FR) **Mr & Mrs William Rucker**
43 **MAC AMARA**, 7, b m Dick Turpin (IRE)—Macnacie (IRE) **Keith & Sue Lowry**
44 **MAC KAYLA**, 6, b m Kayf Tara—Macnacie (IRE) **Keith & Sue Lowry**
45 **MAC NAN**, 5, b m Multiplex—Macnacie (IRE) **Keith & Sue Lowry**
46 **MACK THE MAN (IRE)**, 7, b g Flemensfirth (USA)—Nifty Nuala (IRE) **Mr & Mrs William Rucker**
47 **MARBLE MOON (IRE)**, 9, b g Millenary—Royal Marble (IRE) **Mr Emrys Jones & Partner**
48 **MEMPHIS BELL (IRE)**, 7, b m Yeats (IRE)—Andrea Gale (IRE) **Mr W. P. Bates**
49 **MISS ZIP (IRE)**, 8, b m Getaway (GER)—Lady Lace (IRE) **Tony Cromwell & Partner**
50 **MOTASHAKEL (IRE)**, 5, b g Olympic Glory (IRE)—River Test **Irving Struel Racing**
51 **MOUSEINTHEHOUSE (IRE)**, 7, b g Milan—Mandysue (IRE) **R J Gambarini Racing**
52 **NO REMATCH (IRE)**, 7, b g Westerner—Loadsofability (IRE) **Mr & Mrs William Rucker**
53 **OLYMPIC HONOUR (FR)**, 5, b g Olympic Glory (IRE)—Shamah **Mr R Abbott & Mr M Stavrou**
54 **ON THE QUIET (IRE)**, 6, b m Ballingarry (IRE)—Royale Sulawesie (IRE) **Hush Hush Partnership**
55 **ON TOUR (IRE)**, 13, b g Croco Rouge (IRE)—Galant Tour (IRE) **Mr T. Hywel Jones**
56 **ONLY THE BOLD (IRE)**, 6, b g Jeremy (USA)—Cloghoge Lady (IRE) **Mr & Mrs William Rucker**
57 **OXWICH BAY (IRE)**, 9, b g Westerner—Rose de Beaufai (FR) **T Hywel Jones Racing**
58 **PETERBOROUGH (IRE)**, 8, b g Fuisse (IRE)—Peony Girl (FR) **Norwester Racing Club & Partner**
59 **POBBLES BAY (IRE)**, 11, b g Oscar (IRE)—Rose de Beaufai (FR) **Mr D. M. Williams**
60 **PRESENT VALUE (IRE)**, 7, b g Gold Well—Presenting Shares (IRE) **Mr & Mrs William Rucker**
61 **PRIME PRETENDER**, 6, b g Great Pretender (IRE)—The Prime Viper (IRE) **Mrs Janet Davies**
62 **PRIME VENTURE (IRE)**, 10, br g Primary (USA)—Next Venture (IRE) **Mrs Janet Davies**
63 **QUOI DE NEUF (FR)**, 5, b g Anzillero (GER)—Qualite Controlee (FR) **Mr & Mrs William Rucker**
64 **RAILROAD JUNKIE (IRE)**, 8, b g Thousand Words—Eckbeag (USA) **Mrs J. Davies**
65 **RING THE MOON**, 8, b g Spanish Moon (USA)—Get The Ring (FR) **W. J. Evans**
66 **SABBATHICAL (FR)**, 6, b g Sunday Break (JPN)—Ulcy Pressive (FR) **R. E. R. Williams**

## MR EVAN WILLIAMS - continued

67 **SECRET REPRIEVE (IRE)**, 7, b g Flemensfirth (USA)—Oscar's Reprieve (IRE) **Mr & Mrs William Rucker**
68 **SIGN OF WAR (IRE)**, 7, b g Oscar (IRE)—Irish Wedding (IRE) **R. E. R. Williams**
69 **SILVER STREAK (IRE)**, 8, gr g Dark Angel (IRE)—Happy Talk (IRE) **Mr T. L. Fell**
70 **SKEWIFF**, 9, b m Doyen (IRE)—Skew **Mrs Janet Davies**
71 **STAR GATE (IRE)**, 5, b g Imperial Monarch (IRE)—Supreme Judge (IRE) **Mr & Mrs William Rucker**
72 **STATE CROWN (IRE)**, 4, ch g New Approach (IRE)—Patroness **six franks**
73 **STILL BELIEVING (IRE)**, 13, ch m Blueprint (IRE)—Im A Believer (IRE) **R. E. R. Williams**
74 **SUPREME ESCAPE (IRE)**, 7, b g Milan—Silent Whisper (IRE) **Walters Plant, Spiers & Hartwell, Pt Eng**
75 **THE BOAT (IRE)**, 5, b g Dylan Thomas (IRE)—Whenever Wherever (IRE) **R. E. R. Williams**
76 **THE LAST DAY (IRE)**, 9, b g Oscar (IRE)—The Last Bank (IRE) **Mr & Mrs William Rucker**
77 **TIMASSINI (IRE)**, 6, b m Dr Massini (IRE)—Timoca (IRE) **Mrs J. Davies**
78 **TO BE SURE**, 6, b g Sulamani (IRE)—Egretta Island (IRE) **T Hywel Jones Racing**
79 **TREASURE DILLON (IRE)**, 7, b g Sans Frontieres (IRE)—Treasure Trix (IRE) **Mr R Abbott & Mr M Stavrou**
80 **VIRGINIA CHICK (FR)**, 9, b g Nickname (FR)—Sweet Jaune (FR) **Mrs C. A. Williams**
81 **VOODOO DOLL (IRE)**, 8, b g Getaway (GER)—Voodoo Magic (GER) **R. E. R. Williams**
82 **WINDS OF FIRE (USA)**, 6, b g Kitten's Joy (USA)—Laureldean Gale (USA) **Mr T. L. Fell**

**Other Owners:** R. J. Abbott, Mr J. M. Basquill, Mr O. T. W. Chandler, Mr C. T. Cromwell, Mrs J. Davies, Exors of the Late Mr M. V. Dawson, Mr W. J. Eddy-Williams, W. J. Evans, Mr E. H. M. Frost, GG Thoroughbreds XII, Mr R. J. Gambarini, Mr G. Gill, Mr T. R. Harris, Ms S. A. Howell, Mr E. C. Jones, Mr T. H. Jones, Mr A. Lobo, Mr D. G. Long, K. R. Lowry, Mrs S. B. Lowry, W. J. G. Morse, Norwester Racing Club, Mr F. T. O'Muiri, Opulence Thoroughbreds N, P T Civil Engineering Ltd, POS Partnership, Spiers & Hartwell Ltd, M. Stavrou, Mr K. J. Strangeway, Mr I. Struel, Mr C. Trigg, Walters Plant Hire Ltd, Mrs C. A. Williams, Mr D. M. Williams, R. E. R. Williams, Mr S. Williams.

**Assistant Trainer:** Cath Williams.

**NH Jockey:** Adam Wedge, Conor Ring. **Conditional Jockey:** Isabel Williams.

---

**582**  **MR IAN WILLIAMS, Alvechurch**
Postal: **Dominion Racing Stables, Seafield Lane, Alvechurch, Birmingham, B48 7HL**
Contacts: **PHONE 01564 822392 MOBILE 07976 645384 FAX 01564 829475**
**EMAIL info@ianwilliamsracing.com WEBSITE www.ianwilliamsracing.com**

1 **ABEL TASMAN**, 7, b g Mount Nelson—Helena Molony (IRE) **Mr I. Furlong**
2 **AKARITA LIGHTS (IRE)**, 7, b g Arctic Cosmos (USA)—Akarita (IRE) **Mr Allan Stennett & Mickley Stud**
3 6, B g Winged Love (IRE)—Ally Rose (IRE)
4 **ALMOST GOLD (IRE)**, 8, b g Gold Well—Shining Lights (IRE) **Mr S. Cox**
5 **ALWAYS RESOLUTE**, 10, b g Refuse To Bend (IRE)—Mad Annie (USA) **Ne-Chance**
6 **ARMED (IRE)**, 6, b g Invincible Spirit (IRE)—Ange Bleu (USA) **Turton & O'Shea**
7 **ARTIC NEL**, 7, ch m Haafhd—Artic Bliss **First Chance Racing**
8 **AUTUMN WAR (IRE)**, 6, ch g Declaration of War (USA)—Autumn Leaves (FR) **The JAM Partnership**
9 **BLUE LAUREATE**, 6, b g Poet's Voice—Powder Blue **Mr A. Dale**
10 **BOL D'AIR (FR)**, 10, b g Blue Bresil (FR)—Holding (FR) **Mr P. Hernon**
11 **BOY IN THE BAR**, 10, ch g Dutch Art—Lipsia (IRE) **I. P Williams**
12 **BRAVO BUDDY (IRE)**, 5, b g Leading Light (IRE)—Second Best (IRE) **Deva Racing Bravo Buddy**
13 **BYRON FLYER**, 10, b g Byron—Nursling (IRE) **Anchor Men**
14 **CARDANO (USA)**, 5, b g Oasis Dream—Astorgs Galaxy **R. S. Brookhouse**
15 **CENTRAL CITY (IRE)**, 6, b g Kodiac—She Basic (IRE) **Mr S. Coomes**
16 6, Ch g Sholokhov (IRE)—Chiltern Hills (IRE)
17 **CHOSEN SHANT (IRE)**, 5, b br m Shantou (USA)—Ratheniska (IRE) **Golden Equinox Racing**
18 **COME ON JOSH**, 6, b g Universal (IRE)—Tangolania (FR) **Mr A. Cocum**
19 **COOL TO BE A CAT (FR)**, 4, b g Style Vendome (FR)—Forward Feline (IRE) **Mr P. R. Williams**
20 **DADS LEGACY**, 6, ch g Schiaparelli (GER)—Our Jess (IRE) **Mrs S. J. Vasey**
21 **DRAGON BONES**, 6, br m Passing Glance—Sainte Kadette (FR) **The Ferandlin Peaches**
22 **DYNALI**, 5, b g Dansili—Lunar Phase (IRE) **Golden Equinox Racing**
23 **EJTILAAB (IRE)**, 5, b g Slade Power—Miranda Frost (IRE) **Mr P. E. Wildes**
24 **EMBRACE THE MOMENT (IRE)**, 5, b m Le Havre—Kithonia (IRE) **Middleham Park Racing XCIII**

# MR IAN WILLIAMS - continued

25 **ERNESTO (GER)**, 6, ch g Reliable Man—Enrica **Buxted Partnership**
26 **EVERYTHING FOR YOU (IRE)**, 7, b g Pivotal—Miss Delila (USA) **Mr D. A. Thorpe**
27 **FAMOUS LAST WORD (IRE)**, 6, b br g Fame And Glory—Presenting Tara (IRE) **Mr T. J. & Mrs H. Parrott**
28 **FIFRELET (FR)**, 6, br g Diamond Boy—Unique Star (FR) **ASD Contracts Ltd**
29 5, B g Sholokhov (IRE)—Ginger Bazouka (FR)
30 **GOLDEN GRENADE (FR)**, 5, b g Zanzibari (USA)—King's Parody (IRE) **I. P. Williams**
31 **HARLOW**, 7, b g Harlan's Holiday (USA)—Glowing (IRE) **P. Kelly**
32 **HASANABAD (IRE)**, 6, b g Nathaniel (IRE)—Hasanka (IRE) **Teme Valley 2**
33 **HEAD ON (IRE)**, 5, br g Robin des Champs (FR)—Miss Baloo (IRE) **Mr S. Cox**
34 **HYDROPLANE (IRE)**, 5, b g Pour Moi (IRE)—Walk On Water **John Nicholls Racing**
35 **INDIANAPOLIS (IRE)**, 6, b g Galileo (IRE)—Adoration (USA) **Mr A. Owen**
36 **JAWSHAN (USA)**, 6, b g Denman (AUS)—Diamond Baby (USA) **Ever Hopefuls**
37 **JEN'S FELLA (FR)**, 4, b g Zoffany (IRE)—Heliocentric (FR) **Middleham Park Racing CI**
38 **KANGAROO POINT (IRE)**, 4, b g Australia—Magic Peak (IRE) **Ne Chance & Partner Iii**
39 **KICK ON KICK ON**, 6, b g Swiss Spirit—Catmint **Mr R J Turton & Ian Williams**
40 **KING OF REALMS (IRE)**, 9, b g King's Theatre (IRE)—Sunny South East (IRE) **Chandler Ferguson Hanafin Kelly**
41 **KINGBROOK**, 4, br g c Kingman—Warling (IRE) **R. S. Brookhouse**
42 **LADY SHIROCCO (IRE)**, 6, b m Shirocco (GER)—Estarana (GER) **The DTTW Partnership**
43 **LUCKY'S DREAM**, 6, ch g Yorgunnabelucky (USA)—Dream Esteem **R. S. Brookhouse**
44 6, B g Great Pretender (IRE)—Mewstone **The Ferandlin Peaches**
45 **MISTER PARMA (IRE)**, 8, ch g Iffraaj—Annee Lumiere (IRE) **Mr & Mrs H. Parmar**
46 **MOKAATIL**, 6, br g Lethal Force (IRE)—Moonlit Garden **Midtech**
47 **MONJENI**, 8, b g Montjeu (IRE)—Polly's Mark (IRE) **Deva Racing Value**
48 **MR PERFECT (IRE)**, 6, b g Mustameet (USA)—Crescendor (FR) **Mr S. Coomes**
49 **MRS DOUBTFIRE**, 7, b m Jeremy (USA)—Monsignorita (IRE) **M. C. Denmark**
50 **MUSTARRID (IRE)**, 7, b g Elzaam (AUS)—Symbol of Peace (IRE) **Mr A. Dale**
51 **NORTH HILL (IRE)**, 6, b g Westerner—Hill Fairy **Ms S. A. Howell**
52 **OCEAN VOYAGE (IRE)**, 6, b m Most Improved (IRE)—Minshar **Please Run Faster**
53 **OI THE CLUBB OI'S**, 6, gr g Champs Elysees—Red Boots (IRE) **The Albatross Club**
54 **ONE MORE FLEURIE (IRE)**, 7, b g Mustameet (USA)—Auburn Cherry (IRE) **Mr K. McKenna**
55 **OUR IDIC BOY (IRE)**, 7, b g Royal Anthem (USA)—Next Best Thing (IRE) **Mr K. McKenna**
56 **PADDY THE CHEF (IRE)**, 6, b g Dandy Man (IRE)—The Reek
57 **PARTY BUSINESS (IRE)**, 5, b g Shantou (USA)—Marias Dream (IRE) **Eventmasters Racing**
58 **PORTWAY FLYER**, 13, br g King's Theatre (IRE)—Next Best Thing (IRE) **P. Kelly**
59 **POUR JOIE**, 6, b g Pour Moi (IRE)—Lupa Montana (USA) **Helen Jameson Racing Partnership**
60 **PSYCHEDELIC ROCK**, 10, b g Yeats (IRE)—Gemini Lucy (IRE) **John Nicholls Racing**
61 **RATHBRIDE PRINCE (IRE)**, 6, b g Pour Moi (IRE)—Bright And Clear **Lost In The Summer Wine**
62 **RED INFANTRY (IRE)**, 11, ch g Indian River (FR)—Red Rover **Mr R. Little**
63 **REGABY (IRE)**, 6, b g Stowaway—Anjum (USA) **P. Kelly**
64 **ROBELLI (IRE)**, 6, b g Getaway (GER)—Marhab Dancer (IRE) **John Nicholls Racing**
65 **SAKURA SPIRIT**, 5, gr g Dutch Art—Bite of The Cherry
66 5, B g Sageburg (IRE)—Shining Lights (IRE)
67 **SHIP OF THE FEN**, 6, b g Champs Elysees—Ruffled **Midtech, McKenna, Macable**
68 **SIR MAXIMILIAN (IRE)**, 12, b g Royal Applause—Nebraska Lady (IRE) **Mr P. E. Wildes**
69 **SOMETIMES ALWAYS (IRE)**, 6, b g Presenting—Noras Fancy (IRE) **Mr S. Cox**
70 **SPEED COMPANY (IRE)**, 8, b g Fast Company (IRE)—Trentini (IRE) **A. Stennett**
71 **SPEEDO BOY (FR)**, 7, ch g Vision d'Etat (FR)—Shamardanse (IRE) **Mr P. R. Williams**
72 **TANQEEB**, 5, b g Garswood—Oasis Mirage **ASD Contracts Ltd**
73 **TEEMLUCKY**, 5, ch m Yorgunnabelucky (USA)—Dream Esteem **R. S. Brookhouse**
74 **THUNDER FLASH**, 4, b g Night of Thunder (IRE)—Sultanah Heyam **John Nicholls Racing**
75 **TIDE TIMES (IRE)**, 7, gr g Vinnie Roe (IRE)—Lady Wagtail (IRE) **The DTTW Partnership**
76 **TRAVELLING MAX**, 5, b g Maxios—Raiysina **T & R Kent**
77 **TRIBAL COMMANDER**, 5, gr g Intikhab (USA)—Jessica Ennis (USA) **Mr T. J. & Mrs H. Parrott**
78 **TWOJAYSLAD**, 12, b g Kayf Tara—Fulwell Hill **J. Tredwell**

## THREE-YEAR-OLDS

79 **BUXTED TOO**, ch g Iffraaj—Much Promise **Buxted Partnership**
80 **MRS DIBBLE (FR)**, b br f Dabirsim (FR)—Ossun (FR) **Mr A. Grant**
81 **SELFLESS ACT (IRE)**, br f Swiss Spirit—Shahaama **Salcey Forest Stud Racing**

## MR IAN WILLIAMS - continued

82 **SIR BENEDICT (IRE),** ch g Dandy Man (IRE)—Kingdomforthebride (IRE) **Mr P. E. Wildes**
83 **THIS ONES FOR FRED (IRE),** b br c Markaz (IRE)—Green Chorus (IRE) **Mr P. Coombs**
84 **TYPICAL MAN,** b g Territories (IRE)—Just Like A Woman **Mascalls Stud**

### TWO-YEAR-OLDS

85 B c 16/03 Caravaggio (USA)—Danehurst (Danehill (USA)) (47619) **Mr P. E. Wildes**
86 Gr c 26/04 Gutaifan (IRE)—Miranda Frost (IRE) (Cape Cross (IRE)) (23810) **Mr P. E. Wildes**
87 **TESTING FAITH,** b c 08/04 Time Test—Midnight (IRE) (Galileo (IRE)) (19048) **Midtech 3**

**Other Owners:** Mr G. Anderson, Mr D. E. Carolan, Mr G. Castle, Mr A. Chandler, Mr A. Cocum, M. R. Deeley, Mr A. I. Derry, Mr J. I. Derry, Mr R. M. Faccenda, Sir A. Ferguson, Mr N. D. Ford, Mrs M. Forsyth, Mr C. Hall, Mr D. Hanafin, Ms R. J. Harris, B. M. W. Hearn, Mrs S. J. Hearn, Mr M. Hilton, Mrs H. Jameson, Mr T. Johnson, Mr N. N. Kane, P. Kelly, R. Kent, Mr S. Mackintosh, Mr C. R. Mander, Mr K. McKenna, Mr F. Mooney, Ne-Chance, Mr J. A. M. Nicholls, Mrs J. J. Nicholls, Mr J. O'Shea, Mr H. Parmar, Mrs K. Parmar, Mrs H. Parrott, T. J. Parrott, Mr M. Rapley, Mr P. Ratcliffe, J. L. Rowsell, Mr P. Southall, A. Stennett, J. Tredwell, R. J. Turton, L. P Williams.

**Assistant Trainer:** Ben Brookhouse.

**NH Jockey:** Will Kennedy, Tom O'Brien. **Apprentice Jockey:** Joshua Thorman.

---

### MRS JANE WILLIAMS, South Molton
**583** Postal: **Culverhill Farm, George Nympton, South Molton, Devon, EX36 4JE**
Contacts: **HOME 01769 574174 MOBILE 07977 457350**

1 **ADMIRAL BALKO (FR),** 4, b br g Balko (FR)—Singaminnie (FR) **Culverhill Racing Club III**
2 **AFTER THE FOX,** 6, b g Universal (IRE)—Foxglove **Mrs J. R. Williams**
3 **AGRAPART (FR),** 10, b br g Martaline—Afragha (IRE) **Gascoigne, Brookes & Barker**
4 **AUBUSSON (FR),** 12, b g Ballingarry (IRE)—Katioucha (FR) **Mrs J. R. Williams**
5 **BALKO SAINT (FR),** 4, b g Balko (FR)—Sainte Cupid (FR) **Mrs J. R. Williams**
6 **ERICK LE ROUGE (FR),** 7, ch g Gentlewave (IRE)—Imperia II (FR) **The Culverhill Racing Club**
7 **FOLLY GATE (FR),** 6, b g Montmartre (FR)—Cate Bleue (FR) **Mrs J Williams & Mr R Stark**
8 **FOX PRO (FR),** 6, b g Coastal Path—Devise II (FR) **Mrs J. R. Williams**
9 **GALICE MACALO (FR),** 5, b m Saddler Maker (IRE)—Victoire de Forme (FR) **Culverhill Racing Club II**
10 **GLADIATEUR ALLEN (FR),** 5, b g Saint des Saints (FR)—Une Epoque (FR) **Mrs J. R. Williams**
11 **HERMES BOY (FR),** 4, b g Diamond Boy (FR)—Roche Brune (FR) **Valentine Bloodstock Racing**
12 **HONNEUR D'AJONC (FR),** 4, b g Diamond Boy (FR)—Fleur d'Ajonc (FR) **Valentine Bloodstock Racing**
13 **MONSIEUR LECOQ (FR),** 7, b g Diamond Boy (FR)—Draga (FR) **Mrs J. R. Williams**
14 **PRUDHOMME (FR),** 6, ch g Martaline—Panzella (FR) **Gascoigne, Brookes & Barker**
15 **ROCOCO RIVER,** 7, b g Shirocco (GER)—Noun de La Thinte (FR) **Mrs J Williams & Mr R Stark**
16 **SORELLINA ROYALE,** 4, b f Kayf Tara—Benefique Royale **Len,Burleigh,Downes,Jess,Jon,Ray,Booth**
17 **TEA FOR TWO,** 12, b g Kayf Tara—One For Me **Mrs Jane Williams & Mr Len Jakeman**

### THREE-YEAR-OLDS

18 B c Telescope (IRE)—Fragrant Rose **Mr R Stark & Mrs J Williams**
19 **ILFONCE (FR),** ch g Coastal Path—Une Brik (FR)
20 B c Saint des Saints (FR)—Jolie Menthe (FR)
21 **MOKA DE VASSY (FR),** b g Karaktar (IRE)—Mona Vassy (FR)
22 Ch g Martaline—Panzella (FR) **Gascoigne, Brookes & Barker**
23 **SAINT SEGAL (FR),** b g Saint des Saints (FR)—Bal Celtique (FR)

### TWO-YEAR-OLDS

24 B c 11/03 Great Pretender (IRE)—Rouvraie (FR) (Anabaa (USA))

**Other Owners:** K. Barker, J. N. W. Brookes, D. A. Gascoigne, Mr L. J. Jakeman, Mr E. Partridge, Mrs E. Partridge, Mr R. Stark, Mrs J. R. Williams.

## 584 MR NICK WILLIAMS, South Molton
Postal: Culverhill Farm, George Nympton, South Molton, Devon, EX36 4JE
Contacts: PHONE 01769 574174 MOBILE 07855 450379
EMAIL nandjwilliams@live.co.uk

1 AIMEE DE SIVOLA (FR), 7, ch m Network (GER)—Neva de Sivola (FR) **Larkhills Racing Partnership IV**
2 ALBERIC (FR), 4, b g Poliglote—Khayance (FR) **Corrina Ltd**
3 BORO BABE (FR), 5, ch m Sea The Stars (IRE)—Lockup (IRE) **Mrs E. K. M. J. Morgan Joseph**
4 COLONEL MANDERSON (FR), 5, b g Kapgarde (FR)—Playact (IRE) **Babbit Racing**
5 COO STAR SIVOLA (FR), 9, b g Assessor (IRE)—Santorine (FR) **Babbit Racing**
6 DENTLEY DE MEE (FR), 8, b g Lauro (GER)—Natty Twigy (FR) **Babbit Racing**
7 FAVORI DE SIVOLA (FR), 6, b g Noroit (GER)—Suave de Sivola (FR) **John White & Anne Underhill**
8 FIGHTING TIGER (FR), 4, b g Elvstroem (AUS)—Ma Preference (FR) **My Racing Manager Friends & N Williams**
9 GALAHAD QUEST (FR), 5, b g American Post—Atacames (FR)
10 GENIAL HAWKSTONE (FR), 5, b m Cokoriko (FR)—Silane (FR) **Mrs S. A. Noott & Mr N. S. L. Williams**
11 GINGEMBRE MENTHE (FR), 5, ch g Barastraight—Jolie Menthe (FR) **French Gold**
12 GRAIN DE THAIX (FR), 5, gr g Lord du Sud (FR)—Replique de Thaix (FR) **Tom Chadney & The Mugs**
13 HECTOR DE SIVOLA (FR), 4, b g Noroit (GER)—Little Memories (IRE) **Larkhills Racing Partnership III**
14 HELIOS ALLEN (FR), 4, b g Coastal Path—Silane (FR) **French Gold Racing**
15 HORATIO HORNBLOWER (IRE), 13, b br g Presenting—Countess Camilla **Chasing Gold Limited**
16 HURRICANE SIVOLA (FR), 4, b g Noroit (FR)—Surprise de Sivola (FR) **Mr N. S. L. Williams**
17 LE CAMELEON, 6, b br g Great Pretender (IRE)—Countess Camilla **The Pretenders & Partner**
18 LE ROCHER (FR), 11, b g Saint des Saints (FR)—Belle du Roi (FR) **John White & Anne Underhill**
19 MOONLIGHTER, 8, b g Midnight Legend—Countess Camilla **Huw & Richard Davies & Friends Racing**
20 NIGHT OF SIN (FR), 8, gr g Sinndar (IRE)—Natt Musik (FR) **Simon Brown & Ron Watts**
21 ONE FOR THE TEAM, 7, b g Shirocco (GER)—One Gulp **Forty Winks Syndicate 2 & Partner**
22 ONE OF US, 9, b g Presenting—One Gulp **Forty Winks Syndicate**
23 YGGDRASIL (FR), 4, b g Kapgarde (FR)—Margerie (FR) **John White & Anne Underhill**

### THREE-YEAR-OLDS

24 I'M THE DIVA (FR), b f Network (GER)—Sunny Vic (FR) **Mr N. S. L. Williams**
25 INTERNE DE SIVOLA (FR), b g Noroit (GER)—Kerrana (FR) **Mr R. C. Watts**

**Other Owners:** Mr S. J. Brown, Mr T. H. Chadney, Mrs V. J. Chadney, Mr K. Conlan, Mr H. G. Davies, Mr R. L. Davies, Mr G. Devlin, Mr R. Forster, Forty Winks Syndicate 2, Mr M. J. Freer, French Gold, Mr C. J. Garner, Mr S. D. Garner, Mr A. Holt, Huw & Richard Davies & Friends, Mr J. E. Lawrence, Mrs E. K. M. J. Morgan Joseph, My Racing Manager Friends, Mrs S. A. Noott, Mr I. Paye, M. L. Pepper, Mr J. D. Robinson, Mrs K. Salters, Mr J. Summers, The Pretenders, Mrs A. Underhill, Mr R. C. Watts, Mr A. J. White, Mr N. S. L. Williams.

**Conditional Jockey:** Chester Williams.

## 585 MR NOEL WILLIAMS, Blewbury
Postal: Churn Stables, Churn Estate, Blewbury, Didcot, Oxfordshire, OX11 9HG
Contacts: PHONE 01235 850806 MOBILE 07887 718678
EMAIL info@noelwilliamsracing.co.uk WEBSITE www.noelwilliamsracing.co.uk

1 ANOTHER CRICK, 8, b g Arcadio (GER)—Suetsu (IRE) **Mr D. J. S. Sewell**
2 ANOTHER DRAMA (IRE), 9, b g Gamut (IRE)—Rachrush (IRE) **Churn Racing**
3 BRIERY EXPRESS, 8, b m Rail Link—Blackbriery Thyne (FR) **Mr E. T. D. Leadbeater, Mrs Helen Plumbly**
4 CASHMOLL (IRE), 8, b m Ask—Witness Daughter (IRE) **Mrs S. P. H. Oliver**
5 CUILLIN (USA), 6, b m Arch (USA)—Zahrah (USA) **Mr N. Williams**
6 DELIGHT OF DUBAI (IRE), 7, b br m Dubai Destination (USA)—Bonny Hall (IRE) **Daniel MacAuliffe & Anoj Don**
7 EDWARD BLUE (IRE), 6, b br g Vinnie Roe (IRE)—Gold Shot **Mr R. Skillen**
8 ELLOFAGETAWAY (IRE), 5, b g Getaway (GER)—Ellaway Rose (IRE) **Didntt Partnership**
9 FARNE (IRE), 7, b m Stowaway—Bonnies Island (IRE) **Blyth Currie & Royle**
10 GINO WOTIMEAN (USA), 5, b br g Gio Ponti (USA)—Promulgation (USA) **Mr D. J. S. Sewell**

## MR NOEL WILLIAMS - continued

11 **KALINIHTA (IRE)**, 7, b g Kalanisi (IRE)—Valamareha (IRE)  **Mr J Allison & Mr A Allison**
12 **LARGY G (IRE)**, 7, b m Shantou (USA)—G Day Sile (IRE)  **Mrs Lucie McGarity**
13 **LOCKDOWN LADY**, 5, b m Universal (IRE)—Mays Dream  **Stonepoint Racing Club**
14 **MISS KHARIZMA (IRE)**, 4, b f Kalanisi (IRE)—Aunt Kate (IRE)  **Elaine Chivers Racing**
15 **PURE COUNTRY**, 6, b g Frankel—Plante Rare (IRE)  **Mr N. Williams, Mr Matt Coleman**
16 **SENSULANO (IRE)**, 8, b m Milan—Espresso Lady (IRE)  **Allison, Allison, Williams**
17 **SOL PLUM CREEK (FR)**, 5, b g Canyon Creek (IRE)—Solenrana (FR)  **Stonepoint Racing Club**
18 **SOUND OF MUSIC**, 6, ch m Universal (IRE)—Sounds Familiar (IRE)  **Mrs M. L. Luck**
19 **SPEECH BUBBLE (IRE)**, 6, b m Well Chosen—Teamplin (IRE)  **Mr T. D. J. Syder**
20 **STEP TO THE TOP (IRE)**, 6, b m Doyen (IRE)—Step On My Soul (IRE)  **Mr G. Wragg**
21 **THAT'S A GIVEN (FR)**, 7, b g Great Pretender—Aulne River (FR)  **Mr Andrew L. Cohen**
22 **THEATRE GOER**, 12, b m King's Theatre (IRE)—Clover Green (IRE)  **Waddington & Williams Bloodstock**
23 **TITANEASY**, 6, b g Thewayyouare (USA)—Titian's Pride (USA)  **Pegasus Bloodstock Ltd & David McNeil**
24 **TWIN STAR (IRE)**, 7, ch g Tagula (IRE)—Chronicle  **Happy Star Partnership**
25 **VINNIE DEV (IRE)**, 7, b g Vinnie Roe (IRE)—Nifty Milan (IRE)  **David J S Sewell & Tim Leadbeater**
26 **ZIGGY ROSE (IRE)**, 7, b m Fame And Glory—Koko Rose (IRE)  **Elaine Chivers Racing**

### THREE-YEAR-OLDS

27 B f Scorpion (IRE)—Theatre Goer  **Peace Of Mind Racing Club**

**Other Owners:** Mr J. Allison, S. A. Allison, Mrs H. D. Blyth Currie, Miss C. I. Chivers, Ms E. C. Chivers, Ms L. D. Chivers, Mr E. T. D. Leadbeater, Mr D. E. T. McNeill, Pegasus Bloodstock Limited, Mrs H. M. Royle, Mr D. J. S. Sewell, Ms Kate Waddington, Mr N. Williams.

**NH Jockey:** Paddy Brennan, Robbie Dunne.

---

**586** **MR OLLY WILLIAMS**, Market Rasen
Postal: **Stone Cottage, Nettleton Top, Market Rasen, Lincolnshire, LN7 6SY**
Contacts: **MOBILE 07793 111600**
**EMAIL williams.olly@yahoo.co.uk WEBSITE www.ollywilliamsracing.co.uk**

1 **GOING NATIVE**, 6, ch m Speightstown (USA)—Latin Love (IRE)  **D. L. Bayliss**
2 **INEXORABLE**, 8, b g Sulamani (IRE)—Princess Amelia (IRE)  **Mr D. J. Ablott**
3 **LINCOLN RED**, 5, ch g Monsieur Bond (IRE)—Roxy Hart  **Top of the Wolds Racing**
4 **RASPBERRY**, 5, b m Avonbridge—Spennymoor (IRE)  **Olly Williams Rhys Williams James Hanna**

### THREE-YEAR-OLDS

5 **CORIANO RIDGE**, b g Al Kazeem—Melodica  **Olly Williams Rhys Williams James Hanna**
6 **NORTHERN GENERAL (IRE)**, ch g Ivawood (IRE)—Cealtra Star (IRE)  **Mrs H. R. Townsend**
7 **YOUR FANCY**, b f Showcasing—Whim  **Racing For Life Partnership**

### TWO-YEAR-OLDS

8 **ROANO (IRE)**, ro c 16/04 Buratino (IRE)—She's A Minx (IRE) (Linamix (FR)) (5714)  **David Bayliss,Olly Williams,Trevor Smithson**

**Other Owners:** D. L. Bayliss, Mr W. Belcher, Mr J. Hanna, Mr T. A. Pocklington, Mr T. Smithson, Mr M. C. Waddingham, Mr E. Williams, Mr O. R. Williams, Mr R. T. Williams.

**Assistant Trainer:** Lynsey Williams.

## 587 MR STUART WILLIAMS, Newmarket

Postal: **Diomed Stables, Hamilton Road, Newmarket, Suffolk, CB8 0PD**
Contacts: HOME **01638 560143** PHONE **01638 663984** MOBILE **07730 314102**
EMAIL **stuart@stuartwilliamsracing.co.uk** WEBSITE **www.stuartwilliamsracing.co.uk**
TWITTER **@Williamsstuart**

1 **AGENT SHIFTWELL**, 4, b g Equiano (FR)—Holley Shiftwell **J. W. Parry**
2 **AL MUFFRIH (IRE)**, 6, b g Sea The Stars (IRE)—Scarlet And Gold (IRE) **Mrs M. J. Morley**
3 **ALBUM (IRE)**, 4, gr g Clodovil (IRE)—Michael's Song (IRE) **Opulence Thoroughbreds**
4 **BELLE ANGLAISE**, 4, b f Cable Bay (IRE)—Belle Allemande (CAN) **Graf P. Von Stauffenberg**
5 **BIG BROWN (IRE)**, 4, b g Canford Cliffs (IRE)—Caravan of Dreams (IRE) **Mr S. C. Williams**
6 **CLEGANE**, 4, ch f Iffraaj—Cradle of Life (IRE) **The Pro-Claimers**
7 **DAWN VIEW (IRE)**, 4, b f Dawn Approach (IRE)—Viletta (GER) **Essex Racing Club et al**
8 **DRAMATICA (IRE)**, 4, ch f Lope de Vega (IRE)—Miss Georgie (IRE) **J. W. Parry**
9 **EL RAY (IRE)**, 4, gr c Lope de Vega (IRE)—Lucky Clio (IRE) **Mr S. C. Williams**
10 **EQUITATION**, 7, b g Equiano (FR)—Sakhee's Song (IRE) **Mr A Lyons & Mr T W Morley**
11 **EXCELLENT GEORGE**, 9, b g Exceed And Excel (AUS)—Princess Georgina **Mr Stuart Williams & Mr J W Parry**
12 **GIVE IT SOME TEDDY**, 7, b g Bahamian Bounty—Croeso Cariad **TW Morley, Terry Long & Partners**
13 **GLENN COCO**, 7, gr g Aussie Rules (USA)—Las Hilanderas (USA) **Miss Emily Stevens Partnership**
14 **HERCULEAN**, 6, ch g Frankel—African Rose **Morley, Reynolds, Watkins & Partner**
15 **I'M AVAILABLE (IRE)**, 5, b m Nathaniel (IRE)—Night Carnation **Mr S. C. Williams**
16 **KNOWING GLANCE (IRE)**, 6, b g Kodiac—Shauna's Princess (IRE) **Patrick B Doyle (Construction) Ltd**
17 **LORD RAPSCALLION (IRE)**, 5, gr g Alhebayeb (IRE)—Simply Topping (IRE) **Mr T. W. Morley**
18 **LUNAR DEITY**, 12, b g Medicean—Luminda (IRE) **Mr W E Enticknap & Partner**
19 **MY BOY SEPOY**, 6, ch g Sepoy (AUS)—Emily Carr (IRE) **Mr & Mrs G. Bhatti**
20 **PACTOLUS (IRE)**, 10, b g Footstepsinthesand—Gold Marie (IRE) **T W Morley & Mrs J Morley**
21 **PAPA STOUR (USA)**, 6, b g Scat Daddy (USA)—Illaunglass (IRE) **Mr T. W. Morley**
22 **PASSIONAL**, 4, b f Footstepsinthesand—Cordial **Mr J W Parry and Mrs C Shekells**
23 **PINNATA (IRE)**, 7, b g Shamardal (USA)—Lavande Violet (GER) **Mr David N Reynolds & Mr C D Watkins**
24 **REVOLUTIONISE (IRE)**, 5, gr g Lope de Vega (IRE)—Modeeroch (IRE) **T W Morley & Regents Racing**
25 **RHYTHMIC INTENT (IRE)**, 5, ch h Lope de Vega (IRE)—Kerry Gal (IRE) **Happy Valley Racing & Breeding Limited**
26 **RIVER ROCK (IRE)**, 4, b f Fastnet Rock (AUS)—Knocknagree (IRE) **Mr P. Brosnan**
27 **ROYAL BIRTH**, 10, b g Exceed And Excel (AUS)—Princess Georgina **The Morley Family**
28 **SHAMSHON (IRE)**, 10, b g Invincible Spirit (IRE)—Greenisland (IRE) **T W Morley & Regents Racing**
29 **TAWNY PORT**, 7, ch g Arcano (IRE)—Tawaasul **Morley, Enticknap B Ralph**
30 **THE GILL BROTHERS**, 5, gr g Mukhadram—Si Belle (IRE) **The Gill Brothers**
31 **TONE THE BARONE**, 5, ch g Lope de Vega (IRE)—A Huge Dream (IRE) **Mr B Piper & Partner**
32 **WOLFLET**, 4, ch f Lope de Vega (IRE)—Martlet **J. G. Thom**

### THREE-YEAR-OLDS

33 **AKKERINGA**, b c Dutch Art—Annie's Fortune (IRE) **Mr G Johnson & Mr J W Parry**
34 **BABY SHAM**, b f Sir Percy—Zamzama (IRE) **J. W. Parry**
35 **BEDFORD BLAZE (IRE)**, b c Dandy Man (IRE)—Hawaajib (FR) **Mr George Bhatti & Partner**
36 B g Twilight Son—Cincinnati Kit **Mr J W Parry & Partner**
37 **FINAL FANTASY**, gr f Lethal Force (IRE)—Fantasize **Mr S. C. Williams**
38 **FURY**, b c Zoffany (IRE)—Swiss Dream **Lordship Stud**
39 Ch f Equiano (FR)—Holley Shiftwell **J. W. Parry**
40 **LIBERTINE BELLE**, b f Helmet (AUS)—Cordial **Mr J W Parry & Partner**
41 **LYNNS BOY**, ch c Coach House (IRE)—La Fortunata **Mr M. Ricketts**
42 **MOTORIOUS**, b c Muhaarar—Squash **Opulence Thoroughbreds**
43 **ONALEDGE**, gr f Toronado (IRE)—Tipping Over (IRE) **Essex Racing Club**
44 **TRIBUTO (IRE)**, b c Dragon Pulse (IRE)—Auntie Myrtle (IRE) **Opulence Thoroughbreds**

### TWO-YEAR-OLDS

45 B c 22/03 Oasis Dream—Beach Bunny (IRE) (High Chaparral (IRE)) (47619) **Opulence Thoroughbreds**
46 B c 15/02 The Last Lion (IRE)—Before The Storm (Sadler's Wells (USA)) (10000) **Mr S. C. Williams**
47 B f 25/01 Dabirsim (FR)—Crowning Glory (FR) (Speightstown (USA)) (28000) **Mr J W Parry & Partners**
48 B f 21/04 Zoffany (IRE)—Malmoosa (IRE) (Shamardal (USA)) (21000) **Mr J W Parry and Mrs C Shekells**
49 B f 20/03 Oasis Dream—Pure Innocence (IRE) (Montjeu (IRE)) (20000) **Mr J W Parry and Mrs C Shekells**
50 Ch c 12/05 Profitable (IRE)—Winning Sequence (FR) (Zafonic (USA)) (36000) **Mr B Piper & Mr D Cobill**

## MR STUART WILLIAMS - continued

**Other Owners:** Mrs C. J. Bhatti, Mr G. Bhatti, Mr D. L. Cobill, W. E. Enticknap, Essex Racing Club, Mrs E. A. Harris, T. F. Harris, Mr G. M. C. Johnson, Mr A. A. Lyons, Mrs M. J. Morley, Mr T. W. Morley, J. W. Parry, Mr B. V. Piper, Mr G. R. Pooley, Mr B. Ralph, Mr D. Redvers, Regents Racing, Mr D. N. Reynolds, Mrs J. P. Root, Mr R. B. Root, Mrs C. I. Shekells, Miss E. V. Stevens, P. W. Stevens, Mr C. D. Watkins, Mr S. C. Williams.

**Assistant Trainer:** J W Parry.

**Apprentice Jockey:** Lorenzo Atzori, Marco Ghiani, Adeel Muhammad.

---

## 588 | MISS VENETIA WILLIAMS, Hereford

Postal: **Aramstone, Kings Caple, Hereford, Herefordshire, HR1 4TU**
Contacts: **PHONE 01432 840646 MOBILE 07770 627108**
**EMAIL office@venetiawilliams.com WEBSITE www.venetiawilliams.com**

1 ACHILLE (FR), 11, gr g Dom Alco (FR)—Hase (FR) **Mrs V. A. Bingham**
2 ARQALINA (IRE), 9, b m Arcano (IRE)—Pride Celebre (IRE) **The Hon Lady Heber-Percy & V Williams**
3 ASO (FR), 11, b br g Goldneyev (USA)—Odyssee du Cellier (FR) **The Bellamy Partnership**
4 BELAMI DES PICTONS (FR), 10, b g Khalkevi (IRE)—Nina des Pictons (FR) **Hills of Ledbury Ltd**
5 BELLATRIXSA (IRE), 4, gr f Gregorian (IRE)—Aloisi (IRE) **Mrs S. A. J. Kinsella**
6 4, Br gr f Geordieland (FR)—Bollin Across **Mrs N. S. Harris**
7 BRAVE SEASCA (FR), 6, bl g Brave Mansonnien (FR)—Miss Laveron (FR) **Lds Partnership**
8 BRIANSTORM (IRE), 9, b g Brian Boru—Coco Moon (IRE) **David & Carol Shaw**
9 BURROWS PARK (FR), 9, b g Astarabad (USA)—
La Vie de Boitron (FR) **Venetia Williams Racehorse Syndicate III**
10 CATCH THE SWALLOWS (IRE), 7, b g Masterofthehorse (IRE)—Nafrah (USA) **Carol & David Shaw**
11 CEPAGE (FR), 9, b g Saddler Maker (IRE)—Sience Fiction (FR) **The Bellamy Partnership**
12 CHAMBARD (FR), 9, b g Gris de Gris (IRE)—Regina Park (FR) **David & Carol Shaw**
13 CLOUDY GLEN (IRE), 8, b g Cloudings (IRE)—Ribble (IRE) **Mr T. J. Hemmings**
14 COMMIS D'OFFICE (FR), 9, b g Califet (FR)—Pas de Bal (FR) **Julian Blackwell & Mrs Angus Maclay**
15 COMMODORE (FR), 9, gr g Fragrant Mix (FR)—Morvandelle (FR) **Mrs C Watson & Mrs S Graham**
16 CRYPTO (IRE), 7, b g Gold Well—Top Lot (IRE) **Mr P. Davies**
17 CUBAN PETE (IRE), 9, b g Flemensfirth (USA)—Gee Whizz (FR) **Mrs J. Jones**
18 DESQUE DE L'ISLE (FR), 8, b g Special Kaldoun (FR)—Naiade de L'Isle (FR) **The Hon Lady M. J. Heber-Percy**
19 DESTINEE ROYALE (FR), 8, b m Balko (FR)—Viana (FR) **Mr C. Boultbee-Brooks**
20 DIDERO VALLIS (FR), 8, b g Poliglote—Oreade Vallis (FR) **Normans, Ramsay, Tufnell & Bishop**
21 DON HERBAGER (FR), 7, b g Saddler Maker (IRE)—Marie d'Altoria (FR) **M Willcocks & V Williams**
22 EASY AS THAT (IRE), 6, b g Sans Frontieres (IRE)—Bell Storm (IRE) **Kate & Andrew Brooks**
23 ECEPARTI (FR), 7, b g Enrique—La Pommeraie (FR) **Mrs S. M. Champ**
24 ELEANOR BOB, 6, b m Midnight Legend—Red And White (IRE) **F. M. P. Mahon**
25 ELIXIR DU GOUET (FR), 7, ch g Vision d'Etat (FR)—My Asadore (FR) **Charles & Mary Rose Barlow**
26 ENZO D'AIRY (FR), 7, b g Anzillero (GER)—Panzara d'Airy (FR) **Dr M. A. Hamlin**
27 ESPOIR DE GUYE (FR), 7, b g Khalkevi (FR)—Penelope de Guye (FR) **Mrs J. Hitchings**
28 FALLY JEM (FR), 6, b m Authorized (IRE)—Ballymena Lassie **Bendall & Anderson**
29 FANION D'ESTRUVAL (FR), 6, b g Enrique—Urfe d'Estruval (FR) **Mr David Wilson**
30 FARINET (FR), 6, gr g Lord du Sud (FR)—Mendy Tennise (FR) **Mindy Hammond & Eddie Coombs**
31 FARRANTS WAY (IRE), 7, b g Shantou (USA)—Shuil A Hocht (IRE) **Mr T. J. Hemmings**
32 FONTAINE COLLONGES (FR), 6, b m Saddler Maker (IRE)—Saturne Collonges (FR) **Mr P. Davies**
33 FRANCO D'AUNOU (FR), 6, b g Saint des Saints (FR)—Jimagine II (FR) **Wrap Up Warm Partnership**
34 FREDDIE FLIP FLOP (IRE), 6, b g Imperial Monarch (IRE)—Moon Over Thefirth (IRE) **Sir W. J. A. Timpson**
35 FRENCHY DU LARGE (FR), 6, gr g Al Namix (FR)—Quadence de Sivola (FR) **Mr A. O. Wiles**
36 FRERO BANBOU (FR), 6, b g Apsis—Lady Banbou (FR) **Mr P. Davies**
37 FUJI FLIGHT (FR), 6, b g Day Flight—Silverlea (FR) **George & Drury**
38 FUNAMBULE SIVOLA (FR), 6, b g Noroit (GER)—Little Memories (IRE) **My Racing Manager Friends**
39 GARDEFORT (FR), 12, b br g Agent Bleu (FR)—La Fresnaie (FR) **Venetia Williams' Stable Staff**
40 GEMIRANDE (FR), 5, b g Al Namix (FR)—Queenjo (FR) **The Bellamy Partnership**

## MISS VENETIA WILLIAMS - continued

41  **GRAND TURINA**, 10, b m Kayf Tara—Cesana (IRE)  **Nora's Playmates**
42  **GREEN BOOK (FR)**, 4, b g Authorized (IRE)—Mantissa  **Price, Shaw, Boylan I Tagg**
43  **HILL OF TARA**, 4, b g Kayf Tara—Patsie Magern  **B B Racing Club**
44  **HOLD THAT TAUGHT**, 6, b g Kayf Tara—Belle Magello (FR)  **Mr P. Davies**
45  **HUNTER LEGEND (FR)**, 4, b g Buck's Boum (FR)—Sience Fiction (FR)  **Gaskins Family**
46  **IBLEO (FR)**, 8, b g Dick Turpin (IRE)—Mahendra (GER)  **The Bellamy Partnership**
47  **ISTORIUS (FR)**, 5, b g Pastorius (GER)—Indianapolis (GER)  **The Autumn Partnership**
48  **JACK VALENTINE (IRE)**, 8, b g Scorpion (IRE)—Mangan Rose (IRE)  **Venetia Williams Racehorse Syndicate IV**
49  **JURYS OUT (IRE)**, 8, b g Witness Box (USA)—No Complaints But (IRE)  **Venetia Williams Racehorse Syndicate III**
50  **KAPGA DE LILY (FR)**, 8, ch m Kapgarde (FR)—Louvisy (FR)  **Lady Judith Price & Mrs Carol Shaw**
51  **KHAIRAGASH (FR)**, 8, b g Sinndar (IRE)—Khazina (FR)  **Carol & David Shaw**
52  **L'HOMME PRESSE (FR)**, 6, b g Diamond Boy (FR)—Romance Turgot (FR)  **Mr A. J. Edwards**
53  **LISA DE VASSY (FR)**, 6, b m Cokoriko (FR)—Mona Vassy (FR)  **Falcon's Line Ltd**
54  **MIDNIGHT SONATA (IRE)**, 7, b g Big Bad Bob (IRE)—Symphonique (FR)  **Mrs P. Pink**
55  **MOUNTAIN LEOPARD (IRE)**, 6, b g Shantou (USA)—Laurel Gift (IRE)  **The Shantou Partnership**
56  **ONE STYLE (FR)**, 11, b g Desert Style (IRE)—Arieta (FR)  **The Four Bosses**
57  **OTTOLINE**, 5, b m Kayf Tara—Lily Grey (FR)  **Ottoline Syndicate**
58  **PENNY MALLOW (FR)**, 7, b m Kapgarde (FR)—Louvisy (FR)  **Kate & Andrew Brooks**
59  **PINK LEGEND**, 7, b m Midnight Legend—Red And White (IRE)  **F. M. P. Mahon**
60  **PONIENTE**, 7, br m Shirocco (GER)—Tazzarine (FR)  **Bailey-Carvill Equine**
61  **PUNITIVE DAMAGE**, 4, b f Saint des Saints (FR)—Tazzarine (FR)  **Mr R. F. Bailey**
62  **QUICK WAVE (FR)**, 8, b m Gentlewave (IRE)—Magicaldoun (FR)  **Mrs S. A. J. Kinsella**
63  **QUIETLYFLOWSTHEDON**, 6, ch m Sholokhov (IRE)—Tazzarine (FR)  **Bailey-Carvill Equine**
64  **REALM KEEPER (USA)**, 8, b g Arch (USA)—La Lodola (USA)  **Venetia Williams Racehorse Syndicate V**
65  **REALM OF GLORY (IRE)**, 6, b g Fame And Glory—Ebony Queen  **Venetia Williams Racehorse Syndicate V**
66  **ROCK OF FAME**, 4, b f Fastnet Rock (AUS)—Familliarity  **Caroline Wilson & Lavinia Taylor**
67  **ROYALE PAGAILLE (FR)**, 7, b g Blue Bresil (FR)—Royale Cazoumaille (FR)  **Mrs S. Ricci**
68  **SALOPIAN BOY**, 5, ch g Dunaden (FR)—Red And White (IRE)  **F. M. P. Mahon**
69  **SENDHERVICTORIA'S (IRE)**, 6, b g Shirocco (GER)—Midnight Flirt (IRE)  **Tim & Sarah Stevens**
70  **SNUFF BOX (IRE)**, 10, b g Witness Box (USA)—Dara Supreme (IRE)  **Mrs J. R. L. Young**
71  **STAR ACADEMY (IRE)**, 7, b g Stowaway—Academy Miss (IRE)  **John Nicholls Racing**
72  **STRIKE HOLLOW**, 8, ch m Beat Hollow—Tazzarine (FR)  **Bailey-Carvill Equine**
73  **SUBCONTINENT (IRE)**, 9, b g Dubawi (IRE)—Saree  **Shire Birds**
74  **SUPERVISOR (IRE)**, 7, b g Flemensfirth (USA)—Coolamaine Star (IRE)  **Sarah Williams & Charles Barlow**
75  **TANGO DE JUILLEY (FR)**, 13, b g Lesotho (USA)—Lasalsa de Juilley (FR)  **Venetia Williams' Stable Staff**
76  **TARA CHIEFTAIN**, 6, b g Kayf Tara—Molly Flight (FR)  **The Winter Partnership**
77  **THE CROONER (FR)**, 6, gr g Martaline—Viva Maria (FR)  **The Crooner Partnership**
78  **TOP AND DROP**, 10, b m Kayf Tara—Ismene (FR)  **Lady Judith Price & Mrs Carol Shaw**
79  **UN PROPHETE (FR)**, 10, gr g Carlotamix (FR)—Pollita (FR)  **Sir W. J. A. Timpson**
80  **YALLTAI**, 10, gr g Kayf Tara—Lily Grey (FR)  **Venetia Williams Racehorse Syndicates II**

**NH Jockey:** Charlie Deutsch. **Conditional Jockey:** Hugh Nugent. **Amateur Jockey:** Miss Lucy Turner.

---

**589** **MRS LISA WILLIAMSON, Tarporley**
Postal: **Kelsall Hill Equestrian Centre, Middlewich Road, Tarporley, Cheshire, CW6 0SR**
Contacts: **PHONE 07970 437679**
EMAIL **info@lisawilliamson.co.uk** WEBSITE **www.lisawilliamson.co.uk**

1  **AMBER LILY**, 5, ch m Captain Gerrard (IRE)—Lily Jicaro (IRE)  **Miss H. J. Roberts**
2  **BRANDY STATION (IRE)**, 6, b g Fast Company (IRE)—Kardyls Hope (IRE)  **A V Wilding (Chester) Ltd**
3  **BRAZEN LADY**, 4, br f Brazen Beau (AUS)—Turin (IRE)  **Mr J. P. Coddington**
4  **CELERITY (IRE)**, 7, ch m Casamento (IRE)—Shinko Dancer (IRE)  **Heath House Racing**
5  **DETONATION**, 5, gr g Sun Central (IRE)—Tomintoul Star  **Mrs L. V. Williamson**
6  5, B g Universal (IRE)—Dusky Dancer
7  **GEMINI GLORY (USA)**, 7, b m Tale of Ekati (USA)—Misconduct (USA)  **E. H. Jones (Paints) Ltd**

## MRS LISA WILLIAMSON - continued

8 **GRANNY ROZ,** 7, b m Bahamian Bounty—Hulcote Rose (IRE)  **Mr I. Furlong**
9 **ISABELLA RUBY,** 6, b m Power—Scarlet Rocks (IRE)  **Heath House Racing**
10 **LA CHICA LOBO,** 4, b f Captain Gerrard (IRE)—Senora Lobo (IRE)  **Miss H. J. Roberts**
11 **LILY JICARO (IRE),** 15, ch m Choisir (AUS)—Mourir d'Aimer (USA)
12 **MANY A TALE,** 7, br m Poet's Voice—Rustam  **Heath House Racing**
13 **MARIAH'S MELODY (IRE),** 6, gr m Graydar (USA)—In Seconds (USA)  **E. H. Jones (Paints) Ltd**
14 **MRS TIFFEN,** 4, b f Finjaan—Fancy Rose (USA)  **A V Wilding (Chester) Ltd**
15 **NEW LOOK (FR),** 6, gr g Style Vendome (FR)—Tara's Force (IRE)  **Mr R. M. Heath**
16 **RED DEREK,** 5, b g Steele Tango (USA)—Maydream  **Mr G. L. Shepherd**
17 **RED STRIPES (USA),** 9, b g Leroidesanimaux (BRZ)—Kaleidoscopic (USA)  **E. H. Jones (Paints) Ltd**
18 **SANTINHO (IRE),** 18, b g Double Eclipse (IRE)—Gina's Love
19 **SECRET ASSET (IRE),** 16, gr g Clodovil (IRE)—Skerray  **Simon & Mrs Jeanette Pierpoint**
20 **SHORTBACKANDSIDES (IRE),** 6, b g Fast Company (IRE)—Whatagoodcatch (IRE)  **Mr I. Furlong**
21 **TAN,** 7, b g Aqlaam—Sunburnt  **E. H. Jones (Paints) Ltd**
22 **TWILIGHT HAZE,** 4, b f Heeraat (IRE)—Lily Jicaro (IRE)  **Miss H. J. Roberts**
23 **WHITLEY NEILL (IRE),** 9, b g Shantou (USA)—Maidrin Rua (IRE)  **JMH Racing Limited**

### THREE-YEAR-OLDS

24 **LOCKDOWN LASS,** b f Albaasil (IRE)—Littlemoor Lass  **Lockdown Racing**
25 **RED WALLS,** b c Heeraat (IRE)—Gemini Glory (USA)  **E. H. Jones (Paints) Ltd**
26 Ch f Captain Gerrard (IRE)—Senora Lobo (IRE)  **Miss H. J. Roberts**

Other Owners: Mrs J. T. Pierpoint, Mr S. W. Pierpoint.


---

**590**  **MR ANDREW WILSON, Greystoke**
Postal: Silver Howe, Orton, Penrith, Cumbria, CA10 3RQ
Contacts: PHONE 015396 24071 MOBILE 07813 846768
EMAIL andywilsonorton@gmail.com

1 **FRIENDS IN HEAVEN (IRE),** 9, br g Asian Heights—Native Bev (IRE)  **Mr A. C. Wilson**
2 **KINGS ECLIPSE (IRE),** 11, b g Double Eclipse (IRE)—Good Times Ahead (IRE)  **Mr A. C. Wilson**
3 **MOORE CLOUDS (IRE),** 6, gr m Cloudings (IRE)—Wednesday Girl (IRE)  **Clouds of Orton**
4 **SAINT JUDE (IRE),** 8, ch g Presenting—Native Monk (IRE)  **Mr A. C. Wilson**


---

**591**  **MR KEN WINGROVE, Bridgnorth**
Postal: 6 Netherton Farm Barns, Netherton Lane, Highley, Bridgnorth, Shropshire, WV16 6NJ
Contacts: HOME 01746 861534 MOBILE 07974 411267
EMAIL kenwingrove@btinternet.com

1 **HEY PRETTY (IRE),** 6, b g Society Rock (IRE)—Coffee Date (USA)  **Mr D. G. Wingrove**
2 **LORD MURPHY (IRE),** 8, b g Holy Roman Emperor (IRE)—Tralanza (IRE)  **Mr D. G. Wingrove**
3 **LYME PARK,** 10, gr m Multiplex—So Cloudy  **Mr D. G. Wingrove**
4 **MIDTECH VALENTINE,** 10, b m Act One—Eveon (IRE)  **Mr D. G. Wingrove**
5 **RED REFRACTION (IRE),** 11, b g Red Clubs (IRE)—Dreamalot (IRE)  **Mr D. G. Wingrove**
6 4, B f Yorgunnabelucky (USA)—Seedless  **Mr D. G. Wingrove**
7 **WILD SAM (IRE),** 11, b g Bachelor Duke (USA)—Pure Spin (USA)  **Mr D. G. Wingrove**

Assistant Trainer: Isobel Willer.

**592**
**MR PETER WINKS, Barnsley**
Postal: **Homefield, Rotherham Road, Little Houghton, Barnsley, South Yorkshire, S72 0HA**
Contacts: **MOBILE 07846 899993**
**EMAIL pwracing@outlook.com**

1 AGENTLEMAN (IRE), 11, b g Trans Island—Silvine (IRE)  **Mr R. H. Lee**
2 BALLYFARSOON (IRE), 10, ch g Medicean—Amzara (IRE)  **Barnsley Burglars**
3 CAVALRY, 6, b h Exceed And Excel (AUS)—Queen's Best  **Mr P Rowbottom & Mr R Taberner**
4 GROW NASA GROW (IRE), 10, ch g Mahler—Dereenavurrig (IRE)  **Nature and Science Agriculture Limited**
5 HARTSIDE (GER), 12, b g Montjeu (IRE)—Helvellyn (USA)  **Peter Winks Racing Club**
6 LOUGH SALT (IRE), 10, b g Brian Boru—Castlehill Lady (IRE)  **Mr J Toes & Mr J O'Loan**
7 SCOTTSDALE, 8, b g Cape Cross (IRE)—High Praise (USA)  **Mr P W O'Mara & Mr. P Winks**
8 WEST CLASS (IRE), 10, b g Westerner—Catch The Class (IRE)  **Peter Winks Racing Club**

**Other Owners:** Mr P. Connor, Mr John O'Loan, Mr P. W. O'Mara, Mr P. Rowbottom, Mr R. Taberner, Mr J. Toes, Mr P. Winks.

**Assistant Trainer:** Ryan Winks.

**593**
**MR ADRIAN WINTLE, Westbury-On-Severn**
Postal: **Yew Tree Stables, Rodley, Westbury-On-Severn, Gloucestershire, GL14 1QZ**
Contacts: **MOBILE 07767 351144**

1 AMERICAN CRAFTSMAN (IRE), 7, gr g Mastercraftsman (IRE)—Quiet Mouse (USA)  **Mr M. P. Dunphy**
2 AMLOVI (IRE), 8, b m Court Cave (IRE)—Portanob (IRE)  **Mr S. R. Whistance**
3 BARATINEUR (FR), 10, ch g Vendangeur (IRE)—Olmantina (FR)  **A. A. Wintle**
4 CENTREOFEXCELLENCE (IRE), 10, b g Oscar (IRE)—Calm Approach (IRE)  **Mrs P Corbett & Mrs A Thomas**
5 CREEK HARBOUR (IRE), 6, b g Kodiac—Allegheny Creek (IRE)  **Mrs H. Hawkins**
6 ESPINATOR (FR), 7, b br g Spider Flight (FR)—Santalisa (FR)  **Mr S. R. Whistance**
7 HEY FRANKIE (IRE), 5, gr m Mahler—Flaming Poncho (IRE)  **Mr M. P. Dunphy**
8 JOUR A LA PLAGE (FR), 6, gr g Coastal Path—Juntina (FR)  **Mr S. R. Whistance**
9 KEEPER'S CHOICE (IRE), 7, ch m Intikhab (USA)—Crossing  **A. A. Wintle**
10 KENSTONE (FR), 8, gr g Kendargent (FR)—Little Stone (FR)  **A. A. Wintle**
11 LEBOWSKI (IRE), 6, b g Aizavoski (IRE)—Castle Supreme (IRE)  **Mr M. P. Dunphy**
12 MISTY MOUNTAIN (USA), 7, gr m Lemon Drop Kid (USA)—Saratoga Fling (USA)  **A. A. Wintle**
13 MR PEANUT, 5, b g Aeroplane—Sumingasedit (IRE)  **A. A. Wintle**
14 PLANSINA, 6, b m Planteur (IRE)—Sina (GER)  **Mr S. Davies**
15 ROCKET RONNIE (IRE), 11, b g Antonius Pius (USA)—Ctesiphon (USA)  **Wintle Racing Club**
16 RUNNING CLOUD (IRE), 6, b g Cacique (IRE)—Nimbus Star  **Mr A. Jordan**
17 SEAFORTH (IRE), 9, b g Acclamation—Hendrina (IRE)  **Wintle Racing Club**
18 STAY OUT OF COURT (IRE), 10, b g Court Cave (IRE)—Lucky To Live (IRE)  **A. A. Wintle**
19 SUNNY GIRL (IRE), 7, b m Arcadio (GER)—Vincenta (IRE)  **Mr S. R. Whistance**
20 TAWAAFOQ, 7, b g Showcasing—Gilt Linked  **Mr S. R. Whistance**
21 TEDDY THE KNIGHT, 6, b g Kayf Tara—Michelle's Ella (IRE)  **A. A. Wintle**
22 THAIS TOIR (FR), 6, b g Diamond Boy (FR)—Scotland Act (FR)  **Mr S. R. Whistance**
23 WIFF WAFF, 6, b g Poet's Voice—Eraadaat (IRE)  **A. A. Wintle**
24 YORSEXYANDUKNOWIT (IRE), 8, ch m Curtain Time (IRE)—Mercy Mission  **Mr M. P. Dunphy**

**THREE-YEAR-OLDS**

25 Ch f Toronado (IRE)—Sandy Shaw  **Oracle Horseracing**
26 SOUTH CAROLINA (IRE), b f Footstepsinthesand—Miss Mocca  **Oracle Horseracing**

**Other Owners:** Mrs P. Corbett, Mrs A. P. Thomas.

**594**  **MISS REBECCA WOODMAN, Chichester**
Postal: **Souters Cottage, 21 East Lavant, Chichester, West Sussex, PO18 0AG**
Contacts: **PHONE 01243 527260 MOBILE 07821 603063**
EMAIL rebeccawoodman@msn.com

1 **ECHO BRAVA**, 11, gr g Proclamation (IRE)—Snake Skin  **Miss R. E. Woodman**
2 **MILLDEAN FELIX (IRE)**, 5, br g Red Jazz (USA)—Plausabelle  **Miss R. E. Woodman**
3 **RED ORATOR**, 12, ch g Osorio (GER)—Red Roses Story (FR)  **Miss R. E. Woodman**

**595**  **MR STEVE WOODMAN, Chichester**
Postal: **Parkers Barn Stables, East Lavant, Chichester, West Sussex, PO18 0AU**
Contacts: **PHONE 01243 527136 MOBILE 07889 188519 FAX 01243 527136**
EMAIL stevewoodman83@msn.com

1 **BLACK LACE**, 6, b m Showcasing—Ivory Lace  **The Lacemakers**
2 **LORD ALDERVALE (IRE)**, 14, br g Alderbrook—Monavale (IRE)  **Mr D. N. Boxall**
3 **VICE ROYAL**, 4, b g Swiss Spirit—Ivory Lace  **Vice Royal Partnership**

Other Owners: Dr J. A. H. Miles, Mrs P. M. Tyler.

**596**  **MRS CYNTHIA WOODS, Crowborough**
Postal: **Green Hedges Farm, Mark Cross, Crowborough, East Sussex, TN6 3PA**
Contacts: **PHONE 01892 750567**
EMAIL chaydon@hotmail.co.uk

1 **BIT OF A LEGEND**, 7, b g Midnight Legend—Kitty Wong (IRE)  **Mr G. Woods**
2 **FLORELLA (IRE)**, 11, b m Presenting—Shiminnie (IRE)  **Debs & Sarah Wilkins**
3 **JO MAHLER (IRE)**, 7, b m Mahler—Trendy Gift (IRE)  **Green Hedges Racing**
4 **LEMON SHOULDER (IRE)**, 6, b g Dylan Thomas (IRE)—The Cookie Jar (IRE)  **Mr G. Woods**
5 **UKNOWWHATIMEAN (IRE)**, 7, ch g Shantou (USA)—Presenting Chaos (IRE)  **Mr G. Woods**

Other Owners: Mrs D. Wilkins, Mrs S. L. M. Wilkins.

**597**  **MR SEAN WOODS, Newmarket**
Postal: **Shalfleet Stables, 17 Bury Road, Newmarket, Suffolk, CB8 7BX**
EMAIL spcwoods65@hotmail.com

1 **BLACK CAESAR (IRE)**, 10, b g Bushranger (IRE)—Evictress (IRE)  **The Long Furlong**
2 **CASPIAN QUEEN (IRE)**, 4, b f Sepoy (AUS)—Rhythm Excel  **Davood Vakilgilani 1**

### THREE-YEAR-OLDS
3 **FULL MOON RISING**, b g Sea The Moon (GER)—Lady Hen  **A. Coombs & J. W. Rowley**
4 **GOLDEN WATTLE (IRE)**, ch f Australia—Chrysanthemum (IRE)  **Brook Stud**
5 **KHUFU**, b g Exceed And Excel (AUS)—Miss Chicane  **Brook Stud**
6 **SARRDAR (IRE)**, ch c New Approach (IRE)—Coolnagree (IRE)  **Mr D. Vakilgilani**

# MR SEAN WOODS - continued

## TWO-YEAR-OLDS

7 Ch c 21/03 The Last Lion (IRE)—Blue Crest (FR) (Verglas (IRE)) (27000) **S. P. C. Woods**
8 B c 14/04 Pivotal—Celeste (Green Desert (USA)) (100000) **S. P. C. Woods**
9 B c 09/03 Pride of Dubai (AUS)—Cephalonie (Kris S (USA)) (60000) **S. P. C. Woods**
10 Ch c 13/02 Tagula (IRE)—Concra Girl (IRE) (Footstepsinthesand) (19048) **S. P. C. Woods**
11 B c 15/03 Exceed And Excel (AUS)—Cottonmouth (IRE) (Noverre (USA)) (161905) **S. P. C. Woods**
12 B c 23/04 Holy Roman Emperor (IRE)—Dame Lucy (Refuse To Bend (IRE)) (47619) **Ignited**
13 B c 28/04 Profitable (IRE)—Deora De (Night Shift (USA)) (35238) **Ignited**
14 **EIGHT OF DIAMONDS**, ch c 18/04 Ulysses (IRE)—Mirror City (Street Cry (IRE)) (50000)
15 **ELSAAB**, gr f 24/02 El Kabeir (USA)—
Miss Mediator (USA) (Consolidator (USA)) (29000) **The Storm Again Syndicate**
16 **GENERAL PANIC**, b c 27/01 Outstrip—Dominance (Lilbourne Lad (IRE)) (4000) **Brook Stud**
17 B c 25/03 New Bay—Highlands Queen (FR) (Mount Nelson) (228571) **Mr J. C. H. Hui**
18 **MUMCAT**, b f 02/04 Bobby's Kitten (USA)—Tell Mum (Marju (IRE)) **The Storm Again Syndicate**
19 B c 03/03 Anjaal—One Time (IRE) (Olden Times) (3333) **S. P. C. Woods**
20 Ch c 06/02 Cityscape—Paradise Way (Elusive Quality (USA)) (23000) **S. P. C. Woods**
21 B c 21/04 Caravaggio (USA)—Seagull (IRE) (Sea The Stars (IRE)) (105000) **Mr J. C. H. Hui**
22 B f 19/03 Havana Gold (IRE)—So Funny (USA) (Distorted Humor (USA)) (6667) **Mrs M. Bryce**
23 B c 23/02 Twilight Son—Spin Doctor (Mayson) (59048) **Mr N. O'Keeffe**
24 **UDABERRI (IRE)**, gr c 13/03 Mastercraftsman (IRE)—Eccellente Idea (IRE) (Excellent Art) (55000) **S. P. C. Woods**
25 B c 23/02 Holy Roman Emperor (IRE)—Vibe Queen (IRE) (Invincible Spirit (IRE)) (66667)
26 B c 03/03 Territories (IRE)—Yearbook (Byron) (30000) **S. P. C. Woods**

**Other Owners:** Mr G. W. Brickwood, Mr A. C. Coombs, R. T. Goodes, Mr R. Hine, Mr J. W. F. Rowley, Mr M. G. P. Sanaei, Mr B. Stewart, Mr N. A. D. Thomas, Mr D. Vakilgilani, Mr E. J. Williams, S. P. C. Woods.

---

**598** **MRS KAYLEY WOOLLACOTT, South Molton**
Postal: **Big Brook Park, Rose Ash, South Molton, Devon, EX36 4RQ**
Contacts: **PHONE 01769 550483**
**EMAIL** info@richardwoollacottracing.co.uk **WEBSITE** www.richardwoollacottracing.co.uk

1 **CASPERS COURT (IRE)**, 7, gr g Court Cave (IRE)—Kindle Ball (FR) **Mr D Stevens & Mrs S Stevens**
2 **CLONDAW'S ANSWER (IRE)**, 8, b g Ask—Monabricka Lady (IRE) **D. G. Staddon**
3 **DORRANA (IRE)**, 7, br m Darsi (FR)—Arts Theater (USA) **Gale Force Five**
4 **DREAMS AT MIDNIGHT**, 5, gr g Dream Eater (IRE)—Miss Midnight
5 **DYSANIA (IRE)**, 6, b g Califet (FR)—She's Supersonic (IRE) **Ms G. E. Morgan**
6 **ENORMOUSE**, 8, b g Crosspeace (IRE)—Mousiemay **M. H. Dare**
7 **EROS (FR)**, 7, b g Diamond Boy (FR)—Madame Lys (FR) **Mr D Stevens & Mrs S Stevens**
8 **ESPECIALLY SO**, 6, br m So You Think (NZ)—Behra (IRE) **BumpersToJumpers3**
9 **FAMOUS CLERMONT (FR)**, 6, b g Maresca Sorrento (FR)—Progest des Mottes (FR) **Mrs K. Woollacott**
10 **GENTLE KATE**, 5, b m Gentlewave (IRE)—Himayna **Peter Ingram & Paul Gibson**
11 **GETAWAY CORY (IRE)**, 6, br g Getaway (GER)—Annaru (IRE) **Mr I. G. Thompson**
12 **GETAWAY HONEY (IRE)**, 9, ch m Getaway (GER)—Knappogue Honey (IRE) **Mr S. Payne**
13 **GETAWAY LUCY (IRE)**, 7, br m Getaway (GER)—Courtmac Memories (IRE) **Mr I. G. Thompson**
14 **GOODGIRLTERESA (IRE)**, 11, b m Stowaway—Decheekymonkey (IRE) **Kayley Woollacott Racing Club**
15 **JACK THE FARMER**, 6, b g Kalanisi (IRE)—Deploys Dream (IRE) **Mrs K. Woollacott**
16 **LADY ELLIE**, 6, b m Schiaparelli (GER)—Tara Gale **Mr L. H. Vickery**
17 **LALLYGAG (GER)**, 4, b c It's Gino (GER)—Laviola (GER) **D. G. Staddon**
18 **LALOR (GER)**, 9, b g It's Gino (GER)—Laviola (GER) **D. G. Staddon**
19 **MIDNIGHT JEWEL**, 5, b g Midnight Legend—Follow The Dream **Ms G. E. Morgan**
20 **MINIM MOUSE**, 10, b m Victory Note (USA)—Mousiemay **M. H. Dare**
21 **NICKELSONTHEDIME (IRE)**, 7, b g Shantou (USA)—Penny Fiction (IRE) **T Hamlin, J E Gardener**
22 **OSTUNI (FR)**, 8, b g Great Pretender (IRE)—Mamassita (FR) **Mr D Stevens & Mrs S Stevens**
23 **ROSSDERRIN (IRE)**, 6, b g Getaway (GER)—Fine Call (IRE) **J & Woollacott**
24 **SAKE OF SECRECY (IRE)**, 5, b g El Salvador (IRE)—Springfield Spirit (IRE)

## MRS KAYLEY WOOLLACOTT - continued

25  SHANNON LODGE (IRE), 7, b m Doyen (IRE)—Lady Cadia (FR)
26  SHANNON ROCCO (IRE), 6, b m Shirocco (GER)—Coco Moon (IRE)  **Mr I. G. Thompson**
27  SIXTEEN LETTERS (IRE), 9, b g Well Chosen—Back To Loughadera (IRE)  **J. F. G. Symes**
28  STRATTON OAKMONT (IRE), 5, b g Ask—Foxwood Girl (IRE)  **Kayley Woollacott Racing Club**
29  THE KINGS WRIT (IRE), 10, b g Brian Boru—Letterwoman (IRE)  **Mr D Stevens & Mrs S Stevens**
30  TIPALONG TYLER, 7, br m Winged Love (IRE)—Supreme Cove  **Kayley Woollacott Racing Club**

**Other Owners:** Mr J. E. Gardener, Mr P. D. Gibson, T. Hamlin, Mr P. Ingram, Mr D. J. Stevens, Mrs S. E. Stevens, Mrs K. Woollacott.

---

**599**  **MR PHILLIP YORK, Effingham Common**
Postal: **Mornshill Farm, Banks Lane, Effingham, Leatherhead, Surrey, KT24 5JB**
Contacts: **PHONE 01372 457102**

1   ALONG THE REEKS (IRE), 8, b g Let The Lion Roar—Astalanda (FR)  **Mrs K. H. York**
2   DELIGHTFUL GUEST (IRE), 8, b m Beneficial—Saddlers Green (IRE)  **Mrs K. H. York**
3   GERSJOEYCASEY (IRE), 12, b m Milan—Derrigra Sublime (IRE)  **Mrs K. H. York**
4   GLORIFY (IRE), 7, b g Fame And Glory—Georgia On My Mind (FR)  **Mrs K. H. York**
5   LEGAL OK (IRE), 9, b g Echo of Light—Desert Trail (IRE)  **P. York**
6   MAGEN'S MOON (IRE), 7, b m Henrythenavigator (USA)—Magen's Star (IRE)  **P. York**
7   MOUNT CORBITT (IRE), 6, b g Robin des Champs (FR)—Hanora O'Brien (IRE)  **P. York**
8   RENDEZVOUS PEAK, 12, b g High-Rise (IRE)—Jurado Park (IRE)  **Mrs K. H. York**
9   ROBIN DES MANA (IRE), 10, br g Robin des Pres (FR)—Kokopelli Mana (IRE)  **P. York**
10  SANDYCOVE ISLAND (IRE), 11, b g Lahib (USA)—Twilight Breeze (IRE)  **P. York**
11  SAUCY SINDY, 7, ch m Amber Life—Nessa  **Mrs K. H. York**
12  SPENDABLE, 9, ch m Spendent—Eastern Point  **Mrs K. H. York**
13  SPIRITOFCHARTWELL, 13, ch g Clerkenwell (USA)—Rollin Rock  **Mrs K. H. York**
14  TOUCH TIGHT (IRE), 9, b g Touch of Land (FR)—Classic China  **Mrs K. H. York**
15  UNCLE DANNY (IRE), 12, b g Catcher In The Rye (IRE)—Bobset Leader (IRE)  **Mrs K. H. York**

---

**600**  **MRS LAURA YOUNG, Bridgwater**
Postal: **Rooks Castle Stables, Broomfield, Bridgwater, Somerset, TA5 2EW**
Contacts: **PHONE 01278 664595 MOBILE 07766 514414 FAX 01278 661555**
**EMAIL ljyracing@hotmail.com WEBSITE www.laurayoungracing.com**

1   AUENWIRBEL (GER), 10, b g Sholokhov (IRE)—Auentime (GER)  **Mr T. J. Moynihan**
2   AUMIT HILL, 8, b g Authorized (IRE)—Eurolinka (IRE)  **Mr G. C. Vining**
3   BUCKBORU (IRE), 13, b m Brian Boru—Buckland Filleigh (IRE)  **Mrs L. J. Young**
4   JIGSAW FINANCIAL (IRE), 15, b g Brian Boru—Ardcolm Cailin (IRE)  **Mrs L. J. Young**
5   MOYNIHANS GIRL (IRE), 7, ch m Frammassone (IRE)—Catch Ball  **Mr T. J. Moynihan**
6   SUFFICE (IRE), 12, b g Iffraaj—Shallat (IRE)  **Mrs L. J. Young**
7   VALSHAN TIME (IRE), 9, b br g Atraf—Valshan (IRE)  **Mrs L. J. Young**
8   WHITE NILE (IRE), 12, b h Galileo (IRE)—Super Gift (IRE)  **Mrs L. J. Young**

**Assistant Trainer:** James Young.

**NH Jockey:** Robert Dunne.

## 601 MR MAXWELL YOUNG, Droitwich
Postal: Little Acton Farm, Sneads Green, Droitwich, Worcestershire, WR9 0PZ
Contacts: PHONE 01905 827795
EMAIL max.young@hotmail.com

1 **BABY JAKE (IRE)**, 12, b g Morozov (USA)—Potters Dawn (IRE) **Mr M. J. Young**
2 **CLASSICAL DAYTIME (IRE)**, 8, b g Trans Island—Aintree Baba (FR) **Mr M. J. Young**
3 **DOYENS DE ANTE (IRE)**, 5, b g Doyen (IRE)—De Street (IRE) **Mrs D. Prosser**
4 **FERROBIN (IRE)**, 7, br g Robin des Champs (FR)—Fedaia (IRE) **Mrs D. Prosser**
5 **HELOVAPLAN (IRE)**, 7, b g Helmet (AUS)—Watsdaplan (IRE) **Mrs D. Prosser**
6 5, B g Sans Frontieres (IRE)—Inishbeg House (IRE)
7 6, B g Great Pretender (IRE)—McKyla (IRE)
8 **MEANAZ**, 5, b m Malinas (GER)—Kate Hill Dancer (IRE) **Mr D. R. Broadhurst**
9 **MINNIE MAHLER**, 6, ch m Mahler—Presenteea (IRE) **Mr M. J. Young**
10 **MUILEAN NA MADOG (IRE)**, 10, b g Papal Bull—Truly Precious (IRE) **Mr M. J. Young**
11 **ON THE RISE (IRE)**, 5, b g Valirann (FR)—High Sunshine (IRE) **Miss E. Williams**
12 7, B m Passing Glance—Qualitee **Mrs H. M. Oliver**
13 **SECOND CHAPTER (IRE)**, 6, b g Arcadio (GER)—Tosca Shine (IRE) **Mr M. J. Young**
14 **SHREWDOPERATOR (IRE)**, 11, gr g Medaaly—Fitanga (FR)
15 **SILVRETTA SCHWARZ (IRE)**, 6, b gr m Silver Frost (IRE)—Perruche Grise (FR) **Mr M. J. Young**
16 **STINGGREY (IRE)**, 8, gr g Scorpion (IRE)—Northinn Lady (IRE) **Mrs H. M. Oliver**
17 **TABOO (IRE)**, 12, b m Tikkanen (USA)—Tasari (IRE) **Max Young Racing Club**
18 **TAKODA (IRE)**, 5, b g Doyen (IRE)—Crimson Bow (GER)
19 **THE FECKENHAM FOX,** 7, ch m Malinas (GER)—Broughton Melody **Mr K. E. Hay**
20 **TOP BEAK (IRE)**, 8, b g Lawman (FR)—Tree Tops **Mr M. J. Young**

## 602 MR WILLIAM YOUNG, Carluke
Postal: Watchknowe Lodge, Crossford, Carluke, Lanarkshire, ML8 5QT
Contacts: PHONE 01555 860226, 01555 860856 MOBILE 07900 408210 FAX 01555 860137
EMAIL watchknowe@talktalk.net

1 **APOLLO CREED (IRE)**, 9, b g Vinnie Roe (IRE)—Just Cassandra (IRE) **W. G. Young**
2 **ARDERA CROSS (IRE)**, 10, ch g Shantou (USA)—Fair Maid Marion (IRE) **W. G. Young**
3 **COOL VALLEY (IRE)**, 12, b g Zerpour (IRE)—Jilly Jaffa Cake (IRE) **W. G. Young**
4 **COSTLY DREAM (IRE)**, 9, b g Yeats (IRE)—What Price Love (USA) **W. G. Young**
5 **FORMIDABLEOPPONENT (IRE)**, 14, b g Arakan (USA)—Sliding **W. G. Young**
6 **KICKS BEFORE SIX (IRE)**, 9, b g Scorpion (IRE)—Square Up (IRE) **W. G. Young**
7 **SOME AMBITION (IRE)**, 8, b g Westerner—Heath Heaven **W. G. Young**

**Assistant Trainer:** William G Young Snr.

# Download the free must-have Racing Post app.

**RACING POST**

The Must-Have App
For The Must-Have Info

Use your camera phone
and scan the QR code
on the right to download
the free app now.

Download on the
**App Store**

GET IT ON
**Google Play**

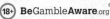

# INDEX TO HORSES

**The figure before** the name of the horse refers to the number of the team in which it appears and
**The figure after** the horse supplies a ready reference to each animal. Horses are indexed strictly alphabetically, e.g.
THE CON MAN appears in the T's, MR NICE GUY in the MR's, ST BASIL in the ST's etc.
Unnamed animals are listed under their dam, along with their sex

527 **AMAZING TANGO** (GER) 1
407 **AMAZON PRINCESS** 1
379 **AMAZONIAN DREAM** (IRE) 34
63 **AMBA** G 41
562 **AMBARELLA** (IRE) 11
492 **AMBASSADOR** (IRE) 8
102 **AMBASSADORIAL** (USA) 1
545 **AMBASSADRICE** F 148
413 **AMBER** 1
27 **AMBER DEW** 78
344 **AMBER ISLAND** (IRE) 1
253 **AMBER LANE** F 136
589 **AMBER LILY** 1
76 **AMBER QUEEN** (GER) F 86
186 **AMBER ROCK** (USA) 1
477 **AMBERINE** 1
461 **AMBEROSE** 1
534 **AMBION HILL** (IRE) 4
241 **AMBITIOUS ICARUS** 1
101 **AMEERA** 29
309 **AMELIA DREAM** F 151
122 **AMELIA R** (IRE) 1
553 **AMELIA'S DANCE** (IRE) 1
378 **AMELIORATE** (IRE) F 35
411 **AMENON** (FR) 4
501 **AMERDALE** 3
563 **AMERICAN ANTHEM** (IRE) 26
593 **AMERICAN CRAFTSMAN** (IRE) 1
494 **AMERICAN GENTLEMAN** (FR) 20
227 **AMERICAN GERRY** (IRE) 3
253 **AMERICAN KESTREL** (IRE) 137
234 **AMERICAN LEGACY** 3
554 **AMERICAN STAR** (IRE) 74
213 **AMETHEA** 1
400 **AMETHYSTOS** (IRE) C 44
243 **AMETIST** 7
415 **AMHRAN NA BHFIANN** (IRE) 1
369 **AMI DESBOIS** (FR) 4
105 **AMIR KABIR** 1
15 **AMISI** 1
167 **AMITOLA** (IRE) F 76
593 **AMLOVI** (IRE) 2
274 **AMLWCH** (IRE) 30
376 **AMMA LORD** (IRE) 2
508 **AMMAYYA** 1
123 **AMMOLITE** (IRE) 57
510 **AMNA** 1
61 **AMNAA** 2
554 **AMNIARIX** (USA) 2
167 **AMODIO** (IRE) C 77
571 **AMOOD** (IRE) 1
492 **AMOOLA GOLD** (GER) 9
563 **AMOR DE MI VIDA** (FR) 27
180 **AMOR FATI** (IRE) 3
411 **AMOUR DE NUIT** (IRE) 5
122 **AMOURI CHIEF** 2
122 **AMOURI GLEAM** 3
122 **AMOURIE** 4
179 **AMSBY** 1
228 **AMTIYAZ** 3
98 **AMY BEACH** (IRE) 30
508 **AMY C** 13
19 **AMZAC MAGIC** 1
256 **AN CAILIN ORGA** (IRE) C 156
309 **AN SAINCHEANN** (IRE) C 152
424 **AN TAILLIUR** (IRE) 3
16 **ANA SHABABIYA** (IRE) C 130

123 **ANAAMIL** (IRE) C 58
421 **ANAHITA** (IRE) C 106
270 **ANAIS COLLONGES** (FR) F 6
120 **ANALYTICAL** (IRE) C 61
309 **ANAM ALLTA** (IRE) F 153
228 **ANASTARSIA** (IRE) 4
449 **ANATOMIC** 40
126 **ANAX** (IRE) 2
98 **ANAZAH** (USA) C 64
379 **ANBELLA** (FR) F 35
251 **ANCIENT ASTRONAUT** 2
256 **ANCIENT SPIRIT** (IRE) 3
179 **ANCIENT TIMES** 13
190 **AND THE NEW** (IRE) 8
369 **ANDALEEP** (IRE) 5
399 **ANDALUSA** (FR) F 5
115 **ANDANTE** (IRE) 1
465 **ANDAPA** (FR) 2
326 **ANDELYSA** 20
309 **ANDONNO** 51
63 **ANDRE AMAR** (IRE) 3
132 **ANDRONICUS BEAU** (IRE) 1
353 **ANDRY BRUSSELLES** C 36
79 **ANEEDAH** (IRE) F 43
394 **ANEEDH** 1
577 **ANEMOI** (FR) 1
309 **ANGE BLEU** (USA) C 154
434 **ANGE ENDORMI** (IRE) 1
101 **ANGEL** 30
132 **ANGEL ALEXANDER** (IRE) 1
462 **ANGEL EYES** 1
194 **ANGEL OF DELIGHT** (IRE) 1
76 **ANGEL OF THE GLEN** (FR) 2
243 **ANGEL OF THE GWAUN** (IRE) F 123
108 **ANGEL OF TRAFALGAR** 32
160 **ANGEL ON HIGH** (IRE) 1
545 **ANGEL POWER** 2
16 **ANGEL TERRACE** (USA) F 131
388 **ANGEL'S ENVY** 3
228 **ANGEL'S KISS** 42
400 **ANGEL'S WHISPER** (IRE) 2
395 **ANGELA'S HOPE** 2
256 **ANGELIC AIR** F 157
256 **ANGELIC GUEST** (IRE) F 158
538 **ANGELS FACES** (IRE) 1
56 **ANGELS ROC** 2
50 **ANGELS WILL RISE** 25
274 **ANGELS WINGS** (IRE) C 76
253 **ANGHAAM** (IRE) 40
119 **ANGLE LAND** 36
76 **ANGLEZARKE** (IRE) C 30
50 **ANIARNOTA** (IRE) F 70
272 **ANIF** (IRE) 1
434 **ANIGHTINLAMBOURN** (IRE) 2
502 **ANIMAL** (IRE) 2
449 **ANIMAL INSTINCT** 3
421 **ANIMATO** 107
300 **ANIMORE** 1
306 **ANISOPTERA** (IRE) 1
6 **ANJAZ** (USA) F 103
393 **ANJELLA** 11
79 **ANMAAT** (IRE) 15
98 **ANN WITHOUT AN E** C 65
395 **ANN'S EMERALD REEL** (FR) 3
6 **ANNA SALAI** (USA) F 104
256 **ANNA STRADA** 75
419 **ANNABELLE JA** (FR) C 132

235 **ANNAHALLA REBEL** (IRE) 3
429 **ANNAJEMIMA** 1
399 **ANNAMIX** (FR) 6
309 **ANNANDALE** (IRE) 52
86 **ANNEBELLE** (IRE) 1
545 **ANNEE LUMIERE** (IRE) F 149
256 **ANNER CASTLE** (IRE) 76
574 **ANNIE BROWN** 3
580 **ANNIE DAY** (IRE) 1
189 **ANNIE GALE** (IRE) 53
345 **ANNIE KENNEY** G 53
424 **ANNIE MC** (IRE) 4
345 **ANNIE MOORE** (IRE) 1
25 **ANNIE ROSE** 26
347 **ANNIE SALTS** G 7
105 **ANNIE'S SONG** 55
23 **ANNIEMATION** (IRE) 1
86 **ANNIES PRAYER** (IRE) 2
113 **ANNIES REGATTA** 1
552 **ANNIMATION** (IRE) G 1
581 **ANNSAM** 1
490 **ANNUAL FLAVOUR** (IRE) 1
227 **ANNUAL INVICTUS** (IRE) 1
369 **ANNUAL REVIEW** (IRE) 6
195 **ANONYMOUS JOHN** (IRE) 1
64 **ANOTHER ANGEL** (IRE) 2
25 **ANOTHER BATT** (IRE) 1
533 **ANOTHER BERTIE** (IRE) 44
473 **ANOTHER BURDEN** F 4
585 **ANOTHER CRICK** 1
51 **ANOTHER DAWN** 20
300 **ANOTHER DAY** C 64
585 **ANOTHER DRAMA** (IRE) 2
234 **ANOTHER EMOTION** (FR) 4
41 **ANOTHER GLANCE** 1
527 **ANOTHER KATE** (IRE) F 40
12 **ANOTHER NIGHTCAP** (IRE) 1
419 **ANOTHER STORM** (USA) C 133
222 **ANOTHER STOWAWAY** (IRE) 5
323 **ANOTHER THEATRE** (IRE) 5
13 **ANOTHER VENTURE** (IRE) 4
330 **ANSILIA** (IRE) 11
495 **ANTAGONIZE** 1
40 **ANTARA** (GER) C 116
337 **ANTEROS** (IRE) 1
399 **ANTEY** (GER) 7
256 **ANTHEM** (IRE) 77
123 **ANTHEM NATIONAL** (IRE) 59
143 **ANTI COOL** (IRE) 1
148 **ANTICO LADY** (IRE) 1
210 **ANTIDOTE** (IRE) 1
110 **ANTILLIA** F 34
6 **ANTIQUITIES** F 105
397 **ANTON DOLIN** (IRE) 1
386 **ANTONY** (FR) 6
492 **ANTUNES** 10
512 **ANY JOB WILL DO** (IRE) 1
395 **ANY NEWS** (IRE) 4
245 **ANYONECANHAVEITALL** 1
570 **ANYONEWHOHADAHEART** 2
503 **ANYTHING WILL DO** (IRE) 1
419 **ANYWAYYOULOOKATIT** (IRE) 5
309 **AOIFE ALAINN** (IRE) C 155
552 **AOIFE'S JOY** (IRE) 2
98 **AONACH MOR** 31

7 **BANCNUANAHEIREANN** (IRE) 7
6 **BANDINELLI** 38
571 **BANDOL** (IRE) 2
507 **BANDSMAN RICE** 1
482 **BANG ON** (IRE) 2
304 **BANG ON THE BELL** 31
434 **BANGERS AND CASH** (IRE) 5
16 **BANGKOK** (IRE) 2
222 **BANISH** (USA) 9
167 **BANKAWI** 7
391 **BANNED** 47
224 **BANNERGIRL** (IRE) 11
253 **BANNERMAN** 43
222 **BANNISTER** (FR) 10
471 **BANNIXTOWN BOY** (IRE) 2
363 **BANNIXTOWN GLORY** (IRE) 8
475 **BANNOW** 36
180 **BANOFFEE** (IRE) 23
159 **BANTAM** (IRE) G 42
108 **BANZARI** C 35
399 **BAPAUME** (FR) 16
537 **BAQQA** (IRE) C 40
445 **BARACALU** (FR) 1
545 **BARADAR** (IRE) 50
162 **BARATHEA DANCER** (IRE) C 10
593 **BARATINEUR** (FR) 3
256 **BARBADOS** (IRE) 7
270 **BARBADOS BLUE** (IRE) 12
411 **BARBADOS BUCK'S** (IRE) 10
362 **BARBARA ANN** 10
73 **BARBARIAN** 4
119 **BARBAROMA** (IRE) 21
372 **BARBARY MASTER** 2
98 **BARBILE** (IRE) 4
276 **BARBROOK STAR** (IRE) 7
494 **BARC** (FR) 21
201 **BARCA** (USA) 1
570 **BARD OF BRITTANY** 3
422 **BARDD** (IRE) 1
580 **BARDEN BELLA** (IRE) 2
101 **BARDO** (FR) 3
308 **BARE GRILS** (IRE) 22
363 **BAREBACK JACK** (IRE) 9
270 **BARELY FAMOUS** (IRE) 13
29 **BARENBOIM** 10
98 **BARGE OF MARGINS** (IRE) 5
243 **BARGAIN BUY** C 125
203 **BARISTA** (IRE) 1
323 **BARLEY BREEZE** 9
360 **BARLEY HILL** (IRE) 2
105 **BARN OWL** 18
363 **BARNABAS COLLINS** (IRE) 10
126 **BARNARD CASTLE** (IRE) 3
62 **BARNAVIDDAUN** (IRE) 3
86 **BARNAY** 3
431 **BARNET** C 54
376 **BARNEY BULLET** (IRE) 6
389 **BARNEY STINSON** (IRE) 1
168 **BARNEY'S BAY** 101
253 **BARNEZET** (GR) C 139
413 **BARNONE** 13
546 **BARNTOWN** (IRE) 5
175 **BARON DE MIDLETON** (IRE) 3
270 **BARON NELSON** (IRE) 14
76 **BARON RUN** 4
419 **BARON SAMEDI** 4
537 **BARON SLICK** (IRE) 2

256 **BARON WILD** (IRE) 79
245 **BARON ZEE** (IRE) 28
180 **BARONESS RACHAEL** 24
98 **BAROQUE STAR** (IRE) 66
328 **BAROSSA RED** (IRE) 1
369 **BARRAKHOV** (IRE) 13
431 **BARRET** (IRE) 21
402 **BARRICANE** 6
363 **BARRICHELLO** 11
444 **BARRIER PEAKS** (FR) 7
7 **BARRINGTON** (IRE) 2
256 **BARRINGTON COURT** 8
120 **BARROCHE** (IRE) C 65
398 **BARROWMOUNT** (IRE) 3
363 **BARRULE PARK** 12
123 **BARSHAA** 17
578 **BARTAT** 2
435 **BARTHOLOMEW J** (IRE) 1
348 **BARTON KNOLL** 2
343 **BARTON ROSE** 3
243 **BARTZELLA** 42
25 **BARYSHNIKOV** 3
290 **BASCULE** (FR) 18
16 **BASHFUL** 50
35 **BASHFUL BOY** (IRE) 1
243 **BASHKIROVA** 43
545 **BASHOSH** (IRE) 1
40 **BASIC BEAUTY** 3
309 **BASILICATA** (IRE) 58
39 **BASK IN THE GLORY** (IRE) 3
532 **BASS ROCK** (FR) 4
98 **BASS STRAIT** 67
546 **BASSARABAD** (FR) 6
298 **BATCH ME** 1
51 **BATCHELOR BOY** (IRE) 4
418 **BATHIVA** 16
411 **BATHSHEBA BAY** (IRE) 11
190 **BATHWICK BRAVE** (IRE) 5
272 **BATOCCHI** 20
415 **BATON ROUGE** (IRE) 19
545 **BATRAAN** (IRE) 52
274 **BATTAASH** (IRE) 5
431 **BATTERED** 7
471 **BATTLE ANTHEM** (IRE) 3
150 **BATTLE MARCH** (USA) 2
419 **BATTLE OF ACTIUM** (IRE) 5
534 **BATTLE OF IDEAS** (IRE) 6
474 **BATTLE OF MARATHON** (USA) 1
372 **BATTLE OF MIDWAY** (IRE) 3
96 **BATTLE OF PAVIA** (IRE) 1
574 **BATTLE OF WILLS** (IRE) 5
239 **BATTLEFIELD** (IRE) 3
415 **BATTLEGROUND** (USA) 20
239 **BATTLETANK** (IRE) 4
167 **BAVARDAGES** (IRE) 8
101 **BAVARIA BABY** (FR) 4
101 **BAVARIA EXPRESS** (FR) 31
249 **BAVINGTON BOB** (IRE) 3
529 **BAWAADER** (IRE) 1
518 **BAWAADY** 33
434 **BAXTER BASICS** (IRE) 6
179 **BAY BELLE** 4
518 **BAY BRIDGE** 34
306 **BAY MAY** 2
522 **BAY OF INTRIGUE** 2
272 **BAY OF NAPLES** (IRE) 4
488 **BAYAANAAT** 2

539 **BAYAMON BELLE** (IRE) 16
473 **BAYFRIARS BOBBY** (IRE) 7
120 **BAYJA** (IRE) C 66
287 **BAYLEY'S DREAM** 2
544 **BAYSTON HILL** 3
563 **BAZAROV** (IRE) 3
200 **BAZOOKA** (IRE) 1
371 **BAZZANA** F 21
25 **BAZZY** 30
408 **BBOLD** (IRE) 7
575 **BE DONN** (IRE) G 3
309 **BE FABULOUS** (GER) F 160
93 **BE FAIR** 3
555 **BE FREE** C 30
179 **BE GLORIOUS** 22
221 **BE JOYFUL** (IRE) F 15
167 **BE LUCKY** F 79
27 **BE LUCKY MY SON** (IRE) 82
344 **BE MY BEAU** 35
6 **BE MY GAL** F 111
93 **BE MY SEA** (IRE) 4
61 **BE PREPARED** 3
225 **BE PROUD** (IRE) 2
313 **BE THANKFUL** 2
490 **BE THE BEST** (USA) 2
323 **BE THE DIFFERENCE** (IRE) 10
304 **BE WITH THE BELL** 24
363 **BEACH BREAK** 13
587 **BEACH BUNNY** (IRE) C 45
419 **BEACH OF FALESA** (IRE) F 136
274 **BEACHES** 78
372 **BEACON EDGE** (IRE) 4
454 **BEACON OF HOPE** (IRE) F 49
386 **BEALACH** (IRE) 10
6 **BEAN FEASA** C 112
424 **BEAN IN TROUBLE** 1
526 **BEAR ATTRACTION** 3
526 **BEAR FORCE ONE** 4
358 **BEAR GHYLLS** (IRE) 1
410 **BEAR ME IN MIND** (IRE) 6
245 **BEAR STORY** (IRE) 29
391 **BEARAWAY** (IRE) 24
290 **BEASTIE BOY** (IRE) 19
185 **BEAT BOX** (FR) 4
253 **BEAT LE BON** (FR) 3
149 **BEAT THE BREEZE** 2
56 **BEAT THE HEAT** 4
386 **BEAT THE JUDGE** (IRE) 11
326 **BEAT THE STARS** (IRE) C 43
326 **BEAT THE STORM** (IRE) 23
64 **BEATBYBEATBYBEAT** 3
421 **BEATIFY** (IRE) C 109
518 **BEATING ALL** (USA) 35
126 **BEATTHEBULLET** (IRE) 4
408 **BEAU BAY** (FR) 8
256 **BEAU BRIDGET** (IRE) G 9
276 **BEAU DU BRIZAIS** (FR) 8
93 **BEAU GESTE** (IRE) 5
130 **BEAU HAZE** 1
545 **BEAU JARDINE** (IRE) 53
228 **BEAU NASH** (IRE) 45
353 **BEAU TINKER** (IRE) 18
234 **BEAUFORT** (IRE) 9
295 **BEAUFORT WEST** (IRE) 1
388 **BEAUTIFUL BEN** (IRE) 5
105 **BEAUTIFUL BERTIE** 19
306 **BEAUTIFUL CROWN** 13

431 **BEAUTIFUL FILLY** C 55
40 **BEAUTIFUL FOREST** F 117
6 **BEAUTIFUL FUTURE** (IRE) 39
373 **BEAUTIFUL MIX** 2
442 **BEAUTIFUL PEOPLE** (FR) 2
6 **BEAUTIFUL ROMANCE** F 113
40 **BEAUTIFUL SCENERY** (IRE) 4
419 **BEAUTY BRIGHT** (IRE) C 137
193 **BEAUTY CHOICE** 2
173 **BEAUTY DRAGON** (IRE) 1
415 **BEAUTY IS TRUTH** C 119
562 **BEAUTY STONE** (IRE) 1
319 **BEAUTY WITHIN** F 16
400 **BEAUVALLON BAY** (IRE) 4
546 **BEBRAVEFORGLORY** (IRE) 7
136 **BECCACCINO** 1
217 **BECKENBAUER** 8
418 **BECKY THE BOO** 17
587 **BEDFORD BLAZE** (IRE) 35
186 **BEDFORD FLYER** (IRE) 10
40 **BEDOUIN'S STORY** 5
475 **BEECHWOOD DONNA** 37
128 **BEECHWOOD EMILY** 77
128 **BEECHWOOD JUDE** (FR) 7
478 **BEENO** (IRE) 1
216 **BEEPEECEE** 2
266 **BEES AND HONEY** 2
6 **BEFORE DAWN** (IRE) 114
527 **BEFORE MIDNIGHT** 2
587 **BEFORE THE STORM** C 46
114 **BEFOREYPUSHDACHAIR** (IRE) 1
12 **BEGIN THE LUCK** (IRE) 2
315 **BEGOODTOYOURSELF** (IRE) 1
105 **BEHELD** 20
473 **BEHINDTHELINES** (IRE) 8
503 **BEHOLDEN** 4
228 **BEHOLDING** 46
427 **BEHRESS** 5
253 **BEIJING BILLY** (IRE) 44
101 **BEL ARISTO** (FR) 32
51 **BELACQUA** (IRE) 29
446 **BELAFONTE** 15
588 **BELAMI DES PICTONS** (FR) 4
223 **BELARGUS** (FR) 1
444 **BELGUARDO** (FR) 8
179 **BELHAVEN** (IRE) 2
243 **BELIEF** 44
545 **BELIEVE IN LOVE** (IRE) 6
415 **BELIEVE'N'SUCCEED** (AUS) F 120
446 **BELISA DE VEGA** (IRE) 41
390 **BELL HEATHER** (IRE) 2
256 **BELL I AM** (IRE) 80
256 **BELL PEPPER** (IRE) 81
16 **BELL ROCK** 3
23 **BELLA AMOURA** 2
51 **BELLA B** 21
264 **BELLA BEAU** (FR) 4
574 **BELLA BLUESKY** 6
510 **BELLA BLUR** 2
215 **BELLA CATALINA** C 19
433 **BELLA COLOROSSA** 4
262 **BELLA FEVER** (URU) 1
574 **BELLA GLENEAGLES** (IRE) 7
159 **BELLA LUCE** (IRE) 18
120 **BELLA LULU** F 67
253 **BELLA NOTTE** 45
240 **BELLA VENETA** 24

325 **BELLA'S PEARL** 22
159 **BELLAGIO** 19
233 **BELLAMY'S GREY** 1
579 **BELLAMYS BELLE** 1
579 **BELLAMYS BOY** 2
159 **BELLARENA LADY** 43
588 **BELLATRIXSA** (IRE) 5
587 **BELLE ANGLAISE** 4
285 **BELLE DE MANECH** (FR) 3
395 **BELLE DORMANT** (IRE) F 113
399 **BELLE METAL** (IRE) 17
250 **BELLE O' THE DALES** (FR) 4
473 **BELLE REBELLE** (IRE) F 9
309 **BELLE ROUGE** 59
451 **BELLETTI** 16
482 **BELLEVARDE** (IRE) 1
493 **BELLEVARDE EXPRESS** (IRE) 3
493 **BELLICA** 3
475 **BELLISSIME** (IRE) 38
375 **BELLOCCIO** (FR) 18
102 **BELLOSA** (IRE) 21
399 **BELLOW MOME** (FR) 18
16 **BELLPORT** (IRE) 137
546 **BELLS OF BARNACK** (IRE) 8
546 **BELLS OF PETERBORO** (IRE) 9
532 **BELLSHILL** (IRE) 5
523 **BELLWETHER** F 52
419 **BELMONT AVENUE** (IRE) 65
6 **BELONGING** C 115
554 **BELOVED** 36
514 **BELTOR** 1
533 **BELVEDERE BLAST** (IRE) 24
488 **BEMBRIDGE** (IRE) 3
4 **BEMPTON CLIFFS** (IRE) 4
303 **BEN BRODY** (IRE) 3
313 **BEN BUIE** (IRE) 3
70 **BEN LILLY** (IRE) 1
475 **BEN MACDUI** (IRE) 39
372 **BEN SIEGEL** 91
372 **BEN THOMSON** (IRE) 5
188 **BENADALID** 1
23 **BENANDGONE** 3
386 **BENATAR** (IRE) 12
419 **BENAUD** (FR) 66
40 **BENBATL** 6
59 **BENDY BOW** 1
318 **BENE REGINA** (IRE) 2
343 **BENEFICIAL BREEZE** (IRE) G 4
68 **BENEFIT** 68
119 **BENEFIT STREET** (IRE) 5
13 **BENEVOLENTDICTATOR** 13
107 **BENI KHIAR** (FR) 15
458 **BENI LIGHT** (FR) 2
399 **BENIE DES DIEUX** (FR) 19
329 **BENITO** (FR) 5
418 **BENNIE BOY** 18
324 **BENNY AND THE JETS** (IRE) 1
291 **BENNY FLIES HIGH** (IRE) 1
20 **BENNY IN MILAN** (IRE) 2
408 **BENNY'S BRIDGE** (IRE) 9
492 **BENNY'S OSCAR** (IRE) 15
1 **BENNY'S SECRET** (IRE) 4
492 **BENNYS KING** (IRE) 16
408 **BENSON** 10
75 **BENTLEY WOOD** 1
554 **BEOWULF** (IRE) 37
399 **BERET ROUGE** (IRE) 20

475 **BERGERAC** (IRE) 40
321 **BERINGER** 4
16 **BERKSHIRE BREEZE** (IRE) 138
16 **BERKSHIRE PHOENIX** (IRE) 139
16 **BERKSHIRE REBEL** (IRE) 140
16 **BERKSHIRE ROCCO** (FR) 4
399 **BERKSHIRE ROYAL** 21
16 **BERKSHIRE SHADOW** 141
190 **BERMEO** (IRE) 6
120 **BERMUDA** 69
314 **BERNARD SPIERPOINT** 2
506 **BERNARDO O'REILLY** 2
365 **BERNIE'S BOY** 1
34 **BERRAHRI** (IRE) 1
148 **BERRY EDGE** (IRE) 33
25 **BERT KIBBLER** 31
470 **BERTHA BURNETT** (IRE) C 14
323 **BERTIE BLAKE** (IRE) 11
424 **BERTIE'S BANDANA** (IRE) 12
120 **BERTIE'S WISH** (IRE) 15
267 **BERTIELICIOUS** 2
348 **BERTOG** 3
301 **BERYL THE PERIL** (IRE) 12
243 **BESHARAH** (IRE) F 126
6 **BESOTTED** (IRE) C 116
309 **BESS OF HARDWICK** C 161
415 **BEST OF MY LOVE** (IRE) C 121
431 **BEST SIDE** (IRE) F 56
145 **BEST TAMAYUZ** 2
420 **BESTFOOTFORWARD** C 18
47 **BESTIARIUS** (IRE) 2
508 **BESTING** (FR) 14
233 **BET ON BETTY** 2
290 **BETHERSDEN BOY** (IRE) 42
40 **BETIMES** C 118
55 **BETTER BY FAR** (IRE) 9
309 **BETTER HALF** 162
288 **BETTERLATETHANNEVA** (IRE) 1
375 **BETTY CREAN L A** (IRE) 19
492 **BETTY GETAWAY** 17
517 **BETTY GRABLE** (IRE) 2
29 **BETWEEN THE SHEETS** (IRE) 44
503 **BETWEEN THE WATERS** (IRE) 5
105 **BETWEEN US** C 57
489 **BEVSBOY** (IRE) 3
270 **BEWARE THE BEAR** (IRE) 15
16 **BEWITCHMENT** F 142
168 **BEXANDELLA** G 102
428 **BEYOND BOUNDARIES** (IRE) 51
325 **BEYOND DESIRE** C 50
402 **BEYOND EQUAL** 1
497 **BEYOND EVERYTHING** (FR) 7
272 **BEYOND FASHION** C 10
459 **BEYOND INFINITY** 5
343 **BEYOND SUPREMACY** (IRE) 1
389 **BEYOND THE CLOUDS** 5
418 **BEYOND THE LAW** (IRE) 2
93 **BEYOND THE PALE** (IRE) 19
84 **BEZZAS LAD** (IRE) 6
103 **BHAJI** 29
308 **BHARANI STAR** (GER) 1
473 **BHUBEZI** 23
29 **BIALCO** (FR) 10
155 **BIARAAFA** (IRE) C 45
1 **BIBBIDIBOBBIDIBOO** (IRE) 3
87 **BIBLICAL** (FR) 5
**BIBULOUS** (IRE) 18

193 **BIBURY** G 34
27 **BIBURY** C 83
76 **BICKERSTAFFE** 32
475 **BIELSA** (IRE) 2
229 **BIG ARTHUR** 2
461 **BIG BAD BEAR** (IRE) 2
575 **BIG BAD DREAM** (IRE) 4
105 **BIG BOY BOBBY** (IRE) 21
222 **BIG BRESIL** 11
587 **BIG BROWN** (IRE) 5
264 **BIG CHIEF** (IRE) 5
321 **BIG CHIEF BENNY** (IRE) 5
580 **BIG CHIP AND PIN** 3
43 **BIG DATA** (IRE) 2
434 **BIG DIFFERENCE** (IRE) 7
105 **BIG DREAM** (IRE) 22
323 **BIG EARS** (IRE) 12
442 **BIG FIDDLE** 3
408 **BIG G** 11
63 **BIG IMPACT** 4
523 **BIG IMPRESSION** 2
128 **BIG JIM DWYER** (IRE) 8
386 **BIG JIMBO** 1
29 **BIG KITTY** 11
84 **BIG LES** (IRE) 2
428 **BIG LITTLE LIE** (FR) 18
271 **BIG MAN CLARENCE** (IRE) 3
322 **BIG MEADOW** (IRE) 5
40 **BIG MEETING** (IRE) 7
507 **BIG MUDDY** 2
506 **BIG NARSTIE** (FR) 31
313 **BIG NASTY** 4
388 **BIG PENNY** (IRE) 6
32 **BIG PETE** 1
190 **BIG PICTURE** 7
473 **BIG RIVER** (IRE) 11
276 **BIG SHARK** (IRE) 9
40 **BIG TEAM** (USA) 8
353 **BIG THANKS** (IRE) 19
133 **BIG TIME DANCER** (IRE) 3
242 **BIG TIME FRANK** (IRE) 1
10 **BIG TIME MAYBE** (IRE) 4
166 **BIG TREE** (IRE) 2
475 **BIG VIOLETT** (IRE) C 88
253 **BIG WING** (IRE) 4
394 **BIGBADBOY** (IRE) 2
441 **BIGBILLRIGLEY** (IRE) 1
23 **BIGGLES** 3
146 **BIGIRONONHISHIP** (IRE) 3
577 **BIGMARTRE** (FR) 3
219 **BIGNORM** (IRE) 1
50 **BIGSALONSUNTOWN** (USA) 28
545 **BILHAYL** (IRE) 54
221 **BILINGUAL** 2
234 **BILL BAXTER** (IRE) 10
84 **BILL CODY** (IRE) 3
372 **BILL DOOLIN** 6
491 **BILL PEYTO** (IRE) 30
418 **BILLAMS LEGACY** 20
399 **BILLAWAY** (IRE) 22
193 **BILLHILLY** (GER) 3
323 **BILLIAN** (IRE) 94
251 **BILLIE ERIA** (IRE) F 13
159 **BILLIE'S GIRL** (IRE) 20
211 **BILLIEBROOKEDIT** (IRE) 4
456 **BILLINGSLEY** (IRE) 2
574 **BILLY BATHGATE** 8

408 **BILLY BRONCO** 12
207 **BILLY DYLAN** (IRE) 2
253 **BILLY MILL** 46
148 **BILLY NO MATES** (IRE) 4
178 **BILLY RAY** 2
576 **BILLY ROBERTS** (IRE) 1
418 **BILLY THE SQUID** (IRE) 21
549 **BILLY WEDGE** 1
400 **BILLY'S ANGEL** (IRE) 5
530 **BILLYFAIRPLAY** (IRE) 1
436 **BILLYOAKES** (IRE) 1
87 **BIMBLE** (IRE) 2
40 **BIN BATTUTA** 9
131 **BINDON LANE** 3
185 **BINGO D'OLIVATE** (FR) 5
6 **BINT ALMATAR** (USA) C 117
253 **BINT ALMUKHTAR** (IRE) C 140
189 **BINT AUSTRALIA** (IRE) 2
557 **BINT DANDY** (IRE) 6
388 **BIOVERDIA** (IRE) 7
424 **BIOWAVEGO** (IRE) 13
270 **BIRCHDALE** (IRE) 16
309 **BIRDIE BOWERS** (IRE) 2
309 **BIRDIE PUTT** (IRE) 163
534 **BIRDMAN BOB** (IRE) 7
186 **BIRKENHEAD** 2
387 **BIRKIE QUEEN** (IRE) 1
596 **BIT OF A LEGEND** 9
552 **BIT OF A QUIRKE** 3
4 **BITASWEETSYMPHONY** (IRE) 5
423 **BITE MY TONGUE** (IRE) 1
168 **BITE YA LEGS** 103
473 **BIX BEIDERBECKE** (FR) 95
189 **BIZ BAR** F 54
4 **BIZERTA** (FR) 6
16 **BIZZARRIA** C 143
577 **BLACK ABBEY** (FR) 4
63 **BLACK BOX** 5
93 **BLACK BUBLE** (FR) 7
597 **BLACK CAESAR** (IRE) 1
475 **BLACK CASPIAN** (IRE) 3
227 **BLACK CENTAUR** (IRE) 8
6 **BLACK CHERRY** C 118
411 **BLACK CORTON** (FR) 12
323 **BLACK EBONY** 13
386 **BLACK GERRY** (IRE) 15
386 **BLACK KALANISI** (IRE) 3
143 **BLACK KALAROSA** (IRE) 2
250 **BLACK KETTLE** (IRE) 5
263 **BLACK KRAKEN** 3
82 **BLACK LABEL** 1
595 **BLACK LACE** 1
288 **BLACK LIGHTNING** (IRE) 2
555 **BLACK LOTUS** 1
414 **BLACK MARKET** (IRE) 2
554 **BLACK MASCARA** (IRE) C 76
385 **BLACK MEDICK** 2
9 **BLACK MINSTER** 1
212 **BLACK MISCHIEF** 5
190 **BLACK NOAH** 5
222 **BLACK OP** (IRE) 12
297 **BLACK OPIUM** 1
313 **BLACK PANTHER** (IRE) 5

253 **BLACK PEARL** (IRE) C 141
256 **BLACK PEPPER** (IRE) 161
185 **BLACK PIRATE** 6
126 **BLACK SAM MELODY** 5
365 **BLACK SPARROW** 12
495 **BLACKBERRY** 16
399 **BLACKBOW** (IRE) 23
290 **BLACKCASTLE STORM** 1
68 **BLACKCURRENT** 2
171 **BLACKFINCH** 3
148 **BLACKHEATH** 5
68 **BLACKJACK** 3
411 **BLACKJACK KENTUCKY** (IRE) 13
19 **BLACKJACK MAGIC** 1
321 **BLACKO** (FR) 6
34 **BLACKROD** 34
569 **BLACKTHIRTYONE** 32
190 **BLACKTHORN WINTER** 9
161 **BLACKWATER BRAMBLE** (IRE) 3
270 **BLAIRGOWRIE** (IRE) 17
385 **BLAIRLOGIE** 3
363 **BLAKENEY POINT** 15
461 **BLAKERIGG** (IRE) 3
98 **BLAKESHALL ROSE** F 33
492 **BLAKLION** 18
356 **BLAME CULTURE** (USA) 1
227 **BLAME THE GAME** (IRE) 9
421 **BLANCHE NEIGE** F 110
295 **BLARNEY BATELEUR** (IRE) 2
258 **BLAS CEOIL** (USA) F 49
501 **BLASTER YEATS** 6
362 **BLAUSEE** (IRE) 1
526 **BLAZEON FIVE** 25
399 **BLAZER** (FR) 24
484 **BLAZER TWO** 46
402 **BLAZER'S MILL** (IRE) 8
482 **BLAZING DREAMS** (IRE) 4
1 **BLAZING PORT** (IRE) 6
482 **BLAZING SADDLES** 1
495 **BLAZING SON** 17
13 **BLAZON** 7
545 **BLENDING** F 155
491 **BLESS HIM** (IRE) 1
87 **BLESSED** (IRE) 3
509 **BLESSING** (USA) F 10
399 **BLEU BERRY** (FR) 25
285 **BLEUE AWAY** (IRE) 4
523 **BLHADAWA** (IRE) F 53
263 **BLINDINGLY** (GER) 5
436 **BLISSFUL SONG** (IRE) 9
315 **BLISTERING BARNEY** (IRE) 2
553 **BLISTERING BOB** 2
107 **BLUSHING** 16
303 **BLOOD EAGLE** (IRE) 4
473 **BLOORIEDOTCOM** (IRE) 12
6 **BLOSSOMTIME** C 119
317 **BLOW BY BLOW** (IRE) 1
518 **BLOW THAT HORN** 36
193 **BLOW YOUR HORN** (IRE) 4
300 **BLOWING DIXIE** 2
148 **BLOWING WIND** (IRE) 35
36 **BLU BOY** (IRE) 12
189 **BLUE ARTEMIS** 27
365 **BLUE BEACON** F 13
135 **BLUE BEIRUT** (IRE) 3
149 **BLUE BERET** 26
171 **BLUE BIKINI** 4

6 **BLUE BUNTING** (USA) C 120
10 **BLUE CABLE** 5
509 **BLUE CABOCHAN** 11
171 **BLUE CATO** (IRE) 5
235 **BLUE COLLAR GLORY** (IRE) 7
597 **BLUE CREST** (IRE) C 7
375 **BLUE CUP** (FR) 3
179 **BLUE DAHLIA** (IRE) C 24
264 **BLUE DAVIS** 6
119 **BLUE DE VEGA** (GER) 6
228 **BLUE DIAMOND** (IRE) 47
544 **BLUE GALAXY** 17
111 **BLUE HAWAII** (IRE) 2
270 **BLUE HEAVEN** 18
7 **BLUE HERO** (CAN) 93
442 **BLUE HOUR BAY** (IRE) 4
250 **BLUE HUSSAR** (IRE) 6
40 **BLUE ILLUSION** F 119
582 **BLUE LAUREATE** 9
110 **BLUE LILY** (USA) 20
399 **BLUE LORD** (FR) 26
418 **BLUE LUNA** 22
345 **BLUE MEDICI** 3
105 **BLUE MIST** 2
418 **BLUE MONDAY** (IRE) 23
180 **BLUE MOONRISE** 25
574 **BLUE NYMPH** G 9
415 **BLUE PLANET** 21
408 **BLUE RIBBON** 13
418 **BLUE SANS** (IRE) 24
399 **BLUE SARI** (FR) 27
424 **BLUE SHARK** (IRE) 14
176 **BLUE SKYLINE** (IRE) 1
60 **BLUE SLATE** (IRE) 1
270 **BLUE STELLO** (FR) 19
145 **BLUE STREAK** 3
93 **BLUE VENTURE** 8
291 **BLUE WHISPER** 2
522 **BLUEBELL POLKA** (IRE) 3
477 **BLUEBELL TIME** (IRE) 2
581 **BLUEBERG** (IRE) 10
363 **BLUEBERRY WINE** (IRE) 16
189 **BLUEBIRD** 55
27 **BLUEBIRD DAY** 33
40 **BLUEFIRE** F 120
185 **BLUEFORTYTWO** 7
7 **BLUELLA** 9
50 **BLUENOSE BELLE** (USA) 29
128 **BLUESKYANDSUNSHINE** (IRE) 9
134 **BLUETECH** 3
76 **BLUEWATER LADY** (USA) 33
218 **BLUFFMEIFYOUCAN** 2
395 **BLUMEN GLORY** (IRE) 7
546 **BLUNDER BUSS** (IRE) 10
450 **BLURRED LINES** (IRE) G 2
308 **BLYNX** C 53
92 **BO BRIDGET** (IRE) C 25
212 **BO KAAP** (IRE) 68
453 **BO TAIFAN** (IRE) 1
283 **BOA** F 2
22 **BOA ISLAND** (IRE) 5
50 **BOADICEE** F 73
222 **BOAGRIUS** (IRE) 13
321 **BOARD OF TRADE** 7
168 **BOARDMAN** 3
411 **BOB AND CO** (FR) 14
285 **BOB BACKUS** (IRE) 5

234 **BOB MAHLER** (IRE) 11
363 **BOB'S BAR** (IRE) 17
397 **BOB'S GIRL** 3
31 **BOB'S OSS** (IRE) 2
396 **BOBBA TEE** 1
307 **BOBBIE THE DAZZLER** (IRE) 1
434 **BOBBY BOW** (IRE) 8
91 **BOBBY JOE LEG** 3
109 **BOBBY KENNEDY** 8
29 **BOBBY ON THE BEAT** (IRE) 12
550 **BOBBY SHAFT** 1
554 **BOBBY THE THIEF** 77
375 **BOBBY'S BLESSING** 40
13 **BOBHOPEORNOHOPE** (IRE) 8
546 **BOBMAHLEY** (IRE) 11
522 **BOBO MAC** (IRE) 4
34 **BOBS LAD** 2
340 **BODROY** (IRE) 13
449 **BODYLINE** (IRE) 4
210 **BOGOSS DU PERRET** (FR) 2
399 **BOHEMIAN BIRCH** (IRE) 28
441 **BOHER LAD** (IRE) 2
582 **BOL D'AIR** (FR) 10
518 **BOLD AND LOYAL** 92
79 **BOLD ASSUMPTION** F 48
534 **BOLD CONDUCT** (IRE) 8
93 **BOLD DECISION** 9
388 **BOLD ENDEAVOUR** 5
388 **BOLD LEADER** 9
343 **BOLD PIMPERNEL** (IRE) 6
581 **BOLD PLAN** (IRE) 11
123 **BOLD PRESENCE** 63
333 **BOLD REASON** (GER) 2
62 **BOLD RED** 4
545 **BOLD RIBB** 156
234 **BOLD SOLDIER** 12
148 **BOLD TERRITORIES** (IRE) 36
89 **BOLD VISION** (IRE) 2
6 **BOLDARRA** (USA) C 121
12 **BOLDMERE** 3
126 **BOLEY BAY** (IRE) 6
419 **BOLLEVILLE** (IRE) 6
168 **BOLLIN ACE** 9
588 **BOLLIN ACROSS** F 6
168 **BOLLIN JOAN** 10
168 **BOLLIN MARGARET** 11
168 **BOLLIN NEIL** 12
168 **BOLLIN PHOENIX** 13
168 **BOLLIN TED** 14
473 **BOLLINGERANDKRUG** (IRE) 13
425 **BOLLY BULLET** (IRE) 1
415 **BOLSHOI BALLET** (IRE) 22
234 **BOLSOVER BILL** (IRE) 13
316 **BOLT N BROWN** 2
105 **BOLTAWAY** 23
29 **BOLTHOLE** (IRE) 46
408 **BOLTISSIME** (FR) 14
51 **BOLTON ABBEY** (IRE) 31
131 **BOLVING** (IRE) 4
193 **BOMA GREEN** 5
189 **BOMB PROOF** (IRE) 3
387 **BOMB SQUAD** (IRE) 3
180 **BOMBASTIC** (IRE) 4
21 **BOMBAY BASIL** (IRE) 1
372 **BOMBAY BLUE** (IRE) 7
140 **BOMBERO** (IRE) 1
548 **BOMBYX** 3

399 **BON RETOUR** (IRE) 29
415 **BONANZA CREEK** (IRE) C 122
360 **BONANZA SAM** 3
337 **BONBON AU MIEL** (FR) 3
145 **BOND ANGEL** 4
426 **BOND ARTIST** (IRE) F 9
495 **BOND CHAIRMAN** 28
495 **BOND POWER** 29
270 **BOND'S LOVER** (IRE) 20
326 **BONDI SPICE** (IRE) 44
345 **BONFIRE HEART** C 54
162 **BONGOALI** G 1
40 **BONHOMIE** C 121
395 **BONNE ANNIVERSAIRE** F 8
15 **BONNET** 29
189 **BONNEVAL** 4
176 **BONNIE BRAE** C 15
470 **BONNIE BURNETT** (IRE) G 15
290 **BONNIE LAD** 20
575 **BONNY HOUXTY** 5
16 **BONNYRIGG** (IRE) 52
256 **BONTE MOI** (FR) 82
56 **BONUS** 5
472 **BOOBOROWIE** (IRE) 1
76 **BOOGIE TIME** (IRE) 34
488 **BOOK OF GOLD** (IRE) 4
473 **BOOK OF INVASIONS** (IRE) 14
245 **BOOK OF VERSE** (USA) 30
29 **BOOKMARK** 13
256 **BOOLA BOOLA** (IRE) 10
577 **BOOLEY BEACH** (IRE) 5
93 **BOOM THE GROOM** (IRE) 10
545 **BOOMSHALAA** 55
303 **BOOMTIME BANKER** (IRE) 5
309 **BOONDOGGLE** 164
475 **BOONIE** (IRE) 89
243 **BOOSALA** (IRE) 8
212 **BOOTHILL** (IRE) 6
133 **BOOTLEGGER** (IRE) 4
256 **BOPEDRO** (FR) 11
175 **BORDEAUX BILL** (IRE) 4
378 **BORDER MINSTRAL** (IRE) F 36
404 **BORDER VICTOR** 2
313 **BORDERLINE** (IRE) 33
333 **BOREHAM BILL** (IRE) 3
566 **BORIC** 1
121 **BORIS THE BRAVE** 1
540 **BORN AT MIDNIGHT** 1
27 **BORN CROSS** (IRE) C 84
534 **BORN IN BORRIS** (IRE) 9
492 **BORN SURVIVOR** (IRE) 19
76 **BORN TO BE ALIVE** (IRE) 5
506 **BORN TO DESTROY** 3
140 **BORN TO FINISH** (IRE) 2
289 **BORN TO FROLIC** (IRE) 1
544 **BORN TO PLEASE** 6
161 **BORN TO REASON** (IRE) 4
557 **BORN TO SIRE** (IRE) 7
243 **BORN WITH PRIDE** (IRE) 9
438 **BORNTOBEALEADER** (IRE) 22
584 **BORO BABE** (FR) 3
178 **BORODIN** (IRE) 3
84 **BORSDANE WOOD** 4
253 **BOSH** (FR) 142
281 **BOSS DES MOTTES** (FR) 2
518 **BOSS POWER** (IRE) 5
235 **BOSSINEY BAY** (IRE) 8

168 **BOSSIPOP** 15
416 **BOSTIN** (IRE) 2
270 **BOTHWELL BRIDGE** (IRE) 21
386 **BOTOX HAS** (FR) 16
154 **BOTUS FLEMING** 2
523 **BOUCHERON** F 12
5 **BOUDICA BAY** (IRE) 2
353 **BOUGAINVILIA** (IRE) F 37
568 **BOUGHTBEFORELUNCH** (IRE) 2
322 **BOULTING FOR GLORY** (IRE) 6
48 **BOUMMA DREAM** 3
16 **BOUNCE THE BLUES** (IRE) 5
491 **BOUNCE THIS WAY** 71
536 **BOUNCING BOBBY** (IRE) 4
235 **BOUNDSY BOY** 68
31 **BOUNTY BOX** G 15
45 **BOUNTY PURSUIT** 1
534 **BOURBALI** (FR) 10
244 **BOURBON BEAUTY** 1
167 **BOW BRIDGE** C 80
229 **BOWDEREK** 3
354 **BOWL IMPERIOR** 2
328 **BOWMAN PARK** 17
15 **BOWLING RUSSIAN** (IRE) 4
309 **BOWMAN** (IRE) 6
86 **BOWSER** (IRE) 4
1 **BOWSTAR** F 44
434 **BOWTOGREATNESS** (IRE) 9
309 **BOY ABOUT TOWN** 165
195 **BOY GEORGE** 2
582 **BOY IN THE BAR** 11
473 **BOY'S ON TOUR** (IRE) 15
222 **BOYHOOD** (IRE) 14
419 **BOYNE RIVER** 67
372 **BRACE YOURSELF** (IRE) 8
419 **BRACELET** (IRE) F 138
58 **BRACHO** 1
168 **BRACING BREEZE** C 152
574 **BRACKENMOSS RORY** 1
29 **BRACKISH** 3
132 **BRAD THE BRIEF** 2
399 **BRAHMA BULL** (IRE) 30
428 **BRAINS** (IRE) 1
386 **BRAMBLEDOWN** 17
171 **BRAN** 6
175 **BRANCASTER** (IRE) 5
309 **BRANDEGORIS** 61
475 **BRANDO** 4
322 **BRANDON CASTLE** 7
222 **BRANDON HILL** (IRE) 15
168 **BRANDY BAY** 104
581 **BRANDY COVE** (IRE) 12
295 **BRANDY CROSS** (IRE) 3
399 **BRANDY LOVE** (IRE) 31
589 **BRANDY STATION** (IRE) 2
93 **BRANSTON PIKKLE** 93
568 **BRAQUEUR D'OR** (FR) 3
27 **BRASCA** 4
420 **BRASINGAMANBELLAMY** 2
63 **BRASS CLANKERS** 6
309 **BRAVADO** (FR) 62
552 **BRAVANTINA** 4
488 **BRAVE BAIRN** (FR) 5
270 **BRAVE EAGLE** (IRE) 22
447 **BRAVE JAQ** (FR) 1
577 **BRAVE KINGDOM** (FR) 6
562 **BRAVE LILY** (IRE) 27

167 **BRAVE MAVE** F 81
588 **BRAVE SEASCA** (FR) 7
411 **BRAVEMANSGAME** (FR) 15
582 **BRAVO BUDDY** (IRE) 12
569 **BRAVO FAISAL** (IRE) 4
498 **BRAWNY** 1
185 **BRAYHILL** (IRE) 8
162 **BRAZEN ARROW** 11
421 **BRAZEN BELLE** 59
410 **BRAZEN BEST** 10
455 **BRAZEN BRUCE** 9
301 **BRAZEN IDOL** 21
589 **BRAZEN LADY** 3
95 **BRAZEN POINT** 1
415 **BRAZIL** (IRE) 23
86 **BREADCRUMBS** (FR) 5
497 **BREAK THE RULES** 2
145 **BREAK THE SILENCE** 5
120 **BREAKAWAY** 16
399 **BREAKEN** (FR) 32
324 **BREAKFASTATIFFANYS** 15
167 **BREAKING RECORDS** (IRE) 9
39 **BREAKING THE ICE** (IRE) 4
577 **BREAKING WAVES** (IRE) 7
492 **BREAKWATER BUOY** (IRE) 20
27 **BREATH CAUGHT** 5
400 **BREATH OF JOY** 6
368 **BREATH OF SPRING** (IRE) 4
120 **BREATH OF SUN** 17
241 **BREATHOFFRESHAIR** 2
243 **BRECCIA** 45
7 **BRECKLAND** 94
291 **BRECON HILL** (IRE) 3
218 **BREDON HILL LEO** 3
401 **BREEZYANDBRIGHT** (IRE) 13
190 **BREFFNIBOY** (FR) 10
128 **BREGUET BOY** (IRE) 10
313 **BREIZH ALKO** (FR) 6
411 **BRELAN D'AS** (FR) 16
290 **BRENTFORD HOPE** 2
411 **BREWERS PROJECT** (IRE) 12
402 **BREWIN'UPASTORM** (IRE) 12
546 **BRIAC** 21
413 **BRIAN BORANHA** (IRE) 2
588 **BRIANSTORM** (IRE) 8
36 **BRIARDALE** (IRE) 2
250 **BRICKADANK** (IRE) 7
333 **BRICKLAGGER** (IRE) 4
228 **BRIDESMAN** (IRE) 48
445 **BRIDEY'S LETTUCE** (IRE) 2
84 **BRIDGETOWN** 30
98 **BRIDIE FFRENCH** F 68
386 **BRIDLE LOANAN** (IRE) 18
53 **BRIEF ACQUAINTANCE** (IRE) 1
418 **BRIEF AMBITION** 25
585 **BRIERY EXPRESS** 3
546 **BRIGADE OF GUARDS** (IRE) 13
336 **BRIGADIER BOB** (IRE) 2
76 **BRIGHT APPARITION** 35
523 **BRIGHT APPROACH** (IRE) F 54
6 **BRIGHT BEACON** C 122
552 **BRIGHT CLOUD** (IRE) G 5
470 **BRIGHT DAWN** (IRE) 3
359 **BRIGHT EDGE** F 1
402 **BRIGHT EYED EAGLE** (IRE) 10
98 **BRIGHT FLASH** C 69
94 **BRIGHT GIRL** (IRE) F 16

245 **BRIGHT GLORY** GB 31
419 **BRIGHT IDEA** (IRE) 7
90 **BRIGHT LIGHTS** (FR) 3
40 **BRIGHT MOONLIGHT** (IRE) 73
277 **BRIGHT SAFFRON** 1
40 **BRIGHT START** (IRE) 10
11 **BRIGHT VIEW** (IRE) 1
40 **BRILLIANT LIGHT** 11
290 **BRILLIANT NEWS** (IRE) 43
270 **BRILLIANT PRESENT** (IRE) 23
264 **BRING THE ACTION** (IRE) 7
236 **BRING THE BACON** 2
98 **BRING THE MONEY** (IRE) 6
7 **BRINGING GLORY** (IRE) 10
128 **BRINGITONBORIS** (USA) 11
488 **BRINGTHEHOUSEDOWN** (IRE) 6
444 **BRINKLEY** (FR) 9
29 **BRISTOL BAY** (FR) F 47
132 **BRITAIN'S PRIDE** F 47
446 **BROAD APPEAL** 1
150 **BROADCLYST** (IRE) 3
511 **BROADFIELD CRUISER** (IRE) G 1
446 **BROADHAVEN** 16
545 **BROADSPEAR** 157
146 **BROADSTRUTHER** (IRE) 4
326 **BROADWAY DIVA** (FR) 24
1 **BROADWAY JOE** (IRE) 7
319 **BROADWAY LAD** (USA) 1
387 **BROCKAGH CAILIN** 2
92 **BROCKHOLES** C 26
47 **BROCTUNE RED** 3
473 **BRODICK** 5
132 **BROGAN** G 48
161 **BROKE AWAY** (IRE) 5
411 **BROKEN HALO** 18
487 **BROKEN QUEST** (IRE) 2
214 **BROKEN RIFLE** 1
121 **BROKEN SPEAR** 1
399 **BRONAGH'S BELLE** (IRE) 33
399 **BROOKLYNN GLORY** (IRE) 34
581 **BROOKSWAY FAIR** (IRE) 13
415 **BROOME** (IRE) 3
270 **BROOMFIELD BURG** (IRE) 24
475 **BROOMY LAW** 41
514 **BROPHIES DOLL** (IRE) 2
295 **BROTHER BENNETT** (FR) 4
93 **BROTHER IN ARMS** (IRE) 11
168 **BROTHER MCGONAGALL** 16
363 **BROTHER PAT** 18
276 **BROTHER TEDD** 10
227 **BROTHER WINDSOR** (IRE) 10
532 **BROTHERLY COMPANY** (IRE) 6
340 **BROUAINS** (FR) 2
42 **BROUGHTONS CHARM** (IRE) F 9
362 **BROUGHTONS CHIEF** 1
275 **BROUGHTONS COMPASS** 1
569 **BROUGHTONS FLARE** (IRE) 5
353 **BROUGHTONS JEWEL** (IRE) F 38
549 **BROUGHTONS MYSTERY** F 17
362 **BROUGHTONS OYSTER** 12
293 **BROUGHTONS RHYTHM** 1
69 **BROUGHTONS RUBY** 1
442 **BROWN ARROW** (IRE) G 5
253 **BROWN BEE** (IRE) C 143
295 **BROWN BULLET** (IRE) 5
50 **BROWN DELIVERS** (USA) 30
475 **BROWN EYED HONEY** F 90

296 **BROXI** (IRE) 24
111 **BRUKIRK LASS** F 3
488 **BRUMMIE BOYS** (IRE) 7
290 **BRUNEL CHARM** 3
76 **BRUNI HEINKE** (IRE) C 91
431 **BRUNNERA** 22
87 **BRUSH CREEK** 34
447 **BRUSHED UP** 2
526 **BRUTE FORCE** 5
296 **BRUYERE** (FR) 2
148 **BRYANWOOD** (IRE) 37
86 **BRYDEN BOY** (IRE) 6
150 **BRYHER** 4
402 **BUBBLES OF GOLD** (IRE) 11
555 **BUCEPHALUS** (GER) 2
458 **BUCK BRAVO** (IRE) 3
28 **BUCK DANCING** (IRE) 1
399 **BUCK'S BILLIONAIRE** (FR) 35
222 **BUCK'S BIN'S** (FR) 16
270 **BUCK'S BLUE** (FR) G 25
222 **BUCK'S BOGGLE** (FR) 17
600 **BUCKBORU** (IRE) 3
534 **BUCKHORN GEORGE** 11
534 **BUCKHORN ROCCO** 12
308 **BUCKINGHAM** (IRE) 3
125 **BUCKLAND BOY** (IRE) 4
532 **BUCKLED** 7
503 **BUCKO'S BOY** 6
450 **BUCKSKIN** (IRE) 3
503 **BUCKSOME** 7
473 **BUDDHA SCHEME** (IRE) 17
411 **BUENA NOTTE** (IRE) G 19
538 **BUFORD** 25
407 **BUG BOY** (IRE) 2
262 **BUILDING YEAR** (IRE) 2
399 **BUILDMEUPBUTTERCUP** 36
371 **BUKHOOR** (IRE) C 22
79 **BULBUL** (IRE) F 17
27 **BULLACE** 39
301 **BULLEIT** 22
185 **BULLION** (FR) 9
461 **BULLION BOSS** (IRE) 4
212 **BULLIONAIRE** (IRE) 7
300 **BULLS AYE** (IRE) 47
277 **BULLSEMPIRE** (IRE) 2
514 **BUMBLE BAY** 3
263 **BUMBLE BEEE** (IRE) 36
347 **BUMMBLE BERRY** 1
384 **BUMPTIOUS** F 22
444 **BUMPY JOHNSON** (IRE) 10
222 **BUN DORAN** (IRE) 18
181 **BUNGLEDUPINBLUE** (IRE) 14
378 **BUIANNN** (IRE) 1
273 **BUNNY BORU** 1
337 **BUONAROTTI BOY** (IRE) 4
383 **BURBANK** (IRE) 4
250 **BURDIGALA** (FR) 8
409 **BURGESS DREAM** (IRE) 1
434 **BURGUNDY BETTY** (IRE) F 10
27 **BURIRAM** (IRE)
367 **BURLINGTON BERT** (FR) 1
274 **BURMA SKY** 34
16 **BURMA SUN** (IRE) C 144
563 **BURMESE WALTZ** 4
175 **BURN SOME DUST** (IRE) 6
400 **BURN THE CAKES** 36
250 **BURNAGE BOY** (IRE) 9

378 **BURNING CASH** (IRE) 28
228 **BURNING SEA** (IRE) 49
94 **BURNING SUN** (IRE) 1
399 **BURNING VICTORY** (FR) 37
491 **BURNISTON ROCKS** 2
321 **BURREN WALK** 8
418 **BURRISTO** (IRE) 147
420 **BURROW SEVEN** 3
501 **BURROWS DIAMOND** (FR) 7
270 **BURROWS EDGE** (FR) 26
501 **BURROWS HALL** (FR) 8
588 **BURROWS PARK** (FR) 9
399 **BURROWS SAINT** (FR) 38
323 **BURROWS SEESIDE** (FR) 14
212 **BURROWS TREAT** (FR) 8
148 **BURSCOUGH** 38
84 **BURTONWOOD** 5
214 **BUSBY** (IRE) 6
391 **BUSHFIRE** 48
323 **BUSHYPARK** (IRE) 15
454 **BUSINESS** (FR) 3
119 **BUSINESS FLIGHT** (USA) 22
33 **BUSLANE** G 1
419 **BUSSELTON** (FR) 8
87 **BUSSELTON** 35
149 **BUSTED ICE** (IRE) 3
444 **BUSTER EDWARDS** (IRE) 11
333 **BUSTER THOMAS** (IRE) 5
552 **BUSTER VALENTINE** (IRE) 6
376 **BUSY STREET** 7
63 **BUTCHEROFSTOCKHOLM** 7
456 **BUTLER'S BRIEF** (IRE) 3
418 **BUTTE MONTANA** (IRE) 26
203 **BUTTERFIELD** (IRE) 2
415 **BUTTERFLIES** (IRE) F 123
417 **BUTTERFLY COVE** (USA) F 28
534 **BUTTERWICK BROOK** (IRE) 13
247 **BUTTEVANT LADY** (IRE) 1
159 **BUTTON UP** (IRE) C 44
449 **BUTTRESS** 44
270 **BUTTSBURY LADY** 27
270 **BUVEUR D'AIR** (FR) 28
582 **BUXTED TOO** 73
345 **BUY ME BACK** 4
14 **BUYER BEWARE** (IRE) 2
105 **BUYING TROUBLE** C 58
270 **BUZZ** (FR) 29
153 **BUZZ DE TURCOING** (FR) 2
550 **BUZZ LIGHTYERE** 2
376 **BUZZKILLBOB** (IRE) 8
9 **BY JOVE** 11
87 **BY STARLIGHT** (IRE) 4
76 **BY THE EDGE** (IRE) C 92
319 **BYBROOK** C 17
446 **BYE DAY** 17
214 **BYFORD** (FR) 7
569 **BYHOOKORBYCROOK** 47
253 **BYKER** 144
582 **BYRON FLYER** 13
193 **BYRON HILL** (IRE) 6
148 **BYRON'S CHOICE** 6
351 **BYRONESS** F 20
539 **BYTHEBAY** 4
470 **BYTON** G 19
193 **BYZANTIA** 7
408 **C'EST LE BONHEUR** (FR) 15
280 **C'EST NO MOUR** (GER) 2

545 **CABALETTA** 7
128 **CABALLERO** (IRE) 12
399 **CABARET QUEEN** 39
416 **CABERNET D'ALENE** (FR) 3
308 **CABINET OF CLOWNS** (IRE) 54
193 **CABLE GUY** 35
149 **CABLE MOUNTAIN** 33
481 **CABLE NEWS** 14
492 **CABOT CLIFFS** (IRE) 21
126 **CABOT HILLS** (IRE) 7
473 **CABOY** (FR) 18
191 **CABRINI** 12
33 **CADDY SHACK** (IRE) 2
456 **CADDYHILL** (IRE) 4
16 **CADEAU D'OR** (FR) 6
88 **CADEAU DU BRESIL** (FR) 1
120 **CADEAUX POWER** C 70
256 **CADILLAC** (IRE) 83
562 **CADIXIA** C 13
227 **CADMAR** 11
16 **CADMUS** (IRE) 145
492 **CADZAND** (IRE) 22
274 **CAESAR NERO** 79
389 **CAESAR ROCK** (IRE) 3
123 **CAESAR'S PALACE** 64
274 **CAESONIA** 6
18 **CAFE ESPRESSO** 4
437 **CAFE EXPRESS** (IRE) G 14
149 **CAFE MILANO** 4
93 **CAFE SYDNEY** (IRE) 12
546 **CAFFE MACCHIATO** (IRE) 14
418 **CAGE OF FEAR** (IRE) 27
295 **CAGLIOSTRO** (FR) 6
94 **CAHORS** 11
408 **CAID DU LIN** (FR) 16
98 **CAIRN GORM** 34
475 **CAIRN ISLAND** (IRE) 42
307 **CAIRNSHILL** (IRE) 2
461 **CAIUS MARCIUS** (IRE) 5
10 **CAJUN MOON** F 45
388 **CAKE DE L'ISLE** (FR) 10
282 **CALAJANI** (FR) 1
6 **CALARE** (IRE) C 123
546 **CALARULES** 15
173 **CALCULUS** (IRE) 2
16 **CALCUTTA CUP** (FR) 53
484 **CALDWELL** 4
421 **CALDY DANCER** (IRE) C 111
23 **CALECO** (IRE) 20
263 **CALEVADE** (IRE) 6
139 **CALGARY TIGER** 3
492 **CALICO** (GER) 23
372 **CALICOJACK** (IRE) 9
577 **CALIDAD** (IRE) 8
400 **CALIDUS MIRABILIS** 7
214 **CALIFORNIA BREEZE** (IRE) 12
214 **CALIFORNIA LAD** 8
464 **CALIFORNIA SOUL** (IRE) 2
264 **CALIN DU BRIZAIS** (FR) 8
93 **CALIN'S LAD** 13
40 **CALIPATRIA** F 122
402 **CALIPSO COLLONGES** (FR) 12
1 **CALIVIGNY** (IRE) 8
185 **CALIX DELAFAYETTE** (FR) 10
291 **CALL AT MIDNIGHT** F 4
291 **CALL AT MIDNIGHT** F 17
420 **CALL CLWYD** (IRE) 27

225 **CALL ME GINGER** 3
111 **CALL ME JEZZA** (IRE) 4
270 **CALL ME LORD** (FR) 30
222 **CALL ME RAFA** (IRE) 19
264 **CALL ME SAINTE** (FR) 9
415 **CALL ME SWEETHEART** (IRE) 24
418 **CALL ME TARA** 28
418 **CALL ME VIC** (IRE) 29
195 **CALL MY BLUFF** (IRE) 3
386 **CALL OFF THE DOGS** (IRE) 19
358 **CALM SIMON** (IRE) 2
473 **CALLE MALVA** (IRE) 19
290 **CALLING THE WIND** (IRE) 4
478 **CALLIOPE** 2
319 **CALM ATTITUDE** (IRE) F 18
316 **CALM DOWN** (FR) 3
503 **CALOMERIA** F 8
254 **CALONNE** (IRE) 1
484 **CALTEX** (FR) 5
2 **CALTON HILL** (IRE) 6
369 **CALUM GILHOOLEY** (IRE) 14
411 **CALVA D'AUGE** (FR) 20
577 **CALVARIO** (FR) 9
324 **CALYPSO CHOIR** C 27
114 **CALYPSO STORM** (IRE) 2
363 **CALZA NERA** (IRE) 19
362 **CAMACHESS** (IRE) 2
148 **CAMACHO CHIEF** (IRE) 7
148 **CAMACHO KING** (IRE) 65
86 **CAMACHO MAN** (IRE) 7
475 **CAMARGUE** F 91
69 **CAMASSIA** (IRE) 3
371 **CAMBRIDGESHIRE** (IRE) 11
419 **CAMDEBOO** (IRE) 68
554 **CAME FROM THE DARK** (IRE) 4
123 **CAMELOT TALES** (FR) 18
533 **CAMERILY JOE** 25
300 **CAMILE** (IRE) 3
353 **CAMMY** (IRE) 20
355 **CAMOUFLAGED** (IRE) 1
180 **CAMP FIRE** (IRE) C 46
63 **CAMPACHOOCHOO** (IRE) 45
256 **CAMPHOR** (IRE) 13
214 **CAMPOSANTO** C 64
276 **CAMPROND** (FR) 11
264 **CAMRON DE CHAILLAC** (FR) 10
70 **CAN CAN GIRL** (IRE) 8
358 **CAN YOU BELIEVE IT** (IRE) 3
581 **CAN YOU CALL** 14
227 **CAN'T STOP NOW** (IRE) 12
509 **CAN'THELPFALLIN** 12
395 **CANADA KID** 9
341 **CANAL ROCKS** 3
168 **CANARIA PRINCE** 105
276 **CANASTERO** (IRE) 12
1 **CANCAN** (FR) 9
344 **CANDELISA** (IRE) 4
552 **CANDESCENCE** 40
16 **CANDLEBERRY** C 146
243 **CANDLEFORD** (IRE) 46
87 **CANDLEMAS** 5
53 **CANDY BURG** (FR) 2
528 **CANDY LOU** 2
421 **CANDY RIDE** (IRE) C 112
293 **CANDYMAN CAN** (IRE) 2
449 **CANDYTUFT** 45
321 **CANELO** (IRE) 9

64 **CANFORD BAY** (IRE) 4
199 **CANFORD STAR** (IRE) 2
14 **CANFORD'S JOY** (IRE) 3
90 **CANICHETTE** (FR) 4
163 **CANIMAX** 2
258 **CANNIE LAD** 5
208 **CANNY TOM** (IRE) 1
243 **CANONIZED** 127
554 **CANOODLED** (IRE) 38
391 **CANTATA** 49
243 **CANTERBURY BELL** (IRE) 128
333 **CANTY BAY** (IRE) 6
322 **CANYON CITY** 8
211 **CANZONE** (IRE) 3
578 **CAP D'ANTIBES** (IRE) 3
411 **CAP DU MATHAN** (FR) 21
580 **CAP DU NORD** (FR) 4
554 **CAP FRANCAIS** 5
107 **CAP SAN ROMAN** (FR) 42
546 **CAP ST VINCENT** (FR) 16
569 **CAP'N** (IRE) 6
569 **CAPALA** (FR) 7
532 **CAPARD KING** (IRE) 8
545 **CAPE BYRON** 8
240 **CAPE COLUMBUS** 15
309 **CAPE DOLLAR** (IRE) C 166
252 **CAPE FEAR** 3
387 **CAPE GOOD HOPE** F 22
342 **CAPE GRECO** (USA) 1
168 **CAPE HORN** 106
415 **CAPE JOY** (IRE) C 124
276 **CAPE MILANO** (IRE) 13
228 **CAPE PALACE** 5
546 **CAPE ROBIN** (IRE) 17
240 **CAPE SUNSET** 3
411 **CAPELAND** (FR) 22
136 **CAPELLIAN CRUSADER** (IRE) 2
309 **CAPITAL THEORY** 167
216 **CAPITOLE** (FR) 3
240 **CAPLA BERRY** 4
164 **CAPLA CRUSADER** 1
50 **CAPLA FEVER** (IRE) 74
555 **CAPLA HUNTRESS** 4
316 **CAPLA KNIGHT** (IRE) 19
167 **CAPLA LASS** 52
316 **CAPLA SPIRIT** 4
132 **CAPO BAY** (IRE) 25
399 **CAPODANNO** (FR) 40
355 **CAPONE** (GER) 2
562 **CAPOTE'S DREAM** (IRE) 2
251 **CAPPADOCIA** (IRE) 3
10 **CAPPANANTY CON** 6
423 **CAPPARATTIN** 2
282 **CAPPELLA FELLA** (IRE) 2
449 **CAPPOQUIN** (IRE) 46
51 **CAPRELLA** C 32
107 **CAPRICE DES DIEUX** (FR) 17
313 **CAPRICIA** (IRE) 7
18 **CAPRICIOUS** 19
159 **CAPRICIOUS CAITLIN** 45
145 **CAPRICIOUS MADAM** 6
386 **CAPRICORN PRINCE** 20
159 **CAPRIOLE** C 46
554 **CAPRIOLETTE** (IRE) 6
402 **CAPTAIN BIGGLES** (IRE) 13
222 **CAPTAIN BLACKPEARL** 20
449 **CAPTAIN BONNY** 13

418 **CAPTAIN CATTISTOCK** 30
492 **CAPTAIN CHAOS** (IRE) 24
308 **CAPTAIN CLARET** 4
285 **CAPTAIN CLAUDE** (IRE) 6
418 **CAPTAIN CLIPPO** (IRE) 31
475 **CAPTAIN COOPER** (IRE) 43
5 **CAPTAIN CORCORAN** (IRE) 3
84 **CAPTAIN CORELLI** (IRE) 6
404 **CAPTAIN COURAGEOUS** (IRE) 3
411 **CAPTAIN DESTINY** 23
212 **CAPTAIN DRAKE** (IRE) 9
50 **CAPTAIN HELMET** 31
449 **CAPTAIN HOWSE** (IRE) 47
190 **CAPTAIN IVAN** (IRE) 11
153 **CAPTAIN JACK** 3
454 **CAPTAIN JAMESON** (IRE) 4
399 **CAPTAIN KANGAROO** (IRE) 41
372 **CAPTAIN MC** (IRE) 10
501 **CAPTAIN MOIRETTE** (FR) 9
270 **CAPTAIN MORGS** (IRE) 31
362 **CAPTAIN PUGWASH** (IRE) 3
113 **CAPTAIN REDBEARD** (IRE) 5
235 **CAPTAIN REVELATION** 9
141 **CAPTAIN RYAN** 3
505 **CAPTAIN SEDGWICK** (IRE) 3
340 **CAPTAIN SPEAKING** (FR) 3
16 **CAPTAIN SQUARE** 147
214 **CAPTAIN ST LUCIFER** 9
408 **CAPTAIN TOM CAT** (IRE) 17
577 **CAPTAIN TOMMY** (IRE) 10
353 **CAPTAIN VALLO** (IRE) 21
426 **CAPTAIN VAN DYKE** 1
144 **CAPTAIN ZEBO** (IRE) 2
396 **CAPTAINHUGHJAMPTON** 3
190 **CAPTAINS RUN** (IRE) 12
554 **CARADOC** (IRE) 7
253 **CARAMELISED** 47
274 **CARAUSIUS** 7
431 **CARAVAN OF HOPE** (IRE) 3
119 **CARBON POSITIVE** (USA) 23
517 **CARD HIGH** (IRE) 3
582 **CARDANO** (USA) 14
343 **CARDIGAN BAY** (FR) 7
27 **CARDINAL ROUGE** (IRE) 85
399 **CAREFULLY SELECTED** (IRE) 42
290 **CAREWELL COVER** (IRE) 44
520 **CAREY STREET** (IRE) 1
108 **CARIBANA** C 36
454 **CARIBBEAN PRINCESS** (USA) C 50
356 **CARIBBEAN SPRING** (IRE) 2
270 **CARIBEAN BOY** (FR) 32
449 **CARIBENO** 5
109 **CARIBOU** 3
133 **CARISBROOK** (IRE) 5
252 **CARLA KOALA** 3
415 **CARLISLE BAY** (IRE) 25
415 **CARLO LANDOLFI** (IRE) 26
492 **CARLOS FELIX** (IRE) 8
552 **CARLOVIAN** 7
343 **CARLOW FARMER** (IRE) 8
304 **CARMELA SOPRANO** 25
109 **CARMENERE** 1
128 **CARN A CHLAMAIN** (USA) 78
183 **CARNAGE** 2
300 **CARNIVAL TIMES** 65
518 **CARNOUSTIE** (FR) F 93
193 **CARNWENNAN** (IRE) 8

496 **CARO DES FLOS** (FR) 1
400 **CAROLE'S TEMPLER** 8
400 **CAROLE'S TZARINA** (FR) 9
344 **CAROLINE DALE** 36
546 **CAROLINE'S QUEST** (IRE) 18
395 **CAROLINES CHARM** (IRE) 10
16 **CAROLUS MAGNUS** (IRE) 54
199 **CARP KID** (IRE) 3
62 **CARPE DIEM** (FR) 29
98 **CARPE DIEM LADY** (IRE) C 70
449 **CARPENTIER** (IRE) 14
581 **CARPOOL** (IRE) 15
283 **CARRIAGE CLOCK** 3
378 **CARRIBEAN QUEEN** 29
534 **CARRICK ROADS** (IRE) 14
168 **CARRIGILLIHY** 107
418 **CARROLLS MILAN** (IRE) 32
491 **CARROTHERS** (USA) 31
363 **CARRY ON** 20
309 **CARRY ON KATIE** (USA) F 168
411 **CARRY ON THE MAGIC** (IRE) 24
330 **CARTAOJAL** (FR) 33
415 **CARTOUCHE** (IRE) 27
216 **CARTRON** (IRE) 4
304 **CARVELLA DA CORSA** C 26
243 **CARYATID** 129
424 **CARYS' COMMODITY** 15
386 **CASA LOUPI** 21
222 **CASA TALL** (FR) 21
453 **CASABLANCA KID** (IRE) 2
270 **CASABLANCA MIX** (FR) 33
7 **CASARUAN** 12
34 **CASAVOLA** 3
270 **CASCOVA** (IRE) 34
7 **CASE KEY** 13
344 **CASE OF THE EX** (FR) 37
263 **CASH AGAIN** (FR) 7
399 **CASH BACK** (FR) 43
108 **CASH MACHINE** (IRE) 16
7 **CASH N CARRIE** (IRE) 14
552 **CASH TO ASH** (IRE) 8
7 **CASHEL** (IRE) 15
51 **CASHEW** (IRE) 33
585 **CASHMOLL** (IRE) 4
309 **CASI CRUDO** 169
520 **CASIET** 2
491 **CASILA** (IRE) C 72
167 **CASILLI** 10
113 **CASIMIR DU CLOS** (FR) 6
50 **CASINA DI NOTTE** (IRE) 3
372 **CASK MATE** (IRE) 1
598 **CASPERS COURT** (IRE) 1
7 **CASPIAN PRINCE** (IRE) 16
597 **CASPIAN QUEEN** (IRE) 2
306 **CASSANDRA ROSE** (IRE) 14
314 **CASSIOPEIA DREAM** 21
168 **CASSIQUE LADY** (IRE) G 17
540 **CASSIS DE REINE** 2
50 **CASSOWARY** (IRE) 32
168 **CASSY O** (IRE) 18
369 **CAST IN GREY** (IRE) 15
497 **CASTALIAN SPRING** (IRE) F 11
555 **CASTANA DIA** (IRE) 18
553 **CASTCARRIE** (IRE) 3
418 **CASTEL GANDOLFO** (IRE) 33
443 **CASTKITELLO** (IRE) 3
80 **CASTLE KING** (IRE) 3

7 **CASTLE QUARTER** (IRE) 17
343 **CASTLE ROBIN** (IRE) 9
461 **CASTLE RUSHEN** (IRE) 6
256 **CASTLE STABLES** (IRE) 84
225 **CASTLE VIEW** (IRE) 4
399 **CASTLEBAWN WEST** (IRE) 44
223 **CASTLEDHEM** (IRE) 3
167 **CASTLEHILL LAD** 11
263 **CASTLEHILL RETREAT** 8
282 **CASTLEREA TESS** 3
468 **CASTLETOWN** (FR) 2
547 **CASTLETROY** (IRE) 1
419 **CASTRA VETERA** (IRE) 9
189 **CASUAL REPLY** 5
27 **CASUARINA** 35
581 **CASWELL BAY** 16
464 **CAT SIX** (USA) F 3
464 **CAT SIX** (USA) G 9
411 **CAT TIGER** (IRE) 25
189 **CAT'S CLAW** (USA) F 56
387 **CATAMARAN** (IRE) C 23
408 **CATAMARAN DU SEUIL** (FR) 18
321 **CATBIRD SEAT** (IRE) 10
415 **CATCH** (IRE) 28
474 **CATCH MY BREATH** 2
534 **CATCH THE CUBAN** 15
588 **CATCH THE SWALLOWS** (IRE) 10
86 **CATCHMEIFYOUCAN** (IRE) 8
508 **CATCHTHESNITCH** (FR) 15
577 **CATELINE** (IRE) 11
145 **CATESBY** 7
484 **CATFISH ROW** 6
461 **CATHAL'S STAR** 7
538 **CATHAYENSIS** (IRE) 26
49 **CATHEADANS FURY** 2
155 **CATHERINE'S GIRL** 9
342 **CATIVO RAGAZZO** 2
318 **CATLIN** 3
136 **CATLOW** (IRE) 3
577 **CAUGHT INTHE SLIPS** 12
533 **CAUSEWAY CHARM** (USA) F 45
399 **CAVALLINO** (IRE) 45
290 **CAVALLUCCIO** (IRE) 45
592 **CAVALRY** 3
120 **CAVE DIVER** 71
235 **CAVE TOP** (IRE) 10
532 **CAVENTARA** 9
303 **CAVICIANA** 6
235 **CAWTHORNE** 11
424 **CAWTHORNE LAD** 16
256 **CAYENNE PEPPER** 14
163 **CAYIRLI** (FR) 3
326 **CAYMAN MOON** 25
330 **CAZALLA** 12
245 **CEALLACH** (IRE) 64
244 **CEARA BE** (IRE) 2
523 **CEASELESS** (IRE) C 55
568 **CECI WELLS** 4
449 **CEDAR CAGE** 6
532 **CEDAR HILL** (IRE) 10
189 **CEDAR'S STARS** 28
193 **CELERIA** 36
589 **CELERITY** (IRE) 4
597 **CELESTE** C 8
419 **CELESTIAL DE LA MER** (IRE) C 139
95 **CELESTIAL BLISS** 2
411 **CELESTIAL FORCE** (IRE) 26

135 **CELESTIAL LIGHT** 4
386 **CELESTIAL POINT** (IRE) 125
76 **CELESTIAL QUEEN** 36
101 **CELESTIN** (FR) 5
185 **CELLAR VIE** 11
471 **CELMA DES BOIS** (FR) 4
108 **CELSIUS** (IRE) 3
371 **CELSIUS DEGRE** (IRE) C 23
110 **CELTIC ART** (FR) 2
376 **CELTIC ARTISAN** (IRE) 9
110 **CELTIC CLASSIC** (IRE) 3
473 **CELTIC FLAMES** (IRE) 20
341 **CELTIC FORCE** (IRE) 4
333 **CELTIC JOY** (IRE) 7
318 **CELTIC SIXPENCE** (IRE) G 17
402 **CELTIC TARA** 14
15 **CEMHAAN** 5
363 **CENOTICE** 21
363 **CENT PRIME** G 22
1 **CENTENIER** (FR) 10
582 **CENTRAL CITY** (IRE) 15
559 **CENTRAL FLAME** 1
87 **CENTRE DRIVE** 36
593 **CENTREOFEXCELLENCE** (IRE) 4
484 **CENTS IN THE CITY** 47
123 **CENTURY DREAM** (IRE) 3
370 **CEOLWULF** 1
588 **CEPAGE** (FR) 11
597 **CEPHALONIE** (USA) C 9
501 **CERENDIPITY** (IRE) 10
98 **CERTAIN LAD** 7
460 **CERTAINLY RED** 1
488 **CERVARO MIX** (FR) 8
388 **CESAR COLLONGES** (FR) 11
90 **CESAR DE BALLON** (FR) 5
287 **CESAR DU GOUET** (FR) 3
395 **CESAR ET ROSALIE** (FR) 11
167 **CESCA** (IRE) G 82
569 **CESIFIRE** (IRE) 8
492 **CH'TIBELLO** (FR) 26
384 **CHACHAMAIDEE** (IRE) F 23
399 **CHACUN POUR SOI** (FR) 46
263 **CHADLINGTON LAD** (IRE) 37
518 **CHAI YO POWER** 6
415 **CHAIN MAIL** (IRE) 29
288 **CHAIN SMOKER** 3
518 **CHAIRMAN POWER** 7
61 **CHAIRMANIC** (IRE) 4
98 **CHAIRMANOFTHEBOARD** (IRE) 8
276 **CHALGROVE** (FR) 14
243 **CHALK STREAM** 47
531 **CHALLOW** (IRE) 1
27 **CHAMADE** 7
588 **CHAMBARD** (FR) 12
270 **CHAMP** (IRE) 35
392 **CHAMPAGNE ANGEL** (IRE) 1
105 **CHAMPAGNE CERI** C 59
222 **CHAMPAGNE CITY** 22
482 **CHAMPAGNE COURT** (IRE) 5
199 **CHAMPAGNE HIGHLIFE** (GER) 4
150 **CHAMPAGNE IDEAS** (IRE) 5
426 **CHAMPAGNE KATIE** G 5
426 **CHAMPAGNE KATIE** G 10
534 **CHAMPAGNE MESDAMES** (FR) 16
456 **CHAMPAGNE MIST** (IRE) 5
270 **CHAMPAGNE MYSTERY** (IRE) 36
343 **CHAMPAGNE NOIR** (IRE) 10

386 **CHAMPAGNE PIAFF** (FR) 126
270 **CHAMPAGNE PLATINUM** (IRE) 37
581 **CHAMPAGNE RHYTHM** (IRE) 17
565 **CHAMPAGNE RULES** 2
506 **CHAMPAGNE SUPANOVA** (IRE) 4
311 **CHAMPAGNE TERRI** (IRE) 1
43 **CHAMPAGNE VINTAGE** (IRE) 3
418 **CHAMPAGNE WELL** (IRE) 34
402 **CHAMPAGNESUPEROVER** (IRE) 15
49 **CHAMPION CHASE** (FR) 3
419 **CHAMPION GREEN** (IRE) 69
420 **CHAMPION PLACE** C 38
45 **CHAMPS DE REVES** 2
315 **CHANCE FINALE** (IRE) 2
190 **CHANCE IT** (IRE) 13
113 **CHANCEANOTHERFIVE** (IRE) 7
473 **CHANCEITON** (IRE) 21
456 **CHANCEUX** (IRE) 6
42 **CHANDON ELYSEES** 2
43 **CHANKAYA** 4
7 **CHANNEL PACKET** 18
481 **CHANSON D'AMOUR** 38
137 **CHANTECLER** 1
421 **CHANTER** F 113
449 **CHANTERELLE** (FR) F 48
130 **CHANTILLY HAZE** 2
119 **CHANTILLY JEWEL** (USA) F 37
1 **CHANTILLY HILL** (IRE) 11
214 **CHANTREYS** 10
270 **CHANTRY HOUSE** (IRE) 38
117 **CHAPATI** (FR) 1
461 **CHAPEL STILE** (IRE) 8
503 **CHAPMANSHYPE** (IRE) 9
110 **CHAPPAQUIDDICK** 21
421 **CHARGING THUNDER** 60
167 **CHARITY** G 83
241 **CHARLEMAGNE DIVA** C 3
263 **CHARLEMAINE** (IRE) 9
446 **CHARLES LE BRUN** 2
97 **CHARLES MOLSON** 2
290 **CHARLIE ARTHUR** (IRE) 5
372 **CHARLIE BASSETT** (IRE) 12
132 **CHARLIE D** (USA) 3
481 **CHARLIE FELLOWES** (IRE) 2
503 **CHARLIE GEORGE** (IRE) 10
534 **CHARLIE MAGRI** 17
165 **CHARLIE MON** (IRE) 1
304 **CHARLIE MY BOY** (IRE) 2
372 **CHARLIE SIRINGO** 13
204 **CHARLIE SNOW ANGEL** 3
357 **CHARLIE'S GLANCE** 1
539 **CHARLIFAN** (IRE) 27
529 **CHARLOTTES WAY** (IRE) 2
1 **CHARM OFFENSIVE** (FR) 12
185 **CHARMANT** (FR) 12
90 **CHARMEUR DE BALLON** (FR) 6
401 **CHARMGOER** (USA) C 19
296 **CHARMING KID** 3
391 **CHARMING PARADISE** 25
473 **CHARMIX** (FR) 22
96 **CHARYN CANYON** (IRE) 2
270 **CHASAMAX** (IRE) 39
309 **CHASE THE DOLLAR** 63
205 **CHASE THE WIND** (IRE) 1
179 **CHASING APHRODITE** 25
305 **CHASING HIGHS** (IRE) 2
93 **CHASMA** 14

492 **CHASSE EN MER** (FR) G 27
375 **CHATEAU D'IF** (FR) 20
175 **CHATEAU MARMONT** (IRE) 7
286 **CHATO** (FR) 1
411 **CHAVEZ** (IRE) 27
13 **CHAZZA** (IRE) 9
509 **CHAZZESMEE** (IRE) 13
355 **CHEAD SOLAS** (IRE) 3
530 **CHEAP JACK** 2
376 **CHECK MY PULSE** (IRE) 10
326 **CHECKANDCHALLENGE** 45
492 **CHECKINFORSQUIRELS** (IRE) 28
86 **CHEDDLETON** 9
545 **CHEEKY AZ** 56
230 **CHEEKY CHES** 3
148 **CHEEKY GIRL** F 66
143 **CHEER'S DELBOY** (IRE) 3
120 **CHEERS STEVE** 18
555 **CHEESE AND WINE** 4
490 **CHEF BOGO** (FR) 3
276 **CHEF D'EQUIPE** (FR) 15
178 **CHEF D'OEUVRE** (FR) 4
408 **CHEF DE TROUPE** (FR) 19
98 **CHELMS PRINCE** 71
98 **CHELMS PRINCESS** 72
314 **CHELSEA SHOWCASE** 3
111 **CHEMICAL WARFARE** (IRE) 5
415 **CHENCHIKOVA** (IRE) F 125
322 **CHENG GONG** 9
386 **CHEQUE EN BLANC** (FR) 22
27 **CHERCHEZ** 36
93 **CHERISH** (FR) 15
427 **CHEROKEE BILL** 5
491 **CHEROKEE DANCE** (USA) 32
311 **CHERREGO** (USA) C 21
570 **CHERRY COLA** 4
309 **CHERRY CREEK** (IRE) C 170
415 **CHERRY HINTON** F 126
454 **CHERUBIC** C 51
434 **CHESS PLAYER** (IRE) 11
337 **CHESTNUT PETE** 5
93 **CHETAN** 16
509 **CHEVAL BLANC** 14
347 **CHEVISE** (FR) F 8
519 **CHEZ CASTEL MAIL** (FR) 5
411 **CHEZ HANS** (GER) 28
484 **CHEZ HANS** (IRE) 7
63 **CHIARA WELLS** (IRE) F 46
362 **CHIARODILUNA** 4
228 **CHIASMA** (IRE) 50
161 **CHIAVARI** (IRE) 6
375 **CHIAVE DI VOLTA** 4
278 **CHIC NAME** (FR) 1
344 **CHICA BELLA** (IRE) 38
554 **CHICA BOOM** (IRE) 39
149 **CHICA DE LA NOCHE** 5
149 **CHICA DEL DIA** 6
76 **CHICAGO FALL** (FR) C 93
417 **CHICAGO GIRL** (FR) C 29
321 **CHICAGO GUY** 11
98 **CHICAGO STAR** C 73
36 **CHICANERY** 23
518 **CHICHEN ITZA** 94
128 **CHICHESTER** 13
400 **CHICITA BANANA** F 46
92 **CHICKENFORTEA** (IRE) 2
120 **CHICKLADE** C 72

461 **CHIDSWELL** (IRE) 9
257 **CHIEF BRODY** 2
168 **CHIEF CRAFTSMAN** 19
415 **CHIEF LITTLE HAWK** (USA) 30
40 **CHIEF OF STAFF** 74
93 **CHIEF SITTINGBULL** 17
290 **CHIEF WHITE FACE** 46
193 **CHIEFOFCHIEFS** 9
211 **CHIEFTAIN'S CHOICE** (IRE) 6
140 **CHIFA** (IRE) 3
415 **CHIFFON** (IRE) 31
326 **CHIFFONADE** (IRE) C 46
431 **CHIGUN** F 57
16 **CHIL CHIL** 7
449 **CHILL OUT** (IRE) 15
36 **CHILLINGHAM** (IRE) 24
272 **CHILLON CASTLE** 6
582 **CHILTERN HILLS** (IRE) G 16
506 **CHIM CHIMNEY** 32
546 **CHIMES OF DYLAN** (IRE) 19
472 **CHINA EXCELS** 2
179 **CHINA IN MY HANDS** C 26
253 **CHINDIT** (IRE) 48
437 **CHINESE SPIRIT** (IRE) 1
321 **CHINESE WHISPERER** (FR) 12
491 **CHING SHIH** (IRE) 73
123 **CHINOOK** 19
395 **CHINWAG** 12
214 **CHIPIRON** (FR) 11
308 **CHIPOTLE** 55
555 **CHIPS AND RICE** 31
526 **CHIPSTEAD** 26
395 **CHIRICO VALLIS** (FR) 13
328 **CHITRA** 2
511 **CHIVERS** (IRE) 2
270 **CHIVES** 40
553 **CHLOE'S COURT** (FR) 4
304 **CHLOELLIE** 3
15 **CHLOHOLTEEN** 30
363 **CHOCCA WOCCA** F 23
18 **CHOCCO STAR** (IRE) 5
316 **CHOCO ICE** 20
316 **CHOCOCO** 5
345 **CHOCOLATE BOX** (IRE) 5
431 **CHOCOYA** 23
247 **CHOIX DES ARMES** (FR) 2
491 **CHOLA EMPIRE** 74
128 **CHOOKIE DUNEDIN** 14
554 **CHOOSE ME** (IRE) C 78
167 **CHOOSEY** (IRE) 12
258 **CHORAL SINGER** G 42
344 **CHORITZO** 39
146 **CHOSEN FLAME** (IRE) 5
321 **CHOSEN PATH** (IRE) 13
402 **CHOSEN PORT** (IRE) 17
582 **CHOSEN SHANT** (IRE) 17
84 **CHOSEN WORLD** 7
105 **CHOUMICHA** F 60
419 **CHOUNGAYA** (FR) 10
546 **CHOZEN** (IRE) 20
235 **CHRIS COOL** 12
534 **CHRISTMAS IN APRIL** (FR) 18
1 **CHRISTMAS IN USA** (IRE) 13
436 **CHRISTMAS NIGHT** 2
547 **CHRISTOPH COLUMBUS** (GER) 2
411 **CHRISTOPHER WOOD** (IRE) 29
28 **CHROI OLD GIRL** (IRE) 2

15 **DANTE'S VIEW** (IRE) 9
431 **DANTORA** 27
308 **DANVILLE** 25
167 **DANVINA** (IRE) F 85
79 **DANYAH** (IRE) 3
168 **DANZAN** (IRE) 26
98 **DANZART** (IRE) 36
7 **DANZENO** 23
125 **DAPA LAD** (IRE) 5
569 **DAPHNE MAY** 34
378 **DAPPER BOB** (IRE) 30
22 **DAPPER DAISY** 6
214 **DARALIMI** (FR) 13
228 **DARAMETHOS** (IRE) 55
344 **DARANOVA** (IRE) 7
419 **DARASSO** (FR) 13
60 **DARAZ LEGACY** 3
378 **DARBY SABINI** 38
19 **DARCY WARD** (FR) 4
48 **DARE** 4
376 **DARE THE BEAR** (IRE) 12
20 **DARE TO BEGIN** (IRE) 3
386 **DAREBIN** (GER) 23
323 **DARES TO DREAM** (IRE) 17
577 **DARGIANNINI** (IRE) 13
132 **DARING DAY** C 52
213 **DARIUS DES BOIS** 2
230 **DARIUS DES SOURCES** (FR) 4
313 **DARIYA** (USA) 12
474 **DARK AGENT** (IRE) 12
566 **DARK AND DANGEROUS** (IRE) 2
123 **DARK CHARM** (USA) 21
309 **DARK COMPANY** (IRE) 68
141 **DARK CROCODILE** (IRE) 3
26 **DARK DEFENDER** 2
526 **DARK ESTEEM** (IRE) 28
471 **DARK FLAME** (IRE) 6
98 **DARK ICON** 11
308 **DARK ILLUSION** 26
351 **DARK ISLAND STAR** (IRE) 21
168 **DARK JEDI** (IRE) 27
123 **DARK LIBERTY** (IRE) C 65
545 **DARK LION** (IRE) 57
128 **DARK LOCHNAGAR** (USA) 17
27 **DARK MOTIVE** 37
419 **DARK NOTE** 141
110 **DARK PHOENIX** (IRE) 4
344 **DARK PINE** (IRE) 8
376 **DARK SARI** (IRE) G 65
50 **DARK SCIMITAR** (USA) 5
475 **DARK SEDUCTRESS** (IRE) C 94
274 **DARK SHIFT** 36
145 **DARK SHOT** 10
347 **DARK SIDE PRINCE** 2
493 **DARK SPEC** 4
554 **DARK SPECTRE** (IRE) 10
540 **DARK STORM** 3
27 **DARK SWAN** (IRE) F 89
120 **DARK SWANSONG** (IRE) 74
253 **DARK TULIP** 147
309 **DARK VISION** (IRE) 4
399 **DARK VOYAGER** (IRE) 56
439 **DARK WHITE** 2
323 **DARK ZEAS** (IRE) 95
386 **DARKEST DAY** (IRE) 24
198 **DARKEST DREAM** 1
395 **DARKSIDEOFTARNSIDE** (IRE) 19

534 **DARLAC** (FR) 23
228 **DARLECTABLE YOU** 56
74 **DARLING ALKO** (FR) 1
222 **DARLING DU LARGE** (FR) 30
228 **DARLING HEART** (IRE) 57
293 **DARSI ROSE** (IRE) 3
501 **DARSI'S DARLING** (IRE) 13
537 **DARTINGTON** (IRE) 3
475 **DARVEL** (IRE) 48
272 **DARWINA** 7
32 **DAS KAPITAL** 2
290 **DASH FOR IT** (IRE) 50
96 **DASH OF BLUE** 6
311 **DASH OF SPICE** 3
189 **DASH TO THE FRONT** C 60
482 **DASHEL DRASHER** 7
516 **DASHING DICK** (IRE) 10
408 **DASHING PERK** 3
516 **DASHING ROGER** 2
409 **DASHING SPIRIT** (IRE) 2
399 **DATA BREACH** 57
393 **DATA PROTECTION** 1
503 **DATSALRIGHTGINO** (GER) 14
490 **DAVE AND BERNIE** (IRE) 6
292 **DAVID JOHN** 1
397 **DAVID'S BEAUTY** (IRE) 4
411 **DAVIDS DELIGHT** (IRE) C 40
186 **DAWAALEEB** (USA) 4
79 **DAWAAM** (USA) 4
576 **DAWN BREAKING** 3
243 **DAWN HORIZONS** F 133
253 **DAWN OF LIBERATION** (IRE) 148
252 **DAWN RAIDER** (IRE) 5
369 **DAWN TREADER** (IRE) 16
264 **DAWN TROUPER** (IRE) 14
587 **DAWN VIEW** (IRE) 7
419 **DAWN WALL** (AUS) F 142
75 **DAWNSLITTLEDIAMOND** 3
253 **DAWSON CITY** 3
253 **DAY TRADER** (IRE) 55
220 **DAYBREAK BOY** (IRE) 1
369 **DAYDREAM AULMES** (FR) 17
308 **DAYEM** (IRE) 56
27 **DAYMAN** (GER) 90
98 **DAYROSE** F 75
240 **DAYS LIKE THIS** 25
345 **DAYSAQ** (IRE) 8
539 **DAYSLEEPER** 28
212 **DAYTIME AHEAD** (IRE) 10
165 **DAZZLE DANCER** (IRE) C 3
6 **DAZZLING BEAUTY** 45
493 **DAZZLING DAN** (IRE) 5
421 **DAZZLING DES** (IRE) 10
492 **DAZZLING GLORY** (IRE) 33
344 **DAZZLING LIGHT** (UAE) C 54
434 **DE BARLEY BASKET** (IRE) 14
237 **DE BRUYNE HORSE** 3
278 **DE FORGOTTEN ONE** 2
14 **DE LATOUR** 4
161 **DE LITTLE ENGINE** (IRE) 9
372 **DE NAME ESCAPES ME** (IRE) 19
418 **DE NAME EVADES ME** (IRE) 43
333 **DE RASHER COUNTER** 10
93 **DE VEGAS KID** (IRE) 20
482 **DE YOUNG WARRIOR** 8
110 **DEACS DELIGHT** 35
395 **DEAD RIGHT** 20

259 **DEADLY ACCURATE** 1
491 **DEAL A DOLLAR** 4
399 **DEAL D'ESTRUVAL** (FR) 58
5 **DEAL DUN** (IRE) 4
411 **DEANA** (FR) G 41
32 **DEAR ALIX** 3
421 **DEAR DANCER** (IRE) C 115
285 **DEAR RALPHY** (IRE) 8
363 **DEAR SIRE** (IRE) 31
402 **DEAUVILLE DANCER** (IRE) 23
194 **DEAUVILLE LEGEND** (IRE) 27
531 **DEAUVILLE SOCIETY** (IRE) 2
353 **DEBATED** 22
495 **DEBAWTRY** (IRE) 3
60 **DEBBONAIR** (IRE) 4
313 **DEBDEN BANK** 13
502 **DEBESTYMAN** (IRE) 5
421 **DEBIT CARD** 116
243 **DEBUETATIN** F 134
167 **DECCAN QUEEN** C 86
98 **DECEPTION VALLEY** (IRE) 12
55 **DECISION MAKER** (IRE) 4
27 **DECLARED INTEREST** 8
309 **DECODING** 69
315 **DECONSO** 5
167 **DECONTRACTE** 87
570 **DECORA** (IRE) 7
567 **DEE DAY LANDING** 1
252 **DEE EIRE** 6
252 **DEE LANE** (IRE) 7
252 **DEE STAR** (IRE) 8
386 **DEEBAJ** (IRE) 25
63 **DEEDS NOT WORDS** (IRE) 11
113 **DEEP CHARM** 10
526 **DEEP DREAM** C 45
309 **DEEP IMPRESSION** (IRE) 70
443 **DEEP INFERNO** (IRE) 4
491 **DEEP SIGH** (FR) 34
40 **DEEP SNOW** 14
212 **DEEPER BLUE** (FR) 11
422 **DEER HUNTER** (IRE) 3
22 **DEERFOOT** 7
25 **DEEVIOUS BEAU** 6
305 **DEEWHY** (IRE) 4
545 **DEFERRED** 161
355 **DEFI DES CARRES** (FR) 5
276 **DEFI DU SEUIL** (FR) 19
278 **DEFI SACRE** (FR) 3
361 **DEFINATELY VINNIE** 7
228 **DEFINED** 58
492 **DEFINING BATTLE** (IRE) 34
439 **DEFINITE DILEMMA** (IRE) 3
111 **DEFINITE GREY** (IRE) G 7
114 **DEFINITE WARRIOR** (IRE) 4
280 **DEFINITE WINNER** (IRE) 4
146 **DEFINITE WISDOM** (IRE) 8
552 **DEFINITELY ALRIGHT** 41
175 **DEFINITELY RED** (IRE) 11
415 **DEFROST MY HEART** (IRE) C 128
324 **DEFTERA LAD** (IRE) 2
580 **DEFUTURE IS BRIGHT** (IRE) 5
518 **DEGREE** 9
369 **DEHRADUN** 18
227 **DEIANIRA** (IRE) G 17
7 **DEINONYCHUS** 24
133 **DEIRA CHAMPION** 20
537 **DEIRA STATION** (IRE) 41

276 **DEISE ABA** (IRE) 20
67 **DEISE VU** (IRE) 3
103 **DEJA** (FR) 2
285 **DEJA VUE** (IRE) 9
16 **DEJAME PASO** (IRE) 58
402 **DEL DUQUE** (IRE) 24
434 **DEL LA MAR ROCKET** (IRE) 15
359 **DEL'S EDGE** 3
10 **DELAGATE THE LADY** 9
10 **DELAGATE THIS LORD** 10
434 **DELAHAYE GOLD** (IRE) 16
159 **DELAQUINN** 7
149 **DELCIA** 5
16 **DELEVIGNE** F 153
243 **DELEYLA** F 135
80 **DELEYLL** 5
444 **DELFACE** (FR) 14
471 **DELGANY MONARCH** (IRE) 7
168 **DELGREY BOY** 28
6 **DELICATE KISS** 5
585 **DELIGHT OF DUBAI** (IRE) 6
599 **DELIGHTFUL GUEST** (IRE) 2
518 **DELIGHTSNSURPRISES** (USA) 40
424 **DELILAH** (IRE) 22
555 **DELILAH PARK** 5
434 **DELIRE D'ESTRUVAL** (FR) 17
180 **DELIZIA** (IRE) F 47
58 **DELKANTRA** (IRE) 4
511 **DELL ORO** (FR) 5
444 **DELL' ARCA** (IRE) 15
93 **DELLA MARE** 21
27 **DELOREAN** (IRE) 91
228 **DELTA BAY** 59
168 **DELTA DIVA** (USA) C 154
223 **DELTA ROSE** (IRE) 5
17 **DELTA RUN** (IRE) 2
84 **DELUXE MUSIC** 8
532 **DELUXE RANGE** (IRE) 14
336 **DEMACHINE** (IRE) 3
384 **DEMBE** 8
263 **DEMERA BAY** 11
128 **DEMOCRATIC OATH** (IRE) 18
460 **DEMOISELLE BOND** G 3
460 **DEMOISELLE BOND** F 10
482 **DEMON FOU** (FR) 9
276 **DEMOPOLIS** (FR) 21
94 **DENABLE** 3
411 **DENILIQUIN** (IRE) 42
449 **DENNING** 49
402 **DENS DELIGHT** (FR) 25
584 **DENTLEY DE MEE** (FR) 6
454 **DENY KNOWLEDGE** (IRE) 30
128 **DENZIL'S LAUGHING** (IRE) 82
20 **DEOLALI** 4
597 **DEORA DE** C 13
399 **DEPLOY THE GETAWAY** (IRE) 59
372 **DEPLOYED** (IRE) 20
475 **DEPP** (IRE) 49
578 **DEPUTISE** 4
193 **DEPUTY** (IRE) 37
395 **DEPUTY JONES** (IRE) 21
256 **DEPUTY SANDY** (IRE) 91
171 **DEPUTY'S OSCAR** (IRE) 8
113 **DEQUALL** 11
228 **DERAB** 60
32 **DEREHAM** 4
35 **DEREK DUVAL** (USA) 3

257 **DEREK LE GRAND** 3
168 **DEREKSSON** (IRE) 111
369 **DERRIANA** (IRE) G 19
28 **DERRICK D'ANJOU** (IRE) 3
65 **DERWENT DEALER** (IRE) 2
250 **DESARAY GIRL** (FR) 17
253 **DESERT** 149
253 **DESERT ANGEL** (IRE) 150
518 **DESERT BERRY** C 99
6 **DESERT BLOSSOM** (IRE) C 127
5 **DESERT CAT** 11
219 **DESERT DE BRUYERE** (FR) 2
554 **DESERT DOCTOR** (IRE) 11
507 **DESERT DREAM** 5
214 **DESERT EMPEROR** 14
491 **DESERT ENCOUNTER** (IRE) 5
40 **DESERT FIRE** (IRE) 15
491 **DESERT FRIEND** (IRE) 6
326 **DESERT GULF** 26
523 **DESERT HISTORY** 13
56 **DESERT LAND** (IRE) 7
179 **DESERT LILY** (IRE) C 28
92 **DESERT MARATHON** 38
376 **DESERT MOON** (IRE) F 13
378 **DESERT PALMS** 2
6 **DESERT PEACE** (USA) 6
574 **DESERT QUEST** (IRE) 49
16 **DESERT RAVINE** 59
309 **DESERT SAFARI** (IRE) 5
446 **DESERT SECRETS** (IRE) G 3
176 **DESERT SKYLINE** (IRE) 2
123 **DESERT TEAM** (IRE) 66
13 **DESIGN ICON** 12
546 **DESIGNER DESTINY** (IRE) 27
330 **DESILUSION** (USA) 34
474 **DESPATCH** C 17
588 **DESQUE DE L'ISLE** (FR) 18
353 **DESTACADO** (IRE) 23
420 **DESTALINK** C 39
424 **DESTIN D'AJONC** (FR) 23
564 **DESTINATION AIM** 1
336 **DESTINED TO SHINE** (IRE) 4
588 **DESTINEE ROYALE** (FR) 19
473 **DESTINY IS ALL** (IRE) 25
15 **DESTINY QUEEN** 38
492 **DESTRIER** (FR) 35
260 **DETACHMENT** 3
427 **DETATCHED** (IRE) 9
478 **DETECTIVE** 3
589 **DETONATION** 5
326 **DEVERON** (USA) F 48
420 **DEVIL'S ANGEL** 5
562 **DEVIL'S CUB** 14
419 **DEVIL'S OUTLAW** (USA) 72
189 **DEVILRY** 30
446 **DEVILS ROC** 4
27 **DEVILWALA** (IRE) 38
132 **DEVIOUS ANGEL** (IRE) 53
295 **DEVIOUS DICKS DAME** 8
439 **DEVIZES** (IRE) 4
379 **DEVON ENVOY** 36
264 **DEVONGATE** 15
6 **DEVONSHIRE** (IRE) F 128
488 **DEVONSHIRE ROCCO** (IRE) 11
15 **DEVORGILLA** 31
545 **DEVOTED POET** 162

115 **DEVOUR** (IRE) 3
51 **DEW LINE** (IRE) C 34
159 **DEW YOU BELIEVE** (IRE) 22
123 **DEWDROP** (IRE) C 67
253 **DEWEY ROAD** (IRE) 56
318 **DEXCITE** (FR) 4
475 **DEXTER BELLE** (IRE) 50
321 **DEYRANN DE CARJAC** (FR) 21
419 **DHABYAH** (IRE) 1
6 **DHAHABI** (IRE) 47
105 **DHAN DHANA** F 66
37 **DHARAN** (FR) 1
277 **DHARMA RAIN** (IRE) 3
123 **DHEYAA** (IRE) C 68
234 **DHOWIN** (IRE) 15
243 **DHUSHAN** (IRE) 54
244 **DI BELLO ROSA** (IRE) 39
386 **DIABLE DE SIVOLA** (FR) 26
309 **DIABLERETTE** C 176
65 **DIABOLEO** (FR) 3
323 **DIAKOSAINT** (FR) 18
415 **DIALAFARA** (FR) F 129
245 **DIAMIL** (FR) 34
253 **DIAMINDA** (IRE) C 151
581 **DIAMON DES FLOS** (IRE) 24
107 **DIAMOND BANGLE** (IRE) F 44
562 **DIAMOND BAY** 15
427 **DIAMOND BRIG** 10
477 **DIAMOND COTTAGE** 4
375 **DIAMOND CUTTER** 21
119 **DIAMOND DOUGAL** (IRE) 7
243 **DIAMOND DROP** (IRE) 55
258 **DIAMOND DUCHESS** (IRE) F 43
258 **DIAMOND DUCHESS** (IRE) G 50
76 **DIAMOND FEVER** (IRE) F 96
415 **DIAMOND FIELDS** (IRE) C 130
274 **DIAMOND FIFE** 37
418 **DIAMOND FORT** (IRE) 44
13 **DIAMOND GAIT** 13
351 **DIAMOND GIRL** 22
148 **DIAMOND HAZE** (IRE) 41
399 **DIAMOND HILL** (IRE) 60
282 **DIAMOND JILL** (IRE) 4
282 **DIAMOND JOEL** 5
253 **DIAMOND OF DUBAI** 57
270 **DIAMOND RIVER** (IRE) 8
367 **DIAMOND ROAD** (IRE) 2
496 **DIAMOND ROSE** 2
199 **DIAMOND SHOWER** (IRE) 6
415 **DIAMOND SKY** (IRE) C 131
473 **DIAMOND STATE** (IRE) 26
259 **DIAMOND VINE** (IRE) 2
148 **DIAMONDONTHEHILL** 42
518 **DIAMONDS ARE KING** (USA) 41
29 **DIAMONDS AT DUSK** 19
98 **DIAMONDS DANCING** 37
42 **DIAMONDS DREAM** 3
16 **DIARY** (IRE) F 154
167 **DIAVOLERIA** F 88
545 **DIAVOLO** (IRE) 58
90 **DIBAMBA PASSION** (FR) 24
421 **DICK DATCHERY** (IRE) 11
321 **DICKENS** (IRE) 129
270 **DICKIE DIVER** (IRE) 49
98 **DICKIEDOODA** (IRE) 92
526 **DICKTATE** 46
563 **DID SHE THOUGH** (IRE) 31

67 **FILBERT STREET** 5
396 **FILE AND PAINT** (IRE) C 11
424 **FILE ILLICO** (FR) 32
323 **FILLE D'AVIGNON** (IRE) 23
562 **FILLE D'OR** (IRE) 17
386 **FILLE DE LA LUNE** 99
419 **FILS D'OUDAIRIES** (FR) 23
399 **FILS SPIRITUEL** (FR) 84
381 **FILTHY LUCCA** 2
363 **FIN AND GAME** (IRE) 37
280 **FINAIR** 5
6 **FINAL APPLAUSE** 53
282 **FINAL ATTACK** (IRE) 6
569 **FINAL CHOICE** 12
419 **FINAL DYNASTY** F 146
391 **FINAL ENCORE** 4
587 **FINAL FANTASY** 37
146 **FINAL FLING** (IRE) 15
91 **FINAL FRONTIER** (IRE) 8
485 **FINAL LEGACY** 7
257 **FINAL LIST** (IRE) 5
418 **FINAL NUDGE** (IRE) 55
393 **FINAL OPTION** 4
1 **FINAL REMINDER** (IRE) 24
481 **FINAL RENDEZVOUS** 16
40 **FINAL SONG** (IRE) 29
6 **FINAL STAGE** C 140
40 **FINAL STORY** (USA) 30
40 **FINAL THOUGHT** (FR) 78
523 **FINAL VOYAGE** (IRE) 17
308 **FINALE** C 59
495 **FINALIZE** F 32
128 **FINALLY MINE** (USA) 23
126 **FINANCIAL OUTCOME** (IRE) 13
336 **FINANCIER** 9
245 **FINANS BAY** (IRE) 6
402 **FINAWN BAWN** (IRE) 39
375 **FINDONO** (FR) 22
210 **FINDUSATGORCOMBE** 3
123 **FINE BALANCE** (IRE) 73
496 **FINE BY HER** 3
434 **FINE CASTING** (IRE) 24
518 **FINE CHINA** 104
60 **FINE INVESTMENT** 5
123 **FINE TIME** F 74
145 **FINE WINE** (IRE) 13
7 **FINERY** 34
415 **FINEST** (IRE) 44
399 **FINEST EVERMORE** (IRE) 85
123 **FINEST SOUND** (IRE) 5
321 **FINEST VIEW** 33
9 **FINGAL'S HILL** (IRE) 2
395 **FINGERONTHESWITCH** (IRE) 30
224 **FINISHER** (USA) 3
363 **FINISK RIVER** 38
492 **FINISTERE** (FR) 53
295 **FINNEGAN'S GARDEN** (IRE) 11
337 **FINNISTON FARM** 10
132 **FINOAH** (IRE) 5
194 **FIORDLAND** (IRE) 16
492 **FIRAK** (FR) 54
148 **FIRBY** (IRE) 12
323 **FIRCOMBE HALL** 96
419 **FIRE ATTACK** (IRE) 24
52 **FIRE AWAY** (IRE) 5
454 **FIRE EATER** (FR) 7

309 **FIRE FIGHTING** (IRE) 10
545 **FIRE HEROINE** (USA) C 165
50 **FIRE IN THE RAIN** 40
569 **FIRE LINE** F 51
495 **FIREBOMB** 33
429 **FIREGUARD** 6
181 **FIRENZE** C 17
61 **FIRENZE ROSA** (IRE) 6
553 **FIRENZO** (FR) 10
270 **FIRESTEP** (IRE) 64
285 **FIRESTREAM** 14
243 **FIREWORKS** (FR) 59
225 **FIRINFEU** 6
421 **FIRMAMENT** 17
533 **FIRMDECISIONS** (IRE) 6
128 **FIRST ACCOUNT** 24
372 **FIRST APPROACH** (IRE) 31
17 **FIRST ASSEMBLY** (IRE) 5
40 **FIRST BLUSH** (IRE) F 127
554 **FIRST CHARGE** (IRE) 15
402 **FIRST CLASS RETURN** (IRE) 40
92 **FIRST COMPANY** (IRE) 14
193 **FIRST CONNECTION** (FR) 39
514 **FIRST DESTINATION** 9
447 **FIRST DU CHARMIL** (FR) 7
120 **FIRST EDITION** (IRE) 24
55 **FIRST EXCEL** 6
13 **FIRST FLOW** (IRE) 21
484 **FIRST FURLOUGH** 16
323 **FIRST GLORY** (IRE) 24
148 **FIRST GREYED** (IRE) 44
115 **FIRST HARMONY** F 28
323 **FIRST ILLUSION** (IRE) 25
454 **FIRST IMPRESSION** (IRE) 8
362 **FIRST LANDING** 13
228 **FIRST LIGHT** (IRE) 24
444 **FIRST LORD DE CUET** (FR) 24
132 **FIRST LOTT** 28
235 **FIRST MAN** (IRE) 21
489 **FIRST OF NEVER** (IRE) 4
303 **FIRST ONE D'ANA** (FR) 10
395 **FIRST QUEST** (USA) 31
520 **FIRST RESPONSE** 3
536 **FIRST REVOLUTION** (IRE) 6
568 **FIRST ROMANCE** 8
40 **FIRST SMILE** (IRE) 79
40 **FIRST SNOWFALL** 31
408 **FIRST SOLDIER** (FR) 29
554 **FIRST STREET** 16
523 **FIRST VERSE** (IRE) 18
6 **FIRST VICTORY** (IRE) C 141
40 **FIRST VIEW** (IRE) 32
179 **FIRST VIOLIN** 29
7 **FIRST VOYAGE** (FR) 35
376 **FIRSTEEN** 16
6 **FIRTH OF LORNE** (IRE) F 142
7 **FISCAL PRUDENCE** (IRE) 36
168 **FISHABLE** 36
22 **FISHER GREEN** (IRE) 12
131 **FISHERMANS COVE** (IRE) 7
212 **FISHKHOV** (FR) 13
37 **FITSAOHA** (FR) 13
36 **FITTONIA** (FR) F 4
526 **FITWOOD STAR** 8
577 **FITZ IN** (IRE) 16
230 **FITZ PARK** (IRE) 7
143 **FITZ WELL** (IRE) 5

107 **FITZCARRALDO** 4
140 **FITZROVIA** 6
402 **FITZROY** (IRE) 41
72 **FITZY** 3
545 **FIUISE** (IRE) C 166
98 **FIUMICINO** F 81
410 **FIVE AND DIME** 8
235 **FIVE BAR BRIAN** (IRE) 22
266 **FIVE GOLD BARS** (IRE) 3
494 **FIVE ICE CUBES** (FR) 3
399 **FIVE O'CLOCK** (FR) 86
324 **FIVE RINGS** 18
580 **FIVE STAR GETAWAY** (IRE) 7
309 **FIVE STARS** 184
363 **FIVEANDTWENTY** 39
16 **FIVETHOUSANDTOONE** (IRE) 65
402 **FIVETOTWELVE** 42
270 **FIX SUN** (FR) 65
227 **FIZZLESTIX** (FR) 18
344 **FIZZY FEET** (IRE) 12
16 **FLAG HIGH** (IRE) 159
545 **FLAG OF TRUTH** (FR) 167
553 **FLAGRANT DELITIEP** (FR) 11
230 **FLAKARNA** 8
501 **FLAMBOYANT JOYAUX** (FR) 15
308 **FLAME OF FREEDOM** (IRE) 30
173 **FLAME OF IRELAND** (IRE) C 19
202 **FLAMENCO DE KERSER** (FR) 3
375 **FLAMENCO FAN** 4
424 **FLAMES OF PASSION** (IRE) 33
341 **FLAMES OF YORK** 7
483 **FLAMING GLORY** (IRE) 9
522 **FLAMING HOT** (IRE) 9
179 **FLAMING LORD** 30
296 **FLAMING SPEAR** (IRE) 10
386 **FLAMINGER** (FR) 41
94 **FLAMINGO ROSE** 5
421 **FLAMMARION** (GER) 18
341 **FLANAGANS FIELD** (IRE) 8
372 **FLANKING MANEUVER** (IRE) 32
369 **FLANN** 26
419 **FLASH BULB** (IRE) 147
411 **FLASH COLLONGES** (FR) 62
577 **FLASH DE CLERVAL** (FR) 17
248 **FLASH MORIVIERE** (FR) 2
549 **FLASH POINT** (FR) 3
492 **FLASH THE STEEL** (FR) 55
214 **FLASH TO BANG** 19
471 **FLASHDANZA** 9
384 **FLASHING COLOUR** (GER) F 27
329 **FLASHING GLANCE** 10
417 **FLASHY WINGS** C 34
176 **FLASHYFRANCES** C 16
98 **FLASHYFRANCES** C 82
280 **FLAT TO THE MAX** (FR) 6
548 **FLAT WHITE** (FR) 11
523 **FLAT WHITE** (FR) F 60
65 **FLAVIUS TITUS** 7
431 **FLAWLESS BEAUTY** F 61
6 **FLECHE D'OR** F 143
17 **FLECK IVY** (IRE) 6
121 **FLEETING BLUE** (FR) 13
274 **FLEETING PRINCE** (IRE) 11
369 **FLEETING VISIT** 27
442 **FLEETSTONE** G 6
492 **FLEGMATIK** (FR) 56
333 **FLEMCARA** (IRE) 18

499 **FOURTH OF JULY** (IRE) 11
96 **FOURTOUT** (FR) 11
399 **FOVEROS** (FR) 88
16 **FOX CHAIRMAN** (IRE) 12
27 **FOX DUTY FREE** (IRE) 10
5 **FOX HILL** 5
314 **FOX LEICESTER** (IRE) 5
534 **FOX NORTON** (FR) 36
253 **FOX POWER** (IRE) 7
16 **FOX PREMIER** (IRE) 13
583 **FOX PRO** (FR) 8
16 **FOX TAL** 14
371 **FOX VARDY** (USA) 4
270 **FOX'S SOCKS** (FR) 69
553 **FOXBORO** (GER) 12
120 **FOXCATCHER** C 77
447 **FOXCUB** (IRE) 8
16 **FOXES TALES** (IRE) 68
185 **FOXEY** 21
402 **FOXINTHEBOX** (IRE) 45
388 **FOXISLE SUNNY JIM** 15
241 **FOXRUSH TAKE TIME** (FR) 6
375 **FOXTROT SIZZLER** (GER) 24
215 **FOXY FEMME** 1
389 **FOXY JACKS** (IRE) 7
277 **FOXY SINGER** (FR) 4
106 **FOYLESIDEVIEW** (IRE) 2
105 **FOZZIE BEAR** (IRE) 67
120 **FRABJOUS** C 78
583 **FRAGRANT ROSE** C 18
309 **FRAGRANT STORM** 80
233 **FRAME RATE** 3
14 **FRAMLEY GARTH** (IRE) 6
263 **FRANCE DE REVE** (FR) 16
194 **FRANCESCO GUARDI** (IRE) 17
16 **FRANCHEMENT** (FR) 160
399 **FRANCIGANE** (FR) 18
211 **FRANCIS XAVIER** (IRE) 10
140 **FRANCISCO BAY** 7
53 **FRANCKY DU BERLAIS** (FR) 11
588 **FRANCO D'AUNOU** (FR) 33
399 **FRANCO DE PORT** (FR) 90
488 **FRANCOLIN** (FR) 15
577 **FRANEGANE** (FR) 18
101 **FRANKEL'S MAGIC** (FR) 7
250 **FRANKELIO** (FR) 27
16 **FRANKELLA** 161
454 **FRANKENSTELLA** (FR) 9
492 **FRANKEUR** (FR) 57
234 **FRANKIE BABY** (IRE) 22
205 **FRANKIE BALLOU** (IRE) 3
435 **FRANKIE JAZ** 5
559 **FRANKIES FIRE** 4
150 **FRANKINCENSE** (IRE) 9
228 **FRANKLET** 69
402 **FRANKLY MR SHANKLY** (GER) 46
230 **FRANKS FANCY** (FR) 9
493 **FRANSHAM** 8
491 **FRANTOIO** 39
475 **FRANZ** 98
452 **FRANZ KLAMMER** 4
81 **FRANZI FURY** (IRE) 5
494 **FRAOULA** 3
424 **FRASCATO BELLO** (FR) 36
235 **FRATERCULUS** (IRE) 24
321 **FRATERNAL** (FR) 35
395 **FRAU GEORGIA** (IRE) 32

234 **FRAUGHAN HILL** (IRE) 23
16 **FRAULEIN** C 162
51 **FREAK OUT** (IRE) 23
270 **FRED** (FR) 70
309 **FRED** 11
98 **FRED BEAR** (IRE) 43
212 **FREDDIE DARLING** (IRE) 16
588 **FREDDIE FLIP FLOP** (IRE) 16
250 **FREDDIE'S FRONTIER** (IRE) 28
325 **FREDDY FANATAPAN** 4
327 **FREE DEGREES** (IRE) 2
7 **FREE LOVE** 37
256 **FREE SOLO** (IRE) 26
27 **FREE WILL** 44
228 **FREE WIND** (IRE) 70
546 **FREEDELIVERY** (IRE) 31
45 **FREEDOM AND WHEAT** (IRE) 4
219 **FREEDOM CHIMES** 4
91 **FREEDOM FLYER** (IRE) 10
431 **FREEDOM PASS** (USA) F 62
424 **FREEDOM SONG** G 37
16 **FREEDOM'S LIGHT** C 163
343 **FREETHINKER** (IRE) 14
289 **FREEZING** (FR) 4
34 **FRENCH ACCENT** G 19
399 **FRENCH ASEEL** (FR) 91
270 **FRENCH CRUSADER** (FR) 71
181 **FRENCH DE GUYE** (FR) 4
389 **FRENCH DYNAMITE** (FR) 8
157 **FRENCH FASHION** (FR) F 3
428 **FRENCH FLIRT** F 54
93 **FRENCH KISS** (FR) 32
326 **FRENCH MINSTREL** (IRE) 6
161 **FRENCH MIX** (USA) 13
490 **FRENCH PARADOXE** (FR) 10
300 **FRENCH RED** (FR) 48
588 **FRENCHY DU LARGE** (FR) 35
217 **FRENZIFIED** C 13
65 **FREQUENCY CODE** (FR) 8
399 **FRERE TUCK** (FR) 92
588 **FRERO BANBOU** (FR) 36
189 **FRESH** 11
193 **FRESH HOPE** 64
263 **FRESH MINT** (IRE) F 49
402 **FRESH NEW DAWN** (IRE) 47
553 **FRESNO EMERY** (FR) 13
309 **FREYJA** (IRE) 12
469 **FRIARY GOLD** (IRE) 2
402 **FRIARY LAND** 48
389 **FRIARY ROCK** (FR) 9
94 **FRICKA** 6
127 **FRIDAY** 4
411 **FRIEND OR FOE** (FR) 66
415 **FRIENDLY** (IRE) 47
128 **FRIENDLY ADVICE** (IRE) 26
387 **FRIENDLY PRINCESS** (IRE) 9
497 **FRIENDS DON'T ASK** 3
174 **FRIENDS DON'T TELL** 3
590 **FRIENDS IN HEAVEN** (IRE) 1
478 **FRIGHTENED RABBIT** (USA) 4
415 **FRILL** (IRE) 48
360 **FRILLY FROCK** (FR) 4
501 **FRIMEUR DE LANCRAY** (FR) 16
424 **FRISCO BAY** (IRE) 38
76 **FRISKY** 100
492 **FRISSON COLLONGES** (FR) 58
446 **FRITH** 42

330 **FRIVOLE** (FR) 37
411 **FRODON** (FR) 67
421 **FROG AND TOAD** (IRE) 68
243 **FRONT HOUSE** (IRE) C 143
101 **FRONT LINE** 38
555 **FRONT OF LINE** 8
351 **FRONT PAGE NEWS** C 25
419 **FRONT VIEW** (FR) 25
330 **FRONTGATE** (USA) 13
438 **FRONTISPIECE** 4
76 **FRONTLINE PHANTOM** (IRE) 8
209 **FROSTY BERRY** G 5
411 **FROSTY LADY** (FR) 68
70 **FROW** (IRE) 3
40 **FROZEN PATH** 80
253 **FROZEN WATERS** (IRE) 8
363 **FRUIT N NUT** (IRE) 40
479 **FRUITCAKE** 5
253 **FRUSTRATING** 165
210 **FS LOLA** 5
473 **FUDGEMAN** (IRE) 37
506 **FUEGO** 46
278 **FUGITIF** (FR) 8
270 **FUGITIVES DRIFT** (IRE) 72
10 **FUJAIRA KING** (USA) 15
545 **FUJAIRA PRINCE** (IRE) 12
588 **FUJI FLIGHT** (FR) 37
534 **FULGURIX** (FR) 37
446 **FULL APPROVAL** (IRE) 19
386 **FULL BACK** (FR) 43
121 **FULL CIRCLE** 5
476 **FULL GLASS** (FR) 1
435 **FULL INTENTION** 6
509 **FULL MANDATE** F 40
597 **FULL MOON RISING** 9
179 **FULL OF BEANS** 31
533 **FULL OF SASS** (IRE) 29
395 **FULL OF SURPRISES** (FR) 33
447 **FULL SHIFT** (FR) 9
234 **FULL SPES** (FR) 24
360 **FULL TROTTLE** (IRE) 5
93 **FUME** (FR) 33
419 **FUN LIGHT** (FR) 26
588 **FUNAMBULE SIVOLA** (FR) 38
228 **FUNDAMENTAL** 71
120 **FUNKY BEAR** (IRE) 26
487 **FUNKY SENSATION** 4
322 **FUNWAY MONARCH** (IRE) 14
372 **FUOCO** 95
250 **FURAX** (FR) 29
735 **FURIOUSLY FAST** (FR) 5
235 **FURIUS DE CIERGUES** (FR) 25
534 **FURKASH** (FR) 38
530 **FURNITURE FACTORS** (IRE) 11
324 **FURTHER MEASURE** (USA) 4
587 **FURY** 38
148 **FURY NIGHT** (IRE) 45
400 **FUSEAU** (FR) 13
270 **FUSIL RAFFLES** (FR) 73
168 **FUSION** (FR) F 157
252 **FUSIONFORCE** (IRE) 9
420 **FUTURE ENERGY** F 41
70 **FUTURE INVESTMENT** 4
27 **FUTURE INVESTMENT** 11
40 **FUTURE KING** (IRE) 33
372 **FUTURE PROOF** (FR) 33
50 **FUTURISTIC** (IRE) 7

181 **FUWAIRT** (IRE) 5
33 **FUZZBUSTER** (IRE) 4
473 **FYFIN PATSY** (IRE) 38
538 **FYRECRACKER** (IRE) 8
432 **G'DAAY** 10
464 **G'DAY AUSSIE** 5
503 **GA LAW** (IRE) 22
243 **GAASSEE** (IRE) 60
387 **GAAZAAL** (IRE) C 25
390 **GABRIAL** (IRE) 3
390 **GABRIAL THE SAINT** (IRE) 4
390 **GABRIAL THE TIGER** (IRE) 5
441 **GABRIEL OATS** 5
285 **GABRIEL'S GETAWAY** (IRE) 16
444 **GABRIELLE DU SEUIL** (FR) 26
194 **GADFLY** F 28
492 **GADJET D'AINAY** (FR) 59
523 **GADWA** F 61
286 **GAELIC BELLE** 2
51 **GAELIC LAW** 24
128 **GAELIC SECRET** 85
286 **GAELIC THUNDER** 3
363 **GAELIC COAST** (FR) 41
36 **GAERWEN** 16
101 **GAGARIN'S MOON** 39
419 **GAHERIS** (GER) 79
12 **GAIA VALLIS** (IRE) 12
399 **GAILLARD DU MESNIL** (FR) 93
36 **GAINSBOURG** 17
253 **GAIUS** 166
372 **GAIUS DE MARCIGNY** (FR) 34
228 **GAL WONDER** 72
276 **GALA BALL** (IRE) 3
411 **GALA DE CORTON** (FR) 69
341 **GALA DES LYS** (FR) 9
523 **GALACTIC HEROINE** F 62
143 **GALACTIC POWER** (IRE) 6
181 **GALACTIC SPIRIT** 6
101 **GALACTICA** (FR) 40
27 **GALAH** 45
584 **GALAHAD QUEST** (FR) 9
98 **GALAHAD THREEPWOOD** 13
270 **GALAN DES PLANCHES** (FR) 74
13 **GALANTE DE ROMAY** (FR) 23
408 **GALATA BRIDGE** 34
6 **GALATEE** (FR) C 144
330 **GALAWI** (IRE) 3
148 **GALE FORCE MAYA** 14
527 **GALES PRESENT** (IRE) G 5
393 **GALIAC** 23
583 **GALICE MACALO** (FR) 9
309 **GALICIAN** C 186
37 **GALIDERMES** (FR) 3
355 **GALIDERMES** (FR) 6
527 **GALILEO SILVER** (IRE) 6
228 **GALLAGHER** 9
52 **GALLAHERS CROSS** (IRE) 6
212 **GALLANT COMMANDER** (FR) 17
371 **GALLANTICUS** (IRE) 34
253 **GALLEY** F 167
136 **GALLIC DESTINY** (IRE) 6
153 **GALLIC GEORDIE** 10
375 **GALLIFREY** F 49
363 **GALLOPONGRAY** (IRE) 42
450 **GALLOW FORD** (IRE) 7
270 **GALLYHILL** (FR) 75
399 **GALOPIN DES CHAMPS** (FR) 94

264 **GALORE DESASSENCES** (FR) 17
408 **GALSWORTHY** 35
403 **GALTEE MOUNTAIN** (IRE) 1
307 **GALUPPI** 5
456 **GALURIN** (FR) 13
547 **GALWAY GIRL** (GER) 4
308 **GAMBON** (GER) 6
33 **GAME BIRD** (IRE) 5
322 **GAME IN THE PARK** (FR) 15
53 **GAME LINE** (IRE) 12
548 **GAME ON FOR GLORY** (IRE) 12
408 **GAME SOCKS** 36
263 **GAMEFACE** (IRE) 17
235 **GAMESTERS ICON** 26
6 **GAMILATI** C 145
399 **GANAPATHI** (FR) 95
389 **GANDY MAN** (IRE) 10
161 **GANG WARFARE** 14
234 **GANGSTER** (FR) 25
92 **GANNON GLORY** (IRE) 27
167 **GAOLBREAKER** (IRE) 23
408 **GARBANZO** 37
376 **GARDE FORESTIER** (FR) 17
276 **GARDE LA VICTOIRE** (FR) 38
588 **GARDEFORT** (FR) 39
168 **GARDEN OASIS** 37
523 **GARDEN PARADISE** (IRE) 3
225 **GARGOYLE GIRL** G 7
225 **GARGOYLE GIRL** G 8
337 **GARO DE JUILLEY** (FR) 11
482 **GARRANE** (IRE) 14
363 **GARRIX DE LA SEE** (FR) 43
274 **GARRUS** (IRE) 13
424 **GARRY CLERMONT** (FR) 39
273 **GARS BAR DINE** (FR) 4
399 **GARS EN NOIR** (FR) 96
401 **GARTH ROCKETT** 3
532 **GASPAISIELLE** F 25
190 **GASTARA** 20
495 **GATAMALATA** (IRE) C 34
6 **GATERIE** (USA) C 146
23 **GATES PASS** 7
322 **GATEWAY TO EUROPE** 16
102 **GATILLO** 9
330 **GAUCHER** 38
399 **GAULOISE** (FR) 97
326 **GAUNTLET** (FR) 7
321 **GAVI DI GAVI** (IRE) 36
379 **GAVIN** 20
10 **GAVLAR** 16
276 **GAVROCHEKA** (FR) 39
493 **GAYTON** 9
96 **GAZETTE BOURGEOISE** (FR) 12
309 **GEAR UP** (IRE) 81
98 **GEARING'S POINT** 44
121 **GEHT FASTEUR** (IRE) F 6
263 **GELBOE DE CHANAY** (FR) 18
399 **GELEE BLANCHE** (FR) 98
428 **GELENSCHIK** (IRE) C 55
411 **GELINO BELLO** (FR) 70
189 **GEMINGA** 34
589 **GEMINI GLORY** (USA) 7
588 **GEMIRANDE** (FR) 40
473 **GEMOLOGIST** (IRE) 39
415 **GEMS** C 136
214 **GEMS JEWEL** 49

425 **GENERAL BROOK** (IRE) 6
337 **GENERAL BUX** 12
153 **GENERAL CONSENSUS** 11
399 **GENERAL COUNSEL** (IRE) 99
402 **GENERAL CUSTARD** 49
110 **GENERAL LEE** (IRE) 23
597 **GENERAL PANIC** 16
402 **GENERAL PROBUS** 50
421 **GENERAL SAGO** (IRE) 69
393 **GENERAL ZOFF** 5
47 **GENERALISATION** (IRE) 8
424 **GENERATION GAP** (IRE) 40
335 **GENERATOR CITY** (IRE) 2
427 **GENEROUS DAY** (IRE) 13
344 **GENEROUS HEART** F 56
449 **GENESIUS** (IRE) 7
29 **GENEVA DIVA** 21
363 **GENEVER DRAGON** (IRE) 44
584 **GENIAL HAWKSTONE** (FR) 10
178 **GENNADY** (IRE) 7
548 **GENTLE ALICE** (IRE) F 13
290 **GENTLE BREEZE** (IRE) F 51
153 **GENTLE FIRE** 12
598 **GENTLE KATE** 10
456 **GENTLE RIVER** 14
493 **GENTLE ROSE** 10
160 **GENTLEMAN AT ARMS** (IRE) 2
266 **GENTLEMAN FARMER** 4
539 **GENTLEMAN JOE** 19
212 **GENTLEMAN KAP** (FR) 18
434 **GENTLEMAN VALLEY** (FR) 26
386 **GENTLEMAN'S DREAM** (IRE) 44
389 **GENTLEMANSGAME** 11
145 **GENTLY SPOKEN** (IRE) 14
253 **GENUFLEX** 70
80 **GENUINE APPROVAL** (IRE) 13
211 **GEOGRAPHY TEACHER** (IRE) 11
402 **GEOMATRICIAN** (FR) 51
518 **GEOMETRIST** 49
454 **GEONICE** (FR) 10
126 **GEORDIE DES CHAMPS** (IRE) 14
264 **GEORDIE WASHINGTON** (IRE) 18
146 **GEORDIELANDGANGSTA** 16
468 **GEORDIES DREAM** 4
15 **GEORGE BAKER** (IRE) 13
545 **GEORGE BANCROFT** 72
397 **GEORGE EDWARD** (IRE) 6
445 **GEORGE MALLORY** 3
87 **GEORGE MORLAND** 20
481 **GEORGE PEABODY** (IRE) 17
167 **GEORGE RIDSDALE** 24
193 **GEORGE SCOTT** (IRE) 40
65 **GEORGE SQUARE** (IRE) 25
170 **GEORGE THOMAS** 5
335 **GEORGIAN FIREBIRD** 3
13 **GERARD MENTOR** (FR) 24
434 **GERBOISE BORGET** (FR) 27
50 **GEREMIA** (FR) 41
444 **GERICAULT ROQUE** (FR) 27
303 **GEROLAMO CARDANO** 12
363 **GEROMINO** (FR) 45
532 **GERONIMO** 26
74 **GERRITZEN** 2
599 **GERSJOEYCASEY** (IRE) 3
526 **GERT LUSH** (IRE) 9
506 **GERTCHA** (IRE) 7
242 **GERTIES GARTER** 5

274 **GERTRUDE GRAY** (IRE) C 84
194 **GERTRUDE VERSED** C 29
492 **GET A TONIC** (IRE) 60
53 **GET AN OSCAR** (IRE) 13
212 **GET BACK GET BACK** (IRE) 19
222 **GET BYE** (IRE) 41
132 **GET FUNKY** (IRE) 30
113 **GET HELP** (IRE) 14
363 **GET IN ROBIN** (IRE) 46
120 **GET IT** 27
148 **GET KNOTTED** (IRE) 15
389 **GET MY DRIFT** (FR) 12
88 **GET ON JEREMY** (IRE) 3
128 **GET ON JOHN** (IRE) 27
532 **GET OUT THE GATE** (IRE) 27
434 **GET PREPARED** 28
323 **GET REAL** (IRE) 26
492 **GET SKY HIGH** (IRE) 61
411 **GET THE APPEAL** (IRE) 71
65 **GET THE FACTS** (IRE) 9
425 **GET UP THEM STEPS** 7
131 **GET WISHING** (IRE) 8
146 **GET WITH IT** (IRE) 17
244 **GET YOUR OWN** (IRE) 11
399 **GETABIRD** (IRE) 100
519 **GETABUCK** (IRE) 9
487 **GETAFRIEND** (IRE) 5
443 **GETALEAD** (IRE) 6
303 **GETAMAN** (IRE) 13
376 **GETAREASON** (IRE) 18
492 **GETARIVER** (IRE) 62
443 **GETAROUND** (IRE) 7
53 **GETASTAR** (IRE) 14
501 **GETAWAY BAY** (IRE) 17
598 **GETAWAY CORY** (IRE) 11
58 **GETAWAY FLYER** (IRE) 7
534 **GETAWAY FRED** (IRE) 39
483 **GETAWAY GERRY** 6
399 **GETAWAY GORGEOUS** (IRE) 101
254 **GETAWAY GUILLAUNE** (IRE) 3
598 **GETAWAY HONEY** (IRE) 12
250 **GETAWAY JEWEL** (IRE) 30
247 **GETAWAY KID** (IRE) 4
598 **GETAWAY LUCY** (IRE) 13
402 **GETAWAY LUV** (IRE) 52
492 **GETAWAY MAG** (IRE) 63
323 **GETAWAY MISSION** (IRE) 27
445 **GETAWAY NORTH** 4
502 **GETAWAY SUZY** (IRE) 6
456 **GETAWAY TOTHEROCK** (IRE) 15
411 **GETAWAY TRUMP** (IRE) 72
13 **GETAWEAPON** (IRE) 25
534 **GETMEGOLD** (IRE) 40
267 **GETONSAM** 3
369 **GETTHEPOT** (IRE) 29
138 **GETTYSBURGH** (IRE) 1
404 **GEYSER** 7
175 **GHADBBAAN** 17
344 **GHAITH** 13
40 **GHALY** 34
537 **GHALYOON** 4
274 **GHANAATI** (USA) C 85
549 **GHANTHANFAR** (IRE) 4
514 **GHAYAHIB** (IRE) 30
574 **GHAYYAR** (IRE) 20
79 **GHAZAALY** (IRE) 18
159 **GHEEDAA** (USA) C 52

97 **GHEPARDO** 6
325 **GHERKIN** 5
309 **GHOST RIDER** (IRE) 82
571 **GHOSTEEM FLECHOIS** (FR) 8
509 **GHOSTFLOWER** F 41
368 **GHOSTFLOWER** (IRE) G 16
20 **GHOSTLY** 22
6 **GHOSTWATCH** (IRE) 8
309 **GHUMAMA** (IRE) 83
50 **GHURFAH** F 79
367 **GIAMAS** 3
20 **GIANT STEPS** (IRE) 6
50 **GIAVELLOTTO** (IRE) 80
73 **GIBB HILL** 7
117 **GIBBERWELL** (IRE) 7
12 **GIBBES BAY** (FR) 9
56 **GIBRALTARIAN** (IRE) 9
523 **GIFT HORSE** 63
108 **GIFT OF KINGS** 6
27 **GIFT OF MUSIC** (IRE) C 98
491 **GIFT OF STARS** (IRE) 40
376 **GIFT WRAPPED** (IRE) C 19
76 **GIFTED GOLD** (IRE) 101
132 **GIFTED RULER** 6
40 **GIFTS OF GOLD** (IRE) 35
581 **GIGA WHITE** (IRE) 28
548 **GIGABIT** 14
168 **GIGGLE BAND** (IRE) 158
148 **GIGI'S BEACH** 16
569 **GILBERT** 52
318 **GILBERTINA** 6
16 **GILDED TRUFFLE** (IRE) C 164
90 **GILOU JAGUEN** (FR) 25
359 **GILT EDGE** 6
581 **GILWEN GRAYSON** 29
581 **GILWEN REACHER** 30
421 **GIMASHA** C 117
355 **GIN COCO** (FR) 7
308 **GIN PALACE** 7
584 **GINGEMBRE MENTHE** (FR) 11
582 **GINGER BAZOUKA** (FR) G 29
63 **GINGER BOX** 15
367 **GINGER BRANDY** F 4
533 **GINGER JAM** 7
1 **GINGER MAIL** (FR) 26
190 **GINGILI** 21
402 **GINISTRELLI** (IRE) 53
329 **GINNY'S DESTINY** (IRE) 11
418 **GINO TRAIL** (IRE) 57
585 **GINO WOTIMEAN** (USA) 10
242 **GIO'S GIRL** 6
145 **GIOGIOBBO** 15
128 **GIOIA CIECA** (USA) 86
415 **GIORGIO VASARI** (IRE) 49
552 **GIOVANNI CHANGE** (FR) 16
456 **GIOVANNI ROYALE** 16
294 **GIOVANNI TIEPOLO** 5
372 **GIPSI JOE** (FR) 35
270 **GIPSY DE CHOISEL** (FR) 76
1 **GIPSY LEE ROSE** (FR) 27
554 **GIRL FROM IPANEMA** (IRE) 45
101 **GIRL ON THE MOON** (FR) 41
253 **GISBURN** (IRE) 168
256 **GIULIANA** (GER) 97
50 **GIUSEPPE CASSIOLI** 8
274 **GIVE 'EM THE SLIP** 41
587 **GIVE IT SOME TEDDY** 12

411 **GIVE ME A COPPER** (IRE) 73
322 **GIVE ME A CUDDLE** (IRE) 17
521 **GIVE OVER** 2
577 **GIVE US A SWIG** 19
137 **GIVEHIMHISDEW** (IRE) 2
289 **GIVEN** (IRE) 5
109 **GIVEPEACEACHANCE** 2
397 **GIZZA JOB** 26
399 **GJOUMI** (FR) 102
297 **GLACEON** (IRE) 3
99 **GLACIER FOX** 2
120 **GLACIER POINT** C 79
217 **GLADE** C 14
583 **GLADIATEUR ALLEN** (IRE) 10
411 **GLAJOU** (FR) 74
554 **GLAM UP** 80
259 **GLAMOROUS AIR** (IRE) C 27
359 **GLAMOROUS ANNA** 7
359 **GLAMOROUS BREEZE** 11
359 **GLAMOROUS CRESCENT** 8
259 **GLAMOROUS FORCE** 7
529 **GLAN Y GORS** (IRE) 6
41 **GLANCE BACK** 4
456 **GLANCE FROM CLOVER** 17
276 **GLASHA'S PEAK** 40
475 **GLASS SLIPPERS** 7
499 **GLASSES UP** (USA) 12
284 **GLASSTREES** 0
141 **GLASTONBERRY** F 5
141 **GLASTONBERRY** G 18
180 **GLASVEGAS** (IRE) 5
479 **GLEAM ON FLORENCE** 2
564 **GLEAMING ARCH** 2
564 **GLEAMING MAIZE** 3
363 **GLEBE AALIN** (IRE) 47
309 **GLEN AGAIN** (IRE) 84
555 **GLEN ESK** 9
301 **GLEN ETIVE** 23
98 **GLEN FORSA** (IRE) 14
436 **GLEN MOLLY** (IRE) F 25
143 **GLEN MOOAR** (IRE) 7
223 **GLEN ROCCO** 11
569 **GLEN ROSA** 36
228 **GLEN SAVAGE** (IRE) 73
563 **GLEN SHIEL** 1
211 **GLEN VINE** 12
86 **GLENAMOY LAD** 18
554 **GLENARTNEY** 46
168 **GLENCADAM GLORY** 38
343 **GLENCASSLEY** (IRE) 15
200 **GLENCOE BOY** (IRE) 2
176 **GLENCORA** (IRE) 5
334 **GLENCOUM LASS** (IRE) 3
216 **GLENDEVON** (USA) 6
461 **GLENDUFF** (IRE) 14
179 **GLENDUN** (USA) 7
193 **GLENEAGLET** 41
65 **GLENGARRY** 10
110 **GLENGOWAN** (IRE) 6
225 **GLENIFFER** 9
449 **GLENISTER** (IRE) 52
225 **GLENLINI** G 33
587 **GLENN COCO** 13
386 **GLENO** (IRE) 45
20 **GLENRUA** (IRE) 7
399 **GLENS OF ANTRIM** (IRE) 103
284 **GLENTON** 1

| | | |
|---|---|---|
| 527 GLENTROOL 7 | 547 GLORY DAB (FR) 5 | 235 GOLD DESERT 27 |
| 431 GLESGA GAL (IRE) 30 | 321 GLORY DAYS (GER) G 37 | 388 GOLD FIELDS 16 |
| 321 GLIDE DOWN (USA) 132 | 300 GLORY FIGHTER 12 | 212 GOLD IN DOHA (FR) 20 |
| 343 GLIMPSE OF GALA 16 | 554 GLORY GALORE 81 | 333 GOLD LINK (FR) 20 |
| 291 GLIMPSE OF GOLD 7 | 230 GLORY HIGHTS 10 | 190 GOLD MAN (IRE) 22 |
| 461 GLINGER FLAME (IRE) 15 | 101 GLORY LIGHT 42 | 545 GOLD MAZE 13 |
| 508 GLINT OF AN EYE (IRE) 3 | 323 GLORY OF PARIS (IRE) 28 | 416 GOLD MERLION (IRE) 6 |
| 415 GLINTING (IRE) 50 | 519 GLORY TIME 10 | 175 GOLD MINER 8 |
| 84 GLITTERBOX GIRL (IRE) 32 | 470 GLORYELLA 4 | 313 GOLD OF WIN POTIER (FR) 19 |
| 132 GLITTERING CHOICE 58 | 371 GLOUCESTERSHIRE (USA) 13 | 270 GOLD PRESENT (IRE) 81 |
| 461 GLITTERING LOVE (IRE) 16 | 578 GLOVES LYNCH 7 | 526 GOLD RIBBON 10 |
| 240 GLITTERING PRIZE (UAE) F 26 | 325 GLOWETH 6 | 178 GOLD RUNNER (IRE) 9 |
| 120 GLOBAL ACCLAIM 28 | 107 GLOWING CLOUD F 46 | 511 GOLD SOUK (IRE) 7 |
| 97 GLOBAL ACCLAMATION 7 | 538 GLYNDEBOURNE (USA) F 28 | 93 GOLD STANDARD (IRE) 35 |
| 258 GLOBAL AGREEMENT 8 | 270 GLYNN (FR) 78 | 173 GOLD TOBOUGG F 17 |
| 120 GLOBAL ALEXANDER (IRE) C 80 | 576 GMASHA 4 | 173 GOLD TOBOUGG 7 |
| 159 GLOBAL ART 4 | 282 GMS PRINCE 7 | 101 GOLD TRIP (FR) 8 |
| 434 GLOBAL CITIZEN (IRE) 29 | 282 GMS PRINCESS 8 | 299 GOLD VENTURE (IRE) 3 |
| 419 GLOBAL DESTINATION (IRE) 5 | 282 GMS TEESSIDE 9 | 40 GOLD WING 81 |
| 222 GLOBAL EFFECT (IRE) 42 | 168 GNAT ALLEY 159 | 228 GOLDEN ACE 74 |
| 419 GLOBAL EQUITY (IRE) 27 | 105 GO ANGELLICA F 68 | 119 GOLDEN AGE (FR) 9 |
| 164 GLOBAL ESTEEM (IRE) 2 | 472 GO ANNIE GO 3 | 10 GOLDEN AMBER (IRE) F 46 |
| 541 GLOBAL EXCEED 3 | 568 GO AS YOU PLEASE (IRE) 11 | 378 GOLDEN ANTHEM (USA) C 40 |
| 418 GLOBAL FAME (IRE) 58 | 499 GO BOB GO (IRE) 13 | 168 GOLDEN APOLLO 39 |
| 492 GLOBAL FAMENGLORY (IRE) 64 | 270 GO CHIQUE (FR) 79 | 386 GOLDEN BOY GREY (FR) 46 |
| 164 GLOBAL FLIGHT 8 | 367 GO COMPLAIN 5 | 228 GOLDEN BUGLE 75 |
| 183 GLOBAL FRONTIER (IRE) 3 | 402 GO DANTE 54 | 52 GOLDEN CHANCER 7 |
| 228 GLOBAL GIANT 10 | 334 GO FORRIT (IRE) 4 | 384 GOLDEN CLAIM 11 |
| 164 GLOBAL GRANDEUR 9 | 20 GO GO LUNA 23 | 533 GOLDEN CLUSTER 30 |
| 492 GLOBAL HARMONY (IRE) 65 | 303 GO HARD OR GO HOME (IRE) 14 | 16 GOLDEN CRUSADER (FR) 69 |
| 40 GLOBAL HEAT (IRE) 36 | 581 GO LONG (IRE) 31 | 440 GOLDEN CYGNET 4 |
| 316 GLOBAL HOPE (IRE) 8 | 171 GO MILLIE GO (IRE) 11 | 228 GOLDEN DARLING (IRE) 76 |
| 225 GLOBAL HUMOR (USA) 10 | 222 GO ON BRYCEY LAD (FR) 44 | 309 GOLDEN DISC 187 |
| 40 GLOBAL HUNTER (IRE) 37 | 7 GO ON GAL (IRE) 38 | 168 GOLDEN DOVE 117 |
| 250 GLOBAL JACKPOT 31 | 485 GO ON MY COCKER 8 | 193 GOLDEN DRAGON (IRE) 12 |
| 365 GLOBAL MELODY 8 | 345 GO OSCAR GO (IRE) 45 | 395 GOLDEN EMBLEM (IRE) 34 |
| 164 GLOBAL MIRAGE 10 | 234 GO PHARISEE FLYER (FR) 26 | 309 GOLDEN FLAME (IRE) 85 |
| 164 GLOBAL PROSPECTOR (USA) 3 | 270 GO SACRE GO (FR) 80 | 193 GOLDEN FORCE 13 |
| 523 GLOBAL RESPONSE 20 | 492 GO STEADY 66 | 436 GOLDEN GAL (IRE) 26 |
| 164 GLOBAL ROMANCE (IRE) 11 | 205 GO TO COURT (IRE) 4 | 123 GOLDEN GLANCE 77 |
| 270 GLOBAL SOCIETY 77 | 387 GO WEST YOUNG LAD (IRE) 4 | 514 GOLDEN GLORY (IRE) 10 |
| 6 GLOBAL STORM (IRE) 9 | 227 GO WHATEVER (IRE) 19 | 582 GOLDEN GRENADE (FR) 30 |
| 93 GLOBAL STYLE (IRE) 34 | 460 GO YOGI (IRE) 4 | 514 GOLDEN GROVE (IRE) 5 |
| 164 GLOBAL TYCOON (IRE) 12 | 422 GOAHEADWITHTHEPLAN (IRE) 4 | 421 GOLDEN HIND 19 |
| 523 GLOBAL VISION (IRE) 21 | 532 GOAST DANCER (IRE) 28 | 102 GOLDEN LOVE 10 |
| 40 GLOBAL WALK (IRE) 38 | 57 GOD KNOWS (IRE) 5 | 256 GOLDEN LYRIC 98 |
| 164 GLOBAL WARNING 4 | 580 GOD KNOWS WHY (IRE) 8 | 51 GOLDEN MAC (IRE) 41 |
| 35 GLOBAL WONDER (IRE) 5 | 253 GOD OF THUNDER (IRE) 169 | 421 GOLDEN MELODY (IRE) 70 |
| 555 GLOBE PLAYER 32 | 474 GODDESS OF FIRE 3 | 385 GOLDEN NECTAR 5 |
| 180 GLOBE THEATRE (USA) 6 | 17 GODREVY POINT (FR) 8 | 431 GOLDEN PASS 8 |
| 65 GLOBETROTTER (IRE) 11 | 475 GOFREEZE 99 | 245 GOLDEN PEARL F 67 |
| 222 GLOCKENSPIEL (IRE) 43 | 344 GOING BACK TO CALI 44 | 77 GOLDEN POET (IRE) 2 |
| 246 GLOI 1 | 56 GOING GONE (IRE) 19 | 259 GOLDEN RIDGE (IRE) 24 |
| 568 GLORIANO (IRE) 10 | 372 GOING IN STYLE 96 | 501 GOLDEN ROBIN (IRE) 18 |
| 371 GLORIFICATION C 35 | 178 GOING MOBILE (IRE) 8 | 234 GOLDEN ROC (IRE) 27 |
| 599 GLORIFY (IRE) 4 | 586 GOING NATIVE 1 | 545 GOLDEN ROSIE (IRE) C 168 |
| 295 GLORIOUS BORU (IRE) 12 | 563 GOING PLACES 7 | 228 GOLDEN RULES 11 |
| 272 GLORIOUS CHARMER 9 | 189 GOING UNDERGROUND 12 | 300 GOLDEN SANDBANKS 13 |
| 6 GLORIOUS JOURNEY 10 | 195 GOINGTOCALIFORNIA (IRE) 13 | 309 GOLDEN SANDS 188 |
| 128 GLORIOUS LADY (IRE) 28 | 448 GOKOTTA (IRE) 15 | 105 GOLDEN SHEEN 69 |
| 434 GLORIOUS OSCAR (IRE) 30 | 86 GOLAN CLOUD (IRE) 19 | 449 GOLDEN SHOT 53 |
| 20 GLORIOUS RIO (IRE) 8 | 377 GOLAN FORTUNE (IRE) 2 | 276 GOLDEN SOVEREIGN (IRE) 41 |
| 461 GLORIOUS SPIRIT (IRE) 17 | 33 GOLAN RIVER (IRE) F 12 | 399 GOLDEN SPREAD 104 |
| 531 GLORY 3 | 7 GOLD BROCADE (IRE) 39 | 534 GOLDEN SUNRISE (IRE) 41 |
| 329 GLORY AND FORTUNE (IRE) 12 | 411 GOLD BULLION (FR) 75 | 418 GOLDEN TAIPAN (IRE) 59 |
| 243 GLORY AND GOLD 144 | 329 GOLD CLERMONT (FR) 14 | 383 GOLDEN TOWN (IRE) 6 |
| 329 GLORY AND HONOUR (IRE) 13 | 95 GOLD CLUB 11 | 245 GOLDEN TWILIGHT (IRE) 7 |

321 **GREENROCK ABBEY** (IRE) 39
87 **GREENSIDE** 7
308 **GREG THE GREAT** 63
165 **GREGARIOUS** (IRE) 5
492 **GREGOR** (FR) 68
375 **GREGORACI** (FR) C 52
160 **GRENADA** 20
485 **GRENADIER GUARD** (IRE) 9
278 **GRENADINE SAVE** (FR) 9
372 **GREY ANGEL** (IRE) 97
340 **GREY D'ARS** (FR) 6
527 **GREY DIAMOND** (FR) 11
115 **GREY EXPECTATIONS** 7
333 **GREY FOX** (IRE) 21
376 **GREY FRONTIERES** (IRE) 20
526 **GREY GALLEON** (USA) 11
549 **GREY MIST** 6
274 **GREY SPARKLE** (IRE) 42
402 **GREY SPIRIT** (IRE) 57
483 **GREY TIKKANA** 7
379 **GREYCIOUS GIRL** (IRE) 21
80 **GREYED FIRST** (IRE) 41
25 **GREYFIRE** 8
98 **GREYSTOKE** 46
419 **GRID** 80
16 **GRIFFIN PARK** 165
125 **GRIGGY** (IRE) 8
475 **GRIGORA** (FR) 57
408 **GRIMM STAR** (FR) 39
7 **GRIMSTHORPE CASTLE** 41
297 **GRIMTHORPE** 4
235 **GRIS DE PRON** (FR) 30
321 **GRISBI DE BERCE** (FR) 40
253 **GROOM** 171
580 **GROOM D'OUDAIRIES** (FR) 10
456 **GROOVEUR** (FR) 18
411 **GROOVY KIND** (FR) 80
321 **GROSVENOR COURT** 41
16 **GROUP ONE POWER** 16
23 **GROUP STAGE** (GER) 8
493 **GROUSEMAN** 11
16 **GROVE FERRY** 17
592 **GROW NASA GROW** (IRE) 4
390 **GROWL** 6
574 **GRUMPY BOOTS** (IRE) 21
286 **GRUMPY CHARLEY** 4
286 **GRUMPY FREYA** 5
128 **GRUMPY MCGRUMPFACE** (IRE) 31
330 **GUADAIZA** (FR) 39
371 **GUAJIRA** (IRE) F 36
333 **GUARD DUTY** 22
68 **GUARDIA SVIZZERA** (IRE) 4
264 **GUARDIA TOP** (FR) 19
434 **GUARDINO** (FR) 32
447 **GUATEMALA LE DUN** (FR) 10
253 **GUBBASS** (IRE) 172
276 **GUERNESEY** (FR) 43
343 **GUETAPAN COLLONGES** (FR) 17
386 **GUGUSS COLLONGES** (FR) 49
76 **GUILDED** (IRE) 102
4 **GUILDHALL** 7
97 **GUILTY PARTY** (IRE) 8
503 **GUINNESS AFFAIR** (FR) 23
256 **GUIRI** (GER) 28
253 **GUITAR** 173
461 **GUITAR PETE** (IRE) 18
167 **GULF OF POETS** 25

94 **GULLAND ROCK** 7
421 **GULLIVER** 20
424 **GULLIVER COLLONGES** (FR) 41
19 **GULSHANIGANS** 9
276 **GUMBALL** (FR) 44
568 **GUMBO FLYER** (FR) 12
574 **GUN CASE** 22
247 **GUN MERCHANT** 5
333 **GUNFLEET** (IRE) 23
25 **GUNMETAL** (IRE) 9
446 **GUNNER BAY** 20
538 **GUNNERSIDE** (IRE) 9
270 **GUNNERY** (FR) 85
581 **GUNS FOR HIRE** (IRE) 34
402 **GUNSIGHT RIDGE** 58
526 **GURKHA GIRL** (IRE) 30
363 **GURKHA'S SURPRISE** (IRE) 122
300 **GURKHALI GIRL** (IRE) 68
50 **GUROOR** 9
228 **GURU** 18
526 **GUSSY MAC** (IRE) 31
295 **GUSTAV** (IRE) 13
36 **GUSTAV GRAVES** 19
253 **GUSTAV HOLST** (IRE) 73
337 **GUSTAVE AITCH** (IRE) 14
285 **GUSTAVIAN** (IRE) 17
538 **GUVENOR'S CHOICE** (IRE) 10
534 **GUY DE GUYE** (FR) 42
483 **GWEEDORE** 8
391 **GWENHWYVAR** (IRE) 28
264 **GWENNOLINE** (FR) 20
16 **GYENYAME** 72
546 **GYLLEN** (USA) 32
492 **GYLO** (IRE) 69
204 **GYPSEY'S SECRET** (IRE) 5
316 **GYPSY BOY** (IRE) 22
345 **GYPSY DANCER** (IRE) 13
29 **GYPSY EYES** F 52
316 **GYPSY LADY** 28
70 **GYPSY STYLE** F 17
107 **GYPSY WHISPER** 5
399 **HA D'OR** (FR) 109
493 **HAAFAPIECE** 12
29 **HAARAR** 53
343 **HAAS BOY** (FR) 18
388 **HAASAB** (FR) 17
305 **HAB SAB** (IRE) 6
316 **HABANERO STAR** 9
50 **HABIT ROUGE** 10
86 **HACHERT** 20
175 **HACKBERRY** 20
439 **HACKBRIDGE** 7
411 **HACKER DES PLACES** (FR) 81
491 **HACKNESS HARRY** 41
317 **HADEED** 4
419 **HADMAN** (FR) 149
495 **HAGAR** (IRE) 21
527 **HAIDEES REFLECTION** F 42
228 **HAIJA** (FR) 79
254 **HAIL SEZER** 4
509 **HAIR OF GOLD** 19
415 **HAIRY ROCKET** C 138
319 **HAITI DANCER** F 10
537 **HAIZOOM** 21
549 **HAJEY** 7
14 **HAJJAM** 7
245 **HAKIMPOUR** (IRE) 39

263 **HALA HALA** (IRE) C 50
475 **HALA HALA HALA** (IRE) 58
419 **HALA JOUD** (IRE) 81
6 **HALAY** F 150
376 **HALCYON DAYS** 21
537 **HALCYON SPIRIT** 22
131 **HALDON HILL** 9
376 **HALF HANGIT MAGGIE** C 75
257 **HALF NELSON** 6
415 **HALFWAY TO HEAVEN** (IRE) C 139
540 **HALFWAYTOPARADISE** G 15
518 **HALIC** 50
328 **HALL HEE** (FR) C 32
151 **HALLO SIXTIES** 3
498 **HALLOWED GROUND** (IRE) 3
463 **HALLWOOD** (FR) 2
237 **HALTWHISTLE** 7
243 **HAMAKI** (IRE) 146
180 **HAMARON** (GER) 7
228 **HAMHAMA** (IRE) 80
13 **HAMILTON DICI** (FR) 26
270 **HAMILTON'S FANTASY** 86
485 **HAMMER GUN** (USA) 10
393 **HAMMY END** (FR) 6
545 **HAMOUDI** 76
256 **HAMWOOD FLIER** (IRE) 100
555 **HAN SOLO BERGER** (IRE) 11
105 **HANA LINA** C 70
43 **HANAFY** (USA) 6
6 **HAND PUPPET** (IRE) C 151
415 **HANDEL** (USA) 51
43 **HANDFUL OF GOLD** (IRE) 7
189 **HANDSOME** (IRE) 37
506 **HANDSOME SAMSON** 8
363 **HANDY HOLLOW** (IRE) 50
379 **HANDYTALK** (IRE) 4
333 **HANG IN THERE** (IRE) 24
424 **HANG TOUGH** 42
323 **HANGARD** 30
475 **HANIYA** 59
519 **HANNALITE** 13
435 **HANOVERIAN KING** (GER) 12
253 **HAPAP** (IRE) 174
309 **HAPPY** (IRE) 86
153 **HAPPY AND CONTENT** (IRE) 13
153 **HAPPY B** (IRE) 14
336 **HAPPY DIVA** (IRE) 10
86 **HAPPY HOLLOW** 21
239 **HAPPY NEWS** 2
16 **HAPPY POWER** (IRE) 18
253 **HAPPY ROMANCE** (IRE) 74
13 **HAPPYGOLUCKY** (IRE) 27
419 **HAPPYWIFEHAPPYLIFE** (IRE) 82
228 **HAQEEQY** (IRE) 13
399 **HARA KIRI** (FR) 110
321 **HARAMBE** 42
81 **HARAZ** (IRE) 6
395 **HARBOUR FORCE** (FR) 37
93 **HARBOUR PROJECT** 36
63 **HARBOUR STORM** 16
70 **HARBOUR VISION** 5
411 **HARD FROST** (FR) 82
126 **HARD GROUND** 15
437 **HARD NUT** (IRE) 3
421 **HARD SOLUTION** 21
168 **HARD TO FAULT** 118
427 **HARD TO FORGET** (IRE) 14

354 **HARD TO HANDEL** 4
2 **HARD TOFFEE** (IRE) 2
492 **HARDKORE** (FR) 70
487 **HARDY ARTICOS** (IRE) 6
434 **HARDY BOY** (FR) 33
227 **HAREFIELD** (IRE) 21
309 **HARLEM SOUL** 87
127 **HARLEQUIN** 1
159 **HARLEQUIN GIRL** F 54
97 **HARLEQUIN ROSE** (IRE) 9
115 **HARLEYS MAX** 8
582 **HARLOW** 31
145 **HARMONIOUS** 17
570 **HARMONISE** 10
132 **HARMONY LIL** (IRE) 31
506 **HAROLD SHAND** (IRE) 35
434 **HARPER'S BROOK** (IRE) 34
120 **HARPIST** (IRE) C 81
256 **HARPOCRATES** (IRE) 29
399 **HARRIE** (FR) 1
159 **HARRIER HAWK** 23
84 **HARRIS CHOICE** 41
563 **HARRISON POINT** (IRE) 9
115 **HARRISONS PROMISE** 9
378 **HARROGATE** (FR) 5
228 **HARROVIAN** 14
16 **HARROW** (FR) 166
321 **HARROWBY** 43
372 **HARRY ALONZO** (IRE) 36
250 **HARRY GO** 35
295 **HARRY HAZARD** 14
130 **HARRY HAZE** 3
436 **HARRY LOVE** (IRE) 3
568 **HARRY THE NORSEMAN** 13
5 **HARRY'S RIDGE** (IRE) 6
120 **HARRYANA TO** C 82
179 **HARSTON** 15
14 **HARSWELL DUCHESS** (IRE) 20
14 **HARSWELL DUKE** (IRE) 21
14 **HARSWELL PRINCE** 22
211 **HART FELL** 13
363 **HART OF STEEL** (IRE) 51
538 **HART STOPPER** 11
264 **HARTLAND QUAY** (IRE) 21
131 **HARTNOLL HERO** (IRE) 10
592 **HARTSIDE** (GER) 5
415 **HARVARD** (IRE) 52
167 **HARVEST DAY** 26
491 **HARVEST TIME** (IRE) 42
70 **HARWORTH** (IRE) 9
244 **HAS TROKE** (FR) 14
79 **HASANAAT** 19
582 **HASANABAD** (IRE) 32
388 **HASANKEY** (IRE) 18
321 **HASEEFAH** 44
428 **HASHTAG BE KIND** (IRE) 28
411 **HASHTAG BOUM** (FR) 83
428 **HASHTAGMETOO** (USA) 4
532 **HASTRUBAL** (FR) 29
274 **HASTY** (FR) C 88
518 **HASTY SAILOR** (IRE) 11
492 **HATCHER** (IRE) 71
271 **HATCHET JACK** (IRE) 11
235 **HATS OFF TO LARRY** 31
369 **HATTAAB** 30
270 **HAUL AWAY** (IRE) 87
473 **HAUL US IN** (IRE) 41

402 **HAURAKI GULF** 59
124 **HAUT BERRY** (FR) 6
399 **HAUT EN COULEURS** (FR) 112
473 **HAUTE ESTIME** (IRE) 42
218 **HAVACUPPA** 7
148 **HAVAGOMECCA** 46
518 **HAVAILA** (IRE) 105
297 **HAVANA BAY** 5
107 **HAVANA BOUND** 6
258 **HAVANA CABANA** 44
514 **HAVANA DAWN** 12
171 **HAVANA HERMANO** (IRE) 13
141 **HAVANA LADY** 16
300 **HAVANA PARTY** 49
214 **HAVANA QUEEN** 50
190 **HAVANA RIVER** (IRE) 23
257 **HAVANA SUNSET** 7
454 **HAVEN LADY** (IRE) 36
494 **HAVENVOUS** (FR) 6
80 **HAVEONEYERSELF** (IRE) 14
433 **HAVERGATE ISLAND** 5
300 **HAVEYOUMISSEDME** 50
375 **HAVRE DE PAIX** (FR) F 53
546 **HAWA BLADI** (IRE) 33
72 **HAWK GOLD** (IRE) 4
576 **HAWK IN THE SKY** 5
576 **HAWK IN THE WIND** 14
434 **HAWK WIND** (IRE) 35
333 **HAWK'S WELL** (IRE) 25
379 **HAWRIDGE FLYER** 5
379 **HAWRIDGE STORM** (IRE) 6
6 **HAWSA** (USA) C 152
400 **HAWTHORN COTTAGE** (IRE) 14
554 **HAY CHEWED** (IRE) C 82
26 **HAYADH** 5
228 **HAYKAL** 81
391 **HAYMAKER** 52
16 **HAYNES** 167
57 **HAYYEL** (IRE) 1
300 **HAZALOU** 51
321 **HAZARD COLLONGES** (FR) 45
105 **HAZARIYA** (FR) F 31
417 **HAZEL** (IRE) 10
424 **HAZEL BANK LASS** (IRE) F 43
508 **HAZEL BLUE** (IRE) F 18
245 **HAZIYA** (IRE) 40
224 **HAZMAT** (IRE) 12
150 **HAZY DREAM** 14
329 **HAZZAAR** (IRE) 15
324 **HE CAN DANCE** (IRE) 19
71 **HE IS A CRACKER** (IRE) 3
326 **HE'S A DREAM** 31
335 **HE'S A GOER** (IRE) 4
132 **HE'S A KEEPER** (IRE) 7
568 **HE'S A KNOWALL** (IRE) 14
386 **HE'S A LATCHICO** (IRE) 128
7 **HE'S A LEGEND** 42
212 **HE'S GOT THE LOT** (FR) 22
207 **HE'S GUILTY** (USA) 3
198 **HE'S MAGIC** 2
93 **HE'S OUR STAR** (IRE) 37
282 **HEAD HIGH** (IRE) 10
547 **HEAD LAD** (FR) 6
582 **HEAD ON** (IRE) 33
309 **HEADINGLEY** (IRE) 88
145 **HEADLAND** 18
149 **HEADLEY GEORGE** (IRE) 9

523 **HEADLINER** (IRE) 22
446 **HEADORA** 21
461 **HEADSCARF LIL** (IRE) 19
7 **HEADSHOT** 99
214 **HEALING POWER** 22
128 **HEAR ME OUT** (IRE) 32
148 **HEAR ME ROAR** (IRE) 47
260 **HEAR THE CHIMES** 5
189 **HEAR THE MUSIC** (IRE) 38
93 **HEART OF A HUNTER** (FR) 38
321 **HEART OF A LION** (IRE) 46
221 **HEART OF AN ANGEL** F 16
264 **HEART OF KERNOW** (IRE) 22
390 **HEART OF SOUL** (IRE) 7
491 **HEART OF THE SUN** 43
495 **HEART THROB** 20
309 **HEART'S CONTENT** (IRE) F 189
214 **HEART'S DESIRE** (IRE) F 67
363 **HEARTBREAK KID** (IRE) 52
87 **HEARTBREAK LASS** 39
29 **HEARTBREAKER** 2
348 **HEARTSTAR** 6
449 **HEAT AND DUST** 19
102 **HEAT OF THE MOMENT** 28
491 **HEATH RISE** 44
29 **HEATHERDOWN HERO** 54
29 **HEATHERDOWN MATRON** 22
195 **HEATON CHAPEL** (IRE) 6
2 **HEAVEN FORFEND** 1
95 **HEAVEN'S BILL** (IRE) 21
328 **HEAVEN'S SAKE** F 33
418 **HEAVENLY PROMISE** (IRE) 64
50 **HEAVENLY ROSE** 4
133 **HEAVENLY TALE** (IRE) 11
76 **HEAVENLY VERSE** C 103
395 **HEAVEY** 38
415 **HECTOR DE MARIS** (IRE) 53
584 **HECTOR DE SIVOLA** (FR) 13
149 **HECTOR LOZA** 10
473 **HECTOR MASTER** (FR) 43
555 **HECTOR'S GIRL** C 33
214 **HECTOR'S HERE** 23
79 **HEDAAYA** (IRE) C 54
239 **HEDGEBIRD** 7
514 **HEDGEINATOR** (IRE) 13
308 **HEDGING** (IRE) 9
401 **HEED MY ADVICE** 15
180 **HEER WE GO AGAIN** 8
539 **HEERS HARRY** 31
481 **HEHO** C 43
475 **HEIGHT OF VANITY** (IRE) F 102
128 **HEIGHTS OF ABRAHAM** (IRE) 87
372 **HEISENBERG** (IRE) 37
280 **HELETA** 7
534 **HELFORD RIVER** 43
164 **HELIAN** (IRE) 5
584 **HELIOS ALLEN** (FR) 14
527 **HELIOS DE GRUGY** (FR) 12
344 **HELIX** 14
256 **HELL BENT** (IRE) 101
347 **HELL OF A YEAR** (FR) 5
372 **HELL OR HIGH WATER** (IRE) 38
411 **HELL RED** (FR) 84
446 **HELLAVAPACE** 22
566 **HELLFIRE KODE** 4
336 **HELLFIRE PRINCESS** 11
153 **HELLO BOB** 15

330 **HIT** (IRE) 40
275 **HIT THE BEAT** 4
287 **HIT THE BOTTLE** 4
523 **HIT THE HEIGHTS** (IRE) 23
386 **HIT THE ROCKS** (IRE) 52
458 **HITDROADJACK** (IRE) 8
27 **HITHER** 101
411 **HITMAN** (FR) 87
146 **HITMAN FRED** (IRE) 18
227 **HIWAY ONE O THREE** (IRE) 24
55 **HIYA MAITE** 10
308 **HMS PRESIDENT** (IRE) 10
415 **HMS SEAHORSE** (IRE) 56
270 **HOB HOUSE** (FR) 91
395 **HOBB'S DELIGHT** 41
419 **HOBSONS BAY** (IRE) 83
309 **HOCHFELD** (IRE) 13
245 **HODD'S GIRL** (IRE) 9
402 **HOGAN** (IRE) 64
419 **HOGAN'S HEIGHT** (IRE) 24
333 **HOI POLLOI** (IRE) 27
253 **HOKKAIDO** (IRE) 176
263 **HOKU** (IRE) C 51
93 **HOLBACHE** 97
182 **HOLD COURT** (IRE) 2
419 **HOLD ME NOW** (USA) C 150
242 **HOLD ME TIGHT** (IRE) 7
588 **HOLD THAT TAUGHT** 44
98 **HOLD THE NOTE** (IRE) 15
319 **HOLDA** (IRE) C 12
581 **HOLDBACKTHERIVER** (IRE) 35
540 **HOLDENHURST** 4
411 **HOLETOWN HERO** (FR) 88
19 **HOLIDAY MAGIC** (IRE) 7
587 **HOLLEY SHIFTWELL** F 39
573 **HOLLOW STYLE** (IRE) 3
509 **HOLLOW TALK** (IRE) 4
581 **HOLLY JAMES** 36
13 **HOLLYMOUNT HOLLY** (IRE) 30
136 **HOLLYWOOD BLACK** (FR) 7
486 **HOLLYWOOD KEN** (IRE) 2
27 **HOLLYWOOD LADY** 46
522 **HOLLYWOODIEN** (FR) 13
243 **HOLOCENE** 148
240 **HOLWAH** 18
29 **HOLY BEE** (IRE) 23
419 **HOLY CAT** (IRE) C 151
263 **HOLY CHALICE** 39
161 **HOLY GUNNER** 15
415 **HOLY MOON** (IRE) C 140
251 **HOLY NORMA** F 14
18 **HOLY TIBER** (IRE) 6
161 **HOLY VEIL** F 41
309 **HOME AND DRY** (IRE) 89
128 **HOME BEFORE DUSK** 35
419 **HOME BY THE LEE** (IRE) 31
444 **HOME FARM HOUSE** (IRE) 32
461 **HOME FIRE** 20
325 **HOME MADE WINE** 7
545 **HOMECOMING QUEEN** (IRE) C 169
474 **HOMEGROWNALLIGATOR** 5
419 **HOMEPAGE** C 152
171 **HOMETOWN BOY** (IRE) 16
105 **HOMILY** C 71
369 **HOMING STAR** 33
235 **HOMME PUBLIC** (FR) 33
354 **HONCHO** (IRE) 5

575 **HONDA FIFTY** (IRE) 10
534 **HONEST EXCHANGE** (IRE) 45
295 **HONEST OSCAR** (IRE) 15
141 **HONEY BOO** 6
391 **HONEY POT** (IRE) 30
76 **HONEY SWEET** (IRE) 105
15 **HONEYSUCKLE MOON** 16
63 **HONG KONG FURY** (IRE) 49
246 **HONKY TONK MAN** (IRE) 72
583 **HONNEUR D'AJONC** (FR) 12
363 **HONNOLD** 56
434 **HONOR GREY** (IRE) 36
276 **HONORARY COLONEL** (IRE) 45
290 **HONORINE** (FR) C 53
15 **HONORLINA** (FR) F 39
146 **HONOURABLE GENT** 19
185 **HONOURARY GIFT** (IRE) 22
160 **HONOURS** 8
16 **HOO YA MAL** 169
167 **HOOFS HAPPY NOW** 55
399 **HOOK UP** (FR) 114
222 **HOOLIGAN** (IRE) 45
270 **HOOPER** 92
131 **HOOPER'S LEGEND** 11
128 **HOOPMALASSIE** (USA) 36
87 **HOORAY HENRY** 8
109 **HOORNBLOWER** 1
402 **HOOROO** (IRE) 65
343 **HOT AT MIDNIGHT** 20
93 **HOOVES LIKE JAGGER** (IRE) 98
421 **HOPE AGAINST HOPE** (IRE) C 119
421 **HOPE OF LIFE** (IRE) 72
454 **HOPE PROBE** (IRE) 37
56 **HOPE SPRINGS** 20
276 **HOPE YOU DO** (FR) 46
499 **HOPEFULL** 15
399 **HOPEFULLY** (IRE) 115
107 **HOPISSIME** (FR) 19
436 **HORACE GREASLEY** (IRE) 13
235 **HORACIO APPLE'S** (FR) 34
584 **HORATIO HORNBLOWER** (IRE) 15
484 **HORIZON BLEU** (FR) 17
492 **HORIZON D'AINAY** (FR) 73
270 **HORN CAPE** (FR) 93
16 **HORN OF PLENTY** 19
10 **HORNBY** 17
415 **HOROSCOPE** (IRE) 57
17 **HORS GUARD** (FR) 9
418 **HORSE POWER** (FR) 65
29 **HORSEFLY** (IRE) 24
421 **HORTZADAR** 22
253 **HOST** (IRE) 75
91 **HOSTELRY** 12
321 **HOSTILE** 48
296 **HOT CHESNUT** 25
387 **HOT DAY** 10
539 **HOT DIVA** 20
478 **HOT GOSSIP** (IRE) 5
93 **HOT HOT HOT** 40
162 **HOT MADRAS** (IRE) 2
119 **HOT PROPERTY** (USA) G 12
568 **HOT REPLY** F 39
286 **HOT RHYTHM** G 16
428 **HOT RYAN** 6
516 **HOT SCOOP** 29
553 **HOT SECRET** C 12
**HOT SMOKED** 14

345 **HOT SUMMER** 14
287 **HOT TO TROT** 5
576 **HOT WIRED** G 15
421 **HOT WOOD** 12
180 **HOTALENA** 29
283 **HOTCITY** 4
529 **HOTELMIKEPAPA** 1
253 **HOTLINE BLING** (IRE) 177
170 **HOTSPUR HARRY** (IRE) 6
421 **HOTTER IN TIME** 121
321 **HOTTER THAN HELL** (FR) 49
140 **HOUI CHERIE** (FR) 8
540 **HOUND MUSIC** G 17
568 **HOUSE ISLAND** (IRE) 17
431 **HOUSE POINT** C 63
110 **HOUSEHOLD NAME** F 37
355 **HOUSTON BERE** (FR) 8
574 **HOUSTON TEXAS** (IRE) 23
411 **HOUX GRIS** (FR) 89
371 **HOVER** (IRE) 5
475 **HOW** (IRE) F 103
14 **HOW BIZARRE** 8
569 **HOW FORTUNATE** F 53
190 **HOW'S THE CRICKET** (IRE) 24
131 **HOWARDIAN HILLS** (IRE) 12
503 **HOWDILYOUDO** (IRE) 25
153 **HOWLING MILAN** (IRE) 11
285 **HOWLINGMADMURDOCK** (IRE) 19
12 **HOWYA HUN** (IRE) 10
4 **HOWYOUPLAYTHEGAME** (FR) 8
63 **HOWZAK** 50
250 **HOWZAT HIRIS** (FR) 37
128 **HOWZER BLACK** (IRE) 37
371 **HOYAM** C 37
324 **HTILOMINLO** 5
475 **HUBOOR** (IRE) 9
391 **HUDDLETON MAC** (IRE) 31
386 **HUDSON DE GRUGY** (FR) 53
503 **HUDSON YARD** (IRE) 26
411 **HUELGOAT** (FR) 90
330 **HUETOR** (FR) 4
444 **HUGO 'N TAZ** 33
96 **HUGO'S REFLECTION** (IRE) 13
411 **HUGOS NEW HORSE** (FR) 91
411 **HUGOS OTHER HORSE** 92
526 **HUGOSTHERE** 32
79 **HUKUM** (IRE) 6
418 **HULLNBACK** 66
301 **HUMAN ACTION** 16
228 **HUMANITARIAN** (USA) 15
135 **HUME LOUGH** 9
63 **HUNDON** 51
98 **HUNDRED ISLES** (IRE) 16
574 **HUNGRY HELEN HIPPO** 24
424 **HUNGRY HILL** (IRE) 47
12 **HUNKY** (FR) 11
108 **HUNNI** 8
418 **HUNNY MOON** 67
588 **HUNTER LEGEND** (FR) 45
400 **HUNTER'S DAWN** 15
402 **HUNTERS CALL** (IRE) 66
508 **HUNTERS STEP** 4
316 **HUNTERS STEP** 10
333 **HUNTING BROOK** (IRE) 28
329 **HUNTING PERCIVAL** 17
244 **HUNTSMAN SON** (IRE) 16
376 **HUNTSMAN'S CALL** (IRE) 22

418 **HUNTSMANS JOG** (IRE) 68
49 **HURCLE** (IRE) 5
270 **HURLING MAGIC** (IRE) 94
42 **HURRICANE ALERT** 4
348 **HURRICANE ALI** (IRE) 8
45 **HURRICANE ARCADIO** (IRE) 6
548 **HURRICANE BAY** 15
527 **HURRICANE DEAL** (FR) 14
515 **HURRICANE DYLAN** (IRE) 2
418 **HURRICANE HARVEY** 69
379 **HURRICANE HELEN** 22
547 **HURRICANE HERO** (FR) 7
243 **HURRICANE IVOR** (IRE) 7
6 **HURRICANE LANE** (IRE) 56
270 **HURRICANE LE DUN** (FR) 95
212 **HURRICANE MITCH** (IRE) 23
584 **HURRICANE SIVOLA** (IRE) 16
8 **HURRICANE VIC** 3
243 **HURRY UP HEDLEY** (IRE) 149
413 **HURSTWOOD** 4
123 **HUSHING** F 78
165 **HY BRASIL** (IRE) 6
505 **HY EALES** (IRE) 5
11 **HYACINTH** (IRE) 2
308 **HYANNA** 11
119 **HYBA** 12
399 **HYBERY** (FR) 116
578 **HYDE PARK BARRACKS** (USA) 18
582 **HYDROPLANE** (IRE) 34
518 **HYDROS** 13
395 **HYGROVE PERCY** 42
270 **HYLAND** (FR) 96
372 **HYMIE WEISS** 43
486 **HYMN AND A PRAYER** 3
419 **HYPE** (IRE) 84
431 **HYPER DREAM** (FR) C 64
168 **HYPERFOCUS** (IRE) 43
274 **HYPHAEMA** (IRE) F 89
330 **HYPOCONDRIAC** (FR) 16
330 **HYPOTENUS** 41
522 **HYSTERY BERE** (FR) 14
378 **I AM A DREAMER** 6
270 **I AM MAXIMUS** (FR) 97
199 **I AM PLASTERED** 9
102 **I AM THE SECRET** (SAF) 11
275 **I AM WILD** 5
13 **I CAN'T EXPLAIN** (IRE) 31
128 **I CAN'T REMEMBER** (IRE) 38
300 **I GOT RHYTHM** G 14
283 **I HAD A DREAM** 5
322 **I HOPE STAR** (IRE) 18
501 **I JUST KNOW** (IRE) 20
402 **I K BRUNEL** 67
84 **I KNOW HOW** (IRE) 10
398 **I SEE YOU WELL** (FR) 8
13 **I SPY A DIVA** 32
31 **I'LL BE GOOD** 4
16 **I'LL BE THERE** 170
499 **I'LL HAVE IT** (IRE) G 16
309 **I'M A GAMBLER** (IRE) 190
463 **I'M A STARMAN** 3
587 **I'M AVAILABLE** (IRE) 15
216 **I'M DIGBY** (IRE) 9
59 **I'M HERE** (IRE) 5
310 **I'M NOTAPARTYGIRL** 3
156 **I'M SHEIKRA** (IRE) C 1
156 **I'M SHEIKRA** (IRE) C 16

408 **I'M SO BUSY** 41
434 **I'M SPELLBOUND** (IRE) 37
584 **I'M THE DIVA** (FR) 24
128 **I'M TO BLAME** (IRE) 39
259 **I'M WATCHING YOU** 8
325 **IBERIO** (GER) 8
278 **IBIS DU RHEU** (FR) 10
274 **IBIZA ROCKS** 43
588 **IBLEO** (FR) 46
82 **IBN AL EMARAT** (IRE) 3
274 **IBN ALDAR** 90
481 **IBN ARABI** (IRE) 19
530 **ICE AGE** (IRE) 4
211 **ICE CANYON** 15
336 **ICE COOL CHAMPS** (IRE) 13
243 **ICE HOUSE** 150
168 **ICE MAYDEN** C 160
217 **ICE PALACE** G 1
580 **ICE PIGEON** (IRE) 11
323 **ICE PYRAMID** (IRE) 32
354 **ICE ROYAL** (IRE) 6
436 **ICE SHADOW** (IRE) 27
27 **ICE STATION ZEBRA** 14
446 **ICKYTOO** 43
323 **ICONIC BELLE** 33
132 **ICONIC CHOICE** 8
299 **ICONIC FIGURE** (IRE) 4
250 **ICONIC HERO** (IRE) 38
554 **ICONIC KNIGHT** (IRE) 18
439 **ICONIC MOVER** 5
386 **ICONIC MUDDLE** 54
27 **ICONIC QUEEN** 47
548 **ICONIC SKY** 16
421 **ICONICDAAY** 122
193 **ICONIQUE** 42
16 **ICY LADY** 171
243 **ICYKEL** (IRE) 151
372 **IDAS BOY** (IRE) 44
541 **IDEAL CANDY** (IRE) 4
76 **IDEALIST** C 106
471 **IDIDITFORYOOOO** (IRE) 10
411 **IDIDNTFORGET** 93
323 **IDILICO** (FR) 34
36 **IDOAPOLOGISE** 5
243 **IDOL** 61
59 **IDOL'S EYE** (FR) 6
258 **IF KARL'S BERG DID** 11
212 **IF THE CAP FITS** (IRE) 24
309 **IF YOU DARE** 90
130 **IFANDABUT** (IRE) 4
76 **IFFRAJA** (FR) C 107
372 **IFICUDIWUD** (IRE) 45
120 **IGHRAA** (IRE) C 83
289 **IGNIGHT** 6
270 **IGOR** 82
563 **IGOTATEXT** (IRE) 35
417 **IGRAINE** (IRE) 11
330 **IKATA** (IRE) 42
217 **IKIGAI** 2
274 **IL BANDITO** (IRE) 44
386 **IL RE DI NESSUNO** (FR) 55
243 **ILARAAB** (IRE) 15
250 **ILAYA** (FR) 39
538 **ILE DE BREHAT** 12
256 **ILE DE CIRCE** (IRE) 169
50 **ILE FLOTTANTE** C 81
351 **ILEACH MATHAN** (IRE) 26

583 **ILFONCE** (FR) 19
93 **ILHABELA FACT** 41
343 **ILLEGAL MODEL** (IRE) 21
400 **ILLEGALLY BLONDE** (IRE) C 47
569 **ILLEGITIMATE GAINS** 14
159 **ILLICO** C 56
274 **ILLIES MEMORIES** (IRE) 45
384 **ILLUMINATING DREAM** (IRE) F 28
538 **ILLUSIONIST** (GER) 13
245 **ILLUSORY** (IRE) 10
523 **ILLUSTRATOR** 24
301 **ILLUZZI** (IRE) 17
98 **ILLYKATO** 48
256 **ILMIG** (IRE) 30
518 **ILTEMAS** (USA) C 106
123 **ILZA'EEM** (IRE) 44
107 **IMAGE INEXPLICABLE** 20
314 **IMAGE OF THE MOON** 6
415 **IMAGINE** (IRE) F 141
323 **IMAJORBLUSH** 35
419 **IMALWAYSHOTFORYOU** (USA) C 153
108 **IMASUMAQ** (IRE) F 38
132 **IMELDA MAYHEM** F 59
309 **IMMACULATE** 91
123 **IMMELMANN** (GER) 25
329 **IMMORTAL FAME** (IRE) 18
415 **IMMORTAL VERSE** (IRE) F 142
305 **IMPACOBLE** 18
256 **IMPACT FACTOR** (IRE) 31
523 **IMPALA** C 65
385 **IMPART** 6
491 **IMPASSE** C 79
256 **IMPEACHD ALEXANDER** (IRE) 170
168 **IMPELLER** 119
418 **IMPERIAL ALCAZAR** (IRE) 70
13 **IMPERIAL AURA** (IRE) 33
345 **IMPERIAL COMMAND** (IRE) 15
110 **IMPERIAL DAWN** 25
421 **IMPERIAL EIGHT** (IRE) 73
418 **IMPERIAL ELYSIAN** (IRE) 71
212 **IMPERIAL ESPRIT** (IRE) 25
581 **IMPERIAL FLEM** (IRE) 37
566 **IMPERIAL FOCUS** (IRE) 5
16 **IMPERIAL FORCE** (IRE) 76
488 **IMPERIAL HOPE** (IRE) 17
522 **IMPERIAL HURLEY** (IRE) 15
13 **IMPERIAL ICON** (IRE) 34
434 **IMPERIAL KNIGHT** (IRE) 38
157 **IMPERIAL PRINCE** (IRE) 4
563 **IMPERIAL SANDS** (IRE) 36
418 **IMPERIAL STORM** (IRE) 72
228 **IMPERIAL SUN** 83
545 **IMPERIAL YELLOW** (IRE) 78
340 **IMPERIL** (FR) 7
105 **IMPERIUM** (IRE) 6
533 **IMPERIUM BLUE** 32
386 **IMPHAL** 56
330 **IMPITOYABLE** (FR) 43
6 **IMPORTANT TIME** (IRE) C 154
401 **IMPRESSIBLE** F 20
344 **IMPRESSIONIST ART** (USA) C 57
120 **IMPRESSIONS DREAM** 29
306 **IMPRESSIVE VICTORY** (USA) G 16
353 **IMPRESSOR** (IRE) 4
29 **IMPROVISE** (FR) 55
295 **IMPULSIVE LEADER** (IRE) 16
243 **IMPULSIVE ONE** (USA) 62

419 **IRWIN** (IRE) 85
411 **ISAAC DES OBEAUX** (FR) 197
484 **ISAAC WONDER** (IRE) 18
120 **ISABELLA GILES** (IRE) 31
589 **ISABELLA RUBY** 9
120 **ISABELLA SWAN** 32
120 **ISAKOVA** 87
386 **ISAYALITTLEPRAYER** 58
189 **ISCHIA** 62
300 **ISHEBAYORGREY** (IRE) 15
212 **ISHKHARA LADY** 27
119 **ISHVARA** 13
501 **ISKABEG LANE** (IRE) 22
109 **ISKAHEEN** (IRE) 18
238 **ISKRABOB** 4
199 **ISLA DI MILANO** (IRE) 10
533 **ISLA KAI** (IRE) 33
180 **ISLA VISTA** 59
386 **ISLA'S DREAM** (IRE) 59
351 **ISLAND BANDIT** 27
386 **ISLAND BRAVE** (IRE) 5
167 **ISLAND MAGIC** G 97
257 **ISLAND MEMORY** 8
402 **ISLAND NATION** (IRE) 68
354 **ISLAND SONG** (IRE) 7
351 **ISLAND STORM** (IRE) 6
546 **ISLE OF ARON** 34
103 **ISLE OF LIGHT** 10
119 **ISLE OF LISMORE** (IRE) 25
234 **ISLE OF RONA** 33
419 **ISLE OF SARK** (USA) 86
37 **ISLE OF WOLVES** 4
241 **ISNTSHESOMETHING** 7
231 **ISOBEL BLEU** 2
189 **ISOLA ROSSA** 40
321 **ISOLATE** (FR) 51
58 **ISOSCELES** (IRE) 8
491 **ISPAHAN** 11
6 **ISPOLINI** 11
444 **ISRAEL CHAMP** (IRE) 36
428 **ISRAFEL** C 57
252 **ISTHEBAROPEN** 12
248 **ISTIMRAAR** (IRE) 4
588 **ISTORIUS** (FR) 47
143 **IT FITZ** 8
189 **IT GIRL** 41
533 **IT JUST TAKES TIME** (IRE) 34
7 **IT MUST BE FAITH** 44
270 **IT SURE IS** (IRE) 100
383 **IT'S A LILY** 8
180 **IT'S A LOVE THING** 31
485 **IT'S A SIN** 11
136 **IT'S FOR ALAN** 8
62 **IT'S FOR YOU MUM** (FR) 30
386 **IT'S GOT LEGS** (IRE) 60
505 **IT'S HOW WE ROLL** (IRE) 6
571 **IT'S JUST TOMMY** (IRE) 9
402 **IT'S O KAY** 69
93 **IT'S WONDERFUL** (FR) 42
118 **IT'S YOUR MOVE** (IRE) 3
420 **ITALIAN BREEZE** 30
270 **ITALIAN LEGEND** (IRE) 101
402 **ITALIAN SPIRIT** (IRE) 70
270 **ITALIAN SUMMER** 102
402 **ITCHY FEET** (FR) 71
79 **ITKAANN** (IRE) 7
167 **ITOJEH** 28

473 **ITS A MIDNIGHT** 44
485 **ITS ALL CLOVER NOW** (IRE) 12
406 **ITSABOUTIME** (IRE) 2
199 **ITSALLABOUTLUCK** (IRE) 11
450 **ITSAMANSLIFE** (IRE) 8
533 **ITSGOODTOBEUS** (IRE) 52
253 **ITSINTHESTARS** C 181
223 **ITSNOTWHATYOUTHINK** (IRE) 12
22 **ITSNOTYOUITSME** 14
227 **ITSONLYROCKNROLL** (IRE) 26
421 **IUR CINN TRA** (IRE) 123
520 **IVA REFLECTION** (IRE) 4
105 **IVADREAM** 7
568 **IVAHUNCH** 20
506 **IVAN DRAGO** 37
149 **IVAQUESTION** (IRE) 11
80 **IVASECRET** (IRE) 42
110 **IVATHEENGINE** (IRE) 9
355 **IVILNOBLE** (IRE) 9
297 **IVORS INVOLVEMENT** (IRE) 6
509 **IVY ROCK** 20
527 **IVY'S SHADOW** (IRE) 15
193 **IVYNATOR** (IRE) 44
168 **IWASTHEFUTUREONCE** (IRE) 44
527 **IWILLDOIT** 14
330 **IZNAJAR** 17
473 **IZZY'S CHAMPION** (IRE) 45
442 **J GAYE** (IRE) 10
78 **J POWERS FORGE** (IRE) 4
378 **J R CAVAGIN** (IRE) 34
179 **J'ADORE** (IRE) 32
388 **J'AI FROID** (IRE) 20
563 **JAARIYAH** (USA) 11
5 **JABBAROCKIE** 1
321 **JABOTICABA** (FR) 52
527 **JABULANI** (FR) 17
246 **JAC BROWN** 2
258 **JACAMAR** (GER) 12
15 **JACARANDA LADY** (USA) 33
5 **JACARANDA RIDGE** G 14
76 **JACATTACK** (IRE) 46
449 **JACK BEAN** 20
554 **JACK D'OR** 19
92 **JACK DANIEL** (IRE) 16
110 **JACK DARCY** (IRE) 38
146 **JACK DEVINE** (IRE) 20
419 **JACK DILLINGER** (IRE) 32
396 **JACK IS BACK** 3
228 **JACK KENNEDY** 86
281 **JACK LAMB** 5
87 **JACK LESLIE** 41
47 **JACK OF ALL SHAPES** (IRE) 10
474 **JACK RYAN** (IRE) 6
456 **JACK SHARP** (IRE) 22
266 **JACK SNIPE** 6
598 **JACK THE FARMER** 15
481 **JACK THE TRUTH** (IRE) 3
355 **JACK THUNDER** (IRE) 10
588 **JACK VALENTINE** (IRE) 48
113 **JACK YEATS** (IRE) 1
310 **JACK'S A LEGEND** 4
108 **JACK'S POINT** 9
92 **JACKAMUNDO** (FR) 4
257 **JACKIE IS BACK** (FR) 9
160 **JACKFINBAR** (FR) 3
478 **JACKHAMMER** (IRE) 7
299 **JACKMAN** 5

367 **JACKOFHEARTS** 6
258 **JACKSON HILL** (IRE) 13
353 **JACKSONIAN** 5
345 **JACKSTAR** (IRE) 17
230 **JACQANINA** 12
6 **JACQUELINE QUEST** (IRE) C 160
123 **JADANNA** (IRE) C 108
123 **JADOOMI** (FR) 26
274 **JADWAL** 81
569 **JAFFATHEGAFFA** 37
183 **JAGANORY** (IRE) 4
59 **JAISALMER** (IRE) 7
92 **JAKACAN** (IRE) 17
59 **JAKAMANI** 8
519 **JALINGO** (IRE) 53
386 **JALWAN** (USA) 61
343 **JAMACHO** 22
399 **JAMES DU BERLAIS** (FR) 117
195 **JAMES PARK WOODS** (IRE) 8
378 **JAMES WATT** (IRE) 8
400 **JAMESSAINTPATRICK** (IRE) 16
297 **JAMIH** 7
297 **JAMIL** (IRE) 8
101 **JAMILYA** (FR) 11
545 **JAMMRAH** 35
90 **JAMMY RUGGER** 13
302 **JAMPOT EDDIE** 5
297 **JAN DE HEEM** 9
472 **JAN VAN HOOF** (IRE) 10
402 **JAN WELLENS** 72
266 **JANESPRICELESS** 7
552 **JANEYMAC** (IRE) 5
399 **JANIDIL** (FR) 118
98 **JANIE JONES** 49
270 **JANIKA** (FR) 103
123 **JANNATTAN** (USA) F 79
552 **JANTE LAW** 18
107 **JANULIS** (FR) 21
258 **JANUS** (IRE) 14
415 **JAPAN** 5
238 **JAPPELOUP** (IRE) 5
545 **JARAMILLO** 81
398 **JARLATH** 10
418 **JARVEYS PLATE** (IRE) 73
123 **JARWAH** (IRE) 27
123 **JASH** (IRE) 7
391 **JASMENO** F 61
256 **JASMINE BLUE** (IRE) F 173
189 **JASMINE JOY** (IRE) 42
63 **JASMINE ROYALE** C 59
185 **JASSAS** (IRE) 23
169 **JAUNTY EXPRESS** 1
169 **JAUNTY FREYJA** 2
395 **JAUNTY SORIA** 45
169 **JAUNTY VIKING** 3
169 **JAUNTY WALK** F 4
13 **JAVA POINT** (IRE) 36
410 **JAWAAYIZ** F 13
79 **JAWHARY** 20
582 **JAWSHAN** (USA) 36
148 **JAWWAAL** 17
335 **JAXLIGHT** 6
321 **JAY BEE WHY** (IRE) 53
492 **JAY JAY REILLY** (IRE) 75
501 **JAYAAAH** (IRE) 23
568 **JAYCEEBEE** 21
450 **JAYCOLS STAR** 9

54 **KING FRANK** 1
309 **KING FRANKEL** (IRE) 95
307 **KING GOLAN** (IRE) 6
235 **KING GYPSY** (IRE) 37
228 **KING LEONIDAS** 17
137 **KING LEWLEW** 3
465 **KING MURO** 5
391 **KING OF CLUBS** 32
256 **KING OF COMEDY** (IRE) 35
157 **KING OF FASHION** (IRE) 6
243 **KING OF ICE** 156
582 **KING OF REALMS** (IRE) 40
119 **KING OF SPEED** (IRE) 40
7 **KING OF STARS** (IRE) 49
415 **KING OF THE CASTLE** (IRE) 65
308 **KING OF THE DANCE** (IRE) 64
295 **KING OF THE SHARKS** (IRE) 18
326 **KING OF THE SOUTH** (IRE) 12
6 **KING OF TOMORROW** 58
421 **KING OF TONGA** (IRE) 25
105 **KING OF TSAVO** 36
475 **KING OF YORK** (IRE) 106
218 **KING ORRY** (IRE) 10
193 **KING OTTOKAR** (FR) 17
569 **KING RAJ** 16
557 **KING ROBERT** 11
212 **KING ROLAND** (IRE) 31
50 **KING TIGER** 47
545 **KING TRITON** (IRE) 85
16 **KING VEGA** 78
175 **KING VIKTOR** 63
309 **KING ZAIN** (IRE) 96
309 **KING'S ADVICE** 15
539 **KING'S CASTLE** (IRE) 8
421 **KING'S COMMANDER** (FR) 75
393 **KING'S COURSE** (IRE) 24
31 **KING'S GUEST** (IRE) F 10
253 **KING'S GUEST** (IRE) C 182
107 **KING'S HARLEQUIN** (IRE) 22
274 **KING'S KNIGHT** (IRE) 15
16 **KING'S LYNN** 2
308 **KING'S MIRACLE** (IRE) C 65
581 **KING'S ODYSSEY** (IRE) 40
258 **KING'S PROCTOR** (IRE) 16
444 **KING'S SOCKS** (FR) 38
333 **KING'S THRESHOLD** (IRE) 33
532 **KING'S WHARF** (IRE) 31
582 **KINGBROOK** 41
264 **KINGCORMAC** (IRE) 28
189 **KINGDOM FOUND** (IRE) 44
526 **KINGHENRYTHENINTH** 34
198 **KINGI COMPTON** 3
555 **KINGMANIA** (IRE) 21
545 **KINGMAX** (IRE) 173
342 **KINGMON'S BOY** 3
323 **KINGS CAVE** (IRE) 39
300 **KINGS CREEK** (IRE) 17
590 **KINGS ECLIPSE** (IRE) 2
223 **KINGS KRACKERTARA** 15
336 **KINGS MONARCH** 14
349 **KINGS OWN** 1
309 **KINGS PRINCE** 97
96 **KINGS TEMPTATION** 16
534 **KINGS WALK** (IRE) 52
444 **KINGSFORT HILL** 39
189 **KINGSHOLM** (IRE) 14
80 **KINGSLEY KLARION** (IRE) 19

154 **KINGSMILL GIN** 5
154 **KINGSMILL LAKE** M 6
16 **KINGSOFTHEMIDLANDS** (FR) 79
491 **KINGSTON JOY** (IRE) 81
458 **KINGSTON KING** (IRE) 11
10 **KINGSTON KURRAJONG** 20
224 **KINGSTON MIMOSA** 5
87 **KINGSTON STAR** (IRE) 21
6 **KINGSWEAR** 12
484 **KINGSWELL THEATRE** 20
105 **KINNI** F 75
27 **KINROSS** 15
253 **KINTBURY** 183
505 **KINZ** (IRE) 14
109 **KIP** F 19
436 **KIPLIN** 4
391 **KIPPS** (IRE) 7
76 **KIRALIK** C 111
518 **KIRILENKO** 109
552 **KIRINGA** C 45
419 **KIRKLAND LADY** (IRE) 89
69 **KIRTLING** 2
465 **KIRUNA PEAK** (IRE) 6
495 **KISKADEE** 7
533 **KISS FROM A ROSE** F 55
175 **KISS MY FACE** 27
415 **KISSED** (IRE) C 148
482 **KISSESFORKATIE** (IRE) 18
330 **KISSING** 44
250 **KISUMU** 46
18 **KIT'S ALLANAH** (IRE) 9
518 **KITEFLYER** 110
4 **KITEINAHURRICANE** (IRE) 10
204 **KITTY FISHER** (IRE) 8
243 **KITTY FOR ME** F 157
461 **KITTY HALL** (IRE) 22
536 **KITTY'S COVE** 8
580 **KITTY'S LIGHT** 17
504 **KIWAYU** 3
494 **KIWI GREEN SUITE** (BRZ) 8
486 **KIWI KATIE** M 4
486 **KIWI MYTH** 5
16 **KIYOSHI** C 174
431 **KIZOMBA** 33
222 **KK LEXION** (IRE) 48
399 **KLASSICAL DREAM** (FR) 125
399 **KLASSY KAY** (IRE) 126
64 **KLOPP** 10
421 **KLOPP OF THE KOP** (IRE) 26
386 **KLOUD GATE** (FR) 67
411 **KNAPPERS HILL** (IRE) 99
456 **KNICKERBOCKERGLORY** (IRE) 24
339 **KNIGHT COMMANDER** 6
425 **KNIGHT CRUSADER** 10
424 **KNIGHT DESTROYER** (IRE) 49
16 **KNIGHT SALUTE** 80
6 **KNIGHT'S TOWN** (IRE) 59
98 **KNIGHTOFPENTACLES** (IRE) 51
93 **KNOCKABOUT QUEEN** 43
252 **KNOCKNAGOSHEL** (IRE) 13
250 **KNOCKNAMONA** (IRE) 47
22 **KNOCKOURA** (IRE) 15
342 **KNOCKOUT BLOW** 4
492 **KNOTTY ASH** (IRE) 157
407 **KNOW NO LIMITS** (IRE) 4
189 **KNOWING** 15
587 **KNOWING GLANCE** (IRE) 16

258 **KNOWWHENTOHOLDEM** (IRE) 17
526 **KNOWWHENTORUN** 35
258 **KOALA BEAR** F 18
368 **KOBENHAVN** 17
492 **KOBRA** (GER) 81
421 **KOCOLLADA** (IRE) F 125
162 **KODI GOLD** (IRE) 14
571 **KODI KOH** (IRE) 12
18 **KODI KUB** (IRE) 7
545 **KODIAC BLUE** 174
63 **KODIAC HARBOUR** (IRE) 18
324 **KODIAK ATTACK** (IRE) 6
253 **KODIAS SANGARIUS** (IRE) 184
84 **KODIKOVA** (IRE) 13
552 **KODIMOOR** (IRE) 20
98 **KOEMAN** 19
256 **KOJIN** (IRE) 103
243 **KOLISI** (IRE) 66
330 **KOLKA** 20
134 **KOLOSSUS** 5
6 **KOMACHI** (IRE) 60
256 **KOMEDY KICKS** (IRE) 176
272 **KOMMANDER KIRKUP** 12
341 **KOMMODITY KID** (IRE) 12
431 **KOMORE** 12
309 **KONDO ISAMI** (IRE) 98
93 **KONDRATIEV WAVE** (IRE) 44
546 **KONIGSBERG** 40
253 **KOOL MOE DEE** (IRE) 77
481 **KOOLA BUALA** (IRE) 4
376 **KOPA KILANA** (IRE) 24
256 **KOREA** (IRE) 104
76 **KORNFLAKE** (IRE) 48
525 **KOROPICK** (IRE) 2
399 **KOSHARI** (FR) 127
386 **KOST A COAT** (FR) 68
321 **KOZIER** (GER) 57
492 **KRACKA NUT** 82
162 **KRAKA** (IRE) 4
128 **KRAKEN FILLY** (IRE) 90
300 **KRAKEN POWER** (IRE) 55
159 **KRANK IT** (FR) 26
545 **KRATOS** 86
402 **KRAZY PAVING** 76
436 **KROY** 15
190 **KRUJERS GIRL** (IRE) 26
300 **KRYNICA** (USA) F 70
32 **KRYPTOS** 6
436 **KRYSTAL MAZE** (IRE) 14
145 **KRYSTALLITE** 20
580 **KUIPER BELT** (USA) 18
327 **KUKRI KLASS** (IRE) 3
256 **KUNA YALA** (GER) C 177
482 **KURAKA** 19
228 **KUSNACHT** 90
421 **KUZNETSOVA** 76
7 **KYBOSH** (IRE) 50
91 **KYLIE RULES** 15
401 **KYLLA LOOKS** 4
489 **KYLLACHY CASTLE** 6
463 **KYLLACHY DRAGON** (IRE) 4
396 **KYLLACHY WARRIOR** (IRE) 4
145 **KYLLARNEY** F 39
535 **KYLLINGA** (IRE) 3
15 **KYLLISHI** 18
557 **KYLLUKEY** 12

534 **LOSTINTRANSLATION** (IRE) 58
529 **LOSTNFOUND** 11
52 **LOSTOCK HALL** (IRE) 8
51 **LOSTWITHIEL** (IRE) 9
296 **LOTHARIO** 15
10 **LOTHIAN** 32
13 **LOTS OF LUCK** (IRE) 40
539 **LOTTIE MARIE** 9
252 **LOU TREK** (FR) 17
92 **LOUBY LOU** (IRE) 19
522 **LOUD AS LIONS** (IRE) 21
105 **LOUGANINI** 8
415 **LOUGH DERG** (IRE) 70
501 **LOUGH DERG FARMER** (IRE) 30
363 **LOUGH DERG JEWEL** (IRE) 62
411 **LOUGH DERG SPIRIT** (IRE) 103
418 **LOUGH HAR** (IRE) 83
501 **LOUGH LEGEND** (IRE) 31
395 **LOUGH RYN** (IRE) 56
592 **LOUGH SALT** (IRE) 6
492 **LOUGHAN** (IRE) 89
566 **LOUGHERMORE** (IRE) 9
120 **LOUIE DE PALMA** 4
148 **LOUIS THE WARRIOR** 48
506 **LOUIS TREIZE** (IRE) 11
323 **LOUIS' VAC POUCH** (IRE) 47
230 **LOUIS'S TEFFIA** (IRE) G 15
91 **LOULIN** 16
22 **LOULOUMILLS** 16
223 **LOUNAOS** (FR) F 17
338 **LOUPGAROU** (FR) 1
343 **LOUSE TALK** (IRE) 27
159 **LOUVE RARE** (IRE) C 60
34 **LOUYA** (FR) F 20
415 **LOVE** (IRE) 8
168 **LOVE ACTION** (IRE) F 161
199 **LOVE AND BE LOVED** 15
404 **LOVE AT DAWN** (IRE) 8
400 **LOVE BAILEYS** 40
309 **LOVE DE VEGA** (IRE) 194
45 **LOVE DREAMS** (IRE) 7
417 **LOVE EXCELLING** (FR) C 38
509 **LOVE IS BLINDLESS** F 43
309 **LOVE IS GOLDEN** (IRE) 101
105 **LOVE IS YOU** (IRE) 38
576 **LOVE ISLAND** C 17
253 **LOVE LOVE** 13
481 **LOVE NEVER ENDING** 45
309 **LOVE OF ZOFFANY** (IRE) 102
274 **LOVE ON THE ROCKS** (IRE) F 93
479 **LOVE POEMS** (IRE) 3
92 **LOVE SENSATION** 20
190 **LOVE THE LEADER** (IRE) 29
518 **LOVE YOU GRANDPA** (IRE) 115
317 **LOVE YOUR WORK** (IRE) 8
419 **LOVED** (IRE) C 159
270 **LOVEHERANDLEAVEHER** (IRE) 114
98 **LOVEISALLAROUNDYOU** (IRE) F 88
393 **LOVEISRECKLESS** (IRE) C 25
289 **LOVELY ACCLAMATION** (IRE) 8
431 **LOVELY BREEZE** (IRE) 37
387 **LOVELY DANCER** (IRE) G 28
419 **LOVELY ESTEEM** 91
80 **LOVELY LOU LOU** 20
27 **LOVELY MANA** (IRE) 108
431 **LOVELY PASS** (IRE) C 65
512 **LOVELY SCHTUFF** (IRE) 7

431 **LOVELY SURPRISE** (IRE) F 66
321 **LOVERBOY** (FR) 62
287 **LOVEYOUTOTHEMOON** 7
541 **LOVING** C 14
105 **LOVING CARE** 78
189 **LOVING DASH** 45
228 **LOVING DREAM** 93
375 **LOVING KISS** (IRE) 28
32 **LOVING PEARL** 7
552 **LOW PROFILE** 22
399 **LOW SUN** 132
491 **LOWER STREET** 49
84 **LOWESWATER** 34
554 **LOWNDES SQUARE** (IRE) 48
6 **LOXLEY** (IRE) 14
415 **LOYAL** (IRE) 71
340 **LOYAL HAVANA** 14
234 **LOYALTY BINDS ME** 39
63 **LUA DE MEL** (IRE) 19
308 **LUANG PRABANG** (IRE) C 66
40 **LUBNA** 90
28 **LUCA BRASI'S BOY** (IRE) 4
27 **LUCANDER** (IRE) 16
317 **LUCARNIP** 9
162 **LUCAYAN** 15
450 **LUCCA LADY** (IRE) 14
301 **LUCHT NA GAEILGE** (IRE) F 25
105 **LUCID DREAMER** 39
373 **LUCINDA LAMB** M 3
420 **LUCINDA LAMB** G 33
363 **LUCK OF CLOVER** 63
402 **LUCKELLO** 79
491 **LUCKINESS** (FR) 50
87 **LUCKY BAY** 22
237 **LUCKY BEGGAR** (IRE) 9
140 **LUCKY BREEZE** (IRE) C 25
293 **LUCKY CIRCLE** 4
309 **LUCKY DEAL** 16
140 **LUCKY DRAW** 9
275 **LUCKY FACE** 6
473 **LUCKY FLIGHT** (FR) 48
323 **LUCKY ICON** (IRE) 48
380 **LUCKY LARA** (IRE) 8
98 **LUCKY LEIGH** F 89
64 **LUCKY LODGE** 11
526 **LUCKY LOUIE** 14
235 **LUCKY LOVER BOY** (IRE) 41
533 **LUCKY LUCKY LUCKY** (IRE) 57
411 **LUCKY ONE** (FR) 104
540 **LUCKY PURCHASE** 8
175 **LUCKY ROBIN** (IRE) 29
123 **LUCKY SHAKE** (FR) 83
101 **LUCKY SIM** (FR) 47
358 **LUCKY SO AND SO** (IRE) 10
256 **LUCKY VEGA** (IRE) 111
437 **LUCKY VIOLET** (IRE) 8
582 **LUCKY'S DREAM** 43
397 **LUCKYANGEL** 9
443 **LUCKYJOHNHOBBS** (IRE) 10
250 **LUCOU** (FR) 50
27 **LUCRECE** F 109
353 **LUCREZIA** C 44
391 **LUCROSA** (IRE) 54
25 **LUCY PARSONS** (IRE) C 35
25 **LUCY PARSONS** (IRE) G 47
436 **LUCY RULES** (IRE) 15
99 **LUDUAMF** (IRE) 4

290 **LUDYNOSA** (USA) F 56
522 **LUGG RIVER** 22
417 **LUGNAQUILLA** (IRE) 2
375 **LUIGI VAMPA** (FR) 9
243 **LUIS FERNANDO** 160
135 **LUIS VAN ZANDT** (IRE) 12
391 **LUISA CALDERON** C 55
562 **LUISA CASATI** (IRE) 19
167 **LUKE** 32
372 **LUKE SHORT** 58
529 **LUKOUTOLDMAKEZEBAK** 12
194 **LULAWIN** C 32
76 **LULLABY BAY** 116
27 **LULLABY MOON** 49
6 **LUMIERE** F 170
428 **LUMINATA** (IRE) C 61
41 **LUMINATION** 5
309 **LUMINOUS** F 195
179 **LUMLEY** (IRE) 33
527 **LUMP SUM** (FR) 46
240 **LUNA BREEZE** 27
333 **LUNA DORA** 37
27 **LUNA DORADA** (IRE) 110
563 **LUNA MAGIC** 13
495 **LUNA MOON** F 38
356 **LUNA WISH** 3
321 **LUNAR BOUNTY** 63
587 **LUNAR DEITY** 18
419 **LUNAR DISPLAY** (IRE) 35
568 **LUNAR FLIGHT** 26
16 **LUNAR GAZE** 181
348 **LUNAR JET** 9
456 **LUNAR LANDER** (IRE) 28
174 **LUNAR MIST** 5
321 **LUNAR SHADOW** 135
418 **LUNAR SOVEREIGN** (IRE) 84
48 **LUNE DE RIO** (FR) 17
105 **LUNEARIA** C 79
27 **LUNESQUE** (IRE) F 111
400 **LUNETTE** (IRE) F 48
418 **LUNGARNO PALACE** (USA) 85
44 **LURE DES PRES** (IRE) 4
93 **LUSCIFER** 50
581 **LUSITANIEN** (FR) 42
270 **LUST FOR GLORY** (IRE) 115
105 **LUSTROUS** F 80
508 **LUTHER CEE** (FR) 19
418 **LUTINEBELLA** 86
276 **LUTTRELL LAD** (IRE) 60
245 **LUV TURBO** (IRE) 70
257 **LUXY LOU** (IRE) 17
475 **LUZIA** F 108
545 **LYDFORD** 18
274 **LYDIA BECKER** C 94
222 **LYDIA VIOLET** (IRE) 50
353 **LYDIA'S PLACE** F 45
541 **LYDITATE LADY** 7
574 **LYFORD** (IRE) 34
591 **LYME PARK** 3
230 **LYNDALE** 16
199 **LYNDON B** (IRE) 16
16 **LYNIQUE** (IRE) C 182
587 **LYNNS BOY** 41
159 **LYNNWOOD CHASE** (USA) C 61
256 **LYNWOOD GOLD** (IRE) 41
411 **LYONS** (IRE) 105
6 **LYRIC OF LIGHT** F 171

253 **MALATHAAT** (IRE) 82
415 **MALAWI** (IRE) 73
411 **MALAYA** (FR) 107
90 **MALAYAN STYLE** (FR) 28
256 **MALAYSIAN** (IRE) 112
132 **MALEFICENT** F 68
27 **MALEX** 112
283 **MALHAM TARN COVE** 17
545 **MALHOOB** (USA) 95
395 **MALIBOO** (IRE) 59
120 **MALILLA** (IRE) F 90
322 **MALINA JAMILA** 22
252 **MALINA OCARINA** 18
395 **MALINAS ISLAND** 60
434 **MALINELLO** 50
167 **MALMESBURY** (IRE) F 100
587 **MALMOOSA** (IRE) F 48
256 **MALOJA** 113
505 **MALORY TOWERS** F 15
363 **MALPAS** (IRE) 66
421 **MALTBY RAIDER** (FR) 77
253 **MALVERN** 17
135 **MALVOLIO** (IRE) 13
413 **MALYSTIC** 5
199 **MAMA AFRICA** (IRE) 17
328 **MAMA QUILLA** (USA) C 36
410 **MAMBA WAMBA** (IRE) 15
120 **MAMBO BEAT** (IRE) 91
29 **MAMBO GOLD** F 60
253 **MAMBO NIGHTS** (IRE) 18
317 **MAMDOOD** (IRE) 11
15 **MAMILLIUS** 20
253 **MAMMASAIDKNOCKUOUT** (IRE) 83
178 **MAMOO** 13
296 **MAMUNIA** 26
337 **MAN OF PLENTY** 18
6 **MAN OF PROMISE** (USA) 15
273 **MAN OF STEEL** (IRE) 6
253 **MAN OF THE NIGHT** (FR) 19
93 **MAN OF THE NORTH** 52
395 **MAN OF THE SEA** (IRE) 61
323 **MAN OF VERVE** (IRE) 51
40 **MANABOO** (USA) C 132
475 **MANASSAS** 62
281 **MANCE RAYDER** (IRE) 7
501 **MANCINELLIE** 32
390 **MANCINI** 8
234 **MANDALAYAN** (IRE) 41
345 **MANDARIN** (GER) 22
102 **MANDARIN DUCK** 24
63 **MANDM** 53
171 **MANDOCELLO** (FR) 18
101 **MANDOLINE** 48
1 **MANETTI** (IRE) 32
211 **MANFADH** (IRE) 17
486 **MANGETOUT** 6
555 **MANGO BOY** 22
259 **MANGO TWITCHER** 25
333 **MANHATTAN BULLET** (IRE) 38
159 **MANHATTANVILLE** (IRE) 62
168 **MANIGORDO** (USA) 52
168 **MANILA SCOUSE** (IRE) 52
343 **MANINSANE** (IRE) 28
424 **MANINTHESHADOWS** (IRE) 53
399 **MANITOPARK AA** (FR) 134
344 **MANJAAM** (IRE) 22
123 **MANKHOOL** (IRE) 31

488 **MANNING ESTATE** (IRE) 27
509 **MANNIX** (IRE) 45
473 **MANNOCHMORE** 50
6 **MANOBO** (IRE) 65
222 **MANOFTHEMOMENT** (IRE) 51
333 **MANOFTHEMOUNTAIN** (IRE) 39
23 **MANOR PARK** 14
411 **MANORBANK** (IRE) 108
418 **MANOTHEPEOPLE** (IRE) 87
20 **MANSFIELD** 11
546 **MANUCCI** (IRE) 49
119 **MANUMISSION** (IRE) 15
553 **MANVERS HOUSE** 15
178 **MANWELL** (IRE) 14
589 **MANY A TALE** 12
577 **MANY DOVES** 23
348 **MANY TALES** 10
95 **MANZIL** (IRE) 13
170 **MANZO DURO** (IRE) 7
258 **MAONTRI** (IRE) G 45
290 **MAORI KNIGHT** (IRE) 9
80 **MAP** (IRE) 46
84 **MAPLE JACK** 35
366 **MAPLE LADY** (IRE) G 2
537 **MAQAASID** C 43
350 **MAQUISARD** (FR) 6
40 **MAR MAR** (FR) F 133
243 **MARAAKIZ** (FR) 76
290 **MARACUJA** C 58
492 **MARADA** 91
399 **MARAJMAN** (FR) 135
411 **MARALYPHA** (FR) G 109
421 **MARAMBA** (USA) F 129
581 **MARBLE MOON** (IRE) 47
502 **MARBLE PALACE** 10
369 **MARBLE SANDS** (FR) 38
63 **MARBLES ARE BLUE** 20
424 **MARCH IS ON** (IRE) 54
309 **MARCH LAW** (IRE) 103
40 **MARCHING ARMY** 91
48 **MARCIE** (IRE) 13
285 **MARCO ISLAND** (IRE) 29
518 **MARDOOF** (IRE) 55
79 **MAREERA** 24
540 **MARETTIMO** (IRE) 9
431 **MARGARET DUMONT** (IRE) 10
243 **MARGARET'S MISSION** (IRE) F 162
42 **MARGARETS MEMORY** 8
350 **MARGIE'S CHOICE** (GER) 7
537 **MARGUB** 5
244 **MARIA MAGDALENA** (IRE) 21
305 **MARIA MILENA** C 23
589 **MARIAH'S MELODY** (IRE) 13
434 **MARIAH'S WAY** G 51
554 **MARIE ANTOINETTE** 49
375 **MARIE ROSSA** C 56
309 **MARIE'S DIAMOND** (IRE) 18
270 **MARIE'S ROCK** (IRE) 117
193 **MARIEGOLD** 49
108 **MARIENPLATZ** 19
419 **MARIESQUE** (IRE) 93
87 **MARIETTY** 12
162 **MARIGAY'S MAGIC** C 17
379 **MARIGOT BOY** 25
285 **MARILYN MONROE** (IRE) 30
16 **MARINE** (IRE) 84
223 **MARINE JAG** (FR) 18

408 **MARINE ONE** 48
527 **MARIO DE PAIL** (FR) 23
526 **MARION'S BOY** (IRE) 15
79 **MARISOL** C 56
253 **MARITIME RULES** (IRE) 189
15 **MARJORAM** (IRE) 21
178 **MARK OF GOLD** 20
446 **MARK OF RESPECT** (IRE) 26
178 **MARK'S CHOICE** (IRE) 15
14 **MARKAZI** (FR) 14
156 **MARKETTA** 13
402 **MARKOV** (IRE) 83
56 **MARLAY PARK** 22
400 **MARLBOROUGH SOUNDS** 20
474 **MARLY** (FR) 7
324 **MARMALADE CAT** C 33
270 **MARMALAID** 118
243 **MARMALASHES** (IRE) 163
145 **MARNIE JAMES** 21
321 **MAROOCHI** 68
461 **MAROWN** (IRE) 27
492 **MARRACUDJA** (FR) 92
228 **MARRAKECH MOON** 95
105 **MARS MAGIC** 82
518 **MARS LANDING** (IRE) 18
391 **MARSABIT** (IRE) 35
535 **MARSDEN CROSS** (IRE) 9
308 **MARSELAN** (IRE) 33
171 **MARSH WREN** 19
351 **MARSHAL DAN** (IRE) 8
228 **MARSHALL PLAN** 96
180 **MARTA BOY** 33
522 **MARTA DES MOTTES** (FR) 23
323 **MARTALINDY** 52
548 **MARTELLO SKY** 18
234 **MARTHA BRAE** 42
86 **MARTHA YEATS** (IRE) 23
466 **MARTHA'S DREAM** 3
468 **MARTILA** (FR) 5
529 **MARTIN'S BRIG** (IRE) 13
304 **MARTIN'S JUSIS** 30
92 **MARTINA FRANCA** F 21
103 **MARTINENGO** (IRE) 3
80 **MARTINEO** 21
444 **MARTINHAL** (IRE) 49
415 **MARTINIQUE** 74
270 **MARTOVIC** (IRE) F 119
329 **MARTY TIME** (FR) 28
396 **MARVE** 7
84 **MARVEL** 18
415 **MARVELLOUS** (IRE) F 155
250 **MARVELLOUS JOE** (IRE) 53
167 **MARWARI** (IRE) 33
474 **MARY BOLEYN** (IRE) G 14
408 **MARY KANE** 49
328 **MARY MOUNT** 37
338 **MARY OF DE SORROWS** (IRE) 2
10 **MARY OF MODENA** 49
51 **MARY PEKAN** (IRE) F 42
25 **MARY THOMAS** (IRE) C 48
1 **MARYLINE TRITT** (FR) 33
434 **MARYS ARTICLE** (IRE) G 52
321 **MASACCIO** (IRE) 69
402 **MASADA KNIGHT** (IRE) 84
193 **MASAYA** C 66
27 **MASCAT** 17
16 **MASEKELA** 183

406 **MENAPIAN** (IRE) 6
354 **MENDACIOUS HARPY** (IRE) 8
50 **MENDENHALL** 50
270 **MENGLI KHAN** (IRE) 120
214 **MENIN GATE** (IRE) 14
214 **MENINA ATREVIDA** 31
214 **MENSOORA** (SAF) F 71
7 **MEONSTOKE** 104
309 **MERAAS** 19
81 **MERCERS** 8
406 **MERCHANT IN MILAN** (IRE) 7
415 **MERCHANTS QUAY** (FR) 76
217 **MERCI PERCY** (FR) 10
535 **MERCIAN HYMN** 10
400 **MERCIAN KNIGHT** (IRE) 21
400 **MERCIAN PRINCE** (IRE) 22
107 **MERCIELAGO** (FR) 29
379 **MERCURIST** 8
16 **MERCURIS POWER** (IRE) 88
251 **MERCURY** 6
424 **MERCUTIO ROCK** (FR) 56
474 **MERCY ME** F 19
514 **MERE ANARCHY** (IRE) 15
74 **MERE DETAIL** (IRE) F 7
74 **MERE DETAIL** (IRE) F 9
25 **MERESIDE MAGIC** (IRE) 36
25 **MERESIDE PEARL** (IRE) 37
474 **MERHOOB** (IRE) 8
228 **MERITORIOUS** 98
290 **MERLIN'S BEARD** 29
475 **MERLIN'S LADY** (IRE) 111
401 **MERLIN'S MISSION** (IRE) 17
300 **MERRICOURT** (IRE) 20
419 **MERROIR** (IRE) 38
274 **MERRY BERRY** 88
274 **MERRY ME** (IRE) C 98
358 **MERRY MILAN** (IRE) 12
487 **MERRY MISTRESS** (IRE) 11
7 **MERRY SECRET** (IRE) 105
259 **MERWEB** (IRE) 10
305 **MERYEMS WAY** (IRE) 7
492 **MESMERIC** (GER) 9
419 **MESSIDOR** (FR) 95
321 **MESSIRE DES OBEAUX** (FR) 71
279 **MET BY MOONLIGHT** 1
15 **METAL PRECIOUS** (FR) C 41
415 **METAPHORICAL** (IRE) 77
522 **METEORITE** 24
244 **METHAG** (FR) 22
371 **METHOD** (IRE) 16
456 **METHOD MADNESS** (IRE) 30
473 **METHODTOTHEMADNESS** (IRE) 51
442 **METHODTOTHEMAGIC** (IRE) 16
488 **METHORP** (IRE) 28
321 **METHUSALAR** (IRE) 72
212 **METIER** (IRE) 36
52 **METRO BOULOT DODO** (IRE) 10
27 **MEU AMOR** (FR) 50
569 **MEWS HOUSE** 19
402 **MEWSTONE** G 44
402 **MEXICAN BOY** (IRE) 86
175 **MEXICAN MILLY** (IRE) G 75
491 **MEXICAN SONG** (IRE) 51
171 **MEXICO** (GER) 22
576 **MEY BLOSSOM** F 18
449 **MEZZANOTTE** (IRE) 56

128 **MI CAPRICHO** (IRE) 45
258 **MI LADDO** (IRE) 21
488 **MI MONEY** G 29
436 **MI RUBINA** (IRE) C 28
253 **MIA MADONNA** F 190
256 **MIA MENTO** (IRE) 45
446 **MIA MIA** 27
18 **MIAELLA** 12
420 **MIAH GRACE** 11
37 **MIAMI PRESENT** (IRE) 6
323 **MICHAEL'S MOUNT** 55
301 **MICHAELS CHOICE** 5
7 **MICHELE STROGOFF** 57
318 **MICK MAESTRO** (FR) 11
456 **MICK MONA** (FR) 31
411 **MICK PASTOR** (FR) 112
386 **MICKEY BUCKMAN** 74
448 **MICKEY DRIPPIN** (IRE) 3
526 **MICKS DREAM** 36
253 **MICKYDEE** 85
546 **MICKYH** (IRE) 51
399 **MICRO MANAGE** (IRE) 138
93 **MID DAY RUSH** (IRE) 101
378 **MID WINSTER** 11
91 **MIDAS** (IRE) 39
173 **MIDDLESCENCE** (IRE) 4
449 **MIDFIELD** 24
505 **MIDNIGHT AIR** 9
150 **MIDNIGHT ANNIE** 12
111 **MIDNIGHT ANTICS** (IRE) 11
492 **MIDNIGHT AURORA** 94
499 **MIDNIGHT BAHIA** (IRE) F 29
540 **MIDNIGHT CALAMITY** 10
285 **MIDNIGHT CALLISTO** 31
503 **MIDNIGHT CENTURION** 31
376 **MIDNIGHT CHIEF** (IRE) 67
27 **MIDNIGHT DANCE** (IRE) C 113
120 **MIDNIGHT DRIFT** 5
532 **MIDNIGHT FIDDLER** 35
579 **MIDNIGHT FRENSI** 4
321 **MIDNIGHT GINGER** 73
321 **MIDNIGHT GLANCE** 74
456 **MIDNIGHT HENRY** 32
501 **MIDNIGHT HUNTER** 33
598 **MIDNIGHT JEWEL** 19
323 **MIDNIGHT LEGACY** (IRE) 56
19 **MIDNIGHT MALIN** 11
120 **MIDNIGHT MARTINI** C 92
171 **MIDNIGHT MARY** 23
279 **MIDNIGHT MIDGE** 2
168 **MIDNIGHT MOJITO** C 163
235 **MIDNIGHT MOSS** 42
357 **MIDNIGHT MUSTANG** 2
501 **MIDNIGHT MYTH** 34
165 **MIDNIGHT OWLE** 8
420 **MIDNIGHT POPPY** (IRE) 34
357 **MIDNIGHT POPSTAR** 3
492 **MIDNIGHT RIVER** 95
131 **MIDNIGHT SAPPHIRE** 14
496 **MIDNIGHT SENSATION** 5
501 **MIDNIGHT SHADOW** 35
588 **MIDNIGHT SONATA** (IRE) 54
168 **MIDNIGHT STRIPPER** 131
120 **MIDNIGHT TRAIN** 93
41 **MIDNIGHT TROUBLE** 9
285 **MIDNIGHT TUNE** 32
540 **MIDNIGHT WAVE** 11

321 **MIDNIGHTREFERENDUM** 75
96 **MIDNIGHTREFLECTION** 17
321 **MIDNIGHTS LEGACY** 76
321 **MIDNIGHT'S GIFT** 77
475 **MIDNITE BRIDE** 16
485 **MIDNITE MOTIVATION** F 24
243 **MIDRARR** (IRE) 19
591 **MIDTECH VALENTINE** 4
491 **MIEN** (USA) C 52
212 **MIGHT I** (IRE) 37
24 **MIGHTASWELLSMILE** 4
419 **MIGHTY BLUE** (FR) 39
442 **MIGHTY ELSA** 17
256 **MIGHTY GIRL** (FR) F 179
563 **MIGHTY GURKHA** (IRE) 8
522 **MIGHTY LEADER** (IRE) 25
235 **MIGHTY MARVEL** (IRE) 43
402 **MIGHTY MEG** 87
435 **MIGHTY MIND** 8
357 **MIGHTY MUSTANG** 4
368 **MIGHTY POWER** (IRE) 18
473 **MIGHTY THUNDER** 52
375 **MIGRATION** (IRE) 10
481 **MIKANDY** (IRE) F 46
240 **MIKASA** 20
571 **MIKE MCCANN** (IRE) 14
168 **MIKMAK** 53
167 **MILADY** G 101
420 **MILAN ATHLETE** (IRE) G 12
285 **MILAN IN MAY** (IRE) 33
418 **MILANESE ROSE** (IRE) 89
380 **MILANFORD** (IRE) 9
415 **MILANOVA** (AUS) C 156
363 **MILANS EDGE** (IRE) 68
323 **MILANVERA** (IRE) 57
381 **MILBERRY** (IRE) 3
446 **MILD REFLECTION** 46
309 **MILDENBERGER** 20
514 **MILE HOUSE** (IRE) 16
279 **MILES OF SUNSHINE** 3
261 **MILEVA ROLLER** 5
26 **MILIANAPOWER** 9
371 **MILIIKA** C 40
234 **MILITAIRE** 43
357 **MILITARIAN** 5
258 **MILITARY DRESS** (IRE) 22
545 **MILITARY MAN** 97
40 **MILITARY MARCH** 48
431 **MILITARY MISSION** (IRE) 38
415 **MILITARY STYLE** (USA) 78
434 **MILITARY TACTIC** (IRE) 53
378 **MILITIA** 12
448 **MILITRY DECORATION** (IRE) 4
395 **MILKWOOD** (IRE) 64
270 **MILL GREEN** 121
321 **MILL POINT** C 149
168 **MILL RACE KING** (IRE) 54
229 **MILLARVILLE** (IRE) 6
212 **MILLBANK FLYER** (IRE) 38
300 **MILLDALE** F 72
429 **MILLDEAN BILLY** (IRE) 11
594 **MILLDEAN FELIX** (IRE) 2
429 **MILLDEAN PANTHER** 12
120 **MILLE MIGLIA** 35
212 **MILLE SUSSURRI** (IRE) 39
244 **MILLERS BANK** 23
494 **MILLFIELD** (FR) 10

| | |
|---|---|
| 448 | **MILLIE MALOO** (IRE) 5 |
| 300 | **MILLIE N AIRE** G 21 |
| 461 | **MILLIE OF MAYO** 29 |
| 222 | **MILLIE ROUND** (IRE) 54 |
| 478 | **MILLIE THE MINX** (IRE) 10 |
| 466 | **MILLIE'S FLYING** 4 |
| 50 | **MILLION REASONS** (IRE) 51 |
| 76 | **MILLIONS** 50 |
| 385 | **MILLIONS MEMORIES** 7 |
| 98 | **MILLTOWN STAR** 20 |
| 113 | **MILLY ON AIR** 23 |
| 488 | **MILLY'S DAUGHTER** 30 |
| 168 | **MILLY'S SECRET** (IRE) F 164 |
| 395 | **MILREU HAS** (FR) 65 |
| 337 | **MILROW** (IRE) 19 |
| 238 | **MILTON** 6 |
| 532 | **MILVALE** (IRE) 36 |
| 80 | **MIME DANCE** 22 |
| 393 | **MIMI'S ODYSSEY** 27 |
| 399 | **MIN** (FR) 139 |
| 120 | **MINALISA** C 94 |
| 253 | **MIND HUNTER** 86 |
| 270 | **MIND SUNDAY** (FR) 122 |
| 392 | **MIND THAT JET** (IRE) 14 |
| 395 | **MIND YOUR BACK** (IRE) 66 |
| 165 | **MIND'S EYE** (IRE) 9 |
| 491 | **MINDSPIN** 53 |
| 364 | **MINDUROWNBUSINESS** (IRE) 1 |
| 120 | **MINE'S A DOUBLE** 36 |
| 77 | **MINE'S A PINT** 7 |
| 76 | **MINEANDYOURS** 51 |
| 434 | **MINELLA AWAY** (IRE) 54 |
| 126 | **MINELLA BOBO** (IRE) 23 |
| 333 | **MINELLA BUSTER** (IRE) 41 |
| 383 | **MINELLA CHARMER** (IRE) 11 |
| 53 | **MINELLA DADDY** (IRE) 22 |
| 363 | **MINELLA DRAMA** (IRE) 69 |
| 408 | **MINELLA ENCORE** (IRE) 52 |
| 234 | **MINELLA EXAMINER** 44 |
| 372 | **MINELLA FAIR** (IRE) 61 |
| 222 | **MINELLA FOR ME** (IRE) 55 |
| 150 | **MINELLA MOJO** (IRE) 13 |
| 448 | **MINELLA RISING** (IRE) 6 |
| 488 | **MINELLA ROYALE** 31 |
| 165 | **MINELLA STYLE** (IRE) 10 |
| 418 | **MINELLA TARA** (IRE) 90 |
| 363 | **MINELLA TRUMP** (IRE) 70 |
| 161 | **MINELLA VOUCHER** 20 |
| 13 | **MINELLA WARRIOR** (IRE) 41 |
| 442 | **MINELLA WHISPER** 18 |
| 450 | **MINELLACELEBRATION** (IRE) 15 |
| 175 | **MING DYNASTY** (FR) 32 |
| 485 | **MING MENG** (IRE) F 27 |
| 10 | **MINHAAJ** (IRE) 23 |
| 484 | **MINI ADVENTURE** (IRE) F 22 |
| 555 | **MINI RIVO** (IRE) 23 |
| 598 | **MINIM MOUSE** 20 |
| 210 | **MINIMALISTIC** (IRE) 9 |
| 105 | **MINISTERIAL** 10 |
| 331 | **MINMORE GREY** (IRE) 4 |
| 431 | **MINNALOUSHE** (IRE) C 67 |
| 298 | **MINNEIGH MOZZE** (FR) 5 |
| 131 | **MINNIE ESCAPE** 15 |
| 601 | **MINNIE MAHLER** 9 |
| 39 | **MINNIMO** 11 |
| 313 | **MINORAS RETURN** (IRE) C 37 |
| 440 | **MINSTER** (IRE) 10 |

| | |
|---|---|
| 498 | **MINSTREL SONG** 5 |
| 86 | **MINT CONDITION** 24 |
| 473 | **MINT GOLD** (IRE) 53 |
| 491 | **MINT JULEP** 54 |
| 1 | **MINUIT CIEL** 36 |
| 413 | **MINUTE WALTZ** 6 |
| 79 | **MINZAAL** (IRE) 26 |
| 563 | **MIQUELON** 15 |
| 420 | **MIRACLE EAGLE** (IRE) 13 |
| 67 | **MIRACLE GARDEN** 7 |
| 51 | **MIRAGE MAC** 26 |
| 296 | **MIRAKUHL** 16 |
| 132 | **MIRAMICHI** (IRE) 35 |
| 411 | **MIRANDA** (IRE) 113 |
| 582 | **MIRANDA FROST** (IRE) C 86 |
| 160 | **MIRIQUE** 21 |
| 438 | **MIRRIE DANCERS** (IRE) 17 |
| 98 | **MIRROR KISSES** 5 |
| 409 | **MIS CASEY** (IRE) 5 |
| 92 | **MIS CHICAF** (IRE) C 28 |
| 168 | **MISCHIEF MANAGED** (IRE) 55 |
| 421 | **MISCHIEF STAR** 30 |
| 40 | **MISE EN ROSE** (USA) F 134 |
| 494 | **MISEREY** (FR) 29 |
| 473 | **MISFITS** (IRE) 54 |
| 562 | **MISHAL STAR** (IRE) 20 |
| 228 | **MISRIFFT** (IRE) 23 |
| 141 | **MISREAD** 10 |
| 523 | **MISS ALBANE** (IRE) F 69 |
| 552 | **MISS AMELIA** 26 |
| 313 | **MISS ANTIPOVA** 21 |
| 263 | **MISS AZEZA** F 52 |
| 348 | **MISS BAMBY** 11 |
| 155 | **MISS BEHAVING** 15 |
| 340 | **MISS BELLA BRAND** 15 |
| 568 | **MISS BLAH BLAH** 28 |
| 537 | **MISS BLONDELL** 6 |
| 574 | **MISS BOBCAT** (IRE) 51 |
| 523 | **MISS CALACATTA** (IRE) 32 |
| 243 | **MISS CARBONIA** (IRE) F 164 |
| 194 | **MISS CELIE** (IRE) C 33 |
| 222 | **MISS CHANTELLE** 56 |
| 276 | **MISS CHINCHILLA** F 66 |
| 505 | **MISS CONDUCT** C 16 |
| 235 | **MISS DELIGHTED** (IRE) 44 |
| 438 | **MISS DOWN UNDER** (IRE) 24 |
| 152 | **MISS DUSKY DIVA** (IRE) 4 |
| 95 | **MISS ELSA** 14 |
| 391 | **MISS FAIRFAX** (IRE) 9 |
| 270 | **MISS FARAGE** (IRE) 123 |
| 431 | **MISS FASTNET** 39 |
| 123 | **MISS FEDORA** (IRE) 86 |
| 347 | **MISS FERNANDA** (IRE) 6 |
| 228 | **MISS FINLAND** (IRE) 99 |
| 13 | **MISS GEMSTONE** 42 |
| 402 | **MISS GOLD DEN** (IRE) 88 |
| 29 | **MISS HARMONY** 67 |
| 242 | **MISS HARRIETT** 8 |
| 548 | **MISS HERITAGE** (IRE) 19 |
| 111 | **MISS HOLLYBELL** F 12 |
| 234 | **MISS HONEY RYDER** (IRE) 45 |
| 395 | **MISS JEANNE MOON** (IRE) 67 |
| 6 | **MISS JINGLES** (IRE) 68 |
| 545 | **MISS KATIE MAE** (IRE) F 178 |
| 585 | **MISS KHARIZMA** (IRE) 14 |
| 98 | **MISS LAHAR** F 90 |
| 420 | **MISS LAMB** 14 |

| | |
|---|---|
| 300 | **MISS LILL** 73 |
| 444 | **MISS M** (IRE) 51 |
| 323 | **MISS MAHMITE** (IRE) 58 |
| 305 | **MISS MALARKY** (IRE) 8 |
| 123 | **MISS MARBLE** 34 |
| 150 | **MISS MARETTE** 14 |
| 308 | **MISS MATTERHORN** 15 |
| 251 | **MISS MAUNA KEA** (IRE) F 7 |
| 20 | **MISS MAWATHEEQ** 14 |
| 33 | **MISS MEMORIES** (IRE) 6 |
| 308 | **MISS METROPOLITAN** 68 |
| 113 | **MISS MISTRAL** (IRE) 24 |
| 283 | **MISS MOCKTAIL** (IRE) 7 |
| 343 | **MISS MOLINARI** 29 |
| 395 | **MISS MOLLY MAE** (IRE) 68 |
| 481 | **MISS MULLIGAN** (IRE) 5 |
| 454 | **MISS NAY NEVER** (IRE) 39 |
| 472 | **MISS NORA ABU** (IRE) 7 |
| 449 | **MISS PALOMA** 25 |
| 243 | **MISS PINKERTON** F 165 |
| 398 | **MISS PLATINUM** (IRE) G 17 |
| 124 | **MISS PLYMWICK** 9 |
| 294 | **MISS POLLYANNA** (IRE) 8 |
| 350 | **MISS RECYCLED** 8 |
| 309 | **MISS ROULETTE** (IRE) 104 |
| 311 | **MISS SALLY** (IRE) F 24 |
| 554 | **MISS SCALETTA** 50 |
| 76 | **MISS SEAFIRE** (IRE) 52 |
| 428 | **MISS SLIGO** (IRE) 7 |
| 326 | **MISS SUZIE** B 33 |
| 235 | **MISS TARA MOSS** 45 |
| 368 | **MISS THOUGHTFUL** 8 |
| 290 | **MISS TIKI** 30 |
| 42 | **MISS TOLDYASO** (IRE) C 10 |
| 283 | **MISS TRIXIE** 14 |
| 253 | **MISS UNDERSTOOD** (IRE) F 191 |
| 430 | **MISS VELVETEEN** (IRE) 1 |
| 340 | **MISS VILLEFRANCHE** C 16 |
| 385 | **MISS YEATS** (IRE) 8 |
| 160 | **MISS ZENLINGUS** (IRE) 12 |
| 581 | **MISS ZIP** (IRE) 49 |
| 323 | **MISSCARLETT** (IRE) 59 |
| 189 | **MISSED CALL** (IRE) F 46 |
| 103 | **MISSED ILLUSION** (IRE) 12 |
| 234 | **MISSED VACATION** (IRE) 46 |
| 20 | **MISSESGEEJAY** 15 |
| 228 | **MISSILE** 100 |
| 50 | **MISSION BOY** 12 |
| 309 | **MISSISIPI STAR** (IRE) F 200 |
| 310 | **MISSMEBUTLETMEGO** 7 |
| 369 | **MISSTHECUDDLES** (IRE) 39 |
| 198 | **MISSTIFY** 4 |
| 417 | **MISSVINSKI** (USA) F 39 |
| 285 | **MISTER ALLEGRO** 51 |
| 29 | **MISTER BLUE** 6 |
| 399 | **MISTER BLUE SKY** (IRE) 140 |
| 351 | **MISTER BLUEBIRD** 18 |
| 408 | **MISTER CHIANG** 53 |
| 270 | **MISTER COFFEY** (FR) 124 |
| 146 | **MISTER DON** (IRE) 24 |
| 84 | **MISTER FALSETTO** 42 |
| 270 | **MISTER FISHER** (IRE) 125 |
| 97 | **MISTER FREEZE** (IRE) 12 |
| 534 | **MISTER MALARKY** 59 |
| 574 | **MISTER MANDURO** (FR) 35 |
| 276 | **MISTER MARBLES** (IRE) 67 |
| 250 | **MISTER MCARTHUR** 55 |

389 **MRS DEMPSEY** (IRE) G 21
582 **MRS DIBBLE** (FR) 80
582 **MRS DOUBTFIRE** 49
391 **MRS FITZHERBERT** (IRE) 36
175 **MRS HYDE** (IRE) 34
32 **MRS MAISEL** 17
191 **MRS MEADER** 3
108 **MRS PENNY** (AUS) F 40
303 **MRS THATCHER** (IRE) 19
589 **MRS TIFFEN** 14
113 **MRS VONN** (IRE) 25
427 **MRSGREY** (IRE) 21
545 **MS GANDHI** (IRE) 102
177 **MS JILLY MAAYE** (IRE) G 7
285 **MS PARFOIS** (IRE) 36
399 **MT LEINSTER** (IRE) 144
428 **MT OF BEATITUDES** (IRE) C 62
244 **MTPOCKETS** (IRE) F 24
209 **MUAJIZA** C 7
550 **MUATADEL** 10
253 **MUAY THAI** (IRE) 90
434 **MUCHO MAS** (IRE) 56
256 **MUCKROSS** (IRE) 55
79 **MUDAWANAH** C 60
32 **MUDAWWAN** (IRE) 7
534 **MUFFINS FOR TEA** 63
243 **MUFFRI'HA** (IRE) C 166
414 **MUFTAKKER** 4
243 **MUHALHEL** (IRE) 85
185 **MUHTAMAR** (IRE) 27
601 **MUILEAN NA MADOG** (IRE) 10
417 **MUJABAHA** F 41
6 **MUJARAH** (IRE) C 178
70 **MUJASSID** (USA) 32
274 **MUJBAR** 53
578 **MUJID** (IRE) 9
243 **MUJTABA** 86
353 **MUKER** (IRE) 29
316 **MUKHA MAGIC** 14
353 **MUKHADRAM WAY** 9
168 **MUKHAYYAM** 59
545 **MULBERRY SILK** 103
234 **MULCAHYS HILL** (IRE) 50
168 **MULTELLIE** 60
287 **MULTISTORY** 9
401 **MULZIM** 6
333 **MUMBO JUMBO** (IRE) 43
597 **MUMCAT** 18
253 **MUMMY BEAR** (IRE) 91
274 **MUMMY'S BOY** 54
253 **MUMS TIPPLE** (IRE) 21
274 **MUMTAAZ** (IRE) 18
253 **MUNDANA** (IRE) F 197
149 **MUNGO'S QUEST** (IRE) 15
110 **MUNIFICENT** 26
21 **MUNSTEAD MOONSHINE** 3
541 **MUQARRED** (USA) 8
79 **MURAAD** (IRE) 19
309 **MURAAQABA** F 202
557 **MURAAQEB** 13
309 **MURAHANA** (IRE) C 203
578 **MURAT ASSET** 10
189 **MURAU** 47
415 **MURAVKA** (IRE) F 158
177 **MURCHISON RIVER** 8
460 **MURHIB** (IRE) 7
198 **MURITZ** 6

531 **MUROOR** 5
128 **MURPHY'S LAW** (IRE) 47
461 **MURVAGH BEACH** (IRE) 30
243 **MUSAANADA** C 167
421 **MUSAHABA** 31
421 **MUSCIKA** 32
239 **MUSE OF FIRE** (IRE) 11
93 **MUSEE D'ORSAY** (IRE) 53
545 **MUSHIRIF** (IRE) 104
417 **MUSIC BOX** (IRE) F 42
159 **MUSIC IN MY HEART** F 64
10 **MUSIC MAJOR** 26
398 **MUSIC ON D WATERS** (IRE) F 22
283 **MUSIC PEARL** (IRE) F 18
92 **MUSIC SEEKER** (IRE) 7
61 **MUSIC SOCIETY** (IRE) 61
419 **MUSIC TO MY EARS** (IRE) 41
40 **MUSIC WRITER** (IRE) 95
429 **MUSICAL COMEDY** 13
159 **MUSICAL REVIEW** (UAE) C 65
276 **MUSICAL SLAVE** (IRE) 71
545 **MUSICALITY** 22
514 **MUSKETEER** 17
344 **MUST BE AN ANGEL** (IRE) 24
507 **MUST DREAM** 10
503 **MUSTANG ALPHA** (IRE) 33
526 **MUSTANG KODI** (IRE) 37
148 **MUSTAQBAL** (IRE) 22
80 **MUSTAQQIR** (IRE) 23
582 **MUSTARRID** (IRE) 50
328 **MUSTAVIM** 25
555 **MUSTAZEED** (IRE) 25
86 **MUTAABEQ** (IRE) 25
545 **MUTABAADAL** 105
64 **MUTABAAHY** (IRE) 13
378 **MUTAFARRID** (IRE) 14
40 **MUTAFAWWIG** 51
545 **MUTAHAMISA** (IRE) 106
436 **MUTAKAAMIL** (IRE) 16
274 **MUTALAAQY** (IRE) 55
91 **MUTAMADED** (IRE) 20
91 **MUTANAASEQ** (IRE) 21
274 **MUTARAAFEQ** (IRE) 56
80 **MUTARABBY** (IRE) 24
274 **MUTARABES** (IRE) 57
274 **MUTASAABEQ** 58
537 **MUTASALLEM** (IRE) 26
159 **MUTAWAARID** 29
79 **MUTEBAH** (IRE) F 61
309 **MUTEELA** C 204
442 **MUTHABIR** (IRE) 20
415 **MUWAKABA** (USA) C 159
261 **MUWALLA** 6
212 **MUY BIEN** (IRE) 43
567 **MUZETTA'S WALTZ** (IRE) 2
138 **MY ANCHOR** 3
223 **MY BAD LUCY** 19
421 **MY BEST FRIEND** (IRE) 79
569 **MY BOY FRANKIE** 40
385 **MY BOY JAMES** (IRE) 9
587 **MY BOY SEPOY** 19
515 **MY BROTHER MIKE** (IRE) 3
40 **MY CALL** C 136
291 **MY DESIGN** (IRE) 11
492 **MY DROGO** 98
535 **MY FOOTSTEPS** 4
556 **MY FOXY LADY** 5

518 **MY FRANKEL** 19
84 **MY FRIEND STAN** (IRE) 20
171 **MY GIRL LOLLIPOP** (IRE) 24
309 **MY GIRL MAGGIE** 22
241 **MY GIRL MAISIE** (IRE) 9
276 **MY KEEPSAKE** 72
97 **MY LADY CLAIRE** 13
534 **MY LADY GREY** 64
358 **MY LAST OSCAR** (IRE) 14
446 **MY LAW** 5
22 **MY MACHO MAN** (IRE) 18
256 **MY MINERVINA** (IRE) 116
554 **MY MIRAGE** (IRE) 51
552 **MY NAME'S NIPPER** 43
243 **MY OBERON** (IRE) 21
461 **MY OLD GOLD** (IRE) 31
479 **MY PERFECT COUSIN** 4
178 **MY RENAISSANCE** 16
399 **MY SISTER SARAH** (IRE) 145
300 **MY SONNY** (IRE) 58
243 **MY SPECIAL J'S** C 168
323 **MY STRONG MAN** (IRE) 62
308 **MY STYLE** (IRE) 16
518 **MY SWALLOW** 62
101 **MY SYMBOL** 51
578 **MY TARGET** (IRE) 11
168 **MY THOUGHT** (IRE) 62
515 **MY TOWN CHICAGO** (USA) 4
411 **MY WAY** 121
270 **MY WHIRLWIND** (IRE) 131
509 **MYBOYCHARLES** 25
250 **MYBOYMAX** (IRE) 91
501 **MYBURG** (IRE) 37
161 **MYFANWY'S JEWEL** 23
433 **MYKINDOFSUNSHINE** (IRE) 1
428 **MYKONOS ST JOHN** 10
428 **MYLIE** (IRE) 33
78 **MYLITTLEOULBUDDY** (IRE) 7
532 **MYMILAN** (IRE) 37
322 **MYPLACEATMIDNIGHT** 23
168 **MYRISTICA** (IRE) 134
273 **MYSPACENOTYOURS** 7
51 **MYSTERY ANGEL** (IRE) 27
563 **MYSTERY SHOW** (IRE) 44
16 **MYSTERY SMILES** (IRE) 90
380 **MYSTIC COURT** (IRE) 11
217 **MYSTIC DRAGON** 5
223 **MYSTIC DREAMER** (IRE) 20
545 **MYSTICAL AIR** 107
80 **MYSTICAL CLOUDS** (IRE) 25
6 **MYSTICAL DAWN** (IRE) 71
415 **MYSTICAL LADY** (IRE) C 160
421 **MYSTICAL MADNESS** 33
175 **MYTHICAL MOLLY** (IRE) 76
290 **MYTHICAL STAR** 65
517 **MYTHICAL WATERS** 10
495 **MYTHMAKER** 8
538 **MYWAYISTHEONLYWAY** (IRE) 18
7 **N OVER J** 62
399 **N'GOLO** (IRE) 146
475 **NA BLIANTA BEO** (IRE) 17
243 **NAAFER** C 169
309 **NAAMOOS** (FR) 106
290 **NAASHA** (IRE) 61
414 **NAASIK** 5
444 **NABVUTIKA** (IRE) 53
264 **NACHI FALLS** 33

363 **NACHO** (IRE) 124
322 **NACHTSTERN** (GER) 24
545 **NADA** F 179
484 **NADA TO PRADA** 25
434 **NADAITAK** 57
105 **NADEIN** 40
547 **NADINE** (IRE) 47
40 **NAFURA** C 137
545 **NAGANO** 108
31 **NAGASAKI DREAM** 11
243 **NAHAARR** (IRE) 22
309 **NAHOODH** (IRE) F 205
418 **NAIZAGAI** 92
105 **NAJEEBA** 41
40 **NAJM KABIR** (IRE) 96
6 **NAJOUM** (USA) C 179
309 **NAJRAAN** F 206
404 **NAKADAM** (FR) 9
173 **NAKED LASS** 5
300 **NAKEETA** 22
494 **NAMASSE** (BRZ) 11
290 **NAMASTE** (IRE) 31
534 **NAME IN LIGHTS** (IRE) 65
128 **NAME OF FAME** (IRE) 48
371 **NANCY O** (IRE) C 41
314 **NANDIGA** (USA) F 31
120 **NANDO PARRADO** 38
251 **NANNY MAKFI** 8
96 **NANNY MAY** 18
175 **NANS GIFT** (IRE) 35
328 **NANTOSUELTA** (IRE) 26
494 **NAO DA MAIS** (BRZ) 12
309 **NAOMH GEILEIS** (USA) C 207
16 **NAPPER TANDY** 91
400 **NAPPING** 23
545 **NARGYS** (IRE) C 180
7 **NARJES** 63
6 **NASH NASHA** 72
523 **NASHMIAH** (IRE) F 73
334 **NASHVILLE NIPPER** (IRE) 7
79 **NASMATT** F 62
538 **NASSAAKH** F 31
386 **NASSALAM** (FR) 77
554 **NASTASIYA** 52
226 **NAT LOVE** (IRE) 4
79 **NATAGORA** (FR) C 63
263 **NATALEENA** (IRE) 22
570 **NATALIE JAY** G 15
92 **NATCHEZ TRACE** 8
16 **NATE THE GREAT** 26
40 **NATION'S HISTORY** (IRE) 97
415 **NATIONAL BALLET** (IRE) 84
419 **NATIONAL GALLERY** (IRE) 163
263 **NATIONAL TREASURE** (IRE) 23
243 **NATIONS ALEXANDER** (IRE) C 170
376 **NATIVE CHOICE** (IRE) 29
383 **NATIVE FIGHTER** (IRE) 12
534 **NATIVE RIVER** (IRE) 66
482 **NATIVE ROBIN** (IRE) 23
170 **NATIVE SILVER** 8
406 **NATIVEGETAWAY** (IRE) 8
289 **NATTY DRESSER** (IRE) 10
428 **NATURAL BLUES** F 63
40 **NATURAL COLOUR** 98
386 **NATURAL HISTORY** 78
539 **NATURAL INSTINCT** (IRE) 21
309 **NATURAL VALUE** 107

386 **NATURALLY HIGH** (FR) 79
27 **NATURE** (IRE) 51
168 **NAUGHTY ANA** (IRE) 135
35 **NAUTICAL HAVEN** 11
1 **NAUTICAL MISS** (IRE) 38
519 **NAVAJO BEAUTY** 29
523 **NAVAJO CHANT** F 74
63 **NAVAJO DAWN** (IRE) 22
453 **NAVAJO EAGLE** 5
363 **NAVAJO PASS** 75
148 **NAVAJO SPRING** (IRE) 51
63 **NAVAL COMMANDER** 23
6 **NAVAL CROWN** 73
209 **NAVAL OFFICER** 1
89 **NAVARRA PRINCESS** (IRE) 3
554 **NAVEGAON GATE** 53
119 **NAVY DRUMS** (USA) 28
568 **NAVY GIRL** (IRE) 30
193 **NAWAFETH** (USA) 24
49 **NAWAR** 7
363 **NAYATI** 76
309 **NAYEF ROAD** (IRE) 23
180 **NAYON** 34
253 **NAZAAHA** (IRE) 92
545 **NAZUNA** (IRE) 109
395 **NEACHELLS BRIDGE** (IRE) 74
16 **NEANDRA** (GER) 187
178 **NEAR KETTERING** 17
168 **NEARLY A GONNA** 63
257 **NEARLY FAMOUS** 11
322 **NEARLY PERFECT** 25
517 **NEARLY THERE** 5
321 **NEBUCHADNEZZAR** (FR) 80
16 **NEBULOSA** 92
419 **NECHITA** (AUS) F 164
466 **NECK OR NOTHING** (GER) 5
475 **NECKLACE** (AUS) F 113
508 **NED** (FR) 20
1 **NED TANNER** (IRE) 39
168 **NED'S ESCAPE** (IRE) 64
386 **NEEDHAMS GAP** (IRE) 80
94 **NEEDWOOD BLOSSOM** 13
16 **NEENEE'S CHOICE** 93
142 **NEETSIDE** (IRE) 1
149 **NEFARIOUS** (IRE) 16
68 **NEFETARI** F 11
386 **NEFF** (GER) 81
363 **NEFYN POINT** 77
545 **NEGLIGENT** 181
545 **NEHALENNIA** (USA) C 182
167 **NEIGE D'ANTAN** G 103
195 **NELL 'N' FLO** (IRE) 9
109 **NELL QUICKLY** (IRE) 12
54 **NELL THE THIEF** 54
363 **NELL'S BELLS** (IRE) 78
571 **NELLIE DEEN** (IRE) 15
483 **NELLIE FRENCH** (IRE) 10
438 **NELLIE MOON** 18
461 **NELLS SON** 32
290 **NELSON GAY** (IRE) 32
93 **NELSON ROAD** (IRE) 13
133 **NELSON ROAD** (IRE) 13
139 **NELSON'S HILL** 3
398 **NELSON'S TOUCH** (IRE) 5
534 **NELSONS ROCK** 67
494 **NEMBO KID** (FR) 30
386 **NEMINOS** (FR) 131

148 **NEON CITY** 52
444 **NEON MOON** (IRE) 54
101 **NEPALAIS** 52
431 **NEPTUNE LEGEND** (IRE) 69
419 **NEPTUNE ROCK** (IRE) 96
6 **NEPTUNE SEAS** (IRE) 74
431 **NEPTUNE'S WONDER** (IRE) 40
389 **NERO ROCK** (IRE) 22
274 **NESHMEYA** F 99
403 **NESSFIELD BLUE** 2
105 **NESSINA** (USA) C 84
399 **NESSUN DORMA** (IRE) 147
434 **NESTOR PARK** (FR) 58
228 **NETHERTON** 107
204 **NETTLEBUSH** (IRE) 10
473 **NETYWELL** (FR) 55
417 **NEUTRAL** C 43
226 **NEVADA** 5
419 **NEVER BUSY** (USA) C 165
417 **NEVER CHANGE** (IRE) C 44
419 **NEVER FORGOTTEN** (IRE) 42
290 **NEVER IN** (IRE) C 62
526 **NEVER IN FOURTH** 48
76 **NEVER IN PARIS** (IRE) 15
446 **NEVER NO TROUBLE** 13
345 **NEVER SAID NOTHING** (IRE) 25
426 **NEVER SAY NEVER** (IRE) 8
518 **NEVER SAY WHEN** (IRE) 63
80 **NEVER SURRENDER** (IRE) 26
80 **NEVER TO FORGET** 27
501 **NEVER UP** (GER) 38
577 **NEVERBEEN TO PARIS** (IRE) 24
256 **NEVERUSHACON** (IRE) 48
326 **NEVEYAH** (IRE) 34
371 **NEVILE CHAMBERLAIN** (IRE) 17
329 **NEVILLE'S CROSS** (IRE) 30
444 **NEW AGE DAWNING** (IRE) 55
385 **NEW ARRIVAL** (IRE) 10
514 **NEW CLARE** 18
309 **NEW DAY** 108
300 **NEW DELHI EXPRESS** (IRE) 23
518 **NEW DIMENSION** 119
523 **NEW DYNASTY** (IRE) 33
6 **NEW EXCEED** (IRE) 75
431 **NEW FORCE** 41
446 **NEW HEIGHTS** 29
6 **NEW KINGDOM** (IRE) 76
589 **NEW LOOK** (FR) 15
27 **NEW MANDATE** (IRE) 52
329 **NEW MOON** (FR) 31
123 **NEW NATION** (IRE) 87
428 **NEW PROVIDENCE** (IRE) C 64
574 **NEW RHYTHM** 36
523 **NEW SEASON** (IRE) 34
534 **NEW TO THIS TOWN** (IRE) 68
369 **NEW ZEALANDER** 40
547 **NEWA** (IRE) 33
37 **NEWBERRY NEW** (IRE) 7
27 **NEWBOLT** (IRE) 19
239 **NEWERA** 12
121 **NEWGATE ANGEL** 8
121 **NEWGATE SQUAL** 9
580 **NEWLANDS CROSS** (IRE) 23
430 **NEWS DESK** C 8
571 **NEWS FOR PASCAL** (IRE) 16
564 **NEWSPEAK** (IRE) 5
76 **NEWSROOM** (IRE) C 120

578 **OMRAN** 12
417 **ON A PEDESTAL** (IRE) C 45
128 **ON A PROMISE** (IRE) 50
25 **ON A SESSION** (USA) 17
257 **ON CALL** (IRE) 12
359 **ON EDGE** 12
415 **ON ICE** (IRE) F 161
16 **ON LOCATION** (USA) F 193
212 **ON MY COMMAND** (IRE) 44
545 **ON MY WAY** 112
434 **ON SPRINGS** (IRE) 62
424 **ON THE BANDWAGON** (IRE) 60
270 **ON THE BLIND SIDE** (IRE) 134
62 **ON THE METER** (IRE) 15
569 **ON THE NOSE** 41
239 **ON THE PLATFORM** (IRE) 13
581 **ON THE QUIET** (FR) 54
376 **ON THE RHINE** (IRE) 31
544 **ON THE RIGHT TRACK** 11
601 **ON THE RISE** (IRE) 11
263 **ON THE RIVER** 53
227 **ON THE SLOPES** 33
6 **ON THE WARPATH** 16
408 **ON THE WILD SIDE** (IRE) 57
417 **ON TIPTOES** (IRE) 15
321 **ON TO VICTORY** 84
581 **ON TOUR** (IRE) 55
307 **ON WE GO** (IRE) 8
418 **ONAGATHERINGSTORM** (IRE) 97
587 **ONALEDGE** 43
379 **ONARAGGATIP** 27
385 **ONE DAY** 19
171 **ONE EYE ON VEGAS** 26
487 **ONE FER MAMMA** (IRE) 12
383 **ONE FINE MAN** (IRE) 15
473 **ONE FOR ARTHUR** (IRE) 56
31 **ONE FOR BRAD** (IRE) 8
553 **ONE FOR DUNSTAN** (IRE) 16
376 **ONE FOR JUNE** (IRE) C 77
421 **ONE FOR NAVIGATION** (IRE) 34
167 **ONE FOR THE LADIES** 61
584 **ONE FOR THE TEAM** 21
276 **ONE FOR YOU** (IRE) 76
270 **ONE HANDSOME DUDE** (IRE) 135
194 **ONE HART** (IRE) 9
244 **ONE IN ALL IN** (IRE) 25
105 **ONE JOURNEY** 42
120 **ONE LAST DANCE** (AUS) C 96
290 **ONE LAST DANCE** (IRE) 34
236 **ONE LAST GLANCE** 9
225 **ONE LAST HUG** 15
290 **ONE MORE DREAM** 64
582 **ONE MORE FLEURIE** (IRE) 54
319 **ONE MORE SU** 14
128 **ONE NIGHT IN MILAN** (IRE) 51
301 **ONE NIGHT STAND** 6
584 **ONE OF US** 22
64 **ONE ONE SEVEN** (IRE) 14
523 **ONE OVER PAR** 36
311 **ONE PUNCH TERRI** 10
253 **ONE RIVER** (FR) C 202
6 **ONE RULER** (IRE) 78
506 **ONE STEP BEYOND** (IRE) 15
205 **ONE STEP TOO FAR** (IRE) 6
588 **ONE STYLE** (IRE) 56
597 **ONE TIME** (IRE) C 19
563 **ONE TO GO** 16

434 **ONE TOUCH** (IRE) 63
19 **ONE WILD NIGHT** F 13
93 **ONEBABA** (IRE) 59
212 **ONEFORTHEROADTOM** 45
143 **ONEIDA TRIBE** (IRE) 11
322 **ONEMOREFORTHEROAD** 28
160 **ONENIGHTINMIAMI** (FR) 13
250 **ONENIGHTINTOWN** (IRE) 57
417 **ONES ARE WILD** 16
491 **ONESMOOTHOPERATOR** (USA) 55
411 **ONETHREEFIVENOTOUT** (IRE) 124
19 **ONEUPMANSHIP** (IRE) 14
274 **ONLINE ALEXANDER** (IRE) C 101
432 **ONLY DEBRIS** (IRE) 13
218 **ONLY GORGEOUS** (IRE) 12
227 **ONLY MONEY** (IRE) 34
256 **ONLY SKY** (IRE) 122
581 **ONLY THE BOLD** (IRE) 56
563 **ONLY THE BRAVE** (USA) 17
420 **ONLY TOGETHER** (IRE) F 47
250 **ONLYFOOLSOWNHORSES** (IRE) 58
256 **ONLYHUMAN** (IRE) 53
483 **ONNA BUGEISHA** (IRE) 17
415 **ONTARIO** (IRE) 85
363 **ONTHEFRONTFOOT** (IRE) 83
399 **ONTHEROPES** (IRE) 148
423 **ONURBIKE** 3
419 **ONWARD ROUTE** (IRE) 32
13 **OO DE LALLY** (IRE) 94
256 **OODNADATTA** (IRE) 123
180 **OOH IS IT** 36
134 **OOH LA LAH** 6
243 **OOJOOBA** C 172
173 **OPECHEE** (IRE) 7
76 **OPEN MYSTERY** 56
309 **OPEN VERSE** (USA) C 210
438 **OPEN WIDE** (IRE) 7
40 **OPENING SCENE** 99
291 **OPERA COMIQUE** (FR) F 181
16 **OPERA GIFT** 27
324 **OPERA GLASS** F 35
123 **OPERATIC** (IRE) 37
408 **OPERATIC EXPORT** (IRE) 58
473 **OPERATION OVERLORD** (IRE) 57
424 **OPINE** (IRE) 61
145 **OPPORTUNIST** 23
76 **OPPRESSIVE** 121
434 **OPTIMISE PRIME** (IRE) 64
181 **OPTIMISTIC BIAS** (IRE) 12
183 **ORANGE GINA** 7
274 **ORAZIO** (IRE) 102
421 **ORBAAN** 35
260 **ORBIT OF IOLITE** 6
276 **ORBYS LEGEND** (IRE) 77
336 **ORCHARD GROVE** (IRE) 19
444 **ORCHARD THIEVES** (IRE) 60
482 **ORCHARDSTOWN CROSS** (IRE) 24
408 **ORCHESTRAL RAIN** (IRE) 59
66 **ORCHESTRATED** (IRE) 1
124 **ORCHID ROSE** (IRE) 16
415 **ORDER OF AUSTRALIA** (IRE) 10
473 **ORDER OF THISTLE** (IRE) 15
418 **ORDERED LIVES** (IRE) 98
105 **ORDEROFSUCCESSION** 43
442 **ORGANDI** (FR) 22
487 **ORGANISED SOLUTION** (FR) 13

420 **ORGANZA** C 48
27 **ORGETORIX** 54
157 **ORIENT SUNSET** 10
491 **ORIENTAL ART** 56
546 **ORIENTAL CROSS** (IRE) 55
225 **ORIENTAL LILLY** 16
491 **ORIENTAL MYSTIQUE** 16
262 **ORIENTAL RELATION** (IRE) 7
63 **ORIENTAL ROMANCE** (IRE) F 54
325 **ORIENTAL SPIRIT** 19
555 **ORIENTAL STEP** (IRE) F 35
340 **ORIGINAL CHOICE** (IRE) 10
537 **ORIGINATOR** (IRE) 27
547 **ORIHIME** (IRE) 14
446 **ORIN SWIFT** (IRE) 6
399 **ORION D'AUBRELLE** (FR) 149
168 **ORION'S BOW** 67
473 **ORIONINVERNESS** (IRE) 59
552 **ORKAN** 28
115 **ORLAS' ABBEY** 16
190 **ORMSKIRK** 33
237 **ORNATE** 6
431 **ORNELIA RUEE** (IRE) F 44
173 **OROBAS** (IRE) 8
314 **ORPHIUCHUS** (IRE) 24
424 **ORRISDALE** (IRE) 62
53 **ORSINO** (IRE) 28
378 **ORVAR** (IRE) 16
546 **OSCA LOCA** (IRE) 56
126 **OSCAR ASCHE** (IRE) 24
367 **OSCAR BLUE** (IRE) 8
175 **OSCAR CEREMONY** (IRE) 38
128 **OSCAR CLOUDS** (IRE) 52
534 **OSCAR ELITE** (IRE) 73
252 **OSCAR NOMINATION** (IRE) 21
222 **OSCAR ROBERTSON** (IRE) 59
418 **OSCAR ROSE** (IRE) 99
501 **OSCAR WILDE** (IRE) 40
86 **OSCARS LEADER** (IRE) 26
411 **OSCARS MOONSHINE** (IRE) 125
502 **OSCARSMAN** (IRE) 12
326 **OSHIPONGA** F 52
418 **OSKI** (IRE) 100
7 **OSLO** 66
456 **OSPREY CALL** (IRE) 33
378 **OSTILIO** 17
598 **OSTUNI** (FR) 22
56 **OTAGO** 11
245 **OTAY** (IRE) 48
473 **OTELLO MOOR** (IRE) 60
243 **OTI MA BOATI** 23
408 **OTTAVIO** 60
210 **OTTER LYNN** 10
509 **OTTEY** 48
25 **OTTO OYL** 38
588 **OTTOLINE** 57
503 **OTTOMAN STYLE** 35
363 **OTTONIAN** 81
228 **OTYRAR** 108
191 **OUD METHA BRIDGE** (IRE) 4
171 **OUR BUBBA** (IRE) 27
124 **OUR CILLA** 10
418 **OUR COLOSSUS** (IRE) 101
295 **OUR DOT'S BABY** (IRE) 23
575 **OUR ELSIE** 14
441 **OUR ETHEL** F 6
582 **OUR IDIC BOY** (IRE) 55

526 **PETITE JACK** 19
253 **PETITE NYMPHE** F 204
418 **PETITE POWER** (IRE) 107
473 **PETITE RHAPSODY** (IRE) 61
134 **PETITIONER** (IRE) 7
303 **PETRASTAR** 22
253 **PETRILA** (IRE) 205
411 **PETROSSIAN** (IRE) 128
303 **PETRUCCI** (IRE) 23
498 **PETRULER** 7
61 **PETTOCHSIDE** 8
547 **PETUNIE** (FR) 16
488 **PEUR DE RIEN** (FR) 37
51 **PHANTASMAGORIC** (IRE) F 43
369 **PHANTOMOFTHEOSCAR** (IRE) 43
376 **PHECDA** (FR) G 68
48 **PHEDRE** (FR) 14
235 **PHIL DE PAIL** (FR) 49
369 **PHIL HEALY** (IRE) 44
424 **PHIL THE THRILL** (FR) 68
506 **PHILAMUNDO** (IRE) 18
369 **PHILLAPA SUE** (IRE) 45
258 **PHILLIPSTOWN ELLEN** (IRE) 26
168 **PHOENIX APPROACH** (IRE) 70
163 **PHOENIX AQUILUS** (IRE) 6
408 **PHOENIX DAWN** 61
423 **PHOENIX SONG** 4
347 **PHOENIX STAR** (IRE) 3
263 **PHOENIX STRIKE** 24
212 **PHOENIX WAY** (IRE) 49
51 **PHOLAS** 10
92 **PHOTOGRAPH** (IRE) 9
132 **PHUKET POWER** (IRE) 12
508 **PIACERE** (IRE) C 28
329 **PIAFF BUBBLES** (IRE) 34
94 **PIANISSIMO** 8
61 **PIAZOLLA** (IRE) 18
65 **PIAZON** 17
411 **PIC D'ORHY** (FR) 129
234 **PICARA'S PROMISE** 53
289 **PICC AN ANGEL** 11
180 **PICCELINA** F 50
221 **PICCOLA SISSI** (IRE) F 17
499 **PICKING PEACHES** (IRE) 20
51 **PICKLE** F 44
318 **PICKNICK PARK** 12
462 **PICKS PINTA** 3
385 **PICKYOUROWN** (IRE) 13
544 **PICOTA** 25
62 **PICTURESQUE VIEW** (IRE) 16
40 **PIECE OF HISTORY** (IRE) 55
167 **PIECE OF MAGIC** F 104
228 **PIED PIPER** 112
372 **PIENTA** (USA) 68
545 **PIERRE LAPIN** (IRE) 23
6 **PIETRAFIORE** (IRE) C 185
554 **PIFFLE** (IRE) 88
165 **PIGEON PIE** G 12
538 **PIGEON PIE** G 32
424 **PIGGY WINKLE** (IRE) 69
494 **PIKES PEAK** (FR) 14
276 **PILEON** (FR) 78
120 **PILGRIM'S LIGHT** (IRE) 40
53 **PILGRIMS KING** (IRE) 30
145 **PILGRIMS PURSUIT** 25
309 **PILLAR OF HOPE** 115
505 **PILLAR OF STEEL** 10

93 **PILOT WINGS** (IRE) 61
6 **PIMPERNEL** (IRE) C 186
296 **PIN CUSHION** C 29
309 **PINA COLLADA** 116
120 **PINBALL WIZARD** (IRE) 41
363 **PINCH OF GINGER** (IRE) 86
16 **PINEAPPLE RING** 95
494 **PINGO** (FR) 31
534 **PINGSHOU** (IRE) 76
375 **PINK CAVIAR** 59
58 **PINK EYED PEDRO** 10
10 **PINK FLAMINGO** 29
431 **PINK GOLD** (IRE) 46
125 **PINK JAZZ** (IRE) 11
588 **PINK LEGEND** 59
455 **PINK SHEETS** (IRE) 4
76 **PINK STORM** 123
372 **PINKERTON** 69
313 **PINNACLE PEAK** 24
587 **PINNATA** (IRE) 23
161 **PINSON DU RHEU** (FR) 26
419 **PIONEER BRIDE** (USA) C 171
419 **PIONEER GIRL** (IRE) C 172
2 **PIPERS DREAM** 3
527 **PIPES OF PEACE** (IRE) 28
270 **PIPESMOKER** (FR) 142
79 **PIPS TUNE** 12
167 **PIRANHA** (IRE) G 105
191 **PIRANHADRAMA** 15
193 **PIRATE KING** 26
57 **PIRATE LASS** (IRE) 2
62 **PIRATE SAM** 17
245 **PIRITA** (IRE) C 72
176 **PIROUETTE QUEEN** 12
105 **PIROUZ** 92
101 **PISANELLO** (IRE) 16
449 **PISELLI MOLLI** (IRE) 26
503 **PISGAH PIKE** (IRE) 37
144 **PISTOL** (IRE) 5
175 **PISTOL PARK** (FR) 40
270 **PISTOL WHIPPED** (IRE) 143
474 **PISTOLETTO** (USA) 9
509 **PITA PINTA** (IRE) 27
333 **PITCH IT UP** 48
97 **PITCHCOMBE** 15
228 **PITCHER'S POINT** (USA) 27
574 **PITEMPTON POWER** (IRE) 37
529 **PIVELLO** 17
16 **PIVOINE** (IRE) 29
27 **PIVOTAL DRIVE** (IRE) F 117
123 **PIVOTAL MISSION** F 90
375 **PIVOTAL TIME** 30
523 **PIVOTAL'S PRINCESS** (IRE) F 77
415 **PIVOTALIA** (IRE) C 162
168 **PIVOTING** 139
139 **PIXELATIT** 4
417 **PIZ BADILE** (IRE) 47
123 **PIZZARRA** F 91
479 **PLACATED** 8
22 **PLACEDELA CONCORDE** 22
6 **PLACIDIA** (IRE) F 187
536 **PLAN OF ESCAPE** (IRE) 10
431 **PLANET LEGEND** (IRE) 73
146 **PLANET NINE** (IRE) 28
593 **PLANSINA** 14
34 **PLANTADREAM** 11
398 **PLANTAGENET** 24

18 **PLASTIC PADDY** 22
29 **PLATFORM NINETEEN** (IRE) 7
386 **PLATINUM PRINCE** 86
128 **PLATINUMCARD** (IRE) 54
438 **PLATITUDE** 9
107 **PLAY ALL DAY** (USA) 31
398 **PLAYA BLANCA** (IRE) 25
492 **PLAYFUL SAINT** (FR) 108
105 **PLEASANT MAN** 44
6 **PLEASCACH** (IRE) C 188
309 **PLEASEMETOO** (IRE) F 213
305 **PLEASURE GARDEN** (USA) 10
523 **PLEASURE PLACE** (FR) F 78
296 **PLEDGE OF HONOUR** 19
385 **PLEDGE OF PEACE** (IRE) 14
546 **PLENEY** 57
402 **PLENTY IN THE TANK** (IRE) 97
484 **PLENTY OF BUTTY** (IRE) 27
379 **PLOVER** F 38
180 **PLUM RUN** (IRE) 37
330 **PLUMAGE** (FR) 48
243 **PLUME ROSE** F 175
464 **PLUMETTE** 6
180 **PLUNGER** 13
344 **PLYMOUTH ROCK** (IRE) 25
581 **POBBLES BAY** (IRE) 59
474 **POCKETEER** (IRE) 16
529 **POCO CONTANTE** 18
228 **POET OF LIFE** (IRE) 113
168 **POET'S DAWN** 71
440 **POET'S EYE** 11
475 **POET'S KING** 64
25 **POET'S LADY** 12
555 **POET'S PARK** 27
44 **POET'S REFLECTION** (IRE) 6
31 **POETIC DANCER** G 17
2 **POETIC DEED** 4
93 **POETIC FORCE** (IRE) 62
288 **POETIC PRESENCE** (IRE) 4
167 **POETIC VERSE** F 62
410 **POETIKEL PIECE** 15
274 **POGO** (IRE) 20
212 **POGO I AM** 50
363 **POGUE** (IRE) 87
160 **POINT LOUISE** 14
274 **POINT LYNAS** (IRE) 104
419 **POINT NEPEAN** (IRE) 97
353 **POINT OF HONOUR** (IRE) 190
546 **POINT OF PRINCIPLE** (IRE) 58
297 **POINT OF WOODS** 12
79 **POINTED AND SHARP** (IRE) 79
310 **POKARI** (FR) 8
362 **POKER MASTER** (IRE) 7
444 **POKER PLAY** (FR) 64
276 **POL CROCAN** (IRE) 80
268 **POL MA CREE** 3
264 **POLA CHANCE** (FR) 39
25 **POLAM LANE** 39
351 **POLAR CLOUD** 12
449 **POLAR ICE** 27
271 **POLAR LIGHT** 21
577 **POLDARK CROSS** (IRE) 26
6 **POLICORO** (IRE) F 189
418 **POLISH** 108
509 **POLISH BELLE** F 49
256 **POLISHED STEEL** (IRE) 55
307 **POLITELYSED** G 9

307 **POLITELYSED** G 11
495 **POLITICISM** 39
16 **POLITICS** (IRE) 96
411 **POLITOLOGUE** (FR) 130
253 **POLKA DOT** (IRE) C 206
87 **POLLINATE** 24
270 **POLLY PEACHUM** (IRE) G 144
243 **POLLY'S MARK** C 176
137 **POLLYAMOROUS** (IRE) 4
329 **POLYDORA** (IRE) 35
348 **POLYPHONY** (IRE) 14
27 **POMELO** 57
264 **POMME** 40
6 **POMOLOGY** (USA) C 190
419 **PONDUS** 46
588 **PONIENTE** 60
309 **PONS AELIUS** 214
399 **PONT AVAL** (FR) 150
399 **PONT AVEN** (FR) 151
274 **PONTIUS** (IRE) 61
488 **PONTRESINA** (IRE) 38
113 **POOKIE PEKAN** (IRE) 26
189 **POOKY** 49
132 **POOL BAR LADY** 37
578 **POOL FUND** (IRE) 13
397 **POOR DUKE** (IRE) 13
93 **POP DANCER** (IRE) 63
442 **POP MISTRESS** (IRE) 23
424 **POP ROCKSTAR** (IRE) 70
369 **POP THE CHAMPAGNE** (FR) 46
424 **POP THE CORK** 71
50 **POP YA COLLAR** (IRE) 55
543 **POPE GREGORY** 3
105 **POPLIN** C 93
554 **POPMASTER** (IRE) 59
437 **POPPING CORKS** (IRE) 9
93 **POPPLE** 64
515 **POPPOP** (FR) 6
211 **POPPY JAG** (IRE) 20
123 **POPULIST** (IRE) C 92
301 **PORFIN** (IRE) 19
87 **PORNSTAR MARTINI** (IRE) 25
99 **PORT LAIRGE** 6
154 **PORT O'CLOCK** (IRE) 11
402 **PORT OF MARS** (IRE) 98
341 **PORT OR STARBOARD** (IRE) 13
419 **PORT PHILIP** (IRE) 98
256 **PORT STANLEY** 56
180 **PORTELBAY** 38
168 **PORTENO** 140
518 **PORTFOLIO** (JPN) 65
495 **PORTH DIANA** (IRE) 22
42 **PORTHGWIDDEN BEACH** (USA) G 6
61 **PORTO FERRO** (IRE) 9
167 **PORTRAITOFMYLOVE** (IRE) G 106
228 **PORTRUSH** 28
234 **PORTRUSH TED** (IRE) 54
157 **PORTSTORM** 11
563 **PORTUGUESEPRINCESS** (IRE) 21
582 **PORTWAY FLYER** (IRE) 58
387 **POSE** (IRE) F 32
555 **POSH GIRL** 28
473 **POSH ROIS** (IRE) 62
545 **POSITANO** 115
120 **POSITIVE** 7
148 **POSITIVE MENTALITY** (IRE) 56
454 **POSSIBLE AMBITION** 40

518 **POSSIBLE MAN** 66
253 **POSTED** 26
179 **POSTIE** 9
545 **POSTILEO** (IRE) 24
398 **POSTMAN** (FR) 26
27 **POSTMARK** 118
132 **POT OF PAINT** 13
518 **POTAPOVA** 67
179 **POTENZA** (IRE) 10
321 **POTTERMAN** 89
580 **POTTERS CORNER** (IRE) 25
557 **POTTERS FREDDIE** 21
548 **POTTERS HEDGER** 25
548 **POTTERS LEGEND** 26
557 **POTTERS QUESTION** 14
276 **POTTERS VENTURE** (IRE) 81
333 **POTTERS VISION** (IRE) 49
334 **POTTLEREAGHEXPRESS** (IRE) 10
335 **POUCOR** 7
539 **POUDRETTEITE** C 32
128 **POUGNE BOBBI** (FR) 55
532 **POULNASHERRY DOVE** (IRE) G 40
47 **POUND OFF YOU** 16
329 **POUNDING POET** (IRE) 36
582 **POUR JOIE** 59
93 **POUR LA VICTOIRE** (IRE) 65
35 **POUR ME A DRINK** 13
381 **POUR UNE RAISON** (FR) 4
6 **POWDER SNOW** (USA) F 191
63 **POWER ABOVE** (IRE) 29
325 **POWER EM** 20
109 **POWER HOME** (IRE) 4
537 **POWER OF DARKNESS** 8
399 **POWER OF PAUSE** (IRE) 152
431 **POWER OF STATES** (IRE) 11
421 **POWER OF TIME** (IRE) 37
63 **POWER OVER ME** (IRE) 30
91 **POWER PLAYER** 24
550 **POWER POINT** 11
253 **POWER STATION** 96
259 **POWERFUL DREAM** (IRE) 11
424 **POWERFUL HERO** (AUS) 72
580 **POWERFUL POSITION** (IRE) 26
372 **POWERFUL TED** (IRE) 70
221 **POWERFULSTORM** F 18
527 **POWERSTOWN PARK** (IRE) 29
107 **POWHATAN** (FR) 32
94 **POY** 15
411 **POZO EMERY** (FR) 131
355 **PRABENI** 13
159 **PRACTICALLYPERFECT** (IRE) C 66
274 **PRADO** 62
545 **PRAIANO** (GER) 116
419 **PRAIRIE DANCER** (IRE) 99
93 **PRAIRIE TOWN** (IRE) 66
50 **PRAISE OF SHADOWS** (IRE) 56
189 **PRAISE THE LORD** 16
344 **PRAXEOLOGY** (IRE) 26
415 **PREAMBLE** (IRE) 86
285 **PRECIOUS** 38
253 **PRECIOUS ANGEL** (IRE) C 207
270 **PRECIOUS CARGO** (IRE) 45
62 **PRECIOUS GEM** (IRE) G 18
43 **PRECIOUS GROUND** 12
557 **PRECIOUS PLUM** 15
80 **PRECISELY** 29
345 **PRECISION STORM** 26

369 **PRELUDE TO GLORY** (IRE) 47
494 **PRELUNA** (FR) 32
545 **PREMIER POWER** 25
308 **PREMIERE DANSEUSE** C 76
534 **PREMIUMACCESS** (IRE) 77
144 **PRESENCE FELT** (IRE) 6
402 **PRESENCE OF MIND** (FR) 99
424 **PRESENT CHIEF** (IRE) 73
168 **PRESENT DAY** F 166
333 **PRESENT DESTINY** (IRE) 50
442 **PRESENT FROM DUBAI** (IRE) 24
532 **PRESENT LEADER** M 41
411 **PRESENT MAN** (IRE) 132
581 **PRESENT VALUE** (IRE) 60
363 **PRESENTANDCOUNTING** (IRE) 88
522 **PRESENTEDWITHWINGS** (IRE) 29
67 **PRESENTING BEARA** (IRE) 8
321 **PRESENTING PETE** (IRE) 90
258 **PRESENTING YEATS** (IRE) 27
210 **PRESGRAVE** (IRE) 11
227 **PRESS YOUR LUCK** (IRE) 36
424 **PRESSURE SENSITIVE** (IRE) 74
276 **PRESUMING ED** (IRE) 82
449 **PRETENDING** (IRE) 61
50 **PRETENDING** (ITY) 14
419 **PRETTY BLUE** (IRE) 173
300 **PRETTY BONNIE** C 76
475 **PRETTY DARLING** (IRE) C 116
123 **PRETTY FAIR** (IRE) 39
236 **PRETTY FANTASY** (IRE) 12
419 **PRETTY GORGEOUS** (FR) 100
50 **PRETTY IN GREY** 15
547 **PRETTY SOLDIER** (GER) 17
256 **PRETTY'N'SMART** (IRE) 126
395 **PRETTYLITTLETHING** (IRE) 82
194 **PREY FOR GLORY** 20
6 **PRICELESS** F 192
421 **PRICELESS JEWEL** C 133
253 **PRIDE ASIDE** 208
214 **PRIDE DAY** 54
160 **PRIDE OF AMERICA** (FR) 4
120 **PRIDE OF ENGLAND** 42
379 **PRIDE OF HAWRIDGE** (IRE) 28
418 **PRIDE OF LECALE** 109
391 **PRIDE OF NEPAL** 37
158 **PRIDE OF PEMBERLEY** (IRE) 2
156 **PRIDE OF PIMLICO** (IRE) 6
243 **PRIDE OF PRIORY** 88
316 **PRIDE OF QATAR** (IRE) 24
316 **PRIDE OF UK** 25
9 **PRIDE PARK** (IRE) 4
580 **PRIMAL FOCUS** (IRE) 27
306 **PRIME APPROACH** (IRE) 1
581 **PRIME PRETENDER** 61
581 **PRIME VENTURE** (IRE) 62
554 **PRIMO BACIO** (IRE) 60
108 **PRIMO LADY** C 42
225 **PRIMO'S COMET** 18
33 **PRIMROSE LADY** (FR) F 13
494 **PRIMUS INCITATUS** (IRE) 15
245 **PRINCE ABAMA** (IRE) 49
485 **PRINCE ABU** (IRE) 16
27 **PRINCE ALEX** 20
353 **PRINCE ALI** 32
527 **PRINCE DES FICHAUX** (FR) 30
473 **PRINCE DUNDEE** (IRE) 63
545 **PRINCE EIJI** 26

243 **QATAR POWER** (FR) F 177
537 **QAWAASEM** (IRE) F 45
167 **QAWAMEES** (IRE) 34
253 **QAYSAR** (FR) 27
258 **QEETHAARA** (USA) F 51
491 **QR PASSION** (USA) 57
537 **QUAIL LANDING** F 46
215 **QUAINT** (FR) 7
6 **QUALIFY** (IRE) F 196
577 **QUALISMART** (FR) 27
601 **QUALITEE** M 12
14 **QUANAH** (IRE) 16
391 **QUARANTINI** 38
424 **QUARENTA** (FR) 78
160 **QUARRY BEACH** 5
344 **QUARTET** 62
424 **QUARTZ DU RHEU** (FR) 79
27 **QUAVERING** (FR) 121
122 **QUAY QUEST** 6
554 **QUAYBIRD** (IRE) 89
148 **QUE AMORO** (IRE) 26
149 **QUE QUIERES** (USA) 19
330 **QUECHUACH** 49
295 **QUEEN AMONG KINGS** (IRE) 25
25 **QUEEN ATHENA** (IRE) C 50
228 **QUEEN CHARLOTTE** 115
415 **QUEEN CLEOPATRA** (IRE) F 165
545 **QUEEN DAENERYS** (IRE) 27
475 **QUEEN JO JO** 18
214 **QUEEN LAGERTHA** 36
253 **QUEEN OF ASIA** (IRE) 99
162 **QUEEN OF BURGUNDY** 7
123 **QUEEN OF CHANGE** (IRE) 96
186 **QUEEN OF KALAHARI** 8
51 **QUEEN OF MEAN** C 46
368 **QUEEN OF RIO** (IRE) 19
88 **QUEEN OF THE COURT** (IRE) 5
111 **QUEEN OF THE ROAD** 14
16 **QUEEN OF THE STARS** F 196
534 **QUEEN OF THE WIND** 79
554 **QUEEN OF THORNS** 61
228 **QUEEN OF ZABEEL** 116
518 **QUEEN POWER** (IRE) 20
93 **QUEEN SARABI** (IRE) 104
417 **QUEEN TITI** (IRE) F 48
384 **QUEEN ZAIN** (IRE) C 31
167 **QUEEN'S CASTLE** C 107
421 **QUEEN'S COURSE** (IRE) 38
518 **QUEEN'S FAIR** 69
107 **QUEEN'S HARLEQUIN** (FR) 57
475 **QUEEN'S HEIR** (IRE) 117
4 **QUEEN'S LAW** G 19
222 **QUEEN'S LEADER** G 62
475 **QUEEN'S ORDER** 19
475 **QUEEN'S SARGENT** (FR) 20
456 **QUEEN'S SOLDIER** (GER) 35
415 **QUEEN'S SPEECH** (IRE) 30
245 **QUEENIE KEEN** (IRE) C 73
171 **QUEENOHEARTS** (IRE) 28
444 **QUEENS CAVE** (IRE) 65
334 **QUEENS PRESENT** (IRE) 11
270 **QUEENS RIVER** 148
540 **QUEENS ROAD** (IRE) 12
419 **QUEENSHIP** (IRE) 101
411 **QUEL DESTIN** (FR) 135
326 **QUEL KAIMA** (GER) 54
362 **QUELLA COSA** 8

449 **QUELLA SPERANZA** 62
160 **QUELLE VITESSE** (GER) 15
110 **QUEMONDA** 14
215 **QUENCH DOLLY** 8
431 **QUENELLE D'OR** 47
155 **QUERCUS** (IRE) 7
518 **QUERULOUS** (USA) C 123
84 **QUEST FOR FUN** 3
552 **QUEST FOR LIFE** 31
481 **QUESTION** (USA) C 48
386 **QUIANA** 89
545 **QUICK APPROACH** 118
446 **QUICK BREATH** 7
22 **QUICK BREW** 23
76 **QUICK CHANGE** 125
329 **QUICK DRAW** (IRE) 37
507 **QUICK GETAWAY** (IRE) 11
418 **QUICK GRABIM** (IRE) 112
167 **QUICK LOOK** 35
260 **QUICK MONET** (IRE) 7
86 **QUICK PICK** (IRE) 29
347 **QUICK THOUGHT** (IRE) G 10
588 **QUICK WAVE** (FR) 62
175 **QUICKLY DOES IT** 43
16 **QUICKSTEP LADY** 30
290 **QUICKSTEP QUEEN** C 66
391 **QUICKTHORN** 13
492 **QUID PRO QUO** (IRE) 111
311 **QUIET ASSASSIN** (IRE) 11
40 **QUIET EVENING** (IRE) 56
492 **QUIET FLOW** 112
503 **QUIET PENNY** 38
272 **QUIET PRIDE** (IRE) 15
371 **QUIET PROTEST** (USA) C 45
326 **QUIET THUNDER** (IRE) 37
588 **QUIETLYFLOWSTHEDON** 63
105 **QUILTED** 45
434 **QUINNSBORO NATIVE** (IRE) G 67
514 **QUINNSBOROTEMPTRES** (IRE) 22
434 **QUINTA DO MAR** (IRE) 68
321 **QUINTESSA** 140
6 **QUINTILLUS** 80
333 **QUIQUILLO** (USA) G 51
56 **QUITA** 14
372 **QUITE INCREDIBLE** (IRE) 71
569 **QUITE SMART** (FR) F 60
92 **QUITEACATCH** 10
117 **QUIVVY LOUGH** (IRE) 11
386 **QULOOB** 90
581 **QUOI DE NEUF** (IRE) 63
250 **QUOTELINE DIRECT** 60
228 **QURTAJANA** (FR) 117
436 **QWICKEN** (IRE) 29
4 **R BERNARD** 14
447 **R BREN** (IRE) 17
64 **RAABEH** 17
7 **RAADEA** 68
545 **RAADOBARG** (IRE) 119
40 **RAAEB** (IRE) 57
43 **RAAJIHAH** 13
40 **RAAJIL** (IRE) 101
491 **RAAKIB ALHAWA** (IRE) 18
79 **RAAQY** (IRE) C 64
258 **RAASEL** 69
7 **RAASEL** 69
217 **RABAT** (IRE) 11
222 **RABBLE ROUSER** (IRE) 63

424 **RABSKI** (IRE) 80
132 **RACE IN FOCUS** (IRE) C 72
124 **RACEMAKER** 11
511 **RACING COUNTRY** (IRE) 10
1 **RACING PULSE** (IRE) 44
424 **RACING SNAKE** 81
464 **RACING SPIRIT** 7
283 **RACY STACEY** 9
253 **RADAD** (IRE) 211
250 **RADDLE AND HUM** (IRE) 61
368 **RADETSKY** (USA) 9
159 **RADHAADH** (IRE) C 67
535 **RADIANT LIGHT** 11
375 **RADIATION** F 60
16 **RADIOACTIVE** (FR) 197
376 **RAECIUS FELIX** (IRE) 35
434 **RAF TAVEL** (FR) 69
376 **RAFFERTY'S RETURN** 36
577 **RAFFLES GITANE** (FR) 28
519 **RAFFLES REBEL** 30
321 **RAFIKI** (FR) 141
386 **RAFIOT** (USA) 91
499 **RAFTA** (IRE) C 31
395 **RAGAMUFFIN** (IRE) 85
76 **RAGGLE TAGGLE** (IRE) F 126
562 **RAGING RASCAL** (IRE) 22
286 **RAGTAG RASCAL** (IRE) 9
274 **RAGTIME DANCER** C 106
191 **RAHA** 8
449 **RAHAALA** (IRE) F 63
141 **RAHMAH** (IRE) 12
323 **RAIFF** (IRE) 66
517 **RAIL DANCER** 7
581 **RAILROAD JUNKIE** (IRE) 64
462 **RAIN CAP** 4
523 **RAIN GAUGE** (IRE) 39
415 **RAIN GODDESS** (IRE) C 166
376 **RAINBOW APPLAUSE** (IRE) 69
321 **RAINBOW DREAMER** 92
228 **RAINBOW FIRE** (IRE) 118
348 **RAINBOW JET** (IRE) 15
463 **RAINBOW MIRAGE** 7
433 **RAINBOW SIGN** 6
488 **RAINBOW STORM** (FR) 39
420 **RAINBOW'S GIFT** 36
253 **RAINBOW'S PONY** (IRE) 100
343 **RAINMAKER** (IRE) 37
98 **RAINS OF CASTAMERE** 22
225 **RAINY CITY** (IRE) 19
411 **RAINYDAY WOMAN** 136
523 **RAISE THE ROOF** (IRE) 40
419 **RAISE YOU** (IRE) 47
39 **RAISE YOUR HAND** (IRE) 14
428 **RAISING SAND** 13
455 **RAIYSINA** F 11
317 **RAJAPUR** 13
333 **RAJARAN** (FR) 52
415 **RAJEEM** C 167
132 **RAJINSKY** (IRE) 14
108 **RAJMEISTER** 20
306 **RAKEMATIZ** 7
303 **RAKHINE STATE** (IRE) 24
363 **RALF DES NOES** (FR) 91
570 **RALLY DRIVER** 17
574 **RALPHY BOY TWO** (IRE) 39
385 **RAMATUELLE** 15
196 **RAMBLING RIVER** 4

399 **RAMILLIES** (IRE) 155
278 **RAMONEX** (GER) 14
227 **RAMORE WILL** (IRE) 37
444 **RAMSES DE TEILLEE** (FR) 66
245 **RANALLAGH ROCKET** (IRE) C 74
16 **RANCH HAND** 31
228 **RANCHERO** 119
237 **RANCHO MONTOYA** (IRE) F 13
444 **RANCO** 67
554 **RANDOM HARVEST** (IRE) 62
254 **RANGEFIELD EXPRESS** (IRE) 5
491 **RANI OF JHANSI** 58
324 **RANIA** (IRE) 21
126 **RANIERI** (IRE) 28
504 **RANN OF KUTCH** (IRE) 7
518 **RANSOM** 21
518 **RAOOF** 22
243 **RAOUL DUFY** 178
74 **RAPAZINE** 4
270 **RAPID FLIGHT** 149
531 **RAPID FRITZ** (IRE) 7
473 **RAPID RAIDER** (IRE) 64
454 **RAPID RECRUIT** (IRE) C 57
256 **RAPID RESPONSE** (FR) 58
420 **RAQISA** 37
537 **RAQRAAQ** (USA) 30
166 **RARE CLOUDS** 4
420 **RARE GROOVE** (IRE) 16
534 **RAREST DIAMOND** (IRE) 80
94 **RASAASY** (IRE) 9
79 **RASHEED** (IRE) 34
586 **RASPBERRY** 4
376 **RATAAR** 70
272 **RATAFIA** 23
369 **RATFACEMCDOUGALL** (IRE) 48
146 **RATH AN IUIR** (IRE) 30
537 **RATHAATH** (IRE) C 47
221 **RATHAGAN** 5
475 **RATHBONE** 21
582 **RATHBRIDE PRINCE** (IRE) 61
270 **RATHER BE** (IRE) 150
263 **RATHHILL** (IRE) 26
39 **RATHLEEK** G 15
444 **RATHLIN ROSE** (IRE) 68
450 **RATHNURE RANGER** (IRE) 17
419 **RATIB** 102
213 **RATOUTE YUTTY** 6
420 **RATTLE OWL** 17
132 **RATTLING ROSIE** 38
87 **RAVELLO SUNSET** 45
343 **RAVEN COURT** (IRE) 38
464 **RAVEN'S RAFT** (IRE) 8
434 **RAVEN'S TOWER** (USA) 70
501 **RAVENHILL ROAD** (IRE) 43
391 **RAVENS ARK** 14
323 **RAVENSCAR** (IRE) 67
300 **RAVENSCRAIG CASTLE** 60
475 **RAVENSWING** (IRE) 118
235 **RAVING BONKERS** 50
110 **RAW HIDE** (IRE) 27
554 **RAY DAY** 63
386 **RAY'S THE ONE** 92
245 **RAYADIYR** (IRE) 50
245 **RAYAGARA** (IRE) 51
253 **RAYAHEEN** C 212
245 **RAYDIYA** (IRE) C 75
128 **RAYMOND** (IRE) 57

321 **RAYMOND TUSK** (IRE) 93
323 **RAYNA'S WORLD** (IRE) 68
76 **RAYONG** 17
111 **RAYTHEHANDYMAN** (IRE) 15
76 **RAYYAN** 18
294 **RAZIEL** 10
119 **RAZOR GLASS** (USA) 29
474 **REACHING AHEAD** (USA) C 21
545 **REACT** 120
211 **REACTION TIME** 21
76 **READMAN** 7
424 **READY AND ABLE** (IRE) 82
436 **READY FREDDIE GO** (IRE) 18
123 **READY TO SHINE** (IRE) 97
243 **READY TO VENTURE** 89
473 **READYSTEADYBEAU** (FR) 65
256 **REAL APPEAL** (GER) 59
558 **REAL ARMANI** 3
10 **REAL ESTATE** (IRE) 31
411 **REAL STEEL** (IRE) 137
492 **REAL STONE** 113
538 **REAL TERMS** 20
40 **REAL WORLD** (IRE) 58
29 **REALIST** 30
410 **REALLY LOVELY** (IRE) F 16
6 **REALLY SPECIAL** F 197
400 **REALLY SUPER** 25
227 **REALLYRADICAL** (IRE) 38
167 **REBEL AT DAWN** (IRE) 58
408 **REBEL FORCE** (IRE) G 108
454 **REBEL LEADER** (IRE) 63
418 **REBEL REDEMPTION** 20
321 **REBEL ROXY** (IRE) 113
526 **REBEL ROYAL** (IRE) 94
438 **REBEL SPIRIT** 38
6 **REBEL TERRITORY** 19
399 **REBEL'S ROMANCE** (IRE) 81
214 **REBELLITO** (FR) 156
455 **RECALL IT ALL** 37
122 **RECALL THE SHOW** 122
25 **RECHERCHER** 122
309 **RECKLESS ENDEAVOUR** (IRE) 19
175 **RECKONING** (IRE) F 216
93 **RECLAIM VICTORY** (IRE) 44
16 **RECON MISSION** (IRE) 68
534 **RECOVERY RUN** 97
259 **RECTORY OAK** (IRE) 81
149 **RECTORY ROAD** 12
93 **RECUERDAME** (USA) 20
453 **RED ALERT** 69
397 **RED ALL STAR** (IRE) 6
250 **RED ALLURE** 15
168 **RED AMAPOLA** 92
365 **RED ASTAIRE** 167
384 **RED BEACON** (IRE) 8
128 **RED BLOODED WOMAN** (USA) C 32
2 **RED BOND** (IRE) 58
371 **RED BOULEVARD** (SAF) 7
397 **RED BOX** C 46
345 **RED BRAE RAINY MAY** 16
317 **RED BRAVO** (IRE) 28
**RED CARAVEL** (IRE) 14

481 **RED CARPET QUEEN** 27
235 **RED CENTRE** (USA) 51
35 **RED CHARMER** (IRE) 15
589 **RED DEREK** 16
493 **RED DIAMOND** (IRE) 18
435 **RED EVELYN** 13
76 **RED FASCINATOR** 59
506 **RED FEZ** 50
562 **RED FLYER** (IRE) 23
323 **RED FORCE ONE** 69
372 **RED GERRY** (IRE) 71
86 **RED GIANT** (IRE) 30
159 **RED GLORY** (IRE) 30
345 **RED GUNNER** 29
159 **RED HALO** (IRE) C 68
429 **RED HANRAHAN** (IRE) 15
376 **RED HEADED TIGER** 71
518 **RED HOT MAMA** 70
189 **RED HOT RADISH** 17
582 **RED INFANTRY** (IRE) 62
7 **RED JASPER** 70
444 **RED LION LAD** (IRE) 69
475 **RED LODGE** (USA) C 119
424 **RED MAPLE** (IRE) 83
309 **RED MIRAGE** (IRE) 120
473 **RED MISSILE** (IRE) 66
386 **RED MIX** (IRE) 93
392 **RED NAOMI** (IRE) 4
329 **RED NIKA** (FR) 38
230 **RED OCHRE** 20
431 **RED OCTOBER** (IRE) 12
594 **RED ORATOR** 3
495 **RED PIKE** (IRE) 11
193 **RED POPPY** 28
518 **RED RAMBLER** 124
591 **RED REFRACTION** (IRE) 5
230 **RED REMINDER** 21
76 **RED RIGHT SAND** (IRE) 60
411 **RED RISK** (FR) 138
333 **RED ROOKIE** 53
171 **RED ROYALIST** 29
148 **RED SAVINA** G 70
250 **RED SKYE DELIGHT** (IRE) 62
557 **RED SPARROW** 2
228 **RED SQUARE** (IRE) 120
567 **RED STAR DANCER** (IRE) 3
80 **RED STARS** (IRE) C 49
589 **RED STRIPES** (USA) 17
188 **RED TORNADO** (IRE) 6
523 **RED TULIP** F 79
159 **RED VERDON** (USA) 10
393 **RED VINEYARD** (IRE) 29
589 **RED WALLS** 25
148 **RED WARNING** (IRE) 71
68 **REDALANI** (IRE) C 12
478 **REDARNA** 11
503 **REDBRIDGE GOLD** (IRE) 39
547 **REDEMPTORIST** (IRE) 18
115 **REDESDALE REBEL** 19
539 **REDGRAVE** (IRE) 11
344 **REDHEADED STRANGER** 48
477 **REDREDROBIN** 7
5 **REDROSEZORRO** 9
473 **REDWING LASS** (FR) 67
495 **REDZONE** 12
439 **REECELTIC** 13
10 **REEDANJAS** (IRE) C 51

474 **REEL OF FORTUNE** (IRE) 22
186 **REEL TIMBA** (IRE) 20
391 **REELEMIN** 57
300 **REELY BONNIE** 29
270 **REFINEMENT** (IRE) G 151
523 **REFLECT ALEXANDER** (IRE) C 80
167 **REFUGE** 36
582 **REGABY** (IRE) 63
180 **REGAL EAGLE** (IRE) 14
285 **REGAL ENCORE** (IRE) 40
120 **REGAL ENVOY** 98
73 **REGAL FLOW** 9
384 **REGAL HAWK** C 33
168 **REGAL MIRAGE** (IRE) 73
518 **REGAL REALITY** 23
16 **REGAL VEGA** (IRE) 98
330 **REGALIS** (FR) 50
548 **REGARDING RUTH** (IRE) 27
415 **REGENCY GIRL** (IRE) C 168
228 **REGENT** 121
179 **REGIMENTAL GENT** 34
495 **REGIMENTO** 24
76 **REGRETTE RIEN** (IRE) C 127
569 **REGULAR INCOME** (IRE) 22
161 **REGULATOR** (IRE) 28
429 **REIGNITE** 16
492 **REILLY** (IRE) 114
328 **REIMS** 7
554 **REINA DEL MAR** (IRE) 64
386 **REINATOR** (FR) 94
375 **REINE DU BAL** 32
393 **REINFORCER** 19
461 **REIVERS LAD** 37
115 **REIVERS LODGE** 20
243 **REKDHAT** F 179
419 **REKERO** (IRE) 103
274 **RELATION ALEXANDER** (IRE) F 107
371 **RELATIVE** (FR) 7
346 **RELATIVE EASE** 4
354 **RELAXED BOY** (FR) 9
353 **RELAXEZ VOUS** (IRE) C 50
461 **RELEASE THE KRAKEN** (IRE) 38
126 **RELENTLESS DREAMER** (IRE) 29
168 **RELKADAM** (FR) 74
481 **RELOADED** (IRE) 6
444 **REMASTERED** 70
253 **REMEDIUM** 101
417 **REMEMBER ALEXANDER** C 49
527 **REMEMBER ALLY** (FR) 48
471 **REMEMBER ME WELL** (IRE) 12
322 **REMEMBER THE MAN** (IRE) 31
243 **REMEMBER YOU** (IRE) F 180
368 **REMEMBERANCE DAY** C 20
81 **REMEMBERTHETITANS** 9
6 **RENAISSANCE QUEEN** 18
419 **RENAISSANCE RIO** (IRE) F 175
6 **RENAISSANCE ROSE** (IRE) 82
519 **RENARDEAU** 13
309 **RENBAWI** (IRE) 121
599 **RENDEZVOUS PEAK** 8
16 **RENDITION** (IRE) 198
395 **RENEGADE ARROW** (FR) 86
87 **RENOIR** 46
276 **RENWICK** (IRE) 83
475 **REPARTEE** (IRE) 22
491 **REPERTOIRE** 19
264 **REPETITIO** (IRE) 41

503 **REPRESENTING BOB** (IRE) 40
308 **REPRIEVAL** (FR) F 77
488 **REPUBLICAN** 40
378 **REQUIEMS DREAM** (IRE) 19
575 **REQUINTO'S ROSE** (IRE) 15
391 **REQUITED** (IRE) 15
534 **RESERVE TANK** (IRE) 82
123 **RESET IN BLUE** (IRE) C 98
390 **RESHOUN** (FR) 10
350 **RESPLENDENT ROSE** 9
50 **RESPONDEZ** C 90
310 **REST AND BE** (IRE) C 9
402 **RESTANDBETHANKFUL** 101
228 **RESTITUTION** (FR) 122
167 **RESTIVE** (IRE) 37
266 **RESTLESS BRIAN** 10
538 **RESTLESS ENDEAVOUR** (IRE) 21
390 **RESTORER** 11
428 **RESTRICTED AREA** (IRE) 38
243 **RESUMPTION** 90
105 **RETAKE** F 95
16 **RETICENT** 199
437 **RETIREMENT BECKONS** 10
393 **RETROSPECT** (IRE) 10
217 **RETROUVAILLES** 12
376 **RETURN TICKET** (IRE) 37
120 **RETURN VOYAGE** (USA) 99
35 **RETURNING GLORY** 16
548 **REVASSER** (IRE) 28
313 **REVE** 25
212 **REVELS HILL** (IRE) 52
330 **REVENTADOR** (IRE) 5
65 **REVERANT CUST** (IRE) 19
253 **REVEREND HUBERT** (IRE) 102
318 **REVEREND JACOBS** 13
51 **REVERENT** (IRE) F 47
481 **REVERENTIAL** (IRE) 28
558 **REVERSE THE CHARGE** (IRE) 4
506 **REVICH** (IRE) 19
125 **REVOLUTIONARY MAN** (IRE) 12
57 **REVOLUTIONISE** (IRE) 24
274 **REWAAYAT** 21
375 **REWIRED** 33
101 **REY PELAYO** (IRE) 17
274 **REYAADAH** C 108
491 **REYAMOUR** F 86
27 **RHEBUS ROAD** (IRE) 58
522 **RHIAN DE SIVOLA** 32
428 **RHIANNON** (IRE) F 67
329 **RHINESTONE BLUE** (IRE) 12
76 **RHINOPLASTY** (IRE) 128
421 **RHOSCOLYN** 86
451 **RHUBARB** 11
7 **RHYME SCHEME** (IRE) 71
253 **RHYTHM** (IRE) 103
411 **RHYTHM IS A DANCER** 139
80 **RHYTHM N ROCK** (IRE) 47
167 **RHYTHMIC BLUES** 63
587 **RHYTHMIC INTENT** (IRE) 25
461 **RIBBLE VALLEY** (IRE) 39
240 **RIBTICKLER** (IRE) 30
36 **RICH DREAM** (IRE) 20
124 **RICH JADE** (USA) C 17
36 **RICH KING** 29
29 **RICH LEGACY** (IRE) C 64
344 **RICHARD R H B** (IRE) 27
268 **RICHARDOFDOCCOMBE** (IRE) 4

239 **RICHARDSON** 15
386 **RICHIDISH** (FR) 95
425 **RICHIE VALENTINE** 12
132 **RICKENBACKER** (IRE) 73
345 **RICKSEN** 30
330 **RICLA** 22
321 **RIDEAU CANAL** (IRE) 95
113 **RIDETHEWAVES** 28
308 **RIDGEWAY** (FR) 19
194 **RIDGEWAY AVENUE** (USA) 21
19 **RIDGEWAY FLYER** 15
417 **RIEN NE VAS PLUS** (IRE) C 50
253 **RIFFAA WONDER** (IRE) 104
228 **RIFLEMAN** (IRE) 123
518 **RIFQAH** (USA) C 125
492 **RIGGS** 115
241 **RIGGSBY** (IRE) 18
418 **RIGHT DESTINATION** (IRE) 114
386 **RIGHT HAND OF GOD** 96
556 **RIGHT ROYALS DAY** 7
448 **RIGHTEOUS RENEE** (USA) F 17
33 **RIGHTY RUE** (IRE) F 14
537 **RIHAAM** (IRE) C 48
123 **RIKNNAH** (IRE) 41
408 **RIKOBOY** (FR) 64
16 **RING FENCED** 200
400 **RING FOR BAILEYS** F 50
271 **RING MINELLA** (IRE) 22
167 **RING OF GOLD** 38
87 **RING OF LIGHT** 26
400 **RING OF LOVE** C 51
419 **RING THE BELL** (IRE) F 176
581 **RING THE MOON** 65
167 **RINGAROUND** C 39
167 **RINGAROUND** C 64
167 **RINGAROUND** F 109
338 **RINGMOYLAN** (IRE) 4
185 **RINGO KID** 30
434 **RINTULLA** (IRE) 71
97 **RINTY MAGINTY** (IRE) 16
402 **RIO QUINTO** (FR) 102
371 **RIO'S CLIFFS** F 47
576 **RIO'S ROSANNA** (IRE) G 19
386 **RIOHACHA** (FR) 97
225 **RIOJA DAY** (IRE) 20
228 **RIOT** (IRE) 29
387 **RIOT OF COLOUR** C 33
292 **RIP ROCKS PADDY OK** (IRE) 2
504 **RIP VAN GO** 8
176 **RIPP OFF** (IRE) 8
402 **RIPPER ROO** (FR) 103
173 **RIPPLET** 10
552 **RISAALAAT** (IRE) 32
426 **RISE HALL** 3
473 **RISING MARIENBARD** (IRE) 68
217 **RISING SEAS** 6
50 **RISING STAR** 57
487 **RISK AND ROLL** (IRE) 14
456 **RISK D'ARGENT** (FR) 36
523 **RISK OF THUNDER** (IRE) 41
417 **RISKIT FORA BISKIT** (IRE) C 51
497 **RISKY BUSINESS** (IRE) 8
466 **RITA O'HARA** 6
25 **RITA R** (IRE) 41
240 **RITA THE CHEETAH** 21
263 **RITCHIE STAR** (IRE) 27
108 **RITCHIE VALENS** (IRE) 11

321 **ROSCOE TARA** 96
120 **ROSE ALL DAY** 44
251 **ROSE BANDIT** (IRE) 9
555 **ROSE CAMIRA** 51
535 **ROSE FANDANGO** 12
578 **ROSE GREY** (USA) 14
93 **ROSE HIP** 10
223 **ROSE OF AGHABOE** (IRE) 23
534 **ROSE OF ARCADIA** (IRE) 85
309 **ROSE OF KILDARE** (IRE) 27
20 **ROSE OF LANCASHIRE** 26
503 **ROSE OHARA** 41
408 **ROSE SEA HAS** (FR) 66
308 **ROSE TIARA** 38
575 **ROSE VIC** (IRE) F 16
407 **ROSE WHISPER** (IRE) 9
352 **ROSE'S EMMA** (IRE) F 1
309 **ROSEABAD** (IRE) 122
519 **ROSEARELLI** 19
25 **ROSECOMB** (IRE) C 51
538 **ROSEHILL ARTIST** (IRE) F 38
450 **ROSEISAROSEISAROSE** (IRE) 18
545 **ROSEMAN** (IRE) 28
391 **ROSEMARY AND THYME** 39
372 **ROSENCRANTZ** (IRE) 75
523 **ROSERAIE** (FR) F 81
580 **ROSERIVER HAS** (FR) 30
415 **ROSES ARE RED** (IRE) 89
256 **ROSES BLUE** (IRE) 129
20 **ROSESATHENDOFTIME** 27
162 **ROSETINTEDGLASSES** (IRE) 19
107 **ROSETTA STONE** (FR) 59
309 **ROSEWATER** (FR) C 218
372 **ROSGALME** (IRE) 76
240 **ROSIDA** 31
484 **ROSIE AND MILLIE** (IRE) 32
256 **ROSIE BASSETT** 130
16 **ROSIE BRIAR** F 202
563 **ROSIE POWERS** (FR) 45
290 **ROSIKA** C 68
94 **ROSLEA LADY** (IRE) F 18
13 **ROSMUC RELAY** (IRE) 50
442 **ROSSBEIGH STRAND** (IRE) 26
598 **ROSSDERRIN** (IRE) 23
43 **ROSSERK ABBEY** (IRE) 14
419 **ROSSO CORSA** (USA) 179
408 **ROSTELLO** (FR) 67
297 **ROSY RYAN** (IRE) 14
502 **ROSY WORLD** 14
511 **ROSYGO** (IRE) F 11
577 **ROUGE VIF** (FR) 39
244 **ROUGH NIGHT** (IRE) 27
123 **ROULSTON SCAR** (IRE) 11
576 **ROUND THE ISLAND** 8
149 **ROUNDABOUT MAGIC** (IRE) 21
49 **ROUNDEL** 1
533 **ROUNDHAY PARK** 14
583 **ROUVRAIE** (FR) C 24
171 **ROWLAND WARD** 30
263 **ROXBORO ROAD** (IRE) 30
250 **ROXYFET** (FR) 65
365 **ROY J** 15
32 **ROY ROCKET** (FR) 8
135 **ROYAL ACT** 16
128 **ROYAL ADVICE** (IRE) 92
123 **ROYAL AIR FORCE** (IRE) 42
143 **ROYAL BASSETT** (FR) 13

587 **ROYAL BIRTH** 27
419 **ROYAL BLEND** 107
91 **ROYAL BLOSSOM** (IRE) G 35
376 **ROYAL BLOSSOM** (IRE) F 78
441 **ROYAL BORN** (IRE) 7
545 **ROYAL CHAMPION** (IRE) 122
522 **ROYAL CLARET** 33
274 **ROYAL COMMANDO** (IRE) 22
305 **ROYAL CONCORDE** (IRE) 11
421 **ROYAL CONFIDENCE** C 134
499 **ROYAL COUNTESS** 21
534 **ROYAL CROWN** (FR) 86
421 **ROYAL CROWN** (IRE) G 135
6 **ROYAL CRUSADE** 1
392 **ROYAL DYNASTY** 5
428 **ROYAL EMPRESS** (IRE) C 68
253 **ROYAL EVENT** (IRE) 106
6 **ROYAL FLEET** 83
566 **ROYAL FLUSH** 12
123 **ROYAL HARMONY** (IRE) 43
159 **ROYAL HEART** (FR) 31
399 **ROYAL ILLUSION** (IRE) 160
40 **ROYAL INVITATION** 102
538 **ROYAL JAZZ** 33
564 **ROYAL LEGEND** 6
527 **ROYAL MAGIC** (IRE) 31
40 **ROYAL MARINE** (IRE) 59
228 **ROYAL MEWS** (FR) 30
274 **ROYAL MUSKETEER** 65
539 **ROYAL OBSESSION** (IRE) F 33
395 **ROYAL OBSESSION** (IRE) F 116
40 **ROYAL PARTNERSHIP** 60
513 **ROYAL PLAZA** 1
449 **ROYAL PLEASURE** (IRE) 9
418 **ROYAL PRACTITIONER** 116
321 **ROYAL PRETENDER** (FR) 97
157 **ROYAL RANK** 12
222 **ROYAL REGARD** (FR) 80
499 **ROYAL REGENT** 22
399 **ROYAL RENDEZVOUS** (IRE) 161
473 **ROYAL RESERVE** 70
155 **ROYAL RESIDENCE** 8
107 **ROYAL RIVER** (FR) 60
189 **ROYAL SCANDAL** (IRE) 67
120 **ROYAL SCIMITAR** (IRE) 45
574 **ROYAL SHAHEEN** (FR) 41
6 **ROYAL TOUCH** 84
253 **ROYAL TRIBUTE** (IRE) 107
534 **ROYAL VACATION** (IRE) 87
250 **ROYAL VILLAGE** (IRE) 66
132 **ROYAL WHISPER** C 75
588 **ROYALE PAGAILLE** (FR) 67
386 **ROYAUME UNI** (IRE) 100
101 **ROYAUMONT** (FR) 20
480 **ROYBUOY** 2
186 **ROZENE** (IRE) F 21
245 **ROZIYNA** (IRE) 53
295 **RUACANA** 26
399 **RUAILLE BUAILLE** (IRE) 162
481 **RUBBELDIEKATZ** 49
61 **RUBEE FORTY** 10
133 **RUBENESQUE** (IRE) 15
80 **RUBY GATES** (IRE) 32
344 **RUBY JULES** 63
415 **RUBY QUEST** (IRE) C 169
421 **RUBY RED** 136
51 **RUBY RED EMPRESS** (IRE) 12

345 **RUBY RIBBONS** 47
139 **RUBY RUBLES** 5
309 **RUBY RUBY** 219
34 **RUBY WEDNESDAY** C 25
386 **RUBY YEATS** 101
285 **RUBYS REWARD** 41
328 **RUE CAMBON** (IRE) C 43
108 **RUE DE LA GAITE** (IRE) 13
50 **RUFFLED** C 91
212 **RUFIO** 53
274 **RUFOOF** F 109
457 **RUINOUS** (IRE) 3
178 **RUKWA** (FR) 21
168 **RULE BRITANNIA** G 75
509 **RULER LEGEND** (IRE) 51
7 **RULER RYDE** 73
419 **RULING** (GER) 108
577 **RULING DE ROOST** (IRE) 30
120 **RUM COCKTAIL** 100
254 **RUM RUNNER** 7
545 **RUMAYTHAH** (IRE) 123
291 **RUMBLE B** (IRE) 14
6 **RUMBLE B** (IRE) 14
6 **RUMH** (GER) C 199
330 **RUMI** 23
105 **RUMI** 46
313 **RUN A RIG** 27
306 **RUN AFTER GENESIS** (IRE) 8
15 **RUN FORREST RUN** (IRE) 35
140 **RUN RED RUN** 21
442 **RUN ROSIE RUN** 27
309 **RUN THIS WAY** 123
87 **RUN TO FREEDOM** 28
131 **RUN TO MILAN** (IRE) 17
395 **RUNASIMI RIVER** 89
215 **RUNNER BEAN** 22
593 **RUNNING CLOUD** (IRE) 16
522 **RUNNING D'OR** (FR) 34
434 **RUNNING WILD** (IRE) G 72
399 **RUNRIZED** (FR) 163
333 **RUNSWICK BAY** 54
563 **RUNWAY QUEEN** 46
318 **RUPERTS REFLECTION** 14
449 **RUSHFORD** 64
16 **RUSHMORE** 101
109 **RUSKIN RED** (IRE) 5
363 **RUSSCO** (IRE) 125
39 **RUSSELL'S QUARTER** (IRE) 16
570 **RUSSIAN EMPRESS** (IRE) F 18
534 **RUSSIAN EXILE** 88
154 **RUSSIAN INVASION** (IRE) 12
464 **RUSSIAN MEMORIES** (IRE) G 10
419 **RUSSIAN RIVER** (IRE) 109
250 **RUSSIAN ROYALE** 67
270 **RUSSIAN RULER** (IRE) 152
446 **RUSSIAN RUMOUR** (IRE) 8
153 **RUSSIAN SERVICE** 21
375 **RUSSIAN VIRTUE** 12
268 **RUSSIAN'S LEGACY** 5
150 **RUSSIES DREAM** 20
126 **RUTHLESS ARTICLE** (IRE) 30
481 **RWANDA MIST** 29
473 **RYALEX** (IRE) 71
1 **RYEDALE RACER** 45
62 **SA ALORS** (FR) 19
318 **SAABOOG** F 18
438 **SAAHEQ** 10
581 **SABBATHICAL** (FR) 66

| | | |
|---|---|---|
| 256 **SABLONNE** 185 | 582 **SAKURA SPIRIT** 65 | 313 **SAMTARA** 28 |
| 518 **SABOUSI** (IRE) 71 | 392 **SALAM YA FAISAL** (IRE) 6 | 404 **SAMTU** (IRE) 10 |
| 400 **SABRE JET** (IRE) 42 | 390 **SALAM ZAYED** 12 | 382 **SAMUEL JACKSON** 5 |
| 305 **SABREFLIGHT** F 19 | 234 **SALAMANCA SCHOOL** (FR) 57 | 329 **SAN AGUSTIN** (IRE) 40 |
| 340 **SACHAMAK** (FR) 11 | 7 **SALATEEN** 74 | 411 **SAN BENEDETO** (FR) 147 |
| 322 **SACKETT** 33 | 135 **SALAZAR** (IRE) 17 | 314 **SAN CARLOS** 12 |
| 355 **SACRE COEUR** (FR) 15 | 399 **SALDIER** (FR) 166 | 545 **SAN DONATO** (IRE) 29 |
| 363 **SACRE PIERRE** (FR) 126 | 95 **SALEH** (IRE) 15 | 193 **SAN FRANCISCO BAY** (IRE) 71 |
| 243 **SACRED** 91 | 123 **SALEYMM** (IRE) 44 | 333 **SAN GIOVANNI** (IRE) 56 |
| 259 **SACRED LEGACY** (IRE) 13 | 105 **SALIGO BAY** (IRE) 47 | 314 **SAN JUAN** (IRE) 13 |
| 256 **SACRED RHYME** (IRE) 131 | 76 **SALINE BAY** (IRE) 20 | 415 **SAN MARTINO** (IRE) 90 |
| 546 **SAD EYED DYLAN** 60 | 253 **SALITEH** 214 | 386 **SAN PEDRO DE SENAM** (FR) 103 |
| 246 **SADDLERS QUEST** 6 | 402 **SALLEY GARDENS** (IRE) 106 | 168 **SAN ROCH** (IRE) 77 |
| 311 **SADIE'S DAY** (IRE) 12 | 400 **SALLY** F 52 | 321 **SAN RUMOLDO** 98 |
| 120 **SADIQAA** (IRE) 46 | 194 **SALOME** (FR) C 35 | 418 **SAN SEB** (GER) 118 |
| 537 **SADLERS BEACH** (IRE) 9 | 588 **SALOPIAN BOY** 68 | 578 **SANAADH** 15 |
| 331 **SADMA** 5 | 324 **SALOUEN** (IRE) 11 | 375 **SANADA** (IRE) F 62 |
| 253 **SAFE PASSAGE** 108 | 420 **SALSADA** (IRE) 19 | 274 **SANAYA** (FR) C 110 |
| 454 **SAFE VOYAGE** (IRE) 21 | 399 **SALSARETTA** (FR) 167 | 87 **SANCTIFIED** 29 |
| 120 **SAFETY FIRST** 101 | 237 **SALSOUL** 12 | 375 **SAND DANCER** C 63 |
| 387 **SAFFA GARDEN** (IRE) G 35 | 388 **SALT OF THE EARTH** (IRE) 26 | 105 **SAND IN MY SHOES** (FR) 48 |
| 345 **SAFFA GARDEN** (IRE) G 48 | 437 **SALTMARKET** 11 | 411 **SANDALWOOD** (FR) 148 |
| 102 **SAFFRON BEACH** (IRE) 26 | 62 **SALTY BOY** (IRE) 20 | 503 **SANDAROC** 42 |
| 354 **SAFIRA MENINA** 10 | 393 **SALTY SUGAR** C 30 | 148 **SANDERLIN** (IRE) 57 |
| 304 **SAGA SPRINT** (IRE) 12 | 388 **SALUTE THE KING** (IRE) 27 | 190 **SANDFORD CASTLE** (IRE) 35 |
| 256 **SAGAR LAKE** (FR) 132 | 378 **SALUTI** (IRE) 20 | 415 **SANDHURST** (IRE) 91 |
| 421 **SAGAUTEUR** (FR) 39 | 532 **SALVINO** (IRE) 43 | 247 **SANDHURST LAD** (IRE) 7 |
| 408 **SAGE ADVICE** (IRE) 68 | 333 **SAM BARTON** 55 | 333 **SANDINISTA** (IRE) 57 |
| 136 **SAGGAZZA** 12 | 309 **SAM BELLAMY** 124 | 263 **SANDRET** (IRE) 31 |
| 386 **SAGHIR** (IRE) 102 | 285 **SAM BROWN** 42 | 541 **SANDS CHORUS** 9 |
| 98 **SAHAFH** (USA) F 93 | 27 **SAM COOKE** (IRE) 22 | 181 **SANDS COVE** (IRE) 13 |
| 523 **SAHARA DESERT** (IRE) 82 | 130 **SAM HAZE** 5 | 309 **SANDS OF TIME** 125 |
| 214 **SAHARA SUNSHINE** C 57 | 420 **SAM SPINNER** 20 | 256 **SANDSTONE** F 186 |
| 314 **SAHARAN SHIMMER** 11 | 175 **SAM'S ADVENTURE** 46 | 91 **SANDY** B 25 |
| 93 **SAHARAN SONG** (IRE) C 105 | 167 **SAM'S CALL** 41 | 276 **SANDY BOY** (IRE) 88 |
| 141 **SAHHAB** (USA) 13 | 167 **SAM'S GUNNER** 42 | 227 **SANDY BROOK** (IRE) 41 |
| 243 **SAIGON** 92 | 212 **SAMARQUAND** 54 | 212 **SANDY MARASCHINO** (IRE) 55 |
| 492 **SAIL AWAY** (FR) 122 | 411 **SAMARRIVE** (FR) 145 | 593 **SANDY SHAW** F 25 |
| 518 **SAILED AWAY** (GER) 72 | 13 **SAMATIAN** (IRE) 51 | 193 **SANDY TIMES** (IRE) F 72 |
| 560 **SAILING AWAY** (IRE) 1 | 395 **SAMBELLA** 91 | 253 **SANDY'S HOPE** (IRE) 215 |
| 22 **SAINT ARVANS** (IRE) 26 | 490 **SAMBEZI** (FR) 14 | 599 **SANDYCOVE ISLAND** (IRE) 10 |
| 577 **SAINT CALVADOS** (FR) 31 | 235 **SAMBLUCKY** 52 | 110 **SANDYMAN** 16 |
| 343 **SAINT DALINA** (FR) 40 | 159 **SAMBORA GIRL** 3 | 256 **SANDYMOUNT BABY** (IRE) 60 |
| 411 **SAINT DE REVE** (FR) 143 | 378 **SAMBUCCA SPIRIT** 21 | 395 **SANDYMOUNT ROSE** (IRE) 92 |
| 522 **SAINT DE VASSY** (FR) 35 | 276 **SAMBURU SHUJAA** (FR) 87 | 108 **SANFELICE** (IRE) 43 |
| 590 **SAINT JUDE** (FR) 4 | 523 **SAMDANIYA** F 83 | 518 **SANGARIUS** 24 |
| 545 **SAINT LAWRENCE** (IRE) 124 | 363 **SAME CIRCUS** (IRE) 94 | 212 **SANGUINAIRE** (IRE) 56 |
| 473 **SAINT LEO** (FR) 72 | 198 **SAME OPINION** (IRE) 8 | 110 **SANITISER** 40 |
| 388 **SAINT MAC** 25 | 168 **SAMEEM** (IRE) 76 | 51 **SANIYAAT** C 48 |
| 17 **SAINT PALAIS** (FR) 12 | 334 **SAMEER** (FR) 12 | 308 **SANKALPA** (IRE) 39 |
| 383 **SAINT PATRIC** 17 | 411 **SAMETEGAL** (FR) 146 | 509 **SANOSUKE** 28 |
| 399 **SAINT ROI** (FR) 164 | 227 **SAMI BEAR** 40 | 444 **SANS LOGIQUE** 71 |
| 399 **SAINT SAM** (FR) 165 | 400 **SAMILLE** (FR) 27 | 243 **SANS PRETENTION** (IRE) 93 |
| 583 **SAINT SEGAL** (FR) 23 | 13 **SAMMEO** (FR) 52 | 50 **SANTA ANABAA** C 92 |
| 411 **SAINT SONNET** (FR) 144 | 369 **SAMMYLOU** (IRE) 49 | 413 **SANTA BARBARA** (IRE) 92 |
| 278 **SAINT XAVIER** (FR) 15 | 518 **SAMOOT** (IRE) 73 | 419 **SANTA FLORENTINA** 110 |
| 418 **SAINTBURY LADY** 117 | 548 **SAMOURAI ONE** (FR) 29 | 6 **SANTE** (IRE) F 200 |
| 395 **SAINTE DOCTOR** (FR) 90 | 145 **SAMOVAR** 26 | 454 **SANTIA** F 22 |
| 210 **SAINTEMILION** (FR) 12 | 7 **SAMPERS SEVEN** (IRE) 75 | 415 **SANTIAGO** (IRE) 12 |
| 420 **SAISONS D'OR** (IRE) 18 | 485 **SAMPHIRE COAST** 17 | 34 **SANTIBURI SPIRIT** 22 |
| 73 **SAKANDI** 10 | 376 **SAMRANA** (FR) F 40 | 29 **SANTIKI** 31 |
| 491 **SAKARYA** (IRE) C 87 | 389 **SAMS PROFILE** 25 | 589 **SANTINHO** (IRE) 18 |
| 598 **SAKE OF SECRECY** (IRE) 24 | 478 **SAMS ROSEABELLE** 12 | 270 **SANTINI** 153 |
| 323 **SAKHEE'S CITY** (FR) 72 | 153 **SAMSON'S REACH** 22 | 321 **SANTON** (IRE) 99 |
| 398 **SAKHEE'S CONQUEST** 29 | 574 **SAMSTOWN** 42 | 61 **SANTORINI SAL** 11 |
| 485 **SAKTOON** (USA) F 25 | | 256 **SANTOSHA** (IRE) 133 |
| 6 **SAKURA PETAL** 20 | | 376 **SAO** (FR) 41 |

570 **SAO JORGE** 19
185 **SAO MAXENCE** (FR) 31
16 **SAORLA** 203
494 **SAPHIRSIDE** (IRE) 16
399 **SAPPHIRE LADY** (IRE) 168
159 **SAPPHIRE WATERS** (IRE) C 70
6 **SAQQARA KING** (USA) 21
62 **SAQUEBOUTE** (FR) 21
408 **SAQUON** (IRE) 69
259 **SARAH'S VERSE** 14
243 **SARAHA** F 181
167 **SARAS CALL** 65
215 **SARAS HOPE** 10
313 **SARASOTA STAR** (IRE) 29
274 **SARATOGA GOLD** 66
191 **SARAY PRINCE** (IRE) 12
161 **SARCEAUX** (FR) 30
243 **SARGASSO SEA** 26
234 **SARIM** (IRE) 58
108 **SARINDA** C 44
29 **SARISKA** C 65
159 **SARKHA** (IRE) 71
597 **SARRDAR** (IRE) 6
274 **SARROOD** (IRE) 67
344 **SARTAJ** (USA) 28
38 **SARTENE'S SON** (FR) 3
481 **SARVAN** 8
225 **SARVI** 22
532 **SARYSHAGANN** (FR) 44
1 **SAS** (IRE) G 36
6 **SASAKIA** (IRE) 85
448 **SASHCORD** 10
484 **SASHENKA** (GER) 33
263 **SASSOON** 32
120 **SASSY GAL** (IRE) F 102
266 **SASTRUGA** (IRE) 11
179 **SATELLITE** G 35
120 **SATELLITE CALL** (IRE) 103
516 **SATIN WATERS** C 17
518 **SATONO CHEVALIER** (IRE) 74
518 **SATONO JAPAN** (JPN) 25
190 **SATOSHI** (IRE) 36
194 **SATSUMA** F 36
71 **SATURDAY SONG** 6
484 **SATURN 'N SILK** 34
399 **SATURNAS** (FR) 169
461 **SAUCE OF LIFE** (IRE) 40
65 **SAUCHIEHALL STREET** (IRE) 20
438 **SAUCY ENCORE** 11
250 **SAUCY SALLY** (IRE) 68
599 **SAUCY SINDY** 11
415 **SAUCY SPIRIT** C 170
9 **SAULIRE STAR** (IRE) 57
161 **SAUSALITO SUNRISE** (IRE) 31
254 **SAVALAS** (IRE) 8
120 **SAVANNAH BELLE** F 104
545 **SAVE A FOREST** (IRE) 126
421 **SAVE THE SPIRIT** (IRE) 40
29 **SAVEASEA** 32
481 **SAVEATREE** 30
508 **SAVISE L'AMOUR** (FR) 22
95 **SAVITAR** (IRE) 16
10 **SAVOY BROWN** 32
39 **SAVOY COURT** (IRE) 17
555 **SAVROLA** (IRE) 37
174 **SAW THE SEA** 8
153 **SAWPIT SIENNA** 23

180 **SAY IT AS IT IS** (IRE) 40
244 **SAY NOTHING** 28
222 **SAY THE WORD** 65
13 **SAYADAM** (FR) 53
318 **SAYAR** (IRE) 15
438 **SAYIFYOUWILL** 20
399 **SAYO** 170
6 **SAYYIDA** 86
503 **SAZERAK** (IRE) 43
421 **SCALDED** 137
316 **SCALE FORCE** 16
16 **SCAMPI** 102
391 **SCANNING** 16
543 **SCAPALLORO** 4
411 **SCARAMANGA** (IRE) 149
190 **SCARAMUCCI** (IRE) 37
148 **SCARBOROUGHDEBUT** 58
577 **SCARDINO** (FR) 32
395 **SCARDURA** (IRE) 93
419 **SCARLET AND DOVE** (IRE) 48
301 **SCARLET BEAR** (IRE) 20
321 **SCARLET DRAGON** 100
185 **SCARLET N' BLACK** 37
425 **SCARLET RUBY** 13
418 **SCARLETT CLIPPER** (IRE) 119
419 **SCARLETT DUBOIS** (IRE) 180
399 **SCARPETA** (FR) 171
270 **SCARPIA** (IRE) 154
219 **SCARTARE** (IRE) 7
344 **SCATINA** (IRE) F 64
6 **SCATTER DICE** (IRE) C 201
243 **SCATTERING** 182
321 **SCEAU ROYAL** (FR) 101
343 **SCENE NOT HERD** (IRE) 41
51 **SCENT OF ROSES** (FR) 49
376 **SCENTED GARDEN** G 72
87 **SCEPTRED ISLE** 13
554 **SCHABANG** (GER) 65
376 **SCHALKE** 12
391 **SCHEHERAZADE** 40
386 **SCHELEM** (FR) 104
352 **SCHIAPARANNIE** 2
357 **SCHIAPARELLI TEDDY** 6
250 **SCHIEHALLION MUNRO** 69
419 **SCHIELE** (IRE) 181
308 **SCHILTHORN** 40
16 **SCHMILSSON** 204
518 **SCHNEEMANN** 127
372 **SCHOOL BOY HOURS** (IRE) 77
51 **SCHOOL OF THOUGHT** 13
107 **SCHOONER RIDGE** (IRE) 33
290 **SCHWARTZ** (IRE) 35
107 **SCIACCA** (IRE) F 45
107 **SCILIAR** (IRE) 34
329 **SCIPION** (IRE) 41
263 **SCOOP THE POT** (IRE) 33
27 **SCOPE** (IRE) 60
376 **SCORCHED BREATH** 43
143 **SCORCHED EARTH** (IRE) 14
501 **SCORCHIN** 44
519 **SCORPION HAZE** (IRE) 20
531 **SCORPO** (IRE) 8
353 **SCOTA BESS** 31
191 **SCOTCH MIST** 18
132 **SCOTS GOLD** (IRE) 41
225 **SCOTS SONNET** 23
346 **SCOTSBROOK NIGHT** 5

346 **SCOTSBROOK RHULA** 6
376 **SCOTTISH ACCENT** (IRE) 44
390 **SCOTTISH BLADE** (IRE) 13
376 **SCOTTISH KING** (IRE) 45
254 **SCOTTISH SUMMIT** (IRE) 9
483 **SCOTTISH WIND** (FR) 18
592 **SCOTTSDALE** 7
509 **SCREAM BLUE MURDER** (IRE) C 52
397 **SCREECHING DRAGON** (IRE) 18
256 **SCREEN STAR** (IRE) F 134
4 **SCRIPTED DESTINY** 16
372 **SCRUM HALF** 100
77 **SCRUMPY BOY** 10
295 **SCRUTINISE** 27
214 **SCUDAMORE** (FR) 38
512 **SCULLYS FORGE** (IRE) 8
85 **SE YOU** 7
454 **SEA ART** 23
199 **SEA CREST** G 20
154 **SEA DESTINATION** (IRE) 13
243 **SEA EMPRESS** (IRE) 94
395 **SEA EWE** 94
16 **SEA FERN** 103
243 **SEA GREY** 205
243 **SEA IS GOLD** (IRE) 95
243 **SEA KARATS** (IRE) 96
449 **SEA KING** 65
243 **SEA LA ROSA** (IRE) 97
160 **SEA OF CHARM** (FR) 16
148 **SEA OF DREAMS** (IRE) F 72
309 **SEA OF GRACE** (IRE) C 220
87 **SEA OF HOPE** (IRE) C 48
7 **SEA OF MYSTERY** (IRE) 76
545 **SEA OF SNOW** (USA) C 186
243 **SEA OSCAR** 98
244 **SEA PRINCE** 29
63 **SEA REGATTA** (IRE) G 56
243 **SEA SPEEDWELL** 99
426 **SEA STORM** 4
243 **SEA SYLPH** (IRE) 100
577 **SEA THE CLOUDS** (IRE) 33
209 **SEA THE GIRL** 2
243 **SEA THE SEVEN** 183
309 **SEA THE SHELLS** 126
429 **SEA THE WAVES** 17
385 **SEA TIDE** 17
516 **SEA TROUT** 8
508 **SEA WILLOW** 11
386 **SEABORN** (IRE) 105
529 **SEABOROUGH** (IRE) 20
330 **SEACHANGE** (FR) 6
475 **SEACLUSION** 67
593 **SEAFORTH** (IRE) 17
597 **SEAGULL** (IRE) C 21
98 **SEAGULLS NEST** 23
440 **SEALED OFFER** 14
243 **SEALIFE** (IRE) C 184
205 **SEAPOINT** (IRE) 8
421 **SEAS OF ELZAAM** (IRE) 41
233 **SEASEARCH** 6
434 **SEASIDE GIRL** (IRE) 73
189 **SEASTAR** 50
488 **SEASTON SPIRIT** 41
428 **SEATONE** (USA) F 40
324 **SEATTLE ROCK** 22
16 **SEB'S WELCOME** (FR) 104
434 **SEBASTIAN BEACH** (IRE) 74

| | |
|---|---|
| 175 | SHAMROCK WINE (IRE) 66 |
| 587 | SHAMSHON (IRE) 28 |
| 492 | SHAN BLUE (IRE) 125 |
| 13 | SHANACOOLE PRINCE (IRE) 54 |
| 534 | SHANAHAN'S TURN (IRE) 90 |
| 58 | SHANANDOA 12 |
| 172 | SHANANN STAR (IRE) 2 |
| 146 | SHANBALLY ROSE (IRE) 33 |
| 545 | SHANDOZ 32 |
| 333 | SHANG TANG (IRE) 58 |
| 253 | SHANGHAI ROCK 112 |
| 61 | SHANI 12 |
| 399 | SHANNING (FR) 173 |
| 492 | SHANNON BRIDGE (IRE) 126 |
| 598 | SHANNON LODGE (IRE) 25 |
| 598 | SHANNON ROCCO (IRE) 26 |
| 421 | SHANNOOAN (USA) C 138 |
| 548 | SHANROE SANTOS (IRE) 30 |
| 202 | SHANROE SMOOCH (IRE) 7 |
| 473 | SHANROE STREET (IRE) 73 |
| 434 | SHANROE TIC TEC (IRE) 77 |
| 363 | SHANTALUZE (IRE) 98 |
| 111 | SHANTOU BOUDICCA 16 |
| 78 | SHANTOU CITY (IRE) 8 |
| 13 | SHANTOU EXPRESS (IRE) 55 |
| 386 | SHANTOU MASTER (IRE) 106 |
| 566 | SHANTOU STREET (IRE) 13 |
| 276 | SHANTOU SUNSET 90 |
| 395 | SHANTOU VILLAGE (IRE) 95 |
| 577 | SHANTOU VOW (IRE) 38 |
| 424 | SHANTOU'S MELODY (IRE) 85 |
| 548 | SHANTUNG (IRE) 31 |
| 96 | SHANTY ALLEY 21 |
| 344 | SHAQEEQA 49 |
| 105 | SHARAAKAH F 99 |
| 326 | SHARE THE PROFITS 55 |
| 345 | SHARED MOMENT (IRE) F 49 |
| 53 | SHAREEF STAR 31 |
| 399 | SHARJAH (FR) 174 |
| 526 | SHARLA 39 |
| 108 | SHARNBERRY C 45 |
| 91 | SHARP EXHIBIT (IRE) 26 |
| 135 | SHARP REPLY (IRE) 19 |
| 501 | SHARP RESPONSE (IRE) 46 |
| 175 | SHARP SUITED 48 |
| 16 | SHARP SUSAN (USA) C 207 |
| 348 | SHARPCLIFF 16 |
| 325 | SHARPENUPABIT 21 |
| 111 | SHARPES EXPRESS (IRE) F 17 |
| 243 | SHARQEYIH F 186 |
| 20 | SHARRABANG 18 |
| 344 | SHARRON MACREADY (IRE) 65 |
| 375 | SHARSTED (GER) 35 |
| 415 | SHASTYE (IRE) F 172 |
| 484 | SHATTERED GLASS (IRE) 35 |
| 247 | SHAUGHNESSY 8 |
| 271 | SHAW'S CROSS (IRE) 23 |
| 92 | SHAWAAMEKH 11 |
| 6 | SHAWANDA (IRE) C 205 |
| 128 | SHAWS BRIDGE (IRE) 61 |
| 317 | SHAWSHANK 19 |
| 496 | SHAYANA F 7 |
| 235 | SHAYMIN 54 |
| 545 | SHE DO 128 |
| 383 | SHE GOT FAST (IRE) 18 |
| 309 | SHE GOT THE LOOK (IRE) 127 |
| 16 | SHE IS FIERCE 106 |

| | |
|---|---|
| 27 | SHE IS NO LADY F 124 |
| 394 | SHE IS WHAT SHE IS 4 |
| 98 | SHE STRIDES ON 24 |
| 418 | SHE'LL BITE (IRE) 120 |
| 33 | SHE'S A CRACKER (IRE) 9 |
| 376 | SHE'S A DANCER (IRE) 47 |
| 533 | SHE'S A DEVA 39 |
| 418 | SHE'S A NOVELTY (IRE) 121 |
| 473 | SHE'S A STEAL (IRE) 74 |
| 495 | SHE'S A WORLDIE (IRE) F 43 |
| 132 | SHE'S ALL IN GOLD (IRE) 16 |
| 492 | SHE'S GINA (GER) 127 |
| 305 | SHE'S HUMBLE (IRE) G 12 |
| 76 | SHE'S NO ANGEL (IRE) 64 |
| 94 | SHE'S ON THE EDGE (IRE) 10 |
| 76 | SHE'S SO NICE (IRE) 65 |
| 311 | SHE'S THE DANGER (IRE) 26 |
| 300 | SHE'SASUPERMACK (IRE) 31 |
| 577 | SHE'SONEOFOUROWN (IRE) 39 |
| 411 | SHEARER (IRE) 155 |
| 245 | SHEDINI (IRE) 18 |
| 533 | SHEEPSCAR LAD (IRE) 15 |
| 419 | SHEER CHANCE (IRE) 112 |
| 308 | SHEER ROCKS 78 |
| 41 | SHEEZA LEGEND 11 |
| 214 | SHEHARZ 58 |
| 431 | SHEILA 13 |
| 577 | SHEILA NASH (IRE) 40 |
| 446 | SHEILA O'SHEA 32 |
| 96 | SHEILA TANIST (IRE) 22 |
| 68 | SHEILA'S LEGACY 9 |
| 109 | SHEILA'S SPIRIT 6 |
| 372 | SHEISBYBRID (IRE) 101 |
| 372 | SHEISDIESEL 80 |
| 265 | SHEKNOWSYOUKNOW G 2 |
| 398 | SHELDON (IRE) 30 |
| 421 | SHELIR (IRE) 43 |
| 309 | SHEM (IRE) 128 |
| 240 | SHEMSA (FR) 11 |
| 4 | SHENEEDEDTHERUN (IRE) 18 |
| 492 | SHENTRI (IRE) 128 |
| 491 | SHENU (USA) 60 |
| 421 | SHEOAK (IRE) F 139 |
| 84 | SHEPHERDS WAY (IRE) 23 |
| 563 | SHERBET LEMON (USA) 48 |
| 534 | SHERBORNE (IRE) 91 |
| 304 | SHERELLA 13 |
| 168 | SHERIFF GARRETT (IRE) 79 |
| 323 | SHERIFF'S SISTER (IRE) 74 |
| 547 | SHERIN (GER) 20 |
| 372 | SHERINGA F 65 |
| 149 | SHERPA TRAIL (USA) 22 |
| 221 | SHERWOOD FORRESTER 6 |
| 397 | SHESADABBER 21 |
| 155 | SHESAHEART 17 |
| 321 | SHESHOON SONNY (FR) 103 |
| 81 | SHESSWEET (IRE) 11 |
| 332 | SHETLAND BUS (GER) 6 |
| 399 | SHEWEARSITWELL (IRE) 175 |
| 340 | SHIELD OF HONOUR 12 |
| 123 | SHIELDED (IRE) 45 |
| 326 | SHIFTING GOLD (IRE) 14 |
| 76 | SHIFTING MOON F 129 |
| 250 | SHIGHNESS 70 |
| 143 | SHILPA (IRE) G 22 |
| 79 | SHIMAH (USA) C 65 |
| 273 | SHIMBA HILLS 9 |

| | |
|---|---|
| 120 | SHIMLA ROLANN 47 |
| 523 | SHIMMERING DAWN (IRE) 5 |
| 120 | SHIMMERING SKY 105 |
| 509 | SHINAPACHI 29 |
| 323 | SHINE BABY SHINE 75 |
| 253 | SHINE FOR YOU 113 |
| 26 | SHINE ON BRENDAN (IRE) 10 |
| 16 | SHINE SO BRIGHT 34 |
| 376 | SHINEDOWN (IRE) 48 |
| 161 | SHINGHARI (IRE) 32 |
| 243 | SHINGWEDZI (SAF) F 187 |
| 56 | SHINING 15 |
| 362 | SHINING AITCH 9 |
| 40 | SHINING BLUE (IRE) 103 |
| 415 | SHINING BRIGHT (IRE) 93 |
| 40 | SHINING EXAMPLE (IRE) 62 |
| 582 | SHINING LIGHTS (IRE) G 66 |
| 491 | SHINING SUCCESS (IRE) 61 |
| 239 | SHININSTAR (IRE) 16 |
| 13 | SHINOBI (IRE) 56 |
| 417 | SHINSENGUMI (IRE) 18 |
| 19 | SHINTORI (IRE) 16 |
| 582 | SHIP OF THE FEN 67 |
| 384 | SHIRIN OF PERSIA (IRE) F 34 |
| 523 | SHIRLEY (IRE) F 84 |
| 333 | SHIROCCAN ROLL 59 |
| 534 | SHIROCCO'S DREAM (IRE) 92 |
| 244 | SHIROCCSMYWORLD (IRE) 30 |
| 333 | SHIROCCY ROAD 60 |
| 270 | SHISHKIN (IRE) 156 |
| 534 | SHOAL BAY (IRE) 93 |
| 274 | SHOBIZ 68 |
| 391 | SHOCKWAVES 58 |
| 575 | SHOESHINE BOY (IRE) 18 |
| 411 | SHOLOKJACK (IRE) 156 |
| 527 | SHOMEN UCHI (FR) 32 |
| 256 | SHONA MEA 61 |
| 446 | SHOOT FOR THE MOON 33 |
| 444 | SHOOT TO FAME (IRE) 74 |
| 481 | SHOOT TO KILL (IRE) 9 |
| 577 | SHORE SHANTY (IRE) 41 |
| 410 | SHORT AFFAIR F 18 |
| 167 | SHORT AFFAIR G 66 |
| 571 | SHORT HEAD (GER) 17 |
| 589 | SHORTBACKANDSIDES (IRE) 20 |
| 120 | SHOSHONI WIND C 106 |
| 229 | SHOUGHALL'S BOY (IRE) 7 |
| 375 | SHOULDERING (IRE) 14 |
| 375 | SHOW AYA (IRE) C 66 |
| 6 | SHOW DAY F 206 |
| 189 | SHOW ME A SUNSET 20 |
| 425 | SHOW ME THE BUBBLY 14 |
| 35 | SHOW OF FORCE 17 |
| 486 | SHOW ON THE ROAD 7 |
| 86 | SHOW PALACE 31 |
| 323 | SHOW PROMISE 76 |
| 523 | SHOW YOURSELF 44 |
| 168 | SHOWALONG 41 |
| 344 | SHOWDANSE 50 |
| 315 | SHOWSHUTAI 9 |
| 76 | SHOWSTOPPA C 130 |
| 549 | SHOWTIME EARNIE 14 |
| 549 | SHOWTIME ELLE 15 |
| 27 | SHRARA (IRE) 62 |
| 601 | SHREWDOPERATOR (IRE) 14 |
| 98 | SHRIMPTON F 95 |
| 450 | SHUDISTAYORSHUDIGO (IRE) 19 |

98 **SOCIETY GAL** (IRE) C 97
159 **SOCIETY LION** 12
145 **SOCIOLOGIST** (FR) 28
131 **SOCKEYE** (IRE) 18
311 **SOCKS OFF** (IRE) 7
569 **SOCRU** (IRE) 23
253 **SODASHY** (IRE) C 217
518 **SOFFIKA** (IRE) 27
492 **SOFIA'S ROCK** (FR) 131
431 **SOFT POWER** (IRE) C 75
461 **SOFT RISK** (FR) 43
40 **SOFT WHISPER** (IRE) 105
492 **SOFTKORE** (FR) 132
328 **SOGNATORE** (IRE) 29
379 **SOI DAO** (IRE) 39
285 **SOJOURN** (IRE) 43
585 **SOL PLUM CREEK** (FR) 17
56 **SOLANDIA** (IRE) C 28
330 **SOLANIA** (IRE) 26
315 **SOLAR IMPULSE** (FR) 10
545 **SOLAR ORBITER** (IRE) 188
10 **SOLAR PARK** (IRE) 34
491 **SOLAR SCREEN** (IRE) 22
74 **SOLAR SOVEREIGN** (IRE) 5
364 **SOLDIER IN ACTION** (FR) 2
308 **SOLDIER LIONS** (IRE) 41
411 **SOLDIER OF LOVE** 163
400 **SOLDIER ON PARADE** 28
334 **SOLDIER TO FOLLOW** 13
128 **SOLDIER'S MINUTE** 63
40 **SOLDIER'S SECRET** (IRE) 106
87 **SOLDIER'S SON** 14
424 **SOLDIEROFTHESTORM** (IRE) 108
132 **SOLENT GATEWAY** (IRE) 42
63 **SOLENT SCENE** 36
392 **SOLID GOLD** 16
518 **SOLID STONE** (IRE) 28
440 **SOLIZA** (IRE) C 24
168 **SOLDER BAY** (FR) 142
411 **SOLO** (FR) 164
145 **SOLO HUNTER** 29
263 **SOLO SAXOPHONE** (IRE) 34
161 **SOLOIST** (IRE) 34
102 **SOLOMONS JUDGEMENT** (IRE) 27
572 **SOLSTALLA** 3
313 **SOLSTICE STAR** 30
230 **SOLSTICE TWILIGHT** 25
395 **SOLWARA ONE** (FR) 98
261 **SOLWAY AVA** 7
261 **SOLWAY BERRY** 8
261 **SOLWAY LARK** 9
261 **SOLWAY MOLLY** 10
261 **SOLWAY MOUSE** 11
261 **SOLWAY PRIMROSE** 12
261 **SOLWAY SPIRIT** 13
602 **SOME AMBITION** (IRE) 7
521 **SOME BUCKLE** (IRE) 6
153 **SOME CAN DANCE** (IRE) 25
171 **SOME CAN SING** (IRE) 31
484 **SOME CHAOS** (IRE) 37
503 **SOME DAY SOON** (IRE) 46
264 **SOME DETAIL** (IRE) 43
143 **SOME FINISH** (IRE) 15
395 **SOME MIGHT SAY** (IRE) 99
425 **SOME NIGHTMARE** (IRE) 15
90 **SOME OPERATOR** (IRE) 19
146 **SOME REIGN** (IRE) 36

235 **SOME SPIN** (IRE) 55
548 **SOMEKINDOFSTAR** (IRE) 32
529 **SOMEONE EXCITING** 22
235 **SOMEONE YOU LOVE** 56
289 **SOMERSET FALLS** (UAE) C 16
43 **SOMERSET JEM** 16
408 **SOMETHINBOUTANGELA** (IRE) 71
300 **SOMETHING BREWING** (FR) 34
176 **SOMETHING ENTICING** (IRE) 14
105 **SOMETHING EXCITING** C 101
10 **SOMETHING LUCKY** (IRE) 35
490 **SOMETHING ROSIE** (IRE) 15
582 **SOMETIMES ALWAYS** (IRE) 69
397 **SOMEWHERE SECRET** 22
387 **SOMMER DAISY** (FR) 16
132 **SOMMORELL** (FR) C 77
315 **SOMTHINGPHENOMENAL** 11
378 **SON AND MANNER** (IRE) 22
270 **SON OF CAMAS** (FR) 157
514 **SON OF OZ** 25
321 **SON OF RED** (IRE) 105
566 **SON OF SUZIE** 15
323 **SON OF THE SOMME** (IRE) 78
193 **SONA** F 73
76 **SONDERBAR** 68
326 **SONG AT TWILIGHT** (IRE) 17
522 **SONG FOR SOMEONE** (GER) 36
554 **SONG LYRIC** (IRE) 69
93 **SONG OF BEAUTY** (FR) 77
415 **SONG OF PEACE** (USA) 99
368 **SONG OF POMPEIA** 11
93 **SONG OF SUMMER** (FR) 78
351 **SONG OF THE ISLES** (IRE) 13
261 **SONG OF THE NIGHT** (IRE) 14
355 **SONG OF THE SKY** 17
180 **SONG TO THE MOON** (IRE) F 53
193 **SONG TWO** (IRE) 53
51 **SONGKRAN** (IRE) 14
258 **SONGO** (IRE) 32
473 **SONGOFTHELARK** (IRE) 77
92 **SONGSEEKER** (IRE) C 32
425 **SONIC GOLD** 16
379 **SONKO** (IRE) F 40
56 **SONNETATION** (IRE) C 29
109 **SONNETINA** 7
321 **SONNING** (IRE) 142
162 **SONNY BROWN** 21
411 **SONNY CROCKETT** (IRE) 165
274 **SONNY LISTON** 111
358 **SONOFTHEKING** (IRE) 16
6 **SOON** (IRE) C 211
105 **SOORAH** F 102
377 **SOPAT** (FR) 5
221 **SOPHIE** 9
532 **SOPHIE FATALE** 48
536 **SOPHIE OLIVIA** (IRE) 12
569 **SOPHIE'JO** F 42
98 **SOPHIGGLIA** 60
539 **SOPHOSC** (IRE) 12
386 **SOPRAN THOR** (FR) 107
16 **SOPRANA** (GER) C 212
79 **SORAAYA** (IRE) C 66
548 **SORBET** 33
25 **SORBONNE** 20
583 **SORELLINA ROYALE** 16
193 **SOROS** 29
297 **SORY** 16

375 **SOTO SIZZLER** 15
492 **SOUL EMOTION** (FR) 133
77 **SOUL ICON** 11
421 **SOUL SEEKER** (IRE) 45
225 **SOUND OF IONA** 25
585 **SOUND OF MUSIC** 18
314 **SOUND OF U A E** (IRE) 28
475 **SOUND REASON** 71
6 **SOUND REFLECTION** (USA) C 212
253 **SOUNDSLIKETHUNDER** (IRE) 118
243 **SOUNDSTRINGS** F 188
330 **SOUPIR** 27
395 **SOUPY SOUPS** (IRE) 100
179 **SOURIRE SECRET** 17
253 **SOUTH AUDLEY** 218
123 **SOUTH BAY** F 100
156 **SOUTH BOSTON** (IRE) 8
593 **SOUTH CAROLINA** (IRE) 26
434 **SOUTH MOUNTAIN** (IRE) 79
323 **SOUTH TERRACE** (IRE) 79
536 **SOUTHEAST ROSE** (IRE) 13
16 **SOUTHERLY STORM** 213
309 **SOUTHERN BELLE** (IRE) C 222
417 **SOUTHERN CAPE** (IRE) 20
473 **SOUTHERN GIRL** (IRE) 78
419 **SOUTHERN LIGHTS** (IRE) 115
563 **SOUTHERN VOYAGE** (FR) 49
411 **SOUTHFIELD HARVEST** 166
59 **SOUTHFIELD LILY** 9
59 **SOUTHFIELD MEGAN** 10
411 **SOUTHFIELD STONE** 167
59 **SOUTHFIELD TORR** 11
575 **SOUTHWAY QUEEN** C 19
107 **SOUTHWEST HARBOR** (IRE) 61
503 **SOVEREIGN DUKE** (GER) 47
120 **SOVEREIGN LEADER** (IRE) 49
70 **SOVEREIGN MOON** 14
87 **SOVEREIGN SLIPPER** 30
407 **SOVEREIGN STATE** 10
202 **SOVEREIGNSFLAGSHIP** (IRE) F 8
253 **SOWS** (IRE) 219
535 **SOYOUNIQUE** (IRE) 6
492 **SOYOUTHINKSOAGAIN** (IRE) 134
149 **SOYUZ** 30
6 **SPACE BLUES** (IRE) 24
311 **SPACE KID** (IRE) 14
532 **SPACE SAFARI** (FR) 49
344 **SPACER** (IRE) 66
401 **SPACESUIT** 8
391 **SPANGLER** (IRE) 41
243 **SPANISH** (IRE) 189
91 **SPANISH ANGEL** (IRE) 27
189 **SPANISH ARCHER** (FR) 21
545 **SPANISH CITY** 33
256 **SPANISH CLASS** (IRE) 138
227 **SPANISH HUSTLE** 55
424 **SPANISH JUMP** (FR) 89
326 **SPANISH KISS** 18
191 **SPANISH MANE** (IRE) 9
16 **SPANISH MISSION** (USA) 35
511 **SPANISH PERSUADER** (FR) 12
97 **SPANISH STAR** (IRE) 17
473 **SPARK OF MADNESS** (FR) 79
368 **SPARK OF MAGIC** 22
537 **SPARKLE** C 49
250 **SPARKLE IN HIS EYE** 73
190 **SPARKLING DAWN** 39

420 **SWEET DIME** 24
550 **SWEET EMBRACE** (IRE) 12
555 **SWEET EXPECTATION** 29
514 **SWEET FAB'S** 26
27 **SWEET FANTASY** 128
307 **SWEET FLORA** (IRE) 10
243 **SWEET IDEA** (AUS) C 192
16 **SWEET MANDOLIN** F 217
65 **SWEET MARMALADE** (IRE) 22
415 **SWEET MOLLY MALONE** (USA) 102
385 **SWEET NATURE** (IRE) 18
308 **SWEET NICOLE** F 44
279 **SWEET NIGHTINGALE** 4
379 **SWEET PURSUIT** 13
446 **SWEET REWARD** (IRE) 9
393 **SWEET SECRET** C 33
344 **SWEET TEMPTATION** (IRE) C 67
47 **SWEET VINETTA** 18
105 **SWEET WILLIAM** 105
417 **SWEETASEVER** (IRE) C 55
263 **SWEETEST COMPANY** (IRE) 56
504 **SWEETEST SMILE** (IRE) 12
15 **SWEETHEART ABBEY** G 44
186 **SWEETNESSANDLIGHT** G 14
408 **SWEETTOWATCH** (IRE) 76
119 **SWELL SONG** 18
153 **SWIFT CRUSADOR** 28
1 **SWIFT GETAWAY** (IRE) F 56
215 **SWIFT PUSEY** 18
211 **SWIFT REMARK** 27
16 **SWILCAN BRIDGE** 218
244 **SWILLY SUNSET** 35
285 **SWINCOMBE FLEAT** 45
421 **SWING LOW** 88
538 **SWINGING EDDIE** 23
250 **SWINTON DIAMOND** (IRE) 77
7 **SWINTON NOON** 110
353 **SWISH DANCER** (IRE) C 52
415 **SWISS ACE** 103
446 **SWISS CHEER** (FR) 10
495 **SWISS CONNECTION** 14
545 **SWISS DIVA** C 191
132 **SWISS DREAM** C 80
10 **SWISS FLAMINGO** 42
428 **SWISS KISS** C 71
167 **SWISS KNIGHT** 44
526 **SWISS PRIDE** (IRE) 23
397 **SWISS SANCERRE** 28
351 **SWISS TIME** 19
425 **SWISSAL** (IRE) 17
415 **SWITCH** (USA) F 181
411 **SWITCH HITTER** (IRE) 172
6 **SWITCHING** (USA) C 215
300 **SWITZER** (IRE) 36
16 **SWIVELSTICK** 114
518 **SWOON** (FR) 77
119 **SWOOPER** 33
308 **SWORD BEACH** (IRE) 20
214 **SWORD EXCEED** (GER) 42
320 **SWORD OF FATE** (IRE) 2
491 **SWORN SOLD** (GER) C 88
371 **SYCAMORE** (IRE) 8
358 **SYKES** (IRE) 18
32 **SYLVIA PLATH** (IRE) 11
168 **SYMBOL OF HOPE** 144
6 **SYMBOLIC GESTURE** 90
98 **SYMBOLINE** F 61

16 **SYMBOLIZE** (IRE) 39
221 **SYMPATHISE** (IRE) 12
253 **SYMPHONY PERFECT** (IRE) 222
40 **SYMPHONY SOUND** (IRE) 11
470 **SYMPHONY STAR** (IRE) G 12
569 **SYNAESTHESIA** (FR) C 62
421 **SYNONYMOUS** 142
253 **SYSTEM** (IRE) 223
431 **SYSTEMIC** 16
7 **SZARRATU** (IRE) 80
132 **TAA LAA** 81
525 **TAAMER** 3
523 **TAAQAH** (USA) F 87
79 **TAAWFAN** (IRE) 9
411 **TABACHINES** (FR) G 173
6 **TABAQAT** (IRE) 1
79 **TABDEED** 10
152 **TABLE BLUFF** (IRE) 6
522 **TABLE MOUNTAIN** 37
333 **TABLE THIRTY FOUR** 63
518 **TABLES TURNED** 131
601 **TABOO** (IRE) 17
376 **TABOU BEACH BOY** 53
253 **TACARIB BAY** 224
16 **TACK** (FR) 219
63 **TACKLESLIKEAFERRET** (IRE) 37
428 **TACORA** (IRE) 41
302 **TACTICAL** 115
482 **TACTICAL MANOEUVRE** (IRE) 29
483 **TADASANA** 13
309 **TADREEB** (IRE) 136
51 **TADRIS** (USA) C 52
40 **TAFANEEN** (USA) C 144
491 **TAHIRAH** F 89
253 **TAHITIAN PRINCE** (FR) 29
475 **TAHONTA** (IRE) 74
146 **TAILSPIN** (IRE) 39
256 **TAIPAN** (IRE) 142
253 **TAJDID** (FR) 121
6 **TAJRIBA** (IRE) C 216
183 **TAKBEER** (IRE) 11
546 **TAKE EM OUT** (IRE) 64
399 **TAKE TEA** (IRE) 180
119 **TAKE UP ARMS** (USA) 34
411 **TAKE YOUR TIME** (IRE) 174
493 **TAKEIT EASY** 20
345 **TAKEONEFORTHETEAM** 38
461 **TAKING FLIGHT** (IRE) 44
363 **TAKINGITALLIN** (IRE) 102
461 **TAKINGRISKS** (IRE) 45
601 **TAKODA** (IRE) 18
309 **TALAMPAYA** (USA) G 137
79 **TALBEYAH** (IRE) 35
422 **TALES OF THE TWEED** (IRE) 5
153 **TALK OF A STORM** 29
13 **TALK OF FAME** 60
13 **TALK OF THE MOON** 61
143 **TALK TO THE MISSUS** (IRE) F 17
125 **TALKING ABOUT YOU** 13
321 **TALKISCHEAP** (IRE) 107
234 **TALKTOMENOW** 64
29 **TALL ORDER** (IRE) 36
503 **TALLOW FOR COAL** (IRE) 50
193 **TALLULAH** (IRE) 55
257 **TALLY'S SON** 15
402 **TAMANGO** (IRE) 117
402 **TAMAR BRIDGE** (IRE) 118

274 **TAMARAMA** 112
337 **TAMARILLO GROVE** (IRE) 24
386 **TAMARIS** (IRE) 111
411 **TAMAROC DU MATHAN** (FR) 175
421 **TAMASKA** 89
107 **TAMBOOTIE** (IRE) 36
6 **TAMBORRADA** 92
84 **TAMBOURINE GIRL** 24
411 **TAMGHO BORGET** (FR) 176
50 **TAMIGI** 63
91 **TAMKEEN** 30
545 **TAMMOOZ** 35
27 **TAMRA'S ROCK** (IRE) 129
253 **TAMYEEZ** (USA) 122
589 **TAN** 21
7 **TAN ARABIQ** 81
101 **TAN TAMASHA** 65
415 **TANAGHUM** F 182
86 **TANARPINO** 8
225 **TANASOQ** (IRE) 28
228 **TANGELO** 132
541 **TANGLED** (IRE) 10
16 **TANGLEWOOD TALES** 116
395 **TANGO BOY** (IRE) 103
588 **TANGO DE JUILLEY** (FR) 75
264 **TANGO DU ROY** (IRE) 45
408 **TANGO ECHO CHARLIE** (IRE) 77
411 **TANGO TARA** 177
274 **TANMAWWY** (IRE) 71
225 **TANNADICE PARK** (IRE) 29
214 **TANNING** G 60
582 **TANQEEB** 72
264 **TANRUDY** (IRE) 46
175 **TANTASTIC** 68
62 **TANTOLI** 62
456 **TAP TAP BOOM** 38
415 **TAPESTRY** (IRE) C 183
76 **TAPETEN TONI** (FR) 74
167 **TAPIS LIBRE** 45
228 **TAQAREER** (IRE) 33
123 **TAQDEES** (IRE) C 106
537 **TAQSEEMAAT** 11
388 **TAQWAA** (IRE) 31
419 **TAR HEEL** (IRE) 120
588 **TARA CHIEFTAIN** 76
159 **TARA ITI** 23
225 **TARA KAY** 30
178 **TARA MILL** (IRE) 23
333 **TARA NIECE** 64
527 **TARA POTTER** G 37
122 **TARA TIARA** 8
243 **TARAASHQQ** (GER) 109
300 **TARAMANDA** 37
6 **TARANTO** F 217
388 **TARAS DAY** 32
120 **TARAVARA** (IRE) 52
32 **TARBAT NESS** 18
415 **TARBELA** (IRE) C 184
378 **TARBOOSH** 23
388 **TARDREE** (IRE) 33
243 **TARHIB** (IRE) 110
407 **TARKA COUNTRY** 13
76 **TARNEEMAT** 75
517 **TARNHELM** 8
128 **TARQUIN STARDUST** (FR) 64
441 **TARRONA** 9
557 **TARSEEKH** 18

110 **TARTAN CHIEF** 41
321 **TARTAN FLYER** (FR) 108
6 **TASADAY** (USA) C 218
276 **TASANAK** (IRE) G 102
537 **TASFEEQ** 32
107 **TASHAROWA** (FR) F 63
7 **TASHBEEH** 111
6 **TASHELKA** (FR) C 219
418 **TASHUNKA** (IRE) 126
228 **TASLIMA** 133
535 **TASMAN BAY** (IRE) 14
71 **TASMANIA** (IRE) 28
384 **TASSINA** (GER) F 36
107 **TASTE OF HEAVEN** (AUS) F 64
408 **TASTE THE FEAR** (IRE) 78
180 **TATABOQ** (IRE) 42
64 **TATHMEEN** (IRE) 21
128 **THATSTHEWAYTODOIT** 95
569 **TATTENHAMS** 25
471 **TATTLETALE** (FR) 14
308 **TATTOO** 45
256 **TAURAN SHAMAN** (IRE) 65
526 **TAUREAN EMERALD** (IRE) 40
127 **TAUREAN STAR** (IRE) 2
314 **TAVRINA** 16
593 **TAWAAFOQ** 20
518 **TAWAAREQ** (IRE) 78
79 **TAWAANY** (IRE) 36
228 **TAWAHUB** 134
228 **TAWLEED** (IRE) 135
587 **TAWNY PORT** 29
363 **TAWSEEF** (IRE) 103
97 **TAWTHEEF** (IRE) 18
399 **TAX FOR MAX** (GER) 181
33 **TAXI RANK** (IRE) 10
147 **TAXMEIFYOUCAN** (IRE) 65
189 **TAYCAN** 70
368 **TAYLOR THE SAILOR** 23
93 **TAYLORS THREE ROCK** (IRE) 79
302 **TAYZAR** 12
386 **TAZKA** (FR) 112
101 **TAZMANIAN DEVIL** 66
447 **TB BROKE HER** (IRE) 20
329 **TEA CLIPPER** (IRE) 47
583 **TEA FOR TWO** 17
218 **TEA TIME FRED** 14
218 **TEA TIME ON MARS** 15
228 **TEARDROP ROCK** 136
6 **TEARLESS** C 220
16 **TEARS OF THE SUN** F 220
379 **TEASE AND SEIZE** (IRE) 30
363 **TEASING GEORGIA** (IRE) 104
304 **TEASYWEASY** 36
34 **TEBAY** (IRE) 14
243 **TEBEE'S OASIS** C 193
371 **TECHNICIAN** (IRE) 9
371 **TECHNIQUE** 19
227 **TECHNO VIKING** (IRE) 56
258 **TECHNOLOGICAL** 36
534 **TECHNOLOGY** (IRE) 107
418 **TED DA TITAN** 127
1 **TED VEALE** (IRE) 50
418 **TED'S FRIEND** (IRE) 128
93 **TEDDY** B 106
467 **TEDDY TEE** (IRE) 6
593 **TEDDY THE KNIGHT** 21
424 **TEDHAM** 92

333 **TEDWIN HILLS** (IRE) 65
582 **TEEMLUCKY** 73
343 **TEENAGE DIRTBAG** (IRE) 46
47 **TEESCOMPONENTS LAD** 19
25 **TEESCOMPONENTSFLY** 21
329 **TEESCOMPONENTSLASS** (IRE) 48
47 **TEESCOMPONENTSTRIG** 20
360 **TEETON SURPRISE** 8
128 **TEFNUT** (USA) 66
424 **TEGEREK** (IRE) 93
323 **TEKIBLUE DE L'ORME** (FR) 84
434 **TEL'ART** (FR) 82
533 **TELE COED** 19
76 **TELE RED** 24
569 **TELEFINA** 43
93 **TELEKINETIC** 80
189 **TELEMACHUS** 71
539 **TELL ME NOW** (IRE) F 23
120 **TELL'EM NOWT** 53
62 **TELLAIRSUE** (GER) 32
137 **TELLEROFTALES** (IRE) 5
309 **TELLMEYOURSTORY** (USA) 138
241 **TELLOVOI** (IRE) 12
369 **TELSON BARLEY** (IRE) 51
536 **TEME SPIRIT** (IRE) 14
258 **TEMPAH** 47
168 **TEMPER TRAP** 87
193 **TEMPEST FUGIT** (IRE) F 76
353 **TEMPESTUOUS** (IRE) 32
554 **TEMPLE BRUER** 72
308 **TEMPLE LOCK** 46
302 **TEMPLE MAN** 13
548 **TEMPLE OF THEBES** (IRE) F 44
418 **TEMPLEPARK** 129
168 **TEMPLEPOINT** 88
513 **TEMPLIER** (IRE) 3
105 **TEMPTATION** 106
326 **TEMPTING** F 58
456 **TEMPURAN** 39
105 **TEMPUS** 13
93 **TEMUR KHAN** 81
180 **TEN CHANTS** 18
475 **TEN IN A ROW** (IRE) 75
313 **TEN PAST MIDNIGHT** 31
276 **TEN SIXTY** (IRE) 103
533 **TENAX** (IRE) 20
554 **TENAYA CANYON** 73
228 **TENBURY WELLS** (USA) 34
421 **TENDENTIOUS** 90
386 **TENFOLD** (IRE) 113
456 **TENNEWROW** (IRE) 40
21 **TENSION TIME** (IRE) 4
311 **TENTH CENTURY** 15
523 **TEODELIGHT** (IRE) F 88
253 **TEODOLINA** (IRE) 123
545 **TEONA** (IRE) 130
415 **TEPIN** (USA) F 185
418 **TEQANY** (IRE) 130
418 **TEQUILA BLAZE** 131
168 **TEQUILA ROYALE** 145
481 **TEQUILA TEQUILA** 33
123 **TERHAAB** (USA) C 107
393 **TERMAGANT** (IRE) C 34
538 **TERMONATOR** 24
518 **TERRA MITICA** (IRE) 132
321 **TERRAFIRMA LADY** (IRE) 109
270 **TERREFORT** (FR) 163

448 **TERRI RULES** (IRE) 11
287 **TERRIBLE DAY** (IRE) G 12
76 **TERRICHANG** 76
492 **TERRIERMAN** (IRE) 138
491 **TERRIFY** (IRE) 63
419 **TERROR** (IRE) C 189
237 **TERUNTUM STAR** (IRE) 11
193 **TESSIE** C 56
395 **TEST RIDE** (IRE) 104
156 **TESTING** (FR) F 19
582 **TESTING FAITH** 87
552 **TESTING TIMES** 48
214 **TESTON** (FR) 43
16 **TEX AUSTRALIA** (IRE) 40
101 **TEXALOULA** C 67
259 **TEXAN NOMAD** 16
378 **TEXAS QUEEN** C 49
232 **TEXAS ROCK** (IRE) 4
392 **TEXTING** 3
461 **TFOU** (FR) 46
272 **THAAYER** 18
84 **THACKTHWAITE** 38
274 **THAFEERA** (USA) F 113
161 **THAHAB IFRAJ** (IRE) 35
309 **THAI TERRIER** (USA) 33
593 **THAIS TOIR** (FR) 22
368 **THAKI** (IRE) 13
518 **THALER** 79
399 **THALITLEOZIBATLER** (AUS) 182
321 **THANIELLE** (FR) 110
253 **THANK YOU NEXT** (IRE) 124
442 **THAT OLE CHESTNUT** (IRE) 30
28 **THAT SHIPS SAILED** (IRE) 5
585 **THAT'S A GIVEN** (FR) 71
448 **THAT'S A SHAME** (IRE) 12
292 **THAT'S MY DUBAI** (IRE) 3
105 **THAT'S MY STYLE** C 107
483 **THAT'S YOUR LOTTIE** 14
287 **THATS THE ONE** 13
424 **THATS THE TRUTH** (IRE) 94
534 **THATSENTERTAINMENT** (IRE) 108
428 **THAWRAH** (IRE) C 72
64 **THAWRY** 22
400 **THE ACCOUNTANT** 30
539 **THE ALCHEMIST** (FR) 34
429 **THE ARISTOCAT** (IRE) 13
188 **THE ARMED MAN** 8
274 **THE ATTORNEY** (IRE) 72
453 **THE BANNER MAN** (IRE) 10
487 **THE BAY BIRCH** (IRE) 16
544 **THE BAY WARRIOR** (IRE) 22
418 **THE BEES KNEES** (IRE) 132
425 **THE BELFRY BOY** 18
353 **THE BELL CONDUCTOR** (IRE) 13
427 **THE BIG BITE** (IRE) 26
534 **THE BIG BREAKAWAY** (IRE) 109
399 **THE BIG GETAWAY** (IRE) 183
410 **THE BIG HOUSE** (IRE) 5
212 **THE BIG STING** (IRE) 60
136 **THE BIG YIN** (IRE) 7
281 **THE BLACK SQUIRREL** (IRE) 8
185 **THE BLAME GAME** (IRE) 32
446 **THE BLUE BOWER** (IRE) 11
256 **THE BLUE BRILLIANT** (IRE) 143
156 **THE BLUE GARTER** (IRE) 15
581 **THE BOAT** (IRE) 75
17 **THE BOLSHOI BANDIT** (IRE) 13

231 **VALENTINE MIST** (IRE) 5
341 **VALENTINE'S TURF** (FR) 16
50 **VALENTINKA** 66
154 **VALENTINO** 17
402 **VALENTINO DANCER** 126
256 **VALERIA MESSALINA** (IRE) 67
529 **VALGOR DU RONCERAY** (FR) 25
6 **VALIANT PRINCE** (FR) 94
256 **VALLE DE LA LUNA** 145
321 **VALLERES** (FR) 123
191 **VALLETTA SUNSET** 10
399 **VALLEY BREEZE** (FR) 191
16 **VALLEY FORGE** 120
421 **VALLEY OF FLOWERS** (IRE) 95
105 **VALORANT** 51
537 **VALPARAISO** 34
105 **VALSAD** 108
190 **VALSE AU TAILLONS** (FR) 42
222 **VALSEUR DU GRANVAL** (FR) 75
600 **VALSHAN TIME** (IRE) 7
270 **VALSHEDA** 170
270 **VALTOR** (FR) 171
309 **VALUE THEORY** (IRE) 230
545 **VALYRIAN STEEL** (IRE) 38
530 **VAMPISH** 9
64 **VAN DIJK** 24
378 **VAN GERWEN** 25
415 **VAN GOGH** (USA) 107
62 **VAN MEEGEREN** (IRE) 25
91 **VAN ZANT** 40
395 **VANCOUVER** 110
392 **VANDAD** (IRE) 9
235 **VANDEMERE** (IRE) 63
224 **VANDERBILT** (IRE) 9
276 **VANGO DE VAIGE** (FR) 109
449 **VANISHING GRACE** (FR) 34
337 **VANITEUX** (FR) 26
495 **VANITY** (IRE) C 44
193 **VANITY AFFAIR** (IRE) 31
330 **VANOUCHE** 29
415 **VANZARA** (FR) C 186
93 **VAPE** 87
563 **VARIYANN** (FR) 24
393 **VARNISH** C 36
316 **VASCO DA GAMA** (FR) 17
6 **VASILAKOS** 95
84 **VASSARIA** (IRE) F 43
506 **VASTITAS** (IRE) C 57
120 **VAUNTED** 114
553 **VAZIANI** (FR) 19
372 **VAZZY** 104
7 **VEE SIGHT** 132
107 **VEFA** (FR) C 67
419 **VEGA MAGNIFICO** (IRE) 195
123 **VEGA SICILIA** (FR) C 110
270 **VEGAS BLUE** (IRE) 172
454 **VEILED BEAUTY** (USA) C 59
522 **VEILED SECRET** (IRE) 38
569 **VELADIYA** (IRE) F 65
329 **VELASCO** (FR) 52
412 **VELKERA** (IRE) 2
188 **VELMA** 19
283 **VELOCISTAR** (IRE) 15
428 **VELOCITY** (IRE) 43
6 **VELORUM** (FR) 27
27 **VELVET AND STEEL** (USA) 69
576 **VELVET BAND** G 21

440 **VELVET CHARM** C 25
273 **VELVET COGNAC** 10
290 **VELVET REVOLVER** (IRE) C 69
401 **VELVET VISION** 10
401 **VELVET VISTA** 11
171 **VELVET VOICE** 32
401 **VELVET VULCAN** 23
460 **VENETIAN LASS** F 9
473 **VENGEUR DE GUYE** (FR) 87
194 **VENTURA** (IRE) C 39
128 **VENTURA FLAME** (IRE) 70
226 **VENTURA GOLD** (IRE) 6
309 **VENTURA KINGDOM** (FR) 144
322 **VENTURA MAGIC** 40
309 **VENTURA MIST** F 231
475 **VENTURA RASCAL** 30
253 **VENTURA TORMENTA** (IRE) 125
309 **VENTURA VISION** (IRE) 145
253 **VENTURA WIZARD** 126
25 **VENTUROUS** (IRE) 22
29 **VENUS DE MILO** C 71
417 **VENUS DE MILO** (IRE) F 57
20 **VENUS RISING** F 31
262 **VENUSTA** (IRE) 9
134 **VERA RICHARDSON** (IRE) C 12
229 **VERAVERA** 8
270 **VERDANA BLUE** (IRE) 173
235 **VEREINA** 64
429 **VERETA** (IRE) 19
232 **VERHOYEN** 5
140 **VERITY** C 27
256 **VERLINGA** (IRE) 196
578 **VERNE CASTLE** 17
568 **VERNIER** 36
61 **VERRE DORE** 20
159 **VERREAUX EAGLE** (IRE) 36
270 **VERSATILITY** 174
479 **VERTICAL** 10
549 **VERTICE** (IRE) 13
345 **VERUS DELICIA** (IRE) F 59
492 **VERY FIRST TIME** 146
322 **VERY INTENSE** (IRE) 41
501 **VERY PATIENT** (IRE) 54
6 **VERY SPECIAL** (IRE) F 223
27 **VESELA** 70
124 **VESHENSKAYA** (IRE) 13
554 **VESNINA** F 92
274 **VESPASIA** F 115
189 **VESTMENT** 72
310 **VETONCALL** (IRE) 13
547 **VEXED** 25
375 **VEZINA** F 70
16 **VIA DE VEGA** (FR) 42
241 **VIA LAZIO** G 19
193 **VIA SERENDIPITY** 32
539 **VIA SISTINA** (IRE) 24
465 **VIA VOLUPTA** 8
145 **VIADUCT** 32
597 **VIBE QUEEN** (FR) C 25
189 **VIBRANCE** 24
595 **VICE ROYAL** 4
227 **VICENZO MIO** (FR) 52
284 **VICKY CRISTINA** (IRE) 5
352 **VICKY JANE** 3
132 **VICTORIA FALLS** (IRE) 84
508 **VICTORIA GROVE** 29
491 **VICTORIA LINE** (IRE) 66

175 **VICTORIANO** (IRE) 59
418 **VICTORIAS PEAK** (IRE) 144
253 **VICTORIOUS NIGHT** (IRE) 127
26 **VICTORY ANGEL** (IRE) 12
27 **VICTORY CHIME** (IRE) 26
449 **VICTORY CLAP** 68
22 **VICTORY ECHO** (IRE) 29
523 **VICTORY HEIGHTS** (IRE) 47
419 **VICTORY ROAD** (IRE) 62
435 **VICTORY ROSE** 11
309 **VICTORY STAR** 38
444 **VIEUX LION ROUGE** (FR) 82
492 **VIGILANCE** (IRE) 147
87 **VIGNONI** 33
475 **VIKING FAIR** C 128
395 **VIKING RUBY** 111
494 **VILARO** (FR) 19
371 **VILLAGE GOSSIP** (IRE) F 49
446 **VILLANELLE** 13
6 **VILLARRICA** (USA) C 224
518 **VILLE DE GRACE** 84
523 **VILLEURBANNE** 48
370 **VIN DE PAIL** (FR) 5
428 **VIN ROUGE** (IRE) 44
324 **VINA BAY** 25
475 **VINCENT VEGA** (IRE) 81
527 **VINCENZO** (FR) 51
97 **VINCENZO COCCOTTI** (USA) 20
98 **VINCITA** (IRE) C 101
549 **VINDOBALA** (IRE) 16
274 **VINDOLANDA** 28
13 **VINNDICATION** (IRE) 70
585 **VINNIE DEV** (IRE) 25
66 **VINNIE RED** (IRE) 7
488 **VINNIE THE HODDIE** (IRE) 46
402 **VINNIE'S GETAWAY** (IRE) 127
233 **VINNIE'S ICON** (IRE) 7
170 **VINO SANTO** 12
391 **VINO VICTRIX** 45
473 **VINO'S CHOICE** (IRE) 88
501 **VINTAGE CLOUDS** (IRE) 55
146 **VINTAGE GLEN** (IRE) 41
376 **VINTAGE POLLY** (IRE) 61
562 **VINTAGE RASCAL** (FR) 7
189 **VIOLA** (IRE) 25
421 **VIOLA D'AMOUR** (IRE) F 144
259 **VIOLA PARK** 21
6 **VIOLANTE** (USA) F 225
7 **VIOLET PRINCESS** 85
547 **VIOLET RUN** (IRE) 38
243 **VIOLET WARDA** (IRE) 113
40 **VIOLET'S GIFT** (IRE) C 147
306 **VIOLET'S LADS** (IRE) 12
533 **VIOLETTE SZABO** (IRE) 21
159 **VIRGIN SNOW** 14
274 **VIRGINIA CELESTE** (IRE) C 116
581 **VIRGINIA CHICK** (FR) 80
475 **VIRGINIA HALL** F 129
454 **VIRGINIA PLANE** 44
415 **VIRGINIA WATERS** (USA) C 187
411 **VIROFLAY** (FR) 187
311 **VIRTUDES** (IRE) F 28
16 **VIRTUOSO** 221
395 **VIS A VIS** 112
399 **VIS TA LOI** (FR) 192
243 **VISALA** 114
145 **VISIBILITY** (IRE) 33

259 **WE'RE REUNITED** (IRE) 22
337 **WE'VE GOT PAYET** 27
397 **WE'VE GOT THE LOVE** (IRE) 25
175 **WEAKFIELD** (IRE) 60
404 **WEAREWEREWEARE** (IRE) 12
300 **WEATHER FRONT** (USA) 44
6 **WEDDING DANCE** (IRE) 97
40 **WEDDING MARCH** (IRE) F 149
134 **WEDGEWOOD STAR** F 13
483 **WEE DRACULA** (IRE) 20
242 **WEE FLY TOO** 9
51 **WEE JEAN** F 54
223 **WEE RUPERT** 27
365 **WEEKEND LADY** (IRE) F 19
545 **WEEKEND STRIKE** (USA) C 195
346 **WEEKLY GOSSIP** (IRE) 11
168 **WEISSE SOCKEN** (IRE) F 171
547 **WELAN** (GER) 26
48 **WELCOME SIGHT** 21
473 **WELL ABOVE PAR** (IRE) 90
339 **WELL BRIEFED** (IRE) 11
575 **WELL DISGUISED** (IRE) G 23
454 **WELL EDUCATED** (IRE) 25
122 **WELL I NEVER** 9
6 **WELL OF WISDOM** 29
454 **WELL PLANTED** (IRE) 26
345 **WELL PREPARED** 42
178 **WELL SMITTEN** (IRE) 24
228 **WELL SPENT** 148
493 **WELLAND** 31
370 **WELLFLEET WITCH** 7
234 **WELLNTYNE** 66
168 **WELLS FARHH GO** (IRE) 96
35 **WELLS GLORY** (IRE) 20
177 **WELLS GOLD** (IRE) 10
80 **WELOOF** (FR) 38
123 **WELSH GOLD** 52
173 **WELSH RAREBIT** 15
270 **WELSH SAINT** (FR) 176
132 **WELSH WAYNE** (IRE) 17
96 **WELSH'S CASTLE** (IRE) 26
415 **WEMBLEY** (IRE) 108
323 **WEMYSS POINT** 89
62 **WENCESLAUS** (GER) 26
180 **WENDEN BELLE** (IRE) F 56
217 **WENDREDA** 7
26 **WENSLEY** 13
419 **WENSUM RIVER** 130
392 **WENTWORTH AMIGO** (IRE) 10
254 **WENTWORTH FALLS** 10
331 **WESSINGTON PARK** 6
534 **WEST APPROACH** 119
592 **WEST CLASS** (IRE) 8
488 **WEST COAST FLYER** 49
499 **WEST DRIVE** (IRE) 26
309 **WEST END CHARMER** (IRE) 42
473 **WEST END LADY** (IRE) 91
574 **WEST END WOODY** (IRE) 45
386 **WEST LAKE** (FR) 121
290 **WEST OF VENUS** (USA) F 70
386 **WEST ON SUNSET** (FR) 122
534 **WEST ORCHARD** (IRE) 120
445 **WEST TO CROSSGALES** (IRE) 9
492 **WEST TO THE BRIDGE** (IRE) 151
76 **WEST WAY NEVER** (IRE) 81
337 **WEST WIZARD** (FR) 28
253 **WESTADORA** (IRE) F 235

382 **WESTBOURNE** (IRE) F 7
273 **WESTBROOK BERTIE** 11
65 **WESTDANTE** (IRE) 24
276 **WESTEND STORY** (IRE) 111
558 **WESTEND THEATRE** (IRE) 6
120 **WESTERN ALLIANCE** (IRE) 57
534 **WESTERN BARON** (IRE) 121
167 **WESTERN BEAT** (IRE) 71
427 **WESTERN CLIMATE** (IRE) 27
15 **WESTERN DAWN** (IRE) 27
343 **WESTERN MILLER** (IRE) 27
25 **WESTERN MUSIC** (IRE) 43
351 **WESTERN PEARL** C 30
373 **WESTERN RAMBLER** (IRE) 5
234 **WESTERN STARLET** (IRE) 67
190 **WESTERN SUNRISE** (IRE) 43
6 **WESTERN SYMPHONY** (IRE) 98
297 **WESTERN WOLF** 19
411 **WESTHILL** (IRE) 188
185 **WESTLAND ROW** (IRE) 35
488 **WESTSTREET** (IRE) 50
238 **WESTTARA** 7
571 **WESTY'S SUPER MARE** (IRE) 20
258 **WETANWINDY** 39
84 **WETHER FELL** 28
461 **WETLANDS** (IRE) 50
304 **WHALEWEIGH STATION** 19
222 **WHAT** (IRE) 76
210 **WHAT A BALOO** (IRE) 18
488 **WHAT A GLANCE** 15
252 **WHAT A LAUGH** 26
444 **WHAT A MOMENT** (IRE) 83
150 **WHAT A PLEASURE** 21
222 **WHAT A STEAL** (IRE) 77
343 **WHAT ABOUT TIME** (IRE) 54
256 **WHAT SAY YOU** (IRE) C 197
402 **WHAT WILL BE** (IRE) 131
19 **WHAT'LLBEWILLBE** (IRE) 17
350 **WHAT'S MY LINE** 13
488 **WHAT'S OCCURRING** (IRE) 52
501 **WHAT'S THE SCOOP** (IRE) 57
128 **WHAT'S THE STORY** 73
421 **WHAT'S UP PUSSYCAT** (IRE) F 97
443 **WHATABOUTWALT** (IRE) 14
399 **WHATDEAWANT** (IRE) 193
387 **WHATELSEABOUTYOU** (IRE) C 39
194 **WHATITIZZ** 23
249 **WHATS THE MATTER** (IRE) 5
408 **WHATSDASTORY** (IRE) 82
467 **WHATSGOINGON** (FR) 7
389 **WHATSNOTOKNOW** (IRE) 29
434 **WHATSUPWITHYOU** (IRE) 89
270 **WHATSWRONGWITHYOU** (IRE) 177
195 **WHATTHEBUTLERSAW** (IRE) 12
241 **WHATWOULDYOUKNOW** (IRE) 14
402 **WHATYA ON ABOUT** 132
481 **WHAZZAT** F 51
495 **WHEAL KITTY** 45
113 **WHEELBAHRI** 33
456 **WHEESHT** (IRE) 43
424 **WHEN YOU'RE READY** (IRE) 104
526 **WHENTHEDEALINSDONE** 41
324 **WHERE YOU AT** 26
25 **WHERE'S BOBBY** 44
533 **WHERE'S BROUGHTON** F 66
167 **WHERE'S JEFF** 47
167 **WHERE'S STEPH** 72

415 **WHERE'S SUE** (IRE) C 190
114 **WHERE'S THE TAPE** 12
350 **WHERE'S TOM** 14
388 **WHERES MAUD GONE** (IRE) 37
177 **WHEREWOULDUGETIT** (IRE) 11
16 **WHIMSY** 223
212 **WHISKEY 'N' CHIPS** 58
175 **WHISKEY AND WATER** 61
107 **WHISKEY LULLABY** 13
411 **WHISKEY LULLABY** (IRE) 189
399 **WHISKEY SOUR** (IRE) 194
137 **WHISKEY TIMES** (IRE) 6
212 **WHISKY EXPRESS** 64
421 **WHISKY SPRINTER** (IRE) 145
492 **WHISPERING GYPSY** (IRE) 152
379 **WHISPERING WINDS** (IRE) 7
256 **WHISPERINTHEBREEZE** 69
63 **WHISTLING SANDS** 39
421 **WHITE AIME** 98
27 **WHITE CAY** F 134
375 **WHITE DRESS** (IRE) C 71
212 **WHITE HART LADY** (IRE) 65
51 **WHITE JASMINE** (IRE) 55
274 **WHITE LADY** (IRE) 74
211 **WHITE MOCHA** (USA) 24
534 **WHITE MOON** (GER) 122
40 **WHITE MOONLIGHT** (USA) 71
384 **WHITE MOONSTONE** (USA) C 38
600 **WHITE NILE** (IRE) 8
237 **WHITE ROSA** (IRE) C 14
364 **WHITE TOWER** (IRE) 6
456 **WHITE TURF** (IRE) 44
492 **WHITE WALKER** 153
391 **WHITE WEDDING** (IRE) F 66
101 **WHITE WHISKY** 74
495 **WHITEANDBLUE** 46
363 **WHITECHURCH** (IRE) 114
254 **WHITEHALL** 11
391 **WHITEHAVEN** (FR) 21
212 **WHITEHOTCHILLIFILI** (IRE) 66
98 **WHITELEY** F 104
363 **WHITEOAK FLEUR** 115
589 **WHITLEY NEILL** (IRE) 23
270 **WHITLOCK** 178
148 **WHITTLE LE WOODS** 61
291 **WHITTON LOCH** (IRE) 16
495 **WHITWELL** 48
321 **WHO CARES WINS** (IRE) 146
321 **WHO DARES WINS** (IRE) 125
227 **WHO IS THAT** (IRE) 53
534 **WHO SHOT JR** (IRE) 123
539 **WHO TOLD JO JO** (IRE) 15
242 **WHO TOLD YOU** 10
366 **WHO WHAT WHEN** 4
318 **WHO'S IN THE BOX** (IRE) 18
404 **WHO'S MY JOCKEY** (IRE) 17
171 **WHO'S THE BOSS** 33
250 **WHO'S THE GUV'NOR** (IRE) 85
512 **WHOA BLACK BETTY** (IRE) 11
387 **WHOLELOTAFUN** (IRE) 19
323 **WHOSHOTTHESHERIFF** (IRE) 90
408 **WHOSHOTWHO** (IRE) 83
534 **WHYDAH GALLY** 124
360 **WICK GREEN** 9
370 **WICKED WEST** (IRE) 8
413 **WICKLOW WARRIOR** 12
51 **WIDAAD** 16

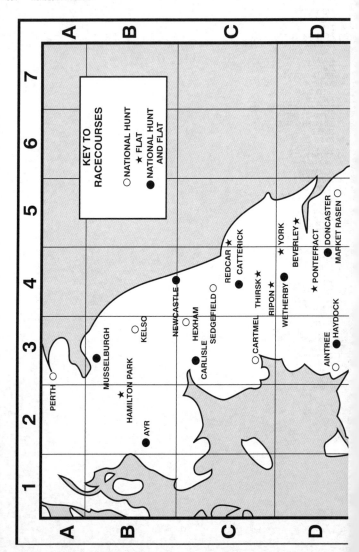

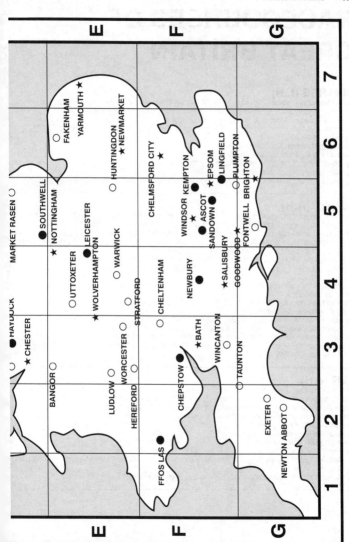

# RACECOURSES OF GREAT BRITAIN

## AINTREE (L.H)
**Grand National Course:** Triangular, 2m2f (16 fences) 494y run-in with elbow. Perfectly flat. A severe test for both horse and rider, putting a premium on jumping ability, fitness and courage.
**Mildmay Course:** Rectangular, 1m4f (8) 260y run-in. A very fast, flat course with sharp bends.
**Address:** Aintree Racecourse, Ormskirk Road, Aintree, Liverpool, L9 5AS Tel: 0151 523 2600
**Website:** www.aintree.co.uk
**Managing Director:** Nicholas Wrigley
**Clerk of the Course:** Sulekha Varma
**By Road:** North of the City, near the junction of the M57 and M58 with the A59 (Preston).
**By Rail:** Aintree Station is adjacent to the Stands, from Liverpool Central.
**By Air:** Liverpool (John Lennon) Airport is 10 miles. Helicopter landing facility by prior arrangement.

## ASCOT (R.H)
**Flat:** Right-handed triangular track just under 1m6f in length. The Round course descends from the 1m4f start into Swinley Bottom, the lowest part of the track. It then turns right-handed and joins the Old Mile Course, which starts on a separate chute. The course then rises to the right-handed home turn over an underpass to join the straight mile course. The run-in is about 3f, rising slightly to the winning post. The whole course is of a galloping nature with easy turns.
**N.H.** Triangular, 1m6f (10), 240y run-in mostly uphill. A galloping course with an uphill finish, Ascot provides a real test of stamina. The fences are stiff and sound jumping is essential, especially for novices.
**Address:** Ascot Racecourse, Ascot, Berkshire SL5 7JX Tel: 08707 271234
**Website:** www.ascot.co.uk
**Clerk of the Course:** Chris Stickels 01344 878502 / 07970 621440
**Chief Executive:** Guy Henderson
**By Road:** West of the town on the A329. Easy access from the M3 (Junction 3) and the M4 (Junction 6). Car parking adjoining the course and Ascot Heath.
**By Rail:** Regular service from Waterloo to Ascot (500y from the racecourse).
**By Air:** Helicopter landing facility at the course. London (Heathrow) Airport 15 miles, White Waltham Airfield 12 miles (01427) 718800.

## AYR (L.H)
**Flat:** A left-handed, galloping, flat oval track of 1m4f with a 4f run-in. The straight 6f is essentially flat.
**N.H.** Oval, 1m4f (9), 210y run-in. Relatively flat and one of the fastest tracks in Great Britain. It is a well-drained course and the ground rarely becomes testing. The track suits the long-striding galloper.
**Address:** Ayr Racecourse, Whitletts Road, Ayr, KA8 0JE Tel: 01292 264179
**Website:** www.ayr-racecourse.co.uk
**Clerk of the Course:** Graeme Anderson
**Managing Director:** David Brown
**By Road:** East of the town on the A758. Free parking for buses and cars.
**By Rail:** Ayr Station (trains on the half hour from Glasgow Central). Journey time 55 minutes. Buses and taxis also to the course.
**By Air:** Prestwick International Airport (10 minutes), Glasgow Airport (1 hour).

# BANGOR-ON-DEE (L.H)

**N.H.** Circular, 1m4f (9), 325y run-in. Apart from some 'ridge and furrow', this is a flat course notable for three sharp bends, especially the paddock turn. Suits handy, speedy sorts.
**Address:** Bangor-On-Dee Racecourse, Overton Road, Bangor-On-Dee, Wrexham, LL13 0DA Tel: 01978 782081
**Website:** www.bangorondeeraces.co.uk
**Clerk of the Course and Racing Manager:** Andrew Morris
**Chief Executive:** Richard Thomas
**General Manager:** Jeannie Chantler
**By Road:** 5 miles south-east of Wrexham, off the B5069.
**By Rail:** Wrexham Station (bus or taxi to the course).
**By Air:** Helicopters may land by prior arrangement with Clerk of the Course.

# BATH (L.H)

**Flat:** Galloping, left-handed, level oval of 1m4f, with long, stiff run-in of about 4f which bends to the left. An extended chute provides for sprint races.
**Address:** The Racecourse, Lansdown, Bath, BA1 9BU Tel: 01225 424609
**Website:** www.bath-racecourse.co.uk
**Clerk of the Course:** Tim Long
**Executive Director:** Liam Johnson
**By Road:** 2 miles northwest of the City (M4 Junction 18) at Lansdown. Unlimited free car and coach parking immediately behind the stands. Special bus services operate from Bath to the racecourse.
**By Rail:** Bath Station (from Paddington).
**By Air:** Bristol or Colerne Airports. Helicopter landing facilities available by prior arrangement.

# BEVERLEY (R.H)

**Flat:** A right-handed oval of 1m3f, generally galloping, with an uphill run-in of two and a half furlongs. The 5f course is very stiff.
**Address:** Beverley Race Co. Ltd., York Road, Beverley, Yorkshire HU17 9QZ Tel: 01482 867488 / 882645
**Website:** www.beverley-racecourse.co.uk
**Chief Executive and Clerk of the Course:** Sally Iggulden 07850 458605
**By Road:** 7 miles from the M62 (Junction 38) off the A1035. Free car parking opposite the course. Owners and trainers use a separate enclosure.
**By Rail:** Beverley Station (Hull-Scarborough line). Occasional bus service to the course (1 mile).

# BRIGHTON (L.H)

**Flat:** Left-handed, 1m4f horseshoe with easy turns and a run-in of three and a half furlongs. Undulating and sharp, the track suits handy types.
**Address:** Brighton Racecourse, Brighton, East Sussex BN2 2XZ Tel: 01273 603580
**Website:** www.brighton-racecourse.co.uk
**Clerk of the Course:** Philip Hide
**Executive Director:** Paul Ellison
**By Road:** East of the city on the A27 (Lewes Road). Car park adjoins the course.
**By Rail:** Brighton Station (from Victoria on the hour, London Bridge or Portsmouth). Special bus service to the course from the station (approx 2 miles).
**By Air:** Helicopters may land by prior arrangement.

# CARLISLE (R.H)

**Flat:** Right-handed, 1m4f pear-shaped track. Galloping and undulating with easy turns and a stiff uphill run-in of three and a half furlongs. The 6f course begins on an extended chute.

**N.H.** Pear-shaped, 1m5f (9), 300y run-in uphill. Undulating and a stiff test of stamina, ideally suited to the long-striding thorough stayer.

**Address:** Carlisle Racecourse, Durdar Road, Carlisle CA2 4TS Tel: 01228 554700

**Website:** www.carlisle-races.co.uk

**Regional Director:** Dickon White

**Joint Clerks of the Course:** Sulekha Varma and Kirkland Tellwright

**General Manager:** Molly Dingwall

**By Road:** 2 miles south of the city (Durdar Road). Easy access from the M6 (Junction 42). The car park is free (adjacent to the course).

**By Rail:** Carlisle Station (2 miles from the course).

**By Air:** Helicopter landing facility by prior arrangement.

# CARTMEL (L.H)

**N.H.** Oval, 1m1f (6), 800y run-in. Almost perfectly flat but very sharp, with the longest run-in in the country, approximately half a mile. The fences are stiff but fair.

**Address:** Cartmel Racecourse, Cartmel, nr Grange-Over-Sands, Cumbria LA11 6QF Tel: 01539 536340 Out of season: 01539 533335

**Website:** www.cartmel-racecourse.co.uk

**General Manager:** Geraldine McKay

**Clerk of the Course:** Anthea Morshead 07837 559861

**By Road:** 1 mile west of the town, 2 miles off the B5277 (Grange-Haverthwaite road). M6 (Junction 36).

**By Rail:** Cark-in-Cartmel Station (2 miles) (Carnforth-Barrow line). Raceday bus service.

**By Air:** Light aircraft facilities available at Cark Airport (4 miles from the course). Helicopter landing facility at the course, by prior arrangement only.

# CATTERICK (L.H)

**Flat:** A sharp, left-handed, undulating oval of 1m180y with a downhill run-in of 3f.

**N.H.** Oval, 1m1f (9), 240y run-in. Undulating, sharp track that favours the handy, front-running sort, rather than the long-striding galloper.

**Address:** The Racecourse, Catterick Bridge, Richmond, North Yorkshire DL10 7PE Tel: 01748 811478

**Website:** www.catterickbridge.co.uk

**General Manager and Clerk of the Course:** Fiona Needham 07831 688625

**By Road:** The course is adjacent to the A1, 1 mile northwest of the town on the A6136. There is a free car park.

**By Rail:** Darlington Station (special buses to course - 14-mile journey).

**By Air:** Helicopters can land by prior arrangement. Fixed wing planes contact RAF Leeming Tel: 01677 423041

# CHELMSFORD CITY (L.H)

**Flat:** A left-handed, floodlit Polytrack oval of 1m with sweeping bends and a 2f home straight. Races over 7f and 1m start from separate chutes.

**Address:** Chelmsford City Racecourse, Great Leighs, Essex, CM3 1QP Tel: 01245 362412

**Website:** www.chelmsfordcityracecourse.com

**Manager:** Fraser Garrity

**Clerk of the Course:** Andy Waitt

**By Road:** At Great Leighs, five miles north of Chelmsford on the A31

**By Rail:** Chelmsford station (from Liverpool Street)

**By Air:** Stansted Airport (17 miles)

# CHELTENHAM (L.H)

**Old Course:** Oval, 1m4f, (9) 350y run-in. A testing, undulating track with stiff fences. The ability to stay is essential.

**New Course:** Oval, 1m5f (10), 220y run-in. Undulating, stiff fences, testing course, uphill for the final half-mile.

**Address:** Cheltenham Racecourse, Prestbury Park, Cheltenham, Gloucestershire GL50 4SH Tel: 01242 513014

**Website:** www.cheltenham.co.uk

**Regional Director:** Ian Renton

**Regional Head of Racing and Clerk of the Course:** Simon Claisse 07785 293966

**By Road:** 1.5 miles north of the town on the A435. M5 (Junction 10 or 11).

**By Rail:** Cheltenham Spa Station. Buses and taxis to course.

**By Air:** Helicopter landing site to the northeast of the stands.

# CHEPSTOW (L.H)

**Flat:** A left-handed, undulating oval of about 2m, with easy turns, and a straight run-in of 5f. There is a straight track of 1m14y.

**N.H.** Oval, 2m (11), 240y run-in. Many changing gradients, five fences in the home straight. Favours the long-striding front-runner, but stamina is important.

**Address:** Chepstow Racecourse, Chepstow, Monmouthshire NP16 6BE Tel: 01291 622260

**Website:** www.chepstow-racecourse.co.uk

**General Manager:** Caroline Williams

**Clerk of the Course:** Libby O'Flaherty 07970 831987

**Executive Director:** Phil Bell

**By Road:** 1 mile north-west of the town on the A466. (1 mile from Junction 22 of the M4 (Severn Bridge) or M48 Junction 2. There is a free public car park opposite the entrance.

**By Rail:** Chepstow Station (from Paddington, change at Gloucester or Newport). The course is a mile from the station.

**By Air:** Helicopter landing facility in the centre of the course.

# CHESTER (L.H)

**Flat:** A level, sharp, left-handed, circular course of 1m73y, with a short run-in of 230y.
Chester is a specialists' track which generally suits the sharp-actioned horse.

**Address:** The Racecourse, Chester CH1 2LY Tel: 01244 304600

**Website:** www.chester-races.co.uk

**Racing Manager and Clerk of the Course:** Andrew Morris

**Chief Executive:** Richard Thomas

**By Road:** The course is near the centre of the city on the A548 (Queensferry Road). The Owners' and Trainers' car park is adjacent to the Leverhulme Stand. There is a public car park in the centre of the course.

**By Rail:** Chester Station (3/4 mile from the course). Services from Euston, Paddington and Northgate.

**By Air:** Hawarden Airport (2 miles). Helicopters are allowed to land on the racecourse by prior arrangement only.

# DONCASTER (L.H)

**Flat:** A left-handed, flat, galloping course of 1m7f 110y, with a long run-in which extends to a straight mile.

**N.H.** Conical, 2m (11), 247y run-in. A very fair, flat track ideally suited to the long-striding galloper.

**Address:** Doncaster Racecourse, Leger Way, Doncaster, DN2 6BB Tel: 01302 304200

**Website:** www.doncaster-racecourse.co.uk

**Clerk of the Course:** Roderick Duncan 07772 958685

**Executive Director:** Rachel Harwood

**General Manager:** Nikki Griffiths

**By Road:** East of the town, off the A638 (M18 Junctions 3 and 4). Club members' car park reserved. Large public car park free and adjacent to the course.

**By Rail:** Doncaster Central Station (from King's Cross). Special bus service from the station (1 mile).

**By Air:** Helicopter landing facility by prior arrangement only. Doncaster Robin Hood Airport is 15 minutes from the racecourse.

# EPSOM (L.H)

**Flat:** Left-handed and undulating with easy turns, and a run-in of just under 4f. The straight 5f course is also undulating and downhill all the way, making it the fastest 5f in the world.
**Address:** The Racecourse, Epsom Downs, Surrey KT18 5LQ Tel: 01372 726311
**Website:** www.epsomderby.co.uk
**Regional Director:** Phil White
**Clerk of the Course:** Andrew Cooper Tel: 01372 726311 Mobile: 07774 230850
**General Manager:** Simon Durrant
**By Road:** Two miles south of the town on the B290 (M25 Junctions 8 and 9). For full car park particulars apply to: The Club Secretary, Epsom Grandstand, Epsom Downs, Surrey KT18 5LQ. Tel: 01372 726311.
**By Rail:** Epsom, Epsom Downs or Tattenham Corner Stations (trains from London Bridge, Waterloo, Victoria). Regular bus services run to the course from Epsom and Morden Underground Station.
**By Air:** London (Heathrow) and London (Gatwick) are both within 30 miles of the course. Heliport (Derby Meeting only) - apply to Hascombe Aviation. Tel: 01279 680291.

# EXETER (R.H)

**N.H.** Oval, 2m (11), 300y run-in uphill. Undulating with a home straight of half a mile. A good test of stamina, suiting the handy, well-balanced sort.
**Address:** Exeter Racecourse, Kennford, Exeter, Devon EX6 7XS Tel: 01392 832599
**Website:** www.exeter-racecourse.co.uk
**Regional Director:** Ian Renton
**Clerk of the Course:** Daniel Cooper  07976 413045
**General Manager:** Jack Parkinson
**By Road:** The course is at Haldon, 5 miles south-west of Exeter on the A38 (Plymouth) road, 2 miles east of Chudleigh.
**By Rail:** Exeter (St Davids) Station. Free bus service to course.
**By Air:** Helicopters can land by prior arrangement.

# FAKENHAM (L.H)

**N.H.** Square, 1m (6), 200y run-in. On the turn almost throughout and undulating, suiting the handy front-runner. The going rarely becomes heavy.
**Address:** The Racecourse, Fakenham, Norfolk NR21 7NY Tel: 01328 862388
**Website:** www.fakenhamracecourse.co.uk
**Clerk of the Course and Chief Executive:** David Hunter Tel: 01328 862388 Mobile: 07767 802206
**By Road:** A mile south of the town on the B1146 (East Dereham) road.
**By Rail:** Norwich Station (26 miles) (Liverpool Street line), King's Lynn (22 miles) (Liverpool Street/Kings Cross).
**By Air:** Helicopter landing facility in the centre of the course by prior arrangement only.

# FFOS LAS (L.H)

Flat The track is a 60m wide, basically flat, 1m4f oval with sweeping bends. Races over 5f and 6f start on a chute.
**N.H.** A flat, 1m4f oval (9). The going is often testing which places the emphasis on stamina.
**Address:** Ffos Las Racecourse, Trimsaran, Carmarthenshire SA17 4DE Tel: 01554 811092
**Website:** www.ffoslasracecourse.com
**Executive Director:** Phil Bell
**Clerk of the Course and General Manager:** Dai Jones
**By Road:** From the east take J48 from the M4 and join the A4138 to Llanelli, then follow the brown tourist signs to the racecourse. From the west take the A48 to Carmarthen then the A484 to Kidwelly before following the brown signs.
**By Air:** The course has the facilities to land helicopters on race days.

# FONTWELL PARK (Fig. 8)

**N.H.** 2m (7), 230y run-in with left-hand bend close home. The figure-of-eight chase course suits handy types and is something of a specialists' track. The left-handed hurdle course is oval and one mile round. The bottom bend, which is shared, has been converted to Fibresand.
**Address:** Fontwell Park Racecourse, nr Arundel, West Sussex BN18 0SX Tel: 01243 543335
**Website:** www.fontwellpark.co.uk
**Clerk of the Course:** Philip Hide
**Executive Director and General Manager:** Jonathan Acott
**By Road:** South of village at the junction of the A29 (Bognor) and A27 (Brighton-Chichester) roads.
**By Rail:** Barnham Station (2 miles). Brighton-Portsmouth line (access via London Victoria).
**By Air:** Helicopter landing facility by prior arrangement with the Clerk of the Course.

# GOODWOOD (R.H)

**Flat:** A sharp, undulating, essentially right-handed track with a long run-in. There is also a straight 6f course.
**Address:** Goodwood Racecourse Ltd., Goodwood, Chichester, West Sussex PO18 0PX Tel: 01243 755022
**Website:** www.goodwood.co.uk
**Managing Director:** Adam Waterworth
**General Manager:** Alex Eade
**Clerk of the Course:** Ed Arkell
**By Road:** 6 miles north of Chichester between the A286 and A285. There is a car park adjacent to the course. Ample free car and coach parking.
**By Rail:** Chichester Station (from Victoria or London Bridge). Regular bus service to the course (6 miles).
**By Air:** Helicopter landing facility by prior arrangement 01243 755030. Goodwood Airport 2 miles (taxi to the course).

# HAMILTON PARK (R.H)

**Flat:** A sharp, undulating, right-handed course of 1m5f with a five and a half-furlong, uphill run-in. There is a straight track of 6f.
**Address:** Hamilton Park Racecourse, Bothwell Road, Hamilton, Lanarkshire ML3 0DW Tel: 01698 283806
**Website:** www.hamilton-park.co.uk
**Clerk of the Course:** Harriet Graham
**Chief Executive:** Vivien Currie 01698 283806
**By Road:** Off the A72 on the B7071 (Hamilton-Bothwell road). (M74 Junction 5). Free parking for cars and buses.
**By Rail:** Hamilton West Station (1 mile).
**By Air:** Glasgow Airport (20 miles).

# HAYDOCK PARK (L.H)

**Flat:** A galloping, almost flat, oval track, 1m5f round, with a run-in of four and a half furlongs and a straight six-furlong course.
**N.H.** Oval, 1m5f (10), 440y run-in. A flat, galloping chase course using portable fences. The hurdles track, which is sharp, is inside the chase course and has some tight bends.
**Address:** Haydock Park Racecourse, Newton-le-Willows, Merseyside WA12 0HQ Tel: 01942 402609
**Website:** www.haydock-park.co.uk
**Regional Director:** Dickon White
**Regional Head of Racing and Clerk of the Course:** Kirkland Tellwright 01942 725963 or 07748 181595
**By Road:** The course is on the A49 near Junction 23 of the M6.
**By Rail:** Newton-le-Willows Station (Manchester-Liverpool line) is 2.5 miles from the course. Earlstown 3 miles from the course. Warrington Bank Quay and Wigan are on the London to Carlisle/Glasgow line.
**By Air:** Landing facilities in the centre of the course for helicopters and planes not exceeding 10,000lbs laden weight.

# HEREFORD (R.H)

**N.H.** Square, 1m4f (9), 300y run-in. The turns, apart from the final one that is on falling ground, are easily negotiated, placing the emphasis on speed rather than stamina. A handy position round the home turn is vital, as winners rarely come from behind. The hurdle track is on the outside of the chase course.

**Address:** Hereford Racecourse, Roman Road, Holmer, Hereford, HR4 9QU Tel: (01432) 273560

**Website:** www.hereford-racecourse.co.uk

**Regional Executive Director:** Rebecca Davies

**Clerk of the Course:** Libby O'Flaherty

**By Road:** 1 mile north-west of the city centre off the A49 (Leominster) road.

**By Rail:** Hereford Station (1 mile from the course).

# HEXHAM (L.H)

**N.H.** Oval, 1m4f (10), 220y run-in. An undulating course that becomes very testing when the ground is soft, it has easy fences and a stiff climb to the finishing straight, which is on a separate spur.

**Address:** Hexham Racecourse, The Riding, Hexham, Northumberland NE46 2JP Tel: 01434 606881 Racedays: 01434 603738

**Website:** www.hexham-racecourse.co.uk

**Chief Executive:** Robert Whitelock

**Clerk of the Course:** James Armstrong 01434 606881 or 07801 166820

**By Road:** 1.5 miles south-west of the town off the B6305.

**By Rail:** Hexham Station (Newcastle-Carlisle line). Free bus to the course.

**By Air:** Helicopter landing facility in centre of course (by special arrangement only).

# HUNTINGDON (R.H)

**N.H.** Oval, 1m4f (9), 200y run-in. A perfectly flat, galloping track with a tricky open ditch in front of the stands. The two fences in the home straight can cause problems for novice chasers. Suits front-runners.

**Address:** The Racecourse, Brampton, Huntingdon, Cambridgeshire PE28 4NL Tel: 01480 453373

**Website:** www.huntingdon-racecourse.co.uk

**Regional Director:** Amy Starkey

**Clerk of the Course:** Jack Pryor

**General Manager:** James Wilcox

**By Road:** The course is situated at Brampton, 2 miles west of Huntingdon on the A14. Easy access from the A1 ($^1$/₂ mile from the course).

**By Rail:** Huntingdon Station. Buses and taxis to course.

**By Air:** Helicopter landing facility by prior arrangement.

# KELSO (L.H)

**N.H.** Oval, 1m1f (8), 200y run-in, uphill run-in of just over a furlong. Rather undulating with two downhill fences opposite the stands, it suits the nippy, front-running sort, though the uphill finish helps the true stayer. The hurdle course is smaller and very sharp with a tight turn away from the stands.

**Address:** Kelso Racecourse, Kelso, Roxburghshire TD5 7SX Tel: 01668 280800

**Website:** www.kelso-races.co.uk

**Clerk of the Course:** Matthew Taylor

**Managing Director:** Jonathan Garratt

**By Road:** 1 mile north of the town, off the B6461.

**By Rail:** Berwick-upon-Tweed Station. 23-mile bus journey to Kelso.

**By Air:** Helicopters can land at course by arrangement, fixed wing aircraft at Winfield, regular aircraft at Edinburgh.

# KEMPTON PARK (R.H)

**Flat:** A floodlit Polytrack circuit. A 1m2f outer track accommodates races over 6f, 7f, 1m, 1m3f, 1m4f and 2m. The 1m inner track caters for races over 5f and 1m2f.

**N.H.** Triangular, 1m5f (10), 175y run-in. A practically flat, sharp course where the long run between the last obstacle on the far side and the first in the home straight switches the emphasis from jumping to speed. The hurdles track is on the outside of the chase track. The course crosses the Polytrack at two points on each circuit.

**Address:** Kempton Park Racecourse, Sunbury-on-Thames, Middlesex TW16 5AQ Tel: 01932 782292

**Website:** www.kempton.co.uk

**Regional Director:** Phil White

**Clerk of the Course and Director of Racing:** Brian Clifford 07880 784484

**Assistant Clerk of the Course:** Sarah Dunster

**General Manager:** Simon Durrant

**By Road:** On the A308 near Junction 1 of the M3.

**By Rail:** Kempton Park Station (from Waterloo).

**By Air:** London (Heathrow) Airport 6 miles.

# LEICESTER (R.H)

**Flat:** A stiff, galloping, right-handed oval of 1m5f, with a 5f run-in. There is a straight course of seven furlongs.

**N.H.** Rectangular, 1m6f (10), 250y run-in uphill. An undulating course with an elbow 150y from the finish, it can demand a high degree of stamina, as the going can become extremely testing and the last three furlongs are uphill.

**Address:** Leicester Racecourse, Oadby, Leicester, LE2 4AL Tel: 01162 716515

**Website:** www.leicester-racecourse.co.uk

**Clerk of the Course:** Jimmy Stevenson 01162 712115 or 07774 497281

**General Manager:** Rob Bracken

**By Road:** The course is 2.5 miles south-east of the city on the A6 (M1, Junction 21). The car park is free.

**By Rail:** Leicester Station (from St Pancras) is 2.5 miles.

**By Air:** Helicopter landing facility in the centre of the course.

# LINGFIELD PARK (L.H)

**Flat, Turf:** A sharp, undulating left-handed circuit, with a 7f 140y straight course.

**Flat, Polytrack:** The left-handed Polytrack is 1m2f round, with an extended chute to provide a 1m5f start. It is a sharp, level track with a short run-in.

**N.H.** Conical, 1m5f (10), 200y run-in. Severely undulating with a tight downhill turn into the straight, the chase course suits front-runners.

**Address:** Lingfield Park Racecourse, Lingfield, Surrey RH7 6PQ Tel: 01342 834800

**Website:** www.lingfield-racecourse.co.uk

**Clerk of the Course:** George Hill

**Executive Director:** Amy Smith

**General Manager:** Russell Bowes

**By Road:** South-east of the town off the A22; M25 (Junction 6). Ample free parking.

**By Rail:** Lingfield Station (regular services from London Bridge and Victoria). Half-mile walk to the course.

**By Air:** London (Gatwick) Airport 10 miles. Helicopter landing facility south of wind-sock.

# LUDLOW (R.H)

**N.H.** Oval, 1m4f (9), 185y run-in. The chase course is flat and has quite sharp bends into and out of the home straight, although long-striding horses never seem to have any difficulties. The hurdle course is on the outside of the chase track and is not so sharp.

**Address:** Ludlow Race Club Ltd, The Racecourse, Bromfield, Ludlow, Shropshire SY8 2BT Tel: 01584 856221 (Racedays) or see below.

**Website:** www.ludlowracecourse.co.uk

**General Manager and Clerk of the Course:** Simon Sherwood

**By Road:** The course is situated at Bromfield, 2 miles north of Ludlow on the A49.

**By Rail:** Ludlow Station (Hereford-Shrewsbury line) 2 miles.

**By Air:** Helicopter landing facility in the centre of the course by arrangement with the Clerk of the Course

# MARKET RASEN (R.H)

**N.H.** Oval, 1m2f (8), 250y run-in. A sharp, undulating course with a long run to the straight, it favours the handy, front-running type.

**Address:** Market Rasen Racecourse, Legsby Road, Market Rasen, Lincolnshire LN8 3EA Tel: 01673 843434

**Website:** www.marketrasenraces.co.uk

**Regional Director:** Amy Starkey

**Clerk of the Course:** Jack Pryor

**General Manager:** Nadia Powell

**By Road:** The town is just off the A46, and the racecourse is one mile east of the town on the A631. Free car parks.

**By Rail:** Market Rasen Station 1 mile (King's Cross - Cleethorpes line).

**By Air:** Helicopter landing facility by prior arrangement only.

# MUSSELBURGH (R.H)

**Flat:** A sharp, level, right-handed oval of 1m2f, with a run-in of 4f. There is an additional 5f straight course.

**N.H.** Rectangular, 1m3f (8), 150y run-in (variable). A virtually flat track with sharp turns, suiting the handy, front-running sort. It drains well. There is a section of Polytrack going away from the stands.

**Address:** Musselburgh Racecourse, Linkfield Road, Musselburgh, East Lothian EH21 7RG

**Tel:** 01316 652859

**Website:** www.musselburgh-racecourse.co.uk

**Clerk of the Course:** Harriet Graham 07843 380401

**General Manager:** Bill Farnsworth 07710 536134

**By Road:** The course is situated at Musselburgh, 5 miles east of Edinburgh on the A1. Car park, adjoining course, free for buses and cars.

**By Rail:** Waverley Station (Edinburgh). Local Rail service to Musselburgh.

**By Air:** Edinburgh (Turnhouse) Airport 30 minutes.

# NEWBURY (L.H)

**Flat:** Left-handed, oval track of about 1m7f, with a slightly undulating straight mile. The round course is level and galloping with a four and a half-furlong straight. Races over the round mile start on the adjoining chute.

**N.H.** Oval, 1m6f (11), 255y run-in. Slightly undulating, wide and galloping in nature. The fences are stiff and sound jumping is essential. One of the fairest tracks in the country.

**Address:** Newbury Racecourse, Newbury, Berkshire RG14 7NZ Tel: 01635 40015

**Website:** www.newbury-racecourse.co.uk

**Chief Executive:** Julian Thick

**Clerk of the Course:** Keith Ottesen 07813 043453

**By Road:** East of the town off the A34 (M4, Junction 12 or 13). Car park, adjoining enclosures, free.

**By Rail:** Newbury Racecourse Station adjoins the course.

**By Air:** Light Aircraft landing strip East/West. 830 metres by 30 metres wide. Helicopter landing facilities.

# NEWCASTLE (L.H)

**Flat:** A 1m6f Tapeta track outside the jumps course. The straight mile is floodlit.
**N.H.** Oval, 1m6f (11), 220y run-in. A gradually rising home straight of four furlongs makes this galloping track a true test of stamina, especially as the ground can become very heavy.
**Address:** High Gosforth Park, Newcastle-Upon-Tyne, NE3 5HP Tel: 01912 362020
**Website:** www.newcastle-racecourse.co.uk
**Clerk of the Course:** James Armstrong 07801 166820
**Executive Director:** David Williamson
**By Road:** 4 miles north of the city on the A6125 (near the A1). Car and coach park free.
**By Rail:** Newcastle Central Station (from King's Cross). A free bus service operates from South Gosforth and Regent Centre Metro Station.
**By Air:** Helicopter landing facility by prior arrangement. The Airport is 4 miles from the course.

# NEWMARKET (R.H)

**Rowley Mile Course:** There is a straight ten-furlong course, which is wide and galloping. Races over 1m4f or more are right-handed. The Rowley Mile course has a long run-in and a stiff finish.
**July Course:** Races up to a mile are run on the Bunbury course, which is straight. Races over 1m2f or more are right-handed, with a 7f run-in. Like the Rowley Mile course, the July Course track is stiff.
 **Address:** Newmarket Racecourse, Westfield House, The Links, Newmarket, Suffolk CB8 0TG Tel: 01638 663482 (Main Office) 01638 663762 (Rowley Mile) 01638 675416 (July) .
**Website:** www.newmarketracecourses.co.uk
**Clerk of the Course and Racing Director:** Michael Prosser 01638 675504 or 07802 844578
**Regional Director:** Amy Starkey
**General Manager:** Sophie Able
**By Road:** South-west of the town on the A1304 London Road (M11 Junction 9). Free car parking at the rear of the enclosure. Annual Badge Holders' car park free all days. Courtesy bus service from Newmarket Station, Bus Station and High Street. , commencing 90 minutes prior to the first race.
**By Rail:** Infrequent rail service to Newmarket Station from Cambridge (Liverpool Street) or direct bus service from Cambridge (13-mile journey).
**By Air:** Landing facilities for light aircraft and helicopters on racedays at both racecourses. See Flight Guide. Cambridge Airport 11 miles.

# NEWTON ABBOT (L.H)

**N.H.** Oval, 1m2f (7), 300y run-in. Flat with two tight bends. The nippy, agile sort is favoured. The run-in can be very short on the hurdle course.
**Address:** Newton Abbot Races Ltd., Kingsteignton Road, Newton Abbot, Devon TQ12 3AF Tel: 01626 353235
**Website:** www.newtonabbotracing.com
**Clerk of the Course:** Jason Loosemore 07766 228109
**Managing Director:** Pat Masterson Tel: 01626 353235 Mobile: 07917 830144
**By Road:** North of the town on the A380. Torquay 6 miles, Exeter 17 miles.
**By Rail:** Newton Abbot Station (from Paddington) 3/4 mile. Buses and taxis operate to and from the course.
**By Air:** Helicopter landing pad in the centre of the course.

# NOTTINGHAM (L.H)

**Flat:** Left-handed, galloping, oval of about 1m4f, and a straight of four and a half furlongs. Flat with easy turns.
**Address:** Nottingham Racecourse, Colwick Park, Nottingham, NG2 4BE Tel: 0870 8507634
**Website:** www.nottinghamracecourse.co.uk
**Regional Director:** Amy Starkey
**Clerk of the Course:** Jane Hedley
**General Manager:** James Wilcox
**By Road:** 2 miles east of the city centre on the B686.
**By Rail:** Nottingham (Midland) Station. Regular bus service to course (2 miles).
**By Air:** Helicopter landing facility in the centre of the course.

# PERTH (R.H)

**N.H.** Rectangular, 1m2f (8), 283y run-in. A flat, easy track with sweeping turns. Not a course for the long-striding galloper.
**Address:** Perth Racecourse, Scone Palace Park, Perth, PH2 6BB Tel: 01738 551597
**Website:** www.perth-races.co.uk
**Clerk of the Course:** Matthew Taylor
**General Manager:** Hazel Peplinski
**By Road:** 4 miles north of the town off the A93.
**By Rail:** Perth Station (from Dundee) 4 miles. There are buses to the course.
**By Air:** Scone Airport (3.75 miles). Edinburgh Airport 45 minutes.

# PLUMPTON (L.H)

**N.H.** Oval, 1m1f (7), 200y run-in uphill. A tight, undulating circuit with an uphill finish, Plumpton favours the handy, fast jumper. The ground often gets heavy, as the course is based on clay soil.
**Address:** Plumpton Racecourse, Plumpton, East Sussex BN7 3AL Tel: 01273 890383
**Website:** www.plumptonracecourse.co.uk
**Clerk of the Course:** Mark Cornford 07759 151617
**Chief Executive:** Daniel Thompson
**By Road:** 2 miles north of the village off the B2116.
**By Rail:** Plumpton Station (from Victoria) adjoins course.
**By Air:** Helicopter landing facility by prior arrangement with the Clerk of the Course.

# PONTEFRACT (L.H)

**Flat:** Left-handed oval, undulating course of 2m133y, with a short run-in of 2f. It is a particularly stiff track with the last 3f uphill.
**Address:** Pontefract Park Race Co. Ltd., The Park, Pontefract, West Yorkshire Tel: 01977 781307
**Website:** www.pontefract-races.co.uk
**Managing Director:** Norman Gundill 01977 781307
**Assistant Manager and Clerk of the Course:** Richard Hamill
**By Road:** 1 mile north of the town on the A639. Junction 32 of M62. Free car park adjacent to the course.
**By Rail:** Pontefract Station (Tanshelf, every hour to Wakefield), 1 1/2 miles from the course. Regular bus service from Leeds.
**By Air:** Helicopters by arrangement only. (Nearest Airfields: Robin Hood (Doncaster), Sherburn-in-Elmet, Yeadon (Leeds Bradford).

# REDCAR (L.H)

**Flat:** Left-handed, level, galloping, oval course of 1m6f with a straight run-in of 5f. There is also a straight mile.
**Address:** Redcar Racecourse, Redcar, Cleveland TS10 2BY Tel: 01642 484068
**Website:** www.redcarracing.com
**Clerk of the Course:** Jonjo Sanderson Tel: 01642 484068 Mobile: 07766 022893
**General Manager:** Amy Fair
**By Road:** In the town off the A1085. Free parking adjoining the course for buses and cars.
**By Rail:** Redcar Station (1/4 mile from the course).
**By Air:** Landing facilities at Turners Arms Farm (600yds runway) Yearby, Cleveland. Two miles south of the racecourse - transport available. Durham Tees Valley airport (18 miles west of Redcar).

# RIPON (R.H)

**Flat:** A sharp, undulating, right-handed oval of 1m5f, with a 5f run-in. There is also a 6f straight course.
**Address:** Ripon Racecourse, Boroughbridge Road, Ripon, North Yorkshire HG4 1UG Tel: 01765 530530
**Website:** www.ripon-races.co.uk
**Clerk of the Course and Managing Director:** James Hutchinson 07860 679904
**By Road:** The course is situated 2 miles south-east of the city, on the B6265. There is ample free parking for cars and coaches.
**By Rail:** Harrogate Station (11 miles) or Thirsk (15 miles). Bus services to Ripon.
**By Air:** Helicopters only on the course. Otherwise Leeds/Bradford airport.

# SALISBURY (R.H)

**Flat:** Right-handed and level, with a run-in of 4f. There is a straight mile track. The last half-mile is uphill, providing a stiff test of stamina.
**Address:** Salisbury Racecourse, Netherhampton, Salisbury, Wiltshire SP2 8PN Tel: 01722 326461
**Website:** www.salisburyracecourse.co.uk
**Clerk of the Course and General Manager:** Jeremy Martin 07880 744999
**By Road:** 3 miles south-west of the city on the A3094 at Netherhampton. Free car park adjoins the course.
**By Rail:** Salisbury Station is 3.5 miles (from London Waterloo). Bus service to the course.
**By Air:** Helicopter landing facility near the 1m2f start.

# SANDOWN PARK (R.H)

**Flat:** An easy right-handed oval course of 1m5f with a stiff, straight uphill run-in of 4f. Separate straight 5f track is also uphill. Galloping.
**N.H.** Oval, 1m5f (11), 220y run-in uphill. Features seven fences on the back straight; the last three (the Railway Fences) are very close together and can often decide the outcome of races. The stiff climb to the finish puts the emphasis very much on stamina, but accurate-jumping, free-running sorts are also favoured. Hurdle races are run on the Flat course.
**Address:** Sandown Park Racecourse, Esher, Surrey KT10 9AJ Tel: 01372 464348
**Website:** www.sandown.co.uk
**Regional Director:** Phil White
**Clerk of the Course:** Andrew Cooper: 01372 461213 Mobile: 07774 230850
**By Road:** Four miles south-west of Kingston-on-Thames, on the A307 (M25 Junction 10).
**By Rail:** Esher Station (from Waterloo) adjoins the course.
**By Air:** London (Heathrow) Airport 12 miles.

# SEDGEFIELD (L.H)

**N.H.** Oval, 1m2f (8), 200y run-in. Undulating with fairly tight turns, it doesn't suit big, long-striding horses.
**Address:** Sedgefield Racecourse, Sedgefield, Stockton-on-Tees, Cleveland TS21 2HW Tel: 01740 621925
**Website:** www.sedgefield-racecourse.co.uk
**Clerk of the Course:** Michael Naughton
**General Manager:** Emma White
**By Road:** ³/₄ mile south-west of the town, near the junction of the A689 (Bishop Auckland) and the A177 (Durham) roads. The car park is free.
**By Rail:** Darlington Station (9 miles). Durham Station (12 miles).
**By Air:** Helicopter landing facility in car park area by prior arrangement only.

# SOUTHWELL (L.H)

**Flat, Fibresand:** Left-handed oval, Fibresand course of 1m2f with a 3f run-in. There is a straight 5f. Track floodlit from 2019. Sharp and level, Southwell suits front-runners.

**N.H.** Oval, 1m 1f (7), 220y run-in. A tight, flat track with a short run-in, it suits front-runners.

**Address:** Southwell Racecourse, Rolleston, Newark, Nottinghamshire NG25 0TS Tel: 01636 814481

**Website:** www.southwell-racecourse.co.uk

**Executive Director:** Mark Clayton

**Clerk of the Course:** Paul Barker

**By Road:** The course is situated at Rolleston, 3 miles south of Southwell, 5 miles from Newark.

**By Rail:** Rolleston Station (Nottingham-Newark line) adjoins the course.

**By Air:** Helicopters can land by prior arrangement.

# STRATFORD-ON-AVON (L.H)

**N.H.** Triangular, 1m2f (8), 200y run-in. Virtually flat with two tight bends, and quite a short home straight. A sharp and turning course, it suits the well-balanced, handy sort.

**Address:** Stratford Racecourse, Luddington Road, Stratford-upon-Avon, Warwickshire CV37 9SE Tel: 01789 267949

**Website:** www.stratfordracecourse.net

**Managing Director:** Ilona Barnett

**Clerk of the Course:** Nessie Chanter

**By Road:** A mile from the town centre, off the A429 (Evesham road).

**By Rail:** Stratford-on-Avon Station (from Birmingham New Street or Leamington Spa) 1 mile.

**By Air:** Helicopter landing facility by prior arrangement.

# TAUNTON (R.H)

**N.H.** Elongated oval, 1m2f (8), 150y run-in uphill. Sharp turns, especially after the winning post, with a steady climb from the home bend. Suits the handy sort.

**Address:** Taunton Racecourse, Orchard Portman, Taunton, Somerset TA3 7BL Tel: 01823 337172

**Website:** www.tauntonracecourse.co.uk

**Clerk of the Course:** Jason Loosemore

**Chief Executive:** Bob Young

**By Road:** Two miles south of the town on the B3170 (Honiton) road (M5 Junction 25).

**By Rail:** Taunton Station 2 miles. There are buses and taxis to course.

**By Air:** Helicopter landing facility by prior arrangement.

# THIRSK (L.H)

**Flat:** Left-handed oval of 1m2f with sharp turns and an undulating run-in of 4f. There is a straight 6f track.

**Address:** The Racecourse, Station Road, Thirsk, North Yorkshire YO7 1QL Tel: 01845 522276

**Website:** www.thirskracecourse.net

**Clerk of the Course and Managing Director:** James Sanderson

**By Road:** West of the town on the A61. Free car park adjacent to the course for buses and cars.

**By Rail:** Thirsk Station (from King's Cross), 1/2 mile from the course.

**By Air:** Helicopters can land by prior arrangement. Tel: Racecourse 01845 522276. Fixed wing aircraft can land at RAF Leeming. Tel: 01677 423041. Light aircraft at Bagby. Tel: 01845 597385 or 01845 537555

# UTTOXETER (L.H)

**N.H.** Oval, 1m2f (8), 170y run-in. A few undulations, easy bends and fences and a flat home straight of over half a mile. Suits front-runners, especially on the 2m hurdle course.
**Address:** The Racecourse, Wood Lane, Uttoxeter, Staffordshire ST14 8BD Tel: 01889 562561
**Website:** www.uttoxeter-racecourse.co.uk
**Clerk of the Course:** Eloise Quayle
**General Manager:** Brian Barrass
**By Road:** South-east of the town off the B5017 (Marchington Road).
**By Rail:** Uttoxeter Station (Crewe-Derby line) adjoins the course.
**By Air:** Helicopters can land by prior arrangement with the raceday office.

# WARWICK (L.H)

**N.H.** Circular, 1m6f (10), 240y run-in. Undulating with tight bends, five quick fences in the back straight and a short home straight, Warwick favours handiness and speed rather than stamina.
**Address:** Warwick Racecourse, Hampton Street, Warwick, CV34 6HN Tel: 01926 491553
**Website:** www.warwickracecourse.co.uk
**Regional Director:** Ian Renton
**Clerk of the Course:** Jane Hedley
**General Manager:** Andre Klein
**By Road:** West of the town on the B4095 adjacent to Junction 15 of the M40.
**By Rail:** Warwick or Warwick Parkway Stations.
**By Air:** Helicopters can land by prior arrangement with the Clerk of the Course.

# WETHERBY (L.H)

**Flat:** First used in 2015, the Flat course is left-handed with a 1m4f circuit.
**N.H.** Oval, 1m4f (9), 200y run-in slightly uphill. A flat, very fair course which suits the long-striding galloper.
**Address:** The Racecourse, York Road, Wetherby, LS22 5EJ Tel: 01937 582035
**Website:** www.wetherbyracing.co.uk
**Clerk of the Course and Chief Executive:** Jonjo Sanderson 07831 437453
**By Road:** East of the town off the B1224 (York Road). Adjacent to the A1. Excellent bus and coach facilities. Car park free.
**By Rail:** Leeds Station 12 miles. Buses to Wetherby.
**By Air:** Helicopters can land by prior arrangement

# WINCANTON (R.H)

**N.H.** Rectangular, 1m3f (9), 200y run-in. Good galloping course where the going rarely becomes heavy. The home straight is mainly downhill.
**Address:** Wincanton Racecourse, Wincanton, Somerset BA9 8BJ Tel: 01963 435840
**Website:** www.wincantonracecourse.co.uk
**Regional Director:** Ian Renton
**Clerk of the Course:** Daniel Cooper  07976 413045
**General Manager:** Jack Parkinson
**By Road:** 1 mile north of the town on the B3081.
**By Rail:** Gillingham Station (from Waterloo) or Castle Cary Station (from Paddington). Buses and taxis to the course.
**By Air:** Helicopter landing area is situated in the centre of the course.

# WINDSOR (Fig. 8)

**Flat:** Figure of eight track of 1m4f 110y. The course is level and sharp with a long run-in. The 6f course is essentially straight.
**Address:** Royal Windsor Racecourse, Maidenhead Road, Windsor, Berkshire SL4 5JJ Tel: 01753 498400
**Website:** www.windsor-racecourse.co.uk
**Clerk of the Course:** Sophie Candy
**Executive Director:** Simon Williams
**By Road:** North of the town on the A308 (M4 Junction 6).
**By Rail:** Windsor Central Station (from Paddington) or Windsor and Eton Riverside Station (from Waterloo).
**By Air:** London (Heathrow) Airport 15 minutes. Also White Waltham Airport (West London Aero Club) 15 minutes.
**River Bus:** Seven minutes from Barry Avenue promenade at Windsor.

# WOLVERHAMPTON (L.H)
**Flat:** Left-handed, floodlit,  oval Tapeta track of 1m, with a run-in of 380y. A level track with sharp bends.
**Address:** Wolverhampton Racecourse, Dunstall Park, Gorsebrook Road, Wolverhampton, WV6 0PE Tel: 01902 390000
**Website:** www.wolverhampton-racecourse.co.uk
**Clerk of the Course:** Fergus Cameron 07971 531162
**General Manager:** Dave Roberts
**By Road:** 1 mile north of the city centre on the A449 (M54 Junction 2 or M6 Junction 12). Car parking free.
**By Rail:** Wolverhampton Station (from Euston) 1 mile.
**By Air:** Halfpenny Green Airport 8 miles.

# WORCESTER (L.H)
**N.H.** Elongated oval, 1m5f (9), 220y run-in. Flat with easy turns, it is a very fair, galloping track.
**Address:** Worcester Racecourse, Pitchcroft, Worcester, WR1 3EJ Tel: 01905 25364
**Website:** www.worcester-racecourse.co.uk
**Clerk of the Course:** Tim Long
**Regional Executive Director:** Rebecca Davies
**General Manager:** Michael Thomas
**By Road:** West of the city centre off the A449 (Kidderminster road) (M5 Junction 8).
**By Rail:** Foregate Street Station, Worcester (from Paddington) ³/₄ mile.
**By Air:** Helicopter landing facility in the centre of the course, by prior arrangement only.

# YARMOUTH (L.H)
**Flat:** Left-handed, level circuit of 1m4f, with a run-in of 5f. The straight course is 1m long.
**Address:** The Racecourse, Jellicoe Road, Great Yarmouth, Norfolk NR30 4AU Tel: 01493 842527
**Website:** www.greatyarmouth-racecourse.co.uk
**Clerk of the Course:** Richard Aldous 07738 507643
**Executive Director:** Glenn Tubby
**By Road:** 1 mile east of town centre (well signposted from A47 and A12).
**By Rail:** Great Yarmouth Station (1 mile). Bus service to the course.
**By Air:** Helicopter landing available by prior arrangement with Racecourse Office

# YORK (L.H)
**Flat:** Left-handed, level, galloping track, with a straight 6f. There is also an adjoining chute for races over 7f.
**Address:** The Racecourse, York, YO23 1EX Tel: 01904 683932
**Website:** www.yorkracecourse.co.uk
**Clerk of the Course and Chief Executive:** William Derby 07812 961176
**Assistant Clerk of the Course:** Anthea Morshead
**By Road:** 1 mile south-east of the city on the A1036.
**By Rail:** 1 1/2 miles York Station (from King's Cross). Special bus service from station to the course.
**By Air:** Light aircraft and helicopter landing facilities available at Rufforth aerodrome (5,000ft tarmac runway). Leeds Bradford airport (25 miles).

# RACING POST
## MEMBERS' CLUB

**What our current members are saying about**

**Video Replays**

" *I use the race video replay facility to review a horse's form to help to analyse races. I also use the Bloodstock section to follow the sales and stallion results, and the extended racecards which show all details including a horse's breeding.* "

## Find out more at
## racingpost.com/members-club

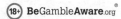

# THE DERBY STAKES (GROUP 1)
# EPSOM DOWNS ON SATURDAY 5TH JUNE 2021

**SECOND ENTRIES BY NOON APRIL 6TH; SUPPLEMENTARY ENTRIES BY NOON MAY 31ST.**

| HORSE | TRAINER | HORSE | TRAINER |
|---|---|---|---|
| ABSTRACT (IRE) | D. K. Weld | DERAB | John & Thady Gosden |
| ACE AUSSIE (IRE) | Mrs J. Harrington | DESTINADO | Francis-Henri Graffard |
| AERION POWER (IRE) | Sir Michael Stoute | DHUSHAN (IRE) | William Haggas |
| ALBANMAN (IRE) | Roger Varian | DIVERGE | F. Head |
| ALBASHEER (IRE) | Owen Burrows | DUBAI EMPEROR (IRE) | David Simcock |
| ALBERT CAMUS | John & Thady Gosden | DUBLIN JOURNAL (IRE) | J. S. Bolger |
| ALGHADEER (IRE) | Owen Burrows | EAGLE TERRACE | John & Thady Gosden |
| ALKHATTAAF | Saeed bin Suroor | EARLSWOOD | John M. Oxx |
| ALNAJEEB (IRE) | Mark Johnston | EAST SEA (IRE) | |
| ALPINE STROLL | Ed de Giles | EBASARI (IRE) | M. Halford |
| ALTO VOLANTE | William Haggas | EL DRAMA (IRE) | Roger Varian |
| ALVANIY (IRE) | D. K. Weld | ENDAVI (FR) | A. de Royer Dupre |
| ANMAAT (IRE) | Owen Burrows | EPIC PASS (IRE) | Mark Johnston |
| ANNANDALE (IRE) | Mark Johnston | EQUUS DEUS (IRE) | Aidan O'Brien |
| ANTHEM (IRE) | Mrs J. Harrington | ERSAAL | William Haggas |
| ANZAC COVE | John & Thady Gosden | ERZINDJAN (IRE) | D. K. Weld |
| ARAMAIC (IRE) | William Haggas | ESTEEM (IRE) | Donnacha Aidan O'Brien |
| ARTHUR'S REALM (IRE) | Ed Dunlop | ETERNAL FLAME (IRE) | Aidan O'Brien |
| ARTURO TOSCANINI (IRE) | Aidan O'Brien | ETONIAN (IRE) | Richard Hannon |
| ATACAMA DESERT (IRE) | Sir Michael Stoute | EVALUATION | Sir Michael Stoute |
| AVIZ (IRE) | Aidan O'Brien | EXUMA (IRE) | Aidan O'Brien |
| BAAEED | William Haggas | FABILIS | Ralph Beckett |
| BAILEYS DERBYDAY | Mark Johnston | FATHER'S DAY (IRE) | Aidan O'Brien |
| BALLANTRUAN | John & Thady Gosden | FERNANDO VICHI (IRE) | Donnacha Aidan O'Brien |
| BANK RATE | | FERRAN STAR | |
| BARATTI | A. Fabre | FIGHT FOR IT (IRE) | Simon & Ed Crisford |
| BARENBOIM | Michael Bell | FIGLIO D'ARTE (IRE) | Aidan O'Brien |
| BASHOSH (IRE) | Roger Varian | FIRST BLOOD (IRE) | Joseph Patrick O'Brien |
| BATON ROUGE (IRE) | Aidan O'Brien | FLINDERS LANE (IRE) | Joseph Patrick O'Brien |
| BEAU NASH (IRE) | John & Thady Gosden | FLYIN' HIGH | Andrew Balding |
| BEOWULF (IRE) | Ed Walker | FRIENDLY FACE (IRE) | Aidan O'Brien |
| BEYOND BOUNDARIES (IRE) | Andrew Balding | GAASSEE | William Haggas |
| BOLSHOI BALLET (IRE) | Aidan O'Brien | GAHERIS (GER) | Joseph Patrick O'Brien |
| BOLTAWAY | Roger Charlton | GEAR UP (IRE) | Mark Johnston |
| BOSPHORUS | John & Thady Gosden | GEORGE MORLAND | Henry Candy |
| BRAZIL (IRE) | Aidan O'Brien | GLEN AGAIN (IRE) | Mark Johnston |
| CADILLAC (IRE) | Mrs J. Harrington | GLOUCESTERSHIRE (USA) | Martyn Meade |
| CAMELOT TALES (FR) | Simon & Ed Crisford | GLOWING FOR GOLD | Ismail Mohammed |
| CANDLEFORD (IRE) | William Haggas | GOING BACK TO CALI | David Loughnane |
| CAPRIOLI | | GOING GONE (IRE) | Jim Boyle |
| CARLISLE BAY (IRE) | Aidan O'Brien | GOLDEN ARMOUR | Richard Fahey |
| CARLO LANDOLFI (IRE) | Aidan O'Brien | GOLDEN CLAIM | Ismail Mohammed |
| CECIL STREET (USA) | Joseph Patrick O'Brien | GOONER BOY | John & Thady Gosden |
| CHAIN MAIL (IRE) | Aidan O'Brien | GRAND REVIVAL (USA) | Aidan O'Brien |
| CHALK STREAM | William Haggas | GRAND SCHEME (IRE) | Richard Hannon |
| CLEVELAND (IRE) | Aidan O'Brien | GREATGADIAN (GER) | Roger Varian |
| COLLINS STREET (IRE) | Joseph Patrick O'Brien | GREAT SUGAR LOAF (IRE) | Aidan O'Brien |
| CONSPIRACY THEORY | Andrew Balding | GRID | Joseph Patrick O'Brien |
| COOLCULLEN (IRE) | J. S. Bolger | GUITAR MAN (IRE) | Aidan O'Brien |
| CRISTAL CLERE (IRE) | William Haggas | HALFBARBERBINGIE (USA) | |
| DAJRAAN | Kevin Ryan | HALIC | Sir Michael Stoute |
| DANTORA | Hugo Palmer | HAPPY (IRE) | Mark Johnston |
| DARAMETHOS (IRE) | John & Thady Gosden | HARLEM SOUL | Mark Johnston |
| DARIYABAD (FR) | A. de Royer dupre | HARVARD (IRE) | Aidan O'Brien |
| DARK SHIFT | Charles Hills | HATHLOOL (IRE) | |
| DAYSHANN (FR) | Jean Claude Rouget | HECTOR DE MARIS (IRE) | Aidan O'Brien |
| DEFINED | John & Thady Gosden | HELL BENT (IRE) | Mrs J. Harrington |
| DEIRA CHAMPION | Andrew Balding | HIGH DEFINITION (IRE) | Aidan O'Brien |

| HORSE | TRAINER |
|---|---|
| HIGH RESILIENCE | |
| HILLCREST AVENUE (IRE) | Joseph Patrick O'Brien |
| HMS SEAHORSE (IRE) | Aidan O'Brien |
| HOME AND DRY (IRE) | Mark Johnston |
| HUDSON RIVER (IRE) | Aidan O'Brien |
| HYPE (IRE) | Joseph Patrick O'Brien |
| IMMELMANN (GER) | Simon & Ed Crisford |
| IMPERIAL SUN | John & Thady Gosden |
| INIGO JONES | Sir Michael Stoute |
| INTERPRETATION (IRE) | Aidan O'Brien |
| IOWA (IRE) | aoki takafumi |
| IWAZU (JPN) | |
| JACK KENNEDY | John & Thady Gosden |
| JACKSONVILLE | John & Thady Gosden |
| JARAMILLO | Roger Varian |
| JERSEY GIFT (IRE) | Jamie Osborne |
| JOHN LEEPER (IRE) | Ed Dunlop |
| JUDGMENT CALL | David Simcock |
| JUMBY (IRE) | Eve Johnson Houghton |
| JUSTUS (IRE) | Aidan O'Brien |
| KEEPER | Roger Charlton |
| KEY TO THE KINGDOM (IRE) | Aidan O'Brien |
| KHARTOUM (USA) | Aidan O'Brien |
| KING CREOLE | David Menuisier |
| KING FRANCIS (IRE) | Roger Varian |
| KING FRANKEL (IRE) | Mark Johnston |
| KING OF CLUBS | Hughie Morrison |
| KING OF THE CASTLE (IRE) | Aidan O'Brien |
| KINGSOFTHEMIDLANDS (FR) | Andrew Balding |
| KOLISI (IRE) | William Haggas |
| KONDO ISAMI (IRE) | Mark Johnston |
| KYPRIOS (IRE) | Aidan O'Brien |
| LANKARAN | Roger Varian |
| LATEST GENERATION | Simon & Ed Crisford |
| LAW OF THE SEA | John & Thady Gosden |
| LE COUTRE (USA) | A. Fabre |
| LEGEND OF DUBAI | Roger Varian |
| LENNY'S SPIRIT (FR) | Ed Dunlop |
| LICENCE | |
| LIFFEY RIVER (FR) | Joseph Patrick O'Brien |
| LIGHT DRAGOON (FR) | |
| LIGHT STARS (FR) | Francis-Henri Graffard |
| LINDWALL (IRE) | Sir Mark Prescott Bt |
| LINE OF DESCENT (IRE) | Simon & Ed Crisford |
| LOFOTEN (IRE) | W. McCreery |
| LONE EAGLE (IRE) | Martyn Meade |
| LORD OF THE MANOR (IRE) | Aidan O'Brien |
| LOS ANDES (USA) | Mrs J. Harrington |
| LOUGH DERG (IRE) | Aidan O'Brien |
| LOVE IS GOLDEN (IRE) | Mark Johnston |
| LUCKY VEGA (IRE) | Mrs J. Harrington |
| MAHOMES | John & Thady Gosden |
| MAHRAJAAN (USA) | William Haggas |
| MALHOOB (USA) | Roger Varian |
| MAN OF PEACE (IRE) | Aidan O'Brien |
| MARINE (IRE) | Andrew Balding |
| MARSHALL PLAN | John & Thady Gosden |
| MASHHOOR | Sir Michael Stoute |
| MAWKEB (USA) | Owen Burrows |
| MAXIMAL | Sir Michael Stoute |
| MAZYAD (IRE) | M. Halford |
| MCPHERSON | Mrs J. Harrington |
| MEDIA STREAM | A. Fabre |
| MEGALLAN | John & Thady Gosden |
| MIRRIE DANCERS (IRE) | Amanda Perrett |
| MOEL ARTHUR (USA) | |

| HORSE | TRAINER |
|---|---|
| MOHAAFETH (IRE) | William Haggas |
| MOJDDEE (IRE) | William Haggas |
| MOKTASAAB | Owen Burrows |
| MONTASHY (IRE) | |
| MOSAAHEB | Sir Michael Stoute |
| MOSHAAWER | Roger Varian |
| MOSTAHDAF (IRE) | John & Thady Gosden |
| MOTARAJJA (IRE) | Marcus Tregoning |
| MOTAZZEN (IRE) | Jean Claude Rouget |
| MOZDAHER (IRE) | |
| MUNSTER BLACKWATER | Joseph Patrick O'Brien |
| NAGANO | Roger Varian |
| NANKEEN | Simon & Ed Crisford |
| NATIONAL BALLET (JPN) | Aidan O'Brien |
| NAVEGAON GATE | Ed Walker |
| NAYON | David Evans |
| NEW FORCE | Hugo Palmer |
| NEW HOLLAND (IRE) | |
| NORTHERN (IRE) | Jamie Osborne |
| OKITA SOUSHI (IRE) | Joseph Patrick O'Brien |
| ONTARIO (IRE) | Aidan O'Brien |
| OTYRAR | John & Thady Gosden |
| OUTBACK BOY (IRE) | Mark Johnston |
| OUTBACK OPAL | |
| O'REILLY (FR) | Mrs J. Harrington |
| PABLO DEL PUEBLO (IRE) | Simon Dow |
| PARACHUTE | Ed Walker |
| PARLIAMENT | John & Thady Gosden |
| PATROLMAN | John & Thady Gosden |
| PERCY'S LAD | Eve Johnson Houghton |
| PETER THE GREAT | John & Thady Gosden |
| PIECEDERESISTANCE (IRE) | Aidan O'Brien |
| PITERAQ (IRE) | Francis-Henri Graffard |
| PLEASANT MAN | Roger Charlton |
| POINT NEPEAN (IRE) | Joseph Patrick O'Brien |
| POLLING DAY (IRE) | John & Thady Gosden |
| POPULAR VERDICT | D.K. Weld |
| PORT PHILIP (IRE) | Joseph Patrick O'Brien |
| PRAIANO (GER) | Roger Varian |
| PRIDE OF PRIORY | William Haggas |
| PRINCE OF VERONA (USA) | Aidan O'Brien |
| PROCELLARUM (IRE) | Donnacha Aidan O'Brien |
| PRYDWEN (IRE) | George Scott |
| RATIB | Joseph Patrick O'Brien |
| REALIST | Michael Bell |
| REAMS OF LOVE | Mark Johnston |
| RECOVERY RUN | Andrew Balding |
| REKERO (IRE) | Joseph Patrick O'Brien |
| RIDGEWAY AVENUE (USA) | James Ferguson |
| ROBIOLA (IRE) | William Haggas |
| ROCK CHANT (USA) | Joseph Patrick O'Brien |
| RODHWAAN | |
| ROMAN EMPIRE (IRE) | Aidan O'Brien |
| ROYAL AIR FORCE (IRE) | Simon & Ed Crisford |
| ROYAL CHAMPION (IRE) | Roger Varian |
| RULING (GER) | Joseph Patrick O'Brien |
| RUSHMORE | Andrew Balding |
| SALIGO BAY (IRE) | Roger Charlton |
| SANDHURST (IRE) | Aidan O'Brien |
| SAN MARTINO (IRE) | Aidan O'Brien |
| SARROOD (IRE) | Charles Hills |
| SCO GUARDI (IRE) | James Ferguson |
| SCOPE (IRE) | Ralph Beckett |
| SEA THE SHELLS | Mark Johnston |
| SEATTLE CREEK | Luke Comer |
| SEATTLE SOUND (IRE) | Luke Comer |

| HORSE | TRAINER |
|---|---|
| SET POINT (IRE) | Hugo Palmer |
| SEVENTH KINGDOM | John & Thady Gosden |
| SHAAHER | Kevin Ryan |
| SHABANDOZ | Roger Varian |
| SHACKLETON HERO (IRE) | Aidan O'Brien |
| SHAFAAF (USA) | Jean Claude Rouget |
| SHAYZAR (FR) | A. de Royer Dupre |
| SHEMENI (IRE) | D. K. Weld |
| SHERINGHAM | Simon & Ed Crisford |
| SHINSENGUMI (IRE) | Aidan O'Brien |
| SHIYRVANN (FR) | A. de Royer Dupre |
| SIDE SHOT | John & Thady Gosden |
| SIGN FROM ABOVE (IRE) | Mrs J. Harrington |
| SIR LAMORAK (IRE) | Aidan O'Brien |
| SIR LUCAN (IRE) | Aidan O'Brien |
| SIR WILLIAM BRUCE (IRE) | Aidan O'Brien |
| SIYAZANN (FR) | A. de Royer Dupre |
| SNOWY OWL (IRE) | Donnacha Aidan O'Brien |
| SOUTHERN CAPE (IRE) | Donnacha Aidan O'Brien |
| SOUTHERN LIGHTS (IRE) | Joseph Patrick O'Brien |
| SOYUZ | Simon Dow |
| STANLEY BALDWIN | Michael Bell |
| STAR CALIBER | Andrew Balding |
| STAR HARBOUR (IRE) | Adrian Mcguinness |
| STAY WELL | Hughie Morrison |
| SUNWALK | A. Slattery |
| SUREFIRE | Ralph Beckett |
| SURREY GOLD (IRE) | Hughie Morrison |
| SWORD ZORRO (IRE) | Mrs J. Harrington |
| TAIPAN (FR) | Mrs J. Harrington |
| TARAASHOQ (GER) | William Haggas |
| TASMAN BAY (FR) | Sir Mark Todd |
| TAWAAREQ (IRE) | Sir Michael Stoute |
| TECHNO VIKING (IRE) | Chris Gordon |
| TEOFILO STAR (IRE) | James Ferguson |
| THALER | Sir Michael Stoute |
| THE GUVNOR (IRE) | Tom Clover |
| THE MEDITERRANEAN (IRE) | Aidan O'Brien |
| THE ORIENT (IRE) | Aidan O'Brien |
| THIRD REALM | Roger Varian |
| TIDES OF WAR (IRE) | Aidan O'Brien |
| TIGER BEETLE | Sir Michael Stoute |
| TIGNANELLO (IRE) | Aidan O'Brien |
| TITLE (IRE) | Roger Varian |
| TONY MONTANA | Roger Varian |
| TOO FRIENDLY | George Scott |
| TOP BRASS | John & Thady Gosden |
| TORINO (IRE) | Aidan O'Brien |
| TRAILA | Sir Michael Stoute |
| TRAWLERMAN (IRE) | John & Thady Gosden |
| TYRRHENIAN SEA (IRE) | Roger Varian |
| UBAHHA | |
| UNCLE BRYN | John & Thady Gosden |
| VALPARAISO | Marcus Tregoning |
| VAN GOGH (USA) | Aidan O'Brien |
| VENGEANCE | |
| VICTORY ROLL | Roger Charlton |
| WAKE UP HARRY | Simon Dow |
| WALLEM | Andrew Balding |
| WEDDELL SEA (IRE) | A. Fabre |
| WEMBLEY (IRE) | Aidan O'Brien |
| WORDSWORTH (IRE) | Aidan O'Brien |
| WUQOOD | D.K. Weld |
| YARRAWONGA (IRE) | Aidan O'Brien |
| YOUTH SPIRIT (IRE) | Andrew Balding |
| ZAGATO | John & Thady Gosden |

| HORSE | TRAINER |
|---|---|
| ZASKAR | A. de Royer Dupre |
| ZOOKEEPER (IRE) | Mark Johnston |
| ZOZIMUS (IRE) | Aidan O'Brien |
| EX AMBITIOUS LADY | Aidan O'Brien |
| EX ATTRACTION | Peter Chapple-Hyam |
| EX CONVOCATE (USA) | Peter Chapple-Hyam |
| EX LARCENY (IRE) | Aidan O'Brien |
| EX LA TRAVIATA (USA) | Aidan O'Brien |
| EX OAKLEY GIRL | Peter Chapple-Hyam |
| EX TUNKWA (FR) | Ismail Mohammed |
| EX WINNER'S WISH | Ismail Mohammed |

# THE BET365
# EUROPEAN FREE HANDICAP STAKES
## NEWMARKET CRAVEN MEETING 2021
## (ON THE ROWLEY MILE COURSE)
## WEDNESDAY APRIL 14TH

The bet365 European Free Handicap Stakes (Class 1) (Listed Race) with total prize fund of £50,000 for **three-year-olds only** (Two-year-olds of 2020 which are included in the European 2-y-o Thoroughbred Rankings or which, in 2020, either ran in Great Britain or ran for a trainer who at the time was licensed by the British Horseracing Authority, and are Rated 100 or above); lowest weight 8st; highest weight 9st 7lb.

Penalty for a winner after December 31st 2020 to be at the discretion of the BHA Handicapper. Seven furlongs.

| Rating | | st | lb | | Rating | | st | lb |
|---|---|---|---|---|---|---|---|---|
| 120 | **St Mark's Basilica** (FR) | 9 | 7 | | 110 | **Umm Kulthum** (IRE) | 8 | 11 |
| 118 | **Supremacy** (IRE) | 9 | 5 | | 109 | **Etonian** (IRE) | 8 | 10 |
| 118 | **Wembley** (IRE) | 9 | 5 | | 109 | **Isabella Giles** (IRE) | 8 | 10 |
| 117 | **Thunder Moon** (IRE) | 9 | 4 | | 109 | **Ontario** (IRE) | 8 | 10 |
| 116 | **Golden Pal** (USA) | 9 | 3 | | 109 | **Winter Power** (IRE) | 8 | 10 |
| 116 | **Lucky Vega** (IRE) | 9 | 3 | | 108 | **Bolshoi Ballet** (IRE) | 8 | 9 |
| 116 | **Mac Swiney** (IRE) | 9 | 3 | | 108 | **Fev Rover** (IRE) | 8 | 9 |
| 116 | **Sealiway** (FR) | 9 | 3 | | 107 | **Cobh** (IRE) | 8 | 8 |
| 115 | **High Definition** (IRE) | 9 | 2 | | 107 | **Poetic Flare** (IRE) | 8 | 8 |
| 114 | **Cadillac** (IRE) | 9 | 1 | | 107 | **Recovery Run** (GB) | 8 | 8 |
| 114 | **One Ruler** (IRE) | 9 | 1 | | 107 | **Sacred** (GB) | 8 | 8 |
| 114 | **Van Gogh** (USA) | 9 | 1 | | 107 | **Tactical** (GB) | 8 | 8 |
| 113 | **Alkumait** (GB) | 9 | 0 | | 106 | **Fancy Man** (IRE) | 8 | 7 |
| 113 | **Campanelle** (IRE) | 9 | 0 | | 106 | **Happy Romance** (IRE) | 8 | 7 |
| 113 | **Chindit** (IRE) | 9 | 0 | | 106 | **Jadoomi** (FR) | 8 | 7 |
| 113 | **Devilwala** (IRE) | 9 | 0 | | 106 | **King Vega** (GB) | 8 | 7 |
| 113 | **Gear Up** (IRE) | 9 | 0 | | 106 | **Method** (IRE) | 8 | 7 |
| 113 | **Pretty Gorgeous** (FR) | 9 | 0 | | 106 | **The Lir Jet** (IRE) | 8 | 7 |
| 113 | **Shale** (IRE) | 9 | 0 | | 105 | **Charterhouse** (GB) | 8 | 6 |
| 112 | **Alcohol Free** (IRE) | 8 | 13 | | 105 | **Dandalla** (IRE) | 8 | 6 |
| 112 | **Battleground** (USA) | 8 | 13 | | 105 | **Lipizzaner** (USA) | 8 | 6 |
| 112 | **Botanik** (IRE) | 8 | 13 | | 105 | **Megallan** (GB) | 8 | 6 |
| 112 | **Indigo Girl** (GB) | 8 | 13 | | 104 | **Acklam Express** (IRE) | 8 | 5 |
| 112 | **Makaloun** (FR) | 8 | 13 | | 104 | **Apollo One** (GB) | 8 | 5 |
| 112 | **Master of The Seas** (IRE) | 8 | 13 | | 104 | **Chief Little Hawk** (USA) | 8 | 5 |
| 112 | **New Mandate** (IRE) | 8 | 13 | | 104 | **La Barrosa** (IRE) | 8 | 5 |
| 111 | **Best of Lips** (IRE) | 8 | 12 | | 104 | **Lullaby Moon** (GB) | 8 | 5 |
| 111 | **Minzaal** (IRE) | 8 | 12 | | 104 | **Naval Crown** (GB) | 8 | 5 |
| 111 | **Monaasib** (IRE) | 8 | 12 | | 104 | **Ventura Tormenta** (IRE) | 8 | 5 |
| 111 | **Mother Earth** (IRE) | 8 | 12 | | 103 | **Cloudbridge** (USA) | 8 | 4 |
| 111 | **Nando Parrado** (GB) | 8 | 12 | | 103 | **Devious Company** (IRE) | 8 | 4 |
| 110 | **Albasheer** (IRE) | 8 | 11 | | 103 | **Dhahabi** (IRE) | 8 | 4 |
| 110 | **Baradar** (IRE) | 8 | 11 | | 103 | **Frenetic** (IRE) | 8 | 4 |
| 110 | **Dubai Fountain** (IRE) | 8 | 11 | | 103 | **Love Is You** (IRE) | 8 | 4 |
| 110 | **Fivethousandtoone** (IRE) | 8 | 11 | | 103 | **Monday** (USA) | 8 | 4 |
| 110 | **Go Athletico** (FR) | 8 | 11 | | 103 | **Muker** (IRE) | 8 | 4 |
| 110 | **Laneqash** (GB) | 8 | 11 | | 103 | **Nazuna** (IRE) | 8 | 4 |
| 110 | **Lone Eagle** (IRE) | 8 | 11 | | 103 | **Royal Scimitar** (IRE) | 8 | 4 |
| 110 | **Miss Amulet** (IRE) | 8 | 11 | | 103 | **Youth Spirit** (IRE) | 8 | 4 |
| 110 | **Plainchant** (FR) | 8 | 11 | | 103 | **Zamaani** (IRE) | 8 | 4 |
| 110 | **Rhythm Master** (IRE) | 8 | 11 | | 102 | **Belloccio** (FR) | 8 | 3 |
| 110 | **State of Rest** (IRE) | 8 | 11 | | 102 | **Burning Cash** (IRE) | 8 | 3 |
| 110 | **Tiger Tanaka** (IRE) | 8 | 11 | | 102 | **Mighty Gurkha** (IRE) | 8 | 3 |
| 110 | **Ubettabelieveit** (IRE) | 8 | 11 | | 102 | **Mujbar** (GB) | 8 | 3 |

| Rating | | st | lb |
|---|---|---|---|
| 102 | **Mystery Smiles** (IRE) | 8 | 3 |
| 102 | **Scarlet Bear** (IRE) | 8 | 3 |
| 102 | **Steel Bull** (IRE) | 8 | 3 |
| 102 | **Time Scale** (GB) | 8 | 3 |
| 102 | **Zabeel Queen** (IRE) | 8 | 3 |
| 101 | **Cairn Gorm** (GB) | 8 | 2 |
| 101 | **Escape Route** (IRE) | 8 | 2 |
| 101 | **First Edition** (IRE) | 8 | 2 |
| 101 | **Just Frank** (GB) | 8 | 2 |
| 101 | **Lilac Road** (IRE) | 8 | 2 |
| 101 | **Pleasant Man** (GB) | 8 | 2 |
| 101 | **Royal Approval** (USA) | 8 | 2 |
| 101 | **Saffron Beach** (IRE) | 8 | 2 |
| 101 | **Santosha** (IRE) | 8 | 2 |
| 101 | **Thinking of You** (USA) | 8 | 2 |
| 100 | **Akmaam** (FR) | 8 | 1 |
| 100 | **Alenquer** (FR) | 8 | 1 |
| 100 | **Bahrain Pride** (GB) | 8 | 1 |
| 100 | **Dark Lion** (IRE) | 8 | 1 |
| 100 | **Gorytus** (IRE) | 8 | 1 |
| 100 | **Legal Attack** (GB) | 8 | 1 |
| 100 | **Lost In Space** (IRE) | 8 | 1 |
| 100 | **Percy's Lad** (GB) | 8 | 1 |
| 100 | **Seventh Kingdom** (GB) | 8 | 1 |
| 100 | **Tetragonal** (IRE) | 8 | 1 |
| 100 | **Yibir** (GB) | 8 | 1 |

# Download the free must-have Racing Post app.

**RACING POST**

The Must-Have App
For The Must-Have Info

Use your camera phone
and scan the QR code
on the right to download
the free app now.

# LONGINES WORLD'S BEST RACEHORSE RANKINGS 2020

for **three-year-olds** rated 115 or greater by the IFHA World's Best Racehorse Rankings Conference.

| Rating | | Trained |
|---|---|---|
| 126 | Authentic (USA) | USA |
| 125 | Palace Pier (GB) | GB |
| 125 | Tiz The Law (USA) | USA |
| 124 | Contrail (JPN) | JPN |
| 122 | Gamine (USA) | USA |
| 122 | In Swoop (IRE) | FR |
| 122 | Kameko (USA) | GB |
| 122 | Love (IRE) | IRE |
| 122 | Pinatubo (IRE) | GB |
| 122 | Swiss Skydiver (USA) | USA |
| 121 | Mogul (GB) | IRE |
| 120 | Armory (IRE) | IRE |
| 120 | Mishriff (IRE) | GB |
| 120 | Order of Australia (IRE) | IRE |
| 120 | Serpentine (IRE) | IRE |
| 119 | Alpine Star (IRE) | IRE |
| 119 | Art Collector (USA) | USA |
| 119 | Charlatan (USA) | USA |
| 119 | Daring Tact (JPN) | JPN |
| 119 | Gold Trip (FR) | FR |
| 119 | Pyledriver (GB) | GB |
| 119 | Salios (JPN) | JPN |
| 119 | Shedaresthedevil (USA) | USA |
| 119 | Siskin (USA) | IRE |
| 118 | Nadal (USA) | USA |
| 118 | Rothfire (AUS) | AUS |
| 118 | Russian Camelot (IRE) | AUS |
| 118 | Wichita (IRE) | IRE |
| 117 | Aristoteles (JPN) | JPN |
| 117 | Galileo Chrome (IRE) | IRE |
| 117 | Happy Saver (USA) | USA |
| 117 | Honor A P (USA) | USA |
| 117 | Lope Y Fernandez (IRE) | IRE |
| 117 | Mr Big News (USA) | USA |
| 117 | Torquator Tasso (GER) | GER |
| 117 | Wonderful Tonight (FR) | GB |
| 116 | Berkshire Rocco (FR) | GB |
| 116 | Cool Day (ARG) | ARG |
| 116 | Dicaprio (GER) | GER |
| 116 | Earthlight (IRE) | FR |
| 116 | Golden Horde (IRE) | GB |
| 116 | Got The Greenlight (SAF) | SAF |
| 116 | Harvey's Lil Goil (USA) | USA |
| 116 | Maxfield (USA) | USA |
| 116 | Ole Kirk (AUS) | AUS |
| 116 | Tiger Moth (IRE) | IRE |
| 115 | Anders (AUS) | AUS |
| 115 | Aysar (AUS) | AUS |
| 115 | Cayenne Pepper (IRE) | IRE |
| 115 | Champers Elysees (IRE) | IRE |
| 115 | Great Escape (ARG) | ARG |
| 115 | Harvest Moon (USA) | USA |
| 115 | Kaspar (GER) | GER |
| 115 | Lauda Sion (JPN) | JPN |
| 115 | Mount Pleasant (AUS) | SAF |
| 115 | Mystic Guide (USA) | USA |
| 115 | North Pacific (AUS) | AUS |
| 115 | Santiago (IRE) | IRE |
| 115 | Sinawann (IRE) | IRE |
| 115 | Sunny Queen (GER) | GER |
| 115 | Tagaloa (AUS) | AUS |
| 115 | Tawkeel (GB) | FR |
| 115 | Victor Ludorum (GB) | FR |

# OLDER HORSES 2020

for **four-year-olds and up** rated 115 or greater by the IFHA World's Best Racehorse Rankings Conference.

| Rating | | Age | Trained |
|---|---|---|---|
| 130 | Ghaiyyath (IRE) | 6 | GB |
| 125 | Addeybb (IRE) | 7 | GB |
| 125 | Bivouac (AUS) | 4 | AUS |
| 125 | Classique Legend (AUS) | 4 | AUS |
| 125 | Persian King (IRE) | 4 | FR |
| 125 | Stradivarius (IRE) | 7 | GB |
| 124 | Almond Eye (JPN) | 6 | JPN |
| 124 | Golden Sixty (AUS) | 6 | HK |
| 124 | Mohaather (GB) | 4 | GB |
| 124 | Nature Strip (AUS) | 7 | AUS |
| 123 | Battaash (IRE) | 7 | GB |
| 123 | Fierement (JPN) | 6 | JPN |
| 123 | Glory Vase (JPN) | 6 | JPN |
| 123 | Improbable (USA) | 4 | USA |
| 123 | Lord North (IRE) | 4 | GB |
| 123 | Sottsass (FR) | 4 | FR |
| 122 | Anthony Van Dyck (IRE) | 4 | IRE |
| 122 | Beauty Generation (NZ) (ex Montaigne) | 9 | HK |
| 122 | Enable (GB) | 7 | GB |
| 122 | Magical (IRE) | 6 | IRE |
| 122 | Maximum Security (USA) | 4 | USA |
| 122 | Tarnawa (IRE) | 4 | IRE |
| 122 | Tom's d'Etat (USA) | 8 | USA |
| 121 | Chrono Genesis (JPN) | 4 | JPN |
| 121 | Do It Again (SAF) | 7 | SAF |
| 121 | Gran Alegria (JPN) | 4 | JPN |
| 121 | Sir Dragonet (IRE) | 4 | AUS |
| 121 | Skalleti (FR) | 6 | FR |
| 120 | Channel Maker (CAN) | 7 | USA |
| 120 | Circus Maximus (IRE) | 4 | IRE |
| 120 | Dream of Dreams (IRE) | 7 | GB |
| 120 | Exultant (IRE) (ex Irishcorrespondent) | 7 | HK |
| 120 | Global Campaign (USA) | 4 | USA |
| 120 | Hawwaam (SAF) | 4 | SAF |
| 120 | Hot King Prawn (AUS) (ex Join In) | 7 | HK |
| 120 | Japan (GB) | 4 | IRE |
| 120 | Mo Forza (USA) | 4 | USA |
| 120 | Monomoy Girl (USA) | 6 | USA |
| 120 | Oxted (GB) | 4 | GB |
| 120 | Saturnalia (JPN) | 4 | JPN |
| 120 | Space Blues (IRE) | 4 | GB |
| 119 | Beat The Clock (AUS) | 8 | HK |
| 119 | Chrysoberyl (JPN) | 4 | JPN |
| 119 | Curren Bouquetd'or (JPN) | 4 | JPN |
| 119 | Danon Premium (JPN) | 6 | JPN |
| 119 | Indy Champ (JPN) | 6 | JPN |
| 119 | Knicks Go (USA) | 4 | USA |
| 119 | One World (SAF) | 4 | SAF |
| 119 | Rainbow Bridge (SAF) | 7 | SAF |
| 119 | Salacia (JPN) | 6 | JPN |
| 119 | Santa Ana Lane (AUS) | 9 | AUS |
| 119 | The Revenant (GB) | 6 | FR |
| 119 | Vardy (SAF) | 4 | SAF |
| 119 | Vekoma (USA) | 4 | USA |
| 119 | Win Bright (JPN) | 7 | JPN |
| 118 | Admire Mars (JPN) | 4 | JPN |
| 118 | Benbatl (GB) | 7 | UAE |
| 118 | Call The Wind (GB) | 6 | FR |
| 118 | Danon Kingly (JPN) | 4 | JPN |
| 118 | Gytrash (AUS) | 6 | AUS |
| 118 | Hello Youmzain (FR) | 4 | GB |
| 118 | Hey Doc (AUS) | 8 | AUS |
| 118 | Midnight Bisou (USA) | 6 | USA |
| 118 | Mr Stunning (AUS) | 9 | HK |
| 118 | Mucho Gusto (USA) | 4 | USA |
| 118 | Pierata (AUS) | 7 | AUS |
| 118 | Redzel (AUS) | 9 | AUS |
| 118 | Regal Power (AUS) | 6 | AUS |
| 118 | Roseman (GB) | 4 | GB |
| 118 | Rushing Fall (USA) | 6 | USA |
| 118 | Southern Legend (AUS) | 9 | HK |
| 118 | Te Akau Shark (NZ) | 7 | NZ |
| 118 | Thanks Forever (AUS) | 6 | HK |
| 118 | Trekking (AUS) | 7 | AUS |
| 118 | Trueshan (FR) | 4 | GB |
| 118 | Waikuku (HK) | 6 | HK |
| 118 | World Premiere (JPN) | 4 | JPN |
| 118 | Zulu Alpha (USA) | 8 | USA |
| 117 | Alligator Blood (AUS) | 4 | AUS |
| 117 | Audarya (FR) | 4 | GB |
| 117 | Behemoth (AUS) | 6 | AUS |
| 117 | Blast Onepiece (JPN) | 6 | JPN |
| 117 | By My Standards (USA) | 4 | USA |
| 117 | Capezzano (USA) | 7 | UAE |
| 117 | Chuwa Wizard (JPN) | 6 | JPN |
| 117 | Code of Honor (USA) | 4 | USA |
| 117 | Dreamforce (AUS) | 9 | AUS |
| 117 | Fierce Impact (JPN) | 7 | AUS |
| 117 | Fifty Stars (IRE) | 6 | AUS |
| 117 | Furore (NZ) | 4 | HK |
| 117 | Glen Shiel (GB) | 7 | GB |
| 117 | Ka Ying Star (GB) (ex Urban Aspect) | 6 | HK |
| 117 | Kolding (NZ) | 6 | AUS |
| 117 | McKinzie (USA) | 6 | USA |
| 117 | Mozu Ascot (USA) | 6 | JPN |
| 117 | Mugatoo (IRE) | 6 | AUS |
| 117 | Normcore (JPN) | 6 | JPN |
| 117 | Stiffelio (JPN) | 7 | JPN |
| 117 | Summer Pudding (SAF) | 4 | SAF |
| 117 | Tacitus (USA) | 4 | USA |
| 117 | Tetaze (ARG) | 4 | ARG |
| 117 | Twilight Payment (IRE) | 8 | IRE |
| 117 | Volatile (USA) | 4 | USA |
| 117 | Whitmore (USA) | 8 | USA |
| 116 | Arcadia Queen (AUS) | 6 | AUS |
| 116 | Arklow (USA) | 7 | USA |
| 116 | Aspetar (FR) | 6 | GB |
| 116 | Belgarion (SAF) | 4 | SAF |
| 116 | Bostonian (NZ) (alt The Bostonian) | 7 | NZ |
| 116 | Brando (GB) | 9 | GB |
| 116 | Cadenas (JPN) | 7 | JPN |
| 116 | Castelvecchio (AUS) | 4 | AUS |
| 116 | Catalyst (NZ) | 4 | NZ |
| 116 | Century Dream (IRE) | 7 | GB |
| 116 | Factor This (USA) | 6 | USA |
| 116 | Got The Greenlight (SAF) | 4 | SAF |
| 116 | Ivar (BRZ) | 4 | USA |
| 116 | Loving Gaby (AUS) | 4 | AUS |
| 116 | Lucky Lilac (JPN) | 6 | JPN |
| 116 | Melody Belle (NZ) | 7 | NZ |

| Rating | | Age | Trained |
|---|---|---|---|
| 116 | Mr Quickie (AUS) | 6 | AUS |
| 116 | Pimper's Paradise (BRZ) | 7 | BRZ |
| 116 | Pinball Wizard (ARG) | 6 | ARG |
| 116 | Regal Reality (GB) | 6 | GB |
| 116 | Safe Voyage (IRE) | 8 | GB |
| 116 | Sceptical (GB) | 4 | IRE |
| 116 | Search For A Song (IRE) | 4 | IRE |
| 116 | Sharp Samurai (USA) | 7 | USA |
| 116 | Strategos (ARG) | 6 | ARG |
| 116 | Superstorm (AUS) | 4 | AUS |
| 116 | Time Warp (GB) | 8 | HK |
| 116 | United (USA) | 6 | USA |
| 116 | Valiance (USA) | 4 | USA |
| 116 | Verry Elleegant (NZ) | 6 | AUS |
| 116 | Way To Paris (GB) | 8 | FR |
| 115 | Ajool (ARG) | 4 | ARG |
| 115 | Ajuste Fiscal (URU) | 4 | URU |
| 115 | Avilius (GB) | 7 | AUS |
| 115 | Barney Roy (GB) | 7 | UAE |
| 115 | Big Time Baby (IRE) | 7 | HK |
| 115 | Bodexpress (USA) | 4 | USA |
| 115 | Ce Ce (USA) | 4 | USA |
| 115 | Cirillo (SAF) | 6 | SAF |
| 115 | Columbus County (NZ) (ex Sword in Stone) | 6 | HK |
| 115 | Complexity (USA) | 4 | USA |
| 115 | Dalasan (AUS) | 4 | AUS |
| 115 | Danon Smash (JPN) | 6 | JPN |
| 115 | Diatonic (JPN) | 6 | JPN |
| 115 | Dirty Work (AUS) | 4 | AUS |
| 115 | Dubai Warrior (GB) | 4 | GB |
| 115 | Dunbar Road (USA) | 4 | USA |
| 115 | Elarqam (GB) | 6 | GB |
| 115 | Fanny Logan (IRE) | 4 | GB |
| 115 | Fighting Mad (USA) | 4 | USA |
| 115 | Fujaira Prince (IRE) | 7 | GB |
| 115 | George Washington (BRZ) | 6 | BRZ |
| 115 | Golden Ducat (SAF) | 4 | SAF |
| 115 | Happy Power (IRE) | 4 | GB |
| 115 | Kiseki (JPN) | 7 | JPN |
| 115 | Kurino Gaudi (JPN) | 4 | JPN |
| 115 | Libertini (AUS) | 4 | AUS |
| 115 | Limato (IRE) | 9 | GB |
| 115 | Magny Cours (USA) | 4 | FR |
| 115 | Midcourt (USA) | 6 | USA |
| 115 | Mikki Swallow (JPN) | 7 | JPN |
| 115 | Mirage Dancer (GB) | 7 | AUS |
| 115 | Nagano Gold (GB) | 7 | CZE |
| 115 | Nayef Road (IRE) | 4 | GB |
| 115 | Nazeef (GB) | 4 | GB |
| 115 | Newspaperofrecord (IRE) | 4 | USA |
| 115 | Omega Perfume (JPN) | 6 | JPN |
| 115 | Persian Knight (JPN) | 7 | JPN |
| 115 | Prince Fawaz (AUS) | 4 | AUS |
| 115 | Quick Thinker (AUS) | 4 | NZ |
| 115 | Raging Bull (FR) | 6 | USA |
| 115 | Romanised (IRE) | 6 | IRE |
| 115 | Serengeti Empress (USA) | 4 | USA |
| 115 | Shadow Hero (AUS) | 4 | AUS |
| 115 | Shaman (IRE) | 4 | FR |
| 115 | Springdom (ARG) | 4 | ARG |
| 115 | Streets of Avalon (AUS) | 7 | AUS |
| 115 | Tavi Mac (NZ) | 6 | NZ |
| 115 | Tofane (NZ) | 6 | AUS |
| 115 | True Timber (USA) | 7 | USA |
| 115 | Twist of Fate (SAF) | 6 | SAF |
| 115 | Vexatious (USA) | 7 | USA |
| 115 | Vin de Garde (JPN) | 4 | JPN |
| 115 | Voyage Warrior (AUS) | 6 | HK |
| 115 | Wet Your Whistle (USA) | 6 | USA |
| 115 | Wide Pharaoh (JPN) | 4 | JPN |

# RACING POST CHAMPIONS 2020

ONLY HORSES WHICH HAVE RUN IN EUROPE ARE INCLUDED

## FOUR-YEAR-OLDS AND UP

| | | | |
|---|---|---|---|
| GHAIYYATH | 131 | STRADIVARIUS | 125 |
| MOHAATHER | 127 | ENABLE | 124 |
| ADDEYBB | 126 | PERSIAN KING | 124 |
| LORD NORTH | 126 | SOTTSASS | 124 |

## THREE-YEAR-OLD COLT

| | | | |
|---|---|---|---|
| PALACE PIER | 127 | PINATUBO | 124 |
| KAMEKO | 125 | IN SWOOP | 122 |
| MOGUL | 124 | SERPENTINE | 121 |

## THREE-YEAR-OLD FILLY

| | | | |
|---|---|---|---|
| LOVE | 124 | ALPINISTA | 116 |
| ALPINE STAR | 119 | CHAMPERS ELYSEES | 116 |
| WONDERFUL TONIGHT | 119 | ONE VOICE | 116 |
| FANCY BLUE | 117 | | |

## SPRINTER

| | | | |
|---|---|---|---|
| BATTAASH | 123 | SPACE BLUES | 121 |
| OXTED | 123 | GLEN SHIEL | 119 |
| DREAM OF DREAMS | 122 | SCEPTICAL | 119 |
| HELLO YOUMZAIN | 121 | | |

## STAYER

| | | | |
|---|---|---|---|
| STRADIVARIUS | 125 | DASHING WILLOUGHBY | 116 |
| TRUESHAN | 121 | NAYEF ROAD | 116 |
| FUJAIRA PRINCE | 118 | PYLEDRIVER | 116 |
| GALILEO CHROME | 118 | SANTIAGO | 116 |
| BERKSHIRE ROCCO | 117 | | |

## TWO-YEAR-OLD COLT

| | | | |
|---|---|---|---|
| ST MARK'S BASILICA | 121 | THUNDER MOON | 117 |
| WEMBLEY | 119 | LUCKY VEGA | 116 |
| SUPREMACY | 118 | SEALIWAY | 116 |

## TWO-YEAR-OLD FILLY

| | | | |
|---|---|---|---|
| CAMPANELLE | 114 | INDIGO GIRL | 112 |
| PRETTY GORGEOUS | 114 | PLAINCHANT | 112 |
| ALCOHOL FREE | 113 | SHALE | 112 |

# MEDIAN TIMES 2020

The following Raceform median times are used in the calculation of the Split Second speed figures. They represent a true average time for the distance, which has been arrived at after looking at the winning times for all races over each distance within the past five years, except for those restricted to two or three-year-old

Some current race distances have been omitted as they have not yet had a sufficient number of races run over them to produce a reliable average time.

## ASCOT

| | | |
|---|---|---|
| 5f........................................ 1m 0.70 | 1m Straight...................... 1m 41.40 | 1m 7f 209y...................... 3m 31.30 |
| 6f...................................... 1m 13.70 | 1m 1f 212y........................ 2m 7.70 | 2m 3f 210y...................... 4m 22.00 |
| 7f...................................... 1m 27.50 | 1m 3f 211y...................... 2m 32.60 | 2m 5f 143y...................... 4m 43.60 |
| 7f 213y Round .................. 1m 41.60 | 1m 6f 34y........................ 3m 4.30 | |

## AYR

| | | |
|---|---|---|
| 5f........................................ 59.10 | 7f 50y............................ 1m 31.00 | 1m 5f 26y...................... 2m 56.40 |
| 5f 110y.............................. 1m 7.20 | 1m................................ 1m 41.50 | 1m 7f.............................. 3m 25.80 |
| 6f...................................... 1m 12.30 | 1m 2f.............................. 2m 10.00 | 2m 1f 105y...................... 4m 1.50 |

## BATH

| | | |
|---|---|---|
| 5f 10y................................ 1m 1.70 | 1m 2f 37y.......................... 2m 9.30 | 1m 6f.............................. 3m 4.10 |
| 5f 160y.............................. 1m 10.50 | 1m 3f 137y...................... 2m 29.20 | 2m 1f 24y...................... 3m 51.40 |
| 1m.................................... 1m 40.50 | 1m 5f 11y........................ 2m 51.50 | |

## BEVERLEY

| | | |
|---|---|---|
| 5f...................................... 1m 2.90 | 1m 100y.......................... 1m 47.00 | 1m 4f 23y...................... 2m 41.40 |
| 7f 96y................................ 1m 33.50 | 1m 1f 207y........................ 2m 6.80 | 2m 32y.......................... 3m 35.00 |

## BRIGHTON

| | | |
|---|---|---|
| 5f 60y................................ 1m 2.60 | 6f 210y............................ 1m 22.70 | 1m 1f 207y........................ 2m 3.40 |
| 5f 215y.............................. 1m 10.30 | 7f 211y............................ 1m 35.40 | 1m 3f 198y...................... 2m 34.10 |

## CARLISLE

| | | |
|---|---|---|
| 5f...................................... 1m 2.10 | 7f 173y............................ 1m 41.90 | 1m 6f 32y...................... 3m 13.00 |
| 5f 193y.............................. 1m 15.10 | 1m 1f................................ 2m 1.00 | 2m 1f 47y...................... 3m 55.00 |
| 6f 195y.............................. 1m 28.00 | 1m 3f 39y........................ 2m 29.70 | |

## CATTERICK

| | | |
|---|---|---|
| 5f...................................... 1m 0.00 | 7f 6y.............................. 1m 26.60 | 1m 5f 192y........................ 3m 0.00 |
| 5f 212y.............................. 1m 14.20 | 1m 4f 13y........................ 2m 39.50 | 1m 7f 189y...................... 3m 39.00 |

## CHELMSFORD (A.W)

| | | |
|---|---|---|
| 5f...................................... 59.40 | 1m................................ 1m 38.50 | 1m 6f.............................. 3m 0.20 |
| 6f...................................... 1m 12.20 | 1m 2f.............................. 2m 6.10 | 2m................................ 3m 29.00 |
| 7f...................................... 1m 25.80 | 1m 5f 66y...................... 2m 53.60 | |

## CHEPSTOW

| | | |
|---|---|---|
| 5f 16y................................ 1m 0.30 | 1m 14y............................ 1m 35.80 | 2m................................ 3m 39.10 |
| 6f 16y................................ 1m 12.30 | 1m 2f.............................. 2m 10.00 | |
| 7f 16y................................ 1m 24.40 | 1m 4f.............................. 2m 37.30 | |

# CHESTER

| Distance | Time | Distance | Time | Distance | Time |
|---|---|---|---|---|---|
| 5f 15y | 1m 3.50 | 1m 2f 70y | 2m 14.30 | 1m 6f 87y | 3m 10.00 |
| 6f 17y | 1m 16.40 | 1m 3f 75y | 2m 30.40 | 1m 7f 196y | 3m 34.00 |
| 7f 1y | 1m 28.00 | 1m 4f 63y | 2m 44.00 | 2m 2f 140y | 4m 4.60 |
| 7f 127y | 1m 35.70 | 1m 5f 84y | 3m 0.60 | | |

# DONCASTER

| Distance | Time | Distance | Time | Distance | Time |
|---|---|---|---|---|---|
| 5f 3y | 1m 0.30 | 7f 6y | 1m 26.40 | 1m 6f 115y | 3m 9.00 |
| 5f 143y | 1m 8.10 | 1m Straight | 1m 38.30 | 2m 1f 197y | 3m 55.00 |
| 6f 2y | 1m 13.10 | 1m 2f 43y | 2m 12.30 | | |
| 6f 111y | 1m 19.60 | 1m 3f 197y | 2m 33.20 | | |

# EPSOM

| Distance | Time | Distance | Time | Distance | Time |
|---|---|---|---|---|---|
| 6f 3y | 1m 9.90 | 1m 113y | 1m 46.40 | 1m 4f 6y | 2m 40.80 |
| 7f 3y | 1m 23.40 | 1m 2f 17y | 2m 10.00 | | |

# GOODWOOD

| Distance | Time | Distance | Time | Distance | Time |
|---|---|---|---|---|---|
| 5f | 59.70 | 1m 1f 11y | 1m 57.30 | 1m 6f | 3m 3.00 |
| 6f | 1m 13.50 | 1m 1f 197y | 2m 9.00 | 2m | 3m 29.00 |
| 7f | 1m 28.50 | 1m 3f 44y | 2m 30.40 | 2m 4f 134y | 4m 31.80 |
| 1m | 1m 41.20 | 1m 3f 218y | 2m 39.40 | | |

# HAMILTON

| Distance | Time | Distance | Time | Distance | Time |
|---|---|---|---|---|---|
| 5f 7y | 1m 0.40 | 1m 1f 35y | 1m 59.10 | 1m 5f 16y | 2m 52.60 |
| 6f 6y | 1m 13.20 | 1m 3f 15y | 2m 24.60 | | |
| 1m 68y | 1m 48.40 | 1m 4f 15y | 2m 39.60 | | |

# HAYDOCK

| Distance | Time | Distance | Time | Distance | Time |
|---|---|---|---|---|---|
| 5f | 59.90 | 7f 212y l | 1m 42.70 | 1m 6f l | 3m 9.40 |
| 5f l | 59.90 | 1m 37y | 1m 45.60 | 1m 6f | 3m 9.40 |
| 6f | 1m 14.70 | 1m 2f 42y l | 2m 13.80 | 2m 45y l | 3m 36.70 |
| 6f l | 1m 14.70 | 1m 2f 100y | 2m 16.60 | 2m 45y | 3m 36.70 |
| 6f 212y l | 1m 28.80 | 1m 3f 140y l | 2m 32.60 | | |
| 7f 37y | 1m 32.20 | 1m 3f 175y | 2m 37.50 | | |

# KEMPTON (A.W)

| Distance | Time | Distance | Time | Distance | Time |
|---|---|---|---|---|---|
| 5f | 1m 0.50 | 1m | 1m 39.40 | 1m 3f 219y | 2m 34.50 |
| 6f | 1m 12.80 | 1m 1f 219y | 2m 8.00 | 1m 7f 218y | 3m 30.10 |
| 7f | 1m 26.20 | 1m 2f 219y | 2m 21.00 | | |

# LEICESTER

| Distance | Time | Distance | Time | Distance | Time |
|---|---|---|---|---|---|
| 5f | 1m 0.50 | 7f | 1m 24.70 | 1m 2f | 2m 14.00 |
| 6f | 1m 11.90 | 1m 53y | 1m 46.80 | 1m 3f 179y | 2m 37.40 |

# LINGFIELD

| Distance | Time | Distance | Time | Distance | Time |
|---|---|---|---|---|---|
| 4f 217y | 58.70 | 7f 135y | 1m 31.70 | 1m 3f 133y | 2m 34.00 |
| 6f | 1m 11.50 | 1m 1f | 1m 56.90 | 1m 6f | 3m 6.20 |
| 7f | 1m 24.30 | 2f | 2m 12.20 | 2m 68y | 3m 36.00 |

# LINGFIELD (A.W)

| Distance | Time | Distance | Time | Distance | Time |
|---|---|---|---|---|---|
| 5f 6y | 58.30 | 1m 1y | 1m 37.30 | 1m 5f | 2m 46.00 |
| 6f 1y | 1m 11.90 | 1m 2f | 2m 5.30 | 1m 7f 169y | 3m 25.70 |
| 7f 1y | 1m 24.80 | 1m 4f | 2m 32.10 | | |

# MUSSELBURGH

| Distance | Time | Distance | Time | Distance | Time |
|---|---|---|---|---|---|
| 5f 1y | 1m 0.10 | 1m 208y | 1m 53.10 | 1m 5f 216y | 3m 3.90 |
| 7f 33y | 1m 29.00 | 1m 4f 104y | 2m 44.50 | 1m 7f 217y | 3m 31.50 |
| 1m 2y | 1m 40.00 | 1m 5f | 2m 51.70 | | |

# NEWBURY

| | | | | | |
|---|---|---|---|---|---|
| 5f 34y | 1m 2.40 | 1m Round | 1m 40.50 | 1m 5f 61y | 2m 54.40 |
| 6f | 1m 13.20 | 1m 1f | 1m 55.70 | 2m | 3m 39.40 |
| 6f 110y | 1m 22.10 | 1m 2f | 2m 9.50 | 2m 110y | 3m 46.30 |
| 7f Straight | 1m 26.90 | 1m 3f | 2m 24.20 | | |
| 1m Straight | 1m 40.90 | 1m 4f | 2m 36.90 | | |

# NEWCASTLE (A.W)

| | | | | | |
|---|---|---|---|---|---|
| 5f | 59.90 | 1m 5y | 1m 41.00 | 2m 56y | 3m 35.00 |
| 6f | 1m 13.00 | 1m 2f 42y | 2m 10.40 | | |
| 7f 14y | 1m 27.70 | 1m 4f 98y | 2m 43.50 | | |

# NEWMARKET

| | | | | | |
|---|---|---|---|---|---|
| 5f | 1m 0.90 | 1m 1f | 1m 53.10 | 2m | 3m 27.30 |
| 6f | 1m 12.50 | 1m 2f | 2m 6.60 | 2m 2f | 3m 53.00 |
| 7f | 1m 27.40 | 1m 4f | 2m 34.50 | | |
| 1m | 1m 40.00 | 1m 6f | 3m 2.00 | | |

# NEWMARKET (JULY)

| | | | | | |
|---|---|---|---|---|---|
| 5f | 58.80 | 1m | 1m 39.00 | 1m 5f | 2m 44.00 |
| 6f | 1m 12.50 | 1m 2f | 2m 6.30 | 1m 6f | 2m 59.10 |
| 7f | 1m 27.20 | 1m 4f | 2m 34.90 | | |

# NOTTINGHAM

| | | | | | |
|---|---|---|---|---|---|
| 5f 8y l | 1m 1.50 | 1m 75y l | 1m 49.50 | 1m 6f | 3m 9.80 |
| 5f 8y | 1m 1.50 | 1m 2f 50y | 2m 18.50 | 2m | 3m 40.00 |
| 6f 18y | 1m 15.00 | 1m 2f 50y l | 2m 18.50 | 2m l | 3m 40.00 |
| 1m 75y | 1m 49.50 | 1m 6fl | 3m 9.80 | | |

# PONTEFRACT

| | | | | | |
|---|---|---|---|---|---|
| 5f 3y | 1m 4.10 | 1m 2f 5y | 2m 15.00 | 2m 2f 2y | 4m 9.80 |
| 6f | 1m 17.10 | 1m 4f 5y | 2m 41.10 | | |
| 1m 6y | 1m 45.90 | 2m 1f 27y | 3m 52.30 | | |

# REDCAR

| | | | | | |
|---|---|---|---|---|---|
| 5f | 58.50 | 7f 219y | 1m 38.10 | 1m 5f 218y | 3m 5.00 |
| 5f 217y | 1m 11.80 | 1m 1f | 1m 54.50 | 1m 7f 217y | 3m 33.70 |
| 7f | 1m 21.10 | 1m 2f 1y | 2m 8.40 | | |

# RIPON

| | | | | | |
|---|---|---|---|---|---|
| 5f | 1m 1.00 | 1m 1f | 1m 52.80 | 1m 4f 10y | 2m 39.30 |
| 6f | 1m 13.50 | 1m 1f 170y | 2m 5.60 | 1m 6f | 3m 4.40 |
| 1m | 1m 42.50 | 1m 2f 190y | 2m 22.00 | 2m | 3m 30.40 |

# SALISBURY

| | | | | | |
|---|---|---|---|---|---|
| 5f | 1m 2.50 | 1m | 1m 43.50 | 1m 6f 44y | 3m 8.00 |
| 6f | 1m 16.50 | 1m 1f 201y | 2m 9.30 | | |
| 6f 213y | 1m 30.50 | 1m 4f 5y | 2m 43.60 | | |

# SANDOWN PARK

| | | | | | |
|---|---|---|---|---|---|
| 5f 10y | 1m 1.30 | 1m 1f | 1m 55.30 | 2m 50y | 3m 34.50 |
| 7f | 1m 30.70 | 1m 1f 209y | 2m 10.20 | | |
| 1m | 1m 43.30 | 1m 6f | 3m 11.00 | | |

# SOUTHWELL (A.W)

| | | | | | |
|---|---|---|---|---|---|
| 4f 214y | 58.80 | 1m 13y | 1m 41.30 | 1m 6f 21y | 3m 6.30 |
| 6f 16y | 1m 15.40 | 1m 3f 23y | 2m 28.00 | 2m 102y | 3m 45.50 |
| 7f 14y | 1m 28.70 | 1m 4f 14y | 2m 38.00 | 2m 2f 98y | 4m 11.50 |

# THIRSK

| | | |
|---|---|---|
| 5f..................................... 59.40 | 7f............................... 1m 28.50 | 1m 4f 8y........................... 2m 41.90 |
| 6f................................ 1m 12.10 | 7f 218y...................... 1m 42.50 | |

# WETHERBY

| | | |
|---|---|---|
| 5f 110y........................ 1m 6.00 | 1m.............................. 1m 43.60 | 1m 6f.............................. 3m 8.00 |
| 7f................................ 1m 28.20 | 1m 2f.......................... 2m 11.50 | |

# WINDSOR

| | | |
|---|---|---|
| 5f 21y.......................... 1m 1.10 | 1m 31y....................... 1m 46.10 | 1m 3f 99y......................... 2m 32.40 |
| 6f 12y........................ 1m 13.20 | 1m 2f.......................... 2m 11.50 | |

# WOLVERHAMPTON (A.W)

| | | |
|---|---|---|
| 5f 21y.......................... 1m 1.90 | 1m 142y..................... 1m 50.10 | 1m 5f 219y...................... 3m 1.00 |
| 6f 20y........................ 1m 14.50 | 1m 1f 104y................. 2m 0.80 | 2m 120y......................... 3m 39.30 |
| 7f 36y........................ 1m 28.80 | 1m 4f 51y................... 2m 40.80 | |

# YARMOUTH

| | | |
|---|---|---|
| 5f 42y.......................... 1m 2.00 | 1m 3y......................... 1m 38.20 | 1m 6f 17y........................ 3m 4.70 |
| 6f 3y.......................... 1m 13.50 | 1m 2f 23y................... 2m 8.80 | |
| 7f 3y.......................... 1m 27.10 | 1m 3f 104y................. 2m 29.90 | |

# YORK

| | | |
|---|---|---|
| 5f.................................. 58.90 | 7f 192y...................... 1m 39.00 | 1m 5f 188y...................... 3m 0.20 |
| 5f 89y........................ 1m 4.60 | 1m 177y..................... 1m 50.40 | 2m 56y........................... 3m 36.50 |
| 6f.............................. 1m 12.60 | 1m 2f 56y................... 2m 12.30 | |
| 7f.............................. 1m 25.50 | 1m 3f 188y................. 2m 32.20 | |

# RACING POST RECORD TIMES (FLAT)

## ASCOT

| DISTANCE | TIME | AGE | WEIGHT | GOING | HORSE | DATE |
|---|---|---|---|---|---|---|
| 5f | 58.80 | 2 | 9-1 | Good To Firm | NO NAY NEVER | Jun 20 2013 |
| 5f | 57.44 | 6 | 9-1 | Good To Firm | MISS ANDRETTI | Jun 19 2007 |
| 6f | 1m 12.39 | 4 | 9-1 | Good To Firm | RAJASINGHE | Jun 20 2017 |
| 6f | 1m 11.05 | 3 | 9-1 | Good To Firm | BLUE POINT | May 3 2017 |
| 7f | 1m 25.73 | 2 | 9-3 | Good | PINATUBO | Jun 22 2019 |
| 7f | 1m 24.28 | 4 | 8-11 | Good To Firm | GALICIAN | Jul 27 2013 |
| 7f 213y (Rnd) | 1m 39.55 | 2 | 8-12 | Good | JOSHUA TREE | Sep 26 2009 |
| 7f 213y (Rnd) | 1m 35.89 | 3 | 9-0 | Good To Firm | ALPHA CENTAURI | Jun 22 2018 |
| 1m (Str) | 1m 36.60 | 4 | 9-0 | Good To Firm | RIBCHESTER | Jun 20 2017 |
| 1m 1f 212y | 2m 1.90 | 5 | 8-11 | Good To Firm | THE FUGUE | Jun 18 2014 |
| 1m 3f 211y | 2m 24.60 | 4 | 9-7 | Good To Firm | NOVELLIST | Jul 27 2013 |
| 1m 7f 209y | 3m 24.12 | 4 | 8-12 | Good To Firm | MIZZOU | Apr 29 2015 |
| 2m 3f 210y | 4m 16.92 | 6 | 9-2 | Good To Firm | RITE OF PASSAGE | Jun 17 2010 |
| 2m 5f 143y | 4m 45.24 | 9 | 9-2 | Good To Firm | PALLASATOR | Jun 23 2018 |

## AYR

| DISTANCE | TIME | AGE | WEIGHT | GOING | HORSE | DATE |
|---|---|---|---|---|---|---|
| 5f | 56.98 | 4 | 8-11 | Good | BOOGIE STREET | Sep 18 2003 |
| 5f | 55.68 | 3 | 8-11 | Good To Firm | LOOK BUSY | Jun 21 2008 |
| 6f | 1m 9.73 | 4 | 7-10 | Firm | SIR BERT | Sep 17 1969 |
| 6f | 1m 8.37 | 5 | 8-6 | Good To Firm | MAISON DIEU | Jun 21 2008 |
| 7f 50y | 1m 28.99 | 2 | 9-0 | Good | TAFAAHUM | Sep 19 2003 |
| 7f 50y | 1m 26.43 | 4 | 9-4 | Good To Firm | HAJJAM | May 22 2018 |
| 1m | 1m 39.18 | 2 | 9-7 | Good | MOONLIGHTNAVIGATOR | Sep 18 2014 |
| 1m | 1m 36.00 | 4 | 7-13 | Firm | SUFI | Sep 16 1959 |
| 1m 1f 20y | 1m 50.30 | 4 | 9-3 | Good | RETIREMENT | Sep 19 2003 |
| 1m 2f | 2m 4.02 | 4 | 9-9 | Good To Firm | ENDLESS HALL | Jul 17 2000 |
| 1m 5f 26y | 2m 45.81 | 4 | 9-7 | Good To Firm | EDEN'S CLOSE | Sep 18 1993 |
| 1m 7f | 3m 13.16 | 3 | 9-4 | Good | ROMANY RYE | Sep 19 1991 |
| 2m 1f 105y | 3m 45.20 | 4 | 6-13 | Firm | CURRY | Sep 16 1955 |

## BATH

| DISTANCE | TIME | AGE | WEIGHT | GOING | HORSE | DATE |
|---|---|---|---|---|---|---|
| 5f 10y | 59.50 | 2 | 9-2 | Firm | AMOUR PROPRE | Jul 24 2008 |
| 5f 10y | 58.75 | 3 | 8-12 | Firm | ENTICING | May 1 2007 |
| 5f 160y | 1m 8.70 | 2 | 8-12 | Firm | QALAHARI | Jul 24 2008 |
| 5f 160y | 1m 7.40 | 4 | 9-10 | Firm | MOTAGALLY | Sep 14 2020 |
| 1m 5y | 1m 39.51 | 2 | 9-2 | Firm | NATURAL CHARM | Sep 14 2014 |
| 1m 5y | 1m 37.20 | 5 | 8-12 | Good To Firm | ADOBE | Jun 17 2000 |
| 1m 5y | 1m 37.20 | 3 | 8-7 | Firm | ALASHA | Aug 18 2002 |
| 1m 2f 37y | 2m 5.80 | 3 | 9-0 | Good To Firm | CONNOISSEUR BAY | May 29 1998 |
| 1m 3f 137y | 2m 25.74 | 3 | 9-0 | Hard | TOP THE CHARTS | Sep 8 2005 |
| 1m 5f 11y | 2m 47.20 | 4 | 10-0 | Firm | FLOWN | Aug 13 1991 |
| 1m 6f | 2m 58.97 | 4 | 9-10 | Firm | CHARLIE D | Sep 15 2019 |
| 2m 1f 24y | 3m 43.41 | 6 | 7-9 | Firm | YAHESKA | Jun 14 2003 |

# BEVERLEY

| DISTANCE | TIME | AGE | WEIGHT | GOING | HORSE | DATE |
|---|---|---|---|---|---|---|
| 5f | 1m 0.85 | 2 | 9-5 | Good To Firm | BILLIAN | Aug 12 2020 |
| 5f | 59.77 | 5 | 9-3 | Good To Firm | JUDICIAL | Jun 20 2017 |
| 7f 96y | 1m 31.10 | 2 | 9-7 | Good To Firm | CHAMPAGNE PRINCE | Aug 10 1995 |
| 7f 96y | 1m 31.10 | 2 | 9-0 | Firm | MAJAL | Jul 30 1991 |
| 7f 96y | 1m 29.50 | 3 | 7-8 | Firm | WHO'S TEF | Jul 30 1991 |
| 1m 100y | 1m 43.30 | 2 | 9-0 | Firm | ARDEN | Sep 24 1986 |
| 1m 100y | 1m 42.20 | 3 | 8-4 | Firm | LEGAL CASE | Jun 14 1989 |
| 1m 1f 207y | 2m 1.00 | 3 | 9-7 | Good To Firm | EASTERN ARIA | Aug 29 2009 |
| 1m 4f 23y | 2m 33.35 | 5 | 9-2 | Good To Firm | TWO JABS | Apr 23 2015 |
| 2m 32y | 3m 28.62 | 4 | 9-11 | Good To Firm | CORPUS CHORISTER | Jul 18 2017 |

# BRIGHTON

| DISTANCE | TIME | AGE | WEIGHT | GOING | HORSE | DATE |
|---|---|---|---|---|---|---|
| 5f 60y | 1m 0.10 | 3 | 9-0 | Firm | BID FOR BLUE | May 6 1993 |
| 5f 60y | 59.30 | 3 | 8-9 | Firm | PLAY HEVER GOLF | May 26 1993 |
| 5f 215y | 1m 8.10 | 2 | 8-9 | Firm | SONG MIST | Jul 16 1996 |
| 5f 215y | 1m 7.12 | 8 | 9-6 | Good To Firm | DIAMOND LADY | Apr 20 2019 |
| 6f 210y | 1m 19.90 | 2 | 8-11 | Hard | RAIN BURST | Sep 15 1988 |
| 6f 210y | 1m 20.10 | 4 | 9-3 | Good To Firm | SAWAKI | Sep 3 1991 |
| 7f 211y | 1m 32.80 | 2 | 9-7 | Firm | ASIAN PETE | Oct 3 1989 |
| 7f 211y | 1m 30.50 | 5 | 8-11 | Firm | MYSTIC RIDGE | May 27 1999 |
| 1m 1f 207y | 2m 4.70 | 2 | 9-0 | Good To Soft | ESTEEMED MASTER | Nov 2 2001 |
| 1m 1f 207y | 1m 57.20 | 3 | 9-0 | Firm | GET THE MESSAGE | Apr 30 1984 |
| 1m 3f 198y | 2m 25.80 | 4 | 8-2 | Firm | NEW ZEALAND | Jul 4 1985 |

# CARLISLE

| DISTANCE | TIME | AGE | WEIGHT | GOING | HORSE | DATE |
|---|---|---|---|---|---|---|
| 5f | 1m 0.10 | 2 | 8-5 | Firm | LA TORTUGA | Aug 2 1999 |
| 5f | 58.80 | 3 | 9-8 | Good To Firm | ESATTO | Aug 21 2002 |
| 5f 193y | 1m 12.30 | 2 | 9-2 | Good To Firm | BURRISHOOLE ABBEY | Jun 22 2016 |
| 5f 193y | 1m 10.83 | 4 | 9-0 | Good To Firm | BO MCGINTY | Sep 11 2005 |
| 6f 195y | 1m 24.30 | 3 | 8-9 | Good To Firm | MARJURITA | Aug 21 2002 |
| 7f 173y | 1m 35.84 | 5 | 8-12 | Good To Firm | WAARIF | Jun 27 2018 |
| 1m 1f | 1m 53.84 | 3 | 9-0 | Firm | LITTLE JIMBOB | Jun 14 2004 |
| 1m 3f 39y | 2m 20.46 | 5 | 10-0 | Good To Firm | AASHEQ | Jun 27 2018 |
| 1m 3f 206y | 2m 29.13 | 5 | 9-8 | Good To Firm | TEMPSFORD | Sep 19 2005 |
| 1m 6f 32y | 3m 2.20 | 6 | 8-10 | Firm | EXPLOSIVE SPEED | May 26 1994 |

# CATTERICK

| DISTANCE | TIME | AGE | WEIGHT | GOING | HORSE | DATE |
|---|---|---|---|---|---|---|
| 5f | 57.60 | 2 | 9-0 | Firm | H HARRISON | Oct 8 2002 |
| 5f | 57.10 | 4 | 8-7 | Firm | KABCAST | Jul 6 1989 |
| 5f 212y | 1m 11.40 | 2 | 9-4 | Firm | CAPTAIN NICK | Jul 11 1978 |
| 5f 212y | 1m 9.86 | 9 | 8-13 | Good To Firm | SHARP HAT | May 30 2003 |
| 7f 6y | 1m 24.10 | 2 | 8-11 | Firm | LINDA'S FANTASY | Sep 18 1982 |
| 7f 6y | 1m 22.56 | 6 | 8-7 | Firm | DIFFERENTIAL | May 31 2003 |
| 1m 5f 192y | 2m 54.80 | 3 | 8-5 | Firm | GERYON | May 31 1984 |
| 1m 7f 189y | 3m 20.80 | 4 | 7-11 | Firm | BEAN BOY | Jul 8 1982 |

# CHELMSFORD (AW)

| DISTANCE | TIME | AGE | WEIGHT | GOING | HORSE | DATE |
|---|---|---|---|---|---|---|
| 5f | 58.19 | 2 | 9-2 | Standard | SHALAA ASKER | Sep 13 2020 |
| 5f | 57.30 | 7 | 8-13 | Standard | BROTHER TIGER | Feb 7 2016 |
| 6f | 1m 10.62 | 2 | 9-4 | Standard | KOEPP | Oct 8 2020 |
| 6f | 1m 10.00 | 4 | 9-2 | Standard | RAUCOUS | Apr 27 2017 |
| 7f | 1m 22.56 | 4 | 9-0 | Standard | MISS CELESTIAL | Jul 4 2020 |
| 1m | 1m 37.15 | 2 | 9-3 | Standard | DRAGON MALL | Sep 26 2015 |
| 1m | 1m 35.23 | 3 | 9-7 | Standard | LASER SHOW | Sep 13 2020 |
| 1m 2f | 2m 1.81 | 5 | 9-7 | Standard | BIN BATTUTA | Sep 28 2019 |
| 1m 5f 66y | 2m 47.00 | 4 | 8-7 | Standard | COORG | Jan 6 2016 |
| 1m 6f | 2m 55.61 | 3 | 9-0 | Standard | BRASCA | Sep 5 2019 |
| 2m | 3m 22.37 | 5 | 9-3 | Standard | NOTARISED | Mar 3 2016 |

# CHEPSTOW

| DISTANCE | TIME | AGE | WEIGHT | GOING | HORSE | DATE |
|---|---|---|---|---|---|---|
| 5f 16y | 57.60 | 2 | 8-11 | Firm | MICRO LOVE | Jul 8 1986 |
| 5f 16y | 56.80 | 3 | 8-4 | Firm | TORBAY EXPRESS | Sep 15 1979 |
| 6f 16y | 1m 8.50 | 3 | 9-2 | Firm | NINJAGO | Jul 27 2012 |
| 6f 16y | 1m 8.10 | 3 | 9-7 | Firm | AMERICA CALLING | Sep 18 2001 |
| 7f 16y | 1m 20.48 | 2 | 9-0 | Good | FESTIVAL DAY | Sep 17 2019 |
| 7f 16y | 1m 19.30 | 3 | 9-0 | Firm | TARANAKI | Sep 18 2001 |
| 1m 14y | 1m 33.10 | 2 | 8-11 | Good To Firm | SKI ACADEMY | Aug 28 1995 |
| 1m 14y | 1m 31.60 | 3 | 8-13 | Firm | STOLI | Sep 18 2001 |
| 1m 2f | 2m 4.58 | 3 | 8-13 | Good To Firm | SHOW OF FORCE | Jul 19 2018 |
| 1m 2f 36y | 2m 4.10 | 3 | 8-5 | Good To Firm | ELA ATHENA | Jul 23 1999 |
| 1m 2f 36y | 2m 4.10 | 5 | 8-9 | Hard | LEONIDAS | Jul 5 1983 |
| 1m 2f 36y | 2m 4.10 | 5 | 7-8 | Good To Firm | IT'S VARADAN | Sep 9 1989 |
| 1m 4f 23y | 2m 31.00 | 5 | 8-11 | Hard | THE FRIEND | Aug 29 1983 |
| 1m 4f 23y | 2m 31.00 | 3 | 8-9 | Good To Firm | SPRITSAIL | Jul 13 1989 |
| 2m 49y | 3m 27.70 | 4 | 9-0 | Good To Firm | WIZZARD ARTIST | Jul 1 1989 |
| 2m 2f | 3m 56.40 | 5 | 8-7 | Good To Firm | LAFFAH | Jul 8 2000 |

# CHESTER

| DISTANCE | TIME | AGE | WEIGHT | GOING | HORSE | DATE |
|---|---|---|---|---|---|---|
| 5f 15y | 59.94 | 2 | 9-2 | Good To Firm | LEIBA LEIBA | Jun 26 2010 |
| 5f 15y | 58.88 | 3 | 8-7 | Good To Firm | PETERKIN | Jul 11 2014 |
| 5f 110y | 1m 6.39 | 2 | 8-7 | Good To Soft | KINEMATIC | Sep 27 2014 |
| 5f 110y | 1m 4.54 | 5 | 8-5 | Good | BOSSIPOP | Sep 1 2018 |
| 6f 17y | 1m 12.54 | 2 | 8-12 | Good | GLASS SLIPPERS | Sep 1 2018 |
| 6f 17y | 1m 12.02 | 5 | 9-5 | Good To Firm | DEAUVILLE PRINCE | Jun 13 2015 |
| 7f 1y | 1m 25.29 | 2 | 9-0 | Good To Firm | DUE RESPECT | Sep 25 2002 |
| 7f 1y | 1m 23.75 | 5 | 8-13 | Good To Firm | THREE GRACES | Jul 9 2005 |
| 7f 127y | 1m 32.29 | 2 | 9-0 | Good To Firm | BIG BAD BOB | Sep 25 2002 |
| 7f 127y | 1m 30.62 | 5 | 9-10 | Good | OH THIS IS US | Sep 1 2018 |
| 1m 2f 70y | 2m 7.15 | 3 | 8-8 | Good To Firm | STOTSFOLD | Sep 23 2006 |
| 1m 3f 75y | 2m 22.17 | 3 | 8-12 | Good To Firm | PERFECT TRUTH | May 6 2009 |
| 1m 5f 84y | 2m 45.43 | 5 | 8-11 | Firm | RAKAPOSHI KING | May 7 1987 |
| 1m 7f 196y | 3m 20.33 | 4 | 9-0 | Good To Firm | GRAND FROMAGE | Jul 13 2002 |
| 2m 2f 140y | 3m 58.89 | 7 | 9-2 | Good To Firm | GREENWICH MEANTIME | May 9 2007 |

# DONCASTER

| DISTANCE | TIME | AGE | WEIGHT | GOING | HORSE | DATE |
|----------|------|-----|--------|-------|-------|------|
| 5f 3y | 58.04 | 2 | 9-1 | Good | GUTAIFAN | Sep 11 2015 |
| 5f 3y | 57.31 | 7 | 9-10 | Good | TABARET | Aug 14 2010 |
| 5f 143y | 1m 5.38 | 4 | 9-7 | Good | MUTHMIR | Sep 13 2014 |
| 6f 2y | 1m 10.33 | 2 | 9-4 | Good To Firm | COMEDY | Jun 29 2018 |
| 6f 2y | 1m 9.36 | 3 | 9-9 | Good To Firm | STARMAN | Aug 15 2020 |
| 6f 111y | 1m 17.19 | 2 | 8-9 | Good | MR LUPTON | Sep 10 2015 |
| 6f 111y | 1m 16.62 | 4 | 8-10 | Good | BADR AL BADOOR | Sep 12 2014 |
| 7f 6y | 1m 22.78 | 2 | 9-5 | Good | BASATEEN | Jul 24 2014 |
| 7f 6y | 1m 21.81 | 6 | 8-7 | Good To Firm | SIGNOR PELTRO | May 30 2009 |
| 7f 213y (Rnd) | 1m 38.37 | 2 | 8-6 | Good To Soft | ANTONIOLA | Oct 23 2009 |
| 7f 213y (Rnd) | 1m 34.46 | 4 | 8-12 | Good To Firm | STAYING ON | Apr 18 2009 |
| 1m (Str) | 1m 36.45 | 2 | 9-0 | Good To Firm | LILAC ROAD | Aug 15 2020 |
| 1m (Str) | 1m 34.95 | 6 | 8-9 | Firm | QUICK WIT | Jul 18 2013 |
| 1m 2f 43y | 2m 4.81 | 4 | 8-13 | Good To Firm | RED GALA | Sep 12 2007 |
| 1m 3f 197y | 2m 27.48 | 3 | 8-4 | Good To Firm | SWIFT ALHAARTH | Sep 10 2011 |
| 1m 6f 115y | 3m 0.27 | 3 | 9-1 | Good To Firm | LOGICIAN | Sep 14 2019 |
| 2m 109y | 3m 34.52 | 7 | 9-0 | Good To Firm | INCHNADAMPH | Nov 10 2007 |
| 2m 1f 197y | 3m 48.41 | 4 | 9-4 | Good To Firm | SEPTIMUS | Sep 14 2007 |

# EPSOM

| DISTANCE | TIME | AGE | WEIGHT | GOING | HORSE | DATE |
|----------|------|-----|--------|-------|-------|------|
| 5f | 55.02 | 2 | 8-9 | Good To Firm | PRINCE ASLIA | Jun 9 1995 |
| 5f | 54.00 | 6 | 8-13 | Good To Firm | ORNATE | Jun 1 2019 |
| 6f 3y | 1m 7.85 | 2 | 8-11 | Good To Firm | SHOWBROOK | Jun 5 1991 |
| 6f 3y | 1m 6.20 | 3 | 8-11 | Good To Firm | WATCHABLE | Jun 1 2019 |
| 7f 3y | 1m 21.30 | 2 | 8-9 | Good To Firm | RED PEONY | Jul 29 2004 |
| 7f 3y | 1m 19.88 | 5 | 9-5 | Good | SAFE VOYAGE | Jul 4 2020 |
| 1m 113y | 1m 42.80 | 2 | 8-5 | Good To Firm | NIGHTSTALKER | Aug 30 1988 |
| 1m 113y | 1m 40.46 | 4 | 9-6 | Good To Firm | ZAAKI | Jun 1 2019 |
| 1m 2f 17y | 2m 3.50 | 5 | 7-11 | Firm | CROSSBOW | Jun 7 1967 |
| 1m 4f 6y | 2m 31.33 | 3 | 9-0 | Good To Firm | WORKFORCE | Jun 5 2010 |

# FFOS LAS

| DISTANCE | TIME | AGE | WEIGHT | GOING | HORSE | DATE |
|----------|------|-----|--------|-------|-------|------|
| 5f | 57.06 | 2 | 9-3 | Good To Firm | MR MAJEIKA | May 5 2011 |
| 5f | 56.35 | 5 | 8-8 | Good | HAAJES | Sep 12 2009 |
| 6f | 1m 9.00 | 2 | 9-5 | Good To Firm | WONDER OF QATAR | Sep 14 2014 |
| 6f | 1m 7.46 | 6 | 10-2 | Good To Firm | HANDYTALK | Jul 29 2019 |
| 1m | 1m 39.36 | 2 | 9-2 | Good To Firm | HALA HALA | Sep 2 2013 |
| 1m | 1m 37.12 | 5 | 9-0 | Good To Firm | ZEBRANO | May 5 2011 |
| 1m 2f | 2m 4.85 | 8 | 8-12 | Good To Firm | PELHAM CRESCENT | May 5 2011 |
| 1m 3f 209y | 2m 31.18 | 3 | 9-9 | Good | TRUESHAN | Aug 29 2019 |
| 1m 6f | 2m 58.61 | 4 | 9-7 | Good To Firm | LADY ECLAIR | Jul 12 2010 |
| 2m | 3m 25.42 | 4 | 9-3 | Good To Firm | LONG JOHN SILVER | Jul 24 2018 |

# GOODWOOD

| DISTANCE | TIME | AGE | WEIGHT | GOING | HORSE | DATE |
|---|---|---|---|---|---|---|
| 5f | 57.14 | 2 | 9-1 | Good | YALTA | Jul 27 2016 |
| 5f | 55.62 | 6 | 9-7 | Good To Firm | BATTAASH | Jul 31 2020 |
| 6f | 1m 9.81 | 2 | 8-11 | Good To Firm | BACHIR | Jul 28 1999 |
| 6f | 1m 9.10 | 6 | 9-0 | Good To Firm | TAMAGIN | Sep 12 2009 |
| 7f | 1m 24.99 | 2 | 8-11 | Good To Firm | EKRAAR | Jul 29 1999 |
| 7f | 1m 23.75 | 4 | 9-3 | Good | BILLESDON BROOK | Aug 2 2019 |
| 1m | 1m 37.21 | 2 | 9-0 | Good | CALDRA | Sep 9 2006 |
| 1m | 1m 35.28 | 3 | 8-13 | Good To Firm | BEAT LE BON | Aug 2 2019 |
| 1m 1f 11y | 1m 56.27 | 2 | 9-3 | Good | DORDOGNE | Sep 22 2010 |
| 1m 1f 11y | 1m 52.81 | 3 | 9-6 | Good | VENA | Jul 27 1995 |
| 1m 1f 197y | 2m 2.81 | 3 | 9-3 | Good To Firm | ROAD TO LOVE | Aug 3 2006 |
| 1m 3f 44y | 2m 22.77 | 3 | 9-3 | Good | KHALIDI | May 26 2017 |
| 1m 3f 218y | 2m 31.39 | 3 | 9-1 | Good To Firm | CROSS COUNTER | Aug 4 2018 |
| 1m 6f | 2m 57.61 | 4 | 9-6 | Good To Firm | MEEZNAH | Jul 28 2011 |
| 2m | 3m 21.55 | 5 | 9-10 | Good To Firm | YEATS | Aug 3 2006 |
| 2m 4f | 4m 11.75 | 3 | 7-10 | Firm | LUCKY MOON | Aug 2 1990 |

# HAMILTON

| DISTANCE | TIME | AGE | WEIGHT | GOING | HORSE | DATE |
|---|---|---|---|---|---|---|
| 5f 7y | 57.95 | 2 | 8-8 | Good To Firm | ROSE BLOSSOM | May 29 2009 |
| 5f 7y | 57.20 | 5 | 9-4 | Good To Firm | DAPPER MAN | Jun 27 2019 |
| 6f 6y | 1m 10.00 | 2 | 8-12 | Good To Firm | BREAK THE CODE | Aug 24 1999 |
| 6f 6y | 1m 9.03 | 6 | 9-5 | Good To Firm | GEORGE BOWEN | Jul 20 2018 |
| 1m 68y | 1m 45.46 | 2 | 9-5 | Good To Firm | LAAFIRAAQ | Sep 20 2015 |
| 1m 68y | 1m 42.70 | 6 | 7-7 | Firm | CRANLEY | Sep 25 1972 |
| 1m 1f 35y | 1m 53.60 | 5 | 9-6 | Good To Firm | REGENT'S SECRET | Aug 10 2005 |
| 1m 3f 15y | 2m 18.66 | 3 | 9-3 | Good | POSTPONED | Jul 18 2014 |
| 1m 4f 15y | 2m 30.52 | 5 | 9-10 | Good To Firm | RECORD BREAKER | Jun 10 2009 |
| 1m 5f 16y | 2m 45.10 | 6 | 9-6 | Firm | MENTALASANYTHIN | Jun 14 1995 |

# HAYDOCK

| DISTANCE | TIME | AGE | WEIGHT | GOING | HORSE | DATE |
|---|---|---|---|---|---|---|
| 5f | 58.56 | 2 | 8-2 | Good To Firm | BARRACUDA BOY | Aug 11 2012 |
| 5f | 56.39 | 5 | 9-4 | Firm | BATED BREATH | May 26 2012 |
| 5f (Inner) | 58.51 | 2 | 9-1 | Good | FOUR DRAGONS | Oct 14 2016 |
| 5f (Inner) | 57.38 | 7 | 9-12 | Good To Firm | FOXY FOREVER | Jul 21 2017 |
| 6f | 1m 10.98 | 4 | 9-9 | Good To Firm | WOLFHOUND | Sep 4 1993 |
| 6f | 1m 8.56 | 3 | 9-0 | Firm | HARRY ANGEL | May 27 2017 |
| 6f (Inner) | 1m 10.58 | 2 | 9-2 | Good To Firm | PRESTBURY PARK | Jul 21 2017 |
| 6f (Inner) | 1m 9.04 | 3 | 8-11 | Good To Firm | PRINCES DES SABLES | Aug 8 2019 |
| 6f 212y (Inner) | 1m 27.20 | 2 | 9-6 | Good | BROGAN | Oct 14 2016 |
| 6f 212y (Inner) | 1m 25.28 | 3 | 9-8 | Good To Firm | MYSTIC FLIGHT | Jun 7 2018 |
| 7f 37y | 1m 27.57 | 2 | 9-2 | Good To Firm | CONTRAST | Aug 5 2016 |
| 7f 37y | 1m 25.50 | 3 | 8-11 | Good | FORGE | Sep 1 2016 |
| 7f 212y (Inner) | 1m 39.41 | 2 | 9-0 | Good | STAR ARCHER | Sep 1 2016 |
| 7f 212y (Inner) | 1m 37.80 | 3 | 9-4 | Good | SIDEWINDER | May 26 2017 |
| 1m 37y | 1m 41.99 | 2 | 9-0 | Good | TOP OF THE GLAS | Aug 8 2013 |
| 1m 37y | 1m 38.50 | 4 | 8-11 | Good To Firm | EXPRESS HIMSELF | Jun 10 2015 |
| 1m 2f 42y (Inner) | 2m 7.25 | 3 | 8-9 | Good To Firm | LARAAIB | May 26 2017 |
| 1m 2f 100y | 2m 7.53 | 4 | 9-5 | Good | TEODORO | Aug 11 2018 |
| 1m 3f 140y (Inner) | 2m 25.52 | 5 | 9-9 | Good To Firm | DECEMBER SECOND | Aug 8 2019 |
| 1m 3f 175y | 2m 25.53 | 4 | 8-12 | Good To Firm | NUMBER THEORY | May 24 2012 |
| 1m 6f | 2m 55.20 | 5 | 9-9 | Good To Firm | HUFF AND PUFF | Sep 7 2012 |
| 2m 45y | 3m 26.98 | 5 | 8-13 | Good To Firm | DE RIGUEUR | Jun 8 2013 |

# KEMPTON (AW)

| DISTANCE | TIME | AGE | WEIGHT | GOING | HORSE | DATE |
|---|---|---|---|---|---|---|
| 5f | 58.96 | 2 | 8-6 | Standard | GLAMOROUS SPIRIT | Nov 28 2008 |
| 5f | 58.07 | 5 | 8-12 | Standard | A MOMENTOFMADNESS | Apr 7 2018 |
| 6f | 1m 11.02 | 2 | 9-1 | Standard To Slow | INVINCIBLE ARMY | Sep 9 2017 |
| 6f | 1m 9.79 | 4 | 8-11 | Standard | TRINITYELITEDOTCOM | Mar 29 2014 |
| 7f | 1m 23.79 | 2 | 8-0 | Standard | ELSAAKB | Nov 8 2017 |
| 7f | 1m 23.10 | 6 | 9-9 | Standard | SIRIUS PROSPECT | Nov 20 2014 |
| 1m | 1m 37.26 | 2 | 9-0 | Standard | CECCHINI | Nov 8 2017 |
| 1m | 1m 35.73 | 3 | 8-9 | Standard | WESTERN ARISTOCRAT | Sep 15 2011 |
| 1m 1f 219y | 2m 2.93 | 3 | 8-11 | Standard To Slow | PLY | Sep 25 2017 |
| 1m 2f 219y | 2m 15.65 | 4 | 8-8 | Standard To Slow | FORBIDDEN PLANET | Mar 30 2019 |
| 1m 3f 219y | 2m 28.99 | 6 | 9-3 | Standard | SPRING OF FAME | Nov 7 2012 |
| 1m 7f 218y | 3m 21.50 | 4 | 8-12 | Standard | COLOUR VISION | May 2 2012 |

# LEICESTER

| DISTANCE | TIME | AGE | WEIGHT | GOING | HORSE | DATE |
|---|---|---|---|---|---|---|
| 5f 2y | 58.40 | 2 | 9-0 | Firm | CUTTING BLADE | Jun 9 1986 |
| 5f 2y | 57.85 | 5 | 9-5 | Good To Firm | THE JOBBER | Sep 18 2006 |
| 5f 218y | 1m 9.99 | 2 | 9-0 | Good | EL MANATI | Aug 1 2012 |
| 5f 218y | 1m 9.12 | 6 | 8-12 | Good To Firm | PETER ISLAND | Apr 25 2009 |
| 7f | 1m 22.83 | 2 | 9-5 | Good To Firm | CLOUDBRIDGE | Aug 2 2020 |
| 7f | 1m 22.24 | 5 | 9-2 | Good To Firm | HOME OF THE BRAVE | Apr 29 2017 |
| 1m 53y | 1m 44.05 | 2 | 8-11 | Good To Firm | CONGRESSIONAL | Sep 6 2005 |
| 1m 53y | 1m 41.89 | 5 | 9-7 | Good To Firm | VAINGLORY | Jun 18 2009 |
| 1m 1f 216y | 2m 5.30 | 2 | 9-1 | Good To Firm | WINDSOR CASTLE | Oct 14 1996 |
| 1m 1f 216y | 2m 2.40 | 4 | 9-6 | Good To Firm | LADY ANGHARAD | Jun 18 2000 |
| 1m 1f 216y | 2m 2.40 | 3 | 8-11 | Firm | EFFIGY | Nov 4 1985 |
| 1m 3f 179y | 2m 27.10 | 5 | 8-12 | Good To Firm | MURGHEM | Jun 18 2000 |

# LINGFIELD (TURF)

| DISTANCE | TIME | AGE | WEIGHT | GOING | HORSE | DATE |
|---|---|---|---|---|---|---|
| 4f 217y | 56.76 | 2 | 9-2 | Good | GLORY FIGHTER | May 11 2018 |
| 4f 217y | 56.09 | 3 | 9-4 | Good To Firm | WHITECREST | Sep 16 2011 |
| 6f | 1m 9.41 | 2 | 9-0 | Good To Firm | COMPANY MINX | Jul 10 2019 |
| 6f | 1m 8.48 | 4 | 9-6 | Good To Firm | REWAAYAT | Jul 17 2019 |
| 7f | 1m 20.55 | 2 | 8-11 | Good To Firm | HIKING | Aug 17 2013 |
| 7f | 1m 20.44 | 3 | 9-5 | Good | ADDITIONAL | Jun 26 2020 |
| 7f 135y | 1m 29.32 | 2 | 9-3 | Good To Firm | DUNDONNELL | Aug 4 2012 |
| 7f 135y | 1m 26.73 | 3 | 8-6 | Good To Firm | HIAAM | Jul 11 1987 |
| 1m 1f | 1m 50.45 | 4 | 9-3 | Good To Firm | ENZEMBLE | May 30 2019 |
| 1m 2f | 2m 4.83 | 5 | 9-8 | Good To Firm | HAIRDRYER | Jul 21 2018 |
| 1m 3f 133y | 2m 23.95 | 3 | 8-5 | Firm | NIGHT-SHIRT | Jul 14 1990 |
| 1m 6f | 2m 58.88 | 3 | 8-13 | Good To Firm | TIMOSHENKO | Jul 21 2018 |
| 2m 68y | 3m 23.71 | 3 | 9-5 | Good To Firm | LAURIES CRUSADOR | Aug 13 1988 |

# LINGFIELD (AW)

| DISTANCE | TIME | AGE | WEIGHT | GOING | HORSE | DATE |
|---|---|---|---|---|---|---|
| 5f 6y | 56.94 | 2 | 10-3 | Standard | BEDFORD FLYER | Nov 25 2020 |
| 5f 6y | 56.67 | 5 | 8-12 | Standard | LADIES ARE FOREVER | Mar 16 2013 |
| 6f 1y | 1m 9.76 | 2 | 9-4 | Standard | RED IMPRESSION | Nov 24 2018 |
| 6f 1y | 1m 8.32 | 6 | 9-0 | Standard | KACHY | Feb 2 2019 |
| 7f 1y | 1m 22.67 | 2 | 9-3 | Standard | COMPLICIT | Nov 23 2013 |
| 7f 1y | 1m 21.90 | 4 | 9-9 | Standard | CARDSHARP | Mar 13 2019 |
| 1m 1y | 1m 35.70 | 2 | 8-13 | Standard | QAADDIM | Oct 3 2019 |
| 1m 1y | 1m 33.90 | 6 | 9-5 | Standard | LUCKY TEAM | Mar 30 2018 |
| 1m 2f | 2m 0.54 | 4 | 9-0 | Standard | BANGKOK | Feb 1 2020 |
| 1m 4f | 2m 26.99 | 6 | 9-11 | Standard | PINZOLO | Jan 21 2017 |
| 1m 5f | 2m 39.70 | 3 | 8-10 | Standard | HIDDEN GOLD | Oct 30 2014 |
| 1m 7f 169y | 3m 15.18 | 4 | 9-1 | Standard | WINNING STORY | Apr 14 2017 |

# MUSSELBURGH

| DISTANCE | TIME | AGE | WEIGHT | GOING | HORSE | DATE |
|----------|------|-----|--------|-------|-------|------|
| 5f 1y | 57.66 | 2 | 9-2 | Good To Firm | IT DONT COME EASY | Jun 3 2017 |
| 5f 1y | 56.77 | 9 | 9-10 | Good To Firm | CASPIAN PRINCE | Jun 9 2018 |
| 7f 33y | 1m 27.46 | 2 | 8-8 | Good | DURHAM REFLECTION | Sep 14 2009 |
| 7f 33y | 1m 25.00 | 9 | 8-8 | Good To Firm | KALK BAY | Jun 4 2016 |
| 1m 2y | 1m 40.34 | 2 | 8-12 | Good To Firm | SUCCESSION | Sep 26 2004 |
| 1m 2y | 1m 36.83 | 3 | 9-5 | Good To Firm | GINGER JACK | Jul 13 2010 |
| 1m 208y | 1m 50.42 | 8 | 8-11 | Good To Firm | DHAULAR DHAR | Sep 3 2010 |
| 1m 4f 104y | 2m 36.80 | 3 | 8-3 | Good To Firm | HARRIS TWEED | Jun 5 2010 |
| 1m 5f | 2m 46.41 | 3 | 9-5 | Good To Firm | ALCAEUS | Sep 29 2013 |
| 1m 5f 216y | 2m 57.98 | 7 | 8-5 | Good To Firm | JONNY DELTA | Apr 18 2014 |
| 1m 7f 217y | 3m 25.62 | 4 | 8-3 | Good To Firm | ALDRETH | Jun 13 2015 |

# NEWBURY

| DISTANCE | TIME | AGE | WEIGHT | GOING | HORSE | DATE |
|----------|------|-----|--------|-------|-------|------|
| 5f 34y | 59.19 | 2 | 8-6 | Good To Firm | SUPERSTAR LEO | Jul 22 2000 |
| 5f 34y | 58.40 | 3 | 9-0 | Good | LAZULI | Sep 19 2020 |
| 6f | 1m 9.70 | 2 | 9-1 | Good | ALKUMAIT | Sep 19 2020 |
| 6f 8y | 1m 9.42 | 3 | 8-11 | Good To Firm | NOTA BENE | May 13 2005 |
| 6f 110y | 1m 18.06 | 2 | 9-5 | Good To Firm | TWIN SAILS | Jun 11 2015 |
| 7f (Str) | 1m 23.04 | 2 | 8-11 | Good To Firm | HAAFHD | Aug 15 2003 |
| 7f (Str) | 1m 20.80 | 3 | 9-0 | Good To Firm | MUHAARAR | Apr 18 2015 |
| 1m (Str) | 1m 37.66 | 2 | 8-12 | Good | YIBIR | Sep 18 2020 |
| 1m (Rnd) | 1m 36.98 | 3 | 9-1 | Good To Firm | HE'S OUR STAR | Jun 26 2018 |
| 1m (Str) | 1m 35.07 | 4 | 8-11 | Good To Firm | RHODODENDRON | May 19 2018 |
| 1m 1f | 1m 49.65 | 3 | 8-0 | Good To Firm | HOLTYE | May 21 1995 |
| 1m 2f | 2m 1.29 | 3 | 8-7 | Good To Firm | WALL STREET | Jul 20 1996 |
| 1m 3f 5y | 2m 16.54 | 3 | 8-9 | Good To Firm | GRANDERA | Sep 22 2001 |
| 1m 4f 5y | 2m 28.26 | 4 | 9-7 | Good To Firm | AZAMOUR | Jul 23 2005 |
| 1m 5f 61y | 2m 44.90 | 5 | 10-0 | Good To Firm | MYSTIC HILL | Jul 20 1996 |

# NEWCASTLE (AW)

| Distance | Time | Age | Weight | Going | HORSE | Date |
|----------|------|-----|--------|-------|-------|------|
| 5f | 58.05 | 2 | 8-6 | Standard | SPIN DOCTOR | Oct 25 2016 |
| 5f | 57.78 | 3 | 8-9 | Standard | ASTRAEA | Dec 15 2018 |
| 6f | 1m 9.95 | 2 | 9-2 | Standard | MAZYOUN | Oct 25 2016 |
| 6f | 1m 9.86 | 3 | 9-2 | Standard | UNABATED | Mar 22 2017 |
| 7f 14y | 1m 25.50 | 2 | 9-5 | Standard | COMMANDER COLE | Oct 18 2016 |
| 7f 14y | 1m 24.10 | 3 | 9-0 | Standard | NORTHERNPOWERHOUSE | Dec 18 2019 |
| 1m 5y | 1m 36.26 | 2 | 9-1 | Standard | KAMEKO | Nov 1 2019 |
| 1m 5y | 1m 36.10 | 4 | 9-8 | Standard | ALFRED RICHARDSON | Nov 9 2018 |
| 1m 2f 42y | 2m 4.88 | 3 | 8-6 | Standard | PALISADE | Oct 16 2016 |
| 1m 4f 98y | 2m 36.76 | 3 | 8-7 | Standard | AJMAN PRINCE | Oct 14 2016 |
| 2m 56y | 3m 29.87 | 4 | 9-8 | Standard | DANNYDAY | Jun 25 2016 |

# NEWMARKET (ROWLEY MILE)

| DISTANCE | TIME | AGE | WEIGHT | GOING | HORSE | DATE |
|---|---|---|---|---|---|---|
| 5f | 58.04 | 2 | 9-5 | Good To Firm | EYE OF HEAVEN | Jun 4 2020 |
| 5f | 56.81 | 6 | 9-2 | Good To Firm | LOCHSONG | Apr 30 1994 |
| 6f | 1m 9.31 | 2 | 9-0 | Good | EARTHLIGHT | Sep 28 2019 |
| 6f | 1m 9.55 | 3 | 9-1 | Good To Firm | CAPTAIN COLBY | May 16 2015 |
| 7f | 1m 22.37 | 2 | 9-1 | Good | U S NAVY FLAG | Oct 14 2017 |
| 7f | 1m 21.98 | 3 | 9-0 | Good To Firm | TUPI | May 16 2015 |
| 1m | 1m 35.13 | 2 | 9-0 | Good | ROYAL DORNOCH | Sep 28 2019 |
| 1m | 1m 34.07 | 4 | 9-0 | Good To Firm | EAGLE MOUNTAIN | Oct 3 2008 |
| 1m 1f | 1m 46.94 | 4 | 8-8 | Good | MAJESTIC DAWN | Sep 26 2020 |
| 1m 2f | 2m 2.76 | 2 | 9-2 | Good | KEW GARDENS | Oct 14 2017 |
| 1m 2f | 2m 0.13 | 3 | 8-12 | Good | NEW APPROACH | Oct 18 2008 |
| 1m 4f | 2m 25.89 | 5 | 9-0 | Good To Firm | GHAIYYATH | Jun 5 2020 |
| 1m 6f | 2m 51.59 | 3 | 8-7 | Good | ART EYES | Sep 29 2005 |
| 2m | 3m 18.64 | 5 | 9-6 | Good To Firm | TIMES UP | Sep 22 2011 |
| 2m 2f | 3m 45.59 | 4 | 8-8 | Good | WITHHOLD | Oct 14 2017 |

# NEWMARKET (JULY COURSE)

Following remeasurement of the track by the BHA and RCA in 2017, some starts were moved to retain traditional race distances.

| DISTANCE | TIME | AGE | WEIGHT | GOING | HORSE | DATE |
|---|---|---|---|---|---|---|
| 5f | 57.31 | 4 | 9-2 | Good To Firm | MOUNTAIN PEAK | Jul 12 2019 |
| 6f | 1m 9.09 | 3 | 9-3 | Good To Firm | RAFFLE PRIZE | Jul 12 2019 |
| 6f | 1m 9.31 | 3 | 9-0 | Good To Firm | TEN SOVEREIGNS | Jul 13 2019 |
| 7f | 1m 23.33 | 2 | 9-1 | Good To Firm | BIRCHWOOD | Jul 11 2015 |
| 7f | 1m 21.78 | 3 | 8-13 | Good To Firm | LIGHT AND DARK | Jul 12 2019 |
| 1m | 1m 37.47 | 2 | 8-13 | Good | WHIPPERS LOVE | Aug 28 2009 |
| 1m | 1m 35.89 | 4 | 9-7 | Good To Firm | VERACIOUS | Jul 12 2019 |
| 1m 2f | 2m 0.61 | 3 | 9-7 | Good To Firm | WALKINTHESAND | Jul 12 2019 |
| 1m 4f | 2m 27.26 | 3 | 8-9 | Good To Firm | KATARA | Aug 1 2020 |
| 1m 5f | 2m 39.96 | 3 | 9-1 | Good To Firm | SPANISH MISSION | Jul 11 2019 |
| 1m 6f | 2m 53.40 | 7 | 9-3 | Good To Firm | WITHHOLD | Aug 1 2020 |

# NOTTINGHAM

| DISTANCE | TIME | AGE | WEIGHT | GOING | HORSE | DATE |
|---|---|---|---|---|---|---|
| 5f 8y (Inner) | 59.05 | 2 | 9-0 | Good To Firm | MAIN DESIRE | May 2 2017 |
| 5f 8y (Inner) | 57.01 | 3 | 8-12 | Good To Firm | GARRUS | Apr 10 2019 |
| 5f 8y | 57.90 | 2 | 8-9 | Firm | HOH MAGIC | May 13 1994 |
| 5f 8y | 57.58 | 5 | 7-11 | Good To Firm | PENNY DREADFUL | Jun 19 2017 |
| 6f 18y | 1m 11.40 | 2 | 8-11 | Firm | JAMEELAPI | Aug 8 1983 |
| 6f 18y | 1m 10.00 | 4 | 9-2 | Firm | AJANAC | Aug 8 1988 |
| 1m 72y (Inner) | 1m 45.14 | 2 | 9-6 | Good | RASHFORD'S DOUBLE | Nov 2 2016 |
| 1m 72y (Inner) | 1m 43.22 | 4 | 9-7 | Good To Firm | REAVER | Apr 22 2017 |
| 1m 75y | 1m 43.50 | 2 | 9-7 | Good | FABILIS | Sep 27 2020 |
| 1m 75y | 1m 42.02 | 3 | 9-0 | Good To Firm | GANAYEM | May 11 2018 |
| 1m 2f 50y | 2m 7.13 | 5 | 9-8 | Good To Firm | VASILY | Jul 19 2013 |
| 1m 2f 52y (Inner) | 2m 16.66 | 2 | 9-3 | Soft | LETHAL GLAZE | Oct 1 2008 |
| 1m 2f 52y (Inner) | 2m 9.40 | 3 | 9-5 | Good | CENTURIUS | Apr 20 2013 |
| 1m 6f | 2m 57.80 | 3 | 8-10 | Firm | BUSTER JO | Oct 1 1985 |
| 1m 7f 219y (Inner) | 3m 34.39 | 3 | 8-0 | Good | BENOZZO GOZZOLI | Oct 28 2009 |
| 2m | 3m 25.25 | 3 | 9-5 | Good | BULWARK | Sep 27 2005 |

# PONTEFRACT

| DISTANCE | TIME | AGE | WEIGHT | GOING | HORSE | DATE |
|---|---|---|---|---|---|---|
| 5f 3y | 1m 1.10 | 2 | 9-0 | Firm | GOLDEN BOUNTY | Sep 20 2001 |
| 5f 3y | 1m 0.49 | 5 | 9-5 | Good To Firm | JUDICIAL | Apr 24 2017 |
| 6f | 1m 14.00 | 2 | 9-3 | Firm | FAWZI | Sep 6 1983 |
| 6f | 1m 12.60 | 3 | 7-13 | Firm | MERRY ONE | Aug 29 1970 |
| 1m 6y | 1m 42.80 | 2 | 9-13 | Firm | STAR SPRAY | Sep 6 1983 |
| 1m 6y | 1m 42.80 | 2 | 9-0 | Firm | ALASIL | Sep 26 2002 |
| 1m 6y | 1m 40.60 | 4 | 9-10 | Good To Firm | ISLAND LIGHT | Apr 13 2002 |
| 1m 2f 5y | 2m 10.10 | 2 | 9-0 | Firm | SHANTY STAR | Oct 7 2002 |
| 1m 2f 5y | 2m 8.20 | 4 | 7-8 | Hard | HAPPY HECTOR | Jul 9 1979 |
| 1m 2f 5y | 2m 8.20 | 3 | 7-13 | Hard | TOM NODDY | Aug 21 1972 |
| 2m 4f 5y | 2m 33.72 | 3 | 8-7 | Firm | AJAAN | Aug 8 2007 |
| 2m 1f 27y | 3m 40.67 | 4 | 8-7 | Good To Firm | PARADISE FLIGHT | Jun 6 2005 |
| 2m 2f 2y | 3m 51.10 | 3 | 8-8 | Good To Firm | KUDZ | Sep 9 1986 |
| 2m 5f 139y | 4m 47.80 | 4 | 8-4 | Firm | PHYSICAL | May 14 1984 |

# REDCAR

| DISTANCE | TIME | AGE | WEIGHT | GOING | HORSE | DATE |
|---|---|---|---|---|---|---|
| 5f | 56.88 | 2 | 9-7 | Good To Soft | WOLFOFWALLSTREET | Oct 27 2014 |
| 5f | 56.01 | 10 | 9-3 | Firm | HENRY HALL | Sep 20 2006 |
| 5f 217y | 1m 8.84 | 3 | 8-3 | Good To Firm | OBE GOLD | Oct 2 2004 |
| 5f 217y | 1m 8.60 | 3 | 9-2 | Good To Firm | SIZZLING SAGA | Jun 21 1991 |
| 7f | 1m 21.28 | 2 | 9-3 | Firm | KAROO BLUE | Sep 20 2006 |
| 7f | 1m 20.67 | 3 | 9-0 | Good To Firm | DREAMLOPER | Jul 27 2020 |
| 7f 219y | 1m 34.37 | 2 | 9-0 | Firm | MASTERSHIP | Sep 20 2006 |
| 7f 219y | 1m 32.42 | 4 | 10-0 | Firm | NANTON | Sep 20 2006 |
| 1m 1f | 1m 52.44 | 2 | 9-0 | Firm | SPEAR | Sep 13 2004 |
| 1m 1f | 1m 48.50 | 5 | 8-12 | Firm | MELLOTTIE | Jul 25 1990 |
| 1m 2f 1y | 2m 10.10 | 2 | 8-11 | Good | ADDING | Nov 10 1989 |
| 1m 2f 1y | 1m 1.40 | 5 | 9-2 | Good | ERADICATE | May 28 1990 |
| 1m 5f 218y | 2m 59.54 | 6 | 8-5 | Good To Firm | LEODIS | Jun 23 2018 |
| 1m 7f 217y | 3m 24.90 | 3 | 9-3 | Good To Firm | SUBSONIC | Oct 8 1991 |

# RIPON

| DISTANCE | TIME | AGE | WEIGHT | GOING | HORSE | DATE |
|---|---|---|---|---|---|---|
| 5f | 57.80 | 2 | 8-8 | Firm | SUPER ROCKY | Aug 5 1991 |
| 5f | 57.80 | 2 | 9-5 | Good | ORNATE | Jul 18 2015 |
| 5f | 57.28 | 5 | 8-12 | Good | DESERT ACE | Sep 24 2016 |
| 6f | 1m 10.40 | 2 | 9-2 | Good | CUMBRIAN VENTURE | Aug 17 2002 |
| 6f | 1m 9.09 | 5 | 8-13 | Good To Firm | SANDRA'S SECRET | May 20 2018 |
| 1m | 1m 38.77 | 2 | 9-4 | Good | GREED IS GOOD | Sep 28 2013 |
| 1m | 1m 36.62 | 4 | 8-11 | Good To Firm | GRANSTON | Aug 29 2005 |
| 1m 1f | 1m 49.97 | 6 | 9-3 | Good To Firm | GINGER JACK | Jun 20 2013 |
| 1m 2f | 2m 2.60 | 3 | 9-4 | Firm | SWIFT SWORD | Jul 20 1991 |
| 1m 4f 10y | 2m 31.04 | 3 | 9-7 | Good To Firm | JUST HUBERT | Jul 8 2019 |
| 2m | 3m 23.90 | 4 | 9-10 | Firm | PANAMA JACK | Jun 23 1988 |

# SALISBURY

| DISTANCE | TIME | AGE | WEIGHT | GOING | HORSE | DATE |
|---|---|---|---|---|---|---|
| 5f | 59.30 | 2 | 9-0 | Good To Firm | AJIGOLO | May 12 2005 |
| 5f | 59.18 | 7 | 8-10 | Good To Firm | EDGED OUT | Jun 18 2017 |
| 6f | 1m 12.10 | 2 | 8-0 | Good To Firm | PARISIAN LADY | Jun 10 1997 |
| 6f | 1m 11.09 | 3 | 9-0 | Firm | L'AMI LOUIS | May 1 2011 |
| 6f 213y | 1m 25.97 | 2 | 9-0 | Firm | MORE ROYAL | Jun 29 1995 |
| 6f 213y | 1m 24.91 | 3 | 9-4 | Good To Firm | CHILWORTH LAD | May 1 2011 |
| 1m | 1m 40.48 | 2 | 8-13 | Firm | CHOIR MASTER | Sep 17 2002 |
| 1m | 1m 38.29 | 3 | 8-7 | Good | LAYMAN | Aug 11 2005 |
| 1m 1f 201y | 2m 4.70 | 3 | 8-8 | Firm | ALPINISTA | Aug 13 2020 |
| 1m 4f 5y | 2m 31.69 | 3 | 9-5 | Good To Firm | ARRIVE | Jun 27 2001 |
| 1m 6f 44y | 3m 0.48 | 7 | 9-2 | Good To Firm | HIGHLAND CASTLE | May 23 2015 |

# SANDOWN PARK

| DISTANCE | TIME | AGE | WEIGHT | GOING | HORSE | DATE |
|----------|------|-----|--------|-------|-------|------|
| 5f 10y | 59.48 | 2 | 9-3 | Firm | TIMES TIME | Jul 22 1982 |
| 5f 10y | 58.57 | 3 | 8-12 | Good To Firm | BATTAASH | Jul 8 2017 |
| 7f | 1m 26.56 | 2 | 9-0 | Good To Firm | RAVEN'S PASS | Sep 1 2007 |
| 7f | 1m 26.36 | 3 | 9-0 | Firm | MAWSUFF | Jun 14 1986 |
| 1m | 1m 43.90 | 2 | 9-5 | Good | VIA DE VEGA | Sep 18 2019 |
| 1m | 1m 39.21 | 4 | 8-12 | Good To Firm | EL HAYEM | Jul 8 2017 |
| 1m 1f | 1m 52.40 | 7 | 9-3 | Good To Firm | BOURGAINVILLE | Aug 11 2005 |
| 1m 1f 209y | 2m 2.14 | 3 | 8-11 | Good | KALAGLOW | May 31 1982 |
| 1m 6f | 3m 1.08 | 3 | 8-9 | Good | JUST HUBERT | Jul 25 2019 |
| 2m 50y | 3m 29.38 | 6 | 9-0 | Good To Firm | CAUCUS | Jul 6 2013 |

# SOUTHWELL (AW)

| DISTANCE | TIME | AGE | WEIGHT | GOING | HORSE | DATE |
|----------|------|-----|--------|-------|-------|------|
| 4f 214y | 57.61 | 2 | 9-2 | Standard | THE BELL CONDUCTOR | Nov 7 2019 |
| 4f 214y | 56.80 | 5 | 9-7 | Standard | GHOSTWING | Jan 3 2012 |
| 6f 16y | 1m 14.00 | 2 | 8-5 | Standard | PANALO | Nov 8 1989 |
| 6f 16y | 1m 13.49 | 4 | 9-7 | Standard | ROCK SOUND | Nov 5 2019 |
| 7f 14y | 1m 26.82 | 2 | 8-12 | Standard | WINGED ICARUS | Aug 28 2012 |
| 7f 14y | 1m 26.29 | 7 | 8-9 | Standard To Slow | WELD AL EMARAT | Feb 27 2019 |
| 1m 13y | 1m 38.00 | 2 | 8-10 | Standard | ANDREW'S FIRST | Dec 30 1989 |
| 1m 13y | 1m 38.00 | 2 | 8-9 | Standard | ALPHA RASCAL | Nov 13 1990 |
| 1m 13y | 1m 37.25 | 3 | 8-6 | Standard | VALIRA | Nov 3 1990 |
| 1m 3f 23y | 2m 21.50 | 4 | 9-7 | Standard | TEMPERING | Dec 5 1990 |
| 1m 4f 14y | 2m 33.90 | 4 | 9-12 | Standard | FAST CHICK | Nov 8 1989 |
| 1m 6f 21y | 3m 1.60 | 3 | 7-8 | Standard | EREVNON | Dec 29 1990 |
| 2m 102y | 3m 37.60 | 9 | 8-12 | Standard | OLD HUBERT | Dec 5 1990 |

# THIRSK

| DISTANCE | TIME | AGE | WEIGHT | GOING | HORSE | DATE |
|----------|------|-----|--------|-------|-------|------|
| 5f | 57.20 | 2 | 9-7 | Good To Firm | PROUD BOAST | Aug 5 2000 |
| 5f | 56.92 | 5 | 9-6 | Firm | CHARLIE PARKES | Apr 11 2003 |
| 6f | 1m 9.20 | 2 | 9-6 | Good To Firm | WESTCOURT MAGIC | Aug 25 1995 |
| 6f | 1m 8.80 | 6 | 9-4 | Firm | JOHAYRO | Jul 23 1999 |
| 7f | 1m 23.70 | 2 | 8-9 | Firm | COURTING | Jul 23 1999 |
| 7f | 1m 22.80 | 4 | 8-5 | Firm | SILVER HAZE | May 21 1988 |
| 7f 218y | 1m 37.97 | 2 | 9-0 | Firm | SUNDAY SYMPHONY | Sep 4 2004 |
| 7f 218y | 1m 34.80 | 4 | 8-13 | Firm | YEARSLEY | May 5 1990 |
| 1m 4f 8y | 2m 29.90 | 5 | 9-12 | Firm | GALLERY GOD | Jun 4 2001 |
| 2m 13y | 3m 22.30 | 3 | 9-0 | Firm | TOMASCHEK | Jul 17 1981 |

# WETHERBY

| DISTANCE | TIME | AGE | WEIGHT | GOING | HORSE | DATE |
|----------|------|-----|--------|-------|-------|------|
| 5f 110y | 1m 6.14 | 2 | 9-5 | Good To Firm | COASTAL MIST | May 30 2019 |
| 5f 110y | 1m 4.25 | 3 | 9-1 | Good To Firm | DAPPER MAN | Jun 19 2017 |
| 7f | 1m 26.23 | 2 | 8-9 | Good | RAYAA | Jul 21 2015 |
| 7f | 1m 24.72 | 4 | 9-2 | Good | SLEMY | Jul 21 2015 |
| 1m | 1m 38.47 | 3 | 9-1 | Good To Firm | SAVAANAH | Jun 22 2018 |
| 1m 2f | 2m 5.13 | 5 | 9-5 | Good | FIRST SARGEANT | Jul 21 2015 |
| 1m 6f | 3m 0.41 | 3 | 9-7 | Good To Firm | DAVY'S DILEMMA | Jun 19 2017 |

# WINDSOR

| DISTANCE | TIME | AGE | WEIGHT | GOING | HORSE | DATE |
|----------|------|-----|--------|-------|-------|------|
| 5f 21y | 58.69 | 2 | 9-0 | Good To Firm | CHARLES THE GREAT | May 23 2011 |
| 5f 21y | 58.08 | 5 | 8-13 | Good To Firm | TAURUS TWINS | Apr 4 2011 |
| 6f 12y | 1m 10.50 | 2 | 9-5 | Good To Firm | CUBISM | Aug 17 1998 |
| 6f 12y | 1m 9.54 | 5 | 9-5 | Good | ALJADY | Jul 13 2020 |
| 1m 31y | 1m 41.73 | 2 | 9-5 | Good To Firm | SALOUEN | Aug 7 2016 |
| 1m 31y | 1m 39.47 | 4 | 9-6 | Good To Firm | MATTERHORN | Jun 29 2019 |
| 1m 1f 194y | 2m 1.62 | 6 | 9-1 | Good | AL KAZEEM | Aug 23 2014 |
| 1m 2f | 2m 4.24 | 7 | 9-8 | Good To Firm | DESERT ENCOUNTER | Aug 24 2019 |
| 1m 3f 99y | 2m 21.50 | 3 | 9-2 | Firm | DOUBLE FLORIN | May 19 1980 |

# WOLVERHAMPTON (AW)

| DISTANCE | TIME | AGE | WEIGHT | GOING | HORSE | DATE |
|----------|------|-----|--------|-------|-------|------|
| 5f 21y | 59.75 | 2 | 9-6 | Standard | QUATRIEME AMI | Nov 13 2015 |
| 5f 21y | 59.33 | 5 | 9-6 | Standard | LOMU | Dec 3 2019 |
| 6f 20y | 1m 12.16 | 2 | 9-2 | Standard | MUBAKKER | Nov 1 2018 |
| 6f 20y | 1m 11.44 | 5 | 9-6 | Standard | KACHY | Dec 26 2018 |
| 7f 36y | 1m 26.77 | 2 | 8-11 | Standard | RICHARD R H B | Nov 23 2019 |
| 7f 36y | 1m 25.35 | 4 | 9-3 | Standard | MISTER UNIVERSE | Mar 12 2016 |
| 1m 142y | 1m 47.38 | 2 | 9-5 | Standard | JACK HOBBS | Dec 27 2014 |
| 1m 142y | 1m 45.43 | 4 | 9-4 | Standard | KEYSTROKE | Nov 26 2016 |
| 1m 1f 104y | 1m 57.99 | 2 | 9-2 | Standard | EMISSARY | Oct 12 2019 |
| 1m 1f 104y | 1m 55.91 | 6 | 8-8 | Standard | STORM AHEAD | Nov 18 2019 |
| 1m 4f 51y | 2m 33.44 | 4 | 9-5 | Standard | PATHS OF GLORY | Oct 19 2019 |
| 1m 5f 219y | 2m 57.83 | 4 | 9-8 | Standard | GIVEN CHOICE | Jan 7 2019 |
| 2m 120y | 3m 31.18 | 4 | 9-0 | Standard | AIRCRAFT CARRIER | Jan 14 2019 |

# YARMOUTH

| DISTANCE | TIME | AGE | WEIGHT | GOING | HORSE | DATE |
|----------|------|-----|--------|-------|-------|------|
| 5f 42y | 59.00 | 2 | 9-2 | Good To Firm | THE LIR JET | Jun 3 2020 |
| 5f 42y | 58.57 | 11 | 9-10 | Good To Firm | CASPIAN PRINCE | Sep 16 2020 |
| 6f 3y | 1m 10.40 | 2 | 9-0 | Firm | LANCHESTER | Sep 15 1988 |
| 6f 3y | 1m 9.14 | 3 | 9-0 | Good To Firm | CARTOGRAPHER | May 24 2017 |
| 7f 3y | 1m 22.20 | 2 | 9-0 | Good To Firm | WARRSHAN | Sep 14 1988 |
| 7f 3y | 1m 21.32 | 3 | 9-7 | Firm | MISTER SNOWDON | Jun 3 2020 |
| 1m 3y | 1m 35.40 | 2 | 9-2 | Good To Firm | FOREST FALCON | Sep 17 2020 |
| 1m 3y | 1m 33.00 | 4 | 9-5 | Firm | MAYDANNY | Jun 3 2020 |
| 1m 1f 21y | 1m 52.00 | 3 | 9-5 | Good To Firm | TOUCH GOLD | Jul 5 2012 |
| 1m 2f 23y | 2m 2.83 | 3 | 8-8 | Firm | REUNITE | Jul 18 2006 |
| 1m 3f 104y | 2m 23.10 | 3 | 8-9 | Firm | RAHIL | Jul 1 1993 |
| 1m 6f 17y | 2m 57.80 | 3 | 8-2 | Good To Firm | BARAKAT | Jul 24 1990 |
| 2m | 3m 26.70 | 4 | 8-2 | Good To Firm | ALHESN | Jul 26 1999 |

# YORK

| DISTANCE | TIME | AGE | WEIGHT | GOING | HORSE | DATE |
|----------|------|-----|--------|-------|-------|------|
| 5f | 57.11 | 2 | 9-0 | Good | BIG TIME BABY | Aug 20 2016 |
| 5f | 55.90 | 5 | 9-11 | Good To Firm | BATTAASH | Aug 23 2019 |
| 5f 89y | 1m 3.20 | 2 | 9-3 | Good To Firm | THE ART OF RACING | Sep 9 2012 |
| 5f 89y | 1m 1.72 | 4 | 9-7 | Good To Firm | BOGART | Aug 21 2013 |
| 6f | 1m 8.90 | 2 | 9-0 | Good | TIGGY WIGGY | Aug 21 2014 |
| 6f | 1m 8.23 | 3 | 8-11 | Good To Firm | MINCE | Sep 9 2012 |
| 7f | 1m 22.32 | 2 | 9-1 | Good To Firm | DUTCH CONNECTION | Aug 20 2014 |
| 7f | 1m 21.00 | 3 | 9-1 | Good To Firm | SHINE SO BRIGHT | Aug 24 2019 |
| 7f 192y | 1m 36.92 | 2 | 9-5 | Good | AWESOMETANK | Oct 14 2017 |
| 7f 192y | 1m 34.95 | 3 | 9-3 | Good To Firm | POGO | Aug 23 2019 |
| 1m 177y | 1m 46.76 | 5 | 9-8 | Good To Firm | ECHO OF LIGHT | Sep 5 2007 |
| 1m 2f 56y | 2m 5.29 | 3 | 8-11 | Good To Firm | SEA THE STARS | Aug 18 2009 |
| 1m 3f 188y | 2m 25.40 | 4 | 8-8 | Good To Firm | TAMREER | Aug 23 2019 |
| 1m 5f 188y | 2m 52.97 | 6 | 9-5 | Good To Firm | MUSTAJEER | Aug 24 2019 |
| 2m 56y | 3m 27.06 | 5 | 9-6 | Good To Firm | STRADIVARIUS | Aug 23 2019 |

# TOP FLAT JOCKEYS IN BRITAIN 2020

**(JANUARY 1st - DECEMBER 31st)**

| WINS-RUNS | % | JOCKEY | 2ND | 3RD | TOTAL PRIZE | WIN PRIZE |
|---|---|---|---|---|---|---|
| 170-1038 | 16% | BEN CURTIS | 147 | 133 | 865,758 | 1,331,676 |
| 151-979 | 15% | HOLLIE DOYLE | 120 | 102 | 1,246,038 | 1,855,216 |
| 147-1015 | 14% | TOM MARQUAND | 136 | 109 | 1,608,927 | 2,454,476 |
| 144-825 | 17% | OISIN MURPHY | 128 | 121 | 1,383,340 | 2,244,392 |
| 139-659 | 21% | WILLIAM BUICK | 107 | 74 | 1,728,817 | 2,591,658 |
| 120-1139 | 11% | LUKE MORRIS | 123 | 127 | 546,320 | 928,034 |
| 103-627 | 16% | JACK MITCHELL | 86 | 82 | 533,170 | 815,365 |
| 101-565 | 18% | JAMES DOYLE | 82 | 77 | 912,734 | 1,468,275 |
| 100-615 | 16% | SILVESTRE DE SOUSA | 80 | 54 | 791,739 | 1,215,746 |
| 98-996 | 10% | DAVID PROBERT | 112 | 122 | 426,752 | 864,565 |
| 93-704 | 13% | RICHARD KINGSCOTE | 94 | 82 | 571,769 | 943,937 |
| 90-602 | 15% | DANIEL TUDHOPE | 78 | 94 | 498,027 | 939,007 |
| 88-520 | 17% | JIM CROWLEY | 57 | 70 | 1,769,637 | 2,263,071 |
| 85-744 | 11% | JOE FANNING | 102 | 78 | 516,124 | 941,689 |
| 84-546 | 15% | ANDREA ATZENI | 69 | 72 | 772,378 | 1,625,636 |
| 82-681 | 12% | PAUL MULRENNAN | 75 | 91 | 462,313 | 745,095 |
| 80-480 | 17% | RYAN MOORE | 76 | 64 | 1,428,090 | 2,610,011 |
| 80-559 | 14% | KEVIN STOTT | 77 | 72 | 558,766 | 836,893 |
| 79-669 | 12% | ROB HORNBY | 75 | 75 | 452,671 | 758,851 |
| 78-668 | 12% | JASON HART | 72 | 71 | 433,720 | 686,519 |
| 77-593 | 13% | CALLUM SHEPHERD | 59 | 59 | 387,702 | 571,141 |
| 72-565 | 13% | ADAM KIRBY | 64 | 74 | 743,360 | 1,102,760 |
| 72-697 | 10% | P J MCDONALD | 87 | 88 | 471,870 | 806,076 |
| 67-439 | 15% | ROBERT HAVLIN | 59 | 50 | 364,869 | 631,669 |
| 63-496 | 13% | ROSSA RYAN | 58 | 65 | 334,619 | 595,496 |
| 63-569 | 11% | CIEREN FALLON | 55 | 64 | 484,657 | 730,989 |
| 60-512 | 12% | KIERAN SHOEMARK | 69 | 46 | 271,534 | 502,157 |
| 59-507 | 12% | FRANNY NORTON | 58 | 54 | 333,033 | 558,534 |
| 57-496 | 11% | DAVID ALLAN | 61 | 48 | 281,965 | 489,333 |
| 53-395 | 13% | DAVID EGAN | 46 | 50 | 492,184 | 742,751 |
| 51-443 | 12% | HARRY BENTLEY | 53 | 45 | 529,469 | 779,990 |
| 51-582 | 9% | GRAHAM LEE | 42 | 56 | 231,231 | 394,114 |
| 49-457 | 11% | SEAN LEVEY | 52 | 37 | 411,146 | 637,320 |
| 47-421 | 11% | HECTOR CROUCH | 40 | 47 | 200,954 | 339,371 |
| 47-484 | 10% | SHANE KELLY | 41 | 48 | 176,215 | 310,736 |
| 45-497 | 9% | DANIEL MUSCUTT | 44 | 45 | 165,088 | 293,100 |
| 45-602 | 7% | CAM HARDIE | 52 | 53 | 188,920 | 343,895 |
| 41-498 | 8% | PHIL DENNIS | 45 | 38 | 143,551 | 264,146 |
| 40-160 | 25% | FRANKIE DETTORI | 21 | 18 | 1,748,113 | 2,401,914 |
| 39-342 | 11% | DAVID NOLAN | 37 | 26 | 145,972 | 242,489 |
| 39-395 | 10% | CALLUM RODRIGUEZ | 43 | 38 | 245,111 | 381,126 |
| 39-472 | 8% | CHARLES BISHOP | 31 | 36 | 182,274 | 304,596 |
| 39-642 | 6% | KIERAN O'NEILL | 48 | 67 | 163,982 | 346,591 |
| 37-426 | 9% | BARRY MCHUGH | 42 | 56 | 157,330 | 302,367 |
| 36-311 | 12% | JASON WATSON | 36 | 28 | 355,663 | 599,726 |
| 36-388 | 9% | ALISTAIR RAWLINSON | 40 | 38 | 155,649 | 269,511 |
| 35-351 | 10% | MARTIN DWYER | 41 | 38 | 277,199 | 480,118 |
| 35-421 | 8% | GEORGE ROOKE | 56 | 42 | 134,908 | 277,430 |
| 34-553 | 6% | JAMES SULLIVAN | 23 | 43 | 124,398 | 235,130 |
| 33-296 | 11% | RAY DAWSON | 30 | 35 | 256,648 | 384,930 |
| 33-477 | 7% | ANDREW MULLEN | 38 | 47 | 115,724 | 229,573 |
| 32-309 | 10% | CLIFFORD LEE | 31 | 42 | 179,511 | 286,188 |
| 32-395 | 8% | HARRISON SHAW | 44 | 36 | 118,009 | 259,590 |
| 30-629 | 5% | TOM EAVES | 55 | 46 | 105,412 | 388,157 |
| 29-250 | 12% | DANE O'NEILL | 35 | 37 | 171,772 | 305,375 |
| 29-296 | 10% | STEVIE DONOHOE | 27 | 32 | 154,011 | 264,598 |
| 29-384 | 8% | TONY HAMILTON | 32 | 35 | 115,051 | 233,241 |

# TOP FLAT TRAINERS IN BRITAIN 2020

| TRAINER | LEADING HORSE | W-R | 2ND | 3RD | 4TH | WIN PRIZE | TOTAL PRIZE |
|---|---|---|---|---|---|---|---|
| JOHN GOSDEN | Enable | 150-647 | 105 | 89 | 71 | 2,346,525 | 3,129,278 |
| A P O'BRIEN | Love | 13-102 | 15 | 14 | 12 | 1,350,447 | 2,463,089 |
| MARK JOHNSTON | Nayef Road | 169-1274 | 177 | 149 | 144 | 1,203,664 | 2,134,036 |
| ANDREW BALDING | Kameko | 106-729 | 105 | 101 | 83 | 1,231,996 | 2,107,155 |
| WILLIAM HAGGAS | Addeybb | 118-624 | 89 | 93 | 68 | 1,362,665 | 2,032,427 |
| ROGER VARIAN | Fujaira Prince | 115-573 | 104 | 85 | 55 | 1,098,188 | 1,885,357 |
| RICHARD HANNON | Happy Romance | 114-1120 | 142 | 123 | 140 | 901,704 | 1,593,807 |
| CHARLIE APPLEBY | Ghaiyyath | 84-296 | 59 | 47 | 22 | 1,063,185 | 1,520,680 |
| RALPH BECKETT | New Mandate | 103-523 | 72 | 63 | 46 | 842,540 | 1,238,108 |
| RICHARD FAHEY | Umm Kulthum | 120-1263 | 124 | 150 | 152 | 627,632 | 1,191,530 |
| SIR MICHAEL STOUTE | Dream Of Dreams | 74-366 | 54 | 58 | 43 | 672,084 | 1,078,004 |
| DAVID O'MEARA | Summerghand | 100-810 | 93 | 88 | 86 | 628,283 | 1,071,598 |
| CHARLES HILLS | Battaash | 53-331 | 39 | 35 | 42 | 640,243 | 908,158 |
| KEVIN RYAN | Hello Youmzain | 52-445 | 55 | 49 | 47 | 472,430 | 885,277 |
| TIM EASTERBY | Art Power | 94-997 | 93 | 83 | 127 | 486,621 | 881,450 |
| CLIVE COX | Golden Horde | 47-394 | 42 | 57 | 45 | 612,211 | 878,961 |
| ARCHIE WATSON | Glen Shiel | 71-440 | 57 | 58 | 53 | 583,250 | 870,948 |
| MICHAEL APPLEBY | Ayr Harbour | 99-983 | 113 | 110 | 111 | 390,138 | 736,836 |
| K R BURKE | Dandalla | 60-543 | 72 | 66 | 61 | 432,796 | 695,937 |
| SIMON & ED CRISFORD | Century Dream | 60-271 | 44 | 37 | 35 | 460,695 | 668,995 |
| ROGER CHARLTON | Extra Elusive | 50-278 | 34 | 28 | 25 | 373,816 | 604,061 |
| ALAN KING | Trueshan | 30-252 | 32 | 28 | 29 | 442,978 | 571,717 |
| JOSEPH PATRICK O'BRIEN | Pretty Gorgeous | 7-22 | 2 | 2 | 1 | 502,127 | 560,310 |
| ED WALKER | Assimilation | 53-403 | 42 | 50 | 61 | 358,867 | 548,091 |
| DAVID SIMCOCK | Desert Encounter | 46-330 | 46 | 51 | 48 | 249,556 | 502,848 |
| TONY CARROLL | Kondratiev Wave | 80-703 | 77 | 70 | 79 | 301,626 | 495,103 |
| MICHAEL DODS | Dakota Gold | 43-412 | 52 | 47 | 44 | 285,789 | 493,133 |
| TOM DASCOMBE | Devious Company | 41-387 | 45 | 46 | 47 | 247,380 | 466,655 |
| JOHN QUINN | Safe Voyage | 44-373 | 47 | 48 | 33 | 279,255 | 459,722 |
| CHARLIE FELLOWES | Onassis | 38-285 | 31 | 33 | 32 | 284,493 | 443,403 |
| KEITH DALGLEISH | Aberama Gold | 43-468 | 40 | 53 | 57 | 248,913 | 420,617 |
| IAN WILLIAMS | Kingbrook | 38-381 | 35 | 39 | 32 | 262,684 | 414,438 |
| SAEED BIN SUROOR | Laser Show | 39-259 | 50 | 31 | 33 | 205,874 | 407,825 |
| STUART WILLIAMS | Tone The Barone | 34-432 | 51 | 36 | 42 | 197,963 | 406,715 |
| HUGO PALMER | Caravan Of Hope | 53-280 | 42 | 32 | 31 | 282,923 | 399,910 |
| F-H GRAFFARD | The Revenant | 1-4 | 0 | 0 | 0 | 368,615 | 368,615 |
| MICK CHANNON | Certain Lad | 41-418 | 50 | 56 | 43 | 213,638 | 366,375 |
| MRS JOHN HARRINGTON | Alpine Star | 2-16 | 4 | 1 | 0 | 210,250 | 365,238 |
| DAVID LOUGHNANE | Tranchee | 41-375 | 43 | 36 | 36 | 209,706 | 362,500 |
| JAMES FANSHAWE | Harry's Bar | 35-262 | 33 | 31 | 26 | 200,179 | 349,387 |
| MARCUS TREGONING | Mohaather | 14-98 | 13 | 15 | 15 | 280,171 | 343,308 |
| MARCO BOTTI | Pas Malotru | 38-322 | 30 | 45 | 42 | 226,190 | 340,361 |
| EVE JOHNSON HOUGHTON | Hyanna | 37-316 | 38 | 38 | 45 | 186,968 | 337,417 |
| OWEN BURROWS | Minzaal | 20-121 | 17 | 18 | 9 | 233,566 | 337,397 |
| ROGER FELL | The Flying Ginger | 39-477 | 54 | 57 | 36 | 161,127 | 331,384 |
| DAVID MENUISIER | Wonderful Tonight | 18-115 | 7 | 14 | 10 | 285,547 | 325,588 |
| WILLIAM MUIR | Pyledriver | 17-183 | 27 | 26 | 20 | 202,763 | 320,972 |
| DAVID EVANS | Snow Ocean | 50-538 | 43 | 50 | 61 | 181,065 | 319,806 |
| SIR MARK PRESCOTT BT | Alpinista | 37-217 | 27 | 21 | 11 | 179,373 | 316,535 |
| ROGER TEAL | Oxted | 18-168 | 10 | 14 | 20 | 262,066 | 310,138 |
| RICHARD HUGHES | Top Breeze | 41-336 | 43 | 41 | 40 | 169,444 | 307,374 |
| JAMES TATE | Top Rank | 28-228 | 32 | 38 | 30 | 193,915 | 305,966 |
| JIM GOLDIE | Euchen Glen | 26-305 | 29 | 29 | 30 | 195,015 | 292,582 |
| HUGHIE MORRISON | Urban Artist | 25-246 | 29 | 31 | 25 | 135,360 | 290,873 |
| ROBERT COWELL | Aljady | 30-246 | 37 | 23 | 27 | 173,553 | 277,427 |
| PAUL MIDGLEY | Tarboosh | 36-306 | 24 | 33 | 29 | 165,761 | 269,068 |
| WILLIAM KNIGHT | Sir Busker | 23-189 | 21 | 24 | 21 | 145,608 | 263,986 |
| PAUL & OLIVER COLE | Majestic Dawn | 16-144 | 13 | 20 | 16 | 156,209 | 260,708 |

# TOP FLAT OWNERS
# IN BRITAIN 2020

| OWNER | LEADING HORSE | W-R | 2ND | 3RD | 4TH | WIN PRIZE | TOTAL PRIZE |
|---|---|---|---|---|---|---|---|
| HAMDAN AL MAKTOUM | Battaash | 116-571 | 74 | 87 | 63 | 1,891,582 | 2,330,768 |
| GODOLPHIN | Ghaiyyath | 139-647 | 123 | 92 | 65 | 1,406,568 | 2,174,064 |
| MICHAEL TABOR & DERRICK SMITH & MRS JOHN MAGNIER | Love | 9-38 | 3 | 3 | 8 | 737,633 | 1,002,532 |
| SHEIKH AHMED AL MAKTOUM | Addeybb | 44-153 | 34 | 20 | 12 | 734,610 | 981,366 |
| K ABDULLAH | Enable | 51-210 | 30 | 24 | 20 | 641,709 | 959,389 |
| SHEIKH MOHAMMED OBAID AL MAKTOUM | Fujaira Prince | 42-221 | 33 | 29 | 23 | 472,183 | 939,920 |
| KING POWER RACING CO LTD | Happy Power | 54-397 | 49 | 44 | 45 | 544,571 | 921,745 |
| SHEIKH HAMDAN BIN MOHAMMED AL MAKTOUM | Palace Pier | 47-310 | 44 | 32 | 38 | 461,594 | 782,452 |
| DERRICK SMITH & MRS JOHN MAGNIER & MICHAEL TABOR | St Mark's Basilica | 2-18 | 2 | 5 | 0 | 287,519 | 624,837 |
| CHEVELEY PARK STUD | Cabaletta | 49-308 | 49 | 42 | 33 | 314,330 | 615,470 |
| MRS JOHN MAGNIER & MICHAEL TABOR & DERRICK SMITH | Serpentine | 2-27 | 5 | 3 | 1 | 286,978 | 536,674 |
| SAEED SUHAIL | Dream Of Dreams | 20-94 | 19 | 13 | 14 | 338,595 | 459,128 |
| QATAR RACING LIMITED | Kameko | 20-120 | 27 | 9 | 16 | 305,280 | 452,957 |
| AL ASAYL FRANCE | The Revenant | 1-1 | 0 | 0 | 0 | 368,615 | 368,615 |
| B E NIELSEN | Stradivarius | 5-20 | 0 | 2 | 5 | 312,872 | 348,386 |
| HAMBLETON RACING XXXVI & PARTNER | Glen Shiel | 4-9 | 2 | 1 | 0 | 250,916 | 308,375 |
| J C SMITH | Alcohol Free | 12-117 | 18 | 18 | 13 | 209,619 | 302,129 |
| THE QUEEN | Tactical | 22-162 | 28 | 21 | 17 | 159,162 | 291,334 |
| ALMOHAMEDIYA RACING | Golden Horde | 6-49 | 6 | 12 | 8 | 172,970 | 257,846 |
| A E OPPENHEIMER | Dame Malliot | 7-56 | 7 | 11 | 5 | 115,865 | 250,018 |
| CHRISTOPHER WRIGHT | Wonderful Tonight | 6-48 | 5 | 7 | 7 | 217,633 | 246,724 |
| AMO RACING LIMITED | Prince Alex | 18-78 | 10 | 13 | 10 | 156,726 | 240,589 |
| CLIPPER LOGISTICS | Eagles By Day | 21-195 | 18 | 27 | 25 | 125,292 | 232,232 |
| SAEED MANANA | Top Rank | 20-160 | 22 | 29 | 22 | 131,726 | 227,519 |
| JOHN C OXLEY | Pretty Gorgeous | 1-1 | 0 | 0 | 0 | 226,840 | 226,840 |
| GEORGE STRAWBRIDGE | Indigo Girl | 9-51 | 8 | 10 | 9 | 84,733 | 224,542 |
| HH SHEIKH ZAYED BIN MOHAMMED RACING | Lord North | 4-13 | 3 | 1 | 0 | 188,001 | 224,483 |
| MRS FITRI HAY | Highland Chief | 11-116 | 14 | 22 | 19 | 76,905 | 216,506 |
| BARBURY LIONS 5 | Trueshan | 5-16 | 1 | 0 | 4 | 210,141 | 216,266 |
| FLAXMAN STABLES, MRS MAGNIER, M TABOR, D SMITH | Circus Maximus | 1-3 | 1 | 0 | 0 | 148,000 | 207,125 |
| MISS K RAUSING | Alpinista | 15-120 | 15 | 15 | 14 | 75,441 | 203,386 |
| THE MCMURRAY FAMILY | Happy Romance | 3-4 | 0 | 0 | 1 | 191,353 | 203,145 |
| MOHAMED OBAIDA | Nayef Road | 7-31 | 6 | 1 | 5 | 60,512 | 198,905 |
| GALILEO CHROME PARTNERSHIP | Galileo Chrome | 1-1 | 0 | 0 | 0 | 198,485 | 198,485 |
| DR MARWAN KOUKASH | Brian The Snail | 18-164 | 16 | 22 | 20 | 127,977 | 194,676 |
| ABDULLA AL MANSOORI | Good Effort | 11-73 | 10 | 8 | 6 | 110,463 | 190,834 |
| SHEIKH JUMA DALMOOK AL MAKTOUM | Shimmering Dawn | 18-133 | 15 | 17 | 17 | 111,404 | 182,920 |
| H H SHEIKH NASSER AL KHALIFA & PARTNER | Line Of Departure | 7-33 | 5 | 4 | 4 | 149,940 | 180,872 |
| HAMAD RASHED BIN GHEDAYER | Summerghand | 12-46 | 9 | 4 | 5 | 124,671 | 179,754 |
| ANTONY BRITTAIN | Tathmeen | 27-243 | 35 | 27 | 37 | 94,253 | 172,827 |
| AL SHAQAB RACING | Katara | 15-105 | 13 | 15 | 10 | 102,682 | 169,978 |
| NIARCHOS FAMILY | Alpine Star | 2-11 | 4 | 1 | 0 | 151,493 | 168,580 |
| IMAD ALSAGAR | Extra Elusive | 12-49 | 7 | 9 | 4 | 110,315 | 163,278 |
| S PIPER,T HIRSCHFELD & D FISH | Oxted | 2-2 | 0 | 0 | 0 | 162,757 | 162,757 |
| JEAN-CLAUDE SEROUL | Skalleti | 0-1 | 1 | 0 | 0 | 0 | 161,250 |
| J GODDARD | Supremacy | 3-4 | 0 | 0 | 0 | 157,257 | 157,257 |
| LAEL STABLE | One Master | 7-24 | 6 | 1 | 1 | 57,562 | 155,847 |
| HARAS D'ETREHAM AND CAMBRIDGE STUD | Hello Youmzain | 1-3 | 0 | 0 | 0 | 148,000 | 154,725 |
| AHMAD AL SHAIKH | Khalifa Sat | 4-28 | 2 | 4 | 5 | 31,334 | 151,139 |
| W M JOHNSTONE | Euchen Glen | 8-25 | 3 | 4 | 3 | 123,176 | 148,414 |
| GEOFF & SANDRA TURNBULL | Makawee | 12-134 | 16 | 17 | 8 | 62,646 | 148,281 |
| PAUL & CLARE ROONEY | Isabella Giles | 16-93 | 8 | 10 | 9 | 120,752 | 147,161 |
| BERKSHIRE PARTS & PANELS LTD | Berkshire Rocco | 2-20 | 6 | 2 | 2 | 27,374 | 143,906 |
| WELDSPEC GLASGOW LIMITED | Soldier's Minute | 9-121 | 10 | 12 | 19 | 77,885 | 138,080 |
| K SOHI | Tranchee | 13-117 | 10 | 12 | 16 | 70,526 | 136,585 |
| T W MORLEY | Papa Stour | 16-103 | 11 | 9 | 11 | 87,799 | 129,995 |
| MALCOLM C DENMARK | Great White Shark | 1-10 | 1 | 1 | 1 | 124,500 | 129,109 |
| MICHAEL PESCOD | Chindit | 8-28 | 3 | 0 | 2 | 101,341 | 128,848 |
| MRS J S BOLGER | Mac Swiney | 1-2 | 0 | 0 | 0 | 127,280 | 127,280 |

# TOP FLAT HORSES
# IN BRITAIN 2020

| HORSE (AGE) | WIN & PLACE £ | W-R | TRAINER | OWNER | BREEDER |
|---|---|---|---|---|---|
| **ADDEYBB** (6) | 497,037 | 2-3 | William Haggas | Sheikh Ahmed Al Maktoum | Rabbah Bloodstock Limited |
| **LOVE** (3) | 425,325 | 3-3 | A P O'Brien | Michael Tabor & Derrick Smith & Mrs John Magnier | Coolmore |
| **THE REVENANT** (5) | 368,615 | 1-1 | F-H Graffard | Al Asayl France | Al Asayl Bloodstock Ltd |
| **BATTAASH** (6) | 360,662 | 3-3 | Charles Hills | Hamdan Al Maktoum | Ballyphilip Stud |
| **GHAIYYATH** (5) | 360,108 | 3-3 | Charlie Appleby | Godolphin | Springbank Way Stud |
| **SERPENTINE** (3) | 323,750 | 1-2 | A P O'Brien | Mrs John Magnier & Michael Tabor & Derrick Smith | Coolmore |
| **ENABLE** (6) | 312,347 | 2-3 | John Gosden | K Abdullah | Juddmonte Farms Ltd |
| **GLEN SHIEL** (6) | 308,375 | 4-9 | Archie Watson | Hambleton Racing Xxxvi & Partner | Darley |
| **STRADIVARIUS** (6) | 301,611 | 2-4 | John Gosden | B E Nielsen | Bjorn Nielsen |
| **NAZEEF** (4) | 299,046 | 4-6 | John Gosden | Hamdan Al Maktoum | Shadwell Estate Company Limited |
| **KAMEKO** (3) | 243,423 | 2-5 | Andrew Balding | Qatar Racing Limited | Calumet Farm |
| **ST MARK'S BASILICA** (2) | 242,151 | 1-1 | A P O'Brien | Derrick Smith & Mrs John Magnier & Michael Tabor | Robert Scarborough |
| **PALACE PIER** (3) | 227,391 | 2-3 | John Gosden | Sheikh Hamdan bin Mohammed Al Maktoum | Highclere Stud And Floors Farming |
| **PRETTY GORGEOUS** (2) | 226,840 | 1-1 | Joseph Patrick O'Brien | John C Oxley | E A R L Ecurie Haras Du Cadran Et Al |
| **DREAM OF DREAMS** (6) | 223,201 | 2-4 | Sir Michael Stoute | Saeed Suhail | Prostock Ltd |
| **HAPPY ROMANCE** (2) | 207,285 | 4-7 | Richard Hannon | The McMurray Family | Redpender Stud Ltd |
| **CIRCUS MAXIMUS** (4) | 207,125 | 1-3 | A P O'Brien | Flaxman Stables, Mrs Magnier, M Tabor, D Smith | Flaxman Stables Ireland Ltd |
| **TRUESHAN** (4) | 200,248 | 3-5 | Alan King | Barbury Lions 5 | Didier Blot |
| **WONDERFUL TONIGHT** (3) | 200,119 | 1-2 | David Menuisier | Christopher Wright | S A R L Ecurie La Cauviniere |
| **GOLDEN HORDE** (3) | 200,077 | 1-3 | Clive Cox | AlMohamediya Racing | Cn Farm Ltd |
| **LORD NORTH** (4) | 198,572 | 2-4 | John Gosden | HH Sheikh Zayed bin Mohammed Racing | Godolphin |
| **GALILEO CHROME** (3) | 198,485 | 1-1 | Joseph Patrick O'Brien | Galileo Chrome Partnership | Mohamed Ali Meddeb |
| **FUJAIRA PRINCE** (6) | 194,921 | 2-3 | Roger Varian | Sheikh Mohammed Obaid Al Maktoum | Rabbah Bloodstock Limited |
| **MOHAATHER** (4) | 189,978 | 2-3 | Marcus Tregoning | Hamdan Al Maktoum | Mrs R F Johnson Houghton |
| **OXTED** (4) | 173,282 | 2-3 | Roger Teal | S Piper,T Hirschfeld, D Fish & J Collins | Homecroft Wealth Racing |
| **SKALLETI** (5) | 161,250 | 0-1 | J Reynier | Jean-Claude Seroul | Guy Pariente Holding |
| **SUPREMACY** (2) | 157,257 | 3-4 | Clive Cox | J Goddard | Kangyu International Racing |
| **HELLO YOUMZAIN** (4) | 154,725 | 1-3 | Kevin Ryan | Haras d'Etreham and Cambridge Stud | Rabbah Bloodstock Limited |
| **ROSEMAN** (4) | 153,725 | 0-2 | Roger Varian | Sheikh Mohammed Obaid Al Maktoum | Knocktoran Stud |
| **PYLEDRIVER** (3) | 153,267 | 2-6 | William Muir | La Pyle Partnership | Knox & Wells Limited & R Devlin |
| **ALPINE STAR** (3) | 148,000 | 1-1 | Mrs John Harrington | Niarchos Family | Niarchos Family |
| **FANCY BLUE** (3) | 141,775 | 1-1 | Donnacha Aidan O'Brien | Michael Tabor & Derrick Smith & Mrs John Magnier | Coolmore |
| **NAYEF ROAD** (4) | 141,467 | 1-4 | Mark Johnston | Mohamed Obaida | B V Sangster |
| **MAGICAL** (4) | 139,825 | 0-2 | A P O'Brien | Derrick Smith & Mrs John Magnier & Michael Tabor | Orpendale, Chelston & Wynatt |
| **LINE OF DEPARTURE** (2) | 136,003 | 3-7 | Roger Varian | H H Shaikh Nasser Al Khalifa & Partner | Cn Farm Ltd |
| **ALCOHOL FREE** (2) | 135,027 | 2-3 | Andrew Balding | J C Smith | Churchtown House Stud |
| **WICHITA** (3) | 134,490 | 1-4 | A P O'Brien | Derrick Smith & Mrs John Magnier & Michael Tabor | W Maxwell Ervine |
| **BERKSHIRE ROCCO** (3) | 132,065 | 1-5 | Andrew Balding | Berkshire Parts & Panels Ltd | Seserve S A G L |
| **ENBIHAAR** (5) | 130,663 | 2-3 | John Gosden | Hamdan Al Maktoum | Haras Du Mezeray |
| **EUCHEN GLEN** (7) | 127,486 | 3-10 | Jim Goldie | W M Johnstone | W M Johnstone |
| **MAC SWINEY** (2) | 127,280 | 1-1 | J S Bolger | Mrs J S Bolger | J S Bolger |
| **KHALIFA SAT** (3) | 126,814 | 1-3 | Andrew Balding | Ahmad Al Shaikh | Declan Phelan & Irish National Stud |

# TOP NH JOCKEYS IN BRITAIN 2019/20

| WINS-RUNS | % | JOCKEY | 2ND | 3RD | TOTAL PRIZE | WIN PRIZE |
|---|---|---|---|---|---|---|
| 141-716 | 20% | BRIAN HUGHES | 102 | 101 | 870,095 | 1,309,714 |
| 122-669 | 18% | RICHARD JOHNSON | 104 | 112 | 787,522 | 1,206,688 |
| 99-589 | 17% | SAM TWISTON-DAVIES | 83 | 91 | 1,163,158 | 1,625,900 |
| 97-473 | 21% | HARRY SKELTON | 88 | 67 | 955,210 | 1,428,847 |
| 83-399 | 21% | HARRY COBDEN | 66 | 52 | 952,358 | 1,513,102 |
| 82-418 | 20% | AIDAN COLEMAN | 62 | 51 | 677,274 | 950,137 |
| 73-318 | 23% | NICO DE BOINVILLE | 54 | 30 | 787,250 | 1,180,683 |
| 70-355 | 20% | GAVIN SHEEHAN | 47 | 42 | 582,195 | 906,097 |
| 65-459 | 14% | ADAM WEDGE | 52 | 52 | 610,087 | 878,194 |
| 61-348 | 18% | JONJO O'NEILL JR | 45 | 47 | 421,964 | 638,948 |
| 54-371 | 15% | SEAN BOWEN | 39 | 40 | 459,681 | 639,908 |
| 52-413 | 13% | TOM SCUDAMORE | 42 | 44 | 304,795 | 521,063 |
| 51-336 | 15% | PADDY BRENNAN | 60 | 44 | 362,481 | 647,220 |
| 47-358 | 13% | LEIGHTON ASPELL | 51 | 55 | 273,370 | 476,823 |
| 45-311 | 14% | BRYONY FROST | 41 | 36 | 327,450 | 640,188 |
| 44-336 | 13% | TOM CANNON | 44 | 37 | 364,519 | 566,936 |
| 41-198 | 21% | BEN JONES | 28 | 28 | 394,935 | 525,680 |
| 39-231 | 17% | DANNY COOK | 26 | 32 | 278,227 | 421,678 |
| 39-249 | 16% | A P HESKIN | 41 | 29 | 334,128 | 521,659 |
| 38-320 | 12% | JONATHAN BURKE | 46 | 31 | 432,519 | 733,137 |
| 36-250 | 14% | DAVID BASS | 37 | 25 | 385,669 | 531,521 |
| 35-235 | 15% | CONNOR BRACE | 44 | 21 | 195,195 | 300,452 |
| 34-231 | 15% | DARYL JACOB | 28 | 37 | 353,613 | 672,640 |
| 34-324 | 10% | RICHIE MCLERNON | 31 | 27 | 317,423 | 508,027 |
| 34-403 | 8% | HENRY BROOKE | 61 | 54 | 250,576 | 488,055 |
| 33-321 | 10% | JAMES BOWEN | 44 | 39 | 289,363 | 505,875 |
| 33-321 | 10% | SEAN QUINLAN | 42 | 37 | 226,906 | 385,492 |
| 32-361 | 9% | TOM O'BRIEN | 46 | 49 | 298,604 | 535,090 |
| 30-229 | 13% | CONOR O'FARRELL | 31 | 37 | 171,085 | 268,714 |
| 29-143 | 20% | ROBBIE POWER | 22 | 16 | 522,969 | 763,085 |
| 28-221 | 13% | DANNY MCMENAMIN | 26 | 33 | 146,238 | 238,622 |
| 27-198 | 14% | CHARLIE DEUTSCH | 28 | 19 | 258,217 | 445,076 |
| 26-186 | 14% | BRENDAN POWELL | 16 | 17 | 203,830 | 323,762 |
| 26-264 | 10% | ALAN JOHNS | 24 | 21 | 142,628 | 239,912 |
| 25-88 | 28% | BARRY GERAGHTY | 10 | 8 | 994,441 | 1,199,524 |
| 25-206 | 12% | JEREMIAH MCGRATH | 21 | 23 | 189,715 | 299,704 |
| 25-227 | 11% | THOMAS DOWSON | 24 | 23 | 178,081 | 281,576 |
| 25-233 | 11% | KIELAN WOODS | 33 | 30 | 134,713 | 272,298 |
| 24-144 | 17% | REX DINGLE | 18 | 10 | 213,398 | 295,455 |
| 24-231 | 10% | PAGE FULLER | 20 | 27 | 90,444 | 170,903 |
| 23-138 | 17% | BRYAN CARVER | 25 | 17 | 102,467 | 210,168 |
| 23-138 | 17% | CHARLIE PRICE | 17 | 17 | 83,885 | 135,883 |
| 23-305 | 8% | DAVID NOONAN | 26 | 43 | 211,347 | 379,656 |
| 23-334 | 7% | JAMIE MOORE | 20 | 39 | 131,969 | 267,382 |
| 21-107 | 20% | RYAN MANIA | 14 | 16 | 126,202 | 183,387 |
| 21-188 | 11% | JAMIE HAMILTON | 16 | 25 | 92,210 | 155,852 |
| 21-192 | 11% | JOSHUA MOORE | 25 | 26 | 104,819 | 200,355 |
| 21-232 | 9% | ROSS CHAPMAN | 18 | 20 | 129,272 | 205,681 |
| 20-164 | 12% | JACK TUDOR | 9 | 17 | 222,506 | 273,010 |
| 20-206 | 10% | CRAIG NICHOL | 27 | 25 | 143,529 | 253,114 |
| 20-209 | 10% | TOM BELLAMY | 22 | 26 | 165,852 | 300,568 |
| 20-307 | 7% | NICK SCHOLFIELD | 26 | 30 | 104,219 | 208,478 |
| 19-134 | 14% | BRIDGET ANDREWS | 23 | 10 | 99,549 | 227,912 |
| 19-199 | 10% | SAM COLTHERD | 14 | 22 | 111,041 | 181,412 |
| 18-55 | 33% | MR DAVID MAXWELL | 11 | 7 | 87,750 | 128,526 |
| 17-69 | 25% | JOE COLLIVER | 10 | 4 | 119,326 | 141,049 |
| 17-222 | 8% | JAMES BEST | 16 | 22 | 157,817 | 240,555 |
| 16-125 | 13% | BLAIR CAMPBELL | 21 | 15 | 78,963 | 133,202 |

# TOP NH TRAINERS IN BRITAIN 2019/20

| TRAINER | LEADING HORSE | W-R | 2ND | 3RD | 4TH | WIN PRIZE | TOTAL PRIZE |
|---|---|---|---|---|---|---|---|
| NICKY HENDERSON | Epatante | 117-452 | 72 | 49 | 42 | 1,861,523 | 2,533,563 |
| PAUL NICHOLLS | Politologue | 95-442 | 78 | 59 | 42 | 1,497,610 | 2,335,983 |
| DAN SKELTON | Oldgrangewood | 117-717 | 110 | 88 | 70 | 838,950 | 1,478,611 |
| W P MULLINS | Al Boum Photo | 8-68 | 11 | 9 | 4 | 856,319 | 1,421,679 |
| NIGEL TWISTON-DAVIES | Riders Onthe Storm | 71-433 | 57 | 61 | 46 | 868,097 | 1,300,788 |
| COLIN TIZZARD | Lostintranslation | 61-408 | 52 | 56 | 42 | 797,698 | 1,216,569 |
| PHILIP HOBBS | Defi Du Seuil | 75-419 | 61 | 57 | 48 | 762,993 | 1,139,199 |
| GORDON ELLIOTT | Samcro | 28-126 | 23 | 21 | 9 | 539,041 | 835,373 |
| DAVID PIPE | Warthog | 64-341 | 45 | 48 | 34 | 493,759 | 734,089 |
| ALAN KING | Harambe | 41-335 | 50 | 41 | 43 | 359,036 | 644,470 |
| EVAN WILLIAMS | Silver Streak | 49-434 | 51 | 46 | 46 | 367,498 | 636,568 |
| TOM GEORGE | Bun Doran | 28-247 | 38 | 25 | 25 | 358,303 | 611,865 |
| OLLY MURPHY | Itchy Feet | 66-348 | 58 | 42 | 43 | 408,586 | 610,452 |
| FERGAL O'BRIEN | Champagne Well | 62-326 | 66 | 45 | 32 | 347,501 | 609,241 |
| DR RICHARD NEWLAND | Le Patriote | 60-276 | 40 | 30 | 38 | 414,512 | 592,660 |
| DONALD MCCAIN | Navajo Pass | 61-451 | 66 | 53 | 57 | 356,185 | 573,542 |
| VENETIA WILLIAMS | Cepage | 39-249 | 36 | 20 | 37 | 333,629 | 553,260 |
| JONJO O'NEILL | Young Wolf | 61-434 | 55 | 60 | 46 | 291,106 | 502,028 |
| NEIL MULHOLLAND | Fingerontheswitch | 50-404 | 53 | 59 | 33 | 312,501 | 475,276 |
| EMMA LAVELLE | De Rasher Counter | 29-181 | 20 | 23 | 20 | 393,480 | 467,331 |
| HARRY FRY | If The Cap Fits | 30-169 | 22 | 19 | 19 | 299,640 | 467,331 |
| KIM BAILEY | Imperial Aura | 32-201 | 37 | 26 | 21 | 306,082 | 453,640 |
| HARRY WHITTINGTON | Saint Calvados | 29-158 | 23 | 11 | 18 | 271,469 | 451,940 |
| ANTHONY HONEYBALL | Regal Encore | 36-126 | 25 | 11 | 8 | 303,759 | 412,749 |
| JAMIE SNOWDEN | Hogan's Height | 46-206 | 23 | 29 | 27 | 274,210 | 375,843 |
| BRIAN ELLISON | Definitly Red | 32-108 | 16 | 7 | 21 | 266,096 | 363,343 |
| TIM VAUGHAN | Eva's Oskar | 45-361 | 42 | 36 | 40 | 216,008 | 362,085 |
| HENRY DE BROMHEAD | Put The Kettle On | 4-26 | 2 | 2 | 3 | 196,292 | 359,332 |
| NICKY RICHARDS | Takingrisks | 34-183 | 24 | 25 | 25 | 229,652 | 352,621 |
| LUCINDA RUSSELL | Mighty Thunder | 32-332 | 52 | 41 | 34 | 177,855 | 343,885 |
| PHILIP KIRBY | Lady Buttons | 26-265 | 20 | 26 | 21 | 211,117 | 339,386 |
| GARY MOORE | Botox Has | 33-322 | 39 | 52 | 32 | 173,475 | 337,606 |
| MICKY HAMMOND | Cornerstone Lad | 31-303 | 39 | 34 | 37 | 197,526 | 319,768 |
| REBECCA CURTIS | Lisnagar Oscar | 20-78 | 8 | 12 | 15 | 259,358 | 318,601 |
| CHRISTIAN WILLIAMS | Potters Corner | 19-239 | 17 | 27 | 16 | 229,327 | 311,373 |
| WARREN GREATREX | Keeper Hill | 18-197 | 26 | 28 | 16 | 175,061 | 305,475 |
| SUE SMITH | Vintage Clouds | 20-183 | 23 | 24 | 28 | 165,623 | 294,046 |
| KEITH DALGLEISH | Amalfi Doug | 33-187 | 36 | 19 | 23 | 180,563 | 291,082 |
| CHARLIE LONGSDON | Western Miller | 29-260 | 22 | 36 | 25 | 168,784 | 287,152 |
| CHRIS GORDON | Go Whatever | 30-188 | 21 | 25 | 15 | 177,426 | 287,143 |
| HENRY DALY | Stoney Mountain | 18-137 | 16 | 25 | 12 | 202,505 | 285,428 |
| TOM LACEY | Kimberlite Candy | 20-152 | 24 | 14 | 17 | 166,124 | 272,488 |
| OLIVER SHERWOOD | Papagana | 27-166 | 27 | 23 | 14 | 159,981 | 272,340 |
| DAVID BRIDGWATER | The Conditional | 19-95 | 11 | 11 | 9 | 175,728 | 264,689 |
| PETER BOWEN | Dr Robin | 18-260 | 30 | 26 | 32 | 155,495 | 264,372 |
| NEIL KING | Nordano | 23-166 | 19 | 18 | 18 | 155,640 | 242,767 |
| KERRY LEE | Happy Diva | 11-84 | 11 | 14 | 11 | 144,239 | 232,361 |
| BEN PAULING | Delire D'Estruval | 17-201 | 15 | 22 | 24 | 122,076 | 226,811 |
| JENNIE CANDLISH | Zolfo | 24-219 | 26 | 36 | 28 | 114,303 | 207,919 |
| ALEX HALES | Smooth Stepper | 20-114 | 17 | 16 | 9 | 136,334 | 202,130 |
| SANDY THOMSON | Seeyouatmidnight | 22-122 | 16 | 14 | 14 | 128,802 | 198,251 |
| N W ALEXANDER | Elvis Mail | 19-143 | 15 | 19 | 24 | 127,818 | 194,402 |
| RICHARD HOBSON | Lord Du Mesnil | 13-49 | 12 | 1 | 5 | 107,440 | 185,476 |
| SEAMUS MULLINS | The Pink'n | 18-218 | 25 | 26 | 33 | 83,738 | 184,973 |
| ROBERT WALFORD | Walk In The Mill | 8-115 | 16 | 19 | 11 | 128,994 | 182,999 |
| IAN WILLIAMS | Royal Village | 9-150 | 17 | 20 | 14 | 81,450 | 175,700 |
| JEREMY SCOTT | Champagne Court | 21-151 | 16 | 16 | 15 | 108,403 | 173,778 |
| NIGEL HAWKE | Repetitio | 17-209 | 23 | 30 | 31 | 92,818 | 172,973 |

# TOP NH OWNERS
# IN BRITAIN 2019/20

| OWNER | LEADING HORSE | W-R | 2ND | 3RD | 4TH | WIN PRIZE | TOTAL PRIZE |
|---|---|---|---|---|---|---|---|
| JOHN P MCMANUS | Epatante | 79-467 | 64 | 40 | 50 | 1,562,339 | 2,138,975 |
| SIMON MUNIR & ISAAC SOUEDE | Call Me Lord | 27-140 | 22 | 23 | 19 | 455,397 | 852,924 |
| MRS J DONNELLY | Al Boum Photo | 4-11 | 2 | 1 | 2 | 443,859 | 498,046 |
| KATE & ANDREW BROOKS | Saint Calvados | 27-92 | 12 | 7 | 13 | 319,239 | 481,826 |
| MRS S RICCI | Min | 3-17 | 3 | 2 | 0 | 275,818 | 421,028 |
| TREVOR HEMMINGS | Stoney Mountain | 26-187 | 25 | 21 | 19 | 294,383 | 403,544 |
| MRS JOHNNY DE LA HEY | Cyrname | 7-50 | 13 | 5 | 6 | 216,528 | 373,725 |
| GIGGINSTOWN HOUSE STUD | Samcro | 2-28 | 4 | 4 | 2 | 125,915 | 320,730 |
| J HALES | Politologue | 3-9 | 2 | 1 | 0 | 233,462 | 254,583 |
| MR & MRS R KELVIN-HUGHES | Santini | 5-13 | 1 | 3 | 1 | 94,496 | 237,231 |
| MCNEILL FAMILY | The Worlds End | 13-50 | 13 | 7 | 4 | 168,749 | 223,684 |
| MR & MRS WILLIAM RUCKER | Esprit Du Large | 14-73 | 11 | 3 | 8 | 175,194 | 217,956 |
| CARL HINCHY AND MARK SCOTT | Riders Onthe Storm | 6-26 | 0 | 0 | 3 | 207,381 | 213,489 |
| TAYLOR & O'DWYER | Lostintranslation | 4-12 | 1 | 2 | 0 | 136,187 | 205,140 |
| PHIL & JULIE MARTIN | Definitly Red | 12-40 | 7 | 2 | 10 | 135,964 | 196,901 |
| RACING FOR FUN | Lisnagar Oscar | 1-6 | 1 | 2 | 0 | 182,877 | 193,116 |
| ANN & ALAN POTTS LIMITED | Magic Of Light | 14-73 | 9 | 14 | 5 | 139,679 | 191,200 |
| T G LESLIE | Navajo Pass | 21-94 | 14 | 10 | 12 | 120,411 | 174,536 |
| CHEVELEY PARK STUD | Envoi Allen | 3-10 | 0 | 4 | 1 | 115,464 | 172,959 |
| PAUL & CLARE ROONEY | If The Cap Fits | 19-69 | 12 | 11 | 4 | 134,406 | 171,004 |
| WALTERS PLANT HIRE & POTTER GROUP | Sir Valentine | 15-65 | 10 | 8 | 7 | 107,581 | 169,769 |
| WILL ROSEFF | Happy Diva | 4-19 | 5 | 3 | 2 | 109,785 | 167,462 |
| BROCADE RACING | Native River | 10-59 | 13 | 8 | 3 | 120,225 | 161,409 |
| P J CAVE | The Conditional | 2-5 | 1 | 1 | 1 | 99,061 | 157,218 |
| MAKIN' BACON PARTNERSHIP | De Rasher Counter | 1-4 | 0 | 0 | 1 | 142,375 | 148,846 |
| MR & MRS P K BARBER, G MASON & SIR A FERGUSON | Clan Des Obeaux | 1-3 | 0 | 1 | 0 | 144,050 | 146,585 |
| OPTIONS O SYNDICATE | Ballyandy | 7-21 | 2 | 2 | 1 | 89,527 | 143,854 |
| STRAIGHTLINE BLOODSTOCK | Taxmeifyoucan | 17-123 | 18 | 10 | 20 | 91,258 | 142,429 |
| MILLS & MASON PARTNERSHIP | Ballyoptic | 4-10 | 1 | 1 | 1 | 124,355 | 140,479 |
| R S BROOKHOUSE | Summerville Boy | 7-51 | 9 | 5 | 3 | 63,369 | 135,900 |
| PROFESSOR CAROLINE TISDALL & BRYAN DREW | Warthog | 5-11 | 1 | 2 | 0 | 111,032 | 132,444 |
| CROSSED FINGERS PARTNERSHIP | Bun Doran | 3-24 | 2 | 2 | 6 | 71,505 | 130,898 |
| MIKE AND EILEEN NEWBOULD | Captain Chaos | 7-38 | 8 | 5 | 5 | 63,247 | 130,453 |
| GORDON & SU HALL | Truckers Lodge | 2-5 | 2 | 0 | 1 | 91,495 | 127,066 |
| COLM DONLON | Silver Forever | 10-45 | 13 | 5 | 1 | 72,967 | 126,409 |
| DAVID MAXWELL RACING LIMITED | Jatiluwih | 17-53 | 10 | 6 | 3 | 84,550 | 125,266 |
| ONE FOR LUCK RACING SYNDICATE | Put The Kettle On | 2-2 | 0 | 0 | 0 | 118,696 | 118,696 |
| WALTERS PLANT HIRE LTD | William Henry | 3-33 | 5 | 10 | 2 | 66,788 | 115,981 |
| THE BELLAMY PARTNERSHIP | Cepage | 3-16 | 3 | 2 | 2 | 53,393 | 115,183 |
| KENNETH ALEXANDER | Honeysuckle | 5-22 | 2 | 6 | 2 | 86,445 | 107,389 |
| LADY BLYTH | Not So Sleepy | 2-4 | 0 | 0 | 0 | 104,193 | 104,193 |
| MICHAEL GEOGHEGAN | Dynamite Dollars | 2-7 | 2 | 2 | 0 | 9,096 | 101,746 |
| MRS JAYNE SIVILLS | Lady Buttons | 4-19 | 2 | 0 | 1 | 89,941 | 101,722 |
| ERIC JONES, GEOFF NICHOLAS, JOHN ROMANS | Slate House | 5-9 | 0 | 0 | 1 | 91,075 | 100,319 |
| P J VOGT | Frodon | 2-15 | 0 | 4 | 2 | 45,216 | 98,840 |
| N A TWISTON-DAVIES | Topofthecotswolds | 12-62 | 10 | 11 | 9 | 61,084 | 97,825 |
| MRS JANE WILLIAMS | Monsieur Lecoq | 1-26 | 5 | 3 | 3 | 31,280 | 97,547 |
| TIM SYDER | Sevarano | 7-47 | 9 | 7 | 5 | 52,497 | 96,811 |
| JOHN WHITE & ANNE UNDERHILL | Ramses De Teillee | 6-25 | 1 | 3 | 1 | 77,114 | 95,918 |
| CHRIS STEDMAN & MARK ALBON | Mcgroarty | 7-17 | 0 | 1 | 3 | 85,625 | 94,486 |
| THE ENGLANDS AND HEYWOODS | Thyme Hill | 4-12 | 1 | 0 | 1 | 82,857 | 94,143 |
| IMPERIAL RACING PARTNERSHIP 2016 | Imperial Aura | 4-17 | 7 | 1 | 1 | 66,310 | 93,635 |
| ALL STARS SPORTS RACING & J DAVIES | Potters Corner | 2-4 | 0 | 0 | 0 | 91,338 | 91,338 |
| MRS KATHY STUART | Capeland | 1-7 | 0 | 1 | 1 | 78,200 | 88,780 |
| MR & MRS DUNCAN DAVIDSON | Bigirononhiship | 6-39 | 9 | 6 | 5 | 59,844 | 88,105 |
| JOHN AND HEATHER SNOOK | West Approach | 3-27 | 4 | 4 | 4 | 44,614 | 87,254 |
| SULLIVAN BLOODSTOCK LIMITED | Duc Des Genievres | 4-24 | 2 | 3 | 3 | 17,525 | 87,019 |
| MRS DIANA L WHATELEY | Thomas Darby | 3-29 | 10 | 4 | 3 | 34,518 | 86,573 |

# TOP NH HORSES
# IN BRITAIN 2019/20

| HORSE (AGE IN 2019) | WIN & PLACE £ | W-R | TRAINER | OWNER | BREEDER |
|---|---|---|---|---|---|
| EPATANTE (5) | 367,119 | 3-3 | Nicky Henderson | John P McManus | Francois-Xavier & Anne Doulce Lefeuvre |
| AL BOUM PHOTO (7) | 351,687 | 1-1 | W P Mullins | Mrs J Donnelly Jacky Rauch | Emmanuel Clayeux & |
| POLITOLOGUE (8) | 244,970 | 1-3 | Paul Nicholls | J Hales | Mme Henri Devin |
| DEFI DU SEUIL (6) | 233,232 | 3-4 | Philip Hobbs | John P McManus | Mme Catherine Boudot |
| SANTINI (7) | 206,852 | 2-3 | Nicky Henderson | Mr & Mrs R Kelvin-Hughes | Mr & Mrs R Kelvin-Hughes |
| MIN (8) | 197,115 | 1-1 | W P Mullins | Mrs S Ricci | Madame Marie-Therese Mimouni |
| LOSTINTRANSLATION (7) | 195,937 | 2-4 | Colin Tizzard | Taylor & O'Dwyer | A R M M Kavanagh |
| LISNAGAR OSCAR (6) | 193,116 | 1-6 | Rebecca Curtis | Racing For Fun | Denis Fitzgerald |
| RIDERS ONTHE STORM (7) | 178,247 | 3-4 | Nigel Twiston-Davies | Carl Hinchy And Mark Scott | Tom Taaffe |
| THE CONDITIONAL (7) | 157,218 | 2-5 | David Bridgwater | P J Cave | Brendan Ferris |
| DE RASHER COUNTER (7) | 148,846 | 1-4 | Emma Lavelle | Makin' Bacon Partnership | Karina Casini |
| CLAN DES OBEAUX (7) | 146,175 | 1-2 | Paul Nicholls | Mr & Mrs P K Barber, G Mason & Sir A Ferguson | Mme Marie Devilder |
| HAPPY DIVA (8) | 139,210 | 1-5 | Kerry Lee | Will Roseff | M Harris & P McKeon |
| SAINT CALVADOS (6) | 130,349 | 1-4 | Harry Whittington | Kate & Andrew Brooks | Jeremy Buez |
| CHAMP (7) | 128,669 | 3-4 | Nicky Henderson | John P McManus | Philip And Mrs Jane Myerscough |
| BALLYOPTIC (9) | 127,938 | 3-5 | Nigel Twiston-Davies | Mills & Mason Partnership | Roger Ryan |
| TRUCKERS LODGE (7) | 127,066 | 2-5 | Paul Nicholls | Gordon & Su Hall | Mrs Ann Hogan |
| PUT THE KETTLE ON (5) | 118,696 | 2-2 | Henry De Bromhead | One For Luck Racing Syndicate | Butlersgrove Stud |
| BUN DORAN (8) | 106,782 | 1-4 | Tom George | Crossed Fingers Partnership | Mrs Mary F Griffin |
| CALL ME LORD (6) | 106,760 | 1-4 | Nicky Henderson | Simon Munir & Isaac Souede | Roger Marot |
| NOT SO SLEEPY (7) | 104,193 | 2-4 | Hughie Morrison | Lady Blyth | Lord Blyth |
| LORD DU MESNIL (6) | 103,612 | 3-8 | Richard Hobson | Paul Porter & Mike & Mandy Smith | Mme Henri Devin |
| JANIKA (6) | 103,098 | 1-5 | Nicky Henderson | Simon Munir & Isaac Souede | Hubert Langot & Michel Langot |
| SHARJAH (6) | 99,692 | 0-1 | W P Mullins | Mrs S Ricci | Ecurie Haras De Beauvoir |
| SIMPLY THE BETTS (6) | 97,906 | 4-5 | Harry Whittington | Kate & Andrew Brooks | Oliver Power |
| CYRNAME (7) | 94,965 | 1-3 | Paul Nicholls | Mrs.Johnny de la Hey | S Follain, E Lecoiffier Et Al |
| SHISHKIN (5) | 92,172 | 3-4 | Nicky Henderson | Mrs J Donnelly | C J & E B Bennett |
| POTTERS CORNER (9) | 91,338 | 2-4 | Christian Williams | All Stars Sports Racing & J Davies | Mrs P J O'Connor |
| BALLYANDY (8) | 91,090 | 1-6 | Nigel Twiston-Davies | Options O Syndicate | Pleasure Palace Racing |
| DYNAMITE DOLLARS (6) | 90,284 | 0-2 | Paul Nicholls | Michael Geoghegan Jacky Rauch | Emmanuel Clayeux & |
| LADY BUTTONS (9) | 90,195 | 3-5 | Philip Kirby | Mrs Jayne Sivills | Keith Sivills |
| WARTHOG (7) | 90,127 | 1-3 | David Pipe | Professor Caroline Tisdall & Bryan Drew | Thierry Seguinotte |
| THE WORLDS END (8) | 88,383 | 2-4 | Tom George | McNeill Family | J Sheehan |
| PIC D'ORHY (4) | 87,888 | 1-2 | Paul Nicholls | Mrs.Johnny de la Hey | J Contou Carrere & Y Broca |
| CAPELAND (7) | 87,550 | 1-5 | Paul Nicholls | Mrs Kathy Stuart | Alain Couetil |
| SLATE HOUSE (7) | 86,416 | 3-6 | Colin Tizzard | Eric Jones, Geoff Nicholas, John Romans | Aaron Metcalfe |
| OLDGRANGEWOOD (8) | 86,364 | 2-5 | Dan Skelton | Chris Giles & Sandra Giles | Mickley Stud |
| REGAL ENCORE (11) | 86,345 | 1-5 | Anthony Honeyball | John P McManus | John Browne |
| WALK IN THE MILL (9) | 85,301 | 1-3 | Robert Walford | Baroness Harding | Alain Jollivet & Mme Celine Lefevre |
| SAMCRO (7) | 84,405 | 1-1 | Gordon Elliott | Gigginstown House Stud | D Taylor |
| MONSIEUR LECOQ (5) | 83,509 | 1-5 | Mrs Jane Williams | Mrs Jane Williams | Jean-Charles Haimet & J-Pascal Liberge |

# LEADING SIRES OF 2020 IN GREAT BRITAIN AND IRELAND

| STALLION | BREEDING | RNRS | WNRS | WINS | TOTAL BEST HORSE |
|---|---|---|---|---|---|
| GALILEO | by Sadler's Wells | 206 | 85 | 116 | £5,349,153 Magical |
| DUBAWI | by Dubai Millennium | 199 | 81 | 107 | £2,458,976 Ghaiyyath |
| DARK ANGEL | by Acclamation | 272 | 106 | 153 | £2,112,342 Battaash |
| KODIAC | by Danehill | 336 | 116 | 156 | £1,889,877 Hello Youmzain |
| PIVOTAL | by Polar Falcon | 80 | 25 | 43 | £1,598,469 Addeybb |
| LOPE DE VEGA | by Shamardal | 202 | 77 | 113 | £1,546,117 Lucky Vega |
| INVINCIBLE SPIRIT | by Green Desert | 168 | 71 | 103 | £1,479,338 Nazeef |
| ZOFFANY | by Dansili | 219 | 72 | 96 | £1,363,721 Thunder Moon |
| KINGMAN | by Invincible Spirit | 154 | 69 | 85 | £1,352,035 Palace Pier |
| SEA THE STARS | by Cape Cross | 155 | 55 | 70 | £1,319,069 Stradivarius |
| AUSTRALIA | by Galileo | 125 | 41 | 62 | £1,255,776 Galileo Chrome |
| FRANKEL | by Galileo | 148 | 57 | 81 | £1,167,933 Frankly Darling |
| DANDY MAN | by Mozart | 218 | 70 | 97 | £1,140,292 Happy Romance |
| CAMELOT | by Montjeu | 147 | 46 | 58 | £1,067,561 Even So |
| SHOWCASING | by Oasis Dream | 164 | 60 | 91 | £969,675 Mohaather |
| EXCEED AND EXCEL | by Danehill | 161 | 56 | 81 | £930,683 Sceptical |
| MEHMAS | by Acclamation | 88 | 46 | 65 | £920,290 Supremacy |
| NATHANIEL | by Galileo | 120 | 40 | 59 | £893,230 Enable |
| NO NAY NEVER | by Scat Daddy | 128 | 45 | 55 | £868,778 Alcohol Free |
| SHAMARDAL | by Giant's Causeway | 119 | 41 | 58 | £867,766 Pinatubo |
| TEOFILO | by Galileo | 105 | 30 | 44 | £837,943 Twilight Payment |
| SIYOUNI | by Pivotal | 107 | 39 | 52 | £827,890 St Mark's Basilica |
| DREAM AHEAD | by Diktat | 73 | 26 | 41 | £814,557 Dream of Dreams |
| AUTHORIZED | by Montjeu | 34 | 11 | 18 | £749,088 Santiago |
| FOOTSTEPSINTHESAND | by Giant's Causeway | 138 | 38 | 67 | £745,145 A Step Too Far |
| BATED BREATH | by Dansili | 147 | 43 | 63 | £742,864 Could Be King |
| MAYSON | by Invincible Spirit | 124 | 43 | 77 | £711,073 Oxted |

# LEADING TWO-YEAR-OLD SIRES OF 2020 IN GREAT BRITAIN AND IRELAND

| STALLION | BREEDING | RNRS | WNRS | WINS | TOTAL | BEST HORSE |
|---|---|---|---|---|---|---|
| MEHMAS | by Acclamation | 88 | 46 | 65 | £920,290 | Supremacy |
| GALILEO | by Sadler's Wells | 58 | 28 | 35 | £802,983 | Shale |
| KODIAC | by Danehill | 107 | 43 | 56 | £802,029 | Frenetic |
| ZOFFANY | by Dansili | 71 | 26 | 30 | £611,695 | Thunder Moon |
| DANDY MAN | by Mozart | 69 | 17 | 26 | £527,907 | Happy Romance |
| SIYOUNI | by Pivotal | 36 | 12 | 16 | £426,812 | St Mark's Basilica |
| DUBAWI | by Dubai Millennium | 64 | 24 | 31 | £424,016 | Indigo Girl |
| LOPE DE VEGA | by Shamardal | 49 | 10 | 13 | £413,402 | Lucky Vega |
| LAWMAN | by Invincible Spirit | 25 | 5 | 8 | £397,924 | Pretty Gorgeous |
| NO NAY NEVER | by Scat Daddy | 48 | 18 | 20 | £318,833 | Alcohol Free |
| KODI BEAR | by Kodiac | 44 | 15 | 22 | £318,124 | Mystery Angel |
| STARSPANGLEDBANNER | by Choisir | 37 | 13 | 17 | £305,953 | Aloha Star |
| SHOWCASING | by Oasis Dream | 59 | 21 | 29 | £297,228 | Sweet Gardenia |
| ADAAY | by Kodiac | 51 | 14 | 18 | £278,239 | Shark Two One |
| BELARDO | by Lope de Vega | 36 | 10 | 16 | £276,401 | Isabella Giles |
| NEW BAY | by Dubawi | 29 | 11 | 17 | £274,375 | New Mandate |
| DARK ANGEL | by Acclamation | 69 | 26 | 29 | £272,287 | Dark Lion |
| NEW APPROACH | by Galileo | 24 | 6 | 8 | £260,866 | Mac Swiney |
| FRANKEL | by Galileo | 58 | 19 | 20 | £242,608 | Zabeel Queen |
| PRIDE OF DUBAI | by Street Cry | 30 | 8 | 14 | £211,187 | Zaffy's Pride |
| AIR FORCE BLUE | by War Front | 9 | 4 | 6 | £210,460 | Chief Little Hawk |
| KINGMAN | by Invincible Spirit | 55 | 24 | 26 | £209,055 | Love Is You |
| MUHARRAR | by Oasis Dream | 47 | 17 | 20 | £195,639 | Baradar |
| EXCEED AND EXCEL | by Danehill | 46 | 13 | 15 | £189,592 | Sacred |
| FOOTSTEPSINTHESAND | by Giant's Causeway | 40 | 9 | 9 | £171,110 | Star of Orion |
| FAST COMPANY | by Danehill Dancer | 39 | 12 | 14 | £170,474 | Devious Company |
| SIR PRANCEALOT | by Tamayuz | 22 | 6 | 9 | £170,150 | Miss Amulet |

# LEADING FIRST CROP SIRES OF 2020 IN GREAT BRITAIN AND IRELAND

| STALLION | BREEDING | RNRS | WNRS | WINS | TOTAL BEST HORSE |
|---|---|---|---|---|---|
| MEHMAS | by Acclamation | 88 | 46 | 65 | £920,290 Supremacy |
| KODI BEAR | by Kodiac | 44 | 15 | 22 | £318,124 Mystery Angel |
| ADAAY | by Kodiac | 51 | 14 | 18 | £278,239 Shark Two One |
| BELARDO | by Lope de Vega | 36 | 10 | 16 | £276,401 Isabella Giles |
| NEW BAY | by Dubawi | 29 | 11 | 17 | £274,375 New Mandate |
| PRIDE OF DUBAI | by Street Cry | 30 | 8 | 14 | £211,187 Zaffy's Pride |
| AIR FORCE BLUE | by War Front | 9 | 4 | 6 | £210,460 Chief Little Hawk |
| BOBBY'S KITTEN | by Kitten's Joy | 29 | 8 | 13 | £163,973 Monaasib |
| TERRITORIES | by Invincible Spirit | 40 | 12 | 13 | £163,931 Uncle Jumbo |
| TWILIGHT SON | by Kyllachy | 68 | 17 | 17 | £156,947 Grammata |
| PRINCE OF LIR | by Kodiac | 27 | 8 | 11 | £144,069 The Lir Jet |
| AWTAAD | by Cape Cross | 52 | 13 | 13 | £136,087 Ebeko |
| SHALAA | by Invincible Spirit | 33 | 12 | 13 | £135,530 No Speak Alexander |
| BURATINO | by Exceed And Excel | 25 | 5 | 7 | £132,861 Snapraeterea |
| THE GURKHA | by Galileo | 39 | 11 | 11 | £108,108 San Martino |
| COULSTY | by Kodiac | 15 | 6 | 9 | £84,172 Santosha |
| VADAMOS | by Monsun | 34 | 8 | 10 | £78,182 Messidor |
| MARKAZ | by Dark Angel | 32 | 5 | 6 | £67,168 Mark of The Man |
| ESTIDHKAAR | by Dark Angel | 30 | 7 | 8 | £64,494 Rania |
| THE LAST LION | by Choisir | 27 | 5 | 5 | £46,123 Kraken Power |
| CHARMING THOUGHT | by Oasis Dream | 18 | 5 | 5 | £45,270 Charterhouse |
| AJAYA | by Invincible Spirit | 10 | 4 | 5 | £36,553 Fourhometwo |
| HARZAND | by Sea The Stars | 13 | 2 | 2 | £30,275 Port Sunlight |
| PEARL SECRET | by Compton Place | 22 | 3 | 3 | £29,992 Little Sunflower |
| FASCINATING ROCK | by Fastnet Rock | 14 | 2 | 2 | £29,577 Split Passion |
| FLINTSHIRE | by Dansili | 6 | 2 | 2 | £23,782 Talace |
| STRATH BURN | by Equiano | 3 | 2 | 2 | £20,009 Burning Cash |

# LEADING MATERNAL GRANDSIRES OF 2020 IN GREAT BRITAIN AND IRELAND

| STALLION | BREEDING | RNRS | WNRS | WINS | TOTAL BEST HORSE |
|---|---|---|---|---|---|
| GALILEO | by Sadler's Wells | 397 | 143 | 205 | £3,531,225 Ghaiyyath |
| PIVOTAL | by Polar Falcon | 307 | 102 | 160 | £3,325,138 Magical |
| DANEHILL DANCER | by Danehill | 263 | 97 | 131 | £2,569,619 Serpentine |
| OASIS DREAM | by Green Desert | 314 | 125 | 187 | £2,348,952 Siskin |
| DANSILI | by Danehill | 268 | 97 | 136 | £2,122,926 Galileo Chrome |
| CAPE CROSS | by Green Desert | 215 | 76 | 109 | £1,760,611 Santiago |
| SADLER'S WELLS | by Northern Dancer | 222 | 66 | 90 | £1,561,106 Enable |
| DANEHILL | by Danzig | 151 | 45 | 70 | £1,471,168 Search For A Song |
| MONTJEU | by Sadler's Wells | 171 | 54 | 86 | £1,433,628 Wonderful Tonight |
| SHAMARDAL | by Giant's Causeway | 184 | 77 | 110 | £1,366,456 Hello Youmzain |
| KINGMAMBO | by Mr. Prospector | 76 | 30 | 51 | £1,181,281 Addeybb |
| DALAKHANI | by Darshaan | 133 | 44 | 62 | £1,004,542 Fujaira Prince |
| DUBAWI | by Dubai Millennium | 141 | 47 | 71 | £996,048 Nazeef |
| EXCEED AND EXCEL | by Danehill | 168 | 57 | 77 | £877,974 Current Option |
| HOLY ROMAN EMPEROR | by Danehill | 99 | 38 | 54 | £810,612 Shale |
| GREEN DESERT | by Danzig | 149 | 46 | 56 | £791,395 Mother Earth |
| INVINCIBLE SPIRIT | by Green Desert | 228 | 57 | 78 | £763,460 Desert Encounter |
| ROYAL APPLAUSE | by Waajib | 154 | 52 | 80 | £762,767 Cobh |
| TEOFILO | by Galileo | 122 | 34 | 47 | £733,505 Mac Swiney |
| SELKIRK | by Sharpen Up | 124 | 42 | 56 | £715,827 Happy Power |
| NAYEF | by Gulch | 108 | 27 | 40 | £707,374 Palace Pier |
| ROCK OF GIBRALTAR | by Danehill | 128 | 34 | 52 | £706,792 Kameko |
| ACCLAMATION | by Royal Applause | 162 | 49 | 66 | £682,866 Yazaman |
| SINGSPIEL | by In the Wings | 145 | 39 | 59 | £680,185 Ecliptical |
| LAWMAN | by Invincible Spirit | 72 | 21 | 32 | £657,215 Battaash |
| STREET CRY | by Machiavellian | 100 | 38 | 53 | £641,933 Make A Challenge |
| MARJU | by Last Tycoon | 88 | 28 | 39 | £628,964 Happy Romance |

# FLAT STALLIONS' EARNINGS FOR 2020

(includes every stallion who sired a winner on the Flat in Great Britain and Ireland in 2020)

| STALLIONS | RNRS | WNRS | WINS | PLACES | TOTAL (£) |
|---|---|---|---|---|---|
| ACCLAMATION (GB) | 152 | 54 | 75 | 171 | 666414.75 |
| ADAAY (IRE) | 51 | 14 | 18 | 41 | 266358.17 |
| ADLERFLUG (GER) | 2 | 1 | 1 | 1 | 8926.16 |
| AIR CHIEF MARSHAL (IRE) | 2 | 2 | 2 | 1 | 8826.57 |
| AIR FORCE BLUE (USA) | 9 | 4 | 6 | 11 | 197148.50 |
| AJAYA (GB) | 10 | 4 | 5 | 6 | 35513.57 |
| AL KAZEEM (GB) | 23 | 5 | 7 | 20 | 91006.63 |
| ALFRED NOBEL (IRE) | 3 | 1 | 1 | 3 | 5470.08 |
| ALHEBAYEB (IRE) | 47 | 15 | 23 | 63 | 269191.59 |
| AMARON (GB) | 2 | 2 | 3 | 4 | 30039.84 |
| AMERICAN PHAROAH (USA) | 20 | 12 | 16 | 14 | 233242.59 |
| ANIMAL KINGDOM (USA) | 8 | 2 | 3 | 7 | 30120.35 |
| ANJAAL (GB) | 59 | 12 | 15 | 43 | 175019.13 |
| ANODIN (IRE) | 6 | 1 | 2 | 3 | 22434.74 |
| ANTONIUS PIUS (USA) | 4 | 2 | 2 | 3 | 10490.66 |
| APPROVE (IRE) | 19 | 7 | 10 | 19 | 92409.20 |
| AQLAAM (GB) | 17 | 5 | 8 | 12 | 97072.25 |
| ARAAFA (IRE) | 1 | 1 | 1 | 1 | 4169.16 |
| ARABIAN GLEAM (GB) | 5 | 1 | 2 | 9 | 17821.97 |
| ARAKAN (USA) | 11 | 2 | 2 | 4 | 13905.63 |
| ARCADIO (GER) | 5 | 1 | 1 | 3 | 9771.03 |
| ARCANO (IRE) | 48 | 16 | 21 | 62 | 226915.54 |
| ARCHIPENKO (USA) | 56 | 16 | 24 | 40 | 140041.33 |
| AREION (GER) | 3 | 1 | 1 | 1 | 17025.70 |
| ART CONNOISSEUR (IRE) | 5 | 2 | 6 | 10 | 37617.46 |
| ARVICO (FR) | 1 | 1 | 2 | 0 | 9000.00 |
| ASK (GB) | 7 | 2 | 4 | 3 | 37367.24 |
| ASSERTIVE (GB) | 14 | 3 | 5 | 13 | 52487.98 |
| ATRAF (GB) | 1 | 1 | 1 | 0 | 3181.67 |
| AUSSIE RULES (USA) | 21 | 4 | 4 | 16 | 45331.25 |
| AUSTRALIA (GB) | 125 | 41 | 62 | 97 | 1208646.48 |
| AUTHORIZED (IRE) | 33 | 11 | 18 | 20 | 719114.84 |
| AVONBRIDGE (GB) | 7 | 2 | 4 | 2 | 17265.73 |
| AWTAAD (IRE) | 52 | 13 | 13 | 27 | 131307.87 |
| AZAMOUR (IRE) | 8 | 1 | 2 | 4 | 17989.07 |
| BAHAMIAN BOUNTY (GB) | 20 | 8 | 12 | 25 | 144432.02 |
| BAHRI (USA) | 5 | 2 | 3 | 3 | 18471.93 |
| BALTIC KING (GB) | 12 | 1 | 2 | 6 | 16692.07 |
| BATED BREATH (GB) | 147 | 43 | 63 | 139 | 729446.33 |
| BATTLE OF MARENGO (IRE) | 17 | 2 | 2 | 10 | 37267.51 |
| BEAT HOLLOW (GB) | 9 | 2 | 4 | 1 | 47207.18 |
| BELARDO (IRE) | 36 | 10 | 16 | 21 | 269678.40 |
| BERNARDINI (USA) | 4 | 2 | 2 | 2 | 8887.92 |
| BERTOLINI (USA) | 5 | 1 | 1 | 3 | 8383.81 |
| BIG BAD BOB (IRE) | 41 | 10 | 15 | 23 | 94242.84 |
| BLAME (USA) | 5 | 1 | 3 | 4 | 16939.18 |
| BOBBY'S KITTEN (USA) | 29 | 8 | 13 | 27 | 157699.95 |
| BORN TO SEA (IRE) | 74 | 14 | 16 | 64 | 193350.49 |
| BRAZEN BEAU (AUS) | 71 | 19 | 31 | 54 | 235386.32 |
| BUNGLE INTHEJUNGLE (GB) | 57 | 13 | 20 | 54 | 204939.05 |
| BURATINO (IRE) | 25 | 5 | 7 | 18 | 126937.19 |
| BURWAAZ (GB) | 4 | 1 | 1 | 3 | 7075.05 |
| BUSHRANGER (IRE) | 13 | 5 | 8 | 16 | 53675.14 |
| CABLE BAY (IRE) | 87 | 21 | 31 | 90 | 404539.23 |
| CACIQUE (IRE) | 18 | 7 | 11 | 22 | 107347.73 |
| CAIRO PRINCE (USA) | 1 | 1 | 1 | 2 | 6103.62 |
| CAMACHO (GB) | 148 | 36 | 50 | 121 | 468704.74 |

| STALLIONS | RNRS | WNRS | WINS | PLACES | TOTAL (£) |
|---|---|---|---|---|---|
| CAMELOT (GB) | 147 | 46 | 58 | 107 | 1028598.20 |
| CAMPANOLOGIST (USA) | 3 | 2 | 3 | 1 | 41839.96 |
| CANDY RIDE (ARG) | 3 | 2 | 2 | 5 | 10217.13 |
| CANFORD CLIFFS (IRE) | 91 | 25 | 37 | 95 | 340046.16 |
| CANNOCK CHASE (USA) | 8 | 1 | 1 | 2 | 6498.03 |
| CAPE BLANCO (IRE) | 3 | 1 | 2 | 3 | 9477.72 |
| CAPE CROSS (IRE) | 59 | 27 | 39 | 49 | 477423.87 |
| CAPPELLA SANSEVERO (GB) | 19 | 3 | 4 | 8 | 31831.46 |
| CAPTAIN GERRARD (IRE) | 29 | 12 | 20 | 31 | 126894.02 |
| CAPTAIN MARVELOUS (IRE) | 2 | 1 | 1 | 2 | 9832.62 |
| CAPTAIN RIO (GB) | 10 | 1 | 1 | 5 | 7687.87 |
| CASAMENTO (IRE) | 83 | 15 | 22 | 73 | 228691.36 |
| CHAMPS ELYSEES (GB) | 86 | 28 | 37 | 98 | 581305.85 |
| CHARM SPIRIT (IRE) | 76 | 27 | 44 | 72 | 377655.67 |
| CHARMING THOUGHT (GB) | 18 | 5 | 5 | 9 | 43975.43 |
| CHOISIR (AUS) | 19 | 4 | 7 | 24 | 89459.80 |
| CITY ZIP (USA) | 6 | 1 | 3 | 7 | 21878.26 |
| CITYSCAPE (GB) | 51 | 15 | 27 | 48 | 252303.78 |
| CLODOVIL (IRE) | 49 | 17 | 29 | 59 | 303651.48 |
| COACH HOUSE (IRE) | 60 | 15 | 25 | 67 | 150847.19 |
| COMPTON PLACE (GB) | 20 | 8 | 13 | 27 | 104292.01 |
| CONGRATS (USA) | 2 | 1 | 2 | 2 | 11850.08 |
| COULSTY (IRE) | 15 | 6 | 9 | 19 | 83304.27 |
| CURLIN (USA) | 1 | 1 | 1 | 0 | 4690.02 |
| DABIRSIM (FR) | 35 | 8 | 11 | 23 | 91638.93 |
| DALAKHANI (IRE) | 13 | 2 | 2 | 11 | 57955.01 |
| DANDY MAN (IRE) | 218 | 70 | 97 | 214 | 1121741.34 |
| DANEHILL DANCER (IRE) | 6 | 2 | 3 | 5 | 18086.61 |
| DANSILI (GB) | 93 | 29 | 35 | 92 | 500680.14 |
| DARIYAN (FR) | 1 | 1 | 1 | 0 | 4375.47 |
| DARK ANGEL (IRE) | 272 | 106 | 152 | 305 | 2088504.76 |
| DAWN APPROACH (IRE) | 112 | 27 | 39 | 84 | 446003.74 |
| DECLARATION OF WAR (USA) | 34 | 12 | 17 | 30 | 212522.74 |
| DEEP IMPACT (JPN) | 8 | 3 | 4 | 6 | 244524.74 |
| DELEGATOR (GB) | 36 | 15 | 27 | 47 | 175952.71 |
| DENOUNCE (GB) | 3 | 1 | 1 | 8 | 27578.05 |
| DICK TURPIN (IRE) | 19 | 8 | 14 | 26 | 74944.99 |
| DISTORTED HUMOR (USA) | 12 | 5 | 8 | 11 | 43398.23 |
| DOYEN (IRE) | 6 | 1 | 1 | 2 | 6034.58 |
| DRAGON PULSE (IRE) | 100 | 27 | 40 | 71 | 321413.17 |
| DREAM AHEAD (USA) | 73 | 26 | 41 | 87 | 796777.98 |
| DUBAWI (IRE) | 199 | 81 | 107 | 147 | 2444012.12 |
| DUE DILIGENCE (USA) | 51 | 15 | 22 | 47 | 174609.27 |
| DUNADEN (FR) | 11 | 4 | 5 | 7 | 78177.66 |
| DUNKERQUE (FR) | 2 | 1 | 1 | 1 | 10602.59 |
| DUTCH ART (GB) | 96 | 43 | 61 | 101 | 569844.99 |
| DYLAN THOMAS (IRE) | 21 | 4 | 5 | 18 | 56294.58 |
| ECHO OF LIGHT (GB) | 3 | 1 | 1 | 1 | 7110.17 |
| ELNADIM (USA) | 11 | 4 | 5 | 10 | 114036.66 |
| ELUSIVE CITY (USA) | 7 | 2 | 8 | 12 | 51804.42 |
| ELUSIVE PIMPERNEL (USA) | 18 | 3 | 5 | 5 | 28958.90 |
| ELUSIVE QUALITY (USA) | 9 | 3 | 7 | 3 | 46277.91 |
| ELZAAM (AUS) | 86 | 26 | 36 | 48 | 495899.48 |
| ENGLISH CHANNEL (USA) | 2 | 2 | 5 | 2 | 32231.85 |
| EPAULETTE (AUS) | 91 | 28 | 38 | 78 | 386580.01 |
| EQUIANO (FR) | 131 | 39 | 62 | 162 | 632153.65 |
| ES QUE LOVE (IRE) | 17 | 7 | 11 | 18 | 155689.94 |
| ESTIDHKAAR (IRE) | 30 | 7 | 8 | 20 | 64287.36 |
| EVASIVE (GB) | 3 | 1 | 2 | 1 | 7068.20 |
| EXCEED AND EXCEL (AUS) | 161 | 56 | 81 | 181 | 923458.46 |
| EXCELEBRATION (IRE) | 65 | 22 | 35 | 63 | 505026.11 |

| STALLIONS | RNRS | WNRS | WINS | PLACES | TOTAL (£) |
|---|---|---|---|---|---|
| EXCELLENT ART (GB) | 11 | 1 | 3 | 3 | 16603.51 |
| EXCHANGE RATE (USA) | 6 | 1 | 1 | 1 | 6755.98 |
| FAIRLY RANSOM (USA) | 1 | 1 | 1 | 1 | 5109.42 |
| FAMOUS NAME (GB) | 18 | 5 | 7 | 18 | 62623.37 |
| FARHH (GB) | 29 | 11 | 17 | 37 | 254068.34 |
| FASCINATING ROCK (IRE) | 14 | 2 | 2 | 9 | 28162.37 |
| FAST COMPANY (IRE) | 110 | 36 | 51 | 85 | 575825.95 |
| FASTNET ROCK (AUS) | 63 | 22 | 23 | 53 | 376383.22 |
| FINJAAN (GB) | 9 | 2 | 3 | 13 | 29346.62 |
| FINSCEAL FIOR (IRE) | 7 | 1 | 1 | 3 | 9809.69 |
| FIREBREAK (GB) | 13 | 2 | 5 | 14 | 36081.44 |
| FIRST DEFENCE (USA) | 10 | 3 | 4 | 14 | 208702.46 |
| FLEMENSFIRTH (USA) | 3 | 1 | 1 | 1 | 20648.30 |
| FLINTSHIRE (GB) | 6 | 2 | 2 | 5 | 22546.66 |
| FOOTSTEPSINTHESAND (GB) | 137 | 38 | 67 | 126 | 724165.78 |
| FOUNTAIN OF YOUTH (IRE) | 57 | 11 | 14 | 35 | 92302.67 |
| FOXWEDGE (AUS) | 35 | 13 | 21 | 61 | 225608.07 |
| FRACAS (IRE) | 12 | 2 | 4 | 11 | 40293.76 |
| FRANKEL (GB) | 148 | 57 | 81 | 134 | 1161853.18 |
| FREE EAGLE (IRE) | 62 | 22 | 30 | 44 | 330137.44 |
| FRENCH NAVY (GB) | 17 | 5 | 5 | 17 | 54892.22 |
| FROZEN POWER (IRE) | 13 | 7 | 11 | 11 | 68109.87 |
| FUISSE (FR) | 1 | 1 | 3 | 0 | 26761.65 |
| FULBRIGHT (GB) | 21 | 1 | 3 | 8 | 24902.55 |
| G FORCE (IRE) | 3 | 1 | 1 | 2 | 8488.99 |
| GALE FORCE TEN (GB) | 24 | 8 | 13 | 34 | 122772.86 |
| GALILEO (IRE) | 206 | 85 | 116 | 177 | 5133190.52 |
| GARSWOOD (GB) | 55 | 21 | 35 | 51 | 232655.06 |
| GETAWAY (GER) | 7 | 1 | 1 | 5 | 41275.62 |
| GIO PONTI (USA) | 3 | 1 | 1 | 4 | 9939.34 |
| GLENEAGLES (IRE) | 94 | 35 | 51 | 92 | 545924.19 |
| GOLDEN HORN (GB) | 95 | 39 | 65 | 87 | 599521.81 |
| GREGORIAN (IRE) | 37 | 14 | 20 | 43 | 177305.28 |
| GUTAIFAN (IRE) | 117 | 30 | 37 | 86 | 307504.85 |
| HAAFHD (GB) | 11 | 2 | 3 | 14 | 24441.86 |
| HAATEF (USA) | 8 | 3 | 3 | 9 | 27731.04 |
| HALLING (USA) | 6 | 3 | 3 | 10 | 88060.76 |
| HALLOWED CROWN (AUS) | 26 | 10 | 12 | 22 | 91470.72 |
| HALLUCINATE (USA) | 1 | 1 | 1 | 0 | 4781.40 |
| HARBOUR WATCH (IRE) | 64 | 25 | 44 | 44 | 463257.09 |
| HARD SPUN (USA) | 9 | 4 | 8 | 12 | 56429.81 |
| HARLAN'S HOLIDAY (USA) | 1 | 1 | 1 | 4 | 7117.02 |
| HARZAND (GB) | 13 | 2 | 2 | 7 | 28666.57 |
| HAVANA GOLD (IRE) | 68 | 18 | 29 | 86 | 248899.71 |
| HEERAAT (IRE) | 66 | 18 | 37 | 56 | 306777.93 |
| HELLVELYN (GB) | 31 | 6 | 10 | 23 | 66235.03 |
| HELMET (AUS) | 126 | 39 | 50 | 103 | 392086.43 |
| HENRYTHENAVIGATOR (USA) | 16 | 3 | 7 | 19 | 47557.65 |
| HIGH CHAPARRAL (IRE) | 24 | 9 | 13 | 13 | 89731.84 |
| HOLY ROMAN EMPEROR (IRE) | 92 | 33 | 37 | 102 | 433050.48 |
| HOT STREAK (IRE) | 50 | 16 | 29 | 49 | 217594.28 |
| HUNTER'S LIGHT (IRE) | 7 | 1 | 1 | 3 | 5097.06 |
| IFFRAAJ (GB) | 168 | 40 | 67 | 130 | 538971.78 |
| INCLUDE (USA) | 2 | 1 | 2 | 5 | 12297.22 |
| INTELLO (GER) | 53 | 13 | 16 | 41 | 190566.57 |
| INTENSE FOCUS (USA) | 27 | 9 | 9 | 20 | 95760.06 |
| INTIKHAB (USA) | 19 | 5 | 9 | 15 | 64276.81 |
| INTO MISCHIEF (USA) | 2 | 1 | 1 | 1 | 5908.92 |
| INTRINSIC (GB) | 13 | 3 | 5 | 9 | 32565.06 |
| INVINCIBLE SPIRIT (IRE) | 167 | 72 | 104 | 177 | 1455311.42 |
| IVAWOOD (IRE) | 55 | 16 | 21 | 34 | 160358.38 |

| STALLIONS | RNRS | WNRS | WINS | PLACES | TOTAL (£) |
|---|---|---|---|---|---|
| JACK MILTON (USA) | 1 | 1 | 1 | 0 | 7000.00 |
| JEREMY (USA) | 15 | 2 | 2 | 3 | 29187.73 |
| JOSHUA TREE (IRE) | 2 | 1 | 2 | 2 | 9004.71 |
| JUKEBOX JURY (IRE) | 5 | 1 | 4 | 3 | 107738.40 |
| KALANISI (IRE) | 7 | 2 | 3 | 3 | 13255.24 |
| KAMSIN (GER) | 1 | 1 | 2 | 0 | 8118.59 |
| KANTHAROS (USA) | 1 | 1 | 1 | 0 | 4471.51 |
| KARAKONTIE (JPN) | 9 | 3 | 3 | 11 | 31700.05 |
| KENDARGENT (FR) | 29 | 10 | 18 | 19 | 332247.51 |
| KHELEYF (USA) | 28 | 8 | 16 | 29 | 113475.02 |
| KINGMAN (GB) | 154 | 69 | 85 | 122 | 1335908.73 |
| KINGSBARNS (IRE) | 2 | 1 | 1 | 3 | 13029.65 |
| KINGSTON HILL (GB) | 10 | 3 | 3 | 10 | 24370.87 |
| KITTEN'S JOY (USA) | 33 | 12 | 16 | 19 | 416586.24 |
| KODI BEAR (IRE) | 44 | 15 | 22 | 46 | 310238.51 |
| KODIAC (GB) | 336 | 116 | 156 | 312 | 1864754.53 |
| KUROSHIO (AUS) | 6 | 2 | 2 | 5 | 19792.85 |
| KYLLACHY (GB) | 83 | 22 | 35 | 104 | 308384.63 |
| LAWMAN (FR) | 100 | 19 | 27 | 84 | 609555.92 |
| LE CADRE NOIR (IRE) | 5 | 3 | 5 | 5 | 63522.34 |
| LE HAVRE (IRE) | 54 | 14 | 18 | 24 | 453332.06 |
| LEMON DROP KID (USA) | 11 | 3 | 3 | 12 | 39928.14 |
| LEROIDESANIMAUX (BRZ) | 15 | 7 | 9 | 24 | 110487.97 |
| LETHAL FORCE (IRE) | 101 | 35 | 51 | 94 | 567709.79 |
| LILBOURNE LAD (IRE) | 25 | 11 | 17 | 33 | 187974.95 |
| LONHRO (AUS) | 10 | 2 | 4 | 10 | 34581.58 |
| LOPE DE VEGA (IRE) | 202 | 77 | 113 | 175 | 1517007.09 |
| LORD KANALOA (JPN) | 1 | 1 | 1 | 0 | 41525.43 |
| LORD OF ENGLAND (GER) | 5 | 2 | 3 | 2 | 12938.44 |
| LORD SHANAKILL (USA) | 18 | 4 | 6 | 20 | 63084.89 |
| LOVELACE (GB) | 2 | 1 | 1 | 2 | 14025.43 |
| LUCAYAN (FR) | 2 | 1 | 1 | 0 | 4053.00 |
| LUCKY STORY (USA) | 3 | 1 | 2 | 7 | 17456.66 |
| MAGICIAN (IRE) | 4 | 1 | 2 | 4 | 15669.64 |
| MAJESTIC MISSILE (IRE) | 5 | 1 | 2 | 7 | 21141.04 |
| MAJOR CADEAUX (GB) | 9 | 4 | 4 | 8 | 34207.56 |
| MAKE BELIEVE (GB) | 59 | 28 | 40 | 54 | 371793.81 |
| MAKFI (GB) | 23 | 9 | 11 | 17 | 93119.65 |
| MANDURO (GER) | 21 | 4 | 6 | 17 | 91540.40 |
| MARESCA SORRENTO (FR) | 1 | 1 | 1 | 0 | 5500.00 |
| MARKAZ (IRE) | 32 | 5 | 6 | 27 | 66847.62 |
| MASTERCRAFTSMAN (IRE) | 121 | 31 | 42 | 104 | 629987.41 |
| MASTEROFTHEHORSE (IRE) | 2 | 1 | 2 | 3 | 14999.99 |
| MAXIOS (GB) | 27 | 7 | 7 | 28 | 89362.16 |
| MAYSON (GB) | 124 | 43 | 77 | 116 | 706595.15 |
| MEDAGLIA D'ORO (USA) | 14 | 7 | 11 | 18 | 89740.65 |
| MEDICEAN (GB) | 29 | 7 | 8 | 24 | 74730.40 |
| MEHMAS (IRE) | 88 | 46 | 65 | 106 | 909702.48 |
| MIDNIGHT LEGEND (GB) | 3 | 1 | 2 | 1 | 12492.19 |
| MILK IT MICK (GB) | 7 | 1 | 2 | 6 | 14274.16 |
| MISTER FOTIS (USA) | 1 | 1 | 1 | 1 | 3795.33 |
| MISU BOND (IRE) | 3 | 3 | 3 | 4 | 15770.03 |
| MIZZEN MAST (USA) | 7 | 2 | 2 | 8 | 25401.72 |
| MONSIEUR BOND (IRE) | 42 | 9 | 14 | 47 | 117722.70 |
| MONTJEU (IRE) | 3 | 1 | 1 | 2 | 14794.37 |
| MONTMARTRE (FR) | 1 | 1 | 1 | 2 | 7286.54 |
| MOOHAAJIM (IRE) | 10 | 1 | 1 | 5 | 14985.84 |
| MORE THAN READY (USA) | 13 | 2 | 2 | 10 | 34826.36 |
| MORPHEUS (GB) | 38 | 14 | 25 | 39 | 167137.01 |
| MOST IMPROVED (IRE) | 22 | 6 | 9 | 19 | 63214.23 |
| MOTIVATOR (GB) | 17 | 1 | 1 | 11 | 36759.05 |

| STALLIONS | RNRS | WNRS | WINS | PLACES | TOTAL (£) |
|---|---|---|---|---|---|
| MOUNT NELSON (GB) | 34 | 9 | 16 | 43 | 149963.68 |
| MOURAYAN (IRE) | 1 | 1 | 1 | 0 | 7500.00 |
| MR VEGAS (IRE) | 1 | 1 | 2 | 5 | 27323.35 |
| MSHAWISH (USA) | 4 | 1 | 1 | 1 | 5258.73 |
| MUHAARAR (GB) | 107 | 44 | 52 | 97 | 498795.18 |
| MUHTATHIR (GB) | 6 | 2 | 2 | 5 | 10969.59 |
| MUKHADRAM (GB) | 87 | 22 | 28 | 70 | 216420.78 |
| MULTIPLEX (GB) | 17 | 5 | 10 | 20 | 67658.95 |
| MUSIC MASTER (GB) | 8 | 1 | 1 | 6 | 8650.80 |
| MUSTAJEEB (GB) | 9 | 1 | 1 | 1 | 6593.17 |
| MYBOYCHARLIE (IRE) | 6 | 1 | 2 | 6 | 18593.06 |
| NATHANIEL (IRE) | 119 | 39 | 58 | 108 | 887902.17 |
| NAYEF (USA) | 25 | 3 | 4 | 11 | 37693.19 |
| NEW APPROACH (IRE) | 115 | 32 | 43 | 80 | 600297.30 |
| NEW BAY (GB) | 29 | 11 | 17 | 24 | 266392.20 |
| NIGHT OF THUNDER (IRE) | 82 | 36 | 47 | 92 | 696127.41 |
| NO NAY NEVER (USA) | 128 | 45 | 55 | 110 | 855878.47 |
| NO RISK AT ALL (FR) | 3 | 2 | 2 | 1 | 7786.86 |
| NOBLE MISSION (GB) | 20 | 7 | 10 | 22 | 177648.46 |
| NOROIT (GER) | 1 | 1 | 1 | 1 | 5262.71 |
| NORTH LIGHT (IRE) | 1 | 1 | 1 | 4 | 6500.09 |
| OASIS DREAM (GB) | 148 | 43 | 61 | 137 | 525704.00 |
| OLYMPIC GLORY (IRE) | 19 | 7 | 12 | 15 | 77545.53 |
| ORIENTOR (GB) | 13 | 5 | 8 | 21 | 57820.04 |
| OSCAR (IRE) | 3 | 1 | 1 | 0 | 13567.80 |
| OUTSTRIP (GB) | 58 | 9 | 15 | 41 | 106416.53 |
| PACO BOY (IRE) | 39 | 12 | 19 | 40 | 151267.24 |
| PALAVICINI (USA) | 4 | 2 | 2 | 2 | 11703.38 |
| PAPAL BULL (GB) | 8 | 3 | 4 | 6 | 34143.63 |
| PASTORAL PURSUITS (GB) | 34 | 12 | 17 | 47 | 180354.53 |
| PASTORIUS (GER) | 6 | 2 | 2 | 3 | 26944.12 |
| PEARL SECRET (GB) | 22 | 3 | 3 | 19 | 29896.53 |
| PEINTRE CELEBRE (USA) | 2 | 1 | 2 | 0 | 7463.34 |
| PHOENIX REACH (IRE) | 9 | 1 | 1 | 8 | 23027.58 |
| PICCOLO (GB) | 23 | 2 | 3 | 17 | 41207.04 |
| PIONEEROF THE NILE (USA) | 4 | 2 | 2 | 1 | 10610.77 |
| PIVOTAL (GB) | 79 | 25 | 43 | 81 | 1581010.66 |
| PLANTEUR (IRE) | 6 | 3 | 8 | 8 | 237977.65 |
| POET'S VOICE (GB) | 103 | 34 | 49 | 115 | 530270.30 |
| POINT OF ENTRY (USA) | 3 | 1 | 1 | 4 | 9158.28 |
| POSEIDON ADVENTURE (IRE) | 1 | 1 | 3 | 1 | 14686.44 |
| POUR MOI (IRE) | 31 | 10 | 12 | 19 | 109481.84 |
| POWER (GB) | 59 | 23 | 30 | 66 | 384255.04 |
| PRIDE OF DUBAI (AUS) | 30 | 8 | 14 | 23 | 200933.57 |
| PRINCE GIBRALTAR (FR) | 2 | 1 | 1 | 1 | 7510.93 |
| PRINCE OF LIR (IRE) | 27 | 8 | 11 | 22 | 141601.84 |
| QUALITY ROAD (USA) | 7 | 4 | 5 | 4 | 37610.61 |
| RAIL LINK (GB) | 12 | 3 | 4 | 7 | 40921.00 |
| RAJJ (IRE) | 3 | 1 | 1 | 2 | 17500.01 |
| RAJSAMAN (FR) | 12 | 1 | 1 | 10 | 16610.46 |
| RAVEN'S PASS (USA) | 72 | 21 | 30 | 65 | 435779.81 |
| RED CLUBS (IRE) | 4 | 1 | 1 | 6 | 10458.77 |
| RED JAZZ (USA) | 41 | 7 | 9 | 29 | 124620.58 |
| REDOUTE'S CHOICE (AUS) | 11 | 1 | 2 | 5 | 152940.02 |
| REFUSE TO BEND (IRE) | 3 | 2 | 4 | 5 | 24409.12 |
| RELIABLE MAN (GB) | 7 | 2 | 4 | 10 | 42282.93 |
| REQUINTO (IRE) | 55 | 17 | 29 | 54 | 215121.69 |
| RIO DE LA PLATA (USA) | 13 | 6 | 6 | 7 | 50524.12 |
| RIP VAN WINKLE (IRE) | 33 | 9 | 12 | 35 | 110570.56 |
| ROCK OF GIBRALTAR (IRE) | 50 | 16 | 21 | 44 | 275163.02 |
| RODERIC O'CONNOR (IRE) | 39 | 13 | 18 | 44 | 286262.79 |

| STALLIONS | RNRS | WNRS | WINS | PLACES | TOTAL (£) |
|---|---|---|---|---|---|
| ROYAL APPLAUSE (GB) | 27 | 9 | 16 | 29 | 121767.34 |
| RULER OF THE WORLD (IRE) | 25 | 8 | 13 | 13 | 61411.04 |
| SABIANGO (GER) | 1 | 1 | 1 | 1 | 4809.42 |
| SAKHEE'S SECRET (GB) | 20 | 9 | 12 | 28 | 79885.91 |
| SALUTINO (GER) | 1 | 1 | 1 | 2 | 8593.22 |
| SANS FRONTIERES (IRE) | 1 | 1 | 1 | 0 | 7000.00 |
| SAYIF (IRE) | 11 | 4 | 7 | 6 | 136076.52 |
| SCAT DADDY (USA) | 19 | 5 | 7 | 12 | 54968.52 |
| SEA THE MOON (GER) | 54 | 17 | 23 | 44 | 528397.67 |
| SEA THE STARS (IRE) | 154 | 54 | 69 | 122 | 1308433.02 |
| SEPOY (AUS) | 86 | 31 | 47 | 83 | 401184.54 |
| SHALAA (IRE) | 33 | 12 | 13 | 29 | 132047.23 |
| SHAMARDAL (USA) | 118 | 40 | 57 | 121 | 856808.92 |
| SHOLOKHOV (IRE) | 1 | 1 | 1 | 1 | 3291.53 |
| SHOOTING TO WIN (AUS) | 8 | 1 | 1 | 2 | 5440.34 |
| SHOWCASING (GB) | 164 | 60 | 91 | 141 | 963391.72 |
| SIDESTEP (AUS) | 7 | 3 | 4 | 13 | 37687.17 |
| SIR PERCY (GB) | 88 | 21 | 29 | 66 | 394267.90 |
| SIR PRANCEALOT (IRE) | 73 | 26 | 42 | 70 | 528850.53 |
| SIXTIES ICON (GB) | 60 | 12 | 15 | 40 | 170526.77 |
| SIYOUNI (FR) | 107 | 39 | 52 | 110 | 815902.40 |
| SLADE POWER (IRE) | 77 | 20 | 37 | 84 | 347869.09 |
| SLEEPING INDIAN (GB) | 15 | 2 | 8 | 13 | 37138.29 |
| SO YOU THINK (NZ) | 11 | 6 | 7 | 12 | 39945.73 |
| SOCIETY ROCK (IRE) | 62 | 20 | 27 | 55 | 283307.74 |
| SOLDIER HOLLOW (GB) | 9 | 2 | 2 | 3 | 16834.10 |
| SOLDIER OF FORTUNE (IRE) | 2 | 1 | 1 | 0 | 5894.75 |
| SPEIGHTSTOWN (USA) | 28 | 12 | 21 | 27 | 183493.82 |
| SPRING AT LAST (USA) | 1 | 1 | 1 | 1 | 4416.25 |
| STARSPANGLEDBANNER (AUS) | 80 | 32 | 41 | 71 | 516903.03 |
| STIMULATION (IRE) | 13 | 5 | 7 | 15 | 41928.08 |
| STRATH BURN (GB) | 3 | 2 | 2 | 4 | 19986.46 |
| STREET BOSS (USA) | 4 | 1 | 1 | 2 | 33078.59 |
| STREET CRY (IRE) | 13 | 5 | 7 | 13 | 63305.89 |
| STRIKING AMBITION (GB) | 1 | 1 | 1 | 0 | 3181.67 |
| STYLE VENDOME (FR) | 6 | 2 | 3 | 5 | 19421.85 |
| SULAMANI (IRE) | 4 | 2 | 6 | 12 | 33516.97 |
| SUPPLICANT (GB) | 4 | 2 | 2 | 0 | 9485.98 |
| SWISS SPIRIT (GB) | 96 | 31 | 44 | 95 | 322289.91 |
| TAGULA (IRE) | 29 | 8 | 13 | 17 | 131597.11 |
| TAMARKUZ (USA) | 2 | 1 | 1 | 4 | 14584.74 |
| TAMAYUZ (GB) | 61 | 22 | 26 | 47 | 222883.83 |
| TAPIT (USA) | 1 | 1 | 2 | 1 | 8330.49 |
| TEMPLE CITY (USA) | 3 | 2 | 2 | 3 | 10735.69 |
| TEOFILO (IRE) | 105 | 30 | 44 | 100 | 813552.63 |
| TERRITORIES (IRE) | 40 | 12 | 13 | 30 | 160644.65 |
| THE CARBON UNIT (USA) | 6 | 2 | 3 | 4 | 16346.64 |
| THE FACTOR (USA) | 8 | 4 | 6 | 6 | 32352.41 |
| THE GURKHA (IRE) | 39 | 11 | 11 | 19 | 100361.90 |
| THE LAST LION (IRE) | 27 | 5 | 5 | 18 | 45294.87 |
| THE WOW SIGNAL (IRE) | 4 | 1 | 5 | 2 | 17586.96 |
| THEWAYYOUARE (USA) | 22 | 8 | 12 | 10 | 74174.08 |
| TIN HORSE (IRE) | 1 | 1 | 2 | 0 | 8816.61 |
| TORONADO (IRE) | 84 | 25 | 40 | 63 | 391791.29 |
| TOUGH AS NAILS (IRE) | 13 | 5 | 8 | 18 | 73364.49 |
| TWILIGHT SON (GB) | 68 | 17 | 17 | 50 | 154879.34 |
| TWIRLING CANDY (USA) | 2 | 1 | 2 | 3 | 10107.97 |
| UNCLE MO (USA) | 7 | 2 | 3 | 7 | 59067.87 |
| UNION RAGS (USA) | 2 | 2 | 5 | 4 | 18452.23 |
| UNIVERSAL (IRE) | 10 | 3 | 4 | 6 | 45573.28 |
| VADAMOS (FR) | 34 | 8 | 10 | 15 | 75973.76 |

| STALLIONS | RNRS | WNRS | WINS | PLACES | TOTAL (£) |
|---|---|---|---|---|---|
| VALE OF YORK (IRE) | 17 | 4 | 5 | 25 | 53499.50 |
| VINNIE ROE (IRE) | 1 | 1 | 1 | 2 | 47720.34 |
| VIRTUAL (GB) | 2 | 2 | 2 | 4 | 9596.96 |
| VOCALISED (USA) | 33 | 6 | 7 | 19 | 98684.69 |
| WAR COMMAND (USA) | 66 | 21 | 31 | 48 | 234319.85 |
| WAR FRONT (USA) | 55 | 21 | 35 | 70 | 485074.45 |
| WELL CHOSEN (GB) | 1 | 1 | 1 | 0 | 5500.00 |
| WHITMORE'S CONN (USA) | 1 | 1 | 2 | 1 | 10101.69 |
| WINDSOR KNOT (IRE) | 3 | 2 | 3 | 4 | 15190.22 |
| WOOTTON BASSETT (GB) | 27 | 12 | 19 | 21 | 225987.08 |
| XTENSION (IRE) | 7 | 4 | 6 | 5 | 63928.45 |
| YEATS (IRE) | 8 | 3 | 4 | 6 | 24486.94 |
| YORGUNNABELUCKY (USA) | 8 | 2 | 4 | 4 | 28263.62 |
| YOUMZAIN (IRE) | 8 | 3 | 3 | 4 | 61197.11 |
| ZAMINDAR (USA) | 5 | 1 | 3 | 3 | 59505.33 |
| ZEBEDEE (GB) | 106 | 38 | 62 | 109 | 614093.35 |
| ZOFFANY (IRE) | 219 | 72 | 96 | 232 | 1318703.59 |

*BY KIND PERMISSION OF WEATHERBYS*

# NH STALLIONS' EARNINGS FOR 2019/20

(includes every stallion who sired a winner over jumps in Great Britain and Ireland in 2019/20)

| STALLIONS | RNRS | STARTS | WNRS | WINS | PLACES | TOTAL (£) |
|---|---|---|---|---|---|---|
| ACAMBARO (GER) | 4 | 19 | 2 | 3 | 9 | 25071.18 |
| ACT ONE (GB) | 5 | 16 | 1 | 1 | 9 | 7307.71 |
| ADMIRE MOON (JPN) | 1 | 2 | 1 | 1 | 1 | 13332.62 |
| AIR CHIEF MARSHAL (IRE) | 5 | 21 | 3 | 7 | 11 | 63039.51 |
| AIZAVOSKI (IRE) | 29 | 79 | 9 | 12 | 36 | 85014.44 |
| ALANADI (FR) | 1 | 6 | 1 | 2 | 3 | 33431.42 |
| ALBANO (IRE) | 2 | 9 | 1 | 1 | 7 | 3741.20 |
| ALBERTO GIACOMETTI (IRE) | 4 | 15 | 1 | 1 | 10 | 11554.66 |
| ALDERBROOK (GB) | 2 | 12 | 1 | 1 | 9 | 8526.56 |
| ALEXANDROS (GB) | 1 | 4 | 1 | 1 | 2 | 4994.42 |
| ALFLORA (IRE) | 25 | 79 | 3 | 3 | 46 | 125422.97 |
| ALFRED NOBEL (IRE) | 5 | 24 | 3 | 5 | 6 | 45270.63 |
| ALKAADHEM (GB) | 14 | 42 | 2 | 3 | 14 | 49395.25 |
| AL NAMIX (FR) | 35 | 112 | 10 | 13 | 66 | 290045.73 |
| AMADEUS WOLF (GB) | 3 | 5 | 1 | 1 | 4 | 6308.52 |
| AMERICAN POST (GB) | 7 | 26 | 3 | 3 | 15 | 35325.98 |
| ANABAA BLUE (GB) | 9 | 25 | 6 | 7 | 12 | 57998.46 |
| AND BEYOND (IRE) | 8 | 20 | 4 | 4 | 8 | 22504.58 |
| ANODIN (IRE) | 1 | 4 | 1 | 1 | 2 | 27324.50 |
| ANTONIUS PIUS (USA) | 6 | 28 | 2 | 3 | 11 | 21066.00 |
| ANZILLERO (GER) | 8 | 25 | 2 | 2 | 13 | 34928.31 |
| APPLE TREE (FR) | 10 | 34 | 3 | 3 | 16 | 40504.69 |
| AQLAAM (GB) | 10 | 34 | 1 | 2 | 19 | 29058.00 |
| ARAAFA (IRE) | 3 | 22 | 1 | 2 | 15 | 19286.21 |
| ARAKAN (USA) | 60 | 280 | 18 | 30 | 134 | 324459.82 |
| ARCADIO (GER) | 132 | 483 | 28 | 45 | 193 | 532078.06 |
| ARCANO (IRE) | 23 | 74 | 3 | 3 | 38 | 33656.90 |
| ARCHIPENKO (USA) | 12 | 40 | 3 | 4 | 19 | 29582.74 |
| ARCTIC COSMOS (USA) | 20 | 71 | 4 | 4 | 28 | 41539.95 |
| AREION (GER) | 1 | 7 | 1 | 3 | 4 | 28235.16 |
| ARVICO (FR) | 26 | 83 | 3 | 4 | 21 | 24131.76 |
| ASHKALANI (IRE) | 1 | 3 | 1 | 1 | 0 | 6659.46 |
| ASK (GB) | 78 | 287 | 16 | 27 | 143 | 319936.09 |
| ASTARABAD (USA) | 9 | 28 | 3 | 3 | 14 | 45493.15 |
| AUSTRALIA (GB) | 9 | 28 | 3 | 3 | 15 | 36610.09 |
| AUTHORIZED (IRE) | 54 | 200 | 22 | 32 | 121 | 441514.67 |
| AXXOS (GER) | 3 | 15 | 2 | 2 | 10 | 34876.90 |
| AZAMOUR (IRE) | 25 | 73 | 6 | 7 | 29 | 62752.48 |
| BACHELOR DUKE (USA) | 2 | 14 | 1 | 2 | 4 | 9952.46 |
| BAHRI (USA) | 10 | 24 | 1 | 2 | 8 | 13916.50 |
| BALKO (FR) | 25 | 83 | 11 | 15 | 41 | 149881.08 |
| BALLINGARRY (IRE) | 19 | 70 | 8 | 9 | 36 | 225408.25 |
| BANDMASTER (USA) | 2 | 13 | 1 | 1 | 4 | 17225.80 |
| BARASTRAIGHT (GB) | 3 | 9 | 1 | 1 | 6 | 38648.74 |
| BARATHEA (IRE) | 2 | 15 | 2 | 2 | 9 | 15010.26 |
| BATTLE OF MARENGO (IRE) | 6 | 26 | 2 | 4 | 11 | 34245.62 |
| BEAT ALL (USA) | 6 | 40 | 1 | 1 | 25 | 22315.86 |
| BEAT HOLLOW (GB) | 73 | 235 | 25 | 34 | 105 | 468312.51 |
| BENEFICIAL (GB) | 172 | 686 | 53 | 81 | 352 | 1254128.71 |
| BERING | 1 | 4 | 1 | 1 | 3 | 6527.60 |
| BERNEBEAU (FR) | 6 | 24 | 4 | 5 | 10 | 56061.29 |
| BIENAMADO (USA) | 5 | 22 | 1 | 1 | 12 | 11224.73 |
| BIG BAD BOB (IRE) | 33 | 120 | 7 | 10 | 59 | 177903.15 |
| BLACK SAM BELLAMY (IRE) | 108 | 378 | 37 | 54 | 186 | 483953.46 |
| BLAME (USA) | 1 | 6 | 1 | 5 | 1 | 50252.12 |
| BLUE BRESIL (FR) | 26 | 83 | 9 | 12 | 41 | 114906.99 |
| BLUEPRINT (IRE) | 11 | 41 | 5 | 8 | 15 | 81266.30 |

| STALLIONS | RNRS | STARTS | WNRS | WINS | PLACES | TOTAL (£) |
|---|---|---|---|---|---|---|
| BOLLIN ERIC (GB) | 17 | 44 | 4 | 4 | 17 | 42028.23 |
| BONBON ROSE (FR) | 9 | 44 | 2 | 4 | 16 | 58585.22 |
| BORIS DE DEAUVILLE (IRE) | 1 | 8 | 1 | 1 | 6 | 5969.48 |
| BORN TO SEA (IRE) | 29 | 131 | 14 | 24 | 66 | 318020.45 |
| BRIAN BORU (GB) | 61 | 265 | 17 | 26 | 149 | 366285.09 |
| BRIER CREEK (USA) | 2 | 12 | 1 | 1 | 10 | 12736.57 |
| BROADWAY FLYER (USA) | 3 | 17 | 1 | 1 | 10 | 18765.39 |
| BUCK'S BOUM (FR) | 13 | 33 | 3 | 5 | 21 | 540060.21 |
| BUSHRANGER (IRE) | 10 | 45 | 2 | 2 | 23 | 29569.73 |
| BYRON (GB) | 4 | 9 | 1 | 2 | 1 | 13900.86 |
| CACIQUE (IRE) | 11 | 41 | 4 | 5 | 21 | 67421.41 |
| CALCUTTA (GB) | 1 | 5 | 1 | 1 | 3 | 8338.39 |
| CALIFET (FR) | 35 | 113 | 8 | 14 | 42 | 194330.51 |
| CAMACHO (GB) | 11 | 37 | 4 | 6 | 20 | 47936.67 |
| CAMELOT (GB) | 27 | 83 | 5 | 5 | 47 | 80854.10 |
| CANFORD CLIFFS (IRE) | 37 | 111 | 9 | 11 | 62 | 216862.08 |
| CAPE CROSS (IRE) | 25 | 97 | 10 | 15 | 44 | 140640.45 |
| CAPTAIN RIO (GB) | 9 | 42 | 4 | 5 | 23 | 43209.32 |
| CARLO BANK (IRE) | 4 | 20 | 2 | 3 | 13 | 23658.88 |
| CARLOTAMIX (FR) | 14 | 50 | 3 | 3 | 17 | 25479.17 |
| CASAMENTO (IRE) | 29 | 77 | 6 | 6 | 27 | 81778.37 |
| CATCHER IN THE RYE (IRE) | 4 | 11 | 1 | 1 | 8 | 14123.50 |
| CELTIC SWING (GB) | 2 | 5 | 1 | 1 | 3 | 7287.02 |
| CENTRAL PARK (IRE) | 14 | 57 | 5 | 8 | 22 | 169048.86 |
| CHAMPS ELYSEES (GB) | 49 | 163 | 13 | 21 | 85 | 213318.00 |
| CHEVALIER (IRE) | 4 | 18 | 1 | 1 | 9 | 21030.65 |
| CIMA DE TRIOMPHE (IRE) | 1 | 4 | 1 | 2 | 1 | 42104.92 |
| CITYSCAPE (GB) | 10 | 31 | 1 | 2 | 9 | 24577.05 |
| CLASSIC CLICHE (IRE) | 5 | 20 | 1 | 1 | 6 | 31826.29 |
| CLODOVIL (IRE) | 11 | 36 | 3 | 5 | 17 | 34989.28 |
| CLOUDINGS (IRE) | 31 | 109 | 10 | 16 | 51 | 180560.89 |
| COACH HOUSE (IRE) | 1 | 5 | 1 | 1 | 4 | 7732.62 |
| COASTAL PATH (GB) | 26 | 78 | 9 | 17 | 38 | 352335.80 |
| COCKNEY REBEL (IRE) | 4 | 19 | 1 | 1 | 10 | 10611.72 |
| COKORIKO (FR) | 20 | 64 | 5 | 7 | 30 | 112086.91 |
| CORONER (IRE) | 4 | 17 | 1 | 2 | 10 | 18744.98 |
| CORRI PIANO (FR) | 2 | 13 | 1 | 1 | 10 | 10659.82 |
| COURT CAVE (IRE) | 142 | 609 | 40 | 63 | 285 | 740582.22 |
| CRAIGSTEEL (GB) | 52 | 228 | 13 | 23 | 122 | 297805.02 |
| CREACHADOIR (IRE) | 9 | 37 | 4 | 6 | 15 | 91161.27 |
| CRILLON (FR) | 8 | 22 | 2 | 4 | 11 | 109859.86 |
| CROSSHARBOUR (GB) | 3 | 14 | 2 | 2 | 11 | 26204.76 |
| CURTAIN TIME (IRE) | 17 | 76 | 5 | 7 | 46 | 86457.33 |
| DADARISSIME (FR) | 1 | 5 | 1 | 1 | 4 | 11006.80 |
| DAHJEE (USA) | 6 | 31 | 1 | 1 | 15 | 11391.36 |
| DALAKHANI (IRE) | 8 | 27 | 1 | 1 | 11 | 14639.38 |
| DANEHILL DANCER (IRE) | 10 | 36 | 3 | 4 | 20 | 44126.44 |
| DANSANT (GB) | 17 | 56 | 3 | 3 | 27 | 45977.88 |
| DANSILI (GB) | 22 | 78 | 9 | 12 | 40 | 106094.36 |
| DAPPER (GB) | 2 | 5 | 1 | 1 | 3 | 8529.74 |
| DARK ANGEL (IRE) | 24 | 83 | 7 | 7 | 36 | 129724.71 |
| DARSI (FR) | 26 | 90 | 4 | 4 | 48 | 97486.63 |
| DAVIDOFF (GER) | 4 | 18 | 2 | 4 | 7 | 133010.99 |
| DAY FLIGHT (GB) | 7 | 23 | 3 | 5 | 11 | 54341.18 |
| DAYLAMI (IRE) | 17 | 61 | 7 | 10 | 27 | 84919.36 |
| DECLARATION OF WAR (USA) | 16 | 37 | 3 | 3 | 13 | 24022.38 |
| DEFINITE ARTICLE (GB) | 38 | 153 | 13 | 20 | 72 | 245896.04 |
| DELEGATOR (GB) | 5 | 11 | 1 | 2 | 3 | 76990.04 |
| DELLA FRANCESCA (USA) | 11 | 48 | 1 | 1 | 27 | 57233.32 |
| DENHAM RED (FR) | 11 | 35 | 2 | 3 | 18 | 93254.10 |
| DESERT KING (IRE) | 8 | 34 | 4 | 7 | 20 | 48859.60 |

| STALLIONS | RNRS | STARTS | WNRS | WINS | PLACES | TOTAL (£) |
|---|---|---|---|---|---|---|
| DESERT STYLE (IRE) | 1 | 4 | 1 | 3 | 0 | 18556.94 |
| DESIDERATUM (GB) | 3 | 9 | 1 | 1 | 6 | 9616.12 |
| DESIR D'UN SOIR (FR) | 2 | 9 | 1 | 2 | 3 | 20234.87 |
| DIAMOND BOY (FR) | 16 | 62 | 7 | 9 | 33 | 196090.81 |
| DICK TURPIN (IRE) | 10 | 33 | 1 | 2 | 10 | 21316.40 |
| DINK (FR) | 1 | 4 | 1 | 2 | 2 | 33610.22 |
| DISCOVER D'AUTEUIL (FR) | 4 | 18 | 2 | 2 | 10 | 17127.22 |
| DOCTOR DINO (FR) | 9 | 36 | 3 | 4 | 22 | 260753.61 |
| DOM ALCO (FR) | 11 | 35 | 5 | 7 | 17 | 56587.75 |
| DOUBLE ECLIPSE (IRE) | 8 | 33 | 4 | 4 | 17 | 30384.07 |
| DOYEN (IRE) | 99 | 423 | 32 | 41 | 197 | 560046.56 |
| DRAGON DANCER (GB) | 1 | 5 | 1 | 1 | 1 | 14311.75 |
| DRAGON PULSE (IRE) | 16 | 50 | 1 | 1 | 22 | 22342.58 |
| DREAM AHEAD (USA) | 4 | 19 | 2 | 2 | 10 | 22450.60 |
| DREAM EATER (IRE) | 2 | 11 | 1 | 1 | 3 | 4270.23 |
| DREAM WELL (FR) | 11 | 35 | 2 | 3 | 22 | 63012.71 |
| DR FONG (USA) | 4 | 10 | 1 | 1 | 7 | 7726.42 |
| DR MASSINI (IRE) | 34 | 142 | 10 | 11 | 77 | 131211.07 |
| DUBAI DESTINATION (USA) | 73 | 281 | 20 | 30 | 140 | 395866.30 |
| DUBAWI (IRE) | 14 | 39 | 3 | 3 | 19 | 27061.03 |
| DUKE OF MARMALADE (IRE) | 26 | 84 | 9 | 11 | 39 | 114119.30 |
| DUNADEN (FR) | 1 | 6 | 1 | 2 | 4 | 20167.14 |
| DUSHYANTOR (USA) | 4 | 29 | 3 | 3 | 11 | 25808.33 |
| DYLAN THOMAS (IRE) | 54 | 194 | 10 | 14 | 81 | 153228.18 |
| EARLY MARCH (GB) | 5 | 16 | 3 | 4 | 7 | 27342.48 |
| EASTERN ANTHEM (IRE) | 5 | 17 | 1 | 1 | 11 | 9520.87 |
| ECHO OF LIGHT (GB) | 10 | 35 | 2 | 2 | 17 | 22325.46 |
| ELECTRIC BEAT (GB) | 1 | 7 | 1 | 2 | 3 | 39468.02 |
| ELUSIVE PIMPERNEL (USA) | 41 | 152 | 14 | 20 | 68 | 253081.38 |
| ELZAAM (AUS) | 7 | 31 | 3 | 4 | 16 | 36113.09 |
| EMPEROR FOUNTAIN | 1 | 5 | 1 | 1 | 3 | 5629.67 |
| ENDOLI (USA) | 1 | 4 | 1 | 2 | 2 | 11394.72 |
| ENGLISH CHANNEL (USA) | 1 | 9 | 1 | 2 | 4 | 21510.74 |
| ENRIQUE (GB) | 15 | 59 | 8 | 10 | 30 | 73353.63 |
| EPAULETTE (AUS) | 5 | 13 | 1 | 1 | 4 | 7260.36 |
| EQUERRY (USA) | 1 | 2 | 1 | 1 | 0 | 17204.00 |
| EXCEED AND EXCEL (AUS) | 7 | 20 | 1 | 2 | 8 | 13856.53 |
| EXCELEBRATION (IRE) | 15 | 54 | 3 | 3 | 28 | 36166.50 |
| EXCELLENT ART (GB) | 12 | 64 | 3 | 7 | 26 | 47634.86 |
| EXCHANGE RATE (USA) | 3 | 14 | 1 | 1 | 4 | 7623.42 |
| EXIT TO NOWHERE (USA) | 10 | 42 | 4 | 6 | 24 | 80041.96 |
| FAIRLY RANSOM (USA) | 9 | 31 | 2 | 2 | 14 | 27755.29 |
| FAIR MIX (IRE) | 63 | 220 | 12 | 14 | 102 | 197658.09 |
| FALCO (USA) | 5 | 19 | 1 | 2 | 11 | 26283.39 |
| FAME AND GLORY (GB) | 128 | 382 | 33 | 49 | 186 | 456492.78 |
| FAMOUS NAME (GB) | 13 | 52 | 2 | 2 | 25 | 25556.26 |
| FARHH (GB) | 2 | 8 | 1 | 1 | 3 | 6671.07 |
| FAST COMPANY (IRE) | 27 | 82 | 5 | 6 | 38 | 108175.42 |
| FASTNET ROCK (AUS) | 9 | 29 | 1 | 1 | 5 | 12074.93 |
| FEEL LIKE DANCING (GB) | 1 | 5 | 1 | 1 | 3 | 7756.30 |
| FINANCIAL REWARD (IRE) | 1 | 7 | 1 | 1 | 5 | 7551.34 |
| FINE GRAIN (JPN) | 1 | 5 | 1 | 2 | 1 | 14968.99 |
| FINSCEAL FIOR (IRE) | 10 | 28 | 2 | 3 | 6 | 26527.00 |
| FLEMENSFIRTH (USA) | 247 | 807 | 69 | 90 | 426 | 1601106.63 |
| FLYING LEGEND (USA) | 8 | 31 | 2 | 3 | 17 | 31868.90 |
| FOOTSTEPSINTHESAND (GB) | 17 | 70 | 4 | 5 | 36 | 50766.8 |
| FORESTIER (FR) | 3 | 5 | 1 | 1 | 3 | 49612.00 |
| FOXWEDGE (AUS) | 13 | 37 | 1 | 2 | 14 | 29751.0 |
| FRACAS (IRE) | 13 | 54 | 7 | 9 | 23 | 70770.0 |
| FRAGRANT MIX (IRE) | 11 | 53 | 4 | 5 | 28 | 49486.2 |
| FRAMMASSONE (IRE) | 6 | 22 | 3 | 4 | 10 | 27191.6 |

| STALLIONS | RNRS | STARTS | WNRS | WINS | PLACES | TOTAL (£) |
|---|---|---|---|---|---|---|
| FRENCH FIFTEEN (FR) | 4 | 9 | 2 | 2 | 5 | 13007.51 |
| FROZEN FIRE (GER) | 6 | 21 | 2 | 2 | 8 | 16281.18 |
| FROZEN POWER (IRE) | 11 | 35 | 2 | 2 | 13 | 17182.95 |
| FRUITS OF LOVE (USA) | 33 | 125 | 12 | 14 | 60 | 157016.84 |
| FUISSE (FR) | 13 | 46 | 3 | 3 | 24 | 42355.86 |
| GALE FORCE TEN (GB) | 6 | 14 | 2 | 3 | 2 | 13045.98 |
| GALILEO (IRE) | 65 | 221 | 14 | 19 | 101 | 229470.26 |
| GAMUT (IRE) | 33 | 100 | 6 | 8 | 53 | 183072.46 |
| GARUDA (IRE) | 2 | 2 | 1 | 1 | 0 | 7116.00 |
| GENEROUS (IRE) | 18 | 73 | 4 | 9 | 39 | 88195.01 |
| GENTLEMAN'S DEAL (IRE) | 1 | 3 | 1 | 1 | 1 | 6075.02 |
| GENTLEWAVE (IRE) | 12 | 40 | 6 | 8 | 23 | 233147.23 |
| GEORDIELAND (FR) | 18 | 50 | 2 | 2 | 12 | 14615.35 |
| GERMANY (USA) | 11 | 47 | 3 | 6 | 18 | 291339.51 |
| GETAWAY (GER) | 244 | 866 | 75 | 98 | 377 | 1081077.64 |
| GLORY OF DANCER (GB) | 1 | 5 | 1 | 1 | 3 | 4455.26 |
| GOLAN (IRE) | 29 | 112 | 8 | 9 | 49 | 166698.57 |
| GOLDEN LARIAT (USA) | 17 | 62 | 3 | 7 | 22 | 55554.03 |
| GOLDEN TORNADO (IRE) | 10 | 43 | 3 | 5 | 14 | 85471.50 |
| GOLD WELL (GB) | 181 | 771 | 66 | 104 | 403 | 1220249.23 |
| GRAND COUTURIER (GB) | 1 | 10 | 1 | 1 | 6 | 8673.64 |
| GRAPE TREE ROAD (GB) | 5 | 25 | 1 | 1 | 18 | 16369.70 |
| GREAT EXHIBITION (USA) | 5 | 24 | 3 | 4 | 13 | 32821.56 |
| GREAT PRETENDER (IRE) | 38 | 136 | 13 | 24 | 59 | 338356.93 |
| GREEN TUNE (USA) | 1 | 5 | 1 | 1 | 2 | 7527.96 |
| GRIS DE GRIS (IRE) | 10 | 45 | 3 | 4 | 32 | 59833.48 |
| HAAFHD (GB) | 9 | 30 | 3 | 4 | 15 | 49817.84 |
| HAATEF (USA) | 7 | 20 | 1 | 1 | 6 | 6515.57 |
| HALLING (USA) | 9 | 31 | 2 | 3 | 19 | 61026.07 |
| HARBOUR WATCH (IRE) | 16 | 58 | 6 | 6 | 29 | 49433.80 |
| HARD SPUN (USA) | 3 | 22 | 2 | 5 | 15 | 56975.87 |
| HAT TRICK (JPN) | 1 | 6 | 1 | 1 | 5 | 11221.65 |
| HAVANA GOLD (IRE) | 7 | 21 | 1 | 1 | 8 | 9923.95 |
| HELIOSTATIC (IRE) | 5 | 12 | 3 | 4 | 3 | 35667.57 |
| HELISSIO (FR) | 9 | 26 | 1 | 1 | 13 | 11926.97 |
| HELLO SUNDAY (FR) | 1 | 7 | 1 | 3 | 3 | 27909.86 |
| HELMET (AUS) | 21 | 65 | 3 | 5 | 36 | 50640.65 |
| HENRYTHENAVIGATOR (USA) | 5 | 25 | 2 | 3 | 12 | 21855.79 |
| HERNANDO (FR) | 2 | 10 | 1 | 1 | 7 | 15447.42 |
| HERON ISLAND (IRE) | 17 | 46 | 5 | 5 | 27 | 54576.03 |
| HIGH CHAPARRAL (IRE) | 49 | 158 | 11 | 16 | 70 | 224553.24 |
| HIGH ROCK (IRE) | 4 | 7 | 1 | 2 | 2 | 19986.66 |
| HIGH ROLLER (IRE) | 1 | 5 | 1 | 1 | 2 | 13184.82 |
| HOLY ROMAN EMPEROR (IRE) | 19 | 72 | 4 | 5 | 49 | 62133.87 |
| HONOLULU (IRE) | 3 | 10 | 2 | 2 | 3 | 18944.85 |
| HUMBEL (USA) | 3 | 10 | 1 | 1 | 3 | 4637.60 |
| HURRICANE CAT (USA) | 3 | 12 | 2 | 4 | 7 | 19433.57 |
| IFFRAAJ (GB) | 24 | 77 | 6 | 9 | 34 | 101338.24 |
| IMPERIAL BALLET (IRE) | 1 | 6 | 1 | 1 | 2 | 6578.39 |
| IMPERIAL MONARCH (IRE) | 15 | 46 | 2 | 4 | 14 | 39792.05 |
| INCLUDE (USA) | 1 | 8 | 1 | 1 | 6 | 6276.84 |
| INDIAN DAFFODIL (IRE) | 2 | 6 | 1 | 3 | 1 | 89061.25 |
| INDIAN DANEHILL (IRE) | 12 | 51 | 5 | 8 | 22 | 143242.42 |
| INDIAN RIVER (FR) | 19 | 71 | 5 | 8 | 42 | 188613.82 |
| INTENSE FOCUS (USA) | 18 | 59 | 2 | 3 | 32 | 31716.16 |
| INTIKHAB (USA) | 17 | 58 | 6 | 7 | 32 | 67487.70 |
| INVINCIBLE SPIRIT (IRE) | 18 | 50 | 4 | 5 | 23 | 39316.79 |
| IRISH WELLS (FR) | 10 | 33 | 3 | 5 | 22 | 66758.54 |
| ISLAND HOUSE (IRE) | 1 | 2 | 1 | 2 | 0 | 5208.85 |
| IT'S GINO (GER) | 6 | 24 | 2 | 3 | 11 | 44423.52 |
| JEREMY (USA) | 150 | 557 | 42 | 56 | 239 | 874263.45 |

| STALLIONS | RNRS | STARTS | WNRS | WINS | PLACES | TOTAL (£) |
|---|---|---|---|---|---|---|
| JIMBLE (FR) | 6 | 22 | 1 | 2 | 12 | 15811.19 |
| JOSR ALGARHOUD (IRE) | 4 | 14 | 1 | 1 | 6 | 6717.22 |
| JUKEBOX JURY (IRE) | 9 | 31 | 6 | 12 | 13 | 112511.04 |
| KADASTROF (FR) | 3 | 5 | 1 | 1 | 1 | 15237.78 |
| KADEED (IRE) | 2 | 16 | 2 | 3 | 7 | 27843.88 |
| KALANISI (IRE) | 127 | 410 | 28 | 44 | 187 | 783424.11 |
| KALLISTO (GER) | 1 | 5 | 1 | 1 | 4 | 6892.54 |
| KAMSIN (GER) | 5 | 13 | 1 | 1 | 3 | 8507.50 |
| KAPGARDE (FR) | 68 | 261 | 21 | 30 | 151 | 741784.49 |
| KAP ROCK (FR) | 9 | 27 | 4 | 5 | 12 | 60330.60 |
| KAYF TARA (GB) | 179 | 569 | 51 | 69 | 284 | 927701.56 |
| KENDARGENT (FR) | 6 | 27 | 2 | 3 | 11 | 56474.24 |
| KENTUCKY DYNAMITE (USA) | 6 | 20 | 4 | 5 | 13 | 39507.34 |
| KEY OF LUCK (USA) | 1 | 7 | 1 | 1 | 5 | 6341.53 |
| KHALKEVI (IRE) | 14 | 42 | 2 | 3 | 25 | 68387.38 |
| KHELEYF (USA) | 11 | 36 | 2 | 4 | 15 | 25222.09 |
| KINGSALSA (USA) | 7 | 31 | 3 | 5 | 12 | 87627.63 |
| KING'S BEST (USA) | 4 | 13 | 1 | 2 | 7 | 48454.71 |
| KING'S THEATRE (IRE) | 102 | 428 | 44 | 71 | 234 | 1393274.63 |
| KODIAC (GB) | 12 | 48 | 1 | 1 | 20 | 20503.63 |
| KONIG TURF (GER) | 8 | 29 | 2 | 3 | 19 | 68352.10 |
| KRIS KIN (USA) | 2 | 9 | 1 | 1 | 0 | 7250.00 |
| KUTUB (IRE) | 11 | 38 | 1 | 1 | 15 | 16946.89 |
| LAURO (GER) | 5 | 14 | 3 | 4 | 7 | 36641.16 |
| LAVERON (GB) | 5 | 13 | 1 | 1 | 3 | 7464.28 |
| LAVIRCO (GER) | 2 | 8 | 1 | 2 | 3 | 56385.48 |
| LAWMAN (FR) | 36 | 109 | 8 | 9 | 45 | 109410.73 |
| LE FOU (IRE) | 26 | 95 | 5 | 5 | 47 | 58119.34 |
| LEGOLAS (JPN) | 1 | 2 | 1 | 1 | 1 | 11935.17 |
| LE HAVRE (IRE) | 14 | 41 | 5 | 8 | 21 | 99163.90 |
| LETHAL FORCE (IRE) | 6 | 35 | 3 | 4 | 17 | 53609.37 |
| LET THE LION ROAR (GB) | 8 | 34 | 1 | 2 | 16 | 23773.98 |
| LIBRETTIST (USA) | 9 | 33 | 3 | 4 | 18 | 43678.68 |
| LILBOURNE LAD (IRE) | 15 | 40 | 1 | 1 | 13 | 29069.48 |
| LINDA'S LAD (GB) | 16 | 69 | 9 | 14 | 40 | 173887.84 |
| LOPE DE VEGA (IRE) | 21 | 70 | 4 | 6 | 21 | 50492.13 |
| LORD DU SUD (FR) | 19 | 61 | 4 | 6 | 33 | 78810.53 |
| LORD OF ENGLAND (GER) | 4 | 13 | 1 | 1 | 4 | 11096.80 |
| LORD SHANAKILL (USA) | 16 | 60 | 4 | 6 | 32 | 65893.87 |
| LOUP BRETON (IRE) | 2 | 10 | 1 | 2 | 2 | 60452.91 |
| LOVELACE (GB) | 2 | 12 | 1 | 3 | 4 | 21650.48 |
| LUCARNO (USA) | 28 | 91 | 5 | 7 | 41 | 126111.40 |
| LUSO (GB) | 2 | 15 | 2 | 2 | 10 | 14841.58 |
| MAHLER (GB) | 201 | 748 | 53 | 72 | 356 | 921206.37 |
| MAJESTIC MISSILE (IRE) | 3 | 10 | 2 | 3 | 4 | 23767.16 |
| MAKFI (GB) | 16 | 49 | 2 | 5 | 18 | 41496.33 |
| MALINAS (GER) | 78 | 227 | 22 | 30 | 111 | 369695.60 |
| MAMOOL (IRE) | 4 | 14 | 1 | 1 | 9 | 10174.19 |
| MANDURO (GER) | 14 | 48 | 5 | 8 | 21 | 69182.23 |
| MARESCA SORRENTO (FR) | 21 | 74 | 8 | 13 | 36 | 99846.64 |
| MARIENBARD (IRE) | 15 | 48 | 2 | 4 | 20 | 25689.70 |
| MARTALINE (GB) | 93 | 306 | 37 | 44 | 147 | 637350.36 |
| MASKED MARVEL (GB) | 2 | 7 | 1 | 1 | 6 | 9937.07 |
| MASTERCRAFTSMAN (IRE) | 61 | 241 | 23 | 31 | 114 | 360181.44 |
| MASTEROFTHEHORSE (IRE) | 11 | 40 | 2 | 2 | 16 | 19154.92 |
| MAWATHEEQ (USA) | 9 | 27 | 2 | 2 | 18 | 18312.11 |
| MAXIOS (GB) | 15 | 51 | 7 | 11 | 23 | 147730.12 |
| MEDAALY (GB) | 3 | 21 | 1 | 1 | 10 | 13120.32 |
| MEDICEAN (GB) | 28 | 109 | 8 | 9 | 60 | 161971.72 |
| MESHAHEER (USA) | 1 | 3 | 1 | 1 | 1 | 4717.48 |
| MIDNIGHT LEGEND (GB) | 147 | 537 | 48 | 66 | 278 | 703814.52 |

| STALLIONS | RNRS | STARTS | WNRS | WINS | PLACES | TOTAL (£) |
|---|---|---|---|---|---|---|
| MILAN (GB) | 263 | 970 | 69 | 104 | 460 | 1871324.99 |
| MILLENARY (GB) | 20 | 81 | 8 | 14 | 33 | 156068.14 |
| MISTER FOTIS (USA) | 3 | 11 | 1 | 4 | 2 | 24347.96 |
| MIZZEN MAST (USA) | 2 | 6 | 1 | 1 | 4 | 6870.96 |
| MONITOR CLOSELY (IRE) | 1 | 6 | 1 | 2 | 4 | 87114.60 |
| MONTJEU (IRE) | 10 | 41 | 3 | 3 | 21 | 67651.11 |
| MONTMARTRE (FR) | 25 | 86 | 6 | 11 | 43 | 145209.95 |
| MOOHAAJIM (IRE) | 1 | 6 | 1 | 1 | 3 | 14188.36 |
| MORES WELLS (GB) | 3 | 5 | 1 | 1 | 2 | 2742.77 |
| MOROZOV (USA) | 45 | 184 | 13 | 17 | 82 | 170175.97 |
| MORPETH (GB) | 2 | 5 | 1 | 1 | 0 | 4808.52 |
| MOSCOW SOCIETY (USA) | 3 | 11 | 1 | 1 | 7 | 7501.91 |
| MOTIVATOR (GB) | 18 | 59 | 7 | 12 | 28 | 142568.44 |
| MOUNTAIN HIGH (IRE) | 53 | 207 | 15 | 21 | 89 | 258762.25 |
| MOUNT NELSON (GB) | 32 | 101 | 9 | 10 | 52 | 110023.08 |
| MR DINOS (IRE) | 16 | 61 | 3 | 3 | 29 | 52019.73 |
| MUHAYMIN (USA) | 3 | 14 | 2 | 2 | 7 | 15909.17 |
| MUHTATHIR (GB) | 19 | 56 | 4 | 9 | 32 | 293811.76 |
| MUKHADRAM (GB) | 4 | 11 | 2 | 2 | 7 | 11677.36 |
| MULLIONMILEANHOUR (IRE) | 1 | 12 | 1 | 1 | 9 | 7862.46 |
| MULTIPLEX (GB) | 52 | 182 | 16 | 21 | 88 | 192569.15 |
| MUSTAMEET (USA) | 24 | 79 | 2 | 2 | 34 | 45573.34 |
| MYBOYCHARLIE (IRE) | 6 | 15 | 2 | 3 | 5 | 23082.01 |
| NATHANIEL (IRE) | 36 | 118 | 16 | 23 | 56 | 339013.67 |
| NATIVE RULER (GB) | 10 | 27 | 1 | 1 | 11 | 12271.30 |
| NAYEF (USA) | 17 | 67 | 4 | 4 | 35 | 41623.25 |
| NAZAR (IRE) | 2 | 13 | 1 | 1 | 5 | 9378.37 |
| NETWORK (GER) | 56 | 195 | 19 | 31 | 98 | 796585.73 |
| NEW APPROACH (IRE) | 24 | 82 | 7 | 9 | 33 | 83187.40 |
| NICKNAME (FR) | 10 | 42 | 5 | 6 | 21 | 283167.95 |
| NICOBAR (GB) | 2 | 7 | 1 | 1 | 4 | 7457.10 |
| NIDOR (FR) | 1 | 4 | 1 | 1 | 3 | 34934.85 |
| NOBLE MISSION (GB) | 3 | 6 | 1 | 2 | 2 | 11038.98 |
| NO RISK AT ALL (FR) | 32 | 103 | 18 | 25 | 46 | 636586.80 |
| NOROIT (GER) | 16 | 54 | 3 | 4 | 25 | 47924.98 |
| NORSE DANCER (IRE) | 20 | 60 | 3 | 3 | 23 | 27247.29 |
| NORTHERN LEGEND (GB) | 1 | 8 | 1 | 2 | 6 | 27772.41 |
| NOTNOWCATO (GB) | 14 | 39 | 1 | 2 | 17 | 17322.69 |
| OASIS DREAM (GB) | 13 | 31 | 1 | 1 | 14 | 16577.38 |
| OCOVANGO (GB) | 4 | 8 | 1 | 2 | 4 | 26522.54 |
| OLDEN TIMES (GB) | 8 | 31 | 1 | 3 | 15 | 29886.71 |
| OLD VIC | 12 | 34 | 2 | 6 | 13 | 148852.99 |
| OLYMPIC GLORY (IRE) | 5 | 19 | 2 | 2 | 13 | 20079.01 |
| ORATORIO (IRE) | 3 | 11 | 1 | 2 | 4 | 8481.06 |
| ORPEN (USA) | 3 | 18 | 1 | 2 | 11 | 17453.43 |
| OSCAR (IRE) | 237 | 862 | 63 | 83 | 437 | 1457106.38 |
| OVERBURY (IRE) | 23 | 87 | 9 | 13 | 53 | 100606.76 |
| PACO BOY (IRE) | 6 | 16 | 2 | 6 | 4 | 43246.50 |
| PADDY O'PRADO (USA) | 4 | 27 | 1 | 1 | 13 | 23549.83 |
| PAINTER'S ROW (IRE) | 1 | 1 | 1 | 1 | 0 | 1247.80 |
| PALACE EPISODE (USA) | 1 | 6 | 1 | 3 | 3 | 43177.37 |
| PANORAMIC | 2 | 3 | 1 | 1 | 0 | 18768.00 |
| PAPAL BULL (GB) | 29 | 114 | 7 | 10 | 48 | 135086.12 |
| PASSING GLANCE (GB) | 49 | 170 | 16 | 22 | 82 | 195530.87 |
| PASTERNAK (GB) | 14 | 36 | 4 | 4 | 18 | 40410.81 |
| PASTORIUS (GER) | 1 | 5 | 1 | 2 | 2 | 11105.64 |
| PERUGINO (USA) | 5 | 20 | 2 | 2 | 11 | 30383.64 |
| PHENOMENA (GB) | 2 | 6 | 1 | 1 | 1 | 2624.30 |
| PHOENIX REACH (IRE) | 17 | 57 | 4 | 5 | 28 | 57849.84 |
| PIERRE (GB) | 7 | 31 | 2 | 3 | 19 | 35645.22 |
| PIVOTAL (GB) | 15 | 60 | 4 | 4 | 25 | 72209.08 |

| STALLIONS | RNRS | STARTS | WNRS | WINS | PLACES | TOTAL (£) |
|---|---|---|---|---|---|---|
| PLANTEUR (IRE) | 6 | 17 | 1 | 1 | 7 | 19142.58 |
| POET'S VOICE (GB) | 25 | 114 | 8 | 11 | 66 | 128136.98 |
| POINTILLISTE (USA) | 1 | 3 | 1 | 2 | 0 | 11018.64 |
| POLICY MAKER (IRE) | 8 | 12 | 2 | 2 | 4 | 101986.60 |
| POLIGLOTE (GB) | 28 | 106 | 16 | 21 | 54 | 716073.85 |
| PORTRAIT GALLERY (IRE) | 11 | 36 | 4 | 5 | 26 | 78918.91 |
| POUR MOI (IRE) | 28 | 89 | 11 | 17 | 51 | 183497.73 |
| POWER (GB) | 7 | 18 | 2 | 2 | 5 | 31025.56 |
| PRESENTING (GB) | 241 | 872 | 68 | 94 | 438 | 1250413.96 |
| PRIMARY (USA) | 11 | 46 | 4 | 8 | 19 | 95049.43 |
| PROCLAMATION (IRE) | 8 | 20 | 2 | 2 | 4 | 13257.36 |
| PROTEKTOR (GER) | 3 | 6 | 1 | 1 | 4 | 13343.62 |
| PUBLISHER (USA) | 8 | 36 | 2 | 3 | 16 | 23278.75 |
| PUIT D'OR (IRE) | 3 | 6 | 1 | 1 | 0 | 3249.00 |
| PUSHKIN (IRE) | 6 | 34 | 1 | 2 | 12 | 22904.32 |
| PUTRA PEKAN (GB) | 1 | 4 | 1 | 1 | 2 | 8946.80 |
| RACINGER (FR) | 8 | 25 | 2 | 4 | 13 | 34068.28 |
| RAIL LINK (GB) | 9 | 20 | 1 | 1 | 9 | 12547.23 |
| RAINBOW HIGH (GB) | 3 | 15 | 2 | 2 | 7 | 12247.70 |
| RAJJ (IRE) | 4 | 8 | 1 | 3 | 2 | 17822.88 |
| RAJSAMAN (FR) | 6 | 12 | 1 | 1 | 2 | 7798.48 |
| RAVEN'S PASS (USA) | 14 | 45 | 1 | 1 | 17 | 14283.02 |
| RECHARGE (IRE) | 3 | 6 | 1 | 1 | 2 | 4893.74 |
| RECITAL (FR) | 6 | 21 | 1 | 1 | 5 | 7225.22 |
| REDOUTE'S CHOICE (AUS) | 3 | 14 | 1 | 1 | 9 | 13753.52 |
| RELIABLE MAN (GB) | 1 | 5 | 1 | 1 | 2 | 7486.48 |
| REQUINTO (IRE) | 5 | 12 | 1 | 2 | 4 | 27500.44 |
| RIP VAN WINKLE (IRE) | 28 | 100 | 10 | 14 | 47 | 117024.48 |
| ROBIN DES CHAMPS (FR) | 88 | 318 | 25 | 37 | 148 | 424853.21 |
| ROBIN DES PRES (FR) | 50 | 227 | 9 | 14 | 117 | 200318.77 |
| ROCK OF GIBRALTAR (IRE) | 30 | 98 | 4 | 4 | 49 | 58099.47 |
| RODERIC O'CONNOR (IRE) | 7 | 16 | 1 | 1 | 6 | 11965.30 |
| ROYAL ANTHEM (USA) | 15 | 48 | 4 | 8 | 27 | 54861.92 |
| ROYAL APPLAUSE (GB) | 8 | 22 | 2 | 2 | 10 | 14470.58 |
| RUDIMENTARY (USA) | 5 | 24 | 1 | 1 | 16 | 11987.24 |
| RULE OF LAW (USA) | 6 | 20 | 2 | 3 | 7 | 16471.01 |
| RULER OF THE WORLD (IRE) | 4 | 10 | 1 | 1 | 7 | 6606.97 |
| SABIANGO (GER) | 1 | 4 | 1 | 1 | 2 | 19648.00 |
| SADDEX (GB) | 11 | 38 | 4 | 4 | 19 | 47933.43 |
| SADDLER MAKER (IRE) | 29 | 103 | 12 | 14 | 66 | 506841.85 |
| SADDLERS' HALL (IRE) | 2 | 11 | 1 | 1 | 8 | 11100.38 |
| SAFFRON WALDEN (FR) | 5 | 12 | 2 | 2 | 2 | 7663.59 |
| SAGAMIX (FR) | 11 | 46 | 6 | 9 | 18 | 59218.86 |
| SAGEBURG (IRE) | 14 | 52 | 5 | 7 | 29 | 142697.84 |
| SAINT DES SAINTS (FR) | 49 | 174 | 21 | 27 | 101 | 640157.66 |
| SAKHEE (USA) | 16 | 61 | 3 | 4 | 31 | 41245.44 |
| SALUTINO (GER) | 13 | 67 | 5 | 11 | 25 | 101110.87 |
| SAMUM (GER) | 5 | 19 | 4 | 8 | 8 | 193070.68 |
| SANDMASON (GB) | 10 | 40 | 5 | 8 | 24 | 129343.99 |
| SANS FRONTIERES (IRE) | 39 | 117 | 6 | 9 | 37 | 92853.64 |
| SATRI (IRE) | 4 | 12 | 3 | 4 | 6 | 24673.84 |
| SAYIF (IRE) | 4 | 15 | 1 | 1 | 12 | 11309.73 |
| SCHIAPARELLI (GER) | 48 | 153 | 10 | 14 | 72 | 280372.41 |
| SCORPION (IRE) | 178 | 717 | 41 | 55 | 318 | 791098.54 |
| SEA THE MOON (GER) | 7 | 25 | 3 | 6 | 12 | 103637.72 |
| SEA THE STARS (IRE) | 28 | 70 | 6 | 7 | 28 | 58254.20 |
| SECRET SINGER (FR) | 10 | 24 | 1 | 1 | 8 | 7710.71 |
| SELKIRK (USA) | 1 | 4 | 1 | 2 | 1 | 11227.00 |
| SEPTEMBER STORM (GER) | 32 | 149 | 9 | 17 | 80 | 176872.77 |
| SHAANMER (IRE) | 4 | 15 | 2 | 2 | 8 | 13548.74 |
| SHAMARDAL (USA) | 9 | 28 | 3 | 4 | 17 | 33458.32 |

| STALLIONS | RNRS | STARTS | WNRS | WINS | PLACES | TOTAL (£) |
|---|---|---|---|---|---|---|
| SHANTARAM (GB) | 3 | 8 | 1 | 1 | 2 | 3332.62 |
| SHANTOU (USA) | 138 | 543 | 55 | 83 | 269 | 944455.10 |
| SHIROCCO (GER) | 144 | 437 | 39 | 55 | 189 | 527198.04 |
| SHOLOKHOV (IRE) | 55 | 164 | 11 | 15 | 73 | 205408.78 |
| SILVER FROST (IRE) | 3 | 16 | 1 | 1 | 9 | 16451.06 |
| SINNDAR (IRE) | 17 | 63 | 5 | 5 | 36 | 77211.51 |
| SIR HARRY LEWIS (USA) | 7 | 23 | 1 | 1 | 15 | 45092.60 |
| SIR PERCY (GB) | 34 | 135 | 10 | 12 | 79 | 147868.90 |
| SIR PRANCEALOT (IRE) | 6 | 18 | 2 | 2 | 9 | 14509.70 |
| SIXTIES ICON (GB) | 32 | 120 | 5 | 7 | 72 | 142498.12 |
| SLADE POWER (IRE) | 2 | 7 | 1 | 1 | 2 | 5116.07 |
| SLEEPING INDIAN (GB) | 3 | 10 | 1 | 1 | 4 | 8317.46 |
| SLICKLY (FR) | 3 | 7 | 1 | 1 | 3 | 106893.78 |
| SMADOUN (FR) | 7 | 26 | 3 | 3 | 15 | 46006.74 |
| SOAPY DANGER (GB) | 1 | 4 | 1 | 1 | 2 | 10661.04 |
| SOLDIER HOLLOW (GB) | 12 | 41 | 3 | 3 | 18 | 76666.05 |
| SOLDIER OF FORTUNE (IRE) | 11 | 45 | 3 | 6 | 22 | 70147.87 |
| SONNY MAC (GB) | 1 | 7 | 1 | 1 | 3 | 7747.73 |
| SO YOU THINK (NZ) | 14 | 64 | 4 | 5 | 21 | 52934.53 |
| SPADOUN (FR) | 9 | 48 | 2 | 3 | 25 | 120571.99 |
| SPANISH MOON (USA) | 17 | 61 | 9 | 12 | 32 | 133958.40 |
| SPARTACUS (IRE) | 3 | 12 | 2 | 2 | 6 | 11190.29 |
| SPECIAL KALDOUN (IRE) | 4 | 20 | 2 | 3 | 11 | 24485.52 |
| SPEEDMASTER (GER) | 2 | 12 | 2 | 2 | 8 | 17480.02 |
| SPIRIT ONE (FR) | 6 | 25 | 2 | 4 | 11 | 49702.72 |
| SPRING AT LAST (USA) | 1 | 8 | 1 | 1 | 4 | 6139.70 |
| STIMULATION (IRE) | 5 | 16 | 3 | 3 | 10 | 16552.95 |
| STOWAWAY (GB) | 250 | 891 | 64 | 97 | 467 | 1607210.97 |
| STREET CRY (IRE) | 5 | 23 | 2 | 2 | 11 | 22277.19 |
| STYLE VENDOME (FR) | 2 | 10 | 1 | 1 | 4 | 11784.95 |
| SUBTLE POWER (IRE) | 7 | 34 | 3 | 4 | 16 | 67784.08 |
| SULAMANI (IRE) | 76 | 303 | 28 | 41 | 154 | 572369.76 |
| SUNDAY BREAK (JPN) | 9 | 30 | 3 | 3 | 18 | 32296.33 |
| TAJRAASI (USA) | 9 | 39 | 4 | 6 | 20 | 47717.75 |
| TAMURE (IRE) | 3 | 12 | 2 | 2 | 8 | 19923.41 |
| TEOFILO (IRE) | 37 | 125 | 8 | 9 | 57 | 90289.64 |
| THEWAYYOUARE (USA) | 30 | 97 | 2 | 2 | 52 | 44992.41 |
| THREE VALLEYS (USA) | 3 | 10 | 1 | 1 | 8 | 17594.06 |
| TIGER GROOM (GB) | 8 | 32 | 1 | 1 | 19 | 47685.22 |
| TIGER HILL (IRE) | 5 | 20 | 1 | 3 | 15 | 25997.48 |
| TIKKANEN (USA) | 33 | 116 | 8 | 9 | 62 | 109617.14 |
| TIRWANAKO (FR) | 3 | 8 | 2 | 3 | 4 | 13968.87 |
| TOBOUGG (IRE) | 19 | 74 | 4 | 5 | 40 | 53335.34 |
| TOP TRIP (GB) | 1 | 10 | 1 | 3 | 6 | 22181.67 |
| TOUCH OF LAND (FR) | 21 | 110 | 8 | 10 | 59 | 101713.27 |
| TRADE FAIR (GB) | 2 | 9 | 1 | 1 | 4 | 10902.94 |
| TRANS ISLAND (GB) | 38 | 177 | 10 | 15 | 102 | 206634.03 |
| TURGEON (USA) | 14 | 44 | 5 | 6 | 25 | 140760.05 |
| TURTLE BOWL (IRE) | 5 | 26 | 3 | 4 | 17 | 43742.11 |
| TURTLE ISLAND (IRE) | 11 | 44 | 6 | 6 | 19 | 44781.80 |
| UNIVERSAL (IRE) | 17 | 47 | 1 | 2 | 14 | 11774.99 |
| VALE OF YORK (IRE) | 9 | 36 | 1 | 3 | 7 | 14356.30 |
| VENDANGEUR (IRE) | 4 | 20 | 1 | 1 | 11 | 13262.91 |
| VERGLAS (IRE) | 4 | 12 | 1 | 2 | 6 | 21384.70 |
| VERTICAL SPEED (FR) | 10 | 34 | 2 | 2 | 13 | 16315.50 |
| VINNIE ROE (IRE) | 60 | 237 | 14 | 21 | 115 | 291581.26 |
| VIRTUAL (GB) | 8 | 31 | 1 | 1 | 14 | 13977.75 |
| VISION D'ETAT (FR) | 13 | 38 | 2 | 4 | 18 | 37383.41 |
| VOCALISED (USA) | 18 | 53 | 3 | 3 | 23 | 33298.46 |
| VOIX DU NORD (FR) | 27 | 107 | 9 | 13 | 64 | 477720.08 |

| STALLIONS | RNRS | STARTS | WNRS | WINS | PLACES | TOTAL (£) |
|---|---|---|---|---|---|---|
| WALK IN THE PARK (IRE) | 21 | 76 | 7 | 9 | 45 | 477895.52 |
| WAREED (IRE) | 8 | 29 | 1 | 1 | 12 | 13122.55 |
| WATAR (IRE) | 16 | 47 | 1 | 2 | 14 | 15787.32 |
| WAVENEY (UAE) | 2 | 11 | 1 | 1 | 2 | 6559.44 |
| WELL CHOSEN (GB) | 34 | 133 | 10 | 14 | 68 | 310958.27 |
| WELL MADE (GER) | 2 | 6 | 2 | 2 | 4 | 21326.80 |
| WESTERNER (GB) | 173 | 711 | 56 | 76 | 379 | 1354068.24 |
| WHIPPER (USA) | 2 | 15 | 1 | 1 | 5 | 6199.59 |
| WHITMORE'S CONN (USA) | 19 | 90 | 8 | 13 | 37 | 123534.29 |
| WINDSOR KNOT (IRE) | 16 | 54 | 3 | 3 | 22 | 41689.81 |
| WINGED LOVE (IRE) | 59 | 213 | 19 | 28 | 91 | 408291.71 |
| WITNESS BOX (USA) | 17 | 47 | 3 | 4 | 21 | 35353.69 |
| WOLFE TONE (IRE) | 1 | 7 | 1 | 1 | 3 | 16581.34 |
| WOOTTON BASSETT (GB) | 3 | 9 | 2 | 2 | 4 | 9790.28 |
| YEATS (IRE) | 213 | 801 | 66 | 87 | 368 | 1402162.35 |
| YOUMZAIN (IRE) | 11 | 38 | 4 | 5 | 20 | 69598.96 |
| ZAGREB (USA) | 11 | 30 | 1 | 1 | 17 | 28671.11 |
| ZAMBEZI SUN (GB) | 10 | 28 | 1 | 1 | 12 | 19523.43 |
| ZAMINDAR (USA) | 7 | 16 | 1 | 1 | 4 | 12670.05 |
| ZEBEDEE (GB) | 13 | 35 | 2 | 2 | 15 | 20147.90 |
| ZERPOUR (IRE) | 1 | 9 | 1 | 3 | 4 | 19313.62 |
| ZOFFANY (IRE) | 31 | 128 | 11 | 17 | 72 | 170599.24 |

*BY KIND PERMISSION OF WEATHERBYS*

# HIGH-PRICED YEARLINGS OF 2020 AT TATTERSALLS SALES

The following yearlings realised 100,000 guineas and over at Tattersalls Sales in 2020:

| Name and Breeding | Purchaser | Guineas |
|---|---|---|
| B F GALILEO (IRE) - SHASTYE (IRE) | M V MAGNIER | 3400000 |
| B F GALILEO (IRE) - PRIZE EXHIBIT (GB) | M V MAGNIER | 2800000 |
| **AKHU NAJLA (GB)** B C KINGMAN (GB) - GALICUIX (GB) | OLIVER ST LAWRENCE BS | 2700000 |
| B C DUBAWI (IRE) - CUSHION (GB) | GODOLPHIN | 2100000 |
| B F FRANKEL (GB) - FLECHE D'OR (GB) | GODOLPHIN | 2000000 |
| B F KINGMAN (GB) - SANTE (IRE) | GODOLPHIN | 1450000 |
| CH F GALILEO (IRE) - VASILIA (GB) | MIKE RYAN AGENT | 1400000 |
| B C FRANKEL (GB) - ATTRACTION (GB) | GODOLPHIN | 1100000 |
| BR C DUBAWI (IRE) - INTRICATELY (IRE) | GODOLPHIN | 1100000 |
| **SPECIAL ENVOY (GB)** B C FRANKEL (GB) - MARLINKA (GB) | VENDOR | 1000000 |
| B C LOPE DE VEGA (IRE) - MOI MEME (GB) | GODOLPHIN | 900000 |
| GR F GALILEO (IRE) - DIALAFARA (FR) | MCCALMONT BS | 850000 |
| CH C LOPE DE VEGA (IRE) - STARLET (IRE) | DAVID REDVERS BS | 825000 |
| B C DUBAWI (IRE) - GREAT AND SMALL (GB) | GODOLPHIN | 800000 |
| CH C DUBAWI (IRE) - PROVENANCE (GB) | GODOLPHIN | 800000 |
| B F SEA THE STARS (IRE) - SWEET FIREBIRD (IRE) | C GORDON WATSON BS | 700000 |
| B F FRANKEL (GB) - PEARLY STEPH (IRE) | GODOLPHIN | 700000 |
| B F SIYOUNI (FR) - MISCHIEF MAKING (USA) | WESTERBERG | 680000 |
| B C SEA THE STARS (IRE) - SMOULDER (GB) | GODOLPHIN | 680000 |
| **SCOTTISH ANTHEM (GB)** GR C LOPE DE VEGA (IRE) - LOCH MA NAIRE (IRE) | GODOLPHIN | 675000 |
| **PARIS LIGHTS (GB)** B C SIYOUNI (FR) - CABARET (IRE) | VENDOR | 650000 |
| CH C NO NAY NEVER (USA) - STRUT (GB) | BEN MCELROY AGENT | 650000 |
| B C SEA THE STARS (IRE) - UMNIYAH (IRE) | SHADWELL ESTATE COMPANY | 625000 |
| B F WOOTTON BASSETT (GB) - GREEN DIAMOND LADY (USA) | C GORDON WATSON BS | 600000 |
| B C INVINCIBLE SPIRIT (IRE) - RAJEEM (GB) | M V MAGNIER | 600000 |
| B F ZOFFANY (IRE) - ENTREAT (GB) | M V MAGNIER | 580000 |
| B C AUSTRALIA (GB) - SWEEPSTAKE (IRE) | M V MAGNIER | 575000 |
| **NOVA LEGEND (IRE)** B C GALILEO (IRE) - GHURRA (USA) | AVENUE BS | 550000 |
| CH C DUBAWI (IRE) - JACQUELINE QUEST (IRE) | GODOLPHIN | 525000 |
| B F DUBAWI (IRE) - BE MY GAL (GB) | GODOLPHIN | 520000 |
| **WIEN (IRE)** B F FRANKEL (GB) - WADYHATTA (GB) | SACKVILLEDONALD | 500000 |
| **DUKEMAN (IRE)** B C KINGMAN (GB) - SHE'S MINE (IRE) | GAINSBOROUGH TB | 500000 |
| B F SEA THE STARS (IRE) - DIAMOND TANGO (IRE) | WESTERBERG | 500000 |
| **SCHNEEMANN (GB)** B C SEA THE MOON (GER) - SNOW BALLERINA (GB) | SHADWELL ESTATE COMPANY | 480000 |
| B C FRANKEL (GB) - AS GOOD AS GOLD (IRE) | GODOLPHIN | 480000 |
| B C DUBAWI (IRE) - BLACK CHERRY (GB) | GODOLPHIN | 480000 |
| B C FRANKEL (GB) - FINE TIME (GB) | STROUD COLEMAN BS | 475000 |
| **COMET LINE (IRE)** B F NO NAY NEVER (USA) - HONOURABLY (IRE) | CANARY BS | 475000 |
| B C KINGMAN (GB) - LOMBATINA (FR) | GODOLPHIN | 475000 |
| B F FRANKEL (GB) - LOVE IS BLINDNESS (IRE) | DE BURGH EQUINE | 460000 |
| B F GALILEO (IRE) - REALTRA (IRE) | C GORDON WATSON BS | 450000 |
| **BLUE BOAT (GB)** B C FRANKEL (GB) - BLUE WALTZ (GB) | JUDDMONTE FARMS | 450000 |
| **SKY LEGEND (GB)** CH C GALILEO (IRE) - SPECTRE (FR) | AVENUE BS | 450000 |
| **STAR LEGEND (IRE)** B C GALILEO (IRE) - THAI HAKU (IRE) | AVENUE BS | 450000 |
| **EPIC POET (IRE)** B C LOPE DE VEGA (IRE) - SAGACIOUSLY (IRE) | WHITE BIRCH FARM | 450000 |
| B C LOPE DE VEGA (IRE) - LAGANORE (IRE) | BLANDFORD BS | 430000 |
| B F LOPE DE VEGA (IRE) - INNEVERA (FR) | GODOLPHIN | 425000 |
| **DR ZEMPF (GB)** B/GR C DARK ANGEL (IRE) - SOUVENIR DELONDRES (FR) | WHITE BIRCH FARM | 420000 |
| **MALEX (GB)** B C KODIAC (GB) - TROIS LUNES (FR) | ROBSON AGUIAR | 420000 |
| B F SIYOUNI (FR) - ELLE SAME (IRE) | VENDOR | 420000 |
| CH F DUBAWI (IRE) - PRICELESS (GB) | GODOLPHIN | 420000 |
| CH C SIYOUNI (FR) - GEISHA GIRL (IRE) | BEN MCELROY AGENT | 410000 |
| **NORTH SOUND (IRE)** CH C NO NAY NEVER (GB) - NEED YOU NOW (IRE) | STROUD COLEMAN BS | 400000 |
| **MONARCHIC (IRE)** B C KINGMAN (GB) - ALLEZ Y (IRE) | GODOLPHIN | 400000 |
| B C LOPE DE VEGA (IRE) - PRANCE (IRE) | SHADWELL ESTATE COMPANY | 400000 |
| B F DARK ANGEL (IRE) - EXTRICATE (IRE) | DAVID REDVERS BS | 390000 |
| B C LOPE DE VEGA (IRE) - MEGERA (FR) | DEVIN | 380000 |
| B C DUBAWI (IRE) - SOON (IRE) | GODOLPHIN | 380000 |
| B C STARSPANGLEDBANNER (AUS) - VIOLET'S GIFT (USA) | STROUD COLEMAN BS | 360000 |
| B C FRANKEL (GB) - ARIS (IRE) | ROGER P VARIAN | 360000 |
| BR C NO NAY NEVER (GB) - MOMENT JUSTE (GB) | M V MAGNIER | 350000 |
| **INFINITE WONDER (IRE)** B F SEA THE STARS (IRE) - CHICAGO DANCER (IRE) | WHITE BIRCH FARM | 350000 |
| **WONDERFUL TIMES (IRE)** B F GOLDEN HORN (GB) - WONDERFULLY (IRE) | STROUD COLEMAN BS | 350000 |
| B F RIBCHESTER (IRE) - SELINKA (IRE) | BEN MCELROY AGENT | 350000 |
| **LA GLOIRE (GB)** B F CHURCHILL (IRE) - DATE WITH DESTINY (IRE) | STROUD COLEMAN BS | 350000 |
| GR F DARK ANGEL (IRE) - DELEVIGNE (GB) | SACKVILLEDONALD | 350000 |
| B C KODIAC (GB) - KHAIMAH (GB) | M V MAGNIER | 350000 |
| **KING OF YORK (IRE)** B C KINGMAN (GB) - ARCHANGEL GABRIEL (USA) | KEVIN RYAN | 350000 |
| **READY TO SHINE (IRE)** B F CAMELOT (GB) - MATORIO (FR) | GAINSBOROUGH TB | 340000 |
| B F CHURCHILL (IRE) - PUSSYCAT LIPS (IRE) | GAINSBOROUGH TB | 340000 |
| B C LE HAVRE (IRE) - WALDNAH (GB) | SHADWELL ESTATE COMPANY | 325000 |

| Name and Breeding | Purchaser | Guineas |
|---|---|---|
| B F MASTERCRAFTSMAN (IRE) - SIMKANA (IRE) | CORMAC MCCORMAC | 325000 |
| BAIKAL (GB) B C NO NAY NEVER (USA) - FOREIGN ASSIGNMENT (IRE) | KEVIN RYAN | 325000 |
| B C INVINCIBLE SPIRIT (IRE) - SWEET ACCLAIM (IRE) | ROGER VARIAN | 320000 |
| SIR ALEX J (IRE) B C MEHMAS (IRE) - ASHTOWN GIRL (IRE) | BLANDFORD BS | 320000 |
| MERLIN'S LADY (IRE) B F CAMELOT (GB) - MORA BAI (IRE) | KEVIN RYAN | 320000 |
| HIGHLAND FROLIC (FR) B C HIGHLAND REEL (IRE) - BEACH FROLIC (GB) | MCCALMONT BS | 320000 |
| B C CHURCHILL (IRE) - WHERE'S SUE (IRE) | M V MAGNIER | 320000 |
| CH C ULYSSES (IRE) - TROARN (FR) | SHADWELL ESTATE COMPANY | 320000 |
| NAZCA (GB) B C OASIS DREAM (GB) - PURE LINE (GB) | JUDDMONTE FARMS | 310000 |
| B F KINGMAN (GB) - LUSTROUS (GB) | BLANDFORD BS | 310000 |
| B C SHOWCASING (GB) - HARLEQUIN TWIST (GB) | WHITE BIRCH FARM | 310000 |
| CH C LOPE DE VEGA (IRE) - EFFERVESCE (IRE) | JOHN & JAKE WARREN | 310000 |
| B F GALILEO (IRE) - NIGHT LAGOON (GER) | BBA IRELAND | 305000 |
| B C FRANKEL (GB) - HOITY TOITY (GB) | SACKVILLEDONALD | 300000 |
| CH C FRANKEL (GB) - MIX AND MINGLE (IRE) | SUNDERLAND HOLDING INC | 300000 |
| CH F SEA THE STARS (IRE) - CRAFTY (AUS) | GODOLPHIN | 300000 |
| CH C DUBAWI (IRE) - HERTFORD DANCER (GB) | STROUD COLEMAN BS | 300000 |
| B C ACCLAMATION (GB) - LADY LIVIUS (IRE) | WHITE BIRCH FARM | 300000 |
| LONGRIDGE FELL (IRE) CH F RIBCHESTER (IRE) - HINT OF PINK (IRE) | STROUD COLEMAN BS | 300000 |
| B C KODIAC (GB) - SUPREME OCCASION (IRE) | ARTHUR HOYEAU AGENT | 300000 |
| B C GALILEO (IRE) - TERROR (IRE) | AGUIAR BS | 300000 |
| UMAX (IRE) B C KINGMAN (GB) - BELLA NOSTALGIA (IRE) | SHADWELL ESTATE COMPANY | 300000 |
| B C KODIAC (GB) - NATIONS ALEXANDER (IRE) | NORTH HILLS | 300000 |
| B F FRANKEL (GB) - AGNES STEWART (IRE) | GODOLPHIN | 300000 |
| HAMNET (GB) B C SIYOUNI (FR) - HAVANT (GB) | STROUD COLEMAN BS | 300000 |
| B C SEA THE STARS (IRE) - TALENT (GB) | BLANDFORD BS | 290000 |
| B C SHALAA (IRE) - ILLAUNMORE (USA) | SHADWELL ESTATE COMPANY | 290000 |
| B C BATED BREATH (GB) - TREMELO POINTE (IRE) | VENDOR | 290000 |
| B F FRANKEL (GB) - BELLA NOUF (IRE) | VENDOR | 290000 |
| B F GALILEO (IRE) - LIGHTNING THUNDER (GB) | GODOLPHIN | 280000 |
| CH C FRANKEL (GB) - ZINDAYA (USA) | STROUD COLEMAN BS | 280000 |
| B G BATED BREATH (GB) - SHY AUDIENCE (IRE) | SHADWELL ESTATE COMPANY | 280000 |
| KABAYIL (GB) B C KODIAC (GB) - ILLAUNGLASS (IRE) | GAINSBOROUGH TB | 280000 |
| THE PRESERVER (GB) B C SEA THE STARS (IRE) - WILLOUGHBY (IRE) | BLANDFORD BS | 280000 |
| B C NATHANIEL (IRE) - DESERT BERRY (GB) | SHADWELL ESTATE COMPANY | 280000 |
| AL AWIR (IRE) B F SIYOUNI (FR) - DRUMFAD BAY (IRE) | SACKVILLEDONALD | 260000 |
| B C DARK ANGEL (IRE) - GOLDEN ROSIE (IRE) | ANDREW BALDING | 260000 |
| ANGEL'S POINT (GB) B/GR F DARK ANGEL (IRE) - MADONNA DELL'ORTO (GB) | GODOLPHIN | 260000 |
| B/BR C SEA THE STARS (IRE) - AWARENESS (USA) | STROUD COLEMAN BS | 260000 |
| B C BATED BREATH (GB) - GUANA (IRE) | SHADWELL ESTATE COMPANY | 260000 |
| B C KINGMAN (GB) - SECRET KEEPER (GB) | ROBSON AGUIAR | 260000 |
| OH GREAT (IRE) B C WOOTTON BASSETT (GB) - TEESLEMEE (FR) | STROUD COLEMAN BS | 260000 |
| B F SEA THE STARS (IRE) - DHUMA (GB) | JOSEPH O'BRIEN | 260000 |
| VEGA MAGNIFICO (IRE) CH C LOPE DE VEGA (IRE) - HIT THE SKY (IRE) | DAVID REDVERS BS | 260000 |
| B F FAST COMPANY (IRE) - ROO (GB) | SHADWELL ESTATE COMPANY | 260000 |
| B C TEOFILO (IRE) - ISLAND REMEDE (GB) | MIKE RYAN AGENT | 260000 |
| B C KINGMAN (GB) - GO WHITE LIGHTNING (IRE) | DE BURGH EQUINE | 260000 |
| GR F SEA THE STARS (IRE) - ALLA SPERANZA (GB) | MCCALMONT BS | 255000 |
| B F SIYOUNI (FR) - OH GOODNESS ME (IRE) | GODOLPHIN | 255000 |
| B C KODIAC (GB) - MONTEFINO (GB) | SHADWELL ESTATE COMPANY | 250000 |
| B C NIGHT OF THUNDER (IRE) - SURPRISE (GB) | SACKVILLEDONALD | 250000 |
| B C SHALAA (IRE) - LADY GORGEOUS (GB) | MIKE RYAN AGENT | 250000 |
| CH C ALMANZOR (FR) - WALDJAGD (GB) | LONGWAYS STABLES | 250000 |
| CH C NO NAY NEVER (USA) - GREAT COURT (IRE) | VENDOR | 250000 |
| B F INVINCIBLE SPIRIT (IRE) - LISCUNE (IRE) | BEN MCELROY AGENT | 250000 |
| B C IFFRAAJ (GB) - AMJAAD (GB) | MIKE RYAN AGENT | 250000 |
| CH F SIYOUNI (FR) - CEISTEACH (IRE) | JOHN & JAKE WARREN | 250000 |
| B C GALILEO (IRE) - ROCK ORCHID (IRE) | BADGERS BS | 240000 |
| B C NO NAY NEVER (USA) - MADAM BAROQUE (GB) | MIKE RYAN AGENT | 240000 |
| B C DUBAWI (IRE) - THE MINIVER ROSE (IRE) | VENDOR | 240000 |
| CH C CURLIN (USA) - AN CAILIN ORGA (IRE) | HONG KONG JOCKEY CLUB | 240000 |
| B C FASTNET ROCK (AUS) - MISS LIGURIA (GB) | VENDOR | 240000 |
| B C NIGHT OF THUNDER (IRE) - HOKKAIDO (GB) | SACKVILLEDONALD | 235000 |
| B C HOLY ROMAN EMPEROR (IRE) - FIRE HEROINE (USA) | MIKE RYAN AGENT | 230000 |
| GR F DARK ANGEL (IRE) - CHARTREUSE (GB) | BLANDFORD BS | 230000 |
| B C SIYOUNI (FR) - MONROE BAY (IRE) | VENDOR | 230000 |
| GR F DARK ANGEL (IRE) - WHITE DAFFODIL (IRE) | SACKVILLEDONALD | 230000 |
| CH C LOPE DE VEGA (IRE) - PRINCESS SERENA (USA) | A C ELLIOTT, AGENT | 230000 |
| PODEROSO (IRE) B C KODIAC (GB) - ONLINE ALEXANDER (IRE) | STROUD COLEMAN BS | 225000 |
| WANDFLOWER (IRE) B F DARK ANGEL (IRE) - WARSHAH (IRE) | WHITE BIRCH FARM | 222000 |
| CAMP VEGA (GB) CH F LOPE DE VEGA (IRE) - YARROW (GB) | MIKE RYAN AGENT | 220000 |
| B C NO NAY NEVER (USA) - RIVALBA (USA) | PETER & ROSS DOYLE BS | 220000 |
| PAS DE FAUX (IRE) B C VADAMOS (FR) - STARRY MESSENGER (GB) | PETER & ROSS DOYLE BS | 220000 |
| PRINCESS OLLY (IRE) B F INVINCIBLE SPIRIT (IRE) - CRISTAL FASHION (IRE) | GAINSBOROUGH TB | 220000 |
| FINE BALANCE (IRE) B F SIYOUNI (FR) - CASH IN THE HAND (USA) | | 220000 |

| Name and Breeding | Purchaser | Guineas |
|---|---|---|
| **RAIN (GER)** B F SEA THE MOON (GER) - RELEVANT (IRE) | STROUD COLEMAN BS | 210000 |
| B C SEA THE STARS (IRE) - AZANARA (IRE) | JOHN & JAKE WARREN | 210000 |
| **MIDNIGHT MOLL (IRE)** B F DARK ANGEL (IRE) - SERENA'S STORM (IRE) | SACKVILLEDONALD | 210000 |
| B F OASIS DREAM (GB) - DIVINE (IRE) | BEN MCELROY AGENT | 210000 |
| **VINTAGE VALLEY (IRE)** GR C MASTERCRAFTSMAN (IRE) - LEA VALLEY (GB) | ANDREW BALDING | 210000 |
| CH C ALMANZOR (FR) - NEHALENNIA (USA) | SACKVILLEDONALD | 210000 |
| B C CHURCHILL (IRE) - RIEN NE VAS PLUS (IRE) | M V MAGNIER | 210000 |
| B F KODIAC (GB) - FORT DEL ORO (IRE) | OLIVER ST LAWRENCE BS | 210000 |
| **IN ECSTASY (IRE)** GR C CARAVAGGIO (USA) - LONGING (IRE) | WHITE BIRCH FARM | 205000 |
| CH C NEW BAY (GB) - LOUVE RARE (IRE) | SHADWELL ESTATE COMPANY | 205000 |
| B C INVINCIBLE SPIRIT (IRE) - LULAWIN (GB) | MICHAEL ROY | 205000 |
| CH F SHAMARDAL (USA) - LAST WALTZ (IRE) | HARAS D'ETREHAM | 200000 |
| B G FASTNET ROCK (AUS) - STELLAR GLOW (IRE) | HONG KONG JOCKEY CLUB | 200000 |
| **SALVATOR MUNDI (IRE)** B C GALILEO (IRE) - BUFERA (IRE) | HUGO MERRY BS | 200000 |
| B C LOPE DE VEGA (IRE) - GREAT HEAVENS (GB) | BBA IRELAND | 200000 |
| B F SEA THE STARS (IRE) - PRAIA (GER) | JEREMY BRUMMITT | 200000 |
| B F FASTNET ROCK (AUS) - HIBISCUS (USA) | STROUD COLEMAN BS | 200000 |
| **BAYSIDE BOY (IRE)** B C NEW BAY (GB) - ALAVA (IRE) | RICHARD RYAN | 200000 |
| B C TEOFILO (IRE) - CAPE MAGIC (IRE) | C GORDON WATSON BS | 200000 |
| CH F SHOWCASING (GB) - SUELITA (GB) | CREIGHTON SCHWARTZ BS | 200000 |
| B F NIGHT OF THUNDER (IRE) - LONDON WELSH (IRE) | SACKVILLEDONALD | 200000 |
| B C WOOTTON BASSETT (GB) - HAREM MISTRESS (IRE) | RICHARD HUGHES RACING | 200000 |
| B C SEA THE MOON (GER) - QATARI PERFECTION (GB) | STROUD COLEMAN BS | 200000 |
| B C NIGHT OF THUNDER (IRE) - GOLD SANDS (IRE) | SHADWELL ESTATE COMPANY | 200000 |
| **FRANTANCK (GB)** B C FRANKEL (GB) - JANEY MUDDLES (IRE) | VENDOR | 200000 |
| B C ULYSSES (IRE) - ON HER TOES (IRE) | STROUD COLEMAN BS | 200000 |
| B F WOOTTON BASSETT (GB) - TABREED (GB) | MIKE RYAN AGENT | 200000 |
| **CAPH STAR (GB)** B C SIYOUNI (FR) - CASKELENA (IRE) | VENDOR | 200000 |
| B C STARSPANGLEDBANNER (AUS) - PRINCESS DESIRE (IRE) | SAM SANGSTER BS | 200000 |
| B C NO NAY NEVER (USA) - MELODRAMA (IRE) | HONG KONG JOCKEY CLUB | 200000 |
| B C NATHANIEL (IRE) - ROBEMA (IRE) | SACKVILLEDONALD | 200000 |
| **WALDSTAR (GB)** CH C SEA THE STARS (IRE) - WALDMARK (GER) | VENDOR | 200000 |
| B C CAMELOT (GB) - PIONEER BRIDE (USA) | JOSEPH O'BRIEN | 200000 |
| B C SEA THE STARS (IRE) - WO DE XIN (GB) | SHADWELL ESTATE COMPANY | 200000 |
| B C LOPE DE VEGA (IRE) - FREEDOM MARCH (GB) | VENDOR | 200000 |
| B/BR F FASTNET ROCK (AUS) - LOPERA (IRE) | MIKE RYAN AGENT | 190000 |
| B C LOPE DE VEGA (IRE) - LADY DARSHAAN (IRE) | BLANDFORD BS | 190000 |
| BR C IFFRAAJ (GB) - SIBILANCE (GB) | STROUD COLEMAN BS | 190000 |
| B/GR F LOPE DE VEGA (IRE) - IROMEA (IRE) | MIKE RYAN AGENT | 190000 |
| B F SEA THE STARS (IRE) - ORIENTAL MAGIC (GER) | SUNDERLAND HOLDING INC | 190000 |
| BR/GR C CARAVAGGIO (USA) - DORA DE GREEN (IRE) | VENDOR | 190000 |
| B C IFFRAAJ (GB) - YELLOWHAMMER (GB) | STEPHEN HILLEN BS | 190000 |
| B F INVINCIBLE SPIRIT (IRE) - WHAT STYLE (IRE) | BLANDFORD BS | 190000 |
| B C LOPE DE VEGA (IRE) - BLACK RUBY (IRE) | VENDOR | 190000 |
| B C ALMANZOR (FR) - HOLBERG SUITE (GB) | FEDERICO BARBERINI | 185000 |
| B F GUTAIFAN (IRE) - WOJHA (IRE) | AVENUE BS FOR MV MAGNIER | 185000 |
| **LONG RIDGE ROAD (IRE)** B F RIBCHESTER (IRE) - SURREY STORM (IRE) | WHITE BIRCH FARM | 185000 |
| B C LOPE DE VEGA (IRE) - SHAHAD (IRE) | STEPHEN HILLEN BS | 185000 |
| B C KODIAC (GB) - ODYSSEE (FR) | JOE FOLEY | 185000 |
| B F NO NAY NEVER (USA) - BEWITCHMENT (GB) | BLANDFORD BS | 185000 |
| CH C FRANKEL (GB) - ONSHORE (GB) | MIKE AKERS AGENT | 185000 |
| **ACER ALLEY (GB)** B F SIYOUNI (FR) - WILLOW VIEW (USA) | VENDOR | 180000 |
| **SALIMAH (IRE)** GR F EL KABEIR (USA) - PROMISED MONEY (USA) | WHITE BIRCH FARM | 180000 |
| **RAVENSWING (IRE)** B C DARK ANGEL (IRE) - FUTURE GENERATION (IRE) | KEVIN RYAN | 180000 |
| B F SEA THE STARS (IRE) - CREGGS PIPES (IRE) | SUNDERLAND HOLDING (P.S.) | 180000 |
| B F FRANKEL (GB) - ASTRELLE (GB) | MIKE RYAN AGENT | 180000 |
| **THUNDERING (GB)** B C NIGHT OF THUNDER (IRE) - COSMEA (GB) | STEPHEN HILLEN BS | 180000 |
| CH F SHOWCASING (GB) - RED INTRIGUE (IRE) | STROUD COLEMAN BS | 180000 |
| CH C NEW BAY (GB) - EVER LOVE (BRZ) | STROUD COLEMAN BS | 180000 |
| B F ALMANZOR (FR) - VIVACITY (GB) | JOHN & JAKE WARREN | 180000 |
| **GLEN BUCK (GB)** B C LOPE DE VEGA (IRE) - PECKING ORDER (IRE) | VENDOR | 180000 |
| CH C SHOWCASING (GB) - EXRATING (GB) | SHADWELL ESTATE COMPANY | 180000 |
| B F MEHMAS (IRE) - TURUQAAT (GB) | STROUD COLEMAN BS | 180000 |
| CH G LOPE DE VEGA (IRE) - GILDED (GB) | HONG KONG JOCKEY CLUB | 180000 |
| CH C COTAI GLORY (GB) - TRIGGERS BROOM (IRE) | SACKVILLEDONALD | 180000 |
| GR C CARAVAGGIO (USA) - GORBAND (USA) | C GORDON WATSON BS | 180000 |
| B F PIVOTAL (GB) - CRYSTAL DIAMOND (GB) | BBA IRELAND | 180000 |
| B F IFFRAAJ (GB) - KAREN'S CAPER (USA) | VENDOR | 180000 |
| B C MAKE BELIEVE (GB) - CRUCK REALTA (GB) | BLANDFORD BS | 175000 |
| CH C NIGHT OF THUNDER (IRE) - CANDLEBERRY (GB) | SACKVILLEDONALD | 175000 |
| B C CAMELOT (GB) - ANOTHER STORM (USA) | JOSEPH O'BRIEN | 175000 |
| **AMERICAN STAR (IRE)** B C STARSPANGLEDBANNER (AUS) - SIGNORA VALENTINA (IRE) | SACKVILLEDONALD | 170000 |
| B F KITTEN'S JOY (USA) - SARANDIA (GER) | VENDOR | 170000 |
| B F KINGMAN (GB) - HAVRE DE PAIX (FR) | VENDOR | 170000 |
| B F TAMAYUZ (GB) - HOLDA (IRE) | SHADWELL ESTATE COMPANY | 170000 |

| Name and Breeding | Purchaser | Guineas |
|---|---|---|
| B C LOPE DE VEGA (IRE) - SPECIAL GAL (FR) | SHADWELL ESTATE COMPANY | 170000 |
| B C ULYSSES (IRE) - TOKEN OF LOVE (GB) | BLANDFORD BS | 170000 |
| **ARTAOIS (GB)** B C KODIAC (GB) - LA PATRIA (GB) | GAINSBOROUGH TB | 170000 |
| B F FRANKEL (GB) - BALANKIYA (IRE) | VENDOR | 170000 |
| **SONIER (IRE)** B C CARAVAGGIO (USA) - SOLAR EVENT (GB) | WHITE BIRCH FARM | 170000 |
| B C LOPE DE VEGA (IRE) - BIBURY (GB) | MCCALMONT BS | 170000 |
| B C BATED BREATH (GB) - UNNATURAL (USA) | PETER & ROSS DOYLE BS | 170000 |
| **LADY SKYE (GB)** B F SEA THE STARS (IRE) - MEMORIA (GB) | A C ELLIOTT, AGENT | 165000 |
| GR C KODIAC (GB) - SYANN (GB) | SHADWELL ESTATE COMPANY | 165000 |
| CH C LOPE DE VEGA (IRE) - GLAMOROUS APPROACH (IRE) | ROGER VARIAN | 160000 |
| B C PROFITABLE (IRE) - IHTIFAL (GB) | SHADWELL ESTATE COMPANY | 160000 |
| B C ZOFFANY (IRE) - LLEW LAW (GB) | ROGER VARIAN | 160000 |
| **SECURITY CODE (GB)** B C TERRITORIES (IRE) - MOMENT OF TIME (GB) | HURWORTH BS | 160000 |
| **ENCOUNTERED (IRE)** B C CHURCHILL (IRE) - ENROL (GB) | SUZANNE ROBERTS | 160000 |
| B F INVINCIBLE SPIRIT (IRE) - RIDGE RANGER (IRE) | VENDOR | 160000 |
| B C CARAVAGGIO (USA) - NICTATE (IRE) | FEDERICO BARBERINI | 160000 |
| B F WOOTTON BASSETT (GB) - MONDELICE (GB) | BBA IRELAND | 160000 |
| **GEOCENTRIC (IRE)** B F KODIAC (GB) - RAJMAHAL (UAE) | SACKVILLEDONALD | 160000 |
| B C MEHMAS (IRE) - DIAMINDA (IRE) | C GORDON WATSON BS | 160000 |
| B G DARK ANGEL (IRE) - RURAL CELEBRATION (IRE) | HONG KONG JOCKEY CLUB | 160000 |
| B F LOPE DE VEGA (IRE) - STAR APPROVAL (IRE) | MIKE RYAN AGENT | 160000 |
| B F FRANKEL (GB) - ALSINDI (IRE) | MIKE RYAN AGENT | 160000 |
| **OLYMPIC ORDER (IRE)** B C TEOFILO (IRE) - SWISS ROLL (IRE) | WHITE BIRCH FARM | 155000 |
| CH C NIGHT OF THUNDER (IRE) - SOUTHERN BELLE (IRE) | SHADWELL ESTATE COMPANY | 155000 |
| **SPANISH BAROQUE (GB)** B F LOPE DE VEGA (IRE) - PACIFICA HIGHWAY (USA) | WHITE BIRCH FARM | 155000 |
| B C SEA THE STARS (IRE) - POLLY'S MARK (IRE) | JOHN & JAKE WARREN | 155000 |
| CH F PROFITABLE (IRE) - BOLD ASSUMPTION (GB) | SHADWELL ESTATE COMPANY | 150000 |
| B C DUBAWI (IRE) - PERIHELION (IRE) | VENDOR | 150000 |
| GR F FRANKEL (GB) - REAL SMART (USA) | VENDOR | 150000 |
| BR C SIYOUNI (FR) - PATRONISING (GB) | JOE FOLEY | 150000 |
| B C TIME TEST (GB) - LYNNWOOD CHASE (USA) | BLANDFORD BS | 150000 |
| B C ALMANZOR (FR) - FAST LILY (IRE) | MIKE RYAN AGENT | 150000 |
| B C OASIS DREAM (GB) - SPANISH FLY (IRE) | JAMES FANSHAWE | 150000 |
| B C CAMELOT (GB) - ATTIRE (IRE) | M V MAGNIER | 150000 |
| B C SIR PERCY (GB) - WILLOW BECK (GB) | A C ELLIOTT, AGENT | 150000 |
| **LUCELLUM (GB)** B C SIR PERCY (GB) - LEADERENE (GB) | STROUD COLEMAN BS | 150000 |
| B C SHOWCASING (GB) - MATHOOL (IRE) | ROGER VARIAN | 150000 |
| B F INVINCIBLE SPIRIT (IRE) - WHEN IN DOUBT (GB) | MIKE RYAN AGENT | 150000 |
| GR F CARAVAGGIO (USA) - SUTTON VENY (IRE) | MEAH / LLOYD BS | 150000 |
| B C LAWMAN (FR) - BIZZARRIA (GB) | ANDREW BALDING | 150000 |
| B C SHOWCASING (GB) - LIFE OF PI (GB) | SHADWELL ESTATE COMPANY | 150000 |
| B C CHURCHILL (IRE) - REGENCY GIRL (GB) | SACKVILLEDONALD | 150000 |
| BR C CABLE BAY - BONHOMIE (GB) | STROUD COLEMAN BS | 150000 |
| CH C SEA THE STARS (IRE) - RASKUTANI (GB) | JOSEPH O'BRIEN | 150000 |
| **BAYAMO (GB)** B C HAVANA GOLD (IRE) - ANICE STELLATO (IRE) | HURWORTH BS | 150000 |
| B C CARAVAGGIO (USA) - INSTANT SPARKLE (IRE) | ARTHUR HOYEAU AGENT | 150000 |
| B C CARAVAGGIO (GB) - CAPRIOLE (GB) | BBA IRELAND | 150000 |
| B F SIYOUNI (FR) - QUEEN PHILIPPA (USA) | TINA RAU BS | 150000 |
| **DANCING EAGLE (GB)** B F GLENEAGLES (IRE) - MAID TO DREAM (GB) | HUGO MERRY BS | 150000 |
| B F GOLDEN HORN (GB) - MIA DILETTA (GB) | VENDOR | 150000 |
| GR F CARAVAGGIO (USA) - ATLANTIC DRIFT (GB) | GAINSBOROUGH TB | 150000 |
| B/BR C MORE THAN READY (USA) - INCONCEIVABLE (IRE) | MIKE RYAN AGENT | 150000 |
| **PIGEONHOLE (GB)** B C POSTPONED (IRE) - SHEMYA (FR) | WHITE BIRCH FARM | 145000 |
| **MAGIC WARRIOR (IRE)** B C KODIAC (GB) - ALKHAWARAH (USA) | PETER & ROSS DOYLE BS | 145000 |
| B F PROFITABLE (IRE) - MISS AZEZA (GB) | AIDAN O'RYAN | 145000 |
| B/BR C ACLAIM (IRE) - KENDAL MINT (GB) | SHADWELL ESTATE COMPANY | 145000 |
| B F DARK ANGEL (IRE) - RELATION ALEXANDER (IRE) | SHADWELL ESTATE COMPANY | 145000 |
| **MOUNT HOTHAM (IRE)** CH C AUSTRALIA (GB) - MARSH DAISY (GB) | STROUD COLEMAN BS | 145000 |
| B C CHURCHILL (IRE) - DANETIME OUT (IRE) | MICHAEL ROY | 145000 |
| B F SHOWCASING (GB) - BIRD KEY (GB) | JS BS | 140000 |
| **CORSINI (IRE)** CH F MASTERCRAFTSMAN (IRE) - IL PALAZZO (USA) | D FARRINGTON | 140000 |
| B C WOOTTON BASSETT (GB) - HOLY CAT (GB) | JOHN & JAKE WARREN | 140000 |
| CH C NO NAY NEVER (USA) - FLASHY WINGS (GB) | ARTHUR HOYEAU AGENT | 140000 |
| B F LAWMAN (FR) - DEBUTANTIN (GB) | JOHN & JAKE WARREN | 140000 |
| BR C KODIAC (GB) - FRAULEIN (GB) | C GORDON WATSON BS | 140000 |
| **FEIGNED FLIGHT (GB)** B C DABIRSIM (FR) - PARTY (IRE) | ANDREW BALDING | 140000 |
| B F MEHMAS (IRE) - FLAT WHITE (IRE) | RABBAH BS | 140000 |
| B F SEA THE STARS (IRE) - FONDLY (IRE) | STROUD COLEMAN BS | 140000 |
| CH F ULYSSES (IRE) - RECKONING (GB) | VENDOR | 140000 |
| **NEW NATION (IRE)** B C STARSPANGLEDBANNER (AUS) - INTERMITTENT (GB) | GAINSBOROUGH TB | 140000 |
| B C RIBCHESTER (IRE) - SUGAR FREE (GER) | BOBBY O'RYAN/BEN HASLAM | 140000 |
| B C NATHANIEL (IRE) - MY SPECIAL J'S (USA) | JOHN & JAKE WARREN | 140000 |
| B C LOPE DE VEGA (IRE) - HUNDI (IRE) | ROGER VARIAN | 140000 |
| B F RIBCHESTER (IRE) - SPIRIT OF DUBAI (IRE) | NIGEL TINKLER RACING | 140000 |
| B F DARK ANGEL (IRE) - RING THE BELL (IRE) | VENDOR | 140000 |

| Name and Breeding | Purchaser | Guineas |
|---|---|---|
| CH C AUSTRALIA (GB) - DEFROST MY HEART (IRE) | M V MAGNIER | 135000 |
| CH C SEA THE STARS (IRE) - CRYSDAL (GB) | JOHN & JAKE WARREN | 135000 |
| B F KINGMAN (GB) - ROEDEAN (IRE) | SACKVILLEDONALD | 135000 |
| CH F LOPE DE VEGA (IRE) - CZABO (GB) | JOHN & JAKE WARREN | 135000 |
| B F CHURCHILL (IRE) - CASERTA (GB) | PETER & ROSS DOYLE BS | 135000 |
| B C SEA THE MOON (GER) - DUBAI CYCLONE (USA) | PETER & ROSS DOYLE BS | 135000 |
| B C DECORATED KNIGHT (GB) - PRINCESS NOOR (IRE) | VENDOR | 130000 |
| B C LOPE DE VEGA (IRE) - WILD IRISH ROSE (GB) | BBA IRELAND | 130000 |
| B G OASIS DREAM (GB) - RIVE GAUCHE (GB) | HONG KONG JOCKEY CLUB | 130000 |
| CH C PROFITABLE (IRE) - PUZZLED (IRE) | SHADWELL ESTATE COMPANY | 130000 |
| B C MASTERCRAFTSMAN (IRE) - CASILA (IRE) | BLANDFORD BS | 130000 |
| **TRIBALIST (GB)** CH C FARHH (GB) - FAIR DAUGHTER (GB) | STROUD COLEMAN BS | 130000 |
| B C FARHH (GB) - FLYCATCHER (IRE) | JEREMY BRUMMITT | 130000 |
| B C DARK ANGEL (IRE) - HAY CHEWED (IRE) | SACKVILLEDONALD | 130000 |
| B C SHOWCASING (GB) - MUST BE ME (GB) | BLANDFORD BS | 130000 |
| **SCAR ROCKS (GB)** B C WOOTTON BASSETT (GB) - JEU DE PLUME (IRE) | JUSTWOW | 130000 |
| B C ACCLAMATION (GB) - LYDIA BECKER (GB) | SHADWELL ESTATE COMPANY | 130000 |
| CH F CHURCHILL (IRE) - PURPLE GLOW (IRE) | JOE FOLEY | 130000 |
| GR C CARAVAGGIO (USA) - BRIGHT SAPPHIRE (IRE) | VENDOR | 130000 |
| **FLAMENCO FAN (GB)** B F DARK ANGEL (IRE) - ANNABELLE'S CHARM (IRE) | VENDOR | 130000 |
| B C KODIAC (GB) - SODASHY (IRE) | SACKVILLEDONALD | 130000 |
| B F STARSPANGLEDBANNER (AUS) - PLYING (USA) | CREIGHTON SCHWARTZ BS | 130000 |
| B C OASIS DREAM (GB) - GUAJARA (GER) | ANDREW BALDING | 130000 |
| CH C NIGHT OF THUNDER (GB) - DOMINIKE (ITY) | GROVE STUD | 130000 |
| B C IFFRAAJ (GB) - SLOANE SQUARE (GB) | MICHAEL BUCKLEY | 130000 |
| B C TAMAYUZ (GB) - FATE (FR) | JEREMY BRUMMITT | 130000 |
| CH C AUSTRALIA (GB) - SNOWFIELDS (IRE) | JOSEPH O'BRIEN | 130000 |
| B C CHURCHILL (IRE) - IMALWAYSHOTFORYOU (USA) | JUSTIN CASSE AGENT | 130000 |
| B C FRANKEL (GB) - SEPTEMBER STARS (IRE) | HUGO MERRY BS | 130000 |
| GR F CARAVAGGIO (USA) - ME AND MISS JONES (USA) | BBA IRELAND | 130000 |
| CH F MEHMAS (IRE) - ARAAJMH (USA) | BLANDFORD BS | 130000 |
| CH C LOPE DE VEGA (IRE) - STONE ROSES (FR) | ANDREW BALDING | 130000 |
| B F NO NAY NEVER (USA) - MISS UNDERSTOOD (IRE) | PETER & ROSS DOYLE BS | 125000 |
| GR C DARK ANGEL (IRE) - SPANGLED (GB) | EBONOS | 125000 |
| B F FARHH (GB) - KITTY FOR ME (GB) | BLANDFORD BS | 125000 |
| B F FASTNET ROCK (AUS) - LOVE CHARM (GB) | BBA IRELAND | 125000 |
| B F STARSPANGLEDBANNER (AUS) - FLORIADE (IRE) | ARTHUR HOYEAU AGENT | 125000 |
| **EGYPTIAN GOD (IRE)** GR C EL KABEIR (USA) - PREQUEL (IRE) | WHITE BIRCH FARM | 125000 |
| B C CAMELOT (GB) - HOMEPAGE (GB) | VENDOR | 125000 |
| B C COTAI GLORY (GB) - WARM WELCOME (GB) | SACKVILLEDONALD | 125000 |
| CH C RIBCHESTER (IRE) - FARTHING (IRE) | STROUD COLEMAN BS | 125000 |
| B C KODIAC (GB) - LEYBURN (GB) | SHADWELL ESTATE COMPANY | 125000 |
| B F HOLY ROMAN EMPEROR (IRE) - LANDELA (GB) | RABBAH BS | 125000 |
| B F AMERICAN PHAROAH (USA) - PARVANEH (IRE) | HUGO MERRY BS | 125000 |
| **LET'S FLY AGAIN (GB)** B C KODIAC (GB) - KINNAIRD (IRE) | HIGHFLYER BS | 125000 |
| CH C SEA THE STARS (IRE) - CRYSDAL (GB) | C GORDON WATSON BS | 125000 |
| B F NATHANIEL (IRE) - NIBBLING (IRE) | MICK PRICE RACING | 125000 |
| **ROYAL SCANDAL (GB)** CH F DUBAWI (IRE) - SEAL OF APPROVAL (GB) | JAMES FANSHAWE | 120000 |
| **BOND CHAIRMAN (GB)** BR C KODIAC (GB) - WUNDERS DREAM (IRE) | B SMART | 120000 |
| CH F BATED BREATH (GB) - DESIRE (GB) | SACKVILLEDONALD | 120000 |
| BR C CARAVAGGIO (USA) - CHICAGO GIRL (IRE) | M V MAGNIER | 120000 |
| **MARHABA THE CHAMP (GB)** CH C GALILEO (IRE) - LADY OF THE DESERT (USA) | RABBAH BS | 120000 |
| B C TIME TEST (GB) - TEBEE'S OASIS (GB) | SHADWELL ESTATE COMPANY | 120000 |
| CH C EXCEED AND EXCEL (AUS) - FALLING PETALS (IRE) | SHADWELL ESTATE COMPANY | 120000 |
| B F KODIAC (GB) - FULL MANDATE (IRE) | DE BURGH EQUINE | 120000 |
| B/BR F FARHH (GB) - LIMBER UP (IRE) | EBONOS | 120000 |
| **OUT FROM UNDER (GB)** B C DUBAWI (IRE) - KOORA (GB) | VENDOR | 120000 |
| **CRUCIAL CHOICE (GB)** B C SIYOUNI (IRE) - PREFER (GB) | ANDREW BALDING | 120000 |
| **NEW DIMENSION (GB)** B C ULYSSES (IRE) - AZHAR (GB) | FLAXMAN STABLES IRELAND | 120000 |
| CH C NIGHT OF THUNDER (IRE) - ASTROMAGICK (GB) | EDDIE LINEHAN BS | 120000 |
| **STOCKPILE (GB)** B C OASIS DREAM (GB) - LA PYLE (FR) | VENDOR | 120000 |
| **LYSANDER (GB)** BR C NEW APPROACH (IRE) - DARTING (USA) | JOHN & JAKE WARREN | 120000 |
| B C SIYOUNI (FR) - ARISTOCRATIC LADY (USA) | VENDOR | 120000 |
| **PROJECT DANTE (GB)** CH C SHOWCASING (GB) - THATSALLIMSAYING (IRE) | B SMART | 115000 |
| **GALASHIELS (IRE)** CH C AUSTRALIA (GB) - GLENMAYNE (IRE) | STROUD COLEMAN BS | 115000 |
| B F DARK ANGEL (IRE) - CLEM FANDANGO (FR) | PADDY TWOMEY | 115000 |
| **LOVELY MANA (IRE)** B F DABIRSIM (FR) - ENRAPTURED (IRE) | A C ELLIOTT, AGENT | 115000 |
| GR C LOPE DE VEGA (IRE) - CLABA DI SAN JORE (IRE) | BBA IRELAND | 115000 |
| B F MASTERCRAFTSMAN (IRE) - MUSIC IN MY HEART (GB) | BBA IRELAND | 115000 |
| CH C NATHANIEL (IRE) - LONG FACE (USA) | JOHN & JAKE WARREN | 115000 |
| CH F CHURCHILL (IRE) - MISS MARIDUFF (USA) | BLANDFORD BS | 115000 |
| BR/GR F DARK ANGEL (IRE) - LORETO (IRE) | O'BYRNE & GRASSICK | 115000 |
| **SIRAJO (GB)** B C SHOWCASING (GB) - BEREKA (GB) | A C ELLIOTT, AGENT | 110000 |
| GR F DARK ANGEL (IRE) - SPIRITUAL LADY (GB) | BEN MCELROY AGENT | 110000 |
| GR C DARK ANGEL (IRE) - PASTORAL GIRL (GB) | VENDOR | 110000 |

| Name and Breeding | Purchaser | Guineas |
|---|---|---|
| B F NO NAY NEVER (USA) - CAUSEWAY QUEEN (IRE) | ROGER VARIAN | 110000 |
| B C MEHMAS (IRE) - SHOSHONI WIND (GB) | BLANDFORD BS | 110000 |
| B C LOPE DE VEGA (IRE) - ANNA'S ROCK (IRE) | VENDOR | 110000 |
| **SEA LODGE (IRE)** B F SEA THE STARS (IRE) - FRALOGA (IRE) | PETER & ROSS DOYLE BS | 110000 |
| B C CARAVAGGIO (USA) - REMEMBER ALEXANDER (GB) | DONNACHA O'BRIEN | 110000 |
| BR F DUBAWI (IRE) - TIANA (GB) | MIKE RYAN AGENT | 110000 |
| B F MUHAARAR (GB) - MOONLIT GARDEN (IRE) | SHADWELL ESTATE COMPANY | 110000 |
| **INVERNESS (IRE)** B C HIGHLAND REEL (IRE) - FOUR ELEVEN (CAN) | C GORDON WATSON | 110000 |
| B C WOOTTON BASSETT (GB) - ZIMIRA (IRE) | SHADWELL ESTATE COMPANY | 110000 |
| BR C CARAVAGGIO (USA) - CAPE JOY (IRE) | AVENUE BS FOR MV MAGNIER | 110000 |
| CH C SIYOUNI (FR) - FOLK OPERA (IRE) | SACKVILLEDONALD | 110000 |
| B C COTAI GLORY (GB) - LADY LUCIA (IRE) | BLANDFORD BS | 110000 |
| B F CAMELOT (GB) - SOFT ICE (IRE) | MARK MCNIFF | 110000 |
| B C MUHAARAR (GB) - MAID FOR WINNING (USA) | SHADWELL ESTATE COMPANY | 110000 |
| B F RIBCHESTER (IRE) - ANEEDAH (IRE) | SHADWELL ESTATE COMPANY | 110000 |
| B C AUSTRALIA (GB) - SIMILU (IRE) | JOSEPH O'BRIEN | 110000 |
| B C SIYOUNI (FR) - IBERIAN SUN (GB) | VENDOR | 110000 |
| **QUE SUERTE (GB)** B C SEA THE MOON (GER) - QUESTABELLA (GER) | C GORDON WATSON BS | 110000 |
| **XAARIA (FR)** GR F KENDARGENT (FR) - XAARINA (FR) | HARAS D'ETREHAM | 110000 |
| CH F NIGHT OF THUNDER (IRE) - HARLEQUIN GIRL (GB) | SHADWELL ESTATE COMPANY | 110000 |
| B C KODIAC (GB) - EAVESDROP (IRE) | SHADWELL ESTATE COMPANY | 110000 |
| B C CHURCHILL (IRE) - BOASTFUL (IRE) | VENDOR | 110000 |
| **PEACE NEGOTIATION (IRE)** B C NO NAY NEVER (USA) - MADEENATY (IRE) | C GORDON WATSON BS | 110000 |
| **DUBAI JEWEL (GB)** B F SHOWCASING - DIAMOND BLAISE (IRE) | ANDREW BALDING | 105000 |
| B C ACCLAMATION (GB) - MIILIKA (GB) | D FARRINGTON | 105000 |
| B C CHURCHILL (IRE) - SPRINKLING (USA) | GLOBAL EQUINE GROUP | 105000 |
| B C AIR FORCE BLUE (USA) - PELLUCID (GB) | D FARRINGTON | 105000 |
| **BROADSPEAR (GB)** B C LE HAVRE (FR) - FLOWER OF LIFE (IRE) | KARL BURKE | 105000 |
| B F LOPE DE VEGA (IRE) - MINWAH (IRE) | BLANDFORD BS | 105000 |
| B F KODIAC (GB) - BLUE CHIP (GB) | BBA IRELAND | 105000 |
| B C PROFITABLE (IRE) - DUTCH HEIRESS (GB) | SHADWELL ESTATE COMPANY | 105000 |
| B F NO NAY NEVER (USA) - DYNACAM (USA) | R O'RYAN / R FAHEY | 105000 |
| B F DARK ANGEL (IRE) - ROSERAIE (IRE) | RABBAH BS | 105000 |
| B C CARAVAGGIO (USA) - SEAGULL (IRE) | DWAYNE WOODS | 105000 |
| B C PROFITABLE (IRE) - LAW OF THE RANGE (IRE) | ROBSON AGUIAR | 105000 |
| B F RIBCHESTER (IRE) - ARTISTI (GB) | DE BURGH EQUINE | 105000 |
| B F EXCEED AND EXCEL (AUS) - CHICA WHOPA (IRE) | GAELIC BS | 105000 |
| CH C NEW APPROACH (IRE) - LA SUPERBA (IRE) | BBA IRELAND | 105000 |
| B C SIYOUNI (FR) - QUSHCHI (GB) | VENDOR | 100000 |
| B C INVINCIBLE SPIRIT (IRE) - AARAAMM (USA) | RICHARD FRISBY BS | 100000 |
| **GOLDEN SHEEN (GB)** CH F FRANKEL (GB) - YELLOW BAND (USA) | VENDOR | 100000 |
| B C ZOFFANY (IRE) - KEBAYA (GB) | RICHARD HUGHES RACING | 100000 |
| GR C SHAMARDAL (USA) - LADY ROSAMUNDE (GB) | BROWN ISLAND STABLES (P.S.) | 100000 |
| B F MUHAARAR (GB) - BELLA LULU (GB) | BLUE DIAMOND STUD | 100000 |
| CH C AUSTRALIA (GB) - PERMISSION SLIP (IRE) | JEREMY BRUMMITT | 100000 |
| B C KODIAC (GB) - SWISS DIVA (GB) | VENDOR | 100000 |
| B C ALMANZOR (FR) - GEMSTONE (IRE) | HARAS D'ETREHAM | 100000 |
| GR F DARK ANGEL (IRE) - KATIE'S DIAMOND (FR) | VENDOR | 100000 |
| CH F NIGHT OF THUNDER (IRE) - CAPE RISING (IRE) | EDDIE LINEHAN BS | 100000 |
| B C NIGHT OF THUNDER (IRE) - BLITHE SPIRIT (GB) | BYRON ROGERS / LONGWAYS | 100000 |
| B C DARK ANGEL (IRE) - CHOOSE ME (IRE) | SACKVILLEDONALD | 100000 |
| B C KINGMAN (GB) - DEUCE AGAIN (GB) | OLIVER ST LAWRENCE BS | 100000 |
| **MR ZIPPI (GB)** B C INTELLO (GER) - IZZI TOP (GB) | VENDOR | 100000 |
| B F SHOWCASING - SHEMDA (IRE) | GROVE STUD | 100000 |
| **DARK SWANSONG (IRE)** B C DARK ANGEL (IRE) - PIXELEEN (GB) | CLIVE COX RACING | 100000 |
| **WOOTTON'SUN (FR)** B C WOOTTON BASSETT (GB) - SOUS LE SOLEIL (USA) | R O'RYAN / R FAHEY | 100000 |
| B C SHAMARDAL (USA) - GWAEL (USA) | BROADHURST AGENCY | 100000 |
| CH C NIGHT OF THUNDER (IRE) - POPULIST (IRE) | SHADWELL ESTATE COMPANY | 100000 |
| B C SHALAA (IRE) - FAZENDERA (IRE) | PETER & ROSS DOYLE BS | 100000 |
| B C PIVOTAL (GB) - CELESTE (GB) | DWAYNE WOODS | 100000 |
| B F IFFRAAJ (GB) - SUNSHINE REGAE (IRE) | & H. | 100000 |
| BL C CARAVAGGIO (USA) - RISKIT FORA BISKIT (IRE) | M V MAGNIER | 100000 |
| **SHOW OF STARS (GB)** BR F SHOWCASING (GB) - GLORYETTE (GB) | PADDY TWOMEY | 100000 |
| B F WOOTTON BASSETT (GB) - RUNNER RUNNER (IRE) | VENDOR | 100000 |
| **MARAYEL (IRE)** B C DANDY MAN (IRE) - LUVMEDO (IRE) | VENDOR | 100000 |
| B F NO NAY NEVER (USA) - DANEHILL'S DREAM (IRE) | JAMIE MCCALMONT | 100000 |
| B C PIVOTAL (GB) - FIELD OF MIRACLES (IRE) | KERN/LILLINGSTON ASSOCIATION | 100000 |
| **BOLD AND LOYAL (GB)** B C FRANKEL (GB) - BIRDWOOD (GB) | VENDOR | 100000 |
| **HAPAP (IRE)** B C DARK ANGEL (IRE) - APPHIA (IRE) | PETER & ROSS DOYLE BS | 100000 |
| B C CHURCHILL (IRE) - LOVE AND BUBBLES (USA) | VENDOR | 100000 |
| **MEDRARA (GB)** B C LOPE DE VEGA (IRE) - MODERAH (USA) | ANDREW SIME | 100000 |
| CH F PROFITABLE (IRE) - KITTY SOFTPAWS (IRE) | SHADWELL ESTATE COMPANY | 100000 |
| B C CHURCHILL (IRE) - MATERIALISTIC (GB) | RABBAH BS | 100000 |
| B F DARK ANGEL (IRE) - VENUS DE MILO (IRE) | JAMIE MCCALMONT | 100000 |
| **PEACHY KEEN (GB)** B F PIVOTAL (GB) - PERFECTLY SPIRITED (GB) | VENDOR | 100000 |

# HIGH-PRICED YEARLINGS OF 2020 AT GOFFS IRELAND
The following yearlings realised 49,560 euros and over at Goffs Ireland Sales in 2020:

| Name and Breeding | Purchaser | Euros |
|---|---|---|
| B F SEA THE STARS (IRE) - GREEN ROOM (USA) | VENDOR | 914500 |
| BR F OASIS DREAM (GB) - PRINCESS DE LUNE (GB) | SHADWELL | 531000 |
| **NAPA SPIRIT (IRE)** B C INVINCIBLE SPIRIT (IRE) - AIMHIRGIN LASS (IRE) | BEN MCELROY | 495600 |
| B F DARK ANGEL (IRE) - FASHIONABLE (GB) | CBR BS | 472000 |
| B F SEA THE STARS (IRE) - LOVE MAGIC (GB) | SUNDERLAND HOLDINGS | 424800 |
| **SCHIELE (IRE)** GR C DARK ANGEL (IRE) - THE HERMITAGE (IRE) | WHITEBIRCH (D.L. O' BYRNE) | 418900 |
| **NEPTUNE LEGEND (IRE)** B C INVINCIBLE SPIRIT (IRE) - KATE THE GREAT (GB) | AVENUE BS | 413000 |
| **WISH FOR ME (IRE)** B F MEHMAS (IRE) - BIG BONED (USA) | HUGO MERRY BS | 389400 |
| **RATHMORE (IRE)** B F KINGMAN (GB) - KNOCKNAGREE (IRE) | JUDDMONTE FARMS | 330400 |
| GR G DARK ANGEL (IRE) - LAYLA JAMIL (IRE) | HKJC | 306800 |
| B F SIYOUNI (FR) - FORK LIGHTNING (USA) | DURCAN BS | 295000 |
| CH F SEA THE STARS (IRE) - GOLDEN REIGN (IRE) | VENDOR | 295000 |
| B C NEW BAY (GB) - HIGHLANDS QUEEN (FR) | DWYANE WOODS | 283200 |
| **SIAMSA (IRE)** B F STARSPANGLEDBANNER (AUS) - SLIABH LUACHRA (IRE) | VENDOR | 283200 |
| B C CHURCHILL (IRE) - PIVOTALIA (IRE) | JAMIE MCCALMONT | 259600 |
| **ORAZIO (IRE)** BR/GR C CARAVAGGIO (USA) - LADY FASHION (GB) | MICHAEL ROY | 253700 |
| B C SHOWCASING (GB) - SPICY (IRE) | AMANDA SKIFFINGTON | 236000 |
| B C NO NAY NEVER (USA) - SEEKING SOLACE (GB) | MITSURU HASHIDA (P.S.) | 236000 |
| B C KODIAC (GB) - SPINAMISS (IRE) | BLANDFORD BS | 224200 |
| B F GALILEO (IRE) - NIGHT VISIT (GB) | B.B.A. IRELAND | 218300 |
| GR C LOPE DE VEGA (IRE) - DIAMOND SKY (IRE) | M V MAGNIER | 212400 |
| B C DARK ANGEL (IRE) - JET SETTING (IRE) | STAR BS (P.S.) | 212400 |
| B F GALILEO (IRE) - BANIMPIRE (IRE) | NEWTOWN ANNER STUD | 200600 |
| B C EXCEED AND EXCEL (AUS) - COTTONMOUTH (IRE) | DWYANE WOODS | 200600 |
| B C CAMELOT (GB) - EDWINSTOWE (IRE) | A.C. ELLIOTT, AGENT | 188800 |
| **TRANQUIL LADY (IRE)** CH F AUSTRALIA (GB) - REPOSE (USA) | RICHARD RYAN | 188800 |
| **PORTO ERCOLE (IRE)** B/BR F CARAVAGGIO (USA) - EUPHRASIA (IRE) | WHITEBIRCH (D.L. O' BYRNE) | 188800 |
| CH F CHURCHILL (IRE) - RIOTICISM (FR) | J.P. MURTAGH RACING | 188800 |
| B C ACCLAMATION (GB) - EXQUISITE RUBY (IRE) | B.B.A. IRELAND | 182900 |
| **HAMAKI (IRE)** B C CHURCHILL (IRE) - SARAWATI (IRE) | HIGHFLYER BS | 177000 |
| GR F DARK ANGEL (IRE) - NIGHT FEVER (IRE) | VENDOR | 177000 |
| B F FAST COMPANY (IRE) - TITIAN SAGA (IRE) | JOE FOLEY | 177000 |
| B F LOPE DE VEGA (IRE) - WITCHES BREW (GB) | RALPH BECKETT | 177000 |
| CH C FRANKEL (GB) - VENTURA (IRE) | AVENUE BS/FERGUSON | 171100 |
| B C CHURCHILL (IRE) - ORCIA (IRE) | PETER & ROSS DOYLE BS | 165200 |
| B F GALILEO (IRE) - NECHITA (AUS) | BRIAN GRASSICK BS | 165200 |
| CH F FRANKEL (GB) - REMEMBER YOU (IRE) | RABBAH BS | 165200 |
| B F FOOTSTEPSINTHESAND (GB) - BREEZE HILL (IRE) | TROY STEVE BS LTD | 159300 |
| **IRISH VIRTUOSO (GB)** GR F MASTERCRAFTSMAN (IRE) - SHENIR (GB) | JAMIE MCCALMONT | 159300 |
| B C NO NAY NEVER (USA) - SAUCY SPIRIT (IRE) | M V MAGNIER | 153400 |
| B G STARSPANGLEDBANNER (AUS) - RELY ON ME (IRE) | HKJC | 153400 |
| **FLASH BULB (IRE)** B F CAMELOT (GB) - ETHEL (GB) | WHITEBIRCH (D.L. O'BYRNE) | 153400 |
| B F ACLAIM (IRE) - ZANZIBAR (IRE) | GROVE STUD | 153400 |
| B C GLENEAGLES (IRE) - DANELETA (IRE) | JOSEPH O'BRIEN | 153400 |
| **SURAC (IRE)** B C FRANKEL (GB) - BELESTA (GB) | HIGHFLYER BS | 153400 |
| BR F NO NAY NEVER (USA) - NOVANTAE (GB) | DAVID REDVERS | 147500 |
| B C INVINCIBLE SPIRIT (IRE) - LOVE STREET (USA) | C GORDON-WATSON | 141600 |
| **KINGMAX (IRE)** B C KINGMAN (GB) - BAINO HOPE (FR) | ROBSON AGUIAR | 141600 |
| **TRIQUETRA (IRE)** B F DARK ANGEL (IRE) - BUTTON DOWN (GB) | PETER & ROSS DOYLE BS | 141600 |
| B C BATED BREATH (GB) - BORAGH JAMAL (IRE) | BEN MCELROY | 135700 |
| CH F SEA THE STARS (IRE) - NINAS TERZ (GER) | JILL LAMB BS | 129600 |
| B C DUBAWI (IRE) - ALL AT SEA (GB) | MAGS O'TOOLE | 129600 |
| **MUSIC MAGIC (IRE)** B C FASTNET ROCK (AUS) - START THE MUSIC (IRE) | RICHARD RYAN | 129600 |
| B G KODIAC (GB) - PEARL OF THE NIGHT (IRE) | HKJC | 129600 |
| B C CARAVAGGIO (USA) - ALCHEMILLA (GB) | OLIVER ST. LAWRENCE | 118000 |
| **KING OF JUNGLE (IRE)** CH C BUNGLE INTHEJUNGLE (GB) - AYR MISSILE (GB) | SACKVILLEDONALD | 118000 |
| **NOVEL LEGEND (IRE)** B C NATHANIEL (IRE) - MAJESTIC DUBAWI (IRE) | AVENUE BS | 118000 |
| **KOMEDY KICKS (IRE)** B F CHURCHILL (IRE) - KOMEDY (IRE) | B.B.A. IRELAND | 118000 |
| B F RIBCHESTER (IRE) - GALLEY (GB) | PETER & ROSS DOYLE BS | 118000 |
| **BRUSH WITH THE LAW (IRE)** B F CARAVAGGIO (USA) - SURPRISINGLY (IRE) | DJ STABLES | 118000 |
| **IRISH FLAME (GB)** B C DARK ANGEL (IRE) - DREAM OF TARA (IRE) | RICHARD RYAN | 118000 |
| CH F NIGHT OF THUNDER (IRE) - ROMANY GYPSY (IRE) | VENDOR | 118000 |
| B C CARAVAGGIO (USA) - SPRING GARDEN (IRE) | STROUD COLEMAN BS | 118000 |
| **BEACHES (GB)** B C CHURCHILL (IRE) - KNOW ME LOVE ME (IRE) | B.B.A. IRELAND | 118000 |
| **SAFETY FIRST (GB)** B F NEW BAY (GB) - SOTERIA (IRE) | CLIVE COX RACING | 118000 |
| **SOUTHWEST HARBOR (IRE)** B F CHURCHILL (IRE) - SQUEEZE (IRE) | VENDOR | 118000 |
| **BELLE COLORA (IRE)** GR F DARK ANGEL (IRE) - OAKLEY GIRL (GB) | BRUMMERHOF STUD | 118000 |

| | | |
|---|---|---|
| **SUNSET SHIRAZ (IRE)** B F TIME TEST (GB) - SUNNY AGAIN (GB) | D. HARVEY FOR HIGHLAND YARD | 118000 |
| B C AUSTRALIA (GB) - APTICANTI (USA) | JOSEPH O'BRIEN (P.S.) | 118000 |
| B F NIGHT OF THUNDER (IRE) - QUENCHED (GB) | BOBBY O'RYAN | 112100 |
| B F LOPE DE VEGA (IRE) - ELLE WOODS (IRE) | DE BURGH EQUINE | 112100 |
| BR/GR F DARK ANGEL (IRE) - LORETO (IRE) | VENDOR | 106200 |
| B C PIVOTAL (GB) - TIPPING OVER (IRE) | B.B.A. IRELAND | 106200 |
| GR F DARK ANGEL (IRE) - SEAFRONT (GB) | DJ STABLES (P.S.) | 106200 |
| B C KODIAC (GB) - BABYLONIAN (IRE) | AIDAN O'RYAN | 106200 |
| BR F WOOTTON BASSETT (GB) - CATALINA BAY (IRE) | JILL LAMB BS | 106200 |
| B F LOPE DE VEGA (IRE) - BLENDING (GB) | ROGER VARIAN (P.S.) | 106200 |
| CH F PROFITABLE (IRE) - CROSSANZA (IRE) | DE BURGH EQUINE | 100300 |
| **KODAMA (IRE)** B F KODIAC (GB) - IT'S TRUE (IRE) | P DOYLE | 100300 |
| B C STARSPANGLEDBANNER (AUS) - BIARAAFA (IRE) | A.C. ELLIOTT, AGENT | 100300 |
| **VICTORIA FAIR (IRE)** B/BR F AUSTRALIA (GB) - HAMMIYA (IRE) | PETER & ROSS DOYLE BS | 96760 |
| CH C ULYSSES (IRE) - DIYAVANA (FR) | S KAVANAGH | 94400 |
| B C DARK ANGEL (IRE) - ORNELIA RUEE (FR) | GAELIC BS | 94400 |
| BR/GR C CARAVAGGIO (USA) - ZEE ZEE GEE (GB) | DJ STABLES | 94400 |
| B F LOPE DE VEGA (IRE) - BABY HOUSEMAN (GB) | VENDOR | 94400 |
| B F GLENEAGLES (IRE) - IN THE MIST (GB) | MERRY GATE BS | 94400 |
| CH C LOPE DE VEGA (IRE) - ALLURE (IRE) | B.B.A. IRELAND | 94400 |
| **AL BAHIA (IRE)** B F ZOFFANY (IRE) - STRAW HAT (IRE) | RABBAH BS | 94400 |
| CH C LOPE DE VEGA (IRE) - GOLDEN SHADOW (IRE) | VENDOR | 94400 |
| B C ZOFFANY (IRE) - LOVED (IRE) | JOSEPH O'BRIEN | 94400 |
| **INIS FAIL (IRE)** CH F SHOWCASING (GB) - FIELD OF STARS (GB) | PADDY TWOMEY | 94400 |
| **ASEAN LEGEND (IRE)** B C AUSTRALIA (GB) - QUEENSCLIFF (IRE) | AVENUE BS | 92040 |
| B/GR C CARAVAGGIO (USA) - FANCY (IRE) | JOSEPH O'BRIEN | 92040 |
| **SEISAI (IRE)** B F GLENEAGLES (IRE) - LILLEBONNE (FR) | HIGHFLYER BS | 92040 |
| B G VADAMOS (FR) - PEARLY SPIRIT (FR) | KEVIN ROSS BS | 92040 |
| B C AUSTRALIA (GB) - CARAVAN OF DREAMS (IRE) | VENDOR | 90860 |
| BR C LOPE DE VEGA (IRE) - PALE MIMOSA (IRE) | DERMOT FARRINGTON | 88500 |
| B F NATIONAL DEFENSE (GB) - THAMES PAGEANT (GB) | BEN MCELROY | 88500 |
| CH F LOPE DE VEGA (IRE) - KERRY GAL (IRE) | AMANDA SKIFFINGTON | 88500 |
| GR C AUSTRALIA (GB) - BEWITCHED (IRE) | RICHARD KNIGHT BS AGENT LTD | 88500 |
| **THUNDER QUEEN (GB)** B F NIGHT OF THUNDER (IRE) - MUZHIL (IRE) | PETER & ROSS DOYLE BS | 84960 |
| B F KODIAC (GB) - ELAYSA (GB) | BLANDFORD BS | 84960 |
| B F HIGHLAND REEL (IRE) - TRIANON (GB) | DAVID REDVERS | 84960 |
| B C HOLY ROMAN EMPEROR (IRE) - VIBE QUEEN (IRE) | DWAYNE WOODS | 82600 |
| CH C SEA THE STARS (IRE) - DAIVIKA (USA) | ANDREW BALDING | 82600 |
| BR/GR F KODIAC (GB) - ENJOYABLE (IRE) | WHITE FEATHER BS | 82600 |
| B C CARAVAGGIO (USA) - LUCY DIAMONDS (IRE) | JOANNA MORGAN | 82600 |
| B F LOPE DE VEGA (IRE) - ORAFINITIS (IRE) | VENDOR | 82600 |
| CH F AUSTRALIA (GB) - ELEKTRA STREET (GB) | OPULENCE THOROUGHBREDS | 82600 |
| B C CHURCHILL (IRE) - NAJMA (GB) | GLENVALE STUD | 82000 |
| B C ALMANZOR (FR) - LADY FAMILY (FR) | VENDOR | 79060 |
| B F OASIS DREAM (GB) - IRIDESCENCE (GB) | MIDDLEHAM PARK RACING | 77880 |
| B C KODIAC (GB) - NIGHT QUEEN (IRE) | GORDON-WATSON BS | 76700 |
| **PROSPEROUS VOYAGE (IRE)** B F ZOFFANY (IRE) - SEATONE (USA) | BADGERS BS | 76700 |
| B C HOLY ROMAN EMPEROR (IRE) - BROADWAY DUCHESS (IRE) | PETER & ROSS DOYLE BS | 76700 |
| B C CARAVAGGIO (USA) - LAP OF LUXURY (IRE) | MIKE AKERS | 76700 |
| **CAVALLUCCIO (IRE)** BR C CARAVAGGIO (USA) - GALE SONG (GB) | RICHARD HUGHES RACING | 76700 |
| B C ALMANZOR (FR) - TIMEPECKER (IRE) | A.C. ELLIOTT, AGENT FOR MPR | 76700 |
| CH C HIGHLAND REEL (IRE) - MOVING HEART (IRE) | BOBBY O'RYAN/D.K. WELD | 76700 |
| CH F PROFITABLE (IRE) - CROSSANZA (IRE) | M O'TOOLE | 75000 |
| **DISSOCIATE (IRE)** B F ALMANZOR (FR) - PARTY ANIMAL (GB) | PADDY TWOMEY | 73160 |
| B F CARAVAGGIO (USA) - HUG AND A KISS (USA) | PHILIPPA MAINS | 73160 |
| B F NO NAY NEVER (USA) - FALLING RAIN (IRE) | EBONOS | 73160 |
| **LITE AND AIRY (GB)** B C TWILIGHT SON (GB) - SPIN DOCTOR (GB) | DWAYNE WOODS | 73160 |
| **MACKENZIE ROSE (IRE)** B F DARK ANGEL (IRE) - KELSEY ROSE (GB) | JOHNSTON RACING | 73160 |
| B F FASTNET ROCK (AUS) - PURE ART (GB) | P. SAVILL | 73160 |
| B F ZOFFANY (IRE) - BRIGHT BANK (IRE) | VENDOR | 70800 |
| CH F LOPE DE VEGA (IRE) - PERFECT ALCHEMY (IRE) | NICK BRADLEY/J. HARRINGTON | 70800 |
| B F NO NAY NEVER (USA) - CASTLE CROSS (IRE) | TOWNLEY HALL BS | 70800 |
| B C ACCLAMATION (GB) - MONCLAIRE (GER) | VENDOR | 70800 |
| CH F MASTERCRAFTSMAN (IRE) - QUADS (IRE) | BEN MCELROY | 70800 |
| **WARHOL (IRE)** B C BELARDO (IRE) - DARSAN (IRE) | HIGHFLYER BS | 70800 |
| **ZOFFANY PORTRAIT (IRE)** CH C ZOFFANY (IRE) - BUNOOD (IRE) | JOSEPH O'BRIEN | 70800 |
| B C PROFITABLE (IRE) - THAKAFAAT (IRE) | JOE FOLEY | 70800 |
| B C NIGHT OF THUNDER (IRE) - SPANGLE (GB) | VENDOR | 70800 |
| B C LOPE DE VEGA (IRE) - DARK CRUSADER (IRE) | VENDOR | 70800 |
| **TURBO TWO (IRE)** B C HOLY ROMAN EMPEROR (IRE) - SWISH (GER) | VENDOR | 70800 |

| | | |
|---|---|---|
| CH C LEA (USA) - SEEKING LUCK (USA) | FILIP ZWICKY | 70800 |
| **BYKER (IRE)** B C LE HAVRE (IRE) - BRIDGE OF PEACE (GB) | PETER & ROSS DOYLE BS | 70800 |
| B C MAKE BELIEVE (GB) - IPSO JURE (IRE) | DERMOT FARRINGTON | 70800 |
| CH C NO NAY NEVER (USA) - ITASCA (FR) | SACKVILLEDONALD | 70800 |
| B F ACCLAMATION (GB) - WESTADORA (IRE) | PETER & ROSS DOYLE BS | 68440 |
| CH C GLENEAGLES (IRE) - CELESTE DE LA MER (IRE) | JOSEPH O'BRIEN | 68440 |
| B F TAMAYUZ (GB) - ABEND (IRE) | JOE FOLEY | 68440 |
| B F FASTNET ROCK (AUS) - LA CONQUERANTE (GB) | GROVE STUD | 64900 |
| B C DANDY MAN (IRE) - HARVEST JOY (IRE) | ROBSON AGUIAR | 64900 |
| B C ZOFFANY (IRE) - INNOCENT AIR (GB) | SAM SANGSTER BS | 64900 |
| B C RIBCHESTER (IRE) - DANCING ON AIR (IRE) | GROVE STUD | 64900 |
| B F NO NAY NEVER (USA) - SOHO SUSIE (IRE) | PETER & ROSS DOYLE BS | 64900 |
| **CHAIN OF DESTINY (IRE)** B C CHURCHILL (IRE) - ALWAYS SPECIAL (IRE) | PADDY TWOMEY | 63720 |
| B C STARSPANGLEDBANNER (AUS) - HOLLOW TALK (GB) | CORMAC MCCORMACK | 63720 |
| BR/GR C ACCLAMATION (GB) - QUEEN OF POWER (IRE) | EOGHAN J. O'NEILL | 61360 |
| **BID FAREWELL (IRE)** B F NO NAY NEVER (USA) - A BID IN TIME (IRE) | DJ STABLES | 61360 |
| B F CHURCHILL (IRE) - IMTIYAAZ (IRE) | EDWARD LYNAM | 59000 |
| CH C SEA THE STARS (IRE) - MISS ELIZABETH (IRE) | BOBBY O'RYAN | 59000 |
| **ZEN (IRE)** B F ZOFFANY (IRE) - MARKET FORCES (GB) | D.J. STABLES (P.S.) | 59000 |
| B C PROFITABLE (GB) - WROOD (USA) | OLIVER ST. LAWRENCE | 59000 |
| B F CAMACHO (GB) - DUTCH TREATY (GB) | VENDOR | 59000 |
| B F NO NAY NEVER (USA) - HIDDEN CHARMS (IRE) | BROWN ISLAND | 59000 |
| **APACHE GREY (IRE)** GR C EL KABEIR (USA) - LAURELITA (IRE) | RICHARD HUGHES RACING | 59000 |
| B C OASIS DREAM (GB) - BEACH BUNNY (IRE) | OPULENCE THOROUGHBREDS | 59000 |
| B F DIVINE PROPHET (AUS) - CLYTHA (GB) | VENDOR | 59000 |
| **BALVANY (IRE)** B F KODIAC (GB) - FANCY VIVID (IRE) | BRUMMERHOF STUD | 59000 |
| B C KODIAC (GB) - ALYAAFEL (IRE) | SACKVILLEDONALD | 59000 |
| B C CARAVAGGIO (USA) - SHIRLEY A STAR (USA) | MITSURU HASHIDA (P.S.) | 59000 |
| B F KODIAC (GB) - EASY TIMES (GB) | SACKVILLEDONALD | 59000 |
| B C MONDIALISTE (IRE) - JUST JEALOUS (IRE) | VENDOR | 59000 |
| B C INVINCIBLE SPIRIT (IRE) - RECITE (JPN) | B.B.A. IRELAND | 59000 |
| B C FOOTSTEPSINTHESAND (GB) - HARPIST (IRE) | KEVIN ROSS BS | 59000 |
| B C DANDY MAN (IRE) - LITTLE KIPLING (GB) | MARGARET O'TOOLE | 59000 |
| GR C DARK ANGEL (IRE) - LA GRANDE ZOA (IRE) | VENDOR | 59000 |
| **GORDONS AURA (IRE)** B C GOLDEN HORN (GB) - SEQUINED (USA) | HIGHFLYER BS | 59000 |
| CH F ACCLAMATION (GB) - SHY BRIDE (IRE) | J.C.H BS | 59000 |
| **CHAMPAGNE PLEASE (IRE)** CH F AUSTRALIA (GB) - CHAMPAGNE OR WATER (IRE) | FILIP ZWICKY | 59000 |
| **QUAVERING (IRE)** B C VOCALISED (USA) - HALLA NA SAOIRE (IRE) | A.C. ELLIOTT, AGENT | 59000 |
| **BERKSHIRE BREEZE (IRE)** B C MASTERCRAFTSMAN (IRE) - BRIGHT AND SHINING (IRE) | ANDREW BALDING (P.S.) | 59000 |
| B C KODIAC (GB) - LEYBURN (GB) | YEOMANSTOWN STUD | 58000 |
| B C DARK ANGEL (IRE) - MAOINEAS (IRE) | HIGHFLYER BS | 56640 |
| B C ZOFFANY (IRE) - HOLD ME NOW (USA) | JOSEPH O'BRIEN | 56640 |
| GR C MASTERCRAFTSMAN (IRE) - ELEGANT PEACE (IRE) | KERN LILLINGSTON | 56640 |
| B C COTAI GLORY (GB) - SOMMORELL (IRE) | SACKVILLEDONALD | 56640 |
| CH C BATED BREATH (GB) - TAKE THE HINT (GB) | VENDOR | 56640 |
| **I'M A GAMBLER (IRE)** B C NO NAY NEVER (USA) - WE ARE NINETY (IRE) | JOHNSTON RACING | 55460 |
| B C DIVINE PROPHET (AUS) - TIP IT ON THE TOP (IRE) | BOBBY O'RYAN | 55460 |
| B C MEHMAS (IRE) - CRAFTY NOTION (IRE) | B.B.A. IRELAND LTD | 55460 |
| B F SEA THE STARS (IRE) - LAUGHING DOVE (IRE) | VENDOR | 55460 |
| B C ZOFFANY (IRE) - ZA'HARA (IRE) | JOSEPH O'BRIEN | 54280 |
| **LILA GIRL (IRE)** B F PRIDE OF DUBAI (AUS) - THE SHREW (GB) | A.C. ELLIOTT AGENT | 54280 |
| B F NO NAY NEVER (USA) - ART OF DANCE (IRE) | EDDIE HARTY (P.S.) | 54280 |
| BR/GR F CARAVAGGIO (USA) - MARASIMA (IRE) | J.B. BS | 54280 |
| **EXMINSTER (IRE)** B C RIBCHESTER (IRE) - SURFACE OF EARTH (USA) | BBA (IRELAND) | 54000 |
| GR C MASTERCRAFTSMAN (IRE) - GELENSCHIK (IRE) | TOWNLEY HALL BS | 53100 |
| B C CHURCHILL (IRE) - DUSTY IN MEMPHIS (USA) | JOE FOLEY | 53100 |
| B F STARSPANGLEDBANNER (AUS) - JE T'ADORE (IRE) | B.B.A. IRELAND | 53100 |
| B C DARK ANGEL (IRE) - TARAKALA (IRE) | RICHARD RYAN | 53100 |
| B F STARSPANGLEDBANNER (AUS) - MEETYOUATTHEMOON (IRE) | CORMAC MCCORMACK | 53100 |
| B F ZOFFANY (IRE) - LISANOR (GB) | BARRY LYNCH/JACK DAVISON | 53100 |
| B C HOLY ROMAN EMPEROR (IRE) - MARIE JOSEPHE (GB) | LEAMORE HORSES | 53100 |
| B F AUSTRALIA (GB) - FILANTE (IRE) | MP BS | 52000 |
| **MEZZANOTTE (IRE)** B F DECORATED KNIGHT (GB) - MIDDLE PERSIA (GB) | BARRY LYNCH/HEATH HOUSE | 51920 |
| B F MEHMAS (IRE) - FADDWA (IRE) | EDWARD LYNAM | 51920 |
| B C ZOFFANY (IRE) - NEVER BUSY (USA) | MAGS O'TOOLE | 51920 |
| B F CAMELOT (GB) - POLISH BELLE (GB) | DE BURGH EQUINE | 49560 |
| CH F NO NAY NEVER (USA) - RAVISH (GB) | EOGHAN J. O'NEILL (P.S.) | 49560 |
| CH C ULYSSES (IRE) - ARWAAH (IRE) | JEREMY BRUMMITT | 49560 |
| CH C MEHMAS (IRE) - PARTY FEET (IRE) | LONGWAYS STABLES | 49560 |

# HIGH-PRICED YEARLINGS OF 2020 AT GOFFS UK (DONCASTER)

**The following yearlings realised £35,000 and over at Goffs UK Sales in 2020:**

| Name and Breeding | Purchaser | Pounds |
|---|---|---|
| **FLAG OF TRUTH (FR)** B C STARSPANGLEDBANNER (AUS) - DALAKANIA (IRE) | RICHARD RYAN | 170000 |
| **HEARTBREAK LASS (GB)** B F COTAI GLORY (GB) - MOTION LASS (GB) | VENDOR | 150000 |
| GR C DARK ANGEL (IRE) - FUTOON (IRE) | JOHN & JAKE WARREN | 140000 |
| B C ACCLAMATION (GB) - DUCHESS POWER (IRE) | SACKVILLEDONALD | 120000 |
| B C HAVANA GOLD (IRE) - MAJESTIC ALEXANDER (IRE) | OLIVER ST LAWRENCE BS | 115000 |
| **CLAIM THE CROWN (IRE)** B C ACCLAMATION (GB) - CROWN LIGHT (GB) | RICHARD RYAN | 115000 |
| GR F SHOWCASING (GB) - SWEET ALABAMA (GB) | MIDDLEHAM PARK RACING | 110000 |
| B C KODI BEAR (IRE) - USEM (GB) | PHIL CUNNINGHAM | 110000 |
| B C DARK ANGEL (IRE) - CUT NO ICE (IRE) | SACKVILLEDONALD | 105000 |
| **OH HERBERTS REIGN (IRE)** B C ACCLAMATION (GB) - WESTERN SAFARI (IRE) | PETER & ROSS DOYLE BS | 105000 |
| B C DARK ANGEL (IRE) - SWISS DREAM (GB) | SACKVILLEDONALD | 100000 |
| B F MEHMAS (IRE) - APPLAUDING (IRE) | JOHN & JAKE WARREN | 100000 |
| **SOWS (IRE)** B F KODIAC (GB) - ZVARKHOVA (FR) | PETER & ROSS DOYLE BS | 100000 |
| B C ACCLAMATION (GB) - BALAYAGE (IRE) | EBONOS | 95000 |
| **MARITIME RULES (IRE)** B C MEHMAS (GB) - BEAUTY OF THE SEA (IRE) | PETER & ROSS DOYLE BS | 95000 |
| B C NIGHT OF THUNDER (IRE) - PEARL SPIRIT (IRE) | LONGWAYS STABLES | 95000 |
| **MR ALAN (GB)** CH C ULYSSES (IRE) - INTERLACE (IRE) | AGUIAR BS | 92000 |
| **LARKIN (IRE)** GR C DARK ANGEL (IRE) - PLAGIARISM (USA) | SACKVILLEDONALD | 88000 |
| **GISBURN (IRE)** CH C RIBCHESTER (IRE) - DISCLOSE (GB) | PETER & ROSS DOYLE BS | 88000 |
| GR C CARAVAGGIO (USA) - PRETTY DARLING (IRE) | HILLEN/RYAN | 85000 |
| **WHISPER MY DREAM (GB)** BR F SHOWCASING (GB) - WELSH ANGEL (GB) | BLANDFORD BLOODSTOCK | 85000 |
| B F RIBCHESTER (IRE) - RUSH (GB) | VENDOR | 85000 |
| **BOLD RIBB (GB)** B C RIBCHESTER (IRE) - BOLD BIDDER (GB) | RICHARD RYAN | 82000 |
| B F EXCEED AND EXCEL (AUS) - STAY SILENT (GB) | RICHARD KNIGHT BS AGENT | 80000 |
| CH F SHOWCASING (GB) - SEOLAN (IRE) | GROVE STUD | 80000 |
| B C HOLY ROMAN EMPEROR (IRE) - BLUE JEAN BABY (GB) | EDDIE LINEHAN | 80000 |
| BR C DUE DILIGENCE (USA) - CHICKLADE (GB) | KEVIN ROSS BS | 80000 |
| **SYSTEM (IRE)** B F GALILEO GOLD (GB) - SPIRITUAL AIR (GB) | PETER & ROSS DOYLE BS | 80000 |
| B C DARK ANGEL (IRE) - KATHOE (IRE) | VENDOR | 78000 |
| **SATELLITE CALL (IRE)** B C KODIAC (GB) - BALL GIRL (IRE) | HOWSON & HOULDSWORTH BS | 78000 |
| B C NIGHT OF THUNDER (IRE) - ELIS ELIZ (IRE) | CHURCH FARM & HORSE PARK STUD | 75000 |
| B C KODIAC (GB) - NIJAH (IRE) | RABBAH BS LTD | 75000 |
| B C LOPE DE VEGA (IRE) - ROYAL EMPRESS (IRE) | JAMIE OSBORNE | 75000 |
| B C NO NAY NEVER (USA) - ELEANOR ROOSEVELT (IRE) | MC BS | 75000 |
| GR C CARAVAGGIO (USA) - VITELLO (IRE) | HOWSON & HOULDSWORTH | 75000 |
| B C NO NAY NEVER (USA) - MADAM VALENTINE (GB) | HILLEN/RYAN | 72000 |
| CH C PROFITABLE (IRE) - FRABJOUS (GB) | KEVIN ROSS BS | 72000 |
| B C RIBCHESTER (IRE) - CROSSED FINGERS (IRE) | GAELIC BS | 72000 |
| B C KODIAC (GB) - BEATIFY (IRE) | VENDOR | 72000 |
| B C KODI BEAR (IRE) - VASTITAS (IRE) | PHIL CUNNINGHAM | 70000 |
| B C DABIRSIM (FR) - HOKU (IRE) | BOBBY O'RYAN/BEN HASLAM | 70000 |
| **KODIAC BLUE (GB)** B C KODIAC (GB) - GRANDE BLEUE (IRE) | VENDOR | 70000 |
| B C COTAI GLORY (GB) - GLOBAL ALEXANDER (IRE) | CLIVE COX RACING LTD | 68000 |
| B C MEHMAS (GB) - CORNAKILL (USA) | DERMOT FARRINGTON | 68000 |
| GR/RO F DARK ANGEL (IRE) - MISS ALBANE (FR) | RABBAH BS LTD | 66000 |
| B C PROFITABLE (IRE) - CROWN (IRE) | DERMOT FARRINGTON | 65000 |
| B F PIVOTAL (GB) - FINAL DYNASTY (GB) | JOSEPH O'BRIEN | 65000 |
| B C CHURCHILL (IRE) - BEYOND DESIRE (GB) | JAMIE OSBORNE | 62000 |
| **THUNDER SKY (GB)** CH F NIGHT OF THUNDER (IRE) - RED ROXANNE (GB) | PETER & ROSS DOYLE BS | 62000 |
| B F CARAVAGGIO (USA) - GOLDEN SHINE (GB) | OLIVER ST LAWRENCE BS | 60000 |
| B C BLUE BRESIL (FR) - HORA (GB) | HIGHFLYER/NJ HENDERSON | 60000 |
| **INDIAN GURU (IRE)** CH F RIBCHESTER (IRE) - TRANSCENDENCE (IRE) | PETER & ROSS DOYLE BS | 60000 |
| **SNOOZE N YOU LOSE (FR)** B F RIBCHESTER (IRE) - WAKE UP CALL (GB) | VENDOR | 60000 |
| **DAYEM (IRE)** B C ACCLAMATION (GB) - SLOVAK (IRE) | OLIVER ST LAWRENCE BS | 58000 |
| B C OLYMPIC GLORY (IRE) - VELVET REVOLVER (IRE) | RICHARD HUGHES RACING LTD | 58000 |
| CH C COTAI GLORY (GB) - JAYLA (IRE) | AGUIAR BS | 58000 |
| B F RIBCHESTER (IRE) - GUAJIRA (IRE) | DERMOT FARRINGTON | 58000 |
| **THE MAD MONK (IRE)** GR C GREGORIAN (IRE) - BROADWAY MUSICAL (IRE) | PHIL CUNNINGHAM | 58000 |
| B C PROFITABLE (IRE) - LA ROUMEGUE (USA) | KARL & KELLY BURKE | 58000 |
| **GREEN TEAM (FR)** B C WOOTTON BASSETT (GB) - ON THE LINE (FR) | HILLEN/RYAN | 55000 |
| B C PROFITABLE (IRE) - VIKING FAIR (GB) | HILLEN/RYAN | 55000 |
| B C KODIAC (GB) - SWEET SUGAR (GER) | GAELIC BS | 55000 |
| B F NO NAY NEVER (USA) - XAPHANIA (GB) | JOSEPH O'BRIEN | 55000 |
| B C PROFITABLE (IRE) - DUTCH COURAGE (GB) | MAGS O'TOOLE | 55000 |
| **HADMAN (IRE)** CH C STARSPANGLEDBANNER (AUS) - ANNELI (IRE) | AVENUE BS (P.S.) | 55000 |
| CH C STARSPANGLEDBANNER (AUS) - MIDNIGHT OASIS (GB) | A ALSABAH | 55000 |
| CH F RIBCHESTER (IRE) - LEXI'S LOVE (USA) | A ALSABAH | 55000 |
| B C BLUE BRESIL (FR) - HIGH BENEFIT (FR) | B A A BS | 55000 |
| B C KODIAC (GB) - HARLEM DANCER (GB) | JOE FOLEY | 54000 |

| | | |
|---|---|---|
| **DESERT ANGEL (IRE)** B/GR C DARK ANGEL (IRE) - SLIEVE MISH (IRE) | PETER & ROSS DOYLE BS | 54000 |
| B C PROFITABLE (IRE) - THRONE (GB) | CLIVE COX RACING LTD | 52000 |
| B C SHOWCASING (GB) - BONFIRE HEART (GB) | CLIVE COX RACING LTD | 52000 |
| B C CARAVAGGIO (USA) - QUEEN BOUDICA (GB) | CHURCH FARM & HORSE PARK | 50000 |
| CH C LOPE DE VEGA (IRE) - VALTINA (IRE) | VENDOR | 50000 |
| **KORKER (IRE)** B C DANDY MAN (IRE) - ADAPTATION (GB) | KARL BURKE | 50000 |
| B C CARAVAGGIO (USA) - DANEHURST (GB) | PAUL WILDES (P.S.) | 50000 |
| **IBN ALDAR (GB)** BR C TWILIGHT SON (GB) - BINT ALDAR (GB) | CHARLIE HILLS | 50000 |
| GR C DARK ANGEL (IRE) - ALONG CAME CASEY (IRE) | RICHARD FAHEY | 50000 |
| B F PRIDE OF DUBAI (AUS) - ARABDA (GB) | PETER & ROSS DOYLE BS | 50000 |
| **ACKLAM GOLD (IRE)** CH G GALILEO GOLD (GB) - TIDES (GB) | VENDOR | 48000 |
| **EVERLOVING (IRE)** B/GR F ACCLAMATION (GB) - CHIRINGUITA (USA) | DAN TUNMORE | 48000 |
| B C KODIAC (GB) - DREAM DANA (IRE) | CON MARNANE | 46000 |
| B C EL KABEIR (USA) - AREYAAM ROSE (IRE) | SACKVILLEDONALD | 46000 |
| CH C CAMACHO (GB) - LADY ARABELLA (IRE) | ROBIN O'RYAN | 46000 |
| CH C RIBCHESTER (IRE) - EMILIA JAMES (GB) | AGUIAR BS | 45000 |
| CH F RIBCHESTER (IRE) - CHEAP THRILLS (GB) | CHURCH FARM & HORSE PARK | 45000 |
| **CRUSH AND RUN (IRE)** B C ZOFFANY (IRE) - MOOCHING ALONG (IRE) | RICHARD HUGHES RACING LTD | 44000 |
| B C KAPGARDE (FR) - FOLIE LOINTAINE (FR) | HAMISH MACAULEY BS | 43000 |
| B C ADAAY (IRE) - RELAXEZ VOUS (IRE) | AIDAN O'RYAN/SYPS LTD | 42000 |
| B F PROFITABLE (IRE) - LUDYNOSA (USA) | RICHARD HUGHES RACING LTD | 42000 |
| B F ACCLAMATION (GB) - CRYING LIGHTENING (GB) | BDSF UK | 42000 |
| **THREE DONS (IRE)** B C FAST COMPANY (IRE) - AVIZARE (IRE) | PETER & ROSS DOYLE BS | 41000 |
| **LUCKY LUCKY LUCKY (IRE)** B G FOOTSTEPSINTHESAND (GB) - LOVERS PEACE (IRE) | JAMIE PIGGOTT | 41000 |
| CH C STARSPANGLEDBANNER (AUS) - BRIGHT NEW DAY (IRE) | CHURCH FARM & HORSE PARK | 40000 |
| **ALDBOURNE (IRE)** B C AWTAAD (IRE) - ALWAYS GENTLE (IRE) | ANDREW BALDING/JS BS | 40000 |
| B C HOLY ROMAN EMPEROR (IRE) - LISA GHERARDINI (IRE) | SACKVILLEDONALD | 40000 |
| **CAREWELL COVER (IRE)** B C FOOTSTEPSINTHESAND (GB) - GOLDEN EASTER (USA) | RICHARD HUGHES RACING | 40000 |
| B C MUHAARAR (GB) - SINGLE (FR) | SAM SANGSTER BS | 40000 |
| **TRUGANINI (IRE)** B F LAWMAN (FR) - TAZMANIA (IRE) | PETER & ROSS DOYLE BS | 40000 |
| **SMULLEN (IRE)** CH C CAMACHO (GB) - DAY BY DAY (GB) | HILLEN/RYAN | 40000 |
| B C COTAI GLORY (GB) - HASTY (IRE) | CHARLIE HILLS | 40000 |
| GR F EL KABEIR (USA) - BEACON OF HOPE (IRE) | A.C. ELLIOTT, AGENT | 40000 |
| B C SHOWCASING (GB) - CARPE DIEM LADY (IRE) | KILBRIDE EQUINE | 40000 |
| **AUSSIE BANKER (GB)** B C MUHAARAR (GB) - ARISTOTELICIENNE (IRE) | RICHARD HUGHES RACING LTD | 40000 |
| B C MEHMAS (IRE) - DITTANDER (GB) | BLANDFORD BS | 40000 |
| B C SHOWCASING (GB) - GLADE (GB) | VENDOR | 40000 |
| B C ESTIDHKAAR (IRE) - CUTE (GB) | ANDREW BALDING/JS BS | 40000 |
| B F PROFITABLE (IRE) - MARAMBA (USA) | VENDOR | 40000 |
| B C COTAI GLORY (GB) - PERFECT VENTURE (GB) | SYPS (UK) LTD | 40000 |
| **MOJOMAKER (IRE)** B C MEHMAS (IRE) - AJLA (IRE) | COMPAS EQUINE | 40000 |
| B C AUSTRALIA (GB) - MARACUJA (GB) | RICHARD HUGHES RACING LTD | 40000 |
| **TOTHENINES (IRE)** BR/GR C DANDY MAN (IRE) - ULTIMATE BEST (GB) | KARL BURKE | 40000 |
| B C AUSTRALIA (GB) - SWEET DREAM (GB) | KEVIN ROSS BS | 40000 |
| B C VADAMOS (FR) - FASHIONABLE SPIRIT (IRE) | KARL & KELLY BURKE | 40000 |
| B C KODI BEAR (IRE) - LIL'S JOY (IRE) | SACKVILLEDONALD | 40000 |
| B C KAYF TARA (GB) - STRAVINSKY DANCE (GB) | R ROHAN | 40000 |
| **PRODIGIOUS BLUE (IRE)** B C BATED BREATH (GB) - HELLOFAHASTE (GB) | NIGEL TINKLER (P.S.) | 39000 |
| B F DANDY MAN (IRE) - BRITAIN'S PRIDE (GB) | SACKVILLEDONALD | 38000 |
| CH C STARSPANGLEDBANNER (AUS) - MADAME CHERIE (USA) | CHURCH FARM & HORSE PARK | 38000 |
| **NOBLE RUN (USA)** B C NOBLE MISSION (GB) - TOXIS (USA) | ANDREW BALDING/JS BS | 38000 |
| B F KENDARGENT (FR) - DOMMYAH (GB) | KEVIN ROSS BS | 38000 |
| B F HAVANA GOLD (IRE) - LITTLEMISSSUNSHINE (IRE) | JILL LAMB BS | 38000 |
| B C GUTAIFAN (IRE) - GLAMOROUS AIR (IRE) | RON HARRIS | 38000 |
| B C ULYSSES (IRE) - FINIDAPREST (IRE) | OLIVER ST LAWRENCE BS | 38000 |
| B F DRAGON PULSE (IRE) - PARADWYS (IRE) | JILL LAMB BS | 38000 |
| CH F NIGHT OF THUNDER (IRE) - AMAMI (IRE) | BROWN ISLAND STABLES LTD | 37000 |
| **GROOM (GB)** BR C ACLAIM (IRE) - TOHAVEANDTOHOLD (GB) | PETER & ROSS DOYLE BS | 36000 |
| GR F ARDAD (IRE) - HEAVENLY ANGEL (GB) | JOE FOLEY | 36000 |
| B F MEHMAS (IRE) - QUICK CHAT (GB) | MARK GRANT | 36000 |
| GR F CARAVAGGIO (USA) - CAPE SUNSHINE (IRE) | VENDOR | 35000 |
| B C BUNGLE INTHEJUNGLE (GB) - CONVIDADA (IRE) | JAMIE OSBORNE | 35000 |
| B C DANDY MAN (IRE) - ISABELLA VITE (IRE) | ROBIN O'RYAN | 35000 |
| CH F BATED BREATH (GB) - RAHAALA (IRE) | OLIVER ST LAWRENCE BS | 35000 |
| B F DANDY MAN (IRE) - NUCLEAR OPTION (IRE) | PETER & ROSS DOYLE BS | 35000 |
| B C MAYSON (GB) - FINAL RHAPSODY (GB) | EDDIE LINEHAN | 35000 |
| **SPACER (IRE)** BR/GR C STARSPANGLEDBANNER (AUS) - FIRST PARTY (GB) | MR MICHEAL ORLANDI (P.S.) | 35000 |
| B G BLUE BRESIL (FR) - LAND OF VIC (GB) | BRIAN GRIFFITHS | 35000 |
| B F STARSPANGLEDBANNER (AUS) - TIME WILL TELL (FR) | LINDA SHANAHAN | 35000 |
| B C INVINCIBLE SPIRIT (IRE) - DISTINCTIVE (GB) | VENDOR | 35000 |
| B C BLUE BRESIL (FR) - PRESENTING DIVA (IRE) | HAMISH MACAULEY BS | 35000 |

# HIGH-PRICED YEARLINGS OF 2020 AT TATTERSALLS IRELAND SALES

**The following yearlings realised 25,960 euros and over at Tattersalls Ireland Sales in 2020:**

| Name and Breeding | Purchaser | Euros |
|---|---|---|
| CH G TEOFILO (IRE) - GEARANAI (USA) | HONG KONG JOCKEY CLUB | 383500 |
| B C MEHMAS (IRE) - LA CUVEE (GB) | JOE FOLEY | 224200 |
| TOOPHAN (IRE) CH C NEW APPROACH (IRE) - MAOINEACH (USA) | EBONOS | 224200 |
| THUNDER MAX (GB) CH C NIGHT OF THUNDER (IRE) - TUOLUMNE MEADOWS (GB) | PETER & ROSS DOYLE BS | 182900 |
| B F TAMAYUZ (GB) - PARDOVAN (IRE) | VENDOR | 118000 |
| MAMBO BEAT (IRE) CH C RED JAZZ (USA) - BULRUSHES (GB) | CLIVE COX RACING | 88500 |
| SO SMART (IRE) B C DANDY MAN (IRE) - MODEL LOOKS (IRE) | SACKVILLEDONALD | 82600 |
| B F KINGMAN (GB) - CONTINENTAL DRIFT (USA) | GREENHILLS FARM | 82600 |
| B C ACCLAMATION (GB) - VOOM VOOM (IRE) | J P MURTAGH | 82600 |
| KODIAS SANGARIUS (IRE) B F KODIAC (GB) - OUI SAY OUI (IRE) | PETER & ROSS DOYLE BS | 80240 |
| B F AUSTRALIA (GB) - DILLYDALLYDO (GB) | DE BURGH EQUINE | 80240 |
| BR C BLUE BRESIL (FR) - WILD BLUEBERRY (IRE) | BALLINCURRIG BS | 80000 |
| B G MEHMAS (IRE) - SHE BU (IRE) | KEVIN ROSS | 76700 |
| B F KODIAC (GB) - DUCHESS ANDORRA (IRE) | YEOMANSTOWN STUD | 76700 |
| MASHMEDIA (IRE) CH C MEHMAS (IRE) - MARK TOO (IRE) | MARCO BOZZI BS | 76700 |
| DOLOMIT (IRE) GR C MASTERCRAFTSMAN (IRE) - DOUALA (GB) | RENELLO BS | 76700 |
| B F GALILEO GOLD (GB) - LADYLISHANDRA (IRE) | VENDOR | 76700 |
| B C EXCELEBRATION (IRE) - CHERRY CREEK (IRE) | PETER & ROSS DOYLE BS | 70800 |
| B F KINGMAN (GB) - LOULWA (IRE) | RABBAH BS | 70800 |
| B C HOLY ROMAN EMPEROR (IRE) - POLKA DOT (IRE) | PETER & ROSS DOYLE BS | 67260 |
| REGAL ENVOY (IRE) B C ARDAD (IRE) - REGINA (GB) | KERN/LILLINGSTON ASSOCIATION | 64900 |
| B G MASTERCRAFTSMAN (IRE) - BRAZILIAN SAMBA (IRE) | HONG KONG JOCKEY CLUB | 64900 |
| CH C AUSTRALIA (GB) - INTO THE LANE (IRE) | AIDAN O'RYAN | 64900 |
| CH C NO RISK AT ALL (FR) - SARDAGNA (FR) | RYAN MAHON/COLM DONLON | 60000 |
| B C KODI BEAR (IRE) - IN DUBAI (USA) | AGUIAR BS | 59000 |
| B C HOLY ROMAN EMPEROR (IRE) - DAME LUCY (IRE) | DWAYNE WOODS | 59000 |
| CH F BATED BREATH (GB) - QUEEN ANDORRA (IRE) | JOE FOLEY | 56640 |
| B C MAYSON (GB) - IDEALIST (GB) | KARL & KELLY BURKE | 55460 |
| B F LOPE DE VEGA (IRE) - LORGNETTE (FR) | EDDIE LINEHAN BS | 55460 |
| CH C MOUNT NELSON (GB) - BATTLE OVER (FR) | AIDEN MURPHY | 55000 |
| CH C PROFITABLE (IRE) - DANCING YEARS (IRE) | BBA IRELAND | 54280 |
| B C DANDY MAN (IRE) - PADDY AGAIN (IRE) | JOE FOLEY | 53100 |
| BL C ROCK OF GIBRALTAR (IRE) - SHANJIA (GER) | HANS STIHL | 53100 |
| NIGHT GLASS (IRE) B C GALILEO GOLD (GB) - HEN NIGHT (IRE) | PETER & ROSS DOYLE BS | 53100 |
| B F LAWMAN (FR) - HIDDEN GIRL (IRE) | ED DUNLOP RACING | 53100 |
| B F DANDY MAN (IRE) - IMELDA MARIE (IRE) | SACKVILLEDONALD | 51920 |
| CH F FOOTSTEPSINTHESAND (GB) - LISFANNON (GB) | DURCAN BS / J P O'BRIEN | 51920 |
| B F DARK ANGEL (IRE) - FREEDOM PASS (USA) | ROB SPEERS | 50740 |
| CH F MEHMAS (IRE) - HEIGHT OF VANITY (IRE) | RABBAH BS | 49560 |
| B F STARSPANGLEDBANNER (AUS) - THE LAST SISTER (IRE) | DE BURGH EQUINE / F STACK | 49560 |
| ATTACHE (IRE) B C DECLARATION OF WAR (USA) - GO KART (IRE) | KERN/LILLINGSTON ASSOCIATION | 49560 |
| PYRRHIC DANCER (IRE) B C HOLY ROMAN EMPEROR (IRE) - KIRK'S DANCER (IRE) | PETER & ROSS DOYLE BS | 47200 |
| CH C COTAI GLORY (GB) - CLEF (GB) | VENDOR | 47200 |
| B C KODIAC (GB) - QUESTION (USA) | OLIVER ST LAWRENCE / JS BS | 47200 |
| B C STARSPANGLEDBANNER (AUS) - CONDENSED (GB) | VENDOR | 47200 |
| B F EL KABEIR (USA) - SHAMARDYH (IRE) | BLANDFORD BS / A WATSON | 47200 |
| GLAMOURISTA (IRE) CH F DAWN APPROACH (IRE) - MY FERE LADY (USA) | CLONGAN HOUSE | 45000 |
| CH F NO NAY NEVER (USA) - MAMBO PARADISE (GB) | D FARRINGTON | 44840 |
| B C KODIAC (GB) - FAITHFUL DUCHESS (IRE) | CON MARNANE | 44840 |
| GLEN ETIVE (GB) B C EXCEED AND EXCEL (AUS) - BETTY LOCH (GB) | JAMES TOLLER | 44840 |
| B C PROFITABLE (IRE) - DEORA DE (GB) | DWAYNE WOODS | 43660 |
| B F FAST COMPANY (IRE) - CLUB PRIVE (IRE) | BELL FOR ED DUNLOP RACING | 43660 |
| CH C TEOFILO (IRE) - SWAY ME NOW (GB) | FREDERIK TYLICKI | 42480 |
| MONITOR (GB) B C DABIRSIM (FR) - DISCIPLINE (GB) | PETER & ROSS DOYLE BS | 42480 |
| B C NETWORK (GER) - HOLLY GIRL (IRE) | J AND J | 42000 |
| B C FOOTSTEPSINTHESAND (GB) - NONETHELESS (IRE) | SACKVILLEDONALD | 41300 |
| AUDIT (IRE) B G FOOTSTEPSINTHESAND (GB) - BAYAN KASIRGA (IRE) | MICHAEL DODS | 40120 |
| B F CAMACHO (GB) - MIA MADONNA (GB) | PETER & ROSS DOYLE BS | 40120 |
| BONDI SPICE (IRE) CH C AUSTRALIA (GB) - LA SPEZIA (IRE) | RICHARD KNIGHT BS AGENT | 40120 |
| CH C FLEMENSFIRTH (USA) - FLORAFERN (GB) | IAN FERGUSON | 40000 |
| B G CHAMPS ELYSEES (GB) - THURINGE (FR) | HAMISH MACAULEY | 40000 |
| B C ACLAIM (IRE) - SNAKE'S HEAD (GB) | AVENUE BS | 38940 |
| B/BR C MAKE BELIEVE (GB) - IN THE HOUSE (IRE) | EDDIE LINEHAN BS | 38940 |
| B C EXCEED AND EXCEL (AUS) - BROADWAY MELODY (GB) | HOWSON & HOULDSWORTH BS | 37760 |
| B C KODI BEAR (IRE) - KATHERINE LEE (IRE) | C DWYER | 37760 |
| B C REQUINTO (IRE) - PAVLOPETRI (IRE) | EDDIE LINEHAN BS | 37760 |
| NORDHALLA (IRE) CH F DIVINE PROPHET (AUS) - CHELLALLA (GB) | JOHNSTON RACING | 37760 |
| B C KODIAC (GB) - YOU DARE TO DREAM (IRE) | A C ELLIOTT, AGENT | 37760 |
| B F KODIAC (GB) - QALAHARI (IRE) | SHAMROCK THOROUGHBREDS | 37760 |
| B F CAMELOT (GB) - GREY SKY BLUE (IRE) | TOMAS JANDA | 37760 |

| | | |
|---|---|---|
| CH C NEW BAY (GB) - NORDKAPPE (GER) | BARRY LYNCH | 36580 |
| **SHENGAI ENKI (FR)** B C BUCK'S BOUM (FR) - LADY NEEDLES (IRE) | MAGS O'TOOLE/KILLEEN GLEBE | 36000 |
| B F STARSPANGLEDBANNER (AUS) - COME SOFTLY (GB) | CORMAC MCCORMACK | 35400 |
| **CASHEW (IRE)** B F BATED BREATH (GB) - TASTE THE SALT (IRE) | JOHN & JAKE WARREN | 35400 |
| CH C CHURCHILL (IRE) - BLUE ANGEL (IRE) | MARK FLANNERY | 35400 |
| B F HOLY ROMAN EMPEROR (IRE) - FANTASTIC ACCOUNT (GB) | BBA IRELAND | 35400 |
| **KING OF THE DANCE (IRE)** B C HAVANA GOLD (IRE) - FIGURANTE (USA) | SHEFFORD BS / HIGHFLYER | 35400 |
| B G WALK IN THE PARK (IRE) - LONESOME DOVE (IRE) | AIDEN MURPHY | 35000 |
| B F CAMELOT (GB) - SPIRITUAL PRAISE (IRE) | VENDOR | 34220 |
| CH C COTAI GLORY (GB) - VULNICURA (IRE) | SACKVILLEDONALD | 33040 |
| B F FAST COMPANY (IRE) - RISING WIND (IRE) | DERMOT FARRINGTON | 33040 |
| B F BELARDO (IRE) - FASHION LINE (IRE) | BBA IRELAND | 33000 |
| B C SOLDIER OF FORTUNE (IRE) - WILD RHUBARB (GB) | ORMOND BS | 32000 |
| B C KODI BEAR (IRE) - MOYNSHA LADY (IRE) | INNISHANNON VALLEY STUD | 31860 |
| CH C DANDY MAN (IRE) - LIGHT SEA (IRE) | CHARLES GREENE | 31860 |
| B F PROFITABLE (IRE) - EBTISAMA (USA) | AIDAN O'RYAN | 31860 |
| B F EXCEED AND EXCEL (AUS) - KHAJOOL (IRE) | MARK GRANT | 31860 |
| **HIGH FIBRE (IRE)** B C VADAMOS (FR) - MULTI GRAIN (GB) | A C ELLIOTT, AGENT / LUCRA II | 31860 |
| B C SOLDIER OF FORTUNE (IRE) - PLAYHARA (IRE) | G HAINE | 31000 |
| BR C MEHMAS (IRE) - FONSECA (IRE) | KEEP DREAMING BS | 30680 |
| **GUBBASS (IRE)** B C MEHMAS (IRE) - VIDA AMOROSA (GB) | C GORDON WATSON BS | 30680 |
| B C SHOWCASING (GB) - FLIRTY THIRTY (IRE) | ETCHINGHAM FENNESSY | 30680 |
| B C MEHMAS (IRE) - NA ZDOROVIE (GB) | CON MARNANE | 30680 |
| B C KODIAC (GB) - ALICE LIDDEL (IRE) | RABBAH BS | 30680 |
| B C DUE DILIGENCE (USA) - SHOWBIZZY (GB) | BBA IRELAND | 30680 |
| B C CAMACHO (GB) - HIGH VINTAGE (IRE) | AIDAN O'RYAN | 30680 |
| B C CABLE BAY (IRE) - SPECTACULAR SHOW (IRE) | BBA IRELAND | 30680 |
| BR C FLEMENSFIRTH (USA) - MY COUSIN RACHEL (IRE) | ELM EQUINE LTD | 30000 |
| B C SOLDIER OF FORTUNE (IRE) - NOW LET GO (IRE) | SLUGGARA FARM | 30000 |
| B C PILLAR CORAL (GB) - QUINE DE SIVOLA (FR) | GEORGE MULLINS | 30000 |
| CH C EL KABEIR (USA) - QUEEN GRACE (IRE) | BEECHLAWN BS | 29500 |
| GR C CARAVAGGIO (USA) - BRIGHT BIRDIE (IRE) | EAM BS | 29500 |
| B C ACLAIM (IRE) - INAGH RIVER (GB) | MARTIN SMITH RACING | 29500 |
| B F AUSTRALIA (GB) - JEALOUS BEAUTY (IRE) | DOLMEN BS | 29500 |
| **HURRY UP HEDLEY (IRE)** B C MEHMAS (IRE) - FOREVERTWENTYONE (IRE) | HURWORTH BS | 29500 |
| B F FOOTSTEPSINTHESAND (GB) - REDINHA (GB) | VENDOR | 29500 |
| CH F MASTERCRAFTSMAN (IRE) - FIUNTACH (IRE) | VENDOR | 29500 |
| CH F NEW BAY (GB) - SCATINA (IRE) | DAVID LOUGHNANE RACING | 29500 |
| B C GALILEO GOLD (GB) - YORK EXPRESS (GB) | TALLY-HO STUD | 29500 |
| B F ARDAD (IRE) - AVENBURY (GB) | KILBRIDE EQUINE | 29500 |
| B C MAKE BELIEVE (GB) - HINT OF GLAS (FR) | CHARLES GREENE | 29500 |
| B C PRINCE OF LIR (IRE) - CONJURING (IRE) | SACKVILLEDONALD | 29500 |
| B C GALILEO GOLD (GB) - BRONZE BABY (USA) | AGUIAR BS | 29500 |
| B C SEA THE MOON (GER) - BRACING BREEZE (GB) | WILLIAM EASTERBY | 29500 |
| B C MUHAARAR (GB) - RAINBOW SPRINGS (GB) | ARDGLAS STABLES | 29500 |
| CH C MEHMAS (IRE) - DARWELL (IRE) | TALLY-HO STUD | 29500 |
| B F KODI BEAR (IRE) - COUP DE MAIN (IRE) | BLANDFORD BS / A WATSON | 29500 |
| GR C ELZAAM (AUS) - SESMEN (GB) | MICHAEL DODS | 29500 |
| **MAHA DEWI (IRE)** B F HIGHLAND REEL (IRE) - GOLD LACE (GB) | BLANDFORD BS | 29500 |
| GR F OASIS DREAM (GB) - ANGELIC GUEST (IRE) | KEN CARROLL | 29500 |
| CH/GR C MASTERCRAFTSMAN (IRE) - MARVELLOUS WAYS (IRE) | ADAM WRYZYK | 29500 |
| B C CAMACHO (GB) - MANDORIA (GER) | J P MURTAGH | 29500 |
| B F MEHMAS (IRE) - DOCTRINE (GB) | LEAMORE HORSES | 28320 |
| B F HOLY ROMAN EMPEROR (IRE) - NANCY ASTOR (GB) | JANDA BS | 28320 |
| B F STARSPANGLEDBANNER (AUS) - CALLISTO STAR (IRE) | BBA IRELAND | 28320 |
| B C BELARDO (IRE) - ALPINE (GB) | MARCO BOTTI | 28320 |
| CH C GALILEO GOLD (GB) - MARIAN HALCOMBE (USA) | RAZZA LATINA | 28320 |
| B F FASCINATING ROCK (IRE) - KAYD KODAUN (IRE) | VENDOR | 28320 |
| **JUVENTUS DE BRION (FR)** B C CREACHADOIR (IRE) - REUNION A BRION (FR) | OAK TREE FARM | 28000 |
| CH C GETAWAY (GER) - ROCK'S FIELD (IRE) | KEVIN ROSS BS | 28000 |
| B F MEHMAS (IRE) - HAZARAYNA (GB) | MARGARET O'TOOLE | 27140 |
| B C EXCEED AND EXCEL (AUS) - ARJEED (IRE) | BUSHYPARK STABLES | 27140 |
| B F KODI BEAR (IRE) - BINT MALYANA (IRE) | RAZZA LATINA | 27140 |
| B C DIVINE PROPHET (AUS) - ESCAPISM (IRE) | BLANDFORD BS / A WATSON | 27140 |
| CH C PIVOTAL (GB) - TESTIMONY (GB) | KILDALLAN FARM | 27140 |
| B C MEHMAS (IRE) - GREEN BRIAR (IRE) | KILRONAN | 27140 |
| CH C GALILEO GOLD (GB) - FUAIGH MOR (IRE) | WILLIAM EASTERBY | 27140 |
| **FLAG HIGH (IRE)** B C STARSPANGLEDBANNER (AUS) - ACID (GB) | ANDREW BALDING | 25960 |
| **SWEETEST COMPANY (IRE)** B F FAST COMPANY (IRE) - FLORIDA CITY (IRE) | BEN HASLAM | 25960 |
| CH C NEW BAY (GB) - HALL HEE (IRE) | KUBLER RACING | 25960 |
| B C DANDY MAN (IRE) - ROMEA (GB) | EDDIE LINEHAN BS | 25960 |
| BR C ADAAY (IRE) - BELATORIO (IRE) | CLIVE COX RACING | 25960 |
| B F NO NAY NEVER (USA) - CLIP ART (GB) | OLIVER ST LAWRENCE / JS RS | 25960 |

# Download the free must-have Racing Post app.

**RACING POST**
The Must-Have App
For The Must-Have Info

Use your camera phone
and scan the QR code
on the right to download
the free app now.

# 2000 GUINEAS STAKES (3y) Newmarket - 1 mile

| Year | Owner | Winner and Price | Jockey | Trainer | Second | Third | Ran | Time |
|------|-------|------------------|--------|---------|--------|-------|-----|------|
| 1983 | R Sangster's | LOMOND (9/1) | Pat Eddery | V O'Brien | Tolomeo | Muscatite | 16 | 1 43.87 |
| 1984 | R Sangster's | EL GRAN SENOR (15/8) | Pat Eddery | V O'Brien | Chief Singer | Lear Fan | 9 | 1 37.41 |
| 1985 | Maktoum Al Maktoum's | SHADEED (4/5) | L Piggott | M Stoute | Bairn | Supreme Leader | 14 | 1 37.41 |
| 1986 | K Abdullah's | DANCING BRAVE (15/8) | G Starkey | G Harwood | Green Desert | Huntingdale | 15 | 1 40.00 |
| 1987 | J Horgan's | DON'T FORGET ME (9/1) | W Carson | R Hannon | Bellotto | Midyan | 13 | 1 36.74 |
| 1988 | H H Aga Khan's | DOYOUN (4/5) | W R Swinburn | M Stoute | Charmer | Bellefella | 14 | 1 41.73 |
| 1989 | Hamdan Al-Maktoum's | NASHWAN (3/1) | W Carson | R Hern | Exbourne | Danehill | 14 | 1 36.44 |
| 1990 | John Horgan's | TIROL (9/1) | M Kinane | R Hannon | Machiavellian | Anshan | 14 | 1 35.84 |
| 1991 | Lady Beaverbrook's | MYSTIKO (13/2) | M Roberts | C Brittain | Lycius | Ganges | 14 | 1 37.83 |
| 1992 | R Sangster's | RODRIGO DE TRIANO (6/1) | L Piggott | P Chapple-Hyam | Lucky Lindy | Pursuit of Love | 16 | 1 38.37 |
| 1993 | K Abdullah's | ZAFONIC (5/6) | Pat Eddery | A Fabre | Barathea | Bin Ajwaad | 14 | 1 35.32 |
| 1994 | G R Bailey Ltd's | MISTER BAILEYS (16/1) | J Weaver | M Johnston | Grand Lodge | Colonel Collins | 23 | 1 35.08 |
| 1995 | Sheikh Mohammed's | PENNEKAMP (9/2) | T Jarnet | A Fabre | Celtic Swing | Bahri | 11 | 1 35.16 |
| 1996 | Godolphin's | MARK OF ESTEEM (8/1) | L Dettori | S bin Suroor | Even Top | Bijou D'Inde | 13 | 1 37.59 |
| 1997 | M Tabor & Mrs J Magnier's | ENTREPRENEUR (11/2) | M Kinane | M Stoute | Revoque | Poteen | 16 | 1 35.64 |
| 1998 | M Tabor & Mrs J Magnier's | KING OF KINGS (7/2) | M Kinane | A O'Brien | Lend A Hand | Border Arrow | 18 | 1 39.25 |
| 1999 | Godolphin's | ISLAND SANDS (10/1) | L Dettori | S bin Suroor | Enrique | Mujahid | 16 | 1 37.14 |
| | | (Run on July Course) | | | | | | |
| 2000 | Saeed Suhail's | KING'S BEST (13/2) | K Fallon | Sir M Stoute | Giant's Causeway | Barathea Guest | 27 | 1 37.77 |
| 2001 | Lord Weinstock's | GOLAN (11/1) | K Fallon | Sir M Stoute | Tamburlaine | Frenchmans Bay | 18 | 1 37.48 |
| 2002 | Sir A Ferguson & Mrs J Magnier's | ROCK OF GIBRALTAR (9/1) | J Murtagh | A O'Brien | Hawk Wing | Redback | 22 | 1 36.50 |
| 2003 | Moyglare Stud Farm's | REFUSE TO BEND (9/1) | P J Smullen | D Weld | Zafeen | Norse Dancer | 20 | 1 37.98 |
| 2004 | Hamdan Al Maktoum's | HAAFHD (11/2) | R Hills | B Hills | Snow Ridge | Azamour | 14 | 1 36.60 |
| 2005 | Mr M Tabor & Mrs John Magnier's | FOOTSTEPSINTHESAND (13/2) | K Fallon | A O'Brien | Rebel Rebel | Kandidate | 19 | 1 36.10 |
| 2006 | Mrs J Magnier, Mr M Tabor & Mr D Smith's | GEORGE WASHINGTON (6/4) | K Fallon | A O'Brien | Sir Percy | Olympian Odyssey | 14 | 1 36.80 |
| 2007 | P Cunningham's | COCKNEY REBEL (25/1) | O Peslier | G Huffer | Vital Equine | Dutch Art | 24 | 1 35.28 |
| 2008 | Mrs J. Magnier's | HENRYTHENAVIGATOR (11/1) | J Murtagh | A O'Brien | New Approach | Stubbs Art | 15 | 1 39.14 |
| 2009 | C Tsui's | SEA THE STARS (8/1) | M Kinane | J Oxx | Delegator | Gan Amhras | 15 | 1 35.88 |
| 2010 | M Offenstadt's | MAKFI (33/1) | C Lemaire | M Delzangles | Dick Turpin | Canford Cliffs | 19 | 1 36.35 |
| 2011 | K Abdullah's | FRANKEL (1/2) | T Queally | H Cecil | French Fifteen | Native Khan | 13 | 1 37.30 |
| 2012 | D Smith, Mrs J Magnier & Mr M D Smith's | CAMELOT (15/8) | J O'Brien | A O'Brien | | Hermival | 18 | 1 42.46 |
| 2013 | Godolphin's | DAWN APPROACH (11/8) | K Manning | J Bolger | Glory Awaits | Van Der Neer | 13 | 1 35.84 |
| 2014 | Saeed Manana's | NIGHT OF THUNDER (40/1) | K Fallon | R Hannon Jnr | Kingman | Australia | 14 | 1 36.61 |
| 2015 | M Tabor, D Smith & Mrs J Magnier's | GLENEAGLES (4/1) | R Moore | A O'Brien | Territories | Ivawood | 18 | 1 37.55 |
| 2016 | Mr J Magnier's | GALILEO GOLD (14/1) | L Dettori | H Palmer | Massaat | Ritchester | 13 | 1 35.91 |
| 2017 | Al Shaqab Racing's | CHURCHILL (6/4) | R Moore | A O'Brien | Barney Roy | Al Wukair | 10 | 1 36.61 |
| 2018 | M Tabor, D Smith & Mrs J Magnier's | SAXON WARRIOR (3/1) | D O'Brien | A O'Brien | Tip Two Win | Masar | 14 | 1 36.55 |
| 2019 | D Smith/Mrs J Magnier/M Tabor & Flaxman Stables's | MAGNA GRECIA (11/2) | D O'Brien | A O'Brien | King of Change | Skardu | 19 | 1 36.84 |
| 2020 | Qatar Racing Limited's | KAMEKO (10/1) | O Murphy | A Balding | Witchita | Pinatubo | 15 | 1 34.72 |

# 1000 GUINEAS STAKES (3y fillies) Newmarket - 1 mile

| Year | Owner | Winner and Price | Jockey | Trainer | Second | Third | Ran | Time |
|---|---|---|---|---|---|---|---|---|
| 1983 | Maktoum Al-Maktoum's | MA BICHE (5/2) | F Head | Mme C Head | Favourite | Habibti | 18 | 1 41.71 |
| 1984 | M Lemos's | PEBBLES (8/1) | P Robinson | C Brittain | Meis El-Reem | Desirable | 15 | 1 38.18 |
| 1985 | Sheikh Mohammed's | OH SO SHARP (2/1) | S Cauthen | H Cecil | Al Bahathri | Bella Colora | 17 | 1 38.65 |
| 1986 | H Ranier's | MIDWAY LADY (10/1) | R Cochrane | B Hanbury | Maysoon | Sonic Lady | 15 | 1 41.54 |
| 1987 | S Niarchos's | MIESQUE (15/8) | F Head | F Boutin | Milligram | Interval | 14 | 1 38.48 |
| 1988 | Ecurie Aland's | RAVINELLA (4/5) | G W Moore | Mme C Head | Dabaweyaa | Diminuendo | 12 | 1 40.88 |
| 1989 | Sheikh Mohammed's | MUSICAL BLISS (7/2) | W R Swinburn | M Stoute | Kerrera | Negligent | 10 | 1 42.69 |
| 1990 | Hamdan Al-Maktoum's | SALSABIL (6/4) | W Carson | J Dunlop | Heart of Joy | Crystal Gazing | 14 | 1 38.06 |
| 1991 | Maktoum Al-Maktoum's | SHADAYID (4/6) | W Carson | J Dunlop | Kooyonga | Kenbu | 14 | 1 38.18 |
| 1992 | Maktoum Al-Maktoum's | HATOOF (5/1) | W R Swinburn | Mme C Head | Marling | Ajfan | 12 | 1 39.45 |
| 1993 | Mohamed Obaida's | SAYYEDATI (5/1) | W R Swinburn | C Brittain | Niche |  | 14 | 1 37.34 |
| 1994 | R Sangster's | LAS MENINAS (12/1) | J Reid | T Stack | Balanchine | Coup de Genie | 15 | 1 36.71 |
| 1995 | Hamdan Al-Maktoum's | HARAYIR (5/1) | R Hills | Major W R Hern | Aqaarid | Moonshell | 14 | 1 36.72 |
| 1996 | Wafic Said's | BOSRA SHAM (10/11) | Pat Eddery | H Cecil | Matiya | Bint Shadayid | 13 | 1 37.75 |
| 1997 | Greenay Stables Ltd's | SLEEPYTIME (5/1) | K Fallon | H Cecil | Shahtoush | Dazzle | 15 | 1 37.66 |
| 1998 | Godolphin's | CAPE VERDI (100/30) | L Dettori | S Bin Suroor | Oh Nellie | Exclusive | 16 | 1 37.86 |
| 1999 | K Abdullah's | WINCE (4/1) | K Fallon | H Cecil | Wannabe Grand | Valentine Waltz | 22 | 1 37.91 |
| (Run on July Course) | | | | | | | | |
| 2000 | Hamdan Al-Maktoum's | LAHAN (14/1) | R Hills | J Gosden | Princess Ellen | Petrushka | 18 | 1 36.38 |
| 2001 | Sheikh Ahmed Al Maktoum's | AMEERAT (11/1) | P Robinson | M Jarvis | Muwakleh | Toroca | 15 | 1 38.36 |
| 2002 | Godolphin's | KAZZIA (14/1) | L Dettori | S Bin Suroor | Snowfire | Alasha | 17 | 1 37.85 |
| 2003 | Cheveley Park Stud's | RUSSIAN RHYTHM (12/1) | K Fallon | Sir M Stoute | Six Perfections | Intercontinental | 19 | 1 38.43 |
| 2004 | Duke of Roxburghe's | ATTRACTION (11/2) | K Darley | M Johnston | Sundrop | Hathrah | 16 | 1 36.70 |
| 2005 | Mrs John Magnier & Mr M Tabor's | VIRGINIA WATERS (12/1) | K Fallon | A O'Brien | Maids Causeway | Vista Bella | 20 | 1 36.50 |
| 2006 | M Sly, Dr Davies & Mrs P Sly's | SPECIOSA (10/1) | M Fenton | Mrs P Sly | Confidential Lady | Nasheej | 13 | 1 36.60 |
| 2007 | M Ryan's | FINSCEAL BEO (5/4) | K Manning | J Bolger | Arch Swing | Simply Perfect | 21 | 1 34.94 |
| 2008 | S. Firborg's | NATAGORA (11/4) | C Lemaire | P Bary | Spacious | Saoirse Abu | 15 | 1 38.99 |
| 2009 | Hamdan Al-Maktoum's | GHANAATI (20/1) | R Hills | B Hills | Cuis Ghaire | Super Sleuth | 14 | 1 34.22 |
| 2010 | K Abdullah's | SPECIAL DUTY (9/2) | S. Pasquier | Mme C Head-Maarek | Jacqueline Quest | Gile Na Greine | 17 | 1 39.66 |
| 2011 | Godolphin's | BLUE BUNTING (16/1) | L Dettori | M Al Zarooni | Together | Maqaasid | 18 | 1 39.27 |
| (The first two placings were reversed by the Stewards) | | | | | | | | |
| 2012 | Mrs John Magnier, M Tabor & D Smith's | HOMECOMING QUEEN (25/1) | R Moore | A O'Brien | Starscope | Maybe | 17 | 1 40.45 |
| 2013 | B Keswick's | SKY LANTERN (9/1) | R Hughes | R Hannon | Just The Judge | Moth | 15 | 1 36.38 |
| 2014 | Ballymore Thoroughbred Ltd's | MISS FRANCE (7/1) | M Guyon | A Fabre | Lightning Thunder | Ihtimal | 17 | 1 37.40 |
| 2015 | M Tabor, D Smith & Mrs J Magnier's | LEGATISSIMO (13/2) | R Moore | D Wachman | Lucida | Tiggy Wiggy | 13 | 1 34.60 |
| 2016 | D Smith, Mrs J Magnier & M Tabor's | MINDING (11/10) | R Moore | A O'Brien | Ballydoyle | Alice Springs | 16 | 1 36.53 |
| 2017 | Ms J Magnier, M Tabor & D Smith's | WINTER (9/1) | W Lordan | A O'Brien | Rhododendron | Daban | 14 | 1 35.66 |
| 2018 | Pall Mall Partners & Partner's | BILLESDON BROOK (66/1) | S Levey | R Hannon | Laurens | Happily | 15 | 1 36.62 |
| 2019 | M Tabor, D Smith & Mrs John Magnier's | HERMOSA (14/1) | W Lordan | A O'Brien | Lady Kaya | Qabala | 15 | 1 36.89 |
| 2020 | M Tabor, D Smith & Mrs John Magnier's | LOVE (4/1) | R Moore | A O'Brien | Cloak Of Spirits | Quadrilateral | 15 | 1 35.80 |

# OAKS STAKES (3y fillies) Epsom - 1 mile 4 furlongs 6 yards

| Year | Owner | Winner and Price | Trainer | Jockey | Second | Third | Ran | Time |
|------|-------|------------------|---------|--------|--------|-------|-----|------|
| 1983 | Sir M Sobell's | SUN PRINCESS (6/1) | R Hern | W Carson | Acclimatise | New Coins | 15 | 2 40.98 |
| 1984 | Sir R McAlpine's | CIRCUS PLUME (4/1) | J Dunlop | L Piggott | Media Luna | Poquito Queen | 15 | 2 38.97 |
| 1985 | Sheikh Mohammed's | OH SO SHARP (6/4) | H Cecil | S Cauthen | Triptych | Dubian | 15 | 2 41.37 |
| 1986 | R Ranier's | MIDWAY LADY (15/8) | B Hanbury | G Starkey | Untold | Maysoon | 15 | 2 35.60 |
| 1987 | Sheikh Mohammed's | UNITE (11/4) | M Stoute | W R Swinburn | Bourbon Girl | Three Tails | 11 | 2 38.17 |
| 1988 | Sheikh Mohammed's | DIMINUENDO (7/4) | H Cecil | S Cauthen | Sudden Love | Animatrice | 9 | 2 35.02 |
| 1989 | Saeed Maktoum Al Maktoum s. | SNOW BRIDE (13/2) | H Cecil | S Cauthen | Roseate Tern | Mamaluna | 9 | 2 34.22 |
| | (Aliysa finished first but was subsequently disqualified) | | | | | | | |
| 1990 | Hamdan Al-Maktoum's | SALSABIL (2/1) | J Dunlop | W Carson | Game Plan | Knight's Baroness | 8 | 2 38.70 |
| 1991 | Maktoum Al-Maktoum's | JET SKI LADY (50/1) | J Bolger | R Cochrane | Shamshir | Shadayid | 9 | 2 37.30 |
| 1992 | W J Gredley's | USER FRIENDLY (5/1) | C Brittain | G Duffield | All At Sea | Pearl Angel | 10 | 2 39.77 |
| 1993 | Sheikh Mohammed's | INTREPIDITY (5/1) | A Fabre | M Roberts | Royal Ballerina | Oakmead | 14 | 2 34.19 |
| 1994 | Godolphin's | BALANCHINE (6/1) | H Ibrahim | L Dettori | Wind In Her Hair | Hawajiss | 10 | 2 40.37 |
| 1995 | Maktoum Al Maktoum/ Godolphin's | MOONSHELL (3/1) | S Bin Suroor | L Dettori | Dance A Dream | Pure Grain | 10 | 2 35.44 |
| 1996 | Wafic Said's | LADY CARLA (100/30) | H Cecil | Pat Eddery | Pricket | Mezzogiorno | 11 | 2 35.55 |
| 1997 | K Abdulla's | REAMS OF VERSE (5/6) | H Cecil | K Fallon | Gazelle Royale | Crown of Light | 12 | 2 35.59 |
| 1998 | Mrs D Nagle & Mrs J Magnier's | SHAHTOUSH (12/1) | A O'Brien | M Kinane | Bahr | Midnight Line | 8 | 2 38.23 |
| 1999 | F Salman's | RAMRUMA (3/1) | H Cecil | K Fallon | Noushkey | Zahrat Dubai | 10 | 2 38.72 |
| 2000 | Lordship Stud's | LOVE DIVINE (9/4) | H Cecil | T Quinn | Kalypso Katie | Melikah | 16 | 2 43.11 |
| 2001 | Mrs D. Nagle & Mrs J Magnier's | IMAGINE (3/1) | A O'Brien | M Kinane | Flight Of Fancy | Relish The Thought | 14 | 2 36.70 |
| 2002 | Godolphin's | KAZZIA (100/30) | S Bin Suroor | L Dettori | Quarter Moon | Shadow Dancing | 14 | 2 44.52 |
| 2003 | W S Farish III's | CASUAL LOOK (10/1) | A Balding | M Dwyer | Yesterday | Summinville | 15 | 2 38.07 |
| 2004 | Lord Derby's | OUIJA BOARD (7/2) | E Dunlop | K Fallon | All Too Beautiful | Punctilious | 7 | 2 35.40 |
| 2005 | Hamdan Al Maktoum's | ESWARAH (11/4) | M Jarvis | R Hills | Something Exciting | Pictavia | 12 | 2 35.00 |
| 2006 | Mrs J. Magnier, Mr M Tabor & Mr D Smith's | ALEXANDROVA (9/4) | A O'Brien | K Fallon | Rising Cross | Short Skirt | 10 | 2 37.70 |
| 2007 | Niarchos Family's | LIGHT SHIFT (13/2) | H Cecil | T Durcan | Peeping Fawn | All My Loving | 14 | 2 40.38 |
| 2008 | J H Richmond-Watson's | LOOK HERE (33/1) | R Beckett | S Sanders | Moonstone | Katiyra | 16 | 2 36.89 |
| 2009 | Lady Bamford's | SARISKA (9/4) | M Bell | J Spencer | Midday | High Heeled | 15 | 2 35.28 |
| 2010 | Aramoine Ltd's | SNOW FAIRY (9/1) | E Dunlop | R Moore | Remember When | Rumoush | | 2 35.77 |
| | (Meeznah finished second but was subsequently disqualified) | | | | | | | |
| 2011 | M J & L A Taylor's | DANCING RAIN (20/1) | W Haggas | J Murtagh | Wonder of Wonders | Izzi Top | 13 | 2 41.73 |
| 2012 | D Smith, Mrs J Magnier & M Tabor's | WAS (20/1) | A O'Brien | S Heffernan | Shirocco Star | The Fugue | 12 | 2 38.68 |
| 2013 | J L Rowsell & M H Dixon's | TALENT (20/1) | R Beckett | R Hughes | Secret Gesture | The Lark | 11 | 2 42.00 |
| 2014 | Hamdan Al Maktoum's | TAGHROODA (5/1) | J Gosden | P Hanagan | Tarfasha | Volume | 17 | 2 34.89 |
| 2015 | Mrs C C Regalado-Gonzalez's | QUALIFY (50/1) | A O'Brien | C O'Donoghue | Legatissimo | Lady of Dubai | 17 | 2 37.41 |
| 2016 | D Smith, Mrs J Magnier & M Tabor's | MINDING (10/11) | A O'Brien | R Moore | Architecture | Harlequeen | 9 | 2 42.66 |
| 2017 | K Abdulla's | ENABLE (6/1) | J Gosden | L Dettori | Rhododendron | Alluringly | 9 | 2 34.13 |
| 2018 | M Tabor, D Smith & Mrs J Magnier's | FOREVER TOGETHER (7/1) | A O'Brien | D O'Brien | Wild Illusion | Bye Bye Baby | 9 | 2 40.39 |
| 2019 | Helena Springfield Ltd's | ANAPURNA (8/1) | J Gosden | L Dettori | Pink Dogwood | Fleeting | 14 | 2 36.09 |
| 2020 | M Tabor, D Smith & Mrs J Magnier's | LOVE (11/10) | A O'Brien | R Moore | Ennistymon | Frankly Darling | 8 | 2 34.06 |

# DERBY STAKES (3y) Epsom - 1 mile 4 furlongs 6 yards

| Year | Owner | Winner and Price | Trainer | Jockey | Second | Third | Ran | Time |
|---|---|---|---|---|---|---|---|---|
| 1983 | E Moller's | TEENOSO (9/2) | G Wragg | L Piggott | Carlingford Castle | Shearwalk | 21 | 2 49.07 |
| 1984 | L Miglitti's | SECRETO (14/1) | D O'Brien | C Roche | El Gran Senor | Mighty Flutter | 17 | 2 39.12 |
| 1985 | Lord H. de Walden's | SLIP ANCHOR (9/4) | H Cecil | S Cauthen | Law Society | Damister | 14 | 2 36.23 |
| 1986 | H Aga Khan's | SHAHRASTANI (11/2) | M Stoute | W Swinburn | Dancing Brave | Mashkour | 17 | 2 37.13 |
| 1987 | I Freedman's | REFERENCE POINT (6/4) | H Cecil | S Cauthen | Most Welcome | Bellotto | 19 | 2 33.90 |
| 1988 | H Aga Khan's | KAHYASI (11/1) | L Cumani | R Cochrane | Glacial Storm | Doyoun | 14 | 2 33.84 |
| 1989 | H Aga Khan's | NASHWAN (5/4) | H Hern | W Carson | Terimon | Cacoethes | 12 | 2 34.90 |
| 1990 | Hamdan Al-Maktoum's | QUEST FOR FAME (7/1) | P Charlton | Pat Eddery | Blue Stag | Elmaamul | 18 | 2 37.26 |
| 1991 | K Salman's | GENEROUS (9/1) | P Cole | A Munro | Marju | Star of Gdansk | 13 | 2 34.00 |
| 1992 | Sidney H Craig's | DR DEVIOUS (8/1) | P Chapple-Hyam | J Reid | St Jovite | Silver Wisp | 18 | 2 36.19 |
| 1993 | K Abdullah's | COMMANDER IN CHIEF (15/2) | H Cecil | M Kinane | Blue Judge | Blues Traveller | 16 | 2 34.51 |
| 1994 | Hamdan Al-Maktoum's | ERHAAB (7/4) | J Dunlop | W Carson | King's Theatre | Colonel Collins | 25 | 2 34.16 |
| 1995 | Saeed Maktoum Al Maktoum's | LAMMTARRA (14/1) | S Bin Suroor | W Swinburn | Tamure | Presenting | 15 | 2 32.31 |
| 1996 | K Dasmal's | SHAAMIT (12/1) | W Haggas | M Hills | Dushyantor | Shantou | 20 | 2 35.25 |
| 1997 | Wafic Said's | BENNY THE DIP (11/1) | J Gosden | W Ryan | Silver Patriarch | Romanov | 20 | 2 35.77 |
| 1998 | Sheikh Mohammed, Obaid Al Maktoum's | HIGH-RISE (20/1) | L Cumani | O Pesier | City Honours | Border Arrow | 15 | 2 33.88 |
| 1999 | The Thoroughbred Corporation's | OATH (13/2) | H Cecil | K Fallon | Dalapour | Beat All | 16 | 2 37.43 |
| 2000 | H H Aga Khan's | SINNDAR (7/1) | J Oxx | J Murtagh | Sakhee | Beat Hollow | 15 | 2 36.75 |
| 2001 | M Tabor & Mrs J Magnier's | GALILEO (11/4) | A O'Brien | M Kinane | Golan | Tobougg | 12 | 2 33.27 |
| 2002 | M Tabor & Mrs J Magnier's | HIGH CHAPARRAL (7/2) | A O'Brien | J Murtagh | Hawk Wing | Moon Ballad | 12 | 2 39.45 |
| 2003 | Saeed Suhail's | KRIS KIN (6/1) | Sir M Stoute | K Fallon | The Great Gatsby | Alamshar | 20 | 2 33.35 |
| 2004 | Ballymacoll Stud's | NORTH LIGHT (7/2) | Sir M Stoute | K Fallon | Rule Of Law | Let The Lion Roar | 14 | 2 33.70 |
| 2005 | The Royal Ascot Racing Club's | MOTIVATOR (3/1) | M Bell | J Murtagh | Walk In The Park | Dubawi | 13 | 2 33.60 |
| 2006 | A E Pakenham's | SIR PERCY (5/4) | M Tregoning | M Dwyer | Dragon Dancer | Dylan Thomas | 18 | 2 35.20 |
| 2007 | Saleh Al Homaizi & Imad Al Sagar's | AUTHORIZED (5/4) | P Chapple-Hyam | L Dettori | Eagle Mountain | Aqaleem | 17 | 2 34.77 |
| 2008 | HRH Princess Haya of Jordan's | NEW APPROACH (5/1) | J Bolger | K Manning | Tartan Bearer | Casual Conquest | 16 | 2 36.50 |
| 2009 | C Tsui's | SEA THE STARS (11/4) | J Oxx | M Kinane | Fame And Glory | Masterofthehorse | 12 | 2 36.74 |
| 2010 | K Abdullah's | WORKFORCE (6/1) | Sir M Stoute | R Moore | At First Sight | Rewilding | 12 | 2 31.33 |
| 2011 | Mrs John Magnier, M Tabor & D Smith's | POUR MOI (4/1) | A Fabre | M Barzalona | Treasure Beach | Carlton House | 13 | 2 34.54 |
| 2012 | D Smith, Mrs J Magnier & M Tabor's | CAMELOT (8/13) | A O'Brien | J O'Brien | Main Sequence | Astrology | 9 | 2 33.90 |
| 2013 | Mrs John Magnier, Michael Tabor & Derrick Smith's | RULER OF THE WORLD (7/1) | A O'Brien | R Moore | Libertarian | Galileo Rock | 12 | 2 39.06 |
| 2014 | D Smith, Mrs J Magnier & T Ah Khing's | AUSTRALIA (11/8) | A O'Brien | J O'Brien | Kingston Hill | Romsdal | 16 | 2 33.63 |
| 2015 | A E Oppenheimer's | GOLDEN HORN (13/8) | J Gosden | L Dettori | Jack Hobbs | Storm The Stars | 12 | 2 32.32 |
| 2016 | H Aga Khan's | HARZAND (13/2) | D Weld | P Smullen | US Army Ranger | Idaho | 16 | 2 40.09 |
| 2017 | D Smith, Mrs J Magnier & M Tabor's | WINGS OF EAGLES (40/1) | A O'Brien | P Beggy | Cliffs of Moher | Cracksman | 18 | 2 33.02 |
| 2018 | Godolphin's | MASAR (16/1) | C Appleby | W Buick | Dee Ex Bee | Roaring Lion | 12 | 2 34.93 |
| 2019 | Mrs J Magnier, M Tabor & D Smith's | ANTHONY VAN DYCK (13/2) | A O'Brien | S Heffernan | Madhmoon | Japan | 13 | 2 33.38 |
| 2020 | Mrs J Magnier, M Tabor & D Smith's | SERPENTINE (25/1) | A O'Brien | E McNamara | Khalifa Sat | Amhran Na Bhfiann | 16 | 2 34.43 |

# ST LEGER STAKES (3y) Doncaster - 1 mile 6 furlongs 115 yards

| Year | Owner | Winner and Price | Jockey | Trainer | Second | Third | Ran | Time |
|---|---|---|---|---|---|---|---|---|
| 1983 | Sir M Sobell's | SUN PRINCESS (11/8) | W Carson | R Hern | Esprit du Nord | Carlingford Castle | 11 | 3 16.65 |
| 1984 | Allan's | COMMANCHE RUN (7/4) | L Piggott | H Cumani | Baynoun | Alphabatim | 11 | 3 09.93 |
| 1985 | Sheikh Mohammed's | OH SO SHARP (8/13) | S Cauthen | H Cecil | Phardante | Lanfranco | 8 | 3 07.13 |
| 1986 | Duchess of Norfolk's | MOON MADNESS (9/2) | Pat Eddery | J Dunlop | Celestial Storm | Untold | 6 | 3 05.03 |
| 1987 | L Freedman's | REFERENCE POINT (4/11) | S Cauthen | H Cecil | Mountain Kingdom | Dry Dock | 7 | 3 05.91 |
| 1988 | Lady Beaverbrook's | MINSTER SON (15/2) | W Carson | N Graham | Diminuendo | Sheriff's Star | 6 | 3 06.80 |
| 1989 | St George's | MICHELOZZO (6/4) | S Cauthen | H Cecil | Sapience | Roseate Tern | 8 | 3 20.72 |

(Run at Ayr)

| Year | Owner | Winner and Price | Jockey | Trainer | Second | Third | Ran | Time |
|---|---|---|---|---|---|---|---|---|
| 1990 | M Arbib's | SNURGE (7/2) | T Quinn | P Cole | Hellenic | River God | 8 | 3 8.78 |
| 1991 | K Abdullah's | TOULON (5/2) | Pat Eddery | A Fabre | Saddlers' Hall | Micheletti | 10 | 3 3.12 |
| 1992 | Mrs G A E Smith's | USER FRIENDLY (7/4) | G Duffield | C Brittain | Sonus | Bonny Scot | 7 | 3 5.48 |
| 1993 | Sheikh Mohammed's | BOB'S RETURN (3/1) | P Robinson | M Tompkins | Armiger | Edbaysaan | 9 | 3 7.85 |
| 1994 | Godolphin's | MOONAX (40/1) | Pat Eddery | B Hills | Broadway Flyer | Double Trigger | 8 | 3 4.19 |
| 1995 | Sheikh Mohammed's | CLASSIC CLICHE (100/30) | L Dettori | S Bin Suroor | Minds Music | Istidaad | 10 | 3 9.74 |
| 1996 | Godolphin's | SHANTOU (8/1) | L Dettori | J Dunlop | Dushyantor | Samraan | 11 | 3 5.10 |
| 1997 | P Winfield's | SILVER PATRIARCH (5/4) | Pat Eddery | J Dunlop | Vertical Speed | The Fly | 10 | 3 6.92 |
| 1998 | Godolphin's | NEDAWI (5/2) | J Reid | S Bin Suroor | High and Low | Sunshine Street | 10 | 3 5.61 |
| 1999 | Godolphin's | MUTAFAWEQ (11/2) | R Hills | S Bin Suroor | Ramruma | Adair | 9 | 3 2.75 |
| 2000 | N Jones' | MILLENARY (11/4) | T Quinn | J Dunlop | Air Marshal | Chimes At Midnight | 11 | 3 2.58 |
| 2001 | M Tabor & Mrs J Magnier's | MILAN (13/8) | M Kinane | A O'Brien | Demophilos | Mr Combustible | 10 | 3 5.16 |
| 2002 | Sir Neil Westbrook's | BOLLIN ERIC (7/1) | K Darley | T Easterby | Highest | Bandari | 8 | 3 2.92 |
| 2003 | Mrs J Magnier's | BRIAN BORU (5/4) | J P Spencer | A O'Brien | High Accolade | Phoenix Reach | 12 | 3 4.64 |
| 2004 | Mrs J Magnier & M M Tabor's | RULE OF LAW | K McEvoy | S Bin Suroor | Quiff | Tycoon | 9 | 3 6.20 |
| 2005 | Mrs S Roy's | SCORPION (10/11) | L Dettori | A O'Brien | The Geezer | Tawgeet | 6 | 3 19.00 |
| 2006 | | SIXTIES ICON (11/8) | L Dettori | J Noseda | The Last Drop | Red Rocks | 11 | 2 57.20 |

(Run at York)

| Year | Owner | Winner and Price | Jockey | Trainer | Second | Third | Ran | Time |
|---|---|---|---|---|---|---|---|---|
| 2007 | G Strawbridge's | LUCARNO (7/2) | J Fortune | J Gosden | Mahler | Honolulu | 10 | 3 1.90 |
| 2008 | Ballymacoll Stud's | CONDUIT (8/1) | L Dettori | Sir M Stoute | Unsung Heroine | Look Here | 14 | 3 7.92 |
| 2009 | Godolphin's | MASTERY (14/1) | T Durcan | S Bin Suroor | Kite Wood | Monitor Closely | 8 | 3 4.81 |
| 2010 | Ms R Hood & R Geffen's | ARCTIC COSMOS (12/1) | W Buick | J Gosden | Midas Touch | Corsica | 10 | 3 3.12 |
| 2011 | B Nielsen's | MASKED MARVEL (15/2) | W Buick | J Gosden | Brown Panther | Sea Moon | 9 | 3 0.44 |
| 2012 | Godolphin's | ENCKE (25/1) | M Barzalona | M A l Zarooni | Camelot | Michelangelo | 9 | 3 3.81 |
| 2013 | Derrick Smith & Mrs John Magnier & Michael Tabor's | LEADING LIGHT (7/2) | J O'Brien | A O'Brien | Talent | Galileo Rock | 11 | 3 9.20 |
| 2014 | Paul Smith's | KINGSTON HILL (9/4) | A Atzeni | R Varian | Romsdal | Snow Sky | 12 | 3 5.42 |
| 2015 | QRL Sheikh Suhaim Al Thani & M Al Kubaisi's | SIMPLE VERSE (8/1) | A Atzeni | R Beckett | Bondi Beach | Fields of Athenry | 7 | 3 7.12 |
| 2016 | Mrs Jackie Cornwell's | HARBOUR LAW (22/1) | G Baker | Mrs L Mongan | Ventura Storm | Housesofparliament | 9 | 3 5.48 |
| 2017 | Derrick Smith & Mrs John Magnier & Michael Tabor's | CAPRI (3/1) | R Moore | A O'Brien | Crystal Ocean | Stradivarius | 11 | 3 4.04 |
| 2018 | Derrick Smith & Mrs John Magnier & Michael Tabor's | KEW GARDENS (3/1) | R Moore | A O'Brien | Lah Ti Dar | Southern France | 12 | 3 3.34 |
| 2020 | Galileo Chrome Partnership's | GALILEO CHROME (4/1) | T Marquand | J O'Brien | Berkshire Rocco | Pyledriver | 11 | 3 1.94 |

# KING GEORGE VI AND QUEEN ELIZABETH STAKES Ascot - 1 mile 3 furlongs 211 yards

| Year | Owner | Winner and Price | Jockey | Trainer | Second | Third | Ran | Time |
|---|---|---|---|---|---|---|---|---|
| 1983 | R Barnett's | TIME CHARTER 4-9-4 (5/1) | J Mercer | H Candy | Diamond Shoal | Sun Princess | 9 | 2 30.78 |
| 1984 | E Moller's | TEENOSO 4-9-7 (13/2) | L Piggott | G Wragg | Sadler's Wells | Tolomeo | 13 | 2 27.95 |
| 1985 | Lady Beaverbrook's | PETOSKI 3-8-8 (12/1) | W Carson | W Hern | Oh So Sharp | Rainbow Quest | 13 | 2 27.61 |
| 1986 | K Abdullah's | DANCING BRAVE 3-8-8 (6/4) | Pat Eddery | G Harwood | Shardari | Triptych | 9 | 2 29.49 |
| 1987 | L Freedman's | REFERENCE POINT 3-8-8 (11/10) | S Cauthen | H Cecil | Celestial Storm | Triptych | 10 | 2 34.63 |
| 1988 | Sheikh Ahmed Al Maktoum | MTOTO 5-9-7 (4/1) | M Roberts | A C Stewart | Unfuwain | Tony Bin | 7 | 2 33.37 |
| 1989 | Hamdan Al-Maktoum's | NASHWAN 3-8-8 (2/9) | W Carson | H Hern | Cacoethes | Top Class | 7 | 2 30.76 |
| 1990 | Sheikh Mohammed's | BELMEZ 3-8-9 (15/2) | M Kinane | H Cecil | Old Vic | Assatis | 11 | 2 30.77 |
| 1991 | F Salman's | GENEROUS 3-8-9 (4/6) | A Munro | P Cole | Sanglamore | Rock Hopper | 9 | 2 30.85 |
| 1992 | Mrs V K Payson's | ST JOVITE 3-8-9 (4/5) | S Craine | J Bolger | Saddlers' Hall | Opera House | 8 | 2 30.95 |
| 1993 | Sheikh Mohammed's | OPERA HOUSE 5-9-7 (8/1) | M Roberts | M Stoute | White Muzzle | Commander in Chief | 10 | 2 33.94 |
| 1994 | Sheikh Mohammed's | KING'S THEATRE 3-8-9 (12/1) | M Kinane | H Cecil | White Muzzle | Wagon Master | 12 | 2 28.92 |
| 1995 | Saeed Maktoum Al Maktoum's | LAMMTARRA 3-8-9 (9/4) | L Dettori | S Bin Suroor | Pentire | Strategic Choice | 7 | 2 31.01 |
| 1996 | Mollers Racing's | PENTIRE 4-9-7 (100/30) | M Hills | G Wragg | Classic Cliche | Shaamit | 8 | 2 28.11 |
| 1997 | Godolphin's | SWAIN 5-9-7 (16/1) | J Reid | S Bin Suroor | Pilsudski | Helissio | 8 | 2 36.45 |
| 1998 | Godolphin's | SWAIN 6-9-7 (11/2) | L Dettori | S Bin Suroor | High-Rise | Royal Anthem | 6 | 2 29.06 |
| 1999 | Godolphin's | DAYLAMI 5-9-7 (3/1) | L Dettori | S Bin Suroor | Nedawi | Fruits Of Love | 8 | 2 29.35 |
| 2000 | M Tabor's | MONTJEU 4-9-7 (1/3) | M Kinane | J Hammond | Fantastic Light | Daliapour | 7 | 2 29.98 |
| 2001 | Mrs J Magnier & M Tabor's | GALILEO 3-8-9 (1/2) | M Kinane | A O'Brien | Fantastic Light | Hightori | 12 | 2 27.71 |
| 2002 | Exors of the late Lord Weinstock's | GOLAN 4-9-7 (11/2) | K Fallon | Sir M Stoute | Nayef | Zindabad | 9 | 2 29.70 |
| 2003 | H H Aga Khan | ALAMSHAR 3-8-9 (3/2) | J Murtagh | J Oxx | Sulamani | Kris Kin | 12 | 2 33.26 |
| 2004 | H H Aga Khan's (Run at Newbury) | DOYEN 4-9-7 (11/10) | L Dettori | S Bin Suroor | Hard Buck | Sulamani | 11 | 2 33.10 |
| 2005 | | AZAMOUR 4-9-7 (5/2) | M Kinane | J Oxx | Norse Dancer | Bago | 12 | 2 28.20 |
| 2006 | M Tabor's | HURRICANE RUN 4-9-7 (5/6) | C Soumillon | A Fabre | Electrocutionist | Heart's Cry | 6 | 2 30.20 |
| 2007 | Mrs J Magnier & M Tabor's | DYLAN THOMAS 4-9-7 (5/4) | J Murtagh | A O'Brien | Youmzain | Marahel | 7 | 2 30.10 |
| 2008 | Mrs J Magnier & M Tabor's | DUKE OF MARMALADE 4-9-7 (4/6) | J Murtagh | A O'Brien | Papal Bull | Youmzain | 9 | 2 27.91 |
| 2009 | Ballymacoll Stud's | CONDUIT 4-9-7 (13/8) | R Moore | Sir M Stoute | Tartan Bearer | Ask | 8 | 2 28.73 |
| 2010 | Highclere Thoroughbred Racing (Adm. Rous)'s | HARBINGER 4-9-7 (4/1) | O Peslier | Sir M Stoute | Cape Blanco | Youmzain | 6 | 2 26.78 |
| 2011 | Lady Rothschild's | NATHANIEL 3-8-9 (11/2) | W Buick | J Gosden | Workforce | St Nicholas Abbey | 5 | 2 35.07 |
| 2012 | Gestut Burg Eberstein & Teruya Yoshida's | DANEDREAM 4-9-4 (9/1) | A Starke | P Schiergen | Nathaniel | St Nicholas Abbey | 10 | 2 31.62 |
| 2013 | Dr Christophe Berglar's | NOVELLIST 4-9-7 (13/2) | J Murtagh | A Wohler | Trading Leather | Hillstar | 8 | 2 24.60 |
| 2014 | Hamdan Al Maktoum's | TAGHROODA 3-8-6 (7/2) | P Hanagan | J Gosden | Telescope | Mukhadram | 7 | 2 28.13 |
| 2015 | Sheikh Mohammed Obaid Al Maktoum's | POSTPONED 4-9-7 (6/1) | A Atzeni | L Cumani | Eagle Top | Romsdal | 8 | 2 31.25 |
| 2016 | D Smith, Mrs J Magnier & M Tabor's | HIGHLAND REEL 4-9-7 (13/8) | R Moore | A O'Brien | Wings of Desire | Dartmouth | 7 | 2 28.97 |
| 2017 | K Abdullah's | ENABLE 3-8-7 (5/4) | L Dettori | J Gosden | Ulysses | Idaho | 10 | 2 36.22 |
| 2018 | S Suhail's | POET'S WORD 5-9-7 (7/4) | J Doyle | Sir M Stoute | Crystal Ocean | Coronet | 7 | 2 25.84 |
| 2019 | K Abdullah's | ENABLE 5-9-4 (8/15) | L Dettori | J Gosden | Crystal Ocean | Waldgeist | 11 | 2 32.42 |
| 2020 | K Abdullah's | ENABLE 6-9-4 (4/9) | L Dettori | J Gosden | Sovereign | Japan | 3 | 2 28.92 |

# PRIX DE L'ARC DE TRIOMPHE ParisLongchamp - 1 mile 4 furlongs

| Year | Owner | Winner and Price | Jockey | Trainer | Second | Third | Ran | Time |
|---|---|---|---|---|---|---|---|---|
| 1983 | D Wildenstein's | ALL ALONG 4-9-5 (173/10) | W Swinburn | P Biancone | Sun Princess | Luth Enchantee | 26 | 2 28.10 |
| 1984 | D Wildenstein's | SAGACE 4-9-4 (29/10) | Y Saint Martin | P Biancone | Northern Trick | All Along | 22 | 2 39.10 |
| 1985 | K Abdullah's | RAINBOW QUEST 4-9-4 (7/10) | Pat Eddery | J Tree | Sagace | Kozana | 15 | 2 39.50 |
| | (The first two placings were reversed by the Stewards) | | | | | | | |
| 1986 | K Abdullah's | DANCING BRAVE 3-8-11 (11/10) | Pat Eddery | G Harwood | Bering | Triptych | 15 | 2 27.70 |
| 1987 | P de Moussac's | TREMPOLINO 3-8-11 (20/1) | Pat Eddery | A Fabre | Tony Bin | Triptych | 11 | 2 26.30 |
| 1988 | Mrs V Gaucci del Bono's | TONY BIN 5-9-3-8-11 (19/1) | J Reid | L Camici | Mtoto | Boyatino | 24 | 2 27.30 |
| 1989 | A Balzarini's | CARROLL HOUSE 4-9-4 (19/1) | M Kinane | M Jarvis | Behera | Saint Andrews | 19 | 2 30.80 |
| 1990 | B McNall's | SAUMAREZ 3-8-11 (5/1) | C Asmussen | N Clement | Epervier Bleu | Snurge | 21 | 2 30.80 |
| 1991 | H Chalhoub's | SUAVE DANCER 3-8-11 (37/10) | C Asmussen | J Hammond | Magic Night | Pistolet Bleu | 14 | 2 31.40 |
| 1992 | O Lecerf's | SUBOTICA 4-9-4 (88/10) | T Jarnet | A Fabre | User Friendly | Vert Amande | 18 | 2 37.90 |
| 1993 | Tsui S's | URBAN SEA 4-9-4 (37/1) | E Saint Martin | J Lesbordes | White Muzzle | Opera House | 23 | 2 31.80 |
| 1994 | Sheikh Mohammed's | CARNEGIE 3-8-11 (3/1) | T Jarnet | A Fabre | Hernando | Apple Tree | 20 | 2 31.80 |
| 1995 | Saeed Maktoum Al Maktoum's | LAMMTARRA 3-8-11 (21/1) | L Dettori | S Bin Suroor | Freedom Cry | Swain | 16 | 2 29.90 |
| 1996 | E Sarasola's | HELISSIO 3-8-11 (18/10) | O Peslier | E Lellouche | Pilsudski | Oscar Schindler | 16 | 2 24.60 |
| 1997 | D Wildenstein's | PEINTRE CELEBRE 3-8-11 (22/10) | O Peslier | A Fabre | Pilsudski | Borgia | 18 | 2 38.50 |
| 1998 | J Lagardère's | SAGAMIX 3-8-11 (5/2) | O Peslier | A Fabre | Leggera | Tiger Hill | 14 | 2 25.80 |
| 1999 | M Tabor's | MONTJEU 3-8-11 (6/4) | M Kinane | J Hammond | El Condor Pasa | Croco Rouge | 14 | 2 36.10 |
| 2000 | H H Aga Khan's | SINNDAR 3-8-11 (6/4) | J Murtagh | J Oxx | Egyptband | Volvoreta | 10 | 2 26.70 |
| 2001 | Godolphin's | SAKHEE 4-9-5 (22/10) | L Dettori | S Bin Suroor | Aquarelliste | Sagacity | 17 | 2 32.30 |
| 2002 | Godolphin's | MARIENBARD 5-9-5 (158/10) | L Dettori | S Bin Suroor | Sulamani | High Chaparral | 16 | 2 25.00 |
| 2003 | H H Aga Khan's | DALAKHANI 3-8-11 (9/4) | C Soumillon | A De Royer-Dupre | Mubtaker | High Chaparral | 13 | 2 27.40 |
| 2004 | Niarchos Family's | BAGO 3-8-11 (11/4) | T Gillet | J E Pease | Cherry Mix | Ouija Board | 13 | 2 26.30 |
| 2005 | M Tabor's | HURRICANE RUN 3-8-11 (11/4) | K Fallon | A Fabre | Westerner | Bago | 15 | 2 27.40 |
| 2006 | K Abdullah's | RAIL LINK 3-8-11 (8/1) | S Pasquier | A Fabre | Pride | Hurricane Run | 8 | 2 26.30 |
| | (Deep Impact disqualified from third place) | | | | | | | |
| 2007 | Mrs J Magnier & M Tabor's | DYLAN THOMAS 4-9-5 (11/2) | K Fallon | A O'Brien | Youmzain | Sagara | 12 | 2 28.50 |
| 2008 | H H Aga Khan's | ZARKAVA 3-8-8 (13/8) | C Soumillon | A De Royer-Dupre | Youmzain | Soldier of Fortune/It's Gino | 16 | 2 28.80 |
| 2009 | C Tsui S's | SEA THE STARS 3-8-11 (4/6) | M Kinane | J Oxx | Youmzain | Cavalryman | 19 | 2 26.30 |
| 2010 | K Abdullah's | WORKFORCE 3-8-11 (6/1) | R Moore | Sir M Stoute | Nakayama Festa | Sarafina | 18 | 2 35.30 |
| 2011 | Gestut Burg Eberstein & Teshida's | DANEDREAM 3-8-8 (20/1) | A Starke | P Schiergen | Shareta | Snow Fairy | 16 | 2 24.49 |
| 2012 | Wertheimer & Frere's | SOLEMIA 4-9-2 (33/1) | O Peslier | C Laffon-Parias | Orfevre | Masterstroke | 18 | 2 37.68 |
| 2013 | H E Sheikh Joaan Bin Hamad. Al Thani's | TREVE 3-8-8 (9/2) | T Jarnet | Mme C Head-Maarek | Orfevre | Intello | 17 | 2 32.04 |
| 2014 | Al Shaqab Racing's | TREVE 4-9-2 (11/1) | T Jarnet | Mme C Head-Maarek | Flintshire | Taghrooda | 20 | 2 26.05 |
| 2015 | A E Oppenheimer's | GOLDEN HORN 3-8-11 (9/2) | L Dettori | J Gosden | Flintshire | New Bay | 17 | 2 27.23 |
| 2016 | M Tabor, D Smith & Mrs J Magnier (Run at Chantilly) | FOUND 4-9-2 (6/1) | R Moore | A O'Brien | Highland Reel | Order of St George | 16 | 2 23.61 |
| 2017 | K Abdullah's (Run at Chantilly) | ENABLE 3-8-9 (10/11) | L Dettori | J Gosden | Cloth of Stars | Ulysses | 18 | 2 28.69 |
| 2018 | K Abdullah's | ENABLE 4-9-2 (Evs) | L Dettori | J Gosden | Sea Of Class | Sottsass | 19 | 2 29.24 |
| 2019 | Gestut Ammerland & Newsells Park's | WALDGEIST 5-9-5 (131/10) | P-C Boudot | A Fabre | Enable | Sottsass | 12 | 2 31.97 |
| 2020 | White Birch Farm's | SOTTSASS 4-9-5 (73/10) | C Demuro | J-C Rouget | In Swoop | Persian King | 11 | 2 39.30 |

# GRAND NATIONAL STEEPLECHASE Aintree - 4m 2f 74y (4m 4f before 2013)

| Year | Winner and Price | Age & Weight | Jockey | Second | Third | Ran | Time |
|---|---|---|---|---|---|---|---|
| 1975 | L'ESCARGOT (13/2) | 12 11 3 | T Carberry | Red Rum | Spanish Steps | 31 | 9.31.10 |
| 1976 | RAG TRADE (14/1) | 10 10 12 | J Burke | Red Rum | Eyecatcher | 32 | 9.20.90 |
| 1977 | RED RUM (9/1) | 12 11 8 | T Stack | Churchtown Boy | Eyecatcher | 42 | 9.30.30 |
| 1978 | LUCIUS (14/1) | 9 10 9 | B R Davies | Sebastian V | Drumroan | 37 | 9.33.90 |
| 1979 | RUBSTIC (25/1) | 10 10 0 | M Barnes | Zongalero | Rough and Tumble | 34 | 9.52.90 |
| 1980 | BEN NEVIS (40/1) | 12 10 12 | Mr C Fenwick | Rough and Tumble | The Pilgarlic | 30 | 10.17.40 |
| 1981 | ALDANITI (10/1) | 11 10 13 | R Champion | Spartan Missile | Royal Mail | 39 | 9.47.20 |
| 1982 | GRITTAR (7/1) | 9 11 5 | E Saunders | Hard Outlook | Loving Words | 39 | 9.12.60 |
| 1983 | CORBIERE (13/1) | 8 11 4 | B de Haan | Greasepaint | Yer Man | 41 | 9.47.04 |
| 1984 | HALLO DANDY (13/1) | 10 10 2 | N Doughty | Greasepaint | Corbiere | 40 | 9.21.04 |
| 1985 | LAST SUSPECT (50/1) | 11 10 5 | N Davies | Mr Snugfit | Corbiere | 40 | 9.42.70 |
| 1986 | WEST TIP (15/2) | 9 10 11 | R Dunwoody | Young Driver | Classified | 40 | 9.33.00 |
| 1987 | MAORI VENTURE (28/1) | 11 10 13 | S C Knight | The Tsarevich | Lean Ar Aghaidh | 40 | 9.19.30 |
| 1988 | RHYME 'N' REASON (10/1) | 9 11 0 | B Powell | Durham Edition | Monanore | 40 | 9.53.50 |
| 1989 | LITTLE POLVEIR (28/1) | 12 10 3 | J Frost | West Tip | The Thinker | 40 | 10.06.80 |
| 1990 | MR FRISK (16/1) | 11 10 6 | Mr M Armytage | Durham Edition | Rinus | 38 | 8.47.80 |
| 1991 | SEAGRAM (12/1) | 11 10 6 | N Hawke | Garrison Savannah | Auntie Dot | 40 | 9.29.90 |
| 1992 | PARTY POLITICS (14/1) | 8 10 7 | C Llewellyn | Romany King | Laura's Beau | 40 | 9.06.30 |
| 1993 | RACE VOID - FALSE START | | | | | | |
| 1994 | MINNEHOMA (16/1) | 11 10 8 | R Dunwoody | Just So | Moorcroft Boy | 36 | 10.18.80 |
| 1995 | ROYAL ATHLETE (40/1) | 12 10 6 | J Titley | Party Politics | Over The Deel | 35 | 9.04.00 |
| 1996 | ROUGH QUEST (7/1) | 10 10 7 | M Fitzgerald | Encore Un Peu | Superior Finish | 27 | 9.00.80 |
| 1997 | LORD GYLLENE (14/1) | 9 10 0 | A Dobbin | Suny Bay | Camelot Knight | 36 | 9.05.80 |
| 1998 | EARTH SUMMIT (7/1) | 10 10 5 | C Llewellyn | Suny Bay | Samlee | 37 | 10.51.40 |
| 1999 | BOBBYJO (10/1) | 9 10 0 | P Carberry | Blue Charm | Call It A Day | 32 | 9.14.20 |
| 2000 | PAPILLON (10/1) | 9 10 12 | R Walsh | Mely Moss | Niki Dee | 40 | 9.09.70 |
| 2001 | RED MARAUDER (33/1) | 11 10 11 | R Guest | Smarty | Blowing Wind | 40 | 11.00.10 |
| 2002 | BINDAREE (20/1) | 8 10 4 | J Culloty | What's Up Boys | Blowing Wind | 40 | 9.09.00 |
| 2003 | MONTY'S PASS (16/1) | 10 10 7 | B J Geraghty | Supreme Glory | Amberleigh House | 40 | 9.21.70 |
| 2004 | AMBERLEIGH HOUSE (16/1) | 12 10 10 | G Lee | Clan Royal | Lord Atterbury | 39 | 9.20.30 |
| 2005 | HEDGEHUNTER (7/1) | 9 11 1 | R Walsh | Royal Auclair | Simply Gifted | 40 | 9.20.80 |
| 2006 | NUMBERSIXVALVERDE (11/1) | 10 10 8 | N Madden | Hedgehunter | Clan Royal | 40 | 9.41.00 |
| 2007 | SILVER BIRCH (33/1) | 10 10 6 | R M Power | McKelvey | Slim Pickings | 39 | 9.13.60 |
| 2008 | COMPLY OR DIE (7/1) | 9 10 9 | T Murphy | King Johns Castle | Snowy Morning | 40 | 9.16.60 |
| 2009 | MON MOME (100/1) | 9 11 0 | L Treadwell | Comply Or Die | My Will | 40 | 9.32.90 |
| 2010 | DON'T PUSH IT (10/1) | 10 11 5 | A P McCoy | Black Apalachi | State Of Play | 40 | 9.04.60 |
| 2011 | BALLABRIGGS (14/1) | 10 11 0 | J Maguire | Oscar Time | Don't Push It | 40 | 9.01.20 |
| 2012 | NEPTUNE COLLONGES (33/1) | 11 11 6 | D Jacob | Sunnyhillboy | Seabass | 40 | 9.05.10 |
| 2013 | AURORAS ENCORE (66/1) | 11 10 3 | R Mania | Cappa Bleu | Teaforthree | 40 | 9.12.00 |
| 2014 | PINEAU DE RE (25/1) | 11 10 6 | L Aspell | Balthazar King | Double Seven | 40 | 9.09.90 |
| 2015 | MANY CLOUDS (25/1) | 8 11 9 | L Aspell | Saint Are | Monbeg Dude | 39 | 8.56.80 |
| 2016 | RULE THE WORLD (33/1) | 9 10 7 | D Mullins | The Last Samuri | Vics Canvas | 39 | 9.29.00 |
| 2017 | ONE FOR ARTHUR (14/1) | 8 10 11 | D Fox | Cause of Causes | Saint Are | 40 | 9.03.50 |
| 2018 | TIGER ROLL (10/1) | 8 10 13 | D Russell | Pleasant Company | Bless The Wings | 38 | 9.40.10 |
| 2019 | TIGER ROLL (4/1) | 9 11 5 | D Russell | Magic of Light | Rathvinden | 40 | 9.01.00 |

# WINNERS OF GREAT RACES

## LINCOLN HANDICAP
Doncaster-1m
| | | |
|---|---|---|
| 2011 | **SWEET LIGHTNING** 6-9-4 | 21 |
| 2012 | **BRAE HILL** 6-9-1 | 22 |
| 2013 | **LEVITATE** 5-8-4 | 22 |
| 2014 | **OCEAN TEMPEST** 5-9-3 | 17 |
| 2015 | **GABRIAL** 6-9-0 | 22 |
| 2016 | **SECRET BRIEF** 4-9-4 | 22 |
| 2017 | **BRAVERY** 4-9-1 | 22 |
| 2018 | **ADDEYBB** 4-9-2 | 20 |
| 2019 | **AUXERRE** 4-9-3 | 19 |
| 2020 | RACE CANCELLED | |

## GREENHAM STAKES (3y)
Newbury-7f
| | | |
|---|---|---|
| 2011 | **FRANKEL** 9-0 | 6 |
| 2012 | **CASPAR NETSCHER** 9-0 | 5 |
| 2013 | **OLYMPIC GLORY** 9-0 | 5 |
| 2014 | **KINGMAN** 9-0 | 10 |
| 2015 | **MUHAARAR** 9-0 | 9 |
| * 2016 | **TASLEET** 9-0 | 3 |
| 2017 | **BARNEY ROY** 9-0 | 10 |
| 2018 | **JAMES GARFIELD** 9-0 | 7 |
| 2019 | **MOHAATHER** 9-0 | 8 |
| 2020 | RACE CANCELLED | |

* Run at Chelmsford City on Polytrack

## EUROPEAN FREE HANDICAP (3y)
Newmarket-7f
| | | |
|---|---|---|
| 2011 | **PAUSANIAS** 8-12 | 6 |
| 2012 | **TELWAAR** 8-11 | 7 |
| 2013 | **GARSWOOD** 9-0 | 10 |
| 2014 | **SHIFTING POWER** 9-1 | 6 |
| 2015 | **HOME OF THE BRAVE** 8-13 | 5 |
| 2016 | **IBN MALIK** 9-6 | 6 |
| 2017 | **WHITECLIFFSOFDOVER** 9-7 | 7 |
| 2018 | **ANNA NERIUM** 8-12 | 10 |
| 2019 | **SHINE SO BRIGHT** 9-3 | 7 |
| 2020 | RACE CANCELLED | |

## CRAVEN STAKES (3y)
Newmarket-1m
| | | |
|---|---|---|
| 2011 | **NATIVE KHAN** 8-12 | 6 |
| 2012 | **TRUMPET MAJOR** 9-1 | 12 |
| 2013 | **TORONADO** 9-1 | 4 |
| 2014 | **TOORMORE** 9-0 | 6 |
| 2015 | **KOOL KOMPANY** 9-3 | 6 |
| 2016 | **STORMY ANTARCTIC** 9-0 | 7 |
| 2017 | **EMINENT** 9-0 | 6 |
| 2018 | **MASAR** 9-0 | 6 |
| 2019 | **SKARDU** 9-0 | 8 |
| 2020 | RACE CANCELLED | |

## JOCKEY CLUB STAKES
Newmarket-1m 4f
| | | |
|---|---|---|
| 2011 | **DANDINO** 4-8-11 | 6 |
| 2012 | **AL KAZEEM** 4-8-12 | 8 |
| 2013 | **UNIVERSAL** 4-8-12 | 4 |
| 2014 | **GOSPEL CHOIR** 5-9-0 | 8 |
| 2015 | **SECOND STEP** 4-9-0 | 4 |
| 2016 | **EXOSPHERE** 4-9-0 | 6 |

## SANDOWN MILE
Sandown-1m
| | | |
|---|---|---|
| 2011 | **DICK TURPIN** 4-9-0 | 5 |
| 2012 | **PENITENT** 6-9-0 | 6 |
| 2013 | **TRUMPET MAJOR** 4-9-0 | 7 |
| 2014 | **TULLIUS** 6-9-1 | 6 |
| 2015 | **CUSTOM CUT** 6-9-5 | 6 |
| 2016 | **TOORMORE** 5-9-4 | 7 |
| 2017 | **SOVEREIGN DEBT** 8-9-1 | 9 |
| 2018 | **ADDEYBB** 4-9-1 | 8 |
| 2019 | **BEAT THE BANK** 5-9-1 | 7 |
| 2020 | RACE CANCELLED | |

## CHESTER VASE (3y)
Chester-1m 4f 63yds
| | | |
|---|---|---|
| 2011 | **TREASURE BEACH** 8-12 | 5 |
| 2012 | **MICKDAAM** 8-12 | 5 |
| 2013 | **RULER OF THE WORLD** 8-12 | 4 |
| 2014 | **ORCHESTRA** 9-0 | 8 |
| 2015 | **HANS HOLBEIN** 9-0 | 6 |
| 2016 | **US ARMY RANGER** 9-0 | 6 |
| 2017 | **VENICE BEACH** 9-0 | 6 |
| 2018 | **YOUNG RASCAL** 9-0 | 10 |
| 2019 | **SIR DRAGONET** 9-0 | 7 |
| 2020 | RACE CANCELLED | |

## CHESTER CUP
Chester-2m 2f 140yds
| | | |
|---|---|---|
| 2011 | **OVERTURN** 7-8-13 | 17 |
| 2012 | **ILE DE RE** 6-8-11 | 16 |
| 2013 | **ADDRESS UNKNOWN** 6-9-0 | 17 |
| 2014 | **SUEGIOO** 5-9-4 | 17 |
| 2015 | **TRIP TO PARIS** 4-8-9 | 17 |
| 2016 | **NO HERETIC** 8-8-13 | 17 |
| 2017 | **MONTALY** 6-9-6 | 17 |
| 2018 | **MAGIC CIRCLE** 6-9-3 | 16 |
| 2019 | **MAKING MIRACLES** 4-9-0 | 15 |
| 2020 | RACE CANCELLED | |

## OAKS TRIAL (3y fillies)
Lingfield-1m 3f 133yds
| | | |
|---|---|---|
| 2011 | **ZAIN AL BOLDAN** 8-12 | 9 |
| * 2012 | **VOW** 8-12 | 6 |
| 2013 | **SECRET GESTURE** 8-12 | 6 |
| 2014 | **HONOR BOUND** 9-0 | 10 |
| 2015 | **TOUJOURS L'AMOUR** 9-0 | 10 |
| 2016 | **SEVENTH HEAVEN** 9-0 | 6 |
| 2017 | **HERTFORD DANCER** 9-0 | 6 |
| 2018 | **PERFECT CLARITY** 9-0 | 7 |
| 2019 | **ANAPURNA** 9-0 | 7 |
| 2020 | **MISS YODA** 9-0 | 8 |

* Run over 1m4f on Polytrack

| | | |
|---|---|---|
| 2017 | **SEVENTH HEAVEN** 4-9-1 | 5 |
| 2018 | **DEFOE** 4-9-1 | 5 |
| 2019 | **COMMUNIQUE** 4-9-1 | 7 |
| 2020 | RACE CANCELLED | |

## DERBY TRIAL (3y)
Lingfield-1m 3f 133yds
| | | |
|---|---|---|
| 2011 | DORDOGNE 8-12 | 6 |
| * 2012 | MAIN SEQUENCE 8-12 | 8 |
| 2013 | NEVIS 8-12 | 4 |
| 2014 | SNOW SKY 9-0 | 9 |
| 2015 | KILIMANJARO 9-0 | 5 |
| 2016 | HUMPHREY BOGART 9-0 | 5 |
| 2017 | BEST SOLUTION 9-0 | 8 |
| 2018 | KNIGHT TO BEHOLD 9-0 | 9 |
| 2019 | ANTHONY VAN DYCK 9-0 | 10 |
| 2020 | ENGLISH KING 9-0 | 8 |

* Run over 1m4f on Polytrack

## MUSIDORA STAKES (3y fillies)
York-1m 2f 56yds
| | | |
|---|---|---|
| 2011 | JOVIALITY 8-12 | 5 |
| 2012 | THE FUGUE 8-12 | 6 |
| 2013 | LIBER NAUTICUS 8-12 | 6 |
| 2014 | MADAME CHIANG 9-0 | 9 |
| 2015 | STAR OF SEVILLE 9-0 | 5 |
| 2016 | SO MI DAR 9-0 | 7 |
| 2017 | SHUTTER SPEED 9-0 | 5 |
| 2018 | GIVE AND TAKE 9-0 | 7 |
| 2019 | NAUSHA 9-0 | 10 |
| 2020 | ROSE OF KILDARE 9-0 | 6 |

## DANTE STAKES (3y)
York-1m 2f 56yds
| | | |
|---|---|---|
| 2011 | CARLTON HOUSE 9-0 | 6 |
| 2012 | BONFIRE 9-0 | 7 |
| 2013 | LIBERTARIAN 9-0 | 8 |
| 2014 | THE GREY GATSBY 9-0 | 6 |
| 2015 | GOLDEN HORN 9-0 | 7 |
| 2016 | WINGS OF DESIRE 9-0 | 12 |
| 2017 | PERMIAN 9-0 | 10 |
| 2018 | ROARING LION 9-0 | 9 |
| 2019 | TELECASTER 9-0 | 8 |
| 2020 | THUNDEROUS 9-0 | 6 |

## MIDDLETON STAKES
## (fillies and mares)
York-1m 2f 56yds
| | | |
|---|---|---|
| 2011 | MIDDAY 5-9-3 | 8 |
| 2012 | IZZI TOP 4-8-12 | 9 |
| 2013 | DALKALA 4-9-0 | 8 |
| 2014 | AMBIVALENT 5-9-0 | 8 |
| 2015 | SECRET GESTURE 5-9-0 | 8 |
| 2016 | BEAUTIFUL ROMANCE 4-9-0 | 7 |
| 2017 | BLOND ME 5-9-0 | 4 |
| 2018 | CORONET 4-9-0 | 7 |
| 2019 | LAH TI DAR 4-9-0 | 6 |
| 2020 | RACE CANCELLED | |

## YORKSHIRE CUP
York-1m 5f 188yds
| | | |
|---|---|---|
| 2011 | DUNCAN 6-9-2 | 8 |
| 2012 | RED CADEAUX 6-9-0 | 8 |
| 2013 | GLEN'S DIAMOND 5-9-0 | 8 |
| 2014 | GOSPEL CHOIR 5-9-0 | 12 |
| 2015 | SNOW SKY 4-9-0 | 6 |
| 2016 | CLEVER COOKIE 8-9-1 | 5 |
| 2017 | DARTMOUTH 5-9-1 | 8 |
| 2018 | STRADIVARIUS 4-9-1 | 8 |
| 2019 | STRADIVARIUS 5-9-4 | 8 |
| 2020 | RACE CANCELLED | |

## DUKE OF YORK STAKES
York-6f
| | | |
|---|---|---|
| 2011 | DELEGATOR 5-9-7 | 14 |
| 2012 | TIDDLIWINKS 6-9-7 | 13 |
| 2013 | SOCIETY ROCK 6-9-13 | 17 |
| 2014 | MAAREK 7-9-13 | 13 |
| 2015 | GLASS OFFICE 5-9-8 | 15 |
| 2016 | MAGICAL MEMORY 4-9-8 | 12 |
| 2017 | TASLEET 4-9-8 | 12 |
| 2018 | HARRY ANGEL 4-9-13 | 5 |
| 2019 | INVINCIBLE ARMY 4-9-8 | 10 |
| 2020 | RACE CANCELLED | |

## LOCKINGE STAKES
Newbury-1m
| | | |
|---|---|---|
| 2011 | CANFORD CLIFFS 4-9-0 | 7 |
| 2012 | FRANKEL 4-9-0 | 6 |
| 2013 | FARHH 5-9-0 | 12 |
| 2014 | OLYMPIC GLORY 4-9-0 | 8 |
| 2015 | NIGHT OF THUNDER 4-9-0 | 16 |
| 2016 | BELARDO 4-9-0 | 12 |
| 2017 | RIBCHESTER 4-9-0 | 8 |
| 2018 | RHODODENDRON 4-8-11 | 14 |
| 2019 | MUSTASHRY 6-9-0 | 14 |
| 2020 | RACE CANCELLED | |

## HENRY II STAKES
Sandown-2m 50yds
| | | |
|---|---|---|
| 2011 | BLUE BAJAN 9-9-2 | 8 |
| 2012 | OPINION POLL 6-9-4 | 10 |
| 2013 | GLOOMY SUNDAY 4-8-11 | 10 |
| 2014 | BROWN PANTHER 6-9-4 | 11 |
| 2015 | VENT DE FORCE 4-9-0 | 7 |
| 2016 | PALLASATOR 7-9-6 | 4 |
| 2017 | BIG ORANGE 6-9-2 | 7 |
| 2018 | MAGIC CIRCLE 6-9-2 | 8 |
| 2019 | DEE EX BEE 4-9-4 | 5 |
| 2020 | DASHING WILLOUGHBY 4-9-2 | 5 |

## TEMPLE STAKES
Haydock-5f
| | | |
|---|---|---|
| 2011 | SOLE POWER 4-9-4 | 12 |
| 2012 | BATED BREATH 4-9-4 | 12 |
| 2013 | KINGSGATE NATIVE 8-9-4 | 10 |
| 2014 | HOT STREAK 3-8-10 | 9 |
| 2015 | PEARL SECRET 6-9-4 | 11 |
| 2016 | PROFITABLE 4-9-4 | 11 |
| 2017 | PRICELESS 4-9-1 | 12 |
| 2018 | BATTAASH 4-9-9 | 11 |
| 2019 | BATTAASH 4-9-2 | 5 |
| 2020 | RACE CANCELLED | |

## BRIGADIER GERARD STAKES
Sandown-1m 1f 209yds
| | | |
|---|---|---|
| 2011 | WORKFORCE 4-9-7 | 8 |
| 2012 | CARLTON HOUSE 4-9-0 | 6 |
| 2013 | MUKHADRAM 4-9-0 | 5 |
| 2014 | SHARESTAN 6-9-0 | 3 |
| 2015 | WESTERN HYMN 4-9-3 | 5 |
| 2016 | TIME TEST 4-9-5 | 7 |
| 2017 | AUTOCRATIC 4-9-0 | 7 |
| 2018 | POET'S WORD 5-9-0 | 5 |
| 2019 | REGAL REALITY 4-9-0 | 6 |
| * 2020 | LORD NORTH 4-9-0 | 5 |

* Run at Haydock Park (1m 2f 42yds)

## CORONATION CUP
Epsom-1m 4f 6yds
| | | |
|---|---|---|
| 2011 | **ST NICHOLAS ABBEY** 4-9-0 | 5 |
| 2012 | **ST NICHOLAS ABBEY** 5-9-0 | 6 |
| 2013 | **ST NICHOLAS ABBEY** 6-9-0 | 7 |
| 2014 | **CIRRUS DES AIGLES** 8-9-0 | 7 |
| 2015 | **PETHER'S MOON** 5-9-0 | 4 |
| 2016 | **POSTPONED** 5-9-0 | 8 |
| 2017 | **HIGHLAND REEL** 5-9-0 | 10 |
| 2018 | **CRACKSMAN** 4-9-0 | 6 |
| 2019 | **DEFOE** 5-9-0 | 9 |
| 2020 | **GHAIYYATH** 5-9-0 | 7 |

* Run at Newmarket

## CHARITY SPRINT HANDICAP
York-6f
| | | |
|---|---|---|
| 2011 | **LEXI'S HERO** 8-11 | 20 |
| 2012 | **SHOLAAN** 8-9 | 17 |
| 2013 | **BODY AND SOUL** 8-11 | 19 |
| 2014 | **SEE THE SUN** 8-7 | 20 |
| 2015 | **TWILIGHT SON** 8-10 | 16 |
| 2016 | **MR LUPTON** 9-7 | 17 |
| 2017 | **GOLDEN APOLLO** 8-3 | 18 |
| 2018 | **ENCRYPTED** 8-8 | 20 |
| 2019 | **RECON MISSION** 9-2 | 22 |
| 2020 | RACE CANCELLED | |

## QUEEN ANNE STAKES
Ascot-1m (st)
| | | |
|---|---|---|
| 2011 | **CANFORD CLIFFS** 4-9-0 | 7 |
| 2012 | **FRANKEL** 4-9-0 | 11 |
| 2013 | **DECLARATION OF WAR** 4-9-0 | 13 |
| 2014 | **TORONADO** 4-9-0 | 10 |
| 2015 | **SOLOW** 5-9-0 | 8 |
| 2016 | **TEPIN** 5-8-11 | 13 |
| 2017 | **RIBCHESTER** 4-9-0 | 16 |
| 2018 | **ACCIDENTAL AGENT** 4-9-0 | 15 |
| 2019 | **LORD GLITTERS** 6-9-0 | 16 |
| 2020 | **CIRCUS MAXIMUS** 4-9-0 | 15 |

## PRINCE OF WALES'S STAKES
Ascot-1m 2f
| | | |
|---|---|---|
| 2011 | **REWILDING** 4-9-0 | 7 |
| 2012 | **SO YOU THINK** 6-9-0 | 11 |
| 2013 | **AL KAZEEM** 5-9-0 | 11 |
| 2014 | **THE FUGUE** 5-8-11 | 8 |
| 2015 | **FREE EAGLE** 4-9-0 | 9 |
| 2016 | **MY DREAM BOAT** 4-9-0 | 6 |
| 2017 | **HIGHLAND REEL** 5-9-0 | 8 |
| 2018 | **POET'S WORD** 5-9-0 | 7 |
| 2019 | **CRYSTAL OCEAN** 5-9-0 | 8 |
| 2020 | **LORD NORTH** 4-9-0 | 7 |

## ST JAMES'S PALACE STAKES (3y)
Ascot-7f 213yds (rnd)
| | | |
|---|---|---|
| 2011 | **FRANKEL** 9-0 | 9 |
| 2012 | **MOST IMPROVED** 9-0 | 16 |
| 2013 | **DAWN APPROACH** 9-0 | 9 |
| 2014 | **KINGMAN** 9-0 | 7 |
| 2015 | **GLENEAGLES** 9-0 | 5 |
| 2016 | **GALILEO GOLD** 9-0 | 7 |
| 2017 | **BARNEY ROY** 9-0 | 8 |
| 2018 | **WITHOUT PAROLE** 9-0 | 10 |
| 2019 | **CIRCUS MAXIMUS** 9-0 | 11 |
| 2020 | **PALACE PIER** 9-0 | 7 |

## COVENTRY STAKES (2y)
Ascot-6f
| | | |
|---|---|---|
| 2011 | **POWER** 9-1 | 23 |
| 2012 | **DAWN APPROACH** 9-1 | 22 |
| 2013 | **WAR COMMAND** 9-1 | 15 |
| 2014 | **THE WOW SIGNAL** 9-1 | 15 |
| 2015 | **BURATINO** 9-1 | 17 |
| 2016 | **CARAVAGGIO** 9-1 | 18 |
| 2017 | **RAJASINGHE** 9-1 | 18 |
| 2018 | **CALYX** 9-1 | 23 |
| 2019 | **ARIZONA** 9-1 | 17 |
| 2020 | **NANDO PARRADO** 9-1 | 15 |

## KING EDWARD VII STAKES (3y)
Ascot-1m 4f
| | | |
|---|---|---|
| 2011 | **NATHANIEL** 8-12 | 10 |
| 2012 | **THOMAS CHIPPENDALE** 8-12 | 5 |
| 2013 | **HILLSTAR** 8-12 | 8 |
| 2014 | **EAGLE TOP** 9-0 | 9 |
| 2015 | **BALIOS** 9-0 | 7 |
| 2016 | **ACROSS THE STARS** 9-0 | 9 |
| 2017 | **PERMIAN** 9-0 | 12 |
| 2018 | **OLD PERSIAN** 9-0 | 9 |
| 2019 | **JAPAN** 9-0 | 8 |
| 2020 | **PYLEDRIVER** 9-0 | 6 |

## JERSEY STAKES (3y)
Ascot-7f
| | | |
|---|---|---|
| 2011 | **STRONG SUIT** 9-6 | 9 |
| 2012 | **ISHVANA** 8-12 | 22 |
| 2013 | **GALE FORCE TEN** 9-1 | 21 |
| 2014 | **MUSTAJEEB** 9-4 | 23 |
| 2015 | **DUTCH CONNECTION** 9-4 | 16 |
| 2016 | **RIBCHESTER** 9-6 | 19 |
| 2017 | **LE BRIVIDO** 9-1 | 20 |
| 2018 | **EXPERT EYE** 9-1 | 21 |
| 2019 | **SPACE TRAVELLER** 9-1 | 18 |
| 2020 | **MOLATHAM** 9-1 | 13 |

## DUKE OF CAMBRIDGE STAKES
## (fillies & mares)
Ascot-1m (st)(Windsor Forest Stakes before 2013)
| | | |
|---|---|---|
| 2011 | **LOLLY FOR DOLLY** 4-8-12 | 13 |
| 2012 | **JOVIALITY** 4-8-12 | 13 |
| 2013 | **DUNTLE** 4-8-12 | 9 |
| 2014 | **INTEGRAL** 4-9-0 | 14 |
| 2015 | **AMAZING MARIA** 4-9-0 | 6 |
| 2016 | **USHERETTE** 4-9-3 | 14 |
| 2017 | **QEMAH** 4-9-0 | 14 |
| 2018 | **ALJAZZI** 5-9-0 | 11 |
| 2019 | **MOVE SWIFTLY** 4-9-0 | 9 |
| 2020 | **NAZEEF** 4-9-0 | 10 |

## QUEEN MARY STAKES (2y fillies)
Ascot-5f
| | | |
|---|---|---|
| 2011 | **BEST TERMS** 8-12 | 14 |
| 2012 | **CEILING KITTY** 8-12 | 27 |
| 2013 | **RIZEENA** 8-12 | 23 |
| 2014 | **ANTHEM ALEXANDER** 9-0 | 21 |
| 2015 | **ACAPULCO** 9-0 | 20 |
| 2016 | **LADY AURELIA** 9-0 | 15 |
| 2017 | **HEARTACHE** 9-0 | 23 |
| 2018 | **SIGNORA CABELLO** 9-0 | 22 |
| 2019 | **RAFFLE PRIZE** 9-0 | 25 |
| 2020 | **CAMPANELLE** 9-0 | 18 |

## CORONATION STAKES (3y fillies)
Ascot-7f 213yds (rnd)

| | | |
|---|---|---|
| 2011 | **IMMORTAL VERSE** 9-0 | 12 |
| 2012 | **FALLEN FOR YOU** 9-0 | 10 |
| 2013 | **SKY LANTERN** 9-0 | 17 |
| 2014 | **RIZEENA** 9-0 | 12 |
| 2015 | **ERVEDYA** 9-0 | 9 |
| 2016 | **QEMAH** 9-0 | 13 |
| 2017 | **WINTER** 9-0 | 7 |
| 2018 | **ALPHA CENTAURI** 9-0 | 12 |
| 2019 | **WATCH ME** 9-0 | 9 |
| 2020 | **ALPINE STAR** 9-0 | 7 |

## COMMONWEALTH CUP (3y)
Ascot-6f

| | | |
|---|---|---|
| 2015 | **MUHAARAR** 9-3 | 18 |
| 2016 | **QUIET REFLECTION** 9-0 | 10 |
| 2017 | **CARAVAGGIO** 9-3 | 12 |
| 2018 | **EQTIDAAR** 9-3 | 22 |
| 2019 | **ADVERTISE** 9-3 | 9 |
| 2020 | **GOLDEN HORDE** 9-0 | 16 |

## ROYAL HUNT CUP
Ascot-1m (st)

| | | |
|---|---|---|
| 2011 | **JULIENAS** 4-8-8 | 28 |
| 2012 | **PRINCE OF JOHANNE** 6-9-3 | 30 |
| 2013 | **BELGIAN BILL** 5-8-11 | 28 |
| 2014 | **FIELD OF DREAM** 7-9-1 | 28 |
| 2015 | **GM HOPKINS** 4-9-3 | 30 |
| 2016 | **PORTAGE** 4-9-5 | 28 |
| 2017 | **ZHUI FENG** 4-9-0 | 29 |
| 2018 | **SETTLE FOR BAY** 4-9-1 | 30 |
| 2019 | **AFAAK** 5-9-3 | 28 |
| 2020 | **DARK VISION** 4-9-1 | 23 |

## QUEEN'S VASE (3y)
Ascot-1m 6f 34yds (2m before 2017)

| | | |
|---|---|---|
| 2011 | **NAMIBIAN** 9-1 | 11 |
| 2012 | **ESTIMATE** 8-12 | 10 |
| 2013 | **LEADING LIGHT** 9-4 | 15 |
| 2014 | **HARTNELL** 9-3 | 10 |
| 2015 | **ALOFT** 9-3 | 13 |
| 2016 | **SWORD FIGHTER** 9-3 | 18 |
| 2017 | **STRADIVARIUS** 9-0 | 13 |
| 2018 | **KEW GARDENS** 9-0 | 12 |
| 2019 | **DASHING WILLOUGHBY** 9-0 | 13 |
| 2020 | **SANTIAGO** 9-0 | 8 |

## DIAMOND JUBILEE STAKES
Ascot-6f
(Golden Jubilee Stakes before 2012)

| | | |
|---|---|---|
| 2011 | **SOCIETY ROCK** 4-9-4 | 16 |
| 2012 | **BLACK CAVIAR** 6-9-1 | 14 |
| 2013 | **LETHAL FORCE** 4-9-4 | 18 |
| 2014 | **SLADE POWER** 5-9-4 | 14 |
| 2015 | **UNDRAFTED** 5-9-3 | 15 |
| 2016 | **TWILIGHT SON** 4-9-3 | 9 |
| 2017 | **THE TIN MAN** 5-9-3 | 19 |
| 2018 | **MERCHANT NAVY** 3-9-3 | 12 |
| 2019 | **BLUE POINT** 5-9-3 | 17 |
| 2020 | **HELLO YOUMZAIN** 4-9-3 | 10 |

## NORFOLK STAKES (2y)
Ascot-5f

| | | |
|---|---|---|
| 2011 | **BAPAK CHINTA** 9-1 | 15 |
| 2012 | **RECKLESS ABANDON** 9-1 | 11 |
| 2013 | **NO NAY NEVER** 9-1 | 14 |
| 2014 | **BAITHA ALGA** 9-1 | 9 |
| 2015 | **WATERLOO BRIDGE** 9-1 | 10 |
| 2016 | **PRINCE OF LIR** 9-1 | 11 |
| 2017 | **SIOUX NATION** 9-1 | 17 |
| 2018 | **SHANG SHANG SHANG** 8-12 | 10 |
| 2019 | **A'ALI** 9-1 | 14 |
| 2020 | **THE LIR JET** 9-1 | 12 |

## GOLD CUP
Ascot-2m 4f

| | | |
|---|---|---|
| 2011 | **FAME AND GLORY** 5-9-2 | 15 |
| 2012 | **COLOUR VISION** 4-9-0 | 9 |
| 2013 | **ESTIMATE** 4-8-11 | 14 |
| 2014 | **LEADING LIGHT** 4-9-0 | 12 |
| 2015 | **TRIP TO PARIS** 4-9-0 | 12 |
| 2016 | **ORDER OF ST GEORGE** 4-9-0 | 17 |
| 2017 | **BIG ORANGE** 6-9-2 | 14 |
| 2018 | **STRADIVARIUS** 4-9-1 | 9 |
| 2019 | **STRADIVARIUS** 5-9-2 | 11 |
| 2020 | **STRADIVARIUS** 6-9-2 | 8 |

## RIBBLESDALE STAKES (3y fillies)
Ascot-1m 4f

| | | |
|---|---|---|
| 2011 | **BANIMPIRE** 8-12 | 12 |
| 2012 | **PRINCESS HIGHWAY** 8-12 | 14 |
| 2013 | **RIPOSTE** 8-12 | 9 |
| 2014 | **BRACELET** 9-0 | 12 |
| 2015 | **CURVY** 9-0 | 10 |
| 2016 | **EVEN SONG** 9-0 | 14 |
| 2017 | **CORONET** 9-0 | 12 |
| 2018 | **MAGIC WAND** 9-0 | 10 |
| 2019 | **STAR CATCHER** 9-0 | 11 |
| 2020 | **FRANKLY DARLING** 9-0 | 11 |

## HARDWICKE STAKES
Ascot-1m 4f

| | | |
|---|---|---|
| 2011 | **AWAIT THE DAWN** 4-9-0 | 9 |
| 2012 | **SEA MOON** 4-9-0 | 12 |
| 2013 | **THOMAS CHIPPENDALE** 4-9-0 | 8 |
| 2014 | **TELESCOPE** 4-9-1 | 10 |
| 2015 | **SNOW SKY** 4-9-1 | 7 |
| 2016 | **DARTMOUTH** 4-9-1 | 9 |
| 2017 | **IDAHO** 4-9-1 | 12 |
| 2018 | **CRYSTAL OCEAN** 4-9-1 | 5 |
| 2019 | **DEFOE** 5-9-1 | 8 |
| 2020 | **FANNY LOGAN** 4-8-12 | 9 |

## WOKINGHAM STAKES
Ascot-6f

| | | |
|---|---|---|
| 2011 | **DEACON BLUES** 4-8-13 | 25 |
| 2012 | **DANDY BOY** 6-9-8 | 28 |
| 2013 | **YORK GLORY** 5-9-2 | 26 |
| 2014 | **BACCARAT** 5-9-2 | 28 |
| 2015 | **INTERCEPTION** 5-9-2 | 25 |
| 2016 | **OUTBACK TRAVELLER** 5-9-1 | 28 |
| 2017 | **OUT DO** 8-8-13 | 27 |
| 2018 | **BACCHUS** 4-9-6 | 28 |
| 2019 | **CAPE BYRON** 5-9-5 | 26 |
| 2020 | **HEY JONESY** 5-9-3 | 22 |

## KING'S STAND STAKES
Ascot-5f
| | | |
|---|---|---|
| 2011 | **PROHIBIT** 6-9-4 | 19 |
| 2012 | **LITTLE BRIDGE** 6-9-4 | 22 |
| 2013 | **SOLE POWER** 6-9-4 | 19 |
| 2014 | **SOLE POWER** 7-9-4 | 16 |
| 2015 | **GOLDREAM** 6-9-4 | 18 |
| 2016 | **PROFITABLE** 4-9-4 | 17 |
| 2017 | **LADY AURELIA** 3-8-9 | 17 |
| 2018 | **BLUE POINT** 4-9-4 | 14 |
| 2019 | **BLUE POINT** 5-9-4 | 12 |
| 2020 | **BATTAASH** 6-9-4 | 11 |

## NORTHUMBERLAND PLATE
Newcastle-2m 56y Tapeta (2m 19y turf before 2016)
| | | |
|---|---|---|
| 2011 | **TOMINATOR** 4-8-5 | 19 |
| 2012 | **ILE DE RE** 6-9-3 | 16 |
| 2013 | **TOMINATOR** 6-9-10 | 18 |
| 2014 | **ANGEL GABRIAL** 5-8-12 | 19 |
| 2015 | **QUEST FOR MORE** 5-9-4 | 19 |
| 2016 | **ANTIQUARIUM** 4-9-5 | 20 |
| 2017 | **HIGHER POWER** 5-9-9 | 20 |
| 2018 | **WITHHOLD** 5-9-1 | 20 |
| 2019 | **WHO DARES WINS** 7-9-1 | 19 |
| 2020 | **CARAVAN OF HOPE** 4-8-5 | 18 |

## ECLIPSE STAKES
Sandown-1m 1f 209yds
| | | |
|---|---|---|
| 2011 | **SO YOU THINK** 5-9-7 | 5 |
| 2012 | **NATHANIEL** 4-9-7 | 9 |
| 2013 | **AL KAZEEM** 5-9-7 | 7 |
| 2014 | **MUKHADRAM** 5-9-7 | 9 |
| 2015 | **GOLDEN HORN** 3-8-10 | 5 |
| 2016 | **HAWKBILL** 3-8-10 | 7 |
| 2017 | **ULYSSES** 4-9-7 | 9 |
| 2018 | **ROARING LION** 3-8-11 | 7 |
| 2019 | **ENABLE** 5-9-4 | 8 |
| 2020 | **GHAIYYATH** 5-9-3 | 7 |

## LANCASHIRE OAKS
### (fillies and mares)
Haydock-1m 3f 175yds
| | | |
|---|---|---|
| 2011 | **GERTRUDE BELL** 4-9-5 | 7 |
| 2012 | **GREAT HEAVENS** 3-8-6 | 9 |
| 2013 | **EMIRATES QUEEN** 4-9-5 | 8 |
| 2014 | **POMOLOGY** 4-9-5 | 9 |
| 2015 | **LADY TIANA** 4-9-5 | 10 |
| 2016 | **ENDLESS TIME** 4-9-5 | 6 |
| 2017 | **THE BLACK PRINCESS** 4-9-5 | 7 |
| 2018 | **HORSEPLAY** 4-9-5 | 7 |
| 2019 | **ENBIHAAR** 4-9-5 | 6 |
| 2020 | **MANUELA DE VEGA** 4-9-5 | 5 |

## DUCHESS OF CAMBRIDGE STAKES
### (2y fillies)
Newmarket-6f
(Cherry Hinton Stakes before 2013)
| | | |
|---|---|---|
| 2011 | **GAMILATI** 8-12 | 11 |
| 2012 | **SENDMYLOVETOROSE** 8-12 | 10 |
| 2013 | **LUCKY KRISTALE** 8-12 | 8 |
| 2014 | **ARABIAN QUEEN** 9-0 | 5 |
| 2015 | **ILLUMINATE** 9-0 | 9 |
| 2016 | **ROLY POLY** 9-0 | 10 |
| 2017 | **CLEMMIE** 9-0 | 8 |
| 2018 | **PRETTY POLLYANNA** 9-0 | 9 |

## BUNBURY CUP
Newmarket-7f
| | | |
|---|---|---|
| 2011 | **BRAE HILL** 5-9-1 | 20 |
| 2012 | **BONNIE BRAE** 5-9-9 | 15 |
| 2013 | **FIELD OF DREAM** 6-9-7 | 19 |
| 2014 | **HEAVEN'S GUEST** 4-9-3 | 13 |
| 2015 | **RENE MATHIS** 5-9-1 | 17 |
| 2016 | **GOLDEN STEPS** 5-9-6 | 16 |
| 2017 | **ABOVE THE REST** 6-8-10 | 18 |
| 2018 | **BURNT SUGAR** 6-9-1 | 18 |
| 2019 | **VALE OF KENT** 4-9-4 | 17 |
| 2020 | **MOTAKHAYYEL** 4-9-7 | 17 |

## PRINCESS OF WALES'S STAKES
Newmarket-1m 4f
| | | |
|---|---|---|
| 2011 | **CRYSTAL CAPELLA** 6-8-13 | 8 |
| 2012 | **FIORENTE** 4-9-2 | 7 |
| 2013 | **AL KAZEEM** 4-9-5 | 6 |
| 2014 | **CAVALRYMAN** 8-9-2 | 6 |
| 2015 | **BIG ORANGE** 4-9-2 | 8 |
| 2016 | **BIG ORANGE** 5-9-2 | 7 |
| 2017 | **HAWKBILL** 4-9-2 | 6 |
| 2018 | **BEST SOLUTION** 4-9-6 | 7 |
| 2019 | **COMMUNIQUE** 4-9-9 | 6 |
| 2020 | **DAME MALLIOT** 4-9-3 | 7 |

## JULY STAKES (2y)
Newmarket-6f
| | | |
|---|---|---|
| 2011 | **FREDERICK ENGELS** 8-12 | 7 |
| 2012 | **ALHEBAYEB** 8-12 | 7 |
| 2013 | **ANJAAL** 8-12 | 11 |
| 2014 | **IVAWOOD** 9-0 | 12 |
| 2015 | **SHALAA** 9-0 | 9 |
| 2016 | **MEHMAS** 9-0 | 9 |
| 2017 | **CARDSHARP** 9-0 | 12 |
| 2018 | **ADVERTISE** 9-0 | 8 |
| 2019 | **ROYAL LYTHAM** 9-0 | 7 |
| 2020 | **TACTICAL** 9-0 | 9 |

## FALMOUTH STAKES
### (fillies & mares)
Newmarket-1m
| | | |
|---|---|---|
| 2011 | **TIMEPIECE** 4-9-5 | 11 |
| 2012 | **GIOFRA** 4-9-5 | 10 |
| 2013 | **ELUSIVE KATE** 4-9-5 | 4 |
| 2014 | **INTEGRAL** 4-9-7 | 7 |
| 2015 | **AMAZING MARIA** 4-9-7 | 7 |
| 2016 | **ALICE SPRINGS** 3-8-12 | 7 |
| 2017 | **ROLY POLY** 3-8-12 | 7 |
| 2018 | **ALPHA CENTAURI** 3-8-12 | 7 |
| 2019 | **VERACIOUS** 4-9-7 | 6 |
| 2020 | **NAZEEF** 4-9-7 | 6 |

## SUPERLATIVE STAKES (2y)
Newmarket-7f
| | | |
|---|---|---|
| 2011 | **RED DUKE** 9-0 | 11 |
| 2012 | **OLYMPIC GLORY** 9-0 | 9 |
| 2013 | **GOOD OLD BOY LUKEY** 9-0 | 8 |
| 2014 | **ESTIDHKAAR** 9-1 | 8 |
| 2015 | **BIRCHWOOD** 9-1 | 8 |
| 2016 | **BOYNTON** 9-1 | 9 |
| 2017 | **GUSTAV KLIMT** 9-1 | 10 |

| | | |
|---|---|---|
| 2018 | **QUORTO** 9-1 | .7 |
| 2019 | **MYSTERY POWER** 9-1 | .8 |
| 2020 | **MASTER OF THE SEAS** 9-1 | .10 |

## JULY CUP
Newmarket-6f

| | | |
|---|---|---|
| 2011 | **DREAM AHEAD** 3-8-13 | 16 |
| 2012 | **MAYSON** 4-9-5 | 12 |
| 2013 | **LETHAL FORCE** 4-9-5 | 11 |
| 2014 | **SLADE POWER** 5-9-6 | 13 |
| 2015 | **MUHAARAR** 3-9-0 | 14 |
| 2016 | **LIMATO** 4-9-6 | 18 |
| 2017 | **HARRY ANGEL** 3-9-0 | 10 |
| 2018 | **U S NAVY FLAG** 3-9-0 | 13 |
| 2019 | **TEN SOVEREIGNS** 3-9-0 | 12 |
| 2020 | **OXTED** 4-9-6 | 12 |

## WEATHERBYS SUPER SPRINT (2y)
Newbury-5f 34 yds

| | | |
|---|---|---|
| 2011 | **CHARLES THE GREAT** 8-11 | 25 |
| 2012 | **BODY AND SOUL** 7-12 | 22 |
| 2013 | **PENIAPHOBIA** 8-8 | 24 |
| 2014 | **TIGGY WIGGY** 9-1 | 24 |
| 2015 | **LATHOM** 9-0 | 22 |
| 2016 | **MRS DANVERS** 8-0 | 23 |
| 2017 | **BENGALI BOYS** 8-7 | 23 |
| 2018 | **GINGER NUT** 8-5 | 25 |
| 2019 | **BETTYS HOPE** 8-4 | 24 |
| 2020 | **HAPPY ROMANCE** 8-5 | 25 |

## SUMMER MILE
Ascot-7f 213yds (rnd)

| | | |
|---|---|---|
| 2011 | **DICK TURPIN** 4-9-4 | .5 |
| 2012 | **FANUNALTER** 6-9-1 | .8 |
| 2013 | **ALJAMAAHEER** 4-9-1 | 11 |
| 2014 | **GUEST OF HONOUR** 5-9-1 | .9 |
| 2015 | **AROD** 4-9-1 | .6 |
| 2016 | **MUTAKAYYEF** 5-9-1 | 10 |
| 2017 | **MUTAKAYYEF** 6-9-1 | .7 |
| 2018 | **BEAT THE BANK** 4-9-4 | .8 |
| 2019 | **BEAT THE BANK** 5-9-4 | .8 |
| 2020 | **MOHAATHER** 4-9-1 | 11 |

## PRINCESS MARGARET STAKES (2y fillies)
Ascot-6f

| | | |
|---|---|---|
| 2011 | **ANGELS WILL FALL** 8-12 | .7 |
| 2012 | **MAUREEN** 8-12 | .6 |
| 2013 | **PRINCESS NOOR** 8-12 | 10 |
| 2014 | **OSAILA** 9-0 | .8 |
| 2015 | **BESHARAH** 9-0 | .6 |
| 2016 | **FAIR EVA** 9-0 | 12 |
| 2017 | **NYALETI** 9-0 | .7 |
| 2018 | **ANGEL'S HIDEAWAY** 9-0 | .7 |
| 2019 | **UNDER THE STARS** 9-0 | .9 |
| 2020 | **SANTOSHA** 9-0 | .7 |

## LENNOX STAKES
Goodwood-7f

| | | |
|---|---|---|
| 2011 | **STRONG SUIT** 3-8-9 | .9 |
| 2012 | **CHACHAMAIDEE** 5-8-13 | .7 |
| 2013 | **GARSWOOD** 3-8-9 | 10 |
| 2014 | **ES QUE LOVE** 5-9-3 | .7 |
| 2015 | **TOORMORE** 4-9-3 | .7 |
| 2016 | **DUTCH CONNECTION** 4-9-3 | .8 |

| | | |
|---|---|---|
| 2017 | **BRETON ROCK** 7-9-3 | 13 |
| 2018 | **SIR DANCEALOT** 4-9-3 | 12 |
| 2019 | **SIR DANCEALOT** 5-9-3 | .9 |
| 2020 | **SPACE BLUES** 4-9-3 | 11 |

## STEWARDS' CUP
Goodwood-6f

| | | |
|---|---|---|
| 2011 | **HOOF IT** 4-10-0 | 27 |
| 2012 | **HAWKEYETHENOO** 6-9-9 | 27 |
| 2013 | **REX IMPERATOR** 4-9-4 | 27 |
| * 2014 | **INTRINSIC** 4-8-11 | 24 |
| 2015 | **MAGICAL MEMORY** 3-8-12 | 27 |
| 2016 | **DANCING STAR** 3-8-12 | 27 |
| 2017 | **LANCELOT DU LAC** 7-9-5 | 26 |
| 2018 | **GIFTED MASTER** 5-9-6 | 26 |
| 2019 | **KHAADEM** 3-9-6 | 27 |
| 2020 | **SUMMERGHAND** 6-9-10 | 27 |

* Run as 32Red Cup in 2014

## GORDON STAKES (3y)
Goodwood-1m 4f

| | | |
|---|---|---|
| 2011 | **NAMIBIAN** 9-3 | 10 |
| 2012 | **NOBLE MISSION** 9-0 | .7 |
| 2013 | **CAP O'RUSHES** 9-0 | .7 |
| 2014 | **SNOW SKY** 9-1 | .7 |
| 2015 | **HIGHLAND REEL** 9-1 | .9 |
| 2016 | **ULYSSES** 9-1 | .9 |
| 2017 | **CRYSTAL OCEAN** 9-1 | .5 |
| 2018 | **CROSS COUNTER** 9-1 | .4 |
| 2019 | **NAYEF ROAD** 9-1 | .9 |
| 2020 | **MOGUL** 9-1 | .6 |

## VINTAGE STAKES (2y)
Goodwood-7f

| | | |
|---|---|---|
| 2011 | **CHANDLERY** 9-0 | .7 |
| 2012 | **OLYMPIC GLORY** 9-3 | 10 |
| 2013 | **TOORMORE** 9-0 | 12 |
| 2014 | **HIGHLAND REEL** 9-1 | .8 |
| 2015 | **GALILEO GOLD** 9-1 | .8 |
| 2016 | **WAR DECREE** 9-1 | .9 |
| 2017 | **EXPERT EYE** 9-1 | 10 |
| 2018 | **DARK VISION** 9-1 | 12 |
| 2019 | **PINATUBO** 9-1 | .7 |
| 2020 | **BATTLEGROUND** 9-1 | 10 |

## SUSSEX STAKES
Goodwood-1m

| | | |
|---|---|---|
| 2011 | **FRANKEL** 3-8-13 | 4 |
| 2012 | **FRANKEL** 4-9-7 | 4 |
| 2013 | **TORONADO** 3-8-13 | 7 |
| 2014 | **KINGMAN** 3-9-0 | 4 |
| 2015 | **SOLOW** 5-9-8 | 8 |
| 2016 | **THE GURKHA** 3-9-0 | 10 |
| 2017 | **HERE COMES WHEN** 7-9-8 | 7 |
| 2018 | **LIGHTNING SPEAR** 7-9-8 | 7 |
| 2019 | **TOO DARN HOT** 3-9-0 | 7 |
| 2020 | **MOHAATHER** 4-9-8 | 7 |

## RICHMOND STAKES (2y)
Goodwood-6f

| | | |
|---|---|---|
| 2011 | **HARBOUR WATCH** 9-0 | 10 |
| 2012 | **HEAVY METAL** 9-0 | 8 |
| 2013 | **SAAYERR** 9-0 | 10 |
| 2014 | **IVAWOOD** 9-3 | 8 |
| 2015 | **SHALAA** 9-0 | 8 |
| 2016 | **MEHMAS** 9-3 | 8 |

| 2017 | **BARRAQUERO** 9-0 | 7 |
| 2018 | **LAND FORCE** 9-0 | 9 |
| 2019 | **GOLDEN HORDE** 9-0 | 8 |
| 2020 | **SUPREMACY** 9-0 | 7 |

## KING GEORGE STAKES
Goodwood-5f

| 2011 | **MASAMAH** 5-9-0 | 11 |
| 2012 | **ORTENSIA** 7-9-5 | 17 |
| 2013 | **MOVIESTA** 3-8-12 | 17 |
| 2014 | **TAKE COVER** 7-9-1 | 15 |
| 2015 | **MUTHMIR** 5-9-6 | 15 |
| 2016 | **TAKE COVER** 9-9-2 | 17 |
| 2017 | **BATTAASH** 3-8-13 | 11 |
| 2018 | **BATTAASH** 4-9-5 | 11 |
| 2019 | **BATTAASH** 5-9-5 | 8 |
| 2020 | **BATTAASH** 6-9-7 | 7 |

## GOODWOOD CUP
Goodwood-2m

| 2011 | **OPINION POLL** 5-9-7 | 15 |
| 2012 | **SADDLER'S ROCK** 4-9-7 | 10 |
| 2013 | **BROWN PANTHER** 5-9-7 | 14 |
| 2014 | **CAVALRYMAN** 8-9-8 | 8 |
| 2015 | **BIG ORANGE** 4-9-8 | 11 |
| 2016 | **BIG ORANGE** 5-9-8 | 14 |
| 2017 | **STRADIVARIUS** 3-8-8 | 14 |
| 2018 | **STRADIVARIUS** 4-9-9 | 9 |
| 2019 | **STRADIVARIUS** 5-9-9 | 9 |
| 2020 | **STRADIVARIUS** 6-9-9 | 7 |

## MOLECOMB STAKES (2y)
Goodwood-5f

| 2011 | **REQUINTO** 9-0 | 13 |
| 2012 | **BUNGLE INTHEJUNGLE** 9-0 | 10 |
| 2013 | **BROWN SUGAR** 9-0 | 8 |
| 2014 | **COTAI GLORY** 9-1 | 8 |
| 2015 | **KACHY** 9-1 | 10 |
| 2016 | **YALTA** 9-1 | 6 |
| 2017 | **HAVANA GREY** 9-1 | 10 |
| 2018 | **RUMBLE INTHEJUNGLE** 9-1 | 11 |
| 2019 | **LIBERTY BEACH** 8-12 | 13 |
| 2020 | **STEEL BULL** 9-1 | 10 |

## NASSAU STAKES
## (fillies and mares)
Goodwood-1m 1f 197yds

| 2011 | **MIDDAY** 5-9-6 | 6 |
| 2012 | **THE FUGUE** 3-8-11 | 8 |
| 2013 | **WINSILI** 3-8-11 | 14 |
| 2014 | **SULTANINA** 4-9-7 | 6 |
| 2015 | **LEGATISSIMO** 3-8-12 | 9 |
| 2016 | **MINDING** 3-8-11 | 5 |
| 2017 | **WINTER** 3-8-13 | 6 |
| 2018 | **WILD ILLUSION** 3-8-13 | 6 |
| 2019 | **DEIRDRE** 5-9-7 | 9 |
| 2020 | **FANCY BLUE** 3-8-12 | 7 |

## HUNGERFORD STAKES
Newbury-7f

| 2011 | **EXCELEBRATION** 3-8-13 | 9 |
| 2012 | **LETHAL FORCE** 3-8-12 | 9 |
| 2013 | **GREGORIAN** 4-9-3 | 6 |
| 2014 | **BRETON ROCK** 4-9-5 | 6 |
| 2015 | **ADAAY** 3-9-2 | 11 |

| 2016 | **RICHARD PANKHURST** 4-9-6 | 6 |
| 2017 | **MASSAAT** 4-9-6 | 8 |
| 2018 | **SIR DANCEALOT** 4-9-9 | 8 |
| 2019 | **GLORIOUS JOURNEY** 4-9-6 | 7 |
| 2020 | **DREAM OF DREAMS** 6-9-6 | 9 |

## GEOFFREY FREER STAKES
Newbury-1m 5f 61yds

| 2011 | **CENSUS** 3-8-6 | 10 |
| 2012 | **MOUNT ATHOS** 5-9-4 | 6 |
| 2013 | **ROYAL EMPIRE** 4-9-4 | 10 |
| 2014 | **SEISMOS** 6-9-4 | 11 |
| 2015 | **AGENT MURPHY** 4-9-5 | 6 |
| 2016 | **KINGS FETE** 5-9-7 | 5 |
| 2017 | **DEFOE** 3-8-10 | 8 |
| 2018 | **HAMADA** 4-9-5 | 6 |
| 2019 | **TECHNICIAN** 3-8-10 | 5 |
| 2020 | **HUKUM** 3-8-9 | 7 |

## INTERNATIONAL STAKES
York-1m 2f 56yds

| 2011 | **TWICE OVER** 6-9-5 | 5 |
| 2012 | **FRANKEL** 4-9-5 | 9 |
| 2013 | **DECLARATION OF WAR** 4-9-5 | 6 |
| 2014 | **AUSTRALIA** 3-8-9 | 6 |
| 2015 | **ARABIAN QUEEN** 3-8-9 | 7 |
| 2016 | **POSTPONED** 5-9-6 | 12 |
| 2017 | **ULYSSES** 4-9-6 | 7 |
| 2018 | **ROARING LION** 3-8-13 | 8 |
| 2019 | **JAPAN** 3-8-13 | 9 |
| 2020 | **GHAIYYATH** 5-9-6 | 6 |

## GREAT VOLTIGEUR STAKES (3y)
York-1m 3f 188yds

| 2011 | **SEA MOON** 8-12 | 8 |
| 2012 | **THOUGHT WORTHY** 8-12 | 6 |
| 2013 | **TELESCOPE** 8-12 | 7 |
| 2014 | **POSTPONED** 9-0 | 9 |
| 2015 | **STORM THE STARS** 9-0 | 7 |
| 2016 | **IDAHO** 9-0 | 6 |
| 2017 | **CRACKSMAN** 9-0 | 6 |
| 2018 | **OLD PERSIAN** 9-3 | 9 |
| 2019 | **LOGICIAN** 9-0 | 5 |
| 2020 | **PYLEDRIVER** 9-3 | 8 |

## LOWTHER STAKES
## (2y fillies)
York-6f

| 2011 | **BEST TERMS** 9-1 | 11 |
| 2012 | **ROSDHU QUEEN** 9-0 | 10 |
| 2013 | **LUCKY KRISTALE** 9-1 | 9 |
| 2014 | **TIGGY WIGGY** 9-0 | 9 |
| 2015 | **BESHARAH** 9-0 | 8 |
| 2016 | **QUEEN KINDLY** 9-0 | 8 |
| 2017 | **THREADING** 9-0 | 9 |
| 2018 | **FAIRYLAND** 9-0 | 9 |
| 2019 | **LIVING IN THE PAST** 9-0 | 10 |
| 2020 | **MISS AMULET** 9-0 | 14 |

## YORKSHIRE OAKS
## (fillies and mares)
York-1m 3f 188yds

| 2011 | **BLUE BUNTING** 3-8-11 | 8 |
| 2012 | **SHARETA** 4-9-7 | 6 |
| 2013 | **THE FUGUE** 4-9--7 | 7 |

| 2014 | TAPESTRY 3-8-11 | 7 |
| 2015 | PLEASCACH 3-8-11 | 11 |
| 2016 | SEVENTH HEAVEN 3-8-11 | 12 |
| 2017 | ENABLE 3-8-12 | 6 |
| 2018 | SEA OF CLASS 3-8-12 | 8 |
| 2019 | ENABLE 5-9-7 | 4 |
| 2020 | LOVE 3-8-12 | 6 |

## EBOR HANDICAP
York-1m 5f 188yds

| 2011 | MOYENNE CORNICHE 6-8-10 | 20 |
| 2012 | WILLING FOE 5-9-2 | 19 |
| 2013 | TIGER CLIFF 4-9-0 | 14 |
| 2014 | MUTUAL REGARD 5-9-4 | 19 |
| 2015 | LITIGANT 7-9-1 | 19 |
| 2016 | HEARTBREAK CITY 6-9-1 | 20 |
| 2017 | NAKEETA 6-9-0 | 19 |
| 2018 | MUNTAHAA 5-9-9 | 20 |
| 2019 | MUSTAJEER 6-9-5 | 22 |
| 2020 | FUJAIRA PRINCE 6-9-8 | 21 |

## GIMCRACK STAKES (2y)
York-6f

| 2011 | CASPAR NETSCHER 8-12 | 9 |
| 2012 | BLAINE 8-12 | 8 |
| 2013 | ASTAIRE 8-12 | 7 |
| 2014 | MUHAARAR 9-0 | 9 |
| 2015 | AJAYA 9-0 | 8 |
| 2016 | BLUE POINT 9-0 | 10 |
| 2017 | SANDS OF MALI 9-0 | 10 |
| 2018 | EMARAATY ANA 9-0 | 9 |
| 2019 | THREAT 9-0 | 12 |
| 2020 | MINZAAL 9-0 | 9 |

## NUNTHORPE STAKES
York-5f

| 2011 | MARGOT DID 3-9-6 | 15 |
| 2012 | ORTENSIA 7-9-8 | 19 |
| 2013 | JWALA 4-9--8 | 17 |
| 2014 | SOLE POWER 7-9-11 | 13 |
| 2015 | MECCA'S ANGEL 4-9-10 | 19 |
| 2016 | MECCA'S ANGEL 5-9-8 | 19 |
| 2017 | MARSHA 4-9-8 | 11 |
| 2018 | ALPHA DELPHINI 7-9-11 | 15 |
| 2019 | BATTAASH 5-9-11 | 11 |
| 2020 | BATTAASH 6-9-11 | 8 |

## LONSDALE CUP
York-2m 56yds

| 2011 | OPINION POLL 5 9-4 | 10 |
| 2012 | TIMES UP 6 9-1 | 11 |
| 2013 | AHZEEMAH 4 9-3 | 7 |
| 2014 | PALE MIMOSA 5-9-0 | 7 |
| 2015 | MAX DYNAMITE 5-9-3 | 8 |
| 2016 | QUEST FOR MORE 6-9-3 | 7 |
| 2017 | MONTALY 6-9-3 | 9 |
| 2018 | STRADIVARIUS 4-9-6 | 9 |
| 2019 | STRADIVARIUS 5-9-6 | 4 |
| 2020 | ENBIHAAR 5 9-0 | 7 |

## PRESTIGE STAKES (2y fillies)
Goodwood-7f

| 2011 | REGAL REALM 9-0 | 6 |
| 2012 | OLLIE OLGA 9-0 | 8 |
| 2013 | AMAZING MARIA 9-0 | 7 |
| 2014 | MALABAR 9-0 | 8 |
| 2015 | HAWKSMOOR 9-0 | 9 |
| 2016 | KILMAH 9-0 | 7 |
| 2017 | BILLESDON BROOK 9-0 | 10 |
| 2018 | ANTONIA DE VEGA 9-0 | 8 |
| 2019 | BOOMER 9-0 | 7 |
| 2020 | ISABELLA GILES 9-0 | 5 |

## CELEBRATION MILE
Goodwood-1m

| 2011 | DUBAWI GOLD 3-8-9 | 7 |
| 2012 | PREMIO LOCO 8-9-1 | 5 |
| 2013 | AFSARE 6-9-1 | 8 |
| 2014 | BOW CREEK 3-8-12 | 8 |
| 2015 | KODI BEAR 3-8-12 | 5 |
| 2016 | LIGHTNING SPEAR 5-9-4 | 5 |
| 2017 | LIGHTNING SPEAR 6-9-4 | 6 |
| 2018 | BEAT THE BANK 4-9-7 | 8 |
| 2019 | DUKE OF HAZZARD 3-8-12 | 6 |
| 2020 | CENTURY DREAM 6-9-4 | 6 |

## SOLARIO STAKES (2y)
Sandown-7f 16yds

| 2011 | TALWAR 9-0 | 4 |
| 2012 | FANTASTIC MOON 9-0 | 7 |
| 2013 | KINGMAN 9-0 | 4 |
| 2014 | AKTABANTAY 9-1 | 5 |
| 2015 | FIRST SELECTION 9-1 | 10 |
| 2016 | SOUTH SEAS 9-1 | 10 |
| 2017 | MASAR 9-1 | 7 |
| 2018 | TOO DARN HOT 9-1 | 6 |
| 2019 | POSITIVE 9-1 | 6 |
| 2020 | ETONIAN 9-1 | 7 |

## SPRINT CUP
Haydock-6f

| 2011 | DREAM AHEAD 3-9-1 | 16 |
| 2012 | SOCIETY ROCK 5-9-3 | 13 |
| 2013 | GORDON LORD BYRON 5-9-3 | 13 |
| 2014 | G FORCE 3-9-1 | 17 |
| 2015 | TWILIGHT SON 3-9-1 | 15 |
| 2016 | QUIET REFLECTION 3-8-12 | 14 |
| 2017 | HARRY ANGEL 3-9-1 | 11 |
| 2018 | THE TIN MAN 5-9-3 | 12 |
| 2019 | HELLO YOUMZAIN 3-9-1 | 11 |
| 2020 | DREAM OF DREAMS 6-9-3 | 13 |

## SEPTEMBER STAKES
Kempton-1m 3f 219yds Polytrack

| 2011 | MODUN 4-9-4 | 7 |
| 2012 | DANDINO 5-9-4 | 9 |
| 2013 | PRINCE BISHOP 6-9-4 | 10 |
| 2014 | PRINCE BISHOP 7-9-12 | 7 |
| 2015 | JACK HOBBS 3-9-3 | 7 |
| 2016 | ARAB SPRING 6-9-5 | 6 |
| 2017 | CHEMICAL CHARGE 5-9-5 | 6 |
| 2018 | ENABLE 4-9-2 | 4 |
| 2019 | ROYAL LINE 5-9-5 | 12 |
| 2020 | ENABLE 6-9-9 | 6 |

## MAY HILL STAKES
### (2y fillies)
Doncaster-1m

| | | |
|---|---|---|
| 2011 | **LYRIC OF LIGHT** 8-12 | 8 |
| 2012 | **CERTIFY** 8-12 | 7 |
| 2013 | **IHTIMAL** 8-12 | 7 |
| 2014 | **AGNES STEWART** 9-0 | 8 |
| 2015 | **TURRET ROCKS** 9-0 | 8 |
| 2016 | **RICH LEGACY** 9-0 | 9 |
| 2017 | **LAURENS** 9-0 | 8 |
| 2018 | **FLEETING** 9-0 | 11 |
| 2019 | **POWERFUL BREEZE** 9-0 | 9 |
| 2020 | **INDIGO GIRL** 9-0 | 9 |

## PORTLAND HANDICAP
Doncaster-5f 143yds

| | | |
|---|---|---|
| 2011 | **NOCTURNAL AFFAIR** 5-9-5 | 21 |
| 2012 | **DOC HAY** 5-8-11 | 20 |
| 2013 | **ANGELS WILL FALL** 4-9-2 | 21 |
| 2014 | **MUTHMIR** 4-9-7 | 20 |
| 2015 | **STEPS** 7-9-7 | 20 |
| 2016 | **CAPTAIN COLBY** 4-9-0 | 20 |
| 2017 | **SPRING LOADED** 5-8-9 | 22 |
| 2018 | **A MOMENTOFMADNESS** 5-9-4 | 21 |
| 2019 | **OXTED** 3-9-4 | 22 |
| 2020 | **STONE OF DESTINY** 5-9-0 | 21 |

## PARK HILL STAKES
### (fillies and mares)
Doncaster-1m 6f 115yds

| | | |
|---|---|---|
| 2011 | **MEEZNAH** 4-9-4 | 7 |
| 2012 | **WILD COCO** 4-9-4 | 9 |
| 2013 | **THE LARK** 3-8-6 | 9 |
| 2014 | **SILK SARI** 4-9-4 | 13 |
| 2015 | **GRETCHEN** 3-8-7 | 11 |
| 2016 | **SIMPLE VERSE** 4-9-5 | 12 |
| 2017 | **ALYSSA** 4-9-5 | 10 |
| 2018 | **GOD GIVEN** 4-9-5 | 7 |
| 2019 | **ENBIHAAR** 4-9-5 | 8 |
| 2020 | **PISTA** 3-8-9 | 7 |

## DONCASTER CUP
Doncaster-2m 1f 197yds

| | | |
|---|---|---|
| 2011 | **SADDLER'S ROCK** 3-8-1 | 7 |
| 2012 | **TIMES UP** 6-9-1 | 10 |
| 2013 | **TIMES UP** 7-9-3 | 7 |
| 2014 | **ESTIMATE** 5-9-0 | 12 |
| 2015 | **PALLASATOR** 6-9-3 | 11 |
| 2016 | **SHEIKHZAYEDROAD** 7-9-3 | 8 |
| 2017 | **DESERT SKYLINE** 3-8-5 | 9 |
| 2018 | **THOMAS HOBSON** 8-9-5 | 8 |
| 2019 | **STRADIVARIUS** 5-9-10 | 5 |
| 2020 | **SPANISH MISSION** 4-9-5 | 7 |

## CHAMPAGNE STAKES (2y)
Doncaster-7f 6yds

| | | |
|---|---|---|
| 2011 | **TRUMPET MAJOR** 8-12 | 5 |
| 2012 | **TORONADO** 8-12 | 5 |
| 2013 | **OUTSTRIP** 8-12 | 4 |
| 2014 | **ESTIDHKAAR** 9-3 | 6 |
| 2015 | **EMOTIONLESS** 9-0 | 6 |
| 2016 | **RIVET** 9-0 | 6 |
| 2017 | **SEAHENGE** 9-0 | 7 |
| 2018 | **TOO DARN HOT** 9-0 | 6 |
| 2019 | **THREAT** 9-3 | 5 |
| 2020 | **CHINDIT** 9-0 | 7 |

## PARK STAKES
Doncaster-7f 6yds

| | | |
|---|---|---|
| 2011 | **PREMIO LOCO** 7-9-4 | 5 |
| 2012 | **LIBRANNO** 4-9-4 | 8 |
| 2013 | **VIZTORIA** 3-8-11 | 9 |
| 2014 | **ANSGAR** 6-9-4 | 7 |
| 2015 | **LIMATO** 3-9-0 | 15 |
| 2016 | **BRETON ROCK** 6-9-4 | 8 |
| 2017 | **ACLAIM** 4-9-4 | 8 |
| 2018 | **MUSTASHRY** 5-9-4 | 9 |
| 2019 | **SIR DANCEALOT** 5-9-7 | 5 |
| 2020 | **WICHITA** 3-9-0 | 8 |

## FLYING CHILDERS STAKES (2y)
Doncaster-5f

| | | |
|---|---|---|
| 2011 | **REQUINTO** 9-0 | 10 |
| 2012 | **SIR PRANCEALOT** 9-0 | 9 |
| 2013 | **GREEN DOOR** 9-0 | 7 |
| 2014 | **BEACON** 9-1 | 14 |
| 2015 | **GUTAIFAN** 9-1 | 9 |
| 2016 | **ARDAD** 9-1 | 11 |
| 2017 | **HEARTACHE** 8-12 | 9 |
| 2018 | **SOLDIER'S CALL** 9-1 | 9 |
| 2019 | **A'ALI** 9-1 | 7 |
| 2020 | **UBETTABELIEVEIT** 9-1 | 10 |

## AYR GOLD CUP
Ayr-6f

| | | |
|---|---|---|
| 2011 | **OUR JONATHAN** 4-9-6 | 26 |
| 2012 | **CAPTAIN RAMIUS** 6-9-0 | 26 |
| 2013 | **HIGHLAND COLORI** 5-8-13 | 26 |
| 2014 | **LOUIS THE PIOUS** 6-9-4 | 27 |
| 2015 | **DON'T TOUCH** 3-9-1 | 25 |
| 2016 | **BRANDO** 4-9-10 | 23 |
| * 2017 | **DONJUAN TRIUMPHANT** 4-9-10 | 17 |
| 2018 | **SON OF REST** 4-9-3 dead heated with | |
| | **BARON BOLT** 5-8-12 | 25 |
| 2019 | **ANGEL ALEXANDER** 3-8-13 | 24 |
| 2020 | **NAHAARR** 4-9-5 | 24 |

*Run at Haydock Park as 32Red Gold Cup

## MILL REEF STAKES (2y)
Newbury-6f 8yds

| | | |
|---|---|---|
| 2011 | **CASPAR NETSCHER** 9-4 | 9 |
| 2012 | **MOOHAAJIM** 9-1 | 8 |
| 2013 | **SUPPLICANT** 9-1 | 7 |
| 2014 | **TOOCOOLFORSCHOOL** 9-1 | 6 |
| 2015 | **RIBCHESTER** 9-1 | 6 |
| 2016 | **HARRY ANGEL** 9-1 | 7 |
| 2017 | **JAMES GARFIELD** 9-1 | 9 |
| 2018 | **KESSAAR** 9-1 | 7 |
| 2019 | **PIERRE LAPIN** 9-1 | 8 |
| 2020 | **ALKUMAIT** 9-1 | 8 |

## ROYAL LODGE STAKES (2y)
Newmarket-1m (run at Ascot before 2011)

| | | |
|---|---|---|
| 2011 | **DADDY LONG LEGS** 8-12 | 6 |
| 2012 | **STEELER** 8-12 | 8 |
| 2013 | **BERKSHIRE** 8-12 | 5 |
| 2014 | **ELM PARK** 9-0 | 6 |
| 2015 | **FOUNDATION** 9-0 | 6 |
| 2016 | **BEST OF DAYS** 9-0 | 8 |
| 2017 | **ROARING LION** 9-0 | 5 |
| 2018 | **MOHAWK** 9-0 | 7 |
| 2019 | **ROYAL DORNOCH** 9-0 | 7 |
| 2020 | **NEW MANDATE** 9-0 | 5 |

## CHEVELEY PARK STAKES (2y fillies)
Newmarket-6f
| | | | |
|---|---|---|---|
| 2011 | **LIGHTENING PEARL** 8-12 | ...................... | 9 |
| 2012 | **ROSDHU QUEEN** 8-12 | ...................... | 11 |
| 2013 | **VORDA** 8-12 | ...................... | 7 |
| 2014 | **TIGGY WIGGY** 9-0 | ...................... | 9 |
| 2015 | **LUMIERE** 9-0 | ...................... | 8 |
| 2016 | **BRAVE ANNA** 9-0 | ...................... | 6 |
| 2017 | **CLEMMIE** 9-0 | ...................... | 11 |
| 2018 | **FAIRYLAND** 9-0 | ...................... | 11 |
| 2019 | **MILLISLE** 9-0 | ...................... | 11 |
| 2020 | **ALCOHOL FREE** 9-0 | ...................... | 8 |

## SUN CHARIOT STAKES
## (fillies and mares)
Newmarket-1m
| | | | |
|---|---|---|---|
| 2011 | **SAHPRESA** 6-9-3 | ...................... | 8 |
| 2012 | **SIYOUMA** 4-9-3 | ...................... | 8 |
| 2013 | **SKY LANTERN** 3-8-13 | ...................... | 7 |
| 2014 | **INTEGRAL** 4-9-3 | ...................... | 7 |
| 2015 | **ESOTERIQUE** 5-9-3 | ...................... | 9 |
| 2016 | **ALICE SPRINGS** 3-9-0 | ...................... | 8 |
| 2017 | **ROLY POLY** 3-9-0 | ...................... | 13 |
| 2018 | **LAURENS** 3-9-0 | ...................... | 9 |
| 2019 | **BILLESDON BROOK** 4-9-3 | ...................... | 9 |
| 2020 | **NAZEEF** 4-9-3 | ...................... | 12 |

## CAMBRIDGESHIRE
Newmarket-1m 1f
| | | | |
|---|---|---|---|
| 2011 | **PRINCE OF JOHANNE** 5-8-9 | ...................... | 32 |
| 2012 | **BRONZE ANGEL** 3-8-8 | ...................... | 33 |
| 2013 | **EDUCATE** 4-9-9 | ...................... | 31 |
| 2014 | **BRONZE ANGEL** 5-8-8 | ...................... | 31 |
| 2015 | **THIRD TIME LUCKY** 3-8-4 | ...................... | 34 |
| 2016 | **SPARK PLUG** 5-9-4 | ...................... | 31 |
| 2017 | **DOLPHIN VISTA** 4-8-7 | ...................... | 34 |
| 2018 | **WISSAHICKON** 3-9-5 | ...................... | 33 |
| 2019 | **LORD NORTH** 3-8-10 | ...................... | 30 |
| 2020 | **MAJESTIC DAWN** 4-8-8 | ...................... | 27 |

## CUMBERLAND LODGE STAKES
Ascot-1m 4f
| | | | |
|---|---|---|---|
| 2011 | **QUEST FOR PEACE** 3-8-7 | ...................... | 7 |
| 2012 | **HAWAAFEZ** 4-8-11 | ...................... | 6 |
| 2013 | **SECRET NUMBER** 3-8-7 | ...................... | 7 |
| 2014 | **PETHER'S MOON** 4-9-6 | ...................... | 5 |
| 2015 | **STAR STORM** 3-8-8 | ...................... | 8 |
| 2016 | **MOVE UP** 3-8-13 | ...................... | 9 |
| 2017 | **DANEHILL KODIAC** 4-9-2 | ...................... | 9 |
| 2018 | **LARAAIB** 4-9-2 | ...................... | 7 |
| 2019 | **MORANDO** 6-9-5 | ...................... | 7 |
| * 2020 | **EUCHEN GLEN** 7-9-0 | ...................... | 4 |
*Run at York

## FILLIES' MILE (2y fillies)
Newmarket-1m
(run at Ascot before 2011)
| | | | |
|---|---|---|---|
| 2011 | **LYRIC OF LIGHT** 8-12 | ...................... | 8 |
| 2012 | **CERTIFY** 8-12 | ...................... | 6 |
| 2013 | **CHRISELLIAM** 8-12 | ...................... | 8 |
| 2014 | **TOGETHER FOREVER** 9-0 | ...................... | 7 |
| 2015 | **MINDING** 9-0 | ...................... | 10 |
| 2016 | **RHODODENDRON** 9-0 | ...................... | 8 |
| 2017 | **LAURENS** 9-0 | ...................... | 11 |
| 2018 | **IRIDESSA** 9-0 | ...................... | 9 |
| 2019 | **QUADRILATERAL** 9-0 | ...................... | 9 |
| 2020 | **PRETTY GORGEOUS** 9-0 | ...................... | 10 |

## MIDDLE PARK STAKES (2y)
Newmarket-6f
| | | | |
|---|---|---|---|
| 2011 | **CRUSADE** 8-12 | ...................... | 16 |
| 2012 | **RECKLESS ABANDON** 8-12 | ...................... | 10 |
| 2013 | **ASTAIRE** 9-0 | ...................... | 10 |
| 2014 | **CHARMING THOUGHT** 9-0 | ...................... | 6 |
| 2015 | **SHALAA** 9-0 | ...................... | 7 |
| 2016 | **THE LAST LION** 9-0 | ...................... | 10 |
| 2017 | **U S NAVY FLAG** 9-0 | ...................... | 12 |
| 2018 | **TEN SOVEREIGNS** 9-0 | ...................... | 8 |
| 2019 | **EARTHLIGHT** 9-0 | ...................... | 8 |
| 2020 | **SUPREMACY** 9-0 | ...................... | 8 |

## CHALLENGE STAKES
Newmarket-7f
| | | | |
|---|---|---|---|
| 2011 | **STRONG SUIT** 3-9-5 | ...................... | 8 |
| 2012 | **FULBRIGHT** 3-9-1 | ...................... | 11 |
| 2013 | **FIESOLANA** 4-9-0 | ...................... | 9 |
| 2014 | **HERE COMES WHEN** 4-9-7 | ...................... | 13 |
| 2015 | **CABLE BAY** 4-9-3 | ...................... | 10 |
| 2016 | **ACLAIM** 3-9-1 | ...................... | 12 |
| 2017 | **LIMATO** 5-9-3 | ...................... | 11 |
| 2018 | **LIMATO** 6-9-3 | ...................... | 8 |
| 2019 | **MUSTASHRY** 6-9-8 | ...................... | 5 |
| 2020 | **HAPPY POWER** 4-9-3 | ...................... | 9 |

## DEWHURST STAKES (2y)
Newmarket-7f
| | | | |
|---|---|---|---|
| 2011 | **PARISH HALL** 9-1 | ...................... | 9 |
| 2012 | **DAWN APPROACH** 9-1 | ...................... | 6 |
| 2013 | **WAR COMMAND** 9-1 | ...................... | 6 |
| 2014 | **BELARDO** 9-1 | ...................... | 6 |
| 2015 | **AIR FORCE BLUE** 9-1 | ...................... | 7 |
| 2016 | **CHURCHILL** 9-1 | ...................... | 7 |
| 2017 | **U S NAVY FLAG** 9-1 | ...................... | 9 |
| 2018 | **TOO DARN HOT** 9-1 | ...................... | 7 |
| 2019 | **PINATUBO** 9-1 | ...................... | 9 |
| 2020 | **ST MARK'S BASILICA** 9-1 | ...................... | 14 |

## CESAREWITCH
Newmarket-2m 2f
| | | | |
|---|---|---|---|
| 2011 | **NEVER CAN TELL** 4-8-11 | ...................... | 33 |
| 2012 | **AAIM TO PROSPER** 8-9-10 | ...................... | 34 |
| 2013 | **SCATTER DICE** 4-8-8 | ...................... | 33 |
| 2014 | **BIG EASY** 7-8-7 | ...................... | 33 |
| 2015 | **GRUMETI** 7-8-2 | ...................... | 34 |
| 2016 | **SWEET SELECTION** 4-8-8 | ...................... | 33 |
| 2017 | **WITHHOLD** 4-8-8 | ...................... | 34 |
| 2018 | **LOW SUN** 5-9-2 | ...................... | 33 |
| 2019 | **STRATUM** 6-9-7 | ...................... | 30 |
| 2020 | **GREAT WHITE SHARK** 6-8-6 | ...................... | 34 |

## ROCKFEL STAKES (2y fillies)
Newmarket-7f
| | | | |
|---|---|---|---|
| 2011 | **WADING** 8-12 | ...................... | 9 |
| 2012 | **JUST THE JUDGE** 8-12 | ...................... | 11 |
| 2013 | **AL THAKHIRA** 8-12 | ...................... | 8 |
| 2014 | **LUCIDA** 9-0 | ...................... | 9 |
| 2015 | **PROMISING RUN** 9-0 | ...................... | 7 |
| 2016 | **SPAIN BURG** 9-0 | ...................... | 8 |
| 2017 | **JULIET CAPULET** 9-0 | ...................... | 10 |
| 2018 | **JUST WONDERFUL** 9-0 | ...................... | 9 |
| 2019 | **DAAHYEH** 9-0 | ...................... | 8 |
| 2020 | **ISABELLA GILES** 9-0 | ...................... | 5 |

## QIPCO BRITISH CHAMPIONS SPRINT STAKES

Ascot-6f (run as Diadem Stakes before 2011)

| | | |
|---|---|---|
| 2011 | **DEACON BLUES** 4-9-0 | 16 |
| 2012 | **MAAREK** 5-9-0 | 15 |
| 2013 | **SLADE POWER** 4-9-0 | 14 |
| 2014 | **GORDON LORD BYRON** 6-9-2 | 15 |
| 2015 | **MUHAARAR** 3-9-1 | 20 |
| 2016 | **THE TIN MAN** 4-9-2 | 13 |
| 2017 | **LIBRISA BREEZE** 5-9-2 | 12 |
| 2018 | **SANDS OF MALI** 3-9-1 | 14 |
| 2019 | **DONJUAN TRIUMPHANT** 6-9-2 | 17 |
| 2020 | **GLEN SHIEL** 6-9-2 | 16 |

## QUEEN ELIZABETH II STAKES (BRITISH CHAMPIONS MILE)

Ascot-1m (st - rnd before 2011)

| | | |
|---|---|---|
| 2011 | **FRANKEL** 3-9-0 | 8 |
| 2012 | **EXCELEBRATION** 4-9-3 | 8 |
| 2013 | **OLYMPIC GLORY** 3-9-0 | 12 |
| 2014 | **CHARM SPIRIT** 3-9-1 | 11 |
| 2015 | **SOLOW** 5-9-4 | 9 |
| 2016 | **MINDING** 3-8-12 | 13 |
| 2017 | **PERSUASIVE** 4-9-1 | 15 |
| 2018 | **ROARING LION** 3-9-1 | 13 |
| 2019 | **KING OF CHANGE** 3-9-1 | 16 |
| 2020 | **THE REVENANT** 5-9-4 | 14 |

## QIPCO BRITISH CHAMPIONS LONG DISTANCE CUP

Ascot-2m

| | | |
|---|---|---|
| 2012 | **RITE OF PASSAGE** 8-9-7 | 9 |
| 2013 | **ROYAL DIAMOND** 7-9-7 | 12 |
| 2014 | **FORGOTTEN RULES** 4-9-7 | 9 |
| 2015 | **FLYING OFFICER** 5-9-7 | 13 |
| 2016 | **SHEIKHZAYEDROAD** 7-9-7 | 10 |
| 2017 | **ORDER OF ST GEORGE** 5-9-7 | 13 |
| 2018 | **STRADIVARIUS** 4-9-7 | 6 |
| 2019 | **KEW GARDENS** 4-9-7 | 6 |
| 2020 | **TRUESHAN** 4-9-7 | 13 |

## QIPCO BRITISH CHAMPIONS FILLIES' AND MARES' STAKES

Ascot-1m 4f

| | | |
|---|---|---|
| 2011 | **DANCING RAIN** 3-8-10 | 10 |
| 2012 | **SAPPHIRE** 4-9-3 | 10 |
| 2013 | **SEAL OF APPROVAL** 4-9-3 | 8 |
| 2014 | **MADAME CHIANG** 3-8-12 | 10 |
| 2015 | **SIMPLE VERSE** 3-8-12 | 12 |
| 2016 | **JOURNEY** 4-9-5 | 13 |
| 2017 | **HYDRANGEA** 3-8-13 | 10 |
| 2018 | **MAGICAL** 3-8-13 | 11 |
| 2019 | **STAR CATCHER** 3-8-13 | 12 |
| 2020 | **WONDERFUL TONIGHT** 3-8-13 | 12 |

## QIPCO CHAMPION STAKES (BRITISH CHAMPIONS MIDDLE DISTANCE)

Ascot-1m 2f (run at Newmarket before 2011)

| | | |
|---|---|---|
| 2011 | **CIRRUS DES AIGLES** 5-9-3 | 12 |
| 2012 | **FRANKEL** 4-9-3 | 6 |
| 2013 | **FARHH** 5-9-3 | 10 |
| 2014 | **NOBLE MISSION** 5-9-5 | 9 |
| 2015 | **FASCINATING ROCK** 4-9-5 | 13 |
| 2016 | **ALMANZOR** 3-9-0 | 10 |
| 2017 | **CRACKSMAN** 3-9-1 | 10 |

| | | |
|---|---|---|
| 2018 | **CRACKSMAN** 4-9-5 | 8 |
| 2019 | **MAGICAL** 4-9-2 | 12 |
| 2020 | **ADDEYBB** 6-9-5 | 10 |

## BALMORAL HANDICAP

Ascot-1m

| | | |
|---|---|---|
| 2014 | **BRONZE ANGEL** 5-9-2 | 27 |
| 2015 | **MUSADDAS** 5-8-2 | 20 |
| 2016 | **YUFTEN** 5-9-1 | 19 |
| 2017 | **LORD GLITTERS** 6-9-3 | 20 |
| 2018 | **SHARJA BRIDGE** 4-9-5 | 20 |
| 2019 | **ESCOBAR** 5-9-6 | 20 |
| 2020 | **NJORD** 4-9-5 | 18 |

## CORNWALLIS STAKES (2y)

Newmarket-5f (run at Ascot before 2014)

| | | |
|---|---|---|
| 2011 | **PONTY ACCLAIM** 8-11 | 16 |
| 2012 | **BUNGLE INTHEJUNGLE** 9-3 | 6 |
| 2013 | **HOT STREAK** 9-0 | 12 |
| 2014 | **ROYAL RAZALMA** 8-12 | 12 |
| 2015 | **QUIET REFLECTION** 8-12 | 11 |
| 2016 | **MRS DANVERS** 8-12 | 9 |
| 2017 | **ABEL HANDY** 9-1 | 12 |
| 2018 | **SERGEI PROKOFIEV** 9-1 | 14 |
| 2019 | **GOOD VIBES** 8-12 | 12 |
| 2020 | **WINTER POWER** 8-12 | 11 |

## TWO-YEAR-OLD TROPHY (2y)

Redcar-6f

| | | |
|---|---|---|
| 2011 | **BOGART** 8-12 | 22 |
| 2012 | **BODY AND SOUL** 8-1 | 21 |
| 2013 | **VENTURA MIST** 8-7 | 23 |
| 2014 | **LIMATO** 8-12 | 23 |
| 2015 | **LOG OUT ISLAND** 9-2 | 20 |
| 2016 | **WICK POWELL** 8-3 | 20 |
| 2017 | **DARKANNA** 8-11 | 23 |
| 2018 | **SUMMER DAYDREAM** 8-9 | 21 |
| 2019 | **SUMMER SANDS** 8-2 | 17 |
| 2020 | **LULLABY MOON** 8-9 | 21 |

## HORRIS HILL STAKES (2y)

Newbury-7f

| | | |
|---|---|---|
| 2011 | **TELL DAD** 8-12 | 14 |
| 2012 | **TAWHID** 8-12 | 8 |
| 2013 | **PIPING ROCK** 8-12 | 11 |
| 2014 | **SMAIH** 9-0 | 6 |
| 2015 | **CRAZY HORSE** 9-0 | 9 |
| 2016 | **PLEASELETMEWIN** 9-0 | 13 |
| 2017 | **NEBO** 9-0 | 6 |
| 2018 | **MOHAATHER** 9-0 | 8 |
| 2019 | ABANDONED | |
| 2020 | **MUJBAR** 9-0 | 12 |

## VERTEM FUTURITY TROPHY (2y)

(Racing Post Trophy before 2018)
Doncaster-1m (St)

| | | |
|---|---|---|
| 2011 | **CAMELOT** 9-0 | 5 |
| 2012 | **KINGSBARNS** 9-0 | 7 |
| 2013 | **KINGSTON HILL** 9-0 | 11 |
| 2014 | **ELM PARK** 9-0 | 8 |
| 2015 | **MARCEL** 9-1 | 7 |
| 2016 | **RIVET** 9-1 | 10 |
| 2017 | **SAXON WARRIOR** 9-1 | 12 |
| 2018 | **MAGNA GRECIA** 9-1 | 11 |
| * 2019 | **KAMEKO** 9-1 | 11 |
| 2020 | **MAC SWINEY** 9-1 | 8 |

* Run at Newcastle 1m 5yds (Tapeta)

## NOVEMBER HANDICAP
Doncaster-1m 3f 197yds

# WINNERS OF PRINCIPAL RACES IN IRELAND

## IRISH 2000 GUINEAS (3y)
The Curragh-1m
| | | |
|---|---|---|
| 2011 | RODERIC O'CONNOR 9-0 | 8 |
| 2012 | POWER 9-0 | 10 |
| 2013 | MAGICIAN 9-0 | 10 |
| 2014 | KINGMAN 9-0 | 11 |
| 2015 | GLENEAGLES 9-0 | 11 |
| 2016 | AWTAAD 9-0 | 8 |
| 2017 | CHURCHILL 9-0 | 6 |
| 2018 | ROMANISED 9-0 | 11 |
| 2019 | PHOENIX OF SPAIN 9-0 | 14 |
| 2020 | SISKIN 9-2 | 11 |

## TATTERSALLS GOLD CUP
The Curragh-1m 2f 110yds
| | | |
|---|---|---|
| 2011 | SO YOU THINK 5-9-1 | 5 |
| 2012 | SO YOU THINK 6-9-1 | 5 |
| 2013 | AL KAZEEM 5-9-3 | 4 |
| 2014 | NOBLE MISSION 5-9-3 | 5 |
| 2015 | AL KAZEEM 7-9-3 | 6 |
| 2016 | FASCINATING ROCK 5-9-3 | 6 |
| 2017 | DECORATED KNIGHT 5-9-3 | 8 |
| 2018 | LANCASTER BOMBER 4-9-3 | 5 |
| 2019 | MAGICAL 4-9-0 | 5 |
| 2020 | MAGICAL 5-9-9 | 6 |

## IRISH 1000 GUINEAS (3y fillies)
The Curragh-1m
| | | |
|---|---|---|
| 2011 | MISTY FOR ME 9-0 | 15 |
| 2012 | SAMITAR 9-0 | 8 |
| 2013 | JUST THE JUDGE 9-0 | 15 |
| 2014 | MARVELLOUS 9-0 | 11 |
| 2015 | PLEASCACH 9-0 | 18 |
| 2016 | JET SETTING 9-0 | 10 |
| 2017 | WINTER 9-0 | 8 |
| 2018 | ALPHA CENTAURI 9-0 | 13 |
| 2019 | HERMOSA 9-0 | 10 |
| 2020 | PEACEFUL 9-2 | 11 |

## IRISH DERBY (3y)
The Curragh-1m 4f
| | | |
|---|---|---|
| 2011 | TREASURE BEACH 9-0 | 8 |
| 2012 | CAMELOT 9-0 | 5 |
| 2013 | TRADING LEATHER 9-0 | 9 |
| 2014 | AUSTRALIA 9-0 | 5 |
| 2015 | JACK HOBBS 9-0 | 8 |
| 2016 | HARZAND 9-0 | 9 |
| 2017 | CAPRI 9-0 | 9 |
| 2018 | LATROBE 9-0 | 12 |
| 2019 | SOVEREIGN 9-0 | 8 |
| 2020 | SANTIAGO 9-2 | 14 |

## PRETTY POLLY STAKES (fillies and mares)
Curragh-1m 2f
| | | |
|---|---|---|
| 2011 | MISTY FOR ME 3-8-12 | 7 |
| 2012 | IZZI TOP 4-9-9 | 4 |
| 2013 | AMBIVALENT 4-9-10 | 9 |

## IRISH 2000 GUINEAS (3y)

## IRISH OAKS (3y fillies)
The Curragh-1m 4f
| | | |
|---|---|---|
| 2011 | BLUE BUNTING 9-0 | 9 |
| 2012 | GREAT HEAVENS 9-0 | 7 |
| 2013 | CHICQUITA 9-0 | 7 |
| 2014 | BRACELET 9--0 | 10 |
| 2015 | COVERT LOVE 9-0 | 9 |
| 2016 | SEVENTH HEAVEN 9-0 | 11 |
| 2017 | ENABLE 9-0 | 10 |
| 2018 | SEA OF CLASS 9-0 | 7 |
| 2019 | STAR CATCHER 9-0 | 8 |
| 2020 | EVEN SO 9-2 | 8 |

## PHOENIX STAKES (2y)
The Curragh-6f
| | | |
|---|---|---|
| 2011 | LA COLLINA 8-12 | 9 |
| 2012 | PEDRO THE GREAT 9-3 | 6 |
| 2013 | SUDIRMAN 9-3 | 5 |
| 2014 | DICK WHITTINGTON 9-3 | 6 |
| 2015 | AIR FORCE BLUE 9-3 | 7 |
| 2016 | CARAVAGGIO 9-3 | 5 |
| 2017 | SIOUX NATION 9-3 | 8 |
| 2018 | ADVERTISE 9-3 | 5 |
| 2019 | SISKIN 9-3 | 5 |
| 2020 | LUCKY VEGA 9-5 | 10 |

## MATRON STAKES (fillies and mares)
Leopardstown-1m
| | | |
|---|---|---|
| 2011 | EMULOUS 4-9-5 | 8 |
| * 2012 | CHACHAMAIDEE 5-9-5 | 11 |
| 2013 | LA COLLINA 4-9-5 | 12 |
| 2014 | FIESOLANA 5-9-5 | 10 |
| 2015 | LEGATISSIMO 3-9-0 | 9 |
| 2016 | ALICE SPRINGS 3-9-0 | 8 |
| 2017 | HYDRANGEA 3-9-0 | 10 |
| 2018 | LAURENS 3-9-0 | 7 |
| 2019 | IRIDESSA 3-9-0 | 7 |
| 2020 | CHAMPERS ELYSEES 3-9-2 | 11 |

* Duntle disqualified from first place

## IRISH CHAMPION STAKES
Leopardstown-1m 2f
| | | |
|---|---|---|
| 2011 | SO YOU THINK 5-9-7 | 6 |
| 2012 | SNOW FAIRY 5-9-4 | 6 |
| 2013 | THE FUGUE 4-9-4 | 6 |
| 2014 | THE GREY GATSBY 3-9-0 | 7 |
| 2015 | GOLDEN HORN 3-9-0 | 7 |
| 2016 | ALMANZOR 3-9-0 | 12 |
| 2017 | DECORATED KNIGHT 5-9-7 | 10 |
| 2018 | ROARING LION 3-9-1 | 7 |

| | | |
|---|---|---|
| 2019 | **MAGICAL** 4-9-4 | 8 |
| 2020 | **MAGICAL** 5-9-6 | 6 |

## IRISH CAMBRIDGESHIRE
The Curragh-1m

| | | |
|---|---|---|
| 2011 | **CASTLE BAR SLING** 6-8-11 | 21 |
| 2012 | **PUNCH YOUR WEIGHT** 3-8-6 | 18 |
| 2013 | **MORAN GRA** 6-8-13 | 20 |
| 2014 | **SRETAW** 5-8-8 | 21 |
| 2015 | **HINT OF A TINT** 5-9-3 | 22 |
| 2016 | **SEA WOLF** 4-9-5 | 24 |
| 2017 | **ELUSIVE TIME** 9-8-9 | 27 |
| 2018 | **KENYA** 3-9-2 | 21 |
| 2019 | **JASSAAR** 4-8-8 | 25 |
| 2020 | **LAUGHIFUWANT** 5-9-10 | 20 |

## MOYGLARE STUD STAKES (2y fillies)
The Curragh-7f

| | | |
|---|---|---|
| 2011 | **MAYBE** 9-1 | 8 |
| 2012 | **SKY LANTERN** 9-0 | 13 |
| 2013 | **RIZEENA** 9-0 | 7 |
| 2014 | **CURSORY GLANCE** 9-0 | 10 |
| 2015 | **MINDING** 9-0 | 9 |
| 2016 | **INTRICATELY** 9-0 | 7 |
| 2017 | **HAPPILY** 9-0 | 8 |
| 2018 | **SKITTER SKATTER** 9-0 | 10 |
| 2019 | **LOVE** 9-0 | 9 |
| 2020 | **SHALE** 9-0 | 13 |

## VINCENT O'BRIEN (NATIONAL) STAKES (2y)
The Curragh-7f

| | | |
|---|---|---|
| 2011 | **POWER** 9-1 | 9 |
| 2012 | **DAWN APPROACH** 9-3 | 7 |
| 2013 | **TOORMORE** 9-3 | 5 |
| 2014 | **GLENEAGLES** 9-3 | 5 |
| 2015 | **AIR FORCE BLUE** 9-3 | 5 |
| 2016 | **CHURCHILL** 9-3 | 7 |
| 2017 | **VERBAL DEXTERITY** 9-3 | 7 |
| 2018 | **QUORTO** 9-3 | 7 |
| 2019 | **PINATUBO** 9-3 | 8 |
| 2020 | **THUNDER MOON** 9-5 | 10 |

## IRISH ST LEGER
The Curragh-1m 6f

| | | |
|---|---|---|
| 2011 | **DUNCAN** 6-9-11 dead heated with | 6 |
| | **JUKEBOX JURY** 5-9-11 | 6 |
| 2012 | **ROYAL DIAMOND** 6-9-11 | 9 |
| 2013 | **VOLEUSE DE COEURS** 4-9-8 | 10 |
| 2014 | **BROWN PANTHER** 6-9-11 | 11 |
| 2015 | **ORDER OF ST GEORGE** 3-9-0 | 11 |
| 2016 | **WICKLOW BRAVE** 7-9-11 | 4 |
| 2017 | **ORDER OF ST GEORGE** 5-9-10 | 10 |
| 2018 | **FLAG OF HONOUR** 3-9-1 | 6 |
| 2019 | **SEARCH FOR A SONG** 3-8-11 | 10 |
| 2020 | **SEARCH FOR A SONG** 4-9-8 | 8 |

## IRISH CESAREWITCH
The Curragh-2m

| | | |
|---|---|---|
| 2011 | **MINSK** 3-8-9 | 19 |
| 2012 | **VOLEUSE DE COEURS** 3-9-1 | 27 |
| 2013 | **MONTEFELTRO** 5-9-4 | 30 |
| 2014 | **EL SALVADOR** 5-9-5 | 21 |
| 2015 | **DIGEANTA** 8-9-10 | 20 |

| | | |
|---|---|---|
| 2016 | **LAWS OF SPIN** 3-8-6 | 20 |
| * 2017 | **LORD ERSKINE** 4-8-5 | 24 |
| 2018 | **BRAZOS** 4-8-12 | 24 |
| 2019 | **ROYAL ILLUSION** 7-8-5 | 18 |
| 2020 | **CAPE GENTLEMAN** 4-9-0 | 21 |

* Run at Navan

## LADBROKES HURDLE (Handicap)
Leopardstown-2m
(Various sponsors)

| | | |
|---|---|---|
| 2012 | **CITIZENSHIP** 6-10-3 | 30 |
| 2013 | **ABBEY LANE** 8-10-8 | 28 |
| 2014 | **GILGAMBOA** 6-10-9 | 24 |
| 2015 | **KATIE T** 6-10-9 | 24 |
| 2016 | **HENRY HIGGINS** 6-10-10 | 23 |
| 2017 | **ICE COLD SOUL** 7-10-2 | 20 |
| 2018 | **OFF YOU GO** 6-10-3 | 28 |
| 2019 | **OFF YOU GO** 6-11-5 | 19 |
| 2020 | **THOSEDAYSAREGONE** 7-9-12 | 22 |
| 2021 | **DROP THE ANCHOR** 7 10-5 | 22 |

## IRISH CHAMPION HURDLE
Leopardstown-2m

| | | |
|---|---|---|
| 2012 | **HURRICANE FLY** 8-11-10 | 5 |
| 2013 | **HURRICANE FLY** 9-11-10 | 5 |
| 2014 | **HURRICANE FLY** 10-11-10 | 4 |
| 2015 | **HURRICANE FLY** 11-11-10 | 6 |
| 2016 | **FAUGHEEN** 8-11-10 | 5 |
| 2017 | **PETIT MOUCHOIR** 6 11-10 | 4 |
| 2018 | **SUPASUNDAE** 8-11-10 | 8 |
| 2019 | **APPLE'S JADE** 7-11-3 | 6 |
| 2020 | **HONEYSUCKLE** 6-11-3 | 9 |
| 2021 | **HONEYSUCKLE** 7-11-5 | 6 |

## IRISH GOLD CUP
Leopardstown-3m(Hennessy Gold Cup before 2016)

| | | |
|---|---|---|
| 2012 | **QUEL ESPRIT** 8-11-10 | 7 |
| 2013 | **SIR DES CHAMPS** 7-11-10 | 4 |
| 2014 | **LAST INSTALMENT** 9-11-10 | 7 |
| 2015 | **CARLINGFORD LOUGH** 9-11-10 | 8 |
| 2016 | **CARLINGFORD LOUGH** 10-11-10 | 10 |
| 2017 | **SIZING JOHN** 7-11-10 | 10 |
| 2018 | **EDWULF** 9-11-10 | 10 |
| 2019 | **BELLSHILL** 9-11-10 | 4 |
| 2020 | **DELTA WORK** 7-11-10 | 8 |
| 2021 | **KEMBOY** 9-11-12 | 5 |

## IRISH GRAND NATIONAL
Fairyhouse-3m 5f

| | | |
|---|---|---|
| 2011 | **ORGANISEDCONFUSION** 6-9-13 | 25 |
| 2012 | **LION NA BEARNAI** 10-10-5 | 29 |
| 2013 | **LIBERTY COUNSEL** 10-9-5 | 28 |
| 2014 | **SHUTTHEFRONTDOOR** 7-10-13 | 26 |
| 2015 | **THUNDER AND ROSES** 7-10-6 | 28 |
| 2016 | **ROGUE ANGEL** 8-10-6 | 27 |
| 2017 | **OUR DUKE** 7-11-4 | 28 |
| 2018 | **GENERAL PRINCIPLE** 9-10-0 | 30 |
| 2019 | **BURROWS SAINT** 6-10-8 | 30 |
| 2020 | RACE CANCELLED | |

# WINNERS OF PRINCIPAL RACES IN FRANCE

## PRIX GANAY
ParisLongchamp-1m 2f 110yds
| | | |
|---|---|---|
| 2011 | **PLANTEUR** 4-9-2 | 7 |
| 2012 | **CIRRUS DES AIGLES** 6-9-2 | 6 |
| 2013 | **PASTORIUS** 4-9-2 | 9 |
| 2014 | **CIRRUS DES AIGLES** 8-9-2 | 8 |
| 2015 | **CIRRUS DES AIGLES** 9-9-2 | 7 |
| * 2016 | **DARIYAN** 4-9-2 | 10 |
| * 2017 | **CLOTH OF STARS** 4-9-2 | 7 |
| 2018 | **CRACKSMAN** 4-9-2 | 7 |
| 2019 | **WALDGEIST** 5-9-2 | 5 |
| ** 2020 | **SOTTSASS** 4-9-2 | 5 |

\* Run at Saint-Cloud
\*\* Run at Chantilly

## POULE D'ESSAI DES POULAINS (3y)
ParisLongchamp-1m
| | | |
|---|---|---|
| 2011 | **TIN HORSE** 9-2 | 14 |
| 2012 | **LUCAYAN** 9-2 | 12 |
| 2013 | **STYLE VENDOME** 9-2 | 18 |
| 2014 | **KARAKONTIE** 9-2 | 12 |
| 2015 | **MAKE BELIEVE** 9-2 | 18 |
| * 2016 | **THE GURKHA** 9-2 | 13 |
| * 2017 | **BRAMETOT** 9-2 | 13 |
| 2018 | **OLMEDO** 9-2 | 11 |
| 2019 | **PERSIAN KING** 9-2 | 10 |
| * 2020 | **VICTOR LUDORUM** 9-2 | 9 |

\* Run at Deauville

## POULE D'ESSAI DES POULICHES (3y fillies)
ParisLongchamp-1m
| | | |
|---|---|---|
| 2011 | **GOLDEN LILAC** 9-0 | 16 |
| 2012 | **BEAUTY PARLOUR** 9-0 | 13 |
| 2013 | **FLOTILLA** 9-0 | 20 |
| 2014 | **AVENIR CERTAIN** 9-0 | 16 |
| 2015 | **ERVEDYA** 9-0 | 14 |
| * 2016 | **LA CRESSONNIERE** 9-0 | 14 |
| * 2017 | **PRECIEUSE** 9-0 | 18 |
| 2018 | **TEPPAL** 9-0 | 14 |
| 2019 | **CASTLE LADY** 9-0 | 10 |
| * 2020 | **DREAM AND DO** 9-0 | 12 |

\* Run at Deauville

## PRIX SAINT-ALARY (3y fillies)
ParisLongchamp-1m 2f
| | | |
|---|---|---|
| 2011 | **WAVERING** 9-0 | 12 |
| 2012 | **SAGAWARA** 9-0 | 8 |
| 2013 | **SILASOL** 9-0 | 8 |
| * 2014 | **VAZIRA** 9-0 | 8 |
| 2015 | **QUEEN'S JEWEL** 9-0 | 9 |
| * 2016 | **JEMAYEL** 9-0 | 9 |
| 2017 | **SOBETSU** 9-0 | 11 |
| 2018 | **LAURENS** 9-0 | 5 |
| 2019 | **SIYARAFINA** 9-0 | 11 |
| * 2020 | **TAWKEEL** 9-0 | 7 |

\* We Are disqualified from first place
\* Run at Deauville
\* Run at Chantilly

## PRIX D'ISPAHAN
ParisLongchamp-1m 1f 55yds
| | | |
|---|---|---|
| 2011 | **GOLDIKOVA** 6-8-13 | 9 |
| 2012 | **GOLDEN LILAC** 4-8-13 | 8 |
| 2013 | **MAXIOS** 5-9-2 | 7 |
| 2014 | **CIRRUS DES AIGLES** 8-9-2 | 6 |
| 2015 | **SOLOW** 5-9-2 | 4 |
| * 2016 | **A SHIN HIKARI** 5-9-2 | 9 |
| * 2017 | **MEKHTAAL** 4-9-2 | 5 |
| 2018 | **RECOLETOS** 4-9-2 | 6 |
| 2019 | **ZABEEL PRINCE** 6-9-2 | 9 |
| * 2020 | **PERSIAN KING** 4-9-6 | 8 |

\* Run at Chantilly

## PRIX DU JOCKEY CLUB (3y)
Chantilly-1m 2f 110yds
| | | |
|---|---|---|
| 2011 | **RELIABLE MAN** 9-2 | 16 |
| 2012 | **SAONOIS** 9-2 | 20 |
| 2013 | **INTELLO** 9-2 | 19 |
| 2014 | **THE GREY GATSBY** 9-2 | 16 |
| 2015 | **NEW BAY** 9-2 | 14 |
| 2016 | **ALMANZOR** 9-2 | 16 |
| 2017 | **BRAMETOT** 9-2 | 12 |
| 2018 | **STUDY OF MAN** 9-2 | 16 |
| 2019 | **SOTTSASS** 9-3 | 15 |
| 2020 | **MISHRIFF** 9-2 | 16 |

## PRIX DE DIANE (3y fillies)
Chantilly-1m 2f 110yds
| | | |
|---|---|---|
| 2011 | **GOLDEN LILAC** 9-0 | 9 |
| 2012 | **VALYRA** 9-0 | 12 |
| 2013 | **TREVE** 9-0 | 11 |
| 2014 | **AVENIR CERTAIN** 9-0 | 12 |
| 2015 | **STAR OF SEVILLE** 9-0 | 17 |
| 2016 | **LA CRESSONNIERE** 9-0 | 16 |
| 2017 | **SENGA** 9-1 | 16 |
| 2018 | **LAURENS** 9-0 | 13 |
| 2019 | **CHANNEL** 9-0 | 16 |
| 2020 | **FANCY BLUE** 9-0 | 11 |

## GRAND PRIX DE SAINT-CLOUD
Saint-Cloud-1m 4f
| | | |
|---|---|---|
| 2011 | **SARAFINA** 4-8-13 | 5 |
| 2012 | **MEANDRE** 4-9-2 | 4 |
| 2013 | **NOVELLIST** 4-9-2 | 11 |
| * 2014 | **NOBLE MISSION** 5-9-2 | 7 |
| 2015 | **TREVE** 5-8-13 | 9 |
| 2016 | **SILVERWAVE** 4-9-2 | 11 |
| 2017 | **ZARAK** 4-9-2 | 10 |
| 2018 | **WALDGEIST** 4-9-3 | 6 |
| 2019 | **CORONET** 5-9-0 | 7 |
| 2020 | **WAY TO PARIS** 7-9-2 | 5 |

\* Spiritjim disqualified from first place

## PRIX JEAN PRAT (3y)
Chantilly-7f (1m before 2019)
| | | |
|---|---|---|
| 2011 | **MUTUAL TRUST** 9-2 | 7 |
| 2012 | **AESOP'S FABLES** 9-2 | 8 |
| 2013 | **HAVANA GOLD** 9-2 | 12 |

| 2014 | **CHARM SPIRIT** 9-2 | 7 |
| 2015 | **TERRITORIES** 9-2 | 8 |
| 2016 | **ZELZAL** 9-2 | 9 |
| 2017 | **THUNDER SNOW** 9-3 | 5 |
| 2018 | **INTELLOGENT** 9-2 | 7 |
| 2019 | **TOO DARN HOT** 9-2 | 12 |
| 2020 | **PINATUBO** 9-2 | 11 |

## GRAND PRIX DE PARIS (3y)
ParisLongchamp-1m 4f

| 2011 | **MEANDRE** 9-2 | 7 |
| 2012 | **IMPERIAL MONARCH** 9-2 | 9 |
| 2013 | **FLINTSHIRE** 9-2 | 8 |
| 2014 | **GALLANTE** 9-2 | 11 |
| 2015 | **ERUPT** 9-2 | 6 |
| * 2016 | **MONT ORMEL** 9-2 | 8 |
| * 2017 | **SHAKEEL** 9-2 | 9 |
| 2018 | **KEW GARDENS** 9-3 | 6 |
| 2019 | **JAPAN** 9-2 | 8 |
| 2020 | **MOGUL** 9-3 | 10 |

* Run at Saint-Cloud

## PRIX ROTHSCHILD
## (fillies and mares)
Deauville-1m
(run as Prix d'Astarte before 2008)

| 2011 | **GOLDIKOVA** 6-9-2 | 8 |
| 2012 | **ELUSIVE KATE** 3-8-9 | 5 |
| 2013 | **ELUSIVE KATE** 4-9-2 | 12 |
| 2014 | **ESOTERIQUE** 4-9-2 | 4 |
| 2015 | **AMAZING MARIA** 4-9-2 | 8 |
| 2016 | **QEMAH** 3-8-9 | 10 |
| 2017 | **ROLY POLY** 3-8-9 | 10 |
| 2018 | **WITH YOU** 3-8-9 | 10 |
| 2019 | **LAURENS** 4-9-3 | 9 |
| 2020 | **WATCH ME** 4-9-4 | 6 |

## PRIX MAURICE DE GHEEST
Deauville-6f 110yds

| 2011 | **MOONLIGHT CLOUD** 3-8-8 | 13 |
| 2012 | **MOONLIGHT CLOUD** 4-8-13 | 9 |
| 2013 | **MOONLIGHT CLOUD** 5-8-13 | 14 |
| 2014 | **GARSWOOD** 4-9-2 | 14 |
| 2015 | **MUHAARAR** 3-8-11 | 12 |
| 2016 | **SIGNS OF BLESSING** 5-9-2 | 15 |
| 2017 | **BRANDO** 5-9-3 | 13 |
| 2018 | **POLYDREAM** 3-8-10 | 20 |
| 2019 | **ADVERTISE** 3-8-13 | 15 |
| 2020 | **SPACE BLUES** 4-9-4 | 11 |

## PRIX JACQUES LE MAROIS
Deauville-1m

| 2011 | **IMMORTAL VERSE** 3-8-8 | 12 |
| 2012 | **EXCELEBRATION** 4-9-4 | 11 |
| 2013 | **MOONLIGHT CLOUD** 5-9-1 | 13 |
| 2014 | **KINGMAN** 3-8-13 | 5 |
| 2015 | **ESOTERIQUE** 5-9-1 | 9 |
| 2016 | **RIBCHESTER** 3-8-13 | 11 |
| 2017 | **AL WUKAIR** 3-8-13 | 6 |
| 2018 | **ALPHA CENTAURI** 3-8-9 | 11 |
| 2019 | **ROMANISED** 4-9-5 | 8 |
| 2020 | **PALACE PIER** 3-8-13 | 7 |

## PRIX MORNY (2y)
Deauville-6f

| 2011 | **DABIRSIM** 9-0 | 7 |
| 2012 | **RECKLESS ABANDON** 9-0 | 11 |
| 2013 | **NO NAY NEVER** 9-0 | 10 |
| 2014 | **THE WOW SIGNAL** 9-0 | 9 |
| 2015 | **SHALAA** 9-0 | 5 |
| 2016 | **LADY AURELIA** 8-10 | 5 |
| 2017 | **UNFORTUNATELY** 9-0 | 8 |
| 2018 | **PRETTY POLLYANNA** 8-10 | 9 |
| 2019 | **EARTHLIGHT** 9-0 | 8 |
| 2020 | **CAMPANELLE** 8-10 | 9 |

## PRIX JEAN ROMANET
## (fillies and mares)
Deauville-1m 2f

| 2011 | **ANNOUNCE** 4-9-0 | 5 |
| * 2012 | **IZZI TOP** 4-9-0 | 8 |
| 2013 | **ROMANTICA** 4-9-0 | 6 |
| 2014 | **RIBBONS** 4-9-0 | 11 |
| 2015 | **ODELIZ** 5-9-0 | 11 |
| 2016 | **SPEEDY BOARDING** 4-9-0 | 10 |
| 2017 | **AJMAN PRINCESS** 4-9-0 | 10 |
| 2018 | **NONZA** 4-9-0 | 9 |
| 2019 | **CORONET** 5-9-0 | 8 |
| 2020 | **AUDARYA** 4-9-0 | 11 |

* Snow Fairy disqualified from first place

## PRIX DU MOULIN DE LONGCHAMP
ParisLongchamp-1m

| 2011 | **EXCELEBRATION** 3-8-11 | 8 |
| 2012 | **MOONLIGHT CLOUD** 4-8-13 | 4 |
| 2013 | **MAXIOS** 5-9-2 | 7 |
| 2014 | **CHARM SPIRIT** 3-8-11 | 10 |
| 2015 | **ERVEDYA** 3-8-9 | 6 |
| * 2016 | **VADAMOS** 5-9-2 | 6 |
| * 2017 | **RIBCHESTER** 4-9-3 | 7 |
| 2018 | **RECOLETOS** 3-8-11 | 11 |
| 2019 | **CIRCUS MAXIMUS** 3-8-13 | 10 |
| 2020 | **PERSIAN KING** 4-9-3 | 6 |

* Run at Chantilly

## PRIX VERMEILLE (fillies and mares)
ParisLongchamp-1m 4f

| 2011 | **GALIKOVA** 3-8-8 | 6 |
| 2012 | **SHARETA** 4-9-2 | 13 |
| 2013 | **TREVE** 3-8-8 | 10 |
| 2014 | **BALTIC BARONESS** 4-9-3 | 9 |
| 2015 | **TREVE** 5-9-3 | 9 |
| * 2016 | **LEFT HAND** 3-8-8 | 6 |
| * 2017 | **BATEEL** 5-9-3 | 11 |
| 2018 | **KITESURF** 4-9-3 | 8 |
| 2019 | **STAR CATCHER** 3-8-9 | 9 |
| 2020 | **TARNAWA** 4-9-5 | 10 |

* Run at Chantilly

## PRIX DE LA FORET
ParisLongchamp-7f

| 2011 | **DREAM AHEAD** 3-9-0 | 8 |
| 2012 | **GORDON LORD BYRON** 4-9-2 | 11 |
| 2013 | **MOONLIGHT CLOUD** 5-8-13 | 11 |
| 2014 | **OLYMPIC GLORY** 4-9-2 | 14 |
| 2015 | **MAKE BELIEVE** 3-9-0 | 13 |
| * 2016 | **LIMATO** 4-9-2 | 11 |
| * 2017 | **ACLAIM** 4-9-2 | 10 |
| 2018 | **ONE MASTER** 4-8-13 | 15 |

| 2019 | **ONE MASTER** 5-8-13 | 12 |
| 2020 | **ONE MASTER** 6-8-13 | 9 |

\* Run at Chantilly

## PRIX DU CADRAN
ParisLongchamp-2m 4f

| 2011 | **KASBAH BLISS** 9-9-2 | 10 |
| 2012 | **MOLLY MALONE** 4-8-13 | 10 |
| 2013 | **ALTANO** 7-9-2 | 10 |
| 2014 | **HIGH JINX** 6-9-2 | 8 |
| 2015 | **MILLE ET MILLE** 5-9-2 | 10 |
| \* 2016 | **QUEST FOR MORE** 6-9-2 | 12 |
| \* 2017 | **VAZIRABAD** 5-9-2 | 6 |
| 2018 | **CALL THE WIND** 4-9-2 | 8 |
| 2019 | **HOLDTHASIGREEN** 7-9-2 | 10 |
| 2020 | **PRINCESS ZOE** 5-8-13 | 9 |

\* Run at Chantilly

## PRIX DE L'ABBAYE DE LONGCHAMP
ParisLongchamp-5f

| 2011 | **TANGERINE TREES** 6-9-11 | 15 |
| 2012 | **WIZZ KID** 4-9-7 | 18 |
| 2013 | **MAAREK** 6-9-11 | 20 |
| 2014 | **MOVE IN TIME** 6-9-11 | 18 |
| 2015 | **GOLDREAM** 6-9-11 | 18 |
| \* 2016 | **MARSHA** 3-9--7 | 17 |
| \* 2017 | **BATTAASH** 3-9-11 | 13 |
| 2018 | **MABS CROSS** 4-9-7 | 16 |
| 2019 | **GLASS SLIPPERS** 3-9-7 | 16 |
| 2020 | **WOODED** 3-9-11 | 11 |

\* Run at Chantilly

## PRIX JEAN-LUC LAGARDERE (2y)
ParisLongchamp-1m (7f before 2015)

| 2011 | **DABIRSIM** 9-0 | 7 |
| 2012 | **OLYMPIC GLORY** 9-0 | 8 |
| 2013 | **KARAKONTIE** 9-0 | 8 |
| \* 2014 | **FULL MAST** 9-0 | 9 |
| 2015 | **ULTRA** 9-0 | 11 |
| \*\* 2016 | **NATIONAL DEFENSE** 9-0 | 7 |
| \*\* 2017 | **HAPPILY** 8-10 | 6 |
| 2018 | **ROYAL MARINE** 9-0 | 6 |
| 2019 | **VICTOR LUDORUM** 9-0 | 7 |
| 2020 | **SEALIWAY** 9-0 | 5 |

\* Gleneagles disqualified from first place
\*\* Run at ParisLongchamp

## PRIX MARCEL BOUSSAC (2y fillies)
ParisLongchamp-1m

| 2011 | **ELUSIVE KATE** 8-11 | 5 |
| 2012 | **SILASOL** 8-11 | 9 |
| 2013 | **INDONESIENNE** 8-11 | 12 |
| 2014 | **FOUND** 8-11 | 12 |
| 2015 | **BALLYDOYLE** 8-11 | 8 |
| \* 2016 | **WUHEIDA** 8-11 | 11 |
| \* 2017 | **WILD ILLUSION** 8-11 | 7 |
| 2018 | **LILY'S CANDLE** 8-11 | 8 |
| 2019 | **ALBIGNA** 8-11 | 9 |
| 2020 | **TIGER TANAKA** 8-11 | 12 |

\* Run at Chantilly

## PRIX DE L'OPERA (fillies and mares)
ParisLongchamp-1m 2f

| 2011 | **NAHRAIN** 3-8-11 | 10 |
| 2012 | **RIDASIYNA** 3-8-11 | 13 |
| 2013 | **DALKALA** 4-9-2 | 9 |
| 2014 | **WE ARE** 3-8-11 | 11 |
| 2015 | **COVERT LOVE** 3-8-11 | 13 |
| \* 2016 | **SPEEDY BOARDING** 4-9-2 | 7 |
| \* 2017 | **RHODODENDRON** 3-8-11 | 13 |
| 2018 | **WILD ILLUSION** 3-8-11 | 15 |
| 2019 | **VILLA MARINA** 3-8-11 | 12 |
| 2020 | **TARNAWA** 4-9-2 | 12 |

\* Run at Chantilly

## PRIX ROYAL-OAK
ParisLongchamp-1m 7f 110yds

| 2011 | **BE FABULOUS** 4-9-1 | 14 |
| 2012 | **LES BEAUFS** 3-8-9 | 9 |
| 2013 | **TAC DE BOISTRON** 6-9-4 | 15 |
| 2014 | **TAC DE BOISTRON** 7-9-4 | 13 |
| 2015 | **VAZIRABAD** 3-8-10 | 13 |
| \* 2016 | **VAZIRABAD** 4-9-4 | 15 |
| \*\* 2017 | **ICE BREEZE** 3-8-10 | 9 |
| 2018 | **HOLDTHASIGREEN** 6-9-4 | 8 |
| 2019 | **TECHNICIAN** 3-8-10 | 6 |
| 2020 | **SUBJECTIVIST** 3-8-10 | 8 |

\* Run at Chantilly
\*\* Run at Saint-Cloud

## CRITERIUM INTERNATIONAL (2y)
Saint-Cloud-1m (7f 2015-2019)

| 2011 | **FRENCH FIFTEEN** 9-0 | 11 |
| 2012 | **LOCH GARMAN** 9-0 | 6 |
| 2013 | **ECTOT** 9-0 | 4 |
| 2014 | **VERT DE GRECE** 9-0 | 9 |
| 2015 | **JOHANNES VERMEER** 9-0 | 8 |
| 2016 | **THUNDER SNOW** 9-0 | 9 |
| 2017 | ABANDONED | |
| \* 2018 | **ROYAL MEETING** 9-0 | 6 |
| \*\* 2019 | **ALSON** 9-0 | 2 |
| 2020 | **VAN GOGH** 9-0 | 6 |

\* Run at Chantilly
\*\* Run at ParisLongchamp

## CRITERIUM DE SAINT-CLOUD (2y)
Saint-Cloud-1m 2f

| 2011 | **MANDAEAN** 9-0 | 8 |
| 2012 | **MORANDI** 9-0 | 8 |
| 2013 | **PRINCE GIBRALTAR** 9-0 | 12 |
| 2014 | **EPICURIS** 9-0 | 6 |
| 2015 | **ROBIN OF NAVAN** 9-0 | 10 |
| 2016 | **WALDGEIST** 9-0 | 13 |
| 2017 | ABANDONED | |
| 2018 | **WONDERMENT** 8-10 | 9 |
| 2019 | **MKFANCY** 9-0 | 8 |
| 2020 | **GEAR UP** 9-0 | 7 |

# WINNERS OF OTHER OVERSEAS RACES

## DUBAI WORLD CUP
Meydan-1m 2f Tapeta
| | | |
|---|---|---|
| 2011 | **VICTOIRE PISA** 4-9-0 | 14 |
| 2012 | **MONTEROSSO** 5-9-0 | 13 |
| 2013 | **ANIMAL KINGDOM** 5-9-0 | 13 |
| 2014 | **AFRICAN STORY** 7-9-0 | 16 |
| 2015 | **PRINCE BISHOP** 8-9-0 | 9 |
| 2016 | **CALIFORNIA CHROME** 5-9-0 | 12 |
| 2017 | **ARROGATE** 4-9-0 | 14 |
| 2018 | **THUNDER SNOW** 4-9-0 | 10 |
| 2019 | **THUNDER SNOW** 5-9-0 | 12 |
| 2020 | RACE CANCELLED | |

## KENTUCKY DERBY
Churchill Downs-1m 2f dirt
| | | |
|---|---|---|
| 2011 | **ANIMAL KINGDOM** 9-0 | 19 |
| 2012 | **I'LL HAVE ANOTHER** 9-0 | 20 |
| 2013 | **ORB** 9-0 | 19 |
| 2014 | **CALIFORNIA CHROME** 9-0 | 19 |
| 2015 | **AMERICAN PHAROAH** 9-0 | 18 |
| 2016 | **NYQUIST** 9-0 | 20 |
| 2017 | **ALWAYS DREAMING** 9-0 | 20 |
| 2018 | **JUSTIFY** 9-0 | 20 |
| * 2019 | **COUNTRY HOUSE** 9-0 | 19 |
| 2020 | **AUTHENTIC** 9-0 | 15 |

* Maximum Security disqualified from first place

## BREEDERS' CUP TURF
Various courses-1m 4f
| | | |
|---|---|---|
| 2011 | **ST NICHOLAS ABBEY** 4-9-0 | 9 |
| 2012 | **LITTLE MIKE** 5-9-0 | 12 |
| 2013 | **MAGICIAN** 3-8-10 | 12 |
| 2014 | **MAIN SEQUENCE** 5-9-0 | 12 |
| 2015 | **FOUND** 3-8-7 | 12 |
| 2016 | **HIGHLAND REEL** 4-9-0 | 12 |
| 2017 | **TALISMANIC** 4-9-0 | 13 |
| 2018 | **ENABLE** 4-8-11 | 13 |
| 2019 | **BRICKS AND MORTAR** 5-9-0 | 12 |
| 2020 | **TARNAWA** 4-8-11 | 10 |

## BREEDERS' CUP CLASSIC
Various courses-1m 2f dirt
| | | |
|---|---|---|
| 2011 | **DROSSELMEYER** 4-9-0 | 12 |
| 2012 | **FORT LARNED** 4-9-0 | 12 |
| 2013 | **MUCHO MACHO MAN** 5-9-0 | 11 |
| 2014 | **BAYERN** 3-8-10 | 14 |
| 2015 | **AMERICAN PHAROAH** 3-8-10 | 8 |
| 2016 | **ARROGATE** 3-8-10 | 9 |
| 2017 | **GUN RUNNER** 4-9-0 | 11 |
| 2018 | **ACCELERATE** 5-9-0 | 14 |
| 2019 | **VINO ROSSO** 4-9-0 | 11 |
| 2020 | **AUTHENTIC** 3-8-10 | 10 |

## MELBOURNE CUP
Flemington-2m
| | | |
|---|---|---|
| 2011 | **DUNADEN** 5-8-8 | 23 |
| 2012 | **GREEN MOON** 5-8-6 | 24 |
| 2013 | **FIORENTE** 5-8-9 | 24 |
| 2014 | **PROTECTIONIST** 4-8-13 | 22 |
| 2015 | **PRINCE OF PENZANCE** 6-8-5 | 24 |
| 2016 | **ALMANDIN** 6-8-3 | 24 |
| 2017 | **REKINDLING** 3-8-2 | 23 |
| 2018 | **CROSS COUNTER** 3-8-0 | 24 |
| 2019 | **VOW AND DECLARE** 4-8-3 | 24 |
| 2020 | **TWILIGHT PAYMENT** 7-8-10 | 23 |

## JAPAN CUP
Tokyo-1m 4f
| | | |
|---|---|---|
| 2011 | **BUENA VISTA** 5-8-9 | 16 |
| 2012 | **GENTILDONNA** 3-8-5 | 17 |
| 2013 | **GENTILDONNA** 4-8-9 | 17 |
| 2014 | **EPIPHANEIA** 4-9-0 | 18 |
| 2015 | **SHONAN PANDORA** 4-8-9 | 18 |
| 2016 | **KITASAN BLACK** 4-9-0 | 17 |
| 2017 | **CHEVAL GRAND** 5-9-0 | 17 |
| 2018 | **ALMOND EYE** 3-8-5 | 14 |
| 2019 | **SUAVE RICHARD** 5-9-0 | 15 |
| 2020 | **ALMOND EYE** 5-8-9 | 15 |

# WINNERS OF PRINCIPAL NATIONAL HUNT RACES

## PADDY POWER GOLD CUP (HANDICAP CHASE)
Cheltenham-2m 4f 78yds
(BetVictor Gold Cup before 2020)
| | | |
|---|---|---|
| 2011 | **GREAT ENDEAVOUR** 7-10-3 | 20 |
| 2012 | **AL FEROF** 7-11-8 | 18 |
| 2013 | **JOHNS SPIRIT** 6-10-2 | 20 |
| 2014 | **CAID DU BERLAIS** 5-10-13 | 18 |
| 2015 | **ANNACOTTY** 7-11-0 | 20 |
| 2016 | **TAQUIN DU SEUIL** 9-11-11 | 17 |
| 2017 | **SPLASH OF GINGE** 9-10-6 | 17 |

| | | |
|---|---|---|
| 2018 | **BARON ALCO** 7-10-11 | 18 |
| 2019 | **HAPPY DIVA** 8-11-0 | 17 |
| 2020 | **COOLE CODY** 9-10-5 | 16 |

## BETFAIR CHASE
Haydock-3m 1f 125yds (3m 24yds before 2017)
| | | |
|---|---|---|
| 2011 | **KAUTO STAR** 11-11-7 | 6 |
| 2012 | **SILVINIACO CONTI** 6-11-7 | 5 |
| 2013 | **CUE CARD** 7-11-7 | 8 |
| 2014 | **SILVINIACO CONTI** 8-11-7 | 9 |
| 2015 | **CUE CARD** 9-11-7 | 5 |

2016 **CUE CARD** 10-11-7 ...................................................6
2017 **BRISTOL DE MAI** 6-11-7 .........................................5
2018 **BRISTOL DE MAI** 7-11-7 .........................................6
2019 **LOSTINTRANSLATION** 7-11-7 ...............................4
2020 **BRISTOL DE MAI** 9-11-7 .........................................5

## LADBROKES TROPHY HANDICAP CHASE

Newbury-3m 1f 214yds
(Run as Hennessy Gold Cup before 2017)

2011 **CARRUTHERS** 8-10-4 .............................................18
2012 **BOBS WORTH** 7-11-6 ............................................19
2013 **TRIOLO D'ALENE** 6-11-1 .......................................21
2014 **MANY CLOUDS** 7-11-6 ..........................................19
2015 **SMAD PLACE** 8-11-4 ............................................15
2016 **NATIVE RIVER** 6-11-1 ...........................................19
2017 **TOTAL RECALL** 8-10-8 ..........................................20
2018 **SIZING TENNESSEE** 10-11-3 ................................12
2019 **DE RASHER COUNTER** 7-10-10 ...........................24
2020 **CLOTH CAP** 8-10-0 ...............................................18

## TINGLE CREEK CHASE

Sandown-2m

2011 **SIZING EUROPE** 9-11-7 ...........................................7
2012 **SPRINTER SACRE** 6-11-7 ........................................7
2013 **SIRE DE GRUGY** 7-11-7 ..........................................9
2014 **DODGING BULLETS** 6-11-7 ................................10
2015 **SIRE DE GRUGY** 9-11-7 .........................................8
2016 **UN DE SCEAUX** 8-11-7 ..........................................6
2017 **POLITOLOGUE** 6-11-7 ...........................................6
2018 **ALTIOR** 8-11-7 .......................................................4
2019 **DEFI DU SEUIL** 6-11-7 ...........................................8
2020 **POLITOLOGUE** 9-11-7 ...........................................5

## CHRISTMAS HURDLE

Kempton-2m

2011 **BINOCULAR** 7-11-7 .................................................5
2012 **DARLAN** 5-11-7 .......................................................7
2013 **MY TENT OR YOURS** 6-11-7 .................................6
2014 **FAUGHEEN** 6-11-7 ................................................6
2015 **FAUGHEEN** 7-11-7 ................................................5
2016 **YANWORTH** 6-11-7 ...............................................5
2017 **BUVEUR D'AIR** 6-11-7 ...........................................4
2018 **VERDANA BLUE** 6-11-0 .........................................5
2019 **EPATANTE** 5-11-0 ...............................................10
2020 **SILVER STREAK** 7-11-7 .........................................5

## KING GEORGE VI CHASE

Kempton-3m

2011 **KAUTO STAR** 11-11-10 ...........................................7
2012 **LONG RUN** 7-11-10 ................................................9
2013 **SILVINIACO CONTI** 7-11-10 ................................10
2014 **SILVINIACO CONTI** 8-11-10 ................................10
2015 **CUE CARD** 9-11-10 ................................................9
2016 **THISTLECRACK** 8-11-10 ........................................8
2017 **MIGHT BITE** 8-11-10 .............................................5
2018 **CLAN DES OBEAUX** 6-11-10 ..............................10
2019 **CLAN DES OBEAUX** 7-11-10 ................................5
2020 **FRODON** 8-11-10 ...................................................9

## WELSH GRAND NATIONAL (HANDICAP CHASE)

Chepstow-3m 5f 110yds

2011 **LE BEAU BAI** 8-10-1 .............................................20
* 2012 **MONBEG DUDE** 8-10-1 .........................................17
2013 **MOUNTAINOUS** 8-10-0 .......................................20
2014 **EMPEROR'S CHOICE** 7-10-8 ..............................19
** 2015 **MOUNTAINOUS** 11-10-6 .....................................20
2016 **NATIVE RIVER** 6-11-12 ........................................20
*** 2017 **RAZ DE MAREE** 13-10-10 ...................................20
2018 **ELEGANT ESCAPE** 6-11-8 ..................................20
2019 **POTTERS CORNER** 9-10-4 ................................17
**** 2020 **SECRET REPRIEVE** 7-10-1 ...................................18
* Run in January 2013
** Run in January 2016
*** Run in January 2018
**** Run in January 2021

## CLARENCE HOUSE CHASE

(Victor Chandler Chase before 2014)
Ascot-2m 167yds

2012 **SOMERSBY** 8-11-7 .................................................8
* 2013 **SPRINTER SACRE** 7-11-7 ........................................7
2014 **SIRE DE GRUGY** 8-11-7 ..........................................7
2015 **DODGING BULLETS** 7-11-7 ..................................5
2016 **UN DE SCEAUX** 8-11-7 ..........................................5
* 2017 **UN DE SCEAUX** 9-11-7 ..........................................7
2018 **UN DE SCEAUX** 10-11-7 ........................................5
2019 **ALTIOR** 9-11-7 .......................................................3
2020 **DEFI DU SEUIL** 7-11-7 ...........................................5
2021 **FIRST FLOW** 9-11-7 ...............................................8
* Run at Cheltenham

## BETFAIR HANDICAP HURDLE

Newbury-2m 69yds(Totesport Trophy before 2012)

2011 **RECESSION PROOF** 5-10-8 ................................15
2012 **ZARKANDAR** 5-11-1 ............................................20
2013 **MY TENT OR YOURS** 6-11-2 ..............................21
2014 **SPLASH OF GINGE** 6-10-3 ................................20
2015 **VIOLET DANCER** 5-10-9 .....................................23
2016 **AGRAPART** 5-10-5 ................................................21
2017 **BALLYANDY** 6-11-1 ..............................................16
2018 **KALASHNIKOV** 5-11-5 .........................................24
* 2019 **AL DANCER** 6-11-8 ..............................................14
2020 **PIC D'ORHY** 5-11-5 ..............................................24
* run at Ascot over 1m 7 1/8f

## SUPREME NOVICES' HURDLE

Cheltenham-2m 87yds

2011 **AL FEROF** 6-11-7 ..................................................15
2012 **CINDERS AND ASHES** 5-11-7 ............................19
2013 **CHAMPAGNE FEVER** 6-11-7 ..............................12
2014 **VAUTOUR** 5-11-7 .................................................18
2015 **DOUVAN** 5-11-7 ...................................................14
2016 **ALTIOR** 6-11-7 .....................................................14
2017 **LABAIK** 6-11-7 .......................................................9
2018 **SUMMERVILLE BOY** 6-11-7 ..............................19
2019 **KLASSICAL DREAM** 5-11-7 ................................16
2020 **SHISHKIN** 6-11-7 .................................................15

## ARKLE CHALLENGE TROPHY (NOVICES' CHASE)
Cheltenham-1m 7f 199yds
| | | |
|---|---|---|
| 2011 | CAPTAIN CHRIS 7-11-7 | 10 |
| 2012 | SPRINTER SACRE 6-11-7 | 6 |
| 2013 | SIMONSIG 7-11-7 | 7 |
| 2014 | WESTERN WARHORSE 6-11-4 | 9 |
| 2015 | UN DE SCEAUX 7-11-4 | 11 |
| 2016 | DOUVAN 6-11-4 | 7 |
| 2017 | ALTIOR 7-11-4 | 9 |
| 2018 | FOOTPAD 6-11-4 | 5 |
| 2019 | DUC DES GENIEVRES 6-11-4 | 12 |
| 2020 | PUT THE KETTLE ON 6-10-11 | 11 |

## CHAMPION HURDLE
Cheltenham-2m 87yds
| | | |
|---|---|---|
| 2011 | HURRICANE FLY 7-11-10 | 11 |
| 2012 | ROCK ON RUBY 7-11-10 | 10 |
| 2013 | HURRICANE FLY 9-11-10 | 9 |
| 2014 | JEZKI 6-11-10 | 9 |
| 2015 | FAUGHEEN 7-11-10 | 8 |
| 2016 | ANNIE POWER 8-11-3 | 12 |
| 2017 | BUVEUR D'AIR 6-11-10 | 11 |
| 2018 | BUVEUR D'AIR 7-11-10 | 11 |
| 2019 | ESPOIR D'ALLEN 5-11-10 | 10 |
| 2020 | EPATANTE 6-11-3 | 17 |

## QUEEN MOTHER CHAMPION CHASE
Cheltenham-1m 7f 199yds
| | | |
|---|---|---|
| 2011 | SIZING EUROPE 9-11-10 | 11 |
| 2012 | FINIAN'S RAINBOW 9-11-10 | 8 |
| 2013 | SPRINTER SACRE 7-11-10 | 7 |
| 2014 | SIRE DE GRUGY 8-11-10 | 11 |
| 2015 | DODGING BULLETS 7-11-10 | 11 |
| 2016 | SPRINTER SACRE 10-11-10 | 10 |
| 2017 | SPECIAL TIARA 10-11-10 | 10 |
| 2018 | ALTIOR 8-11-10 | 9 |
| 2019 | ALTIOR 9-11-10 | 10 |
| 2020 | POLITOLOGUE 9-11-10 | 5 |

## BALLYMORE NOVICES' HURDLE
Cheltenham-2m 5f 26yds
| | | |
|---|---|---|
| 2011 | FIRST LIEUTENANT 6-11-7 | 12 |
| 2012 | SIMONSIG 6-11-7 | 17 |
| 2013 | THE NEW ONE 5-11-7 | 8 |
| 2014 | FAUGHEEN 6-11-7 | 15 |
| 2015 | WINDSOR PARK 6-11-7 | 10 |
| 2016 | YORKHILL 6-11-7 | 11 |
| 2017 | WILLOUGHBY COURT 6-11-7 | 15 |
| 2018 | SAMCRO 6-11-7 | 14 |
| 2019 | CITY ISLAND 6-11-7 | 16 |
| 2020 | ENVOI ALLEN 6-11-7 | 12 |

## RSA CHASE
(Royal & SunAlliance Chase before 2009)
Cheltenham-3m 80yds
| | | |
|---|---|---|
| 2011 | BOSTONS ANGEL 7-11-4 | 12 |
| 2012 | BOBS WORTH 7-11-4 | 9 |
| 2013 | LORD WINDERMERE 7-11-4 | 11 |
| 2014 | O'FAOLAINS BOY 7-11-4 | 15 |
| 2015 | DON POLI 6-11-4 | 8 |
| 2016 | BLAKLION 7-11-4 | 8 |
| 2017 | MIGHT BITE 8-11-4 | 12 |
| 2018 | PRESENTING PERCY 7-11-4 | 10 |
| 2019 | TOPOFTHEGAME 7-11-4 | 12 |
| 2020 | CHAMP 8-11-4 | 10 |

## STAYERS' HURDLE
(World Hurdle before 2017)
Cheltenham-2m 7f 213yds
| | | |
|---|---|---|
| 2011 | BIG BUCK'S 8-11-10 | 13 |
| 2012 | BIG BUCK'S 9-11-10 | 11 |
| 2013 | SOLWHIT 9-11-10 | 13 |
| 2014 | MORE OF THAT 6-11-10 | 10 |
| 2015 | COLE HARDEN 6-11-10 | 16 |
| 2016 | THISTLECRACK 8-11-10 | 12 |
| 2017 | NICHOLS CANYON 7-11-10 | 12 |
| 2018 | PENHILL 7-11-10 | 15 |
| 2019 | PAISLEY PARK 7-11-10 | 18 |
| 2020 | LISNAGAR OSCAR 7-11-10 | 15 |

## TRIUMPH HURDLE (4y)
Cheltenham-2m 179yds
| | | |
|---|---|---|
| 2011 | ZARKANDAR 11-0 | 23 |
| 2012 | COUNTRYWIDE FLAME 11-0 | 20 |
| 2013 | OUR CONOR 11-0 | 17 |
| 2014 | TIGER ROLL 11-0 | 15 |
| 2015 | PEACE AND CO 11-0 | 16 |
| 2016 | IVANOVICH GORBATOV 11-0 | 15 |
| 2017 | DEFI DU SEUIL 11-0 | 15 |
| 2018 | FARCLAS 11-0 | 9 |
| 2019 | PENTLAND HILLS 11-0 | 14 |
| 2020 | BURNING VICTORY 10-7 | 13 |

## CHELTENHAM GOLD CUP
Cheltenham-3m 2f 110yds
| | | |
|---|---|---|
| 2011 | LONG RUN 6-11-0 | 13 |
| 2012 | SYNCHRONISED 9-11-10 | 14 |
| 2013 | BOBS WORTH 8-11-10 | 9 |
| 2014 | LORD WINDERMERE 8-11-10 | 13 |
| 2015 | CONEYGREE 8-11-10 | 16 |
| 2016 | DON COSSACK 9-11-10 | 9 |
| 2017 | SIZING JOHN 7-11-10 | 13 |
| 2018 | NATIVE RIVER 8-11-10 | 15 |
| 2019 | AL BOUM PHOTO 7-11-10 | 16 |
| 2020 | AL BOUM PHOTO 8-11-10 | 12 |

## RYANAIR CHASE (FESTIVAL TROPHY)
Cheltenham-2m 4f 166yds
| | | |
|---|---|---|
| 2011 | ALBERTAS RUN 10-11-10 | 11 |
| 2012 | RIVERSIDE THEATRE 8-11-10 | 12 |
| 2013 | CUE CARD 7-11-10 | 8 |
| 2014 | DYNASTE 8-11-10 | 11 |
| 2015 | UXIZANDRE 7-11-10 | 14 |
| 2016 | VAUTOUR 7-11-10 | 15 |
| 2017 | UN DE SCEAUX 9-11-10 | 8 |
| 2018 | BALKO DES FLOS 7-11-10 | 6 |
| 2019 | FRODON 7-11-10 | 12 |
| 2020 | MIN 9-11-10 | 8 |

## BOWL CHASE
Aintree-3m 210yds
| | | |
|---|---|---|
| 2011 | NACARAT 10-11-7 | 6 |
| 2012 | FOLLOW THE PLAN 9-11-7 | 11 |
| 2013 | FIRST LIEUTENANT 8-11-7 | 8 |
| 2014 | SILVINIACO CONTI 8-11-7 | 6 |
| 2015 | SILVINIACO CONTI 9-11-7 | 7 |
| 2016 | CUE CARD 10-11-7 | 9 |
| 2017 | TEA FOR TWO 8-11-7 | 7 |
| 2018 | MIGHT BITE 9-11-7 | 8 |
| 2019 | KEMBOY 7-11-7 | 6 |
| 2020 | RACE CANCELLED | |

## MELLING CHASE
Aintree-2m 3f 200yds

| | | |
|---|---|---|
| 2011 | **MASTER MINDED** 8-11-10 | 10 |
| 2012 | **FINIAN'S RAINBOW** 9-11-10 | 8 |
| 2013 | **SPRINTER SACRE** 7-11-10 | 6 |
| 2014 | **BOSTON BOB** 9-11-10 | 10 |
| 2015 | **DON COSSACK** 8-11-10 | 10 |
| 2016 | **GOD'S OWN** 8-11-10 | 6 |
| 2017 | **FOX NORTON** 7-11-7 | 9 |
| 2018 | **POLITOLOGUE** 7-11-7 | 6 |
| 2019 | **MIN** 8-11-7 | 6 |
| 2020 | RACE CANCELLED | |

## AINTREE HURDLE
Aintree-2m 4f

| | | |
|---|---|---|
| 2011 | **OSCAR WHISKY** 6-11-7 | 8 |
| 2012 | **OSCAR WHISKY** 7-11-7 | 5 |
| 2013 | **ZARKANDAR** 6-11-7 | 9 |
| 2014 | **THE NEW ONE** 6-11-7 | 7 |
| 2015 | **JEZKI** 7-11-7 | 6 |
| 2016 | **ANNIE POWER** 8-11-0 | 6 |
| 2017 | **BUVEUR D'AIR** 6-11-7 | 6 |
| 2018 | **L'AMI SERGE** 8-11-7 | 9 |
| 2019 | **SUPASUNDAE** 9-11-7 | 7 |
| 2020 | RACE CANCELLED | |

## SCOTTISH GRAND NATIONAL (H'CAP CHASE)
Ayr-3m 7f 176 yds

| | | |
|---|---|---|
| 2011 | **BESHABAR** 9-10-4 | 28 |
| 2012 | **MERIGO** 11-10-2 | 24 |
| 2013 | **GODSMEJUDGE** 7-11-3 | 24 |
| 2014 | **AL CO** 9-10-0 | 29 |
| 2015 | **WAYWARD PRINCE** 11-10-1 | 29 |
| 2016 | **VICENTE** 7-11-3 | 28 |
| 2017 | **VICENTE** 8-11-10 | 30 |
| 2018 | **JOE FARRELL** 9-10-6 | 29 |
| 2019 | **TAKINGRISKS** 10-10-1 | 23 |
| 2020 | RACE CANCELLED | |

## BET365 GOLD CUP (H'CAP CHASE)
Sandown-3m 4f 166yds

| | | |
|---|---|---|
| 2011 | **POKER DE SIVOLA** 8-10-12 | 18 |
| 2012 | **TIDAL BAY** 11-11-12 | 19 |
| 2013 | **QUENTIN COLLONGES** 9-10-12 | 19 |
| 2014 | **HADRIAN'S APPROACH** 7-11-0 | 19 |
| 2015 | **JUST A PAR** 8-10-0 | 20 |
| 2016 | **THE YOUNG MASTER** 7-10-12 | 20 |
| 2017 | **HENLLAN HARRI** 9-10-0 | 13 |
| 2018 | **STEP BACK** 8-10-0 | 20 |
| 2019 | **TALKISCHEAP** 7-10-11 | 15 |
| 2020 | RACE CANCELLED | |

# DISTANCE CONVERSION

| | | | |
|---|---|---|---|
| 5f ............... 1,000m | 10f ............... 2,000m | 15f ............... 3,000m | 20f ............... 4,000m |
| 6f ............... 1,200m | 11f ............... 2,200m | 16f ............... 3,200m | 21f ............... 4,200m |
| 7f ............... 1,400m | 12f ............... 2,400m | 17f ............... 3,400m | 22f ............... 4,400m |
| 8f ............... 1,600m | 13f ............... 2,600m | 18f ............... 3,600m | |
| 9f ............... 1,800m | 14f ............... 2,800m | 19f ............... 3,800m | |

# RACING POST
## MEMBERS' CLUB

**What our current members are saying about**

**Video Replays**

*I use the race video replay facility to review a horse's form to help to analyse races. I also use the Bloodstock section to follow the sales and stallion results, and the extended racecards which show all details including a horse's breeding.*

## Find out more at
## racingpost.com/members-club

# LEADING TRAINERS ON THE FLAT: 1904-2020

| | | |
|---|---|---|
| 1904 P P Gilpin | 1943 W Nightingall | 1982 H Cecil |
| 1905 W T Robinson | 1944 Frank Butters | 1983 W Hern |
| 1906 Hon G Lambton | 1945 W Earl | 1984 H Cecil |
| 1907 A Taylor | 1946 Frank Butters | 1985 H Cecil |
| 1908 C Morton | 1947 F Darling | 1986 M Stoute |
| 1909 A Taylor | 1948 C F N Murless | 1987 H Cecil |
| 1910 A Taylor | 1949 Frank Butters | 1988 H Cecil |
| 1911 Hon G Lambton | 1950 C H Semblat | 1989 M Stoute |
| 1912 Hon G Lambton | 1951 J L Jarvis | 1990 H Cecil |
| 1913 R Wootton | 1952 M Marsh | 1991 P Cole |
| 1914 A Taylor | 1953 J L Jarvis | 1992 R Hannon Snr |
| 1915 P P Gilpin | 1954 C Boyd-Rochfort | 1993 H Cecil |
| 1916 R C Dawson | 1955 C Boyd-Rochfort | 1994 M Stoute |
| 1917 A Taylor | 1956 C F Elsey | 1995 J Dunlop |
| 1918 A Taylor | 1957 C F N Murless | 1996 Saeed bin Suroor |
| 1919 A Taylor | 1958 C Boyd-Rochfort | 1997 M Stoute |
| 1920 A Taylor | 1959 C F N Murless | 1998 Saeed bin Suroor |
| 1921 A Taylor | 1960 C F N Murless | 1999 Saeed bin Suroor |
| 1922 A Taylor | 1961 C F N Murless | 2000 Sir M Stoute |
| 1923 A Taylor | 1962 W Hern | 2001 A O'Brien |
| 1924 R C Dawson | 1963 P Prendergast | 2002 A O'Brien |
| 1925 A Taylor | 1964 P Prendergast | 2003 Sir M Stoute |
| 1926 F Darling | 1965 P Prendergast | 2004 Saeed bin Suroor |
| 1927 Frank Butters | 1966 M V O'Brien | 2005 Sir M Stoute |
| 1928 Frank Butters | 1967 C F N Murless | 2006 Sir M Stoute |
| 1929 R C Dawson | 1968 C F N Murless | 2007 A O'Brien |
| 1930 H S Persse | 1969 A M Budgett | 2008 A O'Brien |
| 1931 J Lawson | 1970 C F N Murless | 2009 Sir M Stoute |
| 1932 Frank Butters | 1971 I Balding | 2010 R Hannon Snr |
| 1933 F Darling | 1972 W Hern | 2011 R Hannon Snr |
| 1934 Frank Butters | 1973 C F N Murless | 2012 J Gosden |
| 1935 Frank Butters | 1974 P Walwyn | 2013 R Hannon Snr |
| 1936 J Lawson | 1975 P Walwyn | 2014 R Hannon Jnr |
| 1937 C Boyd-Rochfort | 1976 H Cecil | 2015 J Gosden |
| 1938 C Boyd-Rochfort | 1977 M V O'Brien | 2016 A O'Brien |
| 1939 J L Jarvis | 1978 H Cecil | 2017 A O'Brien |
| 1940 F Darling | 1979 H Cecil | 2018 J Gosden |
| 1941 F Darling | 1980 W Hern | 2019 J Gosden |
| 1942 F Darling | 1981 M Stoute | 2020 J Gosden |

# CHAMPION JOCKEYS ON THE FLAT: 1903-2020

| | | | | | |
|---|---|---|---|---|---|
| 1903 O Madden | 154 | 1923 C Elliott | 89 | 1944 G Richards | 88 |
| 1904 O Madden | 161 | 1924 C Elliott | 106 | 1945 G Richards | 104 |
| 1905 E Wheatley | 124 | 1925 G Richards | 118 | 1946 G Richards | 212 |
| 1906 W Higgs | 149 | 1926 T Weston | 95 | 1947 G Richards | 269 |
| 1907 W Higgs | 146 | 1927 G Richards | 164 | 1948 G Richards | 224 |
| 1908 D Maher | 139 | 1928 G Richards | 148 | 1949 G Richards | 261 |
| 1909 F Wootton | 165 | 1929 G Richards | 135 | 1950 G Richards | 201 |
| 1910 F Wootton | 137 | 1930 F Fox | 129 | 1951 G Richards | 227 |
| 1911 F Wootton | 187 | 1931 G Richards | 145 | 1952 G Richards | 231 |
| 1912 F Wootton | 118 | 1932 G Richards | 190 | 1953 Sir G Richards | 191 |
| 1913 D Maher | 115 | 1933 G Richards | 259 | 1954 D Smith | 129 |
| 1914 S Donoghue | 129 | 1934 G Richards | 212 | 1955 D Smith | 168 |
| 1915 S Donoghue | 62 | 1935 G Richards | 217 | 1956 D Smith | 155 |
| 1916 S Donoghue | 43 | 1936 G Richards | 174 | 1957 A Breasley | 173 |
| 1917 S Donoghue | 42 | 1937 G Richards | 216 | 1958 D Smith | 165 |
| 1918 S Donoghue | 66 | 1938 G Richards | 206 | 1959 D Smith | 157 |
| 1919 S Donoghue | 129 | 1939 G Richards | 155 | 1960 L Piggott | 170 |
| 1920 S Donoghue | 143 | 1940 G Richards | 68 | 1961 A Breasley | 171 |
| 1921 S Donoghue | 141 | 1941 H Wragg | 71 | 1962 A Breasley | 179 |
| 1922 S Donoghue | 102 | 1942 G Richards | 67 | 1963 A Breasley | 176 |
| 1923 S Donoghue | 89 | 1943 G Richards | 65 | 1964 L Piggott | 140 |

| | | |
|---|---|---|
| 1965 L Piggott ... 160 | 1984 S Cauthen ... 130 | 2003 K Fallon ... 208 |
| 1966 L Piggott ... 191 | 1985 S Cauthen ... 195 | 2004 L Dettori ... 192 |
| 1967 L Piggott ... 117 | 1986 Pat Eddery ... 176 | 2005 J Spencer ... 163 |
| 1968 L Piggott ... 139 | 1987 S Cauthen ... 197 | 2006 R Moore ... 180 |
| 1969 L Piggott ... 163 | 1988 Pat Eddery ... 183 | 2007 S Sanders ... 190 |
| 1970 L Piggott ... 162 | 1989 Pat Eddery ... 171 |     J Spencer ... 190 |
| 1971 L Piggott ... 162 | 1990 Pat Eddery ... 209 | 2008 R Moore ... 186 |
| 1972 W Carson ... 132 | 1991 Pat Eddery ... 165 | 2009 R Moore ... 174 |
| 1973 W Carson ... 164 | 1992 M Roberts ... 206 | 2010 P Hanagan ... 191 |
| 1974 Pat Eddery ... 148 | 1993 Pat Eddery ... 169 | 2011 P Hanagan ... 165 |
| 1975 Pat Eddery ... 164 | 1994 L Dettori ... 233 | 2012 R Hughes ... 172 |
| 1976 Pat Eddery ... 162 | 1995 L Dettori ... 211 | 2013 R Hughes ... 203 |
| 1977 Pat Eddery ... 176 | 1996 Pat Eddery ... 186 | 2014 R Hughes ... 161 |
| 1978 W Carson ... 182 | 1997 K Fallon ... 196 | 2015 S De Sousa ... 132 |
| 1979 J Mercer ... 164 | 1998 K Fallon ... 185 | 2016 J Crowley ... 148 |
| 1980 W Carson ... 166 | 1999 K Fallon ... 200 | 2017 S De Sousa ... 155 |
| 1981 L Piggott ... 179 | 2000 K Darley ... 152 | 2018 S De Sousa ... 148 |
| 1982 L Piggott ... 188 | 2001 K Fallon ... 166 | 2019 O Murphy ... 168 |
| 1983 W Carson ... 159 | 2002 K Fallon ... 144 | 2020 O Murphy ... 142 |

# CHAMPION APPRENTICES ON THE FLAT 1985-2020

| | | |
|---|---|---|
| 1985 G Carter ... 37 | 1997 R Ffrench ... 77 |     D Probert ... 50 |
|     W Ryan ... 37 | 1998 C Lowther ... 72 | 2009 F Tylicki ... 60 |
| 1986 G Carter ... 34 | 1999 R Winston ... 49 | 2010 M Lane ... 41 |
| 1987 G Bardwell ... 27 | 2000 L Newman ... 87 | 2011 M Harley ... 57 |
| 1988 G Bardwell ... 39 | 2001 C Catlin ... 71 | 2012 A Ryan ... 40 |
| 1989 L Dettori ... 71 | 2002 P Hanagan ... 81 | 2013 J Hart ... 51 |
| 1990 J Fortune ... 46 | 2003 R Moore ... 52 | 2014 O Murphy ... 74 |
| 1991 D Holland ... 79 | 2004 T Queally ... 59 | 2015 T Marquand ... 54 |
| 1992 D Harrison ... 56 | 2005 S Golam ... 44 | 2016 J Gordon ... 50 |
| 1993 J Weaver ... 60 |     H Turner ... 44 | 2017 D Egan ... 61 |
| 1994 S Davies ... 45 | 2006 S Donohoe ... 44 | 2018 J Watson ... 77 |
| 1995 S Sanders ... 61 | 2007 G Fairley ... 65 | 2019 C Fallon ... 50 |
| 1996 D O'Neill ... 79 | 2008 W Buick ... 50 | 2020 C Fallon ... 48 |

# LEADING OWNERS ON THE FLAT: 1898-2020

| | | |
|---|---|---|
| 1898 Ld de Rothschild | 1923 Ld Derby | 1948 H.H. Aga Khan |
| 1899 Duke of Westminster | 1924 H.H. Aga Khan | 1949 H.H. Aga Khan |
| 1900 H.R.H. The Prince of Wales | 1925 Ld Astor | 1950 M M Boussac |
| 1901 Sir G Blundell Maple | 1926 Ld Woolavington | 1951 M M Boussac |
| 1902 Mr R S Sievier | 1927 Ld Derby | 1952 H.H. Aga Khan |
| 1903 Sir James Miller | 1928 Ld Derby | 1953 Sir Victor Sassoon |
| 1904 Sir James Miller | 1929 H.H. Aga Khan | 1954 Her Majesty |
| 1905 Col W Hall Walker | 1930 H.H. Aga Khan | 1955 Lady Zia Wernner |
| 1906 Ld Derby (late) | 1931 Mr J A Dewar | 1956 Maj L B Holliday |
| 1907 Col W Hall Walker | 1932 H.H. Aga Khan | 1957 Her Majesty |
| 1908 Mr J B Joel | 1933 Ld Derby | 1958 Mr J McShain |
| 1909 Mr "Fairie" | 1934 H.H. Aga Khan | 1959 Prince Aly Khan |
| 1910 Mr "Fairie" | 1935 H.H. Aga Khan | 1960 Sir Victor Sassoon |
| 1911 Ld Derby | 1936 Ld Astor | 1961 Maj L B Holliday |
| 1912 Mr T Pilkington | 1937 H.H. Aga Khan | 1962 Maj L B Holliday |
| 1913 Mr J B Joel | 1938 Ld Derby | 1963 Mr J R Mullion |
| 1914 Mr J B Joel | 1939 Ld Rosebery | 1964 Mrs H E Jackson |
| 1915 Mr L Neumann | 1940 Lord Rothermere | 1965 M J Ternynck |
| 1916 Mr E Hulton | 1941 Ld Glanely | 1966 Lady Zia Wernher |
| 1917 Mr "Fairie" | 1942 His Majesty | 1967 Mr H J Joel |
| 1918 Lady James Douglas | 1943 Miss D Paget | 1968 Mr Raymond R Guest |
| 1919 Ld Glanely | 1944 H.H. Aga Khan | 1969 Mr D Robinson |
| 1920 Sir Robert Jardine | 1945 Ld Derby | 1970 Mr C Engelhard |
| 1921 Mr S B Joel | 1946 H.H. Aga Khan | 1971 Mr P Mellon |
| 1922 Ld Woolavington | 1947 H.H. Aga Khan | 1972 Mrs J Hislop |

1973 Mr N B Hunt
1974 Mr N B Hunt
1975 Dr C Vittadini
1976 Mr D Wildenstein
1977 Mr R Sangster
1978 Mr R Sangster
1979 Sir M Sobell
1980 S Weinstock
1981 H.H. Aga Khan
1982 Mr R Sangster
1983 Mr R Sangster
1984 Mr R Sangster
1985 Sheikh Mohammed
1986 Sheikh Mohammed
1987 Sheikh Mohammed
1988 Sheikh Mohammed

1989 Sheikh Mohammed
1990 Mr Hamdan Al-Maktoum
1991 Sheikh Mohammed
1992 Sheikh Mohammed
1993 Sheikh Mohammed
1994 Mr Hamdan Al-Maktoum
1995 Mr Hamdan Al-Maktoum
1996 Godolphin
1997 Sheikh Mohammed
1998 Godolphin
1999 Godolphin
2000 H.H. Aga Khan
2001 Godolphin
2002 Mr Hamdan Al-Maktoum
2003 K Abdullah
2004 Godolphin

2005 Mr Hamdan Al-Maktoum
2006 Godolphin
2007 Godolphin
2008 HRH Princess Haya of Jordan
2009 Mr Hamdan Al-Maktoum
2010 K Abdullah
2011 K Abdullah
2012 Godolphin
2013 Godolphin
2014 Mr Hamdan Al-Maktoum
2015 Godolphin
2016 Godolphin
2017 Godolphin
2018 Godolphin
2019 Mr Hamdan Al-Maktoum
2020 Mr Hamdan Al-Maktoum

# LEADING SIRES ON THE FLAT: 1898-2020

1898 Galopin
1899 Orme
1900 St Simon
1901 St Simon
1902 Persimmon
1903 St Frusquin
1904 Gallinule
1905 Gallinule
1906 Persimmon
1907 St Frusquin
1908 Persimmon
1909 Cyllene
1910 Cyllene
1911 Sundridge
1912 Persimmon
1913 Desmond
1914 Polymelus
1915 Polymelus
1916 Polymelus
1917 Bayardo
1918 Bayardo
1919 The Tetrarch
1920 Polymelus
1921 Polymelus
1922 Lemberg
1923 Swynford
1924 Son-in-Law
1925 Phalaris
1926 Hurry On
1927 Buchan
1928 Phalaris
1929 Tetratema
1930 Son-in-Law
1931 Pharos
1932 Gainsborough
1933 Gainsborough
1934 Blandford
1935 Blandford
1936 Fairway
1937 Solario
1938 Blandford

1939 Fairway
1940 Hyperion
1941 Hyperion
1942 Hyperion
1943 Fairway
1944 Fairway
1945 Hyperion
1946 Hyperion
1947 Nearco
1948 Big Game
1949 Nearco
1950 Fair Trial
1951 Nasrullah
1952 Tehran
1953 Chanteur II
1954 Hyperion
1955 Alycidon
1956 Court Martial
1957 Court Martial
1958 Mossborough
1959 Petition
1960 Aureole
1961 Aureole
1962 Never Say Die
1963 Ribot
1964 Chamossaire
1965 Court Harwell
1966 Charlottesville
1967 Ribot
1968 Ribot
1969 Crepello
1970 Northern Dancer
1971 Never Bend
1972 Queen's Hussar
1973 Vaguely Noble
1974 Vaguely Noble
1975 Great Nephew
1976 Wolver Hollow
1977 Northern Dancer
1978 Mill Reef (USA)
1979 Petingo

1980 Pitcairn
1981 Great Nephew
1982 Be My Guest (USA)
1983 Northern Dancer
1984 Northern Dancer
1985 Kris
1986 Nijinsky (CAN)
1987 Mill Reef (USA)
1988 Caerleon (USA)
1989 Blushing Groom (FR)
1990 Sadler's Wells (USA)
1991 Caerleon (USA)
1992 Sadler's Wells (USA)
1993 Sadler's Wells (USA)
1994 Sadler's Wells (USA)
1995 Sadler's Wells (USA)
1996 Sadler's Wells (USA)
1997 Sadler's Wells (USA)
1998 Sadler's Wells (USA)
1999 Sadler's Wells (USA)
2000 Sadler's Wells (USA)
2001 Sadler's Wells (USA)
2002 Sadler's Wells (USA)
2003 Sadler's Wells (USA)
2004 Sadler's Wells (USA)
2005 Danehill (USA)
2006 Danehill (USA)
2007 Danehill (USA)
2008 Galileo (IRE)
2009 Danehill Dancer (IRE)
2010 Galileo (IRE)
2011 Galileo (IRE)
2012 Galileo (IRE)
2013 Galileo (IRE)
2014 Galileo (IRE)
2015 Galileo (IRE)
2016 Galileo (IRE)
2017 Galileo (IRE)
2018 Galileo (IRE)
2019 Galileo (IRE)
2020 Galileo (IRE)

# LEADING BREEDERS ON THE FLAT: 1914-2020

1914 Mr J B Joel
1915 Mr L Neumann
1916 Mr E Hulton
1917 Mr "Fairie"
1918 Lady James Douglas
1919 Ld Derby
1920 Ld Derby
1921 Mr S B Joel
1922 Ld Derby
1923 Ld Derby
1924 Lady Sykes
1925 Ld Astor
1926 Ld Woolavington
1927 Ld Derby
1928 Ld Derby
1929 Ld Derby
1930 Ld Derby
1931 Ld Dewar
1932 H.H. Aga Khan
1933 Sir Alec Black
1934 H.H. Aga Khan
1935 H.H. Aga Khan
1936 Ld Astor
1937 H.H. Aga Khan
1938 Ld Derby
1939 Ld Rosebery
1940 Mr H E Morriss
1941 Ld Glanely
1942 National Stud
1943 Miss D Paget
1944 Ld Rosebery
1945 Ld Derby
1946 Lt- Col H Boyd-Rochfort
1947 H.H. Aga Khan
1948 H.H. Aga Khan
1949 H.H. Aga Khan

1950 M M Boussac
1951 M M Boussac
1952 H. H. Aga Khan
1953 Mr F Darling
1954 Maj L B Holliday
1955 Someries Stud
1956 Maj L B Holliday
1957 Eve Stud
1958 Mr R Ball
1959 Prince Aly Khan and the late
    H.H. Aga Khan
1960 Eve Stud Ltd
1961 Eve Stud Ltd
1962 Maj L B Holliday
1963 Mr H F Guggenheim
1964 Bull Run Stud
1965 Mr J Ternynck
1966 Someries Stud
1967 Mr H J Joel
1968 Mill Ridge Farm
1969 Lord Rosebery
1970 Mr E P Taylor
1971 Mr P Mellon
1972 Mr J Hislop
1973 Claiborne Farm
1974 Mr N B Hunt
1975 Overbury Stud
1976 Dayton Ltd
1977 Mr E P Taylor
1978 Cragwood Estates Inc
1979 Ballymacoll Stud
1980 P Clarke
1981 H.H. Aga Khan
1982 Someries Stud
1983 White Lodge Stud
1984 Mr E P Taylor

1985 Dalham Stud Farms
1986 H.H. Aga Khan
1987 Cliveden Stud
1988 H. H. Aga Khan
1989 Mr Hamdan Al-Maktoum
1990 Capt. Macdonald- Buchanan
1991 Barronstown Stud
1992 Swettenham Stud
1993 Juddmonte Farms
1994 Shadwell Farm & Estate Ltd
1995 Shadwell Farm & Estate Ltd
1996 Sheikh Mohammed
1997 Sheikh Mohammed
1998 Sheikh Mohammed
1999 H. H. The Aga Khan's Studs
2000 H. H. The Aga Khan's Studs
2001 Shadwell Farm & Estate Ltd
2002 Gainsborough Stud
2003 Juddmonte
2004 Juddmonte
2005 Shadwell Farm & Estate Ltd
2006 Darley
2007 Darley
2008 Darley
2009 Darley
2010 Juddmonte
2011 Juddmonte
2012 Juddmonte
2013 Darley
2014 Darley
2015 Darley
2016 Darley
2017 Darley
2018 Godolphin
2019 Godolphin
2020 Godolphin

# LEADING TRAINERS OVER JUMPS: 1949-2020

1949-50 P V F Cazalet
1950-51 T F Rimell
1951-52 N Crump
1952-53 M V O'Brien
1953-54 M V O'Brien
1954-55 H R Price
1955-56 W Hall
1956-57 N Crump
1957-58 F T T Walwyn
1958-59 H R Price
1959-60 P V F Cazalet
1960-61 T F Rimell
1961-62 H R Price
1962-63 K Piggott
1963-64 F T T Walwyn
1964-65 P V F Cazalet
1965-66 H R Price
1966-67 H R Price
1967-68 Denys Smith
1968-69 T F Rimell
1969-70 T F Rimell
1970-71 F T Winter
1971-72 F T Winter
1972-73 F T Winter

1973-74 F T Winter
1974-75 F T Winter
1975-76 T F Rimell
1976-77 F T Winter
1977-78 F T Winter
1978-79 M H Easterby
1979-80 M H Easterby
1980-81 M H Easterby
1981-82 M W Dickinson
1982-83 M W Dickinson
1983-84 M W Dickinson
1984-85 F T Winter
1985-86 N J Henderson
1986-87 N J Henderson
1987-88 D R C Elsworth
1988-89 M C Pipe
1989-90 M C Pipe
1990-91 M C Pipe
1991-92 M C Pipe
1992-93 M C Pipe
1993-94 D Nicholson
1994-95 D Nicholson
1995-96 M C Pipe
1996-97 M C Pipe

1997-98 M C Pipe
1998-99 M C Pipe
1999-00 M C Pipe
2000-01 M C Pipe
2001-02 M C Pipe
2002-03 M C Pipe
2003-04 M C Pipe
2004-05 M C Pipe
2005-06 P F Nicholls
2006-07 P F Nicholls
2007-08 P F Nicholls
2008-09 P F Nicholls
2009-10 P F Nicholls
2010-11 P F Nicholls
2010-11 P F Nicholls
2011-12 P F Nicholls
2012-13 N J Henderson
2013-14 P F Nicholls
2014-15 P F Nicholls
2015-16 P F Nicholls
2016-17 N J Henderson
2017-18 N J Henderson
2018-19 P F Nicholls
2019-20 N J Henderson

# CHAMPION JOCKEYS OVER JUMPS: 1904-2020
Prior to the 1925-26 season the figure relates to racing between January and December

| Year | Jockey | Wins |
|---|---|---|
| 1904 | F Mason | 59 |
| 1905 | F Mason | 73 |
| 1906 | F Mason | 58 |
| 1907 | F Mason | 59 |
| 1908 | P Cowley | 65 |
| 1909 | R Gordon | 45 |
| 1910 | E Piggott | 67 |
| 1911 | W Payne | 76 |
| 1912 | I Anthony | 78 |
| 1913 | E Piggott | 60 |
| 1914 | Mr J R Anthony | 60 |
| 1915 | E Piggott | 44 |
| 1916 | C Hawkins | 17 |
| 1917 | W Smith | 15 |
| 1918 | G Duller | 17 |
| 1919 | Mr H Brown | 48 |
| 1920 | F B Rees | 64 |
| 1921 | F B Rees | 65 |
| 1922 | J Anthony | 78 |
| 1923 | F B Rees | 64 |
| 1924 | F B Rees | 108 |
| 1925 | E Foster | 76 |
| 1925-26 | T Leader | 61 |
| 1926-27 | F B Rees | 59 |
| 1927-28 | W Stott | 88 |
| 1928-29 | W Stott | 65 |
| 1929-30 | W Stott | 77 |
| 1930-31 | W Stott | 81 |
| 1931-32 | W Stott | 77 |
| 1932-33 | G Wilson | 61 |
| 1933-34 | G Wilson | 56 |
| 1934-35 | G Wilson | 73 |
| 1935-36 | G Wilson | 57 |
| 1936-37 | G Wilson | 45 |
| 1937-38 | G Wilson | 59 |
| 1938-39 | T F Rimell | 61 |
| 1939-40 | T F Rimell | 24 |
| 1940-41 | G Wilson | 22 |
| 1941-42 | R Smyth | 12 |
| 1942-43 | No racing | |
| 1943-44 | No racing | |
| 1944-45 | H Nicholson | 15 |
| | T F Rimell | 15 |
| 1945-46 | T F Rimell | 54 |
| 1946-47 | J Dowdeswell | 58 |
| 1947-48 | B Marshall | 66 |
| 1948-49 | T Moloney | 60 |
| 1949-50 | T Moloney | 95 |
| 1950-51 | T Moloney | 83 |
| 1951-52 | T Moloney | 99 |
| 1952-53 | F Winter | 121 |
| 1953-54 | R Francis | 76 |
| 1954-55 | T Moloney | 67 |
| 1955-56 | F Winter | 74 |
| 1956-57 | F Winter | 80 |
| 1957-58 | F Winter | 82 |
| 1958-59 | T Brookshaw | 83 |
| 1959-60 | S Mellor | 68 |
| 1960-61 | S Mellor | 118 |
| 1961-62 | S Mellor | 80 |
| 1962-63 | J Gifford | 70 |
| 1963-64 | J Gifford | 94 |
| 1964-65 | T Biddlecombe | 114 |
| 1965-66 | T Biddlecombe | 102 |
| 1966-67 | J Gifford | 122 |
| 1967-68 | J Gifford | 82 |
| 1968-69 | B R Davies | 77 |
| | T Biddlecombe | 77 |
| 1969-70 | B R Davies | 91 |
| 1970-71 | G Thorner | 74 |
| 1971-72 | B R Davies | 89 |
| 1972-73 | R Barry | 125 |
| 1973-74 | R Barry | 94 |
| 1974-75 | T Stack | 82 |
| 1975-76 | J Francome | 96 |
| 1976-77 | T Stack | 97 |
| 1977-78 | J J O'Neill | 149 |
| 1978-79 | J Francome | 95 |
| 1979-80 | J J O'Neill | 117 |
| 1980-81 | J Francome | 105 |
| 1981-82 | J Francome | 120 |
| | P Scudamore | 120 |
| 1982-83 | J Francome | 106 |
| 1983-84 | J Francome | 131 |
| 1984-85 | J Francome | 101 |
| 1985-86 | P Scudamore | 91 |
| 1986-87 | P Scudamore | 123 |
| 1987-88 | P Scudamore | 132 |
| 1988-89 | P Scudamore | 221 |
| 1989-90 | P Scudamore | 170 |
| 1990-91 | P Scudamore | 141 |
| 1991-92 | P Scudamore | 175 |
| 1992-93 | R Dunwoody | 173 |
| 1993-94 | R Dunwoody | 197 |
| 1994-95 | P Scudamore | 160 |
| 1995-96 | A P McCoy | 175 |
| 1996-97 | A P McCoy | 190 |
| 1997-98 | A P McCoy | 253 |
| 1998-99 | A P McCoy | 186 |
| 1999-00 | A P McCoy | 245 |
| 2000-01 | A P McCoy | 191 |
| 2001-02 | A P McCoy | 289 |
| 2002-03 | A P McCoy | 256 |
| 2003-04 | A P McCoy | 209 |
| 2004-05 | A P McCoy | 200 |
| 2005-06 | A P McCoy | 178 |
| 2006-07 | A P McCoy | 184 |
| 2007-08 | A P McCoy | 140 |
| 2008-09 | A P McCoy | 186 |
| 2009-10 | A P McCoy | 195 |
| 2010-11 | A P McCoy | 218 |
| 2011-12 | A P McCoy | 199 |
| 2012-13 | A P McCoy | 185 |
| 2013-14 | A P McCoy | 218 |
| 2014-15 | A P McCoy | 231 |
| 2015-16 | R Johnson | 235 |
| 2016-17 | R Johnson | 189 |
| 2017-18 | R Johnson | 176 |
| 2018-19 | R Johnson | 200 |
| 2019-20 | B Hughes | 141 |

# LEADING OWNERS OVER JUMPS: 1949-2020
(Please note that prior to the 1994-95 season the leading owner was determined by win prizemoney only)

|  |  |
|---|---|
| 1949-50 | Mrs L Brotherton |
| 1950-51 | Mr J Royle |
| 1951-52 | Miss D Paget |
| 1952-53 | Mr J H Griffin |
| 1953-54 | Mr J H Griffin |
| 1954-55 | Mrs W H E Welman |
| 1955-56 | Mrs L Carver |
| 1956-57 | Mrs Geoffrey Kohn |
| 1957-58 | Mr D J Coughlan |
| 1958-59 | Mr J E Bigg |
| 1959-60 | Miss W H Wallace |
| 1960-61 | Mr C Vaughan |
| 1961-62 | Mr N Cohen |
| 1962-63 | Mr P B Raymond |
| 1963-64 | Mr J K Goodman |
| 1964-65 | Mrs M Stephenson |
| 1965-66 | Duchess of Westminster |
| 1966-67 | Mr C P T Watkins |
| 1967-68 | Mr H S Alper |
| 1968-69 | Mr B P Jenks |
| 1969-70 | Mr E R Courage |
| 1970-71 | Mr F Pontin |
| 1971-72 | Capt T A Forster |
| 1972-73 | Mr N H Le Mare |
| 1973-74 | Mr N H Le Mare |
| 1974-75 | Mr R Guest |
| 1975-76 | Mr P B Raymond |
| 1976-77 | Mr N H Le Mare |
| 1977-78 | Mrs O Jackson |
| 1978-79 | Snailwell Stud Co Ltd |
| 1979-80 | Mr H J Joel |
| 1980-81 | Mr R J Wilson |
| 1981-82 | Sheikh Ali Abu Khamsin |
| 1982-83 | Sheikh Ali Abu Khamsin |
| 1983-84 | Sheikh Ali Abu Khamsin |
| 1984-85 | T Kilroe and Son Ltd |
| 1985-86 | Sheikh Ali Abu Khamsin |
| 1986-87 | Mr H J Joel |
| 1987-88 | Miss Juliet E Reed |
| 1988-89 | Mr R Burridge |
| 1989-90 | Mrs Harry J Duffey |
| 1990-91 | Mr P Piller |
| 1991-92 | Whitcombe Manor Racing Stables Ltd |
| 1992-93 | Mrs J Mould |
| 1993-94 | Pell-Mell Partners |
| 1994-95 | Roach Foods Limited |
| 1995-96 | Mr A T A Wates |
| 1996-97 | Mr R Ogden |
| 1997-98 | Mr D A Johnson |
| 1998-99 | Mr J P McManus |
| 1999-00 | Mr R Ogden |
| 2000-01 | Sir R Ogden |
| 2001-02 | Mr D A Johnson |
| 2002-03 | Mr D A Johnson |
| 2003-04 | Mr D A Johnson |
| 2004-05 | Mr D A Johnson |
| 2005-06 | Mr J P McManus |
| 2006-07 | Mr J P McManus |
| 2007-08 | Mr D A Johnson |

2008-09 Mr J P McManus
2009-10 Mr J P McManus
2010-11 Mr T Hemmings
2011-12 Mr J P McManus
2012-13 Mr J P McManus
2013-14 Mr J P McManus
2014-15 Mr J P McManus
2015-16 Gigginstown House Stud
2016-17 Mr J P McManus
2017-18 Mr J P McManus
2018-19 Mr J P McManus
2019-20 Mr J P McManus

# LEADING AMATEUR RIDERS OVER JUMPS: 1953-2020

| | | |
|---|---|---|
| 1953-54 Mr A H Moralee ............... 22 | 1975-76 Mr P Greenall ................. 25 | 1997-98 Mr S Durack .................... 41 |
| 1954-55 Mr A H Moralee ............... 16 | Mr G Jones ................. 25 | 1998-99 Mr A Dempsey................. 47 |
| 1955-56 Mr R McCreery ................ 13 | 1976-77 Mr P Greenall ................. 27 | 1999-00 Mr P Flynn ..................... 41 |
| Mr A H Moralee ............... 13 | 1977-78 Mr G Sloan ..................... 23 | 2000-01 Mr T Scudamore............... 24 |
| 1956-57 Mr R McCreery ................ 23 | 1978-79 Mr T G Dun.................... 26 | 2001-02 Mr D Crosse ................... 19 |
| 1957-58 Mr J Lawrence ................. 18 | 1979-80 Mr O Sherwood ............... 29 | 2002-03 Mr C Williams ................. 23 |
| 1958-59 Mr J Sutcliffe................... 18 | 1980-81 Mr P Webber .................. 32 | 2003-04 Mr O Nelmes .................. 14 |
| 1959-60 Mr G Kindersley................ 12 | 1981-82 Mr D Browne .................. 28 | 2004-05 Mr T Greenall.................. 31 |
| 1960-61 Sir W Pigott-Brown ........... 28 | 1982-83 Mr D Browne .................. 33 | 2005-06 Mr T O'Brien................... 32 |
| 1961-62 Mr A Biddlecombe............. 30 | 1983-84 Mr S Sherwood................ 28 | 2006-07 Mr T Greenall.................. 31 |
| 1962-63 Sir W Pigott-Brown ........... 20 | 1984-85 Mr S Sherwood................ 30 | 2007-08 Mr T Greenall.................. 23 |
| 1963-64 Mr S Davenport ............... 32 | 1985-86 Mr T Thomson Jones ........ 25 | 2008-09 Mr O Greenall.................. 23 |
| 1964-65 Mr M Gifford ................... 15 | 1986-87 Mr T Thomson Jones ........ 19 | 2009-10 Mr O Greenall.................. 41 |
| 1965-66 Mr C Collins.................... 24 | 1987-88 Mr T Thomson Jones ........ 15 | 2010-11 Mr R Mahon .................... 19 |
| 1966-67 Mr C Collins.................... 33 | 1988-89 Mr P Fenton ................... 18 | 2011-12 Miss E Sayer .................. 16 |
| 1967-68 Mr R Tate....................... 30 | 1989-90 Mr P McMahon................ 15 | 2012-13 Mr N de Boinville............. 16 |
| 1968-69 Mr R Tate....................... 17 | 1990-91 Mr K Johnson .................. 24 | 2013-14 Mr H Bannister ................ 11 |
| 1969-70 Mr M Dickinson ............... 23 | 1991-92 Mr M P Hourigan ............. 24 | 2014-15 Mr H Bannister ................ 15 |
| 1970-71 Mr J Lawrence ................. 17 | 1992-93 Mr A Thornton ................ 26 | 2015-16 Mr D Noonan .................. 19 |
| 1971-72 Mr W Foulkes .................. 26 | 1993-94 Mr J Greenall................... 21 | 2016-17 Mr J King ...................... 15 |
| 1972-73 Mr R Smith..................... 56 | 1994-95 Mr D Parker ................... 16 | 2017-18 Miss P Fuller................... 16 |
| 1973-74 Mr A Webber ................... 21 | 1995-96 Mr J Culloty ................... 40 | 2018-19 Mr D Maxwell.................. 18 |
| 1974-75 Mr R Lamb ..................... 22 | 1996-97 Mr R Thornton ................ 30 | 2019-20 Mr D Maxwell.................. 18 |

# LEADING SIRES OVER JUMPS: 1989-2020

| | | |
|---|---|---|
| 1989-90 Deep Run | 2000-01 Be My Native (USA) | 2011-12 King's Theatre |
| 1990-91 Deep Run | 2001-02 Be My Native (USA) | 2012-13 Beneficial |
| 1991-92 Deep Run | 2002-03 Be My Native (USA) | 2013-14 King's Theatre |
| 1992-93 Deep Run | 2003-04 Be My Native (USA) | 2014-15 King's Theatre |
| 1993-94 Strong Gale | 2004-05 Supreme Leader | 2015-16 King's Theatre |
| 1994-95 Strong Gale | 2005-06 Supreme Leader | 2016-17 King's Theatre |
| 1995-96 Strong Gale | 2006-07 Presenting | 2017-18 King's Theatre |
| 1996-97 Strong Gale | 2007-08 Old Vic | 2018-19 Flemensfirth |
| 1997-98 Strong Gale | 2008-09 Presenting | 2019-20 Milan |
| 1998-99 Strong Gale | 2009-10 Presenting | |
| 1999-00 Strong Gale | 2010-11 Presenting | |

# JOCKEYS' AGENTS

## Jockeys' agents and their contact details

| Agent | Telephone | Mobile/Email |
|---|---|---|
| **NICKY ADAMS** | 01488 72004/72964 | 07796547659<br>nickadams2594@hotmail.com |
| **NEIL ALLAN** | 01243 543870 | 07825549081<br>email: aneilallan@aol.com |
| **NIGEL BAXTER** | 01942 803247 | 07973561521<br>email: sales@clubfactfile.com |
| **PAUL BRIERLEY** | | 07824828750<br>bbjockeys@hotmail.co.uk |
| **CHRIS BROAD** | 01452 760482/447 | 07836622858<br>chrisd.broad@yahoo.co.uk |
| **ADAM BROOK** | | 07399390303<br>info@brooksportsmanagement.com |
| **TOM CASTLE** | | 07912249711<br>whitediamondracing@outlook.com |
| **GLORIA CHARNOCK** | 01653 695004 | 07951576912<br>gloriacharnock@hotmail.com |
| **PAUL CLARKE** | 01638 660804 | 07885914306<br>paul.clarke79@btinternet.com |
| **STEVEN CROFT** | | 07809205556<br>steven.croft6@googlemail.com |
| **SIMON DODDS** | 01509 734496 | 07974924735<br>simon.dodds@btinternet.com |
| **SHELLEY DWYER** | 01638 493123 | 07949612256<br>shelleydwyer4031@outlook.com |
| **SHIPPY ELLIS** | 01638 668484 | 07860864864<br>shippysjockeys@jockeysagent.com |

| Agent | Telephone | Mobile/Email |
|---|---|---|
| **MARK FURNASS** | | 07474242332<br>jockeysagent@gmail.com |
| **AARON GORMAN** | | 07966293350<br>aarongormanjockeysagent@gmail.com |
| **RICHARD HALE** | 01768 88699 | 07909520542<br>richardhale77@hotmail.co.uk |
| **NIALL HANNITY** | 01677 423363 | 07710141084<br>niallhannity@yahoo.co.uk |
| **ALAN HARRISON** | 01969 326248 | 07846187991<br>ahjockagent60@yahoo.co.uk |
| **TONY HIND** | 01638 724997 | 07807908599<br>tonyhind@jockeysagent.com |
| **GAVIN HORNE** | 01392 433610 | 07914897170<br>renoodriver2@gmail.com |
| **CHRIS HUMPLEBY** | | 07712608969<br>chris.humpleby13@gmail.com |
| **ROSS HYSLOP** | | 07894634067<br>r.hyslop91@gmail.com |
| **RUSS JAMES** | 01653 699466 | 07947414001<br>russjames2006@btconnect.com |
| **BRUCE JEFFREY** | 01750 21521 | 07747854684<br>brucejeffrey@live.co.uk |
| **GUY JEWELL** | 01672 861231 | 07765248859<br>guyjewell@btconnect.com |
| **ANDY LEWIS** | | 07838506594<br>andrew.lewis11@sky.com |
| **SARA-LOUISE METCALFE** | 01635 269647 | 07918525354<br>troopersjockeys@hotmail.co.uk |
| **JOHN NEILSON** | 01388 730249 | 07813874970<br>john@jlnjockeys.co.uk |

| Agent | Telephone | Mobile/Email |
|---|---|---|
| **GARETH OWEN** | 01603 569390 | 07958335206<br>garethowenracing@gmail.com |
| **IAN POPHAM** | | 07791225707<br>ianpopham28@outlook.com |
| **WILSON RENWICK** | | 07860949577<br>wilsonrenwick@aol.com |
| **SHASHI RIGHTON** | 01353 688594 | 07825381350<br>srighton.sr@googlemail.com |
| **DAVE ROBERTS** | 01737 221368 | 07860234342<br>daveroberts.racing@gmail.com |
| **PHILIP SHEA** | 01638 667456 | 07585120297<br>psheajockeysagent@gmail.com |
| **COLIN VOYSEY** | 01536 790105 | 07775866911<br>colinvoysey@btinternet.com |
| **ANNA WALLACE** | | 07867923642<br>awallace51@yahoo.com |
| **JAMES WARD** | | 07786146250<br>james@racingroom.co.uk |
| **LAURA WAY** | 01704 834488 | 07775777494<br>laura.way@btconnect.com |
| **IAN WOOD** | | 07733156380<br>ianwood@chase3c.com |

# FLAT JOCKEYS

### Riding weights and contact details
### An index of agents appears on page 755

| Jockey | Weight | Agent |
|---|---|---|
| DAVID ALLAN | 8-10 | Mrs G. S. Charnock |
| ANDREA ATZENI | 8-5 | Mr S. Croft |
| CONNOR BEASLEY | 8-6 | Mr G. R. Owen |
| ALED BEECH | 7-13 | Mr L. R. James |
| CHARLIE BENNETT | 8-6 | Mr G. D. Jewell |
| HARRY BENTLEY | 8-7 | Mr Paul Clarke |
| SHELLEY BIRKETT | 8-4 | 07969777694 |
| CHARLES BISHOP | 8-10 | Mr Neil Allan |
| SEAN BOWEN | 8-12 | Mr Dave Roberts/ M. Furnass |
| DANNY BROCK | 8-6 | Miss S. L. Metcalfe/ Mr Aaron Gorman |
| GEORGE BUCKELL | 8-12 | Andy Lewis |
| WILLIAM BUICK | 8-6 | Mr Tony Hind |
| WILLIAM CARSON | 8-6 | Mr Neil Allan |
| PAT COSGRAVE | 8-9 | Mr Paul Clarke |
| DOUGIE COSTELLO | 8-10 | Mr A. T. Brook |
| LAURA COUGHLAN | 7-13 | Andy Lewis |
| HECTOR CROUCH | 8-11 | Mr G. D. Jewell |
| JIM CROWLEY | 8-7 | Mr Tony Hind |
| NICOLA CURRIE | 8-0 | Mr G. J. Horne |
| BEN CURTIS | 8-5 | Mr S. T. Dodds |
| RAUL DA SILVA | 8-0 | M. Furnass |
| RAY DAWSON | 8-4 | Mr A. T. Brook |
| PHIL DENNIS | 8-6 | Mr Alan Harrison |
| SILVESTRE DE SOUSA | 8-0 | Mrs Shelley Dwyer |
| FRANKIE DETTORI | 8-9 | 07703606162 |
| PAT DOBBS | 8-9 | Mr Tony Hind |
| STEVIE DONOHOE | 8-8 | P.C. Shea |
| ROBBIE DOWNEY | 8-4 | Mr A. T. Brook |
| GEORGE DOWNING | 8-11 | Mr Paul Clarke |
| BRETT DOYLE | 8-5 | M. Furnass |
| HOLLIE DOYLE | 8-0 | Mr G. D. Jewell |
| JAMES DOYLE | 8-10 | Mr Chris Humpleby |
| MARTIN DWYER | 8-3 | Mr S. T. Dodds |
| TOM EAVES | 8-7 | Mr R. A. Hale |
| LEWIS EDMUNDS | 8-9 | Mr S. T. Dodds |
| DAVID EGAN | 8-4 | Mr Tony Hind |
| JOHN EGAN | 8-3 | Mr Paul Brierley |
| ANDREW ELLIOTT | 8-4 | 07709222004 |
| JANE ELLIOTT | 8-0 | Mr S. Croft |
| NATHAN EVANS | 8-2 | Mr R. A. Hale |
| JOHN FAHY | 8-6 | Mr L. R. James |
| CIEREN FALLON | 8-5 | Mr G. J. Horne |
| JOE FANNING | 8-2 | Mr N. Hannity |
| DURAN FENTIMAN | 8-0 | Mr Alan Harrison |
| ROYSTON FFRENCH | 8-3 | M. Furnass |
| JONATHAN FISHER | 8-7 | M. Furnass |
| KIEREN FOX | 8-5 | 07702973759 |
| NOEL GARBUTT | 8-0 | 07447632783 |
| JACK GARRITTY | 8-12 | K. W. Renwick |
| JOSEPHINE GORDON | 8-4 | Mr A. T. Brook |
| JAMIE GORMLEY | 8-0 | Mr R. A. Hale |
| SHANE GRAY | 8-4 | Mr N. Hannity |
| EDWARD GREATREX | 8-8 | Mr G. D. Jewell |
| TONY HAMILTON | 8-8 | Mr N. Hannity |
| PAUL HANAGAN | 8-6 | Mr R. A. Hale |
| CAM HARDIE | 8-0 | Mr R. A. Hale |
| MARTIN HARLEY | 8-11 | Mr Neil Allan |
| RUSSELL HARRIS | 8-5 | Mrs L. H. Way |
| JASON HART | 8-9 | Mr Alan Harrison |
| ROBERT HAVLIN | 8-7 | Mr G. R. Owen |
| JOEY HAYNES | 8-5 | Mr A. T. Brook |
| SAM HITCHCOTT | 8-5 | Mr N. M. Adams |
| DYLAN HOGAN | 8-5 | Mr Paul Brierley |
| ROB HORNBY | 8-10 | Mr N. M. Adams |
| SAM JAMES | 8-6 | K. W. Renwick |
| AARON JONES | 8-0 | 07581002643 |
| LIAM JONES | 8-4 | 01638 554340 |
| SHANE KELLY | 8-7 | Mr N. M. Adams |
| LIAM KENIRY | 8-8 | Mr N. M. Adams |
| RICHARD KINGSCOTE | 8-8 | Mr G. D. Jewell |
| ADAM KIRBY | 9-0 | Mr N. M. Adams |
| RACHEAL KNELLER | 8-4 | 07951820608 |
| CLIFFORD LEE | 8-10 | Mr G. R. Owen |
| GRAHAM LEE | 8-9 | Mr R. A. Hale |
| SEAN LEVEY | 8-10 | Mr S. M. Righton |
| KEVIN LUNDIE | 8-10 | 0790413894 |
| NICKY MACKAY | 8-4 | Mr N. A. Baxter |
| ELLIE MACKENZIE | 8-0 | Andy Lewis |
| GINA MANGAN | 8-0 | Mr L. R. James |
| TOM MARQUAND | 8-7 | Mr S. M. Righton |
| JOANNA MASON | 8-9 | Mr N. Hannity |
| PADDY MATHERS | 8-0 | M. Furnass |
| ADRIAN MCCARTHY | 8-4 | 07852439914 |
| P. J. MCDONALD | 8-2 | Mr G. R. Owen |
| BARRY MCHUGH | 8-6 | Mrs L. H. Way |
| CIARAN MCKEE | 9-0 | 07858355178 |
| FAYE MCMANOMAN | 7-13 | Mr Paul Brierley |
| ADAM MCNAMARA | 8-10 | P.C. Shea |
| JACK MITCHELL | 8-9 | Mr S. Croft |
| RYAN MOORE | 8-9 | Mr Tony Hind |
| LUKE MORRIS | 8-0 | Mr Neil Allan |
| PAULA MUIR | 7-13 | Mr Paul Brierley |
| ANDREW MULLEN | 8-3 | Mr R. A. Hale |
| PAUL MULRENNAN | 8-10 | Mr R. A. Hale |
| OISIN MURPHY | 8-6 | Mr G. J. Horne |
| DANIEL MUSCUTT | 8-10 | Mr Paul Clarke |
| MEGAN NICHOLLS | 8-4 | Mr S. Croft |
| CAMERON NOBLE | 8-9 | 07889633083 |
| DAVID NOLAN | 9-1 | Mr R. A. Hale |
| FRANNY NORTON | 8-7 | Mr N. Hannity |
| DANE O'NEILL | 8-7 | Mr N. M. Adams |
| KIERAN O'NEILL | 8-0 | Mr N. M. Adams |
| RYAN POWELL | 8-0 | 07525337664 |
| PHILIP PRINCE | 8-5 | 07597886396 |
| DAVID PROBERT | 8-7 | Mr Neil Allan |
| TOM QUEALLY | 8-11 | P.C. Shea |
| SOPHIE RALSTON | 7-11 | Miss A. Wallace |
| ALISTAIR RAWLINSON | 8-11 | Mr S. Croft |
| BEN ROBINSON | 8-9 | Mr R. A. Hale |
| CALLUM RODRIGUEZ | 8-10 | Mr R. A. Hale |
| ROSSA RYAN | 8-7 | Mr S. Croft |
| VICTOR SANTOS | 8-0 | 07496534107 |

| | | |
|---|---|---|
| **KIERAN SCHOFIELD** | 8 - 0 | Mr S. T. Dodds |
| **ROWAN SCOTT** | 8 - 5 | Mr N. Hannity |
| **HARRISON SHAW** | 8 - 5 | Mr R. A. Hale |
| **CALLUM SHEPHERD** | 8 - 9 | Mr N. M. Adams |
| **KIERAN SHOEMARK** | 8 - 10 | Mr G. D. Jewell |
| **JAMIE SPENCER** | 8 - 7 | Mr N. Hannity |
| **MICHAEL STAINTON** | 8 - 10 | 07714445806 |
| **LOUIS STEWARD** | 8 - 11 | Mr James Ward |
| **KEVIN STOTT** | 8 - 10 | Mr R. A. Hale |
| **JAMES SULLIVAN** | 8 - 0 | Mr R. A. Hale |
| **RYAN TATE** | 8 - 6 | Mr Neil Allan |
| **DANIEL TUDHOPE** | 8 - 11 | Mrs L. H. Way |
| **HAYLEY TURNER** | 8 - 2 | Mr G. D. Jewell |
| **GEMMA TUTTY** | 8 - 10 | 07970095355 |
| **EOIN WALSH** | 8 - 10 | Mr N. M. Adams |
| **JASON WATSON** | 8 - 4 | Mr Tony Hind |

Are your contact details missing
or incorrect?
If so please update us by
email: hitraceform@weatherbys.co.uk

# APPRENTICES

### Riding weights and contact details
### An index of agents appears on page 755

| | | |
|---|---|---|
| **MUHAMMAD ADEEL** (Stuart Williams) | 8 - 6 | c/o 01638 663984 |
| **JESSICA ANDERSON** (Adrian Keatley) | 7 - 4 | c/o 07934903387 |
| **GAVIN ASHTON** (Roger Varian) | 8 - 0 | c/o 01638 661702 |
| **LORENZO ATZORI** (Stuart Williams) | 8 - 0 | c/o 01638 663984 |
| **GEORGE BASS** (Mick Channon) | 8 - 5 | Mr A. T. Brook |
| **ALICE BOND** (James Ferguson) | 7 - 10 | c/o 01638 599581 |
| **GAIA BONI** (Nigel Tinkler) | 7 - 11 | c/o 07836384225 |
| **JOE BRADNAM** (Michael Bell) | 8 - 3 | c/o 07802264514 |
| **ANDREW BRESLIN** (Mark Johnston) | 7 - 9 | Mr N. Hannity |
| **AIDEN BROOKES** (Micky Hammond) | 7 - 13 | c/o 07808572777 |
| **JOSHUA BRYAN** (Andrew Balding) | 8 - 7 | Mr G. D. Jewell |
| **WILLIAM CARVER** (Andrew Balding) | 8 - 3 | Mr S. T. Dodds |
| **LUKE CATTON** (Richard Hannon) | 8 - 7 | Mr G. D. Jewell |
| **STEFANO CHERCHI** (Marco Botti) | 8 - 3 | Mr Paul Clarke |
| **JACOB CLARK** (Martin Smith) | 8 - 3 | c/o 07712493589 |
| **SOPHIE CLEMENTS** (K. R. Burke) | 7 - 2 | c/o 01969 625088 |
| **RHYS CLUTTERBUCK** (Gary Moore) | 8 - 10 | Mr N. M. Adams |
| **MORGAN COLE** (Marco Botti) | 7 - 11 | M. Furnass |
| **GEORGIA COX** (John Gosden) | 8 - 3 | M. Furnass |
| **WILLIAM COX** (Andrew Balding) | 8 - 2 | Mr N. M. Adams |
| **MARK CREHAN** (George Boughey) | 8 - 7 | P. C. Shea |
| **PAM DU CROCQ** (Chris Wall) | 8 - 7 | c/o 01638 661999 |
| **ELLE-MAY CROOT** (Ivan Furtado) | 8 - 2 | c/o 07783520746 |
| **GEORGIA DOBIE** (Eve Johnson Houghton) | 8 - 3 | P. C. Shea |
| **POPPY FIELDING** (Tom Dascombe) | 8 - 9 | c/o 01948 820485 |
| **ISOBEL FRANCIS** (Mark Usher) | 7 - 7 | Mr L. R. James |
| **HANNAH FRASER** (Ed Walker) | 7 - 4 | c/o 01488 674148 |
| **LOUIS GAROGHAN** (Gary Moore) | 8 - 3 | c/o 01403 891912 |
| **BILLY GARRITTY** (Micky Hammond) | 8 - 8 | K. W. Renwick |
| **MARCO GHIANI** (Stuart Williams) | 8 - 5 | Mr S. M. Righton |
| **ANNA GIBSON** (Gary Moore) | 7 - 7 | c/o 01403 891912 |
| **JADE GOODWIN** (Bryan Smart) | 7 - 5 | c/o 07748634797 |
| **SELMA GRAGE** (Robert Eddery) | 8 - 4 | Mr Aaron Gorman |
| **THOMAS GREATREX** (Roger Charlton) | 8 - 6 | Mr G. D. Jewell |
| **THORE HAMMER HANSEN** (Richard Hannon) | 8 - 0 | Mrs Shelley Dwyer |
| **BRADLEY HARRIS** (Andrew Balding) | 8 - 5 | Mr S. T. Dodds |
| **TYLER HEARD** (Richard Hughes) | 8 - 2 | Mr L. R. James |
| **CHRISTIAN HOWARTH** (Marco Botti) | 8 - 3 | P. C. Shea |
| **WILLIAM HUMPHREY** (Simon & Ed Crisford) | 7 - 5 | P. C. Shea |
| **CALLUM HUTCHINSON** (Andrew Balding) | 8 - 0 | Mr N. M. Adams |
| **KAIA INGOLFSLAND** (Sir Mark Prescott Bt) | 8 - 0 | M. Furnass |
| **RHIAN INGRAM** (Roger Ingram) | 7 - 11 | Mr L. R. James |
| **PIERRE-LOUIS JAMIN** (K. R. Burke) | 8 - 3 | Mr G. D. Jewell |
| **ELINOR JONES** (Sylvester Kirk) | 6 - 10 | Mr G. D. Jewell |
| **SOPHIE JONES** (Michael Appleby) | 7 - 11 | c/o 01572 722772 |
| **AIDAN KEELEY** (Gary Moore) | 8 - 2 | c/o 01403 891912 |
| **DARRAGH KEENAN** (John Ryan) | 8 - 0 | Mr S. T. Dodds |
| **GEORGIA KING** (Alan King) | 7 - 10 | c/o 01793 815 009 |
| **SEAN KIRRANE** (David O'Meara) | 8 - 4 | Mr N. Hannity |
| **THEODORE LADD** (Michael Appleby) | 8 - 0 | Mr G. D. Jewell |
| **FREDERICK LARSON** (Michael Appleby) | 8 - 2 | Mr S. M. Righton |
| **OWEN LEWIS** (Roger Teal) | 8 - 0 | c/o 07710325521 |
| **JAY MACKAY** (Jane Chapple-Hyam) | 9 - 2 | c/o 07917166740 |
| **FINLEY MARSH** (Richard Hughes) | 8 - 9 | c/o 01488 71198 |
| **IMOGEN MATHIAS** (John Flint) | 8 - 3 | Andy Lewis |
| **ELLA MCCAIN** (Tim Easterby) | 8 - 0 | Mr R. A. Hale |
| **GRACE MCENTEE** (Phil McEntee) | 8 - 7 | Mr S. T. Dodds |
| **OISIN MCSWEENEY** (Kevin Ryan) | 8 - 3 | Mr N. Hannity |

**SHARIQ MOHD** (Sylvester Kirk) .................................................. 7 - 10     Andy Lewis
**CONNOR MURTAGH** (Richard Fahey) ...................................... 8 - 6     K. W. Renwick
**ELLIE NORRIS** (Marco Botti) ................................................... 8 - 0     c/o 01638 662416
**JACK OSBORNE** (Andrew Balding) .......................................... 8 - 3     c/o 01635 298210
**SAFFIE OSBORNE** (Jamie Osborne) ....................................... 8 - 4     c/o 01488 73139
**ERIKA PARKINSON** (Michael Appleby) .................................... 8 - 0     Miss S. L. Metcalfe
**OWEN PAYTON** (Jedd O'Keeffe) ............................................. 7 - 4     c/o 07710476705
**LAURA PEARSON** (Tom Clover) .............................................. 8 - 2     Mr S. Croft
**JONNY PEATE** (Mark Johnston) .............................................. 7 - 7     c/o 01969 622237
**MARIE PERRAULT** (Andrew Balding) ...................................... 7 - 13     Miss S. L. Metcalfe
**MOLLIE PHILLIPS** (Tony Carroll) ............................................. 8 - 0     Miss S. L. Metcalfe
**TIA PHILLIPS** (John Ryan) ..................................................... 8 - 3     c/o 01638 664 172
**ABIGAIL PIERCE** (William Knight) ........................................... 7 - 10     c/o 01903 871 188
**RHONA PINDAR** (Liam Bailey) ................................................ 8 - 0     Mr Paul Brierley
**MATTEO PINNA** (Ismail Mohammed) ...................................... 8 - 3     c/o 01638 669074
**MOLLY PRESLAND** (Shaun Keightley) ..................................... 7 - 3     Mrs Shelley Dwyer
**CHARLIE PRICE** (Tim Vaughan) .............................................. 9 - 3     Mr I. P. Popham
**WILLIAM PYLE** (Michael Easterby) .......................................... 7 - 9     c/o 01347 878 368
**AIDAN REDPATH** (Michael Dods) ........................................... 7 - 7     Mr R. A. Hale
**SOPHIE REED** (J. S. Moore) .................................................. 7 - 12     Andy Lewis
**EDWARD REES** (Richard Hannon) .......................................... 8 - 10     c/o 01264 850254
**GEORGE ROOKE** (Richard Hughes) ....................................... 7 - 13     Mr N. M. Adams
**HARRY RUSSELL** (Brian Ellison) ............................................ 8 - 7     Mr R. A. Hale
**GIANLUCA SANNA** (Edward Bethell) ....................................... 8 - 8     Mr R. A. Hale
**TYLER SAUNDERS** (Jonathan Portman) ................................. 8 - 7     Mr Ian Wood
**BENOIT DE LA SAYETTE** (John Gosden) ................................ 8 - 3     Mr Paul Clarke
**OLIVER SEARLE** (Rod Millman) .............................................. 7 - 12     c/o 07885168447
**OLIVER STAMMERS** (Mark Johnston) .................................... 8 - 4     Mr G. R. Owen
**MOHAMMED TABTI** (Paul & Oliver Cole) ................................. 8 - 0     c/o 01488 638433
**EMMA TAFF** (Henry Candy) .................................................... 8 - 7     M. Furnass
**OLIVER TIMMS** (Mick Channon) ............................................. 8 - 3     c/o 01635 281166
**ANGUS VILLIERS** (Richard Spencer) ...................................... 8 - 2     P. C. Shea
**SHANNON WATTS** (Iain Jardine) ............................................ 8 - 8     c/o 07944 722011
**ZAK WHEATLEY** (Declan Carroll) ........................................... 8 - 5     Mr R. A. Hale
**ELISHA WHITTINGTON** (Tony Carroll) .................................... 7 - 10     Mr S. M. Righton
**LEVI WILLIAMS** (Jane Chapple-Hyam) .................................... 7 - 10     c/o 07917166740
**JOE WILLIAMSON** (Philip Kirby) ............................................ 9 - 7     Mr Ian Wood
**SEBASTIAN WOODS** (Chris Wall) .......................................... 8 - 11     Mrs Shelley Dwyer

# JUMP JOCKEYS

### Riding weights and contact details
### An index of agents appears on page 755

| Jockey | Weight | Agent |
|---|---|---|
| LUCY ALEXANDER | 9 - 7 | Mr R. A. Hale |
| AARON ANDERSON | 9 - 7 | Mr Paul Brierley |
| BRIDGET ANDREWS | 9 - 5 | Mr I. P. Popham |
| HARRY BANNISTER | 9 - 7 | Mr C. D. Broad |
| JAMIE BARGARY | 10 - 0 | Mr I. P. Popham |
| LUCY K. BARRY | 9 - 8 | 07889275412 |
| DAVID BASS | 10 - 5 | Mr C. D. Broad |
| MATTIE BATCHELOR | 10 - 0 | 07767400753 |
| TOM BELLAMY | 10 - 5 | Mr C. D. Broad |
| JAMES BEST | 10 - 0 | Mr Dave Roberts |
| CALLUM BEWLEY | 10 - 0 | Mr R. A. Hale |
| JONATHON BEWLEY | 10 - 0 | 01450860651 |
| NICO DE BOINVILLE | 10 - 0 | Mr Dave Roberts |
| JAMES BOWEN | 10 - 0 | Mr Dave Roberts |
| SEAN BOWEN | 9 - 7 | Mr Dave Roberts/ M. Furnass |
| PADDY BRENNAN | 9 - 12 | Mr Dave Roberts |
| HENRY BROOKE | 10 - 0 | Mr R. A. Hale |
| JONATHAN BURKE | 10 - 0 | Mr C. D. Broad |
| DANNY BURTON | 9 - 9 | Mr L. R. James |
| TOM CANNON | 10 - 5 | Mr L. R. James |
| GRAHAM CARSON | 9 - 10 | Mr Dave Roberts |
| ALAIN CAWLEY | 9 - 10 | Mr R. A. Hale |
| ROSS CHAPMAN | 9 - 8 | 07513109598 |
| TOM CHEESMAN | 9 - 9 | Mr Dave Roberts |
| HARRY COBDEN | 10 - 0 | Mr L. R. James |
| GRANT COCKBURN | 10 - 2 | Mr Dave Roberts |
| AIDAN COLEMAN | 9 - 10 | 07927518874 |
| JOE COLLIVER | 10 - 0 | Mr J. B. Jeffrey |
| DANNY COOK | 10 - 7 | Mr A. T. Brook |
| DOUGIE COSTELLO | 10 - 0 | Mr L. R. James |
| JAMES DAVIES | 10 - 0 | Mr R. A. Hale |
| RYAN DAY | 10 - 6 | Mr C. D. Broad |
| CHARLIE DEUTSCH | 10 - 0 | Mr R. A. Hale |
| THOMAS DOWSON | 10 - 0 | Mr Dave Roberts |
| ALAN DOYLE | 9 - 10 | Mr Dave Roberts |
| ROBERT DUNNE | 10 - 0 | Mr L. R. James |
| KIERON EDGAR | 10 - 7 | Mr L. R. James |
| ALEX EDWARDS | 10 - 0 | Mr C. D. Broad |
| LEE EDWARDS | 10 - 0 | Mr C. D. Broad |
| DAVID ENGLAND | 10 - 0 | Mr I. P. Popham |
| JONATHAN ENGLAND | 9 - 10 | 07747390455 |
| WILLIAM FEATHERSTONE | 10 - 7 | Mr I. P. Popham |
| DEREK FOX | 10 - 0 | Mr J. B. Jeffrey |
| BRYONY FROST | 9 - 12 | Mr Dave Roberts |
| LUCY GARDNER | 10 - 0 | 07814979 699 |
| JACK GARRITTY | 9 - 0 | K. W. Renwick |
| CIARAN GETHINGS | 10 - 2 | Mr C. D. Broad |
| MARC GOLDSTEIN | 10 - 0 | Mr Dave Roberts |
| MARK GRANT | 10 - 4 | Mr C. D. Broad |
| MATT GRIFFITHS | 10 - 7 | Mr I. P. Popham |
| JAMIE HAMILTON | 10 - 0 | Mr R. A. Hale |
| A. P. HESKIN | 10 - 0 | Mr Dave Roberts |
| DANIEL HISKETT | 9 - 10 | Mr I. P. Popham |
| BRIAN HUGHES | 9 - 7 | Mr R. A. Hale |
| DARYL JACOB | 10 - 3 | Mr Dave Roberts |
| ALAN JOHNS | 10 - 0 | Mr I. P. Popham |
| ALISON JOHNSON | 9 - 7 | Mr Paul Brierley |
| RICHARD JOHNSON | 10 - 0 | Mr Dave Roberts |
| KEVIN JONES | 10 - 0 | Mr Dave Roberts |
| JONJO O'NEILL JR. | 10 - 4 | Mr Dave Roberts |
| WILLIAM KENNEDY | 10 - 0 | Mr C. D. Broad |
| JOHN KINGTON | 10 - 0 | Mr R. A. Hale |
| RYAN MANIA | 10 - 3 | Mr J. B. Jeffrey |
| COLM MCCORMACK | 10 - 0 | 01287 650456 |
| RACHAEL MCDONALD | 9 - 5 | Mr Ross Hyslop |
| JEREMIAH MCGRATH | 10 - 0 | Mr Dave Roberts |
| RICHIE MCLERNON | 9 - 10 | Mr Dave Roberts |
| JAMIE MOORE | 10 - 0 | Mr Dave Roberts |
| JOSHUA MOORE | 10 - 5 | Mr Dave Roberts |
| NATHAN MOSCROP | 10 - 5 | Mr R. A. Hale |
| STEPHEN MULQUEEN | 10 - 0 | Mr J. B. Jeffrey |
| CRAIG NICHOL | 10 - 0 | K. W. Renwick |
| MEGAN NICHOLLS | 8 - 4 | Mr S. Croft |
| JAMES NIXON | 10 - 2 | Mr L. R. James |
| MICHEAL NOLAN | 10 - 4 | Mr Dave Roberts |
| DAVID NOONAN | 10 - 0 | Mr I. P. Popham |
| PAUL O'BRIEN | 10 - 3 | Mr Dave Roberts |
| TOM O'BRIEN | 10 - 2 | Mr Dave Roberts |
| CONOR O'FARRELL | 10 - 3 | K. W. Renwick |
| KATIE O'FARRELL | 9 - 11 | Mr Dave Roberts |
| TOMMY PHELAN | 10 - 0 | 01386 584209 |
| BEN POSTE | 9 - 10 | Mr Dave Roberts |
| BRENDAN POWELL | 9 - 11 | Mr Dave Roberts |
| DAVID PRICHARD | 10 - 0 | 079830162251 |
| TOM QUEALLY | 9 - 10 | P. C. Shea |
| JACK QUINLAN | 9 - 10 | Mr Dave Roberts |
| SHANE QUINLAN | 9 - 7 | Mr I. P. Popham |
| SEAN QUINLAN | 10 - 0 | Mr R. A. Hale |
| HARRY REED | 9 - 7 | Mr Dave Roberts |
| CONOR RING | 10 - 5 | Mr C. D. Broad |
| BEN ROBINSON | 8 - 9 | Mr R. A. Hale |
| DANIEL SANSOM | 10 - 5 | Mr L. R. James |
| JACK SAVAGE | 10 - 5 | Mr C. D. Broad |
| NICK SCHOLFIELD | 10 - 4 | Mr Dave Roberts |
| TOM SCUDAMORE | 10 - 3 | Mr Dave Roberts |
| WILLIAM SHANAHAN | 10 - 3 | Mr J. L. Neilsor |
| GAVIN SHEEHAN | 10 - 0 | Mr C. D. Broad |
| STAN SHEPPARD | 10 - 0 | Mr C. D. Broad |
| CONOR SHOEMARK | 10 - 0 | 07792125674 |
| HARRY SKELTON | 10 - 0 | Mr I. P. Popham |
| SAM TWISTON-DAVIES | 10 - 0 | Mr C. D. Broad |
| CHRIS WARD | 9 - 12 | Mr L. R. James |
| ADAM WEDGE | 10 - 0 | Mr Dave Robert |
| CALLUM WHILLANS | 9 - 11 | 0789457355 |
| ROBERT WILLIAMS | 10 - 7 | Mr I. P. Pophar |
| KIELAN WOODS | 10 - 3 | Mr C. D. Broa |
| TABITHA WORSLEY | 9 - 9 | Mr L. R. Jame |

# CONDITIONALS

### Their employer and contact details
### An index of agents appears on page 755

| | | | |
|---|---|---|---|
| **JOE ANDERSON** (Nicky Henderson) | 9 - 12 | Mr Dave Roberts |
| **PHILIP ARMSON** (Jonjo O'Neill) | 9 - 7 | Mr Dave Roberts |
| **MITCHELL BASTYAN** (Johnny Farrelly) | 10 - 0 | Mr Dave Roberts |
| **ARCHIE BELLAMY** (Nigel Twiston-Davies) | 9 - 7 | Mr C. D. Broad |
| **HARRISON BESWICK** (Oliver Sherwood) | 10 - 0 | Mr I. P Popham |
| **CONNOR BRACE** (Fergal O'Brien) | 9 - 3 | Mr Dave Roberts |
| **NATHAN BRENNAN** (Chris Gordon) | 9 - 12 | Mr Dave Roberts |
| **POPPY BRIDGWATER** (David Bridgwater) | 9 - 0 | c/o 07831635817 |
| **KEVIN BROGAN** (Jonjo O'Neill) | 10 - 0 | Mr Dave Roberts |
| **MAX BROWNE** (Alan King) | 9 - 4 | Mr C. D. Broad |
| **KIEREN BUCKLEY** (Nigel Hawke) | 10 - 10 | K. W. Renwick |
| **TOM BUCKLEY** (Charlie Longsdon) | 9 - 1 | Mr Dave Roberts |
| **BLAIR CAMPBELL** (Lucinda Russell) | 9 - 10 | K. W. Renwick |
| **BRYAN CARVER** (Paul Nicholls) | 9 - 7 | Mr Dave Roberts |
| **ANGUS CHELEDA** (Paul Nicholls) | 9 - 10 | c/o 01749860656 |
| **PETER COLEMAN** (Keith Dalgleish) | 10 - 0 | K. W. Renwick |
| **SAM COLTHERD** (Sue Smith) | 9 - 12 | Mr J. B. Jeffrey |
| **LEE COSGROVE** (Emma Lavelle) | 10 - 4 | c/o 01672 511544 |
| **PATRICK COWLEY** (L J Morgan) | 10 - 0 | Mr I. P Popham |
| **BEN FFRENCH DAVIS** (Nicky Henderson) | 9 - 12 | Mr Ian Wood |
| **REX DINGLE** (Anthony Honeyball) | 9 - 7 | Mr Dave Roberts |
| **JASON DIXON** (Tom Lacey) | 9 - 7 | Mr C. D. Broad |
| **THOMAS DOGGRELL** (Tom George) | 10 - 4 | Mr C. D. Broad |
| **EDDIE EDGE** (Amy Murphy) | 9 - 10 | Mr Tom Castle |
| **ALEXANDER FIELDING** (Sue Smith) | 9 - 11 | c/o 07903311959 |
| **PAGE FULLER** (Jamie Snowden) | 9 - 3 | Mr L. R. James |
| **BILLY GARRITTY** (Micky Hammond) | 9 - 7 | K. W. Renwick |
| **THEO GILLARD** (David Pipe) | 9 - 7 | c/o 01884 840715 |
| **THEO GILLARD** (Donald McCain) | 10 - 7 | Mr R. A. Hale |
| **BEN GODFREY** (Anthony Honeyball) | 9 - 4 | Mr Dave Roberts |
| **FERGUS GREGORY** (Olly Murphy) | 10 - 0 | Mr I. P Popham |
| **CHARLIE HAMMOND** (Dr Richard Newland) | 9 - 7 | Mr Dave Roberts |
| **LIAM HARRISON** (Fergal O'Brien) | 9 - 6 | Mr Dave Roberts |
| **NIALL HOULIHAN** (Gary Moore) | 9 - 7 | Mr Dave Roberts |
| **SEAN HOULIHAN** (Philip Hobbs) | 9 - 7 | Mr Dave Roberts |
| **MILLAN HURST** (George Bewley) | 9 - 7 | Mr J. B. Jeffrey |
| **BEN JONES** (Philip Hobbs) | 10 - 0 | Mr Dave Roberts |
| **CHARLOTTE JONES** (James Moffatt) | 8 - 11 | Mr J. L. Neilson |
| **ALFIE JORDAN** (Nicky Henderson) | 9 - 1 | c/o 01488 72259 |
| **PETER KAVANAGH** (Donald McCain) | 9 - 0 | c/o 01829 720352 |
| **MAX KENDRICK** (Graeme McPherson) | 9 - 9 | Mr Dave Roberts |
| **HARRY KIMBER** (Colin Tizzard) | 9 - 0 | Mr C. D. Broad |
| **KAI LENIHAN** (Oliver Sherwood) | 9 - 4 | Mr I. P Popham |
| **BRUCE LYNN** (N. W. Alexander) | 9 - 11 | Mr Dave Roberts |
| **KILLIN LEONARD** (Dr Richard Newland) | 10 - 0 | Mr R. A. Hale |
| **AIDAN MACDONALD** (Micky Hammond) | 9 - 10 | c/o 07808572777 |
| **WILLIAM MARSHALL** (Dan Skelton) | 9 - 6 | Mr I. P Popham |
| **ABBIE MCCAIN** (Donald McCain) | 9 - 9 | Mr R. A. Hale |
| **COREY MCGIVERN** (Lucy Wadham) | 9 - 6 | c/o 07980545776 |
| **CALLUM MCKINNES** (Olly Murphy) | 10 - 0 | Mr I. P Popham |
| **DANNY MCMENAMIN** (Nicky Richards) | 9 - 7 | Mr R. A. Hale |
| **TOM MIDGLEY** (Rebecca Menzies) | 9 - 12 | Mr R. A. Hale |
| **NIALL MOORE** (Evan Williams) | 9 - 10 | c/o 01446 754069 |
| **LUCA MORGAN** (Ben Pauling) | 10 - 3 | Mr Dave Roberts |
| **LORCAN MURTAGH** (Harry Fry) | 9 - 11 | Mr C. D. Broad |
| **JORDAN NAILOR** (Nigel Twiston-Davies) | 9 - 7 | Mr C. D. Broad |
| **JAMIE NEILD** (Nigel Twiston-Davies) | 9 - 7 | Mr C. D. Broad |

| | | | |
|---|---|---|---|
| **HUGH NUGENT** (Venetia Williams) | 9 - 7 | Mr C. D. Broad |
| **RICHARD PATRICK** (Kerry Lee) | 9 - 7 | Mr Dave Roberts |
| **LILLY PINCHIN** (Graeme McPherson) | 9 - 10 | Mr C. D. Broad |
| **CHARLIE PRICE** (Tim Vaughan) | 9 - 2 | Mr I. P Popham |
| **CAOILIN QUINN** (Warren Greatrex) | 9 - 10 | c/o 01488 670279 |
| **EMMA SMITH-CHASTON** (Micky Hammond) | 9 - 7 | Mr R. A. Hale |
| **LEWIS STONES** (Olly Murphy) | 9 - 7 | Mr I. P Popham |
| **ALEXANDER THORNE** (Alan King) | 9 - 7 | Mr Dave Roberts |
| **JAY TIDBALL** (Bill Turner) | 10 - 3 | c/o 07967242404 |
| **CHARLIE TODD** (Ian Williams) | 9 - 5 | Mr I. P Popham |
| **JACK TUDOR** (Christian Williams) | 9 - 7 | Mr Dave Roberts |
| **ROSS TURNER** (Oliver Greenall) | 9 - 7 | Mr I. P Popham |
| **PATRICK WADGE** (Lucinda Russell) | 9 - 0 | Mr J. B. Jeffrey |
| **CHESTER WILLIAMS** (Kim Bailey) | 10 - 0 | Mr C. D. Broad |
| **ISABEL WILLIAMS** (Evan Williams) | 9 - 7 | Mr Dave Roberts |
| **LORCAN WILLIAMS** (Paul Nicholls) | 10 - 4 | Mr I. P Popham |
| **JOE WILLIAMSON** (Philip Kirby) | 9 - 7 | Mr Ian Wood |
| **THOMAS WILLMOTT** (Lucinda Russell) | 9 - 7 | Mr J. B. Jeffrey |
| **MILLIE WONNACOTT** (Neil Mulholland) | 9 - 7 | Mr Dave Roberts |

Are your contact details missing
or incorrect?
If so please update us by
email: hitraceform@weatherbys.co.uk

# AMATEUR RIDERS

### Riding weights and contact details
### An index of agents appears on page 755

MORGAN, B. 10 - 0 .................................07475067091
LEWIS, H. 9 - 5 ......................................07593041304
KING, M. 8 - 11 .....................................07946516613
ALEXANDER, C. 9 - 10 ...........................07799191093
ALEXANDER, K. 9 - 7 .............................07950989807
ANDREWS, G. 9 - 12 ..........................Mr C. D. Broad
ANDREWS, J. 10 - 10 ........................Mr I. P Popham
APRAHAMIAN, B. 11 - 3 .........................07739819804
AUSTIN, E. 10 - 0 ...................................07837781877
BAKER, Z. C. N. 10 - 10 ....................Mr C. D. Broad
BAMENT, C. L. 9 - 7 ..............................
BANKS, J. 11 - 0 ....................................01223279210
BARFOOT-SAUNT, G. C. 10 - 12 ..........01684 833227
BARLOW, P. C. F. 9 - 0 ..........................
BARR, F. J. A. 11 - 2 ..............................
BARTLEY, C. A. 8 - 10 ...........................
BARTON, V. 8 - 0 ...................................
BELL, A. 9 - 4 ...................................Mr L. R. James
BIDDICK, W. E. T. 11 - 0 ........................07976556823
BIDDLE, C. 9 - 4 ....................................
BIGGS, M. O. 8 - 0 .................................
BINGHAM, G. F. 11 - 1 ...........................07766204154
BIRKETT, R. A. 9 - 10 .............................07855065036
BLAKEMORE, A. 9 - 0 .............................
BLOSS, A. Z. 8 - 5 ............................Mrs N. Bloss
BOWEN, S. L. 9 - 0 ..........................Mr S. M. Righton
BRACKENBURY, B. E. 10 - 11 ................
BRADSTOCK, L. A. N. 9 - 6 ...................07972161732
BROMLEY, B. W. 9 - 9 ...........................07585973675
BROOKE, L. 9 - 4 ...................................07786962911
BROOKS, C. 9 - 0 ...................................
BROPHY, O. 8 - 8 ...................................
BROTHERTON, S. 8 - 12 ........................
BROUGHTON, T. P. 10 - 0 ......................07769311769
BROWN, L. 10 - 0 ...................................
BROWN, M. W. 9 - 12 ........................Mr J. B. Jeffrey
BROWN, P. J. 9 - 5 .................................
BRYAN, P. J. 10 - 7 .................................07538655128
BRYANT, M. P. 9 - 12 .............................07976217542
BULLOCK, E. 8 - 0 ..................................
BUTTERFIELD, A. 11 - 0 .........................
CAGNEY, E. 9 - 0 .............................Mr Paul Brierley
CASE, C. 10 - 10 ....................................07807652305
CHADWICK, A. 10 - 0 ............................
CHATFEILD-ROBERTS, T. 10 - 7 ..........07876394421
CHENERY, M. 10 - 0 ...............................07967911360
CHERRIMAN, D. J. 10 - 7 .......................07900963271
CLARKE, A. 8 - 10 ..................................
COLLIER, A. 9 - 0 .............................Mrs G. S. Charnock
COTTLE, D. G. G. 10 - 7 .........................01653 698915
COX, A. 8 - 2 ...........................................07813386642
CRANE, C. R. 9 - 8 .................................
CROSS, S. P. 10 - 7 ...............................07774876008
CANDO, A. C. 11 - 4 ...............................07901522080
DAVID, E. 11 - 5 .....................................07500383138
DAVIES, R. A. 9 - 3 ................................

DAVIS, J. 9 - 4 .......................................
DENIEL, A. 8 - 10 ...................................
DISNEY, G. F. 10 - 10 ............................07816847947
DIXON, J. 9 - 7 .......................................07761998988
DOBB, L. 9 - 5 ........................................07960174107
DODD, M. 9 - 0 .......................................
DODS, C. A. 8 - 13 .................................07590048619
DODS, S. E. 9 - 1 ...................................0790048618
DOOLAN, S. M. 10 - 4 ...............doolan@hotmail.co.uk
DUN, C. 9 - 10 ........................................07766592287
DUNNE, M. P. 10 - 0 ...............................
DURRELL, T. 9 - 7 ...........................Mr I. P Popham
EASTERBY, E. A. 8 - 7 ...........................07854733689
EASTERBY, W. H. 9 - 7 ..........................07772216507
EDDERY, G. 9 - 4 ...................................
EDWARDS, D. M. 11 - 4 ..........................07811898002
EDWARDS, H. 10 - 4 ...............................07709506046
ELLIOT, J. A. 9 - 8 .................................
ENNIS, M. C. 9 - 11 ..........................Mrs L. H. Way
EYSTON, T. 9 - 10 ..................................
FEATHERSTONE, W. 9 - 0 ......................
FEILDEN, S. 8 - 0 ...................................
FERGUSON, A. R. D. 10 - 0 .....................07788876161
FIELDING, M. 9 - 10 ................................
FOX, M. 9 - 0 ..........................................
FOX, N. 9 - 7 ..........................................
FURNESS, C. J. W. 10 - 6 .......................07871449210
GARVEN, A. M. 8 - 12 .............................
GEORGE, N. A. C. 10 - 7 ........................07540564499
GERMANY, S. 9 - 0 .................................
GLANVILLE, P. 10 - 0 ..............................
GLASSONBURY, E. 10 - 12 ......................07917167236
GOODWIN, C. L. 8 - 4 .............................
GORMAN, G. 10 - 5 ................................07429557863
GOWING, K. 9 - 0 ...................................
GREASBY, H. 9 - 10 ................................
HAMBLETT, L. S. 9 - 3 ...........................07979102805
HARBISON, J. E. A. 10 - 7 ......................01280 812057
HARDING, D. S. 9 - 4 ..............................
HARDING, J. 9 - 10 .................................07532830029
HARDWICK, C. V. 9 - 10 .........................07808511705
HARRISON, K. 9 - 0 ................................
HARRISON, S. 9 - 10 ..............................01283 567971
HAWKINS, S. 9 - 6 .................................07733265836
HENDERSON, G. 10 - 5 ...........................07765967086
HERBERT, M. 11 - 0 ................................
HISCOCK, G. 10 - 7 ................................07815475518
HODGINS, L. W. 10 - 5 ...........................
HOPKINSON, G. J. 10 - 8 .......................
HOPPER, P. 8 - 7 ...................................07931873497
HOWARTH, R. 9 - 6 ................................
HUGHES, J. 9 - 7 ...................................07884432672
HUMPHREY, L. A. 10 - 2 .........................07557772679
ILES, C. 8 - 8 .........................................
JACKSON-FENNELL, A. 10 - 0 ................
JAKES, V. J. 10 - 2 .................................
JEAVONS, J. 10 - 0 ................................

JOHNSON, M. S. 9 - 10
JONES, J. C. 9 - 7 .................................07794912090
JORDAN, M. 8 - 4
KENIRY, K. L. 9 - 0 ...............................07739414365
KING, J. 10 - 7 .................................. Mr I. P. Popham
KITTS, D. 9 - 7
KYNE, D. B. 10 - 10
LAMBERT, F. 10 - 0
LAW-EADIE, R. 9 - 2
LEAHY, K. 9 - 3 ...................................07470307653
LEE, S. 9 - 7 .......................................07745327430
LEECH, R. 9 - 4
LEGG, M. D. 9 - 7
LEWIS, A. 8 - 7
LLEWELLYN, J. 8 - 5
LYNCH, L. 9 - 4
MAIN, H. 8 - 10
MAINS, C. 9 - 6 ...................................07375496629
MALZARD, V. A. 10 - 0
MARGARSON, R. A. 8 - 2 ....................07595888757
MARSHALL, I. 9 - 0 ..............................07581371480
MARTIN, J. I. 10 - 3 .............................07815698359
MASON, P. W. 11 - 4 ............................07921707292
MAXWELL, D. 11 - 0 ............................0207 7993429
MCBRIDE, A. 10 - 0
MCBRIDE, C. 9 - 7
MCCAIN-MITCHELL, T. 9 - 13
MCCLUNG, A. E. 9 - 4 ..........................07775740004
MCINTYRE, M. J. 10 - 4
METAIREAU, C. 9 - 0
MICKLEWRIGHT, M. 8 - 4 ....................07525466455
MILLMAN, P. B. 9 - 7 ........................... Mr Ian Wood
MITCHELL, G. P 10 - 0
MORGAN, S. A. 9 - 11
MULHALL, C. A. 8 - 2
MULRINE, F. 9 - 5
MYDDELTON, H. 10 - 12 ......................07713837857
NEWCOMBE, H. 9 - 7
NEWMAN, J. 9 - 7
O'BRIEN, D. J. 11 - 0 ...........................07764304906
O'BRIEN, T. M. 10 - 0 ..........................07826516394
O'CONNOR, S. P. 9 - 10 ......................07894425689
O'NEILL, A. J. 10 - 0 ...........................07585400544
O'SHEA, A. 9 - 7 ............................. Mr J. L. Neilson
O'SHEA, C. 10 - 10 .............................07779878748
PAHLMAN, J. V. 9 - 0
PARKER, N. L. 9 - 5
PECK, A. 8 - 7 ................................. Miss A. Wallace
PHILLIPS, N. J. 11 - 4 ..........................07976240874
POTTER, W. E. 10 - 7 ..........................07872933534
POWELL, K. C. 9 - 5
POWNALL, C. L. 9 - 1 ..........................07825064776
PRICE, C. 10 - 4 ..................................07598925913
PROCTER, F. 10 - 0
PUGH, S. 8 - 6 .....................................07391477659
RAHMAN, N. 9 - 7
RAMSAY, W. B. 11 - 0 ..........................07764960054
RAWDON-MOGG, C. J. D. 11 - 0 .........07759451287
REDDINGTON, J. J. 11 - 0 ...................07766767464
RIPPON, S. 9 - 7
ROBERTS, B. 9 - 8 ..............................07871504897
ROBINSON, I. P. B. 9 - 2 .....................07581361986
ROBINSON, M. G. 10 - 10
ROBINSON, S. C. 12 - 0 .......................01424 204190
ROBOTTOM, J. P. 9 - 4
RODGERS, Z. 9 - 0
SANKEY, G. 11 - 1 ...............................07805653696

SCOTT, D. C. 9 - 2 ..................01372 426200
SCOTT, L. R. B. 9 - 4 ........................ Mr I. P. Popham
SENSOY, H. 9 - 8 .................................07595985025
SHARP, M. 9 - 3 ...................................07471823014
SINCLAIR, K. S. 9 - 0 ...........................07554457681
SMITH, R. 9 - 2 ...... Mrs G. S. Charnock/Mr J. L. Neilson
SMITH, S. 7 - 10
SMITH-MAXWELL, J. 11 - 1 ...............07535459701
SOLE, J. D. 10 - 1 ...............................07968947091
SPARKES, G. 8 - 4
SPENCER, L. 9 - 0
SPRAKE, C. G. 10 - 3
STEVENS, A. L. 9 - 7 ........................ Mr I. P. Popham
STEVENS, H. M. 9 - 5 ..........................07925069749
STEVENS, S. 9 - 2
STEVENSON, J. W. 10 - 0
SUMMERS, P. F. 10 - 0 ........................07552219962
SUTTON, B. 10 - 11 .............................07774638398
SWIFT, C. 9 - 7
TAYLOR, R. M. 8 - 12 ..........................07973774660
TEAL, J. 10 - 0 ....................................07984649070
TETT, F. 9 - 0 ......................................07786314587
THIRLBY, W. 11 - 0
THOMAS, P. J. 9 - 0
TRAINOR, M. 9 - 7 ...............................07554992851
TROTT, L. 10 - 5 ..................................07814537290
TUCKER, H. C. 9 - 6 ........................ Mr L. R. James
TUDOR, C. P. 9 - 0
TUFNELL, A. 10 - 7 ..............................07739748736
TURNER, D. I. 9 - 6 ..............................07768094908
TURNER, J. 9 - 0 ..................................07955080203
TURNER, L. M. 10 - 0 ...........................07984531836
VAUGHAN, E. 9 - 6
VOIKHANSKY, M. 9 - 9 .........................01213772133
WADGE, C. 10 - 5 ............................ Mr J. B. Jeffrey
WAGGOTT, J. J. 10 - 7
WALEY-COHEN, S. B. 10 - 0 ................07887848425
WALKER, S. A. 9 - 7 .......................... Mr S. T. Dodds
WALLACE, H. A. R. 11 - 0 ....................07974360462
WARD, J. 10 - 0
WAUGH, A. 8 - 5 .............................. Mr J. B. Jeffrey
WEAVER, A. 10 - 6
WEBB, K. 9 - 3
WELCH, T. 10 - 5
WHITTLE, S. R. 9 - 7
WILKINSON, E. J. 8 - 5 ........................07964145161
WILLIAMS, E. L. 10 - 0 .........................07714170651
WILSON, R. 11 - 0
WINGROVE, M. 9 - 9 ............................07710562173
WOOD, C. 9 - 7
WYNNE, T. S. 10 - 0
YEOMAN, K. 9 - 7 ............................. Mr B. Storey
YORK, P. 10 - 7 ....................................07774962168

# Download the free must-have Racing Post app.

**RACING POST**

The Must-Have App
For The Must-Have Info

Use your camera phone and scan the QR code on the right to download the free app now.

# NOTES

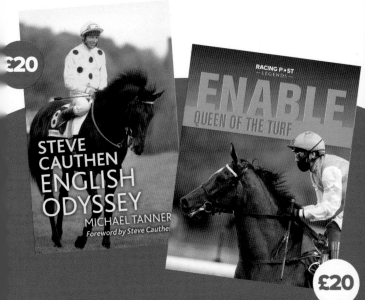

# RACING POST
## MEMBERS' CLUB

**Unlimited access to the Racing Post digital newspaper**

**Premium news and stories from award-winning writers**

**Expert tips from our in-house pros**

**Full video replays of all UK & Irish races**

**Exclusive form study tools and post race analys**

# Find out more at
# racingpost.com/members-club

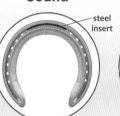

**Farm & Stable**
Enhancing Equine Wellbeing

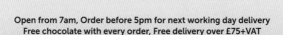

Open from 7am, Order before 5pm for next working day delivery
Free chocolate with every order, Free delivery over £75+VAT

✓ Equine Supplement Specialist
✓ Worming Treatments & Bespoke Programmes
✓ Independent Nutritional Advice
✓ Next Working Day Delivery
✓ Stable & Yard Equipment
✓ Huge UK Stockholding
✓ Fast, Friendly & Reliable Service

**SUPPORTING UK EQUINE PROFESSIONALS**

01730 815800 | farmstable.com

**CALDERS & GRANDIDGE**

**1820**

Timber treated products manufactured on-site

Top quality treated timber
fencing and handmade gates
manufactured on-site.

View the range at
# www.caldersandgrandidge.com

Email **enquiries@caldersandgrandidge.com**
or call our experts on **01205 358866**

BY APPOINTMENT TO
HER MAJESTY THE QUE

Air Cooled Super Lite
Carbon Tech Racing Boots

*Protecting the world's
greatest horses.*

Sire De Gruç

# PREMIER EQUINE

ENGLAND

PROUD SUPPLIERS TO THE RACING COMMUNITY

To apply for a trainer's trade account, please contact:
sales@premierequine.co.uk | Order Line 01469 532279
www.premierequine.co.uk

# EMERALD EQUESTRIAN

### *Excellence in Equestrian Engineering*

Manufactured from high quality materials and designed for maximum efficiency, safety and longevity. Our range of Horse walkers, lunge pens, turn out pens and stabling are used globally by a wide range of industry professionals. Indeed, our satisfied customers extend to US, Saudi Arabia, South Africa, France, the UK and Ireland.

The Errigal Horse Walker is extremely durable with enhanced safety features. Its superior design and workmanship allow for exact specifications in terms of size and features, for both private and professional clients, ensuring excellent value for money.

The Emerald range of Lunge Pens provide a safe controlled environment for lunging and schooling horses. They are available in a range of different sizes.

53 Moneysharvin Road
Maghera,
Northern Ireland
BT46 5PY

Tel: +44 (0)28 7940 1503

Mobile: +44 (0) 77 3020 2745

info@emeraldequestrian.net

**www.emeraldequestrian.net**

Artist & Sculptor

# Moorcroft
### Racehorse Welfare Centre

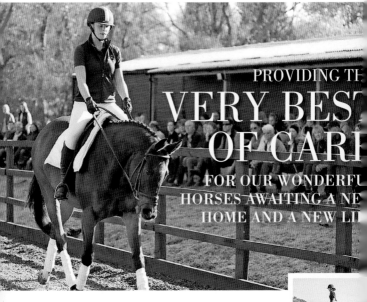

PROVIDING TH
VERY BES'
OF CARI
FOR OUR WONDERFU
HORSES AWAITING A NE
HOME AND A NEW LII

This centre in the south of England was set up to ensure that retired racehorses whatever age, can be re-trained to find another career in life. Much care and attention is given to each individual horse and when fully retrained new homes are found. The centre retains ownership for life and visits these horses every year to ensure that all is well.

This charity depends on generous donations from horse lovers. Many horses need a time for rehabilitation due to injury etc and start to enjoy an easier life after their racing careers. Visits by appointment are welcomed. Please ring Mary Frances, Manager, on 07929 666408 for more information or to arrange a visit.

Huntingrove Stud, Slinfold, West Sussex. RH13 0RB
**Tel: 07929 666408 | moorcroftracehorse@gmail.com | www.moorcroftracehorse.org.u**